SCOTT®

2024
STANDARD POSTAGE STAMP CATALOGUE

ONE HUNDRED AND EIGHTIETH EDITION IN SIX VOLUMES

Volume 1A
U.S., U.N., A-Australia

Released April 2023
Includes New Stamp Listings through the February 2023 *Linn's Stamp News Monthly* Catalogue Update

AMOS MEDIA
1660 Campbell Road, Suite A, Sidney, OH 45365
Publishers of *Linn's Stamp News, Linn's Stamp News Monthly, Coin World* and *Coin World Monthly.*

Table of contents

Scott Catalogue Mission Statement

The Scott Catalogue Team exists to serve the recreational, educational and commercial hobby needs of stamp collectors and dealers.

We strive to set the industry standard for philatelic information and products by developing and providing goods that help collectors identify, value, organize and present their collections.

Quality customer service is, and will continue to be, our highest priority.
We aspire toward achieving total customer satisfaction.

Copyright Notice

Trademark Notice

ISBN 978-0-89487-692-9

Library of Congress Card No. 2-3301

What's new for 2024 Scott Standard Volume 1

Another catalog season is upon us as we continue the journey of the 155-year history of the Scott catalogs. The 2024 volumes are the 180th edition of the Scott *Standard Postage Stamp Catalogue*. Volume 1A includes listings for the United States, United Nations, and countries of the world Aden through Australia. Listings for Austria through B countries of the world can be found in Vol. 1B.

This year's covers feature the 2007 Australia 50¢ Three Male Lifeguards stamp (Scott 2636) from the four-stamp Surf Life Saving Australia Centennial set on the Vol. 1A catalog and the Brazil 2001 40-centavo Ponta Negra Beach stamp (2801b) from a strip of three Beaches stamps on Vol. 1B.

Because Vol. 1B is a continuation of the first part of the Vol. 1 catalog, the introduction pages are not repeated in each volume this year.

Most advisors for the Vol. 1A United States section seem quite satisfied with what we all see as a remarkably stable market. We note that the Scott benchmark grade of very fine for almost all stamp issues remains valid for virtually all auction lots and retail offerings, and these sales have been quite consistent for some time. Therefore, there are relatively few value changes for United States in the 2024 Vol. 1A.

Of course, there always are some values that change in every catalog, as certain stamps or market segments see public offerings that clearly indicate necessary changes. Notable for 2024 are increases for the U.S. 1875 unused reprints of the 1857-60 issue (Scott 40-47). All numbers except Scott 40 see advances of 5 percent to 10 percent. Scott values for all but the 1¢ and 90¢ denominations in this set are for stamps in the grade of fine. A number of attractive examples were sold since the 2023 Scott *Specialized Catalog of United States Stamps and Covers* was published last October, and they all sold for very nice prices.

Several stamps in the 1869 Pictorial definitive set show strength in used condition, and values of the 1¢, 2¢, 3¢, 15¢ types I and II, and the 90¢ carmine and black high denomination all show small advances.

Scott 423B and 423C, the extremely scarce 1914 2¢ and 5¢ Washington issues, perforated 12 by 10, are valued in the grade of fine-very fine. Fortunately, sound examples with neat cancels and fine-very fine centering, exactly what Scott values, sold this past year at auction, and they brought impressive prices. As a result, 423B used moves from $10,000 to $12,500, and 423C used jumps from $15,000 to $17,500.

In the area of errors, Scott 554e, the unused 1923 2¢ Washington definitive imperforate pair, is valued for the first time, at $400.

A new U.S. classic period error was recorded this year. Listed as Scott 542a, the error is the 1920 2¢ Washington definitive, perf 10 by 11, with all color missing, that was offered and sold at auction in a full pane. This error was caused by an extraneous piece of paper falling on the plate or adhering to the pressure roller. Two examples exist in the pane, with 13 surrounding stamps having part of the color missing.

In the modern U.S. listings, a number of new errors were added. Additionally, values moved up for a few of the se-tenant commemorative forever stamp issues, continuing a trend.

Values also increased for the global forever stamps because of the continued uptick in cost for the first-class international letter rate that these stamps satisfy.

Argentina received a thorough review. More than 4,000 value changes were made, most of which were increases. One modern example is the 1990 World Cup Soccer Championships souvenir sheet of four (Scott 1679), which moved from $7 in unused condition to $9 and from $7 to $8 in used condition.

Bolivia was looked at for the 2024 catalog, and more than 200 value changes were recorded. Some values were added for the first time where dashes existed before. One such example is the 2006 Christmas stamp with a red "Agencia Boliviana de Correos" handstamp (Scott 1299A). This stamp is now listed with an unused value of $12.25 and a dash for used. Values for other handstamped stamps were added as well.

Values for Belize were reviewed, and approximately 1,350 changes were made, most of which were increases. An item of note is the 1980 Bird souvenir sheet of six (Scott 500) that went from $55 in unused and used conditions to $62.50.

Lastly, Brazil was thoroughly reviewed, and almost 7,000 value changes were made. There was a mix of increases and decreases, but increases dominated. For example, the 1973 Masonic Emblem stamp (Scott 1303) went from $1.50 unused and 65¢ used to $4.25 and $2.50, respectively.

Many other countries received reviews that are not noted in this letter. We encourage you to pay special attention to the Number Additions, Deletions and Changes listing in this volume. We also suggest reading the catalog introduction, which includes an abundance of useful information.

A digital subscription is also available for the Scott catalogs, and information about the subscription can be found online at www.amosadvantage.com. More than 1,000 images of stamps not pictured in the print edition were added to this year's digital catalog.

Best wishes in your collecting pursuits!

Jay Bigalke, Scott catalog editor-in-chief

Acknowledgments

Our appreciation and gratitude go to the following individuals who have assisted us in preparing information included in this year's Scott catalogues. Some helpers prefer anonymity. These individuals have generously shared their stamp knowledge with others through the medium of the Scott catalogue.

Those who follow provided information that is in addition to the hundreds of dealer price lists and advertisements and scores of auction catalogues and realizations that were used in producing the catalogue values. It is from those noted here that we have been able to obtain information on items not normally seen in published lists and advertisements. Support from these people goes beyond data leading to catalogue values, for they also are key to editorial changes.

A special acknowledgment to Liane and Sergio Sismondo of The Classic Collector for their assistance and knowledge sharing that have aided in the preparation of this year's Standard and Classic Specialized Catalogues.

Clifford J. Alexander
(Carriers and Locals Society)
Roland Austin
Michael & Cecilia Ball (A To Z Stamps)
Jim Bardo (Bardo Stamps)
Brian M. Bleckwenn
(The Philatelic Foundation)
Les Bootman
Roger S. Brody
Tom Brougham
(Canal Zone Study Group)
Paul and Josh Buchsbayew
(Cherrystone Auctions, Inc.)
Timothy Bryan Burgess
Tina and John Carlson (JET Stamps)
Jay T. Carrigan
Carlson Chambliss
Bob Coale
Tony L. Crumbley
(Carolina Coin and Stamp, Inc.)
Christopher Dahle
Charles Deaton
Bob and Rita Dumaine
(Sam Houston Duck Co.)
Charles Epting (H.R. Harmer)
Mike Farrell
David Feldman International Auctioneers
Robert A. Fisher
Jeffrey M. Forster
Robert S. Freeman
Henry L. Gitner
(Henry Gitner Philatelists, Inc.)
Stan Goldfarb
Marc E. Gonzales
Daniel E. Grau
Bruce Hecht (Bruce L. Hecht Co.)
Eric Jackson
Michael Jaffe (Michael Jaffe Stamps, Inc.)
William A. (Bill) Jones
Allan Katz (Ventura Stamp Co.)
Patricia A. Kaufmann
(Civil War Philatelic Society)
Jon Kawaguchi
(Ryukyu Philatelic Specialist Society)
Han Ki Kim
Ingert Kuzych
Ulf Lindahl (Ethiopian Philatelic Society)
Ignacio Llach (Filatelia Llach, S.L.)
William K. McDaniel
Pat McElroy
Brian Metz
Mark S. Miller (India Study Circle)
Gary Morris (Pacific Midwest Co.)
Peter Mosiondz Jr.
Bruce M. Moyer
(Moyer Stamps & Collectables)
Scott Murphy
(Professional Stamp Experts)
Dr. Tiong Tak Ngo
Nik and Lisa Oquist
Don Peterson
(International Philippine Philatelic Society)
Todor Drumev Popov
Dr. Charles Posner
Peter W. W. Powell
Ed Reiser (Century Stamp Co.)
Ghassan D. Riachi
Robert G. Rufe
Theodosios D. Sampson Ph.D.
Dennis W. Schmidt
Joyce and Chuck Schmidt
Guy Shaw
(Mexico-Elmhurst Philatelic Society International)
J. Randall Shoemaker
(Philatelic Stamp Authentication and Grading, Inc.)
Sergio and Liane Sismondo
(The Classic Collector)
Jay Smith
Telah Smith
Mark Stelmacovich
Scott R. Trepel
(Robert A. Siegel Auction Galleries)
Dan Undersander
Steven Unkrich
Herbert R. Volin
Val Zabijaka (Zabijaka Auctions)

Vols. 1A-1B number additions, deletions and changes

Number in 2023 Catalogue	Number in 2024 Catalogue
United States	
new	442a
new	474a
new	542a
new	554e
new	1041Bc
new	1705b
new	1705c
new	2360a
new	2485d
new	5681a
new	5725c
new	5725d
Personal computer postage	
new	1CVP106A
new	1CVP106B
new	1CVP139-1CVP159
Revenue Stamps	
R1f	deleted
Confederate Postmasters' Provisionals	
new	55X2A
Albania	
new	189a
new	200a
Algeria	
new	Q37a
new	Q37b
Argentina	
338a	deleted
Australia	
1937a	1939a
1938c	1940b
1938d	1940c
British Honduras	
J1	J1A
J1b	J1
J2	J2A
J2a	J2
J3	J3A
J3a	J3
J1a	J1B

Addresses, telephone numbers, web sites, email addresses of general and specialized philatelic societies

Collectors can contact the following groups for information about the philately of the areas within the scope of these societies, or inquire about membership in these groups. Aside from the general societies, we limit this list to groups that specialize in particular fields of philately, particular areas covered by the Scott *Standard Postage Stamp Catalogue*, and topical groups. Many more specialized philatelic society exist than those listed below. These addresses are updated yearly, and they are, to the best of our knowledge, correct and current. Groups should inform the editors of address changes whenever they occur. The editors also want to hear from other such specialized groups not listed.

Unless otherwise noted all website addresses begin with http://

General Societies

American Philatelic Society, 100 Match Factory Place, Bellefonte, PA 16823-1367; (814) 933-3803; https://stamps.org; apsinfo@stamps.org

International Society of Worldwide Stamp Collectors, Joanne Murphy, M.D., P.O. Box 19006, Sacramento, CA 95819; www.iswsc.org; executivedirector@iswsc.org

Royal Philatelic Society of Canada, P.O. Box 69080, St. Clair Post Office, Toronto, ON M4T 3A1 Canada; (888) 285-4143; www.rpsc.org; info@rpsc.org

Royal Philatelic Society London, 15 Abchurch Lane, London EX4N 7BW, United Kingdom; +44 (0) 20 7486 1044; www.rpsl.org.uk; secretary@rpsl.org.uk

Libraries, Museums, and Research Groups

American Philatelic Research Library, 100 Match Factory Place, Bellefonte, PA 16823; (814) 933-3803; www.stamplibrary.org; library@stamps.org.

V. G. Greene Philatelic Research Foundation, P.O. Box 69100, St. Clair Post Office, Toronto, ON M4T 3A1, Canada; (416) 921-2073; info@greenefoundation.ca

Aero/Astro Philately

American Air Mail Society, Stephen Reinhard, P.O. Box 110, Mineola, NY 11501; www.americanairmailsociety.org; sreinhard1@optonline.net

Postal History

Auxiliary Markings Club, Jerry Johnson, 6621 W. Victoria Ave., Kennewick, WA 99336; www.postal-markings.org; membership-2010@postal-markings.org

Postage Due Mail Study Group, Bob Medland, Camway Cottage, Nanny Hurn's Lane, Cameley, Bristol BS39 5AJ, United Kingdom; 01761 45959; www.postageduemail.org.uk; secretary.pdmsg@gmail.com

Postal History Society, Yamil Kouri, 405 Waltham St. #347, Lexington, MA 02421; www.postalhistorysociety.org; yhkouri@massmed.org

Post Mark Collectors Club, Bob Milligan, 7014 Woodland Oaks Drive, Magnolia, TX 77354; (281) 259-2735; www.postmarks.org; bob.milligan0@gmail.com

U.S. Cancellation Club, Roger Curran, 18 Tressler Blvd., Lewisburg, PA 17837; rdcnrc@ptd.net

Revenues and Cinderellas

American Revenue Association, Lyman Hensley, 473 E. Elm St., Sycamore, IL 60178-1934; www.revenuer.org; ilrno2@netzero.net

Christmas Seal and Charity Stamp Society, John Denune Jr., 234 E. Broadway, Granville, OH 43023; (740) 814-6031; www.seal-society.org

National Duck Stamp Collectors Society, Anthony J. Monico, P.O. Box 43, Harleysville, PA 19438-0043; www.ndscs.org; ndscs@ndscs.org

State Revenue Society, Kent Gray, P.O. Box 67842, Albuquerque, NM 87193; www.staterevenue.org; srssecretary@comcast.net

Thematic Philately

Americana Unit, Dennis Dengel, 17 Peckham Road, Poughkeepsie, NY 12603-2018; www.americanaunit.org; ddengel@americanaunit.org

American Topical Association, Jennifer Miller, P.O. Box 2143, Greer, SC 29652-2143; (618) 985-5100; americantopical.org; ata@americantopical.org

Astronomy Study Unit, Leonard Zehr, 1411 Chateau Ave., Windsor, ON N8P 1M2, Canada; (416) 833-9317; www.astronomystudyunit.net; lenzehr@gmail.com

Bicycle Stamps Club, Corey Hjalseth, 1102 Broadway, Suite 200, Tacoma, WA 98402; (253) 318-6222; www.bicyclestampsclub.org; coreyh@evergreenhomeloans.com

Biology Unit, Chris Dahle, 1401 Linmar Drive NE, Cedar Rapids, IA 52402-3724; www.biophilately.org; chris-dahle@biophilately.org

Bird Stamp Society, Mr. S. A. H. (Tony) Statham, Ashlyns Lodge, Chesham Road, Berkhamsted, Herts HP4 2ST United Kingdom; www.bird-stamps.org/bss; tony.statham@sky.com

Captain Cook Society, Jerry Yucht, 8427 Leale Ave., Stockton, CA 95212, www.captaincooksociety.com; us@captaincooksociety.com

The CartoPhilatelic Society, Marybeth Sulkowski, 2885 Sanford Ave., SW, #32361, Grandville, MI 49418-1342; www.mapsonstamps.org; secretary@mapsonstamps.org

Casey Jones Railroad Unit, Jeff Lough, 2612 Redbud Land, Apt. C, Lawrence, KS 66046; www.uqp.de/cjr; jeffydplaugh@gmail.com

Cats on Stamps Study Unit, Robert D. Jarvis, 2731 Teton Lane, Fairfield, CA 94533; www.catstamps.info; catmews1@yahoo.com

Chemistry and Physics on Stamps Study Unit, Dr. Roland Hirsch, 13830 Metcalf Ave., Apt. 15218, Overland Park, KS 66223-8017; (301) 792-6296; www.cpossu.org; rfhirsch@cpossu.org

Chess on Stamps Study Unit, Barry Keith, 511 First St. N., Apt. 106; Charlottesville, VA 22902; www.chessonstamps.org; keithfam@embarqmail.com

Cricket Philatelic Society, A. Melville-Brown, 11 Weppons, Ravens Road, Shorham-by-Sea, West Sussex BN43 5AW, United Kingdom; www.cricketstamp.net; mel.cricket.100@googlemail.com

Earth's Physical Features Study Group, Fred Klein, 515 Magdalena Ave., Los Altos, CA 94024; http://epfsu.jeffhayward.com; epfsu@jeffhayward.com

Ebony Society of Philatelic Events and Reflections (ESPER), Don Neal, P.O. Box 5245, Somerset, NJ 08875-5245; www.esperstamps.org; esperdon@verizon.net

Europa Study Unit, Tonny E. Van Loij, 3002 S. Xanthia St.; Denver, CO 80231-4237; (303) 752-0189; www.europastudyunit.org; tvanloij@gmail.com

Fire Service in Philately, John Zaranek, 81 Hillpine Road, Cheektowaga, NY 14227-2259; (716) 668-3352; jczaranek@roadrunner.com

Gastronomy on Stamps Study Unit, David Wolfersburger, 5062 NW 35th Lane Road, Ocala, FL 34482; (314) 494-3795; www.gastronomystamps.org

Gay and Lesbian History on Stamps Club, Joe Petronie, P.O. Box 190842, Dallas, TX 75219-0842; www.glhsonline.org; glhsc@aol.com

Gems, Minerals and Jewelry Study Unit, Fred Haynes, 10 Country Club Drive, Rochester, NY 14618-3720; fredmhaynes55@gmail.com

Graphics Philately Association, Larry Rosenblum. 1030 E. El Camino Real, PMB 107, Sunnyvale, CA 94087-3759; www.graphics-stamps.org; larry@graphics-stamps.org

Journalists, Authors and Poets on Stamps, Christopher D. Cook, 7222 Hollywood Road, Berrien Springs, MI 49103; cdcook2@gmail.com

Lighthouse Stamp Society, www.lighthousestampsociety.org

Lions International Stamp Club, David McKirdy, s-Gravenwetering 248, 3062 SJ Rotterdam, Netherlands; 31(0) 10 212 0313; www.lisc.nl; davidmckirdy@aol.com

Masonic Study Unit, Gene Fricks, 25 Murray Way, Blackwood, NJ 08012-4400; genefricks@comcast.net

Medical Subjects Unit, Dr. Frederick C. Skvara, P.O. Box 6228, Bridgewater, NJ 08807; fcskvara@optonline.net

Napoleonic Age Philatelists, Ken Berry, 4117 NW 146th St., Oklahoma City, OK 73134-1746; (405) 748-8646; www.nap-stamps.org; krb4117@att.net

Old World Archaeological Study Unit, Caroline Scannell, 14 Dawn Drive, Smithtown, NY 11787-176; www.owasu.org; editor@owasu.org

Petroleum Philatelic Society International, Feitze Papa, 922 Meander Drive, Walnut Creek, CA 94598-4239; www.ppsi.org.uk; oildad@astound.net

Rotary on Stamps Fellowship, Gerald L. Fitzsimmons, 105 Calle Ricardo, Victoria, TX 77904; www.rotaryonstamps.org; glfitz@suddenlink.net

Scouts on Stamps Society International, Woodrow (Woody) Brooks, 498 Baldwin Road, Akron, OH 44312; (330) 612-1294; www.sossi.org; secretary@sossi.org

Ships on Stamps Unit, Erik Th. Matzinger, Voorste Havervelden 30, 4822 AL Breda, Netherlands; www.shipsonstamps.org; erikships@gmail.com

Space Topic Study Unit, David Blog, P.O. Box 174, Bergenfield, NJ 07621; www.space-unit.com; davidblognj@gmail.com

Stamps on Stamps Collectors Club, Michael Merritt, 73 Mountainside Road, Mendham, NJ 07945; www.stampsonstamps.org; michael@mischu.me

Windmill Study Unit, Walter J. Hallien, 607 N. Porter St., Watkins Glenn, NY 14891-1345; (607) 229-3541; www.windmillworld.com

Wine On Stamps Study Unit, David Wolfersburger, 5062 NW 35th Lane Road, Ocala, FL 34482; (314) 494-3795; www.wine-on-stamps.org;

United States

American Air Mail Society, Stephen Reinhard, P.O. Box 110, Mineola, NY 11501; www.americanairmailsociety.org; sreinhard1@optonline.net

American First Day Cover Society, P.O. Box 246, Colonial Beach VA 22443-0246; (520) 321-0880; www.afdcs.org; afdcs@afdcs.org

Auxiliary Markings Club, Jerry Johnson, 6621 W. Victoria Ave., Kennewick, WA 99336; www.postal-markings.org; membership-2010@postal-markings.org

American Plate Number Single Society, Rick Burdsall, APNSS Secretary, P.O. BOX 1023, Palatine, IL 60078-1023; www.apnss.org; apnss.sec@gmail.com

American Revenue Association, Lyman Hensley, 473 E. Elm St., Sycamore, IL 60178-1934; www.revenuer.org; ilrno2@netzero.net

American Society for Philatelic Pages and Panels, Ron Walenciak, P.O. Box 1042, Washington Township, NJ 07676; www.asppp.org; ron.walenciak@asppp.org

Canal Zone Study Group, Mike Drabik, P.O. Box 281, Bolton, MA 01740, www.canalzonestudygroup.com; czsgsecretary@gmail.com

Carriers and Locals Society, John Bowman, 14409 Pentridge Drive, Corpus Christi, TX 78410; (361) 933-0757; www.pennypost.org; jbowman@stx.rr.com

Christmas Seal & Charity Stamp Society, John Denune Jr., 234 E. Broadway, Granville, OH 43023; (740) 814-6031; www.seal-society.org; john@christmasseals.net

Civil War Philatelic Society, Patricia A. Kaufmann, 10194 N. Old State Road, Lincoln, DE 19960-3644; (302) 422-2656; www.civilwarphilatelicsociety.org; trishkauf@comcast.net

Error, Freaks, and Oddities Collectors Club, Scott Shaulis, P.O. Box 549, Murrysville, PA 15668-0549; (724) 733-4134; www.efocc.org; scott@shaulisstamps.com

National Duck Stamp Collectors Society, Anthony J. Monico, P.O. Box 43, Harleysville, PA 19438-0043; www.ndscs.org; ndscs@ndscs.org

Plate Number Coil Collectors Club (PNC3), Gene Trinks, 16415 W. Desert Wren Court, Surprise, AZ 85374; (623) 322-4619; www.pnc3.org; gctrinks@cox.net

Post Mark Collectors Club, Bob Milligan, 7014 Woodland Oaks Drive, Magnolia, TX 77354; (281) 259-2735; www.postmarks.org; bob.milligan0@gmail.com

Souvenir Card Collectors Society, William V. Kriebel, www.souvenircards.org; kriebewv@drexel.edu

United Postal Stationery Society, Dave Kandziolka, 404 Sundown Drive, Knoxville, TN 37934; www.upss.org; membership@upss.org

U.S. Cancellation Club, Roger Curran, 18 Tressler Blvd., Lewisburg, PA 17837; rdcnrc@ptd.net

U.S. Philatelic Classics Society, Rob Lund, 2913 Fulton St., Everett, WA 98201-3733; www.uspcs.org; membershipchairman@uspcs.org

US Possessions Philatelic Society, Daniel F. Ring, P.O. Box 113, Woodstock, IL 60098; http://uspps.tripod.com; danielfring@hotmail.com

United States Stamp Society, Rod Juell, P.O. Box 3508, Joliet, IL 60434-3508; www.usstamps.org; execsecretary@usstamps.org

Africa

Bechuanalands and Botswana Society, Otto Peetoom, Roos, East Yorkshire HU12 0LD, United Kingdom; 44(0)1964 670239; www.bechuanalandphilately.com; info@bechuanalandphilately.com

Egypt Study Circle, Mike Murphy, 11 Waterbank Road, Bellingham, London SE6 3DJ United Kingdom; (44) 0203 6737051; www.egyptstudycircle.org.uk; secretary@egyptstudycircle.org.uk

Ethiopian Philatelic Society, Ulf Lindahl, 21 Westview Place, Riverside, CT 06878; (203) 722-0769; https://ethiopianphilatelicsociety.weebly.com; ulindahl@optonline.net

Liberian Philatelic Society, P.O. Box 1570, Parker, CO 80134; www.liberiastamps.org; liberiastamps@comcast.net

Orange Free State Study Circle, J. R. Stroud, RDPSA, 24 Hooper Close, Burnham-on-sea, Somerset TA8 1JQ United Kingdom; 44 1278 782235; www.orangefreestatephilately.org.uk; richard@richardstroud.plus.com

Philatelic Society for Greater Southern Africa, David McNamee, 15 Woodland Drive, Alamo, CA 94507; www.psgsa.org; alan.hanks@sympatico.ca

Rhodesian Study Circle, William R. Wallace, P.O. Box 16381, San Francisco, CA 94116; (415) 564-6069; www.rhodesianstudycircle.org.uk; bwall8rscr@earthlink.net

Society for Moroccan and Tunisian Philately, S.P.L.M., 206, Bld Pereire, 75017 Paris, France; http://splm-philatelie.org; splm206@aol.com

South Sudan Philatelic Society, William Barclay, 1370 Spring Hill Road, South Londonderry, VT 05155; barclayphilatelics@gmail.com

Sudan Study Group, Andy Neal, Bank House, Coedway, Shrewsbury SY5 9AR United Kingdom; www.sudanstamps.org; andywneal@gmail.com

Transvaal Study Circle, c/o 9 Meadow Road, Gravesend, Kent DA11 7LR United Kingdom; www.transvaalstamps.org.uk; transvaalstudycircle@aol.co.uk

West Africa Study Circle, Martin Bratzel, 1233 Virginia Ave., Windsor, ON N8S 2Z1 Canada; www.wasc.org.uk; marty_bratzel@yahoo.ca

Asia

Aden & Somaliland Study Group, Malcom Lacey, 108 Dalestorth Road, Sutton-in-Ashfield, Nottinghamshire NG17 3AA, United Kingdom; www.stampdomain.com/aden; neil53williams@yahoo.co.uk

Burma (Myanmar) Philatelic Study Circle, Michael Whittaker, 1, Ecton Leys, Hillside, Rugby, Warwickshire CV22 5SL United Kingdom; https://burmamyanmarphilately.wordpress.com/burma-myanmar-philatelic-study-circle; manningham8@mypostoffice.co.uk

Ceylon Study Circle, Rodney W. P. Frost, 42 Lonsdale Road, Cannington, Bridgwater, Somerset TA5 2JS United Kingdom; 01278 652592; www.ceylonsc.org; rodney.frost@tiscali.co.uk

China Stamp Society, H. James Maxwell, 1050 W. Blue Ridge Blvd., Kansas City, MO 64145-1216; www.chinastampsociety.org; president@chinastampsociety.org

Hong Kong Philatelic Society, John Tang, G.P.O. Box 446, Hong Kong; www.hkpsociety.com; hkpsociety@outlook.com

Hong Kong Study Circle, Robert Newton, www.hongkongstudycircle.com/index.html; newtons100@gmail.com

India Study Circle, John Warren, P.O. Box 7326, Washington, DC 20044; (202) 488-7443; https://indiastudycircle.org; jw-kbw@earthlink.net

International Philippine Philatelic Society, James R. Larot, Jr., 4990 Bayleaf Court, Martinez, CA 94553; (925) 260-5425; www.theipps.info; jlarot@ccwater.com

International Society for Japanese Philately, P.O. Box 1283, Haddonfield NJ 08033; www.isjp.org; secretary@isjp.org

Iran Philatelic Study Circle, Nigel Gooch, Marchwood, 56, Wickham Ave., Bexhill-on-Sea, East Sussex TN39 3ER United Kingdom; www.iranphilately.org; nigelmgooch@gmail.com

Korea Stamp Society, Peter Corson, 1109 Gunnison Place, Raleigh, NC 27609; (919) 787-7611; koreastampsociety.org; pbcorson@aol.com

Nepal & Tibet Philatelic Study Circle, Colin Hepper, 12 Charnwood Close, Peterborough, Cambs PE2 9BZ United Kingdom; http://fuchs-online.com/ntpsc; ntpsc@fuchs-online.com

Pakistan Philatelic Study Circle, Jeff Siddiqui, P.O. Box 7002, Lynnwood, WA 98046; jeffsiddiqui@msn.com

Society of Indo-China Philatelists, Ron Bentley, 2600 N. 24th St., Arlington, VA 22207; (703) 524-1652; www.sicp-online.org; ron.bentley@verizon.net

Society of Israel Philatelists, Inc., Sarah Berezenko, 100 Match Factory Place, Bellefonte, PA 16823-1367; (814) 933-3803 ext. 212; www.israelstamps.com; israelstamps@gmail.com

Australasia and Oceania

Australian States Study Circle of the Royal Sydney Philatelic Club, Ben Palmer, G.P.O. 1751, Sydney, NSW 2001 Australia; http://club.philas.org.au/states

Fellowship of Samoa Specialists, Trevor Shimell, 18 Aspen Drive, Newton Abbot, Devon TQ12 4TN United Kingdom; www.samoaexpress.org; trevor.shimell@gmail.com

Malaya Study Group, Michael Waugh, 151 Roker Lane, Pudsey, Leeds LS28 9ND United Kingdom; http://malayastudygroup.com; mawpud43@gmail.com

New Zealand Society of Great Britain, Michael Wilkinson, 121 London Road, Sevenoaks, Kent TN13 1BH United Kingdom; 01732 456997; www.nzsgb.org.uk; mwilkin799@aol.com

Pacific Islands Study Circle, John Ray, 24 Woodvale Ave., London SE25 4AE United Kingdom; www.pisc.org.uk; secretary@pisc.org.uk

Papuan Philatelic Society, Steven Zirinsky, P.O. Box 49, Ansonia Station, New York, NY 10023; (718) 706-0616; www.papuanphilatelicsociety.com; szirinsky@cs.com

Pitcairn Islands Study Group, Dr. Everett L. Parker, 207 Corinth Road, Hudson, ME 04449-3057; (207) 573-1686; www.pisg.net; eparker@hughes.net

Ryukyu Philatelic Specialist Society, Laura Edmonds, P.O. Box 240177, Charlotte, NC 28224-0177; (336) 509-3739; www.ryukyustamps.org; secretary@ryukyustamps.org

Society of Australasian Specialists / Oceania, Steve Zirinsky, P.O. Box 230049, New York, NY 10023-0049; www.sasoceania.org; president@sosoceania.org

Sarawak Specialists' Society, Stephen Schumann, 2417 Cabrallo Drive, Hayward, CA 94545; (510) 785-4794; www.britborneostamps.org.uk; vpnam@s-s-s.org.uk

Western Australia Study Group, Brian Pope, P.O. Box 423, Claremont, WA 6910 Australia; (61) 419 843 943; www.wastudygroup.com; wastudygroup@hotmail.com

Europe

American Helvetia Philatelic Society, Richard T. Hall, P.O. Box 15053, Asheville, NC 28813-0053; www.swiss-stamps.org; secretary2@swiss-stamps.org

American Society for Netherlands Philately, Hans Kremer, 50 Rockport Court, Danville, CA 94526; (925) 820-5841; www.asnp1975.com; hkremer@usa.net

Andorran Philatelic Study Circle, David Hope, 17 Hawthorn Drive, Stalybridge, Cheshire SK15 1UE United Kingdom; www.andorranpsc.org.uk; andorranpsc@btinternet.com

Austria Philatelic Society, Ralph Schneider, P.O. Box 978, Iowa Park, TX 76376; (940) 213-5004;

www.austriaphilatelicsociety.com; rschneiderstamps@gmail.com

Channel Islands Specialists Society, Richard Flemming, Burbage, 64 Falconers Green, Hinckley, Leicestershire, LE102SX, United Kingdom; www.ciss.uk; secretary@ciss.uk

Cyprus Study Circle, Rob Wheeler, 47 Drayton Ave., London W13 0LE United Kingdom; www.cyprusstudycircle.org; robwheeler47@aol.com

Danish West Indies Study Unit of Scandinavian Collectors Club, Arnold Sorensen, 7666 Edgedale Drive, Newburgh, IN 47630; (812) 480-6532; www.scc-online.org; valbydwi@hotmail.com

Eire Philatelic Association, John B. Sharkey, 1559 Grouse Lane, Mountainside, NJ 07092-1340; www.eirephilatelicassoc.org; jsharkeyepa@me.com

Faroe Islands Study Circle, Norman Hudson, 40 Queen's Road, Vicar's Cross, Chester CH3 5HB United Kingdom; www.faroeislandssc.org; jntropics@hotmail.com

France & Colonies Philatelic Society, Edward Grabowski, 111 Prospect St., 4C, Westfield, NJ 07090; (908) 233-9318; www.franceandcolsps.org; edjjg@alum.mit.edu

Germany Philatelic Society, P.O. Box 6547, Chesterfield, MO 63006-6547; www.germanyphilatelicusa.org; info@germanyphilatelicsocietyusa.org

Gibraltar Study Circle, Susan Dare, 22, Byways Park, Strode Road, Clevedon, North Somerset BS21 6UR United Kingdom; www.gibraltarstudycircle.wordpress.com; smldare@yahoo.co.uk

International Society for Portuguese Philately, Clyde Homen, 1491 Bonnie View Road, Hollister, CA 95023-5117; www.portugalstamps.com; ispp1962@sbcglobal.net

Italy and Colonies Study Circle, Richard Harlow, 7 Duncombe House, 8 Manor Road, Teddington, Middlesex TW118BE United Kingdom; 44 208 977 8737; www.icsc-uk.com; richardharlow@outlook.com

Liechtenstudy USA, Paul Tremaine, 410 SW Ninth St., Dundee, OR 97115-9731; (503) 538-4500; www.liechtenstudy.org; tremaine@liechtenstudy.org

Lithuania Philatelic Society, Audrius Brazdeikis, 9915 Murray Landing, Missouri City, TX 77459; (281) 450-6224; www.lithuanianphilately.com/lps; audrius@lithuanianphilately.com

Luxembourg Collectors Club, Gary B. Little, 7319 Beau Road, Sechelt, BC V0N 3A8 Canada; (604) 885-7241; http://lcc.luxcentral.com; gary@luxcentral.com

Plebiscite-Memel-Saar Study Group of the German Philatelic Society, Clayton Wallace, 100 Lark Court, Alamo, CA 94507; claytonwallace@comcast.net

Polonus Polish Philatelic Society, Daniel Lubelski, P.O. Box 2212, Benicia, CA 94510; (419) 410-9115; www.polonus.org; info@polonus.org

Rossica Society of Russian Philately, Alexander Kolchinsky, 1506 Country Lake Drive, Champaign, IL 61821-6428; www.rossica.org; alexander.kolchinsky@rossica.org

Scandinavian Collectors Club, Alan Warren, Scandinavian Collectors Club, P.O. Box 39, Exton PA 19341-0039; (612) 810-8640; www.scc-online.org; alanwar@att.net

Society for Czechoslovak Philately, Tom Cossaboom, P.O. Box 4124, Prescott, AZ 86302; (928) 771-9097; www.csphilately.org; klfck1@aol.com

Society for Hungarian Philately, Alan Bauer, P.O. Box 4028, Vineyard Haven, MA 02568; (617) 645-4045; www.hungarianphilately.org; alan@hungarianstamps.com

Spanish Study Circle, Edith Knight, www.spaincircle.wixsite.com/spainstudycircle; spaincircle@gmail.com

Ukrainian Philatelic & Numismatic Society, Martin B. Tatuch, 5117 8th Road N., Arlington, VA 22205-1201; www.upns.org; treasurer@upns.org

Vatican Philatelic Society, Dennis Brady, 4897 Ledyard Drive, Manlius NY 13104-1514; www.vaticanphilately.org; dbrady7534@gmail.com

Yugoslavia Study Group, Michael Chant, 1514 N. Third Ave., Wausau, WI 54401; 208-748-9919; www.yugosg.org; membership@yugosg.org

Interregional Societies

American Society of Polar Philatelists, Alan Warren, P.O. Box 39, Exton, PA 19341-0039; (610) 321-0740; www.polarphilatelists.org; alanwar@att.net

First Issues Collector's Club, Kurt Streepy, 3128 E. Mattatha Drive, Bloomington, IN 47401; www.firstissues.org; secretary@firstissues.org

Former French Colonies Specialist Society, Col.fra, BP 628, 75367 Paris, France; www.colfra.org; postmaster@colfra.org

France & Colonies Philatelic Society, Edward Grabowski, 111 Prospect St., 4C, Westfield, NJ 07090; (908) 233-9318, www.franceandcolsps.org; edjjg@alum.mit.edu

Joint Stamp Issues Society, Richard Zimmermann, 29A, Rue Des Eviats, 67220 Lalaye, France; www.philarz.net; richard.zimmermann@club-internet.fr

The King George VI Collectors Society, Brian Livingstone, 21 York Mansions, Prince of Wales Drive, London SW11 4DL United Kingdom; www.kg6.info; livingstone484@btinternet.com

International Society of Reply Coupon Collectors, Peter Robin, P.O. Box 353, Bala Cynwyd, PA 19004; peterrobin@verizon.net

Italy and Colonies Study Circle, Richard Harlow, 7 Duncombe House, 8 Manor Road, Teddington, Middlesex TW118BE United Kingdom; 44 208 977 8737; www.icsc-uk.com; richardharlow@outlook.com

St. Helena, Ascension & Tristan Da Cunha Philatelic Society, Dr. Everett L. Parker, 207 Corinth Road, Hudson, ME 04449-3057; (207) 573-1686; www.shatps.org; eparker@hughes.net

United Nations Philatelists, Blanton Clement, Jr., P.O. Box 146, Morrisville, PA 19067-0146; www.unpi.com; bclemjunior@gmail.com

Latin America

Asociación Filatélica de Panamá, Edward D. Vianna B. ASOFILPA, 0819-03400, El Dorado, Panama; http://asociacionfilatelicadepanama.blogspot.com; asofilpa@gmail.com

Asociacion Mexicana de Filatelia (AMEXFIL), Alejandro Grossmann, Jose Maria Rico, 129, Col. Del Valle, 3100 Mexico City, DF Mexico; www.amexfil.mx; amexfil@gmail.com

Associated Collectors of El Salvador, Pierre Cahen, Vipsal 1342, P.O. Box 02-5364, Miami FL 33102; www.elsalvadorphilately.org; sfes-aces@elsalvadorphilately.org

Association Filatelic de Costa Rica, Giana Wayman (McCarty), #SJO 4935, P.O. Box 025723, Miami, FL 33102-5723; 011-506-2-228-1947; scotland@racsa.co.cr

Brazil Philatelic Association, William V. Kriebel, www.brazilphilatelic.org, info@brazilphilatelic.org

Canal Zone Study Group, Mike Drabik, P.O. Box 281, Bolton, MA 01740; www.canalzonestudygroup.com; czsgsecretary@gmail.com

Colombia-Panama Philatelic Study Group, Allan Harris, 26997 Hemmingway Ct, Hayward CA 94542-2349; www.copaphil.org; copaphilusa@aol.com

Falkland Islands Philatelic Study Groups, Morva White, 42 Colton Road, Shrivenham, Swindon SN6 8AZ United Kingdom; 44(0) 1793 783245; www.fipsg.org.uk; morawhite@supanet.com

Federacion Filatelica de la Republica de Honduras, Mauricio Mejia, Apartado Postal 1465, Tegucigalpa, D.C. Honduras; 504 3399-7227; www.facebook.com/filateliadehonduras; ffrh@hotmail.com

International Cuban Philatelic Society (ICPS), Ernesto Cuesta, P.O. Box 34434, Bethesda, MD 20827; (301) 564-3099; www.cubafil.org; ecuesta@philat.com

International Society of Guatemala Collectors, Jaime Marckwordt, 449 St. Francis Blvd., Daly City, CA 94015-2136; (415) 997-0295; www.guatemalastamps.com; president@guatamalastamps.com

Mexico-Elmhurst Philatelic Society International, Eric Stovner, P.O. Box 10097, Santa Ana, CA 92711-0097; www.mepsi.org; treasurer@mepsi.org

Nicaragua Study Group, Erick Rodriguez, 11817 S. W. 11th St., Miami, FL 33184-2501; nsgsec@yahoo.com

North America (excluding United States)

British Caribbean Philatelic Study Group, Bob Stewart, 7 West Dune Lane, Long Beach Township, NJ 08008; (941) 379-4108; www.bcpsg.com; bcpsg@comcast.net

British North America Philatelic Society, Andy Ellwood, 10 Doris Ave., Gloucester, ON K1T 3W8 Canada; www.bnaps.org; secretary@bnaps.org

British West Indies Study Circle, Steve Jarvis, 5 Redbridge Drive, Andover, Hants SP10 2LF United Kingdom; 01264 358065; www.bwisc.org; info@bwisc.org

Bermuda Collectors Society, John Pare, 405 Perimeter St., Mount Horeb, WI 53572; (608) 852-7358; www.bermudacollectorssociety.com; pare16@mhtc.net

Haiti Philatelic Society, Ubaldo Del Toro, 5709 Marble Archway, Alexandria, VA 22315; www.haitiphilately.org; u007ubi@aol.com

Hawaiian Philatelic Society, Gannon Sugimura, P.O. Box 10115, Honolulu, HI 96816-0115, www.hpshawaii.com; hiphilsoc@gmail.com

Stamp Dealer Associations

American Stamp Dealers Association, Inc., P.O. Box 513, Centre Hall PA 16828; (800) 369-8207; www.americanstampdealer.com; asda@americanstampdealer.com

National Stamp Dealers Association, Sheldon Ruckens, President, 3643 Private Road 18, Pinckneyville, IL 62274-3426; (618) 357-5497; www.nsdainc.org; nsda@nsdainc.org

Youth Philately

Young Stamp Collectors of America, 100 Match Factory Place, Bellefonte, PA 16823; (814) 933-3803; https://stamps.org/learn/youth-in-philately; ysca@stamps.org

Information on catalogue values, grade and condition

Catalogue value

The Scott Catalogue value is a retail value; that is, an amount you could expect to pay for a stamp in the grade of Very Fine with no faults. Any exceptions to the grade valued will be noted in the text. The general introduction on the following pages and the individual section introductions further explain the type of material that is valued. The value listed for any given stamp is a reference that reflects recent actual dealer selling prices for that item.

Dealer retail price lists, public auction results, published prices in advertising and individual solicitation of retail prices from dealers, collectors and specialty organizations have been used in establishing the values found in this catalogue. Amos Media Co. values stamps, but Amos Media is not a company engaged in the business of buying and selling stamps as a dealer.

Use this catalogue as a guide for buying and selling. The actual price you pay for a stamp may be higher or lower than the catalogue value because of many different factors, including the amount of personal service a dealer offers, or increased or decreased interest in the country or topic represented by a stamp or set. An item may occasionally be offered at a lower price as a "loss leader," or as part of a special sale. You also may obtain an item inexpensively at public auction because of little interest at that time or as part of a large lot.

Stamps that are of a lesser grade than Very Fine, or those with condition problems, generally trade at lower prices than those given in this catalogue. Stamps of exceptional quality in both grade and condition often command higher prices than those listed.

Values for pre-1900 unused issues are for stamps with approximately half or more of their original gum. Stamps with most or all of their original gum may be expected to sell for more, and stamps with less than half of their original gum may be expected to sell for somewhat less than the values listed. On rarer stamps, it may be expected that the original gum will be somewhat more disturbed than it will be on more common issues. Post-1900 unused issues are assumed to have full original gum. From breakpoints in most countries' listings, stamps are valued as never hinged, due to the wide availability of stamps in that condition. These notations are prominently placed in the listings and in the country information preceding the listings. Some countries also feature listings with dual values for hinged and never-hinged stamps.

Grade

A stamp's grade and condition are crucial to its value. The accompanying illustrations show examples of Very Fine stamps from different time periods, along with examples of stamps in Fine to Very Fine and Extremely Fine grades as points of reference. When a stamp seller offers a stamp in any grade from fine to superb without further qualifying statements, that stamp should not only have the centering grade as defined, but it also should be free of faults or other condition problems.

FINE stamps (illustrations not shown) have designs that are quite off center, with the perforations on one or two sides very close to the design but not quite touching it. There is white space between the perforations and the design that is minimal but evident to the unaided eye. Imperforate stamps may have small margins, and earlier issues may show the design just touching one edge of the stamp design. Very early perforated issues normally will have the perforations slightly cutting into the design. Used stamps may have heavier than usual cancellations.

FINE-VERY FINE stamps will be somewhat off center on one side, or slightly off center on two sides. Imperforate stamps will have two margins of at least normal size, and the design will not touch any edge. For perforated stamps, the perfs are well clear of the design, but are still noticeably off center. *However, early issues of a country may be printed in such a way that the design naturally is very close to the edges. In these cases, the perforations may cut into the design very slightly.* Used stamps will not have a cancellation that detracts from the design.

VERY FINE stamps will be just slightly off center on one or two sides, but the design will be well clear of the edge. The stamp will present a nice, balanced appearance. Imperforate stamps will be well centered within normal-sized margins. *However, early issues of many countries may be printed in such a way that the perforations may touch the design on one or more sides. Where this is the case, a boxed note will be found defining the centering and margins of the stamps being valued.* Used stamps will have light or otherwise neat cancellations. This is the grade used to establish Scott Catalogue values.

EXTREMELY FINE stamps are close to being perfectly centered. Imperforate stamps will have even margins that are slightly larger than normal. Even the earliest perforated issues will have perforations clear of the design on all sides.

Amos Media Co. recognizes that there is no formally enforced grading scheme for postage stamps, and that the final price you pay or obtain for a stamp will be determined by individual agreement at the time of transaction.

Condition

Grade addresses only centering and (for used stamps) cancellation. *Condition* refers to factors other than grade that affect a stamp's desirability.

Factors that can increase the value of a stamp include exceptionally wide margins, particularly fresh color, the presence of selvage, and plate or die varieties. Unusual cancels on used stamps (particularly those of the 19th century) can greatly enhance their value as well.

Factors other than faults that decrease the value of a stamp include loss of original gum, regumming, a hinge remnant or foreign object adhering to the gum, natural inclusions, straight edges, and markings or notations applied by collectors or dealers.

Faults include missing pieces, tears, pin or other holes, surface scuffs, thin spots, creases, toning, short or pulled perforations, clipped perforations, oxidation or other forms of color changelings, soiling, stains, and such man-made changes as reperforations or the chemical removal or lightening of a cancellation.

Grading illustrations

On the following two pages are illustrations of various stamps from countries appearing in this volume. These stamps are arranged by country, and they represent early or important issues that are often found in widely different grades in the marketplace. The editors believe the illustrations will prove useful in showing the margin size and centering that will be seen on the various issues.

In addition to the matters of margin size and centering, collectors are reminded that the very fine stamps valued in the Scott catalogues also will possess fresh color and intact perforations, and they will be free from defects.

Examples shown are computer-manipulated images made from single digitized master illustrations.

Stamp illustrations used in the catalogue

It is important to note that the stamp images used for identification purposes in this catalogue may not be indicative of the grade of stamp being valued. Refer to the written discussion of grades on this page and to the grading illustrations on the following two pages for grading information.

Fine-Very Fine →

SCOTT CATALOGUES VALUE STAMPS IN THIS GRADE

Very Fine →

Extremely Fine →

Fine-Very Fine →

SCOTT CATALOGUES VALUE STAMPS IN THIS GRADE

Very Fine →

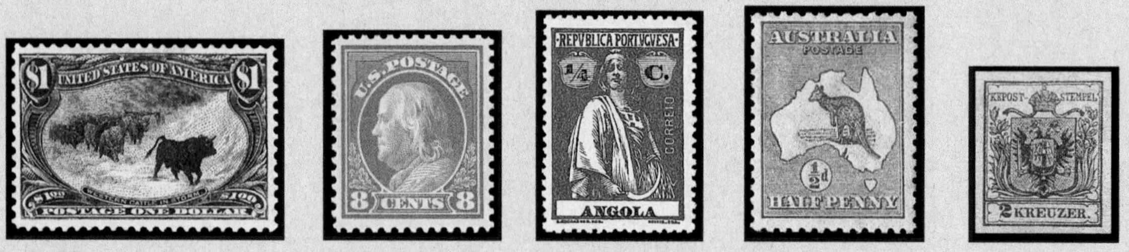

Extremely Fine →

Fine-Very Fine

SCOTT CATALOGUES VALUE STAMPS IN THIS GRADE

Very Fine

Extremely Fine

Fine-Very Fine

SCOTT CATALOGUES VALUE STAMPS IN THIS GRADE

Very Fine

Extremely Fine

Gum Conditions

For purposes of helping to determine the gum condition and value of an unused stamp, Scott presents the following chart which details different gum conditions and indicates how the conditions correlate with the Scott values for unused stamps. Used together, the Illustrated Grading Chart on the previous pages and this Illustrated Gum Chart should allow catalogue users to better understand the grade and gum condition of stamps valued in the Scott catalogues.

Never Hinged (NH; ★★): A never-hinged stamp will have full original gum that will have no hinge mark or disturbance. The presence of an expertizer's mark does not disqualify a stamp from this designation.

Original Gum (OG; ★): Pre-1900 stamps should have approximately half or more of their original gum. On rarer stamps, it may be expected that the original gum will be somewhat more disturbed than it will be on more common issues. Post-1900 stamps should have full original gum. Original gum will show some disturbance caused by a previous hinge(s) which may be present or entirely removed. The actual value of a post-1900 stamp will be affected by the degree of hinging of the full original gum.

Disturbed Original Gum: Gum showing noticeable effects of humidity, climate or hinging over more than half of the gum. The significance of gum disturbance in valuing a stamp in any of the Original Gum categories depends on the degree of disturbance, the rarity and normal gum condition of the issue and other variables affecting quality.

Regummed (RG; (★)): A regummed stamp is a stamp without gum that has had some type of gum privately applied at a time after it was issued. This normally is done to deceive collectors and/or dealers into thinking that the stamp has original gum and therefore has a higher value. A regummed stamp is considered the same as a stamp with none of its original gum for purposes of grading.

Gum Categories:	**MINT N.H.**	**ORIGINAL GUM (O.G.)**				**NO GUM**
	 **Mint Never Hinged** *Free from any disturbance*	 **Lightly Hinged** *Faint impression of a removed hinge over a small area*	 **Hinge Mark or Remnant** *Prominent hinged spot with part or all of the hinge remaining*	 **Large part o.g.** *Approximately half or more of the gum intact*	 **Small part o.g.** Approximately less than half of the gum intact	 **No gum** *Only if issued with gum*
Commonly Used Symbol:	★★	★	★	★	★	(★)
Pre-1900 Issues (Pre-1881 for U.S.)	*Very fine pre-1900 stamps in these categories trade at a premium over Scott value*			Scott Value for "Unused"		Scott "No Gum" listings for selected unused classic stamps
From 1900 to breakpoints for listings of never-hinged stamps	Scott "Never Hinged" listings for selected unused stamps	Scott Value for "Unused" (Actual value will be affected by the degree of hinging of the full o.g.)				
From breakpoints noted for many countries	Scott Value for "Unused"					

Catalogue listing policy

It is the intent of Amos Media Co. to list all postage stamps of the world in the Scott *Standard Postage Stamp Catalogue*. The only strict criteria for listing is that stamps be decreed legal for postage by the issuing country and that the issuing country actually have an operating postal system. Whether the primary intent of issuing a given stamp or set was for sale to postal patrons or to stamp collectors is not part of our listing criteria. Scott's role is to provide basic comprehensive postage stamp information. It is up to each stamp collector to choose which items to include in a collection.

It is Scott's objective to seek reasons why a stamp should be listed, rather than why it should not. Nevertheless, there are certain types of items that will not be listed. These include the following:

1. Unissued items that are not officially distributed or released by the issuing postal authority. If such items are officially issued at a later date by the country, they will be listed. Unissued items consist of those that have been printed and then held from sale for reasons such as change in government, errors found on stamps or something deemed objectionable about a stamp subject or design.

2. Stamps "issued" by non-existent postal entities or fantasy countries, such as Nagaland, Occusi-Ambeno, Staffa, Sedang, Torres Straits and others. Also, stamps "issued" in the names of legitimate, stamp-issuing countries that are not authorized by those countries.

3. Semi-official or unofficial items not required for postage. Examples include items issued by private agencies for their own express services. When such items are required for delivery, or are valid as prepayment of postage, they are listed.

4. Local stamps issued for local use only. Postage stamps issued by governments specifically for "domestic" use, such as Haiti Scott 219-228, or the United States nondenominated stamps, are not considered to be locals, since they are valid for postage throughout the country of origin.

5. Items not valid for postal use. For example, a few countries have issued souvenir sheets that are not valid for postage. This area also includes a number of worldwide charity labels (some denominated) that do not pay postage.

6. Egregiously exploitative issues such as stamps sold for far more than face value, stamps purposefully issued in artificially small quantities or only against advance orders, stamps awarded only to a selected audience such as a philatelic bureau's standing order customers, or stamps sold only in conjunction with other products. All of these kinds of items are usually controlled issues and/or are intended for speculation. These items normally will be included in a footnote.

7. Items distributed by the issuing government only to a limited group, club, philatelic exhibition or a single stamp dealer or other private company. These items normally will be included in a footnote.

8. Stamps not available to collectors. These generally are rare items, all of which are held by public institutions such as museums. The existence of such items often will be cited in footnotes.

The fact that a stamp has been used successfully as postage, even on international mail, is not in itself sufficient proof that it was legitimately issued. Numerous examples of so-called stamps from non-existent countries are known to have been used to post letters that have successfully passed through the international mail system.

There are certain items that are subject to interpretation. When a stamp falls outside our specifications, it may be listed along with a cautionary footnote.

A number of factors are considered in our approach to analyzing how a stamp is listed. The following list of factors is presented to share with you, the catalogue user, the complexity of the listing process.

Additional printings — "Additional printings" of a previously issued stamp may range from an item that is totally different to cases where it is impossible to differentiate from the original. At least a minor number (a small-letter suffix) is assigned if there is a distinct change in stamp shade, noticeably redrawn design, or a significantly different perforation measurement. A major number (numeral or numeral and capital-letter combination) is assigned if the editors feel the "additional printing" is sufficiently different from the original that it constitutes a different issue.

Commemoratives — Where practical, commemoratives with the same theme are placed in a set. For example, the U.S. Civil War Centennial set of 1961-65 and the Constitution Bicentennial series of 1989-90 appear as sets. Countries such as Japan and Korea issue such material on a regular basis, with an announced, or at least predictable, number of stamps known in advance. Occasionally, however, stamp sets that were released over a period of years have been separated. Appropriately placed footnotes will guide you to each set's continuation.

Definitive sets — Blocks of numbers generally have been reserved for definitive sets, based on previous experience with any given country. If a few more stamps were issued in a set than originally expected, they often have been inserted into the original set with a capital-letter suffix, such as U.S. Scott 1059A. If it appears that many more stamps than the originally allotted block will be released before the set is completed, a new block of numbers will be reserved, with the original one being closed off. In some cases, such as the U.S. Transportation and Great Americans series, several blocks of numbers exist. Appropriately placed footnotes will guide you to each set's continuation.

New country — Membership in the Universal Postal Union is not a consideration for listing status or order of placement within the catalogue. The index will tell you in what volume or page number the listings begin.

"No release date" items — The amount of information available for any given stamp issue varies greatly from country to country and even from time to time. Extremely comprehensive information about new stamps is available from some countries well before the stamps are released. By contrast some countries do not provide information about stamps or release dates. Most countries, however, fall between these extremes. A country may provide denominations or subjects of stamps from upcoming issues that are not issued as planned. Sometimes, philatelic agencies, those private firms hired to represent countries, add these later-issued items to sets well after the formal release date. This time period can range from weeks to years. If these items were officially released by the country, they will be added to the appropriate spot in the set. In many cases, the specific release date of a stamp or set of stamps may never be known.

Overprints — The color of an overprint is always noted if it is other than black. Where more than one color of ink has been used on overprints of a single set, the color used is noted. Early overprint and surcharge illustrations were altered to prevent their use by forgers.

Personalized Stamps — Since 1999, the special service of personalizing stamp vignettes, or labels attached to stamps, has been offered to customers by postal administrations of many countries. Sheets of these stamps are sold, singly or in quantity, only through special orders made by mail, in person, or through a sale on a computer website with the postal administrations or their agents for which an extra fee is charged, though some countries offer to collectors at face value personalized stamps having generic images in the vignettes or on the attached labels. It is impossible for any catalogue to know what images have been chosen by customers. Images can be 1) owned or created by the customer, 2) a generic image, or 3) an image pulled from a library of stock images on the stamp creation website. It is also impossible to know the quantity printed for any stamp having a particular image. So from a valuing standpoint, any image is equivalent to any other image for any personalized stamp having the same catalogue number. Illustrations of personalized stamps in the catalogue are not always those of stamps having generic images.

Personalized items are listed with some exceptions. These include:

1. Stamps or sheets that have attached labels that the customer cannot personalize, but which are nonetheless marketed as "personalized," and are sold for far more than the franking value.

2. Stamps or sheets that can be personalized by the customer, but where a portion of the print run must be ceded to the issuing country for sale to other customers.

3. Stamps or sheets that are created exclusively for a particular commercial client, or clients, including stamps that differ from any similar stamp that has been made available to the public.

4. Stamps or sheets that are deliberately conceived by the issuing authority that have been, or are likely to be, created with an excessive number of different face values, sizes, or other features that are changeable.

5. Stamps or sheets that are created by postal administrations using the same system of stamp personalization that has been put in place for use by the public that are printed in limited quantities and sold above face value.

6. Stamps or sheets that are created by licensees not directly affiliated or controlled by a postal administration.

Excluded items may or may not be footnoted.

Se-tenants — Connected stamps of differing features (se-tenants) will be listed in the format most commonly collected. This includes pairs, blocks or larger multiples. Se-tenant units are not always symmetrical. An example is Australia Scott 508, which is a block of seven stamps. If the stamps are primarily collected as a unit, the major number may be assigned to the multiple, with minors going to each component stamp. In cases where continuous-design or other unit se-tenants will receive significant postal use, each stamp is given a major Scott number listing. This includes issues from the United States, Canada, Germany and Great Britain, for example.

Understanding the listings

On the opposite page is an enlarged "typical" listing from this catalogue. Below are detailed explanations of each of the highlighted parts of the listing.

1 Scott number — Scott catalogue numbers are used to identify specific items when buying, selling or trading stamps. Each listed postage stamp from every country has a unique Scott catalogue number. Therefore, Germany Scott 99, for example, can only refer to a single stamp. Although the Scott catalogue usually lists stamps in chronological order by date of issue, there are exceptions. When a country has issued a set of stamps over a period of time, those stamps within the set are kept together without regard to date of issue. This follows the normal collecting approach of keeping stamps in their natural sets.

When a country issues a set of stamps over a period of time, a group of consecutive catalogue numbers is reserved for the stamps in that set, as issued. If that group of numbers proves to be too few, capital-letter suffixes, such as "A" or "B," may be added to existing numbers to create enough catalogue numbers to cover all items in the set. A capital-letter suffix indicates a major Scott catalogue number listing. Scott generally uses a suffix letter only once. Therefore, a catalogue number listing with a capital-letter suffix will seldom be found with the same letter (lower case) used as a minor-letter listing. If there is a Scott 16A in a set, for example, there will seldom be a Scott 16a. However, a minor-letter "a" listing may be added to a major number containing an "A" suffix (Scott 16Aa, for example).

Suffix letters are cumulative. A minor "b" variety of Scott 16A would be Scott 16Ab, not Scott 16b.

There are times when a reserved block of Scott catalogue numbers is too large for a set, leaving some numbers unused. Such gaps in the numbering sequence also occur when the catalogue editors move an item's listing elsewhere or have removed it entirely from the catalogue. Scott does not attempt to account for every possible number, but rather attempts to assure that each stamp is assigned its own number.

Scott numbers designating regular postage normally are only numerals. Scott numbers for other types of stamps, such as air post, semi-postal, postal tax, postage due, occupation and others have a prefix consisting of one or more capital letters or a combination of numerals and capital letters.

2 Illustration number — Illustration or design-type numbers are used to identify each catalogue illustration. For most sets, the lowest face-value stamp is shown. It then serves as an example of the basic design approach for other stamps not illustrated. Where more than one stamp use the same illustration number, but have differences in design, the design paragraph or the description line clearly indicates the design on each stamp not illustrated. Where there are both vertical and horizontal designs in a set, a single illustration may be used, with the exceptions noted in the design paragraph or description line.

When an illustration is followed by a lower-case letter in parentheses, such as "A2(b)," the trailing letter indicates which overprint or surcharge illustration applies.

Illustrations normally are 70 percent of the original size of the stamp. Oversized stamps, blocks and souvenir sheets are reduced even more. Overprints and surcharges are shown at 100 percent of their original size if shown alone, but are 70 percent of original size if shown on stamps. In some cases, the illustration will be placed above the set, between listings or omitted completely. Overprint and surcharge illustrations are not placed in this catalogue for purposes of expertizing stamps.

3 Paper color — The color of a stamp's paper is noted in italic type when the paper used is not white.

4 Listing styles — There are two principal types of catalogue listings: major and minor.

Major listings are in a larger type style than minor listings. The catalogue number is a numeral that can be found with or without a capital-letter suffix, and with or without a prefix.

Minor listings are in a smaller type style and have a small-letter suffix or (if the listing immediately follows that of the major number) may show only the letter. These listings identify a variety of the major item. Examples include perforation and shade differences, multiples (some souvenir sheets, booklet panes and se-tenant combinations), and singles of multiples.

Examples of major number listings include 16, 28A, B97, C13A, 10N5, and 10N6A. Examples of minor numbers are 16a and C13Ab.

5 Basic information about a stamp or set — Introducing each stamp issue is a small section (usually a line listing) of basic information about a stamp or set. This section normally includes the date of issue, method of printing, perforation, watermark and, sometimes, some additional information of note. *Printing method, perforation and watermark apply to the following sets until a change is noted.* Stamps created by overprinting or surcharging previous issues are assumed to have the same perforation, watermark, printing method and other production characteristics as the original. Dates of issue are as precise as Scott is able to confirm and often reflect the dates on first-day covers, rather than the actual date of release.

6 Denomination — This normally refers to the face value of the stamp; that is, the cost of the unused stamp at the post office at the time of issue. When a denomination is shown in parentheses, it does not appear on the stamp. This includes the nondenominated stamps of the United States, Brazil and Great Britain, for example.

7 Color or other description — This area provides information to solidify identification of a stamp. In many recent cases, a description of the stamp design appears in this space, rather than a listing of colors.

8 Year of issue — In stamp sets that have been released in a period that spans more than a year, the number shown in parentheses is the year that stamp first appeared. Stamps without a date appeared during the first year of the issue. Dates are not always given for minor varieties.

9 Value unused and Value used — The Scott catalogue values are based on stamps that are in a grade of Very Fine unless stated otherwise. Unused values refer to items that have not seen postal, revenue or any other duty for which they were intended. Pre-1900 unused stamps that were issued with gum must have at least most of their original gum. Later issues are assumed to have full original gum. From breakpoints specified in most countries' listings, stamps are valued as never hinged. Stamps issued without gum are noted. Modern issues with PVA or other synthetic adhesives may appear ungummed. Unused self-adhesive stamps are valued as appearing undisturbed on their original backing paper. Values for used self-adhesive stamps are for examples either on piece or off piece. For a more detailed explanation of these values, please see the "Catalogue Value," "Condition" and "Understanding Valuing Notations" sections elsewhere in this introduction.

In some cases, where used stamps are more valuable than unused stamps, the value is for an example with a contemporaneous cancel, rather than a modern cancel or a smudge or other unclear marking. For those stamps that were released for postal and fiscal purposes, the used value represents a postally used stamp. Stamps with revenue cancels generally sell for less.

Stamps separated from a complete se-tenant multiple usually will be worth less than a pro-rated portion of the se-tenant multiple, and stamps lacking the attached labels that are noted in the listings will be worth less than the values shown.

10 Changes in basic set information — Bold type is used to show any changes in the basic data given for a set of stamps. These basic data categories include perforation gauge measurement, paper type, printing method and watermark.

11 Total value of a set — The total value of sets of three or more stamps issued after 1900 are shown. The set line also notes the range of Scott numbers and total number of stamps included in the grouping. The actual value of a set consisting predominantly of stamps having the minimum value of 25 cents may be less than the total value shown. Similarly, the actual value or catalogue value of se-tenant pairs or of blocks consisting of stamps having the minimum value of 25 cents may be less than the catalogue values of the component parts.

A6

King George VI
A7

1938-44 **Engr.** **Perf. 12½**

54	A6	½p	green	.25	*2.00*
54A	A6	½p	dk brown ('42)	.25	*2.25*
55	A6	1p	dark brown	2.50	.35
55A	A6	1p	green ('42)	.25	*1.75*
56	A6	1½p	dark carmine	5.00	*6.00*
56A	A6	1½p	gray ('42)	.25	*5.75*
57	A6	2p	gray	5.00	1.25
57A	A6	2p	dark car ('42)	.25	*2.00*
58	A6	3p	blue	.60	1.00
59	A6	4p	rose lilac	1.75	2.00
60	A6	6p	dark violet	2.00	2.00
61	A6	9p	olive bister	2.00	*5.25*
62	A6	1sh	orange & blk	2.10	*3.25*

Typo.
Perf. 14
Chalky Paper

63	A7	2sh	ultra & dl vio, *bl*	7.00	*17.50*
64	A7	2sh6p	red & blk, *bl*	9.00	*24.00*
65	A7	5sh	red & grn, *yel*	35.00	30.00
a.			**5sh dk red & dp grn, *yel* ('44)**	55.00	*140.00*
66	A7	10sh	red & grn, *grn*	35.00	*70.00*

Wmk. 3

67	A7	£1	blk & vio, *red*	30.00	*52.50*
			Nos. 54-67 (18)	138.20	*228.85*
			Set, never hinged	220.00	

1 SCOTT NUMBER

2 ILLUS. NUMBER

3 PAPER COLOR

4 LISTING STYLES — MAJORS — MINORS

5 BASIC INFORMATION ON STAMP OR SET

6 DENOMINATION

7 COLOR OR OTHER DESCRIPTION

8 YEAR OF ISSUE

9 CATALOGUE VALUES — UNUSED — USED

10 CHANGES IN BASIC SET INFORMATION

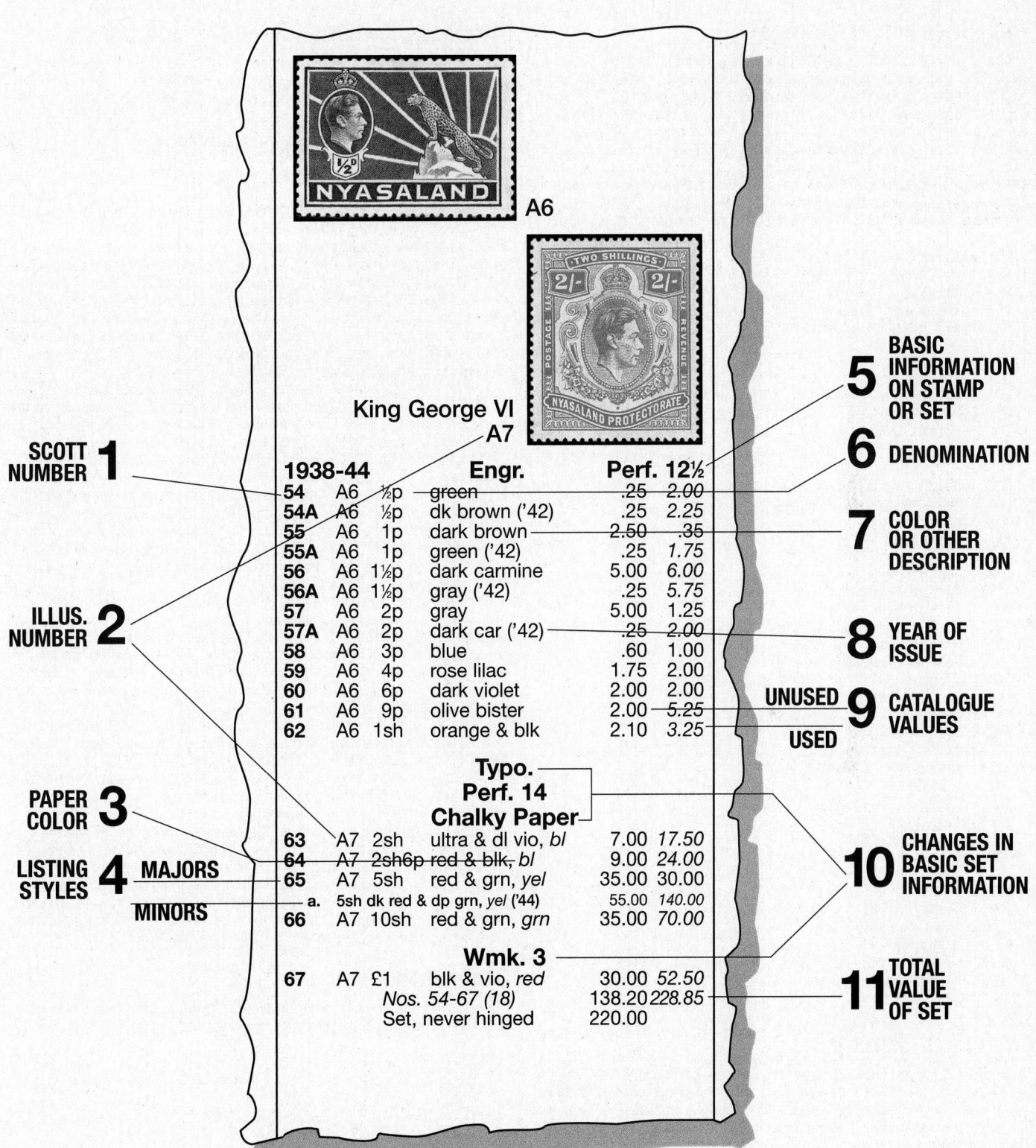

11 TOTAL VALUE OF SET

Special notices

Classification of stamps

The Scott Standard Postage Stamp Catalogue lists stamps by country of issue. The next level of organization is a listing by section on the basis of the function of the stamps. The principal sections cover regular postage, semi-postal, air post, special delivery, registration, postage due and other categories. Except for regular postage, catalogue numbers for all sections include a prefix letter (or number-letter combination) denoting the class to which a given stamp belongs. When some countries issue sets containing stamps from more than one category, the catalogue will at times list all of the stamps in one category (such as air post stamps listed as part of a postage set).

The following is a listing of the most commonly used catalogue prefixes.

Prefix.......Category
C..........Air Post
M.........Military
P..........Newspaper
N..........Occupation - Regular Issues
O..........Official
Q..........Parcel Post
J...........Postage Due
RA.......Postal Tax
B..........Semi-Postal
E..........Special Delivery
MR.......War Tax

Other prefixes used by more than one country include the following:
H..........Acknowledgment of Receipt
I...........Late Fee
CO.......Air Post Official
CQ.......Air Post Parcel Post
RAC.....Air Post Postal Tax
CF........Air Post Registration
CB.......Air Post Semi-Postal
CBO....Air Post Semi-Postal Official
CE.......Air Post Special Delivery
EY........Authorized Delivery
S.........Franchise
G..........Insured Letter
GY.......Marine Insurance
MC.......Military Air Post
MQ......Military Parcel Post
NC.......Occupation - Air Post
NO.......Occupation - Official
NJ........Occupation - Postage Due
NRA.....Occupation - Postal Tax
NB.......Occupation - Semi-Postal
NE.......Occupation - Special Delivery
QY.......Parcel Post Authorized Delivery
AR.......Postal-fiscal
RAJ......Postal Tax Due
RAB.....Postal Tax Semi-Postal
F..........Registration
EB........Semi-Postal Special Delivery
EO.......Special Delivery Official
QE.......Special Handling

New issue listings

Updates to this catalogue appear each month in the *Linn's Stamp News* monthly magazine. Included in this update are additions to the listings of countries found in the Scott *Standard Postage Stamp Catalogue* and the *Specialized Catalogue of United States Stamps and Covers,* as well as corrections and updates to current editions of this catalogue.

From time to time there will be changes in the final listings of stamps from the *Linn's Stamp News* magazine to the next edition of the catalogue. This occurs as more information about certain stamps or sets becomes available.

The catalogue update section of the *Linn's Stamp News* magazine is the most timely presentation of this material available. Annual subscriptions to *Linn's Stamp News* are available from Linn's Stamp News, Box 4129, Sidney, OH 45365-4129.

Number additions, deletions and changes

A listing of catalogue number additions, deletions and changes from the previous edition of the catalogue appears in each volume. See Catalogue Number Additions, Deletions & Changes in the table of contents for the location of this list.

Understanding valuing notations

The *minimum catalogue value* of an individual stamp or set is 25 cents. This represents a portion of the cost incurred by a dealer when he prepares an individual stamp for resale. As a point of philatelic-economic fact, the lower the value shown for an item in this catalogue, the greater the percentage of that value is attributed to dealer mark up and profit margin. In many cases, such as the 25-cent minimum value, that price does not cover the labor or other costs involved with stocking it as an individual stamp. The sum of minimum values in a set does not properly represent the value of a complete set primarily composed of a number of minimum-value stamps, nor does the sum represent the actual value of a packet made up of minimum-value stamps. Thus a packet of 1,000 different common stamps — each of which has a catalogue value of 25 cents — normally sells for considerably less than $250!

The *absence of a retail value* for a stamp does not necessarily suggest that a stamp is scarce or rare. A dash in the value column means that the stamp is known in a stated form or variety, but information is either lacking or insufficient for purposes of establishing a usable catalogue value.

Stamp values in *italics* generally refer to items that are difficult to value accurately. For expensive items, such as those priced at $1,000 or higher, a value in italics indicates that the affected item trades very seldom. For inexpensive items, a value in italics represents a warning. One example is a "blocked" issue where the issuing postal administration may have controlled one stamp in a set in an attempt to make the whole set more valuable. Another example is an item that sold at an extreme multiple of face value in the marketplace at the time of its issue.

One type of warning to collectors that appears in the catalogue is illustrated by a stamp that is valued considerably higher in used condition than it is as unused. In this case, collectors are cautioned to be certain the used version has a genuine and contemporaneous cancellation. The type of cancellation on a stamp can be an important factor in determining its sale price. Catalogue values do not apply to fiscal, telegraph or non-contemporaneous postal cancels, unless otherwise noted.

Some countries have released back issues of stamps in canceled-to-order form, sometimes covering as much as a 10-year period. The Scott Catalogue values for used stamps reflect canceled-to-order material when such stamps are found to predominate in the marketplace for the issue involved. Notes frequently appear in the stamp listings to specify which items are valued as canceled-to-order, or if there is a premium for postally used examples.

Many countries sell canceled-to-order stamps at a marked reduction of face value. Countries that sell or have sold canceled-to-order stamps at *full* face value include United Nations, Australia, Netherlands, France and Switzerland. It may be almost impossible to identify such stamps if the gum has been removed, because official government canceling devices are used. Postally used examples of these items on cover, however, are usually worth more than the canceled-to-order stamps with original gum.

Abbreviations

Scott uses a consistent set of abbreviations throughout this catalogue to conserve space, while still providing necessary information.

Color Abbreviations

amb	amber	crim	crimson	ol	olive
anil	aniline	cr	cream	olvn	olivine
ap	apple	dk	dark	org	orange
aqua	aquamarine	dl	dull	pck	peacock
az	azure	dp	deep	pnksh	pinkish
bis	bister	db	drab	Prus	Prussian
bl	blue	emer	emerald	pur	purple
bld	blood	gldn	golden	redsh	reddish
blk	black	grysh	grayish	res	reseda
bril	brilliant	grn	green	ros	rosine
brn	brown	grnsh	greenish	ryl	royal
brnsh	brownish	hel	heliotrope	sal	salmon
brnz	bronze	hn	henna	saph	sapphire
brt	bright	ind	indigo	scar	scarlet
brnt	burnt	int	intense	sep	sepia
car	carmine	lav	lavender	sien	sienna
cer	cerise	lem	lemon	sil	silver
chlky	chalky	lil	lilac	sl	slate
cham	chamois	lt	light	stl	steel
chnt	chestnut	mag	magenta	turq	turquoise
choc	chocolate	man	manila	ultra	ultramarine
chr	chrome	mar	maroon	Ven	Venetian
cit	citron	mv	mauve	ver	vermilion
cl	claret	multi	multicolored	vio	violet
cob	cobalt	mlky	milky	yel	yellow
cop	copper	myr	myrtle	yelsh	yellowish

When no color is given for an overprint or surcharge, black is the color used. Abbreviations for colors used for overprints and surcharges include: "(B)" or "(Blk)," black; "(Bl)," blue; "(R)," red; and "(G)," green.

Additional abbreviations in this catalogue are shown below:

Adm. ....Administration
AFL ....American Federation of Labor
Anniv. ....Anniversary
APS ....American Philatelic Society
Assoc. ....Association
ASSR. ....Autonomous Soviet Socialist Republic
b...................Born
BEP ....Bureau of Engraving and Printing
Bicent. ....Bicentennial
Bklt. ....Booklet
Brit. ....British
btwn. ....Between
Bur. ....Bureau
c. or ca. ....Circa
Cat. ....Catalogue
Cent. ....Centennial, century, centenary
CIO ....Congress of Industrial Organizations
Conf. ....Conference
Cong. ....Congress
Cpl. ....Corporal
CTO ....Canceled to order
d...................Died
Dbl. ....Double
EDU ....Earliest documented use
Engr. ....Engraved
Exhib. ....Exhibition
Expo. ....Exposition
Fed. ....Federation
GB ....Great Britain
Gen. ....General
GPO ....General post office
Horiz. ....Horizontal
Imperf. ....Imperforate
Impt. ....Imprint
Intl. ....International
Invtd. ....Inverted
L...................Left
Lieut., lt. ....Lieutenant
Litho. ....Lithographed
LL.................Lower left
LR ....Lower right
mm ....Millimeter
Ms. ....Manuscript
Natl. ....National
No. ....Number
NY ....New York
NYC ....New York City
Ovpt. ....Overprint
Ovptd. ....Overprinted
P ....Plate number
Perf. ....Perforated, perforation
Phil. ....Philatelic
Photo. ....Photogravure
PO ....Post office
Pr. ....Pair
P.R. ....Puerto Rico
Prec. ....Precancel, precanceled
Pres. ....President
PTT ....Post, Telephone and Telegraph
R ....Right
Rio ....Rio de Janeiro
Sgt. ....Sergeant
Soc. ....Society
Souv. ....Souvenir
SSR ....Soviet Socialist Republic, see ASSR
St. ....Saint, street
Surch. ....Surcharge
Typo. ....Typographed
UL ....Upper left
Unwmkd. ......Unwatermarked
UPU ....Universal Postal Union
UR ....Upper Right
US ....United States
USPOD ....United States Post Office Department
USSR ....Union of Soviet Socialist Republics
Vert. ....Vertical
VP ....Vice president
Wmk. ....Watermark
Wmkd. ....Watermarked
WWI ....World War I
WWII ....World War II

Examination

Amos Media Co. will not comment upon the genuineness, grade or condition of stamps, because of the time and responsibility involved. Rather, there are several expertizing groups that undertake this work for both collectors and dealers. Neither will Amos Media Co. appraise or identify philatelic material. The company cannot take responsibility for unsolicited stamps or covers sent by individuals.

All letters, emails, etc. are read attentively, but they are not always answered because of time considerations.

How to order from your dealer

When ordering stamps from a dealer, it is not necessary to write the full description of a stamp as listed in this catalogue. All you need is the name of the country, the Scott catalogue number and whether the desired item is unused or used. For example, "Japan Scott 422 unused" is sufficient to identify the unused stamp of Japan listed as "422 A206 5y brown."

Basic stamp information

A stamp collector's knowledge of the combined elements that make a given stamp issue unique determines his or her ability to identify stamps. These elements include paper, watermark, method of separation, printing, design and gum. On the following pages each of these important areas is briefly described.

Paper

Paper is an organic material composed of a compacted weave of cellulose fibers and generally formed into sheets. Paper used to print stamps may be manufactured in sheets, or it may have been part of a large roll (called a web) before being cut to size. The fibers most often used to create paper on which stamps are printed include bark, wood, straw and certain grasses. In many cases, linen or cotton rags have been added for greater strength and durability. Grinding, bleaching, cooking and rinsing these raw fibers reduces them to a slushy pulp, referred to by paper makers as "stuff." Sizing and, sometimes, coloring matter is added to the pulp to make different types of finished paper.

After the stuff is prepared, it is poured onto sieve-like frames that allow the water to run off, while retaining the matted pulp. As fibers fall onto the screen and are held by gravity, they form a natural weave that will later hold the paper together. If the screen has metal bits that are formed into letters or images attached, it leaves slightly thinned areas on the paper. These are called watermarks.

When the stuff is almost dry, it is passed under pressure through smooth or engraved rollers — dandy rolls — or placed between cloth in a press to be flattened and dried.

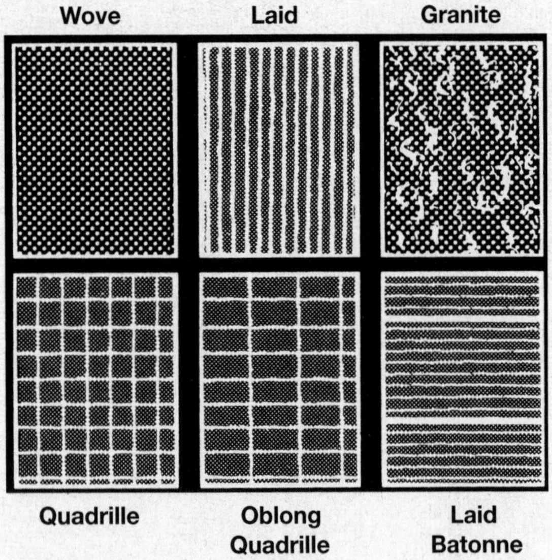

Stamp paper falls broadly into two types: wove and laid. The nature of the surface of the frame onto which the pulp is first deposited causes the differences in appearance between the two. If the surface is smooth and even, the paper will be of fairly uniform texture throughout. This is known as wove paper. Early papermaking machines poured the pulp onto a continuously circulating web of felt, but modern machines feed the pulp onto a cloth-like screen made of closely interwoven fine wires. This paper, when held to a light, will show little dots or points very close together. The proper name for this is "wire wove," but the type is still considered wove. Any U.S. or British stamp printed after 1880 will serve as an example of wire wove paper.

Closely spaced parallel wires, with cross wires at wider intervals, make up the frames used for what is known as laid paper. A greater thickness of the pulp will settle between the wires. The paper, when held to a light, will show alternate light and dark lines. The spacing and the thickness of the lines may vary, but on any one sheet of paper they are all alike. See Russia Scott 31-38 for examples of laid paper.

Batonne, from the French word meaning "a staff," is a term used if the lines in the paper are spaced quite far apart, like the printed ruling on a writing tablet. Batonne paper may be either wove or laid. If laid, fine laid lines can be seen between the batons.

Quadrille is the term used when the lines in the paper form little squares. Oblong quadrille is the term used when rectangles, rather than squares, are formed. Grid patterns vary from distinct to extremely faint. See Mexico-Guadalajara Scott 35-37 for examples of oblong quadrille paper.

Paper also is classified as thick or thin, hard or soft, and by color. Such colors may include yellowish, greenish, bluish and reddish.

Brief explanations of other types of paper used for printing stamps, as well as examples, follow.

Colored — Colored paper is created by the addition of dye in the paper-making process. Such colors may include shades of yellow, green, blue and red. Surface-colored papers, most commonly used for British colonial issues in 1913-14, are created when coloring is added only to the surface during the finishing process. Stamps printed on surface-colored paper have white or uncolored backs, while true colored papers are colored through. See Jamaica Scott 71-73.

Pelure — Pelure paper is a very thin, hard and often brittle paper that is sometimes bluish or grayish in appearance. See Serbia Scott 169-170.

Native — This is a term applied to handmade papers used to produce some of the early stamps of the Indian states. Stamps printed on native paper may be expected to display various natural inclusions that are normal and do not negatively affect value. Japanese paper, originally made of mulberry fibers and rice flour, is part of this group. See Japan Scott 1-18.

Manila — This type of paper is often used to make stamped envelopes and wrappers. It is a coarse-textured stock, usually smooth on one side and rough on the other. A variety of colors of manila paper exist, but the most common range is yellowish-brown.

Silk — Introduced by the British in 1847 as a safeguard against counterfeiting, silk paper contains bits of colored silk thread scattered throughout. The density of these fibers varies greatly and can include as few as one fiber per stamp or hundreds. U.S. revenue Scott R152 is a good example of an easy-to-identify silk paper stamp.

Silk-thread paper has uninterrupted threads of colored silk arranged so that one or more threads run through the stamp or postal stationery. See Great Britain Scott 5-6 and Switzerland Scott 14-19.

Granite — Filled with minute cloth or colored paper fibers of various colors and lengths, granite paper should not be confused with either type of silk paper. Austria Scott 172-175 and a number of Swiss stamps are examples of granite paper.

Chalky — A chalk-like substance coats the surface of chalky paper to discourage the cleaning and reuse of canceled stamps, as well as to provide a smoother, more acceptable printing surface. Because the designs of stamps printed on chalky paper are imprinted on what is often a water-soluble coating, any attempt to remove a cancellation will destroy the stamp. Do not soak these stamps in any fluid. To remove a stamp printed on chalky paper from an envelope, wet the paper from underneath the stamp until the gum dissolves enough to release the stamp from the paper. See St. Kitts-Nevis Scott 89-90 for examples of stamps printed on this type of chalky paper.

India — Another name for this paper, originally introduced from China about 1750, is "China Paper." It is a thin, opaque paper often used for plate and die proofs by many countries.

Double — In philately, the term double paper has two distinct meanings. The first is a two-ply paper, usually a combination of a thick and a thin sheet, joined during manufacture. This type was used experimentally as a means to discourage the reuse of stamps.

The design is printed on the thin paper. Any attempt to remove a cancellation would destroy the design. U.S. Scott 158 and other Banknote-era stamps exist on this form of double paper.

The second type of double paper occurs on a rotary press, when the end of one paper roll, or web, is affixed to the next roll to save time feeding the paper through the press. Stamp designs are printed over the joined paper and, if overlooked by inspectors, may get into post office stocks.

Goldbeater's Skin — This type of paper was used for the 1866 issue of Prussia, and was a tough, translucent paper. The design was printed in reverse on the back of the stamp, and the gum applied over the printing. It is impossible to remove stamps printed on this type of paper from the paper to which they are affixed without destroying the design.

Ribbed — Ribbed paper has an uneven, corrugated surface made by passing the paper through ridged rollers. This type exists on some copies of U.S. Scott 156-165.

Various other substances, or substrates, have been used for stamp manufacture, including wood, aluminum, copper, silver and gold foil, plastic, and silk and cotton fabrics.

Watermarks

Watermarks are an integral part of some papers. They are formed in the process of paper manufacture. Watermarks consist of small designs, formed of wire or cut from metal and soldered to the surface of the mold or, sometimes, on the dandy roll. The designs may be in the form of crowns, stars, anchors, letters or other characters or symbols. These pieces of metal — known in the paper-making industry as "bits" — impress a design into the paper. The design sometimes may be seen by holding the stamp to the light. Some are more easily seen with a watermark detector. This important tool is a small black tray into which a stamp is placed face down and dampened with a fast-evaporating watermark detection fluid that brings up the watermark image in the form of dark lines against a lighter background. These dark lines are the thinner areas of the paper known as the watermark. Some watermarks are extremely difficult to locate, due to either a faint impression, watermark location or the color of the stamp. There also are electric watermark detectors that come with plastic filter disks of various colors. The disks neutralize the color of the stamp, permitting the watermark to be seen more easily.

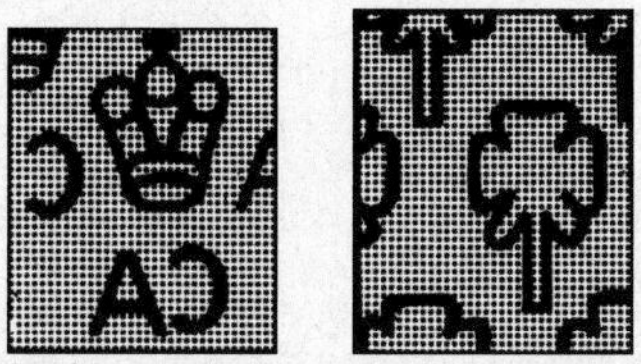

Multiple watermarks of Crown Agents and Burma

Watermarks of Uruguay, Vatican City and Jamaica

WARNING: Some inks used in the photogravure process dissolve in watermark fluids (Please see the section on Soluble Printing Inks). Also, see "chalky paper."

Watermarks may be found normal, reversed, inverted, reversed and inverted, sideways or diagonal, as seen from the back of the stamp. The relationship of watermark to stamp design depends on the position of the printing plates or how paper is fed through the press. On machine-made paper, watermarks normally are read from right to left. The design is repeated closely throughout the sheet in a "multiple-watermark design." In a "sheet watermark," the design appears only once on the sheet, but extends over many stamps. Individual stamps may carry only a small fraction or none of the watermark.

"Marginal watermarks" occur in the margins of sheets or panes of stamps. They occur on the outside border of paper (ostensibly outside the area where stamps are to be printed). A large row of letters may spell the name of the country or the manufacturer of the paper, or a border of lines may appear. Careless press feeding may cause parts of these letters and/or lines to show on stamps of the outer row of a pane.

Soluble printing inks

WARNING: Most stamp colors are permanent; that is, they are not seriously affected by short-term exposure to light or water. Many colors, especially of modern inks, fade from excessive exposure to light. There are stamps printed with inks that dissolve easily in water or in fluids used to detect watermarks. Use of these inks was intentional to prevent the removal of cancellations. Water affects all aniline inks, those on so-called safety paper and some photogravure printings - all such inks are known as fugitive colors. Removal from paper of such stamps requires care and alternatives to traditional soaking.

Separation

"Separation" is the general term used to describe methods used to separate stamps. The three standard forms currently in use are perforating, rouletting and die-cutting. These methods are done during the stamp production process, after printing. Sometimes these methods are done on-press or sometimes as a separate step. The earliest issues, such as the 1840 Penny Black of Great Britain (Scott 1), did not have any means provided for separation. It was expected the stamps would be cut apart with scissors or folded and torn. These are examples of imperforate stamps. Many stamps were first issued in imperforate formats and were later issued with perforations. Therefore, care must be observed in buying single imperforate stamps to be certain they were issued imperforate and are not perforated copies that have been altered by having the perforations trimmed away. Stamps issued imperforate usually are valued as singles. However, imperforate varieties of normally perforated stamps should be collected in pairs or larger pieces as indisputable evidence of their imperforate character.

PERFORATION

The chief style of separation of stamps, and the one that is in almost universal use today, is perforating. By this process, paper between the stamps is cut away in a line of holes, usually round, leaving little bridges of paper between the stamps to hold them together. Some types of perforation, such as hyphen-hole perfs, can be confused with roulettes, but a close visual inspection reveals that paper has been removed. The little perforation bridges, which project from the stamp when it is torn from the pane, are called the teeth of the perforation.

As the size of the perforation is sometimes the only way to differentiate between two otherwise identical stamps, it is necessary to be able to accurately measure and describe them. This is done with a perforation gauge, usually a ruler-like device that has dots or graduated lines to show how many perforations may be counted in the space of two centimeters. Two centimeters is the space universally adopted in which to measure perforations.

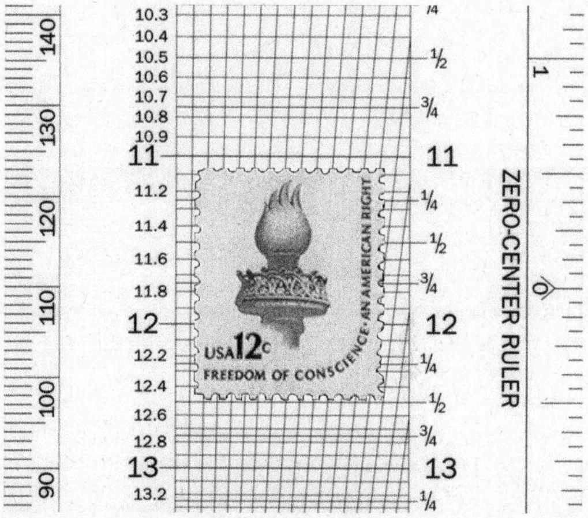

Perforation gauge

To measure a stamp, run it along the gauge until the dots on it fit exactly into the perforations of the stamp. If you are using a graduated-line perforation gauge, simply slide the stamp along the surface until the lines on the gauge perfectly project from the center of the bridges or holes. The number to the side of the line of dots or lines that fit the stamp's perforation is the measurement. For example, an "11" means that 11 perforations fit between two centimeters. The description of the stamp therefore is "perf. 11." If the gauge of the perforations on the top and bottom of a stamp differs from that on the sides, the result is what is known as compound perforations. In measuring compound perforations, the gauge at top and bottom is always given first, then the sides. Thus, a stamp that measures 11 at top and bottom and 10½ at the sides is "perf. 11 x 10½." See U.S. Scott 632-642 for examples of compound perforations.

Stamps also are known with perforations different on three or all four sides. Descriptions of such items are clockwise, beginning with the top of the stamp.

A perforation with small holes and teeth close together is a "fine perforation." One with large holes and teeth far apart is a "coarse perforation." Holes that are jagged, rather than clean-cut, are "rough perforations." *Blind perforations* are the slight impressions left by the perforating pins if they fail to puncture the paper. Multiples of stamps showing blind perforations may command a slight premium over normally perforated stamps.

The term *syncopated perfs* describes intentional irregularities in the perforations. The earliest form was used by the Netherlands from 1925-33, where holes were omitted to create distinctive patterns. Beginning in 1992, Great Britain has used an oval perforation to help prevent counterfeiting. Several other countries have started using the oval perfs or other syncopated perf patterns.

A new type of perforation, still primarily used for postal stationery, is known as microperfs. Microperfs are tiny perforations (in some cases hundreds of holes per two centimeters) that allows items to be intentionally separated very easily, while not accidentally breaking apart as easily as standard perforations. These are not currently measured or differentiated by size, as are standard perforations.

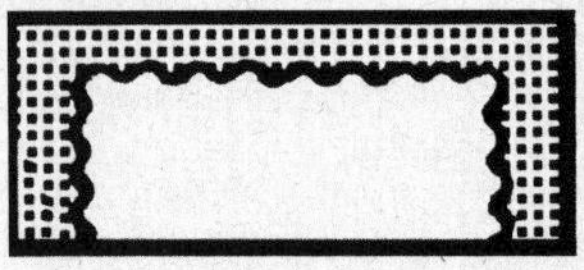

perce en arc

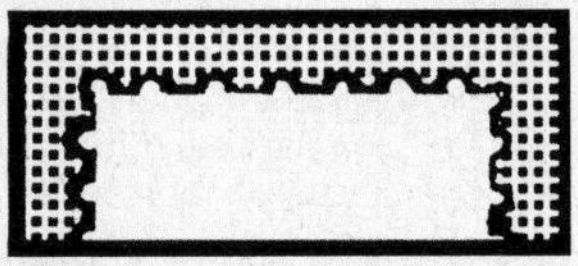

perce en lignes

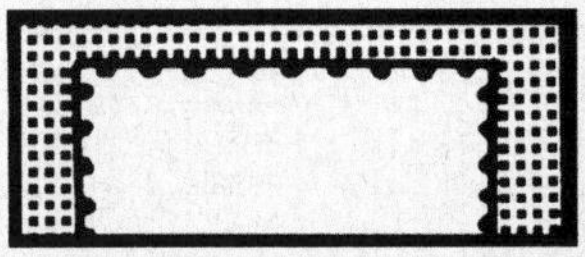

perce en points

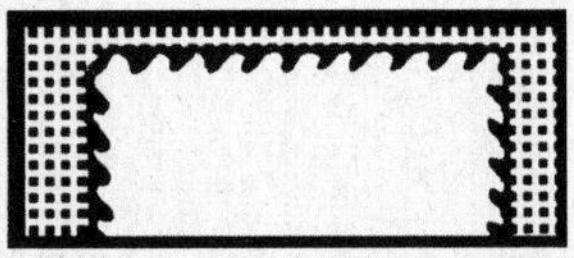

oblique roulette

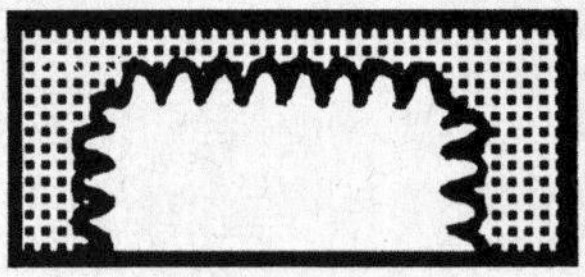

perce en scie

perce serpentin

ROULETTING

In rouletting, the stamp paper is cut partly or wholly through, with no paper removed. In perforating, some paper is removed. Rouletting derives its name from the French roulette, a spur-like wheel. As the wheel is rolled over the paper, each point makes a small cut. The number of cuts made in a two-centimeter space determines the gauge of the roulette, just as the number of perforations in two centimeters determines the gauge of the perforation.

The shape and arrangement of the teeth on the wheels varies. Various roulette types generally carry French names:

Perce en lignes — rouletted in lines. The paper receives short, straight cuts in lines. This is the most common type of rouletting. See Mexico Scott 500.

Perce en points — pin-rouletted or pin-perfed. This differs from a small perforation because no paper is removed, although round, equidistant holes are pricked through the paper. See Mexico Scott 242-256.

Perce en arc and perce en scie — pierced in an arc or saw-toothed designs, forming half circles or small triangles. See Hanover (German States) Scott 25-29.

Perce en serpentin — serpentine roulettes. The cuts form a serpentine or wavy line. See Brunswick (German States) Scott 13-18.

Once again, no paper is removed by these processes, leaving the stamps easily separated, but closely attached.

DIE-CUTTING

The third major form of stamp separation is die-cutting. This is a method where a die in the pattern of separation is created that later cuts the stamp paper in a stroke motion. Although some standard stamps bear die-cut perforations, this process is primarily used for self-adhesive postage stamps. Die-cutting can appear in straight lines, such as U.S. Scott 2522, shapes, such as U.S. Scott 1551, or imitating the appearance of perforations, such as New Zealand Scott 935A and 935B.

Printing processes

ENGRAVING (Intaglio, Line-engraving, Etching)

Master die — The initial operation in the process of line engraving is making the master die. The die is a small, flat block of softened steel upon which the stamp design is recess engraved in reverse.

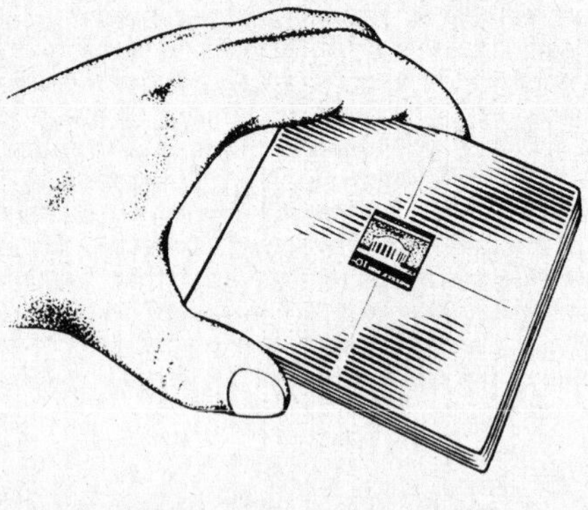

Photographic reduction of the original art is made to the appropriate size. It then serves as a tracing guide for the initial outline of the design. The engraver lightly traces the design on the steel with his graver, then slowly works the design until it is completed. At various points during the engraving process, the engraver hand-inks the die and makes an impression to check his progress. These are known as progressive die proofs. After completion of the engraving, the die is hardened to withstand the stress and pressures of later transfer operations.

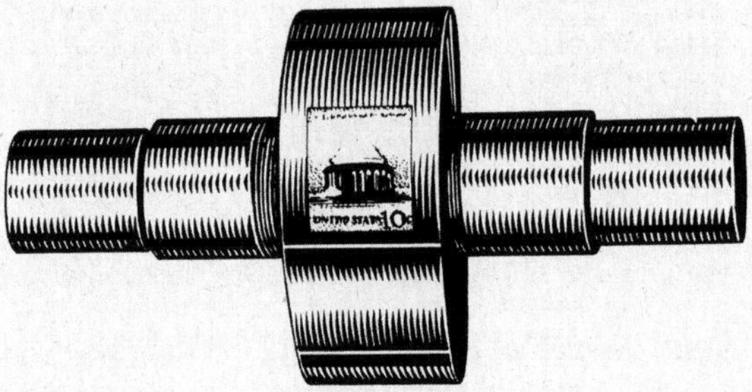

Transfer roll

Transfer roll — Next is production of the transfer roll that, as the name implies, is the medium used to transfer the subject from the master die to the printing plate. A blank roll of soft steel, mounted on a mandrel, is placed under the bearers of the transfer press to allow it to roll freely on its axis. The hardened die is placed on the bed of the press and the face of the transfer roll is applied to the die, under pressure. The bed or the roll is then rocked back and forth under increasing pressure, until the soft steel of the roll is forced into every engraved line of the die. The resulting impression on the roll is known as a "relief" or a "relief transfer." The engraved image is now positive in appearance and stands out from the steel. After the required number of reliefs are "rocked in," the soft steel transfer roll is hardened.

Different flaws may occur during the relief process. A defective relief may occur during the rocking in process because of a minute piece of foreign material lodging on the die, or some other cause. Imperfections in the steel of the transfer roll may result in a breaking away of parts of the design. This is known as a relief break, which will show up on finished stamps as small, unprinted areas. If a damaged relief remains in use, it will transfer a repeating defect to the plate. Deliberate alterations of reliefs sometimes occur. "Altered reliefs" designate these changed conditions.

Plate — The final step in pre-printing production is the making of the printing plate. A flat piece of soft steel replaces the die on the bed of the transfer press. One of the reliefs on the transfer roll is positioned over this soft steel. Position, or layout, dots determine the correct position on the plate. The dots have been lightly marked on the plate in advance. After the correct position of the relief is determined, the design is rocked in by following the same method used in making the transfer roll. The difference is that this time the image is being transferred from the transfer roll, rather than to it. Once the design is entered on the plate, it appears in reverse and is recessed. There are as many transfers entered on the plate as there are subjects printed on the sheet of stamps. It is during this process that double and shifted transfers occur, as well as re-entries. These are the result of improperly entered images that have not been properly burnished out prior to rocking in a new image.

Modern siderography processes, such as those used by the U.S. Bureau of Engraving and Printing, involve an automated form of rocking designs in on preformed cylindrical printing sleeves. The same process also allows for easier removal and re-entry of worn images right on the sleeve.

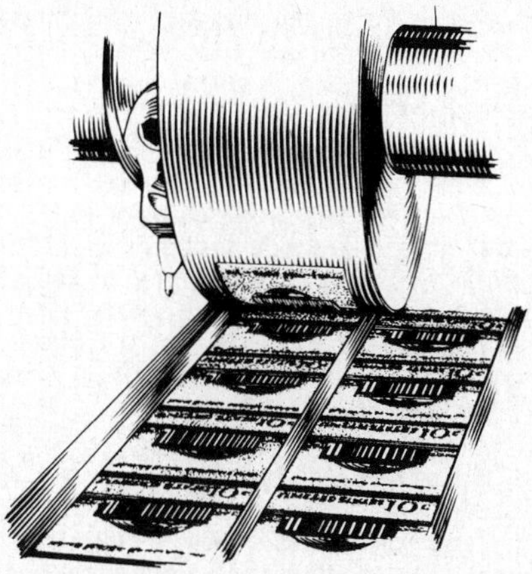

Transferring the design to the plate

Following the entering of the required transfers on the plate, the position dots, layout dots and lines, scratches and other markings generally are burnished out. Added at this time by the siderographer are any required guide lines, plate numbers or other marginal markings. The plate is then hand-inked and a proof impression is taken. This is known as a plate proof. If the impression is approved, the plate is machined for fitting onto the press, is hardened and sent to the plate vault ready for use.

On press, the plate is inked and the surface is automatically wiped clean, leaving ink only in the recessed lines. Paper is then forced under pressure into the engraved recessed lines, thereby receiving the ink. Thus, the ink lines on engraved stamps are slightly raised, and slight depressions (debossing) occur on the back of the stamp. Prior to the advent of modern high-speed presses and more advanced ink formulations, paper had to be dampened before receiving the ink. This sometimes led to uneven shrinkage by the time the stamps were perforated, resulting in improperly perforated stamps, or misperfs. Newer presses use drier paper, thus both *wet and dry printings* exist on some stamps.

Rotary Press — Until 1914, only flat plates were used to print engraved stamps. Rotary press printing was introduced in 1914, and slowly spread. Some countries still use flat-plate printing.

After approval of the plate proof, older rotary press plates require additional machining. They are curved to fit the press cylinder. "Gripper slots" are cut into the back of each plate to receive the "grippers," which hold the plate securely on the press. The plate is then hardened. Stamps printed from these bent rotary press plates are longer or wider than the same stamps printed from flat-plate presses. The stretching of the plate during the curving process is what causes this distortion.

Re-entry — To execute a re-entry on a flat plate, the transfer roll is re-applied to the plate, often at some time after its first use on the press. Worn-out designs can be resharpened by carefully burnishing out the original image and re-entering it from the transfer roll. If the original impression has not been sufficiently removed and the transfer roll is not precisely in line with the remaining impression, the resulting double transfer will make the re-entry obvious. If the registration is true, a re-entry may be difficult or impossible to distinguish. Sometimes a stamp printed from a successful re-entry is identified by having a much sharper and clearer impression than its neighbors. With the advent of rotary presses, post-press re-entries were not possible. After a plate was curved for the rotary press, it was impossible to make a re-entry. This is because the plate had already been bent once (with the design distorted).

However, with the introduction of the previously mentioned modern-style siderography machines, entries are made to the preformed cylindrical printing sleeve. Such sleeves are dechromed and softened. This allows individual images to be burnished out and re-entered on the curved sleeve. The sleeve is then rechromed, resulting in longer press life.

Double Transfer — This is a description of the condition of a transfer on a plate that shows evidence of a duplication of all, or a portion of the design. It usually is the result of the changing of the registration between the transfer roll and the plate during the rocking in of the original entry. Double transfers also occur when only a portion of the design has been rocked in and improper positioning is noted. If the worker elected not to burnish out the partial or completed design, a strong double transfer will occur for part or all of the design.

It sometimes is necessary to remove the original transfer from a plate and repeat the process a second time. If the finished re-worked image shows traces of the original impression, attributable to incomplete burnishing, the result is a partial double transfer.

With the modern automatic machines mentioned previously, double transfers are all but impossible to create. Those partially doubled images on stamps printed from such sleeves are more than likely re-entries, rather than true double transfers.

Re-engraved — Alterations to a stamp design are sometimes necessary after some stamps have been printed. In some cases, either the original die or the actual printing plate may have its "temper" drawn (softened), and the design will be re-cut. The resulting impressions from such a re-engraved die or plate may differ slightly from the original issue, and are known as "re-engraved." If the alteration was made to the master die, all future printings will be consistently different from the original. If alterations were made to the printing plate, each altered stamp on the plate will be slightly different from each other, allowing specialists to reconstruct a complete printing plate.

Dropped Transfers — If an impression from the transfer roll has not been properly placed, a dropped transfer may occur. The final stamp image will appear obviously out of line with its neighbors.

Short Transfer — Sometimes a transfer roll is not rocked its entire length when entering a transfer onto a plate. As a result, the finished transfer on the plate fails to show the complete design, and the finished stamp will have an incomplete design printed. This is known as a "short transfer." U.S. Scott No. 8 is a good example of a short transfer.

TYPOGRAPHY (Letterpress, Surface Printing, Flexography, Dry Offset, High Etch)

Although the word "Typography" is obsolete as a term describing a printing method, it was the accepted term throughout the first century of postage stamps. Therefore, appropriate Scott listings in this catalogue refer to typographed stamps. The current term for this form of printing, however, is "letterpress."

As it relates to the production of postage stamps, letterpress printing is the reverse of engraving. Rather than having recessed areas trap the ink and deposit it on paper, only the raised areas of the design are inked. This is comparable to the type of printing seen by inking and using an ordinary rubber stamp. Letterpress includes all printing where the design is above the surface area, whether it is wood, metal or, in some instances, hardened rubber or polymer plastic.

For most letterpress-printed stamps, the engraved master is made in much the same manner as for engraved stamps. In this instance, however, an additional step is needed. The design is transferred to another surface before being transferred to the transfer roll. In this way, the transfer roll has a recessed stamp design, rather than one done in relief. This makes the printing areas on the final plate raised, or relief areas.

For less-detailed stamps of the 19th century, the area on the die not used as a printing surface was cut away, leaving the surface area raised. The original die was then reproduced by stereotyping or electrotyping. The resulting electrotypes were assembled in the required number and format of the desired sheet of stamps. The plate used in printing the stamps was an electroplate of these assembled electrotypes.

Once the final letterpress plates are created, ink is applied to the raised surface and the pressure of the press transfers the ink impression to the paper. In contrast to engraving, the fine lines of letterpress are impressed on the surface of the stamp, leaving a debossed surface. When viewed from the back (as on a typewritten page), the corresponding line work on the stamp will be raised slightly (embossed) above the surface.

PHOTOGRAVURE (Gravure, Rotogravure, Heliogravure)

In this process, the basic principles of photography are applied to a chemically sensitized metal plate, rather than photographic paper. The design is transferred photographically to the plate through a halftone, or dot-matrix screen, breaking the reproduction into tiny dots. The plate is treated chemically and the dots form depressions, called cells, of varying depths and diameters, depending on the degrees of shade in the design. Then, like engraving, ink is applied to the plate and the surface is wiped clean. This leaves ink in the tiny cells that is lifted out and deposited on the paper when it is pressed against the plate.

Gravure is most often used for multicolored stamps, generally using the three primary colors (red, yellow and blue) and black. By varying the dot matrix pattern and density of these colors, virtually any color can be reproduced. A typical full-color gravure stamp will be created from four printing cylinders (one for each color). The original multicolored image will have been photographically separated into its component colors.

Modern gravure printing may use computer-generated dot-matrix screens, and modern plates may be of various types including metal-coated plastic. The catalogue designation of Photogravure (or "Photo") covers any of these older and more modern gravure methods of printing.

For examples of the first photogravure stamps printed (1914), see Bavaria Scott 94-114.

LITHOGRAPHY (Offset Lithography, Stone Lithography, Dilitho, Planography, Collotype)

The principle that oil and water do not mix is the basis for lithography. The stamp design is drawn by hand or transferred from engraving to the surface of a lithographic stone or metal plate in a greasy (oily) substance. This oily substance holds the ink, which will later be transferred to the paper. The stone (or plate) is wet with an acid fluid, causing it to repel the printing ink in all areas not covered by the greasy substance.

Transfer paper is used to transfer the design from the original stone or plate. A series of duplicate transfers are grouped and, in turn, transferred to the final printing plate.

Photolithography — The application of photographic processes to lithography. This process allows greater flexibility of design, related to use of halftone screens combined with line work. Unlike photogravure or engraving, this process can allow large, solid areas to be printed.

Offset — A refinement of the lithographic process. A rubber-covered blanket cylinder takes the impression from the inked lithographic plate. From the "blanket" the impression is offset or transferred to the paper. Greater flexibility and speed are the principal reasons offset printing has largely displaced lithography. The term "lithography" covers both processes, and results are almost identical.

EMBOSSED (Relief) Printing

Embossing, not considered one of the four main printing types, is a method in which the design first is sunk into the metal of the die. Printing is done against a yielding platen, such as leather or linoleum. The platen is forced into the depression of the die, thus forming the design on the paper in relief. This process is often used for metallic inks.

Embossing may be done without color (see Sardinia Scott 4-6); with color printed around the embossed area (see Great Britain Scott 5 and most U.S. envelopes); and with color in exact registration with the embossed subject (see Canada Scott 656-657).

HOLOGRAMS

For objects to appear as holograms on stamps, a model exactly the same size as it is to appear on the hologram must be created. Rather than using photographic film to capture the image, holography records an image on a photoresist material. In processing, chemicals eat away at certain exposed areas, leaving a pattern of constructive and destructive interference. When the photoresist is developed, the result is a pattern of uneven ridges that acts as a mold. This mold is then coated with metal, and the resulting form is used to press copies in much the same way phonograph records are produced.

A typical reflective hologram used for stamps consists of a reproduction of the uneven patterns on a plastic film that is applied to a reflective background, usually a silver or gold foil. Light is reflected off the background through the film, making the pattern present on the film visible. Because of the uneven pattern of the film, the viewer will perceive the objects in their proper three-dimensional relationships with appropriate brightness. The first hologram on a stamp was produced by Austria in 1988 (Scott 1441).

FOIL APPLICATION

A modern technique of applying color to stamps involves the application of metallic foil to the stamp paper. A pattern of foil is applied to the stamp paper by use of a stamping die. The foil usually is flat, but it may be textured. Canada Scott 1735 has three different foil applications in pearl, bronze and gold. The gold foil was textured using a chemical-etch copper embossing die. The printing of this stamp also involved two-color offset lithography plus embossing.

THERMOGRAPHY

In the 1990s stamps began to be enhanced with thermographic printing. In this process, a powdered polymer is applied over a sheet that has just been printed. The powder adheres to ink that lacks drying or hardening agents and does not adhere to areas where the ink has these agents. The excess powder is removed and the sheet is briefly heated to melt the powder. The melted powder solidifies after cooling, producing a raised, shiny effect on the stamps. See Scott New Caledonia C239-C240.

COMBINATION PRINTINGS

Sometimes two or even three printing methods are combined in producing stamps. In these cases, such as Austria Scott 933 or Canada 1735 (described in the preceding paragraph), the multiple-printing technique can be determined by studying the individual characteristics of each printing type. A few stamps, such as Singapore Scott 684-684A, combine as many as three of the four major printing types (lithography, engraving and typography). When this is done it often indicates the incorporation of security devices against counterfeiting.

INK COLORS

Inks or colored papers used in stamp printing often are of mineral origin, although there are numerous examples of organic-based pigments. As a general rule, organic-based pigments are far more subject to varieties and change than those of mineral-based origin.

The appearance of any given color on a stamp may be affected by many aspects, including printing variations, light, color of paper, aging and chemical alterations.

Numerous printing variations may be observed. Heavier pressure or inking will cause a more intense color, while slight interruptions in the ink feed or lighter impressions will cause a lighter appearance. Stamps printed in the same color by water-based and solvent-based inks can differ significantly in appearance. This affects several stamps in the U.S. Prominent Americans series. Hand-mixed ink formulas (primarily from the 19th century) produced under different conditions (humidity and temperature) account for notable color variations in early printings of the same stamp (see U.S. Scott 248-250, 279B, for example). Different sources of pigment can also result in significant differences in color.

Light exposure and aging are closely related in the way they affect stamp color. Both eventually break down the ink and fade colors, so that a carefully kept stamp may differ significantly in color from an identical copy that has been exposed to light. If stamps are exposed to light either intentionally or accidentally, their colors can be faded or completely changed in some cases.

Papers of different quality and consistency used for the same stamp printing may affect color appearance. Most pelure papers, for example, show a richer color when compared with wove or laid papers. See Russia Scott 181a, for an example of this effect.

The very nature of the printing processes can cause a variety of differences in shades or hues of the same stamp. Some of these shades are scarcer than others, and are of particular interest to the advanced collector.

Luminescence

All forms of tagged stamps fall under the general category of luminescence. Within this broad category is fluorescence, dealing with forms of tagging visible under longwave ultraviolet light, and phosphorescence, which deals with tagging visible only under shortwave light. Phosphorescence leaves an afterglow and fluorescence does not. These treated stamps show up in a range of different colors when exposed to UV light. The differing wavelengths of the light activates the tagging material, making it glow in various colors that usually serve different mail processing purposes.

Intentional tagging is a post-World War II phenomenon, brought about by the increased literacy rate and rapidly growing mail volume. It was one of several answers to the problem of the need for more automated mail processes. Early tagged stamps served the purpose of triggering machines to separate different types of mail. A natural outgrowth was to also use the signal to trigger machines that faced all envelopes the same way and canceled them.

Tagged stamps come in many different forms. Some tagged stamps have luminescent shapes or images imprinted on them as a form of security device. Others have blocks (United States), stripes, frames (South Africa and Canada), overall coatings (United States), bars (Great Britain and Canada) and many other types. Some types of tagging are even mixed in with the pigmented printing ink (Australia Scott 366, Netherlands Scott 478 and U.S. Scott 1359 and 2443).

The means of applying taggant to stamps differs as much as the intended purposes for the stamps. The most common form of tagging is a coating applied to the surface of the printed stamp. Since the taggant ink is frequently invisible except under UV light, it does not interfere with the appearance of the stamp. Another common application is the use of phosphored papers. In this case the paper itself either has a coating of taggant applied before the stamp is printed, has taggant applied during the papermaking process (incorporating it into the fibers), or has the taggant mixed into the coating of the paper. The latter method, among others, is currently in use in the United States.

Many countries now use tagging in various forms to either expedite mail handling or to serve as a printing security device against counterfeiting. Following the introduction of tagged stamps for public use in 1959 by Great Britain, other countries have steadily joined the parade. Among those are Germany (1961); Canada and Denmark (1962); United States, Australia, France and Switzerland (1963); Belgium and Japan (1966); Sweden and Norway (1967); Italy (1968); and Russia (1969). Since then, many other countries have begun using forms of tagging, including Brazil, China, Czechoslovakia, Hong Kong, Guatemala, Indonesia, Israel, Lithuania, Luxembourg, Netherlands, Penrhyn Islands, Portugal, St. Vincent, Singapore, South Africa, Spain and Sweden to name a few.

In some cases, including United States, Canada, Great Britain and Switzerland, stamps were released both with and without tagging. Many of these were released during each country's experimental period. Tagged and untagged versions are listed for the aforementioned countries and are noted in some other countries' listings. For at least a few stamps, the experimentally tagged version is worth far more than its untagged counterpart, such as the 1963 experimental tagged version of France Scott 1024.

In some cases, luminescent varieties of stamps were inadvertently created. Several Russian stamps, for example, sport highly fluorescent ink that was not intended as a form of tagging. Older stamps, such as early U.S. postage dues, can be positively identified by the use of UV light, since the organic ink used has become slightly fluorescent over time. Other stamps, such as Austria Scott 70a-82a (varnish bars) and Obock Scott 46-64 (printed quadrille lines), have become fluorescent over time.

Various fluorescent substances have been added to paper to make it appear brighter. These optical brightners, as they are known, greatly affect the appearance of the stamp under UV light. The brightest of these is known as Hi-Brite paper. These paper varieties are beyond the scope of the Scott Catalogue.

Shortwave UV light also is used extensively in expertizing, since each form of paper has its own fluorescent characteristics that are impossible to perfectly match. It is therefore a simple matter to detect filled thins, added perforation teeth and other alterations that involve the addition of paper. UV light also is used to examine stamps that have had cancels chemically removed and for other purposes as well.

Gum

The Illustrated Gum Chart in the first part of this introduction shows and defines various types of gum condition. Because gum condition has an important impact on the value of unused stamps, we recommend studying this chart and the accompanying text carefully.

The gum on the back of a stamp may be shiny, dull, smooth, rough, dark, white, colored or tinted. Most stamp gumming adhesives use gum arabic or dextrine as a base. Certain polymers such as polyvinyl alcohol (PVA) have been used extensively since World War II.

The *Scott Standard Postage Stamp Catalogue* does not list items by types of gum. The *Scott Specialized Catalogue of United States Stamps and Covers* does differentiate among some types of gum for certain issues.

Reprints of stamps may have gum differing from the original issues. In addition, some countries have used different gum formulas for different seasons. These adhesives have different properties that may become more apparent over time.

Many stamps have been issued without gum, and the catalogue will note this fact. See, for example, United States Scott 40-47. Sometimes, gum may have been removed to preserve the stamp. Germany Scott B68, for example, has a highly acidic gum that eventually destroys the stamps. This item is valued in the catalogue with gum removed.

Reprints and reissues

These are impressions of stamps (usually obsolete) made from the original plates or stones. If they are valid for postage and reproduce obsolete issues (such as U.S. Scott 102-111), the stamps are reissues. If they are from current issues, they are designated as *second, third,* etc., *printing*. If designated for a particular purpose, they are called *special printings*.

When special printings are not valid for postage, but are made from original dies and plates by authorized persons, they are *official reprints*. *Private reprints* are made from the original plates and dies by private hands. An example of a private reprint is that of the 1871-1932 reprints made from the original die of the 1845 New Haven, Conn., postmaster's provisional. *Official reproductions* or imitations are made from new dies and plates by government authorization. Scott will list those reissues that are valid for postage if they differ significantly from the original printing.

The U.S. government made special printings of its first postage stamps in 1875. Produced were official imitations of the first two stamps (listed as Scott 3-4), reprints of the demonetized pre-1861 issues (Scott 40-47) and reissues of the 1861 stamps, the 1869 stamps and the then-current 1875 denominations. Even though the official imitations and the reprints were not valid for postage, Scott lists all of these U.S. special printings.

Most reprints or reissues differ slightly from the original stamp in some characteristic, such as gum, paper, perforation, color or watermark. Sometimes the details are followed so meticulously that only a student of that specific stamp is able to distinguish the reprint or reissue from the original.

Remainders and canceled to order

Some countries sell their stock of old stamps when a new issue replaces them. To avoid postal use, the remainders usually are canceled with a punch hole, a heavy line or bar, or a more-or-less regular-looking cancellation. The most famous merchant of remainders was Nicholas F. Seebeck. In the 1880s and 1890s, he arranged printing contracts between the Hamilton Bank Note Co., of which he was a director, and several Central and South American countries. The contracts provided that the plates and all remainders of the yearly issues became the property of Hamilton. Seebeck saw to it that ample stock remained. The "Seebecks," both remainders and reprints, were standard packet fillers for decades.

Some countries also issue stamps *canceled-to-order (CTO)*, either in sheets with original gum or stuck onto pieces of paper or envelopes and canceled. Such CTO items generally are worth less than postally used stamps. In cases where the CTO material is far more prevalent in the marketplace than postally used examples, the catalogue value relates to the CTO examples, with postally used examples noted as premium items. Most CTOs can be detected by the presence of gum. However, as the CTO practice goes back at least to 1885, the gum inevitably has been soaked off some stamps so they could pass as postally used. The normally applied postmarks usually differ slightly from standard postmarks, and specialists are able to tell the difference. When applied individually to envelopes by philatelically minded persons, CTO material is known as *favor canceled* and generally sells at large discounts.

Cinderellas and facsimiles

Cinderella is a catch-all term used by stamp collectors to describe phantoms, fantasies, bogus items, municipal issues, exhibition seals, local revenues, transportation stamps, labels, poster stamps and many other types of items. Some cinderella collectors include in their collections local postage issues, telegraph stamps, essays and proofs, forgeries and counterfeits.

A *fantasy* is an adhesive created for a nonexistent stamp-issuing authority. Fantasy items range from imaginary countries (Occusi-Ambeno, Kingdom of Sedang, Principality of Trinidad or Torres Straits), to non-existent locals (Winans City Post), or nonexistent transportation lines (McRobish & Co.'s Acapulco-San Francisco Line).

On the other hand, if the entity exists and could have issued stamps (but did not) or was known to have issued other stamps, the items are considered bogus stamps. These would include the Mormon postage stamps of Utah, S. Allan Taylor's Guatemala and Paraguay inventions, the propaganda issues for the South Moluccas and the adhesives of the Page & Keyes local post of Boston.

Phantoms is another term for both fantasy and bogus issues.

Facsimiles are copies or imitations made to represent original stamps, but which do not pretend to be originals. A catalogue illustration is such a facsimile. Illustrations from the Moens catalogue of the last century were occasionally colored and passed off as stamps. Since the beginning of stamp collecting, facsimiles have been made for collectors as space fillers or for reference. They often carry the word "facsimile," "falsch" (German), "sanko" or "mozo" (Japanese), or "faux" (French) overprinted on the face or stamped on the back. Unfortunately, over the years a number of these items have had fake cancels applied over the facsimile notation and have been passed off as genuine.

Forgeries and counterfeits

Forgeries and counterfeits have been with philately virtually from the beginning of stamp production. Over time, the terminology for the two has been used interchangeably. Although both forgeries and counterfeits are reproductions of stamps, the purposes behind their creation differ considerably.

Among specialists there is an increasing movement to more specifically define such items. Although there is no universally accepted terminology, we feel the following definitions most closely mirror the items and their purposes as they are currently defined.

Forgeries (also often referred to as Counterfeits) are reproductions of genuine stamps that have been created to defraud collectors. Such spurious items first appeared on the market around 1860, and most old-time collections contain one or more. Many are crude and easily spotted, but some can deceive experts.

An important supplier of these early philatelic forgeries was the Hamburg printer Gebruder Spiro. Many others with reputations in this craft included S. Allan Taylor, George Hussey, James Chute, George Forune, Benjamin & Sarpy, Julius Goldner, E. Oneglia and L.H. Mercier. Among the noted 20th-century forgers were Francois Fournier, Jean Sperati and the prolific Raoul DeThuin.

Forgeries may be complete replications, or they may be genuine stamps altered to resemble a scarcer (and more valuable) type. Most forgeries, particularly those of rare stamps, are worth only a small fraction of the value of a genuine example, but a few types, created by some of the most notable forgers, such as Sperati, can be worth as much or more than the genuine. Fraudulently produced copies are known of most classic rarities and many medium-priced stamps.

In addition to rare stamps, large numbers of common 19th- and early 20th-century stamps were forged to supply stamps to the early packet trade. Many can still be easily found. Few new philatelic forgeries have appeared in recent decades. Successful imitation of well-engraved work is virtually impossible. It has proven far easier to produce a fake by altering a genuine stamp than to duplicate a stamp completely.

Counterfeit (also often referred to as Postal Counterfeit or Postal Forgery) is the term generally applied to reproductions of stamps that have been created to defraud the government of revenue. Such items usually are created at the time a stamp is current and, in some cases, are hard to detect. Because most counterfeits are seized when the perpetrator is captured, postal counterfeits, particularly used on cover, are usually worth much more than a genuine example to specialists. The first postal counterfeit was of Spain's 4-cuarto carmine of 1854 (the real one is Scott 25). Apparently, the counterfeiters were not satisfied with their first version, which is now very scarce, and they soon created an engraved counterfeit, which is common. Postal counterfeits quickly followed in Austria, Naples, Sardinia and the Roman States. They have since been created in many other countries as well, including the United States.

An infamous counterfeit to defraud the government is the 1-shilling Great Britain "Stock Exchange" forgery of 1872, used on telegraph forms at the exchange that year. The stamp escaped detection until a stamp dealer noticed it in 1898.

Fakes

Fakes are genuine stamps altered in some way to make them more desirable. One student of this part of stamp collecting has estimated that by the 1950s more than 30,000 varieties of fakes were known. That number has grown greatly since then. The widespread existence of fakes makes it important for stamp collectors to study their philatelic holdings and use relevant literature. Likewise, collectors should buy from reputable dealers who guarantee their stamps and make full and prompt refunds should a purchased item be declared faked or altered by some mutually agreed-upon authority. Because fakes always have some genuine characteristics, it is not always possible to obtain unanimous agreement among experts regarding specific items. These students may change their opinions as philatelic knowledge increases. More than 80 percent of all fakes on the philatelic market today are regummed, reperforated (or perforated for the first time), or bear forged overprints, surcharges or cancellations.

Stamps can be chemically treated to alter or eliminate colors. For example, a pale rose stamp can be re-colored to resemble a blue shade of high market value. In other cases, treated stamps can be made to resemble missing color varieties. Designs may be changed by painting, or a stroke or a dot added or bleached out to turn an ordinary variety into a seemingly scarcer stamp. Part of a stamp can be bleached and reprinted in a different version, achieving an inverted center or frame. Margins can be added or repairs done so deceptively that the stamps move from the "repaired" into the "fake" category.

Fakers have not left the backs of the stamps untouched either. They may create false watermarks, add fake grills or press out genuine grills. A thin India paper proof may be glued onto a thicker backing to create the appearance an issued stamp, or a proof printed on cardboard may be shaved down and perforated to resemble a stamp. Silk threads are impressed into paper and stamps have been split so that a rare paper variety is added to an otherwise inexpensive stamp. The most common treatment to the back of a stamp, however, is regumming.

Some in the business of faking stamps have openly advertised fool-proof application of "original gum" to stamps that lack it, although most publications now ban such ads from their pages. It is believed that very few early stamps have survived without being hinged. The large number of never-hinged examples of such earlier material offered for sale thus suggests the widespread extent of regumming activity. Regumming also may be used to hide repairs or thin spots. Dipping the stamp into watermark fluid, or examining it under longwave ultraviolet light often will reveal these flaws.

Fakers also tamper with separations. Ingenious ways to add margins are known. Perforated wide-margin stamps may be falsely represented as imperforate when trimmed. Reperforating is commonly done to create scarce coil or perforation varieties, and to eliminate the naturally occurring straight-edge stamps found in sheet margin positions of many earlier issues. Custom has made straight-edged stamps less desirable. Fakers have obliged by perforating straight-edged stamps so that many are now uncommon, if not rare.

Another fertile field for the faker is that of overprints, surcharges and cancellations. The forging of rare surcharges or overprints began in the 1880s or 1890s. These forgeries are sometimes difficult to detect, but experts have identified almost all. Occasionally, overprints or cancellations are removed to create non-overprinted stamps or seemingly unused items. This is most commonly done by removing a manuscript cancel to make a stamp resemble an unused example. "SPECIMEN" overprints may be removed by scraping and repainting to create non-overprinted varieties. Fakers use inexpensive revenues or pen-canceled stamps to generate unused stamps for further faking by adding other markings. The quartz lamp or UV lamp and a high-powered magnifying glass help to easily detect removed cancellations.

The bigger problem, however, is the addition of overprints, surcharges or cancellations — many with such precision that they are very difficult to ascertain. Plating of the stamps or the overprint can be an important method of detection.

Fake postmarks may range from many spurious fancy cancellations to a host of markings applied to transatlantic covers, to adding normally appearing postmarks to definitives of some countries with stamps that are valued far higher used than unused. With the increased popularity of cover collecting, and the widespread interest in postal history, a fertile new field for fakers has come about. Some have tried to create entire covers. Others specialize in adding stamps, tied by fake cancellations, to genuine stampless covers, or replacing less expensive or damaged stamps with more valuable ones. Detailed study of postal rates in effect at the time a cover in question was mailed, including the analysis of each handstamp used during the period, ink analysis and similar techniques, usually will unmask the fraud.

Restoration and repairs

Scott bases its catalogue values on stamps that are free of defects and otherwise meet the standards set forth earlier in this introduction. Most stamp collectors desire to have the finest copy of an item possible. Even within given grading categories there are variances. This leads to a controversial practice that is not defined in any universal manner: stamp *restoration*.

There are broad differences of opinion about what is permissible when it comes to restoration. Carefully applying a soft eraser to a stamp or cover to remove light soiling is one form of restoration, as is washing a stamp in mild soap and water to clean it. These are fairly accepted forms of restoration. More severe forms of restoration include pressing out creases or removing stains caused by tape. To what degree each of these is acceptable is dependent upon the individual situation. Further along the spectrum is the freshening of a stamp's color by removing oxide build-up or the effects of wax paper left next to stamps shipped to the tropics.

At some point in this spectrum the concept of *repair* replaces that of restoration. Repairs include filling thin spots, mending tears by reweaving or adding a missing perforation tooth. Regumming stamps may have been acceptable as a restoration or repair technique many decades ago, but today it is considered a form of fakery.

Restored stamps may or may not sell at a discount, and it is possible that the value of individual restored items may be enhanced over that of their pre-restoration state. Specific situations dictate the resultant value of such an item. Repaired stamps sell at substantial discounts from the value of sound stamps.

Terminology

Booklets — Many countries have issued stamps in small booklets for the convenience of users. This idea continues to become increasingly popular in many countries. Booklets have been issued in many sizes and forms, often with advertising on the covers, the panes of stamps or on the interleaving.

The panes used in booklets may be printed from special plates or made from regular sheets. All panes from booklets issued by the United States and many from those of other countries contain stamps that are straight edged on the sides, but perforated between. Others are distinguished by orientation of watermark or other identifying features. Any stamp-like unit in the pane, either printed or blank, that is not a postage stamp, is considered to be a *label* in the catalogue listings.

Scott lists and values booklet panes. Modern complete booklets also are listed and valued. Individual booklet panes are listed only when they are not fashioned from existing sheet stamps and, therefore, are identifiable from their sheet stamp counterparts.

Panes usually do not have a used value assigned to them because there is little market activity for used booklet panes, even though many exist used and there is some demand for them.

Cancellations — The marks or obliterations put on stamps by postal authorities to show that they have performed service and to prevent their reuse are known as cancellations. If the marking is made with a pen, it is considered a "pen cancel." When the location of the post office appears in the marking, it is a "town cancellation." A "postmark" is technically any postal marking, but in practice the term generally is applied to a town cancellation with a date. When calling attention to a cause or celebration, the marking is known as a "slogan cancellation." Many other types and styles of cancellations exist, such as duplex, numerals, targets, fancy and others. See also "precancels," below.

Coil Stamps — These are stamps that are issued in rolls for use in dispensers, affixing and vending machines. Those coils of the United States, Canada, Sweden and some other countries are perforated horizontally or vertically only, with the outer edges imperforate. Coil stamps of some countries, such as Great Britain and Germany, are perforated on all four sides and may in some cases be distinguished from their sheet stamp counterparts by watermarks, counting numbers on the reverse or other means.

Covers — Entire envelopes, with or without adhesive postage stamps, that have passed through the mail and bear postal or other markings of philatelic interest are known as covers. Before the introduction of envelopes in about 1840, people folded letters and wrote the address on the outside. Some people covered their letters with an extra sheet of paper on the outside for the address, producing the term "cover." Used airletter sheets, stamped envelopes and other items of postal stationery also are considered covers.

Errors — Stamps that have some major, consistent, unintentional deviation from the normal are considered errors. Errors include, but are not limited to, missing or wrong colors, wrong paper, wrong watermarks, inverted centers or frames on multicolor printing, inverted or missing surcharges or overprints, double impressions, missing perforations, unintentionally omitted tagging and others. Factually wrong or misspelled information, if it appears on all examples of a stamp, are not considered errors in the true sense of the word. They are errors of design. Inconsistent or randomly appearing items, such as misperfs or color shifts, are classified as freaks.

Color-Omitted Errors — This term refers to stamps where a missing color is caused by the complete failure of the printing plate to deliver ink to the stamp paper or any other paper. Generally, this is caused by the printing plate not being engaged on the press or the ink station running dry of ink during printing.

Color-Missing Errors — This term refers to stamps where a color or colors were printed somewhere but do not appear on the finished stamp. There are four different classes of color-missing errors, and the catalog indicates with a two-letter code appended to each such listing what caused the color to be missing. These codes are used only for the United States' color-missing error listings.

FO = A *foldover* of the stamp sheet during printing may block ink from appearing on the face of a stamp. Instead, the color will appear on the back of the foldover (where it might fall on the back of the selvage or perhaps a bit on the back of the stamp or on the back of another stamp. FO also will be used in the case of foldunders, where the paper may fold underneath the other stamp paper and the color will print on the platen.

EP = When the extraneous paper is removed, an unprinted area of stamp paper remains and may show a color or colors to be totally missing on the finished stamp.

CM = A misregistration of the printing plates during printing will result in a *color misregistration*, and such a misregistraion may result in a color not appearing on the finished stamp.

PS = *A perforation shift* after printing may remove a color from the finished stamp. Normally, this will occur on a row of stamps at the edge of the stamp pane.

Measurements – When measurements are given in the Scott catalogues for stamp size, grill size or any other reason, the first measurement given is always for the top and bottom dimension, while the second measurement will be for the sides (just as perforation gauges are measured). Thus, a stamp size of 15mm x 21mm will indicate a vertically oriented stamp 15mm wide at top and bottom, and 21mm tall at the sides. The same principle holds for measuring or counting items such as U.S. grills. A grill count of 22x18 points (B grill) indicates that there are 22 grill points across by 18 grill points down.

Overprints and Surcharges — Overprinting involves applying wording or design elements over an already existing stamp. Overprints can be used to alter the place of use (such as "Canal Zone" on U.S. stamps), to adapt them for a special purpose ("Porto" on Denmark's 1913-20 regular issues for use as postage due stamps, Scott J1-J7) or to commemorate a special occasion (United States Scott 647-648).

A *surcharge* is a form of overprint that changes or restates the face value of a stamp or piece of postal stationery.

Surcharges and overprints may be handstamped, typeset or, occasionally, lithographed or engraved. A few hand-written overprints and surcharges are known.

Personalized Stamps — In 1999, Australia issued stamps with se-tenant labels that could be personalized with pictures of the customer's choice. Other countries quickly followed suit, with some offering to print the selected picture on the stamp itself within a frame that was used exclusively for personalized issues. As the picture used on these stamps or labels vary, listings for such stamps are for any picture within the common frame (or any picture on a se-tenant label), be it a "generic" image or one produced especially for a customer, almost invariably at a premium price.

Precancels — Stamps that are canceled before they are placed in the mail are known as precancels. Precanceling usually is done to expedite the handling of large mailings and generally allow the affected mail pieces to skip certain phases of mail handling.

In the United States, precancellations generally identified the point of origin; that is, the city and state. This information appeared across the face of the stamp, usually centered between parallel lines. More recently, bureau precancels retained the parallel lines, but the city and state designations were dropped. Recent coils have a service inscription that is present on the original printing plate. These show the mail service paid for by the stamp. Since these stamps are not intended to receive further cancellations when used as intended, they are considered precancels. Such items often do not have parallel lines as part of the precancellation.

In France, the abbreviation *Affranchts* in a semicircle together with the word *Postes* is the general form of precancel in use. Belgian precancellations usually appear in a box in which the name of the city appears. Netherlands precancels have the name of the city enclosed between concentric circles, sometimes called a "lifesaver." Precancellations of other countries usually follow these patterns, but may be any arrangement of bars, boxes and city names.

Precancels are listed in the Scott catalogues only if the precancel changes the denomination (Belgium Scott 477-478); if the precanceled stamp is different from the non-precanceled version (such as untagged U.S. precancels); or if the stamp exists only precanceled (France Scott 1096-1099, U.S. Scott 2265).

Proofs and Essays — Proofs are impressions taken from an approved die, plate or stone in which the design and color are the same as the stamp issued to the public. Trial color proofs are impressions taken from approved dies, plates or stones in colors that vary from the final version. An essay is the impression of a design that differs in some way from the issued stamp. "Progressive die proofs" generally are considered to be essays.

Provisionals — These are stamps that are issued on short notice and intended for temporary use pending the arrival of regular issues. They usually are issued to meet such contingencies as changes in government or currency, shortage of necessary postage values or military occupation.

During the 1840s, postmasters in certain American cities issued stamps that were valid only at specific post offices. In 1861, postmasters of the Confederate States also issued stamps with limited validity. Both of these examples are known as "postmaster's provisionals."

Se-tenant — This term refers to an unsevered pair, strip or block of stamps that differ in design, denomination or overprint.

Unless the se-tenant item has a continuous design (see U.S. Scott 1451a, 1694a) the stamps do not have to be in the same order as shown in the catalogue (see U.S. Scott 2158a).

Specimens — The Universal Postal Union required member nations to send samples of all stamps they released into service to the International Bureau in Switzerland. Member nations of the UPU received these specimens as samples of what stamps were valid for postage. Many are overprinted, handstamped or initial-perforated "Specimen," "Canceled" or "Muestra." Some are marked with bars across the denominations (China-Taiwan), punched holes (Czechoslovakia) or back inscriptions (Mongolia).

Stamps distributed to government officials or for publicity purposes, and stamps submitted by private security printers for official approval, also may receive such defacements.

The previously described defacement markings prevent postal use, and all such items generally are known as "specimens."

Tete-Beche — This term describes a pair of stamps in which one is upside down in relation to the other. Some of these are the result of intentional sheet arrangements, such as Morocco Scott B10-B11. Others occurred when one or more electrotypes accidentally were placed upside down on the plate, such as Colombia Scott 57a. Separation of the tete-beche stamps, of course, destroys the tete beche variety.

Currency conversion

Country	Dollar	Pound	S Franc	Yen	HK $	Euro	Cdn $	Aus $
Australia	1.4868	1.7831	1.5651	0.0107	0.1906	1.5417	1.0999	—
Canada	1.3517	1.6211	1.4228	0.0097	0.1733	1.4016	—	0.9091
European Union	0.9644	1.1566	1.0125	0.0069	0.1236	—	0.7135	0.6486
Hong Kong	7.8014	9.3560	8.2120	0.0561	—	8.0894	5.7715	5.2471
Japan	138.98	166.68	146.30	—	17.815	144.11	102.82	93.476
Switzerland	0.9500	1.1393	—	0.0068	0.1218	0.9851	0.7028	0.6390
United Kingdom	0.8338	—	0.8777	0.0060	0.1069	0.8646	0.6169	0.5608
United States	—	1.1993	1.0526	0.0072	0.1282	1.0369	0.7398	0.6726

Country	Currency	U.S. $ Equiv.
Afghanistan	afghani	.0113
Aitutaki	New Zealand dollar	.6237
Albania	lek	.0089
Algeria	dinar	.0072
Andorra (French)	euro	1.0369
Andorra (Spanish)	euro	1.0369
Angola	kwanza	.0020
Anguilla	East Caribbean dollar	.3704
Antigua	East Caribbean dollar	.3704
Argentina	peso	.0060
Armenia	dram	.0025
Aruba	guilder	.5587
Ascension	British pound	1.1993
Australia	dollar	.6726
Australian Antarctic Territory	dollar	.6726
United Nations-New York	U.S. dollar	1.00
United Nations-Geneva	Swiss franc	1.0526
United Nations-Vienna	euro	1.0369
United States	dollar	1.00

Source: xe.com Dec. 1, 2022. Figures reflect values as of Dec. 1, 2022.

British Commonwealth of Nations

Dominions, Colonies, Territories, Offices and Independent Members

Comprising stamps of the British Commonwealth and associated nations.

A strict observance of technicalities would bar some or all of the stamps listed under Burma, Ireland, Kuwait, Nepal, New Republic, Orange Free State, Samoa, South Africa, South-West Africa, Stellaland, Sudan, Swaziland, the two Transvaal Republics and others but these are included for the convenience of collectors.

1. Great Britain

Great Britain: Including England, Scotland, Wales and Northern Ireland.

2. The Dominions, Present and Past

AUSTRALIA

The Commonwealth of Australia was proclaimed on Jan. 1, 1901. It consists of six former colonies as follows:

New South Wales
Queensland
South Australia
Victoria
Tasmania
Western Australia

The following islands and territories are, or have been, administered by Australia: Australian Antarctic Territory, Christmas Island, Cocos (Keeling) Islands, Nauru, New Guinea, Norfolk Island, Papua.

CANADA

The Dominion of Canada was created by the British North America Act in 1867. The following provinces were former separate colonies and issued postage stamps:

British Columbia and Vancouver Island
New Brunswick
Newfoundland
Nova Scotia
Prince Edward Island

FIJI

The colony of Fiji became an independent nation with dominion status on Oct. 10, 1970.

GHANA

This state came into existence March 6, 1957, with dominion status. It consists of the former colony of the Gold Coast and the Trusteeship Territory of Togoland. Ghana became a republic July 1, 1960.

INDIA

The Republic of India was inaugurated on Jan. 26, 1950. It succeeded the Dominion of India which was proclaimed Aug. 15, 1947, when the former Empire of India was divided into Pakistan and the Union of India. The Republic is composed of about 40 predominantly Hindu states of three classes: governor's provinces, chief commissioner's provinces and princely states. India also has various territories, such as the Andaman and Nicobar Islands.

The old Empire of India was a federation of British India and the native states. The more important princely states were autonomous. Of the more than 700 Indian states, these 43 are familiar names to philatelists because of their postage stamps.

CONVENTION STATES

Chamba
Faridkot
Gwalior
Jhind
Nabha
Patiala

FEUDATORY STATES

Alwar
Bahawalpur
Bamra
Barwani
Bhopal
Bhor
Bijawar
Bundi
Bussahir
Charkhari
Cochin
Dhar
Dungarpur
Duttia
Faridkot (1879-85)
Hyderabad
Idar
Indore
Jaipur
Jammu
Jammu and Kashmir
Jasdan
Jhalawar
Jhind (1875-76)
Kashmir
Kishangarh
Kotah
Las Bela
Morvi
Nandgaon
Nowanuggur
Orchha
Poonch
Rajasthan
Rajpeepla
Sirmur
Soruth
Tonk
Travancore
Wadhwan

NEW ZEALAND

Became a dominion on Sept. 26, 1907. The following islands and territories are, or have been, administered by New Zealand:

Aitutaki
Cook Islands (Rarotonga)
Niue
Penrhyn
Ross Dependency
Samoa (Western Samoa)
Tokelau Islands

PAKISTAN

The Republic of Pakistan was proclaimed March 23, 1956. It succeeded the Dominion which was proclaimed Aug. 15, 1947. It is made up of all or part of several Moslem provinces and various districts of the former Empire of India, including Bahawalpur and Las Bela. Pakistan withdrew from the Commonwealth in 1972.

SOUTH AFRICA

Under the terms of the South African Act (1909) the self-governing colonies of Cape of Good Hope, Natal, Orange River Colony and Transvaal united on May 31, 1910, to form the Union of South Africa. It became an independent republic May 3, 1961.

Under the terms of the Treaty of Versailles, South-West Africa, formerly German South-West Africa, was mandated to the Union of South Africa.

SRI LANKA (CEYLON)

The Dominion of Ceylon was proclaimed Feb. 4, 1948. The island had been a Crown Colony from 1802 until then. On May 22, 1972, Ceylon became the Republic of Sri Lanka.

3. Colonies, Past and Present; Controlled Territory and Independent Members of the Commonwealth

Abu Dhabi
Aden
Aitutaki
Alderney
Anguilla
Antigua
Ascension
Australia
Bahamas
Bahrain
Bangladesh
Barbados
Barbuda
Basutoland
Batum
Bechuanaland
Bechuanaland Prot.
Belize
Bermuda
Botswana
British Antarctic Territory
British Central Africa
British Columbia and Vancouver Island

British East Africa
British Guiana
British Honduras
British Indian Ocean Territory
British New Guinea
British Solomon Islands
British Somaliland
Brunei
Burma
Bushire
Cameroons
Canada
Cape of Good Hope
Cayman Islands
Christmas Island
Cocos (Keeling) Islands
Cook Islands
Crete,
  British Administration
Cyprus
Dominica
East Africa & Uganda
  Protectorates
Egypt
Falkland Islands
Fiji
Gambia
German East Africa
Ghana
Gibraltar
Gilbert Islands
Gilbert & Ellice Islands
Gold Coast
Grenada
Griqualand West
Guernsey
Guyana
Heligoland
Hong Kong
Indian Native States
  (see India)
Ionian Islands
Jamaica
Jersey
Jordan
Kenya
Kenya, Uganda & Tanzania
Kiribati
Kuwait
Labuan
Lagos
Leeward Islands
Lesotho
Madagascar
Malawi
Malaya
  Federated Malay States
  Johore
  Kedah
  Kelantan
  Malacca
  Negri Sembilan
  Pahang
  Penang
  Perak
  Perlis
  Selangor
  Singapore
  Sungei Ujong
  Trengganu
Malaysia
Maldive Islands
Malta
Man, Isle of
Mauritius
Mesopotamia
Montserrat
Mozambique
Muscat
Namibia
Natal
Nauru
Nevis
New Britain
New Brunswick
Newfoundland
New Guinea
New Hebrides
New Republic
New South Wales
New Zealand
Niger Coast Protectorate
Nigeria
Niue
Norfolk Island
North Borneo
Northern Nigeria
Northern Rhodesia
North West Pacific Islands
Nova Scotia
Nyasaland Protectorate
Oman
Orange River Colony
Pakistan
Palestine
Papua New Guinea
Penrhyn Island
Pitcairn Islands
Prince Edward Island
Qatar
Queensland
Rhodesia
Rhodesia & Nyasaland
Ross Dependency
Rwanda
Sabah
St. Christopher
St. Helena
St. Kitts
St. Kitts-Nevis-Anguilla
St. Lucia
St. Vincent
Samoa
Sarawak
Seychelles
Sierra Leone
Singapore
Solomon Islands
Somaliland Protectorate
South Africa
South Arabia
South Australia
South Georgia
Southern Nigeria
Southern Rhodesia
South-West Africa
Sri Lanka
Stellaland
Straits Settlements
Sudan
Swaziland
Tanganyika
Tanzania
Tasmania
Tobago
Togo
Tokelau Islands
Tonga
Transvaal
Trinidad
Trinidad and Tobago
Tristan da Cunha
Trucial States
Turks and Caicos
Turks Islands
Tuvalu
Uganda
United Arab Emirates
Vanuatu
Victoria
Virgin Islands
Western Australia
Zambia
Zanzibar
Zimbabwe
Zululand

POST OFFICES IN FOREIGN COUNTRIES

Africa
  East Africa Forces
  Middle East Forces
Bangkok
China
Morocco
Turkish Empire

Colonies, former colonies, offices, territories controlled by parent states

Belgium

Belgian Congo
Ruanda-Urundi

Denmark

Danish West Indies
Faroe Islands
Greenland
Iceland

Finland

Aland Islands

France

COLONIES PAST AND PRESENT, CONTROLLED TERRITORIES

Afars & Issas, Territory of
Alaouites
Alexandretta
Algeria
Alsace & Lorraine
Anjouan
Annam & Tonkin
Benin
Cambodia (Khmer)
Cameroun
Castellorizo
Chad
Cilicia
Cochin China
Comoro Islands
Dahomey
Diego Suarez
Djibouti (Somali Coast)
Fezzan
French Congo
French Equatorial Africa
French Guiana
French Guinea
French India
French Morocco
French Polynesia (Oceania)
French Southern & Antarctic Territories
French Sudan
French West Africa
Gabon
Germany
Ghadames
Grand Comoro
Guadeloupe
Indo-China
Inini
Ivory Coast
Laos
Latakia
Lebanon
Madagascar
Martinique
Mauritania
Mayotte
Memel
Middle Congo
Moheli
New Caledonia
New Hebrides
Niger Territory
Nossi-Be
Obock
Reunion
Rouad, Ile
Ste.-Marie de Madagascar
St. Pierre & Miquelon
Senegal
Senegambia & Niger
Somali Coast
Syria
Tahiti
Togo
Tunisia
Ubangi-Shari
Upper Senegal & Niger
Upper Volta
Viet Nam
Wallis & Futuna Islands

POST OFFICES IN FOREIGN COUNTRIES

China
Crete
Egypt
Turkish Empire
Zanzibar

Germany

EARLY STATES

Baden
Bavaria
Bergedorf
Bremen
Brunswick
Hamburg
Hanover
Lubeck
Mecklenburg-Schwerin
Mecklenburg-Strelitz
Oldenburg
Prussia
Saxony
Schleswig-Holstein
Wurttemberg

FORMER COLONIES

Cameroun (Kamerun)
Caroline Islands
German East Africa
German New Guinea
German South-West Africa
Kiauchau
Mariana Islands
Marshall Islands
Samoa
Togo

Italy

EARLY STATES

Modena
Parma
Romagna
Roman States
Sardinia
Tuscany
Two Sicilies
  Naples
  Neapolitan Provinces
  Sicily

FORMER COLONIES, CONTROLLED TERRITORIES, OCCUPATION AREAS

Aegean Islands
  Calimno (Calino)
  Caso
  Cos (Coo)
  Karki (Carchi)
  Leros (Lero)
  Lipso
  Nisiros (Nisiro)
  Patmos (Patmo)
  Piscopi
  Rodi (Rhodes)
  Scarpanto
  Simi
  Stampalia
Castellorizo
Corfu
Cyrenaica
Eritrea
Ethiopia (Abyssinia)
Fiume
Ionian Islands
  Cephalonia
  Ithaca
  Paxos
Italian East Africa
Libya
Oltre Giuba
Saseno
Somalia (Italian Somaliland)
Tripolitania

POST OFFICES IN FOREIGN COUNTRIES

"ESTERO"*
Austria
China
  Peking
  Tientsin
Crete
Tripoli
Turkish Empire
  Constantinople
  Durazzo
  Janina
Jerusalem
Salonika
Scutari
Smyrna
Valona

**Stamps overprinted "ESTERO" were used in various parts of the world.*

Netherlands

Aruba
Caribbean Netherlands
Curacao
Netherlands Antilles (Curacao)
Netherlands Indies
Netherlands New Guinea
St. Martin
Surinam (Dutch Guiana)

Portugal

COLONIES PAST AND PRESENT, CONTROLLED TERRITORIES

Angola
Angra
Azores
Cape Verde
Funchal
Horta
Inhambane
Kionga
Lourenco Marques
Macao
Madeira
Mozambique
Mozambique Co.
Nyassa
Ponta Delgada
Portuguese Africa
Portuguese Congo
Portuguese Guinea
Portuguese India
Quelimane
St. Thomas & Prince Islands
Tete
Timor
Zambezia

Russia

ALLIED TERRITORIES AND REPUBLICS, OCCUPATION AREAS

Armenia
Aunus (Olonets)
Azerbaijan
Batum
Estonia
Far Eastern Republic
Georgia
Karelia
Latvia
Lithuania
North Ingermanland
Ostland
Russian Turkestan
Siberia
South Russia
Tannu Tuva
Transcaucasian Fed. Republics
Ukraine
Wenden (Livonia)
Western Ukraine

Spain

COLONIES PAST AND PRESENT, CONTROLLED TERRITORIES

Aguera, La
Cape Juby
Cuba
Elobey, Annobon & Corisco
Fernando Po
Ifni
Mariana Islands
Philippines
Puerto Rico
Rio de Oro
Rio Muni
Spanish Guinea
Spanish Morocco
Spanish Sahara
Spanish West Africa

POST OFFICES IN FOREIGN COUNTRIES

Morocco
Tangier
Tetuan

Dies of British colonial stamps

DIE A:

1. The lines in the groundwork vary in thickness and are not uniformly straight.

2. The seventh and eighth lines from the top, in the groundwork, converge where they meet the head.

3. There is a small dash in the upper part of the second jewel in the band of the crown.

4. The vertical color line in front of the throat stops at the sixth line of shading on the neck.

DIE B:

1. The lines in the groundwork are all thin and straight.

2. All the lines of the background are parallel.

3. There is no dash in the upper part of the second jewel in the band of the crown.

4. The vertical color line in front of the throat stops at the eighth line of shading on the neck.

DIE I:

1. The base of the crown is well below the level of the inner white line around the vignette.

2. The labels inscribed “POSTAGE” and “REVENUE” are cut square at the top.

3. There is a white “bud” on the outer side of the main stem of the curved ornaments in each lower corner.

4. The second (thick) line below the country name has the ends next to the crown cut diagonally.

DIE Ia.
1 as die II.
2 and 3 as die I.

DIE Ib.
1 and 3 as die II.
2 as die I.

DIE II:

1. The base of the crown is aligned with the underside of the white line around the vignette.

2. The labels curve inward at the top inner corners.

3. The “bud” has been removed from the outer curve of the ornaments in each corner.

4. The second line below the country name has the ends next to the crown cut vertically.

Wmk. 1
Crown and C C

Wmk. 2
Crown and C A

Wmk. 3
Multiple Crown and C A

Wmk. 4
Multiple Crown and Script C A

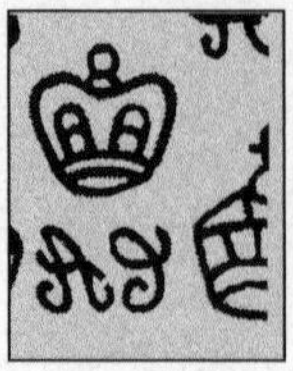

Wmk. 4a

Wmk. 46

Wmk. 314
St. Edward's Crown and C A Multiple

Wmk. 373

Wmk. 384

Wmk. 406

British Colonial and Crown Agents watermarks

Watermarks 1 to 4, 314, 373, 384 and 406, common to many British territories, are illustrated here to avoid duplication.

The letters "CC" of Wmk. 1 identify the paper as having been made for the use of the Crown Colonies, while the letters "CA" of the others stand for "Crown Agents." Both Wmks. 1 and 2 were used on stamps printed by De La Rue & Co.

Wmk. 3 was adopted in 1904; Wmk. 4 in 1921; Wmk. 46 in 1879; Wmk. 314 in 1957; Wmk. 373 in 1974; Wmk. 384 in 1985; Wmk 406 in 2008.

In Wmk. 4a, a non-matching crown of the general St. Edwards type (bulging on both sides at top) was substituted for one of the Wmk. 4 crowns which fell off the dandy roll. The non-matching crown occurs in 1950-52 printings in a horizontal row of crowns on certain regular stamps of Johore and Seychelles, and on various postage due stamps of Barbados, Basutoland, British Guiana, Gold Coast, Grenada, Northern Rhodesia, St. Lucia, Swaziland and Trinidad and Tobago. A variation of Wmk. 4a, with the non-matching crown in a horizontal row of crown-CA-crown, occurs on regular stamps of Bahamas, St. Kitts-Nevis and Singapore.

Wmk. 314 was intentionally used sideways, starting in 1966. When a stamp was issued with Wmk. 314 both upright and sideways, the sideways varieties usually are listed also — with minor numbers. In many of the later issues, Wmk. 314 is slightly visible.

Wmk. 373 is usually only faintly visible.

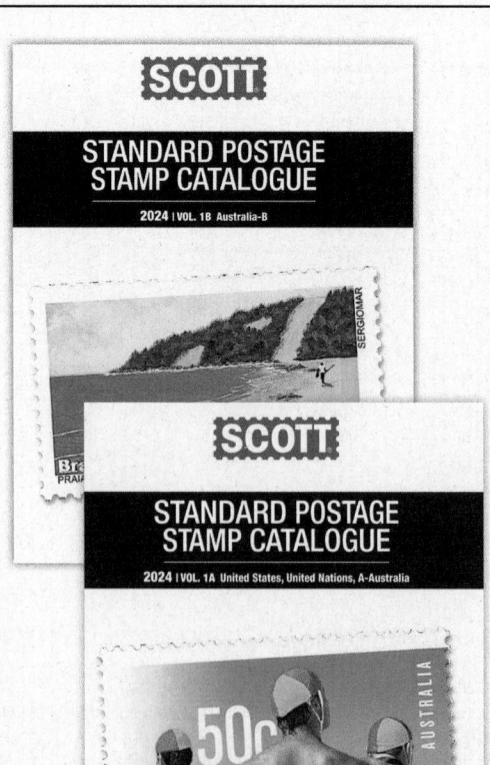

UNITED STATES

yu-ˌnī-təd ˈstāts

GOVT. — Republic
AREA — 3,615,211 sq. mi.
POP. — 308,745,538 (2010)
CAPITAL — Washington, DC

In addition to the 50 States and the District of Columbia, the Republic includes Guam, the Commonwealth of Puerto Rico, the Virgin Islands, American Samoa, Wake, Midway, and a number of small islands in the Pacific Ocean, all of which use stamps of the United States.

100 Cents = 1 Dollar

Catalogue values for unused stamps in this country are for Never Hinged items, beginning with Scott 772 in the regular postage section, Scott C19 in the air post section, Scott E17 in the special delivery section, Scott FA1 in the certified mail section, Scott O127 in officials section, Scott J88 in the postage due section, Scott RW1 in the hunting permit stamps section.

Watermarks

Wmk. 190 — "USPS" in Single-lined Capitals

Wmk. 191 — Double-lined "USPS" in Capitals

Watermark 191 has 9 letters for each horizontal row of 10 stamps. Watermark 190 has 8 to 9 letters for each horizontal row. Each watermark has 9 letters for each vertical row of 10 stamps This results in a number of stamps in each pane showing only a small portion of 1 or more watermark letters. This is especialy true of watermark 190.

Wmk. 190PI — PIPS, used in the Philippines
Wmk. 191PI — PIPS, used in the Philippines
Wmk. 191C — US-C, used for Cuba
Wmk. 191R — USIR

PROVISIONAL ISSUES BY POSTMASTERS

Values for Envelopes are for entires.

ALEXANDRIA, VA.

A1

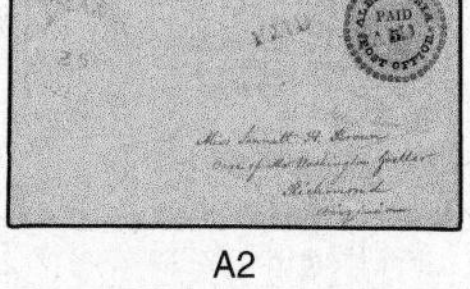

A2

All known examples are cut to shape.
Type I — 40 asterisks in circle.
Type II — 39 asterisks in circle.

1846 **Typeset** ***Imperf.***

1X1 A1 5c black, *buff,* type I *325,000.*
a. 5c black, *buff,* type II *625,000.*
1X2 A2 5c black, *blue,* type I, on cover *1,180,000.*

ANNAPOLIS, MD.

E1

1846

2XU1 E1 5c carmine red, *white* *500,000.*

Handstamped impressions of the circular design with "2" in blue or red exist on envelopes and letter sheets. Values: blue $17,500, red $30,000.

A letter sheet exists with circular design and "5" handstamped in red. Values: blue $10,000, red $12,500.

A similar circular design in blue was used as a postmark.

BALTIMORE, MD.

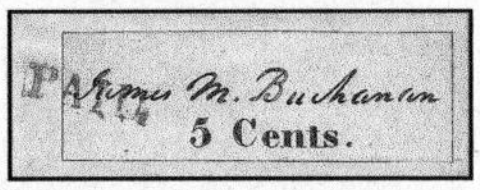

Signature of Postmaster — A1

Printed from a plate of 12 (2x6) containing nine 5c stamps and three 10c.

1845 **Engr.** ***Imperf.***

3X1 A1 5c black *6,000.*
3X2 A1 10c black, on cover *80,000.*
3X3 A1 5c black, *bluish* *65,000.* *8,000.*
3X4 A1 10c black, *bluish* *50,000.*

Nos. 3X1-3X4 were printed from a plate of 12 (2x6) containing nine 5c and three 10c.

Envelopes

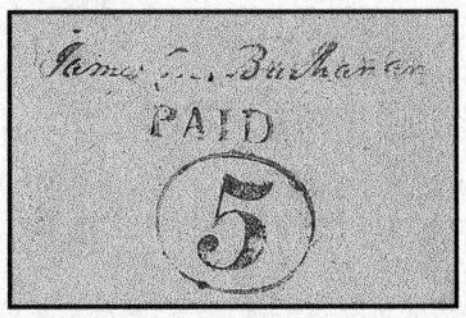

E1

The color given is that of the "PAID 5" and oval. "James M. Buchanan" is handstamped in black, blue or red. The paper is manila, buff, white, salmon or grayish.

1845 **Handstamped**
Various Papers

3XU1 E1 5c blue *4,500.*
3XU2 E1 5c red *10,000.*
3XU3 E1 10c blue *20,000.*
3XU4 E1 10c red *20,000.*

On the formerly listed "5+5" envelopes, the second "5" in oval is believed not to be part of the basic prepaid marking.

BOSCAWEN, N. H.

A1

1846 (?) **Typeset** ***Imperf.***

4X1 A1 5c dull blue, *yellowish,* on cover *300,000.*

BRATTLEBORO, VT.

Initials of Postmaster (FNP) — A1

Plate of 10 (5x2).

1846 ***Imperf.***
Thick Softwove Paper Colored Through

5X1 A1 5c black, *buff* *7,500.*

LOCKPORT, N. Y.

A1

"Lockport, N.Y." oval and "PAID" separately handstamped in red, "5" in black ms.

1846 ***Imperf.***

6X1 A1 5c red, *buff,* on cover *120,000.*

MILLBURY, Mass.

George Washington — A1

Printed from a woodcut, singly, on a hand press.

1846 ***Imperf.***

7X1 A1 5c black, *bluish* — *50,000.*

NEW HAVEN, CONN.

ENVELOPES

E1

Impressed from a brass handstamp at upper right of envelope.

Signed in blue, black or magenta ms., as indicated in parentheses.

1845

8XU1 E1 5c red (M) *100,000.*
8XU2 E1 5c red, *light bluish* (Bk) *125,000.*
8XU3 E1 5c dull blue, *buff* (Bl) *75,000.*
8XU4 E1 5c dull blue (Bl) *60,000.*

Values of Nos. 8XU1-8XU4 are a guide to value. They are based on auction realizations and other sales, and take condition into consideration. All New Haven envelopes are of equal rarity (each is unique), with the exception of No. 8XU2, of which two exist. An entire of No. 8XU2 is the finest example known, and this is reflected in the value shown. The other envelopes are valued according to condition, and cut squares also are valued according to condition as much as rarity.

Reprints were made at various times between 1871 and 1932. They can be distinguished from the originals, primarily due to differences in paper. See the Scott Specialized Catalogue of United States Stamps and Covers for more detail and values.

NEW YORK, N.Y.

George Washington — A1

Plate of 40 (5x8). Nos. 9X1-9X3 and varieties unused are valued without gum. Examples with original gum are extremely scarce and will command higher prices.

9X1 A1 5c black, signed ACM, connected, *1846* 1,500. 450.
a. Signed ACM, AC connected 1,750. 525.
b. Signed A.C.M. *4,500.* *675.*
c. Signed MMJr *10,000.*
d. Signed RHM *13,000.* *3,500.*
e. Without signature *3,750.* 900.

These stamps were usually initialed "ACM" in magenta ink, as a control, before being sold or passed through the mails.

A plate of 9 (3x3) was made from which proofs were printed in black on white and deep blue papers; also in blue, green, brown and red on white bond paper. Stamps from this plate were not issued, and it is possible that it is an essay, as the design differs slightly from the issued stamps from the sheet of 40. No examples from the plate of nine are known used.

1847 **Engr.** ***Imperf.***
Blue Wove Paper

9X2 A1 5c black, signed ACM connected *6,500.* 4,000.
a. Signed RHM —
b. Signed ACM, AC connected *8,000.*
d. Without signature *25,000.* *7,500.*

All used true blue examples carry "ACM" without periods; of the three unused examples, two lack initials.

On the only example known of No. 9X2a the "R" is illegible and does not match those of the other "RHM" signatures.

No. 9X2b is unique.

1847 **Engr.** ***Imperf.***
Gray Wove Paper

9X3 A1 5c black, signed ACM connected 5,250. 3,250.
a. Signed RHM *8,500.*
b. Without signature *13,000.*

PROVIDENCE, R. I.

A1 & A2

10X1 A1 5c gray black 350. *2,250.*
10X2 A2 10c gray black 1,150. *16,500.*
a. Se-tenant with 5c *2,000.*

Plate of 12 (3x4) contains 11-5c and 1-10c.

Reprints were made in 1898. Each stamp bears one of the following letters on the back: B O G E R T D U R B I N. Value of 5c, $65; 10c, $160; sheet, $1,000.

Reprint singles or sheets without back print sell for more.

ST. LOUIS, MO.

A1

A2

Missouri Coat of Arms — A3

Nos. 11X1-11X8 unused are valued without gum.

Wove Paper Colored Through

1845, Nov.-1846 ***Imperf.***

11X1 A1 5c black, *greenish* *47,500.* *8,000.*
11X2 A2 10c black, *greenish* *47,500.* *8,000.*
11X3 A3 20c black, *greenish* *160,000.*

Printed from Plate 1 (3 varieties each of the 5c and 10c) and Plate 2 (1 variety of the 5c, 3 of the 10c, 2 of the 20c).

1846

11X4 A1 5c black, (III), *gray lilac* — *45,000.*
11X5 A2 10c black, *gray lilac* *50,000.* *11,500.*
11X6 A3 20c black, *gray lilac* *100,000.* *60,000.*

One variety of 5c, 3 of 10c, 2 of 20c.
No. 11X6 unused is unique. It is in the grade of fine and valued thus.

1847 **Pelure Paper**

11X7 A1 5c black, *bluish* — *11,000.*
11X8 A2 10c black, *bluish* *17,500.* *15,000.*
a. Impression of 5c on back *77,500.*

Three varieties of 5c, 3 of 10c.
Values of Nos. 11X7-11X8 reflect the usual poor condition of these stamps, which were printed on fragile pelure paper. Attractive examples with minor defects sell for considerably more.
Used values are for pen-canceled stamps.
No. 11X8a is unique.

Please Note:
Stamps are valued in the grade of very fine unless otherwise indicated.
Values for early and valuable stamps are for examples with certificates of authenticity from acknowledged expert committees, or examples sold with the buyer having the right of certification. This applies to examples with original gum as well as examples without gum. Beware of stamps offered "as is," as the gum on some unused stamps offered with "original gum" may be fraudulent, and stamps offered as unused without gum may in some cases be altered or faintly canceled used stamps.

Manuscript Cancels on Used Stamps

Manuscript (pen) cancels reduce the value of used stamps by about 50%. See the Scott U.S. Specialized Catalogue for individual valuations.

GENERAL ISSUES

All Issues from 1847 through 1894 are unwatermarked.

Benjamin Franklin — A1

1847, July 1 **Engr.** ***Imperf.***

Thin Bluish Wove Paper

1 A1 5c red brown 6,000. 425.
No gum 2,100.
a. 5c dark brown 7,000. 525.
No gum 2,400.
b. 5c orange brown 10,000. 675.
No gum 3,500.
c. 5c red orange *25,000.* *8,500.*
No gum *9,500.*
d. 5c brown orange — 1,000.
No gum *4,500.*

George Washington — A2

2 A2 10c black *37,500.* 900.
No gum *16,000.*

REPRODUCTIONS of 1847 ISSUE

A3

A4

Actually, official imitations made from new plates of 50 subjects made by the Bureau of Engraving and Printing by order of the Post Office Department. These were not valid for postal use.

5c. On the originals the left side of the white shirt frill touches the oval on a level with the top of the "F" of "Five." On the reproductions it touches the oval about on a level with the top of the figure "5." On the originals, the bottom of the right leg of the "N" in "CENTS" is blunt. On the reproductions, the "N" comes to a point at the bottom.

10c. On the reproductions, line of coat at left points to right tip of "X" and line of coat at right points to center of "S" of CENTS. On the originals, line of coat points to "T" of TEN and between "T" and "S" of CENTS. The bottom of the right leg of the "N" of "CENTS" shows the same difference as on the 5c originals and reproductions. On the reproductions, the gap between the bottom legs of the left "X" is noticeably wider than the gap on the right "X." On the originals, the gaps are of equal width. On the reproductions, the eyes have a sleepy look, the line of the mouth is straighter, and in the curl of hair near the left cheek is a strong black dot, while the originals have only a faint one.

(See Nos. 948a and 948b for 1947 reproductions — 5c blue and 10c brown orange in larger size.)

1875 ***Imperf.***

Bluish paper, without gum

3 A3 5c red brown *(4779)* 1,000.
4 A4 10c black *(3883)* 1,250.

Numbers in parentheses are quantities sold.

Except as noted here and in footnotes for selected issues, values for 1851-57 issues are for examples that clearly show all of the illustrated type characteristics. Stamps that have weakly defined or missing type characteristics sell for less.

In Nos. 5-17, the 1¢, 3¢ and 12¢ have very small margins between the stamps. The 5¢ and 10¢ have moderate size margins. The values of these stamps take the margin size into consideration.

Values for Nos. 5A, 6b and 19b are for the less distinct positions. Best examples sell for more.

Values for No. 16 are for outer line recut at top. Other recuts sell for more.

Franklin — A5

Type I

Type Ib

ONE CENT

Type I. Has complete curved lines outside the labels with "U. S. Postage" and "One Cent." The scrolls below the lower label are turned under, forming little balls. The ornaments at top are substantially complete.

Type Ib. As type I, but balls below bottom label are not as clear. Plume-like scrolls at bottom are incomplete.

1851-57 ***Imperf.***

5 A5 1c blue, type I (7R1E) *115,000.* *50,000.*

Values for No. 5 are for examples with margins touching or cutting slightly into the design, or for examples with four margins and minor faults. Very few sound examples with the design untouched exist, and these sell for much more than the values shown.

Value for No. 5 unused is for a stamp with no gum. Only one example unused with original gum is recorded. It is in a multiple and is creased.

5A A5 1c blue, type 1b *32,500.* *6,500.*
No gum *12,000.*

Values for No. 5A are for sound examples with margins just clear to just touching the design on one or two sides. Examples with margins well clear of the design all around are scarce and will sell for more than the values shown.

A6

Type Ic

Type Ia. Same as type I at bottom, but top ornaments and outer line at top are partly cut away.

Type Ic. Same as type Ia, but bottom right plume and ball ornament incomplete. Bottom left plume is complete or nearly complete.

6 A6 1c blue, type 1a ('57) *45,000.* *9,250.*
No gum *20,000.*
6b A6 1c blue, type 1c *7,000.* *3,750.*
No gum *3,000.*

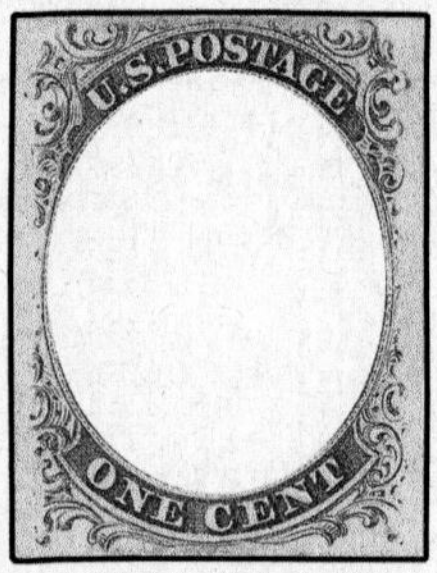

A7

Type II — Same as Type I at top, but the little balls of the bottom scrolls and the bottoms of the lower plume ornaments are missing. The side ornaments are substantially complete.

7 A7 1c blue, type II 1,000. 150.
No gum 375.

A8

Type IIIa

Type III. The top and bottom curved lines outside the labels are broken in the middle. The side ornaments are substantially complete.

Type IIIa. Similar to type III with the outer line broken at top or bottom but not both.

8 A8 1c blue, type III *25,000.* 1,750.
No gum *7,500.*

Values for type III are for at least a 2mm break in each outer line. Examples of type III with wider breaks in outer lines command higher prices; those with smaller breaks sell for much less.

8A A8 1c blue, type IIIa 6,000. 800.
No gum 2,250.

Stamps of type IIIa with bottom line broken command higher prices than those with top line broken. See note after No. 8 on width of break of outer lines.

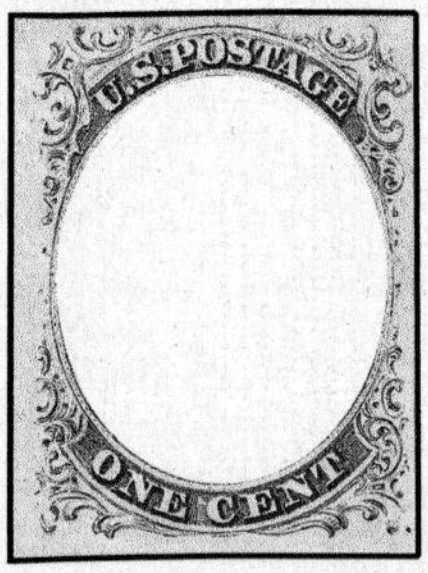

A9

Type IV. Similar to type II, but with the curved lines outside the labels recut at top or bottom or both.

9 A9 1c blue, type IV ('52) 725.00 100.00
No gum 260.00
a. Printed on both sides, reverse inverted *40,000.*

Washington — A10

All of the 3c stamps of the 1851 and 1857 issues were recut at least to the extent of the outer frame lines, sometimes the inner lines at the sides (type II stamps), and often other lines in triangles, diamond blocks, label blocks and/or top/bottom frame lines. Some of the most prominent varieties are listed below each major listing (others are described in "The 3c Stamp of U.S. 1851-57 Issue," by Carroll Chase).

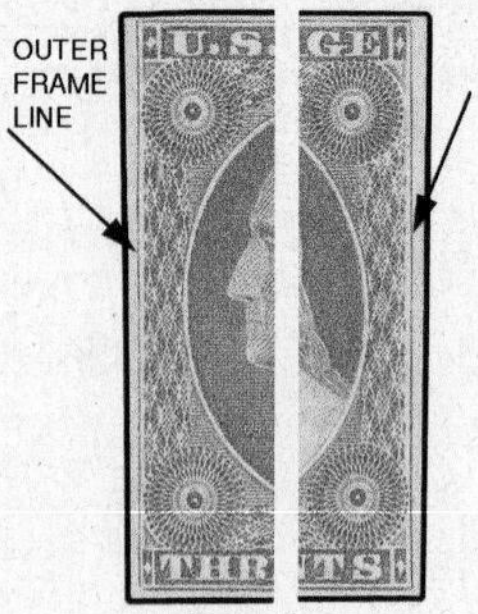

Type I

THREE CENTS

Type I — There is an outer frame line on all four sides. The outer frame lines at the sides are always recut.

10 A10 3c org brown, type I 4,000. 190.00
No gum 1,600.

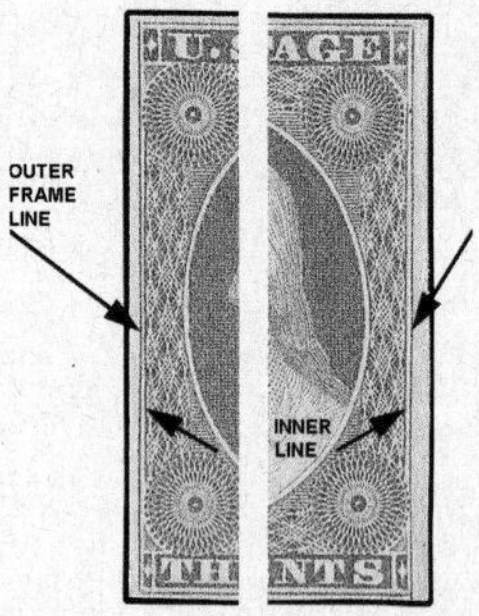

Type II

Type II — As type I, but with the inner lines at the sides added by recutting on the plate.

10A A10 3c org brown, type II 3,250. 150.00
No gum 1,350.
b. Printed on both sides *55,000.*

Only one example of No. 10Ab is recorded.

11 A10 3c dull red, type I ('55) 250.00 17.50
No gum 100.00

11A A10 3c dull red, type II ('53-'55) 250.00 15.00
No gum 85.00
e. Double impression *30,000.*

Thomas Jefferson — A11

FIVE CENTS

Type I — Projections on all four sides.

12 A11 5c red brown, type I ('56) *30,000.* 750.
No gum *11,000.*

Washington — A12

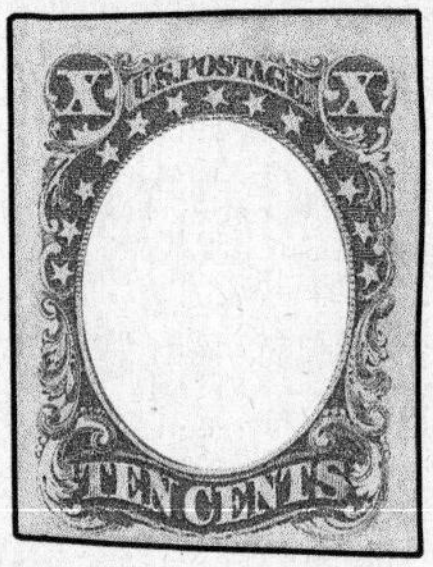

TEN CENTS

Type I — The "shells" at the lower corners are practically complete. The outer line below the label is very nearly complete. The outer lines are broken above the middle of the top label and the "X" in each upper corner.

13 A12 10c green, type I ('55) *19,000.* 750.
No gum *8,500.*

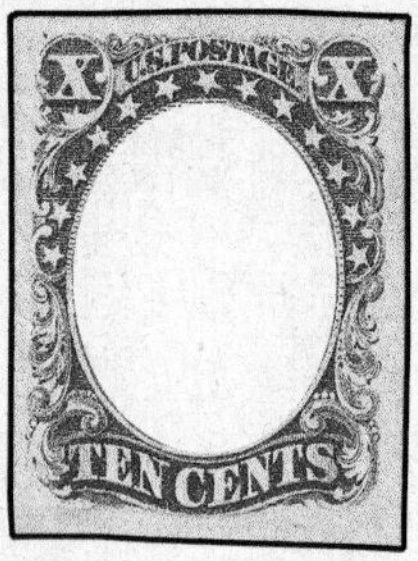

A13

Type II — The design is complete at the top. The outer line at the bottom is broken in the middle. The shells are partly cut away, as shown.

14 A13 10c green, type II ('55) 5,000. 145.
No gum 1,800.

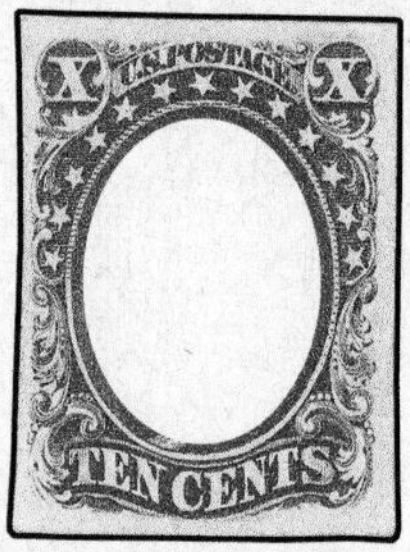

A14

Type III — The outer lines are broken above the top label and the "X" numerals. The outer line at the bottom and the shells are partly cut away, as shown, similar to type II.

15 A14 10c green, type III ('55) 5,000. 145.
No gum 1,800.

A15

Type IV. The outer lines have been recut at top or bottom or both.

Types I, II, III and IV have complete ornaments at the sides of the stamps and three pearls at each outer edge of the bottom panel.

16 A15 10c green, type IV ('55) *50,000.* 1,700.
No gum *27,500.*

Washington — A16

17 A16 12c gray black 6,250. 260.
No gum 2,100.
c. Printed on both sides *35,000.*

Values for 1857-61 issues are for examples that clearly show all the illustrated type characteristics. Stamps that have weakly defined or missing type characteristics sell for less.

Nos. 18-39 have small or very small margins. The values take into account the margin size. See footnotes for more specific information on selected issues.

SAME DESIGNS AS 1851-57 ISSUES

1857-61 ***Perf. 15½***

18 A5 1c blue, type I ('61) 2,100. 500.
No gum 800.
Short ornaments at either top or bottom —

19 A6 1c blue, type Ia *42,500.* *9,500.*
No gum *20,000.*
b. blue, type Ic 4,250. 3,750.
No gum *1,750.*

20 A7 1c blue, type II 850. 275.
No gum 375.

21 A8 1c blue, type III *17,500.* 1,400.
No gum *6,000.*
a. Horiz. pair, imperf between *20,000.*

22 A8 1c blue, type IIIa 2,200. 500.
No gum 850.

Beware of pairs of No. 22 with faint blind perforations between that sometimes are offered as pairs imperf. between.

23 A9 1c blue, type IV *10,000.* 550.
No gum 4,250.

Franklin — A20

Type V — Similar to type III of 1851-57 but with side ornaments partly cut away. About one-half of all positions have side scratches. Wide breaks in top and bottom framelines.

Type Va — Stamps from Plate 5 with almost complete ornaments at right side and no side scratches. Many, but not all, stamps from Plate 5 are Type Va, the remainder being Type V.

24 A20 1c blue, type V 140.00 40.00
No gum 60.00
b. Laid paper *7,500.*

25 A10 3c rose, type I 3,000. 190.00
No gum 1,050.
b. Vert. pair, imperf. horizontally *25,000.*

25A A10 3c rose, type II 9,000. 900.
No gum 4,000.

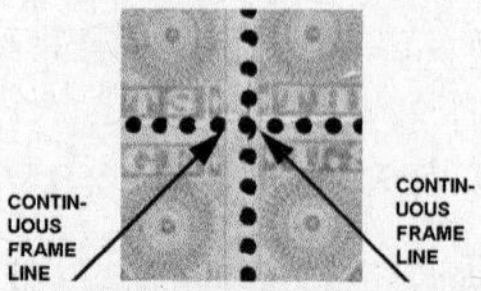

Washington Type III — A21

Type III — There are no outer frame lines at top and bottom. The side frame lines were recut so as to be continuous from the top to the bottom of the plate. **Stamps from the top or bottom rows show the ends of the side frame lines and may be mistaken for Type IV.**

26 A21 3c dull red, type III 65.00 10.00
No gum 27.50
b. Horiz. pair, imperf. vertically *14,000.*
c. Vert. pair, imperf. horizontally *16,000.*
d. Horizontal pair, imperf. between —
e. Double impression *15,000.*

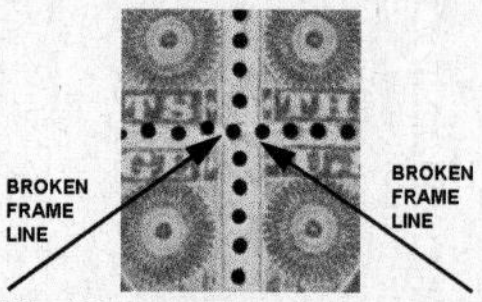

Washington Type IV — A21a

Type IV — As type III, but the side frame lines extend only to the top and bottom of the stamp design. All Type IV stamps are from plates 10 and 11 (each of which exists in three states), and these plates produced only Type IV. The side frame lines were recut individually for each stamp, thus being broken between the stamps vertically.

Beware of type III stamps with frame lines that stop at the top of the design (from top row of plate) or bottom of the design (from bottom row of plate). These are often mistakenly offered as No. 26A.

26A A21a 3c dull red, type IV 600.00 140.00
No gum 260.00
f. Horiz. strip of 3, imperf. vert., on cover *27,000.*

No. 26Af is unique.

27 A11 5c brick red, type I ('58) *80,000.* 1,450.
No gum *20,000.*
N.Y. Ocean Mail +1,000.

28 A11 5c red brown, type I *60,000.* 1,050.
No gum 15,000.
b. Bright red brown *70,000.* *2,000.*
No gum *20,000.*
Defective transfer (23R1) *2,500.*

28A A11 5c Indian red, type I ('58) *160,000.* 3,750.
No gum *40,000.*

No. 28A unused is valued in the grade of fine. Only four examples are recorded with any amount of gum.

29 A11 5c brown, type I ('59) 5,500. 325.
No gum 1,750.

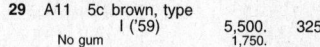

Jefferson — A22

FIVE CENTS.

Type II — The projections at top and bottom are partly cut away.

30 A22 5c orange brown, type II ('61) 1,200. *1,300.*
No gum 500.

30A A22 5c brown, type II ('60) 2,250. 375.
No gum 850.
b. Printed on both sides *35,000.*

31 A12 10c green, type I *35,000.* 1,100.
No gum *11,500.*

32 A13 10c green, type II 5,750. 190.
No gum 2,000.

33 A14 10c green, type III 5,750. 190.
No gum 2,000.

34 A15 10c green, type IV *50,000.* 2,200.
No gum *20,000.*

Example I Example II

Washington (Two typical examples) — A23

TEN CENTS

Type V — The side ornaments are slightly cut away. Usually only one pearl remains at each end of the lower label, but some copies show two or three pearls at the right side. At the bottom the outer line is complete and the shells nearly so. The outer lines at top are complete except over the right "X."

35 A23 10c green, type V ('59) 210.00 55.00
No gum 95.00

No. 36 outer frame lines recut on plate

TWELVE CENTS. Printed from two plates.

Plate 1 (No. 36) — Outer frame lines were recut on the plate and are complete. Very narrow spacing of stamps on the plate.

36 A16 12c black (Plate 1) 1,700. 325.
No gum 600.
c. Horizontal pair, imperf. between *12,500.*

Typical No. 36B, outer frame lines not recut

Plate III (No. 36B) — Weak outer frame lines from the die were not recut and are noticeably uneven or broken, sometimes partly missing. Somewhat wider spacing of stamps on the plate.

36B A16 12c black, plate III ('59) 775. 275.
No gum 375.

Washington A17

Franklin A18

37 A17 24c gray lilac ('60) 1,450. 400.
a. 24c gray 1,450. 400.
No gum 500.

38 A18 30c orange ('60) 1,900. 500.
No gum 700.

Washington — A19

39 A19 90c blue ('60) 3,000. *10,000.*
No gum 1,400.

See Die and Plate proofs in the Scott United States Specialized Catalogue for imperfs. of the 12c, 24c, 30c, 90c.

Genuine cancellations on the 90c are rare. Used examples must be accompanied by certificates of authenticity issued by recognized expertizing committees.

REPRINTS OF 1857-60 ISSUE
White paper, without gum.

1875 ***Perf. 12***

40 A5 1c bright blue *600.*
41 A10 3c scarlet *3,000.*
42 A22 5c orange brown *1,250.*
43 A12 10c blue green *3,000.* 13,000.
44 A16 12c greenish black *2,750.*
45 A17 24c blackish violet *3,250.* 10,000.
46 A18 30c yellow orange *3,250.*
47 A19 90c deep blue *4,000.*

Nos. 41-46 are valued in the grade of fine.

Nos. 40-47 exist imperforate. Very infrequent sales preclude establishing a value at this time. One set of imperforate pairs is recorded and it sold for $110,000 in a 2009 auction.

Essays-Trial Color Proofs

The paper of former Nos. 55-62 (Nos. 63E11e, 65-E15h, 67-E9e, 69-E6e, 72-E7h, Essay section, Nos. 70eTC, 71bTC, Trial Color Proof section, Scott U.S. Specialized) is thin and semitransparent. That of the postage issues is thicker and more opaque, except Nos. 62B, 70c and 70d.

Franklin — A24

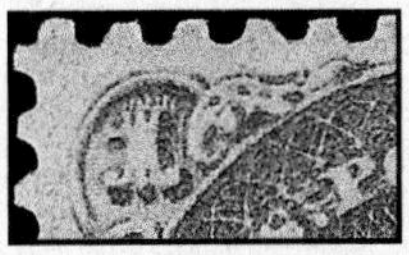

A24

Washington — A25

A25

Jefferson — A26

A26

Washington — A27

A27

A27a

Washington — A28

A28

Washington A29

Franklin A30

Washington — A31

A31

1c — There is a dash under the tip of the ornament at right of the numeral in upper left corner.

3c — Ornaments at corners end in a small ball.

5c — There is a leaflet in the foliated ornaments at each corner.

10c (A27) — A heavy curved line has been cut below the stars and an outer line added to the ornaments above them.

12c — There are corner ornaments consisting of ovals and scrolls.

90c — Parallel lines form an angle above the ribbon with "U. S. Postage"; between these lines there is a row of dashes and a point of color at the apex of the lower line.

1861 ***Perf. 12***

62B A27a 10c dark green *8,500.* 1,800.
No gum *3,600.*

1861-62 ***Perf. 12***

63 A24 1c blue 275.00 45.00
No gum 100.00
a. 1c ultramarine *2,500.* *1,900.*
No gum *1,000.*
b. 1c dark blue 800.00 *875.00*
No gum 300.00
c. Laid paper, horiz. or vert. *8,500.* *4,500.*
d. Vertical pair, imperf. horiz. —
e. Printed on both sides, reverse inverted — *35,000.*

The editors would like to see authenticated evidence of the existence of No. 63d.

The pale milky blue shade of No. 63 is very rare.

64 A25 3c pink *14,000.* 525.00
No gum *5,000.*
a. 3c pigeon blood pink *55,000.* *4,500.*
No gum *17,500.*
b. 3c rose pink, *Aug. 17, 1861* 600.00 140.00
No gum 250.00
65 A25 3c rose 125.00 3.00
No gum 50.00
b. Laid paper, horiz. or vert. — *1,100.*
d. Vertical pair, imperf. horiz. *12,500.* *1,500.*
No gum *5,000.*
e. Printed on both sides, reverse inverted *40,000.* *8,250.*
f. Double impression *11,000.*

The 3c lake can be found under No. 66 in the Trial Color Proofs section of the Scott U.S. Specialized Catalogue. The imperf 3c lake under No. 66P in the same section. The imperf 3c rose can be found in the Die and Plate Proofs section of the Specialized.

67 A26 5c buff *30,000.* 750.
No gum *12,500.*
a. 5c brown yellow *32,500.* 1,100.
No gum *14,000.*
b. 5c olive yellow — 4,850.

Values of Nos. 67, 67a, 67b reflect the normal small margins.

68 A27 10c green 950. 60.00
No gum 375.
a. 10c dark green 1,350. 90.00
No gum 500.
b. Vertical pair, imperf. horiz. *30,000.*
69 A28 12c black 1,700. 95.00
No gum 675.
70 A29 24c red lilac ('62) 2,900. 300.00
No gum 1,100.
a. 24c brown lilac 3,250. 325.00
No gum 1,250.
b. 24c steel blue ('61) *16,500.* 825.00
No gum *6,250.*
c. 24c violet, thin paper, *Aug. 20, 1861* *35,000.* 2,250.
reddish violet —
No gum *13,500.*
d. 24c pale gray violet, thin paper *25,000.* 3,000.
No gum *6,000.*

There are numerous shades of the 24c stamp in this and the following issue.

Color changelings, especially of No. 78, are frequently offered as No. 70b. Obtaining a certificate from an acknowledged expert committee is strongly advised.

Nos. 70c and 70d are on a thinner, harder and more transparent paper than Nos. 70, 70a, 70b or the latter Nos. 78, 78a, 78b and 78c.

71 A30 30c orange 2,600. 250.
No gum 900.
a. Printed on both sides —

Values for No. 71 are for examples with small margins, especially at sides. Large-margined examples sell for much more.

72 A31 90c blue 3,000. 625.
No gum 1,200.
a. 90c pale blue 3,000. 675.
No gum 1,200.
b. 90c dark blue 3,750. 950.
No gum 1,500.

Please Note:

Stamps are valued in the grade of very fine unless otherwise indicated.

Values for early and valuable stamps are for examples with certificates of authenticity from acknowledged expert committees, or examples sold with the buyer having the right of certification.

This applies to examples with original gum as well as examples without gum.

Beware of stamps offered "as is," as the gum on some unused stamps offered with "original gum" may be fraudulent, and stamps offered as unused without gum may in some cases be altered or faintly canceled used stamps.

DESIGNS AS 1861 ISSUE

Andrew Jackson
A32

Abraham Lincoln
A33

1861-66 ***Perf. 12***

73 A32 2c black ('63) 350.00 70.00
No gum 150.00
f. Printed on both sides, reverse not inverted *27,500.*
g. Laid paper — *11,500.*

No. 73f unused is unique. It has perfs cut off on two sides and is valued thus.

The 3c scarlet can be found under No. 74 in the Scott U.S. Specialized Catalogue Trial Color Proofs section.

75 A26 5c red brown ('62) 5,500. 425.
No gum 2,000.

Values for No. 75 reflect the normal small margins.

76 A26 5c brown ('63) 1,400. 115.
No gum 550.
a. 5c black brown 2,250. 400.
No gum 850.
b. Laid paper —

Values of Nos. 76, 76a reflect the normal small margins.

77 A33 15c black ('66) 5,000. 175.
No gum 1,900.
78 A29 24c lilac ('62) 2,750. 400.
No gum 950.
a. 24c grayish lilac 2,750. 425.
No gum 950.
b. 24c gray 2,750. 450.
No gum 950.
c. 24c blackish violet *95,000.* *16,000.*
No gum *30,000.*

Only three examples are recorded of No. 78c unused with original gum. No. 78c unused with and without gum are valued in the grade of fine-very fine.

d. Printed on both sides, reverse inverted *22,500.*

SAME DESIGNS AS 1861-66 ISSUES

Grill

Embossed with grills of various sizes. Some authorities believe that more than one size of grill probably existed on one of the grill rolls.

A peculiarity of the United States issues from 1867 to 1870 is the grill or embossing. The object was to break the fiber of the paper so that the ink of the canceling stamp would soak in and make washing for a second using impossible. The exact date at which grilled stamps came into use is unsettled. Luff's "Postage Stamps of the United States" places the date as probably August 8, 1867.

Horizontal measurements are given first.

GRILL WITH POINTS UP

Grills A and C were made by a roller covered with ridges shaped like an inverted V. Pressing the ridges into the stamp paper forced the paper into the pyramidal pits between the ridges, causing irregular breaks in the paper. Grill B was made by a roller with raised bosses.

A. GRILL COVERING THE ENTIRE STAMP

1867-68 ***Perf. 12***

79 A25 3c rose 8,500. 1,300.
No gum 2,750.
b. Printed on both sides —

Nos. 79, 79b, are valued for fine-very fine centering but with minor perforation faults.

An essay which is often mistaken for No. 79 (#79-E15) shows the points of the grill as small squares faintly impressed in the paper, but not cutting through it.

On No. 79 the grill breaks through the paper. Examples free from defects are rare.

80 A26 5c brown *400,000.*
a. 5c dark brown *400,000.*
81 A30 30c orange *225,000.*

Four examples of Nos. 80 and 80a (two of each shade), and eight examples of No. 81 (one in the New York Public Library Miller collection and not available to collectors) are known. All are more or less faulty and/or off center. Values are for off-center examples with small perforation faults.

B. GRILL ABOUT 18x15mm (22x18 POINTS)

82 A25 3c rose *900,000.*

The four known examples of No. 82 are valued in the grade of fine.

Earliest documented use: Feb. 1?, 1869 (dated cancel on off-cover stamp).

C. GRILL ABOUT 13x16mm (16 TO 17 BY 18 TO 21 POINTS)

The grilled area on each of four C grills in the sheet may total about 18x15mm when a normal C grill adjoins a fainter grill extending to the right or left edge of the stamp.

This is caused by a partial erasure on the grill roller when it was changed to produce C grills instead of the all-over A grill.

The imperf. can be found in the *Scott U.S. Specialized Catalogue* Die and Plate Proofs section.

83 A25 3c rose 5,500. 1,150.
No gum 2,000.

GRILL WITH POINTS DOWN

The grills were produced by rollers with the surface covered, or partly covered, by pyramidal bosses. On the D, E and F grills the tips of the pyramids are vertical ridges. On the Z grill the ridges are horizontal.

D. GRILL ABOUT 12x14mm (15 BY 18 TO 19 POINTS)

84 A32 2c black *16,000.* 5,250.
No gum *6,500.*

No. 84 is valued in the grade of fine.

85 A25 3c rose *8,000.* 1,050.
No gum *2,400.*

Z. GRILL ABOUT 11x14mm (14 TO 15 BY 17 OR 18 POINTS)

(1c, 10c, 15c 17 rows; 2c, 3c, 12c 18 rows)

85A A24 1c blue *3,000,000.*

Two examples of No. 85A are currently recorded. One is contained in the New York Public Library collection, which is on long-term loan to the Smithsonian National Postal Museum.

85B A32 2c black 19,000. 1,100.
No gum 6,750.
85C A25 3c rose *25,000.* 3,500.
No gum *9,000.*
85D A27 10c green *750,000.*

Six examples of No. 85D are known. One is contained in the New York Public Library collection. Value is for a well-centered example with small faults.

85E A28 12c intense black *25,000.* 2,250.
No gum *8,500.*
85F A33 15c black *2,000,000.*

Two examples of No. 85F are documented, one in the grade of very good, the other extremely fine. Value is for the extremely fine example.

E. GRILL ABOUT 11x13mm (14 BY 16 TO 18 POINTS)

86 A24 1c blue 3,000. 450.
No gum 1,100.
a. 1c dull blue 3,000. 425.
No gum 1,100.
87 A32 2c black 1,700. 200.
No gum 650.
88 A25 3c rose 1,050. 30.00
No gum 400.
a. 3c lake red 1,250. 80.00
No gum 475.
89 A27 10c green 5,000. 350.
No gum 2,000.
90 A28 12c black 4,750. 400.
No gum 1,900.
91 A33 15c black 12,500. 575.
No gum 4,500.

F. GRILL ABOUT 9x13mm (12 BY 16 TO 18 POINTS)

92 A24 1c blue 2,800. 450.
No gum 900.
a. 1c pale blue 2,300. 425.
No gum 700.
93 A32 2c black 450. 55.00
No gum 155.
94 A25 3c red 350. 12.50
a. 3c rose 350. 12.50
No gum 150.
c. Vertical pair, imperf. horiz. *15,000.*
d. Printed on both sides *9,000.* *35,000.*

The imperf. 3c can be found in the Scott U.S. Specialized Catalogue Die and Plate Proofs section.

95 A26 5c brown 3,250. 900.
No gum 1,100.
a. 5c black brown 5,000. 2,400.
No gum 2,000.
Double grill —

Values of Nos. 95, 95a reflect the normal small margins.

96 A27 10c yel grn 2,500. 275.
97 A28 12c black 2,800. 250.
No gum 1,000.
98 A33 15c black 4,250. 275.
No gum 1,600.
99 A29 24c gray lilac 8,500. 1,700.
No gum 3,250.
100 A30 30c orange 12,500. 1,000.
No gum 4,500.

Values for No. 100 are for examples with small margins, especially at sides. Large-margined examples sell for much more.

101 A31 90c blue 14,500. 2,500.
No gum 5,750.

RE-ISSUE OF 1861-66 ISSUES
Without Grill, Hard White Paper
White Crackly Gum

1875 ***Perf. 12***

102 A24 1c blue *750.* *1,750.*
No gum *350.*
103 A32 2c black *3,500.* *10,500.*
No gum *1,600.*
104 A25 3c brown red *3,750.* *13,000.*
No gum *1,700.*
105 A26 5c brown *2,500.* *6,500.*
No gum *1,150.*
106 A27 10c green *2,900.* *100,000.*
No gum *1,400.*
107 A28 12c black *3,750.* *12,000.*
No gum *1,750.*
108 A33 15c black *4,500.* *30,000.*
No gum *2,100.*
109 A29 24c deep violet *6,000.* *17,500.*
No gum *2,750.*
110 A30 30c brownish org *6,000.* *17,500.*
No gum *2,750.*
111 A31 90c blue *7,000.* *225,000.*
No gum *3,500.*

These stamps can be distinguished from the 1861-66 issues by the shades and the paper which is hard and very white instead of yellowish. The gum is white and crackly.

Franklin
A34

Post Horse and Rider
A35

G. Grill measuring 9½x9mm (12 by 11 to 11½ points)

1869 **Hard Wove Paper** ***Perf. 12***

112 A34 1c buff 575. 150.
No gum 210.
b. Without grill *32,500.*
113 A35 2c brown 500. 90.
No gum 190.
b. Without grill *14,000.*
d. Printed on both sides *62,500.*

Locomotive
A36

Washington
A37

114 A36 3c ultramarine 225. 20.00
No gum 90.
a. Without grill *13,000.* *18,000.*
Without grill, gray paper 3,750.
e. Printed on both sides, reverse inverted *55,000.*

Two examples recorded of No. 114a on normal paper: one with pen cancel but with original gum, 1994 Philatelic Foundation certificate; and one lifted from a cover, original gum adhering, examined, and placed back, 2011 Philatelic Foundation certificate. Also, four examples of No. 114a on gray paper: a single lifted from cover, examined, and hinged back in place, 1991 Philatelic Foundation certificate; and a strip of three on piece, mostly detached from piece, with full gum, 1978 and 2006 Philatelic Foundation certificates.

No. 114e is unique.

115 A37 6c ultramarine 2,600. 225.
No gum 1,050.

Shield and Eagle
A38

S. S. Adriatic
A39

116 A38 10c yellow 1,850. 110.
No gum 750.
117 A39 12c green 1,850. 130.
No gum 725.

Landing of Columbus — A40

Type I. Picture unframed.

No. 118 has horizontal shading lines at the left and right sides of the vignette.

118 A40 15c brn & bl, type I 9,000. 875.
No gum 3,250.
a. Without grill *11,500.*

A40a

No. 119 has diagonal shading lines at the left and right sides of the vignette.

119 A40a 15c brn & bl, type II 2,600. 200.
No gum 925.
b. Center inverted *1,000,000.* *22,500.*
No gum *700,000.*
c. Center double, one inverted *80,000.*

Declaration of Independence — A41

120 A41 24c green & violet 8,000. 650.
No gum 3,000.
a. Without grill *14,000.*
b. Center inverted *750,000.* *37,500.*

Shield, Eagle and Flags
A42

Lincoln
A43

121 A42 30c ultra & carmine 4,000. 450.
No gum 1,450.
a. Without grill *10,000.*
b. Flags inverted *750,000.* *85,000.*
No gum *300,000.*

Seven examples of No. 121b unused are recorded. Only one has part of its original gum.

122 A43 90c carmine & black 11,000. 2,000.
No gum 4,000.
a. Without grill *22,500.*

Values of varieties of Nos. 112-122 without grill are for examples with original gum.

Most examples of Nos. 119b, 120b are faulty. Values are for stamps with fine centering and only minimal faults. No. 120b unused is valued without gum, as all of the three examples available to collectors are without gum.

RE-ISSUE OF 1869 ISSUE
Without grill, hard white paper, with white crackly gum.

The gum is almost always somewhat yellowed with age, and unused stamps with original gum are valued with such gum.

A new plate of 150 subjects was made for the 1c. The plate for the frame of the 15c was made using the same die as that used to make

the type I frame for No. 118. For No. 118, the lines on each side of the vignette area were entered onto the plate itself, one position at a time. Upon close examination, each stamp position will be found to exhibit minute differences in these horizontal fringe lines.

1875 ***Perf. 12***

123 A34 1c buff	525.	425.
No gum	220.	
124 A35 2c brown	600.	750.
No gum	250.	
125 A36 3c blue	*5,000.*	*25,000.*
No gum	2,500.	

Used value for No. 125 is for an attractive fine to very fine example with minimal faults.

126 A37 6c blue	1,900.	*3,000.*
No gum	900.	
127 A38 10c yellow	1,600.	1,800.
No gum	750.	
128 A39 12c green	2,000.	*3,000.*
No gum	1,000.	

A40b

No. 129 (type III) is similar to No. 118 (type I) but without the shading lines at each side of the vignette.

129 A40b 15c brn & bl, Type III	1,300.	1,000.
No gum	625.	
a. Imperf. horizontally, single	*14,000.*	*30,000.*
No gum	*5,000.*	

Two used examples of No. 129a are recorded. Both have faults and are valued thus.

130 A41 24c grn & violet	2,000.	1,600.
No gum	1,000.	
131 A42 30c ultra & car	2,250.	2,750.
No gum	1,100.	
132 A43 90c car & blk	3,750.	*6,000.*
No gum	2,000.	

Soft Porous Paper

1880-82

133 A34 1c buff, issued with gum	375.	*550.*
No gum	150.	
a. 1c brown orange, issued without gum ('81 and '82)	425.	*650.*

Beware of No. 133 unused without gum offered as No. 133a. Certification is recommended for No. 133a.

PRODUCED BY THE NATIONAL BANK NOTE COMPANY

Franklin — A44

A44

Jackson — A45

A45

Washington — A46

A46

Lincoln — A47

A47

Edwin M. Stanton — A48

A48

Jefferson — A49

A49

Henry Clay — A50

A50

Daniel Webster — A51

A51

Gen. Winfield Scott A52

Alexander Hamilton A53

Commodore O.H. Perry — A54

H. GRILL ABOUT 10x12mm (11 TO 13 BY 14 TO 16 POINTS)

The "H" grills can be separated into early state and late state, based on the shape of the tip of the grill. Early-state grills show a point or very small vertical line at the tip of the pyramid, while late-state grills show the pyramid tips truncated and flat.

Early-state "H" grills tend to be on vertical-mesh wove paper, while later printings and all late-state grills were printed on horizontal-mesh wove paper, resulting in stamp designs being approximately ¼mm shorter than the designs printed on vertical-mesh wove paper. The late-stage "H" grills virtually all seem to have been used only after Jan. 1873.

Poor printing quality often resulted in grills that show only a few grill points or a very few rows of points. This is especially true of the "H" grills. When there are not enough grill points to clearly identify whether the grill is an "H" or an "I," it must be assumed it is the lower-valued "H" grill variety. Authentication is advised for these stamps with high catalogue values.

White Wove Paper, Thin to Medium Thick.

1870-71 ***Perf. 12***

134 A44 1c ultramarine	2,000.	210.00
No gum	700.	
b. Pair, one without grill	—	
135 A45 2c red brown	1,000.	85.00
No gum	360.	
136 A46 3c green	575.	35.00
No gum	190.	
c. Printed on both sides	—	

The imperf. 3c can be found in the Scott U.S. Specialized Catalogue Die and Plate Proofs section.

137 A47 6c carmine	5,000.	425.
No gum	1,750.	
b. Pair, one without grill		—
138 A48 7c vermilion	4,250.	525.
No gum	1,550.	
b. Pair, one without grill	—	
139 A49 10c brown	7,500.	825.
No gum	2,700.	
140 A50 12c dull violet	*32,500.*	3,750.
No gum	*17,500.*	
141 A51 15c orange	7,500.	1,500.
No gum	2,500.	
142 A52 24c purple	—	6,500.
143 A53 30c black	20,000.	3,750.
No gum	7,500.	
144 A54 90c carmine	25,000.	2,250.
No gum	10,000.	

I. GRILL ABOUT 8½x10mm (10 TO 11 BY 10 TO 13 POINTS)

The "I" grills can be separated into early state and late state, based on the shape of the tip of the grill. Early state grills show small tips of the pyramid, while late state grills show the pyramid tips truncated and flat.

Early state "I" grills tend to be on vertical-mesh wove paper, while later printings and all late-state grills were printed on horizontal-mesh wove paper, resulting in stamp designs being approximately ¼mm shorter than the designs printed on vertical-mesh wove paper. The late-stage "I" grills all seem to have been used only after Jan. 1873.

Values are for stamps with grills that are clearly identifiable. Poor printing quality often resulted in grills that show only a few grill points or a very few rows of points. When there are not enough grill points to clearly identify whether the grill is an "H" or an "I," it must be assumed it is the lower-valued "H" grill variety. Authentication is advised for these stamps with high catalogue values.

134A A44 1c ultra	*2,750.*	*400.00*
No gum	*800.00*	
135A A45 2c red brown	*2,000.*	*300.00*
136A A46 3c green	*850.00*	*100.00*
a. Pair, one without grill	—	
137A A47 6c carmine	*8,500.*	*950.00*
138A A48 7c vermilion ('71)	*6,500.*	*800.00*
No gum	*2,200.*	
139A A49 10c brown	*17,500.*	*10,000.*
b. Strip of 3, one without grill, two with split grill		—

There are two unused examples of No. 139A recorded. One is fine and the other is very fine plus. The catalogue value is for the latter.

140A A50 12c dull violet	*30,000.*	—

Two examples are recorded of No. 140A unused, and it is valued in the grade of fine.

One used example is recorded, centered to the left.

141A A51 15c orange	*16,500.*	*8,500.*

Three singles and a block of 4 are recorded of No. 141A unused. Value for unused single is for a fine example.

143A A53 30c black	*75,000.*	

Only one recorded example of No. 143A, which is valued in the grade of fine-very fine.

144A A54 90c carmine	—	*15,000.*

The unused No. 144A has a vertically split grill and is unique.

White Wove Paper Without Grill.

1870-71 ***Perf. 12***

145 A44 1c ultra	650.	20.00
No gum	240.	
146 A45 2c red brown	350.	17.50
No gum	150.	
d. Double impression	*9,000.*	
147 A46 3c green	200.	1.80
No gum	80.	
a. Printed on both sides, reverse inverted		*17,500.*
b. Double impression		*30,000.*

Nos. 147a and 147b are valued in the grade of fine.

The imperf. 3c can be found in the Scott U.S. Specialized Catalogue Die and Plate Proofs section.

148 A47 6c carmine	900.	22.50
No gum	290.	
c. Double paper	—	*100.00*

No. 148b is unique.

149 A48 7c ver ('71)	900.	100.00
No gum	290.	
150 A49 10c brown	2,000.	35.00
No gum	800.	
151 A50 12c dull violet	2,850.	200.00
No gum	1,050.	
152 A51 15c brt org	3,500.	225.00
No gum	1,300.	
a. Double impression		*9,000.*

No. 152a is unique. It has fine centering and faults and is valued thus.

153 A52 24c purple	1,700.	225.00
No gum	650.	
a. Double paper	—	—
154 A53 30c black	7,000.	300.00
No gum	2,600.	
155 A54 90c carmine	5,000.	350.00
No gum	1,800.	

PRINTED BY THE CONTINENTAL BANK NOTE COMPANY

Designs of the 1870-71 Issue with secret marks on the values from 1c to 15c, as described and illustrated:

The object of secret marks was to provide a simple and positive proof that these stamps were produced by the Continental Bank Note Company and not by their predecessors.

Almost all of the stamps of the Continental Bank Note Co. printing including the Department stamps and some of the Newspaper stamps may be found upon a paper that shows more or less the characteristics of a ribbed paper. The ribbing may be oriented either vertically or horizontally, with horizontal ribbing being far more common than vertical ribbing. Values are for the most common varieties.

Franklin — A44a

1c. In the pearl at the left of the numeral "1" there is a small crescent.

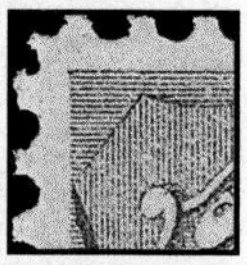
Jackson — A45a

2c. Under the scroll at the left of "U. S." there is a small diagonal line. This mark seldom shows clearly. The stamp, No. 157, can be distinguished by its color.

Washington — A46a

3c. The under part of the upper tail of the left ribbon is heavily shaded.

Lincoln — A47a

6c. The first four vertical lines of the shading in the lower part of the left ribbon have been strengthened.

Stanton — A48a

7c. Two small semi-circles are drawn around the ends of the lines that outline the ball in the lower right hand corner.

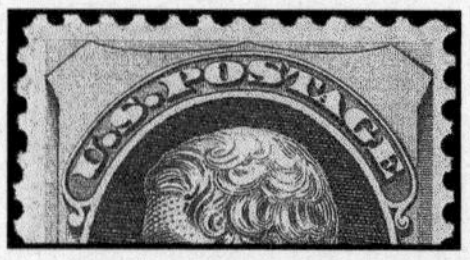
Jefferson — A49a

10c. There is a small semi-circle in the scroll at the right end of the upper label.

Clay — A50a

12c. The balls of the figure "2" are crescent shaped.

Webster — A51a

15c. In the lower part of the triangle in the upper left corner two lines have been made heavier forming a "V." This mark can be found on some of the Continental and American (1879) printings, but not all stamps show it.

Secret marks were added to the dies of the 24c, 30c and 90c but new plates were not made from them. The various printings of the 30c and 90c can be distinguished only by the shades and paper.

Experimental J. Grill about 7x9½mm exists on all values except 24c and 90c. Grill was composed of truncated pyramids and was so strongly impressed that some points often broke through the paper.

White Wove Paper, Thin to Thick
Without Grill

1873, July (?) ***Perf. 12***

156	A44a	1c ultra	200.	5.75
		No gum	90.	
a.		Double paper	2,000.	500.00
e.		With grill	2,000.	
f.		Imperf., pair	—	1,500.
157	A45a	2c brown	325.	25.00
		No gum	125.	
a.		Double paper	1,500.	200.00
c.		With grill	1,850.	750.00
d.		Double impression		16,500.

No. 157d is unique.

158	A46a	3c green	110.	1.00
		No gum	40.	
a.		Double paper	600.	100.00
e.		With grill	550.	
h.		Horizontal pair, imperf. vert.		—
i.		Horizontal pair, imperf. between		1,300.
j.		Double impression		7,000.
k.		Printed on both sides		20,000.

Nos. 158j and 158k are valued in the grade of fine.

The imperf 3c, with and without grill, can be found in the Scott U.S. Specialized Catalogue Die and Plate Proofs section.

159	A47a	6c dull pink	375.	18.00
		No gum	120.	
b.		With grill	1,800.	
c.		Double paper	—	900.00
160	A48a	7c org ver	1,000.	90.00
		No gum	350.	
a.		With grill	3,500.	
b.		Double paper		—
161	A49a	10c brown	800.	25.00
		No gum	275.	
a.		Double paper	3,500.	900.00
c.		With grill	3,750.	
d.		Horizontal pair, imperf. between		15,000.
162	A50a	12c blkish vio	2,200.	150.00
		No gum	775.	
a.		With grill	5,500.	
163	A51a	15c yel org	2,250.	160.00
		No gum	775.	
a.		With grill	5,750.	
b.		Double paper		1,250.
164	A52	24c purple		357,500.

The Philatelic Foundation has certified as genuine a 24c on vertically ribbed paper, and that is the unique stamp listed as No. 164. Specialists believe that only Continental used ribbed paper. It is not known for sure whether or not Continental also printed the 24c value on regular paper; if it did, specialists currently are not able to distinguish these from No. 153. The catalogue value represents a 2004 auction sale price realized.

165	A53	30c gray black	4,000.	150.
		No gum	1,300.	
a.		Double paper	—	
c.		With grill	24,000.	
166	A54	90c rose car	2,100.	325.
		No gum	700.	

Special Printing of the 1873 Issue

Hard, White Wove Paper
Without Gum

1875 ***Perf. 12***

167	A44a	1c ultramarine	14,000.	
168	A45a	2c dark brown	6,000.	
169	A46a	3c blue green	21,500.	—
170	A47a	6c dull rose	20,000.	
171	A48a	7c reddish ver	4,250.	
172	A49a	10c pale brown	19,000.	
173	A50a	12c dark violet	5,500.	
174	A51a	15c bright org	19,000.	
175	A52	24c dull purple	3,500.	22,500.
176	A53	30c greenish blk	12,500.	
177	A54	90c vio carmine	19,000.	

Although perforated, these stamps were usually cut apart with scissors. As a result, the perforations are often much mutilated and the design is frequently damaged.

These can be distinguished from the 1873 issue by the shades; also by the paper, which is very white instead of yellowish.

These and the subsequent issues listed under the heading of "Special Printings" are special printings of stamps then in current use which, together with the reprints and re-issues, were made for sale to collectors. They were available for postage except for the Officials, Newspaper and Periodical, and demonetized issues.

Only three examples of No. 175 used have been certified. They all have small faults and are valued thus.

Yellowish Wove Paper

1875 ***Perf. 12***

178	A45a	2c vermilion	325.	15.00
		No gum	100.	
a.		Double paper	—	—
c.		With grill	1,200.	2,750.

The imperf 2c can be found in the Scott U.S. Specialized Catalogue Die and Plate Proofs section.

Zachary Taylor — A55

179	A55	5c blue	700.	27.50
		No gum	225.	
a.		Double paper	950.	
c.		With grill	9,500.	

SPECIAL PRINTING OF 1875 ISSUE
Hard, White Wove Paper
Without Gum

1875

180	A45a	2c carmine ver	70,000.	
181	A55	5c bright blue	450,000.	

Unlike Nos. 167-177, Nos. 180-181 were seldom cut apart with scissors.

Please Note:
Stamps are valued in the grade of very fine unless otherwise indicated.

Values for early and valuable stamps are for examples with certificates of authenticity from acknowledged expert committees, or examples sold with the buyer having the right of certification.

This applies to examples with original gum as well as examples without gum.

Beware of stamps offered "as is," as the gum on some unused stamps offered with "original gum" may be fraudulent, and stamps offered as unused without gum may in some cases be altered or faintly canceled used stamps.

IMPORTANT INFORMATION
REGARDING VALUES FOR
NEVER-HINGED STAMPS

Collectors should be aware that the values given for never-hinged stamps from No. 182 on are for stamps in the grade of very fine, just as the values for all stamps in the catalogue are for very fine stamps unless indicated otherwise. The never-hinged premium as a percentage of value will be larger for stamps in extremely fine or superb grades, and the premium will be smaller for fine-very fine, fine or poor examples. This is particularly true of the issues of the late-19th and early-20th centuries.

VALUES FOR NEVER-HINGED
STAMPS
PRIOR TO SCOTT 182

This catalogue does not value pre-1879 stamps in never-hinged condition. Premiums for never-hinged condition in the classic era invariably are even larger than those premiums listed for the 1879 and later issues. Generally speaking, the earlier the stamp is listed in the catalogue, the larger will be the never-hinged premium.

For values of the most popular U.S. stamps in various conditions, including never hinged from No. 182 on, and in the grades of very good, fine, fine to very fine, very fine, very fine to extremely fine, extremely fine, extremely fine to superb, and superb, see the *Scott Stamp Values U.S. Specialized by Grade*, updated and issued each year as part of the U.S. specialized catalogue.

PRINTED BY THE AMERICAN BANK NOTE COMPANY

SAME AS 1870-75 ISSUES
Soft Porous Paper
Varying from Thin to Thick

1879 ***Perf. 12***

182	A44a	1c dark ultra	200.	6.00
		Never hinged	675.	
		No gum	80.	
183	A45a	2c vermilion	100.	5.00
		Never hinged	370.	
		No gum	40.	
a.		Double impression	—	5,500.

No. 183a is valued in the grade of fine.

184	A46a	3c green	90.	1.00
		Never hinged	325.	
		No gum	35.	
b.		Double impression		5,000.

No. 184b is valued in the grade of fine.

The imperf 3c can be found in the Scott U.S. Specialized Catalogue Die and Plate Proofs section.

185	A55	5c blue	500.	16.00
		Never hinged	1,600.	
		No gum	155.	
186	A47a	6c pink	900.	22.50
		Never hinged	3,100.	
		No gum	275.	
187	A49	10c brn, without secret mark	3,000.	45.00
		Never hinged	10,000.	
		No gum	1,000.	
a.		Double paper	10,000.	—
188	A49a	10c brn, with secret mark	1,800.	30.00
		Never hinged	6,000.	
		No gum	650.	
189	A51a	15c red orange	180.	27.50
		Never hinged	600.	
		No gum	70.	
190	A53	30c full black	850.	90.00
		Never hinged	2,800.	
		No gum	300.	
191	A54	90c carmine	2,100.	400.00
		Never hinged	7,250.	
		No gum	700.	
a.		Double paper	—	

The Continental Bank Note Co. was consolidated with the American Bank Note Co. on February 4, 1879. The American Bank Note Company used many plates of the Continental Bank Note Company to print the ordinary postage, Departmental and Newspaper stamps. Therefore, stamps bearing the Continental Company's imprint were not always its product.

The A. B. N. Co. also used the 30c and 90c plates of the N. B. N. Co. Some of No. 190 and all of No. 217 were from A. B. N. Co. plate 405.

Early printings of No. 188 were from Continental plates 302 and 303 which contained the normal secret mark of 1873. After those plates were re-entered by the A. B. N. Co. in 1880, pairs or multiple pieces contained combinations of normal, hairline or missing marks. The pairs or other multiples usually found contain at least one hairline mark which tended to disappear as the plate wore.

A. B. N. Co. plates 377 and 378 were made in 1881 from the National transfer roll of 1870. No. 187 from these plates has no secret mark.

The imperf. 90c can be found in the Scott U.S. Specialized Catalogue Die and Plate Proofs section.

Special Printing of the 1879 Issue

Soft Porous Paper
Without Gum

1880 ***Perf. 12***

192	A44a	1c dark ultra	57,500.	
193	A45a	2c brown	16,000.	
194	A46a	3c blue green	120,000.	
195	A47a	6c dull rose	67,500.	
196	A48a	7c scarlet ver	6,750.	
197	A49a	10c deep brown	37,500.	
198	A50a	12c blkish pur	9,500.	
199	A51a	15c orange	30,000.	
200	A52	24c dark violet	9,000.	
201	A53	30c grnish blk	22,500.	
202	A54	90c dull carmine	30,000.	
203	A45a	2c scarlet ver	100,000.	
204	A55	5c deep blue	240,000.	

Nos. 192 and 194 are valued in the grade of fine.

No. 197 was printed from Continental plate 302 (or 303) after plate was re-entered. Therefore, the stamp may show normal, hairline or missing secret mark.

The Post Office Department did not keep separate records of the 1875 and 1880 Special Printings of the 1873 and 1879 issues, but the total quantity sold of both is recorded. Census research indicates that numbers sold of the two sets were approximately equal.

Unlike the 1875 hard-paper Special Printings (Nos. 167-177), the 1880 soft-paper Special Printings were never cut apart with scissors.

While use of Nos. 192-204 for postage was legal, no used examples are recorded. Expertization by competent authorities would be required to establish use.

James A. Garfield — A56

1882

205	A56	5c yellow brown	240.	15.00
		Never hinged	775.	
		No gum	90.	

Special Printing

1882 ***Perf. 12***

Soft porous paper, without gum

205C	A56	5c gray brown	50,000.	

DESIGNS OF 1873 RE-ENGRAVED

Franklin — A44b

1c — The vertical lines in the upper part of the stamp have been so deepened that the background often appears to be solid. Lines of shading have been added to the upper arabesques.

1881-82

206	A44b	1c gray blue	70.00	1.00
		Never hinged	225.00	
		No gum	25.00	
a.		Double impression		—

No. 206a is a partial double impression, with "ONE 1 CENT," etc. at bottom doubled.

Earliest documented use: Oct. 11, 1881.

Washington — A46b

3c. The shading at the sides of the central oval appears only about one-half the previous width. A short horizontal dash has been cut about 1mm below the "TS" of "CENTS."

207	A46b	3c blue green	80.00	.80
		Never hinged	250.00	
		No gum	27.50	
c.		Double impression		10,000.

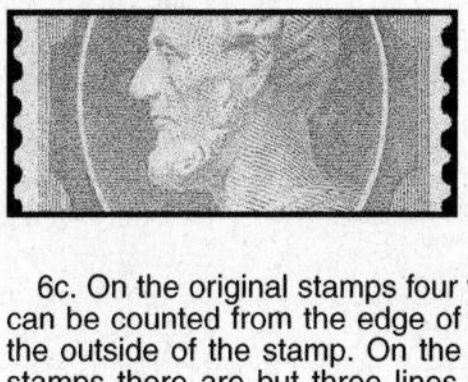

Lincoln — A47b

6c. On the original stamps four vertical lines can be counted from the edge of the panel to the outside of the stamp. On the re-engraved stamps there are but three lines in the same place.

208	A47b	6c rose	825.	110.00
		Never hinged	2,600.	
		No gum	250.	
a.		6c deep brown red	600.	190.00
		Never hinged	1,900.	
		No gum	170.	

Jefferson — A49b

10c. On the original stamps there are five vertical lines between the left side of the oval and the edge of the shield. There are only four lines on the re-engraved stamps. In the lower part of the latter, also, the horizontal lines of the background have been strengthened.

209	A49b	10c brown	175.	6.00
		Never hinged	525.	
		No gum	65.	
b.		10c black brown	3,000.	375.00
		Never hinged	6,000.	
		No gum	950.	
c.		Double impression		—

Specimen stamps (usually overprinted "Sample") without overprint exist in a brown shade that differs from No. 209. The unoverprinted brown specimen is cheaper than No. 209. Expertization is recommended.

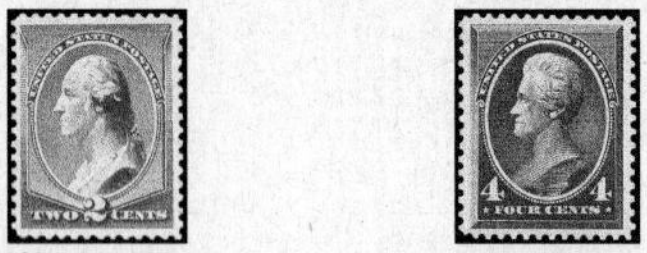

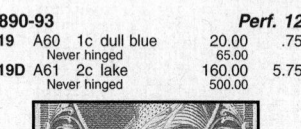

Washington A57 — Jackson A58

Nos. 210-211 were issued to meet the reduced first class rate of 2 cents for each half ounce, and the double rate, which Congress approved Mar. 3, 1883, effective Oct. 1, 1883.

1883, Oct. 1 ***Perf. 12***

210	A57 2c red brown	45.	.75
	Never hinged	135.	
	No gum	17.	
211	A58 4c blue green	225.	25.00
	Never hinged	800.	
	No gum	80.	

Imperfs can be found in the Scott U.S. Specialized Catalogue Die and Plate Proofs section.

Special Printing

1883-85 Soft porous paper ***Perf. 12***

211B	A57 2c pale red brn, with gum ('85)	400.	—
	Never hinged	1,000.	
	No gum	140.	
c.	Horizontal pair, imperf. between	*2,250.*	
	Never hinged	*3,250.*	
211D	A58 4c deep blue grn	*47,500.*	

No. 211D is without gum.

Franklin — A59

1887 ***Perf. 12***

212	A59 1c ultramarine	90.00	2.50
	Never hinged	290.00	
	No gum	35.00	
213	A57 2c green	40.00	.60
	Never hinged	120.00	
	No gum	15.00	
b.	Printed on both sides		—

Imperf 1c, 2c can be found in the Scott U.S. Specialized Catalogue Die and Plate Proofs section.

214	A46b 3c vermilion	65.00	50.00
	Never hinged	190.00	
	No gum	25.00	
	Nos. 212-214 (3)	195.00	53.10

1888 ***Perf. 12***

215	A58 4c carmine	180.	30.00
	Never hinged	525.	
	No gum	60.	
216	A56 5c indigo	220.	20.00
	Never hinged	675.	
	No gum	75.	
217	A53 30c orange brn	300.	90.00
	Never hinged	1,075.	
	No gum	90.	
218	A54 90c purple	800.	225.00
	Never hinged	2,500.	
	No gum	250.	
	Nos. 215-218 (4)	1,500.	365.00

Imperfs can be found in the Scott U.S. Specialized Catalogue Die and Plate Proofs section.

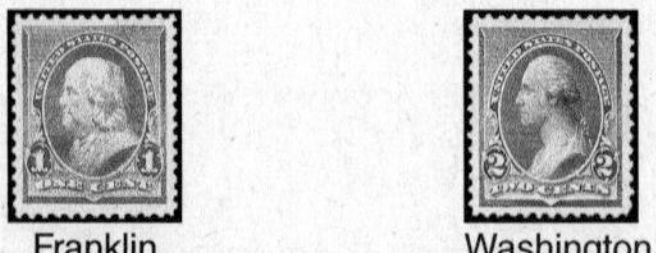

Franklin A60 — Washington A61

Jackson A62 — Lincoln A63

Ulysses S. Grant A64 — Garfield A65

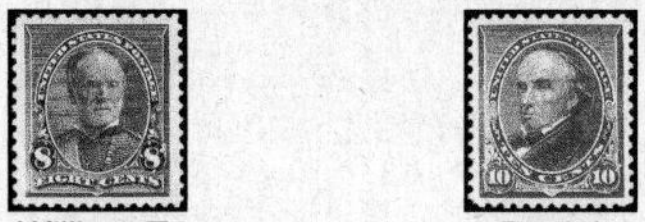

William T. Sherman A66 — Daniel Webster A67

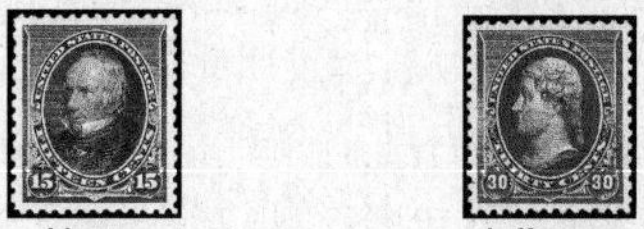

Henry Clay A68 — Jefferson A69

Perry — A70

1890-93 ***Perf. 12***

219	A60 1c dull blue	20.00	.75
	Never hinged	65.00	
219D	A61 2c lake	160.00	5.75
	Never hinged	500.00	

Cap only on left 2

Cap on both 2s

220	A61 2c carmine	20.00	.70
	Never hinged	60.00	
a.	Cap on left "2"	150.00	12.50
	Never hinged	450.00	
c.	Cap on both "2's"	650.00	35.00
	Never hinged	1,800.	
221	A62 3c purple	55.00	9.00
	Never hinged	175.00	
222	A63 4c dark brown	80.00	4.75
	Never hinged	240.00	
223	A64 5c chocolate	60.00	4.75
	Never hinged	185.00	
224	A65 6c brown red	50.00	25.00
	Never hinged	160.00	
225	A66 8c lilac ('93)	45.00	17.00
	Never hinged	135.00	
226	A67 10c green	160.00	5.00
	Never hinged	475.00	
227	A68 15c indigo	180.00	25.00
	Never hinged	550.00	
228	A69 30c black	300.00	30.00
	Never hinged	900.00	
229	A70 90c orange	475.00	140.00
	Never hinged	1,600.	
	Nos. 219-229 (12)	1,605.	267.70

The No. 220 with "cap on right 2" variety is due to imperfect inking, not a plate defect.

Imperfs. can be found in the *Scott U.S. Specialized Catalogue* Die and Plate Proofs section.

COLUMBIAN EXPOSITION ISSUE

Columbus in Sight of Land — A71 — Landing of Columbus — A72

Flagship of Columbus — A73 — Fleet of Columbus — A74

Columbus Soliciting Aid from Isabella — A75 — Columbus Welcomed at Barcelona — A76

Columbus Restored to Favor — A77 — Columbus Presenting Natives — A78

Columbus Announcing his Discovery — A79 — Columbus at La Rábida — A80

Recall of Columbus — A81 — Isabella Pledging her Jewels — A82

Columbus in Chains — A83 — Columbus Describing his Third Voyage — A84

Isabella & Columbus — A85 — Columbus — A86

1893 ***Perf. 12***

230	A71 1c deep blue	14.00	.40
	Never hinged	32.50	
231	A72 2c brn vio	12.50	.30
	Never hinged	31.00	
232	A73 3c green	35.00	15.00
	Never hinged	97.50	
233	A74 4c ultra	55.00	8.00
	Never hinged	150.00	
a.	4c blue (error)	*20,000.*	*15,000.*
	Never hinged	*35,000.*	

No. 233a exists in two shades. No. 233a used is valued with small faults, as almost all examples come thus.

234	A75 5c chocolate	55.00	8.50
	Never hinged	150.00	
235	A76 6c purple	55.00	22.50
	Never hinged	150.00	
a.	6c red violet	65.00	22.50
	Never hinged	175.00	
236	A77 8c brn pur	50.00	10.00
	Never hinged	140.00	
237	A78 10c blk brn	95.00	8.00
	Never hinged	265.00	
238	A79 15c dark green	200.00	80.00
	Never hinged	600.00	
239	A80 30c org brn	225.00	90.00
	Never hinged	675.00	
240	A81 50c slate blue	450.	200.
	Never hinged	1,400.	
	No gum	200.	
241	A82 $1 salmon	1,000.	525.
	Never hinged	3,400.	
	No gum	500.	
242	A83 $2 brown red	1,100.	525.
	Never hinged	3,600.	
	No gum	550.	
243	A84 $3 yel grn	1,500.	775.
	Never hinged	4,750.	
	No gum	750.	
a.	$3 olive green	1,400.	775.
	Never hinged	4,350.	
	No gum	700.	
244	A85 $4 crim lake	2,100.	975.
	Never hinged	7,250.	
	No gum	1,000.	
a.	$4 rose carmine	2,000.	975.
	Never hinged	7,000.	
	No gum	950.	
245	A86 $5 black	2,400.	1,200.
	Never hinged	9,750.	
	No gum	1,250.	

World's Columbia Expo., Chicago, May 1-Oct. 30, 1893.

Nos. 230-245 are known imperf., but were not regularly issues.

See Scott U.S. Specialized Catalogue Die and Plate Proofs section for the 2c.

Never-Hinged Stamps
See note before No. 182 regarding premiums for never-hinged stamps.

Bureau Issues

Starting in 1894, the Bureau of Engraving and Printing at Washington produced most U.S. postage stamps.

Until 1965 Bureau-printed stamps were engraved except Nos. 525-536 which were offset.

The combination of lithography and engraving (see #1253) was first used in 1964, and photogravure (see #1426) in 1971.

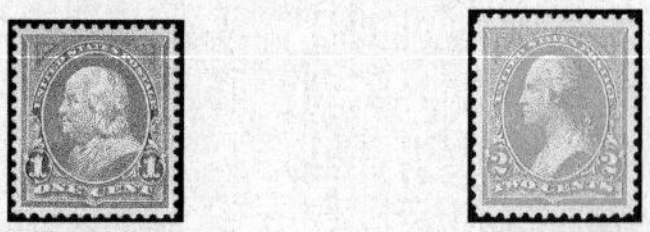

Franklin A87 — Washington A88

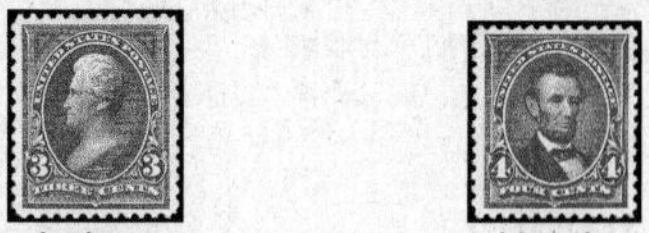

Jackson A89 — Lincoln A90

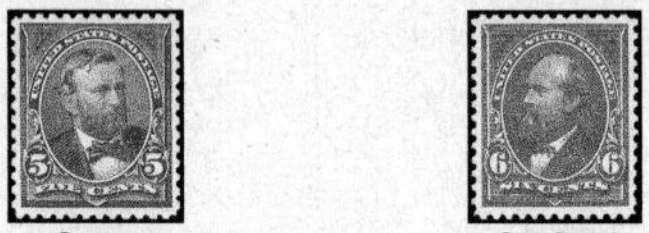

Grant A91 — Garfield A92

Sherman A93 — Webster A94

Clay A95 — Jefferson A96

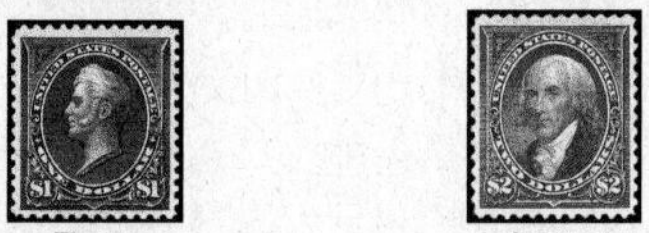

Perry A97 — James Madison A98

John Marshall — A99

1894 **Unwmk.** ***Perf. 12***

246	A87 1c ultramarine	30.00	7.00
	Never hinged	90.00	
247	A87 1c blue	62.50	4.00
	Never hinged	180.00	

Triangle A (Type I)

TWO CENTS

Type I (Triangle A). The horizontal lines of the ground work run across the triangle and are of the same thickness within it as without.

Triangle B (Type II)

Type II (Triangle B). The horizontal lines cross the triangle but are thinner within it than without. Other minor design differences exist, but the change to Triangle B is a sufficient determinant.

Triangle C (Types III and IV)

Type III (Triangle C). The horizontal lines do not cross the double lines of the triangle. The lines within the triangle are thin, as in Type II. The rest of the design is the same as Type II, except that most of the designs had the dot in the "S" of "CENTS" removed. Stamps with this dot present are listed; some specialists refer to them as "Type IIIa" varieties.

Type IV

Type IV (Triangle C). See No. 279B and its varieties. Type IV is from a new die with many major and minor design variations including, (1) re-cutting and lengthening of hairline, (2) shaded toga button, (3) strengthening of lines on sleeve, (4) additional dots on ear, (5) "T" of "TWO" straight at right, (6) background lines extend into white oval opposite "U" of "UNITED." Many other differences exist.

For further information concerning type IV, see also George Brett's article in the Sept. 1993 issue of the "The United States Specialist" and the 23-part article by Kenneth Diehl in the Dec. 1994 through Aug. 1997 issues of the "The United States Specialist."

248	A88	2c pink, type I	32.50	10.00
		Never hinged	97.50	
a.		Vert. pair, imperf horiz.	*5,500.*	
249	A88	2c car lake, type I	175.00	7.00
		Never hinged	500.00	
a.		Double impression		—
250	A88	2c car, type I	29.00	3.00
		Never hinged	85.00	
a.		2c rose, type I	40.00	8.50
		Never hinged	115.00	
b.		2c scarlet, type I	26.00	2.75
		Never hinged	80.00	
d.		Horizontal pair, imperf. between	*2,000.*	
251	A88	2c car, type II	425.00	17.50
		Never hinged	1,250.	
a.		2c scarlet, type II	400.00	15.00
		Never hinged	1,175.	
252	A88	2c car, type III	135.00	13.00
		Never hinged	400.00	
		On cover		22.50
a.		2c scarlet, type III	120.00	15.00
		Never hinged	360.00	
b.		Horiz. pair, imperf. vert.	*5,000.*	
c.		Horiz. pair, imperf. between	*5,500.*	

No. 252b is unique and exists only as a horizontal top plate-number strip of 3. A vertical right plate-number strip of 3 from the same plate exists containing three stamps imperforate at left and right.

253	A89	3c purple	120.00	12.00
		Never hinged	360.00	
254	A90	4c dark brown	200.00	11.00
		Never hinged	600.00	
255	A91	5c chocolate	120.00	9.00
		Never hinged	360.00	
c.		Vert. pair, imperf. horiz.	*4,000.*	
256	A92	6c dull brown	160.00	27.50
		Never hinged	475.00	
a.		Vert. pair, imperf. horiz.	*3,000.*	
257	A93	8c vio brn	170.00	20.00
		Never hinged	525.00	
258	A94	10c dark green	275.00	20.00
		Never hinged	850.00	
259	A95	15c dark blue	275.00	65.00
		Never hinged	850.00	
260	A96	50c orange	475.	140.
		Never hinged	1,425.	

Type I

Type II

ONE DOLLAR

Type I. The circles enclosing "$1" are broken where they meet the curved line below "One Dollar."

Type II. The circles are complete.

261	A97	$1 blk, type I	1,000.	350.
		Never hinged	3,200.	
		No gum	400.	
261A	A97	$1 blk, type II	2,200.	800.
		Never hinged	6,750.	
		No gum	850.	
262	A98	$2 bright blue	2,750.	1,200.
		Never hinged	9,000.	
		No gum	1,100.	
263	A99	$5 dark green	4,000.	2,600.
		Never hinged	15,000.	
		No gum	2,100.	

For imperfs. and the 2c pink, vert. pair, imperf. hoirz., see Scott U.S. Specialized Catalogue Die and plate Proofs.

Same as 1894 Issue

Wmk. 191 Horizontally or Vertically

1895 ***Perf. 12***

264	A87	1c blue	6.00	.60
		Never hinged	17.50	
265	A88	2c car, type I	35.00	3.50
		Never hinged	105.00	
266	A88	2c car, type II	40.00	15.00
		Never hinged	120.00	
267	A88	2c car, type III	5.50	.60
		Never hinged	16.00	
a.		2c pink, type III	20.00	5.00
		Never hinged	60.00	
b.		2c vermilion, type III	*150.00*	*20.00*
c.		2c rose carmine, type III	—	—

The three left vertical rows from plate 170 are type II, the balance being type III.

268	A89	3c purple	37.50	2.25
		Never hinged	115.00	
269	A90	4c dark brown	42.50	3.50
		Never hinged	125.00	
270	A91	5c chocolate	35.00	3.50
		Never hinged	105.00	
271	A92	6c dull brown	110.00	8.50
		Never hinged	325.00	
a.		Wmkd. USIR	*15,000.*	*8,000.*
272	A93	8c violet brown	70.00	2.75
		Never hinged	210.00	
a.		Wmkd. USIR	*7,000.*	950.00
273	A94	10c dark green	95.00	2.25
		Never hinged	280.00	
274	A95	15c dark blue	200.00	17.50
		Never hinged	600.00	
275	A96	50c orange	240.	40.00
		Never hinged	725.	
a.		50c red orange	325.	47.50
		Never hinged	975.	
276	A97	$1 black, type I	600.	95.
		Never hinged	1,800.	
		No gum	250.	
276A	A97	$1 black, type II	1,250.	200.
		Never hinged	3,750.	
		No gum	500.	
277	A98	$2 bright blue	900.	400.
		Never hinged	2,900.	
		No gum	375.	
a.		$2 dark blue	900.	400.
		Never hinged	2,900.	
		No gum	375.	
278	A99	$5 dark green	2,000.	600.
		Never hinged	6,250.	
		No gum	800.	

For imperfs. and the 1c horiz. pair, imperf. vert., see Scott U.S. Specialized Catalogue Die and Plate Proofs.

For "I.R." overprints see Nos. R155, R156-R158.

No. 271a unused is valued in the grade of fine.

Wmk. 191 Horizontally or Vertically

1897-1903 ***Perf. 12***

279	A87	1c dp grn, horiz. wmk ('98)	9.00	.50
		Never hinged	25.00	
a.		Vert. wmk (error)	*80.00*	*7.50*
		Never hinged	*240.00*	
279B	A88	2c red, type IV ('99)	9.00	.40
		Never hinged	25.00	
c.		2c rose carmine, type IV ('99)	275.00	230.00
		Never hinged	850.00	
d.		2c orange red, type IV, horiz. wmk. ('00)	11.50	2.00
		Never hinged	32.50	
e.		2c orange red, type IV, vert. wmk.	*80.00*	*12.50*
		Never hinged	*240.00*	
f.		2c carmine, type IV	10.00	2.00
		Never hinged	27.50	
g.		2c pink, type IV	55.00	7.50
		Never hinged	165.00	
h.		2c vermilion, type IV ('99)	12.50	3.00
		Never hinged	35.00	
i.		2c brown org, type IV ('99)	*400.00*	*100.00*
		Never hinged	*950.00*	
j.		Booklet pane of 6, red, type IV, horiz. wmk. ('00)	500.00	*3,000.*
		Never hinged	1,000.	
k.		Booklet pane of 6, red, type IV, vertical watermark ('02)	500.00	—
		Never hinged	1,000.	
l.		As No. 279B, all color missing (FO)	*500.00*	

No. 279Bl must be collected se-tenant with a partially printed stamp.

280	A90	4c rose brn ('98)	30.00	3.25
		Never hinged	80.00	
a.		4c lilac brown	30.00	3.25
		Never hinged	80.00	
b.		4c orange brown	30.00	3.00
		Never hinged	80.00	
281	A91	5c dk blue ('98)	32.50	2.25
		Never hinged	100.00	
282	A92	6c lake ('98)	45.00	6.50
		Never hinged	140.00	
a.		6c purple lake	80.00	20.00
		Never hinged	240.00	

Type I. The tips of the foliate ornaments do not impinge on the white curved line below "ten cents."

282C	A94	10c brn, type I ('98)	175.00	6.50
		Never hinged	525.00	

Type II. The tips of the ornaments break the curved line below the "e" of "ten" and the "t" of "cents."

283	A94	10c org brn, type II, horiz. wmk.	150.00	6.00
		Never hinged	450.00	
a.		Vert. wmk. ('00)	*250.00*	*15.00*
		Never hinged	*775.00*	
284	A95	15c ol grn ('98)	150.00	13.00
		Never hinged	475.00	
		Nos. 279-284 (8)	600.50	38.40

For "I.R." overprints, see Nos. R153-R155A.

VALUES FOR VERY FINE STAMPS
Please note: Stamps are valued in the grade of Very Fine unless otherwise indicated.

TRANS-MISSISSIPPI EXPOSITION ISSUE

Marquette on the Mississippi
A100

Farming in the West
A101

Indian Hunting Buffalo
A102

Frémont on the Rocky Mountains
A103

Troops Guarding Wagon Train
A104

Hardships of Emigration
A105

Western Mining Prospector
A106

Western Cattle in Storm
A107

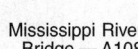

Mississippi River Bridge — A108

1898, June 17 **Wmk. 191** ***Perf. 12***

285	A100	1c dk yel grn	27.50	7.00
		Never hinged	75.00	
286	A101	2c copper red	25.00	2.75
		Never hinged	72.50	
287	A102	4c orange	110.00	25.00
		Never hinged	330.00	
288	A103	5c dull blue	100.00	25.00
		Never hinged	300.00	
289	A104	8c violet brown	140.00	47.50
		Never hinged	425.00	
a.		Vert. pair, imperf. horiz.	*27,500.*	
290	A105	10c gray vio	140.00	35.00
		Never hinged	425.00	
291	A106	50c sage grn	600.00	175.00
		Never hinged	1,750.	
292	A107	$1 black	1,500.	700.
		Never hinged	3,750.	
		No gum	850.	
293	A108	$2 org brn	1,900.	1,000.
		Never hinged	5,750.	
		No gum	950.	
		Nos. 285-293 (9)	4,543.	2,017.

Trans-Mississippi Exposition, Omaha, Neb., June 1 to Nov. 1, 1898.

For "I.R" overprints see #R158A-R158B.

Never-Hinged Stamps
See note before No. 182 regarding premiums for never-hinged stamps.

PAN-AMERICAN EXPOSITION ISSUE

Fast Lake Navigation
A109

"Empire State" Express
A110

Electric Automobile
A111

Bridge at Niagara Falls
A112

Canal Locks at Sault Ste. Marie
A113

Fast Ocean Navigation
A114

1901, May 1 **Wmk. 191** ***Perf. 12***

294	A109	1c grn & blk	17.00	3.00
		Never hinged	42.50	
a.		Center inverted	*12,500.*	*22,500.*
		Never hinged	*22,500.*	
295	A110	2c car & blk	16.00	1.00
		Never hinged	40.00	
a.		Center inverted	*50,000.*	*50,000.*
296	A111	4c dp red brn & blk	70.00	18.00
		Never hinged	170.00	
a.		Center inverted	*80,000.*	—
297	A112	5c ultra & black	75.00	17.00
		Never hinged	180.00	
298	A113	8c brn vio & blk	90.00	50.00
		Never hinged	230.00	
299	A114	10c yel brn & blk	115.00	30.00
		Never hinged	325.00	
		Nos. 294-299 (6)	383.00	119.00
		Nos. 294-299, never hinged	957.50	

No. 296a was a special printing.

Almost all unused examples of Nos. 295a and 296a have partial or disturbed gum. Values are for examples with full original gum that is slightly disturbed.

Franklin
A115

Washington
A116

Jackson
A117

Grant
A118

Lincoln
A119

Garfield
A120

Martha Washington
A121

Webster
A122

Benjamin Harrison
A123

Clay
A124

Jefferson
A125

David G. Farragut
A126

Madison
A127

Marshall
A128

1902-03 Wmk. 191 *Perf. 12*

300	A115 1c blue grn ('03)	12.00	.25
	Never hinged	30.00	
b.	Booklet pane of 6	600.00	*11,500.*
	Never hinged	1,150.	
	Wmk. horiz.	*2,000.*	
301	A116 2c car ('03)	15.00	.50
	Never hinged	37.50	
c.	Booklet pane of 6	500.00	*6,000.*
	Never hinged	950.00	
302	A117 3c brt vio ('03)	55.00	3.75
	Never hinged	140.00	
303	A118 4c brn ('03)	55.00	2.25
	Never hinged	140.00	
304	A119 5c blue ('03)	60.00	2.00
	Never hinged	150.00	
305	A120 6c claret ('03)	60.00	5.50
	Never hinged	150.00	
306	A121 8c vio black	45.00	3.25
	Never hinged	110.00	
307	A122 10c pale red brn ('03)	60.00	3.00
	Never hinged	150.00	
308	A123 13c purple blk	40.00	10.00
	Never hinged	100.00	
309	A124 15c ol grn ('03)	185.00	12.50
	Never hinged	475.00	
310	A125 50c org ('03)	425.	35.00
	Never hinged	1,225.	
311	A126 $1 black ('03)	600.00	90.00
	Never hinged	1,800.	
	No gum	240.00	
312	A127 $2 dk bl ('03)	825.00	200.00
	Never hinged	2,500.	
	No gum	325.00	
313	A128 $5 dk grn ('03)	2,200.	700.00
	Never hinged	*6,500.*	
	No gum	800.00	
	Nos. 300-313 (14)	4,637.	1,068.

For listings of designs A127 and A128 with Perf. 10 see Nos. 479 and 480.

1906-08 *Imperf.*

314	A115 1c blue green	14.00	17.50
	Never hinged	30.00	
314A	A118 4c brn ('08)	*85,000.*	*45,000.*
	Never hinged	*200,000.*	
315	A119 5c blue ('08)	350.	*1,250.*
	Never hinged	600.	

No. 314A was issued imperforate but all examples were privately perforated with large oblong perforations at the sides (Schermack type III).

Beware of examples of No. 303 with trimmed perforations and fake private perfs added.

Used examples of Nos. 314 and 315 must have contemporaneous cancels.

COIL STAMPS

Warning! Imperforate stamps are known fraudulently perforated to resemble coil stamps and part-perforate varieties. Fully perforated stamps and booklet stamps also are known with perforations fraudulently trimmed off to resemble coil stamps.

1908 *Perf. 12 Horizontally*

316	A115 1c blue green	*150,000.*	
317	A119 5c blue	*6,000.*	—
	Never hinged	*12,000.*	

Perf. 12 Vertically

318	A115 1c blue green	*4,500.*	
	Never hinged	*9,500.*	

Coil stamps for use in vending and affixing machines are perforated on two sides only, either horizontally or vertically.

They were first issued in 1908, using perf. 12. This was changed to 8½ in 1910, and to 10 in 1914.

Imperforate sheets of certain denominations were sold to the vending machine companies which applied a variety of private perforations and separations.

Several values of the 1902 and later issues are found on an apparently coarse ribbed paper caused by worn blankets on the printing press and are not true paper varieties.

No. 316 is valued in the grade of fine to very fine. There are no very fine examples recorded.

All examples of Nos. 316-318 must be accompanied by certificates of authenticity issued by recognized expertizing committees.

No. 318 mint never hinged is valued in the grade of fine.

Washington — A129

Type I

Type II

The two large arrows in the illustrations highlight the two major differences of the type II stamps: closing of the thin left border line next to the laurel leaf, and strengthening of the inner frame line at the lower left corner. The small arrows point out three minor differences that are not always easily discernible: strengthening of shading lines under the ribbon just above the "T" of "TWO," a shorter shading line to the left of the "P" in "POSTAGE," and shortening of a shading line in the left side ribbon.

Type I

1903, Nov. 12 Wmk. 191 *Perf. 12*

319	A129 2c car, type I	6.00	.25
	Never hinged	15.00	
a.	2c lake	—	
b.	2c carmine rose	15.00	.40
	Never hinged	45.00	
c.	2c scarlet	10.00	.30
	Never hinged	25.00	
d.	Vert. pair, imperf. horiz., No. 319	*7,500.*	
	Never hinged	*17,500.*	
e.	Vert. pair, imperf. between		—
r.	Vert. pair, rouletted between		*4,000.*

During the use of No. 319, the postmaster of San Francisco discovered in his stock panes that had the perforations missing between the top two rows of stamps. To facilitate their separation, the imperf rows were rouletted, and the stamps were sold over the counter. These vertical pairs with regular perfs all around and rouletted between are No. 319r. No 319e is from a different source. One example has been authenticated, and collectors are warned that other pairs exist with faint blind perfs or indentations from the perforating machine.

g.	Booklet pane of 6, carmine	125.00	*450.00*
	Never hinged	240.00	
n.	Booklet pane of 6, carmine rose	275.00	*700.00*
	Never hinged	500.00	
p.	Booklet pane of 6, scarlet	185.00	*625.00*
	Never hinged	350.00	

Type II

1908 Wmk. 191 *Perf. 12*

319F	A129 2c lake	10.00	.30
	Never hinged	25.00	
i.	2c carmine	65.00	*50.00*
	Never hinged	150.00	
j.	2c carmine rose	100.00	1.75
	Never hinged	225.00	
k.	2c scarlet	70.00	2.00
	Never hinged	160.00	
l.	Booklet pane of 6, scarlet		—
q.	Booklet pane of 6, lake	300.00	*800.00*
	Never hinged	575.00	

Type I

1906, Oct. 2 Wmk. 191 *Imperf.*

320	A129 2c carmine	15.00	*19.00*
	Never hinged	32.50	
c.	2c carmine rose	75.00	42.50
	Never hinged	150.00	

Type II

1908 Wmk. 191 *Imperf.*

320A	A129 2c lake	45.00	50.00
	Never hinged	100.00	
d.	2c carmine	*135.00*	—
	Never hinged	*200.00*	

No. 320Ad was issued imperforate, but all examples were privately perforated with large oblong perforations at the sides (Schermack type III).

COIL STAMPS

1908 *Perf. 12 Horizontally*

321	A129 2c car, type I, pair	*1,000,000.*	*310,000.*

Four authenticated unused pairs of No. 321 are known and available to collectors. A fifth, unauthenticated pair is in the New York Public Library Miller collection, which is on long-term loan to the Smithsonian National Postal Museum. The value for an unused pair is for a fine-very fine example. Two fine pairs are recorded and one very fine pair.

There are no authenticated unused or off-cover used single stamps recorded. The used value is for a single on cover, of which two authenticated examples are known, both used from Indianapolis in 1908.

The Dec. 20, 1908, legal-size cover has not been seen in decades; the Oct. 2, 1908, cover sold in 2018 and is the cover valued.

Numerous counterfeits exist.

322	A129 2c carmine, type II	*7,000.*	—
	Never hinged	*15,000.*	

This Government Coil Stamp should not be confused with those of the International Vending Machine Co., which are perforated 12½.

All examples of Nos. 321-322 must be accompanied by certificates of authenticity issued by recognized expertizing committees.

VALUES FOR VERY FINE STAMPS
Please note: Stamps are valued in the grade of Very Fine unless otherwise indicated.

LOUISIANA PURCHASE EXPOSITION ISSUE

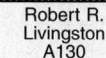

Robert R. Livingston
A130

Thomas Jefferson
A131

James Monroe
A132

William McKinley
A133

Map of Louisiana Purchase — A134

1904, Apr. 30 Wmk. 191 *Perf. 12*

323	A130 1c green	22.50	4.75
	Never hinged	60.00	
324	A131 2c carmine	22.50	2.00
	Never hinged	60.00	
a.	Vertical pair, imperf. horiz.	*25,000.*	
325	A132 3c violet	65.00	27.50
	Never hinged	170.00	
326	A133 5c dark blue	70.00	22.50
	Never hinged	180.00	
327	A134 10c red brown	125.00	27.50
	Never hinged	300.00	
	Nos. 323-327 (5)	305.00	84.25
	Nos. 323-327, never hinged	770.00	

JAMESTOWN EXPOSITION ISSUE

Captain John Smith
A135

Founding of Jamestown
A136

Pocahontas — A137

1907 Wmk. 191 *Perf. 12*

328	A135 1c green	30.00	4.50
	Never hinged	75.00	
329	A136 2c carmine	32.50	4.00
	Never hinged	85.00	
a.	2c carmine lake	—	
330	A137 5c blue	150.00	30.00
	Never hinged	375.00	
	Nos. 328-330 (3)	212.50	38.50
	Nos. 328-330, never hinged	535.00	

Franklin
A138

Washington
A139

There are several types of some of the 2c and 3c stamps of this and succeeding issues. These types are described under the dates at which they first appeared.

Illustrations of Types I-VII of the 2c (A140) and Types I-IV of the 3c (A140) are reproduced by permission of H. L. Lindquist.

1908-09 Wmk. 191 *Perf. 12*

331	A138 1c green	6.50	.40
	Never hinged	16.50	
a.	Booklet pane of 6	150.00	*700.00*
	Never hinged	300.00	

No. 331 exists in horizontal pair, imperforate between, a variety resulting from booklet experiments. Not regularly issued. Value in the grade of fine, $3,750.

No. 331a used is valued with a contemporaneous cancel. A certificate of authenticity is advised.

332	A139 2c carmine	6.00	.35
	Never hinged	14.50	
a.	Booklet pane of 6	135.00	*500.00*
	Never hinged	240.00	
b.	2c lake	*4,250.*	

No. 332a used is valued with a contemporaneous cancel. A certificate of authenticity is advised.

No. 332b is valued in the grade of fine.

Washington — A140

TYPE I

THREE CENTS

Type I. The top line of the toga rope is weak and the rope shading lines are thin. The 5th line from the left is missing. The line between the lips is thin. (For descriptions of 3c types II, III and IV, see notes and illustrations preceding Nos. 484, 529-530.)

Used on both flat plate and rotary press printings.

333 A140 3c dp vio, type I 30.00 3.00
Never hinged 75.00
334 A140 4c org brn 35.00 1.50
Never hinged 87.50
335 A140 5c blue 45.00 2.25
Never hinged 110.00
336 A140 6c red orange 62.50 6.00
Never hinged 145.00
337 A140 8c olive green 45.00 2.75
Never hinged 105.00
338 A140 10c yellow ('09) 70.00 1.80
Never hinged 165.00
339 A140 13c bl grn ('09) 37.50 17.50
Never hinged 90.00
340 A140 15c pale ultra ('09) 67.50 6.00
Never hinged 160.00
341 A140 50c violet ('09) 275.00 20.00
Never hinged 650.00
342 A140 $1 vio brn ('09) 450.00 95.00
Never hinged 1,050.
Nos. 331-342 (12) 1,130. 156.55

For listings of other perforated sheet stamps of A138, A139 and A140 see:

Nos. 357-366 Bluish paper
Nos. 374-382, 405-407 Single line wmk. Perf. 12
Nos. 423A-423C Single line wmk. Perf 12x10
Nos. 423D-423E Single line wmk. Perf 10x12
Nos. 424-430 Single line wmk. Perf. 10
Nos. 461 Single line wmk. Perf. 11
Nos. 462-469 unwmk. Perf. 10
Nos. 498-507 unwmk. Perf. 11
Nos. 519 Double line wmk. Perf. 11
Nos. 525-530 and 536 Offset printing
Nos. 538-546 Rotary press printing

Imperf

343 A138 1c green 5.50 5.00
Never hinged 9.00
344 A139 2c carmine 5.50 2.75
Never hinged 9.00
345 A140 3c dp violet, type I 11.00 *20.00*
Never hinged 19.00
346 A140 4c org brn ('09) 15.00 *20.00*
Never hinged 25.00
347 A140 5c blue ('09) 30.00 *32.50*
Never hinged 50.00
Nos. 343-347 (5) 67.00 *80.25*
Nos. 343-347, never hinged 129.00

For listings of other imperforate stamps of designs A138, A139 and A140 see Nos. 383, 384, 408, 409 and 459 Single line wmk.
Nos. 481-485 unwmk.
Nos. 531-535 Offset printing

The values for used coil stamps are for examples with contemporaneous cancels that can be authenticated by expertizing committees. Used coils with cancels most commonly from the 1950s exist, and these and stamps with other non-contemporaneous cancels sell for less than the values shown.

COIL STAMPS

1908-10 ***Perf. 12 Horizontally***

348 A138 1c green 45.00 *60.00*
Never hinged 80.00
349 A139 2c carmine ('09) 110.00 *160.00*
Never hinged 235.00
350 A140 4c org brn ('10) 155.00 *250.00*
Never hinged 325.00
351 A140 5c blue ('09) 155.00 *300.00*
Never hinged 325.00
Nos. 348-351 (4) 465.00 770.00

1909 ***Perf. 12 Vertically***

352 A138 1c green 110.00 *225.00*
Never hinged 235.00
353 A139 2c carmine 100.00 *220.00*
Never hinged 210.00
354 A140 4c org brn 220.00 *275.00*
Never hinged 425.00
355 A140 5c blue 230.00 *300.00*
Never hinged 450.00
356 A140 10c yellow 3,500. *6,250.*
Never hinged 8,000.

For listings of other coil stamps of designs A138, A139 and A140, see #385-396, 410-413, 441-458 (single line wmk.), #486-496 (unwatermarked).

Beware of stamps offered as No. 356 which may be examples of No. 338 with perfs. trimmed at top and/or bottom. Beware also of plentiful fakes in the marketplace of Nos. 348-355, made by fraudulently perforating imperforate stamps or by fraudulently trimming perforations off fully perforated stamps. Authentication of all these coils is advised.

BLUISH PAPER

This was made with 35 percent rag stock instead of all wood pulp. The "bluish" color (actually grayish blue) goes through the paper showing clearly on the back as well as on the face.

1909 ***Perf. 12***

357 A138 1c green 90.00 *160.00*
Never hinged 190.00
358 A139 2c carmine 80.00 *150.00*
Never hinged 170.00
359 A140 3c dp vio, type I 2,000. *12,500.*
Never hinged 4,000.
360 A140 4c org brn *27,500.*
361 A140 5c blue 6,500. *20,000.*
Never hinged *15,000.*

Only two examples of No. 361 used off cover (three additional on cover) are recorded. Value used is for the better of the two examples, which is well-centered but has two reattached perforations.

362 A140 6c red org 1,300. *12,500.*
Never hinged 3,000.
363 A140 8c olive green *31,500.*
Never hinged *90,000.*
364 A140 10c yellow 1,600. *10,000.*
Never hinged 4,000.
365 A140 13c blue green 2,600. *3,750.*
Never hinged 6,000.
366 A140 15c pale ultra 1,300. *16,000.*
Never hinged 3,000.

Nos. 360 and 363 were not regularly issued.

Used examples of Nos. 357-366 must bear contemporaneous cancels, and Nos. 359-366 used must be accompanied by certificates of authenticity issued by recognized expertizing committees.

LINCOLN CENTENARY OF BIRTH ISSUE

Lincoln — A141

1909, Feb. 12 **Wmk. 191** ***Perf. 12***

367 A141 2c carmine 4.50 1.75
Never hinged 9.50

Imperf

368 A141 2c carmine 12.50 19.00
Never hinged 24.00

BLUISH PAPER

Perf. 12

369 A141 2c carmine 150.00 *225.00*
Never hinged 300.00

Used examples of No. 369 must bear contemporaneous cancels. Expertizing is recommended.

ALASKA-YUKON-PACIFIC EXPOSITION ISSUE

William H. Seward — A142

1909, June 1 **Wmk. 191** ***Perf. 12***

370 A142 2c carmine 6.75 2.00
Never hinged 15.00
a. Imperf. (error), P#5209 block of 6 *3,500.*

No. 370a comes from error panes found in perforated stock. Plate 5209 was used only to print the perforated Alaska-Yukon-Pacific Exposition issue. No 370a can only be collected as a plate-number stamp or multiple. Without an attached plate number 5209, the stamps from this pane cannot be differentiated from No. 371.

Imperf

371 A142 2c carmine 14.00 21.00
Never hinged 30.00

Seattle, Wash., June 1 to Oct. 16.

HUDSON-FULTON CELEBRATION ISSUE

"Half Moon" and Steamship — A143

1909, Sept. 25 **Wmk. 191** ***Perf. 12***

372 A143 2c carmine 10.00 4.75
Never hinged 21.00

Imperf

373 A143 2c carmine 20.00 27.50
Never hinged 40.00

Tercentenary of the discovery of the Hudson River and Centenary of Robert Fulton's steamship.

DESIGNS OF 1908-09 ISSUES

1910-11 **Wmk. 190** ***Perf. 12***

374 A138 1c green 6.00 .25
Never hinged 14.00
a. Booklet pane of 6 225.00 *400.00*
Never hinged 375.00
b. Double impression *300.00*
375 A139 2c carmine 6.00 .25
Never hinged 14.00
a. Booklet pane of 6 125.00 *300.00*
Never hinged 200.00
b. 2c lake *825.00* —
Never hinged *1,800.*
c. As "b," booklet pane of 6 *10,000.*
d. Double impression *750.00* —
Never hinged *1,500.*
376 A140 3c dp vio, type I ('11) 18.00 2.00
Never hinged 40.00
377 A140 4c brown ('11) 27.50 1.00
Never hinged 65.00
378 A140 5c blue ('11) 27.50 .75
Never hinged 65.00
379 A140 6c red org ('11) 37.50 1.25
Never hinged 85.00
380 A140 8c ol grn ('11) 90.00 15.00
Never hinged 200.00
381 A140 10c yellow ('11) 85.00 6.00
Never hinged 200.00
382 A140 15c pale ultra ('11) 225.00 20.00
Never hinged 500.00
Nos. 374-382 (9) 522.50 46.50

1910, Dec. ***Imperf.***

383 A138 1c green 2.50 *2.75*
Never hinged 5.00
384 A139 2c carmine 4.00 2.75
Never hinged 8.00

The values for used coil stamps are for examples with contemporaneous cancels that can be authenticated by expertizing committees. Used coils with cancels most commonly from the 1950s exist, and these and stamps with other non-contemporaneous cancels sell for less than the values shown.

COIL STAMPS

1910, Nov. 1 ***Perf. 12 Horizontally***

385 A138 1c green 50.00 *50.00*
Never hinged 100.00
386 A139 2c carmine 130.00 90.00
Never hinged 260.00

1910-11 ***Perf. 12 Vertically***

387 A138 1c green 200.00 140.00
Never hinged 400.00
388 A139 2c carmine 1,600. *2,250.*
Never hinged 4,000.

Stamps offered as No. 388 frequently are privately perforated examples of No. 384, or examples of No. 375 with top and/or bottom perfs trimmed.

389 A140 3c dp vio, type I ('11) *110,000.* *10,000.*
Never hinged *325,000.*

No. 389 is valued in the grade of fine.

Stamps offered as No. 389 sometimes are examples of No. 376 with top and/or bottom perfs trimmed.

Beware also of plentiful fakes in the marketplace of Nos. 385-387.

Expertization by competent authorities is recommended.

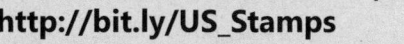

1910 ***Perf. 8½ Horizontally***

390 A138 1c green 4.50 *14.00*
Never hinged 10.00
391 A139 2c carmine 42.50 *50.00*
Never hinged 90.00

1910-13 ***Perf. 8½ Vertically***

392 A138 1c green 32.50 *50.00*
Never hinged 65.00
393 A139 2c carmine 52.50 *55.00*
Never hinged 105.00
394 A140 3c dp vio, type I ('11) 67.50 65.00
Never hinged 135.00
395 A140 4c brown ('12) 67.50 *65.00*
Never hinged 135.00
396 A140 5c blue ('13) 67.50 *65.00*
Never hinged 135.00
Nos. 392-396 (5) 287.50 300.00

Beware also of plentiful fakes in the marketplace of Nos. 390-393.

PANAMA-PACIFIC EXPOSITION ISSUE

Vasco Nunez de Balboa A144

Pedro Miguel Locks, Panama Canal A145

Golden Gate — A146

Discovery of San Francisco Bay — A147

1913 **Wmk. 190** ***Perf. 12***

397 A144 1c green 15.00 2.00
Never hinged 35.00
398 A145 2c carmine 16.00 1.00
Never hinged 35.00
a. 2c carmine lake *1,600.*
Never hinged *2,500.*
b. 2c lake *5,250.* 3,000.
Never hinged *8,500.*
399 A146 5c blue 70.00 10.00
Never hinged 160.00
400 A147 10c orange yel 115.00 20.00
Never hinged 260.00
400A A147 10c orange 175.00 22.50
Never hinged 390.00
Nos. 397-400A (5) 391.00 55.50
Nos. 397-400A, never hinged 850.00

1914-15 ***Perf. 10***

401 A144 1c green 25.00 7.00
Never hinged 60.00
402 A145 2c car ('15) 70.00 3.00
Never hinged 170.00
403 A146 5c blue ('15) 160.00 17.50
Never hinged 400.00
404 A147 10c org ('15) 675.00 70.00
Never hinged 1,650.
Nos. 401-404 (4) 930.00 97.50
Nos. 401-404, never hinged 2,280.

1912-14 **Wmk. 190** ***Perf. 12***

405 A140 1c green 6.50 .25
Never hinged 15.00
a. Vert. pair, imperf. horiz. *2,000.* —
b. Booklet pane of 6 65.00 *90.00*
Never hinged 110.00
c. Double impression *5,500.*

TYPE I

TWO CENTS

Type I. There is one shading line in the first curve of the ribbon above the left "2" and one in the second curve of the ribbon above the right "2."

The button of the toga has only a faint outline.

The top line of the toga rope, from the button to the front of the throat, is also very faint.

The shading lines of the face terminate in front of the ear with little or no joining, to form a lock of hair.

Used on both flat plate and rotary press printings.

406 A140 2c car, type I 6.50 .25
Never hinged 15.00
a. Booklet pane of 6 65.00 *90.00*
Never hinged 110.00
b. Double impression *1,250.* —
c. 2c lake, type I *2,000.* *6,000.*
Never hinged *4,500.*
407 A140 7c black ('14) 70.00 14.00
Never hinged 150.00
Nos. 405-407 (3) 83.00 14.50

1912 ***Imperf.***

408 A140 1c green 1.00 1.00
Never hinged 2.00
409 A140 2c car, type I 1.20 1.20
Never hinged 2.40

COIL STAMPS

1912 ***Perf. 8½ Horizontally***

410 A140 1c green 6.00 *12.50*
Never hinged 13.00
411 A140 2c carmine, type I 10.00 *17.50*
Never hinged 22.50

Perf. 8½ Vertically

412 A140 1c green 25.00 *40.00*
Never hinged 55.00
413 A140 2c carmine, type I 60.00 50.00
Never hinged 130.00
Nos. 410-413 (4) 101.00 120.00

Beware also of plentiful fakes in the marketplace of Nos. 410-413.

Franklin — A148

1912-14 **Wmk. 190** ***Perf. 12***

414 A148 8c pale ol grn 40.00 2.00
Never hinged 100.00
415 A148 9c sal red ('14) 50.00 14.00
Never hinged 120.00
416 A148 10c org yel 40.00 .80
Never hinged 100.00
a. 10c brown yellow *1,250.* —
Never hinged *2,750.*
417 A148 12c cl brn ('14) 40.00 5.00
Never hinged 100.00
418 A148 15c gray 80.00 4.00
Never hinged 190.00
419 A148 20c ultra ('14) 190.00 17.50
Never hinged 400.00
420 A148 30c org red ('14) 115.00 17.50
Never hinged 250.00
421 A148 50c violet ('14) 350.00 27.50
Never hinged 775.00
Nos. 414-421 (8) 905.00 88.30

No. 421 almost always has an offset of the frame lines on the back under the gum. No. 422 does not have this offset.

VALUES FOR VERY FINE STAMPS

Please note: Stamps are valued in the grade of Very Fine unless otherwise indicated.

1912, Feb. 12 **Wmk. 191** ***Perf. 12***

422 A148 50c violet 225.00 25.00
Never hinged 500.00
423 A148 $1 violet brown 475.00 85.00
Never hinged 1,000.

Perforated sheet stamps of type A148: #431-440 (single line wmk., perf. 10), #460 (double line wmk. perf. 10), #470-478 (unwmkd., perf. 10), #508-518 (unwmkd., perf. 11).

1914 **Wmk. 190** ***Perf. 12x10***

423A A140 1c green *12,500.* *5,000.*
Never hinged —
423B A140 2c rose red, type I *175,000.* *12,500.*
423C A140 5c blue *17,500.*

Nos. 423A-423C formerly were Nos. 424a, 425d and 428a, respectively.

No. 423A unused is valued in the grade of fine. Values for 423A used and 423B-423C are for fine-very fine examples.

1914 **Wmk. 190** ***Perf. 10x12***

423D A140 1c green *8,500.*
423E A140 2c rose red, type I —

Nos. 423D and 423E formerly were Nos. 424b and 425c, respectively. Only one example is recorded of No. 423E.

No. 423D is valued in the grade of fine-very fine.

1913-15 **Wmk. 190** ***Perf. 10***

424 A140 1c grn ('14) 2.25 .25
Never hinged 4.75
c. Vert. pair, imperf. horiz. *3,000.* *2,750.*
Never hinged *4,500.*
d. Booklet pane of 6 ('13) 5.25 *7.50*
Never hinged 8.75
f. Vert. pair, imperf. between and with straight edge at top *13,000.*

For former Nos. 424a and 424b, see Nos. 423A and 423D.

The unique example of No. 424f is never hinged, and it is valued thus.

Research has proven beyond doubt that all examples of the previously listed No. 424e, booklet pane of 6, imperforate and without gum, are unissued fabrications made from an ungummed press sheet on stamp paper once undoubtedly housed in the Smithsonian philatelic collection.

425 A140 2c rose red, type I ('14) 2.25 .25
Never hinged 5.00
e. Booklet pane of 6 ('13) 17.50 *25.00*
Never hinged 30.00

For former Nos. 425c and 425d, see Nos. 423A and 423D.

426 A140 3c dp vio, type I ('14) 15.00 1.25
Never hinged 35.00
427 A140 4c brn ('14) 32.50 .90
Never hinged 75.00
428 A140 5c blue ('14) 32.50 .90
Never hinged 75.00

For former No. 428a, see No. 423C.

429 A140 6c red org ('14) 45.00 2.00
Never hinged 105.00
430 A140 7c black ('14) 85.00 4.75
Never hinged 190.00
431 A148 8c pale ol grn ('14) 40.00 3.00
Never hinged 80.00
a. Double impression —
432 A148 9c sal red ('14) 40.00 8.00
Never hinged 80.00
433 A148 10c org yel ('14) 40.00 1.00
Never hinged 80.00
a. 10c brown yellow —
434 A148 11c dk grn ('15) 30.00 8.00
Never hinged 75.00
435 A148 12c clar brn ('14) 30.00 5.50
Never hinged 75.00
a. 12c copper red 30.00 6.50
Never hinged 75.00
437 A148 15c gray ('14) 120.00 8.00
Never hinged 275.00
438 A148 20c ultra ('14) 200.00 7.00
Never hinged 450.00
439 A148 30c org red ('14) 225.00 20.00
Never hinged 500.00
440 A148 50c violet ('15) 450.00 20.00
Never hinged 1,100.
Nos. 424-440 (16) 1,390. 90.80

The values for used coil stamps are for examples with contemporaneous cancels that can be authenticated by expertizing committees. Used coils with cancels most commonly from the 1950s exist, and these and stamps with other non-contemporaneous cancels sell for less than the values shown.

COIL STAMPS

1914 ***Perf. 10 Horizontally***

441 A140 1c green 1.00 *1.50*
Never hinged 2.00
442 A140 2c carmine, type I 10.00 *45.00*
Never hinged 22.50
a. 2c lake, type I, on cover —

1914 ***Perf. 10 Vertically***

443 A140 1c green 30.00 *45.00*
Never hinged 65.00
444 A140 2c car, type I 50.00 40.00
Never hinged 120.00
a. 2c lake *2,000.*
445 A140 3c violet, type I 210.00 *250.00*
Never hinged 500.00
446 A140 4c brown 130.00 *150.00*
Never hinged 280.00
447 A140 5c blue 45.00 *110.00*
Never hinged 100.00
Nos. 443-447 (5) 465.00 595.00

Beware also of plentiful fakes in the marketplace of Nos. 441-447.

ROTARY PRESS STAMPS

The Rotary Press Stamps are printed from plates that are curved to fit around a cylinder. This curvature produces stamps that are slightly larger, either horizontally or vertically, than those printed from flat plates. Designs of stamps from flat plates measure about 18½-19mm wide by 22mm high.

When the impressions are placed sidewise on the curved plates the designs are 19½-20mm wide; when they are placed vertically the designs are 22½ to 23mm high. A line of color (not a guide line) shows where the curved plates meet or join on the press.

ROTARY PRESS COIL STAMPS

Stamp designs: 18½-19x22½mm

1915-16 ***Perf. 10 Horizontally***

448 A140 1c green 12.50 *17.50*
Never hinged 25.00

Type II

TWO CENTS

Type II. Shading lines in ribbons as on type I.

The toga button, rope and rope shading lines are heavy.

The shading lines of the face at the lock of hair end in a strong vertical curved line.

Used on rotary press printings only.

Type III

Type III. Two lines of shading in the curves of the ribbons.

Other characteristics similar to type II.

Used on rotary press printings only.

Fraudulently altered examples of type III (Nos. 455, 488, 492 and 540) have had one line of shading scraped off to make them resemble type II (Nos. 454, 487, 491 and 539).

449 A140 2c red, type I 2,500. 650.00
Never hinged 5,500.
450 A140 2c car, type III ('16) 15.00 *25.00*
Never hinged 30.00

1914-16 ***Perf. 10 Vertically***

Stamp designs: 19½-20x22mm

452 A140 1c green 15.00 *17.50*
Never hinged 30.00
453 A140 2c car rose, type I 140.00 45.00
Never hinged 300.00
454 A140 2c red, type II 70.00 22.50
Never hinged 160.00
455 A140 2c car, type III 8.00 3.50
Never hinged 18.00
456 A140 3c vio, type I ('16) 250.00 170.00
Never hinged 550.00
457 A140 4c brown ('16) 30.00 30.00
Never hinged 60.00
458 A140 5c blue ('16) 32.50 30.00
Never hinged 65.00
Nos. 452-458 (7) 545.50 318.50

Horizontal Coil

1914, June 30 ***Imperf.***

459 A140 2c car, type I 275. *1,300.*
Never hinged 400.

When the value for a used stamp is higher than the unused value, the stamp must have a contemporaneous cancel. Valuable stamps of this type should be accompanied by certificates of authenticity issued by recognized expertizing committees. The used value for No. 459 is for an example with such a certificate.

Beware of examples of No. 453 with perforations fraudulently trimmed to resemble single examples of No. 459.

FLAT PLATE PRINTINGS

1915, Feb. 8 Wmk. 191 *Perf. 10*

460 A148 $1 violet black 650. 140.
Never hinged 1,450.

1915, June 17 Wmk. 190 *Perf. 11*

461 A140 2c pale car red, type I 160. *375.*
Never hinged 330.

Beware of fraudulently perforated examples of No. 409 being offered as No. 461.

See note on used stamps following No. 459.

Unwatermarked

From 1916 onward all postage stamps except Nos. 519 and 832b are on unwatermarked paper.

1916-17 Unwmk. *Perf. 10*

462 A140 1c green 7.00 .35
Never hinged 16.00
a. Booklet pane of 6 9.50 *12.50*
Never hinged 16.00
463 A140 2c car, type I 4.50 .40
Never hinged 10.00 .45
a. Booklet pane of 6 110.00 *110.00*
Never hinged 180.00

See No. 467 for P# block of 6 from plate 7942.

464 A140 3c vio, type I 65.00 17.50
Never hinged 165.00

Beware of fraudulently perforated examples of No. 483 being offered as No. 464.

465 A140 4c org brn 60.00 2.25
Never hinged 125.00
466 A140 5c blue 65.00 2.25
Never hinged 150.00
467 A140 5c car (error in plate of 2c, '17) 425.00 *3,250.*
Never hinged 800.00

No. 467 is an error caused by using a 5c transfer roll in re-entering three subjects: 7942 UL 74, 7942 UL 84, 7942 LR 18; the balance of the subjects on the plate being normal 2c entries. No. 467 imperf. is listed as No. 485. The error perf 11 on unwatermarked paper is No. 505.

468 A140 6c red orange 100.00 8.00
Never hinged 225.00
469 A140 7c black 120.00 13.00
Never hinged 270.00
470 A148 8c olive green 80.00 7.00
Never hinged 165.00
471 A148 9c salmon red 90.00 17.50
Never hinged 190.00
472 A148 10c orange yel 120.00 3.00
Never hinged 250.00
473 A148 11c dark green 50.00 19.00
Never hinged 110.00
474 A148 12c claret brn 55.00 8.00
Never hinged 120.00
a. 12c copper red *75.00* *15.00*
475 A148 15c gray 170.00 15.00
Never hinged 375.00
476 A148 20c lt ultra 240.00 17.50
Never hinged 500.00
476A A148 30c orange red *2,000.*
Never hinged *4,250.*

No. 476A is valued in the grade of fine.

477 A148 50c lt vio ('17) 850. 80.00
Never hinged 2,000.
478 A148 $1 violet black 600. 27.50
Never hinged 1,400.
Nos. 462-466,468-476,477-478 (16) 2,677. 238.25

TYPES OF 1902-03 ISSUE

1917, Mar. 22 Unwmk. *Perf. 10*

479 A127 $2 dark blue 210.00 40.00
Never hinged 475.00
480 A128 $5 light green 170.00 37.50
Never hinged 375.00

1916-17 *Imperf.*

481 A140 1c green 1.25 .95
Never hinged 1.90

Type Ia 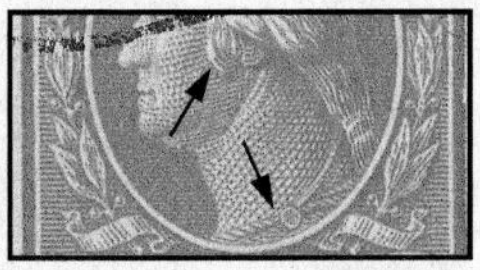

TWO CENTS

Type Ia. The design characteristics are similar to type I except that all of the lines of the design are stronger.

The toga button, toga rope and rope shading lines are heavy.

The latter characteristics are those of type II, which, however, occur only on impressions from rotary plates.

Used only on flat plates 10208 and 10209.

482 A140 2c car, type I 1.50 1.30
Never hinged 2.60
482A A140 2c dp rose, type Ia — *55,000.*

No. 482A was issued imperforate but all examples were privately perforated with large oblong perforations at the sides (Schermack type III).

Type II 

THREE CENTS

Type II. The top line of the toga rope is strong and the rope shading lines are heavy and complete.

The line between the lips is heavy.

Used on both flat plate and rotary press printings.

483 A140 3c vio, type I ('17) 12.00 10.00
Never hinged 24.00
484 A140 3c violet, type II 10.00 8.00
Never hinged 20.00
485 A140 5c car (error in plate of 2c) ('17) *10,000.*
Never hinged *14,000.*

Although No. 485 is valued as a single stamp, such examples are seldom seen in the marketplace.

No. 485 usually is seen as the center stamp in a block of 9 with 8 No. 482 (value with #485 never hinged, $22,500) or as two center stamps in a block of 12 (value with both No. 485 never hinged, $42,500).

ROTARY PRESS COIL STAMPS
(See note over No. 448)

1916-18 *Perf. 10 Horizontally*

Stamp designs: 18½-19x22½mm

486 A140 1c green ('18) .85 .85
Never hinged 1.75
487 A140 2c carmine, type II 12.50 14.00
Never hinged 27.50
488 A140 2c carmine, type III 3.00 *5.00*
Never hinged 6.50
489 A140 3c vio, type I ('17) 4.50 2.25
Never hinged 10.00
Nos. 486-489 (4) 20.85 22.10

1916-22 *Perf. 10 Vertically*

Stamp designs: 19½-20x22mm

490 A140 1c green .50 *.60*
Never hinged 1.05
491 A140 2c car, type II 2,500. 800.00
Never hinged 5,250.
492 A140 2c car, type III 9.00 1.00
Never hinged 19.00
493 A140 3c vio, type I ('17) 14.00 4.50
Never hinged 30.00
494 A140 3c vio, type II ('18) 10.00 2.50
Never hinged 21.50
495 A140 4c org brn ('17) 10.00 7.00
Never hinged 21.50
496 A140 5c blue ('19) 3.25 2.50
Never hinged 7.00
497 A148 10c org yel ('22) 17.50 17.50
Never hinged 35.00

Blind Perfs

Listings of imperforate-between varieties are for examples which show no trace of "blind perfs," traces of impressions from the perforating pins which do not cut into the paper.

Some unused stamps have had the gum removed to eliminate the impressions from the perforating pins. These stamps do not qualify as the listed varieties.

TYPES OF 1913-15 ISSUE

FLAT PLATE PRINTINGS

1917-19 Unwmk. *Perf. 11*

498 A140 1c green .50 .25
Never hinged 1.00
a. Vertical pair, imperf. horiz. 800.00
Never hinged *1,600.*
b. Horizontal pair, imperf. between 700.00
Never hinged *1,500.*
c. Vertical pair, imperf. between *700.00* —
d. Double impression 250.00 *3,750.*
e. Booklet pane of 6 2.50 *2.00*
Never hinged 4.25
f. Booklet pane of 30 *1,050.* *12,500.*
Never hinged *1,700.*
g. Perf. 10 at top or bottom *15,000.* *20,000.*
Never hinged *27,500.*

No. 498g used is valued in the grade of fine.

499 A140 2c rose, type I .50 .25
Never hinged 1.00
a. Vertical pair, imperf. horiz., type I *3,000.* *2,500.*
Never hinged *4,250.*
b. Horiz. pair, imperf. vert., type I *550.00* *600.00*
Never hinged *1,100.*
c. Vert. pair, imperf. btwn., type I *900.00* *300.00*
e. Booklet pane of 6, type I 4.00 *2.50*
Never hinged 6.75
f. Booklet pane of 30, type I *20,000.* —
Never hinged *28,000.*
g. Double impression, type I 200.00 *2,000.*
Never hinged *400.00*
h. 2c lake, type I 600.00 800.00
Never hinged *1,250.*
i. As "e," single stamp, lake *3,250.*

No. 499b is valued in the grade of fine. No 499g used is valued in the grade of fine.

500 A140 2c deep rose, type Ia 260.00 240.00
Never hinged 570.00
501 A140 3c lt vio, type I 9.00 .40
Never hinged 20.00
b. Booklet pane of 6, type I 75.00 *80.00*
Never hinged 125.00
c. Vert. pair, imper. horiz., type I *2,100.*
Never hinged *3,250.*
d. Double impression *3,500.* *3,500.*
Never hinged *5,000.*

No. 501d is valued in the grade of fine.

502 A140 3c dk vio, type II 12.00 .75
Never hinged 27.50
b. Bklt. pane of 6, type II 60.00 *75.00*
Never hinged 100.00
c. Vert. pair, imperf. horiz., type II *1,400.* *850.00*
Never hinged *2,750.*
d. Double impression 800.00 *1,000.*
Never hinged 1,600.
e. Perf. 10 at top or bottom — *30,000.*
503 A140 4c brown 8.50 .40
Never hinged 19.00
b. Double impression —
504 A140 5c blue 7.50 .35
Never hinged 17.00
a. Horizontal pair, imperf. between *20,000.* —
b. Double impression *1,750.* *1,600.*
505 A140 5c rose (error in plate of 2c) 325.00 *600.00*
Never hinged 625.00
506 A140 6c red orange 11.00 .40
Never hinged 25.00
a. Perf. 10 at top or bottom *30,000.* *8,000.*
b. Double impression, never hinged *2,000.*

No. 506a also exists as a transitional stamp gauging partly perf 10 and partly perf 11 at top. Value thus the same as normal 506a.

No. 506b is a partial double impression. Two authenticated examples are documented.

507 A140 7c black 24.00 1.25
Never hinged 55.00
508 A148 8c olive bister 11.00 .65
Never hinged 25.00
b. Vertical pair, imperf. between — —
c. Perf. 10 at top or bottom *9,000.*
509 A148 9c salmon red 11.00 1.60
Never hinged 25.00
a. Perf. 10 at top or bottom *7,500.*
Never hinged *37,500.*

No. 509a also exists as a transitional stamp gauging partly perf 10 and partly perf 11 at top or bottom. Value thus the same as normal 509a.

510 A148 10c org yel 15.00 .25
Never hinged 34.00
a. 10c brown yellow *1,400.*
Never hinged *3,250.*
511 A148 11c lt green 7.50 2.25
Never hinged 17.00
a. Perf. 10 at top or bottom *3,000.* *3,250.*
Never hinged *6,000.*

No. 511a also exists as a transitional stamp gauging partly perf 10 and partly perf 11 at top or bottom. Value thus the same as normal 511a.

512 A148 12c claret brown 8.50 .50
Never hinged 19.00
a. 12c brown carmine 8.50 .50
Never hinged 19.00
b. Perf. 10 at top or bottom *25,000.* *15,000.*
c. 12c claret red 8.50 .50
Never hinged 19.00
513 A148 13c apple grn ('19) 9.50 5.50
Never hinged 21.00
514 A148 15c gray 32.50 1.40
Never hinged 75.00
a. Perf. 10 at bottom *10,000.*
515 A148 20c lt ultra 40.00 .45
Never hinged 85.00
b. Vertical pair, imperf. between *1,750.* *3,250.*
c. Double impression *1,250.*
Never hinged *2,750.*
d. Perf. 10 at top or bottom — *11,000.*

No. 515b is valued in the grade of fine.

Beware of pairs with blind perforations inside the design of the top stamp that are offered as No. 515b.

No. 515c is a partial double impression.

516 A148 30c orange red 30.00 1.50
Never hinged 70.00
a. Perf. 10 at top or bottom *20,000.* *15,000.*
Never hinged *37,500.*
b. Double impression —

No. 516a used is valued in the grade of fine.

517 A148 50c red violet 50.00 .75
Never hinged 120.00
b. Vertical pair, imperf. between & with natural straight edge at bottom *6,000.*
c. Perf. 10 at top or bottom *17,000.*

No. 517b is valued in average condition and may be a unique used pair (precanceled). The editors would like to see authenticated evidence of an unused pair.

518 A148 $1 violet brown 37.50 1.50
Never hinged 95.00
b. $1 deep brown *2,000.* *1,100.*
Never hinged *4,000.*
Nos. 498-504,506-518 (20) 585.50 260.40

No. 518b is valued in the grade of fine to very fine.

TYPE OF 1908-09 ISSUE

This is the result of an old stock of No. 344 which was returned to the Bureau in 1917 and perforated with the then current gauge 11. Only lower left panes of No. 344 were perforated 11, and therefore only left and bottom plate blocks exist.

1917, Oct. 10 Wmk. 191 *Perf. 11*

519 A139 2c carmine 425.00 *1,800.*
Never hinged 900.00

Beware of examples of No. 344 fraudulently perforated and offered as No. 519. Obtaining a certificate from a recognized expertizing committee is strongly recommended.

Warning: See note following No. 459 regarding used stamps.

Franklin — A149

1918, Aug. Unwmk. *Perf. 11*

523	A149 $2 org red & blk	525.	240.
	Never hinged	1,175.	
524	A149 $5 dp grn & blk	160.	40.
	Never hinged	340.	

See No. 547 for $2 carmine & black.

TYPES OF 1917-19 ISSUE

OFFSET PRINTING

1918-20 Unwmk. *Perf. 11*

525	A140 1c gray green	2.50	.90
	Never hinged	6.00	
a.	1c dark green	10.00	1.75
	Never hinged	25.00	
c.	Horizontal pair, imperf. between	*750.00*	*650.00*
d.	Double impression	40.00	*750.00*
	Never hinged	90.00	

No. 525c is valued in the grade of fine and with natural straight edge at right, as virtually all recorded examples come thus. No. 525d used is valued in the grade of very good.

Type IV

TWO CENTS

Type IV — Top line of the toga rope is broken.

The shading lines in the toga button are so arranged that the curving of the first and last form "D (reversed) ID."

The line of color in the left "2" is very thin and usually broken.

Used on offset printings only.

Type V

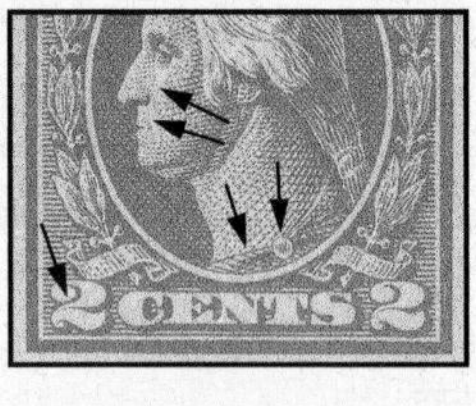

Type V — Top line of the toga is complete.

There are five vertical shading lines in the toga button.

The line of color in the left "2" is very thin and usually broken.

The shading dots on the nose are as shown on the diagram.

Used on offset printings only.

Type Va

Type Va — Characteristics are the same as type V except in the shading dots of the nose. The third row of dots from the bottom has four dots instead of six. The overall height is ⅓mm shorter than the other types.

Used on offset printings only.

Type VI

Type VI — General characteristics the same as type V except that the line of color in the left "2" is very heavy.

Used on offset printings only.

TYPE VII

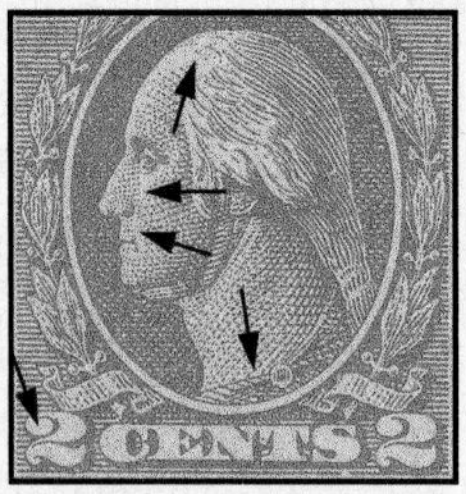

Type VII — The line of color in the left "2" is invariably continuous, clearly defined and heavier than in type V or Va but not as heavy as type VI.

An additional vertical row of dots has been added to the upper lip.

Numerous additional dots have been added to the hair on top of the head.

Used on offset printings only.

526	A140 2c car, type IV ('20)	25.00	4.00
	Never hinged	57.50	
527	A140 2c car, type V ('20)	18.00	1.25
	Never hinged	40.00	
a.	Double impression	100.00	—
	Never hinged	225.00	
b.	Vert. pair, imperf. horiz.	*850.00*	
c.	Horiz. pair, imperf. vert.	*1,000.*	—
d.	Double impression	—	—
528	A140 2c car, type Va ('20)	10.00	.40
	Never hinged	22.50	
c.	Double impression	62.50	
	Never hinged	150.00	
g.	Vert. pair, imperf. between	*3,250.*	
528A	A140 2c car, type VI ('20)	47.50	2.00
	Never hinged	115.00	
d.	Double impression	200.00	*900.00*
	Never hinged	450.00	
f.	Vert. pair, imperf. horiz.	—	
h.	Vert. pair, imperf. between	*5,000.*	
528B	A140 2c car, type VII ('20)	20.00	.75
	Never hinged	50.00	
e.	Double impression	77.50	*400.00*

No. 528Be used is valued in the grade of very good to fine.

TYPE III

THREE CENTS

Type III — The top line of the toga rope is strong but the 5th shading line is missing as in type I.

Center shading line of the toga button consists of two dashes with a central dot.

The "P" and "O" of "POSTAGE" are separated by a line of color.

The frame line at the bottom of the vignette is complete.

Used on offset printings only.

TYPE IV

Type IV — The shading lines of the toga rope are complete.

The second and fourth shading lines in the toga button are broken in the middle and the third line is continuous with a dot in the center.

The "P" and "O" of "POSTAGE" are joined.

The frame line at the bottom of the vignette is broken.

Used on offset printings only.

529	A140 3c vio, type III	3.50	.50
	Never hinged	7.75	
a.	Double impression	50.00	*1,250.*
	Never hinged	115.00	
b.	Printed on both sides	*2,500.*	

No. 529a used is valued in the grade of fine.

530	A140 3c pur, type IV	2.00	.30
	Never hinged	4.50	
a.	Double impression	40.00	*800.00*
	Never hinged	90.00	
b.	Printed on both sides	*750.00*	
	Never hinged	*1,100.*	
c.	Triple impression	*1,750.*	—
	Nos. 525-530 (8)	128.50	10.10

No. 530a used is valued in the grade of fine.

1918-20 *Imperf.*

531	A140 1c green ('19)	14.00	12.00
	Never hinged	21.00	
532	A140 2c car rose, type IV ('20)	50.00	42.50
	Never hinged	80.00	
533	A140 2c car, type V ('20)	120.00	*150.00*
	Never hinged	200.00	
534	A140 2c car, type Va ('20)	16.50	15.00
	Never hinged	26.50	
534A	A140 2c car, type VI ('20)	52.50	40.00
	Never hinged	90.00	
534B	A140 2c car, type VII ('20)	2,500.	1,500.
	Never hinged	3,750.	
535	A140 3c vio, type IV	11.00	6.00
	Never hinged	18.00	
a.	Double impression	100.00	—
	Never hinged	200.00	
	Nos. 531-534A,535 (6)	264.00	265.50

1919, Aug. 12 *Perf. 12½*

536	A140 1c gray green	20.00	*35.00*
	Never hinged	45.00	
a.	Horiz. pair, imperf. vert.	*900.00*	
	Never hinged	*1,400.*	

VICTORY ISSUE

"Victory" and Flags of the Allies — A150

FLAT PLATE PRINTING

1919, Mar. 3 Engr. *Perf. 11*

537	A150 3c violet	10.00	3.25
	Never hinged	20.00	
a.	3c deep red violet	*1,300.*	*1,800.*
	Never hinged	*2,400.*	
b.	3c light reddish violet	150.00	50.00
	Never hinged	300.00	
c.	3c red violet	200.00	60.00
	Never hinged	400.00	

Victory of the Allies in World War I.

No. 537a is valued in the grade of fine.

ROTARY PRESS PRINTINGS

1919 *Perf. 11x10*

Stamp designs: 19½-20x22-22¼mm

538	A140 1c green	10.00	9.00
	Never hinged	23.00	
a.	Vert. pair, imperf. horiz.	60.00	*125.00*
	Never hinged	125.00	
539	A140 2c car rose, type II	2,700.	*16,000.*
	Never hinged	5,000.	
540	A140 2c car rose, type III	12.00	9.50
	Never hinged	27.50	
a.	Vert. pair, imperf horiz.	60.00	*140.00*
	Never hinged	125.00	
b.	Horiz. pair, imperf. vert.	*2,750.*	
541	A140 3c vio, type II	40.00	37.50
	Never hinged	100.00	

The part perforate varieties of Nos. 538a and 540a were issued in sheets and may be had in blocks; similar part perforate varieties, Nos. 490 and 492, are from coils and are found only in strips.

See note over No. 448 regarding No. 539.

No. 539 is valued in the grade of fine.

No. 540b is valued in the grade of fine.

1920, May 26 *Perf. 10x11*

Stamp design: 19x22½-22¾mm

542	A140 1c green	12.50	1.50
	Never hinged	30.00	
a.	All color missing (EP)	—	

1921 *Perf. 10*

Stamp design: 19x22½mm

543	A140 1c green	.70	.40
	Never hinged	1.75	
a.	Horizontal pair, imperf. between	*4,500.*	

1922 *Perf. 11*

Stamp design: 19x22½mm

544	A140 1c green	*22,500.*	*3,500.*
	Never hinged	*35,000.*	

No. 544 is valued in the grade of fine.

1921

Stamp designs: 19½-20x22mm

545	A140 1c green	225.00	200.00
	Never hinged	550.00	
546	A140 2c car rose, type III	105.00	*190.00*
	Never hinged	230.00	
a.	Perf. 10 on left side	*7,500.*	*17,500.*

No. 546a used is valued in the grade of very good. It is unique used.

FLAT PLATE PRINTING

1920, Nov. 1 *Perf. 11*

547	A149 $2 carmine & black	125.	40.
	Never hinged	275.	
a.	$2 lake & black	200.	40.
	Never hinged	425.	

PILGRIM TERCENTENARY ISSUE

"Mayflower" A151

Landing of the Pilgrims A152

Signing of the Compact — A153

1920, Dec. 21 *Perf. 11*

548	A151 1c green	4.00	2.00
	Never hinged	10.00	
549	A152 2c carmine rose	5.50	1.60
	Never hinged	14.00	
550	A153 5c deep blue	32.50	12.50
	Never hinged	70.00	
	Nos. 548-550 (3)	42.00	16.10
	Nos. 548-550, never hinged	94.00	

Tercentenary of the landing of the Pilgrims at Plymouth, Mass.

Nathan Hale A154

Franklin A155

Harding A156

Washington A157

Lincoln A158

Martha Washington A159

Theodore Roosevelt A160

Garfield A161

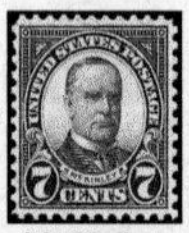

McKinley A162

Grant A163

Jefferson A164

Monroe A165

Rutherford B. Hayes A166

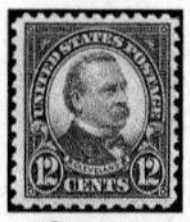
Grover Cleveland A167

American Indian A168

Statue of Liberty A169

Golden Gate A170

Niagara Falls A171

American Buffalo A172

Arlington Amphitheater A173

Lincoln Memorial A174

U.S. Capitol A175

Head of Freedom Statue, Capitol Dome — A176

FLAT PLATE PRINTINGS

1922-25 Unwmk. *Perf. 11*

551 A154 ½c ol brn ('25) .30 .25
Never hinged .50
552 A155 1c dp grn ('23) 1.25 .25
Never hinged 2.75
a. Booklet pane of 6 7.50 *4.00*
Never hinged 12.50
553 A156 1½c yel brn ('25) 2.00 .25
Never hinged 4.10
554 A157 2c carmine ('23) 1.10 .25
Never hinged 2.50
a. Horiz. pair, imperf. vert. 250.00
Never hinged 400.00
b. Vert. pair, imperf. horiz. *6,000.*
Never hinged *10,000.*
c. Booklet pane of 6 7.00 *3.00*
Never hinged 12.00
d. Perf. 10 at top or bottom *9,000.* *5,000.*
Never hinged *12,000.*
e. Imperf., pair *400.00*
555 A158 3c violet ('23) 13.00 1.20
Never hinged 27.50
556 A159 4c yel brn ('23) 16.00 .50
Never hinged 35.00
a. Vert. pair, imperf. horiz. *12,500.*
b. Perf. 10 at top or bottom *7,000.* *7,000.*

No. 556a is unique. It resulted from a sheet that was damaged and patched during production.

No. 556b used also exists as a transitional stamp gauging 10 at left top and 11 at right top. Value the same.

557 A160 5c dark blue 16.00 .30
Never hinged 35.00
a. Imperf., pair *2,000.*
Never hinged *3,500.*
b. Horiz. pair, imperf. vert. —
c. Perf. 10 at top or bottom — *9,500.*
558 A161 6c red orange 30.00 1.00
Never hinged 65.00
559 A162 7c black ('23) 7.25 .75
Never hinged 15.50
560 A163 8c ol grn ('23) 37.50 1.00
Never hinged 80.00
561 A164 9c rose ('23) 11.00 1.25
Never hinged 25.00
562 A165 10c orange ('23) 13.50 .35
Never hinged 30.00
a. Vert. pair, imperf. horiz. *2,000.*
Never hinged *3,250.*
b. Imperf., pair *1,850.*
c. Perf. 10 at top or bottom *25,000.* *7,500.*

No. 562a is valued in the grade of fine, with gum and without blue defacing lines. No. 562b is valued without gum and without blue pencil defacing lines. No. 562c is valued in the grade of fine.

563 A166 11c greenish blue 1.25 .60
Never hinged 2.75
a. 11c light bluish green 1.25 .60
Never hinged 2.75
d. Imperf., horiz. pair *15,000.*
Imperf., vert. strip of 3 *20,000.*

Many other intermediate shades exist for Nos. 563 and 563a, all falling within the blue or green color families.

No. 563d is known only as the two listings shown.

564 A167 12c brn vio ('23) 4.75 .35
Never hinged 10.50
a. Horiz. pair, imperf. vert. *3,750.*
565 A168 14c blue ('23) 4.25 .90
Never hinged 9.50
566 A169 15c gray 16.00 .30
Never hinged 35.00
567 A170 20c car rose ('23) 16.00 .30
Never hinged 35.00
a. Horiz. pair, imperf. vert. *2,500.*
Never hinged *5,000.*

No. 567a is valued in the grade of fine.

568 A171 25c yel grn 13.50 .75
Never hinged 30.00
b. Vert. pair, imperf. horiz. *3,250.*
c. Perf. 10 at one side *12,000.* *9,000.*
Never hinged *16,000.*

No. 568b is valued in the grade of fine. No. 568c used is valued in the grade of fine.

569 A172 30c ol brn ('23) 22.50 .60
Never hinged 50.00
570 A173 50c lilac 32.50 .40
Never hinged 70.00
571 A174 $1 vio brn ('23) 35.00 .80
Never hinged 75.00
572 A175 $2 dp blue ('23) 55.00 9.00
Never hinged 120.00
573 A176 $5 car & bl ('23) 90.00 15.00
Never hinged 180.00
a. $5 car lake & dk bl 180.00 30.00
Never hinged 375.00
Nos. 551-573 (23) 439.65 36.35
Nos. 551-573, never hinged 940.60

No. 556a is unique. No. 554b is valued in the grade of fine. No. 562b is valued without gum and without blue pencil defacing lines. No. 568b is valued in the grade of fine.

For other listings of perforated stamps of designs A154 to A173 see:
Nos. 578 & 579, Perf. 11x10
Nos. 581-591, Perf. 10
Nos. 594-596, Perf. 11
Nos. 632-642, 653, 692-696, Perf. 11x10½
Nos. 697-701, Perf. 10½x11
This series also includes #622-623 (perf. 11), 684-687 & 720-723.

1923-25 *Imperf.*
Stamp design 19¼x22¼mm

575 A155 1c green 6.00 5.00
Never hinged 11.00
576 A156 1½c yel brn ('25) 1.50 *1.50*
Never hinged 2.70

The 1½c A156 Rotary press imperforate is listed as No. 631.

577 A157 2c carmine 1.50 1.25
Never hinged 2.70
a. 2c carmine lake —
Nos. 575-577 (3) 9.00 7.75
Nos. 575-577, never hinged 16.40

ROTARY PRESS PRINTINGS
(See note over No. 448)

1923 *Perf. 11x10*
Stamp designs: 19¾x22¼mm

578 A155 1c green 75.00 *160.00*
Never hinged 150.00
579 A157 2c carmine 70.00 *140.00*
Never hinged 140.00

Nos. 578-579 were made from coil waste of Nos. 597, 599 and measure approximately 19¾x22¼mm.

1923-26 *Perf. 10*
Stamp designs: 19¼x22½mm

581 A155 1c green 10.00 .75
Never hinged 21.00
582 A156 1½c brown ('25) 6.00 .65
Never hinged 13.00
583 A157 2c car ('24) 3.00 .30
Never hinged 6.25
a. Booklet pane of 6 110.00 *150.00*
Never hinged 200.00
584 A158 3c violet ('25) 27.50 3.00
Never hinged 60.00
585 A159 4c yel brn ('25) 17.50 .65
Never hinged 37.50
586 A160 5c blue ('25) 17.50 .40
Never hinged 37.50
a. Horizontal pair, imperf. vertically *7,500.*

No. 586a is unique, precanceled, with average centering and small faults, and it is valued as such.

587 A161 6c red org ('25) 9.25 .60
Never hinged 20.00
588 A162 7c black ('26) 12.50 6.25
Never hinged 26.00
589 A163 8c ol grn ('26) 27.50 4.50
Never hinged 57.50
590 A164 9c rose ('26) 6.00 2.50
Never hinged 12.50
591 A165 10c org ('25) 40.00 .50
Never hinged 85.00
Nos. 581-591 (11) 176.75 20.10
Nos. 581-591, never hinged 371.25

Issued in sheets of 70 or 100 stamps, coil waste of Nos. 597, 599.

1923 *Perf. 11*
Stamp designs approximately 19¾x22¼mm

594 A155 1c green *35,000.* *10,500.*
With gum *65,000.*

The main listing for No. 594 unused is for an example without gum; both unused and used are valued with perforations just touching frameline on one side.

595 A157 2c carmine 240.00 *375.00*
Never hinged 450.00
V-shaped gouge from eye down into cheek and back to hair in front of ear, plate 14731, pos.3 — —

Nos. 594-595 were made from coil waste of Nos. 597 and 599, and measure approximately 19¾x22¼mm.

596 A155 1c green *250,000.*
Precanceled *200,000.*

No. 596 was made from rotary press sheet waste and measures approximately 19¼x22½mm. A majority of the examples carry the Bureau precancel "Kansas City, Mo." No. 596 is valued in the grade of fine.

COIL STAMPS
ROTARY PRESS

1923-29 *Perf. 10 Vertically*
Stamp designs approximately 19¾x22¼mm

597 A155 1c green .30 .25
Never hinged .60
598 A156 1½c brown ('25) .90 .25
Never hinged 1.80

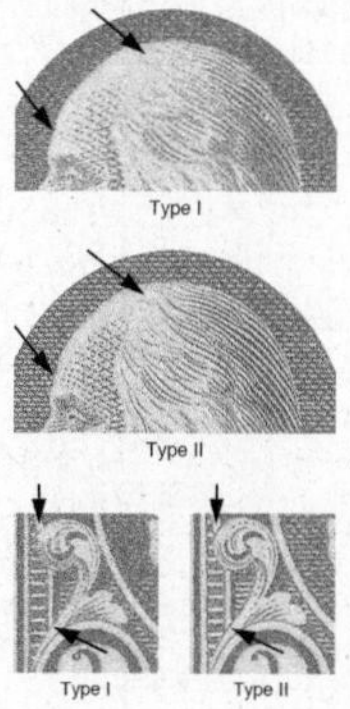
Type I
Type II
Type I Type II

TYPE I. No line outlining forehead. No heavy hair lines at top center of head. Outline of left acanthus scroll generally faint at top and toward base at left side.

TYPE II. Thin line outlining forehead. Three heavy hair lines at top center of head; two being outstanding in the white area. Outline of left acanthus scroll very strong and clearly defined at top (under left edge of lettered panel) and at lower curve (above and to left of numeral oval). This type appears only on Nos. 599A and 634A.

599 A157 2c car, type I .35 .25
Never hinged .70
b. 2c carmine lake, type I, never hinged *300.00* —
599A A157 2c car, type II ('29) 120.00 16.00
Never hinged 240.00
600 A158 3c violet ('24) 5.25 .25
Never hinged 10.50
601 A159 4c yel brn 3.75 .35
Never hinged 7.50
602 A160 5c dk blue ('24) 1.75 .25
Never hinged 3.50
603 A165 10c orange ('24) 3.50 .25
Never hinged 7.00

The 6c design A161 coil stamp is listed as No. 723.

1923-25 *Perf. 10 Horizontally*
Stamp designs: 19¼x22½mm

604 A155 1c green ('24) .40 .25
Never hinged .80
605 A156 1½c yel brn ('25) .40 .25
Never hinged .80
606 A157 2c carmine .40 .25
Never hinged .80
a. 2c carmine lake *70.00* —
Never hinged *140.00*
Nos. 597-599,600-606 (10) 17.00 2.60
Nos. 597-599, 600-606, never hinged 36.00

HARDING MEMORIAL ISSUE

Warren G. Harding — A177

FLAT PLATE PRINTING
Stamp designs: 19¼x22¼mm

1923 *Perf. 11*

610 A177 2c black .50 .25
Never hinged 1.00
a. Horiz. pair, imperf. vert. *2,000.*
b. Imperf. (error), P#14870 block of 6 *20,000.*

No. 610a is valued in the grade of fine.

No. 610b comes from left side error panes found in a normal pad of No. 610 stamps before No. 611 was issued. Two left side plate blocks and one top position plate block are recorded. Plate #14870 was not used to print No. 611. Loose stamps separated from the top and left plate blocks are indistinguishable from No. 611.

Imperf

611 A177 2c black 4.50 4.00
Never hinged 9.00

ROTARY PRESS PRINTING
Stamp designs: 19¼x22½mm

Perf. 10

612 A177 2c black 15.00 1.75
Never hinged 32.50

Perf. 11

613 A177 2c black *35,000.*

Tribute to President Warren G. Harding, who died August 2, 1923.

No. 613 was produced from rotary press sheet waste. It is valued in the grade of fine.

HUGUENOT-WALLOON TERCENTENARY ISSUE

"New Netherland" A178

Landing at Fort Orange A179

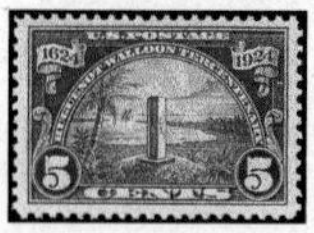
Monument to Jan Ribault at Duvall County, Fla. — A180

FLAT PLATE PRINTINGS

1924, May 1 *Perf. 11*

614 A178 1c dark green 2.30 *3.00*
Never hinged 4.25
615 A179 2c carmine rose 3.75 2.25
Never hinged 7.00
616 A180 5c dark blue 15.00 13.00
Never hinged 27.50
Nos. 614-616 (3) 21.05 18.25
Nos. 614-616, never hinged 38.75

Tercentenary of the settling of the Walloons and in honor of the Huguenots.

LEXINGTON-CONCORD ISSUE

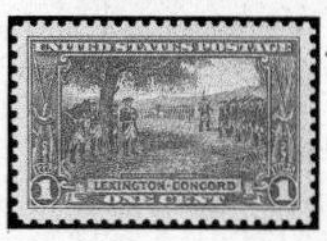
Washington at Cambridge A181

"Birth of Liberty," by Henry Sandham — A182

The Minute Man, by Daniel Chester French — A183

1925, Apr. 4 *Perf. 11*

617 A181 1c deep green 2.00 2.50
Never hinged 3.75
618 A182 2c carmine rose 3.50 4.00
Never hinged 6.50
619 A183 5c dark blue 14.00 13.00
Never hinged 26.00
Nos. 617-619 (3) 19.50 19.50
Nos. 617-619, never hinged 36.25

150th anniv. of the Battle of Lexington-Concord.

NORSE-AMERICAN ISSUE

A184

Viking Ship — A185

1925, May 18 *Perf. 11*

620 A184 2c carmine & black 3.00 2.75
Never hinged 6.00
621 A185 5c dark blue & black 9.00 9.00
Never hinged 19.00

100th anniv. of the arrival in NY on Oct. 9, 1825, of the sloop "Restaurationen" with the first group of immigrants from Norway to the U.S.

Benjamin Harrison A186

Woodrow Wilson A187

1925-26 *Perf. 11*

622 A186 13c green ('26) 9.00 .75
Never hinged 19.00
623 A187 17c black 9.00 .30
Never hinged 19.00

SESQUICENTENNIAL EXPOSITION ISSUE

Liberty Bell — A188

1926, May 10 *Perf. 11*

627 A188 2c carmine rose 2.25 .50
Never hinged 4.00

150th anniv. of the Declaration of Independence, Philadelphia, June 1-Dec. 1.

ERICSSON MEMORIAL ISSUE

Statue of John Ericsson — A189

1926, May 29 *Perf. 11*

628 A189 5c gray lilac 5.00 3.25
Never hinged 8.50

John Ericsson, builder of the "Monitor."

BATTLE OF WHITE PLAINS ISSUE

Alexander Hamilton's Battery — A190

1926, Oct. 18 *Perf. 11*

629 A190 2c carmine rose 1.60 1.70
Never hinged 2.75

Battle of White Plains, NY, 150th anniv.

INTERNATIONAL PHILATELIC EXHIBITION ISSUE

Souvenir Sheet

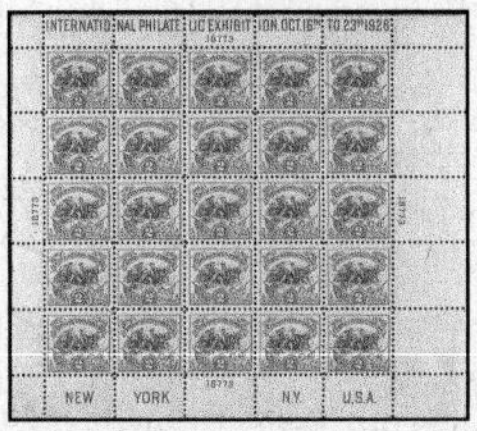

A190a

Condition valued:
Centering: Overall centering will average very fine, but individual stamps may be better or worse.
Perforations: No folds along rows of perforations.
Gum: There may be some light gum bends but no gum creases.
Hinging: There may be hinge marks in the selvage and on up to two or three stamps, but no heavy hinging or hinge remnants (except in the ungummed portion of the wide selvage.
Margins: Top panes should have about ½ inch bottom margin and 1 inch top margin.
Bottom panes should have about ½ inch top margin and just under ¾ inch bottom margin. Both will have one wide side (usually 1 inch plus) and one narrow (½ inch) side margin. The wide margin corner will have a small diagonal notch on top panes.

1926, Oct. 18 *Perf. 11*

630 A190a 2c car rose, pane of 25 275.00 *450.00*
Never hinged 500.00
a. Single stamp (see footnote) *10.00* —
Never hinged 14.00

Issued in panes measuring 158-160¼x136-146½mm containing 25 stamps with inscription "International Philatelic Exhibition, Oct. 16th to 23rd, 1926" in top margin.

No. 630a can be identified only when attached to the distinctive selvage as shown in illustration A190a. The four plate numbers used to print the White Plains souvenir sheets were distinct from the plate numbers used to print No. 629, and therefore all stamps in a plate block, for instance, are identifiable as No. 630a.

VALUES FOR VERY FINE STAMPS
Please note: Stamps are valued in the grade of Very Fine unless otherwise indicated.

TYPES OF 1922-26 ISSUE

REGULAR ISSUE
ROTARY PRESS PRINTINGS
(See note above No. 448.)

1926, Aug. 27 ***Imperf.***

631 A156 1½c yellow brown 2.00 1.70
Never hinged 3.00

1926-34 ***Perf. 11x10½***

632 A155 1c green ('27) .25 .25
Never hinged .35
a. Booklet pane of 6 5.00 *4.00*
Never hinged 8.00
b. Vertical pair, imperf. between *3,000.* *3,250.*
Never hinged *5,500.*
c. Horiz. pair, imperf. between *5,000.*

No. 632b is valued in the grade of fine. No. 632c is valued in the grade of fine and never hinged. It is possibly unique.

633 A156 1½c yel brn ('27) 1.70 .25
Never hinged 2.60
634 A157 2c car, type I .25 .25
Never hinged .30
b. 2c carmine lake *180.00* *500.00*
Never hinged *425.00*
c. Horiz. pair, imperf. btwn. *6,000.*
d. Booklet pane of 6, carmine 1.50 1.50
Never hinged 2.50
e. As "d," carmine lake *400.00* *1,000.*
Never hinged *750.00*

Shades of the carmine exist.
No. 634c is valued in the grade of fine.

634A A157 2c car, type II ('28) 300.00 13.50
Never hinged 600.00
635 A158 3c violet ('27) .75 .25
Never hinged 1.20
a. 3c bright violet ('34) .35 .25
Never hinged .45
636 A159 4c yel brn ('27) 1.90 .25
Never hinged 3.00
637 A160 5c dk blue ('27) 1.90 .25
Never hinged 3.00
638 A161 6c red org ('27) 2.00 .25
Never hinged 3.20
639 A162 7c black ('27) 2.00 .25
Never hinged 3.20
a. Vertical pair, imperf. between 550.00 400.00
Never hinged 1,000.
640 A163 8c yel brn ('27) 2.00 .25
Never hinged 3.20
641 A164 9c rose ('27) 1.90 .25
Never hinged 3.00
642 A165 10c org ('27) 3.25 .25
Never hinged 5.50
Nos. 632-634,635-642 (11) 17.90 2.75
Nos. 632-634, 635-642 never hinged 28.00

The 1½c, 2c, 4c, 5c, 6c, 8c imperf. (dry print) are printer's waste.
For ½c, 11c-50c see Nos. 653, 692-701.

VERMONT SESQUICENTENNIAL ISSUE

Battle of Bennington, 150th anniv. and State independence.

Green Mountain Boy — A191

FLAT PLATE PRINTING

1927, Aug. 3 *Perf. 11*

643 A191 2c carmine rose 1.20 .80
Never hinged 2.00

BURGOYNE CAMPAIGN ISSUE

Battles of Bennington, Oriskany, Fort Stanwix and Saratoga.

"The Surrender of General Burgoyne at Saratoga," by John Trumbull — A192

1927, Aug. 3 *Perf. 11*

644 A192 2c carmine rose 3.00 2.10
Never hinged 5.25

VALLEY FORGE ISSUE

150th anniversary of Washington's encampment at Valley Forge, Pa.

Washington at Prayer — A193

1928, May 26 *Perf. 11*

645 A193 2c carmine rose 1.15 .50
Never hinged 1.80
a. 2c lake —
Never hinged —

BATTLE OF MONMOUTH ISSUE

150th anniv. of the Battle of Monmouth, N.J., and "Molly Pitcher" (Mary Ludwig Hayes), the heroine of the battle.

No. 634 Overprinted

ROTARY PRESS PRINTING

1928, Oct. 20 ***Perf. 11x10½***

646 A157 2c carmine 1.00 1.00
Never hinged 1.60
a. "Pitcher" only *1,000.*
b. 2c carmine lake *2,500.*

No. 646a is valued in the grade of fine.
Normally the overprints were placed 18mm apart vertically, but pairs exist with a space of 28mm between the overprints.

HAWAII SESQUICENTENNIAL ISSUE

Sesquicentennial Celebration of the discovery of the Hawaiian Islands.

Nos. 634 and 637 Overprinted

ROTARY PRESS PRINTING

1928, Aug. 13 ***Perf. 11x10½***

647 A157 2c carmine 4.00 4.00
Never hinged 7.25
648 A160 5c dark blue 11.00 12.50
Never hinged 21.50

Nos. 647-648 were sold at post offices in Hawaii and at the Postal Agency in Washington, D.C. They were valid throughout the nation.
Normally the overprints were placed 18mm apart vertically, but pairs exist with a space of 28mm between the overprints.

AERONAUTICS CONFERENCE ISSUE

Intl. Civil Aeronautics Conf., Washington, D.C., Dec. 12 - 14, 1928, and 25th anniv. of the 1st airplane flight by the Wright Brothers, Dec. 17, 1903.

Wright Airplane — A194

Globe and Airplane — A195

FLAT PLATE PRINTING

1928, Dec. 12 *Perf. 11*

649 A194 2c carmine rose 1.10 .80
Never hinged 1.75
650 A195 5c blue 4.50 3.25
Never hinged 7.00

GEORGE ROGERS CLARK ISSUE

150th anniv. of the surrender of Fort Sackville, the present site of Vincennes, Ind., to Clark.

Surrender of Fort Sackville — A196

1929, Feb. 25 *Perf. 11*

651 A196 2c carmine & black .70 .50
Never hinged 1.15

TYPE OF 1922-26 ISSUE

ROTARY PRESS PRINTING

1929, May 25 ***Perf. 11x10½***

653 A154 ½c olive brown .25 .25
Never hinged .35

ELECTRIC LIGHT'S GOLDEN JUBILEE ISSUE

Invention of the 1st incandescent electric lamp by Thomas Alva Edison, Oct. 21, 1879, 50th anniv.

Edison's First Lamp — A197

FLAT PLATE PRINTING

1929 *Perf. 11*

654 A197 2c carmine rose .65 .65
Never hinged 1.10
a. 2c lake —

ROTARY PRESS PRINTING
Perf. 11x10½

655 A197 2c carmine rose .65 .25
Never hinged 1.10
Pair with full horiz. gutter btwn. —

ROTARY PRESS COIL STAMP
Perf. 10 Vertically

656 A197 2c carmine rose 10.00 1.75
Never hinged 20.00

SULLIVAN EXPEDITION ISSUE

150th anniversary of the Sullivan Expedition in New York State during the Revolutionary War.

Maj. Gen. John Sullivan — A198

FLAT PLATE PRINTING

1929, June 17 ***Perf. 11***

657	A198 2c carmine rose	.55	.55
	Never hinged	.95	
a.	2c lake	375.00	250.00
	Never hinged	625.00	
b.	Vert. pair, imperf. btwn.	*4,000.*	

The unique No. 657b resulted from a paper foldover before perfing, and it has angled errant perfs from another row of horiz. perfs through the left side of the stamps.

Nos. 632-634, 635-642 Overprinted

This special issue was authorized as a measure of preventing losses from post office burglaries. Approximately a year's supply was printed and issued to postmasters. The P.O. Dept. found it desirable to discontinue the State overprinted stamps after the initial supply was used.

ROTARY PRESS PRINTING

1929, May 1 ***Perf. 11x10½***

658	A155 1c green	2.50	2.00
	Never hinged	5.00	
a.	Vertical pair, one without ovpt.	*300.00*	
	Never hinged	*500.00*	
659	A156 1½c brown	3.25	2.90
	Never hinged	6.50	
a.	Vertical pair, one without ovpt.	*475.00*	
660	A157 2c carmine	4.00	1.00
	Never hinged	7.50	
661	A158 3c violet	17.50	15.00
	Never hinged	35.00	
a.	Vertical pair, one without ovpt.	*600.00*	
	Never hinged	*800.00*	
662	A159 4c yellow brown	17.50	9.00
	Never hinged	35.00	
a.	Vertical pair, one without ovpt.	*500.00*	
663	A160 5c deep blue	12.50	9.75
	Never hinged	25.00	
664	A161 6c red orange	25.00	18.00
	Never hinged	50.00	
665	A162 7c black	25.00	27.50
	Never hinged	50.00	
666	A163 8c olive green	72.50	65.00
	Never hinged	145.00	
667	A164 9c light rose	14.00	11.50
	Never hinged	27.50	
668	A165 10c org yel	22.50	12.50
	Never hinged	45.00	
	Nos. 658-668 (11)	216.25	174.15
	Nos. 658-668, never hinged	431.50	

See notes following No. 679.

Overprinted

1929, May 1

669	A155 1c green	3.25	2.25
	Never hinged	6.50	
b.	No period after "Nebr." (19338, 19339 UR 26, 36 and 19339 LR 26, 36)	50.00	
670	A156 1½c brown	3.00	2.50
	Never hinged	6.00	
671	A157 2c carmine	3.00	1.30
	Never hinged	6.00	
672	A158 3c violet	11.00	12.00
	Never hinged	22.00	
a.	Vertical pair, one without ovpt.	*500.00*	
673	A159 4c yellow brown	17.50	15.00
	Never hinged	35.00	
674	A160 5c deep blue	15.00	15.00
	Never hinged	30.00	
675	A161 6c red orange	35.00	24.00
	Never hinged	70.00	
676	A162 7c black	22.50	18.00
	Never hinged	45.00	
677	A163 8c olive green	30.00	25.00
	Never hinged	60.00	
678	A164 9c light rose	35.00	27.50
	Never hinged	70.00	
a.	Vertical pair, one without ovpt.	*800.00*	
679	A165 10c org yel	90.00	22.50
	Never hinged	180.00	
	Nos. 669-679 (11)	265.25	165.05
	Nos. 669-679, never hinged	530.50	

Nos. 658-661, 669-673, 677-678 are known with the overprints on vertical pairs spaced 32mm apart instead of the normal 22mm.

Important: Nos. 658-679 with original gum have either one horizontal gum breaker ridge per stamp or portions of two at the extreme top and bottom of the stamps, 21mm apart. Multiple complete gum breaker ridges indicate a fake overprint. Absence of the gum breaker ridge indicates either regumming or regumming and a fake overprint.

BATTLE OF FALLEN TIMBERS ISSUE

Memorial to Gen. Anthony Wayne and for 135th anniv. of the Battle of Fallen Timbers, Ohio.

Gen. Anthony Wayne Memorial — A199

FLAT PLATE PRINTING

1929, Sept. 14 ***Perf. 11***

680	A199 2c carmine rose	.65	.65
	Never hinged	1.00	

OHIO RIVER CANALIZATION ISSUE

Completion of the Ohio River Canalization Project, between Cairo, Ill. and Pittsburgh, Pa.

Lock No. 5, Monongahela River — A200

1929, Oct. 19 ***Perf. 11***

681	A200 2c carmine rose	.55	.55
	Never hinged	.90	
a.	2c lake	*425.00*	—
	Never hinged	*650.00*	
b.	2c carmine lake, never hinged	—	

MASSACHUSETTS BAY COLONY ISSUE

300th anniversary of the founding of the Massachusetts Bay Colony.

Mass. Bay Colony Seal — A201

1930, Apr. 8 ***Perf. 11***

682	A201 2c carmine rose	.65	.50
	Never hinged	.95	

CAROLINA-CHARLESTON ISSUE

260th anniv. of the founding of the Province of Carolina and the 250th anniv. of the city of Charleston, S.C.

Gov. Joseph West & Chief Shadoo, a Kiowa — A202

1930, Apr. 10 ***Perf. 11***

683	A202 2c carmine rose	1.00	1.00
	Never hinged	1.50	

TYPES OF 1922-26 ISSUE

Warren G. Harding A203

William H. Taft A204

ROTARY PRESS PRINTING

1930 ***Perf. 11x10½***

684	A203 1½c brown	.50	.25
	Never hinged	.70	
685	A204 4c brown	.80	.25
	Never hinged	1.25	

ROTARY PRESS COIL STAMPS

Perf. 10 Vertically

686	A203 1½c brown	1.75	.25
	Never hinged	2.60	
687	A204 4c brown	3.00	.45
	Never hinged	4.50	

BRADDOCK'S FIELD ISSUE

175th anniversary of the Battle of Braddock's Field, otherwise the Battle of Monongahela.

Statue of Col. George Washington — A205

FLAT PLATE PRINTING

1930, July 9 ***Perf. 11***

688	A205 2c carmine rose	.85	.85
	Never hinged	1.30	

VON STEUBEN ISSUE

Baron Friedrich Wilhelm von Steuben (1730-1794), participant in the American Revolution.

General von Steuben — A206

FLAT PLATE PRINTING

1930, Sept. 17 ***Perf. 11***

689	A206 2c carmine rose	.50	.50
	Never hinged	.75	
a.	Imperf., pair	*2,000.*	
	Never hinged	*3,000.*	
b.	2c carmine lake	*950.00*	

PULASKI ISSUE

150th anniversary (in 1929) of the death of Gen. Casimir Pulaski, Polish patriot and hero of the American Revolutionary War.

General Casimir Pulaski — A207

1931, Jan. 16 ***Perf. 11***

690	A207 2c carmine rose	.30	.25
	Never hinged	.40	

TYPE OF 1922-26 ISSUES

ROTARY PRESS PRINTING

1931 ***Perf. 11x10½***

692	A166 11c light blue	2.50	.25
	Never hinged	3.75	
693	A167 12c brown violet	5.00	.25
	Never hinged	8.00	
694	A186 13c yellow green	2.25	.25
	Never hinged	3.50	
695	A168 14c dark blue	4.00	.60
	Never hinged	6.25	
696	A169 15c gray	7.75	.25
	Never hinged	12.00	

Perf. 10½x11

697	A187 17c black	4.75	.25
	Never hinged	7.25	
698	A170 20c carmine rose	7.75	.25
	Never hinged	12.50	
699	A171 25c blue green	8.00	.25
	Never hinged	13.00	
700	A172 30c brown	12.50	.25
	Never hinged	21.00	
701	A173 50c lilac	30.00	.25
	Never hinged	50.00	
	Nos. 692-701 (10)	84.50	2.85
	Nos. 692-701, never hinged	137.25	

RED CROSS ISSUE

50th anniversary of the founding of the American Red Cross Society.

"The Greatest Mother" — A208

FLAT PLATE PRINTING

1931, May 21 ***Perf. 11***

702	A208 2c black & red	.25	.25
	Never hinged	.35	
a.	Red cross missing (FO)	*40,000.*	

One example of No. 702a is documented; believed to be unique. Value reflects most recent sale price at auction in 1994.

YORKTOWN ISSUE

Surrender of Cornwallis at Yorktown, 1781.

Count de Rochambeau, Washington, Count de Grasse — A209

1931, Oct. 19 ***Perf. 11***

703	A209 2c car rose & blk	.35	.25
	Never hinged	.50	
a.	2c lake & black	4.50	.75
	Never hinged	6.25	
b.	2c dark lake & black	*500.00*	
	Never hinged	*950.00*	
c.	Horiz. pair, imperf. vertically	*7,000.*	
	Never hinged	*8,500.*	

No. 703c is valued in the grade of fine.

WASHINGTON BICENTENNIAL ISSUE

200th anniversary of the birth of George Washington. Various Portraits of George Washington.

A210

A211

A212

A213

A214

A215

A216

A217

A218

A219

A220

A221

ROTARY PRESS PRINTINGS

1932, Jan. 1 ***Perf. 11x10½***

704 A210 ½c olive brown .25 .25
Never hinged .35
705 A211 1c green .25 .25
Never hinged .35
706 A212 1½c brown .45 .25
Never hinged .60
707 A213 2c carmine rose .30 .25
Never hinged .45
708 A214 3c purple .55 .25
Never hinged .80
709 A215 4c light brown .60 .25
Never hinged .85
710 A216 5c blue 1.40 .25
Never hinged 2.25
711 A217 6c red orange 2.75 .25
Never hinged 4.50
712 A218 7c black .60 .25
Never hinged .85
713 A219 8c olive bister 2.50 .50
Never hinged 4.00
714 A220 9c pale red 2.00 .25
Never hinged 3.25
715 A221 10c orange yellow 9.00 .25
Never hinged 15.00
Nos. 704-715 (12) 20.65 3.25
Nos. 704-715, never hinged 33.25

OLYMPIC WINTER GAMES ISSUE

3rd Olympic Winter Games, held at Lake Placid, N.Y., Feb. 4-13, 1932.

Skier — A222

FLAT PLATE PRINTING

1932, Jan. 25 ***Perf. 11***

716 A222 2c carmine rose .35 .25
Never hinged .55
a. 2c lake *700.00*
Never hinged *1,050.*

No. 716a should be accompanied by a certificate of authenticity issued by a recognized exertizing committee.

ARBOR DAY ISSUE

Boy and Girl Planting Tree — A223

ROTARY PRESS PRINTING

1932, Apr. 22 ***Perf. 11x10½***

717 A223 2c carmine rose .25 .25
Never hinged .35

60th anniv. of the 1st observance of Arbor Day in Nebr., April, 1872.

Birth centenary of Julius Sterling Morton, who conceived the plan and the name "Arbor Day," while a member of the Nebr. State Board of Agriculture.

OLYMPIC GAMES ISSUE

Issued in honor of the 10th Olympic Games, held at Los Angeles, Calif., July 30 to Aug. 14, 1932.

Runner at Starting Mark A224

Myron's Discobolus A225

ROTARY PRESS PRINTING

1932, June 15 ***Perf. 11x10½***

718 A224 3c purple 1.50 .25
Never hinged 2.00
719 A225 5c blue 2.25 .25
Never hinged 2.90

Washington — A226

ROTARY PRESS PRINTING

1932, June 16 ***Perf. 11x10½***

720 A226 3c purple .35 .25
Never hinged .45
b. Booklet pane of 6 35.00 *12.50*
Never hinged 60.00
c. Vertical pair, imperf. between *725.00* *1,750.*
Never hinged *1,450.*

ROTARY PRESS COIL STAMPS

1932 ***Perf. 10 Vertically***

721 A226 3c purple 2.75 .25
Never hinged 3.50

Perf. 10 Horizontally

722 A226 3c purple 1.50 .35
Never hinged 2.00

Issued: #721, 6/24; #722, 10/12.

TYPE OF 1922-26 ISSUES

1932, Aug. 18 ***Perf. 10 Vertically***

723 A161 6c deep orange 11.00 .30
Never hinged 15.00

WILLIAM PENN ISSUE

250th anniv. of the arrival in America of Penn (1644-1718), English Quaker and founder of Pennsylvania.

William Penn — A227

FLAT PLATE PRINTING

1932, Oct. 24 ***Perf. 11***

724 A227 3c purple .45 .25
Never hinged .60
a. Vert. pair, imperf. horiz. —

DANIEL WEBSTER ISSUE

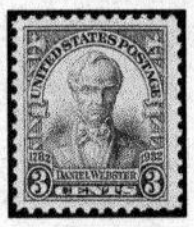
Daniel Webster — A228

FLAT PLATE PRINTING

1932, Oct. 24 ***Perf. 11***

725 A228 3c purple .45 .25
Never hinged .60

Daniel Webster (1782-1852), statesman.

GEORGIA BICENTENNIAL ISSUE

200th anniv. of the founding of the Colony of Georgia, and honoring Oglethorpe, who landed from England, Feb. 12, 1733, and personally supervised the establishing of the colony.

Gen. James Edward Oglethorpe — A229

FLAT PLATE PRINTING

1933, Feb. 12 ***Perf. 11***

726 A229 3c purple .50 .25
Never hinged .65

PEACE OF 1783 ISSUE

150th anniv. of the issuance by George Washington of the official order containing the Proclamation of Peace marking officially the ending of hostilities in the War for Independence.

Washington's Headquarters, Newburgh, NY — A230

ROTARY PRESS PRINTING

1933, Apr. 19 ***Perf. 10½x11***

727 A230 3c violet .25 .25
Never hinged .30

See No. 752.

CENTURY OF PROGRESS ISSUES

"Century of Progress" Intl. Exhibition, Chicago, which opened June 1, 1933, and centenary of the incorporation of Chicago as a city.

Restoration of Fort Dearborn A231

Federal Building at Chicago, 1933 A232

ROTARY PRESS PRINTING

1933, May 25 ***Perf. 10½x11***

728 A231 1c yellow green .25 .25
Never hinged .30
729 A232 3c purple .25 .25
Never hinged .35

AMERICAN PHILATELIC SOCIETY ISSUE

SOUVENIR SHEETS

Restoration of Fort Dearborn — A231a

Federal Building at Chicago, 1933 — A232a

FLAT PLATE PRINTING

1933, Aug. 25 ***Imperf.***

Without Gum

730 A231a 1c dp yel grn, pane of 25 20.00 *25.00*
a. Single stamp .70 .50
731 A232a 3c pur, pane of 25 20.00 *22.50*
a. Single stamp .65 .50

Issued in panes measuring 134x120mm. See Nos. 766-767.

NATIONAL RECOVERY ACT ISSUE

Issued to direct attention to and arouse the support of the nation for the National Recovery Act.

Group of Workers — A233

ROTARY PRESS PRINTING

1933, Aug. 15 ***Perf. 10½x11***

732 A233 3c purple .25 .25
Never hinged .30

BYRD ANTARCTIC ISSUE

Issued in connection with the Byrd Antarctic Expedition of 1933 and for use on letters mailed through the Little America Post Office established at the Base Camp of the Expedition in the territory of the South Pole.

World Map on van der Grinten's Projection — A234

FLAT PLATE PRINTING

1933, Oct. 9 ***Perf. 11***

733 A234 3c dark blue .50 .50
Never hinged .60

See Nos. 735, 753.

KOSCIUSZKO ISSUE

Kosciuszko (1746-1817), Polish soldier and statesman served in the American Revolution, on the 150th anniv. of the granting to him of American citizenship.

Statue of Gen. Tadeusz Kosciuszko — A235

FLAT PLATE PRINTING

1933, Oct. 13 ***Perf. 11***

734 A235 5c blue .55 .25
Never hinged .65
a. Horiz. pair, imperf. vert. *1,750.*
Never hinged *2,750.*

NATIONAL STAMP EXHIBITION ISSUE

SOUVENIR SHEET

A235a

1934, Feb. 10 ***Imperf.***

Without Gum

735 A235a 3c dk blue, pane of 6 10.00 9.00
a. Single stamp 1.60 1.25

Issued in panes measuring 87x93mm. See No. 768.

MARYLAND TERCENTENARY ISSUE

300th anniversary of the founding of Maryland.

"The Ark" and "The Dove" — A236

FLAT PLATE PRINTING

1934, Mar. 23 ***Perf. 11***

736 A236 3c carmine rose .30 .25
Never hinged .40
a. Horizontal pair, imperf between *4,000.*
b. 3c lake *1,000.* —
c. 3c carmine lake, never hinged —

The unique No. 736a resulted from a paper foldover before perfing, and it has angled errant perfs from another column of vert. perfs through the upper-left corner of the left stamp.

MOTHERS OF AMERICA ISSUE

Issued to commemorate Mother's Day.

Adaptation of Whistler's Portrait of his Mother — A237

ROTARY PRESS PRINTING

1934, May 2 ***Perf. 11x10½***

737 A237 3c purple .25 .25
Never hinged .30

FLAT PLATE PRINTING
Perf. 11

738 A237 3c purple .25 .25
Never hinged .30

See No. 754.

WISCONSIN TERCENTENARY ISSUE

Arrival of Jean Nicolet, French explorer, on the shores of Green Bay, 300th anniv. According to historical records, Nicolet was the 1st white man to reach the territory now comprising the State of Wisconsin.

Nicolet's Landing — A238

FLAT PLATE PRINTING

1934. July 7 *Perf. 11*

739 A238 3c purple .25 .25
Never hinged .40
a. Vert. pair, imperf. horiz. *575.00*
Never hinged *1,050.*
b. Horiz. pair, imperf. vert. *1,000.*
Never hinged *1,750.*

See No. 755.

NATIONAL PARKS YEAR ISSUE

El Capitan, Yosemite (California) A239

Old Faithful, Yellowstone (Wyoming) A243

Grand Canyon (Arizona) — A240

Mt. Rainier and Mirror Lake (Washington) A241

Mesa Verde (Colorado) A242

Crater Lake (Oregon) — A244

Great Head, Acadia Park (Maine) A245

Great White Throne, Zion Park (Utah) A246

Great Smoky Mts. (North Carolina) A248

Mt. Rockwell (Mt. Sinopah) and Two Medicine Lake, Glacier Natl. Park (Montana) A247

FLAT PLATE PRINTING

1934 **Unwmk.** *Perf. 11*

740 A239 1c green .25 .25
Never hinged .40
a. Vert. pair, imperf. horiz., with gum *1,500.*
Never hinged *2,500.*
741 A240 2c red .30 .25
Never hinged .40
a. Vert. pair, imperf. horiz., with gum *800.00*
Never hinged *1,450.*
b. Horiz. pair, imperf. vert., with gum *1,000.*
Never hinged *1,750.*
c. Imperf. P# 21261 block of 20 *7,500.*

No. 741c is a unique bottom margin plate #21261 block of 20. This plate was not used to print the imperforate Farley special printing, No. 757. Loose stamps separated from this block or from other possible imperforate No. 741 Plate #21261 blocks are indistinguishable from gummed examples of No. 757.

742 A241 3c purple .40 .25
Never hinged .50
a. Vert. pair, imperf. horiz., with gum *1,150.*
Never hinged *2,000.*
743 A242 4c brown .50 .40
Never hinged .70
a. Vert. pair, imperf. horiz., with gum *3,750.*
Never hinged *8,500.*
744 A243 5c blue .80 .65
Never hinged 1.10
a. Horiz. pair, imperf. vert., with gum *1,250.*
Never hinged *2,750.*
745 A244 6c dark blue 1.20 .85
Never hinged 1.65
746 A245 7c black .80 .75
Never hinged 1.10
a. Horiz. pair, imperf. vert., with gum *1,250.*
Never hinged *2,000.*
747 A246 8c sage green 1.75 1.50
Never hinged 2.70
748 A247 9c red orange 1.60 .65
Never hinged 2.40
749 A248 10c gray black 3.25 1.25
Never hinged 5.00
Nos. 740-749 (10) 10.85 6.80
Nos. 740-749, never hinged 15.95

Beware of fakes of the part-perforate errors of Nos. 740-749, including those with gum (see "without gum" note before No. 752).

See Nos. 750-751, 756-765, 769-770, 797.

AMERICAN PHILATELIC SOCIETY ISSUE

SOUVENIR SHEET

A248a

1934, Aug. 28 *Imperf.*

750 A248a 3c pur, pane of 6 20.00 *27.50*
Never hinged 30.00
a. Single stamp 3.25 3.25
Never hinged 4.00

Issued in panes measuring approximately 98x93mm.

See No. 770.

TRANS-MISSISSIPPI PHILATELIC EXPOSITION ISSUE

SOUVENIR SHEET

A248b

1934, Oct. 10 *Imperf.*

751 A248b 1c grn, pane of 6 10.00 12.50
Never hinged 15.00
a. Single stamp 1.65 1.60
Never hinged 2.25

Issued in panes measuring approximately 92x99mm.

See No. 769.

SPECIAL PRINTING

(Nos. 752-771 inclusive)

"Issued for a limited time in full sheets as printed, and in blocks thereof, to meet the requirements of collectors and others who may be interested." — From Postal Bulletin No. 16614.

Issuance of the following 20 stamps in complete sheets resulted from the protest of collectors and others at the practice of presenting, to certain government officials, complete sheets of unsevered panes, imperforate (except Nos. 752 and 753) and generally ungummed.

Designs of Commemorative Issues

Without Gum

NOTE: In 1940 the P.O. Department offered to and did gum full sheets of Nos. 756-765 and 769-770 sent in by owners. No other Special Printings were accepted for gumming.

TYPE OF PEACE ISSUE

Issued in sheets of 400

ROTARY PRESS PRINTING

Perf. 10½x11

1935, Mar. 15 **Unwmk.**

752 A230 3c purple .25 .25

TYPE OF BYRD ISSUE

Issued in sheets of 200

FLAT PLATE PRINTING

Perf. 11

753 A234 3c dark blue .50 .45

No. 753 is similar to No. 733. Positive identification is by blocks or pairs showing guide line between stamps. These lines between stamps are found only on No. 753.

TYPE OF MOTHERS OF AMERICA ISSUE

Issued in sheets of 200

FLAT PLATE PRINTING

Imperf

754 A237 3c deep purple .60 .60

TYPE OF WISCONSIN ISSUE

Issued in sheets of 200

FLAT PLATE PRINTING

Imperf

755 A238 3c deep purple .60 .60

TYPES OF NATIONAL PARKS ISSUE

Issued in sheets of 200

FLAT PLATE PRINTING

Imperf

756 A239 1c green .25 .25
757 A240 2c red .25 .25
758 A241 3c deep purple .50 .45
759 A242 4c brown 1.00 .95
760 A243 5c blue 1.60 1.40
761 A244 6c dark blue 2.40 2.25
762 A245 7c black 1.60 1.40
763 A246 8c sage green 1.90 1.50
764 A247 9c red orange 2.00 1.75
765 A248 10c gray black 4.00 3.50
Nos. 756-765 (10) 15.50 13.70
Nos. 756-765, with original gum, never hinged 114.35

SOUVENIR SHEETS

Note: Single items from these sheets are identical with other varieties, 766 and 730, 766a and 730a, 767 and 731, 767a and 731a, 768 and 735, 768a and 735a, 769a and 756, 770a and 758.

Positive identification is by blocks or pairs showing wide gutters between stamps. These wide gutters occur only on Nos. 766-770 and measure, horizontally, 13mm on Nos. 766-767; 16mm on No. 768, and 23mm on Nos. 769-770.

TYPE OF CENTURY OF PROGRESS ISSUE

Issued in sheets of 9 panes of 25 stamps each

FLAT PLATE PRINTING

Imperf

766 A231a 1c yel grn, pane of 25 32.50 32.50
a. Single stamp .90 .50
767 A232a 3c dp pur, pane of 25 32.50 32.50
a. Single stamp .90 .50

NATIONAL EXHIBITION ISSUE TYPE OF BYRD ISSUE

Issued in sheets of 25 panes of 6 stamps each

FLAT PLATE PRINTING

Imperf

768 A235a 3c dk blue, pane of 6 20.00 15.00
a. Single stamp 2.80 2.40

TYPES OF NATIONAL PARKS ISSUE

Issued in sheets of 20 panes of 6 stamps each

FLAT PLATE PRINTING

Imperf

769 A248b 1c grn, pane of 6 11.00 11.00
a. Single stamp 1.85 1.80
770 A248a 3c dp pur, pane of 6 30.00 24.00
a. Single stamp 3.25 3.10

TYPE OF AIR POST SPECIAL DELIVERY

Issued in sheets of 200

FLAT PLATE PRINTING

Imperf

771 APSD1 16c dark blue 2.50 2.60

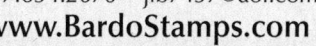

Catalogue values for unused stamps in this section, from this point to the end, are for Never Hinged items.

VALUES FOR HINGED STAMPS AFTER NO. 771
This catalogue does not value unused stamps after No. 771 in hinged condition. Hinged unused stamps from No. 772 to the present are worth considerably less than the values given for unused stamps, which are for never-hinged examples.

CONNECTICUT TERCENTENARY ISSUE

300th anniv. of the settlement of Connecticut.

Charter Oak — A249

ROTARY PRESS PRINTING
Perf. 11x10½

1935, Apr. 26 **Unwmk.**
772 A249 3c rose purple .35 .25

CALIFORNIA PACIFIC EXPOSITION ISSUE

California Pacific Exposition at San Diego.

View of San Diego Exposition A250

1935, May 29 **Unwmk.**
773 A250 3c purple .35 .25

BOULDER DAM ISSUE

Dedication of Boulder Dam.

Boulder Dam — A251

FLAT PLATE PRINTING

1935, Sept. 30 **Unwmk.** ***Perf. 11***
774 A251 3c purple .35 .25

MICHIGAN CENTENARY ISSUE

Advance celebration of Michigan Statehood centenary.

Michigan State Seal — A252

ROTARY PRESS PRINTING

1935, Nov. 1 **Unwmk.** ***Perf. 11x10½***
775 A252 3c purple .35 .25

TEXAS CENTENNIAL ISSUE

Centennial of Texas independence.

Sam Houston, Stephen F. Austin and the Alamo — A253

1936, Mar. 2 **Unwmk.**
776 A253 3c purple .35 .25

RHODE ISLAND TERCENTENARY ISSUE

300th anniv. of the settlement of Rhode Island.

Statue of Roger Williams — A254

1936, May 4 **Unwmk.** ***Perf. 10½x11***
777 A254 3c purple .35 .25

THIRD INTERNATIONAL PHILATELIC EXHIBITION ISSUE

SOUVENIR SHEET

A254a

FLAT PLATE PRINTING

1936, May 9 **Unwmk.** ***Imperf.***

778 A254a	purple, pane of 4	1.75	1.25
a.	3c Type A249	.40	.30
b.	3c Type A250	.40	.30
c.	3c Type A252	.40	.30
d.	3c Type A253	.40	.30

Issued in panes measuring 98x66mm containing four stamps, inscribed in the margins: "Printed by the Treasury Department, Bureau of Engraving and Printing, under authority of James A. Farley, Postmaster General, in compliment to the third International Philatelic Exhibition of 1936. New York, N. Y., May 9-17, 1936. Plate No. 21557."

Also used was plate 21558. Each different plate number used is inscribed in the bottom selvage of the respective souvenir sheets.

ARKANSAS CENTENNIAL ISSUE

100th anniv. of the State of Arkansas.

Arkansas Post, Old and New State Houses — A255

ROTARY PRESS PRINTING
Perf. 11x10½

1936, June 15 **Unwmk.**
782 A255 3c purple .35 .25

OREGON TERRITORY ISSUE

Opening of the Oregon Territory, 1836, 100th anniv.

Map of Oregon Territory — A256

1936, July 14 **Unwmk.**
783 A256 3c purple .35 .25

SUSAN B. ANTHONY ISSUE

Susan Brownell Anthony (1820-1906), woman-suffrage advocate, and 16th anniv. of the ratification of the 19th Amendment which grants American women the right to vote.

Susan B. Anthony — A257

1936, Aug. 26 **Unwmk.**
784 A257 3c purple .30 .25

ARMY ISSUE

Issued in honor of the United States Army.

George Washington, Nathanael Greene and Mount Vernon — A258

Andrew Jackson, Winfield Scott and the Hermitage A259

Generals Sherman, Grant and Sheridan — A260

Generals Robert E. Lee, "Stonewall" Jackson and Stratford Hall — A261

U.S. Military Academy, West Point — A262

1936-37 **Unwmk.**

785 A258	1c green	.30	.25
786 A259	2c carmine ('37)	.30	.25
787 A260	3c purple ('37)	.40	.25
788 A261	4c bl gray ('37)	.60	.25
789 A262	5c ultra ('37)	.75	.25
	Nos. 785-789 (5)	2.35	1.25

NAVY ISSUE

Issued in honor of the United States Navy.

John Paul Jones and John Barry — A263

Stephen Decatur and Thomas MacDonough A264

Admirals David G. Farragut and David D. Porter — A265

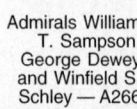

Admirals William T. Sampson, George Dewey and Winfield S. Schley — A266

Seal of U.S. Naval Academy and Naval Midshipmen A267

1936-37 **Unwmk.**

790 A263	1c green	.30	.25
791 A264	2c carmine ('37)	.30	.25
792 A265	3c purple ('37)	.40	.25
793 A266	4c gray ('37)	.60	.25
794 A267	5c ultra ('37)	.75	.25
	Nos. 790-794 (5)	2.35	1.25

ORDINANCE OF 1787 SESQUICENTENNIAL ISSUE

150th anniv. of the adoption of the Ordinance of 1787 and the creation of the Northwest Territory.

Manasseh Cutler, Rufus Putnam and Map of Northwest Territory — A268

1937, July 13 **Unwmk.**
795 A268 3c rose purple .30 .25

VIRGINIA DARE ISSUE

350th anniv. of the birth of Virginia Dare, 1st child born in America of English parents (Aug. 18, 1587), and the settlement at Roanoke Island.

Virginia Dare and Parents — A269

FLAT PLATE PRINTING

1937, Aug. 18 **Unwmk.** ***Perf. 11***
796 A269 5c gray blue .35 .25

SOCIETY OF PHILATELIC AMERICANS ISSUE

SOUVENIR SHEET

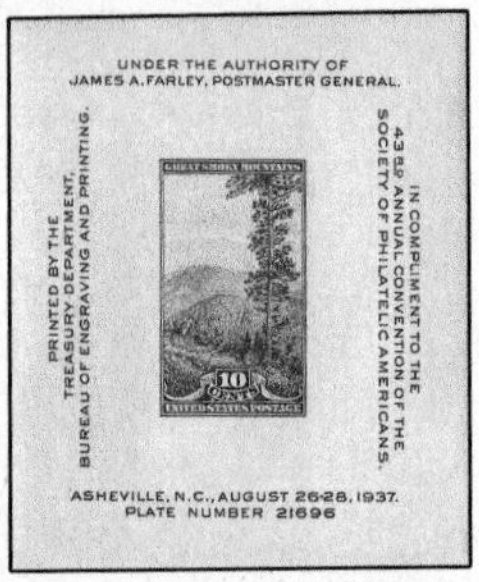

A269a

TYPE OF NATIONAL PARKS ISSUE

1937, Aug. 26 **Unwmk.** ***Imperf.***
797 A269a 10c blue green .60 .40

Issued in panes measuring 67x78mm.

CONSTITUTION SESQUICENTENNIAL ISSUE

150th anniversary of the signing of the Constitution on September 17, 1787.

Signing of the Constitution A270

Perf. 11x10½

1937, Sept. 17 **Unwmk.**
798 A270 3c brt reddsh pur .40 .25

TERRITORIAL ISSUES

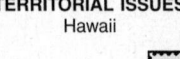

Hawaii

Statue of Kamehameha I, Honolulu — A271

Alaska

Landscape with Mt. McKinley — A272

Puerto Rico

La Fortaleza, San Juan — A273

Virgin Islands

Charlotte Amalie — A274

1937 **Unwmk.** ***Perf. 10½x11***

799 A271 3c violet .35 .25

Perf. 11x10½

800 A272 3c violet .40 .25
801 A273 3c bright purple .40 .25
802 A274 3c rose violet .40 .25
Nos. 799-802 (4) 1.55 1.00

PRESIDENTIAL ISSUE

Benjamin Franklin A275

George Washington A276

Martha Washington A277

John Adams A278

Thomas Jefferson A279

James Madison A280

White House A281

James Monroe A282

John Q. Adams A283

Andrew Jackson A284

Martin Van Buren A285

William H. Harrison A286

John Tyler A287

James K. Polk A288

Zachary Taylor A289

Millard Fillmore A290

Franklin Pierce A291

James Buchanan A292

Abraham Lincoln A293

Andrew Johnson A294

Ulysses S. Grant A295

Rutherford B. Hayes A296

James A. Garfield A297

Chester A. Arthur A298

Grover Cleveland A299

Benjamin Harrison A300

William McKinley A301

Theodore Roosevelt A302

William Howard Taft A303

Woodrow Wilson A304

Warren G. Harding A305

Calvin Coolidge A306

1938 **Unwmk.**

803 A275 ½c deep orange .30 .25
804 A276 1c green .30 .25
b. Booklet pane of 6 2.00 *.50*
c. Horiz. pair, imperf between (from booklet pane) —
805 A277 1½c bister brown .30 .25
b. Horiz. pair, imperf. between 100.00 20.00

No. 805b unused is not precanceled. Precanceled examples are considered used and are valued in the used column. They are valued with gum; pairs without gum are worth less.

806 A278 2c rose carmine .30 .25
b. Booklet pane of 6 5.50 *1.00*
807 A279 3c light violet .30 .25
a. Booklet pane of 6 8.50 *2.00*
b. Horiz. pair, imperf. between *2,000.* —
c. Imperf., pair *3,500.*
d. As "a," imperf between vert. *5,000.*
808 A280 4c brt rose pur .75 .25
809 A281 4½c dark gray .40 .25
810 A282 5c bright blue .35 .25
811 A283 6c red orange .40 .25
812 A284 7c sepia .40 .25
813 A285 8c olive green .40 .25
814 A286 9c rose pink .45 .25
815 A287 10c brown red .40 .25
816 A288 11c ultramarine .75 .25
817 A289 12c bright mauve 1.00 .25
818 A290 13c blue green 1.30 .25
819 A291 14c blue 1.00 .25
820 A292 15c blue gray .80 .25
821 A293 16c black 1.50 .25
822 A294 17c rose red 1.00 .25
823 A295 18c brn car 2.25 .25
824 A296 19c bright mauve 1.30 .35
825 A297 20c brt bl grn 1.20 .25
826 A298 21c dull blue 1.30 .25
827 A299 22c vermilion 1.20 .40
828 A300 24c gray black 3.25 .25
829 A301 25c deep red lilac 1.20 .25
830 A302 30c dp ultra 3.50 .25
a. 30c blue 20.00 —
b. 30c deep blue *375.00* —
831 A303 50c mauve 5.50 .25

FLAT PLATE PRINTING

1938 ***Perf. 11***

832 A304 $1 pur & blk 7.00 .25
a. Vert. pair, imperf. horiz. *1,100.*
b. Watermarked USIR ('51) 200.00 65.00
c. $1 red violet & black ('54) 6.00 .25
d. As "c," vert. pair, imperf. horiz. *900.00*
e. Vert. pair, imperf. btwn. *7,500.*
f. As "c," vert. pair, imperf. btwn. *10,000.*
g. As "c," bright magenta & black *70.00* 50.00
h. As No. 832, red violet & black — —

No. 832c is dry printed from 400-subject flat plates on thick white paper with smooth, colorless gum.

No. 832g is the far end of the color spectrum for the No. 832c stamp, trending toward a more pinkish shade, but the shade is not pink. No. 832g is known in bright magenta and in deep bright magenta; both shades qualify as No. 832g.

No. 832h is a shade variety of the wet printing (No. 832), but the shade essentially matches the red violet normally seen on the dry printing (No. 832c).

833 A305 $2 yel grn & blk 16.00 3.75
834 A306 $5 car & blk 75.00 3.00
a. $5 red brown & black *3,000.* *7,000.*
Nos. 803-834 (32) 131.10 14.50

No. 834 can be chemically altered to resemble Scott 834a. No. 834a should be purchased only with competent expert certification.

Watermarks

All stamps from No. 835 on are unwatermarked.

CONSTITUTION RATIFICATION ISSUE

150th anniversary of the ratification of the United States Constitution.

Old Court House, Williamsburg, Va. — A307

ROTARY PRESS PRINTING

1938, June 21 ***Perf. 11x10½***

835 A307 3c deep violet .45 .25

SWEDISH-FINNISH TERCENTENARY ISSUE

Tercentenary of the founding of the Swedish and Finnish Settlement at Wilmington, Delaware.

Landing of the Swedes and Finns — A308

FLAT PLATE PRINTING

1938, June 27 ***Perf. 11***

836 A308 3c brt reddsh pur .35 .25

NORTHWEST TERRITORY SESQUICENTENNIAL

Statue Symbolizing Colonization of the West — A309

ROTARY PRESS PRINTING

1938, July 15 ***Perf. 11x10½***

837 A309 3c bright rose purple .30 .25

IOWA TERRITORY CENTENNIAL ISSUE

Old Capitol, Iowa City — A310

1938, Aug. 24

838 A310 3c violet .40 .25

TYPES OF 1938

ROTARY PRESS COIL STAMPS

1939, Jan. 20 ***Perf. 10 Vertically***

839	A276	1c	green	.30	.25
840	A277	1½c	bister brown	.30	.25
841	A278	2c	rose carmine	.40	.25
842	A279	3c	light violet	.50	.25
843	A280	4c	red violet	7.50	.40
844	A281	4½c	dark gray	.70	.40
845	A282	5c	bright blue	5.00	2.50
846	A283	6c	red orange	1.10	.55
847	A287	10c	brown red	11.00	1.00

1939, Jan. 27 ***Perf. 10 Horizontally***

848	A276	1c	green	.85	.25
849	A277	1½c	bister brown	1.25	.30
850	A278	2c	rose carmine	2.50	.40
851	A279	3c	light violet	2.50	.40
	Nos. 839-851 (13)			33.90	7.20

GOLDEN GATE INTL. EXPOSITION, SAN FRANCISCO

"Tower of the Sun" — A311

ROTARY PRESS PRINTING

1939, Feb. 18 ***Perf. 10½x11***

852 A311 3c bright purple .30 .25

NEW YORK WORLD'S FAIR ISSUE

Trylon and Perisphere — A312

1939, Apr. 1

853 A312 3c violet .30 .25

WASHINGTON INAUGURATION ISSUE

Sesquicentennial of the inauguration of George Washington as First President.

George Washington Taking Oath of Office — A313

FLAT PLATE PRINTING

1939, Apr. 30 ***Perf. 11***

854 A313 3c bright purple .60 .25

BASEBALL CENTENNIAL ISSUE

Sand-lot Baseball Game — A314

ROTARY PRESS PRINTING

1939, June 12 ***Perf. 11x10½***

855 A314 3c violet 1.75 .25

PANAMA CANAL ISSUE

25th anniv. of the opening of the Panama Canal.

Theodore Roosevelt, Gen. George W. Goethals and Gaillard Cut — A315

FLAT PLATE PRINTING

1939, Aug. 15 ***Perf. 11***

856 A315 3c reddish purple .40 .25

PRINTING TERCENTENARY ISSUE

Issued in commemoration of the 300th anniversary of printing in Colonial America. The Stephen Daye press is in the Harvard University Museum.

Stephen Daye Press — A316

ROTARY PRESS PRINTING

1939, Sept. 25 ***Perf. 10½x11***

857 A316 3c violet .30 .25

50th ANNIVERSARY OF STATEHOOD ISSUE

Map of North and South Dakota, Montana and Washington A317

1939, Nov. 2 ***Perf. 11x10½***

858 A317 3c rose purple .35 .25

FAMOUS AMERICANS ISSUES
AMERICAN AUTHORS

Washington Irving A318

James Fenimore Cooper A319

Ralph Waldo Emerson A320

Louisa May Alcott A321

Samuel L. Clemens (Mark Twain) — A322

1940 ***Perf. 10½x11***

859	A318	1c	bright blue green	.30	.25
860	A319	2c	rose carmine	.30	.25
861	A320	3c	bright purple	.30	.25
862	A321	5c	ultramarine	.35	.25
863	A322	10c	dark brown	1.75	1.20
	Nos. 859-863 (5)			3.00	2.20

AMERICAN POETS

Henry W. Longfellow A323

John Greenleaf Whittier A324

James Russell Lowell A325

Walt Whitman A326

James Whitcomb Riley — A327

864	A323	1c	bright blue green	.30	.25
865	A324	2c	rose carmine	.30	.25
866	A325	3c	bright purple	.30	.25
867	A326	5c	ultramarine	.50	.25
868	A327	10c	dark brown	1.75	1.25
	Nos. 864-868 (5)			3.15	2.25

AMERICAN EDUCATORS

Horace Mann A328

Mark Hopkins A329

Charles W. Eliot A330

Frances E. Willard A331

Booker T. Washington — A332

869	A328	1c	bright blue green	.30	.25
870	A329	2c	rose carmine	.30	.25
871	A330	3c	bright purple	.30	.25
872	A331	5c	ultramarine	.50	.25
873	A332	10c	dark brown	2.25	1.10
	Nos. 869-873 (5)			3.65	2.10

AMERICAN SCIENTISTS

John James Audubon A333

Dr. Crawford W. Long A334

Luther Burbank A335

Dr. Walter Reed A336

Jane Addams — A337

874	A333	1c	bright blue green	.30	.25
875	A334	2c	rose carmine	.30	.25
876	A335	3c	bright purple	.30	.25
877	A336	5c	ultramarine	.50	.25
878	A337	10c	dark brown	1.50	.85
	Nos. 874-878 (5)			2.90	1.85

AMERICAN COMPOSERS

Stephen Collins Foster A338

John Philip Sousa A339

Victor Herbert A340

Edward MacDowell A341

Ethelbert Nevin — A342

879	A338	1c	bright blue green	.30	.25
880	A339	2c	rose carmine	.30	.25
881	A340	3c	bright purple	.30	.25
882	A341	5c	ultramarine	.50	.25
883	A342	10c	dark brown	3.75	1.35
	Nos. 879-883 (5)			5.15	2.35

AMERICAN ARTISTS

Gilbert Charles Stuart A343

James A. McNeill Whistler A344

Augustus Saint-Gaudens A345

Daniel Chester French A346

Frederic Remington — A347

884	A343	1c	bright blue green	.30	.25
885	A344	2c	rose carmine	.30	.25
886	A345	3c	bright purple	.30	.25
887	A346	5c	ultramarine	.50	.25
888	A347	10c	dark brown	1.75	1.25
	Nos. 884-888 (5)			3.15	2.25

AMERICAN INVENTORS

Eli Whitney A348

Samuel F. B. Morse A349

Cyrus Hall McCormick A350

Elias Howe A351

Alexander Graham Bell — A352

889	A348	1c	brt blue grn	.30	.25
890	A349	2c	rose carmine	.30	.25
891	A350	3c	bright purple	.30	.25
892	A351	5c	ultramarine	1.10	.30
893	A352	10c	dark brown	11.00	2.00
	Nos. 889-893 (5)			13.00	3.05
	Nos. 859-893 (35)			34.00	16.05

PONY EXPRESS, 80th ANNIV. ISSUE

Pony Express Rider — A353

1940, Apr. 3 ***Perf. 11x10½***
894 A353 3c henna brown .50 .25

PAN AMERICAN UNION ISSUE

Founding of the Pan American Union, 50th anniv.

The Three Graces from Botticelli's "Spring" — A354

1940, Apr. 14 ***Perf. 10½x11***
895 A354 3c bright rose purple .30 .25

IDAHO STATEHOOD, 50th ANNIV.

Idaho Capitol, Boise — A355

1940, July 3 ***Perf. 11x10½***
896 A355 3c bright mauve .35 .25

WYOMING STATEHOOD, 50th ANNIV.

Wyoming State Seal — A356

1940, July 10 ***Perf. 10½x11***
897 A356 3c brown violet .35 .25

CORONADO EXPEDITION, 400th ANNIV.

"Coronado and His Captains," painted by Gerald Cassidy — A357

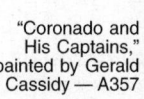

1940, Sept. 7 ***Perf. 11x10½***
898 A357 3c bright violet .35 .25

NATIONAL DEFENSE ISSUE

Statue of Liberty — A358

90-millimeter Anti-aircraft Gun — A359

Torch of Enlightenment — A360

1940, Oct. 16
899 A358 1c bright blue green .30 .25
a. Vertical pair, imperf. between 600.00 —
b. Horizontal pair, imperf. between 32.50 —
900 A359 2c rose carmine .30 .25
a. Horizontal pair, imperf. between 37.50 —
901 A360 3c bright mauve .30 .25
a. Horizontal pair, imperf. between 22.50 —
Nos. 899-901 (3) .90 .75

THIRTEENTH AMENDMENT ISSUE

75th anniv. of the 13th Amendment to the Constitution abolishing slavery.

"Emancipation," Statue of Lincoln and Slave, by Thomas Ball — A361

1940, Oct. 20 ***Perf. 10½x11***
902 A361 3c violet .50 .25

VERMONT STATEHOOD, 150th ANNIV.

Vermont Capitol, Montpelier A362

1941, Mar. 4 ***Perf. 11x10½***
903 A362 3c light violet .45 .25

KENTUCKY STATEHOOD, 150th ANNIV.

Daniel Boone and Three Frontiersmen, from mural by Gilbert White — A363

1942, June 1
904 A363 3c purple .30 .25

WIN THE WAR ISSUE

American Eagle — A364

1942, July 4
905 A364 3c bright lilac .30 .25
b. 3c reddish purple 750.00 500.00

All examples of No. 905b are precanceled either Los Angeles, Calif., Fremont, Ohio, or St. Paul, Minn. Value is for Los Angeles, which is the more common. Value of Fremont, unused, $1,500. Value of St. Paul, used (without gum), $2,500. The stamps with St. Paul precancel are slightly less reddish than Los Angeles or Fremont, but they are in the same reddish purple/purple color family.

CHINESE RESISTANCE ISSUE

Issued to commemorate the Chinese people's five years of resistance to Japanese aggression.

Lincoln, Sun Yat-sen & Map — A365

1942, July 7
906 A365 5c bright blue *4.00* .50

ALLIED NATIONS ISSUE

Allegory of Victory — A366

1943, Jan. 14
907 A366 2c rose carmine .30 .25

Bureau Precancels: Denver, Baltimore.

FOUR FREEDOMS ISSUE

A367

1943, Feb. 12
908 A367 1c bright blue green .30 .25

OVERRUN COUNTRIES ISSUE

Flag of Poland — A368

No. 909, Poland. No. 910, Czechoslovakia. No. 911, Norway. No. 912, Luxembourg. No. 913, Netherlands. No. 914, Belgium. No. 915, France. No. 916, Greece. No. 917, Yugoslavia. No. 918, Albania. No. 919, Austria. No. 920, Denmark. No. 921, Korea.

Printed by the American Bank Note Co.
FRAMES ENGRAVED, CENTERS OFFSET LETTERPRESS
ROTARY PRESS PRINTING
Plates of 200 subjects in four panes of 50.

1943-44 ***Perf. 12***
909 A368 5c blue vio, brt red & blk .30 .25
a. Double impression of "Poland" 200.00
b. Double impression of black flag color and red "Poland" —
910 A368a 5c blue vio, blue, brt red & blk .30 .25
a. Double impression of "Czechoslovakia" 600.00
911 A368b 5c blue vio, dk rose, dp blue & blk .30 .25
a. Double impression of "Norway" 225.00
912 A368c 5c blue vio, dk rose, lt blue & blk .30 .25
a. Double impression of "Luxembourg" —
913 A368d 5c blue vio, dk rose, blue & blk .30 .25
914 A368e 5c blue vio, dk rose, yel & blk .30 .25
a. Double impression of "Belgium" 200.00
915 A368f 5c blue vio, dp blue, dk rose & blk .30 .25
916 A368g 5c blue vio, pale blue, grnsh blue & blk .50 .25
917 A368h 5c blue vio, blue, dk rose & blk .40 .25
b. Double impression of black 250.00 200.00
918 A368i 5c blue vio, dk red & blk .30 .25
a. Double impression of "Albania" — 600.00
919 A368j 5c blue vio, red & blk .30 .25
a. Double impression of "Austria" 300.00
c. Double impression of black —
920 A368k 5c blue vio, red & blk .30 .25
b. 5c blue violet, red & gray .30 .25
921 A368m 5c blue vio, red, lt blue & gray .30 .25
a. Double impression of light blue (including "Korea") — —
c. Double impression of red —
Nos. 909-921 (13) 4.20 3.25

TRANSCONTINENTAL RAILROAD ISSUE

Completion of the 1st transcontinental railroad, 75th anniv.

"Golden Spike Ceremony" Painting by John McQuarrie A369

ENGRAVED
ROTARY PRESS PRINTING

1944, May 10 ***Perf. 11x10½***
922 A369 3c violet .30 .25

STEAMSHIP ISSUE

1st steamship to cross the Atlantic, 125th anniv.

"Savannah" A370

1944, May 22
923 A370 3c violet .30 .25

TELEGRAPH ISSUE

1st message transmitted by telegraph, cent.

Telegraph Wires & the First Transmitted Words "What Hath God Wrought" — A371

1944, May 24
924 A371 3c bright purple .30 .25

PHILIPPINE ISSUE

Final resistance of the US and Philippine defenders on Corregidor to the Japanese invaders in 1942.

View of Corregidor A372

1944, Sept. 27
925 A372 3c deep violet .30 .25

MOTION PICTURE, 50th ANNIV.

Motion Picture Showing for the Armed Forces in South Pacific — A373

1944, Oct. 31
926 A373 3c deep violet .30 .25

FLORIDA STATEHOOD, CENTENARY

Old Florida Seal, St. Augustine Gates and State Capitol — A374

1945, Mar. 3
927 A374 3c bright red violet .30 .25

UNITED NATIONS CONFERENCE ISSUE

United Nations Conference, San Francisco, Calif.

A375

1945, Apr. 25
928 A375 5c ultramarine .30 .25

IWO JIMA (MARINES) ISSUE

Battle of Iwo Jima and honoring the achievements of the US Marines.

Marines Raising the Flag on Mt. Suribachi, Iwo Jima, from a Photograph by Joel Rosenthal — A376

1945, July 11 *Perf. 10½x11*

929 A376 3c yellow green .30 .25

FRANKLIN D. ROOSEVELT ISSUE

Franklin Delano Roosevelt (1882-1945).

Roosevelt and Hyde Park Home — A377

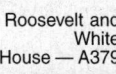

Roosevelt and "Little White House," Warm Springs, Georgia — A378

Roosevelt and White House — A379

Roosevelt, Globe and Four Freedoms — A380

1945-46 *Perf. 11x10½*

930 A377 1c blue green .30 .25
931 A378 2c carmine rose .30 .25
932 A379 3c purple .30 .25
933 A380 5c bright blue .30 .25
Nos. 930-933 (4) 1.20 1.00

ARMY ISSUE

Achievements of the US Army in World War II.

U.S. Troops Passing Arch of Triumph, Paris — A381

1945, Sept. 28

934 A381 3c olive .30 .25

NAVY ISSUE

Achievements of the U.S. Navy in World War II.

U.S. Sailors — A382

1945, Oct. 27

935 A382 3c blue .30 .25

COAST GUARD ISSUE

Achievements of the US Coast Guard in World War II.

Coast Guard Landing Craft and Supply Ship — A383

1945, Nov. 10

936 A383 3c bright blue green .30 .25

ALFRED E. SMITH ISSUE

Alfred E. Smith — A384

1945, Nov. 26

937 A384 3c purple .30 .25

TEXAS STATEHOOD, 100th ANNIV.

U.S. and Texas State Flags — A385

1945, Dec. 29

938 A385 3c dark blue .30 .25

MERCHANT MARINE ISSUE

Achievements of the US Merchant Marine in World War II.

Liberty Ship Unloading Cargo — A386

1946, Feb. 26

939 A386 3c blue green .30 .25

VETERANS OF WORLD WAR II ISSUE

Issued to honor all veterans of World War II.

Honorable Discharge Emblem — A387

1946, May 9

940 A387 3c dark violet .30 .25

TENNESSEE STATEHOOD, 150th ANNIV.

Andrew Jackson, John Sevier & Tennessee Capitol — A388

1946, June 1

941 A388 3c dark violet .30 .25

IOWA STATEHOOD, 100th ANNIV.

Iowa State Flag & Map — A389

1946, Aug. 3

942 A389 3c deep blue .30 .25

SMITHSONIAN INSTITUTION ISSUE

100th anniversary of the establishment of the Smithsonian Institution, Washington, D.C.

Smithsonian Institution — A390

1946, Aug. 10

943 A390 3c violet brown .30 .25

KEARNY EXPEDITION ISSUE

100th anniversary of the entry of General Stephen Watts Kearny into Santa Fe.

"Capture of Santa Fe" by Kenneth M. Chapman — A391

1946, Oct. 16

944 A391 3c brown violet .30 .25

THOMAS A. EDISON ISSUE

Thomas A. Edison, Birth Centenary — A392

1947, Feb. 11 *Perf. 10½x11*

945 A392 3c bright red violet .30 .25

JOSEPH PULITZER ISSUE

Joseph Pulitzer & Statue of Liberty — A393

1947, Apr. 10 *Perf. 11x10½*

946 A393 3c purple .30 .25

POSTAGE STAMP CENTENARY ISSUE

Centenary of the first postage stamps issued by the United States Government

Washington & Franklin; Early and Modern Mail-carrying Vehicles — A394

1947, May 17

947 A394 3c deep blue .30 .25

CENTENARY INTERNATIONAL PHILATELIC EXHIBITION ISSUE

SOUVENIR SHEET

A395

FLAT PLATE PRINTING

1947, May 19 *Imperf.*

948 A395 Pane of 2 .60 .45
a. 5c blue, type A1 .30 .25
b. 10c brown orange, type A2 .30 .25

Pane size varies: 96-98x66-68mm.

DOCTORS ISSUE

Issued to honor the physicians of America.

"The Doctor," by Sir Luke Fildes — A396

ROTARY PRESS PRINTING

1947, June 9 *Perf. 11x10½*

949 A396 3c brown violet .30 .25

UTAH ISSUE

Centenary of the settlement of Utah.

Pioneers Entering the Valley of Great Salt Lake — A397

1947, July 24

950 A397 3c dark violet .30 .25

U.S. FRIGATE CONSTITUTION ISSUE

150th anniversary of the launching of the U.S. frigate Constitution ("Old Ironsides").

Naval Architect's Drawing of Frigate Constitution A398

1947, Oct. 21

951 A398 3c blue green .30 .25

EVERGLADES NATIONAL PARK ISSUE

Dedication of the Everglades National Park, Florida, Dec. 6, 1947.

Great White Heron and Map of Florida — A399

1947, Dec. 5 *Perf. 10½x11*

952 A399 3c bright green .30 .25

GEORGE WASHINGTON CARVER ISSUE

5th anniversary of the death of Dr. George Washington Carver, (1864-1943), botanist.

Dr. George Washington Carver — A400

1948, Jan. 5

953 A400 3c bright red violet .30 .25

CALIFORNIA GOLD CENTENNIAL ISSUE

Sutter's Mill, Coloma, California — A401

1948, Jan. 24 *Perf. 11x10½*

954 A401 3c dark violet .30 .25

MISSISSIPPI TERRITORY ISSUE

Mississippi Territory establishment, 150th anniv.

Map, Seal and Gov. Winthrop Sargent — A402

1948, Apr. 7

955 A402 3c brown violet .30 .25

FOUR CHAPLAINS ISSUE

George L. Fox, Clark V. Poling, John P. Washington and Alexander D. Goode, the 4 chaplains who sacrificed their lives in the sinking of the S.S. Dorchester, Feb. 3, 1943.

Four Chaplains and Sinking S.S. Dorchester A403

1948, May 28

956 A403 3c gray black .30 .25

WISCONSIN STATEHOOD, 100th ANNIV.

Map on Scroll & State Capitol — A404

1948, May 29
957 A404 3c dark violet .30 .25

SWEDISH PIONEER ISSUE

Centenary of the coming of the Swedish pioneers to the Middle West.

Swedish Pioneer with Covered Wagon Moving Westward — A405

1948, June 4
958 A405 5c deep blue .30 .25

PROGRESS OF WOMEN ISSUE

Century of progress of American Women.

Elizabeth Stanton, Carrie C. Catt & Lucretia Mott — A406

1948, July 19
959 A406 3c dark violet .30 .25

WILLIAM ALLEN WHITE ISSUE

William Allen White, Editor and Author — A407

1948, July 31 ***Perf. 10½x11***
960 A407 3c bright red violet .30 .25

UNITED STATES-CANADA FRIENDSHIP ISSUE

Century of friendship between the US and Canada.

Niagara Railway Suspension Bridge — A408

1948, Aug. 2 ***Perf. 11x10½***
961 A408 3c blue .30 .25

FRANCIS SCOTT KEY ISSUE

Francis Scott Key (1779-1843), Maryland lawyer and author of "The Star-Spangled Banner" (1813).

Key and American Flags of 1814 and 1948 — A409

1948, Aug. 9
962 A409 3c rose pink .30 .25

SALUTE TO YOUTH ISSUE

Issued to honor the Youth of America and to publicize "Youth Month," September, 1948.

Girl and Boy Carrying Books — A410

1948, Aug. 11
963 A410 3c deep blue .30 .25

OREGON TERRITORY ISSUE

Centenary of the establishment of Oregon Territory.

John McLoughlin, Jason Lee & Wagon on Oregon Trail — A411

1948, Aug. 14
964 A411 3c brown red .30 .25

HARLAN F. STONE ISSUE

Chief Justice Harlan Fiske Stone — A412

1948, Aug. 25 ***Perf. 10½x11***
965 A412 3c bright red violet .30 .25

PALOMAR MOUNTAIN OBSERVATORY ISSUE

Dedication, August 30, 1948.

Observatory, Palomar Mt., Cal. — A413

1948, Aug. 30
966 A413 3c blue .30 .25
a. Vert. pair, imperf. between *300.00*

CLARA BARTON ISSUE

Founder of the American Red Cross (1882) — A414

Designed by Charles R. Chickering.

1948, Sept. 7 ***Perf. 11x10½***
967 A414 3c rose pink .30 .25

POULTRY INDUSTRY CENTENNIAL ISSUE

Light Brahma Rooster — A415

1948, Sept. 9
968 A415 3c sepia .30 .25

GOLD STAR MOTHERS ISSUE

Issued to honor the mothers of deceased members of the United States armed forces.

Star and Palm Frond — A416

1948, Sept. 21 ***Perf. 10½x11***
969 A416 3c orange yellow .30 .25

FORT KEARNY ISSUE

Establishment of Fort Kearny, Neb., centenary.

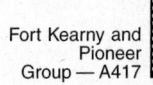

Fort Kearny and Pioneer Group — A417

1948, Sept. 22 ***Perf. 11x10½***
970 A417 3c violet .30 .25

VOLUNTEER FIREMEN ISSUE

300th anniv. of the organization of the 1st volunteer firemen in America by Peter Stuyvesant.

Peter Stuyvesant; Early and Modern Fire Engines — A418

1948, Oct. 4
971 A418 3c bright rose carmine .30 .25

INDIAN CENTENNIAL ISSUE

Centenary of the arrival in Indian Territory, later Oklahoma, of the Five Civilized Indian Tribes: Cherokee, Chickasaw, Choctaw, Muscogee and Seminole.

Map of Indian Territory & Seals of Five Tribes — A419

1948, Oct. 15
972 A419 3c dark brown .30 .25

ROUGH RIDERS ISSUE

50th anniversary of the organization of the Rough Riders of the Spanish-American War.

Statue of Capt. William O. (Bucky) O'Neill — A420

1948, Oct. 27
973 A420 3c violet brown .30 .25

JULIETTE LOW ISSUE

Low (1860-1927), founder of the Girl Scouts of America. Mrs. Low organized the 1st Girl Guides troop in 1912 at Savannah. The name was changed to Girl Scouts in 1913 and headquarters moved to New York.

Low and Girl Scout Emblem — A421

1948, Oct. 29
974 A421 3c blue green .30 .25

WILL ROGERS ISSUE

Will Rogers — A422

1948, Nov. 4 ***Perf. 10½x11***
975 A422 3c bright red violet .30 .25

Will Rogers, 1879-1935, humorist and political commentator.

FORT BLISS CENTENNIAL ISSUE

Fort Bliss and Rocket — A423

1948, Nov. 5
976 A423 3c henna brown .30 .25

MOINA MICHAEL ISSUE

Moina Michael (1870-1944), educator who originated (1918) the Flanders Field Poppy Day idea as a memorial to the war dead.

Moina Michael and Poppy Plant — A424

1948, Nov. 9 ***Perf. 11x10½***
977 A424 3c rose pink .30 .25

GETTYSBURG ADDRESS ISSUE

85th anniversary of Abraham Lincoln's address at Gettysburg, Pennsylvania.

Lincoln and Quotation from Gettysburg Address — A425

1948, Nov. 19
978 A425 3c bright blue .30 .25

AMERICAN TURNERS ISSUE

Formation of the American Turners Soc., cent.

Torch and American Turners' Emblem — A426

1948, Nov. 20 ***Perf. 10½x11***
979 A426 3c carmine .30 .25

JOEL CHANDLER HARRIS ISSUE

Joel Chandler Harris — A427

1948, Dec. 9
980 A427 3c bright red violet .30 .25

Harris (1848-1908), editor and author.

MINNESOTA TERRITORY ISSUE

Establishment of Minnesota Territory, cent.

Pioneer and Red River Oxcart — A428

1949, Mar. 3 ***Perf. 11x10½***
981 A428 3c blue green .30 .25

WASHINGTON AND LEE UNIVERSITY ISSUE

Bicentenary of Washington and Lee University.

George Washington, Robert E. Lee and University Building — A429

1949, Apr. 12
982 A429 3c ultramarine .30 .25

PUERTO RICO ELECTION ISSUE

First gubernatorial election in the Territory of Puerto Rico, Nov. 2, 1948.

Puerto Rican Farmer Holding Cogwheel and Ballot Box — A430

1949, Apr. 27
983 A430 3c green .30 .25

ANNAPOLIS TERCENTENARY ISSUE

Founding of Annapolis, Maryland, 300th anniv.

Stoddert's 1718 Map of Regions about Annapolis, Redrawn — A431

1949, May 23
984 A431 3c aquamarine .30 .25

G.A.R. ISSUE

Final encampment of the Grand Army of the Republic, Indianapolis, Aug. 28 - Sept. 1, 1949.

Union Soldier and GAR Veteran of 1949 — A432

1949, Aug. 29
985 A432 3c bright rose carmine .30 .25

EDGAR ALLAN POE ISSUE

Edgar Allan Poe (1809-1849), Poet, Story Writer and Editor — A433

1949, Oct. 7 ***Perf. 10½x11***
986 A433 3c bright red violet .30 .25

AMERICAN BANKERS ASSOCIATION ISSUE

75th anniv. of the formation of the Association.

Coin, Symbolizing Fields of Banking Service — A434

1950, Jan. 3 ***Perf. 11x10½***
987 A434 3c yellow green .30 .25

SAMUEL GOMPERS ISSUE

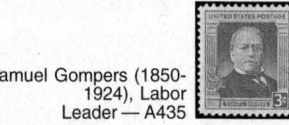

Samuel Gompers (1850-1924), Labor Leader — A435

1950, Jan. 27 ***Perf. 10½x11***
988 A435 3c bright red violet .30 .25

NATIONAL CAPITAL SESQUICENTENNIAL ISSUE

150th anniversary of the establishment of the National Capital, Washington, D.C.

Statue of Freedom on Capitol Dome A436

Executive Mansion A437

Supreme Court Building — A438

United States Capitol — A439

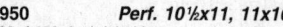

1950 ***Perf. 10½x11, 11x10½***
989 A436 3c bright blue .30 .25
990 A437 3c deep green .30 .25
991 A438 3c light violet .30 .25
992 A439 3c bright red violet .30 .25
Nos. 989-992 (4) 1.20 1.00

RAILROAD ENGINEERS ISSUE

Issued to honor the Railroad Engineers of America. Stamp portrays John Luther (Casey) Jones (1864-1900), locomotive engineer killed in train wreck near Vaughn, Miss.

"Casey" Jones and Locomotives of 1900 and 1950 — A440

1950, Apr. 29 ***Perf. 11x10½***
993 A440 3c violet brown .30 .25

KANSAS CITY, MISSOURI, CENTENARY ISSUE

Kansas City, Missouri, incorporation.

Kansas City Skyline, 1950 and Westport Landing, 1850 — A441

1950, June 3
994 A441 3c violet .30 .25

BOY SCOUTS ISSUE

Honoring the Boy Scouts of America on the occasion of the 2nd National Jamboree, Valley Forge, Pa.

Three Boys, Statue of Liberty and Scout Badge — A442

1950, June 30
995 A442 3c sepia .30 .25

INDIANA TERRITORY ISSUE

Establishment of Indiana Territory, 150th anniv.

Gov. William Henry Harrison & First Indiana Capitol, Vincennes A443

1950, July 4
996 A443 3c bright blue .30 .25

CALIFORNIA STATEHOOD ISSUE

Gold Miner, Pioneers and S.S. Oregon — A444

1950, Sept. 9
997 A444 3c yellow orange .30 .25

UNITED CONFEDERATE VETERANS FINAL REUNION ISSUE

Final reunion of the United Confederate Veterans, Norfolk, Virginia, May 30, 1951.

Confederate Soldier & United Confederate Veteran — A445

1951, May 30
998 A445 3c gray .30 .25

NEVADA CENTENNIAL ISSUE

Centenary of the settlement of Nevada.

Carson Valley, c. 1851 — A446

Designed by Charles R. Chickering.

1951, July 14
999 A446 3c light olive green .30 .25

LANDING OF CADILLAC ISSUE

250th anniversary of the landing of Antoine de la Mothe Cadillac at Detroit.

Detroit Skyline and Cadillac Landing — A447

1951, July 24
1000 A447 3c blue .30 .25

COLORADO STATEHOOD, 75th ANNIV.

Colorado Capitol and Mount of the Holy Cross — A448

1951, Aug. 1
1001 A448 3c blue violet .30 .25

AMERICAN CHEMICAL SOCIETY ISSUE

75th anniv. of the formation of the Society.

A.C.S. Emblem and Symbols of Chemistry A449

1951, Sept. 4
1002 A449 3c violet brown .30 .25

BATTLE OF BROOKLYN, 175th ANNIV.

Gen. George Washington Evacuating Army — A450

1951, Dec. 10
1003 A450 3c violet .30 .25

BETSY ROSS ISSUE

200th anniv. of the birth of Betsy Ross, maker of the first American flag.

Betsy Ross Showing Flag to Gen. George Washington, Robert Morris & George Ross — A451

1952, Jan. 2
1004 A451 3c carmine rose .30 .25

4-H CLUB ISSUE

Farm, Club Emblem, Boy and Girl — A452

1952, Jan. 15
1005 A452 3c blue green .30 .25

B. & O. RAILROAD ISSUE

125th anniv. of the granting of a charter to the Baltimore and Ohio Railroad Company by the Maryland Legislature.

Charter and Three Stages of Rail Transportation A453

1952, Feb. 28
1006 A453 3c bright blue .30 .25

A. A. A. ISSUE

50th anniversary of the formation of the American Automobile Association.

School Girls and Safety Patrolman, Automobiles of 1902 and 1952 — A454

1952, Mar. 4
1007 A454 3c deep blue .30 .25

NATO ISSUE

Signing of the North Atlantic Treaty, 3rd anniv.

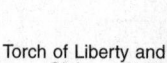

Torch of Liberty and Globe — A455

1952, Apr. 4
1008 A455 3c deep violet .30 .25

GRAND COULEE DAM ISSUE

50 years of Federal cooperation in developing the resources of rivers and streams in the West.

Spillway, Grand Coulee Dam — A456

1952, May 15
1009 A456 3c blue green .30 .25

LAFAYETTE ISSUE

175th anniversary of the arrival of Marquis de Lafayette in America.

Marquis de Lafayette, Flags, Cannon and Landing Party — A457

1952, June 13
1010 A457 3c bright blue .30 .25

MT. RUSHMORE MEMORIAL ISSUE

Dedication of the Mt. Rushmore National Memorial in the Black Hills of South Dakota, 25th anniv.

Sculptured Heads on Mt. Rushmore — A458

1952, Aug. 11 ***Perf. 10½x11***
1011 A458 3c blue green .30 .25

ENGINEERING CENTENNIAL ISSUE

American Society of Civil Engineers founding.

George Washington Bridge & Covered Bridge of 1850s — A459

1952, Sept. 6 ***Perf. 11x10½***
1012 A459 3c violet blue .30 .25

SERVICE WOMEN ISSUE

Women in the United States Armed Services.

Women of the Marine Corps, Army, Navy and Air Force — A460

1952, Sept. 11
1013 A460 3c deep blue .30 .25

GUTENBERG BIBLE ISSUE

Printing of the 1st book, the Holy Bible, from movable type, by Johann Gutenberg, 500th anniv.

Gutenberg Showing Proof to the Elector of Mainz — A461

1952, Sept. 30
1014 A461 3c violet .30 .25

NEWSPAPER BOYS ISSUE

Newspaper Boy, Torch and Group of Homes — A462

1952, Oct. 4
1015 A462 3c violet .30 .25

RED CROSS ISSUE

Globe, Sun and Cross — A463

1952, Nov. 21
1016 A463 3c dp blue & car .30 .25

NATIONAL GUARD ISSUE

National Guardsman and Amphibious Landing — A464

1953, Feb. 23
1017 A464 3c bright blue .30 .25

OHIO STATEHOOD, 150th ANNIV.

Map and Ohio State Seal — A465

1953, Mar. 2
1018 A465 3c chocolate .30 .25

WASHINGTON TERRITORY ISSUE

Organization of Washington Territory, cent.

Medallion, Pioneers and Washington Scene — A466

1953, Mar. 2
1019 A466 3c green .30 .25

LOUISIANA PURCHASE, 150th ANNIV.

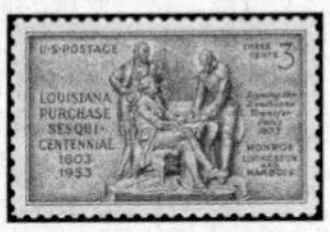

Monroe, Livingston and Barbé-Marbois A467

1953, Apr. 30
1020 A467 3c violet brown .30 .25

OPENING OF JAPAN CENTENNIAL ISSUE

Centenary of Commodore Matthew Calbraith Perry's negotiations with Japan, which opened her doors to foreign trade.

Commodore Perry and 1st Anchorage off Tokyo Bay — A468

1953, July 14
1021 A468 5c green .30 .25

AMERICAN BAR ASSOCIATION, 75th ANNIV.

Section of Frieze, Supreme Court Room — A469

1953, Aug. 24
1022 A469 3c rose violet .30 .25

SAGAMORE HILL ISSUE

Opening of Sagamore Hill, Theodore Roosevelt's home, as a national shrine.

Home of Theodore Roosevelt — A470

1953, Sept. 14
1023 A470 3c yellow green .30 .25

FUTURE FARMERS ISSUE

25th anniversary of the organization of Future Farmers of America.

Agricultural Scene and Future Farmer — A471

1953, Oct. 13
1024 A471 3c deep blue .30 .25

TRUCKING INDUSTRY ISSUE

50th anniv. of the Trucking Industry in the US.

Truck, Farm and Distant City — A472

1953, Oct. 27
1025 A472 3c violet .30 .25

GENERAL PATTON ISSUE

Honoring Gen. George S. Patton, Jr. (1885-1945), and the armored forces of the US Army.

Gen. George S. Patton, Jr., and Tank in Action — A473

1953, Nov. 11
1026 A473 3c blue violet .30 .25

NEW YORK CITY, 300th ANNIV.

Dutch Ship in New Amsterdam Harbor — A474

1953, Nov. 20
1027 A474 3c bright red violet .30 .25

GADSDEN PURCHASE ISSUE

Centenary of James Gadsden's purchase of territory from Mexico to adjust the US-Mexico boundary.

Map and Pioneer Group — A475

1953, Dec. 30
1028 A475 3c copper brown .30 .25

COLUMBIA UNIVERSITY, 200th ANNIV.

Low Memorial Library — A476

1954, Jan. 4
1029 A476 3c blue .30 .25

Wet and Dry Printings

In 1953 the Bureau of Engraving and Printing began experiments in printing on "dry" paper (moisture content 5-10 per cent). In previous "wet" printings the paper had a moisture content of 13-35 per cent.

The new process required a thicker, stiffer paper, special types of inks and greater pressure to force the paper into the recessed plates. The "dry" printings show whiter paper, a higher sheen on the surface, feel thicker and stiffer, and the designs stand out more clearly than on the "wet" printings.

Nos. 832c and 1041 (flat plate) were the first "dry" printings to be issued of flat-plate, regular-issue stamps. No. 1063 was the first rotary-press stamp to be produced entirely by "dry" printing. Nos. QE1a, QE2a and QE3a, RF26A and RW21 (all flat plate) were the first "dry" printings of back-of-the-book issue stamps.

All postage stamps have been printed by the "dry" process since the late 1950's.

See the Scott *Specialized Catalogue of United States Stamps* for listings of the wet and dry printings and for No. 1033 on Silkote paper.

LIBERTY ISSUE

Franklin A477

Washington A478

Palace of the Governors, Santa Fe — A478a 1031A

Mount Vernon A479

Thomas Jefferson A480

Bunker Hill Monument, Mass. Flag, 1776 A481

Statue of Liberty A482

Abraham Lincoln A483

The Hermitage A484

James Monroe A485

Theodore Roosevelt A486

Woodrow Wilson A487

A488

Statue of Liberty A489

The Alamo A490

Independence Hall — A491

Statue of Liberty — A491a

Benjamin Harrison A492

John Jay A493

Monticello A494

Paul Revere A495

Robert E. Lee A496

John Marshall A497

Susan B. Anthony A498

Patrick Henry A499

Alexander Hamilton — A500

ROTARY PRESS PRINTING

1954-68 ***Perf. 11x10½, 10½x11***

1030 A477 ½c red org ('55) .30 .25

1031 A478 1c dark grn .30 .25

1031A A478a 1¼c turq ('60) .30 .25

1032 A479 1½c brn car ('56) .30 .25

1033 A480 2c car rose .30 .25

1034 A481 2½c gray blue ('59) .30 .25

1035 A482 3c dp vio .30 .25

a. Booklet pane of 6, *June 30, 1954* 3.50 *1.25*

b. Horiz. pairs, imperf. btwn in #1035a with foldover (two pairs recorded in two full panes) or miscut (three pairs from pane) *5,000.*

e. Tagged ('66) .35 .25

f. Imperf., pair *3,000.*

g. Horiz. pair, imperf. between *1,000.*

No. 1057b measures about 19½x22mm; No. 1035f, about 18¾x22½mm.

1036 A483 4c red vio .30 .25

b. Booklet pane of 6 ('58) 2.75 *1.25*

c. As "b," imperf. horiz. *10,000.*

d. Horiz. pair, imperf between *4,150.*

e. Tagged ('63) .65 .40

1037 A484 4½c blue grn ('59) .30 .25

1038 A485 5c dp blue .30 .25

1039 A486 6c car ('55) .40 .25

Pair with full vert. gutter btwn. *2,750.*

b. Imperf, block of 4 (unique) *23,000.*

1040 A487 7c rose car ('56) .30 .25

a. dk rose car .30 .25

FLAT PLATE PRINTING

Size: 22.7mm high

Perf. 11

1041 A488 8c dk vio blue & car .30 .25

a. Double impression of carmine *575.00* —

ROTARY PRESS PRINTING

Size: 22.9mm high

1041B A488 8c dk vio blue & car .40 .25

c. Double impression of carmine —

GIORI PRESS PRINTING

Redrawn design

1042 A489 8c dk vio bl & car rose ('58) .30 .25

The 8c John J. Pershing stamp, formerly No. 1042A, is now included with the regular issue of 1961-66. See No. 1214.

ROTARY PRESS PRINTING

Perf. 10½x11

1043 A490 9c rose lil ('56) .30 .25

a. 9c dark rose lilac .30 .25

1044 A491 10c rose lake ('56) .30 .25

b. 10c dark rose lake .30 .25

d. Tagged 2.00 1.00

GIORI PRESS PRINTING

Perf. 11

1044A A491a 11c car & dk vio bl ('61) .30 .25

c. Tagged 3.00 1.60

Perf. 11x10½, 10½x11

1045 A492 12c red ('59) .35 .25

a. Tagged ('68) .35 .25

1046 A493 15c rose lake ('58) .60 .25

a. Tagged 1.10 .80

1047 A494 20c ultra ('56) .50 .25

a. deep bright ultra .50 .25

1048 A495 25c grn ('58) 1.00 .75

1049 A496 30c blk ('55) 1.20 .75

b. 30c intense black .80 .25

No. 1049b is from later printings and is on a harder, whiter paper than No. 1049.

1050 A497 40c brn red ('55) 1.75 .25

1051 A498 50c brt pur ('55) 1.75 .25

1052 A499 $1 purple ('55) 5.00 1.00

FLAT PLATE PRINTING

Perf. 11

1053 A500 $5 black 47.50 6.75

Nos. 1030-1053 (27) 65.25 15.00

Luminescence

During 1963 quantities of certain issues (Nos. C64a, 1213b, 1213c and 1229a) were overprinted with phosphorescent coating, "tagged," for use in testing automated facing and canceling machines. Listings for tagged varieties of stamps previously issued without tagging start with Nos. 1035b and C59a.

The entire printings of Nos. 1238, 1278, 1280-1281, 1283B, 1286-1288, 1298-1305, 1323-1340, 1342-1362, 1364, and C69-C75 and all following listings, unless otherwise noted, were tagged.

Stamps tagged with zinc orthosilicate glow yellow green. Airmail stamps with calcium silicate overprint glow orange red. Both tagging overprints are activated only by shortwave ultraviolet light.

ROTARY PRESS COIL STAMPS

Perf. 10 Vert., Horiz. (1¼c, 4½c)

1954-80

1054 A478 1c dk grn .60 .25

c. Imperf., pair — —

1054A A478a 1¼c turq ('60) .30 .25

d. Imperf., pair —

All examples of No. 1054Ad are precanceled "SEATTLE/WASH." No. 1054A with large holes exists non-precanceled as well as precanceled. The values shown are for the non-precanceled variety; precanceled stamps with large holes are quite common.

1055 A480 2c car rose .60 .25

b. Tagged ('68) .30 .25

c. Imperf. pair, (Bureau precanceled) *325.00*

d. As "b," Imperf. pair *425.00*

1056 A481 2½c gray blue ('59) .30 .25

1057 A482 3c dp vio .35 .25

b. Imperf., pair *1,250.* *800.00*

d. Tagged ('66) 1.00 .50

No. 1057b measures about 19½x22mm; No. 1035f, about 18¾x22½mm.

1058 A483 4c red vio ('58) .75 .25

a. Imperf., pair 75.00 70.00

1059 A484 4½c bl grn ('59) 1.50 1.00

1059A A495 25c grn ('65) .50 .30

b. Tagged .80 .25

d. Imperf., pair, tagged 30.00

Value for No. 1059Ad is for fine centering.

NEBRASKA TERRITORY ISSUE

Establishment of the Nebraska Territory, centenary.

Mitchell Pass, Scotts Bluff & "The Sower," by Lee Lawrie — A507

ROTARY PRESS PRINTING

1954, May 7 ***Perf. 11x10½***

1060 A507 3c violet .30 .25

KANSAS TERRITORY ISSUE

Establishment of the Kansas Territory, centenary.

Wheat Field and Pioneer Wagon Train — A508

1954, May 31

1061 A508 3c brown orange .30 .25

GEORGE EASTMAN ISSUE

George Eastman (1854-1932), Inventor & Philanthropist — A509

1954, July 12 ***Perf. 10½x11***

1062 A509 3c violet brown .30 .25

LEWIS AND CLARK EXPEDITION

150th anniv. of the Lewis and Clark expedition.

Landing of Lewis and Clark — A510

1954, July 28 ***Perf. 11x10½***

1063 A510 3c violet brown .30 .25

PENNSYLVANIA ACADEMY OF THE FINE ARTS ISSUE

150th anniversary of the founding of the Pennsylvania Academy of the Fine Arts, Philadelphia.

Charles Willson Peale in his Museum, Self-portrait — A511

1955, Jan. 15 ***Perf. 10½x11***

1064 A511 3c rose brown .30 .25

LAND GRANT COLLEGES ISSUE

Centenary of the founding of Michigan State College and Pennsylvania State University, first of the land grant institutions.

Open Book and Symbols of Subjects Taught — A512

1955, Feb. 12 ***Perf. 11x10½***

1065 A512 3c green .30 .25

ROTARY INTERNATIONAL, 50th ANNIV.

Torch, Globe and Rotary Emblem — A513

1955, Feb. 23

1066 A513 8c deep blue .30 .25

ARMED FORCES RESERVE ISSUE

Marine, Coast Guard, Army, Navy, & Air Force Personnel — A514

1955, May 21

1067 A514 3c bright red violet .30 .25

NEW HAMPSHIRE ISSUE

Sesquicentennial of the discovery of the "Old Man of the Mountains."

Great Stone Face — A515

1955, June 21 ***Perf. 10½x11***

1068 A515 3c green .30 .25

SOO LOCKS ISSUE

Centenary of the opening of the Soo Locks.

Map of Great Lakes and Two Steamers — A516

1955, June 28 ***Perf. 11x10½***

1069 A516 3c blue .30 .25

ATOMS FOR PEACE ISSUE

Issued to promote an Atoms for Peace policy.

Atomic Energy Encircling the Hemispheres A517

1955, July 28

1070 A517 3c deep blue .30 .25

FORT TICONDEROGA ISSUE

Bicentenary of Fort Ticonderoga, New York.

Map of the Fort, Ethan Allen and Artillery — A518

1955, Sept. 18

1071 A518 3c light brown .30 .25

ANDREW W. MELLON ISSUE

Andrew W. Mellon — A519

1955, Dec. 20 ***Perf. 10½x11***

1072 A519 3c rose carmine .30 .25

Mellon, U.S. Sec. of the Treasury (1921-32), financier and art collector.

BENJAMIN FRANKLIN ISSUE

250th anniv. of the birth of Benjamin Franklin.

"Franklin Taking Electricity from the Sky," by Benjamin West — A520

1956, Jan. 17

1073 A520 3c bright carmine .30 .25

BOOKER T. WASHINGTON ISSUE

Washington (1856-1915), black educator, founder and head of Tuskegee Institute in Alabama.

Log Cabin — A521

1956, Apr. 5 ***Perf. 11x10½***

1074 A521 3c deep blue .30 .25

FIFTH INTERNATIONAL PHILATELIC EXHIBITION ISSUES

FIPEX, New York City, Apr. 28 - May 6, 1956.

SOUVENIR SHEET

A522

FLAT PLATE PRINTING

1956, Apr. 28 ***Imperf.***
1075 A522 Pane of 2 1.20 1.50
a. A482 3c deep violet .75 .60
b. A488 8c dark violet blue & carmine .85 .75

No. 1075 measures 108x73mm. Nos. 1075a and 1075b measure 24x28mm.
Inscriptions printed in dark violet blue; scrolls and stars in carmine.

New York Coliseum & Columbus Monument A523

ROTARY PRESS PRINTING

1956, Apr. 30 ***Perf. 11x10½***
1076 A523 3c deep violet .30 .25

WILDLIFE CONSERVATION ISSUE

Issued to emphasize the importance of Wildlife Conservation in America.

Wild Turkey — A524

Pronghorn Antelope — A525

King Salmon — A526

1956
1077 A524 3c rose lake .30 .25
1078 A525 3c brown .30 .25
1079 A526 3c blue green .30 .25
Nos. 1077-1079 (3) .90 .75

PURE FOOD AND DRUG LAWS, 50th ANNIV.

Harvey W. Wiley — A527

1956, June 27 ***Perf. 10½x11***
1080 A527 3c dark blue green .30 .25

WHEATLAND ISSUE

President Buchanan's Home, "Wheatland," Lancaster, PA — A528

1956, Aug. 5
1081 A528 3c black brown .30 .25

LABOR DAY ISSUE

Mosaic, AFL-CIO Headquarters — A529

1956, Sept. 3 ***Perf. 10½x11***
1082 A529 3c deep blue .30 .25

NASSAU HALL ISSUE

200th anniv. of Nassau Hall, Princeton University.

Nassau Hall, Princeton, NJ — A530

1956, Sept. 22
1083 A530 3c black, *orange* .30 .25

DEVILS TOWER ISSUE

Issued to commemorate the 50th anniversary of the Federal law providing for protection of American natural antiquities. Devils Tower National Monument, Wyoming, is an outstanding example.

Devils Tower — A531

1956, Sept. 24 ***Perf. 10½x11***
1084 A531 3c violet .30 .25

CHILDREN'S ISSUE

Issued to promote friendship among the children of the world.

Children of the World — A532

1956, Dec. 15 ***Perf. 11x10½***
1085 A532 3c dark blue .30 .25

ALEXANDER HAMILTON (1755-1804)

Alexander Hamilton (1757-1804) and Federal Hall — A533

1957, Jan. 11
1086 A533 3c rose red .30 .25

POLIO ISSUE

Honoring "those who helped fight polio," and on for 20th anniv. of the Natl. Foundation for Infantile Paralysis and the March of Dimes.

Allegory — A534

1957, Jan. 15 ***Perf. 10½x11***
1087 A534 3c red lilac .30 .25

COAST AND GEODETIC SURVEY ISSUE

150th anniversary of the establishment of the Coast and Geodetic Survey.

Flag of Coast and Geodetic Survey and Ships at Sea — A535

1957, Feb. 11 ***Perf. 11x10½***
1088 A535 3c dark blue .30 .25

ARCHITECTS ISSUE

American Institute of Architects, centenary.

Corinthian Capital and Mushroom Type Head & Shaft — A536

1957, Feb. 23
1089 A536 3c red lilac .30 .25

STEEL INDUSTRY ISSUE

Centenary of the steel industry in America.

American Eagle and Pouring Ladle — A537

1957, May 22 ***Perf. 10½x11***
1090 A537 3c bright ultramarine .30 .25

INTERNATIONAL NAVAL REVIEW ISSUE

Issued to commemorate the International Naval Review and the Jamestown Festival.

Aircraft Carrier and Jamestown Festival Emblem — A538

1957, June 10 ***Perf. 11x10½***
1091 A538 3c blue green .30 .25

OKLAHOMA STATEHOOD, 50th ANNIV.

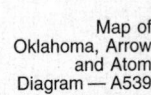

Map of Oklahoma, Arrow and Atom Diagram — A539

1957, June 14
1092 A539 3c dark blue .30 .25

SCHOOL TEACHERS ISSUE

Teacher and Pupils — A540

1957, July 1
1093 A540 3c rose lake .30 .25

FLAG ISSUE

"Old Glory" (48 Stars) — A541

GIORI PRESS PRINTING

1957, July 4 ***Perf. 11***
1094 A541 4c dark blue & deep carmine .30 .25

SHIP BUILDING ISSUE

350th anniversary of shipbuilding in America.

"Virginia of Sagadahock" and Seal of Maine — A542

ROTARY PRESS PRINTING

1957, Aug. 15 ***Perf. 10½x11***
1095 A542 3c deep violet .30 .25

CHAMPION OF LIBERTY ISSUE

Magsaysay (1907-57), Pres. of the Philippines.

Ramon Magsaysay, (1907-1957), Philippines President — A543

GIORI PRESS PRINTING

1957, Aug. 31 ***Perf. 11***
1096 A543 8c car, ultra & ocher .30 .25

For other Champion of Liberty issues, see Nos. 1110-1111, 1117-1118, 1125-1126, 1136-1137, 1147-1148, 1159-1160, 1165-1166, 1168-1169, 1174-1175.

LAFAYETTE BICENTENARY ISSUE

Marquis de Lafayette — A544

1957. Sept. 6 ***Perf. 10½x11***
1097 A544 3c rose lake .30 .25

WILDLIFE CONSERVATION ISSUE

Issued to emphasize the importance of Wildlife Conservation in America.

Whooping Cranes — A545

GIORI PRESS PRINTING

1957, Nov. 22 ***Perf. 11***
1098 A545 3c blue, ocher & green .30 .25

RELIGIOUS FREEDOM ISSUE

300th anniv. of the Flushing Remonstrance.

Bible, Hat and Quill Pen — A546

ROTARY PRESS PRINTING

1957, Dec. 27 ***Perf. 10½x11***
1099 A546 3c black .30 .25

GARDENING HORTICULTURE ISSUE

Issued to honor the garden clubs of America and in connection with the centenary of the birth of Liberty Hyde Bailey, horticulturist.

"Bountiful Earth" — A547

1958, Mar. 15
1100 A547 3c green .30 .25

BRUSSELS EXHIBITION ISSUE

Issued in honor of the opening of the Universal and International Exhibition at Brussels, April 17.

U.S. Pavilion at Brussels — A551

1958, Apr. 17 ***Perf. 11x10½***
1104 A551 3c deep claret .30 .25

JAMES MONROE ISSUE

James Monroe, by Gilbert Stuart — A552

1958, Apr. 28
1105 A552 3c purple .30 .25

MINNESOTA STATEHOOD, 100th ANNIV.

Minnesota Lakes and Pines — A553

1958, May 11
1106 A553 3c green .30 .25

GEOPHYSICAL YEAR ISSUE

International Geophysical Year, 1957-58.

Solar Disc and Hands from Michelangelo's "Creation of Adam" — A554

GIORI PRESS PRINTING

1958, May 31 ***Perf. 11***
1107 A554 3c black & red orange .30 .25

GUNSTON HALL ISSUE

Issued for the bicentenary of Gunston Hall and to honor George Mason, author of the Constitution of Virginia and the Virginia Bill of Rights.

Gunston Hall, Virginia — A555

ROTARY PRESS PRINTING

1958, June 12 ***Perf. 11x10½***
1108 A555 3c light green .30 .25

MACKINAC BRIDGE ISSUE

Dedication of Mackinac Bridge, Michigan.

Mackinac Bridge — A556

1958, June 25 ***Perf. 10½x11***
1109 A556 3c brt greenish blue .30 .25

CHAMPION OF LIBERTY ISSUE

Simon Bolívar, South American freedom fighter.

Simon Bolivar — A557

1958, July 24
1110 A557 4c olive bister .30 .25

GIORI PRESS PRINTING
Perf. 11

1111 A557 8c car, ultra & ocher .30 .25

ATLANTIC CABLE CENTENNIAL ISSUE

Centenary of the Atlantic Cable, linking the Eastern and Western hemispheres.

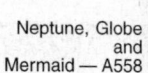

Neptune, Globe and Mermaid — A558

ROTARY PRESS PRINTING

1958, Aug. 15 ***Perf. 11x10½***
1112 A558 4c reddish purple .30 .25

LINCOLN SESQUICENTENNIAL ISSUE

Sesquicentennial of the birth of Abraham Lincoln. No. 1114 also for the centenary of the founding of Cooper Union, New York City. No. 1115 marks the centenary of the Lincoln-Douglas Debates.

Lincoln, by George Healy
A559

Lincoln, by Gutzon Borglum
A560

Abraham Lincoln and Stephen A. Douglas Debating — A561

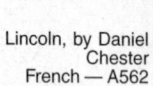

Lincoln, by Daniel Chester French — A562

1958-59 ***Perf. 10½x11***
1113 A559 1c green ('59) .30 .25
1114 A560 3c dark rose ('59) .30 .25

Perf. 11x10½

1115 A561 4c sepia .30 .25
1116 A562 4c dark blue ('59) .30 .25
Nos. 1113-1116 (4) 1.20 1.00

CHAMPION OF LIBERTY ISSUE

Lajos Kossuth, Hungarian freedom fighter.

Lajos Kossuth, (1802-1892) — A563

1958, Sept. 19 ***Perf. 10½x11***
1117 A563 4c green .30 .25

GIORI PRESS PRINTING
Perf. 11

1118 A563 8c car, ultra & ocher .30 .25

FREEDOM OF PRESS ISSUE

Honoring Journalism and freedom of the press in connection with the 50th anniv. of the 1st School of Journalism at the University of Missouri.

Early Press and Hand Holding Quill — A564

ROTARY PRESS PRINTING

1958, Sept. 22 ***Perf. 10½x11***
1119 A564 4c black .30 .25

OVERLAND MAIL ISSUE

Centenary of Overland Mail Service.

Mail Coach and Map of Southwest U.S. — A565

1958, Oct. 10 ***Perf. 11x10½***
1120 A565 4c crimson rose .30 .25

NOAH WEBSTER ISSUE

Webster (1758-1843), lexicographer and author.

Noah Webster — A566

1958, Oct. 16 ***Perf. 10½x11***
1121 A566 4c dark carmine rose .30 .25

FOREST CONSERVATION ISSUE

Issued to publicize forest conservation and the protection of natural resources and to honor Theodore Roosevelt, a leading forest conservationist, on the centenary of his birth.

Forest Scene — A567

GIORI PRESS PRINTING

1958, Oct. 27 ***Perf. 11***
1122 A567 4c green, yellow & brown .30 .25

FORT DUQUESNE ISSUE

Bicentennial of Fort Duquesne (Fort Pitt) at future site of Pittsburgh.

Occupation of Fort Duquesne — A568

ROTARY PRESS PRINTING

1958, Nov. 25 ***Perf. 11x10½***
1123 A568 4c blue .30 .25

OREGON STATEHOOD, 100th ANNIV.

Covered Wagon and Mt. Hood — A569

1959, Feb. 14
1124 A569 4c blue green .30 .25

CHAMPION OF LIBERTY ISSUE

San Martin, So. American soldier and statesman.

José de San Martin — A570

1959, Feb. 25 ***Perf. 10½x11***
1125 A570 4c blue .30 .25
a. Horiz. pair, imperf. between *900.00*

GIORI PRESS PRINTING
Perf. 11

1126 A570 8c car, ultra & ocher .30 .25

NATO ISSUE

North Atlantic Treaty Organization, 10th anniv.

NATO Emblem — A571

ROTARY PRESS PRINTING

1959, Apr. 1 ***Perf. 10½x11***
1127 A571 4c blue .30 .25

ARCTIC EXPLORATIONS ISSUE

Conquest of the Arctic by land by Rear Admiral Robert Edwin Peary in 1909 and by sea by the submarine "Nautilus" in 1958.

North Pole, Dog Sled and "Nautilus" — A572

1959, Apr. 6 ***Perf. 11x10½***
1128 A572 4c brt grnsh blue .30 .25

WORLD PEACE THROUGH WORLD TRADE ISSUE

Issued in conjunction with the 17th Congress of the International Chamber of Commerce, Washington, D.C., April 19-25.

Globe and Laurel — A573

1959, Apr. 20
1129 A573 8c rose lake .30 .25

SILVER CENTENNIAL ISSUE

Discovery of silver at the Comstock Lode, Nevada.

Henry Comstock at Mount Davidson Site — A574

1959, June 8
1130 A574 4c black .30 .25

ST. LAWRENCE SEAWAY ISSUE

Opening of the St. Lawrence Seaway.

Great Lakes, Maple Leaf and Eagle Emblems — A575

GIORI PRESS PRINTING

1959, June 26 ***Perf. 11***
1131 A575 4c red & dark blue .30 .25

See Canada No. 387.

49-STAR FLAG ISSUE

U.S. Flag, 1959 — A576

1959, July 4
1132 A576 4c ocher, dark blue & deep carmine .30 .25

SOIL CONSERVATION ISSUE

Issued as a tribute to farmers and ranchers who use soil and water conservation measures.

Modern Farm — A577

1959, Aug. 26
1133 A577 4c blue, green & ocher .30 .25

PETROLEUM INDUSTRY ISSUE

Centenary of the completion of the nation's first oil well at Titusville, Pa.

Oil Derrick — A578

ROTARY PRESS PRINTING

1959, Aug. 27 ***Perf. 10½x11***
1134 A578 4c brown .30 .25

DENTAL HEALTH ISSUE

Issued to publicize Dental Health and for the centenary of the American Dental Association.

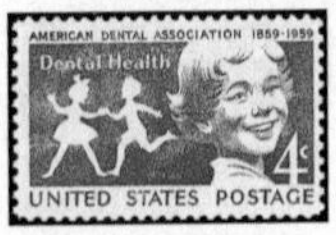

Children — A579

1959, Sept. 14 ***Perf. 11x10½***
1135 A579 4c green .30 .25

CHAMPION OF LIBERTY ISSUE

Ernst Reuter, Mayor of Berlin, 1948-53.

Ernst Reuter — A580

1959, Sept. 29 ***Perf. 10½x11***
1136 A580 4c gray .30 .25

GIORI PRESS PRINTING
Perf. 11

1137 A580 8c car, ultra & ocher .30 .25
a. Ocher missing (EP) *3,000.*
b. Ultramarine missing (EP) *3,750.*
c. Ocher & ultramarine missing (EP) *4,000.*
d. All colors missing (EP) *2,000.*

DR. EPHRAIM McDOWELL ISSUE

Honoring McDowell (1771-1830) on the 150th anniv. of the 1st successful ovarian operation in the US, performed at Danville, Ky., 1809.

Dr. Ephraim McDowell — A581

ROTARY PRESS PRINTING

1959, Dec. 3 ***Perf. 10½x11***
1138 A581 4c rose lake .30 .25
a. Vert. pair, imperf. btwn. *375.00*
b. Vert. pair, imperf. horiz. *200.00*

AMERICAN CREDO ISSUE

Issued to re-emphasize the ideals upon which America was founded and to honor those great Americans who wrote or uttered the credos.

Quotation from Washington's Farewell Address, 1796 — A582

Benjamin Franklin Quotation — A583

Thomas Jefferson Quotation — A584

Francis Scott Key Quotation — A585

Abraham Lincoln Quotation — A586

Patrick Henry Quotation — A587

Designed by Frank Conley.

GIORI PRESS PRINTING

Plates of 200 subjects in four panes of 50.

1960-61 ***Perf. 11***
1139 A582 4c dk vio bl & car .30 .25
1140 A583 4c ol bister & grn .30 .25
1141 A584 4c gray & vermilion .30 .25
1142 A585 4c car & dark blue .30 .25
1143 A586 4c magenta & green .30 .25
1144 A587 4c green & brown .30 .25
Nos. 1139-1144 (6) 1.80 1.50

Issued: 1/20; 3/31; 5/8; 9/14; 11/19; 1/11/61.

BOY SCOUT JUBILEE ISSUE

50th anniv. of the Boy Scouts of America.

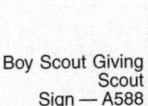

Boy Scout Giving Scout Sign — A588

1960, Feb. 8
1145 A588 4c red, dark blue & dark bister .30 .25

OLYMPIC WINTER GAMES ISSUE

Opening of the 8th Olympic Winter Games, Squaw Valley, Feb. 18-29, 1960.

Olympic Rings and Snowflake — A589

ROTARY PRESS PRINTING

1960, Feb. 18 ***Perf. 10½x11***
1146 A589 4c dull blue .30 .25

CHAMPION OF LIBERTY ISSUE

Issued to honor Thomas G. Masaryk, founder and president of Czechoslovakia (1918-35), on the 110th anniversary of his birth.

Thomas G. Masaryk — A590

1960, Mar. 7
1147 A590 4c blue .30 .25
a. Vert. pair, imperf. between *1,900.*

GIORI PRESS PRINTING
Perf. 11

1148 A590 8c car, ultra & ocher .30 .25
a. Horiz. pair, imperf. between —

WORLD REFUGEE YEAR ISSUE

World Refugee Year, July 1, 1959-June 30, 1960.

Refugee Family Walking Toward New Life — A591

ROTARY PRESS PRINTING

1960, Apr. 7 ***Perf. 11x10½***
1149 A591 4c gray black .30 .25

WATER CONSERVATION ISSUE

Issued to stress the importance of water conservation and to commemorate the 7th Watershed Congress, Washington, D.C.

Water, from Watershed to Consumer A592

GIORI PRESS PRINTING

1960, Apr. 18 ***Perf. 11***
1150 A592 4c dk bl, brn org & grn .30 .25
a. Brown orange missing (EP) *2,750.*

SEATO ISSUE

South-East Asia Treaty Organization and for the SEATO Conf., Washington, D.C., May 31-June 3.

SEATO Emblem — A593

ROTARY PRESS PRINTING

1960, May 31 ***Perf. 10½x11***
1151 A593 4c blue .30 .25
a. Vertical pair, imperf. between *125.00*

AMERICAN WOMAN ISSUE

Issued to pay tribute to American women and their accomplishments in civic affairs, education, arts and industry.

Mother and Daughter — A594

1960, June 2 ***Perf. 11x10½***
1152 A594 4c deep violet .30 .25

50-STAR FLAG ISSUE

U.S. Flag, 1960 — A595

GIORI PRESS PRINTING

1960, July 4 ***Perf. 11***
1153 A595 4c dark blue & red .30 .25

PONY EXPRESS CENTENNIAL ISSUE

Pony Express Rider — A596

ROTARY PRESS PRINTING

1960, July 19 ***Perf. 11x10½***
1154 A596 4c sepia .30 .25

EMPLOY THE HANDICAPPED ISSUE

Promoting the employment of the physically handicapped and publicizing the 8th World Congress of the Intl. Soc. for the Welfare of Cripples, New York City.

Man in Wheelchair Operating Drill Press — A597

1960, Aug. 28 ***Perf. 10½x11***
1155 A597 4c dark blue .30 .25

WORLD FORESTRY CONGRESS ISSUE

5th World Forestry Cong., Seattle, Wash., Aug. 29-Sept. 10.

5th World Forestry Congress Seal — A598

1960, Aug. 29
1156 A598 4c green .30 .25

MEXICAN INDEPENDENCE, 150th ANNIV.

A599

GIORI PRESS PRINTING

1960, Sept. 16 ***Perf. 11***
1157 A599 4c green & rose red .30 .25

See Mexico No. 910.

US-JAPAN TREATY ISSUE

Centenary of the United States-Japan Treaty of Amity and Commerce.

A600

1960, Sept. 28
1158 A600 4c blue & pink .30 .25

CHAMPION OF LIBERTY ISSUE

Jan Paderewski, Polish statesman and musician.

Ignacy Jan Paderewski — A601

ROTARY PRESS PRINTING

1960, Oct. 8 ***Perf. 10½x11***
1159 A601 4c blue .30 .25

GIORI PRESS PRINTING
Perf. 11

1160 A601 8c car, ultra & ocher .30 .25

SENATOR TAFT MEMORIAL ISSUE

Senator Robert A. Taft (1889-1953) of Ohio.

Robert A. Taft — A602

ROTARY PRESS PRINTING

1960, Oct. 10 *Perf. 10½x11*
1161 A602 4c dull violet .30 .25

WHEELS OF FREEDOM ISSUE

Issued to honor the automotive industry and in connection with the National Automobile Show, Detroit, Oct. 15-23.

Globe and Steering Wheel with Tractor, Car and Truck — A603

1960, Oct. 15 *Perf. 11x10½*
1162 A603 4c dark blue .30 .25

BOYS' CLUBS OF AMERICA ISSUE

Boys' Clubs of America movement, centenary.

Profile of a Boy — A604

GIORI PRESS PRINTING

1960, Oct. 18 *Perf. 11*
1163 A604 4c indigo, slate & rose red .30 .25

FIRST AUTOMATED POST OFFICE IN THE US ISSUE

Publicizing the opening of the 1st automated post office in the US at Providence, R.I.

Architect's Sketch of New Post Office, Providence, RI — A605

1960, Oct. 20
1164 A605 4c dark blue & carmine .30 .25
a. Red missing (PS) 250.00

CHAMPION OF LIBERTY ISSUE

Baron Karl Gustaf Emil Mannerheim (1867-1951), Marshal and President of Finland.

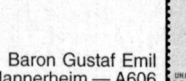

Baron Gustaf Emil Mannerheim — A606

ROTARY PRESS PRINTING

1960, Oct. 26 *Perf. 10½x11*
1165 A606 4c blue .30 .25

GIORI PRESS PRINTING

Plates of 288 subjects in four panes of 72 each.

Perf. 11

1166 A606 8c car, ultra & ocher .30 .25

CAMP FIRE GIRLS ISSUE

50th anniv. of the Camp Fire Girls' movement and in connection with the Golden Jubilee Convention celebration of the Camp Fire Girls.

Camp Fire Girls Emblem — A607

GIORI PRESS PRINTING

1960, Nov. 1 *Perf. 11*
1167 A607 4c dark blue & bright red .30 .25

CHAMPION OF LIBERTY ISSUE

Giuseppe Garibaldi (1807-1882), Italian patriot and freedom fighter.

Giuseppe Garibaldi (1807-1882) — A608

ROTARY PRESS PRINTING

1960, Nov. 2 *Perf. 10½x11*
1168 A608 4c green .30 .25

GIORI PRESS PRINTING

Perf. 11

1169 A608 8c car, ultra & ocher .30 .25

SENATOR GEORGE MEMORIAL ISSUE

Walter F. George (1878-1957) of Georgia.

Walter F. George (1878-1957) — A609

ROTARY PRESS PRINTING

1960, Nov. 5 *Perf. 10½x11*
1170 A609 4c dull violet .30 .25

ANDREW CARNEGIE ISSUE

Carnegie (1835-1919), industrialist & philanthropist.

Andrew Carnegie — A610

1960, Nov. 25
1171 A610 4c deep claret .30 .25

JOHN FOSTER DULLES MEMORIAL ISSUE

Dulles (1888-1959), Secretary of State (1953-59).

John Foster Dulles — A611

1960, Dec. 6
1172 A611 4c dull violet .30 .25

ECHO I — COMMUNICATIONS FOR PEACE ISSUE

World's 1st communications satellite, Echo I, placed in orbit by the Natl. Aeronautics and Space Admin., Aug. 12, 1960.

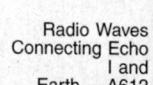

Radio Waves Connecting Echo I and Earth — A612

1960, Dec. 15 *Perf. 11x10½*
1173 A612 4c deep violet .30 .25

CHAMPION OF LIBERTY ISSUE

Mohandas K. Gandhi, leader in India's struggle for independence.

Mahatma Gandhi — A613

1961, Jan. 26 *Perf. 10½x11*
1174 A613 4c red orange .30 .25

GIORI PRESS PRINTING

Perf. 11

1175 A613 8c car, ultra & ocher .30 .25

RANGE CONSERVATION ISSUE

Issued to stress the importance of range conservation and to commemorate the meeting of the American Society of Range Management. "The Trail Boss" from a drawing by Charles M. Russell is the Society's emblem.

The Trail Boss and Modern Range — A614

1961, Feb. 2 *Perf. 11*
1176 A614 4c blue, slate & brown orange .30 .25

HORACE GREELEY ISSUE

Horace Greeley (1811-1872), Publisher and Editor — A615

ROTARY PRESS PRINTING

1961, Feb. 3 *Perf. 10½x11*
1177 A615 4c dull violet .30 .25

CIVIL WAR CENTENNIAL ISSUE

Centenaries of the firing on Fort Sumter (No. 1178), the Battle of Shiloh (No. 1179), the Battle of Gettysburg (No. 1180), the Battle of the Wilderness (No. 1181) and the surrender at Appomattox (No. 1182).

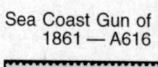

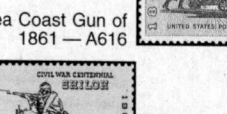

Sea Coast Gun of 1861 — A616

Rifleman at Shiloh, 1862 — A617

Blue and Gray at Gettysburg, 1863 — A618

Battle of the Wilderness, 1864 A619

Appomattox, 1865 A620

1961-65 *Perf. 11x10½*
1178 A616 4c light green .30 .25
1179 A617 4c black, *peach blossom* .30 .25

GIORI PRESS PRINTING

Plates of 200 subjects in four panes of 50.

Perf. 11

1180 A618 5c gray & blue .30 .25
1181 A619 5c dk red & black .30 .25
1182 A620 5c Prus. blue & blk .30 .25
a. Horiz. pair, imperf. vert. 3,500.
Nos. 1178-1182 (5) 1.50 1.25

Issued: #1178-1182, 4/12; 4/7/62; 7/1/63; 5/5/64; 4/9/65.

KANSAS STATEHOOD, 100th ANNIV.

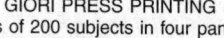

Sunflower, Pioneer Couple and Stockade — A621

1961, May 10 *Perf. 11*
1183 A621 4c brown, dark red & green, *yellow* .30 .25

SENATOR NORRIS ISSUE

Norris and Norris Dam, Tenn. — A622

ROTARY PRESS PRINTING

1961, July 11 *Perf. 11x10½*
1184 A622 4c blue green .30 .25

NAVAL AVIATION, 50th ANNIV.

Navy's First Plane (Curtiss A-1 of 1911) and Naval Air Wings — A623

1961, Aug. 20
1185 A623 4c blue .30 .25

WORKMEN'S COMPENSATION ISSUE

50th anniv. of the 1st successful Workmen's Compensation Law, enacted by the Wisconsin legislature.

Scales of Justice, Factory, Worker and Family — A624

1961, Sept. 4 *Perf. 10½x11*
1186 A624 4c ultramarine, *grayish* .30 .25

FREDERIC REMINGTON ISSUE

Remington (1861-1909), artist of the West. The design is from an oil painting, Amon Carter Museum of Western Art, Fort Worth, Texas.

Remington's "Smoke Signal" — A625

GIORI PRESS PRINTING

1961, Oct. 4 *Perf. 11*
1187 A625 4c multicolored .30 .25

REPUBLIC OF CHINA ISSUE

50th anniversary of the Republic of China.

Sun Yat-sen — A626

ROTARY PRESS PRINTING

1961, Oct. 10 *Perf. 10½x11*
1188 A626 4c blue .35 .25

NAISMITH — BASKETBALL ISSUE

Honoring basketball and James Naismith (1861-1939), Canada-born director of physical education, who invented the game in 1891 at Y.M.C.A. College, Springfield, Mass.

Basketball — A627

1961, Nov. 6
1189 A627 4c brown .30 .25

NURSING ISSUE

Issued to honor the nursing profession.

Student Nurse Lighting Candle — A628

GIORI PRESS PRINTING

1961, Dec. 28 *Perf. 11*
1190 A628 4c bl, grn, org & blk .30 .25

NEW MEXICO STATEHOOD, 50th ANNIV.

Shiprock — A629

1962, Jan. 6
1191 A629 4c lt. blue, maroon & bister .30 .25

ARIZONA STATEHOOD, 50th ANNIV.

Giant Saguaro Cactus — A630

1962, Feb. 14
1192 A630 4c carmine, violet blue & green .30 .25

PROJECT MERCURY ISSUE

1st orbital flight of a US astronaut, Lt. Col. John H. Glenn, Jr., Feb. 20, 1962.

"Friendship 7" Capsule and Globe — A631

1962, Feb. 20
1193 A631 4c dark blue & yellow .30 .25

Imperfs. are printers waste.

MALARIA ERADICATION ISSUE

World Health Organization's drive to eradicate malaria.

Great Seal of U.S. and WHO Symbol — A632

1962, Mar. 30
1194 A632 4c blue & bister .30 .25

CHARLES EVANS HUGHES ISSUE

Hughes (1862-1948), Governor of New York, Chief Justice of the US.

Charles Evans Hughes — A633

ROTARY PRESS PRINTING

1962, Apr. 11 *Perf. 10½x11*
1195 A633 4c black, *buff* .30 .25

SEATTLE WORLD'S FAIR ISSUE

"Century 21" International Exposition, Seattle, Wash., Apr. 21-Oct. 21.

Space Needle and Monorail — A634

GIORI PRESS PRINTING

1962, Apr. 25 *Perf. 11*
1196 A634 4c red & dark blue .30 .25

LOUISIANA STATEHOOD, 150th ANNIV.

Riverboat on the Mississippi A635

1962, Apr. 30
1197 A635 4c blue, dark slate green & red .30 .25

HOMESTEAD ACT, CENTENARY

Sod Hut and Settlers — A636

ROTARY PRESS PRINTING

1962, May 20 *Perf. 11x10½*
1198 A636 4c slate .30 .25

GIRL SCOUTS ISSUE

50th anniversary of the Girl Scouts of America.

Senior Girl Scout & Flag — A637

1962, July 24
1199 A637 4c rose red .30 .25

SENATOR BRIEN McMAHON ISSUE

McMahon (1903-52) of Connecticut had a role in opening the way to peaceful uses of atomic energy through the Atomic Energy Act establishing the Atomic Energy Commission.

Brien McMahon & Atomic Diagram — A638

1962, July 28
1200 A638 4c purple .30 .25

APPRENTICESHIP ISSUE

National Apprenticeship Program and 25th anniv. of the National Apprenticeship Act.

Machinist Handing Micrometer to Apprentice A639

1962, Aug. 31
1201 A639 4c blk, *yellow bister* .30 .25

SAM RAYBURN ISSUE

Sam Rayburn and Capitol — A640

GIORI PRESS PRINTING

1962, Sept. 16 *Perf. 11*
1202 A640 4c dark blue & red brown .30 .25

DAG HAMMARSKJOLD ISSUE

UN Headquarters & Dag Hammarskjold, U.N. Sec. Gen., 1953-61 — A641

1962, Oct. 23
1203 A641 4c blk, brn & yel .30 .25

No. 1203a can only be collected on a cover postmarked before Nov. 16, 1962 (the date the Hammarskjold Special Printing, No. 1204, was issued), or tied on dated piece (unique used pair). Covers are known machine postmarked Cuyahoga Falls, Ohio, Nov. 14, 1962, and notarized in the lower left corner by George W. Schwartz, Notary Public. Other covers are reported postmarked Oct. 26, 1962, Brooklyn, NY, Vanderveer Station. Unaddressed, uncacheted first day covers also exist, but are believed by experts to have been backdated using examples of No. 1204.

An unused pane of 50 was signed in the selvage by ten well-known philatelists attesting to its genuineness. This pane was donated to the American Philatelic Society in 1987.

An unknown number of "first day covers" exist bearing Artmaster cachets. These were contrived using examples of No. 1204.

Hammarskjold Special Printing

1962, Nov. 16
1204 A641 4c black, brown & yel (yellow inverted) .30 .25

No. 1204 was issued following discovery of No. 1203 with yellow background inverted.

CHRISTMAS ISSUE

Wreath and Candles — A642

1962, Nov. 1
1205 A642 4c green & red .30 .25

HIGHER EDUCATION ISSUE

Higher education's role in American cultural and industrial development and the centenary celebrations of the signing of the law creating land-grant colleges and universities.

Map of U.S. and Lamp — A643

1962, Nov. 14
1206 A643 4c blue green & black .30 .25

WINSLOW HOMER ISSUE

Homer (1836-1910), painter, showing his oil, "Breezing Up," which hangs in the National Gallery, Washington, D.C.

"Breezing Up" — A644

1962, Dec. 15
1207 A644 4c multicolored .30 .25
a. Horiz. pair, imperf. btwn. and at right *7,000.*

FLAG ISSUE

Flag over White House — A645

1963-66
1208 A645 5c blue & red .30 .25
a. Tagged ('68) .30 .25
b. Horiz. pair, imperf. between, tagged *2,250.*

Beware of pairs with faint blind perfs between offered as No. 1208b.

REGULAR ISSUE

Andrew Jackson A646

George Washington A650

John J. Pershing A651

ROTARY PRESS PRINTING

1961-66 *Perf. 11x10½*
1209 A646 1c green ('63) .30 .25
a. Tagged ('66) .30 .25
1213 A650 5c dk gray blue .30 .25
a. Booklet pane of 5 + label 2.00 *2.00*
b. Tagged ('63) .50 .25
c. As "a," tagged, ('63) 2.00 *1.50*
d. Horiz. pair, imperf. between, in #1213a with foldover or miscut *1,750.*
1214 A651 8c brown ('61) .30 .25

See Luminescence note after No. 1053.

Three different messages are found on the label in No. 1213a, and two messages on that of No. 1213c.

No. 1213d resulted from a paper foldover after perforating and before cutting into panes.

Unused catalogue numbers were left vacant for additional denominations.

COIL STAMPS
(Rotary Press)

1962-66 *Perf. 10 Vertically*
1225 A646 1c green ('63) .40 .25
a. Tagged ('66) .40 .25
1229 A650 5c dk blue gray 1.50 .25
a. Tagged ('63) 2.50 .25
b. Imperf., pair *300.00*

CAROLINA CHARTER ISSUE

Tercentenary of the Carolina Charter granting to 8 Englishmen lands extending coast-to-coast roughly along the present border of Virginia to the north and Florida to the south. Original charter on display at Raleigh.

First Page of Carolina Charter — A662

GIORI PRESS PRINTING

1963, Apr. 6 *Perf. 11*

1230 A662 5c dark carmine & brown .30 .25

FOOD FOR PEACE-FREEDOM FROM HUNGER ISSUE

American "Food for Peace" program and the "Freedom from Hunger" campaign of the FAO.

Wheat — A663

1963, June 4

1231 A663 5c green, buff & red .30 .25

WEST VIRGINIA STATEHOOD, 100th ANNIV.

Map of West Virginia & State Capitol — A664

1963, June 20

1232 A664 5c green, red & black .30 .25

EMANCIPATION PROCLAMATION ISSUE

Centenary of Lincoln's Emancipation Proclamation freeing about 3,000,000 slaves in 10 southern states.

Severed Chain — A665

1963, Aug. 16

1233 A665 5c dark blue, black & red .30 .25

ALLIANCE FOR PROGRESS ISSUE

2nd anniv. of the Alliance for Progress, which aims to stimulate economic growth and raise living standards in Latin America.

Alliance Emblem — A666

1963, Aug. 17

1234 A666 5c ultramarine & green .30 .25

CORDELL HULL ISSUE

Hull (1871-1955), Secretary of State (1933-44).

Cordell Hull (1871-1955), Sec. of State (1933-44) — A667

ROTARY PRESS PRINTING

1963, Oct. 5 *Perf. 10½x11*

1235 A667 5c blue green .30 .25

ELEANOR ROOSEVELT ISSUE

Mrs. Franklin D. Roosevelt (1884-1962).

Mrs. Franklin D. Roosevelt (1884-1962) A668

1963, Oct. 11 *Perf. 11x10½*

1236 A668 5c bright purple .30 .25

SCIENCE ISSUE

Honoring the sciences and in connection with the centenary of the Natl. Academy of Science.

"The Universe" — A669

GIORI PRESS PRINTING

1963, Oct. 14 *Perf. 11*

1237 A669 5c Prussian blue & black .30 .25

CITY MAIL DELIVERY ISSUE

Centenary of free city mail delivery.

Letter Carrier, 1863 — A670

1963, Oct. 26 **Tagged**

1238 A670 5c gray, dark blue & red .30 .25
- *b.* Dark blue missing (PS) —

RED CROSS CENTENARY ISSUE

A671

1963, Oct. 29

1239 A671 5c bluish black & red .30 .25

CHRISTMAS ISSUE

Natl. Christmas Tree & White House — A672

1963, Nov. 1

1240 A672 5c dk bl, bluish blk & red .30 .25
- *a.* Tagged .65 .50
- *b.* Horiz. pair, imperf between 7,500.
- *c.* Red missing (PS) 500.00

JOHN JAMES AUDUBON ISSUE

Audubon (1785-1851), ornithologist and artist. The birds pictured are actually Collie's magpie jays. See No. C71.

Columbia Jays — A673

1963, Dec. 7

1241 A673 5c dk blue & multi .30 .25

SAM HOUSTON ISSUE

Houston (1793-1863), soldier, president of Texas, US senator.

Sam Houston — A674

ROTARY PRESS PRINTING

1964, Jan. 10 *Perf. 10½x11*

1242 A674 5c black .30 .25

CHARLES M. RUSSELL ISSUE

Russell (1864-1926), painter. The design is from a painting, Thomas Gilcrease Institute of American History and Art, Tulsa, Okla.

"Jerked Down" — A675

GIORI PRESS PRINTING

1964, Mar. 19 *Perf. 11*

1243 A675 5c multicolored .30 .25

NEW YORK WORLD'S FAIR ISSUE

New York World's Fair, 1964-65.

Mall with Unisphere & "Rocket Thrower," by Donald De Lue — A676

ROTARY PRESS PRINTING

1964, Apr. 22 *Perf. 11x10½*

1244 A676 5c blue green .30 .25
- *a.* All color omitted —

On No. 1244a, a clear albino impression of the design is present.

JOHN MUIR ISSUE

Muir (1838-1914), naturalist and conservationist.

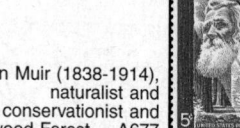

John Muir (1838-1914), naturalist and conservationist and Redwood Forest — A677

GIORI PRESS PRINTING

1964, Apr. 29 *Perf. 11*

1245 A677 5c brn, grn, yel grn & ol .30 .25

KENNEDY MEMORIAL ISSUE

President John Fitzgerald Kennedy, (1917-1963).

Pres. John F. Kennedy (1917-63) and Eternal Flame — A678

ROTARY PRESS PRINTING

1964, May 29 *Perf. 11x10½*

1246 A678 5c blue gray .30 .25

NEW JERSEY TERCENTENARY ISSUE

300th anniv. of English colonization of New Jersey. The design is from a mural by Howard Pyle in the Essex County Courthouse, Newark, N.J.

Philip Carteret Landing at Elizabethtown & Map of New Jersey — A679

1964, June 15 *Perf. 10½x11*

1247 A679 5c brt ultramarine .30 .25

NEVADA STATEHOOD, 100th ANNIV.

Virginia City and Map of Nevada — A680

GIORI PRESS PRINTING

1964, July 22 *Perf. 11*

1248 A680 5c red, yellow & blue .30 .25

REGISTER AND VOTE ISSUE

Campaign to draw more voters to the polls.

Flag — A681

1964, Aug. 1

1249 A681 5c dark blue & red .30 .25

SHAKESPEARE ISSUE

William Shakespeare (1564-1616).

William Shakespeare — A682

ROTARY PRESS PRINTING

1964, Aug. 14 *Perf. 10½x11*

1250 A682 5c black brown, *tan* .30 .25

DOCTORS MAYO ISSUE

Dr. William James Mayo (1861-1939) and his brother, Dr. Charles Horace Mayo (1865-1939), surgeons who founded the Mayo Foundation for Medical Education and Research in affiliation with the Univ. of Minnesota at Rochester. Heads on stamp are from a sculpture by James Earle Fraser.

Drs. William and Charles Mayo — A683

1964, Sept. 11

1251 A683 5c green .30 .25

AMERICAN MUSIC ISSUE

50th anniv. of the founding of the American Society of Composers, Authors and Publishers (ASCAP).

Lute, Horn, Laurel, Oak and Music Score — A684

GIORI PRESS PRINTING

1964, Oct. 15 *Perf. 11*

Gray Paper with Blue Threads

1252 A684 5c red, black & blue .30 .25
- *a.* Blue omitted 450.00
- *b.* Blue missing (PS) 500.00

Beware of examples offered as No. 1252a which have traces of blue.

HOMEMAKERS ISSUE

Honoring American women as homemakers and for the 50th anniv. of the passage of the Smith-Lever Act. By providing economic experts under an extension service of the U.S. Dept. of Agriculture, this legislation helped to improve homelife.

Farm Scene Sampler — A685

Engraved (Giori Press); Background Lithographed

1964, Oct. 26

1253 A685 5c multicolored .30 .25

CHRISTMAS ISSUE

Holly A686

Mistletoe A687

Poinsettia A688

Sprig of Conifer A689

GIORI PRESS PRINTING

1964, Nov. 9

1254	A686 5c green, car & black	.30	.25
a.	Tagged	.75	.50
b.	Printed on gummed side	*1,850.*	
c.	All color missing (FO)	2,000.	
1255	A687 5c car, green & black	.30	.25
a.	Tagged	.75	.50
1256	A688 5c car, green & black	.30	.25
a.	Tagged	.75	.50
1257	A689 5c black, green & car	.30	.25
a.	Tagged	.75	.50
b.	Block of 4, #1254-1257	1.00	1.00
c.	Block of 4, tagged	3.00	2.25

Tagged stamps issued Nov. 10.

No. 1254b resulted from a paper foldover before printing and perforating.

No. 1254c is unique and is in a block of four with the other three stamps missing parts of the designs.

VERRAZANO-NARROWS BRIDGE ISSUE

Opening of the Verrazano-Narrows Bridge connecting Staten Island and Brooklyn.

Verrazano-Narrows Bridge and Map of NY Bay — A690

ROTARY PRESS PRINTING

1964, Nov. 21 ***Perf. 10½x11***

1258 A690 5c blue green .30 .25

FINE ARTS ISSUE

Abstract Design by Stuart Davis — A691

GIORI PRESS PRINTING

1964, Dec. 2 ***Perf. 11***

1259 A691 5c ultra., black & dull red .30 .25

AMATEUR RADIO ISSUE

Issued to honor the radio amateurs on the 50th anniversary of the American Radio Relay League.

Radio Waves and Dial — A692

ROTARY PRESS PRINTING

1964, Dec. 15 ***Perf. 10½x11***

1260 A692 5c red lilac .30 .25

BATTLE OF NEW ORLEANS ISSUE

Battle of New Orleans, Chalmette Plantation, Jan. 8-18, 1815, established 150 years of peace and friendship between the US and Great Britain.

General Andrew Jackson and Sesquicentennial Medal — A693

GIORI PRESS PRINTING

1965, Jan. 8 ***Perf. 11***

1261 A693 5c deep carmine, violet blue & gray .30 .25

PHYSICAL FITNESS-SOKOL ISSUE

Publicizing the importance of physical fitness and for the centenary of the founding of the Sokol (athletic) organization in America.

Discus Thrower — A694

1965, Feb. 15

1262 A694 5c maroon & black .30 .25

CRUSADE AGAINST CANCER ISSUE

Issued to publicize the "Crusade Against Cancer" and to stress the importance of early diagnosis.

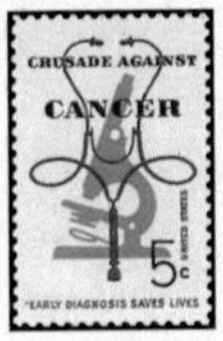

Microscope and Stethoscope — A695

1965, Apr. 1

1263 A695 5c black, purple & red orange .30 .25

CHURCHILL MEMORIAL ISSUE

Sir Winston Spencer Churchill (1874-1965), British statesman and World War II leader.

Winston Churchill — A696

ROTARY PRESS PRINTING

1965, May 13 ***Perf. 10½x11***

1264 A696 5c black .30 .25

MAGNA CARTA ISSUE

750th anniversary of the Magna Carta, the basis of English and American common law.

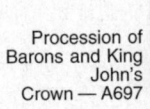

Procession of Barons and King John's Crown — A697

GIORI PRESS PRINTING

1965, June 15 ***Perf. 11***

1265 A697 5c black, yellow ocher & red lilac .30 .25

INTERNATIONAL COOPERATION YEAR

ICY, 1965, and 20th anniv. of the UN.

ICY Emblem — A698

1965, June 26

1266 A698 5c dull blue & black .30 .25

SALVATION ARMY ISSUE

Centenary of the founding of the Salvation Army by William Booth in London.

A699

1965, July 2

1267 A699 5c red, black & dark blue .30 .25

DANTE ISSUE

Dante Alighieri (1265-1321), Italian poet.

A700

ROTARY PRESS PRINTING

1965, July 17 ***Perf. 10½x11***

1268 A700 5c maroon, *tan* .30 .25

HERBERT HOOVER ISSUE

President Herbert Clark Hoover, (1874-1964).

A701

1965, Aug. 10

1269 A701 5c rose red .30 .25

ROBERT FULTON ISSUE

Fulton (1765-1815), inventor of the 1st commercial steamship.

Robert Fulton & Clermont — A702

GIORI PRESS PRINTING

1965, Aug. 19 ***Perf. 11***

1270 A702 5c black & blue .30 .25

FLORIDA SETTLEMENT ISSUE

400th anniv. of the settlement of Florida, and the 1st permanent European settlement in the continental US, St. Augustine, Fla.

Spanish Explorer, Royal Flag of Spain and Ships — A703

1965, Aug. 28

1271 A703 5c red, yel & blk .30 .25

a. Yellow omitted *200.00*

See Spain No. 1312.

TRAFFIC SAFETY ISSUE

Issued to publicize traffic safety and the prevention of traffic accidents.

Traffic Signal — A704

1965, Sept. 3

1272 A704 5c emer, red & blk .30 .25

JOHN SINGLETON COPLEY ISSUE

Copley (1738-1815), painter. The portrait of the artist's daughter is from the oil painting "The Copley Family," which hangs in the National Gallery of Art, Washington, D.C.

Elizabeth Clarke Copley — A705

1965, Sept. 17

1273 A705 5c blk, brn & olive .30 .25

INTERNATIONAL TELECOMMUNICATION UNION, 100th ANNIV.

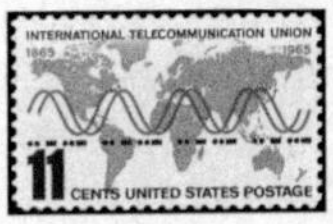

Gall Projection World Map & Radio Sine Wave — A706

1965, Oct. 6

1274 A706 11c blk, car & bister .35 .25

ADLAI STEVENSON ISSUE

Adlai Ewing Stevenson (1900-65), governor of Illinois, US ambassador to the UN.

Adlai E. Stevenson — A707

LITHOGRAPHED, ENGRAVED (Giori)

1965, Oct. 23

1275 A707 5c pale bl, blk, car & vio bl .30 .25

CHRISTMAS ISSUE

Angel with Trumpet — A708

GIORI PRESS PRINTING

1965, Nov. 2

1276 A708 5c carmine, dark olive green & bister .30 .25

a. Tagged .75 .25

PROMINENT AMERICANS ISSUE

Thomas Jefferson A710

Albert Gallatin A711

Frank Lloyd Wright & Guggenheim Museum A712

Francis Parkman A713

Lincoln A714

Washington A715

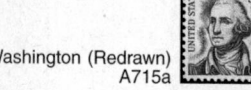

Washington (Redrawn) A715a

Franklin D. Roosevelt A716

Albert Einstein A717

Andrew Jackson — A718

Henry Ford, 1909 Model T — A718a

John F. Kennedy A719

Oliver Wendell Holmes A720

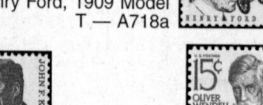

Type 3 — A720a

George Catlett Marshall A721

Frederick Douglass A722

John Dewey A723

Thomas Paine A724

Lucy Stone A725

Eugene O'Neill A726

John Bassett Moore — A727

ROTARY PRESS PRINTING

1965-78 ***Perf. 11x10½, 10½x11***

1278 A710 1c green, tagged .30 .25
a. Booklet pane of 8 1.00 .75
b. Bklt. pane of 4+2 labels .75 .60
c. Untagged (Bureau precanceled) 6.25 1.25
1279 A711 1¼c light green .30 .25
1280 A712 2c dk blue gray, tagged .30 .25
a. Bklt. pane of 5 + label 1.25 .80
b. Untagged (Bureau precanceled) 2.00 .40
c. Bklt. pane of 6 1.00 .75
1281 A713 3c violet, tagged .30 .25
a. Untagged (Bureau precanceled) 3.00 .75
1282 A714 4c black .30 .25
a. Tagged .30 .25
1283 A715 5c blue .30 .25
a. Tagged .30 .25
1283B A715a 5c blue, tagged .30 .25
d. Untagged (Bureau precanceled) 12.50 1.00

No. 1283B is redrawn; highlights, shadows softened.

1284 A716 6c gray brn .30 .25
a. Tagged .30 .25
b. Booklet pane of 8 1.50 1.00
c. Bklt. pane of 5+ label 1.40 1.00
d. Horiz. pair, imperf. between 2,250.
1285 A717 8c violet .30 .25
a. Tagged .30 .25
1286 A718 10c lilac, tagged .30 .25
b. Untagged (Bureau precanceled) 50.00 1.75
1286A 718a 12c black, tagged .30 .25
c. Untagged (Bureau precanceled) 4.75 1.00
1287 A719 13c brn, tagged .30 .25
a. Untagged (Bureau precanceled) 6.00 1.00
1288 A720 15c mag, type I, tagged .30 .25
a. Untagged (Bureau precanceled) .75 .75
d. Type II .55 .25

Imperforates exist from printer's waste.
Values for No. 1288a are for the bars-only precancel. Also exists with city precancels, and worth more thus.

Perf. 10 on 2 or 3 Sides

1288B A720a 15c mag, type III .35 .25
c. Booklet pane of 8 2.80 1.75
e. As "c," vert. imperf. between 1,500.

No. 1288B issued in booklets only. All stamps have one or two straight edges. Plates made from redrawn die.

Perf. 11x10½, 10½x11

1289 A721 20c deep olive .40 .25
a. Tagged .40 .25
b. black olive .50 .25
c. As "a," double impression 500.00
d. As "b," tagging omitted —
1290 A722 25c rose lake .55 .25
a. Tagged .45 .25
b. 25c magenta 25.00 —

Shades of No. 1290 rose lake exist that tend toward magenta, but are not. Competent identification is important for No. 1290b.

1291 A723 30c red lilac .65 .25
a. Tagged .50 .25
1292 A724 40c blue black .80 .25
a. Tagged .75 .25
1293 A725 50c rose mag 1.00 .25
a. Tagged .80 .25
1294 A726 $1 dull purple 2.25 .25
a. Tagged 1.75 .25
b. $1 black violet 200.00 350.00
1295 A727 $5 gray black 10.00 2.25
a. Tagged 8.50 2.00
Nos. 1278-1295 (21) 19.90 7.25

Issued (without tagging) — 1965: 4c, 11/19.
1966: 5c, 2/22; 6c, 1/29; 8c, 3/14; $5, 12/3.
1967: 1¼c, 1/30; 20c, 10/24; 25c, 2/14; $1, 10/16.
1968: 30c, 10/21; 40c, 1/29; 50c, 8/13.
Dates for tagged: 1965: 4c, 12/1.
1966: 2c, 6/8; 5c, 2/23; 6c, 12/29; 8c, 7/6.
1967: 3c, 9/16; #1283B, 11/17; #1284b, 12/28; 10c, 3/15; 13c, 5/29.
1968: 1c, #1284c, 1/12; #1280a, 1/8; 12c, 7/30; 15c, 3/8.
1973: 20c, 25c, 30c, 40c, 50c, $1, $5, 4/3.
1978: No. 1288B, 6/14.

COIL STAMPS

Perf. 10 Horizontally

1966-81 **Tagged**

1297 A713 3c violet .30 .25
a. Imperf., pair 22.50
b. Untagged (Bureau precanceled) .40 .25
c. As "b," imperf. pair 8.00 —
1298 A716 6c gray brn .30 .25
a. Imperf., pair 1,500.

Franklin D. Roosevelt — A727a

Perf. 10 Vertically

1299 A710 1c green .30 .25
a. Untagged (Bureau precanceled) 8.00 1.75
b. Imperf., pair 22.50 —
1303 A714 4c black .30 .25
a. Untagged (Bureau precanceled) 8.75 .75
b. Imperf., pair 400.00
1304 A715 5c blue .30 .25
a. Untagged (Bureau precanceled) 6.50 .65
b. Imperf., pair 110.00
e. As "a," imperf., pair 250.00
f. Tagging omitted (not Bureau precanceled) — —

No. 1304b is valued in the grade of fine.
No. 1304e is precanceled Mount Pleasant, Iowa. Also exists from Chicago, Illinois; value $1,500 for pair.

1304C A715a 5c blue .30 .25
d. Imperf., pair 375.00
1305 A727a 6c gray brn .30 .25
a. Imperf., pair 55.00
b. Untagged (Bureau precanceled) 20.00 1.00
m. Pair, imperf. between 250.00
1305E A720 15c mag, type I .30 .25
f. Untagged (Bureau precanceled) 32.50 —
g. Imperf., pair, type I 20.00
h. Pair, imperf. between 125.00
i. Type II 1.50 .25
j. Imperf., pair, type II 55.00
1305C A726 $1 dull pur 3.25 .40
d. Imperf., pair 1,250.
Nos. 1297-1305C (9) 5.65 2.40

Issued: 1c, 1/12/68; 3c, 11/4/75; 4c, 5/28/66; #1304, 9/8/66; 6c, #1298, 12/28/67; #1305, 2/28/68;
$1, 1/12/73; 15c, 6/14/78.

MIGRATORY BIRD TREATY ISSUE

Migratory Birds over Canada-U.S. Border — A728

GIORI PRESS PRINTING

1966, Mar. 16 ***Perf. 11***
1306 A728 5c blk, crim & dk blue .30 .25

HUMANE TREATMENT OF ANIMALS ISSUE

Issued to promote humane treatment of all animals and for the centenary of the American Society for the Prevention of Cruelty to Animals.

Mongrel — A729

LITHOGRAPHED, ENGRAVED (Giori)

1966, Apr. 9
1307 A729 5c orange brown & black .30 .25

INDIANA STATEHOOD, 150th ANNIV.

Sesquicentennial Seal — A730

GIORI PRESS PRINTING

1966, Apr. 16
1308 A730 5c ocher, brn & vio blue .30 .25

AMERICAN CIRCUS ISSUE

Issued to honor the American Circus on the centenary of the birth of John Ringling.

Clown — A731

1966, May 2
1309 A731 5c multicolored .30 .25

SIXTH INTERNATIONAL PHILATELIC EXHIBITION ISSUES

Sixth International Philatelic Exhibition (SIPEX), Washington, D.C., May 21-30.

Stamped Cover — A732

LITHOGRAPHED, ENGRAVED (Giori)

1966
1310 A732 5c multicolored .30 .25

Souvenir Sheet

A733

Imperf

1311 A733 5c multicolored .30 .25
No. 1311 measures 108x74mm.

BILL OF RIGHTS, 175th ANNIV.

"Freedom" Checking "Tyranny" — A734

GIORI PRESS PRINTING

1966, July 1 ***Perf. 11***
1312 A734 5c carmine, dark & light blue .30 .25

POLISH MILLENNIUM ISSUE

Adoption of Christianity in Poland, 1000th anniv.

Polish Eagle and Cross — A735

ROTARY PRESS PRINTING

1966, July 30 ***Perf. 10½x11***
1313 A735 5c red .30 .25

Tagging Extended

During 1966, experimental use of tagged stamps was extended to the Cincinnati Postal Region covering offices in Indiana, Kentucky and Ohio. To supply these offices about 12 percent of the following nine issues (Nos. 1314-1322) were tagged.

NATIONAL PARK SERVICE ISSUE

50th anniv. of the Natl. Park Service of the Interior Dept. The design "Parkscape U.S.A." identifies Natl. Park Service facilities.

National Park Service Emblem — A736

LITHOGRAPHED, ENGRAVED (Giori)

1966, Aug. 25 *Perf. 11*

1314 A736 5c yellow, black & green .30 .25
  a. Tagged .35 .35

MARINE CORPS RESERVE ISSUE

US Marine Corps Reserve founding, 50th anniv.

A737

1966, Aug. 29

1315 A737 5c black, bister, red & ultra .30 .25
  a. Tagged .40 .25
  b. Black & bister (engraved) missing (EP) 16,000.

GENERAL FEDERATION OF WOMEN'S CLUBS ISSUE

75 years of service by the General Federation of Women's Clubs.

Women of 1890 and 1966 — A738

GIORI PRESS PRINTING

1966, Sept. 12

1316 A738 5c black, pink & blue .30 .25
  a. Tagged .40 .25

AMERICAN FOLKLORE ISSUE
Johnny Appleseed

Issued to honor Johnny Appleseed (John Chapman 1774-1845), who wandered over 100,000 square miles planting apple trees, and who gave away and sold seedlings to Midwest pioneers.

Johnny Appleseed — A739

1966, Sept. 24

1317 A739 5c green, red & black .30 .25
  a. Tagged .40 .25

BEAUTIFICATION OF AMERICA ISSUE

Issued to publicize President Johnson's "Plant for a more beautiful America" campaign.

Jefferson Memorial — A740

1966, Oct. 5

1318 A740 5c emerald, pink & black .30 .25
  a. Tagged .40 .25

Compare with No. 4716c.

GREAT RIVER ROAD ISSUE

Issued to publicize the 5,600-mile Great River Road connecting New Orleans with Kenora, Ontario, and following the Mississippi most of the way.

Central U.S. Map With Great River Road — A741

LITHOGRAPHED, ENGRAVED (Giori)

1966, Oct. 21

1319 A741 5c vermilion, yellow, blue & green .30 .25
  a. Tagged .45 .25

SAVINGS BOND-SERVICEMEN ISSUE

25th anniv. of US Savings Bonds, and honoring American servicemen.

Statue of Liberty & "Old Glory" — A742

1966, Oct. 26

1320 A742 5c red, dk bl, lt bl & blk .30 .25
  a. Tagged .40 .25
  b. Red, dark blue & black missing (EP) 3,750.
  c. Dark blue (engr.) missing (EP) 5,000.

CHRISTMAS ISSUE

Madonna and Child — A743

Modeled after "Madonna and Child with Angels," by the Flemish artist Hans Memling (c.1430-1494), Mellon Collection, National Gallery of Art, Washington, D.C.

1966, Nov. 1

1321 A743 5c multicolored .30 .25
  a. Tagged .40 .25

MARY CASSATT ISSUE

Cassatt (1844-1926), painter. The painting "The Boating Party" is in the Natl. Gallery of Art, Washington, D.C.

"The Boating Party" — A744

GIORI PRESS PRINTING

1966, Nov. 17

1322 A744 5c multicolored .30 .25
  a. Tagged .40 .25

Cassatt (1844-1926), painter. The original painting is in the Natl. Gallery of Art, Washington, DC.

NATIONAL GRANGE ISSUE

Centenary of the founding of the National Grange, American farmers' organization.

Grange Poster, 1870 — A745

1967, Apr. 17

1323 A745 5c org, yel, brn, grn & blk .30 .25

Phosphor Tagging

From No. 1323 onward, all postage issues are tagged, unless otherwise noted.

Tagging Omitted

Inadvertent omissions of tagging occurred on Nos. 1238, 1278, 1281, 1298 and 1305. In addition many tagged issues from 1967 on exist with tagging unintentionally omitted. These errors are listed in the *Scott Specialized Catalogue of United States Stamps and Covers.*

CANADA CENTENARY ISSUE

Centenary of Canada's emergence as a nation.

Canadian Landscape A746

1967, May 25

1324 A746 5c lt bl, dp grn, ultra, olive & blk .30 .25

ERIE CANAL ISSUE

150th anniversary of the Erie Canal ground-breaking ceremony at Rome, N.Y. The canal links Lake Erie and New York City.

Stern of Early Canal Boat — A747

LITHOGRAPHED, ENGRAVED (Giori)

1967, July 4

1325 A747 5c ultra, grnsh blue, blk & crim .30 .25

"SEARCH FOR PEACE" — LIONS ISSUE

Issued to publicize the search for peace. "Search for Peace" was the theme of an essay contest for young men and women sponsored by Lions International on its 50th anniversary.

Peace Dove — A748

GIORI PRESS PRINTING

1967, July 5

Gray Paper with Blue Threads

1326 A748 5c blue, red & black .30 .25

HENRY DAVID THOREAU ISSUE

Henry David Thoreau (1817-1862), Writer — A749

1967, July 12

1327 A749 5c carmine, black & blue green .30 .25
  b. Carmine missing (PS) 700.00

NEBRASKA STATEHOOD, 100th ANNIV.

Hereford Steer and Corn — A750

LITHOGRAPHED, ENGRAVED (Giori)

1967, July 29

1328 A750 5c dark red brown, lemon & yellow .30 .25

VOICE OF AMERICA ISSUE

25th anniv. of the radio branch of the United States Information Agency (USIA).

Radio Transmission Tower and Waves — A751

1967, Aug. 1

1329 A751 5c red, blue, black & carmine .30 .25

AMERICAN FOLKLORE ISSUE

Davy Crockett (1786-1836), frontiersman, hunter, and congressman from Tennessee who died at the Alamo.

Davy Crockett & Scrub Pines — A752

1967, Aug. 17

1330 A752 5c green, black, & yellow .30 .25
  a. Vertical pair, imperf. between 7,500.
  b. Green (engr.) missing (FO) —
  c. Black & green (engr.) missing (FO) —

A foldover on a pane of No. 1330 resulted in one example each of Nos. 1330b-1330c. Part of the colors appear on the back of the selvage and one freak stamp. An engraved black-and-green-only impression appears on the gummed side of one almost-complete "stamp."

ACCOMPLISHMENTS IN SPACE ISSUE

US accomplishments in space. Printed with continuous design in horizontal rows of 5. In the left panes the astronaut stamp is 1st, 3rd and 5th, the spaceship 2nd and 4th. This arrangement is reversed in the right panes.

Space-Walking Astronaut A753

Gemini 4 Capsule and Earth — A754

1967, Sept. 29

1331 A753 5c multicolored .55 .25
1332 A754 5c multicolored .55 .25
  b. Pair, #1331-1332 1.25 1.25

URBAN PLANNING ISSUE

Publicizing the importance of Urban Planning in connection with the Intl. Conf. of the American Institute of Planners, Washington, D.C., Oct. 1-6.

View of Model City — A755

1967, Oct. 2

1333 A755 5c dark blue, light blue & black .30 .25

FINNISH INDEPENDENCE, 50th ANNIV.

Finnish Coat of Arms — A756

ENGRAVED (Giori)

1967, Oct. 6

1334 A756 5c blue .30 .25

THOMAS EAKINS ISSUE

Eakins (1844-1916), painter and sculptor. The painting is in the Natl. Gallery of Art, Washington, D.C.

"The Biglin Brothers Racing" (Sculling on Schuylkill River, Philadelphia) A757

Printed by Photogravure & Color Co., Moonachie, N.J.

PHOTOGRAVURE

1967, Nov. 2 ***Perf. 12***

1335 A757 5c gold & multicolored .30 .25

CHRISTMAS ISSUE

Madonna and Child, by Hans Memling — A758

LITHOGRAPHED, ENGRAVED (Giori)

1967, Nov. 6 ***Perf. 11***

1336 A758 5c multicolored .30 .25

See note on painting above No. 1321.

MISSISSIPPI STATEHOOD, 150th ANNIV.

Magnolia — A759

GIORI PRESS PRINTING

1967, Dec. 11

1337 A759 5c brt grnsh bl, grn & red brn .30 .25

FLAG ISSUE

Flag and White House — A760

1968, Jan. 24

Size: 19x22mm

1338 A760 6c dk bl, red & grn .30 .25
- *k.* Vert. pair, imperf. btwn. *250.00* *150.00*
- *s.* Red missing (FO) —
- *u.* Vert. pair, imperf horiz. *275.00*
- *v.* All color omitted —
- *w.* Green missing (FO) —

No. 1338s is unique.

Beware of regumming on No. 1338u. Most examples have had the gum washed off to make it difficult or impossible to detect blind perfs. Check carefully for blind perfs. Value is for pair with original gum.

On No. 1338v, an albino impression of the engraved plate is present.

COIL STAMP

MULTICOLOR HUCK PRESS

1969, May 30 ***Perf. 10 Vertically***

Size: 18¼x21mm

1338A A760 6c dk bl, red & grn .30 .25
- *b.* Imperf., pair *350.00*

MULTICOLOR HUCK PRESS

1970-71 ***Perf. 11x10½***

Size: 18¼x21mm

1338D A760 6c dk bl, red & grn .30 .25
- *e.* Horiz. pair, imperf. between *115.00*

1338F A760 8c dk bl, red & slate gren ('71) .30 .25
- *i.* Imperf., vert. pair 35.00
- *j.* Horiz. pair, imperf. between 45.00
- *p.* Slate green omitted *350.00*
- *t.* Horiz. pair, imperf. vertically —

Issued: #1338D, 8/7/70

COIL STAMP

MULTICOLOR HUCK PRESS

1971, May 10 ***Perf. 10 Vertically***

Size: 18¼x21mm

1338G A760 8c dk bl, red & slate grn .30 .25
- *h.* Imperf., pair *45.00*

ILLINOIS STATEHOOD, 150th ANNIV.

Farm House & Fields of Ripening Grain — A761

LITHOGRAPHED, ENGRAVED (Giori)

1968, Feb. 12 ***Perf. 11***

1339 A761 6c dk blue, blue, red & ocher .30 .25

HEMISFAIR '68 ISSUE

HemisFair '68 exhibition, San Antonio, Texas, Apr. 6-Oct. 6, for the 250th anniv. of San Antonio.

Map of North & South America — A762

1968, Mar. 30

1340 A762 6c blue, rose red & white .30 .25
- *a.* White omitted *650.00*

AIRLIFT ISSUE

Eagle Holding Pennant — A763

1968, Apr. 4 **Untagged**

1341 A763 $1 sepia, dk. blue, ocher & brown red 2.00 1.25

Issued to pay for airlift of parcels from and to U.S. ports to servicemen overseas and in Alaska, Hawaii and P.R. Valid for all regular postage.

On Apr. 26, 1969, the POD ruled that henceforth No. 1341 "may be used toward paying the postage or fees for special services on airmail articles."

"SUPPORT OUR YOUTH" — ELKS ISSUE

Support Our Youth program, and honoring the Benevolent and Protective Order of Elks, which extended its youth service program in observance of its centennial year.

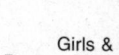

Girls & Boys — A764

1968, May 1 **Tagged**

1342 A764 6c ultramarine & orange red .30 .25

LAW AND ORDER ISSUE

Publicizing the policeman as protector and friend and to encourage respect for law and order.

Policeman and Small Boy — A765

GIORI PRESS PRINTING

1968, May 17

1343 A765 6c chalky blue, black & red .30 .25

REGISTER AND VOTE ISSUE

Campaign to draw more voters to the polls. The weather vane is from an old house in the Russian Hill section of San Francisco, Cal.

Eagle Weather Vane — A766

LITHOGRAPHED, ENGRAVED (Giori)

1968, June 27

1344 A766 6c black, yellow & orange .30 .25

HISTORIC FLAG SERIES

Flags carried by American colonists and by citizens of the new United States. Printed se-tenant in vertical columns of 10. The flag sequence on the 2 upper panes is as listed. On the 2 lower panes the sequence is reversed with the Navy Jack in the 1st row and the Fort Moultrie flag in the 10th.

Ft. Moultrie, 1776 — A767

Ft. McHenry, 1795-1818 A768

Washington's Cruisers, 1775 — A769

Bennington, 1777 — A770

Rhode Island, 1775 — A771

First Stars and Stripes, 1777 — A772

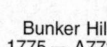

Bunker Hill, 1775 — A773

Grand Union, 1776 — A774

Philadelphia Light Horse, 1775 — A775

First Navy Jack, 1775 — A776

ENGR. (Giori) (#1345-1348, 1350); ENGR. & LITHO. (#1349, 1351-1354)

1968, July 4

1345 A767 6c dark blue .40 .25

1346 A768 6c dark blue & red .40 .25

1347 A769 6c dark blue & olive green .30 .25

1348 A770 6c dark blue & red .30 .25

1349 A771 6c dark blue, yellow & red .30 .25

1350 A772 6c dark blue & red .30 .25

1351 A773 6c dark blue, olive green & red .30 .25

1352 A774 6c dark blue & red .30 .25

1353 A775 6c dark blue, yellow & red .30 .25

1354 A776 6c dark blue, red & yellow .30 .25
- *a.* Strip of ten, #1345-1354 3.25 *3.25*
- *b.* #1345b-1354b, any single, tagging omitted *65.00*
- *c.* As "a," imperf *4,500.*

WALT DISNEY ISSUE

Walt Disney (1901-1966), cartoonist, film producer and creator of Mickey Mouse.

Disney and Children of the World — A777

Printed by Achrovure Division of Union-Camp Corp., Englewood, N.J.

PHOTOGRAVURE

1968, Sept. 11 ***Perf. 12***

1355 A777 6c multicolored .40 .25
- *a.* Ocher omitted ("Walt Disney," "6c," etc.) *300.00* —
- *b.* Vert. pair, imperf. horiz. *575.00*
- *c.* Imperf., pair *425.00*
- *d.* Black omitted *1,750.*
- *e.* Horiz. pair, imperf. between *5,000.*
- *f.* Blue omitted *1,500.*

FATHER MARQUETTE ISSUE

Father Jacques Marquette (1637-1675), French Jesuit missionary, who together with Louis Jolliet explored the Mississippi River and its tributaries.

Father Marquette and Louis Jolliet Exploring the Mississippi A778

LITHOGRAPHED, ENGRAVED (Giori)

1968, Sept. 20 ***Perf. 11***

1356 A778 6c black, apple green & orange brown .30 .25

AMERICAN FOLKLORE ISSUE

Daniel Boone (1734-1820), frontiersman and trapper.

Pennsylvania Rifle, Powder Horn, Tomahawk Pipe & Knife — A779

LITHOGRAPHED, ENGRAVED (Giori)

1968, Sept. 26

1357 A779 6c yel, dp yel, mar & blk .30 .25

ARKANSAS RIVER NAVIGATION ISSUE

Opening of the Arkansas River to commercial navigation.

Ship's Wheel, Power Transmission Tower & Barge — A780

1968, Oct. 1

1358 A780 6c bright blue, dark blue & black .30 .25

LEIF ERIKSON ISSUE

Leif Erikson, 11th century Norse explorer, called the 1st European to set foot on the American continent, at a place he called Vinland. The statue by the American sculptor A. Stirling Calder is in Reykjavik, Iceland.

Leif Erikson, by Stirling Calder — A781

1968, Oct. 9

1359 A781 6c light gray brown & black brown .30 .25

The luminescent element is in the light gray brown ink of the background. The engraved parts were printed on a rotary currency press.

CHEROKEE STRIP ISSUE

75th anniversary of the opening of the Cherokee Strip to settlers, Sept. 16, 1893.

Homesteaders Racing to Cherokee Strip — A782

ROTARY PRESS PRINTING

1968, Oct. 15 ***Perf. 11x10½***

1360 A782 6c brown .30 .25

JOHN TRUMBULL ISSUE

Trumbull (1756-1843), painter. The stamp shows Lt. Thomas Grosvenor and his attendant Peter Salem. The painting hangs at Yale University.

Detail from "The Battle of Bunker's Hill" — A783

LITHOGRAPHED, ENGRAVED (Giori)

1968, Oct. 18 ***Perf. 11***

1361 A783 6c multicolored .30 .25
b. Black (engr.) missing (FO) *11,000.* —

WATERFOWL CONSERVATION ISSUE

Wood Ducks — A784

1968, Oct. 24

1362 A784 6c blk & multi .30 .25
a. Vertical pair, imperf. between *250.00* —
b. Red & dark blue omitted *350.00*
c. Red omitted *1,750.*

Dangerous fakes exist of Nos. 1362b and 1362c. Authentication by experts is required.

CHRISTMAS ISSUE

"The Annunciation" by the 15th century Flemish painter Jan van Eyck is in the National Gallery of Art, Washington, D.C.

Gabriel, from van Eyck's Annunciation — A785

ENGRAVED (Multicolor Huck press)

1968, Nov. 1

1363 A785 6c multicolored .30 .25
a. Untagged .30 .25
b. Imperf., pair, tagged *140.00*
c. Light yellow omitted *60.00* —
d. Imperf., pair, untagged *200.00*

AMERICAN INDIAN ISSUE

Honoring the American Indian and to celebrate the opening of the Natl. Portrait Gallery, Washington, D.C. Chief Joseph (Indian name, Thunder Traveling over the Mountains), a leader of the Nez Percé, was born in eastern Oregon about 1840 and died at the Colville Reservation in Washington State in 1904.

Chief Joseph, by Cyrenius Hall — A786

LITHOGRAPHED, ENGRAVED (Giori)

1968, Nov. 4

1364 A786 6c black & multi .30 .25

BEAUTIFICATION OF AMERICA ISSUE

Publicizing the Natural Beauty Campaign for more beautiful cities, parks, highways and streets. In the left panes Nos. 1365 and 1367 appear in 1st, 3rd and 5th place, Nos. 1366 and 1368 in 2nd and 4th place. This arrangement is reversed in the right panes.

Capitol, Azaleas and Tulips — A787

Washington Monument, Potomac River and Daffodils — A788

Poppies and Lupines along Highway — A789

Blooming Crab Apples along Street — A790

1969, Jan. 16 **Tagged**

1365 A787 6c multicolored .30 .25
1366 A788 6c multicolored .30 .25
1367 A789 6c multicolored .30 .25
1368 A790 6c multicolored .30 .25
a. Block of 4, #1365-1368 1.00 *1.25*

Compare with Nos. 4716a, 4716b, 4716d, 4716e.

AMERICAN LEGION, 50th ANNIV.

Eagle from Great Seal of U.S. — A791

1969, Mar. 15

1369 A791 6c red, blue & black .30 .25

AMERICAN FOLKLORE ISSUE

Grandma Moses (Anna Mary Robertson Moses, 1860-1961), primitive painter of American life.

July Fourth, by Grandma Moses — A792

1969, May 1

1370 A792 6c multicolored .30 .25
a. Horizontal pair, imperf. between *140.00* —
b. Engraved black ("6c U.S. Postage") & Prus. blue ("Grandma Moses") omitted *400.00*

Beware of pairs with blind perfs. being offered as No. 1370a.

No. 1370b often comes with mottled or disturbed gum. Such stamps sell for about two-thirds as much as examples with perfect gum.

APOLLO 8 ISSUE

Apollo 8 mission, which 1st put men into orbit around the moon, Dec. 21-27, 1968. The astronauts were: Col. Frank Borman, Capt. James Lovell and Maj. William Anders.

Moon Surface and Earth — A793

LITHOGRAPHED, ENGRAVED (Giori)

1969, May 5

1371 A793 6c black, blue & ocher .30 .25

Imperfs. exist from printer's waste.

W.C. HANDY ISSUE

Handy (1873-1958), jazz musician and composer.

W. C. Handy (1873-1958), Jazz Musician and Composer — A794

LITHOGRAPHED, ENGRAVED (Giori)

1969, May 17

1372 A794 6c violet, deep lilac & blue .30 .25

CALIFORNIA SETTLEMENT, 200th ANNIV.

Carmel Mission Belfry — A795

1969, July 16

1373 A795 6c orange, red, black & light blue .30 .25
b. Red (engr.) missing (CM) *400.00*

JOHN WESLEY POWELL ISSUE

Powell (1834-1902), geologist who explored the Green and Colorado Rivers 1869-75, and ethnologist.

Powell Exploring Colorado River — A796

1969, Aug. 1

1374 A796 6c black, ocher & light blue .30 .25

ALABAMA STATEHOOD, 150th ANNIV.

Camellia & Yellow-shafted Flicker — A797

1969, Aug. 2

1375 A797 6c mag, rose red, yel, dk, grn & brn .30 .25

BOTANICAL CONGRESS ISSUE

11th Intl. Botanical Cong., Seattle, Wash., Aug. 24-Sept. 2. In left panes Nos. 1376 and 1378 appear in 1st, 3rd and 5th place; Nos. 1377 and 1379 in 2nd and 4th place. This arrangement is reversed in right panes.

Douglas Fir (Northwest) A798

Lady's-slipper (Northeast) A799

Ocotillo (Southwest) A800

Franklinia (Southeast) A801

1969, Aug. 23

1376 A798 6c multicolored .35 .25
1377 A799 6c multicolored .35 .25
1378 A800 6c multicolored .35 .25
1379 A801 6c multicolored .35 .25
a. Block of 4, #1376-1379 1.40 *1.75*

DARTMOUTH COLLEGE CASE ISSUE

150th anniv. of the Dartmouth College Case, which Daniel Webster argued before the Supreme Court, reasserting the sanctity of contracts.

Daniel Webster & Dartmouth Hall — A802

ROTARY PRESS PRINTING

1969, Sept. 22 ***Perf. 10½x11***

1380 A802 6c green .30 .25

PROFESSIONAL BASEBALL, 100th ANNIV.

Batter — A803

LITHOGRAPHED, ENGRAVED (Giori)

1969, Sept. 24 ***Perf. 11***

1381 A803 6c yellow, red, black & green .45 .25
- *a.* Black omitted ("1869-1969, United States, 6c, Professional Baseball") *500.00*
- *c.* Double impression of black (engr.) *5,750.*

INTERCOLLEGIATE FOOTBALL, 100th ANNIV.

Football Player & Coach — A804

1969, Sept. 26

1382 A804 6c red & green .30 .25
- *b.* Vert. pair, imperf horiz. *5,750.*
- *c.* Double impression *2,500.*

The engraved parts were printed on a rotary currency press.

No. 1382b is unique.

Two examples of No. 1382c are recorded, with the double impression on the left part of the left stamps within a lower left plate block of 4. Value given is for the plate block.

DWIGHT D. EISENHOWER ISSUE

Dwight D. Eisenhower — A805

Designed by Robert J. Jones; photograph by Bernie Noble.

GIORI PRESS PRINTING

1969, Oct. 14

1383 A805 6c blue, black & red .30 .25
- *b.* Blue ("U.S. 6c Postage") missing (PS) *600.00*

CHRISTMAS ISSUE

The painting, painted about 1870 by an unknown primitive artist, is the property of the N.Y. State Historical Association, Cooperstown, N.Y.

Winter Sunday in Norway, Maine — A806

ENGRAVED (Multicolor Huck)

1969, Nov. 3 ***Perf. 11x10½***

1384 A806 6c dark green & multicolored .30 .25
- Precancel .60 .25
- *b.* Imperf., pair *700.00*
- *c.* Light green omitted *30.00*
- *d.* Light green, red & yellow omitted *600.00* —
- *e.* Yellow omitted *1,250.*
- *g.* Red & yellow omitted *2,250.*
- *h.* Light green and yellow omitted *500.00*
- *i.* Light green and red omitted —
- *j.* Vert. pair, top stamp Baltimore precancel, bottom stamp precancel missing (FO) —
- *k.* Baltimore precancel printed on gum side *175.00*
- *l.* Baltimore precancel, vert. pair, one stamp missing precancel, other stamp with precancel printed inverted on reverse (FO) *500.00*
- *m.* Inverted Baltimore precancel *225.00*
- *n.* Baltimore precancel printed inverted on reverse (FO) *150.00*
- *p.* Double impression of New Haven precancel —
- *q.* Inverted Memphis precancel *100.00*
- *t.* Inverted Atlanta precancel *500.00*

The precancel value applies to the least expensive of experimental precancels printed locally in four cities, on tagged stamps, with the names between lines 4½mm apart: in black or green, "ATLANTA, GA" and in green only "BALTIMORE, MD," "MEMPHIS, TN" and "NEW HAVEN, CT." They were sold freely to the public and could be used on any class of mail at all post offices during the experimental program and thereafter.

Most examples of No. 1384c show orange where the offset green was. Value is for this variety. Examples without orange sell for more.

On No. 1384i, almost all of the yellow is also omitted. Do not confuse with No. 1384d.

HOPE FOR CRIPPLED ISSUE

Issued to encourage the rehabilitation of crippled children and adults and to honor the National Society for Crippled Children and Adults (Easter Seal Society) on its 50th anniversary.

Cured Child — A807

LITHOGRAPHED, ENGRAVED (Giori)

1969, Nov. 20 ***Perf. 11***

1385 A807 6c multicolored .30 .25

WILLIAM M. HARNETT ISSUE

Harnett (1848-1892), painter. The painting hangs in the Museum of Fine Arts, Boston.

"Old Models" — A808

1969, Dec. 3

1386 A808 6c multicolored .30 .25
- *a.* Red (engr.) missing (CM) —

NATURAL HISTORY ISSUE

Centenary of the American Museum of Natural History, New York City. Nos. 1387-1388 alternate in 1st row, Nos. 1389-1390 in 2nd row. This arrangement is repeated throughout the pane.

American Bald Eagle A809

African Elephant Herd — A810

Tlingit Chief in Haida Ceremonial Canoe A811

Brontosaurus, Stegosaurus & Allosaurus — A812

1970, May 6

1387 A809 6c multicolored .30 .25
1388 A810 6c multicolored .30 .25
1389 A811 6c multicolored .30 .25
1390 A812 6c multicolored .30 .25
- *a.* Block of 4, #1387-1390 1.00 *1.00*

MAINE STATEHOOD, 150th ANNIV.

The painting hangs in the Metropolitan Museum of Art, New York City.

Lighthouse at Two Lights, Maine — A813

1970, July 9 **Tagged** ***Perf. 11***

1391 A813 6c black & multi .30 .25

WILDLIFE CONSERVATION ISSUE

American Buffalo — A814

ROTARY PRESS PRINTING

1970, July 20 ***Perf. 11x10½***

1392 A814 6c black, *light brown* .30 .25

REGULAR ISSUE
Dwight David Eisenhower

Dot between "R" and "U" A815

No dot between "R" and "U" — A815a

Benjamin Franklin A816

USPS Emblem A817

Fiorello H. LaGuardia A817a

Ernest Taylor Pyle — A818

Dr. Elizabeth Blackwell A818a

Amadeo P. Giannini A818b

ROTARY PRESS PRINTING

1970-74

1393 A815 6c dk blue gray .30 .25
- *a.* Booklet pane of 8 2.00 2.00
- *b.* Booklet pane of 5 + label 1.40 1.40
- *c.* Untagged (Bureau precanceled) 12.75 3.00

Perf. 10½x11

1393D A816 7c bright blue ('73) .30 .25
- *e.* Untagged (Bureau precanceled) 4.25 1.00

GIORI PRESS PRINTING
Perf. 11

1394 A815a 8c blk, red & bl gray ('71) .30 .25
- *b.* Red missing (PS) *150.00*
- *c.* Red missing (FO) *1,250.*
- *d.* Red and blue gray missing (PS) —
- *e.* Red and blue gray missing (FO or preprinting paper crease) *1,000.*
- *f.* All colors and tagging missing (FO) *1,000.*
- *g.* Printed on gum side, tagged *1,000.*

No. 1394f must be collected se-tenant with No. 1394c, 1394e, or with a partially printed No. 1394.

ROTARY PRESS PRINTING
Perf. 11x10½ on 2 or 3 Sides

1395 A815 8c deep claret ('71) .30 .25
- *a.* Booklet pane of 8 2.00 2.00
- *b.* Booklet pane of 6 1.50 1.50
- *c.* Booklet pane of 4 +2 ('72) 1.65 1.10
- *d.* Booklet pane of 7 + label ('72) 1.90 1.90
- *e.* Vert. pair, imperf. between, in #1395a or 1395d with foldover *750.00*

No. 1395 was issued only in booklets.

At least 4 pairs of No. 1395e are recorded from 3 panes (one No. 1395a and two 1395d) with different foldover patterns. A pane of No. 1395d also is known with a foldover resulting in a vertical pair of stamp and label, imperf between.

PHOTOGRAVURE (Andreotti)

Plates of 400 subjects in four panes of 100.

Perf. 11x10½

1396 A817 8c multi ('71) .30 .25

ROTARY PRESS PRINTING

1397 A817a 14c gray brown ('72) .30 .25
- *a.* Untagged (Bureau precanceled) *100.00* 17.50

1398 A818 16c brown ('72) .35 .25
- *a.* Untagged (Bureau precanceled) 22.50 5.00

1399 A818a 18c violet ('74) .35 .25
1400 A818b 21c green ('73) .40 .25
- *Nos. 1393-1400 (9)* 2.90 2.25

Issued: 6c, 8/6/70; 7c, 10/20/72; #1394-1395, 5/10/71; #1396, 7/1/71; 14c, 4/24/72; 16c, 5/7/71; 18c, 1/23/74; 21c, 6/27/73.

COIL STAMPS
ROTARY PRESS PRINTING

1970-71 ***Perf. 10 Vert.***

1401 A815 6c dk blue gray .30 .25
- *a.* Untagged (Bureau precanceled) 19.50 3.00
- *b.* Imperf., pair *2,500.*

1402 A815 8c dp claret ('71) .30 .25
- *a.* Imperf., pair 37.50
- *b.* Untagged (Bureau precanceled) 6.75 .75
- *c.* Pair, imperf. between *6,250.*

No. 1401b often found with small faults and/or without gum. Such examples sell for considerably less.

Issue dates: 6c, Aug. 6; 8c, May 10, 1971.

EDGAR LEE MASTERS ISSUE

A819

LITHOGRAPHED, ENGRAVED (Giori)

1970, Aug. 22 ***Perf. 11***

1405 A819 6c black & olive bister .30 .25

WOMAN SUFFRAGE ISSUE

50th anniversary of the 19th Amendment, which gave the vote to women.

Suffragettes, 1920 & Woman Voter, 1970 — A820

GIORI PRESS PRINTING

1970, Aug. 26

1406 A820 6c blue .30 .25

SOUTH CAROLINA ISSUE

300th anniv. of the founding of Charles Town (Charleston), the 1st permanent settlement of South Carolina. Against a background of pine wood the line drawings of the design represent the economic and historic development of South Carolina: the spire of St. Philip's Church, Capitol, state flag, a ship, 17th century man and woman, a Fort Sumter cannon, barrels, cotton, tobacco and yellow jasmine.

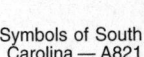

Symbols of South Carolina — A821

LITHOGRAPHED, ENGRAVED (Giori)

1970, Sept. 12

1407 A821 6c bister, black & red .30 .25

STONE MOUNTAIN MEMORIAL ISSUE

Dedication of the Stone Mountain Confederate Memorial, Georgia, May 9, 1970.

A822

GIORI PRESS PRINTING

1970, Sept. 19

1408 A822 6c gray .30 .25

FORT SNELLING ISSUE

150th anniv. of Fort Snelling, Minnesota, an important outpost for the opening of the Northwest.

Fort Snelling, Keelboat & Tepees — A823

LITHOGRAPHED, ENGRAVED (Giori)

1970, Oct. 17

1409 A823 6c yellow & multi .30 .25

ANTI-POLLUTION ISSUE

Issued to focus attention on the problems of pollution.

In left panes Nos. 1410 and 1412 appear in 1st, 3rd and 5th place; Nos. 1411 and 1413 in 2nd and 4th place. This arrangement is reversed in right panes.

Globe and Wheat — A824

Globe and City — A825

Globe and Bluegill — A826

Globe and Seagull — A827

PHOTOGRAVURE

1970, Oct. 28 ***Perf. 11x10½***

1410 A824 6c multicolored .30 .25
1411 A825 6c multicolored .30 .25
1412 A826 6c multicolored .30 .25
1413 A827 6c multicolored .30 .25
a. Block of 4, #1410-1413 1.00 *1.25*

CHRISTMAS ISSUE

In left panes Nos. 1415 and 1417 appear in 1st, 3rd and 5th place; Nos. 1416 and 1418 in 2nd and 4th place. This arrangement is reversed in right panes.

Nativity A828

Tin and Cast-iron Locomotive A829

Toy Horse on Wheels — A830

Mechanical Tricycle — A831

Doll Carriage — A832

1970, Nov. 5 ***Perf. 10½x11***

1414 A828 6c multicolored .30 .25
a. Precanceled .30 .25
b. Black omitted *400.00*
c. As "a," blue omitted *1,100.*
d. Type II .30 .25
e. Type II, precanceled .30 .25

No. 1414 has a slightly blurry impression, snowflaking in the sky and no gum breaker ridges. No. 1414d has shiny surfaced paper, sharper impression, no snowflaking and vertical and horizontal gum breaker ridges.

No. 1414a has a slightly blurry impression, snowflaking in the sky, no gum breaker ridges and the precancel is grayish black. No. 1414e has sharper impression, no snowflaking, gum breaker ridges and the precancel is intense black.

Perf. 11x10½

1415 A829 6c multicolored .30 .25
a. Precanceled .65 .25
b. Black omitted *1,750.*
1416 A830 6c multicolored .30 .25
a. Precanceled .65 .25
b. Black omitted 1,750.
c. Imperf., pair (#1416, 1418) *2,500.*
1417 A831 6c multicolored .30 .25
a. Precanceled .65 .25
b. Black omitted *1,750.*
1418 A832 6c multicolored .30 .25
a. Precanceled .65 .25
b. Block of 4, #1415-1418 1.25 *1.40*
c. As "b," precanceled 3.75 *3.50*
d. Black omitted *1,750.*
e. As "b," black omitted *8,000.*
f. As "b," black omitted on #1417 & 1418 *4,000.*
g. P# block of 8, black omitted on #1415 & 1416 *4,000.*
Nos. 1415-1418 (4) 1.20 1.00

Nos. 1415-1418 and 1415a-1418a are known both without gum breaker ridges (common) and with gum breaker ridges (scarce).

The precanceled stamps, Nos. 1414a-1418a, were furnished to 68 cities. The plates include two straight (No. 1414a) or two wavy (Nos. 1415a-1418a) black lines that make up the precancellation. Unused values are for stamps with gum and used values are for stamps with an additional cancellation or without gum.

UNITED NATIONS, 25th ANNIV.

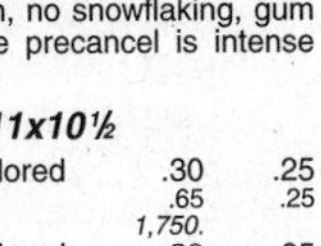

"UN" & UN Emblem — A833

LITHOGRAPHED, ENGRAVED (Giori)

1970, Nov. 20 ***Perf. 11***

1419 A833 6c blk, verm & ultra .30 .25

LANDING OF THE PILGRIMS ISSUE

350th anniv. of the landing of the Mayflower.

Mayflower & Pilgrims — A834

1970, Nov. 21

1420 A834 6c blk, org, yel, mag, bl & brn .30 .25
a. Orange & yellow omitted *425.00*

DISABLED AMERICAN VETERANS AND SERVICEMEN ISSUE

No. 1421 for the 50th anniv. of the Disabled Veterans of America Organization; No. 1422 honors the contribution of servicemen, particularly those who were prisoners of war, missing or killed in action. Nos. 1421-1422 are printed se-tenant in horizontal rows of 10.

A835

A836

1970, Nov. 24

1421 A835 6c dark blue, red & multicolored .30 .25

ENGRAVED

1422 A836 6c dark blue, black & red .30 .25
a. Pair, #1421-1422 .50 .50

AMERICAN WOOL INDUSTRY ISSUE

450th anniv. of the introduction of sheep to the North American continent and the beginning of the American wool industry.

Ewe and Lamb — A837

Plates of 200 subjects in four panes of 50.

1971, Jan. 19

1423 A837 6c multicolored .30 .25
b. Teal blue ("United States") missing (CM) *325.00*

GEN. DOUGLAS MacARTHUR ISSUE

MacArthur (1880-1964), Chief of Staff, Supreme Commander for the Allied Powers in the Pacific Area during World War II and Supreme Commander in Japan after the war.

Douglas MacArthur — A838

GIORI PRESS PRINTING

1971, Jan. 26

1424 A838 6c black, red & dark blue .30 .25
a. Red missing (PS) —
c. Blue missing (PS) —

BLOOD DONOR ISSUE

Salute to blood donors and spur to increased participation in the blood donor program.

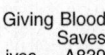

Giving Blood Saves Lives — A839

LITHOGRAPHED, ENGRAVED (Giori)

1971, Mar. 12

1425 A839 6c bl, scarlet & ind .30 .25

MISSOURI STATEHOOD, 150th ANNIV.

The stamp design shows a Pawnee facing a hunter-trapper and a group of settlers. It is from a mural by Thomas Hart Benton in the Harry S Truman Library, Independence, Mo.

"Independence and the Opening of the West" — A840

PHOTOGRAVURE (Andreotti)

1971, May 8 ***Perf. 11x10½***

1426 A840 8c multicolored .30 .25

See note on Andreotti printings and their color control markings in Information for Collectors under Printing, Photogravure.

WILDLIFE CONSERVATION ISSUE

Nos. 1427-1428 alternate in first row, Nos. 1429-1430 in second row. This arrangement repeated throughout pane.

Trout — A841

Alligator A842

Polar Bear, Cubs — A843

California Condor A844

LITHOGRAPHED, ENGRAVED (Giori)

1971, June 12 ***Perf. 11***

1427 A841 8c multicolored .30 .25
a. Red omitted *1,250.*
b. Green (engr.) omitted —
1428 A842 8c multicolored .30 .25
1429 A843 8c multicolored .30 .25
1430 A844 8c multicolored .30 .25
a. Block of 4, #1427-1430 1.00 1.00
b. As "a," light green & dark green omitted from #1427-1428 *3,250.*
c. As "a," red omitted from #1427, 1429-1430 *3,000.*

ANTARCTIC TREATY ISSUE

Map of Antarctica A845

Adapted from emblem on official documents of Consultative Meetings.

GIORI PRESS PRINTING

1971, June 23

1431 A845 8c red & dark blue .30 .25
  b. Both colors missing (EP) *500.00*

No. 1431b should be collected se-tenant with a normal stamp and/or a partially printed stamp.

AMERICAN REVOLUTION BICENTENNIAL

Bicentennial Commission Emblem — A846

LITHOGRAPHED, ENGRAVED (Giori)

1971, July 4

1432 A846 8c gray, red, blue & black .30 .25
  a. Gray & black missing (EP) *325.00*
  b. Gray ("U.S. Postage 8c") missing (EP) *650.00*

JOHN SLOAN ISSUE

John Sloan (1871-1951), painter. The painting hangs in the Phillips Gallery, Washington, D.C.

The Wake of the Ferry — A847

1971, Aug. 2

1433 A847 8c multicolored .30 .25
  b. Red engr. ("John Sloan" and "8") missing (CM) *1,000.*

SPACE ACHIEVEMENT DECADE ISSUE

Decade of space achievements and the Apollo 15 moon exploration mission, July 26-Aug. 7. In the left panes the earth and sun stamp is 1st, 3rd and 5th, the rover 2nd and 4th. This arrangement is reversed in the right panes.

Earth, Sun, Landing Craft on Moon — A848

Lunar Rover — A849

1971, Aug. 2

1434 A848 8c blk, bl, gray, yel & red .30 .25
1435 A849 8c blk, bl, gray, yel & red .30 .25
  b. Pair, #1434-1435 .50 .50
  d. As "b," blue & red (litho.) omitted *950.00*

EMILY DICKINSON ISSUE

Emily Elizabeth Dickinson — A850

1971, Aug. 28

1436 A850 8c multi, *grnsh* .30 .25
  a. Black & olive (engr.) omitted *500.00*
  b. Pale rose missing (EP) *5,000.*
  c. Red omitted —

SAN JUAN ISSUE

450th anniversary of San Juan, Puerto Rico.

Sentry Box, Morro Castle, San Juan — A851

1971, Sept. 12

1437 A851 8c pale brn, blk, yel, red brn & dk brn .30 .25
  b. Dark brown (engr.) omitted *1,500.* —

VALUES FOR HINGED STAMPS AFTER NO. 771

This catalogue does not value unused stamps after No. 771 in hinged condition. Hinged unused stamps from No. 772 to the present are worth considerably less than the values given for unused stamps, which are for never-hinged examples.

PREVENT DRUG ABUSE ISSUE

Drug Abuse Prevention Week, Oct. 3-9.

Young Woman Drug Addict — A852

PHOTOGRAVURE (Andreotti)

1971, Oct. 4 ***Perf. 10½x11***

1438 A852 8c blue, deep blue & black .30 .25

CARE ISSUE

25th anniversary of CARE, a US-Canadian Cooperative for American Relief Everywhere.

Hands Reaching for CARE — A853

1971, Oct. 27

1439 A853 8c blue, blk, vio & red lilac .30 .25
  a. Black omitted *1,100.*

HISTORIC PRESERVATION ISSUE

Nos. 1440-1441 alternate in 1st row, Nos. 1442-1443 in 2nd row. This arrangement is repeated throughout the pane.

Decatur House, Washington, DC — A854

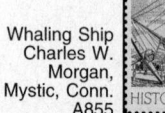

Whaling Ship Charles W. Morgan, Mystic, Conn. A855

Cable Car, San Francisco A856

San Xavier del Bac Mission, Tucson, Ariz. — A857

LITHOGRAPHED, ENGRAVED (Giori)

1971, Oct. 29 **Tagged** ***Perf. 11***

1440 A854 8c blk brn & ocher, *buff* .30 .25
1441 A855 8c blk brn & ocher, *buff* .30 .25
1442 A856 8c blk brn & ocher, *buff* .30 .25
1443 A857 8c blk brn & ocher, *buff* .30 .25
  a. Block of 4, #1440-1443 1.00 *1.00*
  b. As "a," black brown omitted *600.00*
  c. As "a," ocher omitted *2,500.*

CHRISTMAS ISSUE

Adoration of the Shepherds, by Giorgione A858

Partridge in a Pear Tree, by Jamie Wyeth A859

No. 1444 after a painting by Giorgione in the National Gallery of Art, Washington D.C.

PHOTOGRAVURE (Andreotti)

1971, Nov. 10 ***Perf. 10½x11***

1444 A858 8c gold & multi .30 .25
  a. Gold omitted *350.00*
1445 A859 8c dark green, red & multicolored .30 .25

SIDNEY LANIER ISSUE

Lanier (1842-81), poet, musician, lawyer, educator.

Sidney Lanier (1842-1881) — A860

GIORI PRESS PRINTING

1972, Feb. 3 ***Perf. 11***

1446 A860 8c black, brown & light blue .30 .25

PEACE CORPS ISSUE

Peace Corps Poster, by David Battle — A861

PHOTOGRAVURE (Andreotti)

1972, Feb. 11 ***Perf. 10½x11***

1447 A861 8c dark blue, light blue & red .30 .25

NATIONAL PARKS CENTENNIAL ISSUE

Centenary of Yellowstone National Park, the 1st National Park, and of the entire National Park System. See No. C84.

Hulk of Ship A862 | Cape Hatteras Lighthouse A863

Laughing Gulls on Driftwood A864 | Laughing Gulls and Dune A865

Wolf Trap Farm, Vienna, Va. A866

Old Faithful, Yellowstone A867

Mt. McKinley, Alaska — A868

LITHOGRAPHED, ENGRAVED (Giori)

1972 ***Perf. 11***

Plates of 400 subjects in 4 panes of 100 each

1448 A862 2c black & multi .30 .25
1449 A863 2c black & multi .30 .25
1450 A864 2c black & multi .30 .25
1451 A865 2c black & multi .30 .25
  a. Block of 4, #1448-1451 .50 .50
  b. As "a," black (litho.) omitted *800.00*
1452 A866 6c black & multi .30 .25
1453 A867 8c blk, bl, brn & multi .30 .25
1454 A868 15c black & multi .30 .25
  b. Yellow omitted *3,000.*

FAMILY PLANNING ISSUE

Family — A869

1972, Mar. 18

1455 A869 8c blk & multi .30 .25
  a. Yellow omitted *300.00*
  c. Dark brown missing (FO) *9,500.*

AMERICAN BICENTENNIAL ISSUE
Colonial American Craftsmen

In left panes Nos. 1456 and 1458 appear in 1st, 3rd and 5th place; Nos. 1457 and 1459 in 2nd and 4th place. This arrangement is reversed in right panes.

Glassmaker A870

Silversmith A871

Wigmaker — A872

Hatter — A873

ENGRAVED

1972, July 4 ***Perf. 11x10½***

1456 A870 8c deep brown .30 .25
1457 A871 8c deep brown .30 .25
1458 A872 8c deep brown .30 .25
1459 A873 8c deep brown .30 .25
a. Block of 4, #1456-1459 1.00 1.00

OLYMPIC GAMES ISSUE

11th Winter Olympic Games, Sapporo, Japan, Feb. 3-13 and 20th Summer Olympic Games, Munich, Germany, Aug. 26-Sept. 11. See No. C85.

Bicycling and Olympic Rings — A874

Bobsledding A875

Running — A876

PHOTOGRAVURE (Andreotti)

1972, Aug. 17 ***Perf. 11x10½***

1460 A874 6c blk, bl, red, emer & yel .30 .25
1461 A875 8c blk, bl, red, emer & yel .30 .25
1462 A876 15c blk, bl, red, emer & yel .30 .25
Nos. 1460-1462 (3) .90 .75

PARENT TEACHER ASSN., 75th ANNIV.

Blackboard A877

1972, Sept. 15

1463 A877 8c yellow & black .30 .25

WILDLIFE CONSERVATION ISSUE

Nos. 1464-1465 alternate in 1st row, Nos. 1468-1469 in 2nd row. This arrangement repeated throughout pane.

Fur Seals — A878

Cardinal A879

Brown Pelican A880

Bighorn Sheep A881

LITHOGRAPHED, ENGRAVED (Giori)

1972, Sept. 20 ***Perf. 11***

1464 A878 8c multicolored .30 .25
1465 A879 8c multicolored .30 .25
1466 A880 8c multicolored .30 .25
1467 A881 8c multicolored .30 .25
a. Block of 4, #1464-1467 1.00 1.00
b. As "a," brown omitted *2,750.*
c. As "a," green & blue omitted *2,750.*
d. As "a," red & brown omitted *3,250.*

MAIL ORDER BUSINESS ISSUE

Centenary of mail order business, originated by Aaron Montgomery Ward, Chicago. Design based on Headsville, W.Va., post office in Smithsonian Institution, Washington, D.C.

Rural Post Office Store — A882

PHOTOGRAVURE (Andreotti)

1972, Sept, 27 ***Perf. 11x10½***

1468 A882 8c multicolored .30 .25

OSTEOPATHIC MEDICINE ISSUE

75th anniv. of the American Osteopathic Assoc., founded by Dr. Andrew T. Still (1828-1917), who developed the principles of osteopathy in 1874.

Man's Quest for Health — A883

1972, Oct. 9 ***Perf. 10½x11***

1469 A883 8c multicolored .30 .25

AMERICAN FOLKLORE ISSUE

Tom Sawyer, by Norman Rockwell — A884

Designed by Bradbury Thompson.

LITHOGRAPHED, ENGRAVED (Giori)

1972, Oct. 13 ***Perf. 11***

1470 A884 8c blk, red, yel, tan, bl & rose red .30 .25
a. Horiz. pair, imperf. between *6,750.*
b. Red & black (engr.) omitted *800.00*
c. Yellow & tan (litho.) omitted *1,300.*
e. Red (engr. 8c) missing (CM) *750.*

CHRISTMAS ISSUE

Angel from "Mary, Queen of Heaven" A885

Santa Claus A886

No. 1471, detail from a painting by the Master of the St. Lucy Legend in the National Gallery of Art, Washington, D.C.

PHOTOGRAVURE (Andreotti)

1972, Nov. 9 ***Perf. 10½x11***

1471 A885 8c multicolored .30 .25
a. Pink omitted *100.00*
b. Black omitted *2,500.*
1472 A886 8c multicolored .30 .25

PHARMACY ISSUE

Honoring American druggists in connection with the 120th anniversary of the American Pharmaceutical Association.

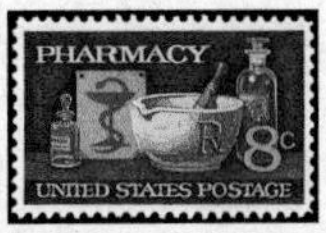

Mortar & Pestle, Bowl of Hygeia, 19th Century Medicine Bottles — A887

LITHOGRAPHED, ENGRAVED (Giori)

1972, Nov. 10 ***Perf. 11***

1473 A887 8c black & multi .30 .25
a. Blue & orange omitted *600.00*
b. Blue omitted *1,250.*
c. Orange omitted *1,250.*
e. Vertical pair, imperf horiz. *2,000.*

STAMP COLLECTING ISSUE

Issued to publicize stamp collecting.

U.S. No. 1 Under Magnifying Glass — A888

1972, Nov. 17

1474 A888 8c multicolored .30 .25
a. Black (litho.) omitted *325.00*

LOVE ISSUE

"Love," by Robert Indiana — A889

PHOTOGRAVURE (Andreotti)

1973, Jan. 26 ***Perf. 11x10½***

1475 A889 8c red, emer & vio blue .30 .25

AMERICAN BICENTENNIAL ISSUE
Communications in Colonial Times

Printer and Patriots Examining Pamphlet — A890

Posting a Broadside A891

Postrider — A892

Drummer — A893

GIORI PRESS PRINTING

1973 ***Perf. 11***

1476 A890 8c ultra, greenish blk & red .30 .25
b. Red missing (PS) *300.00*
1477 A891 8c blk, vermilion & ultra .30 .25

LITHOGRAPHED, ENGRAVED (Giori)

1478 A892 8c bl, blk, red & grn .30 .25
a. Red missing (CM) *1,300.*
1479 A893 8c bl, blk, yel & red .30 .25
a. Blue missing (CM) —
b. Red missing (CM) —
Nos. 1476-1479 (4) 1.20 1.00

AMERICAN BICENTENNIAL ISSUE
Boston Tea Party

In left panes Nos. 1480 and 1482 appear in 1st, 3rd and 5th place, Nos. 1481 and 1483 appear in 2nd and 4th place. This arrangement is reversed in right panes.

British Merchantman A894

British Three-master A895

Boats and Ship's Hull — A896

Boat and Dock — A897

1973, July 4

1480 A894 8c blk & multi .30 .25
1481 A895 8c blk & multi .30 .25
1482 A896 8c blk & multi .30 .25
1483 A897 8c blk & multi .30 .25
a. Block of 4, #1480-1483 1.00 1.00
b. As "a," black (engraved) omitted *750.00*
c. As "a," black (litho.) omitted *900.00*
e. As "a," dk blue omitted *1,500.* *750.00*

AMERICAN ARTS ISSUE

Gershwin, Sportin' Life, Porgy & Bess — A898

Robinson Jeffers, Man & Children of Carmel with Burro — A899

Henry Ossawa Tanner, Palette & Rainbow — A900

Willa Cather, Pioneer Family & Covered Wagon — A901

PHOTOGRAVURE (Andreotti)

1973

1484 A898 8c dp grn & multi .30 .25
a. Vertical pair, imperf. horiz. *160.00*
1485 A899 8c Prus bl & multi .30 .25
a. Vertical pair, imperf. horiz. *160.00*
1486 A900 8c yel brn & multi .30 .25
1487 A901 8c dp brn & multi .30 .25
a. Vertical pair, imperf. horiz. *175.00*
Nos. 1484-1487 (4) 1.20 1.00

Honoring: No. 1484, George Gershwin (1898-1937), composer. No. 1485, Robinson Jeffers (1887-1962), poet. No. 1486, Henry Ossawa Tanner (1859-1937), black painter (portrait by Thomas Eakins). No. 1487, Willa Sibert Cather (1873-1947), novelist.

Issued: No. 1484, Feb. 28; No. 1485, Aug. 13; No. 1486, Sept. 10; No. 1487, Sept. 20.

COPERNICUS ISSUE

Nicolaus Copernicus (1473-1543), Polish Astronomer — A902

LITHOGRAPHED, ENGRAVED (Giori)

1973, Apr. 23

1488 A902 8c black & orange	.30	.25
a. Orange omitted	400.00	
b. Black (engraved) omitted	600.00	

The orange can be chemically removed. Expertization of No. 1488a is required.

POSTAL SERVICE EMPLOYEES ISSUE

A tribute to US Postal Service employees. Nos. 1489-1498 are printed se-tenant in horizontal rows of 10. Emerald inscription on back, printed beneath gum in water-soluble ink, includes Postal Service emblem, "People Serving You" and a statement, differing for each of the 10 stamps, about some aspect of postal service.

Each stamp in top or bottom row has a tab with blue inscription enumerating various jobs in postal service.

Stamp Counter A903

Mail Collection A904

Letter Facing on Conveyor Belt A905

Parcel Post Sorting A906

Mail Canceling A907

Manual Letter Routing A908

Electronic Letter Routing A909

Loading Mail on Truck A910

Mailman A911

Rural Mail Delivery A912

PHOTOGRAVURE (Andreotti)

1973, Apr. 30 ***Perf. 10½x11***

1489 A903 8c multicolored	.30	.25
1490 A904 8c multicolored	.30	.25
1491 A905 8c multicolored	.30	.25
1492 A906 8c multicolored	.30	.25
1493 A907 8c multicolored	.30	.25
1494 A908 8c multicolored	.30	.25
1495 A909 8c multicolored	.30	.25
1496 A910 8c multicolored	.30	.25
1497 A911 8c multicolored	.30	.25
1498 A912 8c multicolored	.30	.25
a. Strip of 10, #1489-1498	2.50	2.50

HARRY S. TRUMAN ISSUE

Harry S Truman, 33rd President (1884-1972) — A913

GIORI PRESS PRINTING

1973, May 8 ***Perf. 11***

1499 A913 8c carmine rose, black & blue	.30	.25

ELECTRONICS PROGRESS ISSUE

Marconi's Spark Coil and Gap — A914

Transistors and Printed Circuit Board — A915

Microphone, Speaker, Vacuum Tube, TV Camera Tube — A916

LITHOGRAPHED, ENGRAVED (Giori)

1973, July 10

1500 A914 6c lilac & multi	.30	.25
1501 A915 8c tan & multi	.30	.25
a. Black (inscriptions & "U.S. 8c") omitted	300.00	
b. Tan (background) & lilac omitted	600.00	

Many examples of No. 1501b are hinged. Value about one-half never hinged value.

1502 A916 15c gray green & multicolored	.30	.25
a. Black (inscriptions & "U.S. 15c") omitted	850.00	
Nos. 1500-1502 (3)	.90	.75

See No. C86.

LYNDON B. JOHNSON ISSUE

Lyndon B. Johnson (1908-1973), 36th President — A917

PHOTOGRAVURE (Andreotti)

1973, Aug. 27

1503 A917 8c black & multi	.30	.25
a. Horiz. pair, imperf. vert.	200.00	

RURAL AMERICA ISSUE

Centenary of the introduction of Aberdeen Angus cattle into the US (#1504); of the Chautauqua Institution (#1505); and of the introduction of hard winter wheat into Kansas by Mennonite immigrants (#1506).

Angus and Longhorn Cattle — A918

Chautauqua Tent and Buggies — A919

Wheat Fields and Train — A920

No. 1504 after painting by F.C. "Frank" Murphy.

LITHOGRAPHED, ENGRAVED (Giori)

1973-74

1504 A918 8c multi	.30	.25
a. Green & red brown omitted	600.00	
b. Vert. pair, imperf. between		5,000.
d. Blue (engr.) missing (PS)		—
1505 A919 10c multi	.30	.25
a. Black (litho.) omitted		1,750.
1506 A920 10c multi	.30	.25
a. Black and blue (engr.) omitted	500.00	
Nos. 1504-1506 (3)	.90	.75

CHRISTMAS ISSUE

Small Cowper Madonna, by Raphael A921

Christmas Tree in Needlepoint A922

No. 1507 after painting in the National Gallery of Art, Washington, D.C.

PHOTOGRAVURE (Andreotti)

1973, Nov. 7 ***Perf. 10½x11***

1507 A921 8c multicolored	.30	.25
1508 A922 8c multicolored	.30	.25
a. Vertical pair, imperf. between	225.00	

50-Star & 13-Star Flags A923

Jefferson Memorial & Signature A924

Mail Transport A925

Liberty Bell A926

MULTICOLOR HUCK PRESS

1973-74 ***Perf. 11x10½***

1509 A923 10c red & blue	.30	.25
a. Horizontal pair, imperf. between	40.00	—
b. Blue omitted	150.00	—
c. Imperf., vert. pair	450.00	
d. Horiz. pair, imperf. vert.	900.00	
f. Vert. pair, imperf between		—

No. 1509 exists imperf and with red omitted from printer's waste.

ROTARY PRESS PRINTING

1510 A924 10c blue	.30	.25
a. Untagged (Bureau precanceled)	4.00	1.00
b. Booklet pane of 5 + label	1.65	1.25
c. Booklet pane of 8	2.00	2.00
d. Booklet pane of 6 ('74)	5.00	1.75
e. Vert. pair, imperf. horiz.	300.00	
f. Vert. pair, imperf. btwn., in #1510c with miscut or with foldover	600.00	
l. As "b," double booklet pane of 10 plus stamps with 2 horiz. pairs imperf. btwn. plus stamp and label imperf. btwn. (FO)	1,750.	

No. 1510f resulted from a paper foldover after perforating and before cutting into booklet panes.

PHOTOGRAVURE (Andreotti)

1511 A925 10c multi	.30	.25
a. Yellow omitted	40.00	

Beware of stamps with yellow chemically removed offered as No. 1511a.

COIL STAMPS
ROTARY PRESS PRINTING

1973-74 ***Perf. 10 Vert.***

1518 A926 6.3c brick red	.30	.25
a. Untagged (Bureau precanceled)	.35	.25
b. Imperf., pair	130.00	
c. As "a," imperf., pair	75.00	

No. 1518c is precanceled Washington, DC. Columbus, Ohio and Garden City, N.Y. Values for Columbus pair $400, for Garden City pair $850.

MULTICOLOR HUCK PRESS

1519 A923 10c red & blue	.30	.25
a. Imperf., pair	35.00	

Huck press printings often show parts of a joint line, but this feature is not consistent.

ROTARY PRESS PRINTING

1520 A924 10c blue	.30	.25
a. Untagged (Bureau precanceled)	5.50	1.25
b. Imperf., pair	30.00	

VETERANS OF FOREIGN WARS ISSUE

75th anniversary of Veterans of Spanish-American and Other Foreign Wars.

V.F.W. Emblem — A928

GIORI PRESS PRINTING

1974, Mar. 11 ***Perf. 11***

1525 A928 10c red & dark blue	.30	.25
b. Blue missing (PS)	350.00	

ROBERT FROST ISSUE

Robert Frost (1874-1963), Poet — A929

1974, Mar. 26 ***Perf. 10½x11***

1526 A929 10c black	.30	.25

EXPO '74 WORLD'S FAIR ISSUE

EXPO '74 World's Fair "Preserve the Environment," Spokane, Wash., May 4-Nov. 4.

"Cosmic Jumper" — A930

PHOTOGRAVURE (Andreotti)

1974, Apr. 18 ***Perf. 11***

1527 A930 10c multicolored	.30	.25

HORSE RACING ISSUE

Kentucky Derby, Churchill Downs, centenary.

Horses Rounding Turn — A931

1974, May 4 ***Perf. 11x10½***

1528 A931 10c yel & multi	.30	.25
a. Blue ("Horse Racing") omitted	500.00	
b. Red ("U.S. postage 10 cents") omitted	1,750.	

Beware of stamps offered as No. 1528b that have traces of red.

SKYLAB ISSUE

First anniversary of the launching of Skylab I, honoring all who participated in the Skylab project.

Skylab — A932

LITHOGRAPHED, ENGRAVED (Giori)

1974, May 14 ***Perf. 11***

1529 A932 10c multicolored .30 .25
- *a.* Vert. pair, imperf. between —
- *c.* Vert. pair, imperf. horiz. —
- *d.* Double impression of magenta —

UNIVERSAL POSTAL UNION ISSUE

UPU cent. In the 1st row Nos. 1530-1537 are in sequence as listed. In the 2nd row Nos. 1534-1537 are followed by Nos. 1530-1533. Every row of 8 and every horizontal block of 8 contains all 8 designs. The letter writing designs are from famous works of art; some are details. The quotation on every second stamp, "Letters mingle souls," is from a letter by poet John Donne.

Michelangelo, from School of Athens — A933

Five Feminine Virtues — A934

Old Time Letter Rack — A935

Mlle. La Vergne — A936

Lady Writing Letter — A937

Inkwell and Quill — A938

Mrs. John Douglas A939

Don Antonio Noreiga A940

PHOTOGRAVURE (Andreotti)

1974, June 6

1530 A933 10c multicolored .30 .25
1531 A934 10c multicolored .30 .25
1532 A935 10c multicolored .30 .25
1533 A936 10c multicolored .30 .25
1534 A937 10c multicolored .30 .25
1535 A938 10c multicolored .30 .25
1536 A939 10c multicolored .30 .25
1537 A940 10c multicolored .30 .25
- *a.* Block or strip of 8 (#1530-1537) 2.40 2.00
- *b.* As "a," (block), imperf. vert. *2,500.*

MINERAL HERITAGE ISSUE

The sequence of stamps in 1st horizontal row is Nos. 1538-1541, 1538-1539. In 2nd row Nos. 1540-1541 are followed by Nos. 1538-1541.

Petrified Wood — A941

Tourmaline A942

Amethyst A943

Rhodochrosite A944

1974, June 13

1538 A941 10c blue & multi .30 .25
- *a.* Light blue & yellow (litho.) omitted —

1539 A942 10c blue & multi .30 .25
- *a.* Light blue (litho.) omitted —
- *b.* Black & purple (engr.) omitted —

1540 A943 10c blue & multi .30 .25
- *a.* Light blue & yellow (litho.) omitted —

1541 A944 10c blue & multi .30 .25
- *a.* Block or strip of 4, #1538-1541 1.20 1.00
- *b.* As "a," light blue & yellow (litho.) omitted *900.00* —
- *c.* Light blue (litho.) omitted —
- *d.* Black & red (engr.) omitted —
- *e.* Block of 4, two right stamps being Nos. 1539b and 1541d *7,000.*

No. 1541e is usually collected as a transition block of six or larger.

KENTUCKY SETTLEMENT, 200th ANNIV.

Fort Harrod, first settlement in Kentucky.

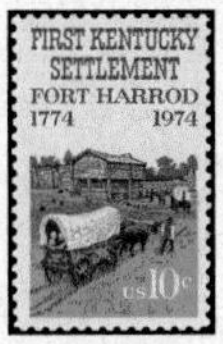

Fort Harrod — A945

1974, June 15

1542 A945 10c green & multi .30 .25
- *a.* Dull black (litho.) omitted *400.00*
- *b.* Green (engr. & litho.), black (engr. & litho.) & blue missing (EP) *1,750.*
- *c.* Green (engr.) missing (EP) *3,000.*
- *d.* Green (engr.) & black (litho.) missing (EP) —
- *f.* Blue (litho.) omitted —

No. 1542f was caused by an occurrence that seems to be unique for U.S. total color omitted/missing errors. According to the BEP, oil on the printing blanket made a small area unreceptive to the blue ink. No blue at all was printed on one unique error stamp.

AMERICAN REVOLUTION BICENTENNIAL ISSUE

First Continental Congress

Nos. 1543-1544 alternate in 1st row, Nos. 1545-1546 in 2nd row. This arrangement is repeated throughout the pane.

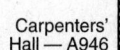

Carpenters' Hall — A946

A947

A948

Independence Hall — A949

1974, July 4

1543 A946 10c dark blue & red .30 .25
1544 A947 10c gray, dark blue & red .30 .25
1545 A948 10c gray, dark blue & red .30 .25
1546 A949 10c red & dark blue .30 .25
- *a.* Block of 4, #1543-1546 1.20 1.00

ENERGY CONSERVATION ISSUE

Publicizing the importance of conserving all forms of energy.

A950

LITHOGRAPHED, ENGRAVED (Giori)

1974, Sept. 23

1547 A950 10c multicolored .30 .25
- *a.* Blue & orange omitted *400.00*
- *b.* Orange & green omitted *275.00*
- *c.* Green omitted *400.00*

AMERICAN FOLKLORE ISSUE

Legend of Sleepy Hollow

The Headless Horseman in pursuit of Ichabod Crane from "Legend of Sleepy Hollow," by Washington Irving.

Legend of Sleepy Hollow — A951

1974, Oct. 10

1548 A951 10c dk bl, blk, org & yel .30 .25

RETARDED CHILDREN ISSUE

Retarded Children Can Be Helped, theme of annual convention of the National Association of Retarded Citizens.

Retarded Child — A952

GIORI PRESS PRINTING

1974, Oct. 12

1549 A952 10c brown red & dark brown .30 .25

WARNING ABOUT SELF-ADHESIVE STAMPS

Many, though not all, self-adhesive stamps, which first appear with No. 1552, will not separate from paper or otherwise respond well to a standard warm-water soak. Consult the listings in the Scott U.S. Specialized Catalogue for information about which self-adhesives will and which will not soak.The editors strongly recommend that stamps that will not soak be collected on piece.

CHRISTMAS ISSUE

Angel From Pérussis Altarpiece, 1480 — A953

"The Road-Winter," by Currier & Ives — A954

Designers: No. 1550, Bradbury Thompson, using detail from the Pérussis altarpiece painted by anonymous French artist, 1480, in Metropolitan Museum of Art, New York City. No. 1551, Stevan Dohanos, using Currier and Ives print from drawing by Otto Knirsch.

PHOTOGRAVURE (Andreotti)

1974, Oct. 23 ***Perf. 10½x11***

1550 A953 10c multicolored .30 .25

Perf. 11x10½

1551 A954 10c multicolored .30 .25
- *a.* Buff omitted 12.50

No. 1551a is difficult to identify. Competent expertization is necessary.

Dove Weather Vane — A955

Die Cut, Paper Backing Rouletted

1974, Nov. 15 **Untagged**

Self-adhesive; Inscribed "Precanceled"

1552 A955 10c multicolored .30 .25
Nos. 1550-1552 (3) .90 .75

Unused value of No. 1552 is for stamp on rouletted paper backing as issued. Used value is for stamp on piece, with or without postmark. **Most examples are becoming discolored from the adhesive. The Catalogue value is for discolored examples.**

Die cutting includes crossed slashes through dove, applied to prevent removal and re-use of the stamp. The stamp will separate into layers if soaked.

AMERICAN ARTS ISSUE

Benjamin West (1738-1820), painter (No. 1553); Paul Laurence Dunbar (1872-1906), poet (No. 1554); David (Lewelyn) Wark Griffith (1875-1948), motion picture producer (No. 1555).

Benjamin West A956

Paul Laurence Dunbar A957

D. W. Griffith & Projector — A958

PHOTOGRAVURE (Andreotti)

1975 ***Perf. 10½x11***

1553 A956 10c multicolored .30 .25

Perf. 11

1554 A957 10c multicolored .30 .25
- *a.* Imperf., pair *600.00*

LITHOGRAPHED, ENGRAVED (Giori)

Perf. 11

1555 A958 10c brown & multicolored .30 .25
- *a.* Brown (engr.) omitted *450.00*
- *Nos. 1553-1555 (3)* .90 .75

SPACE ISSUES

US space accomplishments with unmanned craft. Pioneer 10 passed within 81,000 miles of Jupiter, Dec. 10, 1973. Mariner 10 explored Venus and Mercury in 1974 and Mercury again in 1975.

Pioneer 10 Passing Jupiter — A959

Mariner 10, Venus & Mercury — A960

LITHOGRAPHED, ENGRAVED (Giori)

1975 ***Perf. 11***

1556 A959 10c lt yel, dk yel, red, bl & 2 dk blues .30 .25
- *a.* Red & dark yellow omitted *750.00*
- *b.* Dark blues (engr.) omitted *400.00*
- *d.* Dark yellow omitted —

Imperfs. exist from printer's waste.

1557 A960 10c blk, red, ultra & bister .30 .25
- *a.* Red omitted *275.00* —
- *b.* Ultramarine & bister omitted *750.00*
- *d.* Red missing (PS) *525.00*

COLLECTIVE BARGAINING ISSUE

Collective Bargaining law, enacted 1935, in Wagner Act.

"Labor and Management" A961

PHOTOGRAVURE (Andreotti)

1975, Mar. 13

1558 A961 10c multicolored .30 .25

Imperforates exist from printer's waste.

AMERICAN BICENTENNIAL ISSUE

Contributors to the Cause

Sybil Ludington, age 16, rallied militia, Apr. 26, 1777; Salem Poor, black freeman, fought in Battle of Bunker Hill; Haym Salomon, Jewish immigrant, raised money to finance Revolutionary War; Peter Francisco, Portuguese-French immigrant, joined Continental Army at 15. Emerald inscription on back, printed beneath gum in water-soluble ink, gives thumbnail sketch of portrayed contributor.

Sybil Ludington — A962

Salem Poor — A963

Haym Salomon — A964

Peter Francisco — A965

1975, Mar. 25 ***Perf. 11x10½***

1559 A962 8c multicolored .30 .25
- *a.* Back inscriptions omitted *110.00*

1560 A963 10c multicolored .30 .25
- *a.* Back inscription omitted *110.00*
- *b.* Black missing (PS) —

1561 A964 10c multicolored .30 .25
- *a.* Back inscription omitted *110.00*

1562 A965 18c multicolored .35 .25
- *Nos. 1559-1562 (4)* 1.25 1.00

On No. 1560, two black plates were used. No. 1560b is missing the impression from one of those plates ("Salem Poor - U.S. Bicentennial symbol - Gallant Soldier") due to an upward shift of the horizontal perforations.

Dangerous fakes exist of No. 1561 with red apparently omitted. Professional authentication is mandatory in order to establish such a stamp as a genuine error.

Lexington-Concord Battle, 200th Anniv.

"Birth of Liberty," by Henry Sandham — A966

1975, Apr. 19 ***Perf. 11***

1563 A966 10c multicolored .30 .25
- *a.* Vert. pair, imperf. horiz. *300.00*

Bunker Hill Battle, 200th Anniv.

Battle of Bunker Hill, by John Trumbull — A967

1975, June 17

1564 A967 10c multicolored .30 .25

Military Uniforms

Bicentenary of US Military Services. Nos. 1565-1566 alternate in one row, Nos. 1567-1568 in next row.

Soldier with Flintlock Musket, Uniform Button A968

Sailor with Grappling Hook, First Navy Jack, 1775 A969

Marine with Musket, Full-rigged Ship A970

Militiaman with Musket, Powder Horn A971

1975, July 4

1565 A968 10c multicolored .30 .25
1566 A969 10c multicolored .30 .25
1567 A970 10c multicolored .30 .25
1568 A971 10c multicolored .30 .25
- *a.* Block of 4, #1565-1568 1.20 1.00

APOLLO SOYUZ SPACE ISSUE

Apollo Soyuz space test project, Russo-American cooperation, launched July 15; link-up, July 17. Nos. In the 1st row, No. 1569 is in 1st and 3rd space, No. 1570 is 2nd space; in the 2nd row No. 1570 is in 1st and 3rd space, No. 1569 in 2nd space, etc.

Participating US and USSR crews: Thomas P. Stafford, Donald K. Slayton, Vance D. Brand, Aleksei A. Leonov, Valery N. Kubasov.

Apollo & Soyuz After Docking, Earth A972

Spacecraft Before Docking, Earth & Project Emblem — A973

1975, July 15

1569 A972 10c multicolored .30 .25
1570 A973 10c multicolored .30 .25
- *a.* Pair, #1569-1570 .60 .50
- *c.* As "a," vert. pair, imperf. horiz. *800.00*
- *d.* As "a," yellow omitted *900.00*

Nos. 1569-1570 totally imperforate are printer's waste.

See Russia Nos. 4339-4340.

INTERNATIONAL WOMEN'S YEAR ISSUE

International Women's Year 1975.

Worldwide Equality for Women — A974

1975, Aug. 26 ***Perf. 11x10½***

1571 A974 10c blue, orange & dark blue .30 .25

US POSTAL SERVICE BICENTENNIAL ISSUE

Nos. 1572-1573 alternate in 1st row, Nos. 1574-1575 in 2nd row. This arrangement is repeated throughout the pane.

Stagecoach and Trailer Truck — A975

Old and New Locomotives A976

Early Mail Plane and Jet — A977

Satellite for Transmission of Mailgrams A978

1975, Sept. 3

1572 A975 10c multicolored .30 .25
1573 A976 10c multicolored .30 .25
1574 A977 10c multicolored .30 .25
1575 A978 10c multicolored .30 .25
- *a.* Block of 4, #1572-1575 1.20 1.00
- *b.* As "a," red "10c" omitted, tagging omitted —

WORLD PEACE THROUGH LAW ISSUE

A prelude to 7th World Law Conference of the World Peace Through Law Center at Washington, D.C., Oct. 12-17.

Law Book, Olive Branch and Globe — A979

GIORI PRESS PRINTING

1975, Sept. 29 ***Perf. 11***

1576 A979 10c green, Prussian blue & rose brown .30 .25
- *b.* Horiz. pair, imperf vert. *7,500.*
- *c.* All colors omitted *725.00*

No. 1576c is collected in a horiz. strip as two errors se-tenant with a partially printed stamp.

BANKING AND COMMERCE ISSUE

Banking and commerce in the U.S., and for the Centennial Convention of the American Bankers Association.

Engine Turning, Indian Head Penny & Morgan Silver Dollar — A980

Seated Liberty Quarter, $20 Gold (Double Eagle), Engine Turning — A981

LITHOGRAPHED, ENGRAVED (Giori)

1975, Oct. 6

1577 A980 10c multicolored .30 .25
1578 A981 10c multicolored .30 .25
- *a.* Pair, #1577-1578 .60 .50
- *b.* As "a," brown & blue (litho) omitted *1,100.*
- *c.* As "a," brown, blue & yellow (litho) omitted *1,750.*

CHRISTMAS ISSUE

Madonna, by Domenico Ghirlandaio A982

Christmas Card, by Louis Prang, 1878 A983

PHOTOGRAVURE (Andreotti)

1975, Oct. 14

1579 A982 (10c) multicolored .30 .25
- *a.* Imperf., pair *75.00*

Perf. 11.2

1580 A983 (10c) multicolored .30 .25
- *a.* Imperf., pair *85.00*
- *c.* Perf. 10.9 .30 .25

Perf. 10.5x11.3

1580B A983 (10c) multicolored .65 .25

AMERICANA ISSUE

Inkwell and Quill A984

Speaker's Stand A985

Early Ballot Box A987

Books, Bookmark, Eyeglasses A988

Dome of Capitol A994

Contemplation of Justice A995

Early American Printing Press A996

Torch A997

Liberty Bell A998

Eagle and Shield A999

Fort McHenry Flag A1001

Head, Statue of Liberty A1002

Old North Church, Boston A1003

Fort Nisqually A1004

Sandy Hook Lighthouse, NJ A1005

Morris Township School No. 2, Devils Lake, ND A1006

Iron "Betty" Lamp, 17th-18th Cent. A1007

Rush Lamp and Candle Holder A1008

Kerosene Table Lamp A1009

Railroad Conductor's Lantern, c. 1850 A1010

ROTARY PRESS PRINTING

1975-81 ***Perf. 11¼x10½***

Size: 18½x22½mm

1581 A984 1c dk bl, *grnish* .30 .25
 a. Untagged (Bureau precanceled) 4.50 1.50
 c. White paper, dull gum — —
1582 A985 2c red brn, *grnsh* .30 .25
 a. Untagged (Bureau precanceled) 4.50 1.50
 b. Cream paper ('81) .30 .25
1584 A987 3c olive, *grnsh* .30 .25
 a. Untagged (Bureau precanceled), dull gum .75 .50

Values for No. 1584a are for the lines-only precancel. Also known with city precancels, and valued at $50 thus.

1585 A988 4c rose mag, *cream* .30 .25
 a. Untagged (Bureau precanceled) 1.00 .75

The pair with horiz. gutter between also is misperfed through the stamps horizontally.

Also known with city precancels, and valued at $100 thus.

Size: 17½x20½mm

Perf. 11x10½ on 3 Sides

1590 A994 9c slate green .45 *1.00*

From bklt. pane #1623a.

Perf. 10x9¾ on 3 Sides

1590A A994 9c slate green 12.50 12.50

From bklt. pane #1623Bc.

Size: 18½x22½mm

Perf. 11¼x10½

1591 A994 9c sl grn, *gray* .30 .25
 a. Untagged (Bureau precanceled) 1.75 1.00

Values for No. 1591a are for the lines-only precancel. Also known with city precancels, and valued at $32.50 thus.

1592 A995 10c violet, *gray* .30 .25
 a. Untagged (Bureau precanceled, Chicago) 9.50 5.00
1593 A996 11c orange, *gray* .30 .25
1594 A997 12c red brown, *beige* .30 .25

Perf. 11¼x10½ on 2 or 3 Sides

1595 A998 13c brown .30 .25
 a. Booklet pane of 6 2.25 1.50
 b. Booklet pane of 7 + label 2.25 1.50
 c. Booklet pane of 8 2.25 1.50
 d. Booklet pane of 5 + label, *Apr. 2, 1976* 1.75 1.25
 e. Vert. pair, imperf. btwn., in #1595c with foldover *1,500.*
 g. Horiz. pair, imperf. btwn., in #1595d with foldover —

Nos. 1595e and 1595g resulted from paper foldovers after perforating and before cutting into panes. Beware of printer's waste consisting of complete panes with perfs around all outside edges.

PHOTOGRAVURE (Andreotti)

Perf. 11¼ Bullseye

1596 A999 13c multicolored .30 .25
 a. Imperf., pair *40.00* —
 b. Yellow omitted *75.00*

ENGRAVED (Combination Press)

Perf. 11x11¼

1597 A1001 15c gray, dk bl & red .30 .25
 b. Gray omitted *300.00*
 c. Vert. pair, imperf btwn and with natural straight edge at bottom *350.00*
 e. Imperf., vert. pair *15.00*

ENGRAVED

Perf. 11x10½ on 2 or 3 Sides

1598 A1001 15c gray, dk bl & red .40 .25
 a. Booklet pane of 8 3.75 1.50

Perf. 11¼x10½

1599 A1002 16c blue .35 .25
1603 A1003 24c red, *blue* .50 .25
 b. red, *greenish blue* .50 .25
1604 A1004 28c brown, *blue* .55 .25
1605 A1005 29c blue, *blue* .60 .25
1606 A1006 30c green, *blue* .55 .25

LITHOGRAPHED AND ENGRAVED

Perf. 11

1608 A1007 50c tan, blk & org .85 .25
 a. Black omitted *375.00*
 b. Vert. pair, imperf. horiz. *1,200.*

Beware of examples offered as No. 1608b that have blind perfs.

1610 A1008 $1 tan, brn, org & yel 2.00 .25
 a. Brown (engraved) omitted *175.00*
 b. Tan, orange & yellow omitted *175.00*
 c. Brown (engraved) inverted *17,000.*
1611 A1009 $2 tan, dk grn, org & yel 3.75 .75
1612 A1010 $5 tan, red brn, yel & org 8.50 1.75
 Nos. 1581-1612 (23) 34.30 20.75

Nos. 1590, 1590A, 1595, 1598, 1623 and 1623b were issued only in booklets. All stamps have one or two straight edges.

Years of issue: #1591, 1595-1596, 11c, 24c, 1975. #1590, 1c-4c, 10c, 1977. #1597-1598, 16c, 28c, 29c, $2, 1978. 30c-$1, $5, 1979. 12c, 1981.

Guitar A1011

Saxhorns A1012

Drum A1013

Piano A1014

Designers: 3.1c, George Mercer. 7.7c, Susan Robb. 7.9c, Bernard Glassman. 10c, Walter Brooks. 15c, V. Jack Ruther.

COIL STAMPS
ENGRAVED

1975-79 ***Perf. 10 Vertically***

1613 A1011 3.1c brown ('79) .30 .25
 a. Untagged (Bureau precanceled, lines only) .35 .35
 b. Imperf., pair *850.00*
1614 A1012 7.7c brown ('76) .30 .25
 a. Untagged (Bureau precanceled) .40 .30
 b. As "a," imperf., pair *1,250.*

No. 1614b is precanceled Washington, DC. Also exists with Marion, OH precancel; value $1,950 for pair.

1615 A1013 7.9c carmine ('76) .30 .25
 a. Untagged (Bureau precanceled) .40 .40
 b. Imperf., pair *300.00*
1615C A1014 8.4c dak blue ('78) .30 .25
 d. Untagged (Bureau precanceled) .50 .40
 e. As "d," pair, imperf. between 45.00
 f. As "d," imperf. pair, shiny gum 15.00

No. 1615Ce is precanceled with lines only. No. 1615Cf is precanceled with lines only (value shown) and also exists in pairs precanceled Newark, N.J. ($25)., Brownstown, Ind. ($900), Oklahoma City, Okla. ($1,500.) and Washington, DC ($900).

1616 A994 9c slate green ('75) .30 .25
 a. Imperf., pair *125.00*
 b. Untagged (Bureau precanceled) .75 .75
 c. As "b," imperf., pair *600.00*

Value for No. 1616b is for stamp with dull gum.

No. 1616c is precanceled Pleasantville, NY.

1617 A995 10c violet ('77) .30 .25
 a. Untagged (Bureau precanceled) 1.35 1.35
 b. Imperf., pair 55.00
 c. As "a," imperf pair *3,750.*

Values for No. 1617a and 1617b are for stamps with dull gum. These varieties with shiny gum are worth considerably more.

1618 A998 13c brown ('75) .30 .25
 a. Untagged (Bureau precanceled) .75 .75
 b. Imperf., pair 22.50
 g. Pair, imperf. between *600.00*
 h. As "a," imperf., pair —

Value for No. 1618a is for stamp with dull gum.

1618C A1001 15c gray, dk bl & red ('78) .75 .25
 d. Imperf., pair 20.00
 e. Pair, imperf. between *100.00*
 f. Gray omitted 30.00
1619 A1002 16c ultra ('78) .35 .25
 a. Huck Press Printing .50 .25
 Nos. 1613-1619 (9) 3.20 2.25

No. 1619a (the B press printing) has a white background without bluish tinge, is a fraction of a millimeter smaller than No. 1619 (the Cottrell press printing) and has no joint lines.

See Nos. 1811, 1813, 1816.

13-Star Flag, Independence Hall — A1015

1975-81 ***Perf. 11x10¾***

1622 A1015 13c dk bl, red & brn red .30 .25
 a. Horiz. pair, imperf. between 40.00
 b. Vertical pair, imperf. *225.00*
 e. Horiz. pair, imperf. vert. —

No. 1622 was printed on the Multicolored Huck Press. Plate markings are at top or bottom of pane.

Perf. 11¼

1622C A1015 13c dk bl, red & brn red ('81) 1.00 .25
 d. Vertical pair, imperf 100.00

No. 1622C was printed on the Combination Press. Plate markings are at sides of pane.

Flag over Capitol — A1016

BOOKLET STAMPS

Perf. 11x10½ on 2 or 3 Sides

1977, Mar. 11

1623 A1016 13c blue & red .30 .25
 a. Booklet pane, 1 #1590 + 7 #1623 2.25 2.00
 d. Pair, #1590 & #1623 .70 *1.25*

Perf. 10x9¾ on 2 or 3 Sides

1623B A1016 13c blue & red .65 .75
 c. Booklet pane, 1 #1590A + 7 #1623B 15.00 15.00
 e. Pair, #1590A & #1623B 14.00 14.00

COIL STAMP

1975, Nov. 15 ***Perf. 10 Vertically***

1625 A1015 13c dk blue, red & brown red .35 .25
 a. Imperf., pair 20.00

AMERICAN BICENTENNIAL ISSUE
The Spirit of '76

Designed after painting by Archibald M. Willard in Abbot Hall, Marblehead, Massachusetts. Nos. 1629-1631 printed in continuous design.

Left panes contain 3 No. 1631a and one No. 1629; right panes contain one No. 1631 and 3 No. 1631a.

Drummer Boy A1019

Old Drummer A1020

Fifer — A1021

PHOTOGRAVURE (Andreotti)

1976, Jan. 1 ***Perf. 11***

1629 A1019 13c blue violet & multi .30 .25
 a. Imperf., vert. pair —
1630 A1020 13c blue violet & multi .30 .25
1631 A1021 13c blue violet & multi .30 .25
 a. Strip of 3, #1629-1631 .75 .75
 b. As "a," imperf. *700.00*
 c. Imperf., vert. pair, #1631 *500.00*

INTERPHIL ISSUE

Interphil 76 International Philatelic Exhibition, Philadelphia, Pa., May 29-June 6.

"Interphil 76" — A1022

LITHOGRAPHED, ENGRAVED (Giori)

1976, Jan. 17

1632 A1022 13c dark blue & red (engr.), ultra. & red (litho.) .30 .25
- *a.* Dark blue & red (engr.) missing (CM) —
- *c.* Red (engr.) missing (CM) —

State Flags — A1023

Photo.

1976, Feb. 23

1633	A1023	13c	Delaware	.30	.25
1634	A1024	13c	Pennsylvania	.30	.25
1635	A1025	13c	New Jersey	.30	.25
1636	A1026	13c	Georgia	.30	.25
1637	A1027	13c	Connecticut	.30	.25
1638	A1028	13c	Massachusetts	.30	.25
1639	A1029	13c	Maryland	.30	.25
1640	A1030	13c	South Carolina	.30	.25
1641	A1031	13c	New Hampshire	.30	.25
1642	A1032	13c	Virginia	.30	.25
1643	A1033	13c	New York	.30	.25
1644	A1034	13c	North Carolina	.30	.25
1645	A1035	13c	Rhode Island	.30	.25
1646	A1036	13c	Vermont	.30	.25
1647	A1037	13c	Kentucky	.30	.25
1648	A1038	13c	Tennessee	.30	.25
1649	A1039	13c	Ohio	.30	.25
1650	A1040	13c	Louisiana	.30	.25
1651	A1041	13c	Indiana	.30	.25
1652	A1042	13c	Mississippi	.30	.25
1653	A1043	13c	Illinois	.30	.25
1654	A1044	13c	Alabama	.30	.25
1655	A1045	13c	Maine	.30	.25
1656	A1046	13c	Missouri	.30	.25
1657	A1047	13c	Arkansas	.30	.25
1658	A1048	13c	Michigan	.30	.25
1659	A1049	13c	Florida	.30	.25
1660	A1050	13c	Texas	.30	.25
1661	A1051	13c	Iowa	.30	.25
1662	A1052	13c	Wisconsin	.30	.25
1663	A1053	13c	California	.30	.25
1664	A1054	13c	Minnesota	.30	.25
1665	A1055	13c	Oregon	.30	.25
1666	A1056	13c	Kansas	.30	.25
1667	A1057	13c	West Virginia	.30	.25
1668	A1058	13c	Nevada	.30	.25
1669	A1059	13c	Nebraska	.30	.25
1670	A1060	13c	Colorado	.30	.25
1671	A1061	13c	North Dakota	.30	.25
1672	A1062	13c	South Dakota	.30	.25
1673	A1063	13c	Montana	.30	.25
1674	A1064	13c	Washington	.30	.25
1675	A1065	13c	Idaho	.30	.25
1676	A1066	13c	Wyoming	.30	.25
1677	A1067	13c	Utah	.30	.25
1678	A1068	13c	Oklahoma	.30	.25
1679	A1069	13c	New Mexico	.30	.25
1680	A1070	13c	Arizona	.30	.25
1681	A1071	13c	Alaska	.30	.25
1682	A1072	13c	Hawaii	.30	.25
a.			Pane of 50	17.50	15.00

TELEPHONE CENTENNIAL ISSUE

Centenary of first telephone call by Alexander Graham Bell, March 10, 1876.

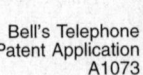

Bell's Telephone Patent Application A1073

ENGRAVED (Giori)

1976, Mar. 10

1683 A1073 13c blk, pur & red, *tan* .30 .25
- *a.* Black & purple missing (EP) *450.00*
- *b.* Red missing (EP) —
- *c.* All colors missing (EP) 725.00

On No. 1683a, the errors have only tiny traces of red present, so are best collected as a horiz. strip of 5 with 2 or 3 error stamps. No. 1683c also must be collected as a transitional strip.

COMMERCIAL AVIATION ISSUE

50th anniversary of first contract airmail flights: Dearborn, Mich. to Cleveland, Ohio, Feb. 15, 1926; and Pasco, Wash. to Elko, Nev., Apr. 6, 1926.

A1074

PHOTOGRAVURE (Andreotti)

1976, Mar. 19 Tagged *Perf. 11*

1684 A1074 13c blue & multicolored .30 .25

CHEMISTRY ISSUE

Honoring American chemists, in conjunction with the centenary of the American Chemical Society.

A1075

PHOTOGRAVURE (Andreotti)

1976, Apr. 6

1685 A1075 13c multicolored .30 .25

AMERICAN BICENTENNIAL ISSUES
SOUVENIR SHEETS

Designs, from Left to Right, No. 1686: a, Two British officers. b, Gen. Benjamin Lincoln. c, George Washington. d, John Trumbull, Col. Cobb, von Steuben, Lafayette, Thomas Nelson. e, Alexander Hamilton, John Laurens, Walter Stewart (all vert.).

No. 1687: a, John Adams, Roger Sherman, Robert R. Livingston. b, Jefferson, Franklin. c, Thomas Nelson, Jr., Francis Lewis, John Witherspoon, Samuel Huntington. d, John Hancock, Charles Thomson. e, George Read, John Dickinson, Edward Rutledge (a, d, vert., b, c, e, horiz.).

No. 1688: a, Boatsman. b, Washington. c, Flag bearer. d, Men in boat. e, Men on shore (a, d, horiz., b, c, e, vert.).

No. 1689: a, Two officers. b, Washington. c, Officer, black horse. d, Officer, white horse. e, Three soldiers (a, c, e, horiz., b, d, vert.).

LITHOGRAPHED

1976, May 29

1686 A1076 Pane of 5 2.75 2.25
- *a.-e.* 13c multicolored .40 .40
- *f.* "USA/13c" omitted on "b," "c" & "d," imperf., tagging omitted — *1,750.*
- *g.* "USA/13c" omitted on "a" & "e" *500.00* *300.00*
- *h.* Imperf., tagging omitted *2,000.*
- *i.* "USA/13c" omitted on "b," "c" & "d" *500.00*
- *j.* "USA/13c" double on "b" —
- *k.* "USA/13c" omitted on "c" & "d" *750.00*
- *l.* "USA/13c" omitted on "e" *475.00*
- *m.* "USA/13c" omitted, imperf., tagging omitted —
- *n.* As "g," imperf., tagging omitted *1,400.*
- *o.* "USA/13c" missing on "a" (PS) *450.00*
- *q.* "USA/13c" omitted on "a" *750.00*
- *r.* Imperf., tagged —
- *s.* "USA/13c" missing on "b" and "d" (PS) —

1687 A1077 Pane of 5 3.75 3.25
- *a.-e.* 18c multicolored .50 .50
- *f.* Design & marginal inscriptions omitted *2,500.*
- *g.* "USA/18c" omitted on "a" & "c" *550.00* *1,800.*
- *h.* "USA/18c" omitted on "b," "d" & "e" *350.00*
- *i.* "USA/18c" omitted on "d" *425.00* *475.00*
- *j.* Black omitted in design *1,500.*
- *k.* "USA/18c" omitted, imperf., tagging omitted *1,250.*
- *m.* "USA/18c" omitted on "b" & "e" *500.00*
- *n.* "USA/18c" omitted on "b" & "d" *1,000.*
- *p.* Imperf. (tagged) *1,000.*
- *q.* "USA/18c" missing on "c" (CM) —
- *r.* Yellow omitted *5,000.*
- *s.* "USA/18c" missing on "a," "c" and "d" (PS) —
- *t.* "USA/18c" missing on "a" and "d" (PS) *300.00*
- *u.* "USA/18c" omitted on "a" *5,000.*

1688 A1078 Pane of 5 4.75 4.25
- *a.-e.* 24c multicolored .65 .65
- *f.* "USA/24c" omitted, imperf., tagging omitted *950.00*
- *g.* "USA/24c" omitted on "d" & "e" *400.00* *400.00*
- *h.* Design & marginal inscriptions omitted *2,500.*
- *i.* "USA/24c" omitted on "a," "b" & "c" *400.00* *400.00*
- *j.* Imperf., tagging omitted *1,250.*
- *k.* "USA/24c" of "d" & "e" inverted *12,500.*
- *l.* As "i," imperf, tagging omitted *3,250.* —
- *n.* As No. 1688, perfs inverted and reversed *7,500.*
- *p.* "USA/24c" missing on "d" and "e" (CM) —
- *q.* "USA/24c" omitted on "b" and "c" —
- *r.* "USA/24c" omitted on "a" *400.00*
- *s.* As No. 1688, imperf. *1,250.*

1689 A1079 Pane of 5 5.75 5.25
- *a.-e.* 31c multicolored .80 .80
- *f.* "USA/31c" omitted, imperf. *1,600.*
- *g.* "USA/31c" omitted on "a" & "c" *375.00*
- *h.* "USA/31c" omitted on "b," "d" & "e" *450.00* —
- *i.* "USA/31c" omitted on "e" *375.00*
- *j.* Black omitted in design *1,700.*
- *k.* Imperf., tagging omitted *2,000.*
- *l.* "USA/31c" omitted on "b" & "d" *300.00*
- *m.* "USA/31c" omitted on "a," "c" & "e" *750.00*
- *n.* As "m," imperf., tagging omitted —
- *p.* As "h," imperf., tagging omitted *1,250.*
- *q.* As "g," imperf., tagging omitted *2,500.*
- *r.* "USA/31c" omitted on "d" & "e" *600.00*
- *s.* As "f," tagging omitted *2,000.*
- *t.* "USA/31c" omitted on "d" *500.00*
- *v.* As No. 1689, perfs and tagging inverted *10,000.*
- *w.* "USA/31c" missing on "a," "b," "c" and "d" (PS) *500.00*
- *x.* "USA/31c" missing on "e" (CM) —
- *y.* "USA/31c" omitted on "a" —

Nos. 1686-1689 (4) 17.00

Issued in connection with Interphil 76 International Philatelic Exhibition, Philadelphia, Pa., May 29-June 6. Size of panes: 203x152mm.

Benjamin Franklin

American Bicentennial: Benjamin Franklin (1706-1790), deputy postmaster general for the colonies (1753-1774) and statesman. Design based on marble bust by anonymous Italian sculptor after terra cotta bust by Jean Jacques Caffieri, 1777. Map published by R. Sayer and J. Bennett in London.

Franklin & Map of North America, 1776 — A1080

LITHOGRAPHED, ENGRAVED (Giori)

1976, June 1

1690 A1080 13c multicolored .30 .25
- *a.* Light blue omitted *150.00*

See Canada No. 691.

A1076

The Surrender of Lord Cornwallis at Yorktown
From a Painting by John Trumbull

A1077

The Declaration of Independence, 4 July 1776 at Philadelphia
From a Painting by John Trumbull

Washington Crossing the Delaware
From a Painting by Emanuel Leutze/Eastman Johnson

A1078

Washington Reviewing His Ragged Army at Valley Forge
From a Painting by William T. Trego

A1079

American Bicentennial Issue

A1081

A1082

A1083

A1084

Declaration of Independence, by John Trumbull

PHOTOGRAVURE (Andreotti)

1976, July 4

1691 A1081 13c multicolored .30 .25
1692 A1082 13c multicolored .30 .25
1693 A1083 13c multicolored .30 .25
1694 A1084 13c multicolored .30 .25
a. Strip of 4, #1691-1694 1.20 1.10

OLYMPIC GAMES ISSUE

12th Winter Olympic Games, Innsbruck, Austria, Feb. 4-15, and 21st Summer Olympic Games, Montreal, Canada, July 17-Aug. 1. Nos. 1695-1696 alternate in one row, Nos. 1697-1698 in other row.

Diving
A1085

Skiing
A1086

Running
A1087

Skating
A1088

1976, July 16

1695 A1085 13c multicolored .30 .25
1696 A1086 13c multicolored .30 .25
1697 A1087 13c multicolored .30 .25
1698 A1088 13c multicolored .30 .25
a. Block of 4, #1695-1698 1.20 1.20
b. As "a," imperf. 375.00

CLARA MAASS ISSUE

Clara Louise Maass (1876-1901), volunteer in fight against yellow fever, birth centenary.

Clara Maass, Newark German Hospital Pin — A1089

1976, Aug. 18

1699 A1089 13c multicolored .30 .25
a. Horiz. pair, imperf. vert. 350.00
b. Dark blue missing (PS) 700.00

On No. 1699, two blue plates were used. No 1699b is missing the dark blue ("She gave her life") at bottom due to an upward shift of the horizontal perforations.

ADOLPH S. OCHS ISSUE

Adolph S. Ochs, Publisher of the NY Times, 1896-1935 — A1090

GIORI PRESS PRINTING

1976, Sept. 18

1700 A1090 13c black & gray .30 .25

CHRISTMAS ISSUE

Nativity, by John Singleton Copley — A1091

Winter Pastime, by Nathaniel Currier — A1092

PHOTOGRAVURE (Andreotti)

1976, Oct. 27

1701 A1091 13c multicolored .30 .25
a. Imperf., pair 85.00
1702 A1092 13c multi, overall tagging .30 .25
a. Imperf., pair 75.00

COMBINATION PRESS

1703 A1092 13c multicolored .30 .25
a. Imperf., pair 75.00
b. Vert. pair, imperf. between 275.00
d. Red omitted 500.00
e. Yellow omitted 675.00

No. 1702 has overall tagging. Lettering at base is black and usually ½mm below design. As a rule, no "snowflaking" in sky or pond. Pane of 50 has margins on 4 sides with slogans. Plate Nos. 37465-37478.

No. 1703 has block tagging the size of printed area. Lettering at base is gray black and usually ¾mm below design. "Snowflaking" generally in sky and pond. Plate Nos. 37617-37621 or 37634-37638.

Examples of No. 1703 are known with various amounts of red or yellow missing. Nos. 1703d-1703e are stamps with the colors totally omitted. Expertization is recommended.

AMERICAN BICENTENNIAL ISSUE
Washington at Princeton

Washington's Victory over Lord Cornwallis at Princeton, N.J., bicentenary.

Washington, Nassau Hall, Hessians, 13-Star Flag — A1093

1977, Jan. 3

1704 A1093 13c multicolored .30 .25
a. Horiz. pair, imperf. vert. 425.00
b. Black (inscriptions) missing (PS) —

SOUND RECORDING ISSUE

Centenary of the invention of the phonograph by Thomas Alva Edison and development of sophisticated recording industry.

Tin Foil Phonograph A1094

LITHOGRAPHED, ENGRAVED (Giori)

1977, Mar. 23

1705 A1094 13c black & multi .30 .25
b. Black (engr.) and brown (engr.) missing (EP) 1,500.
c. Black (engr.) missing (EP) 1,000.

AMERICAN FOLK ART SERIES
Pueblo Pottery

Pueblo art, 1880-1920, from Museums in New Mexico, Arizona and Colorado.

Zia
A1095

San Ildefonso
A1096

Hopi
A1097

Acoma
A1098

PHOTOGRAVURE (Andreotti)

1977, Apr. 13

1706 A1095 13c multicolored .30 .25
1707 A1096 13c multicolored .30 .25
1708 A1097 13c multicolored .30 .25
1709 A1098 13c multicolored .30 .25
a. Block or strip of 4, #1706-1709 1.20 1.00
b. As "a," imperf. vert. 1,100.

LINDBERGH FLIGHT ISSUE

Charles A. Lindbergh's solo transatlantic flight from New York to Paris, 50th anniversary.

Spirit of St. Louis — A1099

1977, May 20

1710 A1099 13c multicolored .30 .25
a. Imperf., pair 700.00

COLORADO STATEHOOD ISSUE

Issued to honor Colorado as the "Centennial State." It achieved statehood in 1876.

Columbine & Rocky Mountains — A1100

1977, May 21

1711 A1100 13c multicolored .30 .25
a. Horiz. pair, imperf. between and with natural straight edge at right 650.00
b. Horiz. pair, imperf. vertically 500.00
c. Perf. 11.2 .75 .25

BUTTERFLY ISSUE

Nos. 1712-1713 alternate in 1st row, Nos. 1714-1715 in 2nd row. This arrangement is repeated throughout the pane. Butterflies represent different geographic US areas.

Swallowtail A1101

Checkerspot A1102

Dogface — A1103

Orange Tip — A1104

1977, June 6 **Tagged** ***Perf. 11***

1712 A1101 13c tan & multi .30 .25
1713 A1102 13c tan & multi .30 .25
1714 A1103 13c tan & multi .30 .25
1715 A1104 13c tan & multi .30 .25
a. Block of 4, #1712-1715 1.20 1.00
b. As "a," imperf. horiz. 9,500.

AMERICAN BICENTENNIAL ISSUES
Marquis de Lafayette

200th anniversary of Lafayette's Landing on the coast of South Carolina, north of Charleston.

Marquis de Lafayette — A1105

GIORI PRESS PRINTING

1977, June 13

1716 A1105 13c blue, black & red .30 .25
a. Red missing (PS) 300.00

Skilled Hands for Independence

Nos. 1717-1718 alternate in 1st row, Nos. 1719-1720 in 2nd row. This arrangement is repeated throughout the pane.

Seamstress A1106

Blacksmith A1107

Wheelwright A1108

Leatherworker A1109

1977, July 4

1717 A1106 13c multicolored .30 .25
1718 A1107 13c multicolored .30 .25
1719 A1108 13c multicolored .30 .25
1720 A1109 13c multicolored .30 .25
a. Block of 4, #1717-1720 1.20 1.00

PEACE BRIDGE ISSUE

50th anniversary of the Peace Bridge, connecting Buffalo (Fort Porter), N.Y. and Fort Erie, Ontario.

Peace Bridge & Dove — A1110

ENGRAVED

1977, Aug. 4 ***Perf. 11x10½***

1721 A1110 13c blue .30 .25

AMERICAN BICENTENNIAL ISSUE
Battle of Oriskany

200th anniv. of the Battle of Oriskany, American Militia led by Brig. Gen. Nicholas Herkimer (1728-77).

Herkimer at Oriskany, by Yohn — A1111

PHOTOGRAVURE (Andreotti)

1977, Aug. 6 *Perf. 11*
1722 A1111 13c multicolored .30 .25

ENERGY ISSUE

Conservation and development of nation's energy resources. Nos. 1723-1724 se-tenant vertically.

Energy Conservation A1112

Energy Development A1113

1977, Oct. 20
1723 A1112 13c multicolored .30 .25
1724 A1113 13c multicolored .30 .25
a. Pair, #1723-1724 .60 .50

ALTA CALIFORNIA ISSUE

Founding of El Pueblo de San José de Guadalupe, first civil settlement in Alta California, 200th anniversary.

Farm Houses — A1114

LITHOGRAPHED, ENGRAVED (Giori)

1977, Sept. 9 **Tagged** *Perf. 11*
1725 A1114 13c black & multi .30 .25

AMERICAN BICENTENNIAL ISSUE
Articles of Confederation

200th anniversary of drafting the Articles of Confederation, York Town, Pa.

Members of Continental Congress in Conference A1115

ENGRAVED (Giori)

1977, Sept. 30
1726 A1115 13c red & brn, *cream* .30 .25
b. Red omitted 500.00
c. Red & brown omitted 300.00

No. 1726b also has most of the brown omitted. No. 1726c must be collected as a transition multiple, certainly with No. 1726b and preferably also with No. 1726.

TALKING PICTURES, 50th ANNIV.

Movie Projector and Phonograph A1116

LITHOGRAPHED, ENGRAVED (Giori)

1977, Oct. 6
1727 A1116 13c multicolored .30 .25
a. Brown & black omitted —

AMERICAN BICENTENNIAL ISSUE
Surrender at Saratoga

200th anniversary of Gen. John Burgoyne's surrender at Saratoga.

Surrender of Burgoyne, by John Trumbull — A1117

PHOTOGRAVURE (Andreotti)

1977, Oct. 7
1728 A1117 13c multicolored .30 .25

CHRISTMAS ISSUE

Washington at Valley Forge A1118

Rural Mailbox A1119

PHOTOGRAVURE (Combination Press)

1977, Oct. 21
1729 A1118 13c multicolored .30 .25
a. Imperf., pair 50.00

See Combination Press note after No. 1703.

PHOTOGRAVURE (Andreotti)

1730 A1119 13c multicolored .30 .25
a. Imperf., pair 175.00

CARL SANDBURG ISSUE

Carl Sandburg (1878-1967), poet, biographer and collector of American folk songs, birth centenary.

Carl Sandburg, by William A. Smith, 1952 — A1120

GIORI PRESS PRINTING

1978, Jan. 6
1731 A1120 13c black & brown .30 .25
a. Brown omitted 1,750.
c. All colors omitted —

No. 1731c is tagged and has a faint black tagging ghost. Authentication is advised.

CAPTAIN COOK ISSUE

Capt. James Cook, 200th anniversary of his arrival in Hawaii, at Waimea, Kauai, Jan. 20, 1778, and of his anchorage in Cook Inlet, near Anchorage, Alaska, June 1, 1778. Nos. 1732-1733 printed in panes of 50, containing 25 each of Nos. 1732-1733 including 5 No. 1733b.

Capt. Cook, by Nathaniel Dance, 1776 A1121

"Resolution" and "Discovery," by John Webber A1122

1978, Jan. 20
1732 A1121 13c dark blue .30 .25
1733 A1122 13c green .30 .25
a. Vert. pair, imperf. horiz. 1,000.
b. Pair, #1732-1733 .60 .50
c. As "b," imperf. between 4,000.

Indian Head Penny, 1877 A1123

Eagle A1124

Roses — A1126

ENGRAVED (Giori)

1978
1734 A1123 13c brown & blue green, *bister, Jan. 11, 1978* .30 .25
a. Horiz. pair, imperf. vert. 175.00

PHOTOGRAVURE (Andreotti)

1735 A1124 (15c) orange, *May 22, 1978* .30 .25
a. Imperf., pair 70.00
b. Vert. pair, imperf. horiz. 500.00
c. Perf. 11.2 .35 .25

BOOKLET STAMPS
ENGRAVED

Perf. 11x10½ on 2 or 3 Sides

1736 A1124 (15c) orange .30 .25
a. Booklet pane of 8, *May 22, 1978* 2.50 1.50
c. Vert. pair, imperf. btwn., in #1736a with foldover 1,000.

Perf. 10 on 2 or 3 Sides

1737 A1126 15c multi .30 .25
a. Booklet pane of 8, *July 11, 1978* 2.50 2.00
b. Imperf, pair 450.00
c. As "a," imperf 2,250.

Robertson Windmill, Williamsburg A1127

Old Windmill, Portsmouth A1128

Cape Cod Windmill, Eastham A1129

Dutch Mill, Batavia A1130

Southwestern Windmill — A1131

BOOKLET STAMPS
ENGRAVED

Perf. 11 on 2 or 3 Sides

1980, Feb. 7
1738 A1127 15c sepia, *yellow* .30 .25
1739 A1128 15c sepia, *yellow* .30 .25
1740 A1129 15c sepia, *yellow* .30 .25
1741 A1130 15c sepia, *yellow* .30 .25
1742 A1131 15c sepia, *yellow* .30 .25
a. Booklet pane of 10, 2 each #1738-1742 3.50 3.00
b. Strip of 5, #1738-1742 1.50 1.40

COIL STAMP

1978, May 22 ***Perf. 10 Vert.***
1743 A1124 (15c) orange .30 .25
a. Imperf., pair 65.00

No. 1743a is valued in the grade of fine.

BLACK HERITAGE SERIES

Harriet Tubman (1820-1913), born a slave, helped more than 300 slaves escape to freedom.

Harriet Tubman (1820-1913), Cart Carrying Slaves — A1133

PHOTOGRAVURE (Andreotti)

1978, Feb. 1 ***Perf. 10½x11***
1744 A1133 13c multicolored .30 .25

AMERICAN FOLK ART SERIES
Quilts
Basket Design

A1134

A1135

A1136

A1137

1978, Mar. 8 ***Perf. 11***
1745 A1134 13c multicolored .30 .25
1746 A1135 13c multicolored .30 .25
1747 A1136 13c multicolored .30 .25
1748 A1137 13c multicolored .30 .25
a. Block of 4, #1745-1748 1.20 1.00

AMERICAN DANCE ISSUE

Ballet — A1138

Theater A1139

Folk Dance — A1140

Modern Dance — A1141

1978, Apr. 26
1749 A1138 13c multicolored .30 .25
1750 A1139 13c multicolored .30 .25
1751 A1140 13c multicolored .30 .25
1752 A1141 13c multicolored .30 .25
a. Block of 4, #1749-1752 1.20 1.00

AMERICAN BICENTENNIAL ISSUE

French Alliance, signed in Paris, Feb. 6, 1778 and ratified by Continental Congress, May 4, 1778.

Louis XVI and Franklin, Porcelain Sculpture by C. G. Sauvage — A1142

GIORI PRESS PRINTING

1978, May 4

1753	A1142 13c blue, black & red		.30	.25
a.	Red missing (PS)		—	

EARLY CANCER DETECTION ISSUE

George Papanicolaou, M.D. (1883-1962), cytologist and developer of Pap Test, early cancer detection in women.

Dr. George Papanicolaou (1883-1962) — A1143

ENGRAVED

1978, May 18 ***Perf. 10½x11***

1754	A1143 13c brown	.30	.25

PERFORMING ARTS SERIES

Jimmie Rodgers (1897-1933), the "Singing Brakeman, Father of Country Music" (No. 1755); George M. Cohan (1878-1942), actor and playwright (No. 1756).

Jimmie Rodgers and Locomotive A1144

George M. Cohan, "Yankee Doodle Dandy" and Stars A1145

PHOTOGRAVURE (Andreotti)

1978 ***Perf. 11***

1755	A1144 13c multicolored	.30	.25
1756	A1145 15c multicolored	.30	.25

CAPEX ISSUE

CAPEX '78, Canadian International Philatelic Exhibition, Toronto, Ont., June 9-18.

Wildlife from Canadian-U.S. Border — A1146

LITHOGRAPHED, ENGRAVED (Giori)

1978, June 10

1757	A1146 Block of 8, multi	2.40	2.00
a.	13c Cardinal	.30	.25
b.	13c Mallard	.30	.25
c.	13c Canada goose	.30	.25
d.	13c Blue jay	.30	.25
e.	13c Moose	.30	.25
f.	13c Chipmunk	.30	.25
g.	13c Red fox	.30	.25
h.	13c Raccoon	.30	.25
i.	As No. 1757, yellow, green, red, brown, blue, black (litho) omitted	*6,000.*	
j.	Strip of 4 (a-d), imperf. vert.	*5,000.*	
k.	Strip of 4 (e-h), imperf. vert.	*2,000.*	
l.	As No. 1757, "d" and "h" with black (engr.) omitted	—	
m.	As No. 1757, "b" with blue missing (PS)	—	
o.	Strip of 4 (e-h), all colors except black missing on "e," "f" and "g," all colors except black and brown missing on "h" (PS)	*1,250.*	
p.	As No. 1757, yellow, red, brown omitted, pane of 48	—	

No. 1757k is worth more when contained in the block of 8. Value is for strip only.

PHOTOGRAPHY ISSUE

Photography's contribution to communications and understanding.

Photographic Equipment — A1147

PHOTOGRAVURE (Andreotti)

1978, June 26

1758	A1147 15c multicolored	.30	.25

VIKING MISSIONS TO MARS ISSUE

Second anniv. of landing of Viking 1 on Mars.

Viking 1 Lander Scooping Up Soil on Mars — A1148

LITHOGRAPHED, ENGRAVED (Giori)

1978, July 20

1759	A1148 15c multicolored	.30	.25

WILDLIFE CONSERVATION

Nos. 1760-1761 alternate in one horizontal row. Nos. 1762-1763 in the next.

Great Gray Owl A1149

Saw-whet Owl A1150

Barred Owl A1151

Great Horned Owl A1152

1978, Aug. 26

1760	A1149 15c multicolored	.30	.25
1761	A1150 15c multicolored	.30	.25
1762	A1151 15c multicolored	.30	.25
1763	A1152 15c multicolored	.30	.25
a.	Block of 4, #1760-1763	1.25	1.25
c.	As "a," yellow and orange (litho.) omitted	—	

Two panes of No. 1763c have been reported. On one pane, the black (engr.) is shifted to the left.

AMERICAN TREES ISSUE

Giant Sequoia — A1153

White Pine — A1154

White Oak — A1155

Gray Birch — A1156

PHOTOGRAVURE (Andreotti)

1978, Oct. 9

1764	A1153 15c multicolored	.30	.25
1765	A1154 15c multicolored	.30	.25
1766	A1155 15c multicolored	.30	.25
1767	A1156 15c multicolored	.30	.25
a.	Block of 4, #1764-1767	1.25	1.25
b.	As "a," imperf. horiz.	*17,500.*	

No. 1767b is unique.

CHRISTMAS ISSUE

Madonna and Child with Cherubim, by Andrea della Robbia A1157

Child on Hobby-horse and Christmas Trees A1158

No. 1768, after terra cotta sculpture in National Gallery, Washington, D.C.

1978, Oct. 18 ***Perf. 11***

1768	A1157 15c blue & multi	.30	.25
a.	Imperf., pair	*70.00*	

Value for No. 1768a is for an uncreased pair.

1769	A1158 15c red & multi	.30	.25
a.	Imperf., pair	*75.00*	
b.	Vert. pair, imperf. horiz.	*900.00*	

ROBERT F. KENNEDY ISSUE

Robert F. Kennedy (1925-68), U.S. Attorney General — A1159

ENGRAVED

1979, Jan. 12

1770	A1159 15c blue	.35	.25

BLACK HERITAGE SERIES

Dr. Martin Luther King, Jr. (1929-1968), Civil Rights leader.

Dr. Martin Luther King, Jr. (1929-68), and Civil Rights Marchers — A1160

PHOTOGRAVURE (Andreotti)

1979, Jan. 13

1771	A1160 15c multicolored	.40	.25
a.	Imperf., pair	*800.00*	

INTERNATIONAL YEAR OF THE CHILD ISSUE

Children — A1161

ENGRAVED

1979, Feb. 15

1772	A1161 15c orange red	.30	.25

LITERARY ARTS SERIES

John Steinbeck — A1162

1979, Feb. 27 ***Perf. 10½x11***

1773	A1162 15c dark blue	.30	.25

ALBERT EINSTEIN ISSUE

Albert Einstein — A1163

1979, Mar. 4

1774	A1163 15c chocolate	.30	.25

AMERICAN FOLK ART SERIES

Pennsylvania Toleware, c. 1800.

Coffeepot A1164

Tea Caddy A1165

Sugar Bowl A1166

Coffeepot A1167

PHOTOGRAVURE (Andreotti)

1979, Apr. 19 ***Perf. 11***

1775	A1164 15c multicolored	.30	.25
1776	A1165 15c multicolored	.30	.25
1777	A1166 15c multicolored	.30	.25
1778	A1167 15c multicolored	.30	.25
a.	Block of 4, #1775-1778	1.25	1.25
b.	As "a," imperf. horiz.	*2,000.*	

AMERICAN ARCHITECTURE SERIES

Virginia Rotunda, by Thomas Jefferson A1168

Baltimore Cathedral, by Benjamin Latrobe A1169

Boston State House, by Charles Bulfinch A1170

Philadelphia Exchange, by William Strickland A1171

ENGRAVED (Giori)

1979, June 4

1779	A1168 15c blk & brick red	.30	.25
1780	A1169 15c blk & brick red	.30	.25
1781	A1170 15c blk & brick red	.30	.25
1782	A1171 15c blk & brick red	.30	.25
a.	Block of 4, #1779-1782	1.25	1.25

ENDANGERED FLORA ISSUE

Persistent Trillium
A1172

Hawaiian Wild Broadbean
A1173

Contra Costa Wallflower
A1174

Antioch Dunes Evening Primrose
A1175

PHOTOGRAVURE (Andreotti)

1979, June 7

1783 A1172 15c multicolored .30 .25
1784 A1173 15c multicolored .30 .25
1785 A1174 15c multicolored .30 .25
1786 A1175 15c multicolored .30 .25
a. Block of 4, #1783-1786 1.25 1.25
b. As "a," imperf. *200.00*

SEEING EYE DOGS ISSUE

1st guide dog program in the US, 50th anniv.

German Shepherd Leading Man — A1176

PHOTOGRAVURE (Combination Press)

1979, June 15

1787 A1176 15c multicolored .30 .25
a. Imperf., pair *325.00*

SPECIAL OLYMPICS ISSUE

Special Olympics for special children, Brockport, N.Y., Aug. 8-13.

Child Holding Winner's Medal — A1177

PHOTOGRAVURE (Andreotti)

1979, Aug. 9

1788 A1177 15c multicolored .30 .25

JOHN PAUL JONES ISSUE

John Paul Jones (1747-1792), Naval Commander, American Revolution.

John Paul Jones, by Charles Willson Peale — A1178

PHOTOGRAVURE (Champlain)

1979, Sept. 23 ***Perf. 11x12***

1789 A1178 15c multi .30 .25
c. Vert. pair, imperf. horiz. *125.00*

Imperforates on gummed stamp paper, including gutter pairs and blocks, are proofs from the ABNCo. archives. See No. 1789P in Proofs section of the Scott United States Specialized Catalogue.

Perf. 11

1789A A1178 15c multi .55 .25
d. Vertical pair, imperf. horiz. *115.00*

Perf. 12

1789B A1178 15c multi *3,000. 3,500.*

OLYMPIC GAMES ISSUE

22nd Summer Olympic Games, Moscow, July 19-Aug. 3, 1980. Nos. 1791-1792 alternate in one horizontal row, Nos. 1793-1794 in next.

Javelin — A1179

Running — A1180

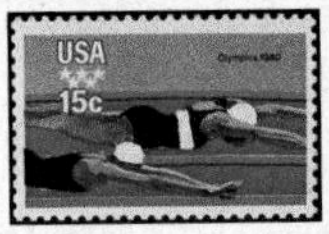

Swimming A1181

Rowing — A1182

Equestrian A1183

PHOTOGRAVURE

1979, Sept. 5 ***Perf. 11***

1790 A1179 10c multicolored .30 .25

1979, Sept. 28

1791 A1180 15c multicolored .30 .25
1792 A1181 15c multicolored .30 .25
1793 A1182 15c multicolored .30 .25
1794 A1183 15c multicolored .30 .25
a. Block of 4, #1791-1794 1.25 1.25
b. As "a," imperf. *900.00*

OLYMPIC GAMES ISSUE

13th Winter Olympic Games, Lake Placid, N.Y., Feb. 12-24. Nos. 1795-1796 alternate in one horizontal row, Nos. 1797-1798 in next.

Speed Skating — A1184

Downhill Skiing — A1185

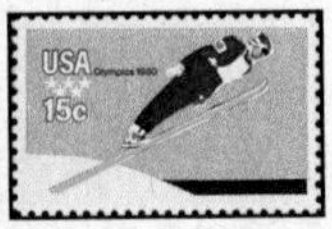

Ski Jump — A1186

Ice Hockey — A1187

1980, Feb. 1 ***Perf. 11¼x10½***

1795 A1184 15c multicolored .35 .25
1796 A1185 15c multicolored .35 .25
1797 A1186 15c multicolored .35 .25
1798 A1187 15c multicolored .35 .25
b. Block of 4, #1795-1798 1.50 1.40

Perf. 11

1795A A1184 15c multicolored 1.00 .60
1796A A1185 15c multicolored 1.00 .60
1797A A1186 15c multicolored 1.00 .60
1798A A1187 15c multicolored 1.00 .60
c. Block of 4, #1795A-1798A 4.00 3.50

CHRISTMAS ISSUE

Virgin and Child, by Gerard David
A1188

Santa Claus, Christmas Tree Ornament
A1189

No. 1799 is designed after a painting in National Gallery of Art, Washington, D.C.

PHOTOGRAVURE (Andreotti)

1979, Oct. 18 ***Perf. 11***

1799 A1188 15c multicolored .30 .25
a. Imperf., pair 70.00
b. Vert. pair, imperf. horiz. *450.00*
c. Vert. pair, imperf. between *950.00*

Perf. 11x10½

1800 A1189 15c multicolored .30 .25
a. Green & yellow omitted *400.00*
b. Green, yellow & tan omitted *400.00*
c. Vert. se-tenant pair, #1800a & 1800b *850.00*

Nos. 1800a and 1800b always have the remaining colors misaligned.

Nos. 1800a, 1800b and 1800c are valued in the grade of fine.

VALUES FOR HINGED STAMPS AFTER NO. 771

This catalogue does not value unused stamps after No. 771 in hinged condition. Hinged unused stamps from No. 772 to the present are worth considerably less than the values given for unused stamps, which are for never-hinged examples.

PERFORMING ARTS SERIES

Will Rogers (1879-1935), Actor and Humorist — A1190

1979, Nov. 4 **Tagged** ***Perf. 11***

1801 A1190 15c multicolored .30 .25
a. Imperf., pair *135.00*

VIETNAM VETERANS ISSUE

A tribute to veterans of the Vietnam War.

Ribbon for Viet Nam Service Medal — A1191

1979, Nov. 11

1802 A1191 15c multicolored .30 .25

PERFORMING ARTS SERIES

W.C. Fields (1880-1946), actor and comedian.

W.C. Fields (1880-1946), Actor and Comedian — A1192

PHOTOGRAVURE

1980, Jan. 29

1803 A1192 15c multicolored .30 .25
a. Imperf., pair

BLACK HERITAGE SERIES

Benjamin Banneker (1731-1806), astronomer and mathematician.

Benjamin Banneker (1731-1806), Astronomer and Mathematician, Transverse — A1193

1980, Feb. 15

1804 A1193 15c multicolored .30 .25
a. Horiz. pair, imperf. vert. *275.00*

Imperfs, including gutter pairs and blocks, exist from printer's waste. These have been fraudulently perforated to simulate No. 1804a. Genuine examples of No. 1804a do not have colors misregistered.

NATIONAL LETTER WRITING WEEK ISSUE

National Letter Writing Week, Feb. 24-Mar. 1. Nos. 1805-1810 are printed vertically se-tenant.

Letters Preserve Memories
A1194

P.S. Write Soon
A1195

Letters Lift Spirits
A1196

Letters Shape Opinions
A1197

1980, Feb. 25

1805 A1194 15c multicolored .30 .25
1806 A1195 15c purple & multi .30 .25
1807 A1196 15c multicolored .30 .25
1808 A1195 15c green & multi .30 .25
1809 A1197 15c multicolored .30 .25
1810 A1195 15c red & multi .30 .25
a. Vertical strip of 6, #1805-1810 1.85 *2.00*
Nos. 1805-1810 (6) 1.80 1.50

AMERICANA TYPE

Weaver Violins — A1199

COIL STAMPS

1980-81 **Engr.** ***Perf. 10 Vertically***

1811 A984 1c dk blue, *grnish* .30 .25
a. Imperf., pair *60.00*
1813 A1199 3.5c pur, *yel* .30 .25
a. Untagged (Bureau precanceled, lines only) .25 .25
b. Imperf., pair *125.00*
1816 A997 12c red brown, *beige ('81)* .30 .25
a. Untagged (Bureau precanceled), red brown, *beige* 1.25 1.25
b. Imperf., pair 135.00
c. As "a," brownish red, *reddish beige* 1.25 1.25
Nos. 1811-1816 (3) .90 .75

A1207

PHOTOGRAVURE

1981, Mar. 15 **Tagged** ***Perf. 11x10½***

1818 A1207 (18c) violet .35 .25

BOOKLET STAMP
ENGRAVED
Perf. 10 on 2 or 3 Sides

1819 A1207 (18c) violet .40 .25
a. Booklet pane of 8 3.50 2.25

COIL STAMP
Perf. 10 Vert.

1820 A1207 (18c) violet .40 .25
a. Imperf., pair 75.00

FRANCES PERKINS ISSUE

Frances Perkins (1882-1965), Secretary of Labor, 1933-1945 (first woman cabinet member).

Frances Perkins — A1208

ENGRAVED

1980, Apr. 10 ***Perf. 10½x11***
1821 A1208 15c Prussian blue .30 .25

DOLLEY MADISON ISSUE

Dolley Madison (1768-1849), First Lady, 1809-1817.

Dolley Madison — A1209

1980, May 20 ***Perf. 11***
1822 A1209 15c red brown & sepia .30 .25
a. Red brown missing (PS) 575.00

EMILY BISSELL ISSUE

Emily Bissell (1861-1948), social worker; introduced Christmas seals in United States.

Emily Bissell — A1210

1980, May 31
1823 A1210 15c black & red .30 .25
a. Vert. pair, imperf. horiz. 250.00
b. All colors missing (EP) —
c. Red missing (FO) —
d. Red omitted —

On No. 1823d, traces of black are present.

HELEN KELLER ISSUE

Helen Keller (1880-1968), blind and deaf writer and lecturer taught by Anne Sullivan (1867-1936).

Helen Keller and Anne Sullivan — A1211

LITHOGRAPHED AND ENGRAVED

1980, June 27
1824 A1211 15c multicolored .30 .25

VETERANS ADMINISTRATION, 50th ANNIV.

Veterans Admin-istration Emblem — A1212

PHOTOGRAVURE

Plates of 200 subjects in four panes of 50.

1980, July 21
1825 A1212 15c car & vio blue .30 .25
a. Horiz. pair, imperf. vert. 375.00

BERNARDO DE GALVEZ ISSUE

Gen. Bernardo de Galvez (1746-1786), helped defeat British in Battle of Mobile, 1780.

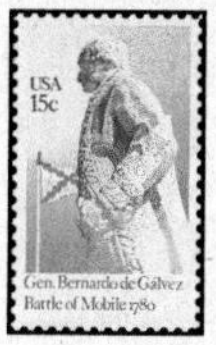

Gen. Bernardo de Galvez — A1213

LITHOGRAPHED & ENGRAVED

1980, July 23
1826 A1213 15c multicolored .30 .25
a. Red, brown & blue (engr.) omitted 550.00
b. Light yellow, red, blue & brown (litho.) omitted 550.00

CORAL REEFS ISSUE

Brain Coral, Beaugregory Fish A1214

Elkhorn Coral, Porkfish A1215

Chalice Coral, Moorish Idol Fish A1216

Finger Coral, Sabertooth Blenny Fish A1217

PHOTOGRAVURE

1980, Aug. 26
1827 A1214 15c multi .30 .25
1828 A1215 15c multi .30 .25
1829 A1216 15c multi .30 .25
1830 A1217 15c multi .30 .25
a. Block of 4, #1827-1830 1.25 1.10
b. As "a," imperf. 250.00
c. As "a," vert. imperf. between 1,750.
d. As "a," imperf. vert. 2,750.

ORGANIZED LABOR ISSUE

American Bald Eagle — A1218

1980, Sept. 1
1831 A1218 15c multi .30 .25
a. Imperf., pair 275.00

LITERARY ARTS SERIES

Edith Wharton (1862-1937), novelist.

Edith Wharton — A1219

ENGRAVED

1980, Sept. 5 ***Perf. 10½x11***
1832 A1219 15c purple .30 .25

EDUCATION ISSUE

"Homage to the Square: Glow," by Josef Albers — A1220

PHOTOGRAVURE

1980, Sept. 12 ***Perf. 11***
1833 A1220 15c multi .30 .25
a. Horiz. pair, imperf. vert. 150.00

AMERICAN FOLK ART SERIES

Pacific Northwest Indian Masks

Heiltsuk, Bella Bella Tribe — A1221

Chilkat Tlingit Tribe — A1222

Tlingit Tribe — A1223

Bella Coola Tribe — A1224

1980, Sept. 25
1834 A1221 15c multi .35 .25
1835 A1222 15c multi .35 .25
1836 A1223 15c multi .35 .25
1837 A1224 15c multi .35 .25
a. Block of 4, #1834-1837 1.50 1.25

AMERICAN ARCHITECTURE SERIES

Smithsonian Institution, by James Renwick — A1225

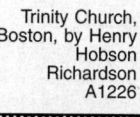

Trinity Church, Boston, by Henry Hobson Richardson A1226

Pennsylvania Academy of Fine Arts, by Frank Furness — A1227

Lyndhurst, Tarrytown, NY, by Alexander Jackson Davis — A1228

ENGRAVED (Giori)

1980, Oct. 9
1838 A1225 15c black & red .30 .25
a. Red missing (PS) —
1839 A1226 15c black & red .30 .25
1840 A1227 15c black & red .30 .25
1841 A1228 15c black & red .30 .25
a. Block of 4, #1838-1841 1.25 1.25
b. As "a," red missing on Nos. 1838, 1839 (PS) 400.00

CHRISTMAS ISSUE

Madonna and Child A1229

Wreath, Toys on Windowsill A1230

Design of No. 1842 after Epiphany Window, Washington Cathedral.

PHOTOGRAVURE

1980, Oct. 31
1842 A1229 15c multi .30 .25
a. Imperf., pair 40.00

PHOTOGRAVURE (Combination Press)

1843 A1230 15c multi .30 .25
a. Imperf., pair 45.00
b. Buff omitted 22.50
c. Vert. pair, imperf. horiz. —
d. Horiz. pair, imperf. between 3,250.

No. 1843b is difficult to identify and should have a competent certificate.

GREAT AMERICANS ISSUE

Dorothea Dix A1231

Igor Stravinsky A1232

Henry Clay A1233

Carl Schurz A1234

Pearl Buck A1235

Walter Lippmann A1236

Abraham Baldwin A1237

Henry Knox A1238

Sylvanus Thayer A1239

Richard Russell A1240

Alden Partridge A1241

Crazy Horse A1242

Sinclair Lewis A1243

Rachel Carson A1244

George Mason
A1245

Sequoyah
A1246

Ralph Bunche
A1247

Thomas H. Gallaudet
A1248

Harry S. Truman
A1249

John J. Audubon
A1250

Frank C. Laubach
A1251

Charles R. Drews MD
A1252

Robert Millikan
A1253

Grenville Clark
A1254

Lillian M. Gilbreth
A1255

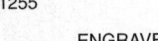

Chester W. Nimitz
A1256

ENGRAVED

Perf. 11x10½, 11 (1c, 6c-11c, 14c, No. 1862, 22c, 30c, 39c, 40c, 50c)

1980-85

1844 A1231 1c black ('83) .30 .25
a. Imperf., pair *250.00*
b. Vert. pair, imperf. btwn. and with natural straight edge at bottom *1,000.*
e. Vert. pair, imperf. horiz. *1,000.*
1845 A1232 2c brn blk ('82) .30 .25
1846 A1233 3c ol grn ('83) .30 .25
1847 A1234 4c violet ('83) .30 .25
1848 A1235 5c henna brn ('83) .30 .25
1849 A1236 6c org verm ('85) .30 .25
a. Vert. pair, imperf. between and with natural straight edge at bottom *1,000.*
1850 A1237 7c brt car ('85) .30 .25
1851 A1238 8c ol blk ('85) .30 .25
1852 A1239 9c dk grn ('86) .30 .25
1853 A1240 10c Prussian bl ('84) .30 .25
b. Vert. pair, imperf. between *550.00*
c. Horiz. pair, imperf. between *1,250.*
d. Vert. pair, imperf horiz. —

Almost all examples of No. 1853b also have a natural straight edge at bottom. At least one pair has perfs at bottom and partial perfs at top.

Completely imperforate tagged or untagged stamps are from printer's waste. Known unused and used.

1854 A1241 11c dk blue ('85) .40 .25
1855 A1242 13c lt maroon ('82) .40 .25
1856 A1243 14c slate grn ('85) .30 .25
b. Vert. pair, imperf. horiz. *90.00*
c. Horiz. pair, imperf. between 8.00 —
d. Vert. pair, imperf. between *1,250.*
e. All color omitted —

No. 1856e comes from a partially printed pane and should be collected as a vertical strip of 10, one stamp normal, one stamp transitional and 8 stamps with color omitted.

1857 A1244 17c green ('81) .35 .25
1858 A1245 18c dk blue ('81) .35 .25
1859 A1246 19c brown .45 .25
1860 A1247 20c claret ('82) .40 .25
1861 A1248 20c green ('83) .50 .25
1862 A1249 20c black ('84) .40 .25
1863 A1250 22c dk chalky bl ('85) .75 .25
d. Vert. pair, imperf. horiz. *1,300.*
f. Horiz. pair, imperf. between *1,300.*
g. Vert. pair, imperf. between —
1864 A1251 30c ol gray ('84) .60 .25
b. Perf. 11.2, overall tagging 3.75 .25
1865 A1252 35c gray ('81) .75 .25
1866 A1253 37c blue ('82) .80 .25
1867 A1254 39c rose lilac ('85) 1.00 .25
a. Vert. pair, imperf. horiz. *350.00*
b. Vert. pair, imperf. between *1,500.*
1868 A1255 40c dk green ('84) 1.00 .25
1869 A1256 50c brown ('85) 1.00 .25
Nos. 1844-1869 (26) 12.45 6.50

EVERETT DIRKSEN (1896-1969)

Senate minority leader, 1960-1969.

A1261

ENGRAVED

1981, Jan. 4 ***Perf. 11***
1874 A1261 15c gray .30 .25
a. All color omitted *500.00*

No. 1874a comes from a partially printed pane and may be collected as a vertical strip of 3 or 5 (1 or 3 stamps normal, one stamp transitional and one stamp with color omitted) or as a pair with one partially printed stamp.

BLACK HERITAGE SERIES

Whitney Moore Young, Jr. (1921-1971), civil rights leader.

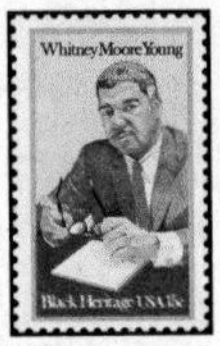

A1262

PHOTOGRAVURE

1981, Jan. 30
1875 A1262 15c multi .35 .25

FLOWER ISSUE

A1263

A1264

A1265

A1266

1981, Apr. 23
1876 A1263 18c multicolored .35 .25
1877 A1264 18c multicolored .35 .25
1878 A1265 18c multicolored .35 .25
1879 A1266 18c multicolored .35 .25
a. Block of 4, #1876-1879 1.40 1.25

AMERICAN WILDLIFE

A1267

A1268

A1269

A1270

A1271

A1272

A1273

A1274

A1275

A1276

No. 1880, Bighorn. No. 1881, Puma. No. 1882, Harbor seal. No. 1883, American Buffalo. No. 1884, Brown bear. No. 1885, Polar bear. No. 1886, Elk (wapiti). No. 1887, Moose. No. 1888, White-tailed deer. No. 1889, Pronghorn.

ENGRAVED

1981, May 14
1880 A1267 18c multicolored .50 .25
1881 A1268 18c multicolored .50 .25
1882 A1269 18c multicolored .50 .25
1883 A1270 18c multicolored .50 .25
1884 A1271 18c multicolored .50 .25
1885 A1272 18c multicolored .50 .25
1886 A1273 18c multicolored .50 .25
1887 A1274 18c multicolored .50 .25
1888 A1275 18c multicolored .50 .25
1889 A1276 18c multicolored .50 .25
a. Booklet pane of 10, #1880-1889 5.00 5.00
Nos. 1880-1889 (10) 5.00 2.50

Nos. 1880-1889 issued in booklet only. All stamps have one or two straight edges.
Imperfs are from printer's waste.

FLAG AND ANTHEM ISSUE

A1277

A1278

A1279

A1280

ENGRAVED

1981, Apr. 24 ***Perf. 11***
1890 A1277 18c multicolored .35 .25
a. Imperf., pair *75.00*
b. Vert. pair, imperf. horiz. *550.00*
c. Vert. pair, imperf. between *550.00*

Coil Stamp

Perf. 10 Vert.

1891 A1278 18c multicolored .35 .25
a. Imperf., pair 17.50 —
b. Pair, imperf. between *1,750.*

Beware of pairs offered as No. 1891b that have faint blind perfs.
Vertical pairs and blocks exist from printer's waste.

Booklet Stamps

Perf. 11x10½ on 3 Sides

1892 A1279 6c dark blue & red .50 .25

Perf. 11x10½ on 2 or 3 Sides

1893 A1280 18c multicolored .30 .25
a. Booklet pane of 8 (2 #1892, 6 #1893) 3.00 2.50
b. As "a," vert. imperf. between 60.00
c. Se-tenant pair, #1892 & #1893 .90 1.00

Bureau Precanceled Coils
Starting with No. 1895b, Bureau precanceled coil stamps are valued unused as well as used. The coils issued with dull gum may be difficult to distinguish.
When used normally these stamps do not receive any postal markings so that used stamps with an additional postal cancellation of any kind are worth considerably less than the values shown here.

FLAG OVER SUPREME COURT ISSUE

A1281

1981, Dec. 17 ***Perf. 11***
1894 A1281 20c blk, dk bl & red .40 .25
a. Vert. pair, imperf. 30.00
b. Vert. pair, imperf. horiz. *250.00*
c. Dark blue omitted *60.00*
d. Black omitted *225.00*

Coil Stamp

Perf. 10 Vert.

1895 A1281 20c blk, dk bl & red .40 .25
b. Untagged (Bureau precanceled, lines only) .50 .50
d. Imperf., pair 8.00 —
e. Pair, imperf. between *600.00*
f. Black omitted *45.00*
g. Dark blue omitted *1,000.*
h. Black field of stars instead of blue —

BOOKLET STAMP

Perf. 11x10½ on 2 or 3 Sides

1896 A1281 20c blk, dk bl & red .40 .25
a. Booklet pane of 6 3.00 2.25
b. Booklet pane of 10, *June 1, 1982* 5.25 3.25
Scored perforations 7.50 5.00

TRANSPORTATION ISSUE

Omnibus 1880s
A1283

Locomotive 1870s
A1284

COIL STAMPS
ENGRAVED

1981-84 ***Perf. 10 Vert.***
1897 A1283 1c violet ('83) .30 .25
b. Imperf., pair *325.00*

See No. 2225.

1897A A1284 2c black ('82) .30 .25
c. Imperf., pair 45.00

See No. 2226.

Handcar 1880s — A1284a

Stagecoach 1890s — A1285

1898 A1284a 3c dk grn ('83) .30 .25
1898A A1285 4c reddish brn ('82) .30 .25
b. Untagged (Bureau precanceled, Nonprofit Org.) .30 .25
c. As "b," imperf., pair *300.00*
d. As No. 1898A, imperf. pair *400.00* —

See No. 2228.

Motorcycle 1913
A1286

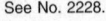

Sleigh 1880s
A1287

1899 A1286 5c gray grn ('83) .30 .25
a. Imperf., pair *1,500.*
1900 A1287 5.2c car ('83) .30 .25
a. Untagged (Bureau precanceled, lines only) .30 .25

Bicycle 1870s A1288

Baby Buggy 1880s A1289

1901 A1288 5.9c blue ('82) .30 .25
a. Untagged (Bureau precanceled, lines only) .30 .25
b. As "a," imperf., pair 140.00
1902 A1289 7.4c brown ('84) .30 .25
a. Untagged (Bureau precanceled, Blk. Rt. CAR-RT SORT) .30 .25

Mail Wagon 1880s A1290

Hansom Cab 1890s A1291

1903 A1290 9.3c car rose .30 .25
a. Untagged (Bureau precanceled, lines only) .30 .25
b. As "a," imperf., pair 90.00
1904 A1291 10.9c pur ('82) .30 .25
a. Untagged (Bureau precanceled, lines only) .30 .25
b. As "a," imperf., pair 125.00

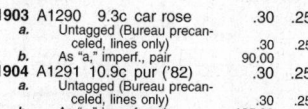

RR Caboose 1890s A1292

Electric Auto 1917 A1293

1905 A1292 11c red ('84) .30 .25
a. Untagged *Sept. 1991* .25 .25

Untagged stamps from plate 1 come only Bureau precanceled with lines. Untagged stamps from plate 2 come only without precancel lines.

1906 A1293 17c ultra .35 .25
a. Untagged (Bureau precanceled, Presorted First Class) .35 .35
b. Imperf., pair 130.00
c. As "a," imperf., pair 400.00

Surrey 1890s A1294

Fire Pumper 1860s A1295

1907 A1294 18c dk brn .35 .25
a. Imperf., pair 95.00
1908 A1295 20c vermilion .35 .25
a. Imperf., pair 75.00
Nos. 1897-1908 (14) 4.35 3.50

A1296

Booklet Stamp
PHOTOGRAVURE
Perf. 10 Vert. on 1 or 2 Sides
1983, Aug. 12 **Untagged**
1909 A1296 $9.35 multicolored 19.00 15.00
a. Booklet pane of 3 57.50 —

AMERICAN RED CROSS CENTENNIAL

A1297

Plates of 200 subjects in four panes of 50.

1981, May 1 ***Perf. 10½x11***
1910 A1297 18c multicolored .35 .25

SAVINGS & LOAN SESQUICENTENNIAL

A1298

1981, May 8 ***Perf. 11***
1911 A1298 18c multicolored .35 .25

SPACE ACHIEVEMENT ISSUE

A1299

A1302

A1300

A1301

A1303

A1306

A1304

A1305

Designs: A1299, Moon walk. A1300-A1301, A1304-A1305, Columbia space shuttle. A1302, Skylab. A1303, Pioneer 11. A1306, Telescope.

1981, May 21
1912 A1299 18c multicolored .35 .25
1913 A1300 18c multicolored .35 .25
1914 A1301 18c multicolored .35 .25
1915 A1302 18c multicolored .35 .25
1916 A1303 18c multicolored .35 .25
1917 A1304 18c multicolored .35 .25
1918 A1305 18c multicolored .35 .25
1919 A1306 18c multicolored .35 .25
a. Block of 8, #1912-1919 2.80 3.00
b. As "a," imperf. 5,500.
c. As "a," imperf. vert. 2,000.
e. As "a," top 4 stamps part perf, bottom 4 stamps imperf 2,700.

No. 1919c is unique and has blind horiz. perfs.

PROFESSIONAL MANAGEMENT EDUCATION CENTENARY

Joseph Wharton — A1307

1981, June 18
1920 A1307 18c blue & black .35 .25

PRESERVATION OF WILDLIFE HABITATS

A1308

A1309

A1310

A1311

1981, June 26
1921 A1308 18c multicolored .35 .25
1922 A1309 18c multicolored .35 .25
1923 A1310 18c multicolored .35 .25
1924 A1311 18c multicolored .35 .25
a. Block of 4, #1921-1924 1.50 1.25

INTERNATIONAL YEAR OF THE DISABLED

Man Looking through Microscope A1312

1981, June 29
1925 A1312 18c multicolored .35 .25
a. Vert. pair, imperf. horiz. 1,500.

EDNA ST. VINCENT MILLAY ISSUE

A1313

LITHOGRAPHED AND ENGRAVED
1981, July 10
1926 A1313 18c multicolored .35 .25
a. Black (engr., inscriptions) omitted 200.00 —

ALCOHOLISM

A1314

ENGRAVED
1981, Aug. 19
1927 A1314 18c blue & black .45 .25
a. Imperf., pair 325.00
b. Vert. pair, imperf. horiz. 2,000.

AMERICAN ARCHITECTURE SERIES

New York University Library by Sanford White — A1315

Biltmore House by Richard Morris Hunt — A1316

Palace of the Arts by Bernard Maybeck A1317

National Farmer's Bank by Louis Sullivan — A1318

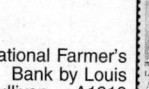

1981, Aug. 28
1928 A1315 18c black & red .40 .25
1929 A1316 18c black & red .40 .25
a. Red missing (PS) —
1930 A1317 18c black & red .40 .25
b. Red missing (PS) —
1931 A1318 18c black & red .40 .25
a. Block of 4, #1928-1931 1.65 1.65

SPORTS PERSONALITIES

Mildred Didrikson Zaharias A1319

Robert Tyre Jones A1320

1981, Sept. 22 ***Perf. 10½x11***
1932 A1319 18c purple .40 .25
1933 A1320 18c green .60 .25

FREDERIC REMINGTON

Coming Through the Rye — A1321

LITHOGRAPHED AND ENGRAVED
1981, Oct. 9 ***Perf. 11***
1934 A1321 18c gray, olive green & brown .35 .25
a. Vert. pair, imperf. between 160.00
b. Brown omitted 190.00

JAMES HOBAN

Irish-American Architect of White House — A1322

PHOTOGRAVURE
1981, Oct. 13
1935 A1322 18c multicolored .35 .25
1936 A1322 20c multicolored .35 .25

See Ireland No. 504.

AMERICAN BICENTENNIAL

Battle of Yorktown A1323

Battle of Virginia Capes — A1324

LITHOGRAPHED AND ENGRAVED
1981, Oct. 16
1937 A1323 18c multicolored .35 .25
1938 A1324 18c multicolored .35 .25
a. Pair, #1937-1938 .90 .75
b. As "a," black (engr., inscriptions) omitted 275.00
d. As "a," black (litho.) omitted —

CHRISTMAS

Madonna and Child, Botticelli A1325

Felt Bear on Sled A1326

PHOTOGRAVURE

1981, Oct. 28

1939	A1325	(20c) multi	.40	.25
a.		Imperf., pair	90.00	
b.		Vert. pair, imperf. horiz.	750.00	
1940	A1326	(20c) multi	.40	.25
a.		Imperf., pair	175.00	
b.		Vert. pair, imperf. horiz.	1,750.	

JOHN HANSON

First President of Continental Congress — A1327

1981, Nov. 5

1941	A1327	20c multicolored	.40	.25

DESERT PLANTS

Barrel Cactus A1328

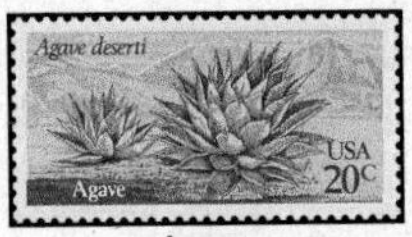

Agave A1329

Beavertail Cactus A1330

Saguaro A1331

LITHOGRAPHED AND ENGRAVED

1981 Dec. 11

1942	A1328	20c multicolored	.35	.25
1943	A1329	20c multicolored	.35	.25
1944	A1330	20c multicolored	.35	.25
1945	A1331	20c multicolored	.35	.25
a.		Block of 4, #1942-1945	1.50	1.25
b.		As "a," deep brown (litho.) omitted	3,000.	
c.		No. 1945 imperf., vert. pair	3,000.	
d.		As "a," dark green & dark blue (engr.) missing (EP)	1,800.	
e.		As "a," dark green (engr.) missing on left stamp (EP)	2,500.	

A1332

A1333

PHOTOGRAVURE

1981, Oct. 11 ***Perf. 11x10½***

1946	A1332	(20c) brown	.40	.25
b.		All color omitted	425.00	

No. 1946b comes from a partially printed pane with most stamps normal. It must be collected as a vertical pair or strip with normal or partially printed stamps attached.

ENGRAVED
COIL STAMP
Perf. 10 Vert.

1947	A1332	(20c) brown	.60	.25
a.		Imperf. pair	700.00	

BOOKLET STAMPS
Perf. 11 on 2 or 3 Sides

1948	A1333	(20c) brown	.40	.25
a.		Booklet pane of 10	4.50	3.25

A1334

BOOKLET STAMP
ENGRAVED
Perf. 11 on 2 or 3 Sides

1982, Jan. 8

1949	A1334	20c dark blue	.50	.25
a.		Booklet pane of 10	4.75	2.50
b.		As "a," imperf. vert.	90.00	
c.		Type II	1.25	.25
d.		Type II, booklet pane of 10	12.50	—

No. 1949 is 18¾mm wide and has overall tagging. No. 1949c is 18½mm wide and has block tagging.
See No. 1880.

FRANKLIN DELANO ROOSEVELT

A1335

1982, Jan. 30 ***Perf. 11***

1950	A1335	20c blue	.40	.25

LOVE ISSUE

A1336

PHOTOGRAVURE

1982, Feb. 1 ***Perf. 11¼***

1951	A1336	20c multicolored	1.00	.25
b.		Imperf., pair	200.00	
c.		Blue omitted	200.00	
d.		Yellow omitted	600.00	
e.		Purple omitted	—	

No. 1951c is valued in the grade of fine.

Perf. 11¼x10½

1951A	A1336	20c multicolored	1.00	.25

GEORGE WASHINGTON

A1337

1982, Feb. 22 ***Perf. 11***

1952	A1337	20c multicolored	.40	.25

STATE BIRDS AND FLOWERS ISSUE

A1338

1982, Apr. 14 ***Perf. 10½x11¼***

1953	A1338	20c Alabama	.55	.30
1954	A1339	20c Alaska	.55	.30
1955	A1340	20c Arizona	.55	.30
1956	A1341	20c Arkansas	.55	.30
1957	A1342	20c California	.55	.30
1958	A1343	20c Colorado	.55	.30
1959	A1344	20c Connecticut	.55	.30
1960	A1345	20c Delaware	.55	.30
1961	A1346	20c Florida	.55	.30
1962	A1347	20c Georgia	.55	.30
1963	A1348	20c Hawaii	.55	.30
1964	A1349	20c Idaho	.55	.30
1965	A1350	20c Illinois	.55	.30
1966	A1351	20c Indiana	.55	.30
1967	A1352	20c Iowa	.55	.30
1968	A1353	20c Kansas	.55	.30
1969	A1354	20c Kentucky	.55	.30
1970	A1355	20c Louisiana	.55	.30
1971	A1356	20c Maine	.55	.30
1972	A1357	20c Maryland	.55	.30
1973	A1358	20c Massachusetts	.55	.30
1974	A1359	20c Michigan	.55	.30
1975	A1360	20c Minnesota	.55	.30
1976	A1361	20c Mississippi	.55	.30
1977	A1362	20c Missouri	.55	.30
1978	A1363	20c Montana	.55	.30
1979	A1364	20c Nebraska	.55	.30
1980	A1365	20c Nevada	.55	.30
1981	A1366	20c New Hampshire	.55	.30
b.		Black missing (EP)	4,000.	
1982	A1367	20c New Jersey	.55	.30
1983	A1368	20c New Mexico	.55	.30
1984	A1369	20c New York	.55	.30
1985	A1370	20c North Carolina	.55	.30
1986	A1371	20c North Dakota	.55	.30
1987	A1372	20c Ohio	.55	.30
1988	A1373	20c Oklahoma	.55	.30
1989	A1374	20c Oregon	.55	.30
1990	A1375	20c Pennsylvania	.55	.30
1991	A1376	20c Rhode Island	.55	.30
b.		Black missing (EP)	4,000.	
1992	A1377	20c South Carolina	.55	.30
1993	A1378	20c South Dakota	.55	.30
1994	A1379	20c Tennessee	.55	.30
1995	A1380	20c Texas	.55	.30
1996	A1381	20c Utah	.55	.30
1997	A1382	20c Vermont	.55	.30
1998	A1383	20c Virginia	.55	.30
1999	A1384	20c Washington	.55	.30
2000	A1385	20c West Virginia	.55	.30
2001	A1386	20c Wisconsin	.55	.30
b.		Black missing (EP)	4,000.	
2002	A1387	20c Wyoming	.55	.30
b.		A1338-A1387 Pane of 50, Nos. 1953-2002	27.50	20.00
d.		Pane of 50, imperf.	21,000.	

Perf. 11¼x11

1953A	A1338	20c Alabama	.60	.30
1954A	A1339	20c Alaska	.60	.30
1955A	A1340	20c Arizona	.60	.30
1956A	A1341	20c Arkansas	.60	.30
1957A	A1342	20c California	.60	.30
1958A	A1343	20c Colorado	.60	.30
1959A	A1344	20c Connecticut	.60	.30
1960A	A1345	20c Delaware	.60	.30
1961A	A1346	20c Florida	.60	.30
1962A	A1347	20c Georgia	.60	.30
1963A	A1348	20c Hawaii	.60	.30
1964A	A1349	20c Idaho	.60	.30
1965A	A1350	20c Illinois	.60	.30
1966A	A1351	20c Indiana	.60	.30
1967A	A1352	20c Iowa	.60	.30
1968A	A1353	20c Kansas	.60	.30
1969A	A1354	20c Kentucky	.60	.30
1970A	A1355	20c Louisiana	.60	.30
1971A	A1356	20c Maine	.60	.30
1972A	A1357	20c Maryland	.60	.30
1973A	A1358	20c Massachusetts	.60	.30
1974A	A1359	20c Michigan	.60	.30
1975A	A1360	20c Minnesota	.60	.30
1976A	A1361	20c Mississippi	.60	.30
1977A	A1362	20c Missouri	.60	.30
1978A	A1363	20c Montana	.60	.30
1979A	A1364	20c Nebraska	.60	.30
1980A	A1365	20c Nevada	.60	.30
1981A	A1366	20c New Hampshire	.60	.30
1982A	A1367	20c New Jersey	.60	.30
1983A	A1368	20c New Mexico	.60	.30
1984A	A1369	20c New York	.60	.30
1985A	A1370	20c North Carolina	.60	.30
1986A	A1371	20c North Dakota	.60	.30
1987A	A1372	20c Ohio	.60	.30
1988A	A1373	20c Oklahoma	.60	.30
1989A	A1374	20c Oregon	.60	.30
1990A	A1375	20c Pennsylvania	.60	.30
1991A	A1376	20c Rhode Island	.60	.30
1992A	A1377	20c South Carolina	.60	.30
1993A	A1378	20c South Dakota	.60	.30
1994A	A1379	20c Tennessee	.60	.30
1995A	A1380	20c Texas	.60	.30
1996A	A1381	20c Utah	.60	.30
1997A	A1382	20c Vermont	.60	.30
1998A	A1383	20c Virginia	.60	.30
1999A	A1384	20c Washington	.60	.30
2000A	A1385	20c West Virginia	.60	.30
2001A	A1386	20c Wisconsin	.60	.30
2002A	A1387	20c Wyoming	.60	.30
c.		A1338-A1387 Pane of 50, Nos. 1953A-2002A	30.00	22.50

Nos. 1953-2002 are line perforated. The perforations do not meet perfectly at the corners of each stamp and extend into the narrow selvage margins of an intact pane. Nos. 1953A-2002A are comb perforated. The perforations meet perfectly at the corners of each stamp and do not extend into the narrow selvage margins of an intact pane.

US-NETHERLANDS

200th Anniv. of Diplomatic Recognition by the Netherlands A1388

1982, Apr. 20 ***Perf. 11***

2003	A1388	20c multicolored	.40	.25
a.		Imperf., pair	250.00	

See Netherlands Nos. 640-641.

LIBRARY OF CONGRESS

A1389

ENGRAVED

1982, Apr. 21

2004	A1389	20c red & black	.40	.25
a.		All color missing	—	

No. 2004a must be collected as a right margin horiz. strip of 3, 4 or 5 with one No. 2004a, one transitional stamp and one or more normal stamps.

CONSUMER EDUCATION

A1390

Coil Stamp

1982, Apr. 27 ***Perf. 10 Vert.***

2005	A1390	20c sky blue	.55	.25
a.		Imperf., pair	70.00	

KNOXVILLE WORLD'S FAIR

A1391

A1392

A1393

A1394

PHOTOGRAVURE

1982, Apr. 29 ***Perf. 11***

2006	A1391	20c multicolored	.45	.25
2007	A1392	20c multicolored	.45	.25
2008	A1393	20c multicolored	.45	.25
2009	A1394	20c multicolored	.45	.25
a.		Block of 4, #2006-2009	1.80	1.50

HORATIO ALGER

Frontispiece from "Ragged Dick" — A1395

ENGRAVED

1982, Apr. 30

2010	A1395	20c red & black, *tan*	.40	.25
a.		Red and black omitted	—	

The Philatelic Foundation has issued a certificate for a pane of 50 with red and black colors omitted. Recognition of this error is by the paper and by a tiny residue of red ink from the tagging roller. The engraved plates did not strike the paper.

AGING TOGETHER

A1396

ENGRAVED

1982, May 21

2011	A1396	20c brown	.40	.25

PERFORMING ARTS SERIES

A1397

PHOTOGRAVURE

1982, June 8

2012 A1397 20c multicolored .40 .25
a. Black missing (EP) —

John (1882-1942), Ethel (1879-1959), and Lionel (1878-1954) Barrymore, actors.

DR. MARY WALKER

A1398

1982, June 10

2013 A1398 20c multicolored .40 .25

Dr. Mary Walker (1832-1919), 1865 recipient of Medal of Honor.

INTERNATIONAL PEACE GARDEN

A1399

LITHOGRAPHED AND ENGRAVED

1982, June 30

2014 A1399 20c multicolored .45 .25
a. Black (engr.) omitted *200.00*

AMERICA'S LIBRARIES

A1400

ENGRAVED

1982, July 13

2015 A1400 20c red & black .40 .25
a. Vert. pair, imperf. horiz. *200.00*
c. All colors missing (EP) *175.00*
d. Imperf. pair *500.00*
e. Horz. pair, imperf. vert. —

On No. 2015c, an albino impression of the design is present.

BLACK HERITAGE SERIES

Jackie Robinson (1919-72), baseball player.

A1401

PHOTOGRAVURE

1982, Aug. 2 ***Perf. 10½x11***

2016 A1401 20c multicolored 1.00 .25

TOURO SYNAGOGUE

A1402

PHOTOGRAVURE AND ENGRAVED

1982, Aug. 22 ***Perf. 11***

2017 A1402 20c multicolored .40 .25
a. Imperf., pair *1,400.*

WOLF TRAP FARM PARK

A1403

PHOTOGRAVURE

1982, Sept. 1

2018 A1403 20c multicolored .40 .25

AMERICAN ARCHITECTURE SERIES

Fallingwater, Mill Run, Pa., by Frank Lloyd Wright — A1404

Illinois Institute of Technology by Ludwig Mies van der Rohe — A1405

Gropius House, Lincoln, Mass., by Walter Gropius — A1406

Dulles Airport, by Eero Saarinen A1407

ENGRAVED

1982, Sept. 30

2019 A1404 20c black & brown .45 .25
b. Red missing (PS) —
2020 A1405 20c black & brown .45 .25
a. Red missing (PS) —
2021 A1406 20c black & brown .45 .25
2022 A1407 20c black & brown .45 .25
a. Block of 4, #2019-2022 2.00 1.75

FRANCIS OF ASSISI

A1408

PHOTOGRAVURE

1982, Oct. 7

2023 A1408 20c multicolored .40 .25

PONCE DE LEON

A1409

PHOTOGRAVURE (Combination press)

1982, Oct. 12

2024 A1409 20c multicolored .40 .25
a. Imperf., pair *250.00*
b. Vert. pair, imperf. between and at top *500.00*

CHRISTMAS ISSUES

A1410

A1411

A1412

A1413

A1414

A1415

PHOTOGRAVURE

1982, Nov. 3

2025 A1410 13c multicolored .30 .25
a. Imperf., pair *300.00*

PHOTOGRAVURE (Combination Press)

1982, Oct. 28

2026 A1411 20c multicolored .40 .25
a. Imperf. pair 90.00
b. Horiz. pair, imperf. vert. *900.00*
c. Vert. pair, imperf. horiz. —

PHOTOGRAVURE

2027 A1412 20c multicolored .60 .25
2028 A1413 20c multicolored .60 .25
2029 A1414 20c multicolored .60 .25
2030 A1415 20c multicolored .60 .25
a. Block of 4, #2027-2030 2.40 1.50
b. As "a," imperf. *1,250.*
c. As "a," imperf. horiz. *700.00*
Nos. 2025-2030 (6) 3.10 1.50

SCIENCE & INDUSTRY

A1416

LITHOGRAPHED AND ENGRAVED

1983, Jan. 19

2031 A1416 20c multicolored .40 .25
a. Black (engr.) omitted *750.00*

BALLOONS

A1417

A1420

A1418

A1419

PHOTOGRAVURE

1983, Mar. 31 **Tagged** ***Perf. 11***

2032 A1417 20c multicolored .50 .25
2033 A1418 20c multicolored .50 .25
2034 A1419 20c multicolored .50 .25
2035 A1420 20c multicolored .50 .25
a. Block of 4, #2032-2035 2.00 1.50
b. As "a," imperf. *2,750.*
c. As "a," right stamp perf., otherwise imperf. *2,750.*

US-SWEDEN

A1421

ENGRAVED

1983, Mar. 24

2036 A1421 20c blue, blk & red brn .40 .25

See Sweden No. 1453.

CCC, 50th ANNIV.

A1422

PHOTOGRAVURE

1983, Apr. 5

2037 A1422 20c multicolored .40 .25
a. Imperf., pair *2,250.*
b. Vert. pair, imperf. horiz. —

JOSEPH PRIESTLEY

A1423

1983, Apr. 13

2038 A1423 20c multicolored .40 .25

VOLUNTEERISM

A1424

ENGRAVED (Combination Press)

1983, Apr. 20

2039 A1424 20c red & black .40 .25
a. Imperf., pair *225.00*

US-GERMANY

Concord, 1683 — A1425

ENGRAVED

1983, Apr. 29

2040 A1425 20c brown .40 .25

See Germany No. 1397.

BROOKLYN BRIDGE

A1426

1983, May 17

2041 A1426 20c blue .40 .25
b. All color missing (EP) *90.00*

On No. 2041b, an albino impression of part of the design is evident.

TVA

A1427

PHOTOGRAVURE AND ENGRAVED (Combination Press)

1983, May 18

2042 A1427 20c multicolored .40 .25

A1428

PHOTOGRAVURE (Combination Press)

1983, May 14

2043 A1428 20c multicolored .40 .25

BLACK HERITAGE SERIES

A1429

PHOTOGRAVURE

1983, June 9

2044 A1429 20c multicolored .50 .25
a. Imperf., pair *300.00*

MEDAL OF HONOR

A1430

LITHOGRAPHED AND ENGRAVED

1983, June 7

2045 A1430 20c multicolored .55 .25
a. Red omitted *150.00*

GEORGE HERMAN RUTH (1895-1948)

A1431

ENGRAVED

1983, July 6 ***Perf. 10½x11***

2046 A1431 20c blue 1.00 .25

LITERARY ARTS SERIES

Nathaniel Hawthorne (1804-1864), novelist.

A1432

PHOTOGRAVURE

1983, July 8 ***Perf. 11***

2047 A1432 20c multicolored .40 .25

1984 SUMMER OLYMPICS

Discus — A1433

High Jump — A1434

Archery — A1435

Boxing — A1436

1983, July 28

2048 A1433 13c multicolored .35 .25
2049 A1434 13c multicolored .35 .25
2050 A1435 13c multicolored .35 .25
2051 A1436 13c multicolored .35 .25
a. Block of 4, #2048-2051 1.50 1.25

SIGNING OF TREATY OF PARIS

John Adams, Franklin, John Jay, David Hartley — A1437

1983, Sept. 2

2052 A1437 20c multicolored .40 .25

CIVIL SERVICE

A1438

PHOTOGRAVURE AND ENGRAVED

1983, Sept. 9

2053 A1438 20c buff, blue & red .40 .25

METROPOLITAN OPERA

A1439

LITHOGRAPHED AND ENGRAVED

1983, Sept. 14

2054 A1439 20c yellow & maroon .40 .25

AMERICAN INVENTORS

A1440

A1441

A1442

A1443

LITHOGRAPHED AND ENGRAVED

1983, Sept. 21

2055 A1440 20c multicolored .50 .25
2056 A1441 20c multicolored .50 .25
2057 A1442 20c multicolored .50 .25
2058 A1443 20c multicolored .50 .25
a. Block of 4, #2055-2058 2.00 1.50
b. As "a," black omitted *275.00*

STREETCARS

A1444

A1445

A1446

A1447

PHOTOGRAVURE AND ENGRAVED

1983, Oct. 8

2059 A1444 20c multicolored .50 .25
2060 A1445 20c multicolored .50 .25
a. Horiz. pair, black (engr.) missing on Nos. 2059, 2060 (EP) —
2061 A1446 20c multicolored .50 .25
a. Vert. pair, black (engr.) missing on Nos. 2059, 2061 (EP) —
2062 A1447 20c multicolored .50 .25
a. Block of 4, #2059-2062 2.00 1.50
b. As "a," black (engr.) omitted *250.00*
c. As "a," black (engr.) omitted on #2059, 2061 —

CHRISTMAS

A1448

A1449

PHOTOGRAVURE

1983, Oct. 28

2063 A1448 20c multicolored .40 .25
2064 A1449 20c multicolored .40 .25
a. Imperf., pair *100.00*

MARTIN LUTHER (1483-1546)

Martin Luther (1483-1546), German Religious Leader — A1450

1983, Nov. 11

2065 A1450 20c multicolored .40 .25

ALASKA STATEHOOD, 25th ANNIV.

Caribou and Alaska Pipeline — A1451

1984, Jan. 3

2066 A1451 20c multicolored .40 .25
a. Vert. pair, imperf. horiz. —

14th WINTER OLYMPIC GAMES

Ice Dancing A1452

Downhill Skiing A1453

Cross-country Skiing A1454

Hockey A1455

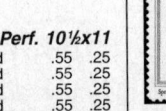

1984, Jan. 6 ***Perf. 10½x11***

2067 A1452 20c multicolored .55 .25
2068 A1453 20c multicolored .55 .25
2069 A1454 20c multicolored .55 .25
2070 A1455 20c multicolored .55 .25
a. Block of 4, #2067-2070 2.20 1.75

FEDERAL DEPOSIT INSURANCE CORPORATION, 50TH ANNIV.

A1456

1984, Jan. 12 ***Perf. 11***

2071 A1456 20c multicolored .40 .25

LOVE

A1457

PHOTOGRAVURE AND ENGRAVED (Combination Press)

1984, Jan. 31 ***Perf. 11x10½***

2072 A1457 20c multicolored .40 .25
a. Horiz. pair, imperf. vert. *125.00*

BLACK HERITAGE SERIES

Carter G. Woodson (1875-1950), Historian.

A1458

PHOTOGRAVURE

1984, Feb. 1 ***Perf. 11***

2073 A1458 20c multicolored .40 .25
a. Horiz. pair, imperf. vert. *800.00*

SOIL & WATER CONSERVATION

A1459

1984, Feb. 6

2074 A1459 20c multicolored .40 .25

50TH ANNIV. OF CREDIT UNION ACT

Dollar Sign, Coin — A1460

1984, Feb. 10

2075 A1460 20c multicolored .40 .25

ORCHIDS

A1461

A1462

A1463

A1464

1984, Mar. 5

2076 A1461 20c multicolored .50 .25
2077 A1462 20c multicolored .50 .25
2078 A1463 20c multicolored .50 .25
2079 A1464 20c multicolored .50 .25
a. Block of 4, #2076-2079 2.00 1.50

HAWAII STATEHOOD, 25th ANNIV.

Eastern Polynesian Canoe, Golden Plover, Mauna Loa Volcano — A1465

1984, Mar. 12

2080 A1465 20c multicolored .40 .25

50TH ANNIV., NATIONAL ARCHIVES

Abraham Lincoln, George Washington — A1466

1984, Apr. 16

2081 A1466 20c multicolored .40 .25

LOS ANGELES SUMMER OLYMPICS

Diving A1467

Long Jump A1468

Wrestling A1469

Kayak A1470

1984, May 4

2082 A1467 20c multicolored .55 .25
2083 A1468 20c multicolored .55 .25
2084 A1469 20c multicolored .55 .25
2085 A1470 20c multicolored .55 .25
a. Block of 4, #2082-2085 2.40 1.90
b. As "a," imperf between vertically *9,500.*

LOUISIANA WORLD EXPOSITION

River Wildlife — A1471

1984, May 11

2086 A1471 20c multicolored .50 .25

HEALTH RESEARCH

Lab Equipment A1472

1984, May 17

2087 A1472 20c multicolored .40 .25

PERFORMING ARTS

A1473

PHOTOGRAVURE AND ENGRAVED
(Combination Press)

1984, May 23

2088 A1473 20c multicolored .40 .25
b. Horiz. pair, imperf between —

JIM THORPE

A1474

ENGRAVED

1984, May 24

2089 A1474 20c dark brown .60 .25
a. All color omitted —

On No. 2089a, an albino impression of the design is evident.

PERFORMING ARTS

Tenor John McCormack (1884-1945) — A1475

PHOTOGRAVURE

1984, June 6

2090 A1475 20c multicolored .40 .25

See Ireland No. 594.

ST. LAWRENCE SEAWAY, 25th ANNIV.

Aerial View of Seaway, Freighters A1476

1984, June 26

2091 A1476 20c multicolored .40 .25

WATERFOWL PRESERVATION ACT, 50th ANNIV.

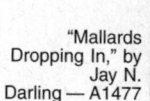

"Mallards Dropping In," by Jay N. Darling — A1477

ENGRAVED

1984, July 2 ***Perf. 11***

2092 A1477 20c blue .50 .25
a. Horiz. pair, imperf. vert. *275.00*

ROANOKE VOYAGES

The Elizabeth — A1478

PHOTOGRAVURE

1984, July 13

2093 A1478 20c multicolored .40 .25

LITERARY ARTS SERIES

Herman Melville (1819-1891), Author — A1479

ENGRAVED

1984, Aug. 1

2094 A1479 20c sage green .40 .25

HORACE MOSES (1862-1947), FOUNDER OF JUNIOR ACHIEVEMENT

Junior Achievement Founder — A1480

ENGRAVED (Combination Press)

1984, Aug. 6

2095 A1480 20c org & dark brn .40 .25

SMOKEY BEAR

Smokey Bear — A1481

LITHOGRAPHED AND ENGRAVED

1984, Aug. 13

2096 A1481 20c multicolored .40 .25
a. Horiz. pair, imperf. btwn. *175.00*
b. Vert. pair, imperf. btwn. *150.00*
c. Block of 4, imperf. btwn. vert. and horiz. *2,500.*
d. Horiz. pair, imperf. vert. *450.00*

ROBERTO CLEMENTE (1934-1972)

Clemente, Puerto Rican Flag — A1482

PHOTOGRAVURE

1984, Aug. 17

2097 A1482 20c multicolored 1.00 .25
a. Horiz. pair, imperf. vert. *1,250.*

DOGS

Beagle, Boston Terrier — A1483

Chesapeake Bay Retriever, Cocker Spaniel — A1484

Alaskan Malamute, Collie — A1485

Black & Tan Coonhound, American Foxhound A1486

1984, Sept. 7

2098 A1483 20c multicolored .50 .25
2099 A1484 20c multicolored .50 .25
2100 A1485 20c multicolored .50 .25
2101 A1486 20c multicolored .50 .25
a. Block of 4, #2098-2101 2.00 1.90
b. As "a," imperf horiz. *5,500.*

CRIME PREVENTION

McGruff, The Crime Dog — A1487

1984, Sept. 26

2102 A1487 20c multicolored .40 .25

HISPANIC AMERICANS

A1488

1984, Oct. 31

2103 A1488 20c multicolored .40 .25
a. Vert. pair, imperf. horiz. *1,250.*

FAMILY UNITY

A1489

PHOTOGRAVURE AND ENGRAVED
(Combination Press)

1984, Oct. 1

2104 A1489 20c multicolored .40 .25
a. Horiz. pair, imperf. vert. *325.00*
c. Vert. pair, imperf. btwn. and at bottom —
d. Horiz. pair, imperf. between *900.00*

ELEANOR ROOSEVELT (1884-1962)

A1490

ENGRAVED

1984, Oct. 11

2105 A1490 20c deep blue .40 .25

NATION OF READERS

Lincoln, Son Tad — A1491

1984, Oct. 16

2106 A1491 20c brown & maroon .40 .25

CHRISTMAS

Madonna and Child by Fra Filippo Lippi A1492

Santa Claus A1493

PHOTOGRAVURE

1984, Oct. 30

2107 A1492 20c multicolored .40 .25
a. Imperf., pair *1,400.*
2108 A1493 20c multicolored .40 .25
a. Horiz. pair, imperf. vert. *750.00*

No. 2108a is valued in the grade of fine.

VIETNAM VETERANS MEMORIAL

Memorial Wall A1494

ENGRAVED

1984, Nov. 10

2109 A1494 20c multicolored .50 .25

PERFORMING ARTS

Composer Jerome Kern (1885-1945) — A1495

PHOTOGRAVURE

1985, Jan. 23

2110 A1495 22c multicolored .45 .25

A1496

A1497

PHOTOGRAVURE

1985, Feb. 1 *Perf. 11*

2111 A1496 (22c) green .60 .25
- *a.* Vert. pair, imperf. 35.00
- *b.* Vert. pair, imperf. horiz. *750.00*

COIL STAMP

Perf. 10 Vert.

2112 A1496 (22c) green .60 .25
- *a.* Imperf., pair *45.00*

BOOKLET STAMP

ENGRAVED

Perf. 11 on 2 or 3 Sides

2113 A1497 (22c) green .70 .25
- *a.* Booklet pane of 10 6.75 3.00
- *b.* As "a," Horiz. imperf. btwn. *1,850.*

Two examples of No. 2113b are reported, both in an unexploded booklet.

A1498

Flag over Capitol Dome — A1499

ENGRAVED

1985, Mar. 29 *Perf. 11*

2114 A1498 22c blue, red & black .45 .25
- *a.* All color missing (EP) —

No. 2114a should be collected se-tenant with a normal or a partially printed stamp.

COIL STAMP

Perf. 10 Vert.

2115 A1498 22c blue, red & black .45 .25
- *c.* Inscribed "T" at bottom ('87) .55 .40
- *d.* Black field of stars instead of blue — —
- *f.* Imperf., pair, wide block tagging 10.00
- *g.* Imperf., pair, narrow block tagging 10.00

BOOKLET STAMP

Perf. 10 Horiz.

2116 A1499 22c blue, red & black .50 .25
- *a.* Booklet pane of 5 2.50 1.25

BOOKLET STAMPS

Frilled Dogwinkle A1500

Reticulated Helmet A1501

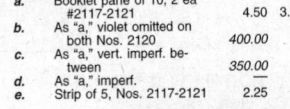

New England Neptune A1502

Calico Scallop A1503

Lightning Whelk — A1504

ENGRAVED

Perf. 10 on 2 or 3 Sides

1985, Apr. 4

2117 A1500 22c black & brown .45 .25
2118 A1501 22c black & multi .45 .25
2119 A1502 22c black & brown .45 .25
2120 A1503 22c black & violet .45 .25
2121 A1504 22c black & multi .45 .25
- *a.* Booklet pane of 10, 2 ea #2117-2121 4.50 3.00
- *b.* As "a," violet omitted on both Nos. 2120 *400.00*
- *c.* As "a," vert. imperf. between *350.00*
- *d.* As "a," imperf. —
- *e.* Strip of 5, Nos. 2117-2121 2.25 —

Eagle and Half Moon A1505

Type I

Type II

TYPE I: washed out, dull appearance most evident in the black of the body of the eagle, and the red in the background between the eagle's shoulder and the moon. "$10.75" appears splotchy or grainy (P# 11111).

TYPE II: brighter, more intense colors most evident in the black on the eagle's body, and red in the background. "$10.75" appears smoother, brighter, and less grainy (P# 22222).

PHOTOGRAVURE

Perf. 10 Vert. on 1 or 2 Sides

1985, Apr. 29 **Untagged**

2122 A1505 $10.75 multi, type I 20.00 7.50
- *a.* Booklet pane of 3 60.00 —
- *b.* Type II, *June 19, 1989* 20.00 10.00
- *c.* As "b," booklet pane of 3 60.00 —

TRANSPORTATION ISSUE

School Bus 1920s A1506

Buckboard 1880s A1507

Star Route Truck 1910s A1508

Tricycle 1880s A1509

Tractor 1920s A1510

Ambulance 1860s A1511

Tow Truck 1920s A1512

Oil Wagon 1890s A1513

Stutz Bearcat 1933 A1514

Stanley Steamer 1909 A1515

Pushcart 1880s A1516

Iceboat 1880s A1517

Dog Sled 1920s A1518

Bread Wagon 1880s A1519

COIL STAMPS

ENGRAVED

1985-89 **Tagged** ***Perf. 10 Vert.***

2123 A1506 3.4c dk bluish green .30 .25
- *a.* Untagged (Bureau precancel, Nonprofit Org. CAR-RT SORT) .30 .25

2124 A1507 4.9c brn blk .30 .25
- *a.* Untagged (Bureau precancel, Nonprofit Org.) .30 .25

2125 A1508 5.5c dp mag ('86) .30 .25
- *a.* Untagged (Bureau precancel, Nonprofit Org. CAR-RT SORT) .30 .25

2126 A1509 6c red brn .35 .25
- *a.* Untagged (Bureau precancel, Nonprofit Org.) .30 .25
- *b.* As "a," imperf., pair *175.00*

2127 A1510 7.1c lake ('87) .30 .25
- *a.* Untagged (Bureau precancel) .30 .25
- *c.* As "a," black (precancel) omitted —

On. No. 2127c, an albino impression of the precancel is present.

2128 A1511 8.3c green .30 .25
- *a.* Untagged (Bureau precancel, Blk. Rt. CAR-RT SORT) .30 .25

On No. 2231 "Ambulance 1860s" is 18mm long; on No. 2128, 18⅓mm long.

2129 A1512 8.5c dk Prus grn ('87) .30 .25
- *a.* Untagged (Bureau precancel, Nonprofit Org.) .30 .25

2130 A1513 10.1c slate blue .55 .25
- *a.* Untagged (Bureau precancel "Bulk Rate Carrier Route Sort" in red) ('88) .30 .25
- *b.* As "a," red precancel, imperf, pair 15.00
- As "a," black precancel, imperf, pair 70.00

2131 A1514 11c dk green .30 .25
2132 A1515 12c dk bl, I .35 .25
- *a.* Untagged, type I (Bureau precancel, PRESORTED FIRST-CLASS), *Apr. 2* .30 .25
- *b.* Untagged, type II (Bureau precancel, PRESORTED FIRST-CLASS) ('87) .40 .30

Type II has "Stanley Steamer 1909" ⅓mm shorter (17⅔mm) than No. 2132 (18mm).

2133 A1516 12.5c ol grn .35 .25
- *a.* Untagged (Bureau precancel, Bulk Rate) .30 .25
- *b.* As "a," imperf., pair 45.00

2134 A1517 14c sky bl, I .30 .25
- *a.* Imperf., pair 75.00
- *b.* Type II ('86) .30 .25
- *c.* Tagging omitted, type I 35.00 —

Type II design is ¼mm narrower (17¼mm) than the original stamp (17½mm) and has block tagging. No. 2134 has overall tagging.

2135 A1518 17c brt bl ('86) .75 .25
- *a.* Imperf., pair *300.00*

2136 A1519 25c org brn ('86) .50 .25
- *a.* Imperf., pair 10.00
- *b.* Pair, imperf. between *525.00*

Nos. 2123-2136 (14) 5.25 3.50

See Nos. 1897-1908, 2225-2231, 2252-2266, 2451-2468.

BLACK HERITAGE SERIES

Mary McLeod Bethune (1875-1955), Educator — A1520

PHOTOGRAVURE

1985, Mar. 5 *Perf. 11*

2137 A1520 22c multicolored .60 .25

AMERICAN FOLK ART SERIES

Duck Decoys

Broadbill A1521

Mallard — A1522

Canvasback A1523

Redhead A1524

1985, Mar. 22

2138 A1521 22c multicolored .90 .25
2139 A1522 22c multicolored .90 .25
2140 A1523 22c multicolored .90 .25
2141 A1524 22c multicolored .90 .25
- *a.* Block of 4, #2138-2141 3.60 2.75

WINTER SPECIAL OLYMPICS

Ice Skater, Emblem, Skier — A1525

1985, Mar. 25

2142 A1525 22c multicolored .50 .25
- *a.* Vert. pair, imperf. horiz. *300.00*

LOVE

A1526

1985, Apr. 17

2143 A1526 22c multicolored .45 .25
- *a.* Imperf., pair *800.00*

RURAL ELECTRIFICATION ADMINISTRATION

Electrified Farm — A1527

PHOTOGRAVURE & ENGRAVED
(Combination Press)

1985, May 11

2144 A1527 22c multicolored .50 .25
a. Vert. pair, imperf between —

AMERIPEX '86

U.S. No. 134 — A1528

LITHOGRAPHED & ENGRAVED

1985, May 25

2145 A1528 22c multicolored .45 .25
a. Red, black & blue (engr.) omitted *110.00*
b. Red & black omitted *1,250.*
c. Red omitted *1,750.*
d. Black missing (PS) 450.00

ABIGAIL ADAMS (1744-1818)

Abigail Adams (1744-1818) — A1529

PHOTOGRAVURE

1985, June 14

2146 A1529 22c multicolored .45 .25
a. Imperf., pair *200.00*

FREDERIC AUGUSTE BARTHOLDI (1834-1904)

Frederic Auguste Bartholdi (1834-1904), Statue of Liberty — A1530

LITHOGRAPHED & ENGRAVED

1985, July 18

2147 A1530 22c multicolored .45 .25

Examples of No. 2147 exist with most, but not all, of the engraved black omitted.

George Washington, Washington Monument A1532

Envelopes A1533

COIL STAMPS
PHOTOGRAVURE

1985 ***Perf. 10 Vertically***

2149 A1532 18c multicolored .40 .25
a. Untagged (Bureau precancel) .35 .35
b. Imperf., pair *750.00*
c. As "a," imperf., pair *575.00*
2150 A1533 21.1c multicolored .40 .25
a. Untagged (Bureau Precancel) .40 .40
c. Imperf., pair —

Precancellations on Nos. 2149a ("PRESORTED FIRST-CLASS") and 2150a ("ZIP+4") do not have lines.

KOREAN WAR VETERANS

American Troops in Korea — A1535

ENGRAVED

1985, July 26 ***Perf. 11***

2152 A1535 22c gray green & rose red .45 .25

SOCIAL SECURITY ACT, 50th ANNIV.

Men, Women, Children, Corinthian Columns — A1536

PHOTOGRAVURE

1985, Aug. 14

2153 A1536 22c deep & light blue .45 .25

WORLD WAR I VETERANS

The Battle of Marne, France, by Harvey Dunn — A1537

ENGRAVED

1985, Aug. 26

2154 A1537 22c gray green & rose red .45 .25
a. Red missing (PS) *300.00*

HORSES

Quarter Horse — A1538

Morgan — A1539

Saddlebred A1540

Appaloosa A1541

PHOTOGRAVURE

1985, Sept. 25

2155 A1538 22c multicolored 1.10 .25
2156 A1539 22c multicolored 1.10 .25
2157 A1540 22c multicolored 1.10 .25
2158 A1541 22c multicolored 1.10 .25
a. Block of 4, #2155-2158 4.40 4.00

PUBLIC EDUCATION IN AMERICA

Quill Pen, Apple, Spectacles, Penmanship Quiz — A1542

1985, Oct. 1

2159 A1542 22c multicolored .45 .25

INTERNATIONAL YOUTH YEAR

YMCA Youth Camping, Cent. — A1543

Boy Scouts, 75th Anniv. — A1544

Big Brothers/Big Sisters Fed., 40th Anniv. — A1545

Camp Fire, Inc., 75th Anniv. — A1546

1985, Oct. 7

2160 A1543 22c multicolored .70 .25
2161 A1544 22c multicolored .70 .25
2162 A1545 22c multicolored .70 .25
2163 A1546 22c multicolored .70 .25
a. Block of 4, #2160-2163 3.00 2.25

HELP END HUNGER

Youths and the Elderly Suffering from Malnutrition A1547

PHOTOGRAVURE

1985, Oct. 15

2164 A1547 22c multicolored .45 .25

CHRISTMAS

Genoa Madonna, Enameled Terra-Cotta by Luca Della Robbia (1400-1482) A1548

Poinsettia Plants A1549

1985, Oct. 30

2165 A1548 22c multicolored .45 .25
a. Imperf., pair *55.00*
2166 A1549 22c multicolored .45 .25
a. Imperf., pair *50.00*

ARKANSAS STATEHOOD, 150th ANNIV.

Old State House, Little Rock — A1550

1986, Jan. 3

2167 A1550 22c multicolored .65 .25
a. Vert. pair, imperf. horiz. *500.00*

GREAT AMERICANS ISSUE

Margaret Mitchell A1551

Mary Lyon A1552

Paul Dudley White MD A1553

Father Flanagan A1554

ENGRAVED

Perf. 11, 11½x11 (#2185), 11.2x11.1 (#2179)

1986-94

2168 A1551 1c brnsh ver .30 .25
b. 1c red brown .30 .30
Pane of 100 30.00
2169 A1552 2c brt bl ('87) .30 .25
a. Untagged .40 .25
2170 A1553 3c bright blue .30 .25
a. Untagged ('94) .30 .25
2171 A1554 4c blue violet .30 .25
a. 4c grayish violet, untagged .25 .25
b. 4c deep grayish blue, untagged .35 .25
d. All color missing (EP) —

No. 2171d has an albino impression, and it also may be collected with a fully or partially printed stamp.

Hugo L. Black A1555

Louis Munoz Marin A1556

2172 A1555 5c dk ol grn .30 .25
b. 5c lt ol grn .35 .25
2173 A1556 5c car ('90) .30 .25
a. Untagged .30 .25

Red Cloud A1557

Julia Ward Howe A1558

2175 A1557 10c lake ('87) .30 .25
e. 10c carmine .80 .25
f. All color omitted *125.00*

No. 2175f may be collected se-tenant with a partially printed stamp or longer vertical strip. Stamps not se-tenant with a partially printed stamp are identified by a light setoff on the gum side.

2176 A1558 14c crimson ('87) .30 .25

Buffalo Bill Cody A1559

Belva Ann Lockwood A1560

2177 A1559 15c claret ('88) 1.00 .25
d. All color omitted *200.00*

No. 2177d resulted from partially printed panes. It must be collected se-tenant with a partially printed stamp or in a longer horizontal strip showing error stamps plus partially/completely printed stamps.

2178 A1560 17c dull bl grn .35 .25

Virginia Apgar A1561

Chester Carlson A1562

2179 A1561 20c red brn ('94) .40 .25
a. 20c orange brown .75 .25
b. 20c bright red brown 1.25 .25
2180 A1562 21c bl vio ('88) .45 .25

Mary Cassatt A1563

Jack London A1564

2181 A1563 23c pur ('88) .45 .25
2182 A1564 25c blue ('88) .50 .25
a. Booklet pane of 10, perf. 11¼, *May 3, 1988* 5.00 3.75
d. Horiz. pair, imperf between *750.00*

e. As "a," all color omitted on right stamps 1,250.

f. As No. 2182 (sheet stamp), vert. pair, bottom stamp all color omitted —

h. As "a," all color omitted on left stamps 1,250.

No. 2182f may be collected se-tenant with a partially printed stamp or longer vertical strip.

See Nos. 2197, 2197a.

Sitting Bull A1565

Earl Warren A1566

2183 A1565 28c myrtle grn ('89) .65 .35

2184 A1566 29c blue ('92) .70 .25

Thomas Jefferson A1567

Dennis Chavez A1568

2185 A1567 29c indigo ('93) .65 .25

2186 A1568 35c black ('91) .75 .25

Claire Chennault A1569

Harvey Cushing MD A1570

2187 A1569 40c dk bl ('90) .85 .25

2188 A1570 45c brt bl ('88) 1.00 .25

a. 45c blue ('90) 2.75 .25

Almost all examples of No. 2188a are in the grade of fine or fine-very fine. Values are for stamps in the grade of fine-very fine.

Hubert H. Humphrey A1571

John Harvard A1572

2189 A1571 52c pur ('91) 1.10 .25

2190 A1572 56c scarlet 1.20 .25

H.H. Hap Arnold A1573

Wendell Willkie A1574

2191 A1573 65c dk bl ('88) 1.30 .25

2192 A1574 75c dp mag ('92) 1.75 .25

Bernard Revel A1575

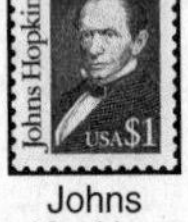

Johns Hopkins A1576

2193 A1575 $1 dk Prus grn 3.00 .50

a. All color omitted —

No. 2193a must be collected se-tenant vertically with partially printed stamps.

2194 A1576 $1 intense dp bl ('89) 2.25 .50

b. $1 dp bl ('90) 2.50 .50

d. $1 dk bl ('92) 2.50 .50

e. $1 blue ('93) 2.75 .60

The intense deep blue of No. 2194 is much deeper than the deep blue and dark blue of the other $1 varieties.

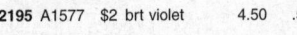

William Jennings Bryan A1577

Bret Harte A1578

2195 A1577 $2 brt violet 4.50 .50

2196 A1578 $5 copper red ('87) 9.00 1.00

Nos. 2168-2196 (28) 34.25 8.60

Booklet Stamp

Perf. 10 on 2 or 3 Sides

2197 A1564 25c blue ('88) .55 .25

a. Booklet pane of 6 3.30 2.50

Issued: No. 2182, 1/11; No. 2172, 2/27; $2, 3/19; 17c, 6/18; 1c, 6/30; 4c, 7/14; 56c, 9/3; 3c, 9/15; No. 2193, 9/23; 14c, 2/12/87; 2c, 2/28/87; 10c, 8/15/87; $5, 8/25/87; Nos. 2182a, 2197, 5/3/88; 15c, 6/6/88; 45c, 6/17/88; 21c, 10/21/88; 23c, 11/4/88; 65c, 11/5/88; No. 2194, 6/7/89; 28c, 9/14/89; No. 2173, 2/18/90; 40c, 9/6/90; Nos. 2188a, 2194b, 1990; 35c, 4/3/91; 52c, 6/3/91; No. 2173a, 1991; 75c, 2/16/92; No. 2184, 3/9/92; No. 2194d, 1992; No. 2185, 4/13/93; Nos. 2171b, 2194e, 1993; 20c, 10/24/94; Nos. 2170a, 2175e, 1994.

UNITED STATES - SWEDEN STAMP COLLECTING

Handstamped Cover, No. 213, Philatelic Memorabilia A1581

Boy Examining Stamp Collection A1582

No. 836 Under Magnifying Glass, Sweden Nos. 268, 271 — A1583

1986 Presidents Miniature Sheet on First Day Cover — A1584

BOOKLET STAMPS

LITHOGRAPHED & ENGRAVED

Perf. 10 Vert. on 1 or 2 Sides

1986, Jan. 23

2198 A1581 22c multicolored .45 .25

2199 A1582 22c multicolored .45 .25

2200 A1583 22c multicolored .45 .25

2201 A1584 22c multicolored .45 .25

a. Bklt. pane of 4, #2198-2201 2.00 1.75

b. As "a," black omitted on Nos. 2198, 2201 50.00 —

c. As "a," blue (litho.) omitted on Nos. 2198-2200 1,500.

d. As "a," buff (litho.) omitted —

See Sweden Nos. 1585-1588.

LOVE ISSUE

A1585

PHOTOGRAVURE

1986, Jan. 30 ***Perf. 11***

2202 A1585 22c multicolored .55 .25

BLACK HERITAGE SERIES

Sojourner Truth (c. 1797-1883), Abolitionist — A1586

PHOTOGRAVURE

1986, Feb. 4

2203 A1586 22c multicolored .55 .25

REPUBLIC OF TEXAS, 150th ANNIV.

San Jacinto, 1836, Texas State Flag and Silver Spur — A1587

1986, Mar. 2

2204 A1587 22c dk bl, dk red & grayish blk .50 .25

a. Horiz. pair, imperf. vert. 600.00

b. Dark red omitted 1,750.

c. Dark blue omitted 5,000.

FISH

Muskellunge A1588

Atlantic Cod — A1589

Largemouth Bass — A1590

Bluefin Tuna — A1591

Catfish A1592

BOOKLET STAMPS

PHOTOGRAVURE

Perf. 10 Horiz. on 1 or 2 Sides

1986, Mar. 21

2205 A1588 22c multicolored .90 .25

2206 A1589 22c multicolored .90 .25

2207 A1590 22c multicolored .90 .25

2208 A1591 22c multicolored .90 .25

2209 A1592 22c multicolored .90 .25

a. Bklt. pane of 5, #2205-2209 4.50 2.75

The magenta used to print this issue is extremely fugitive. Dangerous fakes purported to be magenta omitted exist. No genuine examples are known. Panes apparently lacking red must be certified, and examples presently with certificates should be recertified.

PUBLIC HOSPITALS

A1593

1986, Apr. 11 ***Perf. 11***

2210 A1593 22c multicolored .45 .25

a. Vert. pair, imperf. horiz. 250.00

b. Horiz. pair, imperf. vert. 800.00

PERFORMING ARTS

Edward Kennedy "Duke" Ellington (1899-1974), Jazz Composer — A1594

1986, Apr. 29

2211 A1594 22c multicolored .45 .25

a. Vert. pair. imperf. horiz. 500.00

AMERIPEX '86 ISSUE

Miniature Sheets

35 Presidents — A1599a

No. 2216: a, George Washington. b, John Adams. c, Thomas Jefferson. d, James Madison. e, James Monroe. f, John Quincy Adams. g, Andrew Jackson. h, Martin Van Buren. i, William H. Harrison.

No. 2217: a, John Tyler. b, James Knox Polk. c, Zachary Taylor. d, Millard Fillmore. e, Franklin Pierce. f, James Buchanan. g, Abraham Lincoln. h, Andrew Johnson. i, Ulysses S. Grant.

No. 2218: a, Rutherford B. Hayes. b, James A. Garfield. c, Chester A. Arthur. d, Grover Cleveland. e, Benjamin Harrison. f, William McKinley. g, Theodore Roosevelt. h, William H. Taft. i, Woodrow Wilson.

No. 2219: a, Warren G. Harding. b, Calvin Coolidge. c, Herbert Hoover. d, Franklin Delano Roosevelt. e, White House. f, Harry S. Truman. g, Dwight D. Eisenhower. h, John F. Kennedy. i, Lyndon B. Johnson.

LITHOGRAPHED & ENGRAVED

1986, May 22

2216 A1599a Pane of 9 6.50 4.00

a.-i. 22c, any single .65 .40

j. Blue (engr.) omitted 1,800.

k. Black inscription omitted 1,000.

l. Imperf. 10,500.

m. As "k," double impression of red 1,700.

n. Blue omitted on b-c, e-f, i —

q. Double impression of red 600.00

2217 A1599b Pane of 9 6.50 4.00

a-i. 22c, any single .65 .40

j. Black inscription omitted 1,500.

2218 A1599c Pane of 9 6.50 4.00

a.-i. 22c, any single .65 .40

j. Brown (engr.) omitted —

k. Black inscription omitted 1,500.

2219 A1599d Pane of 9 6.50 4.00

a.-i. 22c, any single .65 .40

j. Blackish blue (engr.) inscription omitted on a-b, d-e, g-h 2,250.

l. Blackish blue (engr.) omitted on all stamps —

Nos. 2216-2219 (4) 26.00 16.00

Issued in conjunction with AMERIPEX '86 Intl. Philatelic Exhibition, Chicago, IL May 22-June 1.

ARCTIC EXPLORERS

Elisha Kent Kane — A1600

Adolphus W. Greely — A1601

Vilhjalmur Stefansson A1602

Robert E. Peary and Matthew Alexander Henson — A1603

PHOTOGRAVURE

1986, May 28

2220 A1600 22c multicolored .65 .25
2221 A1601 22c multicolored .65 .25
2222 A1602 22c multicolored .65 .25
2223 A1603 22c multicolored .65 .25
a. Block of 4, #2220-2223 2.75 2.25
b. As "a," black omitted *3,500.*
c. As "a," Nos. 2220, 2221 black omitted *1,000.*
d. As "a," Nos. 2222, 2223 black omitted *1,000.*

STATUE OF LIBERTY, 100th ANNIVERSARY

Statue of Liberty, Cent. — A1604

ENGRAVED

1986, July 4

2224 A1604 22c scar & dk bl .45 .25
a. Scarlet omitted —

On No. 2224a, virtually all of the dark blue also is omitted, so the error stamp should be collected as part of a transition strip.
See France No. 2014.

TRANSPORTATION ISSUE

Types of 1982-85 and

A1604a — Omnibus 1880s

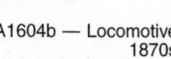

A1604b — Locomotive 1870s

COIL STAMPS
ENGRAVED

1986-90 ***Perf. 10 Vert.***

2225 A1604a 1c violet .30 .25
b. Untagged .30 .25
c. Imperf., pair *1,500.*
2226 A1604b 2c black .30 .25
a. Untagged .30 .25

REDUCED SIZE

2228 A1285 4c reddish brown .30 .25
b. Imperf., pair 175.00

Untagged

2231 A1511 8.3c green (Bureau precancel) .65 .25
Nos. 2225-2231 (4) 1.55 1.00

Issued: 1c, 11/26; 2c, 3/6/87. Earliest known usage of 4c, 8/15/86; 8.3c, 8/29.
On No. 2228 "Stagecoach 1890s" is 17¾mm long, on No. 1898A, 19½mm long. On No. 2231 "Ambulance 1860s" is 18mm long, on No. 2128, 18½mm long.
No. 2226 inscribed "2 USA"; No. 1897A inscribed "USA 2c".

AMERICAN FOLK ART SERIES
Navajo Art

A1605

A1606

A1607

A1608

LITHOGRAPHED & ENGRAVED

1986, Sept. 4 ***Perf. 11***

2235 A1605 22c multicolored .80 .25
a. Black (engr.) omitted 65.00
2236 A1606 22c multicolored .80 .25
a. Black (engr.) omitted 65.00
2237 A1607 22c multicolored .80 .25
a. Black (engr.) omitted 65.00
2238 A1608 22c multicolored .80 .25
a. Black (engr.) omitted 65.00
b. Block of 4, #2235-2238 3.25 2.25
c. As "b," black (engr.) omitted *275.00*

LITERARY ARTS SERIES

T. S. Eliot (1888-1965), Poet — A1609

ENGRAVED

1986, Sept. 26

2239 A1609 22c copper red .45 .25

AMERICAN FOLK ART SERIES
Woodcarved Figurines

Highlander Figure A1610

Ship Figurehead A1611

Nautical Figure A1612

Cigar Store Figure A1613

PHOTOGRAVURE

1986, Oct. 1

2240 A1610 22c multicolored .50 .25
2241 A1611 22c multicolored .50 .25
2242 A1612 22c multicolored .50 .25
2243 A1613 22c multicolored .50 .25
a. Block of 4, #2240-2243 2.00 1.50
b. As "a," imperf. vert. *750.00*

CHRISTMAS

Madonna, by Perugino (c. 1450-1523) A1614

Village Scene A1615

1986, Oct. 24

2244 A1614 22c multicolored .45 .25
a. Imperf., pair *400.00*
2245 A1615 22c multicolored .45 .25

MICHIGAN STATEHOOD, 150th ANNIV.

White Pine — A1616

1987, Jan. 26

2246 A1616 22c multicolored .50 .25

PAN AMERICAN GAMES

Runner in Full Stride — A1617

1987, Jan. 29

2247 A1617 22c multicolored .45 .25
a. Silver omitted *550.00*

No. 2247a is valued in the grade of fine.

LOVE ISSUE

A1618

PHOTOGRAVURE

1987, Jan. 30 ***Perf. 11½x11***

2248 A1618 22c multicolored .45 .25

BLACK HERITAGE SERIES

Jean Baptiste Pointe du Sable (c. 1750-1818), Pioneer Trader, Founder of Chicago — A1619

1987, Feb. 20 ***Perf. 11***

2249 A1619 22c multicolored .40 .25

PERFORMING ARTS SERIES

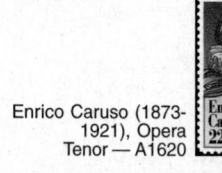

Enrico Caruso (1873-1921), Opera Tenor — A1620

PHOTOGRAVURE

1987, Feb. 27

2250 A1620 22c multicolored .45 .25
a. Black omitted *3,500.*

GIRL SCOUTS, 75TH ANNIVERSARY

Fourteen Achievement Badges — A1621

LITHOGRAPHED & ENGRAVED

1987, Mar. 12

2251 A1621 22c multicolored .45 .25
a. All litho. colors omitted *1,600.*
b. Red & black (engr.) omitted *1,500.*

All known examples of No. 2251a have been expertized and certificate must accompany purchase. The unique pane of No. 2251b has been expertized and a certificate exists for the pane of 50.

TRANSPORTATION ISSUE

Conestoga Wagon 1800s A1622

Milk Wagon 1900s A1623

Elevator 1900s A1624

Carreta 1770s A1625

Wheel Chair 1920s A1626

Canal Boat 1880s A1627

Patrol Wagon 1880s A1628

Coal Car 1870s A1629

Tugboat 1900s A1630

Popcorn Wagon 1902 A1631

Racing Car 1911 A1632

Cable Car 1880s A1633

Fire Engine 1900s A1634

Railroad Mail Car 1920s A1635

Tandem Bicycle 1890s — A1636

COIL STAMPS
ENGRAVED

1987-88 ***Perf. 10 Vert.***

2252 A1622 3c claret ('88) .30 .25
a. Untagged .30 .25
b. As "a," imperf. pair *1,350.*
2253 A1623 5c black .30 .25
2254 A1624 5.3c black (Bureau precancel in red), untagged ('88) .30 .25
2255 A1625 7.6c brown (Bureau precancel in red), untagged ('88) .30 .25
2256 A1626 8.4c dp clar (Bureau precancel in red), untagged ('88) .30 .25
a. Imperf., pair *350.00*

2257 A1627 10c blue .40 .25
e. Imperf. pair *1,000.*
2258 A1628 13c black (Bureau precancel in red), untagged ('88) .65 .25
2259 A1629 13.2c slate grn (Bureau precancel in red), untagged ('88) .30 .25
a. Imperf., pair 75.00
2260 A1630 15c violet ('88) .30 .25
c. As "a," imperf. pair *500.00*
2261 A1631 16.7c rose (Bureau precancel in black), untagged ('88) .30 .30
a. Imperf., pair *300.00*
2262 A1632 17.5c dk vio .75 .25
a. Untagged (Bureau precancel in red) .65 .30
b. Imperf., pair *1,250.*
2263 A1633 20c blue vio ('88) .35 .25
a. Imperf., pair 50.00
2264 A1634 20.5c rose (Bureau precancel in black), untagged ('88) .75 .40
2265 A1635 21c olive grn (Bureau precancel in red), untagged ('88) .50 .40
a. Imperf., pair 35.00
2266 A1636 24.1c deep ultra (Bureau precancel in red), untagged ('88) .80 .45
Nos. 2252-2266 (15) 6.60 4.30

5.3c, 7.6c, 8.4c, 13.2c, 16.7c, 20.5c, 21c and 24.1c only available precanceled.

See Nos. 1897-1908, 2123-2136, 2225-2231, 2451-2468.

SPECIAL OCCASIONS

A1637

A1638

A1639

A1640

A1641

A1642

A1643

A1644

BOOKLET STAMPS
PHOTOGRAVURE

Perf. 10 on 1, 2 or 3 Sides

1987, Apr. 20

2267 A1637 22c multicolored .75 .25
2268 A1638 22c multicolored .90 .25
2269 A1639 22c multicolored .90 .25
2270 A1640 22c multicolored .90 .25
2271 A1641 22c multicolored .90 .25
2272 A1642 22c multicolored .75 .25
2273 A1643 22c multicolored 1.50 .25
2274 A1644 22c multicolored .90 .25
a. Bklt. pane of 10 (#2268-2271, 2273-2274, 2 each #2267, 2272) 9.00 5.00
Nos. 2267-2274 (8) 7.50 2.00

UNITED WAY, 100th ANNIV.

Six Profiles — A1645

LITHOGRAPHED & ENGRAVED

1987, Apr. 28 ***Perf. 11***

2275 A1645 22c multicolored .45 .25

A1646

A1647

A1648

Yosemite — A1649

Pheasant A1649a

Grosbeak A1649b

Owl — A1649c

Honeybee A1649d

Photo., Engr. (No. 2280). Litho. & Engr. (No. 2281)

1987-88 ***Perf. 11***

2276 A1646 22c multi .45 .25
a. Booklet pane of 20, *Nov. 30* 9.00 —
b. As "a," vert. pair, imperf. btwn. *1,450.*
c. As "a," miscut and inserted upside down into booklet cover, imperf between stamps and right selvage —
d. Yellow omitted —

All documented examples of No. 2276d show significant misregistration of the red ink.

2277 A1647 (25c) multi ('88) .50 .25
2278 A1648 25c multi ('88) .50 .25
Nos. 2276-2278 (3) 1.45 .75

COIL STAMPS

Perf. 10 Vert.

2279 A1647 (25c) multi ('88) .50 .25
a. Imperf., pair 60.00 —
2280 A1649 25c multi ('88) .50 .25
c. Imperf. pair 10.00
e. Black trees *90.00* —
f. Pair, imperf. between *375.00*
2281 A1649d 25c multi ('88) .50 .25
a. As No. 2281, imperf. pair 45.00
c. Black (litho. - "25 USA") omitted *500.00*
d. Pair, imperf. between *600.00*
e. Yellow (litho.) omitted *700.00*
Nos. 2279-2281 (3) 1.50 .75

Beware of stamps with traces of the litho. black that are offered as No. 2281c.

Vertical pairs or blocks of No. 2281 and imperfs. with the engr. black missing are from printer's waste.

BOOKLET STAMPS

PHOTOGRAVURE

Perf. 10 on 2 or 3 Sides

2282 A1647 (25c) multi ('88) .50 .25
a. Booklet pane of 10 6.50 3.50

Perf. 11 on 2 or 3 Sides

2283 A1649a 25c multi ('88) .50 .25
a. Booklet pane of 10 6.00 3.50
b. 25c multicolored, red removed from sky 4.50 .25
c. As "b," bklt. pane of 10 45.00 —
d. Vert. pair, imperf. btwn. *275.00*

Imperf. panes exist from printers waste, and a large number exist. No. 2283d resulted from a foldover. Non-foldover pairs and multiples are printer's waste.

Perf. 10 on 2 or 3 Sides

2284 A1649b 25c multi ('88) .50 .25
2285 A1649c 25c multi ('88) .50 .25
b. Bklt. pane of 10, 5 each #2284-2285 5.00 3.50
d. Pair, Nos. 2284-2285 1.10 .50
2285A A1648 25c multi ('88) .50 .25
c. Booklet pane of 6 3.00 2.00
Nos. 2282-2285A (5) 2.50 1.25

Issued: #2276, 5/9; #2277, 2279, 2282, 3/22; #2278, 5/6; #2280, 5/20; #2281, 9/2; #2283, 4/29; #2284-2285, 5/28; #2285A, 7/5.

NORTH AMERICAN WILDLIFE

North American Wildlife — A1650

PHOTOGRAVURE

1987, June 13 ***Perf. 11***

2286 A1650 22c Barn swallow 1.00 .50
2287 A1651 22c Monarch butterfly 1.00 .50
2288 A1652 22c Bighorn sheep 1.00 .50
2289 A1653 22c Broad-tailed humming-bird 1.00 .50
2290 A1654 22c Cottontail 1.00 .50
2291 A1655 22c Osprey 1.00 .50
2292 A1656 22c Mountain lion 1.00 .50
2293 A1657 22c Luna moth 1.00 .50
2294 A1658 22c Mule deer 1.00 .50
2295 A1659 22c Gray squirrel 1.00 .50
2296 A1660 22c Armadillo 1.00 .50
2297 A1661 22c Eastern chipmunk 1.00 .50
2298 A1662 22c Moose 1.00 .50
2299 A1663 22c Black bear 1.00 .50
2300 A1664 22c Tiger swallowtail 1.00 .50
2301 A1665 22c Bobwhite 1.00 .50
2302 A1666 22c Ringtail 1.00 .50
2303 A1667 22c Red-winged blackbird 1.00 .50
2304 A1668 22c American lobster 1.00 .50
2305 A1669 22c Black-tailed jack rabbit 1.00 .50
2306 A1670 22c Scarlet tanager 1.00 .50
2307 A1671 22c Woodchuck 1.00 .50
2308 A1672 22c Roseate spoonbill 1.00 .50
2309 A1673 22c Bald eagle 1.00 .50
2310 A1674 22c Alaskan brown bear 1.00 .50
2311 A1675 22c Iiwi 1.00 .50
2312 A1676 22c Badger 1.00 .50
2313 A1677 22c Pronghorn 1.00 .50
2314 A1678 22c River otter 1.00 .50
2315 A1679 22c Ladybug 1.00 .50
2316 A1680 22c Beaver 1.00 .50
2317 A1681 22c White-tailed deer 1.00 .50
2318 A1682 22c Blue jay 1.00 .50
2319 A1683 22c Pika 1.00 .50
2320 A1684 22c Bison 1.00 .50
2321 A1685 22c Snowy egret 1.00 .50
2322 A1686 22c Gray wolf 1.00 .50
2323 A1687 22c Mountain goat 1.00 .50
2324 A1688 22c Deer mouse 1.00 .50
2325 A1689 22c Black-tailed prairie dog 1.00 .50
2326 A1690 22c Box turtle 1.00 .50
2327 A1691 22c Wolverine 1.00 .50
2328 A1692 22c American elk 1.00 .50
2329 A1693 22c California sea lion 1.00 .50
2330 A1694 22c Mockingbird 1.00 .50
2331 A1695 22c Raccoon 1.00 .50
2332 A1696 22c Bobcat 1.00 .50
2333 A1697 22c Black-footed ferret 1.00 .50
2334 A1698 22c Canada goose 1.00 .50
2335 A1699 22c Red fox 1.00 .50
a. Pane of 50, #2286-2335 50.00 35.00
2286b-2335b Any single, red omitted *2,000.*

RATIFICATION OF THE CONSTITUTION BICENTENNIAL

Delaware A1700

Pennsylvania A1701

New Jersey A1702

Georgia A1703

Connecticut A1704

Massachusetts A1705

Maryland A1706

South Carolina A1707

New Hampshire A1708

Virginia A1709

New York A1710

North Carolina A1711

Rhode Island — A1712

LITHOGRAPHED & ENGRAVED, PHOTOGRAVURE (#2337-2339, 2343-2344, 2347), ENGRAVED (#2341).

1987-90

2336 A1700 22c multi .55 .25
2337 A1701 22c multi .55 .25
2338 A1702 22c multi .55 .25
a. Black (engr.) omitted *2,750.*
2339 A1703 22c multi .55 .25
2340 A1704 22c multi .55 .25
2341 A1705 22c dk bl & dk red .55 .25
2342 A1706 22c multi .55 .25
2343 A1707 25c multi .55 .25
a. Strip of 3, vert. imperf btwn. *12,500.*
b. Red missing (PS) —
2344 A1708 25c multi .55 .25
2345 A1709 25c multi .55 .25
2346 A1710 25c multi .55 .25
2347 A1711 25c multi .55 .25
2348 A1712 25c multi .55 .25
Nos. 2336-2348 (13) 7.15 3.25

No. 2343b resulted either from a shifting of all colors or from a shift of both the perforations and the cutting of the pane.

Issued: No. 2336, 7/4; No. 2337, 8/26; No. 2338, 9/11; No. 2339, 1/6/88; No. 2340, 1/9/88; No. 2341, 2/6/88; No. 2342, 2/15/88; No. 2343, 5/23/88; No. 2344, 6/21/88; No. 2345, 6/25/88; No. 2346, 7/26/88; No. 2347, 8/22/89; No. 2348, 5/29/90.

US-MOROCCO DIPLOMATIC RELATIONS, 200th ANNIV.

Arabesque, Dar Batha Palace, Fez — A1713

LITHOGRAPHED & ENGRAVED

1987, July 17

2349 A1713 22c scar & blk .50 .25
a. Black (engr.) omitted *180.00*

See Morocco No. 642.

LITERARY ARTS SERIES

William Cuthbert Faulkner (1897-1962), Novelist — A1714

ENGRAVED

1987, Aug. 3

2350 A1714 22c bright green .50 .25

Used untagged imperfs exist from printer's waste.

AMERICAN FOLK ART SERIES
Lacemaking

A1715

A1716

A1717

A1718

LITHOGRAPHED & ENGRAVED

1987, Aug. 14

2351 A1715 22c ultra & white .45 .25
2352 A1716 22c ultra & white .45 .25
2353 A1717 22c ultra & white .45 .25
2354 A1718 22c ultra & white .45 .25
a. Block of 4, #2351-2354 1.90 1.90
b. As "a," white omitted *350.00*
c. Any single stamp, white omitted *90.00*

DRAFTING OF THE CONSTITUTION BICENTENNIAL
Excerpts from the Preamble

A1719

A1720

A1721

A1722

A1723

BOOKLET STAMPS
PHOTOGRAVURE

Perf. 10 Horiz. on 1 or 2 Sides

1987, Aug. 28

2355 A1719 22c multicolored .70 .25
a. Grayish green (background) omitted *400.00*
2356 A1720 22c multicolored .70 .25
a. Grayish green (background) omitted *400.00*
2357 A1721 22c multicolored .70 .25
a. Grayish green (background) omitted *400.00*
2358 A1722 22c multicolored .70 .25
a. Grayish green (background) omitted *400.00*
2359 A1723 22c multicolored .70 .25
a. Bklt. pane of 5, #2355-2359 3.50 2.25
b. Grayish green (background) omitted *400.00*

SIGNING OF THE CONSTITUTION

A1724

LITHOGRAPHED & ENGRAVED

1987, Sept. 17 *Perf. 11*

2360 A1724 22c multicolored .55 .25
a. Black (engr.) omitted *1,000.*

CERTIFIED PUBLIC ACCOUNTING

A1725

1987, Sept. 21

2361 A1725 22c multicolored .70 .25
a. Black (engr.) omitted *425.00*

LOCOMOTIVES

Stourbridge Lion, 1829 — A1726

Best Friend of Charleston, 1830 — A1727

John Bull, 1831 — A1728

Brother Jonathan, 1832 — A1729

Gowan & Marx, 1839 — A1730

BOOKLET STAMPS

Perf. 10 Horiz. on 1 or 2 Sides

1987, Oct. 1

2362 A1726 22c multi .50 .25
a. Red (litho.) omitted —
2363 A1727 22c multi .50 .25
a. Red (litho.) omitted —
2364 A1728 22c multi .50 .25
a. Red (litho.) omitted —
2365 A1729 22c multi .50 .25
a. Red omitted *1,000. 250.00*
2366 A1730 22c multi .50 .25
a. Bklt. pane of 5, #2362-2366 2.50 2.00
b. As No. 2366, black (engr.) omitted (single) —
c. As No. 2366, blue omitted (single) —

CHRISTMAS

Moroni Madonna A1731

Christmas Ornaments A1732

PHOTOGRAVURE

1987, Oct. 23 *Perf. 11*

2367 A1731 22c multicolored .45 .25
2368 A1732 22c multicolored .45 .25

1988 WINTER OLYMPICS, CALGARY

Skiing — A1733

1988, Jan. 10

2369 A1733 22c multicolored .50 .25

AUSTRALIA BICENTENNIAL

Caricature of Australian Koala & American Bald Eagle — A1734

1988, Jan. 26

2370 A1734 22c multicolored .45 .25

See Australia No. 1052.

BLACK HERITAGE SERIES

James Weldon Johnson, Author, Lyricist — A1735

1988, Feb. 2

2371 A1735 22c multicolored .50 .25

CATS

Siamese, Exotic Shorthair A1736

Abyssinian, Himalayan A1737

Maine Coon, Burmese A1738

American Shorthair, Persian — A1739

1988, Feb. 5

2372 A1736 22c multicolored .70 .25
2373 A1737 22c multicolored .70 .25
2374 A1738 22c multicolored .70 .25
2375 A1739 22c multicolored .70 .25
a. Block of 4, #2372-2375 2.80 1.90

AMERICAN SPORTS

Knute Rockne (1888-1931), Notre Dame football coach.

A1740

LITHOGRAPHED & ENGRAVED

1988, Mar. 9

2376 A1740 22c multicolored .50 .25

AMERICAN SPORTS

Francis Ouimet (1893-1967), 1st amateur golfer to win the US Open championship.

A1741

PHOTOGRAVURE

1988, June 13

2377 A1741 25c multicolored .60 .25

LOVE ISSUE (Roses)

Rose A1742

Roses A1743

1988

2378 A1742 25c multi .50 .25
a. Imperf., pair *1,500.*
2379 A1743 45c multi .85 .25

1988 SUMMER OLYMPICS, SEOUL

Gymnastic Rings — A1744

1988, Aug. 19

2380	A1744	25c multicolored		.50	.25

CLASSIC AUTOMOBILES

1928 Locomobile A1745

1929 Pierce-Arrow — A1746

1931 Cord — A1747

1932 Packard A1748

1935 Duesenberg A1749

LITHOGRAPHED & ENGRAVED
BOOKLET STAMPS

Perf. 10 Horiz. on 1 or 2 Sides

1988, Aug. 25

2381	A1745 25c multicolored		.65	.25
2382	A1746 25c multicolored		.65	.25
2383	A1747 25c multicolored		.65	.25
2384	A1748 25c multicolored		.65	.25
2385	A1749 25c multicolored		.65	.25
a.	Bklt. pane of 5, #2381-2385		3.25	2.50

ANTARCTIC EXPLORERS

Nathaniel Palmer (1799-1877) A1750

Lt. Charles Wilkes (1798-1877) A1751

Richard E. Byrd (1888-1957) A1752

Lincoln Ellsworth (1880-1951) A1753

PHOTOGRAVURE

1988, Sept. 14 ***Perf. 11***

2386	A1750 25c multicolored		.65	.25
2387	A1751 25c multicolored		.65	.25
2388	A1752 25c multicolored		.65	.25
2389	A1753 25c multicolored		.65	.25
a.	Block of 4, #2386-2389		2.75	2.00
b.	As "a," black omitted		*600.00*	
c.	As "a," imperf. horiz.		*1,500.*	

AMERICAN FOLK ART SERIES

Carousel Animals

Deer A1754

Horse A1755

Camel A1756

Goat A1757

LITHOGRAPHED & ENGRAVED

1988, Oct. 1

2390	A1754 25c multicolored		.75	.25
2391	A1755 25c multicolored		.75	.25
2392	A1756 25c multicolored		.75	.25
2393	A1757 25c multicolored		.75	.25
a.	Block of 4, #2390-2393		3.00	2.00
b.	As "a," red omitted		*800.00*	

EXPRESS MAIL RATE

Eagle in Flight A1758

1988, Oct. 4

2394	A1758 $8.75 multicolored		16.00	8.00

SPECIAL OCCASIONS

Happy Birthday — A1759

Best Wishes — A1760

Thinking of You — A1761

Love You — A1762

BOOKLET STAMPS
PHOTOGRAVURE

Perf. 11 on 2 or 3 Sides

1988, Oct. 22

2395	A1759 25c multicolored		.50	.25
2396	A1760 25c multicolored		.50	.25
a.	Bklt. pane of 6, 3 #2395 + 3 #2396 with gutter between		3.50	3.25
2397	A1761 25c multicolored		.50	.25
2398	A1762 25c multicolored		.50	.25
a.	Bklt. pane of 6, 3 #2397 + 3 #2398 with gutter between		3.50	3.25
b.	As "a," imperf. horiz.		*2,250.*	
c.	As "a," imperf.		—	
	Nos. 2395-2398 (4)		2.00	1.00

CHRISTMAS

Madonna and Child, by Botticelli A1763

One-horse Open Sleigh & Village Scene A1764

LITHOGRAPHED & ENGRAVED (No. 2399), PHOTOGRAVURE (No. 2400)

1988, Oct. 20 ***Perf. 11½***

2399	A1763 25c multicolored		.50	.25
a.	Gold omitted		25.00	
2400	A1764 25c multicolored		.50	.25

MONTANA STATEHOOD, 100th ANNIV.

C.M. Russell and Friends, by Charles M. Russell (1865-1926) A1765

LITHOGRAPHED & ENGRAVED

1989, Jan. 15 ***Perf. 11***

2401	A1765 25c multicolored		.55	.25

Imperfs without gum exist from printer's waste.

BLACK HERITAGE SERIES

Asa Philip Randolph (1889-1979), Labor & Civil Rights Leader — A1766

PHOTOGRAVURE

1989, Feb. 3

2402	A1766 25c multicolored		.50	.25

NORTH DAKOTA STATEHOOD, 100th ANNIV.

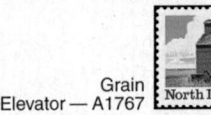

Grain Elevator — A1767

1989, Feb. 21

2403	A1767 25c multicolored		.50	.25

WASHINGTON STATEHOOD, 100th ANNIV.

Mt. Rainier — A1768

1989, Feb. 22

2404	A1768 25c multicolored		.50	.25

STEAMBOATS

Experiment, 1788-1790 — A1769

Phoenix, 1809 — A1770

New Orleans, 1812 — A1771

Washington, 1816 — A1772

Walk in the Water, 1818 — A1773

LITHOGRAPHED & ENGRAVED
BOOKLET STAMPS

Perf. 10 Horiz. on 1 or 2 Sides

1989, Mar. 3

2405	A1769 25c multicolored		.60	.25
2406	A1770 25c multicolored		.60	.25
2407	A1771 25c multicolored		.60	.25
2408	A1772 25c multicolored		.60	.25
2409	A1773 25c multicolored		.60	.25
a.	Booklet pane of 5, #2405-2409		3.00	1.75

WORLD STAMP EXPO '89

Nov. 17-Dec. 3. Washington, D.C.

No. 122 — A1774

1989, Mar. 16 ***Perf. 11***

2410	A1774 25c grayish brn, blk & car rose		.50	.25

PERFORMING ARTS

Arturo Toscanini (1867-1957), Conductor — A1775

PHOTOGRAVURE

1989, Mar. 25

2411	A1775 25c multicolored		.50	.25

CONSTITUTION BICENTENNIAL SERIES

House of Representatives A1776

Senate A1777

Executive Branch A1778

Supreme Court A1779

LITHOGRAPHED & ENGRAVED

1989-90

2412	A1776 25c multi		.50	.25
2413	A1777 25c multi		.50	.25
2414	A1778 25c multi		.50	.25
2415	A1779 25c multi		.50	.25
	Nos. 2412-2415 (4)		2.00	1.00

Issued: No. 2412, 4/4; No. 2413, 4/6; No. 2414, 4/16; No. 2415, 2/2/90.

SOUTH DAKOTA STATEHOOD, 100th ANNIV.

Pasque Flowers, Pioneer Woman and Sod House on Grasslands A1780

PHOTOGRAVURE

1989, May 3

2416 A1780 25c multicolored .60 .25

Imperfs exist from printer's waste.

AMERICAN SPORTS

Lou Gehrig (1903-1941), New York Yankee Baseball Player — A1781

1989, June 10

2417 A1781 25c multicolored .60 .25

LITERARY ARTS SERIES

Ernest Hemingway (1899-1961), Nobel Prize-winner for Literature, 1954 — A1782

1989, July 17

2418 A1782 25c multicolored .50 .25
- *a.* Vert. pair, imperf horiz. 600.00

Imperforates on gummed stamp paper, including gutter pairs and blocks, are proofs from the ABNCo. archives. See No. 2418P in Proofs section of the Scott U.S. Specialized Catalogue.

MOON LANDING, 20TH ANNIVERSARY

Raising the Flag on Lunar Surface, July 20, 1969 — A1783

LITHOGRAPHED & ENGRAVED

1989, July 20 ***Perf. 11x11½***

2419 A1783 $2.40 multi 4.75 2.00
- *a.* Black (engr.) omitted 1,350.
- *b.* Imperf., pair 375.00
- *c.* Black (litho.) omitted 1,500.

LETTER CARRIERS

Letter Carriers — A1784

PHOTOGRAVURE

2420 A1784 25c multicolored .50 .25

CONSTITUTION BICENTENNIAL

Bill of Rights — A1785

LITHOGRAPHED & ENGRAVED

1989, Sept. 25

2421 A1785 25c multicolored .50 .25
- *a.* Black (engr.) omitted 225.00

PREHISTORIC ANIMALS

Tyrannosaurus Rex — A1786

Pteranodon A1787

Stegosaurus A1788

Brontosaurus A1789

1989, Oct. 1

2422 A1786 25c multicolored .70 .25
- *a.* Black (engr.) omitted 80.00 —

2423 A1787 25c multicolored .70 .25
- *a.* Black (engr.) omitted 80.00

2424 A1788 25c multicolored .70 .25
- *a.* Black (engr.) omitted 80.00 —

2425 A1789 25c multicolored .70 .25
- *a.* Black (engr.) omitted 80.00
- *b.* Block of 4, #2422-2425 2.80 2.00
- *c.* As "b," black (engr.) omitted 325.00

No. 2425c is valued in the grade of fine. Very fine blocks exist and sell for approximately $600.

PRE-COLUMBIAN AMERICA ISSUE

Southwest Carved Figure, A. D. 1150-1350 — A1790

PHOTOGRAVURE

1989, Oct. 12

2426 A1790 25c multicolored .60 .25

See No. C121.

CHRISTMAS

Madonna and Child, by Caracci A1791

Sleigh Full of Presents A1792

LITHOGRAPHED & ENGRAVED, PHOTOGRAVURE (#2428-2429)

1989, Oct. 19 ***Perf. 11¼***

2427 A1791 25c multicolored .50 .25
- *a.* Booklet pane of 10 5.00 3.50
- *b.* Red (litho.) omitted 300.00
- *c.* As "a," imperf. —

Perf. 11½

2428 A1792 25c multicolored .50 .25
- *a.* Vert. pair, imperf. horiz. 500.00

BOOKLET STAMP

Perf. 11½ on 2 or 3 Sides

2429 A1792 25c multicolored .50 .25
- *a.* Booklet pane of 10 5.00 3.50
- *b.* Vert. pair, imperf. btwn. (from miscut bklt pane) 500.00
- *c.* As "a," horiz. imperf. between 2,250.
- *d.* As "a," red omitted 3,250.
- *e.* Imperf., pair 750.00

Marked differences exist between Nos. 2428 and 2429: No. 2429 was printed in four colors, No. 2428 in five colors. The runners on the sleigh in No. 2429 are twice as thick as those on No. 2428. On No. 2429 the package at the upper left in the sleigh has a red bow, whereas the same package in No. 2428 has a red and black bow; and the ribbon on the upper right package in No. 2429 is green, whereas the same ribbon in No. 2428 is black.

Eagle and Shield — A1793

PHOTOGRAVURE
BOOKLET STAMP

1989, Nov. 10 ***Die Cut***

Self-Adhesive

2431 A1793 25c multicolored .50 .25
- *a.* Booklet pane of 18 10.00
- *b.* Vert. pair, die cutting omitted between 325.00
- *c.* Die cutting omitted, pair 200.00

Panes sold for $5.

Also available in strips of 18 with stamps spaced for use in affixing machines to service first day covers. Sold for $5.

No. 2431c will include part of the margins around the stamps.

Sold only in 15 test cities (Atlanta, Chicago, Cleveland, Columbus, OH, Dallas, Denver, Houston, Indianapolis, Kansas City, MO, Los Angeles, Miami, Milwaukee, Minneapolis, Phoenix, St. Louis) and through the philatelic agency.

WORLD STAMP EXPO '89

World Stamp Expo, Washington, DC, Nov. 17-Dec. 3 — A1794

LITHOGRAPHED & ENGRAVED

1989, Nov. 17 ***Imperf.***

2433 A1794 Pane of 4 16.00 14.00
- *a.* 90c like No. 122 4.00 3.00
- *b.* 90c like 132TC4j 4.00 3.00
- *c.* 90c like 132TC4i 4.00 3.00
- *d.* 90c like 132TC4d 4.00 3.00
- *f.* Double impression of all 4 frames —

20th UPU CONGRESS
Traditional Mail Delivery

Stagecoach, c. 1850 A1795

Paddlewheel Steamer A1796

Biplane A1797

Depot-hack Type Automobile A1798

1989, Nov. 19 ***Perf. 11***

2434 A1795 25c multicolored .50 .25

2435 A1796 25c multicolored .50 .25

2436 A1797 25c multicolored .50 .25

2437 A1798 25c multicolored .50 .25
- *a.* Block of 4, #2434-2437 2.00 1.75
- *b.* As "a," dark blue (engr.) omitted 300.00

No. 2437b is valued in the grade of fine. Very fine blocks exist and sell for approximately $450.

Souvenir Sheet

1989, Nov. 28 ***Imperf.***

2438 Sheet of 4 5.00 3.75
- *a.* A1795 25c multicolored 1.25 .80
- *b.* A1796 25c multicolored 1.25 .80
- *c.* A1797 25c multicolored 1.25 .80
- *d.* A1798 25c multicolored 1.25 .80
- *e.* Dark blue & gray (engr.) omitted 4,000.

20th Universal Postal Union Congress.

VALUES FOR HINGED STAMPS AFTER NO. 771

This catalogue does not value unused stamps after No. 771 in hinged condition. Hinged unused stamps from No. 772 to the present are worth considerably less than the values given for unused stamps, which are for never-hinged examples.

IDAHO STATEHOOD, 100th ANNIV.

Mountain Bluebird, Sawtooth Mountains — A1799

PHOTOGRAVURE

1990, Jan. 6 ***Perf. 11***

2439 A1799 25c multicolored .55 .25

LOVE

A1800

PHOTOGRAVURE

1990, Jan. 18 ***Perf. 12½x13***

2440 A1800 25c multi .50 .25
- *a.* Imperf., pair 550.00

BOOKLET STAMP

Perf. 11½ on 2 or 3 Sides

2441 A1800 25c multi .50 .25
- *a.* Booklet pane of 10 5.00 3.50
- *b.* Bright pink omitted 80.00
- *c.* As "a," bright pink omitted 750.00

No. 2441b may be obtained from booklet panes containing both normal and color-omitted stamps.

BLACK HERITAGE SERIES

Ida B. Wells (1862-1931), Journalist — A1801

1990, Feb. 1 ***Perf. 11***

2442 A1801 25c multicolored .75 .25

Beach Umbrella — A1802

BOOKLET STAMP

Perf. 11 on 2 or 3 Sides

1990, Feb. 3

2443 A1802 15c multicolored .30 .25
- *a.* Booklet pane of 10 3.00 2.50
- *b.* Blue omitted 100.00
- *c.* As "a," blue omitted 900.00

WYOMING STATEHOOD, 100th ANNIV.

High Mountain Meadows, by Conrad Schwiering A1803

LITHOGRAPHED & ENGRAVED

1990, Feb. 23 ***Perf. 11***

2444 A1803 25c multicolored .80 .25
- *a.* Black (engr.) omitted 900.00 —

CLASSIC FILMS

Judy Garland and Toto (The Wizard of Oz) — A1804

Clark Gable & Vivien Leigh (Gone With the Wind) — A1805

Gary Cooper (Beau Geste) A1806

John Wayne (Stagecoach) A1807

PHOTOGRAVURE

1990, Mar. 23

2445 A1804 25c multicolored 1.25 .25
2446 A1805 25c multicolored 1.25 .25
2447 A1806 25c multicolored 1.25 .25
2448 A1807 25c multicolored 1.25 .25
a. Block of 4, #2445-2448 5.00 3.50

LITERARY ARTS SERIES

Marianne Craig Moore (1887-1972), Poet — A1808

1990, Apr. 18

2449 A1808 25c multicolored .55 .25
a. All colors missing (EP) —

No. 2449a must be collected se-tenant with a partially printed stamp or in longer horizontal strips with a partially printed stamp and normal stamps.

TRANSPORTATION ISSUE

Steam Carriage 1866 A1810

Circus Wagon 1900s A1811

A1811a

Canoe 1800s A1812

Tractor Trailer 1930s A1816

Cog Railway 1870s A1822

Lunch Wagon 1890s A1823

Ferryboat 1900s A1825

Seaplane 1914 A1827

COIL STAMPS
ENGRAVED, PHOTOGRAVURE
(#2452B, 2452D, 2454, 2458)

1990-95 ***Perf. 9.8 Vert.***

Untagged (Nos. 2452B, 2452D, 2453, 2454, 2457-2458)

Bureau Precancel in Gray (#2453-2458)

2451 A1810 4c claret .30 .25
a. Imperf., pair *450.00*
b. Untagged .30 .25
2452 A1811 5c carmine .30 .25
a. Untagged, dull gum .30 .25
c. Imperf., pair *350.00*

No. 2452c is valued in the grade of fine.

2452B A1811 5c carmine .30 .25
2452D A1811a 5c carmine .30 .25
e. Imperf., pair *115.00*
2453 A1812 5c brown .40 .25
a. Imperf., pair *225.00*
b. Gray omitted 1,200.
2454 A1812 5c red .45 .25
2457 A1816 10c green .45 .25
a. Imperf., pair *110.00*
b. All color omitted —

No. 2457b must be accompanied by a 2012 certificate of authentication confirming that stamps are from the discovery coil roll that also contained normal and partially printed stamps.

2458 A1816 10c green .55 .25
2463 A1822 20c green .40 .25
a. Imperf., pair *75.00*
2464 A1823 23c dark blue .45 .25
b. Imperf., pair *100.00*
2466 A1825 32c blue .80 .25
a. Imperf., pair, shiny gum *375.00*
b. bright blue 3.00 2.25

Some specialists refer to No. 2466b as "Bronx blue," and it is considered to be an error of color.

2468 A1827 $1 bl & scar 2.25 .50
a. Imperf., pair *1,750.* *1,150.*
Nos. 2451-2468 (12) 6.95 3.25

Some mint pairs of No. 2468 appear to be imperf. but have faint blind perforations on the gum. Beware of examples with the gum removed.

Issued: $1, 4/20; No. 2452, 8/31; 4c, 1/25/91; 23c, 4/12/91; Nos. 2453, 2457, 5/25/91; No. 2454, 10/22/91; No. 2452B, 12/8/92; No. 2458, 5/25/94; Nos. 2452D, 3/20/95; 32c, 6/2/95; 20c, 6/9/95.

LIGHTHOUSES

Admiralty Head, WA A1829

Cape Hatteras, NC A1830

West Quoddy Head, ME A1831

American Shoals, FL A1832

Sandy Hook, NJ — A1833

BOOKLET STAMPS
LITHOGRAPHED & ENGRAVED

Perf. 10 Vert. on 1 or 2 Sides

1990, Apr. 26

2470 A1829 25c multicolored 1.50 .25
2471 A1830 25c multicolored 1.50 .25
2472 A1831 25c multicolored 1.50 .25
2473 A1832 25c multicolored 1.50 .25
2474 A1833 25c multicolored 1.50 .25
a. Bklt. pane of 5, #2470-2474 7.50 2.00
b. As "a," white ("USA 25") omitted 85.00 —

Perforations on Lighthouse booklet panes separate very easily. Careful handling is required.

FLAG

A1834

PHOTOGRAVURE

1990, May 18 Untagged *Die Cut*

Self-adhesive

Printed on Plastic

2475 A1834 25c dk red & dk bl .55 .25
a. Pane of 12 6.60

Sold only in panes of 12; peelable plastic backing inscribed in light ultramarine. Available for a test period of six months at 22 First National Bank automatic teller machines in Seattle.

FLORA AND FAUNA

A1840

American Kestrel A1841

Eastern Bluebird A1842

Fawn A1843

Cardinal A1844

Pumpkinseed Sunfish A1845

Bobcat A1846

LITHOGRAPHED

Perf. 11, 11.2 (#2477)

1990-95 Untagged (1c, 3c)

2476 A1840 1c multi .30 .25
a. Quadruple impression of black inscriptions and denomination *850.00*
b. Quintuple impression of black inscriptions and denomination *1,500.*
2477 A1841 1c multi .30 .25
2478 A1842 3c multi .30 .25
a. Vert. pair, imperf horiz. —
b. Double impression of all colors except yellow *200.00*
c. Double impression of blue, triple impression of black —

Imperforates on gummed stamp paper, plus imperforate and perforated gutter pairs and blocks (including imperforate and perforated gutter pairs and blocks of No. 2476 se-tenant with No. 2478), are proofs from the ABNCo. archives. See Nos. 2476P and 2478P in Proofs section of the Scott U.S. Specialized Catalogue.

See Nos. 3031, 3031A, 3044. Compare design A1842 with design A2336.

PHOTOGRAVURE

2479 A1843 19c multi .35 .25
b. Red omitted *425.00*
c. Imperf, pair *900.00*

On No. 2479b other colors are shifted.

2480 A1844 30c multicolored, *June 22, 1991* .60 .25

LITHOGRAPHED & ENGRAVED

2481 A1845 45c multi .90 .25
a. Black (engr.) omitted *300.00* —
2482 A1846 $2 multi 3.50 1.25
a. Black (engr.) omitted *200.00*
Nos. 2476-2482 (7) 6.25 2.75

Issued: $2, 6/1; 19c, 3/11/91; No. 2476, 3c, 30c, 6/22/91; 45c, 12/2/92; No. 2477, 5/10/95.

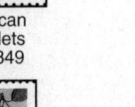

Blue Jay A1847

Wood Duck A1848

African Violets A1849

Peach A1850

Pear A1851

Red Squirrel A1852

Rose A1853

Pine Cone A1854

PHOTOGRAVURE
BOOKLET STAMPS

Perf. 10.9x9.8 on 2 or 3 Sides

1991-95

2483 A1847 20c multi .50 .25
a. Booklet pane of 10 5.25 2.50
b. As "a," imperf —

Perf. 10 on 2 or 3 sides

2484 A1848 29c blk & multi .60 .25
a. Booklet pane of 10 6.00 3.75
b. Vert. pair, imperf. horiz. *175.00*
c. As "b," bklt. pane of 10 *875.00*
f. Vert. pair, imperf between and with natural straight edge at top or bottom *175.00*
g. As "f," bklt. pane of 10 *875.00*

Perf. 11 on 2 or 3 Sides

2485 A1848 29c red & multi .60 .25
a. Booklet pane of 10 6.00 4.00
b. Vert. pair, imperf. between *2,500.*
c. Imperf, pair *4,500.*
d. Pane of 10 with horiz. pairs, imperf. between —

No. 2485d is a pane of 10 with vertical blind perfs between stamps 4 and 5 and 9 and 10.

Perf. 10x11 on 2 or 3 Sides

2486 A1849 29c multi .60 .25
a. Booklet pane of 10 6.00 4.00

Perf. 11x10 on 2 or 3 Sides

2487 A1850 32c multi .65 .25
2488 A1851 32c multi .65 .25
a. Booklet pane, 5 each #2487-2488 6.50 4.25
b. Pair, #2487-2488 1.30 .30

Issued: Nos. 2484-2485, 4/12; No. 2486, 10/8/93; 20c, 6/15/95; 32c, 7/8/95.

PHOTOGRAVURE, ENGRAVED
(#2491)

1993-95 ***Die Cut***

Self-Adhesive

Booklet Stamps

2489 A1852 29c multi .60 .25
a. Booklet pane of 18 11.00
b. As "a," die cutting omitted —
2490 A1853 29c red, green & black .60 .25
a. Booklet pane of 18 11.00

2491 A1854 29c multi .60 .25
- *a.* Booklet pane of 18 11.00
- *b.* Horiz. pair, die cutting omitted between *175.00* *125.00*
- *c.* Coil with plate # B1 — 6.00

Stamps without plate number from coil strips are indistinguishable from booklet stamps once they are removed from the backing paper.

Serpentine Die Cut 11.3x11.7 on 2, 3 or 4 Sides

2492 A1853 32c pink, green & black .65 .25
- *a.* Booklet pane of 20 + label 13.00
- *b.* Booklet pane of 15 + label 9.75
- *c.* Horiz. pair, die cutting omitted between —
- *d.* As "a," 2 stamps and parts of 7 others printed on backing liner —
- *e.* Booklet pane of 14 20.00
- *f.* Booklet pane of 16 20.00
- *g.* Coil with plate # S111 — 5.50
- *h.* Vert. pair, die cutting omitted between (from No. 2492b) *400.00*
- *i.* As "a," 6 pairs plus stamp and label die cutting omitted vert. btwn. (due to mis-cutting) *800.00*
- *j.* As "f," with 2 vert. pairs at bottom die cutting omitted horiz., in full bklt. #BK178D —
- *k.* As "a," horiz. die cutting omitted —

Serpentine Die Cut 8.8 on 2, 3 or 4 Sides

2493 A1850 32c multi .65 .25
2494 A1851 32c multi .65 .25
- *a.* Booklet pane of 20, 10 each #2493-2494 + label 13.00
- *b.* Pair, #2493-2494 1.30
- *c.* As "b," die cutting omitted —

COIL STAMPS

Serpentine Die Cut 8.8 Vert.

2495 A1850 32c multi 2.00 .25
2495A A1851 32c multi 2.00 .25
- *b.* Pair, #2495-2495A 4.00

Issued: No. 2489, 6/25; No. 2490, 8/19; No. 2491, 11/5; No. 2492, 6/2/95; Nos. 2493-2495A, 7/8/95.

See Nos. 3048-3049, 3053-3054.

Values for used self-adhesive stamps are for examples either on piece or off piece.

OLYMPIANS

Jesse Owens, 1936 — A1855

Ray Ewry, 1900-08 — A1856

Hazel Wightman, 1924 — A1857

Eddie Eagan, 1920, 1932 — A1858

Helene Madison, 1932 — A1859

PHOTOGRAVURE

1990, July 6 ***Perf. 11***

2496 A1855 25c multicolored .60 .25
2497 A1856 25c multicolored .60 .25
2498 A1857 25c multicolored .60 .25
2499 A1858 25c multicolored .60 .25
2500 A1859 25c multicolored .60 .25
- *a.* Strip of 5, #2496-2500 3.25 2.50
- *b.* As "a," blue omitted 1,750.

Imperforates on gummed stamp paper, including gutter pairs, strips and blocks, are proofs from the ABNCo. archives. See No. 2500aP in Proofs section of the Scott U.S. Specialized Catalogue.

INDIAN HEADDRESSES

Assiniboin A1860

Cheyenne A1861

Comanche A1862

Flathead — A1863

Shoshone A1864

LITHOGRAPHED & ENGRAVED
BOOKLET STAMPS

Perf. 11 on 2 or 3 Sides

1990, Aug. 17

2501 A1860 25c multicolored .80 .25
2502 A1861 25c multicolored .80 .25
2503 A1862 25c multicolored .80 .25
- *a.* Black (engr.) omitted *125.00* —

2504 A1863 25c multicolored .80 .25
- *a.* Black (engr.) omitted *125.00* —

2505 A1864 25c multicolored .80 .25
- *a.* Bklt. pane of 10, 2 each #2501-2505 8.00 6.00
- *b.* As "a," black (engr.) omitted *2,500.*
- *c.* Strip of 5, #2501-2505 4.00 2.50
- *d.* As "a," horiz. imperf. between *2,250.*

At least one of the examples of No. 2505d that have been reported is actually split at the booklet fold and is a block of 4 and a block of 6.

MICRONESIA & MARSHALL ISLANDS

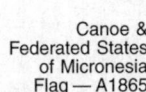

Canoe & Federated States of Micronesia Flag — A1865

Stick Chart, Canoe & Republic of the Marshall Islands Flag — A1866

1990, Sept. 28 ***Perf. 11***

2506 A1865 25c multicolored .50 .25
2507 A1866 25c multicolored .50 .25
- *a.* Pair, #2506-2507 1.00 .75
- *b.* As "a," black (engr.) omitted *1,400.*

See Micronesia Nos. 124-126, Marshall Islands No. 381.

SEA CREATURES

Killer Whales — A1867

Northern Sea Lions — A1868

Sea Otter — A1869

Common Dolphin — A1870

1990, Oct. 3

2508 A1867 25c multicolored .55 .25
2509 A1868 25c multicolored .55 .25
2510 A1869 25c multicolored .55 .25
2511 A1870 25c multicolored .55 .25
- *a.* Block of 4, #2508-2511 2.25 1.90
- *b.* As "a," black (engr.) omitted *250.00*

See Russia Nos. 5933-5936.

PRE-COLUMBIAN AMERICA ISSUE

Grand Canyon — A1871

PHOTOGRAVURE

1990, Oct. 12

2512 A1871 25c multicolored .55 .25

See No. C127.

DWIGHT D. EISENHOWER, BIRTH CENTENARY

A1872

1990, Oct. 13 **Tagged** ***Perf. 11***

2513 A1872 25c multicolored .80 .25

Imperforates on gummed stamp paper are proofs from the ABNCo. archives. See No. 2513P in Proofs section of the Scott U.S. Specialized Catalogue.

CHRISTMAS

Madonna and Child by Antonello da Messina A1873

Christmas Tree A1874

LITHOGRAPHED & ENGRAVED

1990, Oct. 18 ***Perf. 11¼x11½***

2514 A1873 25c multi .50 .25
- *b.* Booklet pane of 10 5.00 3.25

PHOTOGRAVURE

Perf. 11

2515 A1874 25c multicolored .50 .25
- *a.* Vert. pair, imperf. horiz. *500.00*
- *b.* All colors missing (EP) —

No. 2515b must be collected se-tenant with normal and/or partially printed stamp(s).

BOOKLET STAMP

Perf. 11½x11 on 2 or 3 Sides

2516 A1874 25c multicolored .60 .25
- *a.* Booklet pane of 10 6.00 3.25

Marked differences exist between Nos. 2515 and 2516. The background red on No. 2515 is even while that on No. 2516 is splotchy. The bands across the tree and "Greetings" are blue green on No. 2515 and yellow green on No. 2516.

A1875

A1876

1991, Jan. 22 ***Perf. 13***

2517 A1875 (29c) yel, blk, red & yel grn .60 .25
- *a.* Imperf., pair *1,000.*
- *b.* Horiz. pair, imperf. vert. *1,000.*

See note after No. 2518.

Gutter pairs and blocks, and cross gutter blocks, all perforated, are proofs from the ABNCo. archives. See No. 2517P in Proofs section of the Scott U.S. Specialized Catalogue.

No. 2517a is usually collected as a vertical pair, though No. 2517 can be distinguished from the other "F" stamp issues.

COIL STAMP

Perf. 10 Vert.

2518 A1875 (29c) yel, blk, dull red & dk yel grn .60 .25
- *a.* Imperf., pair 25.00

"For U.S. addresses only" is 17½mm long on No. 2517, 16½mm long on No. 2518. Design of No. 2517 measures 21½x17½mm, No. 2518, 21x18mm.

BOOKLET STAMPS

Perf. 11 on 2 or 3 Sides

2519 A1875 (29c) yel, blk, dull red & dk grn .60 .25
- *a.* Booklet pane of 10 6.50 4.50

2520 A1875 (29c) pale yel, blk, red & brt grn 1.50 .25
- *a.* Booklet pane of 10 15.00 4.50
- *b.* As "a," imperf. horiz. —
- *c.* Horiz. pair, imperf btwn., in error booklet pane of 12 stamps *450.00*
- *d.* Imperf. vert., pair —

No. 2519 has bullseye perforations that measure approximately 11.2. No. 2520 has less pronounced black lines in the leaf, which is a much brighter green than on No. 2519.

No. 2520c is from a paper foldover before perforating.

LITHOGRAPHED

1991, Jan. 22 **Untagged** ***Perf. 11***

2521 A1876 (4c) bister & carmine .30 .25
- *a.* Vert. pair, imperf. horiz. 70.00
- *b.* Imperf., pair 60.00

FLAG

A1877

PHOTOGRAVURE

1991, Jan. 22 **Untagged** ***Die Cut***

Self-Adhesive

Printed on Plastic

2522 A1877 (29c) blk, blue & dk red .60 .25
- *a.* Pane of 12 7.25

Sold only in panes of 12; peelable plastic backing inscribed in light ultramarine. Available during a test period at First National Bank automatic teller machines in Seattle.

Flag Over Mt. Rushmore — A1878

COIL STAMPS
ENGRAVED

1991, Mar. 29 **Tagged** ***Perf. 10 Vert.***

2523 A1878 29c bl, red & claret .75 .25
- *b.* Imperf., pair 20.00
- *c.* blue, red & brown 3.00 —

Specialists often call No. 2523c the "Toledo brown" variety.

PHOTOGRAVURE

1991, July 4

2523A A1878 29c bl, red, lt brn, med brn & dk brn .75 .25
- *e.* Medium brown omitted —

On No. 2523A, USA and 29 are not outlined in white and are farther from the bottom of the design.

Flower — A1879

PHOTOGRAVURE

1991-92 ***Perf. 11***

2524 A1879 29c dull yel, blk, red & yel grn .60 .25

See note after No. 2527.

Perf. 13x12¾

2524A A1879 29c dull yel, blk, red & yel grn 1.00 .25

COIL STAMPS

Rouletted 10 Vert.

2525 A1879 29c pale yel, blk, red & yel grn .60 .25

Perf. 10 Vert.

2526 A1879 29c pale yel, blk, red & yel grn .80 .25

BOOKLET STAMP

Perf. 11 on 2 or 3 Sides

2527 A1879 29c pale yel, blk, red & bright grn .60 .25
- *a.* Booklet pane of 10 6.00 3.50
- *b.* Horiz. pair, imperf. between — —
- *c.* Horiz. pair, imperf. vert. *150.00*
- *d.* As "a," imperf. horiz. *750.00*
- *e.* As "a," imperf. vert. *500.00*

Flower on Nos. 2524-2524A has grainy appearance, inscriptions look rougher.
Issued: Nos. 2524, 2524A, 2527, 4/5; No. 2525, 8/16; No. 2526, 3/3/92.

Flag, Olympic Rings — A1880

BOOKLET STAMP

Perf. 11 on 2 or 3 Sides

1991, Apr. 21

2528 A1880 29c multicolored .60 .25
- *a.* Booklet pane of 10 6.00 3.50
- *b.* As "a," imperf. horiz. *2,750.*
- *c.* Vert. pair, imperf. between, perfed at top and bottom *225.00*
- *d.* Vert. strip of 3, top or bottom pair imperf. between —
- *e.* Vert. pair, imperf. horiz. *650.00*
- *f.* As "d," two pairs in #2528a with foldover —

No. 2528c comes from misperfed booklet panes. No. 2528d resulted from paper foldovers after normal perforating and before cutting into panes. Two No. 2528d are known. No. 2528e is valued in the grade of fine.

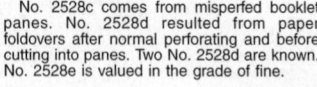

Fishing Boat — A1881

Type I

Type II

Type I: Vertical sides of "1" are jagged. Type II stamps are created by a finer dot pattern. Vertical sides of "1" are smooth.
Nos. 2529 and 2529a have two loops of rope tying boat to piling.

COIL STAMPS

1991, Aug. 8 ***Perf. 9.8 Vert.***

2529 A1881 19c **multi,** type I .40 .25
- *a.* Type II ('93) .40 .25
- *b.* As "a," untagged ('93) 1.00 .40

Imperforates are from printer's waste.

1994, June 25

2529C A1881 19c multicolored .50 .25

No. 2529C has one loop of rope tying boat to piling.

Balloon — A1882

BOOKLET STAMP

Perf. 10 on 2 or 3 Sides

1991, May 17

2530 A1882 19c multicolored .40 .25
- *a.* Booklet pane of 10 4.00 2.75

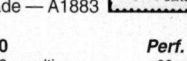

Flags on Parade — A1883

1991, May 30 ***Perf. 11***

2531 A1883 29c multi .60 .25

Liberty Torch — A1884

1991, June 25 ***Die Cut***

Self-Adhesive

2531A A1884 29c blk, gold & grn .60 .25
- *b.* Booklet pane of 18 11.00
- *c.* Die cutting omitted, pair *1,000.*

Sold only in panes of 18; peelable paper backing inscribed in light blue. Available for consumer testing at First National Bank automatic teller machines in Seattle, WA.

SWITZERLAND

Switzerland, 700th Anniv. — A1887

1991, Feb. 22 ***Perf. 11***

2532 A1887 50c multi 1.00 .25
- *a.* Vert. pair, imperf. horiz. *1,400.*

See Switzerland No. 888.
Imperfs exist from printer's waste.

VERMONT STATEHOOD, 200th ANNIV.

A1888

1991, Mar. 1

2533 A1888 29c multicolored .80 .25

SAVINGS BONDS, 50TH ANNIVERSARY

A1889

1991, Apr. 30 ***Perf. 11***

2534 A1889 29c multicolored .60 .25

LOVE

A1890

1991, May 9 ***Perf. 12½x13***

2535 A1890 29c multi .60 .25
- *b.* Imperf., pair *1,650.*

Perf. 11

2535A A1890 29c multi 1.00 .25

BOOKLET STAMP (#2536)

Perf. 11.1x11.3 on 2 or 3 Sides

2536 A1890 29c multi .60 .25
- *a.* Booklet pane of 10 6.00 3.50

"29" is closer to edge of design on No. 2536 than on No. 2535.

A1891

Perf. 11

2537 A1891 52c multi .90 .25

LITERARY ARTS SERIES

William Saroyan — A1892

1991, May 22 ***Perf. 11***

2538 A1892 29c multicolored .60 .25
- *a.* All colors missing (EP) —
- *b.* All colors except black missing (EP) 11,000.

No. 2538a must be collected se-tenant with a partially printed stamp. On No. 2538b, only part of the black is present; it is unique.
See Russia No. 6002.

Eagle, Olympic Rings — A1893

A1894

A1895

A1896

Futuristic Space Shuttle — A1897

Space Shuttle Challenger A1898

Space Shuttle Endeavour — A1898a

1991, Sept. 29

2539 A1893 $1 gold & multi 2.00 .50
- *a.* Black omitted —

LITHOGRAPHED & ENGRAVED

1991, July 7

2540 A1894 $2.90 multicolored 6.00 1.50
- *a.* Vert. pair, imperf horiz. *900.00*
- *b.* Black (engr.) omitted *750.00*

Imperforates on gummed stamp paper, including gutter pairs and blocks, are proofs from the ABNCo. archives. From the same source also come imperforate progressive proofs. See No. 2540P in Proofs section of the Scott U.S. Specialized Catalogue.

1991, June 16 **Untagged**

2541 A1895 $9.95 multicolored 20.00 6.00
- *a.* Imperf., pair —

No. 2541 exists imperf plus black (engr.) omitted from printer's waste.

1991, Aug. 31 **Untagged**

2542 A1896 $14 multicolored 25.00 15.00
- *a.* Red (engr. inscriptions) omitted *750.00*

No. 2542 exists imperf plus red omitted from printer's waste.

PHOTOGRAVURE

1993, June 3 ***Perf. 11x10¾***

2543 A1897 $2.90 multicolored 6.00 1.75

Faked examples of No. 2543, unused and used, exist with red omitted due to bleaching.

1995, June 22 ***Perf. 11.2***

2544	A1898 $3 multicolored, dated "1995"	5.75	1.75
b.	Dated "1996"	5.75	1.75
c.	As "b," horiz. pair, imperf between	*1,000.*	
d.	As "b," imperf pair	*700.00*	

Imperf examples of No. 2544 with "1995" date are believed to be printer's waste.

1995, Aug. 4 ***Perf. 11***

2544A	A1898a $10.75 multi	20.00	9.00

No. 2544A was printed on paper embedded with red fibers.

Imperf examples of No. 2544A are believed to be printer's waste.

FISHING FLIES

Royal Wulff — A1899

Jock Scott — A1900

Apte Tarpon Fly — A1901

Lefty's Deceiver — A1902

Muddler Minnow — A1903

PHOTOGRAVURE
BOOKLET STAMPS

Perf. 11 Horiz. on 1 or 2 Sides

1991, May 31

2545	A1899 29c multicolored	1.10	.25
a.	Black omitted	—	
b.	Horiz. pair, imperf. btwn., in #2549a with foldover	*2,400.*	
2546	A1900 29c multicolored	1.10	.25
a.	Black omitted	—	
2547	A1901 29c multicolored	1.10	.25
a.	Black omitted	—	
2548	A1902 29c multicolored	1.10	.25
2549	A1903 29c multicolored	1.10	.25
a.	Bklt. pane of 5, #2545-2549	5.50	3.00

Horiz. pairs, imperf vert., exist from printer's waste.

No. 2545b is unique and resulted from a foldover after perfing but before cutting. Both stamps are creased.

PERFORMING ARTS

Cole Porter (1891-1964), Composer — A1904

1991, June 8 ***Perf. 11***

2550	A1904 29c multicolored	.60	.25
a.	Vert. pair, imperf. horiz.	*400.00*	

OPERATIONS DESERT SHIELD & DESERT STORM

S. W. Asia Service Medal — A1905

1991, July 2

2551	A1905 29c multicolored	.60	.25
a.	Vert. pair, imperf. horiz.	*600.00*	

No. 2551 is 21mm wide.

BOOKLET STAMP

Perf. 11 Vert. on 1 or 2 Sides

2552	A1905 29c multicolored	.60	.25
a.	Booklet pane of 5	3.00	2.25

No. 2552 is 20½mm wide. Inscriptions are shorter than on No. 2551.

No. 2552 Vert. pairs, imperf horiz., are from printer's waste.

1992 SUMMER OLYMPICS, BARCELONA

Pole Vault — A1907

Discus — A1908

Women's Sprints — A1909

Javelin — A1910

Women's Hurdles — A1911

1991, July 12 ***Perf. 11***

2553	A1907 29c multicolored	.60	.25
2554	A1908 29c multicolored	.60	.25
2555	A1909 29c multicolored	.60	.25
2556	A1910 29c multicolored	.60	.25
2557	A1911 29c multicolored	.60	.25
a.	Strip of 5, #2553-2557	3.00	2.25

NUMISMATICS

1858 Flying Eagle Cent, 1907 Standing Liberty Double Eagle, Series 1875 $1 Note, Series 1902 $10 National Currency Note — A1912

LITHOGRAPHED & ENGRAVED

1991, Aug. 13

2558	A1912 29c multicolored	.60	.25

WORLD WAR II

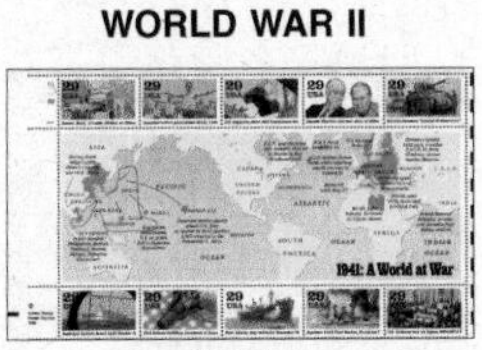

A1913

Designs and events of 1941: a, Military vehicles (Burma Road, 717-mile lifeline to China). b, Recruits (America's first peacetime draft). c, Shipments for allies (U.S. supports allies with Lend-Lease Act). d, Franklin D. Roosevelt, Winston Churchill (Atlantic Charter sets war aims of allies). e, Tank (America becomes the "arsenal of democracy.") f, Sinking of Destoyer Reuben James, Oct. 31. g, Gas mask, helmet (Civil defense mobilizes Americans at home). h, Liberty Ship, sea gull (First Liberty ship delivered December 30). i, Sinking ships (Japanese bomb Pearl Harbor, December 7). j, Congress in session (U.S. declares war on Japan, December 8). Central label is the size of 15 stamps and shows world map, extent of axis control.

LITHOGRAPHED & ENGRAVED

1991, Sept. 3

2559	A1913 Block of 10	7.50	5.00
a.-j.	29c any single	.75	.45
k.	Black (engr.) omitted	*6,500.*	

No. 2559 has selvage at left and right and either top or bottom.

BASKETBALL, 100TH ANNIVERSARY

Basketball, Hoop, Players' Arms — A1914

PHOTOGRAVURE

1991, Aug. 28

2560	A1914 29c multicolored	.60	.25

DISTRICT OF COLUMBIA BICENTENNIAL

Capitol Building from Pennsylvania Avenue, Circa 1903 — A1915

LITHOGRAPHED & ENGRAVED

1991, Sept. 7

2561	A1915 29c multicolored	.60	.25
a.	Black (engr.) omitted	*85.00*	

COMEDIANS

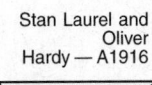

Stan Laurel and Oliver Hardy — A1916

Edgar Bergen and Charlie McCarthy A1917

Jack Benny — A1918

Fanny Brice — A1919

Bud Abbott and Lou Costello — A1920

BOOKLET STAMPS

Perf. 11 on 2 or 3 Sides

1991, Aug. 29

2562	A1916 29c multicolored	1.00	.25
2563	A1917 29c multicolored	1.00	.25
2564	A1918 29c multicolored	1.00	.25
2565	A1919 29c multicolored	1.00	.25
2566	A1920 29c multicolored	1.00	.25
a.	Strip of 5, #2562-2566	5.00	2.25
b.	Bklt. pane of 10, 2 each #2562-2566	10.00	5.00
c.	As "b," scar & brt violet (engr.) omitted	*350.00*	

BLACK HERITAGE SERIES

Jan E. Matzeliger (1852-1889), Inventor — A1921

PHOTOGRAVURE

1991, Sept. 15 ***Perf. 11***

2567	A1921 29c multicolored	.60	.25
a.	Horiz. pair, imperf. vert.	*600.00*	
b.	Vert. pair, imperf. horiz.	*550.00*	
c.	Imperf., pair	*275.00*	

SPACE EXPLORATION

Mercury, Mariner 10 A1922

Venus, Mariner 2 A1923

Earth, Landsat — A1924

Moon, Lunar Orbiter — A1925

Mars, Viking Orbiter — A1926

Jupiter, Pioneer 11 A1927

Saturn, Voyager 2 A1928

Uranus, Voyager 2 A1929

Neptune, Voyager 2 A1930

Pluto — A1931

PHOTOGRAVURE
BOOKLET STAMPS

Perf. 11 on 2 or 3 Sides

1991, Oct. 1

2568	A1922 29c multicolored	.90	.25
2569	A1923 29c multicolored	.90	.25
2570	A1924 29c multicolored	.90	.25
2571	A1925 29c multicolored	.90	.25
2572	A1926 29c multicolored	.90	.25
2573	A1927 29c multicolored	.90	.25
2574	A1928 29c multicolored	.90	.25
2575	A1929 29c multicolored	.90	.25
2576	A1930 29c multicolored	.90	.25
2577	A1931 29c multicolored	.90	.25
a.	Bklt. pane of 10, #2568-2577	9.00	4.50

CHRISTMAS

Madonna and Child by Antoniazzo Romano A1933

Santa Claus in Chimney A1934

Santa Checking List A1935

Santa with Present A1936

Santa at Fireplace A1937

Santa and Sleigh A1938

LITHOGRAPHED & ENGRAVED

1991, Oct. 17 ***Perf. 11¼***

2578 A1933 (29c) multi .60 .25
a. Booklet pane of 10 6.00 3.25
b. Red & black (engr.) omitted *2,250.*

PHOTOGRAVURE

Perf. 11

2579 A1934 (29c) multi .60 .25
P# block of 4, 3#+A 2.50 —
Zip block of 4 2.25 —
Pane of 50 30.00
a. Horiz. pair, imperf. vert. 175.00
b. Vert. pair, imperf. horiz. *350.00*

BOOKLET STAMPS

Size: 25x18½mm

Perf. 11 on 2 or 3 Sides

2580 A1934 (29c) multi, type I 2.00 .25
2581 A1934 (29c) multi, type II 2.00 .25
a. Pair #2580-2581 4.00 .55
b. Bklt. pane, 2 each, #2580-2581 8.00 1.25
2582 A1935 (29c) multi .60 .25
a. Bklt. pane of 4 2.40 1.25
2583 A1936 (29c) multi .60 .25
a. Bklt. pane of 4 2.40 1.25
2584 A1937 (29c) multi .60 .25
a. Bklt. pane of 4 2.40 1.25
2585 A1938 (29c) multi .60 .25
a. Bklt. pane of 4 2.40 1.25
Nos. 2578-2585 (8) 7.60 2.00

The far left brick from the top row of the chimney is missing from Type II, No. 2581.

Imperfs of Nos. 2581, 2583-2585 are printer's waste.

A1939

A1942

A1944

ENGRAVED

1994-95 ***Perf. 11.2***

2587 A1939 32c red brown .65 .25

Perf. 11.5

2590 A1942 $1 blue 1.90 .50
2592 A1944 $5 slate green 8.00 2.50

Issued: $2, 5/5; $5, 8/19; 32c, 11/2/95.

Flag — A1946

BOOKLET STAMPS
PHOTOGRAVURE

Perf. 10 on 2 or 3 Sides

1992, Sept. 8

2593 A1946 29c black & multi .60 .25
a. Booklet pane of 10 6.00 4.25
d. Imperf, pair *500.00*

Perf. 11x10 on 2 or 3 Sides

2593B A1946 29c blk & multi 2.50 .50
c. Bklt. pane of 10, shiny gum 30.00 7.50

Perf. 11x10 on 2 or 3 Sides

1993, Apr. 8 (?)

2594 A1946 29c red & multi .65 .25
a. Booklet pane of 10 6.50 4.25

Denomination is red on #2594 and black on #2593 and 2593B.

Eagle and Shield — A1947

LITHOGRAPHED & ENGRAVED (#2595), PHOTOGRAVURE

1992, Sept. 25 ***Die Cut***

Self-Adhesive

2595 A1947 29c brn & multi .75 .25
a. Bklt. pane of 17 + label 12.75
b. Die cutting omitted, pair *90.00*
c. Brown omitted *250.00*
d. As "a," die cutting omitted *725.00*
2596 A1947 29c bl grn & multi .75 .25
a. Bklt. pane of 17 + label 12.75
2597 A1947 29c red & multi .75 .25
a. Bklt. pane of 17 + label 12.75

Plate No. and inscription reads down on No. 2595a and up on Nos. 2596a-2597a. Design is sharper and more finely detailed on Nos. 2595, 2597.

Nos. 2595a-2597a sold for $5 each.

Nos. 2595-2597 also available in strips with stamps spaced for use in affixing machines to service first day covers.

A1950

Statue of Liberty — A1951

Designed by Richard Sheaff (#2598), Tom Engeman (#2599).

Printed by Dittler Brothers, Inc. (#2599), National Label Co. for 3M (#2598).

1994 ***Die Cut***

Self-Adhesive

2598 A1950 29c red, cream & blue .60 .25
a. Booklet pane of 18 11.00
b. Coil with P#111 — 5.00
c. Die cutting omitted, pair *1,000.*
2599 A1951 29c multi .60 .25
a. Booklet pane of 18 11.00
b. Coil with P#D1111 — 5.00

Except for Nos. 2598b and 2599b with plate numbers, coil stamps of Nos. 2595-2599 are indistinguishable from booklet stamps once they are removed from the backing paper.

See Nos. 3122-3122E.

Issued: No. 2598, 2/4; No. 2599, 6/24.

Scott values for used self-adhesive stamps are for examples either on piece or off piece.

A1956

A1957

A1959

A1960

Flag Over White House — A1961

COIL STAMPS

1991-93 Untagged ***Perf. 10 Vert.***

2602 A1956 (10c) multi .30 .25
a. Imperf., pair *3,500.*
2603 A1957 (10c) org yel & multi .30 .25
a. Imperf., pair 20.00
2604 A1957 (10c) gold & multi .30 .25
2605 A1959 23c multi .45 .40
a. Imperf, pair —

Vertical pairs uncut between on gummed stamp paper are proofs from the ABNCo. archives. See No. 2605P in Proofs section of the Scott U.S. Specialized Catalogue.

2606 A1960 23c multi .45 .40

"First-Class" is 9½mm long and "23" is 6mm long on No. 2606.

2607 A1960 23c multi .45 .40
c. Imperf., pair 65.00

"First-Class" is 9mm long and "23" is 6½mm long on No. 2607.

2608 A1960 23c vio bl, red & blk .80 .40

"First-Class" is 8½mm long and "23" is 6½mm long on No. 2608.

Nos. 2602-2608 are considered precancels by the USPS.

ENGRAVED

Tagged

2609 A1961 29c blue & red .60 .25
a. Imperf., pair 15.00 *25.00*
b. Pair, imperf. between 60.00
c. Indigo blue & red *22.50* —
Nos. 2602-2609 (8) 3.65 2.60

Beware of pairs with blind perfs sometimes offered as No. 2609b.

Issued: No. 2605, 9/27; No. 2602, 12/31; 29c, 4/23/92; No. 2606, 7/21/92; No. 2607, 10/9/92; Nos. 2603-2604, 5/29/93; No. 2608, 5/14/93.

See Nos. 2907, 3270-3271.

WINTER OLYMPICS

Hockey — A1963

Figure Skating — A1964

Speed Skating — A1965

Skiing — A1966

Bobsledding A1967

PHOTOGRAVURE

1992, Jan. 11 ***Perf. 11***

2611 A1963 29c multicolored .60 .25
2612 A1964 29c multicolored .60 .25
2613 A1965 29c multicolored .60 .25
2614 A1966 29c multicolored .60 .25
2615 A1967 29c multicolored .60 .25
a. Strip of 5, #2611-2615 3.00 2.50

WORLD COLUMBIAN STAMP EXPO

Portion of Vignette of No. 129 — A1968

LITHOGRAPHED & ENGRAVED

1992, Jan. 24

2616 A1968 29c multicolored .60 .25

BLACK HERITAGE SERIES

W.E.B. Du Bois (1868-1963), Civil Rights Leader — A1969

1992, Jan. 31

2617 A1969 29c multicolored .60 .25

LOVE

A1970

PHOTOGRAVURE

1992, Feb. 6

2618 A1970 29c multicolored .60 .25
a. Horiz. pair, imperf. vert. *300.00*
b. As "a," green omitted on right stamp *1,250.*

OLYMPIC BASEBALL

A1971

1992, Apr. 3 Tagged ***Perf. 11***

2619 A1971 29c multicolored .60 .25

VOYAGES OF COLUMBUS

Seeking Queen Isabella's Support — A1972

Crossing the Atlantic — A1973

Approaching Land — A1974

Coming Ashore — A1975

LITHOGRAPHED & ENGRAVED

1992, Apr. 24

2620 A1972 29c multicolored .65 .25
2621 A1973 29c multicolored .65 .25
2622 A1974 29c multicolored .65 .25
2623 A1975 29c multicolored .65 .25
a. Block of 4, #2620-2623 2.60 2.00

See Italy Nos. 1877-1880.

Souvenir Sheets

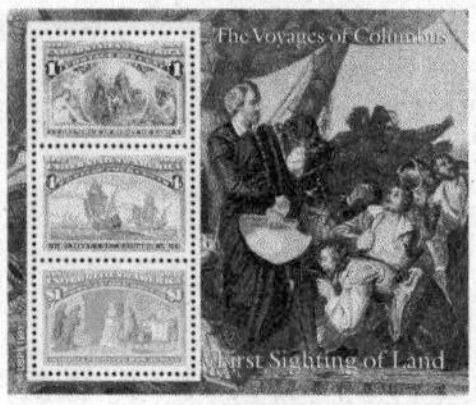

A1976

A1977

A1978

A1979

A1980

A1981

1992, May 22 ***Perf. 10½***

Tagged (15c-$5), Untagged

2624	A1976	Pane of 3	2.35	1.50
a.	A71	1c deep blue	.30	.25
b.	A74	4c ultramarine	.30	.25
c.	A82	$1 salmon	1.75	1.00
2625	A1977	Pane of 3	7.50	5.00
a.	A72	2c brown violet	.30	.25
b.	A73	3c green	.30	.25
c.	A85	$4 crimson lake	7.00	4.00
2626	A1978	Pane of 3	1.80	1.25
a.	A75	5c chocolate	.30	.25
b.	A80	30c orange brown	.60	.30
c.	A81	50c slate blue	.90	.50
2627	A1979	Pane of 3	6.10	3.75
a.	A76	6c purple	.30	.25
b.	A77	8c magenta	.30	.25
c.	A84	$3 yellow green	5.50	3.00
2628	A1980	Pane of 3	4.30	3.00
a.	A78	10c black brown	.30	.25
b.	A79	15c dark green	.30	.25
c.	A83	$2 brown red	3.50	2.00
2629	A1981	$5 Pane of 1	8.75	6.00
a.	A86	$5 black, single stamp	8.50	5.00
		Nos. 2624-2629 (6)	30.80	20.50

See Italy Nos. 1883-1888, Portugal Nos. 1918-1923 and Spain Nos. 2677-2682.

Imperforate souvenir sheets on gummed stamp paper, singly or in pairs and blocks, are proofs from the ABNCo. archives. Additionally, one imperforate essay, with the background of No. 2622 combined with the stamps of No. 2620, is recorded. See Nos. 2624P-2629P in Proofs section of the Scott U.S. Specialized Catalogue.

NEW YORK STOCK EXCHANGE BICENTENNIAL

A1982

1992, May 17 ***Perf. 11***

2630	A1982 29c green, red & black		.60	.25
a.	Black missing (EP)	4,000.		
b.	Black missing (CM)	4,000.		
c.	Center (black engr.) inverted	17,000.		
d.	Se-tenant pair, #2630b and #2630c	22,500.		

No. 2630a resulted from extraneous paper that blocked the black from appearing on the stamp paper. It is from a unique pane that contained four color-missing errors plus a fifth stamp missing half the black center.

No. 2630a must be collected se-tenant with a normal stamp or with a stamp with half of black engraving missing, or se-tenant with a normal stamp and an additional 2630a.

No. 2630b may be collected alone or se-tenant with No. 2630c.

Two panes, each containing 28 No. 2630c and 12 No. 2630b, have been documented.

SPACE ACCOMPLISHMENTS

Cosmonaut, U.S. Space Shuttle A1983

Astronaut, Russian Space Station A1984

Sputnik, Vostok, Apollo Command & Lunar Modules A1985

Soyuz, Mercury and Gemini Spacecraft A1986

PHOTOGRAVURE

1992, May 29

2631	A1983 29c multicolored		.60	.25
2632	A1984 29c multicolored		.60	.25
2633	A1985 29c multicolored		.60	.25
2634	A1986 29c multicolored		.60	.25
a.	Block of 4, #2631-2634		2.40	2.00
b.	As "a," yellow omitted	4,750.		

The yellow color in Nos. 2631-2634 is easily removed by exposure to sunlight. Expertization of No. 2634b is essential.

See Russia Nos. 6080-6083.

ALASKA HIGHWAY, 50th ANNIVERSARY

A1987

LITHOGRAPHED & ENGRAVED

1992, May 30

2635	A1987 29c multicolored	.60	.25
a.	Black (engr.) omitted	575.00	—

Almost half the recorded No. 2635a errors are poorly centered. These sell for approximately $400.

KENTUCKY STATEHOOD BICENTENNIAL

A1988

PHOTOGRAVURE

1992, June 1

2636	A1988 29c multicolored	.60	.25
a.	Dark blue missing (EP)	—	
b.	Dark blue and red missing (EP)	—	
c.	All colors missing (EP)	—	

Nos. 2636a-2636c must be collected se-tenant with normal stamps.

SUMMER OLYMPICS

Soccer — A1989

Gymnastics A1990

Volleyball A1991

Boxing — A1992

Swimming A1993

1992, June 11

2637	A1989 29c multicolored	.60	.25
2638	A1990 29c multicolored	.60	.25
2639	A1991 29c multicolored	.60	.25
2640	A1992 29c multicolored	.60	.25
2641	A1993 29c multicolored	.60	.25
a.	Strip of 5, #2637-2641	3.00	2.50

HUMMINGBIRDS

Ruby-throated A1994

Broad-billed A1995

Costa's A1996

Rufous A1997

Calliope — A1998

BOOKLET STAMPS

Perf. 11 Vert. on 1 or 2 Sides

1992, June 15

2642	A1994 29c multicolored	.60	.25
2643	A1995 29c multicolored	.60	.25
2644	A1996 29c multicolored	.60	.25
2645	A1997 29c multicolored	.60	.25
2646	A1998 29c multicolored	.60	.25
a.	Bklt. pane of 5, #2642-2646	3.00	2.50

Imperforate singles, booklet panes and pane multiples or varieties on gummed stamp paper are proofs from the ABNCo. archives. From the same source also come imperforate progressive proofs. See No. 2646aP in Proofs section of the Scott U.S. Specialized Catalogue.

WILDFLOWERS

A1999

LITHOGRAPHED

1992, July 24 ***Perf. 11***

2647	A1999 29c Indian paintbrush	.60	.60
2648	A2000 29c Fragrant water lily	.60	.60
2649	A2001 29c Meadow beauty	.60	.60
2650	A2002 29c Jack-in-the-pulpit	.60	.60
2651	A2003 29c California poppy	.60	.60
2652	A2004 29c Large-flowered trillium	.60	.60
2653	A2005 29c Tickseed	.60	.60
2654	A2006 29c Shooting star	.60	.60
2655	A2007 29c Stream violet	.60	.60
2656	A2008 29c Bluets	.60	.60
2657	A2009 29c Herb Robert	.60	.60
2658	A2010 29c Marsh marigold	.60	.60
2659	A2011 29c Sweet white violet	.60	.60
2660	A2012 29c Claret cup cactus	.60	.60
2661	A2013 29c White mountain avens	.60	.60
2662	A2014 29c Sessile bellwort	.60	.60
2663	A2015 29c Blue flag	.60	.60
2664	A2016 29c Harlequin lupine	.60	.60
2665	A2017 29c Twinflower	.60	.60
2666	A2018 29c Common sunflower	.60	.60
2667	A2019 29c Sego lily	.60	.60
2668	A2020 29c Virginia bluebells	.60	.60
2669	A2021 29c Ohi'a lehua	.60	.60
2670	A2022 29c Rosebud orchid	.60	.60
2671	A2023 29c Showy evening primrose	.60	.60
2672	A2024 29c Fringed gentian	.60	.60
2673	A2025 29c Yellow lady's slipper	.60	.60
2674	A2026 29c Passionflower	.60	.60
2675	A2027 29c Bunchberry	.60	.60
2676	A2028 29c Pasqueflower	.60	.60
2677	A2029 29c Round-lobed hepatica	.60	.60
2678	A2030 29c Wild columbine	.60	.60
2679	A2031 29c Fireweed	.60	.60
2680	A2032 29c Indian pond lily	.60	.60
2681	A2033 29c Turk's cap lily	.60	.60
2682	A2034 29c Dutchman's breeches	.60	.60
2683	A2035 29c Trumpet honeysuckle	.60	.60
2684	A2036 29c Jacob's ladder	.60	.60
2685	A2037 29c Plains prickly pear	.60	.60
2686	A2038 29c Moss campion	.60	.60
2687	A2039 29c Bearberry	.60	.60
2688	A2040 29c Mexican hat	.60	.60
2689	A2041 29c Harebell	.60	.60
2690	A2042 29c Desert five spot	.60	.60
2691	A2043 29c Smooth Solomon's seal	.60	.60
2692	A2044 29c Red maids	.60	.60
2693	A2045 29c Yellow skunk cabbage	.60	.60
2694	A2046 29c Rue anemone	.60	.60
2695	A2047 29c Standing cypress	.60	.60
2696	A2048 29c Wild flax	.60	.60
a.	A1999-A2048 Pane of 50, #2647-2696	30.00	—

WORLD WAR II

A2049

No. 2697 — Events of 1942: a, B-25's take off to raid Tokyo, Apr. 18. b, Ration coupons (Food and other commodities rationed). c, Divebomber and deck crewman (US wins Battle of the Coral Sea, May). d, Prisoners of war (Corregidor falls to Japanese, May 6). e, Dutch Harbor buildings on fire (Japan invades Aleutian Islands, June). f, Headphones, coded message (Allies decipher secret enemy codes). g, Yorktown lost, U.S. wins at Midway. h, Woman with drill (Millions of women join war effort). i, Marines land on Guadalcanal, Aug. 7. j, Tank in desert (Allies land in North Africa, Nov.).

Central label is the size of 15 stamps and shows world map, extent of axis control.

LITHOGRAPHED & ENGRAVED

1992, Aug. 17

2697	A2049	Block of 10	7.50	5.00
a.-j.		29c any single	.75	.30
k.		Red (litho.) omitted	*4,000.*	

No. 2697 has selvage at left and right and either top or bottom.

LITERARY ARTS SERIES

A2050

PHOTOGRAVURE

1992, Aug. 22

2698	A2050	29c multicolored	.60	.25

Dorothy Parker (1893-1967), author.

THEODORE VON KARMAN

A2051

1992, Aug. 31

2699	A2051	29c multicolored	.60	.25

Von Karman (1881-1963), rocket scientist.

MINERALS

Azurite A2052

Copper A2053

Variscite A2054

Wulfenite A2055

LITHOGRAPHED & ENGRAVED

1992, Sept. 17

2700	A2052	29c multicolored	.60	.25
2701	A2053	29c multicolored	.60	.25
2702	A2054	29c multicolored	.60	.25
2703	A2055	29c multicolored	.60	.25
a.		Block or strip of 4, #2700-2703	2.40	2.00
b.		As "a," silver (litho.) omitted	*6,000.*	
d.		As "a," silver omitted on two stamps	*900.00*	

JUAN RODRIGUEZ CABRILLO

Cabrillo, Ship, Map of San Diego Bay Area — A2056

1992, Sept. 28

2704	A2056	29c multicolored	.60	.25
a.		Black (engr.) omitted	*1,500.*	

WILD ANIMALS

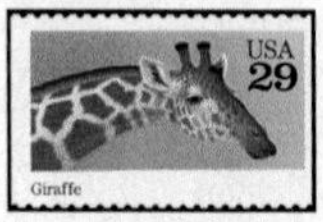

Giraffe — A2057

Giant Panda — A2058

Flamingo — A2059

King Penguins A2060

White Bengal Tiger — A2061

PHOTOGRAVURE
BOOKLET STAMPS

Perf. 11 Horiz. on 1 or 2 Sides

1992, Oct. 1

2705	A2057	29c multicolored	.65	.25
2706	A2058	29c multicolored	.65	.25
2707	A2059	29c multicolored	.65	.25
2708	A2060	29c multicolored	.65	.25
2709	A2061	29c multicolored	.65	.25
a.		Booklet pane of 5, #2705-2709	3.25	2.25
b.		As "a," imperf.	*2,000.*	

CHRISTMAS

Madonna and Child, by Giovanni Bellini — A2062

Horse and Rider A2063

Fire Pumper A2064

Train Engine A2065

Riverboat A2066

LITHOGRAPHED & ENGRAVED

1992 ***Perf. 11¼***

2710	A2062	29c multicolored	.60	.25
a.		Booklet pane of 10	6.00	3.50

LITHOGRAPHED

Perf. 11¼x11

2711	A2063	29c multicolored	.75	.25
2712	A2064	29c multicolored	.75	.25
2713	A2065	29c multicolored	.75	.25
2714	A2066	29c multicolored	.75	.25
a.		Block of 4, #2711-2714	3.00	1.10

Booklet Stamps

PHOTOGRAVURE

Perf. 11 on 2 or 3 Sides

2715	A2063	29c multicolored	.90	.25
2716	A2064	29c multicolored	.90	.25
2717	A2065	29c multicolored	.90	.25
2718	A2066	29c multicolored	.90	.25
a.		Booklet pane of 4, #2715-2718	3.60	1.25

Imperforates and part-perforates on gummed stamp paper are proofs from the ABNCo. archives. From the same source come imperforates with Toys only and imperforates without denominations. See No. 2718aP in Proofs section of the Scott U.S. Specialized Catalogue.

Self-Adhesive

Die Cut

2719	A2065	29c multicolored	.65	.25
a.		Booklet pane of 18	12.00	

"Greetings" is 27mm long on Nos. 2711-2714, 25mm long on Nos. 2715-2718 and 21½mm long on No. 2719. Nos. 2715-2719 differ in color from Nos. 2711-2714.

Issued: #2710-2718, 10/22; #2719, 10/28.

CHINESE NEW YEAR

Year of the Rooster — A2067

LITHOGRAPHED & ENGRAVED

1992, Dec. 30 ***Perf. 11***

2720	A2067	29c multicolored	.60	.25

See Nos. 3895j, 3997j.

AMERICAN MUSIC SERIES

Elvis Presley — A2068

Oklahoma! A2069

Hank Williams — A2070

Elvis Presley — A2071

Bill Haley — A2072

Clyde McPhatter A2073

Ritchie Valens — A2074

Otis Redding — A2075

Buddy Holly — A2076

Dinah Washington A2077

PHOTOGRAVURE

1993 ***Perf. 11***

2721	A2068	29c multicolored	.60	.25
a.		Imperf, pair	—	

Perf. 10

2722	A2069	29c multicolored	.60	.25
2723	A2070	29c multicolored	.75	.25

Perf. 11.2x11.5

2723A	A2070	29c multicolored	12.00	10.00

1993, June 16 ***Perf. 10***

2724	A2071	29c multicolored	.70	.25
2725	A2072	29c multicolored	.70	.25
2726	A2073	29c multicolored	.70	.25
2727	A2074	29c multicolored	.70	.25
2728	A2075	29c multicolored	.70	.25
2729	A2076	29c multicolored	.70	.25
2730	A2077	29c multicolored	.70	.25
a.		Vert. strip of 7, #2724-2730	5.50	3.00

Booklet Stamps

Perf. 11 Horiz. on 1 or 2 Sides

2731	A2071	29c multicolored	.65	.25
2732	A2072	29c multicolored	.65	.25
2733	A2073	29c multicolored	.65	.25
2734	A2074	29c multicolored	.65	.25
2735	A2075	29c multicolored	.65	.25
2736	A2076	29c multicolored	.65	.25
2737	A2077	29c multicolored	.65	.25
a.		Booklet pane, 2 #2731, 1 each #2732-2737	5.25	2.25
b.		Booklet pane, #2731, 2735-2737 + tab	2.60	1.50

Nos. 2731-2737 have smaller design sizes, brighter colors and shorter inscriptions than Nos. 2724-2730, as well as framelines around the designs and other subtle design differences.

No. 2737b without tab is indistinguishable from broken No. 2737a.

Imperforates of both No. 2737a and 2737b on gummed stamp paper are proofs from the ABNCo. archives. Perforated booklet pane multiples and varieties also exist from the same source. See Nos. 2737aP-2737bP in Proofs section of the Scott U.S. Specialized Catalogue.

See Nos. 2769, 2771, 2775 and designs A2112-A2117.

SPACE FANTASY

A2086

A2087

A2088

A2089

A2090

BOOKLET STAMPS

1993, Jan. 25 *Perf. 11 Vert.*

2741	A2086	29c multicolored	.60	.25
2742	A2087	29c multicolored	.60	.25
2743	A2088	29c multicolored	.60	.25
2744	A2089	29c multicolored	.60	.25
2745	A2090	29c multicolored	.60	.25
a.		Booklet pane of 5, #2741-2745	3.00	2.25

BLACK HERITAGE SERIES

Percy Lavon Julian (1899-1975), Chemist — A2091

LITHOGRAPHED & ENGRAVED

1993, Jan. 29 *Perf. 11*

2746	A2091	29c multicolored	.60	.25

OREGON TRAIL

A2092

1993, Feb. 12

2747	A2092	29c multicolored	.60	.25
b.		Blue omitted	*650.00*	

WORLD UNIVERSITY GAMES

A2093

PHOTOGRAVURE

1993, Feb. 25

2748	A2093	29c multicolored	.60	.25

GRACE KELLY (1929-1982)

Actress, Princess of Monaco — A2094

ENGRAVED

1993, Mar. 24

2749	A2094	29c deep ultra	.60	.25

See Monaco No. 1851.

CIRCUS

Clown A2095

Ringmaster A2096

Trapeze Artist A2097

Elephant A2098

LITHOGRAPHED

1993, Apr. 6

2750	A2095	29c multicolored	.60	.25
2751	A2096	29c multicolored	.60	.25
2752	A2097	29c multicolored	.60	.25
2753	A2098	29c multicolored	.60	.25
a.		Block of 4, #2750-2753	2.40	1.75

CHEROKEE STRIP LAND RUN, CENTENNIAL

A2099

LITHOGRAPHED & ENGRAVED

1993, Apr. 17

2754	A2099	29c multicolored	.60	.25

Imperforates on gummed stamp paper, including gutter pairs and blocks, are proofs from the ABNCo. archives. From the same source also come perforated gutter pairs and blocks, plus imperforates missing the red text and black denomination and "USA." An approved die proof also is recorded. See No. 2754P in Proofs section of the Scott U.S. Specialized Catalogue.

DEAN ACHESON (1893-1971)

Secretary of State — A2100

ENGRAVED

1993, Apr. 21

2755	A2100	29c greenish gray	.60	.25

SPORTING HORSES

Steeplechase A2101

Thoroughbred Racing — A2102

Harness Racing — A2103

Polo — A2104

LITHOGRAPHED & ENGRAVED

1993, May 1 *Perf. 11x11½*

2756	A2101	29c multicolored	.60	.25
2757	A2102	29c multicolored	.60	.25
2758	A2103	29c multicolored	.60	.25
2759	A2104	29c multicolored	.60	.25
a.		Block of 4, #2756-2759	2.40	2.00
b.		As "a," black (engr.) omitted	*500.00*	

GARDEN FLOWERS

Hyacinth A2105

Daffodil A2106

Tulip A2107

Iris A2108

Lilac — A2109

LITHOGRAPHED & ENGRAVED
BOOKLET STAMPS

1993, May 15 *Perf. 11 Vert.*

2760	A2105	29c multicolored	.60	.25
2761	A2106	29c multicolored	.60	.25
2762	A2107	29c multicolored	.60	.25
2763	A2108	29c multicolored	.60	.25
2764	A2109	29c multicolored	.60	.25
a.		Booklet pane of 5, #2760-2764	3.00	2.25
b.		As "a," black (engr.) omitted	*135.00*	
c.		As "a," imperf.	*700.00*	

WORLD WAR II

A2110

Designs and events of 1943: a, Destroyers (Allied forces battle German U-boats). b, Military medics treat the wounded. c, Amphibious landing craft on beach (Sicily attacked by Allied forces, July). d, B-24s hit Ploesti refineries, August. e, V-mail delivers letters from home. f, PT boat (Italy invaded by Allies, Sept.). g, Nos. WS7, WS8, savings bonds, (Bonds and stamps help war effort). h, "Willie and Joe" keep spirits high. i, Banner in window (Gold Stars mark World War II losses). j, Marines assault Tarawa, Nov.

Central label is the size of 15 stamps and shows world map with extent of Axis control and Allied operations.

1993, May 31 *Perf. 11*

2765	A2110	Block of 10	7.50	5.00
a.-j.		29c any single	.75	.40

No. 2765 has selvage at left and right and either top or bottom.

JOE LOUIS (1914-1981)

A2111

LITHOGRAPHED & ENGRAVED

1993, June 22

2766	A2111	29c multicolored	.60	.25

AMERICAN MUSIC SERIES

Oklahoma! Type and

Show Boat — A2112

Porgy & Bess — A2113

My Fair Lady — A2114

BOOKLET STAMPS
PHOTOGRAVURE

Perf. 11 Horiz. on 1 or 2 Sides

1993, July 14

2767	A2112	29c multicolored	.60	.25
2768	A2113	29c multicolored	.60	.25
2769	A2069	29c multicolored	.60	.25
2770	A2114	29c multicolored	.60	.25
a.		Booklet pane of 4, #2767-2770	2.75	2.25

No. 2769 has smaller design size, brighter colors and shorter inscription than No. 2722, as well as a frameline around the design and other subtle design differences.

Imperforate booklet panes, singly or in multiples, on gummed stamp paper are proofs from the ABNCo. archives. From the same source come imperforate progressive proofs, plus imperforate proofs/essays showing slightly altered designs. See No. 2770aP in Proofs section of the Scott U.S. Specialized Catalogue.

AMERICAN MUSIC SERIES

Hank Williams Type and

Patsy Cline — A2115

The Carter Family — A2116

Bob Wills — A2117

PHOTOGRAVURE

1993, Sept. 25 *Perf. 10*

2771	A2070	29c multicolored	.75	.25
2772	A2115	29c multicolored	.75	.25
2773	A2116	29c multicolored	.75	.25
2774	A2117	29c multicolored	.75	.25
a.		Block or horiz. strip of 4, #2771-2774	3.00	1.75

Booklet Stamps

Perf. 11 Horiz. on one or two sides

With Black Frameline

2775	A2070	29c multicolored	.60	.25
2776	A2116	29c multicolored	.60	.25
2777	A2115	29c multicolored	.60	.25
2778	A2117	29c multicolored	.60	.25
a.		Booklet pane of 4, #2775-2778	2.50	2.00

Inscription at left measures 27½mm on No. 2723, 27mm on No. 2771 and 22mm on No. 2775. No. 2723 shows only two tuning keys on guitar, while No. 2771 shows those two and parts of two others.

Imperforate booklet panes on gummed stamp paper, singly or in multiples, are proofs from the ABNCo. archives. From the same source come panes perfed horiz. but uncut vertically, plus imperforate progressive proofs and other die proof varieties. See No. 2778aP in Proofs section in the Scott U.S. Specialized Catalogue.

NATIONAL POSTAL MUSEUM

Independence Hall, Benjamin Franklin, Printing Press, Colonial Post Rider — A2118

Pony Express Rider, Civil War Soldier, Concord Stagecoach A2119

JN-4H Biplane, Charles Lindbergh, Railway Mail Car, 1931 Model A Ford Mail Truck — A2120

California Gold Rush Miner's Letter, Nos. 39, 295, C3a, C13, Barcode & Circular Date Stamp — A2121

LITHOGRAPHED AND ENGRAVED

1993, July 30 Tagged ***Perf. 11***

2779 A2118 29c multicolored .60 .25
2780 A2119 29c multicolored .60 .25
2781 A2120 29c multicolored .60 .25
2782 A2121 29c multicolored .60 .25
a. Block or strip of 4, #2779-2782 2.40 2.00
b. As "a," engr. maroon (USA/29) and black ("My dear...") omitted *2,500.*
c. As "a," imperf *2,500.*

AMERICAN SIGN LANGUAGE

A2122

A2123

PHOTOGRAVURE

1993, Sept. 20 ***Perf. 11½***

2783 A2122 29c multicolored .60 .25
2784 A2123 29c multicolored .60 .25
a. Pair, #2783-2784 1.20 .75

CLASSIC BOOKS

A2124

A2125

A2126

A2127

Designs: No. 2785, Rebecca of Sunnybrook Farm, by Kate Douglas Wiggin. No. 2786, Little House on the Prairie, by Laura Ingalls Wilder. No. 2787, The Adventures of Huckleberry Finn, by Mark Twain. No. 2788, Little Women, by Louisa May Alcott.

LITHOGRAPHED & ENGRAVED

1993, Oct. 23 ***Perf. 11***

2785 A2124 29c multicolored .60 .25
2786 A2125 29c multicolored .60 .25
2787 A2126 29c multicolored .60 .25
2788 A2127 29c multicolored .60 .25
a. Block or horiz. strip of 4, #2785-2788 2.40 2.00

Imperforates on gummed stamp paper, including gutter pairs and blocks, are proofs from the ABNCo. archives. See No. 2788aP in Proofs section of the Scott U.S. Specialized Catalogue.

CHRISTMAS

Madonna and Child in a Landscape, by Giovanni Battista Cima — A2128

Jack-in-the-Box
A2129

Red-Nosed Reindeer
A2130

Snowman
A2131

Toy Soldier Blowing Horn
A2132

1993, Oct. 21

2789 A2128 29c multicolored .60 .25

Booklet Stamp

Size: 18x25mm

Perf. 11½x11 on 2 or 3 Sides

2790 A2128 29c multicolored .60 .25
a. Booklet pane of 4 2.40 1.75
b. Imperf., pair —
c. As "a," imperf —

Nos. 2789-2790 have numerous design differences.

1993 ***Perf. 11½***

PHOTOGRAVURE

2791 A2129 29c multicolored .60 .25
2792 A2130 29c multicolored .60 .25
2793 A2131 29c multicolored .60 .25
2794 A2132 29c multicolored .60 .25
a. Block or strip of 4, #2791-2794 2.40 2.00

Booklet Stamps

Size: 18x21mm

Perf. 11x10 on 2 or 3 Sides

2795 A2132 29c multicolored .85 .25
2796 A2131 29c multicolored .85 .25
2797 A2130 29c multicolored .85 .25
2798 A2129 29c multicolored .85 .25
a. Booklet pane, 3 each #2795-2796, 2 each #2797-2798 8.50 4.00
b. Booklet pane, 3 each #2797-2798, 2 each #2795-2796 8.50 4.00
c. Block of 4, #2795-2798 3.40 1.75

Self-Adhesive

Size: 19½x26½mm

Die Cut

2799 A2131 29c multicolored .75 .25
a. Coil with plate # V1111111 — 6.00
b. Horiz. coil strip of 4, #2799-2802 3.00
2800 A2132 29c multicolored .75 .25
2801 A2129 29c multicolored .75 .25
2802 A2130 29c multicolored .75 .25
a. Booklet pane, 3 each #2799-2802 9.00
b. Block of 4, #2799-2802 3.00

Except for No. 2799a with plate number, coil stamps are indistinguishable from booklet stamps once they are removed from the backing paper.

Size: 17x20mm

2803 A2131 29c multicolored .60 .25
a. Booklet pane of 18 11.00

Snowman on Nos. 2793, 2799 has three buttons and seven snowflakes beneath nose (placement differs on both stamps). No. 2796 has two buttons and five snowflakes beneath nose. No. 2803 has two orange buttons and four snowflakes beneath nose.

Issued: #2791-2798, 10/21; #2799-2803, 10/28.

MARIANA ISLANDS

A2133

LITHOGRAPHED AND ENGRAVED

1993, Nov. 4 ***Perf. 11***

2804 A2133 29c multicolored .60 .25

COLUMBUS' LANDING IN PUERTO RICO, 500th ANNIVERSARY

A2134

PHOTOGRAVURE

1993, Nov. 19 ***Perf. 11.2***

2805 A2134 29c multicolored .60 .25

AIDS AWARENESS

A2135

1993, Dec. 1

2806 A2135 29c black & red .60 .25
a. Perf. 11 vert. on 1 or 2 sides, from bklt. pane .70 .25
b. As "a," booklet pane of 5 3.50 2.00

WINTER OLYMPICS

Slalom
A2136

Luge
A2137

Ice Dancing
A2138

Cross-Country Skiing
A2139

Ice Hockey — A2140

LITHOGRAPHED

1994, Jan. 6

2807 A2136 29c multicolored .60 .25
2808 A2137 29c multicolored .60 .25
2809 A2138 29c multicolored .60 .25
2810 A2139 29c multicolored .60 .25
2811 A2140 29c multicolored .60 .25
a. Strip of 5, #2807-2811 3.00 2.50

EDWARD R. MURROW, JOURNALIST (1908-65)

A2141

ENGRAVED

1994, Jan. 21

2812 A2141 29c brown .60 .25

LOVE

A2142

A2143

A2144

Booklet Stamps

LITHOGRAPHED & ENGRAVED

1994 ***Die Cut***

Self-adhesive

2813 A2142 29c multicolored .60 .25
a. Booklet pane of 18 11.00
b. Coil with plate # B1 — 5.00

Except for No. 2813b with plate number, coil stamps are indistinguishable from booklet stamps once they are removed from the backing paper.

PHOTOGRAVURE

Perf. 10.9x11.1 on 2 or 3 sides

2814 A2143 29c multicolored .60 .25
a. Booklet pane of 10 6.00 3.50
b. Imperf, pair —
d. As "a," imperf. —

Horiz. pairs, imperf between, are printer's waste.

No. 2814 was issued in booklets only.

LITHOGRAPHED & ENGRAVED

Perf. 11.1

2814C A2143 29c multicolored .70 .25

Size of No. 2814C is 20x28mm. No. 2814 is 18x24½mm.

PHOTOGRAVURE & ENGRAVED

Perf. 11.2

2815 A2144 52c multicolored 1.00 .25

Issued: No. 2813, Jan. 27; Nos. 2814-2815, Feb. 14; No. 2814C, June 11.

BLACK HERITAGE SERIES

Dr. Allison Davis (1902-83), Social Anthropologist, Educator — A2145

ENGRAVED

1994, Feb. 1 ***Perf. 11.2***

2816 A2145 29c red brown & brown .60 .25

CHINESE NEW YEAR

Year of the Dog — A2146

PHOTOGRAVURE

1994, Feb. 5

2817 A2146 29c multicolored .80 .25

See Nos. 3895k, 3997k.

BUFFALO SOLDIERS

A2147

LITHOGRAPHED & ENGRAVED

1994, Apr. 22 ***Perf. 11.5x11.2***

2818 A2147 29c multicolored .60 .25
a. Double impression (second impression light) of red brown (engr. inscriptions) —

SILENT SCREEN STARS

Rudolph Valentino (1895-1926)
A2148

Clara Bow (1905-65)
A2149

Charlie Chaplin (1889-1977) A2150

Lon Chaney (1883-1930) A2151

John Gilbert (1895-1936) A2152

Zasu Pitts (1898-1963) A2153

Harold Lloyd (1894-1971) A2154

Keystone Cops A2155

Theda Bara (1885-1955) A2156

Buster Keaton (1895-1966) A2157

1994, Apr. 27			*Perf. 11.2*	
2819	A2148 29c red, blk & brt vio		1.10	.30
2820	A2149 29c red, blk & brt vio		1.10	.30
2821	A2150 29c red, blk & brt vio		1.10	.30
2822	A2151 29c red, blk & brt vio		1.10	.30
2823	A2152 29c red, blk & brt vio		1.10	.30
2824	A2153 29c red, blk & brt vio		1.10	.30
2825	A2154 29c red, blk & brt vio		1.10	.30
2826	A2155 29c red, blk & brt vio		1.10	.30
2827	A2156 29c red, blk & brt vio		1.10	.30
2828	A2157 29c red, blk & brt vio		1.10	.30
a.	Block of 10, #2819-2828		11.00	5.00
b.	As "a," black (litho.) omitted		—	
c.	As "a," blk, red & brt vio (litho.) omitted		—	

GARDEN FLOWERS

Lily A2158

Zinnia A2159

Gladiola A2160

Marigold A2161

Rose — A2162

1994, Apr. 28 *Perf. 10.9 Vert.*

Booklet Stamps

2829	A2158 29c multicolored	.60	.25
2830	A2159 29c multicolored	.60	.25
2831	A2160 29c multicolored	.60	.25
2832	A2161 29c multicolored	.60	.25
2833	A2162 29c multicolored	.60	.25
a.	Booklet pane of 5, #2829-2833	3.00	2.25
b.	As "a," imperf	*400.00*	
c.	As "a," black (engr.) omitted	*125.00*	

1994 WORLD CUP SOCCER CHAMPIONSHIPS

A2163

A2163a

A2164

A2165

Design: 40c, Soccer player, diff.

PHOTOGRAVURE

1994, May 26		*Perf. 11.1*	
2834	A2163 29c multicolored	.60	.25
2835	A2163a 40c multicolored	.80	.25
2836	A2164 50c multicolored	1.00	.25
	Nos. 2834-2836 (3)	2.40	.75

Souvenir Sheet of 3

2837	A2165 #a.-#c.	4.50	3.00

No. 2837c has a portion of the yellow map in the LR corner.

WORLD WAR II

A2166

Designs and events of 1944: a, Allied forces retake New Guinea. b, P-51s escort B-17s on bombing raids. c, Troops running from landing craft (Allies in Normandy, D-Day, June 6). d, Airborne units spearhead attacks. e, Officer at periscope (Submarines shorten war in Pacific). f, Parade (Allies free Rome, June 4; Paris, Aug. 25).

g, Soldier firing flamethrower (US troops clear Saipan bunkers). h, Red Ball Express speeds vital supplies. i, Battleship firing main battery (Battle for Leyte Gulf, Oct. 23-26). j, Soldiers in snow (Bastogne and Battle of the Bulge, Dec.).

Central label is size of 15 stamps and shows world map with extent of Axis control and Allied operations.

Illustration reduced.

LITHOGRAPHED & ENGRAVED

1994, June 6		*Perf. 10.9*	
2838	A2166 Block of 10	17.00	10.00
a.-j.	29c any single	1.70	.50

No. 2838 has selvage at left and right and either top or bottom.

NORMAN ROCKWELL

A2167

A2168

1994, July 1		*Perf. 10.9x11.1*	
2839	A2167 29c multicolored	.60	.25

Souvenir Sheet

LITHOGRAPHED

2840	A2168 Sheet of 4	4.50	2.75
a.	50c Freedom From Want	1.10	.65
b.	50c Freedom From Fear	1.10	.65
c.	50c Freedom of Speech	1.10	.65
d.	50c Freedom of Worship	1.10	.65

Moon Landing, 25th Anniv.

A2169

A2170

Miniature Sheet

1994, July 20		*Perf. 11.2x11.1*	
2841	A2169 29c Sheet of 12	10.50	—
a.	Single stamp	.85	.60

LITHOGRAPHED & ENGRAVED

Perf. 10.7x11.1

2842	A2170 $9.95 multicolored	20.00	16.00

LOCOMOTIVES

Hudson's General — A2171

McQueen's Jupiter — A2172

Eddy's No. 242 — A2173

Ely's No. 10 — A2174

Buchanan's No. 999 — A2175

PHOTOGRAVURE

1994, July 28 *Perf. 11 Horiz.*

Booklet Stamps

2843	A2171 29c multicolored	.75	.25
2844	A2172 29c multicolored	.75	.25
2845	A2173 29c multicolored	.75	.25
2846	A2174 29c multicolored	.75	.25
2847	A2175 29c multicolored	.75	.25
a.	Booklet pane of 5, #2843-2847	3.75	2.00
b.	As "a," imperf.	*2,500.*	

GEORGE MEANY, LABOR LEADER (1894-1980)

A2176

ENGRAVED

1994, Aug. 16		*Perf. 11.1x11*	
2848	A2176 29c blue	.60	.25

AMERICAN MUSIC SERIES

Popular Singers

Al Jolson (1886-1950) A2177

Bing Crosby (1904-77) A2178

Ethel Waters (1896-1977) A2179

Nat "King" Cole (1919-65) A2180

Ethel Merman (1908-84) A2181

Jazz Singers

Bessie Smith (1894-1937) A2182

Muddy Waters (1915-83) A2183

Billie Holiday (1915-59) A2184

Robert Johnson (1911-38) A2185

Jimmy Rushing (1902-72) A2186

"Ma" Rainey (1886-1939) A2187

Mildred Bailey (1907-51) A2188

Howlin' Wolf (1910-76) A2189

PHOTOGRAVURE

1994, Sept. 1 *Perf. 10.1x10.2*

2849 A2177 29c multicolored .85 .25
2850 A2178 29c multicolored .85 .25
2851 A2179 29c multicolored .85 .25
2852 A2180 29c multicolored .85 .25
2853 A2181 29c multicolored .85 .25
a. Vert. strip of 5, #2849-2853 4.25 2.00
b. Pane of 20, imperf *10,000.*

1994, Sept. 17 *Perf. 11x10.8*

LITHOGRAPHED

2854 A2182 29c multicolored 1.50 .25
2855 A2183 29c multicolored 1.50 .25
2856 A2184 29c multicolored 1.50 .25
2857 A2185 29c multicolored 1.50 .25
2858 A2186 29c multicolored 1.50 .25
2859 A2187 29c multicolored 1.50 .25
2860 A2188 29c multicolored 1.50 .25
2861 A2189 29c multicolored 1.50 .25
a. Block of 10, #2854-2861 +2 additional stamps 15.00 4.50

LITERARY ARTS SERIES

James Thurber (1894-1961) — A2190

LITHOGRAPHED & ENGRAVED

1994, Sept. 10 *Perf. 11*

2862 A2190 29c multicolored .60 .25

WONDERS OF THE SEA

Diver, Motorboat A2191

Diver, Ship A2192

Diver, Ship's Wheel — A2193

Diver, Coral — A2194

LITHOGRAPHED

1994, Oct. 3 *Perf. 11x10.9*

2863 A2191 29c multicolored .75 .25
2864 A2192 29c multicolored .75 .25
2865 A2193 29c multicolored .75 .25
2866 A2194 29c multicolored .75 .25
a. Block of 4, #2863-2866 3.00 1.50
b. As "a," imperf *350.00*

CRANES

Black-Necked A2195

Whooping A2196

LITHOGRAPHED & ENGRAVED

1994, Oct. 9 *Perf. 10.8x11*

2867 A2195 29c multicolored .70 .25
2868 A2196 29c multicolored .70 .25
a. Pair, #2867-2868 1.40 .75
b. As "a," black & magenta (engr.) omitted *1,250.*
c. As "a," double impression of engr. black (Birds' names and "USA") & magenta ("29") *3,000.*
d. As "a," double impression of engr. black ("USA") & magenta ("29") *3,000.*

See People's Republic of China Nos. 2528-2529.

LEGENDS OF THE WEST

A2197

g. Bill Pickett (1870-1932) (Revised)

Designs: a, Home on the Range. b, Buffalo Bill Cody (1846-1917). c, Jim Bridger (1804-81). d, Annie Oakley (1860-1926). e, Native American Culture. f, Chief Joseph (c. 1840-1904). h, Bat Masterson (1853-1921). i, John C. Fremont (1813-90). j, Wyatt Earp (1848-1929). k, Nellie Cashman (c. 1849-1925). l, Charles Goodnight (1826-1929). m, Geronimo (1823-1909). n, Kit Carson (1809-68). o, Wild Bill Hickok (1837-76). p, Western Wildlife. q, Jim Beckwourth (c. 1798-1866). r, Bill Tilghman (1854-1924). s, Sacagawea (c. 1787-1812). t, Overland Mail.

PHOTOGRAVURE

1994, Oct. 18 *Perf. 10.1x10*

2869 A2197 Pane of 20 15.00 10.00
a.-t. 29c any single .75 .50
u. As No. 2869, a.-e. imperf. f.-j. part perf. —

LEGENDS OF THE WEST (Recalled)

g. Bill Pickett (Recalled)

Nos. 2870b-2870d, 2870f-2870o, 2870q-2870s have a frameline around the vignette that is half the width of the frameline on similar stamps in No. 2869. Other design differences may exist.

1994

2870 A2197 29c Pane of 20 125.00 —

150,000 panes of No. 2870 were made available through a drawing. Panes were delivered in an envelope. Value is for pane without envelope. Panes with envelopes sell for somewhat more.

CHRISTMAS

Madonna and Child, by Elisabetta Sirani A2200

Stocking A2201

Santa Claus A2202

Cardinal in Snow A2203

LITHOGRAPHED & ENGRAVED

1994, Oct. 20 *Perf. 11¼*

2871 A2200 29c multi .60 .25

BOOKLET STAMP

Perf. 9¾x11

2871A A2200 29c multi .60 .25
b. Booklet pane of 10 6.25 3.50
c. Imperf, pair *350.00*

LITHOGRAPHED

Perf. 11¼

2872 A2201 29c multi .60 .25
a. Booklet pane of 20 12.50 6.00
b. Imperf., pair —
c. Vert. pair, imperf. horiz. —
d. Quadruple impression of black, triple impression of blue, double impressions of red and yellow, green normal *900.00*
e. Vert. pair, imperf. between *125.00*
f. As "a," imperf. —

PHOTOGRAVURE

BOOKLET STAMPS

Self-Adhesive

Die Cut

2873 A2202 29c multi .70 .25
a. Booklet pane of 12 8.50
b. Coil with plate #V1111 — 5.75

Except for No. 2873b with plate number, coil stamps are indistinguishable from booklet stamps once they are removed from the backing paper.

2874 A2203 29c multi .60 .25
a. Booklet pane of 18 11.00

BUREAU OF ENGRAVING & PRINTING

Souvenir Sheet

A2204

LITHOGRAPHED & ENGRAVED

1994, Nov. 3 *Perf. 11*

2875 A2204 $2 Pane of 4 16.00 13.50
a. Single stamp 4.00 2.00
b. Pane of 4 with double impression of the brown lettering panel *1,000.* —

The double impression is clear, but may be seen best in the scrolls at lower right.

CHINESE NEW YEAR

Year of the Boar — A2205

PHOTOGRAVURE

1994, Dec. 30 *Perf. 11.2x11.1*

2876 A2205 29c multicolored .70 .25

See Nos. 3895l, 3997l.

A2206

Type I

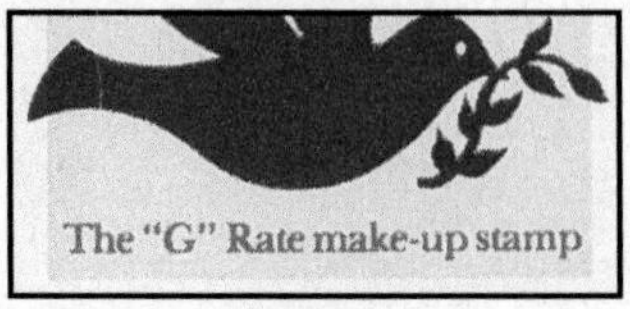

Type II

Inscriptions on No. 2877 are in a thin typeface. Those on No. 2878 are in heavy, bold type.

LITHOGRAPHED

Perf. 11x10.8

1994, Dec. 13 **Untagged**

2877 A2206 (3c) tan, brt bl & red, type I .30 .25
a. Imperf., pair *115.00*
b. Double impression of red *175.00*

No. 2877 imperf and with blue omitted is known from printer's waste.

Perf. 10.8x10.9

Untagged

2878 A2206 (3c) tan, dk bl & red, type II .30 .25

A2207

PHOTOGRAVURE

Perf. 11.2x11.1

2879 A2207 (20c) black "G," yel & multi .40 .25
a. Imperf., pair —

Perf. 11x10.9

2880 A2207 (32c) red "G," yel & multi .75 .25

A2208

Perf. 11.2x11.1

2881 A2208 (32c) black "G" & multi 1.25 .25
a. Booklet pane of 10 12.50 5.00

Perf. 11x10.9

2882 A2208 (32c) red "G" & multi .60 .25

Distance on #2882 from bottom of red G to top of flag immediately above is 13¾mm.

BOOKLET STAMPS

Perf. 10x9.9 on 2 or 3 Sides

2883 A2208 (32c) black "G" & multi .65 .25
a. Booklet pane of 10 6.50 3.75

Perf. 10.9 on 2 or 3 Sides

2884 A2208 (32c) blue "G" & multi .65 .25
a. Booklet pane of 10 6.50 3.75
b. As "a," imperf *4,500.*
c. Horiz. pair, imperf. btwn. due to miscut —
d. Horiz. pair, imperf. vert. —

Perf. 11x10.9 on 2 or 3 Sides

2885 A2208 (32c) red "G" & multi .90 .25
a. Booklet pane of 10 9.00 4.50
b. Horiz. pair, imperf vert. *750.00*
c. Horiz. pair, imperf. btwn., in #2885a with foldover —

Distance on #2885 from bottom of red G to top of flag immediately above is 13½mm. See note below #2882.

No. 2885c resulted from a paper foldover after perforating and before cutting into panes.

No. 2886

No. 2887

Die Cut

Self-Adhesive

2886 A2208 (32c) gray, bl, lt bl, red & blk .70 .25
a. Booklet pane of 18 12.50
b. Coil with plate # V11111 — 9.50

No. 2886 is printed on prephosphored paper that is opaque, thicker and brighter than that of No. 2887 and has only a small number of blue shading dots in the white stripes immediately below the flag's blue field.

Except for No. 2886b with plate number, coil stamps are indistinguishable from booklet stamps once they are removed from the backing paper.

2887 A2208 (32c) black, blue & red .70 .25
a. Booklet pane of 18 12.50

No. 2887 has noticeable blue shading in the white stripes immediately below the blue field and has overall tagging. The paper is translucent, thinner and duller than No. 2886.

A2209

COIL STAMPS

Perf. 9.8 Vert.

2888 A2209 (25c) black "G" .90 .50
2889 A2208 (32c) black "G" 1.50 .25
a. Imperf., pair *250.00*
2890 A2208 (32c) blue "G" .65 .25
2891 A2208 (32c) red "G" .85 .25

Rouletted 9.8 Vert.

2892 A2208 (32c) red "G" .75 .25

A2210

PHOTOGRAVURE

1995 Untagged *Perf. 9.8 Vert.*

2893 A2210 (5c) green & multi .50 .25

Flag Over Porch — A2212

1995, May 19 *Perf. 10.4*

2897 A2212 32c multicolored .75 .25
a. Imperf., vert. pair 55.00

See Nos. 2913-2916, 2920-2921, 3133.

Butte — A2217

COIL STAMPS

1995-97 *Perf. 9.8 Vert.*

Untagged (Nos. 2902-2912B)

Self-Adhesive (#2902B)

2902 A2217 (5c) yel, red & bl .30 .25
a. Imperf., pair 350.00

Serpentine Die Cut 11.5 Vert.

Untagged

2902B A2217 (5c) yel, red & bl ('96) .35 .25

Perf. 9.8 Vert.

Mountain — A2218

Self-Adhesive (#2904A-2904B)

Untagged

2903 A2218 (5c) purple & multi ('96) .30 .25

Letters of inscription "USA NONPROFIT ORG." outlined in purple on No. 2903. No. 2903 has purple "1996" at left bottom.

Untagged

2904 A2218 (5c) blue & multi ('96) .30 .25
c. Imperf., pair 250.00

Letters of inscription have no outline on No. 2904. No. 2904 has blue "1996" at bottom left.

Serpentine Die Cut 11.2 Vert.

Untagged

2904A A2218 (5c) purple & multi ('96) .40 .25

Serpentine Die Cut 9.8 Vert.

Untagged

2904B A2218 (5c) purple & multi ('97) .25 .25

Letters of inscription outlined in purple on No. 2904B, not outlined on No. 2904A. No. 2904A has large purple "1996" at bottom left. No. 2904B has small purple "1997" at bottom left.

Auto — A2220

Self-Adhesive (#2906-2907)

Perf. 9.8 Vert.

Untagged

2905 A2220 (10c) blk, red brn & brn, small "1995" date .30 .25
a. Medium "1995" date .35 .25
b. Large "1995" date ('96) .60 .25
c. As "b," brown omitted, P#S33 single *400.00*

Date on 2905 is approximately 1.9mm long, on No. 2905a 2mm long, and on No. 2905b 2.1mm long.

Serpentine Die Cut 11.5 Vert.

Untagged

2906 A2220 (10c) blk, brn & red brn ('96) .50 .25

Untagged

2907 A1957 (10c) gold & multi ('96) .75 .25

Auto Tail Fin — A2223

Self-Adhesive (#2910)

Perf. 9.8 Vert.

Untagged

2908 A2223 (15c) dk org yel & multi .30 .30

No. 2908 has "1995" in blue and has dark, bold colors, heavy shading lines and heavily shaded chrome.

Untagged

2909 A2223 (15c) buff & multi .30 .30

No. 2909 has "1995" in black and has shinier chrome, more subdued colors and finer details than No. 2908.

Serpentine Die Cut 11.5 Vert.

Untagged

2910 A2223 (15c) buff & multi ('96) .30 .30

Juke Box — A2225

Perf. 9.8 Vert.

Untagged

2911 A2225 (25c) dk red, dk yel grn & multi .50 .50
a. Imperf, pair *400.00*

No. 2911 has dark, saturated colors and dark blue lines in the music selection board.
See No. 3132.

Untagged

2912 A2225 (25c) brt org red, brt yel grn & multi .75 .50

No. 2912 has bright colors, less shading and light blue lines in the music selection board.

Serpentine Die Cut 11.5 Vert.

Untagged

Self-Adhesive

2912A A2225 (25c) brt org red, brt yel grn & multi ('96) .50 .50

Serpentine Die Cut 9.8 Vert.

Untagged

2912B A2225 (25c) dk red, dk yel grn & multi ('97) .75 .50

Perf. 9.8 Vert.

2913 A2212 32c bl, tan, brn, red & lt bl .65 .25
a. Imperf., pair 30.00

No. 2913 has pronounced light blue shading in the flag and red "1995" at left bottom. See No. 3133.

2914 A2212 32c bl, yel brn, red & gray .80 .25

No. 2914 has pale gray shading in the flag and blue "1995" at left bottom.

Serpentine Die Cut 8.7 Vert.

Self-Adhesive (#2915-2915D)

2915 A2212 32c multi 1.25 .30

No. 2915 has blue "1995" at bottom left.

Serpentine Die Cut 9.8 Vert.

2915A A2212 32c dk bl, tan, brn, red & lt bl ('96) .65 .25
h. Die cutting omitted, pair 32.50
i. Tan omitted —
j. Double die cutting 30.00

No. 2915A has red "1996" at left bottom.
Sky on No. 3133 shows color gradation at LR not on No. 2915A.
On No. 2915Ai all other colors except brown are severely shifted.
On No. 2915Aj, the second die cutting is a different gauge than the normal 9.8.

Examples of a self-adhesive Flag Over Porch coil stamp resembling Scott 2915C with a "1995" year date are test stamps and listed in that section of this catalog.

Serpentine Die Cut 11.5 Vert.
2915B A2212 32c dk bl, tan, brn, red & lt bl ('96) 1.00 90

Serpentine Die Cut 10.9 Vert.
2915C A2212 32c dk bl, tan, brn, red & lt bl

Flag Over Field — A2230

Self-Adhesive (#2919-2921)

Die Cut

2919 A2230 32c multi .65 .25
a. Booklet pane of 18 12.00
b. Vert. pair, die cutting omitted btwn. —

Serpentine Die Cut 8.7 on 2, 3 or 4 Adjacent Sides

2920 A2212 32c multi, dated blue "1995" .65 .25
a. Booklet pane of 20+label 13.00
b. Small date 6.00 .35
c. As "b," booklet pane of 20+label 110.00
f. As No. 2920, pane of 15+label 9.75
g. As "a," partial pane of 10, 3 stamps and parts of 7 stamps printed on backing liner —
h. As No. 2920, booklet pane of 15 *47.50*
i. As No. 2920, die cutting omitted, pair —
j. Dark blue omitted (from No. 2920a) *2,100.*
k. Vert. pair, die cutting missing btwn., three examples in No. 2920a with shift in die cutting (PS) —

Date on No. 2920 is nearly twice as large as date on No. 2920b. No. 2920f comes in various configurations.

No. 2920h is a pane of 16 with one stamp removed. The missing stamp is the lower right stamp in the pane or (more rarely) the upper left stamp. No. 2920h cannot be made from No. 2920f, a pane of 15 + label. The label is located in the sixth or seventh row of the pane and is die cut. If the label is removed, an impression of the die cutting appears on the backing paper.

Serpentine Die Cut 11.3 on 3 sides

2920D A2212 32c multi, dated blue "1996" ('96) .80 .25
e. Booklet pane of 10 8.00
l. As "e," die cutting omitted —

Serpentine Die Cut 9.8 on 2 or 3 Adjacent Sides

2921 A2212 32c dk bl, tan, brn, red & lt bl, dated red "1996" ('96) .90 .25
a. Booklet pane of 10, dated red "1996" 9.00
b. As No. 2921, dated red "1997," *Jan. 24, 1997* 1.20 .25
c. As "a," dated red "1997" 12.00
d. Booklet pane of 5 + label, dated red "1997," *Jan. 24, 1997* 8.00
e. As "a," die cutting omitted *200.00*

Issued: #2902, 2905, 3/10/95; #2908-2909, 2911-2912, 2919, 3/17/95; #2915, 2920, 4/18/95; #2897, 2913-2914, 2916, 5/19/95; #2920d, 1/20/96; #2904B, 2912B, 2915D, 2921b-2921d, 1/24/97; #2903-2904, 3/16/96; #2915A, 5/21/97; #2907, 2921, 5/21/96; #2902B, 2904A, 2906, 2910, 2912A, 2915B, 6/15/96; #2915C, 5/21/96.
See Nos. 3132-3133.

Scott values for used self-adhesive stamps are for examples either on piece or off piece.

GREAT AMERICANS ISSUE

Milton S. Hershey A2248

Cal Farley A2249

Henry R. Luce A2250

Lila and DeWitt Wallace A2251

Ruth Benedict A2253

Alice Hamilton, MD A2255

Justin S. Morrill A2256

Mary Breckinridge A2257

Alice Paul — A2258

ENGRAVED

1995-99

Self-Adhesive (#2941-2942)

Perf. 11.2, Serpentine Die Cut 11.7x11.5 (#2941-2942)

2933 A2248 32c brown .75 .25
2934 A2249 32c green ('96) .75 .25
2935 A2250 32c lake ('98) .65 .35
2936 A2251 32c gray blue ('98) .65 .35
a. 32c light blue 2.00 .50
2938 A2253 46c carmine .90 .30
2940 A2255 55c green 1.15 .25
a. Imperf, pair —
2941 A2256 55c black ('99) 1.10 .25
2942 A2257 77c blue ('98) 1.50 .40
2943 A2258 78c bright violet 1.60 .25
a. 78c dull violet 1.60 .25
b. 78c pale violet 3.00 .30
Nos. 2933-2943 (9) 9.05 2.65

The pale violet ink on No. 2943b luminesces bright pink under long-wave ultraviolet light.

LOVE

A2263

Cherub from Sistine Madonna, by Raphael — A2264

LITHOGRAPHED & ENGRAVED

1995, Feb. 1 ***Perf. 11.2***

2948 A2263 (32c) multi .65 .25

Self-Adhesive

Die Cut

2949 A2264 (32c) multi .65 .25
a. Booklet pane of 20 + label 13.00
b. Red (engr.) omitted *100.00*
c. As "a," red (engr.) omitted *2,000.*
d. Red (engr.) missing (CM) —

No. 2949d must be collected se-tenant with a normal stamp. The error comes from the top row of three stamps of the booklet pane of 20 plus label.

See Nos. 2957-2960, 3030.

FLORIDA STATEHOOD

A2265

LITHOGRAPHED

1995, Mar. 3 ***Perf. 11.1***

2950 A2265 32c multicolored .65 .25

EARTH DAY

Earth Clean-Up A2266

Solar Energy — A2267

Tree Planting — A2268

Beach Clean-Up A2269

1995, Apr. 20 ***Perf. 11.1x11***

2951 A2266 32c multicolored .65 .25
2952 A2267 32c multicolored .65 .25
2953 A2268 32c multicolored .65 .25
2954 A2269 32c multicolored .65 .25
a. Block of 4, #2951-2954 2.60 1.75

RICHARD M. NIXON

37th President (1913-94)

Richard M. Nixon, 37th President (1913-94) — A2270

LITHOGRAPHED & ENGRAVED

1995, Apr. 26 ***Perf. 11.2***

2955 A2270 32c multicolored .65 .25
a. Red (engr.) missing (CM) *800.00*

No. 2955 is known with red (engr. "Richard Nixon") inverted, and with red engr. omitted but only half the Nixon portrait present, both from printer's waste. No. 2955a shows a complete Nixon portrait.

BLACK HERITAGE SERIES

Bessie Coleman, Aviator — A2271

ENGRAVED

1995, Apr. 27

2956 A2271 32c red & black .85 .25

LOVE

A2272

A2273

A2274

LITHOGRAPHED & ENGRAVED

1995, May 12

2957 A2272 32c multicolored .65 .25

Compare with No. 3030.

2958 A2273 55c multicolored 1.10 .25

BOOKLET STAMPS

Perf. 9.8x10.8

2959 A2272 32c multicolored .65 .25
a. Booklet pane of 10 6.50 3.25
b. Imperf, pair *100.00*
c. As "a," imperf. *500.00*

Self-Adhesive

Die Cut

2960 A2274 55c multicolored 1.10 .25
a. Booklet pane of 20 + label 22.50

See Nos. 2948-2949, 3030.

RECREATIONAL SPORTS

Volleyball A2275

Softball — A2276

Bowling — A2277

Tennis — A2278

Golf — A2279

LITHOGRAPHED

1995, May 20

2961 A2275 32c multicolored .65 .25
2962 A2276 32c multicolored .65 .25
2963 A2277 32c multicolored .65 .25
2964 A2278 32c multicolored .65 .25
2965 A2279 32c multicolored .65 .25
a. Vert. strip of 5, #2961-2965 3.25 2.00
b. As "a," imperf *1,750.*
c. As "a," yellow omitted *1,200.*
d. As "a," yellow, blue & magenta omitted *1,600.*

PRISONERS OF WAR & MISSING IN ACTION

A2280

1995, May 29

2966 A2280 32c multicolored .65 .25

LEGENDS OF HOLLYWOOD

Marilyn Monroe (1926-62) — A2281

PHOTOGRAVURE

1995, June 1 ***Perf. 11.1***

2967 A2281 32c multicolored .80 .25
a. Imperf., pair *225.00*

Perforations in corner of each stamp are star-shaped.

TEXAS STATEHOOD

A2282

LITHOGRAPHED

1995, June 16 ***Perf. 11.2***

2968 A2282 32c multicolored .70 .25

GREAT LAKES LIGHTHOUSES

Split Rock, Lake Superior A2283

St. Joseph, Lake Michigan A2284

Spectacle Reef, Lake Huron A2285

Marblehead, Lake Erie A2286

Thirty Mile Point, Lake Ontario — A2287

PHOTOGRAVURE

BOOKLET STAMPS

1995, June 17 ***Perf. 11.2 Vert.***

2969 A2283 32c multicolored .90 .30
2970 A2284 32c multicolored .90 .30
2971 A2285 32c multicolored .90 .30
2972 A2286 32c multicolored .90 .30
2973 A2287 32c multicolored .90 .30
a. Booklet pane of 5, #2969-2973 4.50 2.50
b. As "a," two vert. pairs imperf. horiz. of #2972 and 2973, in pane of 7+ stamps in cplt. bklt. #BK230 (due to foldover) —

U.N., 50th ANNIV.

A2288

ENGRAVED

1995, June 26 ***Perf. 11.2***

2974 A2288 32c blue .65 .25

CIVIL WAR

A2289

Designs: a, Monitor and Virginia. b, Robert E. Lee. c, Clara Barton. d, Ulysses S. Grant. e, Battle of Shiloh. f, Jefferson Davis. g, David Farragut. h, Frederick Douglass. i, Raphael Semmes. j, Abraham Lincoln. k, Harriet Tubman. l, Stand Watie. m, Joseph E. Johnston. n, Winfield Hancock. o, Mary Chesnut. p, Battle of Chancellorsville. q, William T. Sherman. r, Phoebe Pember. s, "Stonewall" Jackson. t, Battle of Gettysburg.

PHOTOGRAVURE

1995, June 29 ***Perf. 10.1***

2975 A2289 Pane of 20 32.50 17.50
a.-t. 32c any single 1.50 .60
u. As No. 2975, a.-e. imperf, f.-j. part perf, others perf *800.00*
v. As No. 2975, k.-t. imperf, f.-j. part perf, others perf *1,250.*
w. As No. 2975, imperf *800.00*
x. Block of 9 (f.-h., k.-m., p.-r.) k.-l. & p.-q. imperf. vert. *800.00*
y. As No. 2975, a.-b. perf, c., f.-h. part perf, others imperf *800.00*
z. As No. 2975, o. and t. imperf, j., n. & s. part perf, others perf —
aa. As No. 2975, c.-e. imperf, b., g.-j. part perf, others perf *500.00*

AMERICAN FOLK ART SERIES

Carousel Horses

A2290

A2291

A2292

A2293

LITHOGRAPHED

1995, July 21 *Perf. 11*

2976	A2290 32c multicolored	.65	.25
2977	A2291 32c multicolored	.65	.25
2978	A2292 32c multicolored	.65	.25
2979	A2293 32c multicolored	.65	.25
a.	Block or strip of 4, #2976-2979	2.60	2.00

WOMAN SUFFRAGE

A2294

LITHOGRAPHED & ENGRAVED

1995, Aug. 26 *Perf. 11.1x11*

2980	A2294 32c multicolored	.65	.25
a.	Black (engr.) omitted	*275.00*	
b.	Imperf., pair	*750.00*	
c.	Vert. pair, imperf between and at bottom	*500.00*	

No. 2980a is valued in the grade of fine. Very fine examples exist and sell for much more.

WORLD WAR II

A2295

Designs and events of 1945: a, Marines raise flag on Iwo Jima. b, Fierce fighting frees Manila by March 3, 1945. c, Soldiers advancing (Okinawa, the last big battle). d, Destroyed bridge (US and Soviets link up at Elbe River). e, Allies liberate Holocaust survivors. f, Germany surrenders at Reims. g, Refugees (By 1945, World War II has uprooted millions). h, Truman announces Japan's surrender. i, Sailor kissing nurse (News of victory hits home). j, Hometowns honor their returning veterans.

Central label is size of 15 stamps and shows world map with extent of Axis control and Allied operations.

1995, Sept. 2 *Perf. 11.1*

2981	A2295 Block of 10	15.00	7.50
a.-j.	32c any single	1.50	.50

No. 2981 has selvage at left and right and either top or bottom.

AMERICAN MUSIC SERIES

Louis Armstrong A2296

Coleman Hawkins — A2297

James P. Johnson — A2298

Jelly Roll Morton — A2299

Charlie Parker — A2300

Eubie Blake — A2301

Charles Mingus — A2302

Thelonious Monk — A2303

John Coltrane — A2304

Erroll Garner — A2305

LITHOGRAPHED

Plates of 120 in six panes of 20

1995 *Perf. 11.1x11*

2982	A2296 32c white denomination	.90	.25
a.	Imperf, pair	—	
2983	A2297 32c multicolored	2.25	.30
2984	A2296 32c black denomination	2.25	.30
2985	A2298 32c multicolored	2.25	.30
2986	A2299 32c multicolored	2.25	.30
2987	A2300 32c multicolored	2.25	.30
2988	A2301 32c multicolored	2.25	.30
2989	A2302 32c multicolored	2.25	.30
2990	A2303 32c multicolored	2.25	.30
2991	A2304 32c multicolored	2.25	.30
2992	A2305 32c multicolored	2.25	.30
a.	Vert. block of 10, #2983-2992	23.00	7.50
b.	Pane of 20, dark blue (inscriptions) omitted	—	
c.	Imperf pair of Nos. 2991-2992	*5,000.*	

An imperf. block of Nos. 2983-2992 is believed to be printer's waste.

GARDEN FLOWERS

A2306

A2307

A2308

A2309

A2310

LITHOGRAPHED & ENGRAVED
BOOKLET STAMPS

1995, Sept. 19 *Perf. 10.9 Vert.*

2993	A2306 32c multi	.65	.25
2994	A2307 32c multi	.65	.25
2995	A2308 32c multi	.65	.25
2996	A2309 32c multi	.65	.25
2997	A2310 32c multi	.65	.25
a.	Booklet pane of 5, #2993-2997	3.25	2.25
b.	As "a," imperf	*2,250.*	
c.	As "a," black (engr.) omitted	—	

EDDIE RICKENBACKER (1890-1973), AVIATOR

A2311

Small Date

Large Date

PHOTOGRAVURE

1995, Sept. 25 *Perf. 11¼*

2998	A2311 60c multi, small "1995" year date	1.40	.50
a.	Large "1995" date, *Oct., 1999*	2.00	.50

Date on No. 2998 is 1mm long, on No. 2998a 1½mm long.

REPUBLIC OF PALAU

A2312

LITHOGRAPHED

1995, Sept. 29 *Perf. 11.1*

2999	A2312 32c multicolored	.65	.25

See Palau Nos. 377-378.

COMIC STRIPS

A2313

Designs: a, The Yellow Kid. b, Katzenjammer Kids. c, Little Nemo in Slumberland. d, Bringing Up Father. e, Krazy Kat. f, Rube Goldberg's Inventions. g, Toonerville Folks. h, Gasoline Alley. i, Barney Google. j, Little Orphan Annie. k, Popeye. l, Blondie. m, Dick Tracy. n, Alley Oop. o, Nancy. p, Flash Gordon. q, Li'l Abner. r, Terry and the Pirates. s, Prince Valiant. t, Brenda Starr, Reporter.

PHOTOGRAVURE

1995, Oct. 1 *Perf. 10.1*

3000	A2313 Pane of 20	13.00	10.00
a.-t.	32c any single	.65	.50
u.	As No. 3000, a.-h. imperf., i.-l. part perf	*3,250.*	
v.	As No. 3000, m.-t. imperf., i.-l. part perf	*3,250.*	
w.	As No. 3000, a.-l. imperf.,m.-t. imperf vert.	*3,250.*	
x.	As No. 3000, imperf	*4,250.*	

U.S. NAVAL ACADEMY, 150th ANNIVERSARY

A2314

LITHOGRAPHED

1995, Oct. 10 *Perf. 10.9*

3001	A2314 32c multicolored	.65	.25

LITERARY ARTS SERIES

Tennessee Williams (1911-83) A2315

1995, Oct. 13 *Perf. 11.1*

3002	A2315 32c multicolored	.65	.25

CHRISTMAS

Madonna and Child — A2316

LITHOGRAPHED & ENGRAVED

1995 *Perf. 11.2*

3003	A2316 32c multi	.65	.25
c.	Black (engr., denomination) omitted	*200.00*	—

BOOKLET STAMP

Perf. 9.8x10.9

3003A	A2316 32c multi	.65	.25
b.	Booklet pane of 10	6.50	4.00

Santa Claus Entering Chimney A2317

Child Holding Jumping Jack A2318

Child Holding Tree A2319

Santa Claus Working on Sled A2320

LITHOGRAPHED

Perf. 11.25

3004	A2317 32c multi	.70	.25
3005	A2318 32c multi	.70	.25
3006	A2319 32c multi	.70	.25
3007	A2320 32c multi	.70	.25
a.	Block or strip of 4, #3004-3007	2.80	1.25
b.	Booklet pane of 10, 3 each #3004-3005, 2 each #3006-3007	8.00	4.00
c.	Booklet pane of 10, 2 each #3004-3005, 3 each #3006-3007	8.00	4.00
d.	As "a," imperf	*325.00*	
e.	As "b," miscut and inserted upside down into booklet cover, with full bottom selvage	—	

PHOTOGRAVURE

Self-Adhesive Stamps

Serpentine Die Cut 11.25 on 2, 3 or 4 sides

3008	A2320 32c multi	.95	.25
3009	A2318 32c multi	.95	.25
3010	A2317 32c multi	.95	.25
3011	A2319 32c multi	.95	.25
a.	Booklet pane of 20, 5 each #3008-3011 + label	19.00	
b.	Strip of 4, #3008-3011	3.80	

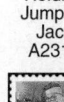

Midnight Angel A2321

Children Sledding A2322

LITHOGRAPHED

Serpentine Die Cut 11.3x11.6 on 2, 3 or 4 sides

3012 A2321 32c multi .65 .25
- *a.* Booklet pane of 20 + label 13.00
- *b.* Vert. pair, die cutting omitted between —
- *c.* Booklet pane of 15 + label, *1996* 12.00
- *d.* Booklet pane of 15 *30.00*

No. 3012a comes either with no die cutting in the label (1995 printing) or with the die cutting from the 1996 printing.

No. 3012d is a pane of 16 with one stamp removed. The missing stamp can be from either row 1, 2, 3, 7 or 8 of the pane. No. 3012d cannot be made from No. 3012c, a pane of 15 + label. The label is die cut. If the label is removed, an impression of the die cutting appears on the backing paper.

PHOTOGRAVURE

Die Cut

3013 A2322 32c multi .65 .25
- *a.* Booklet pane of 18 12.00

Self-Adhesive Coil Stamps

Serpentine Die Cut 11.2 Vert.

3014 A2320 32c multi 3.00 .30
3015 A2318 32c multi 3.00 .30
3016 A2317 32c multi 3.00 .30
3017 A2319 32c multi 3.00 .30
- *a.* Strip of 4, #3014-3017 12.00

LITHOGRAPHED

Serpentine Die Cut 11.6 Vert.

3018 A2321 32c multi 1.10 .30

Nos. 3005-3006 have "USA" printed in green. It is red on the self-adhesive stamps.

Issued: #3003-3003A, 3012-3013, 3018, 10/19; #3004-3011, 3014-3017, 9/30.

ANTIQUE AUTOMOBILES

1893 Duryea — A2323

1894 Haynes — A2324

1898 Columbia A2325

1899 Winton — A2326

1901 White — A2327

PHOTOGRAVURE

1995, Nov. 3 ***Perf. 10.1x11.1***

3019 A2323 32c multicolored .90 .25
3020 A2324 32c multicolored .90 .25
3021 A2325 32c multicolored .90 .25
3022 A2326 32c multicolored .90 .25
3023 A2327 32c multicolored .90 .25
- *a.* Vert. or horiz. strip of 5, #3019-3023 4.50 2.00

Vert. and horiz. strips are all in different order.

UTAH STATEHOOD CENTENARY

Delicate Arch, Arches Natl. Park — A2328

LITHOGRAPHED

1996, Jan. 4 ***Perf. 11.1***

3024 A2328 32c multicolored .75 .25

GARDEN FLOWERS

Crocus A2329

Winter Aconite A2330

Pansy A2331

Snowdrop A2332

Anemone — A2333

LITHOGRAPHED & ENGRAVED BOOKLET STAMPS

1996, Jan. 19 ***Perf. 10.9 Vert.***

3025 A2329 32c multi .65 .25
3026 A2330 32c multi .65 .25
3027 A2331 32c multi .65 .25
3028 A2332 32c multi .65 .25
3029 A2333 32c multi .65 .25
- *a.* Booklet pane of 5, #3025-3029 3.25 2.50
- *b.* As "a," imperf. —

LOVE

Cherub from Sistine Madonna, by Raphael — A2334

BOOKLET STAMP

Serpentine Die Cut 11.3x11.7

1996, Jan. 20

Self-Adhesive

3030 A2334 32c multicolored .65 .25
- *a.* Booklet pane of 20 + label 13.00
- *b.* Booklet pane of 15 + label 9.75
- *c.* Red (engr. "Love") omitted *75.00*
- *d.* Red (engr. "Love") missing (CM) —
- *e.* Double impression of red (engr. "Love") *450.00*
- *f.* Die cutting omitted, pair *225.00*
- *g.* As "a," stamps 1-5 double impression of red (engr. "LOVE") *1,000.*
- *h.* As "a," red (engr. "LOVE") omitted *1,000.*
- *i.* As "a," die cutting omitted —
- *j.* As "e," two examples in booklet pane of 20 (No. 3030a) *1,000.*
- *k.* As "d," three examples in booklet pane of 20 (No. 3030a) *310.00*

No. 3030d must be collected se-tenant with a stamp bearing the red engraving.

See Nos. 2948-2949, 2957-2960.

FLORA AND FAUNA SERIES

Kestrel, Blue Jay and Rose Types of 1993-95 and

Serpentine Die Cut 10½

1996-2002 **Untagged**

Self-Adhesive (#3031, 3031A)

3031 A1841 1c multicolored .30 .25
- *c.* Die cutting omitted, pair —

Serpentine Die Cut 11¼

Untagged

3031A A1841 1c multicolored .30 .25
- *b.* Die cutting omitted, pane of 50 *325.00*

No. 3031A has blue inscription and year. See No. 2477.

Red-headed Woodpecker A2335

Eastern Bluebird A2336

Sheets of 400 in four panes of 100

Perf. 11

Untagged

3032 A2335 2c multicolored .30 .25
3033 A2336 3c multicolored .30 .25

Red Fox — A2339

Serpentine Die Cut 11½x11¼

Self-Adhesive

3036 A2339 $1 multicolored *10.00* *.50*
- *a.* Serpentine die cut 11¾x11 ('02) *11.00* *.50*

Beginning with Nos. 3036 and 3036a, hidden 3-D images can be seen on some stamps when they are viewed with a special "Stamp Decoder" lens sold by the USPS. See the *Scott Specialized Catalogue of U.S. Stamps and Covers* for descriptions of these images. Stamps with 3-D images are 3036-3036a, 3167, 3168-3172, 3178, 3206, 3230-3234, 3238-3242, 3261-3262, 3321-3324, 3472-3473, 3647-3648, 3651, 3771, 3787-3791, 3808-3811, 3838 and 3862.

COIL STAMPS

Untagged

Perf. 9¾ Vert.

3044 A1841 1c multicolored, small date .30 .25
- *a.* Large date .30 .25

Date on No. 3044 is 1mm long, on No. 3044a 1.5mm long.

Untagged

3045 A2335 2c multicolored .30 .25

Issued: #3032, 2/2/96; #3033, 4/3/96; #3044, 1/20/96; #3036, 8/14/98; #3045, 6/22/99; #3031, 11/19/99; #3031A, 10/00.

BOOKLET STAMPS

PHOTOGRAVURE

Serpentine Die Cut 10.4x10.8 on 3 Sides

Tagged

Self-Adhesive

3048 A1847 20c multi .40 .25
- *a.* Booklet pane of 10 4.00
- *b.* Booklet pane of 4 70.00
- *c.* Booklet pane of 6 100.00

Nos. 3048b-3048c are from the vending machine booklet No. BK237 that has a glue strip at the top edge of the top pane, the peelable strip removed and the rouletting line 2mm lower than on No. 3048a on some booklets, when the panes are compared with bottoms aligned. Vending booklets with plate #S2222 always have gauge 8½ rouletting on booklet covers. Convertible booklets (No. 3048a) with plate #S2222 always have gauge 12½ rouletting on booklet covers. Vending booklets with plate #S1111 can have either 8½ or 12½ gauge rouletting on booklet cover, and it may be impossible to tell a vending booklet with 12½ gauge rouletting and plate #S1111 from a convertible booklet with peelable strip removed.

Serpentine Die Cut 11.3x11.7 on 2, 3 or 4 Sides

3049 A1853 32c yel, org, grn & blk .65 .25
- *a.* Booklet pane of 20 + label 13.00
- *b.* Booklet pane of 4 2.60
- *c.* Booklet pane of 5 + label 3.50
- *d.* Booklet pane of 6 4.00

Ring-necked Pheasant — A2350

Serpentine Die Cut 11.2 on 3 Sides

3050 A2350 20c multi .65 .25
- *a.* Booklet pane of 10, all stamps upright 6.50
- *b.* Serpentine die cut 11 3.25 .25
- *c.* As "b," booklet pane of 10, all stamps upright 35.00

Serpentine Die Cut 10½x11 on 3 Sides

3051 A2350 20c multi 1.25 .25

Serpentine Die Cut 10.6x10.4 on 3 Sides

3051A A2350 20c multicolored 7.00 .50
- *b.* Booklet pane of 5, 4 #3051, 1 #3051A turned sideways at top 10.00
- *c.* Booklet pane of 5, 4 #3051, 1 #3051A turned sideways at bottom 10.00

No. 3051 represents the eight upright stamps on the booklet panes Nos. 3051Ab and 3051Ac. The two stamps turned sideways on those panes are No. 3051A.

Coral Pink Rose — A2351

Serpentine Die Cut 11½x11¼ on 2, 3 or 4 Sides

3052 A2351 33c multi .90 .25
- *a.* Booklet pane of 4 3.60
- *b.* Booklet pane of 5 + label 4.50
- *c.* Booklet pane of 6 5.50
- *d.* Booklet pane of 20 + label 17.50
- *j.* Die cutting omitted, pair —
- *k.* As "d," die cutting omitted *5,500.*

Serpentine Die Cut 10¾x10½ on 2 or 3 sides

3052E A2351 33c multi .75 .25
- *f.* Booklet pane of 20 15.00
- *g.* Black ("33 USA," etc.) omitted 350.00
- *h.* As "f," all 12 stamps on one side with black omitted —
- *i.* Horiz. pair, die cutting missing between due to miscutting of the pane —
- *j.* As "f," vert. die cutting missing between due to miscutting of the pane —

No. 3052Ef is a double-sided booklet pane with 12 stamps on one side and 8 stamps plus label on the other side.

COIL STAMPS

Serpentine Die Cut 11½ Vert.

3053 A1847 20c multi .50 .25
- *a.* Die cutting omitted, pair *2,100.*

Yellow Rose, Ring-necked Pheasant Types of 1996-98

LITHOGRAPHED

Self-Adhesive

3054 A1858 32c yel, mag, blk & grn .65 .25
- *a.* Die cutting omitted, pair *85.00*
- *b.* Black, yellow & green omitted —
- *c.* Black, yellow & green omitted, die cutting omitted, pair —
- *d.* Black omitted *250.00*
- *e.* Black omitted, die cutting omitted, pair *550.00*
- *f.* All colors omitted, die cutting omitted —
- *g.* Pair, die cutting omitted, containing one stamp each of "c" and "e" —

Nos. 3054b and 3054d also are miscut and with shifted die cuttings.

No. 3054f must be collected se-tenant with a partially printed stamp(s).

3055 A2350 20c multi .40 .25
- *a.* Die cutting omitted, pair *125.00*

No. 3055a exists miscut. It is more common in this form and is valued thus.

Issued: #3048, 3053, 8/2/96; #3049, 10/24/96; #3054, 8/1/97; #3050, 3055, 7/31/98; #3051, 7/99; #3052, 8/13/99; #3052E, 4/7/00.

BLACK HERITAGE SERIES

Ernest E. Just (1883-1941), Marine Biologist — A2358

LITHOGRAPHED

1996, Feb. 1 *Perf. 11.1*

3058 A2358 32c gray & black .65 .25

SMITHSONIAN INSTITUTION, 150TH ANNIVERSARY

A2359

1996, Feb. 7

3059 A2359 32c multicolored .65 .25

CHINESE NEW YEAR

Year of the Rat — A2360

PHOTOGRAVURE

1996, Feb. 8

3060 A2360 32c multicolored .90 .25
a. Imperf., pair *550.00*

See Nos. 3895a, 3997a.

PIONEERS OF COMMUNICATION

Eadweard Muybridge A2361

Ottmar Mergenthaler A2362

Frederic E. Ives — A2363

William Dickson — A2364

LITHOGRAPHED

1996, Feb. 22 *Perf. 11.1x11*

3061 A2361 32c multicolored .65 .25
3062 A2362 32c multicolored .65 .25
3063 A2363 32c multicolored .65 .25
3064 A2364 32c multicolored .65 .25
a. Block or strip of 4, #3061-3064 2.60 2.00

Muybridge (1830-1904), Photographer; Mergenthaler (1854-99), Inventor of Linotype; Ives (1856-1937), Developer of Halftone Process; Dickson (1860-1935), Co-developer of Kinetoscope.

FULBRIGHT SCHOLARSHIPS, 50th ANNIVERSARY

A2365

LITHOGRAPHED & ENGRAVED

1996, Feb. 28 *Perf. 11.1*

3065 A2365 32c multicolored .75 .25

JACQUELINE COCHRAN (1910-80), PILOT

A2366

1996, Mar. 9

3066 A2366 50c multicolored 1.00 .40
a. Black (engr.) omitted 45.00

MARATHON

A2367

LITHOGRAPHED

1996, Apr. 11

3067 A2367 32c multicolored .65 .25

1996 SUMMER OLYMPIC GAMES

A2368

Designs: a, Decathlon (javelin). b, Men's canoeing. c, Women's running. d, Women's diving. e, Men's cycling. f, Freestyle wrestling. g, Women's gymnastics. h, Women's sailboarding. i, Men's shot put. j, Women's soccer. k, Beach volleyball. l, Men's rowing. m, Men's sprints. n, Women's swimming. o, Women's softball. p, Men's hurdles. q, Men's swimming. r, Men's gymnastics (pommel horse). s, Equestrian. t, Men's basketball.

PHOTOGRAVURE

1996, May 2 *Perf. 10.1*

3068 A2368 Pane of 20 14.00 10.00
a.-t. 32c any single .70 .50
u. As No. 3068, imperf *700.00*
v. As No. 3068, back inscriptions omitted on a., f., k. & p., incorrect back inscriptions on others —
w. As No. 3068, e. imperf, d., i.-j. part perf, all others perf *750.00*

GEORGIA O'KEEFFE (1887-1986)

A2369

PHOTOGRAVURE

1996, May 23 *Perf. 11.6x11.4*

3069 A2369 32c multicolored .85 .25
a. Imperf., pair *110.00*

TENNESSEE STATEHOOD BICENTENNIAL

A2370

1996, May 31 *Perf. 11.1*

3070 A2370 32c multicolored .65 .25
a. Imperf., pair —

One pane of 3070 containing 3069a is known. Some stamps on that pane have blind horizontal perforations.

Booklet Stamp
Self-Adhesive
Serpentine Die Cut 9.9x10.8

3071 A2370 32c multicolored .65 .30
a. Booklet pane of 20, #S11111 13.00
b. Horiz. pair, die cutting omitted btwn. *300.00* —
c. Die cutting omitted, pair —
d. Horiz. pair, die cutting omitted vert. — —

AMERICAN INDIAN DANCES

A2371

A2372

A2373

A2374

A2375

LITHOGRAPHED

1996, June 7 *Perf. 11.1*

3072 A2371 32c Fancy 1.20 .25
3073 A2372 32c Butterfly 1.20 .25
3074 A2373 32c Traditional 1.20 .25
3075 A2374 32c Raven 1.20 .25
3076 A2375 32c Hoop 1.20 .25
a. Strip of 5, #3072-3076 6.00 2.50

PREHISTORIC ANIMALS

A2376

A2377

A2378

A2379

1996, June 8 *Perf. 11.1x11*

3077 A2376 32c Eohippus .65 .25
3078 A2377 32c Woolly Mammoth .65 .25
3079 A2378 32c Mastodon .65 .25
3080 A2379 32c Saber-tooth Cat .65 .25
a. Block or strip of 4, #3077-3080 2.60 2.00

BREAST CANCER AWARENESS

A2380

1996, June 15 *Perf. 11.1*

3081 A2380 32c multicolored .65 .25

LEGENDS OF HOLLYWOOD

A2381

PHOTOGRAVURE

1996, June 24

3082 A2381 32c multicolored .65 .25
a. Imperf., pair *100.00*
b. As "a," red (USA 32c) missing (CM) and tan (JAMES DEAN) omitted —
c. As "a," tan (JAMES DEAN) omitted —
d. As "a," top stamp red missing (CM) and tan (JAMES DEAN) omitted, bottom stamp tan omitted —
e. As No. 3082 pane of 20, right two columns perf, left three columns imperf *1,750.*

Perforations in corner of each stamp are star-shaped. No. 3082 was also available on the first day of issue in at least 127 Warner Bros. Studio stores.

Nos. 3082b-3082d come from the same error pane. The top row is No. 3082b; rows 2-4 are No. 3082c. No. 3082d is a vertical pair with one stamp from No. 3082b at top and one stamp from No. 3082c at bottom.

FOLK HEROES

A2382

A2383

A2384

A2385

LITHOGRAPHED

1996, July 11 *Perf. 11.1x11*

3083 A2382 32c multicolored .65 .25
3084 A2383 32c multicolored .65 .25
3085 A2384 32c multicolored .65 .25
3086 A2385 32c multicolored .65 .25
a. Block or strip of 4, #3083-3086 2.60 2.00

CENTENNIAL OLYMPIC GAMES

Myron's Discobolus — A2386

ENGRAVED

1996, July 19 **Tagged** *Perf. 11.1*

3087 A2386 32c brown .75 .25

Sheet margin of the pane of 20 is lithographed.

IOWA STATEHOOD, 150TH ANNIVERSARY

Young Corn, by Grant Wood — A2387

LITHOGRAPHED

1996, Aug. 1

3088 A2387 32c multicolored .80 .25

BOOKLET STAMP
Self-Adhesive
Serpentine Die Cut 11.6x11.4

3089 A2387 32c multicolored .65 .30
a. Booklet pane of 20 13.00

RURAL FREE DELIVERY, CENT.

A2388

LITHOGRAPHED & ENGRAVED

1996, Aug. 7 ***Perf. 11.2x11***

3090 A2388 32c multicolored .80 .25

RIVERBOATS

Robt. E. Lee — A2389

Sylvan Dell — A2390

Far West — A2391

Rebecca Everingham A2392

Bailey Gatzert — A2393

PHOTOGRAVURE
Serpentine Die Cut 11x11.1

1996, Aug. 22
Self-Adhesive

3091 A2389 32c multicolored .65 .40
3092 A2390 32c multicolored .65 .40
3093 A2391 32c multicolored .65 .40
3094 A2392 32c multicolored .65 .40
3095 A2393 32c multicolored .65 .40
a. Vert. strip of 5, #3091-3095 3.25
b. Strip of 5, #3091-3095, with special die cutting, die cut 11 ¼ *45.00 45.00*

The serpentine die cutting runs through the peelable backing to which Nos. 3091-3095 are affixed. No. 3095a exists with stamps in different sequences.

On the long side of each stamp in No. 3095b, the die cutting is missing 3 "perforations" between the stamps, one near each end and one in the middle. This allows a complete strip to be removed from the backing paper for use on a first day cover.

AMERICAN MUSIC SERIES
Big Band Leaders

Count Basie — A2394

Tommy & Jimmy Dorsey — A2395

Glenn Miller — A2396

Benny Goodman A2397

Songwriters

Harold Arlen — A2398

Johnny Mercer — A2399

Dorothy Fields — A2400

Hoagy Carmichael A2401

LITHOGRAPHED

1996, Sept. 11 ***Perf. 11.1x11***

3096 A2394 32c multicolored .75 .25
3097 A2395 32c multicolored .75 .25
3098 A2396 32c multicolored .75 .25
3099 A2397 32c multicolored .75 .25
a. Block or strip of 4, #3096-3099 3.00 2.00
3100 A2398 32c multicolored .75 .25
3101 A2399 32c multicolored .75 .25
3102 A2400 32c multicolored .75 .25
3103 A2401 32c multicolored .75 .25
a. Block or strip of 4, #3100-3103 3.00 2.00

LITERARY ARTS SERIES

F. Scott Fitzgerald (1896-1940) A2402

PHOTOGRAVURE

1996, Sept. 27 ***Perf. 11.1***

3104 A2402 23c multicolored .55 .25

ENDANGERED SPECIES

A2403

Designs: a, Black-footed ferret. b, Thick-billed parrot. c, Hawaiian monk seal. d, American crocodile. e, Ocelot. f, Schaus swallowtail butterfly. g, Wyoming toad. h, Brown pelican. i, California condor. j, Gila trout. k, San Francisco garter snake. l, Woodland caribou. m, Florida panther. n, Piping plover. o, Florida manatee.

LITHOGRAPHED

1996, Oct. 2 ***Perf. 11.1x11***

3105 A2403 Pane of 15 12.00 8.00
a.-o. 32c any single .80 .50

See Mexico No. 1995.

COMPUTER TECHNOLOGY

A2404

LITHOGRAPHED & ENGRAVED

1996, Oct. 8 ***Perf. 10.9x11.1***

3106 A2404 32c multicolored .65 .25

CHRISTMAS

Madonna and Child from Adoration of the Shepherds, by Paolo de Matteis — A2405

Family at Fireplace A2406

Decorating Tree A2407

Dreaming of Santa Claus A2408

Holiday Shopping A2409

LITHOGRAPHED & ENGRAVED

1996 ***Perf. 11.1x11.2***

3107 A2405 32c multicolored .65 .25
a. Black (engr.) omitted at bottom *600.00*

On No. 3107a, an albino impression of the lettering at bottom is present, but there is no trace of black ink.

No. 3107b is missing the black lettering at bottom due to a small upward shift of the horizontal perforations. This lettering is the only engraved black on the stamp.

LITHOGRAPHED
Perf. 11.3

3108 A2406 32c multicolored .65 .25
3109 A2407 32c multicolored .65 .25
3110 A2408 32c multicolored .65 .25
3111 A2409 32c multicolored .65 .25
a. Block or strip of 4, #3108-3111 2.60 1.75
b. Strip of 4, #3110-3111, 3108-3109, with #3109 imperf., #3108 imperf. at right *1,000.*
c. Strip of 4, #3108-3111, with #3111 imperf, #3110 imperf at right *1,000.*

BOOKLET STAMPS
Self-Adhesive

LITHOGRAPHED & ENGRAVED
Serpentine Die Cut 10 on 2, 3 or 4 Sides

3112 A2405 32c multicolored .75 .25
a. Booklet pane of 20 + label 15.00
b. Die cutting omitted, pair 40.00
c. As "a," die cutting omitted *400.00*
d. As "a," top seven stamps with black (engr.) missing (PS) —

No. 3112d is missing the black lettering at bottom due to a small upward shift of the horizontal perforations. This lettering is the only engraved black on the stamp.

LITHOGRAPHED
Serpentine Die Cut 11.8x11.5 on 2, 3 or 4 Sides

3113 A2406 32c multicolored .65 .25
3114 A2407 32c multicolored .65 .25
3115 A2408 32c multicolored .65 .25
3116 A2409 32c multicolored .65 .25
a. Booklet pane of 20, 5 ea #3113-3116 13.00
b. Strip of 4, #3113-3116 2.60
c. As "a," die cutting omitted *1,250.*
d. As "b," die cutting omitted *500.00*
e. Block of 6, die cutting omitted *700.00*

Skaters — A2410

PHOTOGRAVURE
Die Cut

3117 A2410 32c multicolored .65 .25
a. Booklet pane of 18 12.00

Issued: #3108-3111, 3113-3117, 10/8; #3107, 3112, 11/1.

HANUKKAH

A2411

Serpentine Die Cut 11.1

1996, Oct. 22
Self-Adhesive

3118 A2411 32c multicolored .65 .25

See Nos. 3352, 3547, 3672, Israel No. 1289. For booklet see No. BK258.

CYCLING
Souvenir Sheet

A2412

1996, Nov. 1 ***Perf. 11x11.1***

3119 A2412 Sheet of 2 2.75 2.00
a. 50c orange & multi 1.30 1.00
b. 50c blue green & multi 1.30 1.00

No. 3119 exists overprinted in gold and in silver for the Tour of China '96. This overprint is a private production. Value, set of 2 sheets $12.50.

CHINESE NEW YEAR

Year of the Ox — A2413

1997, Jan. 5 ***Perf. 11.2***

3120 A2413 32c multicolored .80 .25

See Nos. 3895b, 3997b.

BLACK HERITAGE SERIES

Brig. Gen. Benjamin O. Davis, Sr. (1880-1970) — A2414

LITHOGRAPHED
Serpentine Die Cut 11.4

1997, Jan. 28
Self-Adhesive

3121 A2414 32c multicolored .70 .25

Statue of Liberty Type of 1994
PHOTOGRAVURE
Serpentine Die Cut 11 on 2, 3 or 4 Sides
1997, Feb. 1
Self-Adhesive

3122 A1951 32c red, lt bl, dk bl & yel .70 .25
a. Booklet pane of 20 + label 14.00
b. Booklet pane of 4 2.80
c. Booklet pane of 5 + label 3.75
d. Booklet pane of 6 4.25
h. As "a," die cutting omitted —

Serpentine Die Cut 11.5x11.8 on 2, 3 or 4 Sides
1997
Self-Adhesive

3122E A1951 32c red, lt bl, dk bl & yel 1.50 .25
f. Booklet pane of 20 + label 40.00
g. Booklet pane of 6 9.00

LOVE

A2415

Swans — A2416

LITHOGRAPHED
Serpentine Die Cut 11.8x11.6 on 2, 3 or 4 Sides
1997, Feb. 4
Self-Adhesive

3123 A2415 32c multicolored .65 .25
a. Booklet pane of 20 + label 13.00
b. Die cutting omitted, pair *100.00*
c. As "a," die cutting omitted *675.00*
d. As "a," black omitted —

Serpentine Die Cut 11.6x11.8 on 2, 3 or 4 Sides

3124 A2416 55c multicolored 1.10 .25
a. Booklet pane of 20 + label 22.00

HELPING CHILDREN LEARN

A2417

PHOTOGRAVURE
Serpentine Die Cut 11.6x11.7
1997, Feb. 18
Self-Adhesive

3125 A2417 32c multicolored .65 .25

MERIAN BOTANICAL PRINTS

Citron, Moth, Larvae, Pupa, Beetle
A2418

Flowering Pineapple, Cockroaches
A2419

No. 3128 (r), No. 3129 (l), No. 3128a below

Serpentine Die Cut 10.9x10.2 on 2, 3 or 4 Sides
1997, Mar. 3
Self-Adhesive

3126 A2418 32c multicolored .65 .25
3127 A2419 32c multicolored .65 .25
a. Booklet pane, 10 ea #3126-3127 + label 13.00
b. Pair, #3126-3127 1.30
c. Vert. pair, die cutting omitted between *350.00*

Size: 18.5x24mm
Serpentine Die Cut 11.2x10.8 on 2 or 3 Sides

3128 A2418 32c multicolored 1.00 .25
a. See footnote 2.50 .25
b. Booklet pane, 2 ea #3128-3129, 1 #3128a 6.50
3129 A2419 32c multicolored 1.00 .25
a. See footnote 4.50 .35
b. Booklet pane, 2 ea #3128-3129, 1 #3129a 8.50
c. Pair, #3128-3129 2.00

Nos. 3128a-3129a are placed sideways on the pane and are serpentine die cut 11.2 on top and bottom, 10.8 on left side. One of the two No. 3128a per pane has a straight edge at left. The right side is 11.2 broken by a sloping die cut where the stamp meets the vertical die cutting of the two stamps above it. See illustration above.

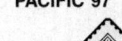

PACIFIC 97

Sailing Ship
A2420

Stagecoach — A2421

ENGRAVED
1997, Mar. 13 Tagged *Perf. 11.2*

3130 A2420 32c blue .65 .30
3131 A2421 32c red .65 .30
a. Pair, #3130-3131 1.30 .75

Juke Box — A2225a

PHOTOGRAVURE
COIL STAMPS
1997, Mar. 14 Untagged *Imperf.*
Self-Adhesive

3132 A2225a (25c) brt org red, brt yel grn & multi 1.50 .50

Tagged
Serpentine Die Cut 9.9 Vert.

3133 A2212 32c dk bl, tan, brn, red & lt bl 1.75 .25

Nos. 3132-3133 were issued without backing paper. No. 3132 has simulated perforations in black bars at the top and bottom edges of the stamp. Sky on No. 3133 shows color gradation at LR not on Nos. 2915A or 2915D, and it has blue "1996" at left bottom.

See Nos. 2897, 2913-2916, 2920-2921.

LITERARY ARTS SERIES

Thornton Wilder (1897-1975)
A2422

LITHOGRAPHED
1997, Apr. 17 *Perf. 11.1*

3134 A2422 32c multicolored .65 .25

RAOUL WALLENBERG (1912-47)

Wallenberg and Jewish Refugees
A2423

1997, Apr. 24

3135 A2423 32c multicolored .65 .25

DINOSAURS

A2424

Designs: a, Ceratosaurus. b, Camptosaurus. c, Camarasaurus. d, Brachiosaurus. e, Goniopholis. f, Stegosaurus. g, Allosaurus. h, Opisthias. i, Edmontonia. j, Einiosaurus. k, Daspletosaurus. l, Palaeosaniwa. m, Corythosaurus. n, Ornithomimus. o, Parasaurolophus.

1997, May 1 *Perf. 11x11.1*

3136 A2424 Sheet of 15 10.00 8.00
a.-o. 32c any single .65 .50
p. As No. 3136, bottom 7 stamps imperf. *2,500.*
q. As No. 3136, top 8 stamps imperf *2,500.*
r. As No. 3136, all colors and tagging missing (EP) —

No. 3136r resulted from double sheeting in the sheet-fed press. It is properly gummed and perforated.

No. 3136 completely imperf. is believed to be printer's waste.

BUGS BUNNY

A2425

PHOTOGRAVURE
1997, May 22 *Serpentine Die Cut 11*
Self-Adhesive

3137 Pane of 10 #3137a 6.75
a. A2425 32c single .65 .25
b. Pane of 9 #3137a 6.00
c. Pane of 1 #3137a .65

Die cutting on #3137 does not extend through the backing paper.

3138 Pane of 10, #3138c, 9 #3138a 130.00
a. A2425 32c single 2.75
b. Pane of 9 #3138a 20.00
c. Pane of 1, no die cutting 100.00

Die cutting on No. 3138b extends through the backing paper.

An untagged promotional piece similar to No. 3137c exists on the same backing paper as the pane, with the same design image, but without Bugs' signature and the single stamp. Replacing the stamp is an enlarged "32 / USA" in the same style as used on the stamp. This promotional piece was not valid for postage.

PACIFIC 97

Franklin
A2426

Washington
A2427

LITHOGRAPHED & ENGRAVED
1997 *Perf. 10.5x10.4*

3139 Pane of 12 12.00 9.00
a. A2426 50c single 1.00 .50
3140 Pane of 12 14.50 11.00
a. A2427 60c single 1.20 .60

Selvage on Nos. 3139-3140 is lithographed.
Issued: No. 3139, 5/29; No. 3140, 5/30.

MARSHALL PLAN, 50TH ANNIV.

Gen. George C. Marshall, Map of Europe — A2428

1997, June 4 *Perf. 11.1*

3141 A2428 32c multicolored .65 .25

CLASSIC AMERICAN AIRCRAFT

A2429

Designs: a, Mustang. b, Model B. c, Cub. d, Vega. e, Alpha. f, B-10. g, Corsair. h, Stratojet. i, GeeBee. j, Staggerwing. k, Flying Fortress. l, Stearman. m, Constellation. n, Lightning. o, Peashooter. p, Tri-Motor. q, DC-3. r, 314 Clipper. s, Jenny. t, Wildcat.

PHOTOGRAVURE
1997, July 19 *Perf. 10.1*

3142 A2429 Pane of 20 13.00 10.00
a.-t. 32c any single .65 .50

FOOTBALL COACHES

Bear Bryant — A2430

Pop Warner — A2431

Vince Lombardi
A2432

George Halas — A2433

LITHOGRAPHED
1997 *Perf. 11.2*

3143 A2430 32c multicolored .65 .25
3144 A2431 32c multicolored .65 .25
3145 A2432 32c multicolored .65 .25
3146 A2433 32c multicolored .65 .25
a. Block or strip of 4, #3143-3146 2.60 1.50

With Red Bar Above Coach's Name
Perf. 11

3147 A2432 32c multicolored .65 .45
3148 A2430 32c multicolored .65 .45
3149 A2431 32c multicolored .65 .45
3150 A2433 32c multicolored .65 .45

Issued: #3143-3146, 7/25; #3147, 8/5; #3148, 8/7; #3149, 8/8; #3150, 8/16.

AMERICAN DOLLS

A2434

Designs: a, “Alabama Baby,” and doll by Martha Chase. b, “Columbian Doll.” c, Johnny Gruelle's “Raggedy Ann.” d, Doll by Martha Chase. e, “American Child.” f, “Baby Coos.” g, Plains Indian. h, Doll by Izannah Walker. i, “Babyland Rag.” j, “Scootles.” k, Doll by Ludwig Greiner. l, “Betsy McCall.” m, Percy Crosby's “Skippy.” n, “Maggie Mix-up.” o, Dolls by Albert Schoenhut.

1997, July 28 ***Perf. 10.9x11.1***

3151	A2434	Pane of 15	13.50	—
a.-o.		32c any single	.90	.60

LEGENDS OF HOLLYWOOD

Humphrey Bogart (1899-1957).

A2435

PHOTOGRAVURE

1997, July 31 ***Perf. 11.1***

3152	A2435	32c multicolored	.85	.25

Perforations in corner of each stamp are star-shaped.

“THE STARS AND STRIPES FOREVER!”

A2436

1997, Aug. 21

3153	A2436	32c multicolored	.65	.25

AMERICAN MUSIC SERIES
Opera Singers

Lily Pons — A2437

Richard Tucker — A2438

Lawrence Tibbett — A2439

Rosa Ponselle — A2440

LITHOGRAPHED

1997, Sept. 10 ***Perf. 11***

3154	A2437	32c multicolored	.75	.25
3155	A2438	32c multicolored	.75	.25
3156	A2439	32c multicolored	.75	.25
3157	A2440	32c multicolored	.75	.25
a.		Block or strip of 4, #3154-3157	3.00	2.00

AMERICAN MUSIC SERIES
Classical Composers & Conductors

Leopold Stokowski A2441

Arthur Fiedler — A2442

George Szell — A2443

Eugene Ormandy A2444

Samuel Barber — A2445

Ferde Grofé — A2446

Charles Ives — A2447

Louis Moreau Gottschalk A2448

LITHOGRAPHED

1997, Sept. 12 ***Perf. 11***

3158	A2441	32c multicolored	1.50	.25
3159	A2442	32c multicolored	1.50	.25
3160	A2443	32c multicolored	1.50	.25
3161	A2444	32c multicolored	1.50	.25
3162	A2445	32c multicolored	1.50	.25
3163	A2446	32c multicolored	1.50	.25
3164	A2447	32c multicolored	1.50	.25
3165	A2448	32c multicolored	1.50	.25
a.		Block of 8, #3158-3165	12.00	4.00

PADRE FÉLIX VARELA (1788-1853)

A2449

1997, Sept. 15 ***Perf. 11.2***

3166	A2449	32c purple	.65	.25

DEPARTMENT OF THE AIR FORCE, 50TH ANNIV.

Thunderbirds Aerial Demonstration Squadron — A2450

1997, Sept. 18 ***Perf. 11.2x11.1***

3167	A2450	32c multicolored	.65	.25

CLASSIC MOVIE MONSTERS

A2451

A2452

A2453

A2454

A2455

PHOTOGRAVURE

1997, Sept. 30 ***Perf. 10.2***

3168	A2451	32c multicolored	.75	.25
3169	A2452	32c multicolored	.75	.25
3170	A2453	32c multicolored	.75	.25
3171	A2454	32c multicolored	.75	.25
3172	A2455	32c multicolored	.75	.25
a.		Strip of 5, #3168-3172	3.75	2.25

FIRST SUPERSONIC FLIGHT, 50TH ANNIV.

A2456

LITHOGRAPHED

Serpentine Die Cut 11.4

1997, Oct. 14

Self-Adhesive

3173	A2456	32c multicolored	.65	.25

WOMEN IN MILITARY SERVICE

A2457

1997, Oct. 18 ***Perf. 11.1***

3174	A2457	32c multicolored	.65	.25

KWANZAA

A2458

PHOTOGRAVURE

1997, Oct. 22 ***Serpentine Die Cut 11***

Self-Adhesive

3175	A2458	32c multicolored	.65	.25

See Nos. 3368, 3548, 3673.

CHRISTMAS

Madonna and Child A2459

Holly A2460

LITHOGRAPHED

Serpentine Die Cut 9.9 on 2, 3 or 4 Sides

1997

Booklet Stamps

Self-Adhesive

3176	A2459	32c multicolored	.65	.25
a.		Booklet pane of 20 + label	13.00	

Serpentine Die Cut 11.2x11.6 on 2, 3 or 4 Sides

3177	A2460	32c multicolored	.65	.25
a.		Booklet pane of 20 + label	13.00	
b.		Booklet pane of 4	2.60	
c.		Booklet pane of 5 + label	3.25	
d.		Booklet pane of 6	3.90	

Madonna and Child, by Sano di Pietro. Issued: No. 3176, 10/27; No. 3177, 10/30.

MARS PATHFINDER
Souvenir Sheet

Mars Rover Sojourner — A2461

PHOTOGRAVURE

1997, Dec. 10 Tagged ***Perf. 11x11.1***

3178	A2461	$3 multicolored	6.00	4.00
a.		$3, single stamp	5.50	3.00
b.		Single souvenir sheet from sheet of 18	7.50	—
c.		As No. 3178, imperf.	—	

The perforations at the bottom of the stamp contain the letters “USA.” Vertical rouletting extends from the vertical perforations of the stamp to the bottom of the souvenir sheet.

Sheet of 18 has vertical perforations separating the three columns of souvenir sheets. These were cut away when No. 3178 was produced. Thus, the souvenir sheet from the sheet of 18 is wider and has vertical perforations on one or two sides.

CHINESE NEW YEAR

Year of the Tiger — A2462

1998, Jan. 5 ***Perf. 11.2***

3179	A2462	32c multicolored	.80	.25

See Nos. 3895c, 3997c.

ALPINE SKIING

A2463

LITHOGRAPHED

1998, Jan. 22 ***Perf. 11.2***

3180	A2463	32c multicolored	.75	.25

BLACK HERITAGE SERIES

A2464

Serpentine Die Cut 11.6x11.3

1998, Jan. 28

Self-Adhesive

3181	A2464	32c sepia & black	.70	.25

CELEBRATE THE CENTURY

1900s A2465

No. 3182: a, Model T Ford. b, Theodore Roosevelt. c, Motion picture "The Great Train Robbery," 1903. d, Crayola Crayons introduced, 1903. e, St. Louis World's Fair, 1904. f, Design used on Hunt's Remedy stamp (#RS56), Pure Food & Drug Act, 1906. g, Wright Brothers first flight, Kitty Hawk, 1903. h, Boxing match shown in painting "Stag at Sharkey's," by George Bellows of the Ash Can School. i, Immigrants arrive. j, John Muir, preservationist. k, "Teddy" Bear created. l, W.E.B. Du Bois, social activist. m, Gibson Girl. n, First baseball World Series, 1903. o, Robie House, Chicago, designed by Frank Lloyd Wright.

1910s A2466

No. 3183: a, Charlie Chaplin as the Little Tramp. b, Federal Reserve System created, 1913. c, George Washington Carver. d, Avant-garde art introduced at Armory Show, 1913. e, First transcontinental telephone line, 1914. f, Panama Canal opens, 1914. g, Jim Thorpe wins decathlon at Stockholm Olympics, 1912. h, Grand Canyon National Park, 1919. i, U.S. enters World War I. j, Boy Scouts started in 1910, Girl Scouts formed in 1912. k, Woodrow Wilson. l, First crossword puzzle published, 1913. m, Jack Dempsey wins heavyweight title, 1919. n, Construction toys. o, Child labor reform.

1920s A2467

No. 3184: a, Babe Ruth. b, The Gatsby style. c, Prohibition enforced. d, Electric toy trains. e, 19th Amendment (woman voting). f, Emily Post's Etiquette. g, Margaret Mead, anthropologist. h, Flappers do the Charleston. i, Radio entertains America. j, Art Deco style (Chrysler Building). k, Jazz flourishes. l, Four Horsemen of Notre Dame. m, Lindbergh flies the Atlantic. n, American realism (Automat, by Edward Hopper). o, Stock Market crash, 1929.

1930s A2468

No. 3185: a, Franklin D. Roosevelt. b, The Empire State Building. c, 1st Issue of Life Magazine, 1936. d, Eleanor Roosevelt. e, FDR's New Deal. f, Superman arrives, 1938. g, Household conveniences. h, "Snow White and the Seven Dwarfs," 1937. i, "Gone with the Wind," 1936. j, Jesse Owens. k, Streamline design. l, Golden Gate Bridge. m, America survives the Depression. n, Bobby Jones wins golf Grand Slam, 1938. o, The Monopoly Game.

1940s A2469

No. 3186: a, World War II. b, Antibiotics save lives. c, Jackie Robinson. d, Harry S Truman. e, Women support war effort. f, TV entertains America. g, Jitterbug sweeps nation. h, Jackson Pollock, Abstract Expressionism. i, GI Bill, 1944. j, Big Band Sound. k, Intl. style of architecture (UN Headquarters). l, Postwar baby boom. m, Slinky, 1945. n, "A Streecar Named Desire," 1947. o, Orson Welles' "Citizen Kane."

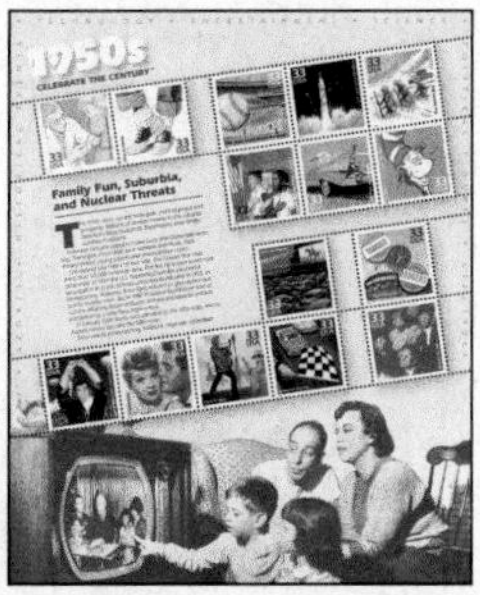

1950s A2470

No. 3187: a, Polio vaccine developed. b, Teen fashions. c, The "Shot Heard 'Round the World." d, US launches satellites. e, Korean War. f, Desegregating public schools. g, Tail fins, chrome. h, Dr. Seuss' "The Cat in the Hat." i, Drive-in movies. j, World Series rivals. k, Rocky Marciano, undefeated boxer. l, "I Love Lucy." m, Rock 'n Roll. n, Stock car racing. o, Movies go 3-D.

1960s A2471

No. 3188: a, Martin Luther King, Jr., "I Have a Dream." b, Woodstock. c, Man walks on the moon. d, Green Bay Packers. e, Star Trek. f, The Peace Corps. g, Viet Nam War. h, Ford Mustang. i, Barbie Doll. j, Integrated circuit. k, Lasers. l, Super Bowl I. m, Peace symbol. n, Roger Maris, 61 in '61. o, The Beatles "Yellow Submarine."

1970s A2472

No. 3189: a, Earth Day celebrated. b, "All in the Family" television series. c, "Sesame Street" television series character, Big Bird. d, Disco music. e, Pittsburgh Steelers win four Super Bowls. f, US Celebrates 200th birthday. g, Secretariat wins Triple Crown. h, VCRs transform entertainment. i, Pioneer 10. j, Women's rights movement. k, 1970s fashions. l, "Monday Night Football." m, Smiley face buttons. n, Jumbo jets. o, Medical imaging.

1980s A2473

No. 3190: a, Space shuttle program. b, "Cats" Broadway show. c, San Francisco 49ers. d, Hostages in Iran come home. e, Figure skating. f, Cable TV. g, Vietnam Veterans Memorial. h, Compact discs. i, Cabbage Patch Kids. j, "The Cosby Show" television series. k, Fall of the Berlin Wall. l, Video games. m, "E. T. The Extra-Terrestrial" movie. n, Personal computers. o, Hip-hop culture.

1990s A2474

No. 3191: a, New baseball records. b, Gulf War. c, "Seinfeld" television series. d, Extreme sports. e, Improving education. f, Computer art and graphics. g, Recovering species. h, Return to space. i, Special Olympics. j, Virtual reality. k, Movie "Jurassic Park." l, Movie "Titanic." m, Sport utility vehicles. n, World Wide Web. o, Cellular phones.

LITHOGRAPHED, ENGRAVED (#3182m, 3183f, 3184m, 3185b, 3186k, 3187a, 3188c, 3189h)

1998-2000 ***Perf. 11½***

3182	A2465	Pane of 15	10.00	8.50
a.-o.		32c any single	.75	.65
p.		Engr. red (No. 3182m, Gibson girl) omitted, in pane of 15	*3,000.*	
3183	A2466	Pane of 15	10.00	8.50
a.-o.		32c any single	.75	.65
p.		Nos. 3183g, 3183 l-3183o imperf, in pane of 15	*7,000.*	
3184	A2467	Pane of 15	12.50	8.50
a.-o.		32c any single	.80	.65
3185	A2468	Pane of 15	12.50	8.50
a.-o.		32c any single	.80	.65
3186	A2469	Pane of 15	13.00	8.50
a.-o.		33c any single	.85	.65
3187	A2470	Pane of 15	13.00	8.50
a.-o.		33c any single	.85	.65
3188	A2471	Pane of 15	13.00	8.50
a.-o.		33c any single	.85	.65
3189	A2472	Pane of 15	13.00	8.50
a.-o.		33c any single	.85	.65
3190	A2473	Pane of 15	13.00	8.50
a.-o.		33c any single	.85	.65
3191	A2474	Pane of 15	13.00	8.50
a.-o.		33c any single	.85	.65
		Nos. 3182-3191 (10)	123.00	85.00

Issued: #3182-3183, 2/3; #3184, 5/28; #3185, 9/10; #3186, 2/18/99; #3187, 5/26/99; #3188, 9/17/99; #3189, 11/18/99; #3190, 1/12/00; #3191, 5/2/00.

"REMEMBER THE MAINE"

A2475

LITHOGRAPHED & ENGRAVED

1998, Feb. 15 ***Perf. 11.2x11***

3192 A2475 32c red & black .70 .25

FLOWERING TREES

Southern Magnolia A2476

Blue Paloverde A2477

Yellow Poplar A2478

Prairie Crab Apple A2479

Pacific Dogwood — A2480

LITHOGRAPHED

1998, Mar. 19 ***Die Cut Perf 11.3***

Self-Adhesive

3193	A2476	32c multicolored		2.00	.40
3194	A2477	32c multicolored		2.00	.40
3195	A2478	32c multicolored		2.00	.40
3196	A2479	32c multicolored		2.00	.40
3197	A2480	32c multicolored		2.00	.40
a.		Strip of 5, #3193-3197		10.00	
b.		As "a," die cutting omitted			—

ALEXANDER CALDER (1898-1976), SCULPTOR

Black Cascade, 13 Verticals, 1959 — A2481

Untitled, 1965 — A2482

Rearing Stallion, 1928 — A2483

Portrait of a Young Man, c. 1945 — A2484

Un Effet du Japonais, 1945 — A2485

PHOTOGRAVURE

1998, Mar. 25 *Perf. 10.2*

3198 A2481 32c multicolored .65 .25
3199 A2482 32c multicolored .65 .25
3200 A2483 32c multicolored .65 .25
3201 A2484 32c multicolored .65 .25
3202 A2485 32c multicolored .65 .25
a. Strip of 5, #3198-3202 3.25 2.25

CINCO DE MAYO

A2486

Serpentine Die Cut 11.7x10.9

1998, Apr. 16

Self-Adhesive

3203 A2486 32c multicolored .65 .25

See Mexico No. 2066. For 33c version, see No. 3309.

SYLVESTER & TWEETY

A2487

Serpentine Die Cut 11.1

1998, Apr. 27

Self-Adhesive

3204 Pane of 10 #3204a 6.75
a. A2487 32c single .65 .25
b. Pane of 9 #3204a 6.00
c. Pane of 1 #3204a .65

Die cutting on No. 3204b does not extend through the backing paper.

3205 Pane of 10, #3205c, 9 #3205a 11.00
a. A2487 32c single .90
b. Pane of 9 #3205a *7.00*
c. Pane of 1, no die cutting *3.00*

Die cutting on #3205a extends through the backing paper.

WISCONSIN STATEHOOD

A2488

Serpentine Die Cut 10.8x10.9

1998, May 29

Self-Adhesive

3206 A2488 32c multicolored .65 .30

Wetlands A2489

Diner A2490

COIL STAMPS

1998 Untagged ***Perf. 10 Vert.***

3207 A2489 (5c) multicolored .30 .25

Serpentine Die Cut 9.8 Vert.

Self-adhesive

Untagged

3207A A2489 (5c) multicolored, small date .30 .25
b. Large date .30 .25

Date on No. 3207A is approximately 1.4mm long, on No. 3207Ab approx. 1.6mm long.

Perf. 10 Vert.

Untagged

3208 A2490 (25c) multicolored .50 .50

Serpentine Die Cut 9.8 Vert.

Self-Adhesive

Untagged

3208A A2490 (25c) multicolored .50 .50

Issued: #3207-3208, 6/5; #3208A, 9/30; #3207A, 12/14.

1898 TRANS-MISSISSIPPI STAMPS, CENT.

A2491

LITHOGRAPHED & ENGRAVED

1998, June 18 *Perf. 12x12.4*

3209 A2491 Pane of 9 9.50 7.00
a. A100 1c green & black .30 .25
b. A108 2c red brown & black .30 .25
c. A102 4c orange & black .30 .25
d. A103 5c blue & black .30 .25
e. A104 8c dark lilac & black .30 .25
f. A105 10c purple & black .30 .25
g. A106 50c green & black 1.25 .60
h. A107 $1 red & black 2.50 1.25
i. A101 $2 red brown & black 4.25 2.50

Vignettes on Nos. 3209b and 3209i are reversed in comparison to the original issue.

3210 A107 $1 Pane of 9 #3209h 22.50 —

BERLIN AIRLIFT, 50th ANNIV.

A2492

PHOTOGRAVURE

1998, June 26 *Perf. 11.2*

3211 A2492 32c multicolored .65 .25

AMERICAN MUSIC SERIES
Folk Singers

Huddie "Leadbelly" Ledbetter A2493

Woody Guthrie — A2494

Sonny Terry — A2495

Josh White — A2496

1998, June 26 *Perf. 10.1x10.2*

3212 A2493 32c multicolored .90 .25
3213 A2494 32c multicolored .90 .25
3214 A2495 32c multicolored .90 .25
3215 A2496 32c multicolored .90 .25
a. Block or strip of 4, #3212-3215 3.60 2.00

AMERICAN MUSIC SERIES
Gospel Singers

Mahalia Jackson — A2497

Roberta Martin — A2498

Clara Ward — A2499

Sister Rosetta Tharpe — A2500

1998, July 15 *Perf. 10.1x10.3*

3216 A2497 32c multicolored 1.00 .25
3217 A2498 32c multicolored 1.00 .25
3218 A2499 32c multicolored 1.00 .25
3219 A2500 32c multicolored 1.00 .25
a. Block or strip of 4, #3216-3219 4.00 2.00

SPANISH SETTLEMENT OF THE SOUTHWEST

La Mision de San Miguel de San Gabriel, Española, NM — A2501

LITHOGRAPHED

1998, July 11 *Perf. 11.2*

3220 A2501 32c multicolored .65 .25

LITERARY ARTS SERIES

Stephen Vincent Benét — A2502

1998, July 22 *Perf. 11.2*

3221 A2502 32c multicolored .65 .25

TROPICAL BIRDS

Antillean Euphonia — A2503

Green-throated Carib — A2504

Crested Honeycreeper A2505

Cardinal Honeyeater A2506

1998, July 29

3222 A2503 32c multicolored .65 .25
3223 A2504 32c multicolored .65 .25
3224 A2505 32c multicolored .65 .25
3225 A2506 32c multicolored .65 .25
a. Block or strip of 4, #3222-3225 2.60 2.00

LEGENDS OF HOLLYWOOD

A2507

PHOTOGRAVURE

1998, Aug. 3 *Perf. 11.1*

3226 A2507 32c multicolored .75 .25

Perforations in corner of each stamp are star-shaped.

ORGAN & TISSUE DONATION

A2508

Serpentine Die Cut 11.7

1998, Aug. 5

Self-Adhesive

3227 A2508 32c multicolored .65 .25

MODERN BICYCLE

A2509

Small Date

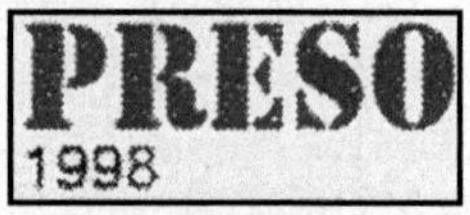

Large Date

COIL STAMP

Serpentine Die Cut 9.8 Vert.

1998, Aug. 14 Untagged

Self-Adhesive (#3228)

3228 A2509 (10c) multicolored, small "1998" year date .30 .25
a. Large date .35 .25

Date on No. 3228a is approximately 1 ½mm; on No. 3228 approximately 1mm.

Untagged

Perf. 9.9 Vert.

3229 A2509 (10c) multicolored .30 .25

Date on No. 3229 is approximately 2mm wide.

BRIGHT EYES

Dog — A2510

Fish — A2511

Cat — A2512

Parakeet A2513

Hamster — A2514

Serpentine Die Cut 9.9

1998, Aug. 20

Self-Adhesive

3230 A2510 32c multicolored	.75	.40
3231 A2511 32c multicolored	.75	.40
3232 A2512 32c multicolored	.75	.40
3233 A2513 32c multicolored	.75	.40
3234 A2514 32c multicolored	.75	.40
a. Strip of 5, #3230-3234	3.75	

KLONDIKE GOLD RUSH, CENTENNIAL

A2515

LITHOGRAPHED

1998, Aug. 21 ***Perf. 11.1***

3235 A2515 32c multicolored .65 .25

AMERICAN ART

A2516

Paintings: a, "Portrait of Richard Mather," by John Foster. b, "Mrs. Elizabeth Freake and Baby Mary," by The Freake Limner. c, "Girl in Red Dress with Cat and Dog," by Ammi Phillips. d, "Rubens Peale with a Geranium," by Rembrandt Peale. e, "Long-billed Curlew, Numenius Longrostris," by John James Audubon. f, "Boatmen on the Missouri," by George Caleb Bingham. g, "Kindred Sprits," by Asher B. Durand. h, "The Westwood Children," by Joshua Johnson. i, "Music and Literature," by William Harnett. j, "The Fog Warning," by Winslow Homer. k, "The White Cloud, Head Chief of the Iowas," by George Catlin. l, "Cliffs of Green River," by Thomas Moran. m, "The Last of the Buffalo," by Alfred Bierstadt. n, "Niagara," by Frederic Edwin Church. o, "Breakfast in Bed," by Mary Cassatt. p, "Nighthawks," by Edward Hopper. q, "American Gothic," by Grant Wood. r, "Two Against the White," by Charles Sheeler. s, "Mahoning," by Franz Kline. t, "No. 12," by Mark Rothko.

PHOTOGRAVURE

1998, Aug. 27 ***Perf. 10.2***

3236 A2516 Pane of 20 18.00 10.00
a.-t. 32c any single .90 .60

AMERICAN BALLET

A2517

LITHOGRAPHED

1998, Sept. 16 ***Perf. 10.9x11.1***

3237 A2517 32c multicolored .65 .25

SPACE DISCOVERY

A2518

A2519

A2520

A2521

A2522

PHOTOGRAVURE

1998, Oct. 1 ***Perf. 11.1***

3238 A2518 32c multicolored	.65	.25
3239 A2519 32c multicolored	.65	.25
3240 A2520 32c multicolored	.65	.25
3241 A2521 32c multicolored	.65	.25
3242 A2522 32c multicolored	.65	.25
a. Strip of 5, #3238-3242	3.25	2.25

GIVING AND SHARING

A2523

PHOTOGRAVURE

Serpentine Die Cut 11.1

1998, Oct. 7

Self-Adhesive

3243 A2523 32c multicolored .65 .25

CHRISTMAS

Madonna and Child, Florence, 15th Cent. — A2524

Evergreen A2525

Victorian A2526

Chili Pepper A2527

Tropical A2528

LITHOGRAPHED

Serpentine Die Cut 10.1x9.9 on 2, 3 or 4 Sides

1998, Oct. 15

Self-Adhesive

Booklet Stamps

3244 A2524 32c multicolored	.65	.25
a. Booklet pane of 20 + label	13.00	
b. Die cutting omitted, pair	—	

Size: 22x25mm

Serpentine Die Cut 11.3x11.7 on 2 or 3 Sides

3245 A2525 32c multicolored	3.25	.25
3246 A2526 32c multicolored	3.25	.25
3247 A2527 32c multicolored	3.25	.25
3248 A2528 32c multicolored	3.75	.25
a. Booklet pane of 4, #3245-3248	13.00	
b. Booklet pane of 5, #3245-3246, 3248, 2 #3247 + label	16.25	
c. Booklet pane of 6, #3247-3248, 2 each #3245-3246	19.50	
d. As "a," die cutting omitted	—	
e. As "b," die cutting omitted	—	
f. As "c," die cutting omitted	—	
g. Block of 4, #3245-3248	13.00	

Size: 23x30mm

Serpentine Die Cut 11.4x11.5 on 2, 3, or 4 Sides

3249 A2525 32c multicolored	1.35	.25
a. Serp. die cut 11.7x11.6 on 2, 3, or 4 sides	1.75	.25
3250 A2526 32c multicolored	1.35	.25
a. Serp. die cut 11.7x11.6 on 3 or 4 sides	1.75	.25
3251 A2527 32c multicolored	1.35	.25
a. Serp. die cut 11.7x11.6 on 3 or 4 sides	1.75	.25
3252 A2528 32c multi + label	1.35	.25
a. Serp. die cut 11.7x11.6 on 2, 3, or 4 sides	1.75	.25
b. Block or strip of 4, #3249-3252	5.40	
c. Booklet pane of 20, 5 each #3249-3252 + label	30.00	
d. Block or strip of 4, #3249a-3252a	7.00	
e. Booklet pane of 20, 5 each #3249a-3252a + label	35.00	
f. Block or strip of 4, #3249-3252, red ("Greetings 32 USA" and "1998") omitted on #3249, 3252	*625.00*	
g. Block or strip of 4, #3249-3252, red ("Greetings 32 USA" and "1998") omitted on #3249, 3252; green (same) omitted on #3250, 3251	—	
h. As "b," die cutting omitted	—	
i. As "c," die cutting omitted	*4,500.*	

Dedicated printing plates were used to print the red and green denominations, salutations and dates. Red and green appearing in the wreaths come from other plates and, therefore, are not part of the color omissions.

Weather Vane — A2529

LITHOGRAPHED

1998 **Untagged** ***Perf. 11.2***

3257 A2529 (1c) multi	.30	.25
a. Black omitted	125.00	
b. Horiz. pair, imperf. vert. and at top	—	

Untagged

3258 A2529 (1c) multi	.30	.25
a. Black missing (PS)		

No. 3257 is 18mm high, has thin letters, white USA, and black 1998. No. 3258 is 17mm high, has thick letters, pale blue USA and blue 1998.

Uncle Sam A2530

Uncle Sam's Hat A2531

PHOTOGRAVURE

Serpentine Die Cut 10.8

Self-Adhesive (#3259, 3261-3263, 3265-3269)

3259 A2530 22c multi	.45	.25
a. Die cut 10.8x10.5	2.50	.25
b. Vert. pair, No. 3259 + 3259a	3.50	

See No. 3353.

Perf. 11.2

3260 A2531 (33c) multi .65 .25

Space Shuttle Landing — A2532

Piggyback Space Shuttle — A2533

LITHOGRAPHED

Sheets of 120 in six panes of 20 (#3261-3262)

Serpentine Die Cut 11.5

3261 A2532 $3.20 multi	6.00	1.50
3262 A2533 $11.75 multi	22.50	10.00

Hidden 3-D images (ENTERPRISE/COLUMBIA/CHALLENGER/ATLANTIS/ENDEAVOR/DISCOVERY) can be seen on Nos. 3261 and 3262 when viewed with a special "Stamp Decoder" lens sold by the USPS.

COIL STAMPS

PHOTOGRAVURE

Serpentine Die Cut 9.9 Vert.

3263 A2530 22c multi	.45	.25
a. Die cutting omitted, pair	*600.00*	

See No. 3353.

Perf. 9.8 Vert.

3264 A2531 (33c) multi	.65	.25
a. Imperf, pair	*325.00*	

Serpentine Die Cut 9.9 Vert.

3265 A2531 (33c) multi	.80	.25
a. Die cutting omitted, pair	65.00	—
b. Red omitted	*300.00*	
c. Black omitted	*1,400.*	
d. Black omitted, die cutting omitted, pair	*700.00*	
e. Red omitted, die cutting omitted, pair	*500.00*	
f. Blue omitted	—	

Unused examples of No. 3265 are on backing paper the same size as the stamps. Corners of the stamp are 90 degree angles.

On No. 3265b, the blue and gray colors are shifted down and to the right.

On No. 3265f, the red is misregistered to right by 10½ stamps and gray by 3mm.

Serpentine Die Cut 9.9 Vert.

3266 A2531 (33c) multi 2.25 .25

Unused examples of No. 3266 are on backing paper larger than the stamps, and the stamps are spaced approximately 2mm. apart. Corners of stamps are rounded.

BOOKLET STAMPS

Serpentine Die Cut 9.9 on 2 or 3 Sides

3267 A2531 (33c) multi	.75	.25
a. Booklet pane of 10	7.50	

Serpentine Die Cut 11¼ on 3 Sides (#3268, 3268a) or 11 on 2, 3 or 4 sides (#3268b, 3268c)

3268 A2531 (33c) multi	.75	.25
a. Booklet pane of 10	7.50	
b. Serpentine die cut 11	.75	.25
c. As "b," booklet pane of 20 + label	15.00	

Die Cut 8 on 2, 3 or 4 Sides

3269 A2531 (33c) multi	.65	.25
a. Booklet pane of 18	12.00	

Issued: No. 3262, 11/19; others, 11/9.

Unused and used examples of an "H" nondenominated stamp inscribed "Postcard Rate" exist in the marketplace. There is no evidence that these stamps were ever officially issued. Values: unused $2,400; used $1,750.

A2534

PHOTOGRAVURE

COIL STAMPS

Perf. 9.8 Vert.

1998, Dec. 14 **Untagged**

3270 A2534 (10c) multi, small date	.30	.25
a. Large date	.75	.25

Self-Adhesive

Untagged

Serpentine Die Cut 9.9 Vert.

3271 A2534 (10c) multi, small date	.30	.25
a. Large date	1.00	.25

Dates on Nos. 3270a and 3271a are approximately 1¾mm; on Nos. 3270-3271 approximately 1¼mm.

Compare to Nos. 2602-2604, 2907.

Scott values for used self-adhesive stamps are for examples either on piece or off piece.

CHINESE NEW YEAR

Year of the Rabbit — A2535

1999, Jan. 5 ***Perf. 11.2***

3272 A2535 33c multicolored .80 .25

See Nos. 3895d, 3997d.

BLACK HERITAGE SERIES

Malcolm X — A2536

LITHOGRAPHED

Serpentine Die Cut 11.4

1999, Jan. 20

Self-Adhesive

3273 A2536 33c multicolored 1.00 .25

VICTORIAN LOVE

A2537

A2538

PHOTOGRAVURE

1999, Jan. 28 ***Die Cut***

Booklet Stamp

Self-Adhesive

3274 A2537 33c multicolored .65 .25
a. Booklet pane of 20 13.00
b. Die cutting omitted, pair *100.00*
c. As "a," die cutting omitted *800.00*
3275 A2538 55c multicolored 1.10 .25

HOSPICE CARE

A2539

LITHOGRAPHED

Serpentine Die Cut 11.4

1999, Feb. 9

3276 A2539 33c multicolored .65 .25
a. Horiz. pair, vert. die cutting omitted *650.00*

Flag & City — A2540

PHOTOGRAVURE

1999, Feb. 25 ***Perf. 11.2***

Self-Adhesive (#3278, 3278F, 3279, 3281-3282)

3277 A2540 33c multi .70 .25

No. 3277 has red date.

Serpentine Die Cut 11 on 2, 3 or 4 Sides

3278 A2540 33c multi .65 .25
a. Booklet pane of 4 2.60
b. Booklet pane of 5 + label 3.25
c. Booklet pane of 6 3.90
d. Booklet pane of 10 13.00
e. Booklet pane of 20 + label 17.00
h. As "e," die cutting omitted —
i. Serpentine die cut 11¼ .90 .25
j. As "i," booklet pane of 10 9.00

No. 3278 has black date.

BOOKLET STAMPS

Serpentine Die Cut 11½x11¾ on 2, 3 or 4 Sides

3278F A2540b33c multi 1.40 .25
g. Booklet pane of 20 + label 28.00

No. 3278F has black date.

Serpentine Die Cut 9.8 on 2 or 3 Sides

3279 A2540 33c multi .85 .25
a. Booklet pane of 10 8.50

No. 3279 has red date.

COIL STAMPS

Perf. 9.9 Vert.

3280 A2540 33c multi, small "1999" year date .65 .25
a. Large date 2.00 .25
b. As No. 3280, imperf pair *125.00* *150.00*

Serpentine Die Cut 9.8 Vert.

Two types of No. 3281: Type I, Long vertical feature at left and right of tallest building consists of 3 separate lines; Type II, Same features consist of solid color.

3281 A2540 33c multi, type I, large "1999" year date .65 .25
a. As No. 3281, die cutting omitted, pair 30.00
b. Light blue and yellow omitted *275.00*
c. Small date, type II .65 .25
d. Small date, type I 5.00 .30
e. As "c," die cutting omitted, pair —

Corners are square on No. 3281. Unused examples are on backing paper the same size as the stamps, and the stamps are adjoining.

Date on Nos. 3280a and 3281 is approximately 1¾mm; on Nos. 3280, 3281c and 3281d approximately 1¼mm.

3282 A2540 33c multi .65 .25

Corners are rounded on #3282. Unused examples are on backing paper larger than the stamps, and the stamps are spaced approximately 2mm. apart.

Flag & Chalkboard — A2541

Printed by Avery Dennison.

PHOTOGRAVURE

Serpentine Die Cut 7.9 on 2, 3 or 4 Sides

1999, Mar. 13

Self-Adhesive

BOOKLET STAMP

3283 A2541 33c multicolored .65 .25
a. Booklet pane of 18 12.00
b. Die cutting omitted, pair —

IRISH IMMIGRATION

A2542

LITHOGRAPHED

1999, Feb. 26 ***Perf. 11.2***

3286 A2542 33c multicolored .65 .25

See Ireland No. 1168.

PERFORMING ARTS SERIES

Alfred Lunt (1892-1977), Lynn Fontanne (1887-1983), Actors

A2543

LITHOGRAPHED

1999, Mar. 2 ***Perf. 11.2***

3287 A2543 33c multicolored .65 .25

ARCTIC ANIMALS

A2544

A2545

A2546

A2547

A2548

LITHOGRAPHED

1999, Mar. 12 ***Perf. 11***

3288 A2544 33c Arctic Hare .85 .25
3289 A2545 33c Arctic Fox .85 .25
3290 A2546 33c Snowy Owl .85 .25
3291 A2547 33c Polar Bear .85 .25
3292 A2548 33c Gray Wolf .85 .25
a. Strip of 5, #3288-3292 4.25 —

SONORAN DESERT

A2549

Designs: a, Cactus wren, brittlebush, teddy bear cholla. b, Desert tortoise. c, White-winged dove, prickly pear. d, Gambel quail. e, Saguaro cactus. f, Desert mule deer. g, Desert cottontail, hedgehog cactus. h, Gila monster. i, Western diamondback rattlesnake, cactus mouse. j, Gila woodpecker.

LITHOGRAPHED

Serpentine Die Cut Perf 11.2

1999, Apr. 6

Self-Adhesive

3293 A2549 Pane of 10 8.00
a.-j. 33c any single .80 .50

BERRIES

Blueberries A2550

Raspberries A2551

Strawberries A2552

Blackberries A2553

PHOTOGRAVURE

Serpentine Die Cut 11¼x11½ on 2, 3 or 4 Sides (Nos. 3294-3297), or 2 or 3 sides (Nos. 3294a-3297a)

1999, Apr. 10

Self-Adhesive

3294 A2550 33c multicolored .85 .25
a. Dated "2000" 1.25 .25
3295 A2551 33c multicolored .85 .25
a. Dated "2000" 1.25 .25
3296 A2552 33c multicolored .85 .25
a. Dated "2000" 1.25 .25
3297 A2553 33c multicolored .85 .25
a. Dated "2000" 1.25 .25
b. Booklet pane of 20, 5 each #3294-3297 + label 17.50
c. Block or strip of 4, #3294-3297 3.50
d. Booklet pane of 20, 5 #3297e + label 25.00
e. Block of 4, #3294a-3297a 5.00

No. 3297d is a double-sided booklet pane, with 12 stamps on one side and eight stamps plus label on the other side.

Serpentine Die Cut 9½x10 on 2 or 3 Sides

3298 A2550 33c multicolored 1.00 .25
3299 A2552 33c multicolored 1.00 .25
3300 A2551 33c multicolored 1.00 .25
3301 A2553 33c multicolored 1.00 .25
a. Booklet pane of 4, #3298-3301 4.00
b. Booklet pane of 5, #3298, 3299, 3301, 2 #3300 + label 5.00
c. Booklet pane of 6, #3300, 3301, 2 #3298, 3299 6.00
d. Block of 4, #3298-3301 4.00

COIL STAMPS

Serpentine Die Cut 8.5 Vert.

3302 A2550 33c multicolored 2.25 .25
3303 A2551 33c multicolored 2.25 .25
3304 A2553 33c multicolored 2.25 .25
3305 A2552 33c multicolored 2.25 .25
a. Strip of 4, #3302-3305 9.00

See Nos. 3404-3407.

DAFFY DUCK

A2554

PHOTOGRAVURE

Serpentine Die Cut 11.1

1999, Apr. 16

Self-Adhesive

3306 Pane of 10 #3306a 6.75
a. A2554 33c single .65 .25
b. Pane of 9 #3306a 6.00
c. Pane of 1 #3306a .65

Die cutting on #3306b does not extend through the backing paper.

3307 Pane of 10, #3307c, 9 #3307a 13.00
a. A2554 33c single 1.10
b. Pane of 9 #3307a 10.00
c. Pane of 1, no die cutting 2.75
d. As "a," vert. pair, die cutting omitted btwn. pos. 6 and 9 (unique) *4,250.*

Die cutting on #3307b extends through the backing paper.

LITERARY ARTS SERIES

Ayn Rand (1905-82) — A2555

LITHOGRAPHED

1999, Apr. 22 ***Perf. 11.2***

3308 A2555 33c multicolored .65 .25

Cinco De Mayo Type of 1998

LITHOGRAPHED

Serpentine Die Cut 11.6x11.3

1999, Apr. 27

Self-Adhesive

3309 A2486 33c multicolored .70 .25

TROPICAL FLOWERS

Bird of Paradise — A2556

Royal Poinciana A2557

Gloriosa Lily — A2558

Chinese Hibiscus — A2559

PHOTOGRAVURE
BOOKLET STAMPS

Serpentine Die Cut 10.9 on 2 or 1 Sides

1999, May 1

Self-Adhesive

3310	A2556	33c multicolored		.65	.30
3311	A2557	33c multicolored		.65	.30
3312	A2558	33c multicolored		.65	.30
3313	A2559	33c multicolored		.65	.30
a.		Block of 4, #3310-3313		2.60	
b.		Booklet pane, 5 each #3313a		13.00	

No. 3313b is a double-sided booklet pane with 12 stamps on one side and 8 stamps plus label on the other side.

JOHN (1699-1777) & WILLIAM (1739-1823) BARTRAM, BOTANISTS

A2560

LITHOGRAPHED

Serpentine Die Cut 11½

1999, May 18

Self-Adhesive

3314	A2560	33c multicolored	.65	.25

PROSTATE CANCER AWARENESS

A2561

PHOTOGRAVURE

1999, May 28 ***Serpentine Die Cut 11***

Self-Adhesive

3315	A2561	33c multicolored	.65	.25

CALIFORNIA GOLD RUSH, 150TH ANNIV.

A2562

LITHOGRAPHED

1999, June 18 ***Perf. 11¼***

3316	A2562	33c multicolored	.65	.25

AQUARIUM FISH

A2563

A2564

A2565

Reef Fish — A2566

Designs: No. 3317, Yellow fish, red fish, cleaner shrimp. No. 3318, Fish, thermometer. No. 3319, Red fish, blue & yellow fish. No. 3320, Fish, heater/aerator.

LITHOGRAPHED

Serpentine Die Cut 11½

1999, June 24

Self-Adhesive

3317	A2563	33c multicolored	.65	.30
3318	A2564	33c multicolored	.65	.30
3319	A2565	33c multicolored	.65	.30
3320	A2566	33c multicolored	.65	.30
b.		Strip of 4, #3317-3320	2.60	

EXTREME SPORTS

A2567

A2568

A2569

A2570

PHOTOGRAVURE

Serpentine Die Cut 11

1999, June 25

Self-Adhesive

3321	A2567	33c multicolored	.75	.30
3322	A2568	33c multicolored	.75	.30
3323	A2569	33c multicolored	.75	.30
3324	A2570	33c multicolored	.75	.30
a.		Block or strip of 4, #3321-3324	3.00	

AMERICAN GLASS

Free-Blown Glass A2571

Mold-Blown Glass A2572

Pressed Glass A2573

Art Glass A2574

LITHOGRAPHED

1999, June 29 ***Perf. 11***

3325	A2571	33c multicolored	1.90	.25
3326	A2572	33c multicolored	1.90	.25
3327	A2573	33c multicolored	1.90	.25
3328	A2574	33c multicolored	1.90	.25
a.		Strip or block of 4, #3325-3328	7.75	3.00

LEGENDS OF HOLLYWOOD

James Cagney (1899-1986) — A2575

PHOTOGRAVURE

1999, July 22 ***Perf. 11***

3329	A2575	33c multicolored	.80	.25

Perforations in corner of each stamp are star-shaped.

GEN. WILLIAM "BILLY" L. MITCHELL (1879-1936), AVIATION PIONEER

A2576

Serpentine Die Cut 9¾x10

1999, July 30

Self-Adhesive

3330	A2576	55c multicolored	1.10	.30

HONORING THOSE WHO SERVED

A2577

Serpentine Die Cut 11

1999, Aug. 16

Self-Adhesive

3331	A2577	33c black, blue & red	.65	.25

UNIVERSAL POSTAL UNION

A2578

LITHOGRAPHED

1999, Aug. 25 ***Perf. 11***

3332	A2578	45c multicolored	1.00	.45

FAMOUS TRAINS

Daylight — A2579

Congressional A2580

20th Century Limited — A2581

Hiawatha A2582

Super Chief — A2583

1999, Aug. 26

3333	A2579	33c multicolored	.75	.25
3334	A2580	33c multicolored	.75	.25
3335	A2581	33c multicolored	.75	.25
3336	A2582	33c multicolored	.75	.25
3337	A2583	33c multicolored	.75	.25
a.		Strip of 5, #3333-3337	3.75	—

Stamps in No. 3337a are arranged in four different orders.

FREDERICK LAW OLMSTED (1822-1903), LANDSCAPE ARCHITECT

A2584

1999, Sept. 12

3338	A2584	33c multicolored	.65	.25

AMERICAN MUSIC SERIES
Hollywood Composers

Max Steiner (1888-1971) A2585

Dimitri Tiomkin (1894-1975) A2586

Bernard Herrmann (1911-75) A2587

Franz Waxman (1906-67) A2588

Alfred Newman (1907-70) A2589

Erich Wolfgang Korngold (1897-1957) A2590

1999, Sept. 16 ***Perf. 11***

3339	A2585	33c multicolored	1.40	.25
3340	A2586	33c multicolored	1.40	.25
3341	A2587	33c multicolored	1.40	.25
3342	A2588	33c multicolored	1.40	.25
3343	A2589	33c multicolored	1.40	.25
3344	A2590	33c multicolored	1.40	.25
a.		Block of 6, #3339-3344	8.50	4.50

AMERICAN MUSIC SERIES
Broadway Songwriters

Ira (1896-1983) & George (1898-1937) Gershwin A2591

Alan Jay Lerner (1918-86) & Frederick Loewe (1901-88) A2592

Lorenz Hart (1895-1943) A2593

Richard Rodgers (1902-79) & Oscar Hammerstein II (1895-1960) A2594

Meredith Willson (1902-84) A2595

Frank Loesser (1910-69) A2596

1999, Sept. 21

3345 A2591 33c multicolored 1.25 .25
3346 A2592 33c multicolored 1.25 .25
3347 A2593 33c multicolored 1.25 .25
3348 A2594 33c multicolored 1.25 .25
3349 A2595 33c multicolored 1.25 .25
3350 A2596 33c multicolored 1.25 .25
a. Block of 6, #3345-3350 7.50 4.50

INSECTS & SPIDERS

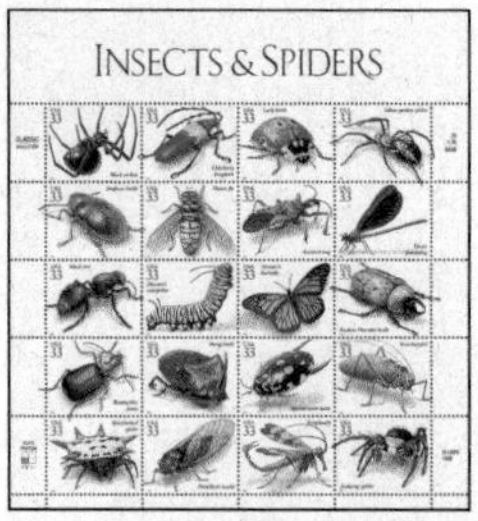

A2597

Designs: a, Black widow. b, Elderberry longhorn. c, Lady beetle. d, Yellow garden spider. e, Dogbane beetle. f, Flower fly. g, Assassin bug. h, Ebony jewelwing. i, Velvet ant. j, Monarch caterpillar. k, Monarch butterfly. l, Eastern Hercules beetle. m, Bombardier beetle. n, Dung beetle. o, Spotted water beetle. p, True katydid. q, Spinybacked spider. r, Periodical cicada. s, Scorpionfly. t, Jumping spider.

1999, Oct. 1 ***Perf. 11***

3351 A2597 Pane of 20 14.00 10.00
a.-t. 33c any single .70 .50

Hanukkah Type of 1996
PHOTOGRAVURE

1999, Oct. 8 ***Serpentine Die Cut 11***
Self-Adhesive

3352 A2411 33c multicolored .65 .25

See Nos. 3352, 3547, 3672, Israel No. 1289.

Uncle Sam Type of 1998
COIL STAMP

1999, Oct. 8 ***Perf. 9¾ Vert.***

3353 A2530 22c multicolored .45 .25

See Nos. 3259, 3263.

NATO, 50TH ANNIV.

A2598

LITHOGRAPHED

1999, Oct. 13 ***Perf. 11¼***

3354 A2598 33c multicolored .65 .25

CHRISTMAS

Madonna and Child, by Bartolomeo Vivarini — A2599

Serpentine Die Cut 11¼ on 2 or 3 sides

1999, Oct. 20
Booklet Stamp
Self-Adhesive

3355 A2599 33c multicolored .90 .25
a. Booklet pane of 20 18.00

Deer — A2600

Serpentine Die Cut 11¼

3356 A2600 33c gold & red 2.25 .25
3357 A2260 33c gold & blue 2.25 .25
3358 A2260 33c gold & purple 2.25 .25
3359 A2260 33c gold & green 2.25 .25
a. Block or strip of 4, #3356-3359 9.00

Booklet Stamps

Serpentine Die Cut 11¼ on 2, 3 or 4 sides

3360 A2260 33c gold & red 1.10 .25
3361 A2260 33c gold & blue 1.10 .25
3362 A2260 33c gold & purple 1.10 .25
3363 A2600 33c gold & green 1.10 .25
a. Booklet pane of 20, 5 each #3360-3363 22.50
b. Block or strip of 4, #3360-3363 4.40
c. As "b," die cutting omitted *100.00*
d. As "a," die cutting omitted *500.00*

Size: 21x19mm

Serpentine Die Cut 11½x11¼ on 2 or 3 sides

3364 A2260 33c gold & red 1.35 .25
3365 A2260 33c gold & blue 1.35 .25
3366 A2260 33c gold & purple 1.35 .25
3367 A2260 33c gold & green 1.35 .25
a. Booklet pane of 4, #3364-3367 5.50
b. Booklet pane of 5, #3364, 3366, 3367, 2 #3365 + label 7.00
c. Booklet pane of 6, #3365, 3367, 2 each #3364 & 3366 8.00
d. Block of 4, #3364-3367 5.50

The frame on Nos. 3356-3359 is narrow and the space between it and the hoof is a hairline. The frame on Nos. 3360-3363 is much thicker, and the space between it and the hoof is wider.

Kwanzaa Type of 1997
PHOTOGRAVURE

1999, Oct. 29 ***Serpentine Die Cut 11***
Self-Adhesive

3368 A2458 33c multicolored .65 .25

See Nos. 3175, 3548, 3673.

YEAR 2000

Baby New Year — A2601

LITHOGRAPHED
Serpentine Die Cut 11¼

1999, Dec. 27
Self-Adhesive

3369 A2601 33c multicolored .65 .25

CHINESE NEW YEAR

Year of the Dragon — A2602

2000, Jan. 6 ***Perf. 11¼***

3370 A2602 33c multicolored .80 .25

See Nos. 3895e, 3997e.

BLACK HERITAGE SERIES

Patricia Roberts Harris — A2603

Serpentine Die Cut 11½x11¼

2000, Jan. 27
Self-Adhesive

3371 A2603 33c indigo .65 .25

SUBMARINES

S Class — A2604

Los Angeles Class — A2605

Ohio Class — A2606

USS Holland — A2607

Gato Class A2608

2000, Mar. 27 ***Perf. 11***

3372 A2605 33c **multi,** with microprinted "USPS" at base of sail .75 .25

BOOKLET STAMPS

3373 A2604 22c multicolored .75 .75
3374 A2605 33c **multi,** no microprinting 1.00 1.00
3375 A2606 55c multicolored 1.50 1.25
3376 A2607 60c multicolored 1.75 1.50
3377 A2608 $3.20 multicolored 10.00 5.00
a. Booklet pane of 5, #3373-3377 15.00 —

No. 3377a was issued with two types of text in the selvage.

PACIFIC COAST RAIN FOREST

A2609

Designs: a, Harlequin duck. b, Dwarf oregongrape, snail-eating ground beetle. c, American dipper, horiz. d, Cutthroat trout, horiz. e, Roosevelt elk. f, Winter wren. g, Pacific giant salamander, Rough-skinned newt. h, Western tiger swallowtail, horiz. i, Douglas squirrel, foliose lichen. j, Foliose lichen, banana slug.

Serpentine Die Cut 11¼x11½, 11½ (horiz. stamps)

2000, Mar. 29
Self-Adhesive

3378 A2609 Pane of 10 10.00
a.-j. 33c any single 1.00 .50

LOUISE NEVELSON (1899-1988), SCULPTOR

Silent Music I — A2610

Royal Tide I — A2611

Black Chord A2612

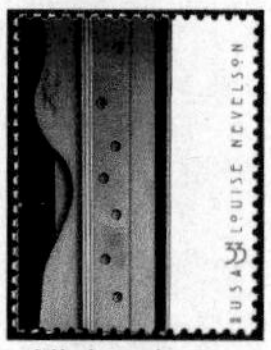

Nightsphere-Light A2613

Dawn's Wedding Chapel I — A2614

2000, Apr. 6 ***Perf. 11x11¼***

3379 A2610 33c multicolored .65 .25
3380 A2611 33c multicolored .65 .25
3381 A2612 33c multicolored .65 .25
3382 A2613 33c multicolored .65 .25
3383 A2614 33c multicolored .65 .25
a. Strip of 5, #3379-3383 3.25 —

HUBBLE SPACE TELESCOPE IMAGES

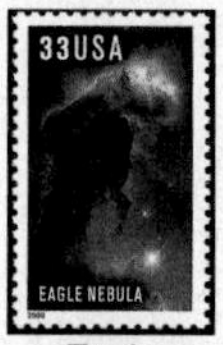

Eagle Nebula A2615

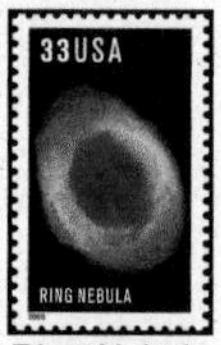

Ring Nebula A2616

Lagoon Nebula A2617

Egg Nebula A2618

Galaxy NGC 1316 — A2619

PHOTOGRAVURE

2000, Apr. 10 ***Perf. 11***

3384 A2615 33c multicolored .65 .25
3385 A2616 33c multicolored .65 .25
3386 A2617 33c multicolored .65 .25
3387 A2618 33c multicolored .65 .25
3388 A2619 33c multicolored .65 .25
a. Strip of 5, #3384-3388 3.25 2.00
b. As "a," imperf *900.00*

AMERICAN SAMOA

Samoan Double Canoe — A2620

LITHOGRAPHED

2000, Apr. 17

3389 A2620 33c multicolored .85 .25

LIBRARY OF CONGRESS

A2621

2000, Apr. 24

3390 A2621 33c multicolored .65 .25

ROAD RUNNER & WILE E. COYOTE

A2622

Serpentine Die Cut 11

2000, Apr. 26

Self-Adhesive

3391 Pane of 10 #3391a 10.00
- *a.* A2622 33c single .85 .25
- *b.* Pane of 9 #3391a 8.00
- *c.* Pane of 1 #3391a 1.50
- *d.* All die cutting omitted, pane of 10 2,250.

Die cutting on #3391b does not extend through the backing paper.

3392 Pane of 10, #3392c, 9 #3392a 30.00
- *a.* A2622 33c single 2.75
- *b.* Pane of 9 #3392a 25.00
- *c.* Pane of 1, no die cutting 5.00

Die cutting on #3392a extends through the backing paper. Used examples of No. 3392a are identical to those of No. 3391a.

Nos. 3391b-3391c and 3392b-3392c are separated by a vertical line of microperforations.

DISTINGUISHED SOLDIERS

A2623

A2624

A2625

A2626

Designs: No. 3393, Maj. Gen. John L. Hines. No. 3394, Gen. Omar N. Bradley. No. 3395, Sgt. Alvin C. York. No. 3396, Second Lt. Audie L. Murphy.

2000, May 3 ***Perf. 11***

3393 A2623 33c multicolored .70 .25
3394 A2624 33c multicolored .70 .25
3395 A2625 33c multicolored .70 .25
3396 A2626 33c multicolored .70 .25
- *a.* Block or strip of 4, #3393-3396 2.80 1.50

SUMMER SPORTS

Runners — A2627

2000, May 5

3397 A2627 33c multicolored .65 .25

ADOPTION

Stick Figures — A2628

Serpentine Die Cut 11½

2000, May 10

Self-Adhesive

3398 A2628 33c multicolored .65 .25
- *a.* Die cutting omitted, pair *2,500.*

See note after No. 1549.

YOUTH TEAM SPORTS

A2629

A2630

A2631

A2632

2000, May 27 ***Perf. 11***

3399 A2629 33c Basketball .70 .25
3400 A2630 33c Football .70 .25
3401 A2631 33c Soccer .70 .25
3402 A2632 33c Baseball .70 .25
- *a.* Block or strip of 4, #3399-3402 2.80 1.75

THE STARS AND STRIPES

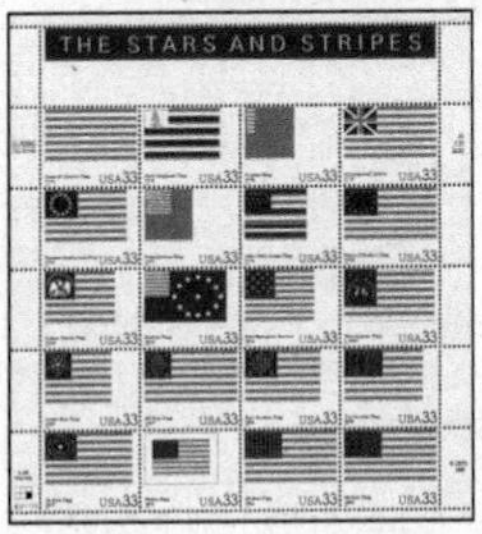

A2633

Designs: a, Sons of Liberty Flag, 1775. b, New England Flag, 1775. c, Forster Flag, 1775. d, Continental Colors, 1776. e, Francis Hopkinson Flag, 1777. f, Brandywine Flag, 1777. g, John Paul Jones Flag, 1779. h, Pierre L'Enfant Flag, 1783. i, Indian Peace Flag, 1803. j, Easton Flag, 1814. k, Star-Spangled Banner, 1814. l, Bennington Flag, c. 1820. m, Great Star Flag, 1837. n, 29-Star Flag, 1847. o, Fort Sumter Flag, 1861. p, Centennial Flag, 1876. q, 38-Star Flag, 1877. r, Peace Flag, 1891. s, 48-Star Flag, 1912. t, 50-Star Flag, 1960.

2000, June 14 ***Perf. 10½x11***

3403 A2633 Pane of 20 15.00 11.00
- *a.-t.* 33c any single .75 .50

BERRIES

Blueberries
A2634

Strawberries
A2635

Blackberries
A2636

Raspberries
A2637

See designs A2550-A2553.

PHOTOGRAVURE
COIL STAMPS

Serpentine Die Cut 8½ Horiz.

2000, June 16 **Tagged**

Self-Adhesive

3404 A2634 33c multicolored 3.50 .25
3405 A2635 33c multicolored 3.50 .25
3406 A2636 33c multicolored 3.50 .25
3407 A2637 33c multicolored 3.50 .25
- *a.* Strip of 4, #3404-3407 15.00

Nos. 3404-3407 are linerless coils issued without backing paper. The adhesive is strong and can remove the ink from stamps in the roll.

LEGENDS OF BASEBALL

A2638

Designs: a, Jackie Robinson. b, Eddie Collins. c, Christy Mathewson. d, Ty Cobb. e, George Sisler. f, Rogers Hornsby. g, Mickey Cochrane. h, Babe Ruth. i, Walter Johnson. j, Roberto Clemente. k, Lefty Grove. l, Tris Speaker. m, Cy Young. n, Jimmie Foxx. o, Pie Traynor. p, Satchel Paige. q, Honus Wagner. r, Josh Gibson. s, Dizzy Dean. t, Lou Gehrig.

LITHOGRAPHED

Serpentine Die Cut 11¼

2000, July 6

Self-Adhesive

3408 A2638 Pane of 20 15.00
- *a.-t.* 33c any single .75 .50

SPACE

Souvenir Sheets

A2639

A2640

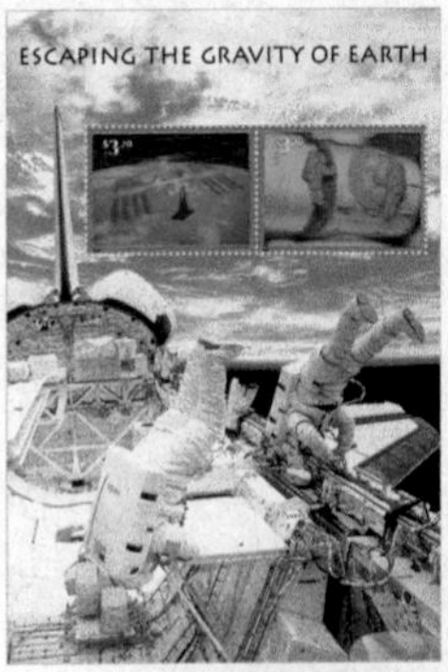

A2641

A2642

A2643

Designs: No. 3409: a, Hubble Space Telescope. b, Radio interferometer very large array, New Mexico. c, Optical and infrared telescopes, Keck Observatory, Hawaii. d, Optical telescopes, Cerro Tololo Observatory, Chile. e, Optical telescope, Mount Wilson Observatory, California. f, Radio telescope, Arecibo Observatory, Puerto Rico.

No. 3410: a, Sun and corona. b, Cross-section of sun. c, Sun and earth. d, Sun and solar flare. e, Sun and clouds.

No. 3411: a, Space Shuttle and Space Station. b, Astronauts working in space.

PHOTOGRAVURE

2000 ***Perf. 10½x11***

3409 A2639 Sheet of 6 15.00 7.00
- *a.-f.* 60c any single 2.25 1.00

Perf. 10¾

3410 A2640 Sheet of 5 + label 17.50 10.00
- *a.-e.* $1 any single 3.00 1.75
- *f.* As No. 3410, imperf *2,000.*
- *g.* As No. 3410, with hologram from No. 3411b applied *1,500.*

Untagged

Photogravure with Hologram Affixed

Perf. 10½, 10¾ (#3412)

3411 A2641 Sheet of 2 22.50 10.00
- *a.-b.* $3.20 any single 10.00 4.00
- *c.* Hologram omitted on right stamp —

3412 A2642 multicolored 40.00 17.50
- *a.* $11.75 single 35.00 15.00
- *b.* Hologram omitted —
- *c.* Hologram omitted on No. 3412 in uncut sheet of 5 panes —

3413 A2643 multicolored 40.00 17.50
- *a.* $11.75 single 35.00 15.00
- *b.* Double hologram *3,500.*
- *c.* Double hologram on No. 3413 in uncut sheet of 5 panes —
- *d.* Hologram omitted on No. 3413 in uncut sheet of 5 panes —

Nos. 3409-3413 (5) 135.00 62.00

Issued: No. 3409, 7/10; No. 3410, 7/11; No. 3411, 7/9; No. 3412, 7/7; No. 3413, 7/8.

The holograms on Nos. 3411-3413 scratch easily. Values are for examples with minimal scratches. Examples without scratches are worth more.

Warning: Soaking in water may affect holographic images.

STAMPIN' THE FUTURE CHILDREN'S STAMP DESIGN CONTEST WINNERS

by Zachary Canter — A2644

by Sarah Lipsey — A2645

by Morgan Hill — A2646

by Ashley Young — A2647

LITHOGRAPHED

Serpentine Die Cut 11¼

2000, July 13

Self-Adhesive

3414 A2644 33c multicolored .65 .30
3415 A2645 33c multicolored .65 .30
3416 A2646 33c multicolored .65 .30
3417 A2647 33c multicolored .65 .30
a. Horiz. strip of 4, #3414-3417 2.60

DISTINGUISHED AMERICANS

Gen. Joseph W. Stilwell A2650

Wilma Rudolph (1940-94), Athlete A2652

Sen. Claude Pepper A2656

Sen. Margaret Chase Smith (1897-1995) A2657

James A. Michener (1907-97), Author — A2657a

Dr. Jonas Salk (1914-95), Polio Vaccine Pioneer A2658

Harriet Beecher Stowe (1811-96), Author A2660

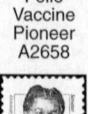

Sen. Hattie Caraway (1878-1950) — A2661

Edward Trudeau (1848-1915), Phthisiologist — A2661b

Mary Lasker (1900-94), Philanthropist — A2661c

Edna Ferber (1887-1968), Writer A2662

Edna Ferber (With Curving Shoulder) A2663

Dr. Albert Sabin (1906-93), Polio Vaccine Pioneer — A2664

LITHOGRAPHED & ENGRAVED, LITHOGRAPHED (#3427A, 3432A, 3432B)

Perf. 11 (#3420, 3426), Serpentine Die Cut 11¼x10¾ (#3422, 3430, 3432B), 11¼x11 (#3427A, 3428, 3432A, 3435), 11 (#3427, 3431), 11½x11 (#3432), 11x11¾ (#3433), 11¼ (#3434)

2000-09

Self-Adhesive (All Except #3420, 3426)

3420 A2650 10c red & blk .30 .25
a. Imperf, pair *300.00*
3422 A2652 23c red & blk .45 .25
a. Imperf, pair *600.00*
3426 A2656 33c red & blk .65 .25
3427 A2657 58c red & blk 1.25 .25
b. Black (engr.) omitted *200.00*
3427A A2657a 59c multi 1.30 .25
c. Blue, magenta and yellow omitted *1,500.*
d. Blue and yellow omitted —

On No. 3427Ad, traces of magenta, where it would not normally appear, are present.

3428 A2658 63c red & blk 1.25 .25
a. Black (litho.) omitted *275.00*
3430 A2660 75c red & blk 1.50 .25
3431 A2661 76c red & blk 1.50 .25
3432 A2661 76c red & blk 4.00 2.00
3432A A2661b 76c multi 2.00 .25
3432B A2661c 78c multi 1.60 .25
3433 A2662 83c red & blk 1.70 .30
3434 A2663 83c red & blk 1.60 .30
3435 A2664 87c red & blk 1.75 .30

LITHOGRAPHED

BOOKLET STAMP

Serpentine Die Cut 11¼x10¾ on 3 Sides

Self-Adhesive

3436 A2652 23c red & blk .45 .25
a. Booklet pane of 4 1.80
b. Booklet pane of 6 2.70
c. As "a" & "b" in cplt booklet of 10 (No. BK279A), die cutting omitted and peel strip intact, P#P44 —
d. Booklet pane of 10 4.50
e. As "d," die cutting omitted — —

The backing on No. 3436b has a different product number (672900) than that found on the lower portion of No. 3436d (673000).

Issued: 10c, 8/24; 33c, 9/7; No. 3432, 2/21/01; No. 3433, 7/29/02; No. 3434, Aug. 2003; 23c, 7/14/04; 63c, 87c, 3/2/06; 58c, 75c, 6/13/07; 59c, No. 3432A, 5/12/08; No. 3432B, 5/15/09.

CALIFORNIA STATEHOOD, 150TH ANNIV.

Big Sur and Iceplant — A2668

PHOTOGRAVURE

2000, Sept. 8 ***Serpentine Die Cut 11***

Self-Adhesive

3438 A2668 33c multicolored 1.00 .25

DEEP SEA CREATURES

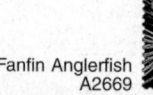

Fanfin Anglerfish A2669

Sea Cucumber A2670

Fangtooth A2671

Amphipod A2672

Medusa — A2673

2000, Oct. 2 Tagged ***Perf. 10x10¼***

3439 A2669 33c multicolored .75 .25
3440 A2670 33c multicolored .75 .25
3441 A2671 33c multicolored .75 .25
3442 A2672 33c multicolored .75 .25
3443 A2673 33c multicolored .75 .25
a. Vert. strip of 5, #3439-3443 3.75 2.00

LITERARY ARTS SERIES

Thomas Wolfe (1900-38), Novelist — A2674

LITHOGRAPHED

2000, Oct. 3 ***Perf. 11***

3444 A2674 33c multicolored .65 .25

WHITE HOUSE, 200TH ANNIV.

A2675

Serpentine Die Cut 11¼

2000, Oct. 18

Self-Adhesive

3445 A2675 33c multicolored 1.00 .25

LEGENDS OF HOLLYWOOD

Edward G. Robinson (1893-1973), Actor — A2676

PHOTOGRAVURE

2000, Oct. 24 ***Perf. 11***

3446 A2676 33c multicolored 1.60 .25

Perforations in corner of each stamp are star-shaped.

New York Public Library Lion — A2677

PHOTOGRAVURE

COIL STAMP

Serpentine Die Cut 11½ Vert.

2000, Nov. 9 **Untagged**

Self-Adhesive

3447 A2677 (10c) multi, "2000" year date .30 .25
a. "2003" year date .30 .25

See No. 3769.

Flag Over Farm — A2678

LITHOGRAPHED (#3448-3449), PHOTOGRAVURE (#3450)

2000, Dec. 15 ***Perf. 11¼***

3448 A2678 (34c) multicolored 1.00 .25

Self-Adhesive

Serpentine Die Cut 11¼

3449 A2678 (34c) multicolored 1.00 .25

Booklet Stamp

Self-Adhesive

Serpentine Die Cut 8 on 2, 3 or 4 Sides

3450 A2678 (34c) multicolored .85 .25
a. Booklet pane of 18 16.00
b. Die cutting omitted, pair —

A2679

PHOTOGRAVURE

Serpentine Die Cut 11 on 2, 3 or 4 Sides

2000, Dec. 15

Self-Adhesive

Booklet Stamp

3451 A2679 (34c) multicolored 1.10 .25
a. Booklet pane of 20 22.00
b. Booklet pane of 4 4.40
c. Booklet pane of 6 6.60
d. As "a," die cutting omitted —

Statue of Liberty — A2680

Coil Stamps

Perf. 9¾ Vert.

3452 A2680 (34c) multicolored 1.10 .25

Serpentine Die Cut 10 Vert.

Self-Adhesive

3453 A2680 (34c) multi, small date .70 .25
a. Die cutting omitted, pair *300.00*
b. Large date .75 .25

The date on No. 3453 is 1.4mm long, on No. 3453b 1.55mm long and darker in color.

A2681

A2682

A2683

Flowers — A2684

PHOTOGRAVURE

Serpentine Die Cut 10½x10¾ on 2 or 3 Sides

2000, Dec. 15

Booklet Stamps

Self-Adhesive

3454	A2681	(34c) purple & multi	1.10	.25
3455	A2682	(34c) tan & multi	1.10	.25
3456	A2683	(34c) green & multi	1.10	.25
3457	A2684	(34c) red & multi	1.10	.25
a.		Block of 4, #3454-3457	4.40	
b.		Booklet pane of 4, #3454-3457	4.40	
c.		Booklet pane of 6, #3456, 3457, 2 each #3454-3455	7.00	
d.		Booklet pane of 6, #3454, 3455, 2 each #3456-3457	7.00	
e.		Booklet pane of 20, 5 each #3454-3457 + label	22.50	

No. 3457e is a double-sided booklet pane, with 12 stamps on one side and eight stamps plus label on the other side.

Serpentine Die Cut 11½x11¾ on 2 or 3 Sides

3458	A2681	(34c) purple & multi	5.00	.25
3459	A2682	(34c) tan & multi	5.00	.25
3460	A2683	(34c) green & multi	5.00	.25
3461	A2684	(34c) red & multi	5.00	.25
a.		Block of 4, #3458-3461	20.00	
b.		Booklet pane of 20, 2 each #3461a, 3 each #3457a	55.00	
c.		Booklet pane of 20, 2 each #3457a, 3 each #3461a	90.00	

Nos. 3461b and 3461c are double-sided booklet panes, with 12 stamps on one side and eight stamps plus label on the other side.

Coil Stamps

Serpentine Die Cut 8½ Vert.

3462	A2683	(34c) green & multi	4.50	.25
3463	A2684	(34c) red & multi	4.50	.25
3464	A2682	(34c) tan & multi	4.50	.25
3465	A2681	(34c) purple & multi	4.50	.25
a.		Strip of 4, #3462-3465	20.00	

Lettering on No. 3462 has black outline not found on No. 3456. Zeroes of "2000" are rounder on Nos. 3454-3457 than on Nos. 3462-3465.

Statue of Liberty — A2685

Serpentine Die Cut 9¾ Vert.

2001, Jan. 7

Coil Stamp

Self-Adhesive

3466	A2685	34c multi	.70	.25

George Washington A2686

American Buffalo A2687

Designed by Carl Herrman (#3467, 3468), Richard Sheaff (#3468A).

Printed by Sterling Sommer for Ashton-Potter (USA) Ltd. (#3467), Avery Dennison (#3468), Banknote Corporation of America (#3468A).

Sheets of 400 in four panes of 100 (#3467), Sheets of 200 in 10 panes of 20 (#3468), Sheets of 120 in six panes of 20 (#3468A)

Self-Adhesive (#3468-3468A)

2001 ***Perf. 11¼x11***

3467	A2687	21c multi	.50	.25

Serpentine Die Cut 11

3468	A2687	21c multi	.50	.25

Litho.

Serpentine Die Cut 11¼x11¾

3468A	A2686	23c green	.50	.25

Flag Over Farm — A2688

Photo.

Perf. 11¼

3469	A2688	34c multi	.75	.25

Serpentine Die Cut 11¼

3470	A2688	34c multi	1.00	.25

Eagle — A2696

Serpentine Die Cut 10¾

3471	A2696	55c multi	1.10	.25
3471A	A2696	57c multi	1.10	.25

Capitol Dome A2697

Washington Monument A2698

Serpentine Die Cut 11¼x11½

Litho.

Self-Adhesive (#3473)

3472	A2697	$3.50 multi	7.00	2.00
a.		Die cutting omitted, pair	*500.00*	
3473	A2698	$12.25 multi	22.50	10.00

COIL STAMPS

Self-Adhesive (#3475-3475A, 3477-3481)

Photo.

Serpentine Die Cut 8½ Vert.

3475	A2687	21c multi	.50	.25
3475A	A2686	23c green	.75	.25

Compare No. 3475A ("2001" date at lower left) with No. 3617 ("2002" date at lower left).

Perf. 9¾ Vert.

3476	A2685	34c multi	.90	.25

Serpentine Die Cut 9¾ Vert.

3477	A2685	34c multi	.80	.25
a.		Die cutting omitted, pair	*65.00*	

No. 3477 has right angle corners and backing paper as high as the stamp. No. 3466 has rounded corners and is on backing paper larger than the stamp.

A2690

A2691

A2692

Flowers — A2693

Serpentine Die Cut 8½ Vert.

3478	A2690	34c green & multi	1.50	.25
3479	A2691	34c red & multi	1.50	.25
3480	A2692	34c tan & multi	1.50	.25
3481	A2693	34c purple & multi	1.50	.25
a.		Strip of 4, #3478-3481	6.00	

BOOKLET STAMPS

Litho.

Self-Adhesive

Serpentine Die Cut 11¼x11 on 3 Sides

3482	A2686	20c dk car	.55	.25
a.		Booklet pane of 10	5.50	
b.		Booklet pane of 4	2.20	
c.		Booklet pane of 6	3.30	

Serpentine Die Cut 10½x11 on 3 Sides

3483	A2686	20c dk car	5.50	1.25
a.		Booklet pane of 4, 2 #3482 at L, 2 #3483 at R	12.50	
b.		Booklet pane of 6, 3 #3482 at L, 3 #3483 at R	20.00	
c.		Booklet pane of 10, 5 #3482 at L, 5 #3483 at R	30.00	
d.		Booklet pane of 4, 2 #3483 at L, 2 #3482 at R	12.50	
e.		Booklet pane of 6, 3 #3483 at L, 3 #3482 at R	20.00	
f.		Booklet pane of 10, 5 #3483 at L, 5 #3482 at R	30.00	
g.		Pair, #3482 at L, #3483 at R	6.00	
h.		Pair, #3483 at L, #3482 at R	6.00	

Serpentine Die Cut 11¼ on 3 Sides

3484	A2687	21c multi	.60	.25
b.		Booklet pane of 4	2.40	
c.		Booklet pane of 6	3.60	
d.		Booklet pane of 10	6.00	

Serpentine Die Cut 10½x11¼

3484A	A2687	21c multi	5.50	1.50
e.		Booklet pane of 4, 2 #3484 at L, 2 #3484A at R	12.50	
f.		Booklet pane of 6, 3 #3484 at L, 3 #3484A at R	20.00	
g.		Booklet pane of 10, 5 #3484 at L, 5 #3484A at R	30.00	
h.		Booklet pane of 4, 2 #3484A at L, 2 #3484 at R	12.50	
i.		Booklet pane of 6, 3 #3484A at L, 3 #3484 at R	20.00	
j.		Booklet pane of 10, 5 #3484A at L, 5 #3484 at R	30.00	
k.		Pair, #3484 at L, #3484A at R	6.00	
l.		Pair, #3484A at L, #3484 at R	6.00	

Statue of Liberty — A2689

Photo.

Serpentine Die Cut 11 on 2, 3 or 4 Sides

3485	A2689	34c multi	.70	.25
a.		Booklet pane of 10	7.00	
b.		Booklet pane of 20	14.00	
c.		Booklet pane of 4	3.00	
d.		Booklet pane of 6	4.50	
e.		Die cutting omitted, pair (from No. 3485b)	—	
f.		As "e," booklet pane of 20	—	

Serpentine Die Cut 10½x10¾ on 2 or 3 Sides

3487	A2693	34c purple & multi	.85	.25
3488	A2692	34c tan & multi	.85	.25
3489	A2690	34c green & multi	.85	.25
3490	A2691	34c red & multi	.85	.25
a.		Block of 4, #3487-3490	3.50	
b.		Booklet pane of 4, #3487-3490	3.50	
c.		Booklet pane of 6, #3489-3490, 2 each #3487-3488	5.00	
d.		Booklet pane of 6, #3487-3488, 2 each #3489-3490	5.00	
e.		Booklet pane of 20, 5 each #3490a + label	20.00	

No. 3490e is a double-sided booklet pane, with 12 stamps on one side and eight stamps plus label on the other side.

Apple A2694

Orange A2695

Litho.

Serpentine Die Cut 11¼ on 2, 3 or 4 Sides

3491	A2694	34c multi	.70	.25
3492	A2695	34c multi	.70	.25
a.		Pair, #3491-3492	1.40	
b.		Booklet pane, 10 each #3491-3492	14.00	
c.		As "a," black ("34 USA") omitted	—	
d.		As "a," die cutting omitted	*1,100.*	
e.		As "b," die cutting omitted	*5,500.*	
f.		As "b," right four stamps yellow omitted	*3,500.*	

Serpentine Die Cut 11½x10¾ on 2 or 3 Sides

3493	A2694	34c multi	1.05	.25
3494	A2695	34c multi	1.05	.25
a.		Pair, #3493-3494	2.10	
b.		Booklet pane, 2 each #3493-3494	4.20	
c.		Booklet pane, 3 each #3493-3494, #3493 at UL	6.30	
d.		Booklet pane, 3 each #3493-3494, #3494 at UL	6.30	

Serpentine Die Cut 8 on 2, 3, or 4 Sides

3495	A2688b	34c multi	1.10	.25
a.		Booklet pane of 18	18.00	

Issued: Nos. 3472-3473, 1/29; Nos. 3469, 3476-3481, 3485, 3487-3490, 2/7; Nos. 3468, 3471, 3475, 3482, 3483, 2/22; Nos. 3470, 3491-3492, 3/6; Nos. 3493-3494, May; Nos. 3467, 3468A, 3471A, 3475A, 3483, 3484A, 9/20; No. 3495, 12/17.

See Nos. 3616-3619.

LOVE

Rose, Apr. 20, 1763 Love Letter by John Adams A2699

Rose, Apr. 20, 1763 Love Letter by John Adams A2700

Rose, Aug. 11, 1763 Love Letter by Abigail Smith (Abigail Adams in 1764) — A2701

LITHOGRAPHED

Serpentine Die Cut 11¼ on 2, 3 or 4 Sides

2001

Self-Adhesive

Booklet Stamps (Nos. 3496-3498)

3496	A2699	(34c) multi	1.10	.25
a.		Booklet pane of 20	22.00	
b.		Vert. pair, die cutting omitted between	—	

Serpentine Die Cut 11¼ on 2, 3 or 4 Sides

3497	A2700	34c multi	.90	.25
a.		Booklet pane of 20	18.00	
b.		Vertical pair, die cutting omitted between	—	

Size: 18x21mm

Serpentine Die Cut 11½x10¾ on 2 or 3 Sides

3498	A2700	34c multi	.85	.25
a.		Booklet pane of 4	3.50	
b.		Booklet pane of 6	5.10	

Serpentine Die Cut 11¼

3499	A2701	55c multi	1.10	.25

Issued: No. 3496, 1/19; others, 2/14.

See No. 3551.

CHINESE NEW YEAR

Year of the Snake — A2702

2001, Jan. 20 ***Perf. 11¼***

3500	A2702	34c multicolored	.75	.25

See Nos. 3895f, 3997f.

BLACK HERITAGE SERIES

Roy Wilkins (1901-81), Civil Rights Leader — A2703

Serpentine Die Cut 11½x11¼

2001, Jan. 24

Self-Adhesive

3501	A2703	34c blue	.70	.25

AMERICAN ILLUSTRATORS

A2704

No. 3502: a, Marine Corps poster "First in the Fight, Always Faithful," by James Montgomery Flagg. b, "Interlude (The Lute Players)," by Maxfield Parrish. c, Advertisement for Arrow Collars and Shirts, by J. C. Leyendecker. d, Advertisement for Carrier Corp. Refrigeration, by Robert Fawcett. e, Advertisement for Luxite Hosiery, by Coles Phillips. f, Illustration for correspondence school lesson, by Al Parker. g, "Br'er Rabbit," by A. B. Frost. h, "An Attack on a Galleon," by Howard Pyle. i, Kewpie and Kewpie Doodle Dog, by Rose O'Neill. j, Illustration for cover of True Magazine, by Dean Cornwell. k, "Galahad's Departure," by Edwin Austin Abbey. l, "The First Lesson," by Jessie Willcox Smith. m, Illustration for cover of McCall's Magazine, by Neysa McMein. n, "Back Home For Keeps," by Jon Whitcomb. o, "Something for Supper," by Harvey Dunn. p, "A Dash for the Timber," by Frederic Remington. q, Illustration for "Moby Dick," by Rockwell Kent. r, "Captain Bill Bones," by N. C. Wyeth. s, Illustration for cover of The Saturday Evening Post, by Norman Rockwell. t, "The Girl He Left Behind," by John Held, Jr.

PHOTOGRAVURE

Serpentine Die Cut 11¼

2001, Feb. 1

Self-Adhesive

3502 A2704 Pane of 20 19.00
a.-t. 34c any single .90 .60

DIABETES AWARENESS

A2705

LITHOGRAPHED

Serpentine Die Cut 11¼x11½

2001, Mar. 16

Self-Adhesive

3503 A2705 34c multicolored .65 .25

NOBEL PRIZE CENTENARY

Alfred Nobel and Obverse of Medals — A2706

LITHOGRAPHED & ENGRAVED

2001, Mar. 22 ***Perf. 11***

3504 A2706 34c multicolored .70 .25
a. Imperf, pair 500.00

See Sweden No. 2415.

PAN-AMERICAN EXPOSITION INVERT STAMPS, CENT.

A2707

No. 3505: Reproductions (dated 2001) of: a, #294a. b, #295a. c, #296a. d, Commemorative "cinderella" stamp depicting a buffalo.

LITHOGRAPHED (#3505d), ENGRAVED (others)

Perf. 12 (#3505d), 12½x12 (others)

2001, Mar. 29

Tagged (#3505d), Untagged (others)

3505 A2707 Pane of 7, #3505a-3505c, 4 #3505d 10.00 7.00
a. A109 1c green & black .75 .25
b. A110 2c carmine & black .75 .25
c. A111 4c deep red brown & black .75 .25
d. 80c red & blue 1.90 .35
e. As #3505, all colors except black (vignettes) missing on a.-c. (CM) *15,000.*

On No. 3505e, the green, carmine and deep red brown frames appear 4mm above Nos. 3505a-3505c on the pane.

GREAT PLAINS PRAIRIE

A2708

No. 3506 — Wildlife and flowers: a, Pronghorns, Canada geese. b, Burrowing owls, American buffalos. c, American buffalo, Black-tailed prairie dogs, wild alfalfa, horiz. d, Black-tailed prairie dog, American buffalos,. e, Painted lady butterfly, American buffalo, prairie coneflowers, prairie wild roses, horiz. f, Western meadowlark, camel cricket, prairie coneflowers, prairie wild roses. g, Badger, harvester ants. h, Eastern short-horned lizard, plains pocket gopher. i, Plains spadefoot, dung beetle, prairie wild roses, horiz. j, Two-striped grasshopper, Ord's kangaroo rat.

LITHOGRAPHED

Serpentine Die Cut 10

2001, Apr. 19

Self-Adhesive

3506 A2708 Pane of 10 10.00
a.-j. 34c Any single 1.00 .50

PEANUTS COMIC STRIP

Snoopy — A2709

Serpentine Die Cut 11¼x11½

2001, May 17

Self-Adhesive

3507 A2709 34c multicolored .80 .25

HONORING VETERANS

A2710

2001, May 23

Self-Adhesive

3508 A2710 34c multicolored .80 .25

FRIDA KAHLO (1907-54), PAINTER

Self-portrait — A2711

2001, June 21 ***Perf. 11¼***

3509 A2711 34c multicolored .70 .25

LEGENDARY PLAYING FIELDS

Ebbets Field — A2712

Tiger Stadium A2713

Crosley Field — A2714

Yankee Stadium A2715

Polo Grounds A2716

Forbes Field — A2717

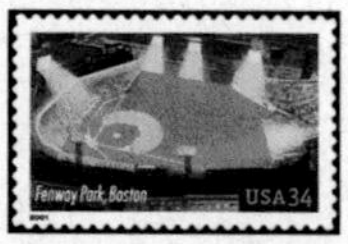

Fenway Park — A2718

Comiskey Park — A2719

Shibe Park — A2720

Wrigley Field — A2721

PHOTOGRAVURE

Serpentine Die Cut 11¼x11½

2001, June 27 **Self-Adhesive**

3510 A2712 34c multicolored .90 .60
3511 A2713 34c multicolored .90 .60
3512 A2714 34c multicolored .90 .60
3513 A2715 34c multicolored .90 .60
3514 A2716 34c multicolored .90 .60
3515 A2717 34c multicolored .90 .60
3516 A2718 34c multicolored .90 .60
3517 A2719 34c multicolored .90 .60
3518 A2720 34c multicolored .90 .60
3519 A2721 34c multicolored .90 .60
a. Block of 10, #3510-3519 9.00

ATLAS STATUE, NEW YORK CITY

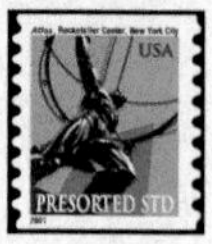

A2722

COIL STAMP

Serpentine Die Cut 8½ Vert.

2001, June 29 **Untagged**

Self-Adhesive

3520 A2722 (10c) multicolored .30 .25

No. 3520 is dated 2001. See No. 3770.

No. 3520 is known with extremely faint tagging, most likely from contamination in the paper-making process.

LEONARD BERNSTEIN (1918-90), CONDUCTOR

A2723

LITHOGRAPHED

2001, July 10 ***Perf. 11¼***

3521 A2723 34c multicolored .70 .25

WOODY WAGON

A2724

PHOTOGRAVURE

COIL STAMP

Serpentine Die Cut 11½ Vert.

2001, Aug. 3 **Untagged**

Self-Adhesive

3522 A2724 (15c) multicolored .30 .25

LEGENDS OF HOLLYWOOD

Lucille Ball (1911-89) — A2725

LITHOGRAPHED

2001, Aug. 6 ***Serpentine Die Cut 11***

Self-Adhesive

3523 A2725 34c multicolored 1.00 .25
a. Die cutting omitted, pair 700.00

AMERICAN TREASURES SERIES

Amish Quilts

Diamond in the Square, c. 1920 — A2726

Lone Star, c. 1920 — A2727

Sunshine and Shadow, c. 1910 A2728

Double Ninepatch Variation A2729

Serpentine Die Cut 11¼x11½

2001, Aug. 9

Self-Adhesive

3524 A2726 34c multicolored .70 .30
3525 A2727 34c multicolored .70 .30
3526 A2728 34c multicolored .70 .30
3527 A2729 34c multicolored .70 .30
a. Block or strip of 4, #3524-3527 2.80

CARNIVOROUS PLANTS

Venus Flytrap A2730

Yellow Trumpet A2731

Cobra Lily A2732

English Sundew A2733

PHOTOGRAVURE

Serpentine Die Cut 11½

2001, Aug. 23

Self-Adhesive

3528 A2730 34c multicolored .70 .25
3529 A2731 34c multicolored .70 .25
3530 A2732 34c multicolored .70 .25
3531 A2733 34c multicolored .70 .25
a. Block or strip of 4, #3528-3531 2.80

EID

"Eid Mubarak" — A2734

Serpentine Die Cut 11¼

2001, Sept. 1

Self-Adhesive

3532 A2734 34c multicolored .70 .25

See Nos. 3674, 4117, 4202, 4351, 4416.

ENRICO FERMI (1901-54), PHYSICIST

A2735

LITHOGRAPHED

2001, Sept. 29 *Perf. 11*

3533 A2735 34c multicolored .70 .25

THAT'S ALL FOLKS!

Porky Pig at Mailbox — A2736

PHOTOGRAVURE

2001, Oct. 1 *Serpentine Die Cut 11*

Self-Adhesive

3534 Pane of 10 #3534a 7.00
a. A2736 34c single .70 .25
b. Pane of 9 #3534a 6.25
c. Pane of 1 #3534a .70

Die cutting on No. 3534b does not extend through the backing paper.

3535 Pane of 10, #3535c, 9 #3535a 50.00
a. A2736 34c single 2.75
b. Pane of 9 #3535a 25.00
c. Pane of 1, no die cutting 25.00

Die cutting on No. 3535a extends through backing paper.

Nos. 3534b-3534c and 3535b-3535c are separated by a vertical line of microperforations.

CHRISTMAS

Virgin and Child, by Lorenzo Costa — A2737

Serpentine Die Cut 11½ on 2, 3 or 4 Sides

2001, Oct. 10

Self-Adhesive

Booklet Stamps (#3536, 3537a-3540a, 3537b, 3538b, 3539b, 3540e, 3541-3544)

3536 A2737 34c multicolored .75 .25
a. Booklet pane of 20 15.00

A2738

A2739

A2740

19th Century Chromolithographs of Santa Claus — A2741

Serpentine Die Cut 10¾x11

Black Inscriptions

3537 A2738 34c multi, large date .70 .25
a. Small date (from booklet pane) .90 .25
b. Large date (from booklet pane) 2.00 .25
3538 A2739 34c multi, large date .70 .25
a. Small date (from booklet pane) .90 .25
b. Large date (from booklet pane) 2.00 .25
3539 A2740 34c multi, large date .70 .25
a. Small date (from booklet pane) .90 .25
b. Large date (from booklet pane) 2.00 .25
3540 A2741 34c multi, large date .70 .25
a. Small date (from booklet pane) .90 .25
b. Block or strip of 4, #3537-3540 2.80
c. Block of 4, small date, #3537a-3540a 3.60
d. Booklet pane of 20, 5 #3540c + label 18.00
e. Large date (from booklet pane) 2.00 .25
f. Block of 4, large date, #3537b-3539b, 3540e 8.00
g. Booklet pane of 20, 5 #3540f + label 40.00

Nos. 3540d and 3540g are double-sided booklet panes, with 12 stamps on one side and eight stamps plus label on the other side.

Numerals "3" and "4" are distinctly separate on Nos. 3537-3540, and touching or separated by a slight hairline on the booklet pane stamps.

Designs of booklet stamps Nos. 3537a-3539a and 3537b-3539b are slightly taller than Nos. 3537-3539. Nos. 3540a and 3540e measure the same as No. 3540.

Serpentine Die Cut 11 on 2 or 3 Sides

Size: 21x18½mm

Green and Red Inscriptions

3541 A2738 34c multicolored .90 .25
3542 A2739 34c multicolored .90 .25
3543 A2740 34c multicolored .90 .25
3544 A2741 34c multicolored .90 .25
a. Block of 4, #3541-3544 3.60
b. Booklet pane of 4, #3541-3544 3.60
c. Booklet pane of 6, #3543-3544, 2 #3541-3542 5.40
d. Booklet pane of 6, #3541-3542, 2 #3543-3544 5.40
Nos. 3536-3544 (9) 7.15 2.25

JAMES MADISON (1751-1836)

Madison and His Home, Montpelier A2742

LITHOGRAPHED & ENGRAVED

2001, Oct. 18 *Perf. 11x11¼*

3545 A2742 34c green & black .70 .25

THANKSGIVING

Cornucopia — A2743

LITHOGRAPHED

Serpentine Die Cut 11¼

2001, Oct. 19

Self-Adhesive

3546 A2743 34c multicolored .70 .25

Hanukkah Type of 1996

PHOTOGRAVURE

2001, Oct. 21 *Serpentine Die Cut 11*

Self-Adhesive

3547 A2411 34c multicolored .70 .25

Kwanzaa Type of 1997

2001, Oct. 21

Self-Adhesive

3548 A2458 34c multicolored .70 .25

UNITED WE STAND

A2744

LITHOGRAPHED

BOOKLET STAMPS

Serpentine Die Cut 11¼ on 2, 3, or 4 Sides

2001, Oct. 24

Self-Adhesive

3549 A2744 34c multicolored .75 .25
a. Booklet pane of 20 15.00

PHOTOGRAVURE

Serpentine Die Cut 10½x10¾ on 2 or 3 Sides

2002, Jan.

Self-Adhesive

3549B A2744 34c multicolored .85 .25
c. Booklet pane of 4 3.40
d. Booklet pane of 6 5.10
e. Booklet pane of 20 18.00

No. 3549Be is a double-sided booklet pane, with 12 stamps on one side and eight stamps plus label on the other side.

"First day covers" of No. 3549B are dated Oct. 24, 2001.

COIL STAMPS Self-Adhesive

Serpentine Die Cut 9¾ Vert.

2001, Oct. 24

3550 A2744 34c multicolored 1.25 .25
3550A A2744 34c multicolored 1.75 .25

No. 3550 has right angle corners and backing paper as high as the stamp. No. 3550A has rounded corners, the backing paper larger than the stamp, and the stamps are spaced approximately 2mm apart.

Love Letters Type of 2001

LITHOGRAPHED

Serpentine Die Cut 11¼

2001, Nov. 19

Self-Adhesive

3551 A2701 57c multicolored 1.20 .25

WINTER OLYMPICS

Ski Jumping — A2745

Snowboarding A2746

Ice Hockey — A2747

Figure Skating — A2748

PHOTOGRAVURE

Serpentine Die Cut 11½x10¾

2002, Jan. 8

Self-Adhesive

3552 A2745 34c multicolored .70 .35
3553 A2746 34c multicolored .70 .35
3554 A2747 34c multicolored .70 .35
3555 A2748 34c multicolored .70 .35
a. Block or strip of 4, #3552-3555 2.80
b. Die cutting inverted, pane of 20 *100.00*
c. Die cutting omitted, block of 4 *825.00*

MENTORING A CHILD

Child and Adult — A2749

Serpentine Die Cut 11x10¾

2002, Jan. 10

Self-Adhesive

3556 A2749 34c multicolored .70 .25

BLACK HERITAGE SERIES

Langston Hughes (1902-67), Writer — A2750

LITHOGRAPHED

Serpentine Die Cut 10¼x10½

2002, Feb. 1

Self-Adhesive

3557 A2750 34c multicolored .70 .25
a. Die cutting omitted, pair *725.00*

Beware of pairs/panes with extremely faint die cutting offered as imperf errors.

HAPPY BIRTHDAY

A2751

PHOTOGRAVURE

2002, Feb. 8 *Serpentine Die Cut 11*

Self-Adhesive

3558 A2751 34c multicolored .75 .25

See Nos. 3695, 4079.

CHINESE NEW YEAR

Year of the Horse — A2752

LITHOGRAPHED

Serpentine Die Cut 10½x10¼

2002, Feb. 11

Self-Adhesive

3559 A2752 34c multicolored .75 .25
a. Horiz. pair, vert. die cutting omitted *5,000.*

See Nos. 3895g, 3997g.

U.S. MILITARY ACADEMY, BICENT.

Military Academy Coat of Arms — A2753

PHOTOGRAVURE

Serpentine Die Cut 10½x11

2002, Mar. 16

Self-Adhesive

3560 A2753 34c multicolored .75 .25

GREETINGS FROM AMERICA

Alabama A2754

Serpentine Die Cut 10¾

2002, Apr. 4

Self-Adhesive

3561	A2754	34c	Alabama	.70	.60
3562	A2755	34c	Alaska	.70	.60
3563	A2756	34c	Arizona	.70	.60
3564	A2757	34c	Arkansas	.70	.60
3565	A2758	34c	California	.70	.60
3566	A2759	34c	Colorado	.70	.60
3567	A2760	34c	Connecticut	.70	.60
3568	A2761	34c	Delaware	.70	.60
3569	A2762	34c	Florida	.70	.60
3570	A2763	34c	Georgia	.70	.60
3571	A2764	34c	Hawaii	.70	.60
3572	A2765	34c	Idaho	.70	.60
3573	A2766	34c	Illinois	.70	.60
3574	A2767	34c	Indiana	.70	.60
3575	A2768	34c	Iowa	.70	.60
3576	A2769	34c	Kansas	.70	.60
3577	A2770	34c	Kentucky	.70	.60
3578	A2771	34c	Louisiana	.70	.60
3579	A2772	34c	Maine	.70	.60
3580	A2773	34c	Maryland	.70	.60
3581	A2774	34c	Massachusetts	.70	.60
3582	A2775	34c	Michigan	.70	.60
3583	A2776	34c	Minnesota	.70	.60
3584	A2777	34c	Mississippi	.70	.60
3585	A2778	34c	Missouri	.70	.60
3586	A2779	34c	Montana	.70	.60
3587	A2780	34c	Nebraska	.70	.60
3588	A2781	34c	Nevada	.70	.60
3589	A2782	34c	New Hampshire	.70	.60
3590	A2783	34c	New Jersey	.70	.60
3591	A2784	34c	New Mexico	.70	.60
3592	A2785	34c	New York	.70	.60
3593	A2786	34c	North Carolina	.70	.60
3594	A2787	34c	North Dakota	.70	.60
3595	A2788	34c	Ohio	.70	.60
3596	A2789	34c	Oklahoma	.70	.60
3597	A2790	34c	Oregon	.70	.60
3598	A2791	34c	Pennsylvania	.70	.60
3599	A2792	34c	Rhode Island	.70	.60
3600	A2793	34c	South Carolina	.70	.60
3601	A2794	34c	South Dakota	.70	.60
3602	A2795	34c	Tennessee	.70	.60
3603	A2796	34c	Texas	.70	.60
3604	A2797	34c	Utah	.70	.60
3605	A2798	34c	Vermont	.70	.60
3606	A2799	34c	Virginia	.70	.60
3607	A2800	34c	Washington	.70	.60
3608	A2801	34c	West Virginia	.70	.60
3609	A2802	34c	Wisconsin	.70	.60
3610	A2803	34c	Wyoming	.70	.60
a.			Pane of 50, #3561-3610	35.00	

See Nos. 3696-3745.

LONGLEAF PINE FOREST

A2804

No. 3611 — Wildlife and flowers: a, Bachman's sparrow. b, Northern bobwhite, yellow pitcher plants. c, Fox squirrel, red-bellied woodpecker. d, Brown-headed nuthatch. e, Broadhead skink, yellow pitcher plants, pipeworts. f, Eastern towhee, yellow pitcher plants, Savannah meadow beauties, toothache grass. g, Gray fox, gopher tortoise, horiz. h, Blind click beetle, sweetbay, pine woods treefrog. i, Rosebud orchid, pipeworts, southern toad, yellow pitcher plants. j, Grass-pink orchid, yellow-sided skimmer, pipeworts, yellow pitcher plants, horiz.

Serpentine Die Cut 10½x10¾, 10¾x10½

2002, Apr. 26

Self-Adhesive

3611 A2804 Pane of 10 19.00
a.-j. 34c Any single 1.90 .50
k. As No. 3611, die cutting omitted *2,500.*

AMERICAN DESIGN SERIES

Toleware Coffeepot — A2805

PHOTOGRAVURE

COIL STAMP

Perf. 9¾ Vert.

2002, May 31 **Untagged**

3612 A2805 5c multicolored .30 .25
a. Imperf, pair 1,200.

No. 3612a is valued with disturbed gum. It is also known without gum and is valued only slightly less thus.

See Nos. 3756-3756A.

Star — A2806

LITHOGRAPHED

Serpentine Die Cut 11

2002, June 7 **Untagged**

Self-Adhesive (#3613-3614)

Year at Lower Left

3613 A2806 3c red, blue & black .30 .25
a. Die cutting omitted, pair —

PHOTOGRAVURE

Serpentine Die Cut 10

Year at Lower Right

Untagged

3614 A2806 3c red, blue & black .30 .25

Coil Stamp

Perf. 9¾ Vert.

Year at Lower Left

Untagged

3615 A2806 3c red, blue & black .30 .25

Washington Type of 2001

LITHOGRAPHED, PHOTOGRAVURE (#3617)

2002, June 7 ***Perf. 11¼***

3616 A2686 23c green .50 .25

Self-Adhesive

Coil Stamp

Serpentine Die Cut 8½ Vert.

3617 A2686 23c gray green .45 .25
a. Die cutting omitted, pair 500.00

Compare No. 3617 ("2002" date at lower left) with No. 3475A ("2001" date at lower left).

LITHOGRAPHED

Booklet Stamps

Serpentine Die Cut 11¼x11 on 3 Sides

3618 A2686 23c green .50 .25
a. Booklet pane of 4 2.00
b. Booklet pane of 6 3.00
c. Booklet pane of 10 5.00
d. Nos. 3619c and 3619d, in bklt. of 10 (#BK289A), imperf. vert. btwn. on both panes *1,100.*

Serpentine Die Cut 10½x11 on 3 Sides

3619 A2686 23c green 4.50 1.75
a. Booklet pane of 4, 2 #3619 at L, 2 #3618 at R 10.00
b. Booklet pane of 6, 3 #3619 at L, 3 #3618 at R 15.00
c. Booklet pane of 4, 2 #3618 at L, 2 #3619 at R 10.00
d. Booklet pane of 6, 3 #3618 at L, 3 #3619 at R 15.00
e. Booklet pane of 10, 5 #3619 at L, 5#3618 at R 27.50
f. Booklet pane of 10, 5 #3618 at L, 5 #3619 at R 27.50
g. Pair, #3619 at L, #3618 at R 5.00
h. Pair, #3618 at L, #3619 at R 5.00

See Nos. 3468A, 3475A, 3482-3483, 3819.

Flag — A2807

LITHOGRAPHED

2002, June 7 ***Perf. 11¼x11***

3620 A2807 (37c) multicolored 1.10 .25

LITHOGRAPHED, PHOTOGRAVURE (#3622)

Self-Adhesive

Serpentine Die Cut 11¼x11

3621 A2807 (37c) multicolored 1.10 .25

Coil Stamp

Serpentine Die Cut 10 Vert.

3622 A2807 (37c) multicolored 1.10 .25
a. Die cutting omitted, pair *475.00*
b. Yellow omitted —

Booklet Stamps

Serpentine Die Cut 11¼ on 2, 3 or 4 Sides

3623 A2807 (37c) multicolored 1.10 .25
a. Booklet pane of 20 22.00

No. 3623 has "USPS" microprinted in the top red stripe of the flag.

Serpentine Die Cut 10½x10¾ on 2 or 3 Sides

3624 A2807 (37c) multicolored 1.10 .25
a. Booklet pane of 4 4.40
b. Booklet pane of 6 6.60
c. Booklet pane of 20 22.00

No. 3624 does not have a microprinted "USPS."

Serpentine Die Cut 8 on 2, 3 or 4 Sides

3825 A2807e(37c) multicolored 1.10 .25
a. Booklet pane of 18 19.00

Toy Mail Wagon A2808

Toy Locomotive A2809

Toy Taxicab A2810

Toy Fire Pumper A2811

PHOTOGRAVURE

Serpentine Die Cut 11 on 2, 3 or 4 Sides

2002, June 7

Booklet Stamps

Self-Adhesive

3626 A2808 (37c) multicolored 1.10 .25
3627 A2809 (37c) multicolored 1.10 .25
3628 A2810 (37c) multicolored 1.10 .25
3629 A2811 (37c) multicolored 1.10 .25
a. Block or strip of 4, #3626-3629 4.40
b. Booklet pane of 4, #3626-3629 4.40
c. Booklet pane of 6, #3627, 3629, 2 each #3626, 3628 6.60
d. Booklet pane of 6, #3626, 3628, 2 each #3627, 3629 6.60
e. Booklet pane of 20, 5 each #3626-3629 22.00

Flag — A2812

LITHOGRAPHED

2002-05 ***Perf. 11¼***

3629F A2812 37c multi .90 .25
g. Imperf, pair *100.00*

No. 3629F has microprinted "USA" in top red stripe of flag.

Serpentine Die Cut 11¼x11

Self-Adhesive (#3630, 3632-3637)

3630 A2812 37c multi .90 .25

No. 3630 has microprinted "USA" in top red stripe of flag.

COIL STAMPS

Perf. 9¾ Vert.

3631 A2812 37c multi .75 .25

Serpentine Die Cut 9¾ Vert.

3632 A2812 37c multi .75 .25
b. Die cutting omitted, pair 55.00 55.00

Serpentine Die Cut 10¼ Vert.

3632A A2812 37c multi .75 .25
f. Die cutting omitted, pair *250.00*
g. Vert. pair, horiz. die-cut slits omitted *750.00*

No. 3632A lacks points of stars at margin at left top, and was printed in "logs" of adjacent coil rolls that are connected at the top or bottom, wherein each roll could be separated from an adjacent roll as needed.

No. 3632 has "2002" date at left bottom. No. 3632A has "2003" date at left bottom.

Serpentine Die Cut 11¾ Vert.

3632C A2812 37c multi 1.50 .25

No. 3632C is the only 37c Flag coil stamp with a "2004" date at left bottom.

LITHOGRAPHED, PHOTOGRAVURE (#3633)

Serpentine Die Cut 8½ Vert.

3633 A2812 37c multi .75 .25
3633A A2812 37c multi 2.25 .25

No. 3633A has right angle corners and backing paper as high as the stamp, and is dated "2003." No. 3633 is dated "2002," has rounded corners, the backing paper larger than the stamp, and the stamps are spaced approximately 2mm apart.

Serpentine Die Cut 9½ Vert.

3633B A2812 37c multi 9.00 .25

No. 3633B has microprinted "USA" in top red stripe of flag, and has "2005" date at bottom left.

LITHOGRAPHED, PHOTOGRAVURE (#3634, 3636, 3636D)

Booklet Stamps

Serpentine Die Cut 11.1 on 3 Sides (#3634)

3634 A2812 37c multi, large "2002" year date .75 .25
a. Booklet pane of 10 7.50
b. Small "2003" date, die cut 11 .75 .25
c. Booklet pane, 4 #3634b 3.00
d. Booklet pane, 6 #3634b 4.50
e. As #3634, die cut 11.3 1.00 .25
f. As "e," booklet pane of 10 10.00

Serpentine Die Cut 11.3 on 2, 3 or 4 Sides

3635 A2812 37c multi .75 .25
a. Booklet pane of 20 15.00
b. Black omitted *3,000.*

No. 3635 has "USPS" microprinted in the top red flag stripe and has a small "2002" year date.

Serpentine Die Cut 10½x10¾ on 2 or 3 Sides

3636 A2812 37c multi .75 .25
a. Booklet pane of 4 3.00
b. Booklet pane of 6 4.50
c. Booklet pane of 20 15.00
f. As "c," 11 stamps and part of 12th stamp on reverse printed on backing liner, the 8 stamps on front side die cutting omitted 1,700.

No. 3636c is a double-sided booklet pane, with 12 stamps on one side and eight stamps plus label on the other side.

Serpentine Die Cut 11¼x11 on 2 or 3 Sides

3636D A2812 37c multi 1.25 .25
e. Booklet pane of 20 25.00

No. 3636D lacks points of stars at margin at UL. No. 3636D is the only 37c Flag booklet stamp with a "2004" date at left bottom. No. 3636De is a double-sided booklet pane with 12 stamps on one side and eight stamps plus label on the other side.

LITHOGRAPHED

Serpentine Die Cut 8 on 2, 3 or 4 Sides

3637 A2812 37c multi .75 .25
a. Booklet pane of 18 13.50

Issued: Nos. 3630-3632, 3633, 3634, 3635-3636, 6/7; No. 3637, 2/4/03; No. 3633A, Apr. 2003; No. 3632A, 8/7/03; No. 3634b, 10/23/03; No. 3629F, 11/24/03; No. 3636D, July 2004; No. 3632C, 2004; No. 3633B, 6/7/05.

Toy Locomotive A2813

Toy Mail Wagon A2814

Toy Fire Pumper A2815

Toy Taxicab A2816

PHOTOGRAVURE

Serpentine Die Cut 8½ Horiz.

2002-03

Self-Adhesive

Coil Stamps

3638 A2813 37c multi 1.50 .25
3639 A2814 37c multi 1.50 .25
3640 A2815 37c multi 1.50 .25
3641 A2816 37c multi 1.50 .25
a. Strip of 4, #3638-3641 6.00

Serpentine Die Cut 11 on 2, 3 or 4 Sides

Booklet Stamps

3642 A2814 37c multi, "2002" year date .75 .25
a. Serpentine die cut 11x11¼ on 2 or 3 sides, dated "2003" .75 .25
3643 A2813 37c multi, "2002" year date .75 .25
a. Serpentine die cut 11x11¼ on 2 or 3 sides, dated "2003" .75 .25
3644 A2816 37c multi, "2002" year date .75 .25
a. Serpentine die cut 11x11¼ on 2 or 3 sides, dated "2003" .75 .25
3645 A2815 37c multi, "2002" year date .75 .25
a. Block or strip of 4, #3642-3645 3.00
b. Booklet pane of 4, #3642-3645 3.00
c. Booklet pane of 6, #3643, 3645, 2 each #3642, 3644 4.50
d. Booklet pane of 6, #3642, 3644, 2 each #3643, 3645 4.50
e. Booklet pane of 20, 5 each #3642-3645 15.00
f. Serpentine die cut 11x11¼ on 2 or 3 sides, dated "2003" .75 .25
g. Block of 4, #3642a, 3643a, 3644a, 3645f 3.00
h. Booklet pane of 20, 5 #3645g 15.00

No. 3645h is a double-sided booklet with 12 stamps on one side and 8 stamps plus label (booklet cover) on the other side. Nos. 3642a, 3643a, 3644a and 3645f have slightly narrower designs than Nos. 3642-3645.

Issued: Nos. 3638-3645, 7/26; Nos. 3642a, 3643a, 3644a, 3645f, 9/3/03.

Coverlet Eagle — A2817

LITHOGRAPHED

Serpentine Die Cut 11x11¼

2002, July 12

Self-Adhesive

3646 A2817 60c multicolored 1.25 .25

Jefferson Memorial A2818

Capitol Dome A2819

Serpentine Die Cut 11¼ (#3647, 3648), 11x10¾ (#3647A)

2002-03 **Tagged**

Self-Adhesive

3647 A2818 $3.85 multi 7.50 2.00
3647A A2818 $3.85 multi 9.00 2.00
3648 A2819 $13.65 multi 27.50 10.00

No. 3647 is dated 2002, and No. 3647A is dated 2003.

MASTERS OF AMERICAN PHOTOGRAPHY

A2820

No. 3649: a, Portrait of Daniel Webster, by Albert Sands Southworth and Josiah Johnson Hawes. b, Gen. Ulysses S. Grant and Officers, by Timothy H. O'Sullivan. c, "Cape Horn, Columbia River," by Carleton E. Watkins. d, "Blessed Art Thou Among Women," by Gertrude Käsebier. e, "Looking for Lost Luggage, Ellis Island," by Lewis W. Hine. f, "The Octopus," by Alvin Langdon Coburn. g, "Lotus, Mount Kisco, New York," by Edward Steichen. h, "Hands and Thimble," by Alfred Stieglitz. i, "Rayograph," by Man Ray. j, "Two Shells," by Edward Weston. k, "My Corsage," by James VanDerZee. l, "Ditched, Stalled, and Stranded, San Joaquin Valley, California," by Dorothea Lange. m, "Washroom and Dining Area of Floyd Burroughs' Home, Hale County, Alabama," by Walker Evans. n, "Frontline Soldier with Canteen, Saipan," by W. Eugene Smith. o, "Steeple," by Paul Strand. p, "Sand Dunes, Sunrise," by Ansel Adams. q, "Age and Its Symbols," by Imogen Cunningham. r, New York cityscape, by André Kertész. s, Photograph of pedestrians, by Garry Winogrand. t, "Bristol, Vermont," by Minor White.

PHOTOGRAVURE

Serpentine Die Cut 10½x10¾

2002, June 13

Self-Adhesive

3649 A2820 Pane of 20 22.50
a.-t. 37c Any single 1.00 .50
u. As No. 3649, die cutting omitted —

AMERICAN TREASURES SERIES

Scarlet and Louisiana Tanagers, by John James Audubon — A2821

Serpentine Die Cut 10¾

2002, June 27

Self-Adhesive

3650 A2821 37c multicolored 1.00 .25

HARRY HOUDINI (1874-1926), MAGICIAN

A2822

LITHOGRAPHED

Serpentine Die Cut 11¼

2002, July 3

Self-Adhesive

3651 A2822 37c multicolored .75 .25

ANDY WARHOL (1928-87), ARTIST

Self-Portrait — A2823

PHOTOGRAVURE

Serpentine Die Cut 10½x10¾

2002, Aug. 9

Self-Adhesive

3652 A2823 37c multicolored .75 .25

TEDDY BEARS, CENTENNIAL

Bruin Bear, c. 1907 — A2824

"Stick" Bear, 1920s — A2825

Gund Bear, c. 1948 — A2826

Ideal Bear, c. 1905 — A2827

Serpentine Die Cut 10½

2002, Aug. 15

Self-Adhesive

3653 A2824 37c multicolored 1.00 .30
3654 A2825 37c multicolored 1.00 .30
3655 A2826 37c multicolored 1.00 .30
3656 A2827 37c multicolored 1.00 .30
a. Block or vert. strip of 4, #3653-3656 4.00

LOVE

A2828

A2829

LITHOGRAPHED (#3657), PHOTOGRAVURE

Serpentine Die Cut 11 on 2, 3 or 4 Sides

2002, Aug. 16

Booklet Stamp (#3657)

Self-Adhesive

3657 A2828 37c multicolored .75 .25
a. Booklet pane of 20 15.00
b. As "a," silver ("Love 37 USA") missing on top five stamps (CM) *750.00*
c. Strip of 5, silver ("Love 37 USA") omitted on one stamp *1,000.*

Serpentine Die Cut 11

3658 A2829 60c multicolored 1.25 .25

Beware of examples of No. 3658 with gold ink fraudulently removed.

LITERARY ARTS

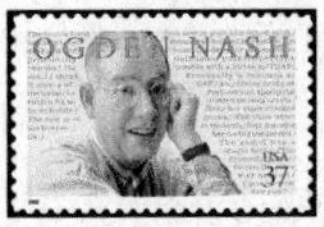

Ogden Nash (1902-71), Poet — A2830

PHOTOGRAVURE

Serpentine Die Cut 11

2002, Aug. 19

Self-Adhesive

3659 A2830 37c multicolored .75 .25

DUKE KAHANAMOKU (1890-1968), "FATHER OF SURFING" AND OLYMPIC SWIMMER

Kahanamoku and Surfers at Waikiki Beach — A2831

PHOTOGRAVURE

Serpentine Die Cut 11½x11¾

2002, Aug. 24

Self-Adhesive

3660 A2831 37c multicolored .75 .25

AMERICAN BATS

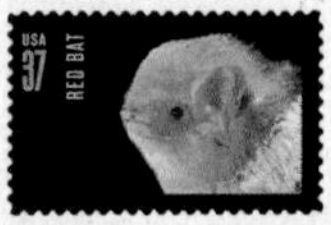

Red Bat — A2832

Leaf-nosed Bat — A2833

Pallid Bat — A2834

Spotted Bat — A2835

Serpentine Die Cut 10¾

2002, Sept. 13

Self-Adhesive

3661 A2832 37c multicolored .75 .30
3662 A2833 37c multicolored .75 .30
3663 A2834 37c multicolored .75 .30
3664 A2835 37c multicolored .75 .30
a. Block or strip of 4, #3661-3664 3.00

WOMEN IN JOURNALISM

Nellie Bly (1864-1922) A2836

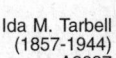

Ida M. Tarbell (1857-1944) A2837

Ethel L. Payne (1911-91) A2838

Marguerite Higgins (1920-66) A2839

Serpentine Die Cut 11x10½

2002, Sept. 14

Self-Adhesive

3665 A2836 37c multicolored 1.25 .35
3666 A2837 37c multicolored 1.25 .35
3667 A2838 37c multicolored 1.25 .35
3668 A2839 37c multicolored 1.25 .35
a. Block or horiz. strip of 4, #3665-3668 5.00

IRVING BERLIN (1888-1989), COMPOSER

Berlin and Score of "God Bless America" — A2840

Serpentine Die Cut 11

2002, Sept. 15

Self-Adhesive

3669 A2840 37c multicolored .75 .25

NEUTER AND SPAY

Kitten — A2841

Puppy — A2842

Serpentine Die Cut 10¾x10½

2002, Sept. 20

Self-Adhesive

3670	A2841	37c	multicolored	1.00	.25
3671	A2842	37c	multicolored	1.00	.25
a.			Horiz. or vert. pair, #3670-3671	2.00	

Hanukkah Type of 1996

2002, Oct. 10 *Serpentine Die Cut 11*

Self-Adhesive

3672	A2411	37c	multicolored	.75	.25

Kwanzaa Type of 1997

2002, Oct. 10 *Serpentine Die Cut 11*

Self-Adhesive

3673	A2458	37c	multicolored	.75	.25

Eid Type of 2001

2002, Oct. 10 *Serpentine Die Cut 11*

Self-Adhesive

3674	A2734	37c	multicolored	.75	.25

CHRISTMAS

Madonna and Child, by Jan Gossaert — A2843

LITHOGRAPHED

Serpentine Die Cut 11x11¼ on 2, 3 or 4 Sides

2002, Oct. 10

Self-Adhesive

Booklet Stamp

Design size: 19x27mm

3675	A2843	37c	multicolored	.75	.25
a.			Booklet pane of 20	15.00	

Compare to No. 3820, which measures 19½x28mm.

See No. 3820.

CHRISTMAS

Snowman with Red and Green Plaid Scarf A2844

Snowman with Blue Plaid Scarf A2845

Snowman with Pipe A2846

Snowman with Top Hat A2847

PHOTOGRAVURE

Serpentine Die Cut 11

2002, Oct. 28 Tagged

Self-Adhesive

3676	A2844	37c	multicolored	.90	.25
3677	A2845	37c	multicolored	.90	.25
3678	A2846	37c	multicolored	.90	.25
3679	A2847	37c	multicolored	.90	.25
a.			Block or vert. strip of 4, #3676-3679	3.75	

Snowman with Blue Plaid Scarf A2848

Snowman with Pipe A2849

Snowman with Top Hat A2850

Snowman with Red and Green Plaid Scarf A2851

COIL STAMPS

Serpentine Die Cut 8½ Vert.

3680	A2848	37c	multicolored	3.25	.25
3681	A2849	37c	multicolored	3.25	.25
3682	A2850	37c	multicolored	3.25	.25
3683	A2851	37c	multicolored	3.25	.25
a.			Strip of 4, #3680-3683	13.00	

BOOKLET STAMPS

Serpentine Die Cut 10¾x11 on 2 or 3 Sides

3684	A2844	37c	multicolored	1.25	.25
3685	A2845	37c	multicolored	1.25	.25
3686	A2846	37c	multicolored	1.25	.25
3687	A2847	37c	multicolored	1.25	.25
a.			Block of 4, #3684-3687	5.00	
b.			Booklet pane of 20, 5 #3687a + label	25.00	

No. 3687b is a double-sided booklet pane with 12 stamps on one side and eight stamps plus label on the other side.

Colors of Nos. 3684-3687 are deeper and designs are slightly smaller than those found on Nos. 3676-3679.

Serpentine Die Cut 11 on 2 or 3 Sides

3688	A2851	37c	multicolored	1.15	.25
3689	A2848	37c	multicolored	1.15	.25
3690	A2849	37c	multicolored	1.15	.25
3691	A2850	37c	multicolored	1.15	.25
a.			Block of 4, #3688-3691	4.60	
b.			Booklet pane of 4, #3688-3691	4.60	
c.			Booklet pane of 6, #3690-3691, 2 each #3688-3689	7.00	
d.			Booklet pane of 6, #3688-3689, 2 each #3690-3691	7.00	
			Nos. 3676-3691 (16)	26.20	4.00

LEGENDS OF HOLLYWOOD

Cary Grant (1904-86), Actor — A2852

Serpentine Die Cut 10¾

2002, Oct. 15

Self-Adhesive

3692	A2852	37c	multicolored	1.25	.25

Sea Coast — A2853

PHOTOGRAVURE

COIL STAMP

Serpentine Die Cut 8½ Vert.

2002, Oct. 21

Self-Adhesive

3693	A2853	(5c)	multicolored	.30	.25

See Nos. 3775, 3785, 3864, 3874-3875, 4348.

HAWAIIAN MISSIONARY STAMPS

A2854

No. 3694: a, 2c stamp of 1851 (Hawaii Scott 1). b, 5c stamp of 1851 (Hawaii Scott 2) c, 13c stamp of 1851 (Hawaii Scott 3). d, 13c stamp of 1852 (Hawaii Scott 4).

LITHOGRAPHED

2002, Oct. 24 Tagged *Perf. 11*

3694	A2854		Pane of 4	5.00	2.50
a.-d.		37c	Any single	1.25	.50

Happy Birthday Type of 2002

PHOTOGRAVURE

2002, Oct. 25 *Serpentine Die Cut 11*

Self-Adhesive

3695	A2751	37c	multicolored	.75	.25

GREETINGS FROM AMERICA TYPE OF 2002

Serpentine Die Cut 10¾

2002, Oct. 25

Self-Adhesive

3696	A2754	37c	Alabama	.75	.60
3697	A2755	37c	Alaska	.75	.60
3698	A2756	37c	Arizona	.75	.60
3699	A2757	37c	Arkansas	.75	.60
3700	A2758	37c	California	.75	.60
3701	A2759	37c	Colorado	.75	.60
3702	A2760	37c	Connecticut	.75	.60
3703	A2761	37c	Delaware	.75	.60
3704	A2762	37c	Florida	.75	.60
3705	A2763	37c	Georgia	.75	.60
3706	A2764	37c	Hawaii	.75	.60
3707	A2765	37c	Idaho	.75	.60
3708	A2766	37c	Illinois	.75	.60
3709	A2767	37c	Indiana	.75	.60
3710	A2768	37c	Iowa	.75	.60
3711	A2769	37c	Kansas	.75	.60
3712	A2770	37c	Kentucky	.75	.60
3713	A2771	37c	Louisiana	.75	.60
3714	A2772	37c	Maine	.75	.60
3715	A2773	37c	Maryland	.75	.60
3716	A2774	37c	Massachusetts	.75	.60
3717	A2775	37c	Michigan	.75	.60
3718	A2776	37c	Minnesota	.75	.60
3719	A2777	37c	Mississippi	.75	.60
3720	A2778	37c	Missouri	.75	.60
3721	A2779	37c	Montana	.75	.60
3722	A2780	37c	Nebraska	.75	.60
3723	A2781	37c	Nevada	.75	.60
3724	A2782	37c	New Hampshire	.75	.60
3725	A2783	37c	New Jersey	.75	.60
3726	A2784	37c	New Mexico	.75	.60
3727	A2785	37c	New York	.75	.60
3728	A2786	37c	North Carolina	.75	.60
3729	A2787	37c	North Dakota	.75	.60
3730	A2788	37c	Ohio	.75	.60
3731	A2789	37c	Oklahoma	.75	.60
3732	A2790	37c	Oregon	.75	.60
3733	A2791	37c	Pennsylvania	.75	.60
3734	A2792	37c	Rhode Island	.75	.60
3735	A2793	37c	South Carolina	.75	.60
3736	A2794	37c	South Dakota	.75	.60
3737	A2795	37c	Tennessee	.75	.60
3738	A2796	37c	Texas	.75	.60
3739	A2797	37c	Utah	.75	.60
3740	A2798	37c	Vermont	.75	.60
3741	A2799	37c	Virginia	.75	.60
3742	A2800	37c	Washington	.75	.60
3743	A2801	37c	West Virginia	.75	.60
3744	A2802	37c	Wisconsin	.75	.60
3745	A2803	37c	Wyoming	.75	.60
a.			Pane of 50, #3696-3745	37.50	

See Nos. 3561-3610.

BLACK HERITAGE SERIES

Thurgood Marshall (1908-93), Supreme Court Justice — A2855

LITHOGRAPHED

Serpentine Die Cut 11½

2003, Jan. 7

Self-Adhesive

3746	A2855	37c	black & gray	.75	.25

CHINESE NEW YEAR

Year of the Ram — A2856

Serpentine Die Cut 11½

2003, Jan. 15

Self-Adhesive

3747	A2856	37c	multicolored	.75	.25

See Nos. 3895h, 3997h.

LITERARY ARTS

Zora Neale Hurston (1891-1960), Writer — A2857

PHOTOGRAVURE

Serpentine Die Cut 10¾

2003, Jan. 24

Self-Adhesive

3748	A2857	37c	multicolored	.90	.25

AMERICAN DESIGN SERIES

Toleware Coffeepot Type of 2002 and

Tiffany Lamp A2866

Navajo Necklace A2858

LITHOGRAPHED, PHOTOGRAVURE (#3750, 3751)

Self-Adhesive (#3749-3757)

2003-14 *Serpentine Die Cut 11¼x11*

3749	A2866	1c	multi	.30	.25
3749A	A2866	1c	multi	.30	.25

No. 3749A has "USPS" microprinted on a white field high on the lamp stand, just below the shade and is dated "2008." No. 3749 has "USPS" microprinted lower on the lamp stand and not on a white field and is dated "2007."

Serpentine Die Cut 11

3750	A2858	2c	multi	.30	.25

A reprinting of No. 3750 shows the borders in a much brighter deep turquoise blue shade.

Serpentine Die Cut 11¼x11½

3751	A2858	2c	multi	1.00	.25

Serpentine Die Cut 11¼x11

With "USPS" Microprinting

3752	A2858	2c	multi	.30	.25

Serpentine Die Cut 11¼x10¾

3753	A2858	2c	multi	.30	.25

Silver Coffeepot — A2868

LITHOGRAPHED

Serpentine Die Cut 11¼x11

3754	A2868	3c	multi	.30	.25

Microprinted "USPS" on No. 3752 is found on top silver appendage next to and below the middle turquoise stone on the right side of the necklace. Microprinting on No. 3753 is found on the top silver appendage next to and below the lower turquoise stone on the left side of the necklace. Nos. 3751 and 3752 are dated "2006." No. 3753 is dated "2007."

Chippendale Chair — A2859

LITHOGRAPHED

Serpentine Die Cut 10¾x10¼

3755 A2859 4c multi .30 .25

LITHOGRAPHED, PHOTOGRAVURE (#3756)

Serpentine Die Cut 11¼x11¾

3756 A2805 5c multi .30 .25

Serpentine Die Cut 11¼x10¾

3756A A2805 5c multi .30 .25
 b. Die cutting omitted, pair *400.00*

No. 3756A has microprinting on the lower part of the coffeepot handle and is dated "2007." No. 3756 has no microprinting and is dated "2004." Existence of No. 3756A was reported in Aug. 2008.

No. 3756A is known printed with non-reactive cream-colored background ink and also with luminescent cream-colored ink that glows orange under both shortwave and longwave ultraviolet light.

American Clock — A2860

LITHOGRAPHED

3757 A2860 10c multi .30 .25
 a. Die cutting omitted, pair —

PHOTOGRAVURE

Perf. 9¾ Vert.

COIL STAMPS

3758 A2866 1c multi .30 .25
3758A A2866 1c multi .30 .25
3758B A2858 2c multi .30 .25
3759 A2868 3c multi .30 .25
3761 A2859 4c multi, dated "2007" at LL .30 .25
3761A A2859 4c multi, dated "2013" at UL .30 .25

On plate number singles, the plate number is at the lower right on No. 3761 and centered at bottom on No. 3761A.

LITHOGRAPHED, PHOTOGRAVURE (#3762)

3762 A2860 10c multi .30 .25
3763 A2860 10c multi .30 .25

No. 3763 is dated "2008," has a microprinted "USPS" as the middle "I" in "VIII," and has a network of beige dots on clock face. No. 3762 is dated "2006," lacks microprinting, and has network of gray dots on clock face.

Issued: No. 3757, 1/24; No. 3758, 3/1; No. 3755, 3/5/04; No. 3756, 6/25/04; No. 3750, 8/20/04; No. 3759, 9/16/05; Nos. 3751-3752, 12/8/05; No. 3762, 8/4/06; Nos. 3749, 3754, 3/16/07; No. 3753, 5/12/07; No. 3761, 7/19/07; No. 3749A, 3/7/08; No. 3758A, 6/7/08; No. 3758B, 2/12/11; No. 3763, 7/15/08; No. 3756A, Aug. 2008.

This is an ongoing set. Numbers may change.

See No. 3612.

AMERICAN CULTURE SERIES

Wisdom, Rockefeller Center, New York City — A2875

LITHOGRAPHED

Serpentine Die Cut 11¼x11

2003, Feb. 28

Self-Adhesive

3766 A2875 $1 multicolored 2.00 .40
 a. Dated "2008" 2.00 .40

New York Public Library Lion Type of 2000

PHOTOGRAVURE

COIL STAMP

Perf. 9¾ Vert.

2003, Feb. 4 Untagged

3769 A2677 (10c) multicolored .30 .25

Atlas Statue Type of 2001

PHOTOGRAVURE

Serpentine Die Cut 11 Vert.

2003, Oct. Untagged

Coil Stamp

Self-Adhesive

3770 A2722 (10c) multicolored .30 .25

No. 3770 is dated 2003.

See No. 3520.

SPECIAL OLYMPICS

Athlete with Medal — A2879

Serpentine Die Cut 11

2003, Feb. 13

Self-Adhesive

3771 A2879 80c multicolored 1.60 .35

AMERICAN FILMMAKING: BEHIND THE SCENES

A2880

No. 3772: a, Screenwriting (segment of script from *Gone With the Wind*). b, Directing (John Cassavetes). c, Costume design (Edith Head). d, Music (Max Steiner working on score). e, Makeup (Jack Pierce working on Boris Karloff's makeup for *Frankenstein*). f, Art direction (Perry Ferguson working on sketch for *Citizen Kane*). g, Cinematography (Paul Hill, assistant cameraman for *Nagana*). h, Film editing (J. Watson Webb editing *The Razor's Edge*). i, Special effects (Mark Siegel working on model for *E.T. The Extra-Terrestrial*). j, Sound (Gary Summers works on control panel).

Serpentine Die Cut 11 Horiz.

2003, Feb. 25

Self-Adhesive

3772 A2880 Pane of 10 12.00
 a.-j. 37c Any single 1.20 .50

OHIO STATEHOOD BICENTENNIAL

Aerial View of Farm Near Marietta — A2881

LITHOGRAPHED

Serpentine Die Cut 11¾x11½

2003, Mar. 1

Self-Adhesive

3773 A2881 37c multicolored .75 .25

PELICAN ISLAND NATIONAL WILDLIFE REFUGE, CENT.

Brown Pelican — A2882

Serpentine Die Cut 12x11½

2003, Mar. 14

Self-Adhesive

3774 A2882 37c multicolored .75 .25

Sea Coast Type of 2002

PHOTOGRAVURE

COIL STAMP

Perf. 9¾ Vert.

2003, Mar. 19 Untagged

3775 A2853 (5c) multicolored .30 .25

See No. 3864. No. 3775 has "2003" year date in blue, dots that run together in surf area, and a distinct small orange cloud. No. 3864 has "2004" year date in black, rows of distinctly separated dots in surf area, and the small orange cloud is indistinct.

See Nos. 3693, 3785, 3864, 3874-3875, 4348.

OLD GLORY

Uncle Sam on Bicycle with Liberty Flag, 20th Cent. A2883

1888 Presidential Campaign Badge A2884

1893 Silk Bookmark A2885

Modern Hand Fan A2886

Carving of Woman with Flag and Sword, 19th Cent. — A2887

LITHOGRAPHED

BOOKLET STAMPS

Serpentine Die Cut 10x9¾

2003, Apr. 3

Self-Adhesive

3776 A2883 37c multicolored .75 .50
3777 A2884 37c multicolored .75 .50
3778 A2885 37c multicolored .75 .50
3779 A2886 37c multicolored .75 .50
3780 A2887 37c multicolored .75 .50
 a. Horiz. strip of 5, #3776-3780 3.75
 b. Booklet pane, 2 #3780a 7.50

Nos. 3776-3780 were issued in booklets containing two No. 3780b, each with a different backing.

CESAR E. CHAVEZ (1927-93), LABOR ORGANIZER

A2888

Serpentine Die Cut 11¾x11½

2003, Apr. 23

Self-Adhesive

3781 A2888 37c multicolored .75 .25

LOUISIANA PURCHASE, BICENTENNIAL

English Translation of Treaty, Map of U.S., Treaty Signers — A2889

PHOTOGRAVURE

Serpentine Die Cut 10¾

2003, Apr. 30

Self-Adhesive

3782 A2889 37c multicolored .95 .40

FIRST FLIGHT OF WRIGHT BROTHERS, CENT.

Orville Wright Piloting 1903 Wright Flyer — A2890

2003, May 22 ***Serpentine Die Cut 11***

Self-Adhesive

3783 Pane of 10 9.00
 a. A2890 37c single .90 .40
 b. Pane of 9 #3783a 8.00
 c. Pane of 1 #3783a .90

PURPLE HEART

A2891

LITHOGRAPHED

2003 ***Serpentine Die Cut 11¼x10¾***

Self-Adhesive

3784 A2891 37c multi .75 .25
 b. Printed on back of backing paper —
 d. Die cutting omitted, pair —

Serpentine Die Cut 10¾x10¼

3784A A2891 37c multi .75 .25
 e. Die cutting omitted, pair 150.00

See Nos. 4032, 4164, 4263-4264, 4390.

Sea Coast Type of 2002

COIL STAMP

PHOTOGRAVURE

Serpentine Die Cut 9½x10

2003, June Untagged

Self-Adhesive

3785 A2853 (5c) multicolored .30 .25
 a. Serp. die cut 9¼x10 .30 .25

On No. 3785, the stamps are spaced on backing paper that is taller than the stamps.

One printing of No. 3785 has more of a scarlet shade in the sky than do other examples of Nos. 3785 and 3785a. Nos. 3785 and 3785a have black "2003" year date.

See Nos. 3693, 3775, 3864, 3874-3875, 4348.

LEGENDS OF HOLLYWOOD

Audrey Hepburn (1929-93), Actress — A2892

Serpentine Die Cut 10¾

2003, June 11

Self-Adhesive

3786 A2892 37c multicolored 1.25 1.00

SOUTHEASTERN LIGHTHOUSES

Old Cape Henry, Virginia A2893

Cape Lookout, North Carolina A2894

Morris Island, South Carolina A2895

Tybee Island, Georgia A2896

Hillsboro Inlet, Florida — A2897

Serpentine Die Cut 10¾

2003, June 13

Self-Adhesive

3787 A2893 37c multicolored 1.10 .30
3788 A2894 37c multicolored 1.10 .30
a. Bottom of "USA" even with top of upper half-diamond of lighthouse (pos. 2) 4.00 2.50
3789 A2895 37c multicolored 1.10 .30
3790 A2896 37c multicolored 1.10 .30
3791 A2897 37c multicolored 1.10 .30
a. Strip of 5, #3787-3791 5.50
b. Strip of 5, #3787, 3788a, 3789-3791 9.50

Eagle in Gold on Colored Background A2898

Colored Eagle on Gold Background A2899

COIL STAMPS
Dated "2003"

Serpentine Die Cut 11¾ Vert.

2003, June 26 **Untagged**

Self-Adhesive

3792 A2898 (25c) gray & gold .50 .25
3793 A2899 (25c) gold & red .50 .25
3794 A2898 (25c) dull blue & gold .50 .25
3795 A2899 (25c) gold & Prussian blue .50 .25
3796 A2898 (25c) green & gold .50 .25
3797 A2899 (25c) gold & gray .50 .25
3798 A2898 (25c) Prussian blue & gold .50 .25
3799 A2899 (25c) gold & dull blue .50 .25
3800 A2898 (25c) red & gold .50 .25
3801 A2899 (25c) gold & green .50 .25
b. Strip of 10, #3792-3801 5.00

Dated "2005"

Serpentine Die Cut 11½ Vert.

2005, Aug. 5 **Untagged**

3792d A2898 (25c) gray & gold .50 .25
3793d A2899 (25c) gold & red .50 .25
3794d A2898 (25c) dull blue & gold .50 .25
3795d A2899 (25c) gold & Prussian blue .50 .25
3796d A2898 (25c) green & gold .50 .25
3797d A2899 (25c) gold & gray .50 .25
3798d A2898 (25c) Prussian blue & gold .50 .25
3799d A2899 (25c) gold & dull blue .50 .25
3800d A2898 (25c) red & gold .50 .25
3801d A2899 (25c) gold & green .50 .25
e. Strip of 10, #3792d-3801d 5.00

See Nos. 3844-3853.

ARCTIC TUNDRA

A2900

LITHOGRAPHED

Serpentine Die Cut 10¾x10½, 10½x10¾

2003, July 2

Self-Adhesive

3802 A2900 Pane of 10 8.50
a.-j. 37c Any single .85 .50

No. 3802 — Wildlife and vegetation: a, Gyrfalcon. b, Gray wolf, vert. c, Common raven, vert. d, Musk oxen and caribou, vert. e, Grizzly bears, caribou. f, Caribou, willow ptarmigans. g, Arctic ground squirrel, vert. h, Willow ptarmigan, bearberry. i, Arctic grayling. j, Singing vole, thin-legged wolf spider, lingonberry, Labrador tea.

KOREAN WAR VETERANS MEMORIAL

Memorial in Snow — A2901

Serpentine Die Cut 11½x11¾

2003, July 27

Self-Adhesive

3803 A2901 37c multicolored .75 .25

MARY CASSATT PAINTINGS

Young Mother, 1888 A2902

Children Playing on the Beach, 1884 A2903

On a Balcony, 1878-79 A2904

Child in a Straw Hat, c. 1886 A2905

PHOTOGRAVURE

Serpentine Die Cut 10¾ on 2 or 3 Sides

2003, Aug. 7

Self-Adhesive

Booklet Stamps

3804 A2902 37c multicolored .75 .30
3805 A2903 37c multicolored .75 .30
3806 A2904 37c multicolored .75 .30
3807 A2905 37c multicolored .75 .30
a. Block of 4, #3804-3807 3.00
b. Booklet pane of 20, 5 #3807a 15.00

No. 3807b is a double-sided booklet with 12 stamps on one side and 8 stamps plus label (booklet cover) on the other side.

EARLY FOOTBALL HEROES

Bronko Nagurski (1908-90) A2906

Ernie Nevers (1903-76) A2907

Walter Camp (1859-1925) A2908

Red Grange (1903-91) A2909

Serpentine Die Cut 11½x11¾

2003, Aug. 8

Self-Adhesive

3808 A2906 37c multicolored .75 .35
3809 A2907 37c multicolored .75 .35
3810 A2908 37c multicolored .75 .35
3811 A2909 37c multicolored .75 .35
a. Block or strip of 4, #3808-3811 3.00

ROY ACUFF

Acuff (1903-92), Country Music Artist, and Fiddle — A2910

Serpentine Die Cut 11

2003, Sept. 13

Self-Adhesive

3812 A2910 37c multicolored .75 .25

DISTRICT OF COLUMBIA

Map, National Mall, Row Houses and Cherry Blossoms A2911

2003, Sept. 23

Self-Adhesive

3813 A2911 37c multicolored .80 .25

REPTILES AND AMPHIBIANS

Scarlet Kingsnake A2912

Blue-Spotted Salamander A2913

Reticulate Collared Lizard — A2914

Ornate Chorus Frog — A2915

Ornate Box Turtle — A2916

2003, Oct. 7

Self-Adhesive

3814 A2912 37c multicolored .80 .40
3815 A2913 37c multicolored .80 .40
3816 A2914 37c multicolored .80 .40
3817 A2915 37c multicolored .80 .40
3818 A2916 37c multicolored .80 .40
a. Vert. strip of 5, #3814-3818 4.00

Washington Type of 2002

PHOTOGRAVURE

2003, Oct. *Serpentine Die Cut 11*

Self-Adhesive

3819 A2686 23c gray green 2.00 .25

Christmas Type of 2002

LITHOGRAPHED

Serpentine Die Cut 11¼ on 2 or 3 Sides

2003, Oct. 23

Self-Adhesive

Booklet Stamp

Size: 19½x28mm

3820 A2843 37c multicolored .75 .25
a. Booklet pane of 20 15.00
b. Die cutting omitted, pair —

See No. 3675.

No. 3820a is a double-sided booklet with 12 stamps on one side and 8 stamps plus label (booklet cover) on the other side.

Compare to No. 3675, which measures 19x27mm.

CHRISTMAS

Reindeer with Pan Pipes A2917

Santa Claus with Drum A2918

Santa Claus with Trumpet A2919

Reindeer with Horn A2920

Reindeer with Pan Pipes A2921

Santa Claus with Drum A2922

Santa Claus with Trumpet A2923

Reindeer with Horn A2924

PHOTOGRAVURE

Serpentine Die Cut 11¾x11

2003, Oct. 23

Self-Adhesive

3821 A2917 37c multicolored 1.00 .25
3822 A2918 37c multicolored 1.00 .25
3823 A2919 37c multicolored 1.00 .25
3824 A2920 37c multicolored 1.00 .25
a. Block or strip of 4, #3821-3824 4.00
b. Booklet pane of 20, 5 each #3821-3824 20.00

No. 3824b is a double-sided booklet with 12 stamps on one side and 8 stamps plus label (booklet cover) on the other side.

BOOKLET STAMPS

Serpentine Die Cut 10½x10¾ on 2 or 3 Sides

3825 A2921 37c multicolored 1.00 .25
3826 A2922 37c multicolored 1.00 .25
3827 A2923 37c multicolored 1.00 .25
3828 A2924 37c multicolored 1.00 .25
a. Block of 4, #3825-3828 4.00
b. Booklet pane of 4, #3825-3828 4.00
c. Booklet pane of 6, #3827-3828, 2 each #3825-3826 6.00
d. Booklet pane of 6, #3825-3826, 2 each #3827-3828 6.00

Snowy Egret — A2925

COIL STAMPS
PHOTOGRAVURE

Serpentine Die Cut 8½ Vert.

2003-04 **Tagged**

Self-Adhesive

3829 A2925 37c multi .75 .25
b. Black omitted — —

LITHOGRAPHED

Serpentine Die Cut 9½ Vert.

3829A A2925 37c multi .85 .25

Serpentine Die Cut 11¼x11 on 2, 3 or 4 Sides

Booklet Stamps

PHOTOGRAVURE

3830 A2925 37c multi .75 .25
a. Booklet pane of 20 15.00
b. As "a," die cutting omitted *250.00*

With "USPS" Microprinted on Bird's Breast

Litho.

3830D A2925 37c multi 5.00 .25
e. Booklet pane of 20 *100.00*
f. Die cutting omitted, pair *150.00*
g. As "e," die cutting omitted *1,200.*

Issued: No. 3829, 10/24; No. 3830, 1/30/04; No. 3829A, Mar. 2004; No. 3830D, 2004.

Nos 3829, 3829A, 3830 and 3830D all have "2003" year dates even though some were issued in 2004.

PACIFIC CORAL REEF

A2926

No. 3831 — Marine life: a, Emperor angelfish, blue coral, mound coral, vert. b, Humphead wrasse, Moorish idol. c, Bumphead parrotfish, vert. d, Black-spotted puffer, threadfin butterflyfish, staghorn coral. e, Hawksbill turtle, palette surgeonfish. f, Pink anemonefish, magnificent sea anemone, vert. g, Snowflake moray eel, Spanish dancer. h, Lionfish, vert. i, Triton's trumpet. j, Oriental sweetlips, bluestreak cleaner wrasse, mushroom coral, vert.

PHOTOGRAVURE

Serpentine Die Cut 10¾

2004, Jan. 2

Self-Adhesive

3831 A2926 Pane of 10 9.00
a.-j. 37c Any single .90 .40

CHINESE NEW YEAR

Year of the Monkey — A2927

Serpentine Die Cut 10¾

2004, Jan. 13

Self-Adhesive

3832 A2927 37c multicolored .75 .25
a. Yellow omitted —

See Nos. 3895i, 3997i.

LOVE

Candy Hearts — A2928

BOOKLET STAMP

Serpentine Die Cut 10¾ on 2, 3 or 4 Sides

2004, Jan. 14

Self-Adhesive

3833 A2928 37c multicolored .75 .25
a. Booklet pane of 20 15.00

BLACK HERITAGE SERIES

Paul Robeson (1898-1976), Actor, Singer, Athlete and Activist — A2929

PHOTOGRAVURE

Serpentine Die Cut 10¾

2004, Jan. 20

Self-Adhesive

3834 A2929 37c multicolored .85 .25

THEODOR SEUSS GEISEL (DR. SEUSS)

Dr. Seuss (1904-91), Children's Book Writer, and Book Characters A2930

PHOTOGRAVURE

Serpentine Die Cut 10¾x10½

2004, Mar. 2

Self-Adhesive

3835 A2930 37c multicolored .85 .25
a. Die cutting omitted, pair *1,400.*

FLOWERS

White Lilacs and Pink Roses A2931

Five Varieties of Pink Roses A2932

LITHOGRAPHED (#3836), PHOTOGRAVURE
BOOKLET STAMP (#3836)

Serpentine Die Cut 10¾ on 2, 3 or 4 Sides

2004, Mar. 4

Self-Adhesive

3836 A2931 37c multicolored .75 .25
a. Booklet pane of 20 15.00

Serpentine Die Cut 11½x11

3837 A2932 60c multicolored 2.00 .25

UNITED STATES AIR FORCE ACADEMY, 50TH ANNIV.

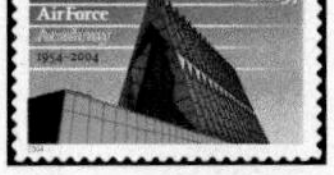

Cadet Chapel — A2933

PHOTOGRAVURE

Serpentine Die Cut 10¾

2004, Apr. 1

Self-Adhesive

3838 A2933 37c multicolored .75 .25

HENRY MANCINI

Henry Mancini (1924-94), Composer, and Pink Panther — A2934

2004, Apr. 13

Self-Adhesive

3839 A2934 37c multicolored .75 .25

AMERICAN CHOREOGRAPHERS

Martha Graham (1893-1991) A2935

Alvin Ailey (1931-89), and Dancers — A2936

Agnes de Mille (1909-93), and Dancers — A2937

George Balanchine (1904-83), and Dancers — A2938

LITHOGRAPHED

2004, May 4

Self-Adhesive

3840 A2935 37c multicolored .75 .35
3841 A2936 37c multicolored .75 .35
3842 A2937 37c multicolored .75 .35
3843 A2938 37c multicolored .75 .35
a. Horiz. strip of 4, #3840-3843 3.00
b. Strip of 4, die cutting omitted *300.00*
c. Pane of 20 misprinted and miscut to show 5 #3843 and half of 5 #3842 at left, lower center plate position diagram at center, and 10 blank stamps at right. —

Eagle Types of 2003

PHOTOGRAVURE

COIL STAMPS

Perf. 9¾ Vert.

2004, May 12 **Untagged**

3844 A2898 (25c) gray & gold 1.25 .25
3845 A2899 (25c) gold & green 1.25 .25
3846 A2898 (25c) red & gold 1.25 .25
3847 A2899 (25c) gold & dull blue 1.25 .25
3848 A2898 (25c) Prussian blue & gold 1.25 .25
3849 A2899 (25c) gold & gray 1.25 .50
3850 A2898 (25c) green & gold 1.25 .25
3851 A2899 (25c) gold & Prussian blue 1.25 .25
3852 A2898 (25c) dull blue & gold 1.25 .25
3853 A2899 (25c) gold & red 1.25 .25
a. Strip of 10, #3844-3853 12.50 —

LEWIS & CLARK EXPEDITION, BICENTENNIAL

Meriwether Lewis (1774-1809) and William Clark (1770-1838) On Hill — A2939

Lewis — A2940

Clark — A2941

LITHOGRAPHED & ENGRAVED

Serpentine Die Cut 10¾

2004, May 14

Self-Adhesive

3854 A2939 37c green & multi 1.10 .25

Booklet Stamps

Serpentine Die Cut 10½x10¾

3855 A2940 37c blue & multi .90 .45
3856 A2941 37c red & multi .90 .45
a. Horiz. or vert. pair, #3855-3856 1.80
b. Booklet pane, 5 each #3855-3856 9.00

Nos. 3855-3856 were issued in booklets containing two No. 3856b, each with a different backing. The booklets sold for $8.95.

ISAMU NOGUCHI (1904-88), SCULPTOR

Akari 25N A2942

Margaret La Farge Osborn A2943

Black Sun — A2944

Mother and Child — A2945

Figure (Detail) — A2946

LITHOGRAPHED

Serpentine Die Cut 10½x10¾

2004, May 18

Self-Adhesive

3857 A2942 37c black .90 .40
3858 A2943 37c black .90 .40
3859 A2944 37c black .90 .40
3860 A2945 37c black .90 .40
3861 A2946 37c black .90 .40
a. Horiz. strip of 5, #3857-3861 4.50

NATIONAL WORLD WAR II MEMORIAL

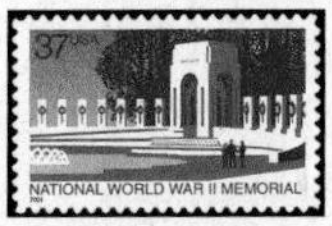

A2947

Serpentine Die Cut 10¾

2004, May 29

Self-Adhesive

3862 A2947 37c multicolored .75 .25

Scott values for used self-adhesive stamps are for examples either on piece or off piece.

OLYMPIC GAMES, ATHENS, GREECE

Stylized Runner — A2948

2004, June 9

Self-Adhesive

3863 A2948 37c multicolored .75 .25

Sea Coast Type of 2002

PHOTOGRAVURE
COIL STAMP

Perf. 9¾ Vert.

2004, June 11 **Untagged**

3864 A2853 (5c) multicolored .30 .25

No. 3864 has "2004" year date in black, rows of distinctly separated dots in surf area, and the small orange cloud is indistinct.

No. 3775 has "2003" year date in blue, dots that run together in surf area, and a distinct small orange cloud.

See Nos. 3693, 3775, 3785, 3874-3875, 4348.

THE ART OF DISNEY: FRIENDSHIP

Goofy, Mickey Mouse, Donald Duck
A2949

Bambi, Thumper
A2950

Mufasa, Simba
A2951

Jiminy Cricket, Pinocchio
A2952

LITHOGRAPHED

Serpentine Die Cut 10½x10¾

2004, June 23

Self-Adhesive

3865 A2949 37c multicolored 1.00 .30
3866 A2950 37c multicolored 1.00 .30
3867 A2951 37c multicolored 1.00 .30
3868 A2952 37c multicolored 1.00 .30
a. Block or vert. strip of 4, #3865-3868 4.00

U.S.S. CONSTELLATION

A2953

ENGRAVED

Serpentine Die Cut 10½

2004, June 30

Self-Adhesive

3869 A2953 37c brown .75 .25

R. BUCKMINSTER FULLER (1895-1983), ENGINEER

Time Magazine Cover Depicting Fuller, by Boris Artzybasheff — A2954

LITHOGRAPHED

Serpentine Die Cut 10½x10¾

2004, July 12

Self-Adhesive

3870 A2954 37c multicolored .75 .25

LITERARY ARTS

James Baldwin (1924-87), Writer — A2955

Serpentine Die Cut 10¾

2004, July 23

Self-Adhesive

3871 A2955 37c multicolored .75 .25
a. Die cutting omitted, pair *750.00*

AMERICAN TREASURES SERIES

Giant Magnolias on a Blue Velvet Cloth, by Martin Johnson Heade — A2956

PHOTOGRAVURE
BOOKLET STAMP

Serpentine Die Cut 10¾ on 2 or 3 Sides

2004, Aug. 12

Self-Adhesive

3872 A2956 37c multicolored .70 .25
a. Booklet pane of 20 15.00
b. Die cutting omitted, pair, in #3872a with foldover —

No. 3872a is a double-sided booklet pane with 12 stamps on one side and eight stamps plus label on the other side.

ART OF THE AMERICAN INDIAN

A2957

No. 3878: a, Mimbres bowl. b, Kutenai parfleche. c, Tlingit sculptures. d, Ho-Chunk bag. e, Seminole doll. f, Mississippian effigy. g, Acoma pot. h, Navajo weaving. i, Seneca carving. j, Luiseño basket.

Serpentine Die Cut 10¾x11

2004, Aug. 21

Self-Adhesive

3873 A2957 Pane of 10 25.00
a.-j. 37c Any single 2.50 .40

Sea Coast Type of 2002

LITHOGRAPHED
COIL STAMPS

Serpentine Die Cut 10 Vert.

2004-05 Untagged

Self-Adhesive

3874 A2853 (5c) multi, large "2003" year date .30 .25
a. Small "2003" year date ('05) .30 .25

Serpentine Die Cut 11½ Vert.

Untagged

3875 A2853 (5c) multi, "2004" year date .30 .25

On Nos. 3874, 3874a and 3875, the stamps are spaced on backing paper that is taller than the stamps.

See Nos. 3693, 3775, 3785, 3864, 4348.

LEGENDS OF HOLLYWOOD

John Wayne (1907-79), Actor — A2958

Serpentine Die Cut 10¾

2004, Sept. 9

Self-Adhesive

3876 A2958 37c multicolored .85 .25

SICKLE CELL DISEASE AWARENESS

Mother and Child — A2959

Serpentine Die Cut 11

2004, Sept. 29

Self-Adhesive

3877 A2959 37c multicolored .75 .25

CLOUDSCAPES

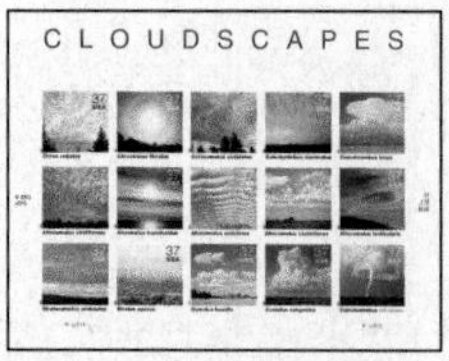

A2960

No. 3878 — Clouds: a, Cirrus radiatus. b, Cirrostratus fibratus. c, Cirrocumulus undulatus. d, Cumulonimbus mammatus. e, Cumulonimbus incus. f, Altocumulus stratiformis. g, Altostratus translucidus. h, Altocumulus undulatus. i, Altocumulus castellanus. j, Altocumulus lenticularis. k, Stratocumulus undulatus. l, Stratus opacus. m, Cumulus humilis. n, Cumulus congestus. o, Cumulonimbus with tornado.

2004, Oct. 4

Self-Adhesive

3878 A2960 Pane of 15 15.00
a.-o. 37c Any single 1.00 .50

CHRISTMAS

Madonna and Child, by Lorenzo Monaco — A2961

LITHOGRAPHED
BOOKLET STAMP

Serpentine Die Cut 10¾x11 on 2 or 3 Sides

2004, Oct. 14

Self-Adhesive

3879 A2961 37c multicolored .75 .25
a. Booklet pane of 20 15.00
b. As "a," die cutting omitted —

No. 3879a is a double-sided booklet pane with 12 stamps on one side and eight stamps plus label that serves as a booklet cover on the other side.

HANUKKAH

Dreidel — A2962

Serpentine Die Cut 10¾

2004, Oct. 15

Self-Adhesive

3880 A2962 37c multicolored .75 .25
a. Die cuts applied to wrong sides of stamp (hyphen-hole die cuts and wavy line on face, die cut 10¾ on reverse) — —

See Nos. 4118, 4219, 4372.

KWANZAA

People in Robes — A2963

Serpentine Die Cut 10¾

2004, Oct. 16

Self-Adhesive

3881 A2963 37c multicolored .75 .25

See Nos. 4119, 4220, 4373.

Moss Hart (1904-61), Playwright A2964

PHOTOGRAVURE

2004, Oct. 25 ***Serpentine Die Cut 11***

Self-Adhesive

3882 A2964 37c multicolored .75 .25

CHRISTMAS

Purple Santa Ornament
A2965

Green Santa Ornament
A2966

Blue Santa Ornament
A2967

Red Santa Ornament
A2968

Serpentine Die Cut 11½x11

2004, Nov. 16

Self-Adhesive

3883 A2965 37c purple & multi 1.00 .25
3884 A2966 37c green & multi 1.00 .25
3885 A2967 37c blue & multi 1.00 .25
3886 A2968 37c red & multi 1.00 .25
a. Block or strip of 4, #3883-3886 4.00
b. Booklet pane of 20, 5 #3886a blocks 20.00

Purple Santa Ornament
A2969

Green Santa Ornament
A2970

Blue Santa Ornament
A2971

Red Santa Ornament
A2972

Booklet Stamps

Serpentine Die Cut 10½x10¾ on 2 or 3 Sides

3887 A2969 37c purple & multi .90 .25
3888 A2970 37c green & multi .90 .25
3889 A2971 37c blue & multi .90 .25
3890 A2972 37c red & multi .90 .25
a. Block of 4, #3887-3890 3.60
b. Booklet pane of 4, #3887-3890 3.60
c. Booklet pane of 6, #3889-3890, 2 each #3887-3888 5.50
d. Booklet pane of 6, #3887-3888, 2 each #3889-3890 5.50

Serpentine Die Cut 8 on 2, 3 or 4 Sides

3891 A2970 37c green & multi 2.00 .25
3892 A2969 37c purple & multi 2.00 .25
3893 A2972 37c red & multi 2.00 .25
3894 A2971 37c blue & multi 2.00 .25
a. Block of 4, #3891-3894 8.00
b. Booklet pane of 18, 6 each #3891, 3893, 3 each # 3892, 3894 36.00
Nos. 3883-3894 (12) 15.60 3.00

No. 3886b is a double-sided booklet with 12 stamps on one side and 8 stamps plus label that serves as a booklet cover on the other side.

The design of No. 3894b shows ornaments in a wooden box. The pattern of the wooden box dividers creates three types of each design. Rows 1 and 4 are Type 1, with a top horizontal strip of frame extending from edge to edge while the bottom strip of frame stops at the design's width. Rows 2 and 5 are Type 2, with both top and bottom strips of frame stopping at the design's width. Rows 3 and 6 are Type 3, with the top strip of frame stopping at design's width while the bottom strip of frame extends from edge to edge. Each variety is equally common.

Chinese New Year Types of 1992-2004

PHOTOGRAVURE

Serpentine Die Cut 10¾

2005, Jan. 6

Self-Adhesive

3895 Double sided pane of 24, 2 each #a-l 18.00
- *a.* A2360 37c Rat .75 .40
- *b.* A2413 37c Ox .75 .40
- *c.* A2462 37c Tiger .75 .40
- *d.* A2535 37c Rabbit .75 .40
- *e.* A2602 37c Dragon .75 .40
- *f.* A2702 37c Snake .75 .40
- *g.* A2752 37c Horse .75 .40
- *h.* A2856 37c Ram .75 .40
- *i.* A2927 37c Monkey .75 .40
- *j.* A2067 37c Rooster .75 .40
- *k.* A2146 37c Dog .75 .40
- *l.* A2205 37c Boar .75 .40
- *m.* As No. 3895, die cutting missing on "a," "b," and "c" on reverse side (PS) *900.00*

No. 3895h has "2005" year date and is photogravure while No. 3747 has "2003" year date and is lithographed.

Stamps are on the right side of the front and on the left side of the reverse.

See Nos. 2720, 2817, 2876, 3060, 3120, 3179, 3272, 3370, 3500, 3559, 3747, 3832, 3997.

BLACK HERITAGE SERIES

Marian Anderson (1897-1993), Singer — A2973

2005, Jan. 27

Self-Adhesive

3896 A2973 37c multicolored .85 .25

RONALD REAGAN

Ronald Reagan (1911-2004), 40th President — A2974

2005, Feb. 9

Self-Adhesive

3897 A2974 37c multicolored .75 .25

See No. 4078.

LOVE

Hand and Flower Bouquet — A2975

BOOKLET STAMP

Serpentine Die Cut 10¾x11 on 2, 3 or 4 Sides

2005, Feb. 18

Self-Adhesive

3898 A2975 37c multicolored .75 .25
- *a.* Booklet pane of 20 15.00

NORTHEAST DECIDUOUS FOREST

A2976

No. 3899 — Wildlife: a, Eastern buckmoth, vert. b, Red-shouldered hawk. c, Eastern red bat. d, White-tailed deer. e, Black bear. f, Long-tailed weasel, vert. g, Wild turkey, vert. h, Ovenbird, vert. i, Red eft. j, Eastern chipmunk.

Serpentine Die Cut 10¾

2005, Mar. 3

Self-Adhesive

3899 A2976 Pane of 10 8.50
- *a.-j.* 37c Any single .85 .40

SPRING FLOWERS

Hyacinth A2977

Daffodil A2978

Tulip A2979

Iris A2980

LITHOGRAPHED

BOOKLET STAMPS

Serpentine Die Cut 10¾ on 2 or 3 Sides

2005, Mar. 15

Self-Adhesive

3900 A2977 37c multicolored .85 .30
3901 A2978 37c multicolored .85 .30
3902 A2979 37c multicolored .85 .30
3903 A2980 37c multicolored .85 .30
- *a.* Block of 4, #3900-3903 3.40
- *b.* Booklet pane of 20, 5 each #3900-3903 17.00
- *c.* As "b," die cutting omitted on side with 8 stamps —

No. 3903b is a double-sided booklet with 12 stamps on one side and 8 stamps plus label (booklet cover) on the other side.

LITERARY ARTS

Robert Penn Warren (1905-89), Writer — A2981

PHOTOGRAVURE

Serpentine Die Cut 10¾

2005, Apr. 22

Self-Adhesive

3904 A2981 37c multicolored .75 .25

EDGAR Y. "YIP" HARBURG

Harburg (1896-1981), Lyricist — A2982

LITHOGRAPHED

2005, Apr. 28

Self-Adhesive

3905 A2982 37c multicolored .75 .25

AMERICAN SCIENTISTS

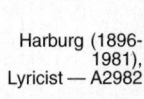

Barbara McClintock (1902-92), Geneticist A2983

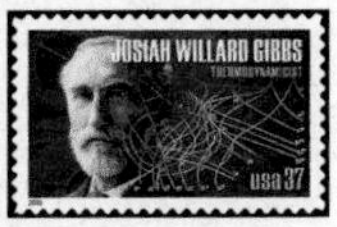

Josiah Willard Gibbs (1839-1903), Thermodynamicist A2984

John von Neumann (1903-57), Mathematician A2985

Richard Feynman (1918-88), Physicist A2986

2005, May 4

Self-Adhesive

3906 A2983 37c multicolored 1.00 .35
3907 A2984 37c multicolored 1.00 .35
3908 A2985 37c multicolored 1.00 .35
- *a.* Vert. pair, die cutting omitted, #3906 & 3908 —

3909 A2986 37c multicolored 1.00 .35
- *a.* Block or horiz. strip of 4, #3906-3909 4.00
- *b.* All colors omitted, tagging omitted, pane of 20 —
- *c.* As "a," printing on back of stamps omitted —
- *d.* Vert. pair, die cutting omitted, #3907 & 3909 —

On No. 3909b, the printing on the back of the pane and all die cutting is normal.

MODERN AMERICAN ARCHITECTURE

A2987

No. 3910 — Buildings: a, Guggenheim Museum, New York. b, Chrysler Building, New York. c, Vanna Venturi House, Philadelphia. d, TWA Terminal, New York. e, Walt Disney Concert Hall, Los Angeles. f, 860-880 Lake Shore Drive, Chicago. g, National Gallery of Art, Washington, DC. h, Glass House, New Canaan, CT. i, Yale Art and Architecture Building, New Haven, CT. j, High Museum of Art, Atlanta. k, Exeter Academy Library, Exeter, NH. l, Hancock Center, Chicago.

Serpentine Die Cut 10¾x11

2005, May 19

Self-Adhesive

3910 A2987 Pane of 12 11.00
- *a.-l.* 37c Any single .90 .50
- *m.* As No. 3910, orange yellow omitted *400.00* —

LEGENDS OF HOLLYWOOD

Henry Fonda (1905-82), Actor — A2988

Sheets of 180 in nine panes of 20

Serpentine Die Cut 11x10¾

2005, May 20

Self-Adhesive

3911 A2988 37c multicolored .90 .25

THE ART OF DISNEY: CELEBRATION

Pluto, Mickey Mouse A2989

Mad Hatter, Alice A2990

Flounder, Ariel A2991

Snow White, Dopey A2992

Serpentine Die Cut 10½x10¾

2005, June 30

Self-Adhesive

3912 A2989 37c multi .85 .30
3913 A2990 37c multi .85 .30
3914 A2991 37c multi .85 .30
3915 A2992 37c multi .85 .30
- *a.* Block or vert. strip of 4, #3912-3915 3.40
- *b.* Die cutting omitted, pane of 20 *5,500.* *1,400.*
- *c.* Printed on backing paper, pane of 20 —

On the unique used pane of No. 3915b, the outer selvage was removed by cutting.

ADVANCES IN AVIATION

Boeing 247 — A2993

Consolidated PBY Catalina — A2994

Grumman F6F Hellcat — A2995

Republic P-47 Thunderbolt A2996

Engineering and Research Corporation Ercoupe 415 — A2997

Lockheed P-80 Shooting Star — A2998

Consolidated B-24 Liberator A2999

Boeing B-29 Superfortress A3000

Beechcraft 35 Bonanza A3001

Northrop YB-49 Flying Wing — A3002

Serpentine Die Cut 10¾x10½

2005, July 29

Self-Adhesive

3916 A2993 37c multicolored .80 .40
3917 A2994 37c multicolored .80 .40
3918 A2995 37c multicolored .80 .40
3919 A2996 37c multicolored .80 .40
3920 A2997 37c multicolored .80 .40
3921 A2998 37c multicolored .80 .40
3922 A2999 37c multicolored .80 .40
3923 A3000 37c multicolored .80 .40
3924 A3001 37c multicolored .80 .40
3925 A3002 37c multicolored .80 .40
- *a.* Block of 10, #3916-3925 8.00

RIO GRANDE BLANKETS

A3003

A3004

A3005

A3006

LITHOGRAPHED
BOOKLET STAMPS

Serpentine Die Cut 10¾ on 2 or 3 Sides

2005, July 30

Self-Adhesive

3926 A3003 37c multicolored .75 .30
3927 A3004 37c multicolored .75 .30
3928 A3005 37c multicolored .75 .30
3929 A3006 37c multicolored .75 .30
a. Block of 4, #3926-3929 3.00
b. Booklet pane, 5 each #3926-3929 15.00

No. 3929b is a double-sided booklet with 12 stamps on one side and 8 stamps plus label (booklet cover) on the other side.

PRESIDENTIAL LIBRARIES ACT, 50th ANNIV.

Presidential Seal — A3007

Serpentine Die Cut 10¾

2005, Aug. 4

Self-Adhesive

3930 A3007 37c multicolored .80 .25

SPORTY CARS OF THE 1950S

1953 Studebaker Starliner — A3008

1954 Kaiser Darrin — A3009

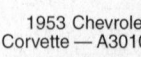

1953 Chevrolet Corvette — A3010

1952 Nash Healey — A3011

1955 Ford Thunderbird A3012

BOOKLET STAMPS

Serpentine Die Cut 10¾ on 2 or 3 Sides

2005, Aug. 20 **Tagged**

Self-Adhesive

3931 A3008 37c multicolored 1.60 .40
3932 A3009 37c multicolored 1.60 .40
3933 A3010 37c multicolored 1.60 .40
3934 A3011 37c multicolored 1.60 .40
3935 A3012 37c multicolored 1.60 .40
a. Vert. strip of 5, #3931-3935 8.00
b. Booklet pane, 4 each #3931-3935 32.00

Stamps in No. 3935a are not adjacent, as rows of selvage are between stamps one and two, and between stamps three and four.

No. 3935b is a double-sided booklet pane with 12 stamps on one side (2 each #3931, 3933, 3935, and 3 each #3932, 3934) and eight stamps (1 each #3932, 3934, and 2 each #3931, 3933, 3935) plus label on the other side.

ARTHUR ASHE

Arthur Ashe (1943-93), Tennis Player — A3013

Serpentine Die Cut 10¾

2005, Aug. 27

Self-Adhesive

3936 A3013 37c multicolored .75 .25

TO FORM A MORE PERFECT UNION

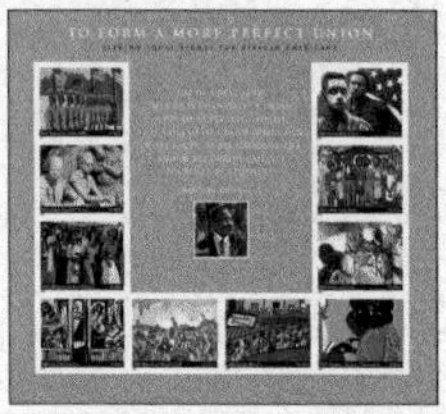
A3014

No. 3937 — Inscriptions and artwork: a, 1948 Executive Order 9981 (Training for War, by William H. Johnson). b, 1965 Voting Rights Act (Youths on the Selma March, 1965, photograph by Bruce Davidson). c, 1960 Lunch Counter Sit-ins (National Civil Rights Museum exhibits, by StudioEIS). d, 1957 Little Rock Nine (America Cares, by George Hunt). e, 1955 Montgomery Bus Boycott (Walking, by Charles Alston). f, 1961 Freedom Riders (Freedom Riders, by May Stevens). g, 1964 Civil Rights Act (Dixie Café, by Jacob Lawrence). h, 1963 March on Washington (March on Washington, by Alma Thomas). i, 1965 Selma March (Selma March, by Bernice Sims). j, 1954 Brown v. Board of Education (The Lamp, by Romare Bearden).

Serpentine Die Cut 10¾x10½

2005, Aug. 30

Self-Adhesive

3937 A3014 Pane of 10 11.00
a.-j. 37c Any single 1.10 .40

CHILD HEALTH

Child and Doctor — A3015

PHOTOGRAVURE

Serpentine Die Cut 10½x11

2005, Sept. 7

Self-Adhesive

3938 A3015 37c multicolored .75 .25

LET'S DANCE

Merengue A3016

Salsa A3017

Cha Cha Cha A3018

Mambo A3019

Serpentine Die Cut 10¾

2005, Sept. 17

Self-Adhesive

3939 A3016 37c multicolored 1.00 .35
3940 A3017 37c multicolored 1.00 .35
3941 A3018 37c multicolored 1.00 .35
3942 A3019 37c multicolored 1.00 .35
a. Vert. strip of 4, #3939-3942 4.00

Stamps in the vertical strip are not adjacent as rows of selvage are between the stamps. The backing paper of stamps from the 2nd and 4th columns have Spanish inscriptions, while the other columns have English inscriptions.

GRETA GARBO

Garbo (1905-90), Actress — A3020

ENGRAVED

2005, Sept. 23

Self-Adhesive

3943 A3020 37c black .75 .25

See Sweden No. 2517.

JIM HENSON AND THE MUPPETS

A3021

No. 3944: a, Kermit the Frog. b, Fozzie Bear. c, Sam the Eagle and flag. d, Miss Piggy. e, Statler and Waldorf. f, The Swedish Chef and fruit. g, Animal. h, Dr. Bunsen Honeydew and Beaker. i, Rowlf the Dog. j, The Great Gonzo and Camilla the Chicken. k, Jim Henson.

Nos. 3944a-3944j are 30x30mm; No. 3944k, 28x37mm.

PHOTOGRAVURE

Serpentine Die Cut 10½, 10½x10¾ (#3944k)

2005, Sept. 28

Self-Adhesive

3944 A3021 Pane of 11 9.00
a.-k. 37c Any single .80 .50

CONSTELLATIONS

Leo A3022

Orion A3023

Lyra A3024

Pegasus A3025

LITHOGRAPHED

Serpentine Die Cut 10¾

2005, Oct. 3

Self-Adhesive

3945 A3022 37c multicolored .85 .35
3946 A3023 37c multicolored .85 .35
3947 A3024 37c multicolored .85 .35
3948 A3025 37c multicolored .85 .35
a. Block or vert. strip of 4, #3945-3948 3.40
b. As "a," die cutting omitted 750.00

CHRISTMAS COOKIES

Santa Claus A3026

Snowmen A3027

Angel A3028

Elves A3029

LITHOGRAPHED

Serpentine Die Cut 10¾x11

2005, Oct. 20

Self-Adhesive

Design Size: 19x26mm

3949 A3026 37c multicolored .85 .25
3950 A3027 37c multicolored .85 .25
3951 A3028 37c multicolored .85 .25
3952 A3029 37c multicolored .85 .25
a. Block or vert. strip of 4, #3949-3952 3.50

Booklet Stamps

Serpentine Die Cut 10¾x11 on 2 or 3 Sides

Design Size: 19½x27mm

3953 A3026 37c multicolored 1.00 .25
3954 A3027 37c multicolored 1.00 .25
3955 A3028 37c multicolored 1.00 .25
3956 A3029 37c multicolored 1.00 .25
a. Block of 4, #3953-3956 4.00
b. Booklet pane of 20, 5 #3956a 20.00

Santa Claus A3030

Snowmen A3031

Angel A3032

Elves A3033

Serpentine Die Cut 10½x10¾

3957 A3030 37c multicolored 1.10 .25
3958 A3031 37c multicolored 1.10 .25
3959 A3032 37c multicolored 1.10 .25
3960 A3033 37c multicolored 1.10 .25
a. Block of 4, #3957-3960 4.50
b. Booklet pane of 4, #3957-3960 4.50
c. Booklet pane of 6, #3959-3960, 2 each #3957-3958 7.00
d. Booklet pane of 6, #3957-3958, 2 each #3959-3960 7.00

No. 3956b is a double-sided booklet pane with 12 stamps on one side and eight stamps plus label that serves as a booklet cover on the other side. Nos. 3949-3952 have a small "2005" year date, while Nos. 3953-3956 have a large year date. Other design differences caused by different cropping of the images can be found, with Nos. 3953-3956 showing slightly more design features on one or more sides.

DISTINGUISHED MARINES

Lt. Gen. John A. Lejeune (1867-1942), 2nd Infantry Division Insignia — A3034

Lt. Gen. Lewis B. Puller (1898-1971), 1st Marine Division Insignia — A3035

Sgt. John Basilone (1916-45), 5th Marine Division Insignia — A3036

Sgt. Major Daniel J. Daly (1873-1937), 73rd Machine Gun Company, 6th Marine Regiment Insignia — A3037

LITHOGRAPHED

Serpentine Die Cut 11x10½

2005, Nov. 10

Self-Adhesive

3961 A3034 37c multicolored 1.00 .35
3962 A3035 37c multicolored 1.00 .35
3963 A3036 37c multicolored 1.00 .35
3964 A3037 37c multicolored 1.00 .35
a. Block or horiz. strip of 4, #3961-3964 4.00

Flag and Statue of Liberty — A3038

LITHOGRAPHED

2005, Dec. 8 ***Perf. 11¼***

3965 A3038 (39c) multicolored 1.10 .25

Self-Adhesive (#3966, 3968-3975)

Serpentine Die Cut 11¼x10¾

3966 A3038 (39c) multicolored 1.10 .25
a. Booklet pane of 20 22.00
b. As "a," die cutting omitted 3,100.

LITHOGRAPHED (#3970), PHOTOGRAVURE

COIL STAMPS

Perf. 9¾ Vert.

3967 A3038 (39c) multicolored 1.10 .25

Serpentine Die Cut 8½ Vert.

3968 A3038 (39c) multicolored 1.10 .25

Serpentine Die Cut 10¼ Vert.

3969 A3038 (39c) multicolored 1.50 .25

Serpentine Die Cut 9½ Vert.

3970 A3038 (39c) multicolored 3.50 .25

LITHOGRAPHED (#3974), PHOTOGRAVURE

BOOKLET STAMPS

Serpentine Die Cut 11¼x10¾ on 2 or 3 Sides

3972 A3038 (39c) multicolored 1.10 .25
a. Booklet pane of 20 22.00

Serpentine Die Cut 10½x10¾ on 2 or 3 Sides

3973 A3038 (39c) multicolored 1.10 .25
a. Booklet pane of 20 22.00

On both Nos. 3972 and 3973, the sky immediately above the date is bright blue and extends from the left side to beyond the "6" in the date, the left arm of the star at the upper left barely touches the frame line and is without the "USPS" microprinting. They are distinguishable by the die cutting. Nos. 3872a and 3973a are double-sided booklet panes with 12 stamps on one side and eight stamps plus label that serves as a booklet cover on the other side.

No. 3973 was not available until January 2006.

Serpentine Die Cut 11¼x10¾ on 2 or 3 Sides

3974 A3038 (39c) multicolored 1.10 .25
a. Booklet pane of 4 4.40
b. Booklet pane of 6 6.60

Serpentine Die Cut 8 on 2, 3 or 4 Sides

3975 A3038 (39c) multicolored 1.10 .25
a. Booklet pane of 18 20.00
Nos. 3965-3975 (10) 13.80 2.50

Nos. 3965-3975 are dated "2006."

On No. 3966, the sky immediately above the date is bright blue and extends from the left side to beyond the "6" in the date, the left arm of the star at upper left is clear of the top frame, and "USPS" is microprinted on the top red flag stripe.

On No. 3974, the sky immediately above the date is dark blue and extends from the left side to the second "0" in the date, the left arm of the star at upper left touches the top frame, and lacks the microprinting found on No. 3966.

Nos. 3965 and 3970 also have "USPS" microprinted on the top red flag stripe.

Nos. 3966a and 3972a are double-sided booklet panes with 12 stamps on one side and eight stamps plus label that serves as a booklet cover on the other side. On No. 3966a, the stamps on one side are upside-down with relation to the stamps on the other side. On No. 3972a the stamps are all aligned the same on both sides.

LOVE

Birds — A3039

PHOTOGRAVURE

Serpentine Die Cut 11 on 2, 3, or 4 Sides

2006, Jan. 3

BOOKLET STAMP

Self-Adhesive

3976 A3039 (39c) multicolored 1.10 .25
a. Booklet pane of 20 22.00

See No. 4029.

Flag and Statue of Liberty — A3040

LITHOGRAPHED

2006 ***Serpentine Die Cut 11¼x10¾***

Self-Adhesive (#3978, 3980-3985)

3978 A3040 39c multi .85 .25
a. Booklet pane of 10 8.50
b. Booklet pane of 20 17.00
c. As "b," die cutting omitted on side with 8 stamps —

No. 3978 has "USPS" microprinted on top red flag stripe.

No. 3978b is a double-sided booklet with 12 stamps on one side and 8 stamps plus label (booklet cover) on the other side.

LITHOGRAPHED (#3981), PHOTOGRAVURE (#3979-3980, 3982-3983)

COIL STAMPS

Perf. 9¾ Vert.

3979 A3040 39c multi 1.00 .25

Serpentine Die Cut 11 Vert.

3980 A3040b 39c multi .80 .25

No. 3980 has rounded corners and lacks microprinting. Unused examples are on backing paper taller than the stamp, and the stamps are spaced approximately 3mm apart.

Serpentine Die Cut 9½ Vert.

3981 A3040 39c multi 1.40 .25
a. Die cutting omitted, pair *150.00*

No. 3981 has "USPS" microprinted on top red flag stripe.

Serpentine Die Cut 10¼ Vert.

3982 A3040 39c multi 1.25 .25
a. Vert. pair, unslit between *500.00*

Serpentine Die Cut 8½ Vert.

3983 A3040 39c multi .80 .25

PHOTOGRAVURE

BOOKLET STAMP

Serpentine Die Cut 11¼x10¾ on 2 or 3 Sides

3985 A3040 39c multi .80 .25
a. Booklet pane of 20 16.00
b. Serpentine die cut 11.1 on 2 or 3 sides .80 .25
c. Booklet pane of 4 #3985b 3.20
d. Booklet pane of 6 #3985b 4.80

Nos. 3983 and 3985 lack the microprinting found on Nos. 3978 and 3981. No. 3982 was not made available until June, despite the official first day of issue. No. 3983 was not made available until July and No. 3985 was not made available until August, despite the official first day of issue. No. 3985a is a double-sided booklet with 12 stamps on one side and 8 stamps plus label (booklet cover) on the other side.

Issued: No. 3980, 1/9; No. 3979, 3/8; Nos. 3978, 3981, 3982, 3985, 4/8.

CHILDREN'S BOOK ANIMALS

The Very Hungry Caterpillar, from *The Very Hungry Caterpillar,* by Eric Carle — A3041

Wilbur, from *Charlotte's Web,* by E. B. White — A3042

Fox in Socks, from *Fox in Socks,* by Dr. Seuss A3043

Maisy, from *Maisy's ABC,* by Lucy Cousins A3044

Wild Thing, from *Where the Wild Things Are,* by Maurice Sendak — A3045

Curious George, from *Curious George,* by Margaret and H. A. Rey — A3046

Olivia, from *Olivia,* by Ian Falconer A3047

Frederick, from *Frederick,* by Leo Lionni A3048

PHOTOGRAVURE

Serpentine Die Cut 10¾

2006, Jan. 10

Self-Adhesive

3987 A3041 39c multicolored .80 .40
3988 A3042 39c multicolored .80 .40
3989 A3043 39c multicolored .80 .40
3990 A3044 39c multicolored .80 .40
3991 A3045 39c multicolored .80 .40
3992 A3046 39c multicolored .80 .40
3993 A3047 39c multicolored .80 .40
3994 A3048 39c multicolored .80 .40
a. Block of 8, #3987-3994 6.50

See Great Britain Nos. 2340-2341.

2006 WINTER OLYMPICS, TURIN, ITALY

Skier — A3049

LITHOGRAPHED

2006, Jan. 11

Self-Adhesive

3995 A3049 39c multicolored .80 .25

BLACK HERITAGE SERIES

Hattie McDaniel (1895-1952), Actress — A3050

2006, Jan. 25

Self-Adhesive

3996 A3050 39c multicolored .80 .25

Chinese New Year Types of 1992-2004

2006, Jan. 29

Self-Adhesive

3997 Pane of 12 12.00
a. A2360 39c Rat 1.00 .50
b. A2413 39c Ox 1.00 .50
c. A2462 39c Tiger 1.00 .50
d. A2535 39c Rabbit 1.00 .50
e. A2602 39c Dragon 1.00 .50
f. A2702 39c Snake 1.00 .50
g. A2752 39c Horse 1.00 .50
h. A2856 39c Ram 1.00 .50
i. A2927 39c Monkey 1.00 .50
j. A2067 39c Rooster 1.00 .50
k. A2146 39c Dog 1.00 .50
l. A2205 39c Boar 1.00 .50

See Nos. 2720, 2817, 2876, 3060, 3120, 3179, 3272, 3370, 3500, 3559, 3747, 3832, 3895.

WEDDING DOVES

Dove Facing Left A3051

Dove Facing Right A3052

BOOKLET STAMPS

Serpentine Die Cut 10¾x11 on 2, 3 or 4 Sides

2006, Mar. 1

Self-Adhesive

3998 A3051 39c pale lilac .80 .25
a. Booklet pane of 20 16.00
b. As "a," die cutting omitted —

Serpentine Die Cut 10¾x11

3999 A3052 63c pale yellow green 1.40 .50
a. Booklet pane, 20 each #3998-3999 45.00
b. Horiz. pair, #3998-3999 with vertical gutter between 2.25 1.50

Common Buckeye Butterfly — A3053

LITHOGRAPHED (#4000), PHOTOGRAVURE (#4001-4002)

2006, Mar. 8 ***Perf. 11¼***

4000 A3053 24c multicolored .50 .25

Self-Adhesive

Serpentine Die Cut 11

4001 A3053 24c multicolored .55 .25
a. Serpentine die cut 10¾x11¼ on 3 sides (from booklet panes) .50 .25
b. Booklet pane of 10 #4001a 5.00
c. Booklet pane of 4 #4001a 2.00
d. Booklet pane of 6 #4001a 3.00

No. 4001b is a convertible booklet that was sold flat. It has a self-adhesive panel that covers the rouletting on the inside of the booklet cover. Nos. 4001c and 4001d are component panes of a vending machine booklet, which was sold pre-folded and sealed, and which does not have the self-adhesive panel covering the rouletting on the inside of the booklet cover.

COIL STAMP

Serpentine Die Cut 8½ Horiz.

4002 A3053 24c multicolored .50 .25

CROPS OF THE AMERICAS

Chili Peppers A3054

Beans A3055

Sunflower and Seeds A3056

Squashes A3057

Corn — A3058

PHOTOGRAVURE

Serpentine Die Cut 10¼ Horiz.

2006, Mar. 16

Self-Adhesive

Coil Stamps

4003 A3054 39c multicolored 2.40 .35
4004 A3055 39c multicolored 2.40 .35
4005 A3056 39c multicolored 2.40 .35
4006 A3057 39c multicolored 2.40 .35
4007 A3058 39c multicolored 2.40 .35
a. Strip of 5, #4003-4007 12.00

Booklet Stamps

Serpentine Die Cut 10¾x10½ on 2 or 3 Sides

4008 A3058 39c multicolored 1.25 .35
4009 A3057 39c multicolored 1.25 .35
4010 A3056 39c multicolored 1.25 .35
4011 A3055 39c multicolored 1.25 .35
4012 A3054 39c multicolored 1.25 .35
a. Horiz. strip of 5, #4008-4012 6.25
b. Booklet pane, 4 each #4008-4012 25.00

LITHOGRAPHED

Serpentine Die Cut 10¾x11¼ on 2 or 3 Sides

4013 A3054 39c multicolored 1.50 .35
4014 A3058 39c multicolored 1.50 .35
4015 A3057 39c multicolored 1.50 .35
4016 A3056 39c multicolored 1.50 .35
a. Booklet pane of 4, #4013-4016 6.00
4017 A3055 39c multicolored 1.50 .35
a. Horiz. strip of 5, #4013-4017 7.50
b. Booklet pane of 4, #4013-4015, 4017 6.00
c. Booklet pane of 6, #4013-4016, 2 #4017 9.00
d. Booklet pane of 6, #4013-4015, 4017, 2 #4016 9.00

Stamps in Nos. 4012a and 4017a are not adjacent, as one or two rows of selvage is between stamps (or a blank space where selvage was removed by the manufacturer).

No. 4012b is a double-sided booklet with 12 stamps on one side and 8 stamps plus label (booklet cover) on the other side.

"USA" is at right of "39" on No. 4004, at left of "39" on Nos. 4011, 4017. Top of "USA" is aligned with top of "39" on No. 4013, with bottom of "39" on Nos. 4003, 4012.

X-PLANES

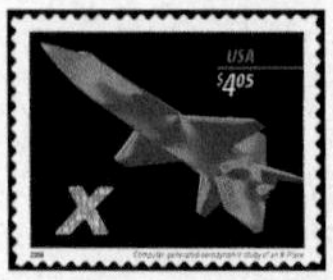

A3059

A3060

LITHOGRAPHED WITH HOLOGRAM AFFIXED

Serpentine Die Cut 10¾x10½

2006, Mar. 17 Self-Adhesive

4018 A3059 $4.05 multi 8.00 5.00
a. Silver foil ("X") omitted —
4019 A3060 $14.40 multi 27.50 15.00

Beware of Nos. 4018 and 4019 with "X" hologram chemically removed. Certification is strongly recommended.

SUGAR RAY ROBINSON (1921-89), BOXER

A3061

PHOTOGRAVURE

2006, Apr. 7 *Serpentine Die Cut 11*

Self-Adhesive

4020 A3061 39c red & blue .80 .25

BENJAMIN FRANKLIN (1706-90)

Statesman A3062

Scientist — A3063

Printer — A3064

Postmaster A3065

2006, Apr. 7

4021 A3062 39c multicolored 1.25 .35
4022 A3063 39c multicolored 1.25 .35
4023 A3064 39c multicolored 1.25 .35
4024 A3065 39c multicolored 1.25 .35
a. Block or horiz. strip of 4 5.00

THE ART OF DISNEY: ROMANCE

Mickey and Minnie Mouse A3066

Cinderella and Prince Charming A3067

Beauty and the Beast A3068

Lady and Tramp A3069

LITHOGRAPHED

Serpentine Die Cut 10½x10¾

2006, Apr. 21

Self-Adhesive

4025 A3066 39c multicolored .80 .30
4026 A3067 39c multicolored .80 .30
4027 A3068 39c multicolored .80 .30
4028 A3069 39c multicolored .80 .30
a. Block or vert. strip of 4, #4025-4028 3.20

LOVE

Birds — A3070

PHOTOGRAVURE

Serpentine Die Cut 11 on 2, 3 or 4 Sides

2006, May 1

Self-Adhesive

Booklet Stamp

4029 A3070 39c multicolored .95 .25
a. Booklet pane of 20 19.00

See No. 3976.

LITERARY ARTS

Katherine Anne Porter (1890-1980), Author — A3071

LITHOGRAPHED

Serpentine Die Cut 10¾

2006, May 15

Self-Adhesive

4030 A3071 39c multicolored .80 .25

AMBER ALERT

Mother and Child — A3072

PHOTOGRAVURE

Serpentine Die Cut 10¾

2006, May 25

Self-Adhesive

4031 A3072 39c multicolored .80 .25

Purple Heart Type of 2003

LITHOGRAPHED

Serpentine Die Cut 11¼x11

2006, May 26

Self-Adhesive

4032 A2891 39c multicolored .80 .25
a. Die cutting omitted, pair —

See Nos. 3784-3784A, 4164, 4263-4264, 4390.

WONDERS OF AMERICA

American Alligator — A3073

Designs: No. 4033, American alligator, largest reptile. No. 4034, Moloka'i, highest sea cliffs. No. 4035, Saguaro, tallest cactus. No. 4036, Bering Glacier, largest glacier. No. 4037, Great Sand Dunes, tallest dunes. No. 4038, Chesapeake Bay, largest estuary. No. 4039, Cliff Palace, largest cliff dwelling. No. 4040, Crater Lake, deepest lake. No. 4041, American bison, largest land mammal. No. 4042, Off the Florida Keys, longest reef. No. 4043, Pacific Crest Trail, longest hiking trail. No. 4044, Gateway Arch, tallest man-made monument. No. 4045, Appalachians, oldest mountains. No. 4046, American lotus, largest flower. No. 4047, Lake Superior, largest lake. No. 4048, Pronghorn, fastest land animal. No. 4049, Bristlecone pines, oldest trees. No. 4050, Yosemite Falls, tallest waterfall. No. 4051, Great Basin, largest desert. No. 4052, Verrazano-Narrows Bridge, longest span. No. 4053, Mount Washington, windiest place. No. 4054, Grand Canyon, largest canyon. No. 4055, American bullfrog, largest frog. No. 4056, Oroville Dam, tallest dam. No. 4057, Peregrine falcon, fastest bird. No. 4058, Mississippi River Delta, largest delta. No. 4059, Steamboat, tallest geyser. No. 4060, Rainbow Bridge, largest natural bridge. No. 4061, White sturgeon, largest freshwater fish. No. 4062, Rocky Mountains, longest mountain chain. No. 4063, Coast redwoods, tallest trees. No. 4064, American beaver, largest rodent. No. 4065, Mississippi-Missouri, longest river system. No. 4066, Mount Wai'ale'ale, rainiest spot. No. 4067, Kilauea, most active volcano. No. 4068, Mammoth Cave, longest cave. No. 4069, Blue whale, loudest animal. No. 4070, Death Valley, hottest spot. No. 4071, Cornish-Windsor Bridge, longest covered bridge. No. 4072, Quaking aspen, largest plant.

PHOTOGRAVURE

Serpentine Die Cut 10¾

2006, May 27

Self-Adhesive

4033 A3073 39c multicolored .80 .60
4034 A3074 39c multicolored .80 .60
4035 A3075 39c multicolored .80 .60
4036 A3076 39c multicolored .80 .60
4037 A3077 39c multicolored .80 .60
4038 A3078 39c multicolored .80 .60
4039 A3079 39c multicolored .80 .60
4040 A3080 39c multicolored .80 .60
4041 A3081 39c multicolored .80 .60
4042 A3082 39c multicolored .80 .60
4043 A3083 39c multicolored .80 .60
4044 A3084 39c multicolored .80 .60
4045 A3085 39c multicolored .80 .60
4046 A3086 39c multicolored .80 .60
4047 A3087 39c multicolored .80 .60
4048 A3088 39c multicolored .80 .60
4049 A3089 39c multicolored .80 .60
4050 A3090 39c multicolored .80 .60
4051 A3091 39c multicolored .80 .60
4052 A3092 39c multicolored .80 .60
4053 A3093 39c multicolored .80 .60
4054 A3094 39c multicolored .80 .60
4055 A3095 39c multicolored .80 .60
4056 A3096 39c multicolored .80 .60
4057 A3097 39c multicolored .80 .60
4058 A3098 39c multicolored .80 .60
4059 A3099 39c multicolored .80 .60
4060 A3100 39c multicolored .80 .60
4061 A3101 39c multicolored .80 .60
4062 A3102 39c multicolored .80 .60
4063 A3103 39c multicolored .80 .60
4064 A3104 39c multicolored .80 .60
4065 A3105 39c multicolored .80 .60
4066 A3106 39c multicolored .80 .60
4067 A3107 39c multicolored .80 .60
4068 A3108 39c multicolored .80 .60
4069 A3109 39c multicolored .80 .60
4070 A3110 39c multicolored .80 .60
4071 A3111 39c multicolored .80 .60
4072 A3112 39c multicolored .80 .60
a. Pane of 40, #4033-4072 32.00

EXPLORATION OF EAST COAST BY SAMUEL DE CHAMPLAIN, 400TH ANNIV.

Ship and Map — A3113

A3114

LITHOGRAPHED & ENGRAVED

Serpentine Die Cut 10¾

2006, May 28

Self-Adhesive (#4073)

4073 A3113 39c multicolored .85 .25

Souvenir Sheet

Perf. 11

4074 A3114 Pane of 4, 2 each #4074a, Canada #2156a 8.50 8.50
a. A3113 39c multicolored 2.00 .25

Washington 2006 World Philatelic Exhibition (#4074). Canada No. 2156, which was sold only by Canada Post, has a bar code in the lower left margin of the pane. No. 4074, which was sold only by the United States Postal Service for $1.75, lacks this bar code.

WASHINGTON 2006 WORLD PHILATELIC EXHIBITION
Souvenir Sheet

A3115

LITHOGRAPHED (MARGIN) & ENGRAVED

2006, May 29 *Perf. 10¾x10½*
4075 A3115 Pane of 3 16.00 6.00
a. A174 $1 violet brown 2.00 .50
b. A175 $2 deep blue 4.00 1.00
c. A176 $5 carmine & blue 10.00 2.50

DISTINGUISHED AMERICAN DIPLOMATS
Souvenir Sheet

A3116

No. 4076: a, Robert D. Murphy (1894-1978). b, Frances E. Willis (1899-1983). c, Hiram Bingham IV (1903-88). d, Philip C. Habib (1920-92). e, Charles E. Bohlen (1904-74). f, Clifton R. Wharton, Sr. (1899-1990).

PHOTOGRAVURE
Serpentine Die Cut 10¾
2006, May 29
Self-Adhesive
4076 A3116 Pane of 6 6.00
a.-f. 39c any single 1.00 .40

LEGENDS OF HOLLYWOOD

Judy Garland (1922-69), Actress — A3117

LITHOGRAPHED
2006, June 10
Self-Adhesive
4077 A3117 39c multicolored 1.00 .25
a. Pair, die cutting omitted 750.00

Ronald Reagan Type of 2005
PHOTOGRAVURE
2006, June 14
Self-Adhesive
4078 A2974 39c multicolored .90 .25
See No. 3897.

Happy Birthday Type of 2002
Serpentine Die Cut 11
2006, June 23
Self-Adhesive
4079 A2751 39c multicolored .80 .25
See Nos. 3558, 3695.

BASEBALL SLUGGERS

Roy Campanella (1921-93) A3118

Hank Greenberg (1911-86) A3119

Mel Ott (1909-58) A3120

Mickey Mantle (1931-95) A3121

Serpentine Die Cut 10¾
2006, July 15
Self-Adhesive
4080 A3118 39c multicolored .80 .30
4081 A3119 39c multicolored .80 .30
4082 A3120 39c multicolored .80 .30
4083 A3121 39c multicolored .80 .30
a. Block or vert. strip of 4, #4080-4083 3.20

DC COMICS SUPERHEROES

A3122

No. 4084: a, Superman. b, Green Lantern. c, Wonder Woman. d, Green Arrow. e, Batman. f, The Flash. g, Plastic Man. h, Aquaman. i, Supergirl. j, Hawkman. k, Cover of *Superman #11*. l, Cover of *Green Lantern #4*. m, Cover of *Wonder Woman #22 (Second Series)*. n, Cover of *Green Arrow #15*. o, Cover of *Batman #1*. p, Cover of *The Flash #111*. q, Cover of *Plastic Man #4*. r, Cover of *Aquaman #5 (of 5)*. s, Cover of *The Daring New Adventures of Supergirl #1*. t, Cover of *The Brave and the Bold Presents Hawkman #36*.

Serpentine Die Cut 10½x10¾
2006, July 20
Self-Adhesive
4084 A3122 Pane of 20 16.00
a.-t. 39c Any single .80 .50
u. As No. 4084, all inscriptions omitted on reverse *2,000.*

MOTORCYCLES

1940 Indian Four — A3123

1918 Cleveland A3124

Generic "Chopper," c. 1970 — A3125

1965 Harley-Davidson Electra-Glide A3126

Serpentine Die Cut 10¾x10½
2006, Aug. 7
Self-Adhesive
4085 A3123 39c multicolored 1.00 .35
4086 A3124 39c multicolored 1.00 .35
4087 A3125 39c multicolored 1.00 .35
4088 A3126 39c multicolored 1.00 .35
a. Block or horiz. strip of 4, #4085-4088 4.00

AMERICAN TREASURES SERIES
Quilts of Gee's Bend, Alabama

Housetop Variation, by Mary Lee Bendolph A3127

Pig in a Pen Medallion, by Minnie Sue Coleman A3128

Nine Patch, by Ruth P. Mosely A3129

Housetop Four Block Half Log Cabin Variation, by Lottie Mooney A3130

Roman Stripes Variation, by Loretta Pettway A3131

Chinese Coins Variation, by Arlonzia Pettway A3132

Blocks and Strips, by Annie Mae Young A3133

Medallion, by Loretta Pettway A3134

Bars and String-pieced Columns, by Jessie T. Pettway A3135

Medallion With Checkerboard Center, by Patty Ann Williams A3136

BOOKLET STAMPS
Serpentine Die Cut 10¾ on 2 or 3 Sides
2006, Aug. 24
Self-Adhesive
4089 A3127 39c multicolored 1.10 .40
4090 A3128 39c multicolored 1.10 .40
4091 A3129 39c multicolored 1.10 .40
4092 A3130 39c multicolored 1.10 .40
4093 A3131 39c multicolored 1.10 .40
4094 A3132 39c multicolored 1.10 .40
4095 A3133 39c multicolored 1.10 .40
4096 A3134 39c multicolored 1.10 .40
4097 A3135 39c multicolored 1.10 .40
4098 A3136 39c multicolored 1.10 .40
a. Block of 10, #4089-4098 11.00
b. Booklet pane of 20, 2 each #4089-4098 22.50

No. 4098b is a double-sided booklet pane with 12 stamps on one side (1 each #4090-4093, 4095-4098, and 2 each #4089, 4094) and eight stamps (1 each #4090-4093, 4095-4098) plus label (booklet cover) on the other side.

SOUTHERN FLORIDA WETLAND

A3137

No. 4099 — Wildlife: a, Snail kite. b, Wood storks. c, Florida panther. d, Bald eagle, horiz. e, American crocodile, horiz. f, Roseate spoonbills, horiz. g, Everglades mink. h, Cape Sable seaside sparrow, horiz. i, American alligator, horiz. j, White ibis.

Serpentine Die Cut 10¾
2006, Oct. 4
Self-Adhesive
4099 A3137 Pane of 10 9.00
a.-j. 39c any single .90 .40

CHRISTMAS

Madonna and Child with Bird, by Ignacio Chacón A3138

Snowflake A3139

Snowflake A3140

Snowflake A3141

Snowflake — A3142

LITHOGRAPHED
Serpentine Die Cut 10¾x11 on 2 or 3 Sides
2006
Self-Adhesive
Booklet Stamps (#4100, 4105-4116)
4100 A3138 39c multi .80 .25
a. Booklet pane of 20 16.00

Base of Denomination Higher Than Year Date
Serpentine Die Cut 11¼x11
4101 A3139 39c multi .90 .25
4102 A3140 39c multi .90 .25
4103 A3141 39c multi .90 .25
4104 A3142 39c multi .90 .25
a. Block or vert. strip of 4, #4101-4104 3.60

Base of Denominations Even With Year Date
Serpentine Die Cut 11¼x11½ on 2 or 3 Sides
4105 A3139 39c multi .90 .25
a. Red missing (PS) —
4106 A3140a39c multi .90 .25
a. Red missing (PS) —
4107 A3141 39c multi .90 .25
4108 A3142 39c multi .90 .25
a. Block of 4, #4105-4108 3.60
b. Booklet pane of 20, 5 #4108a 18.00
c. As "a," red ("USA") and green ("39") omitted —

Serpentine Die Cut 11¼x10¾ on 2 or 3 Sides
4109 A3139 39c multi 1.00 .25
4110 A3140 39c multi 1.00 .25
4111 A3141 39c multi 1.00 .25
4112 A3142 39c multi 1.00 .25
a. Block of 4, #4109-4112 4.00
b. Booklet pane of 4, #4109-4112 4.00
c. Booklet pane of 6, #4111-4112, 2 each #4109-4110 6.00
d. Booklet pane of 6, #4109-4110, 2 each #4111-4112 6.00

Serpentine Die Cut 8 on 2, 3 or 4 Sides

PHOTOGRAVURE

4113 A3139 39c multi 1.50 .35
a. Red and green missing (PS) —
4114 A3141 39c multi 1.50 .35
4115 A3140 39c multi 1.50 .35
4116 A3142 39c multi 1.50 .35
a. Block or strip of 4, #4113-4116 6.00
b. Booklet pane of 18, 4 each #4114, 4116, 5 each #4113, 4115 27.00
Nos. 4100-4116 (17) 18.00 4.65

No. 4108b is a double-sided booklet pane with 12 stamps on one side and eight stamps plus label that serves as a booklet cover on the other side. Snowflakes on Nos. 4101-4104 are slightly smaller than those on Nos. 4105-4116.

Issued: No. 4100, 10/17, Nos. 4101-4116, 10/5.

Eid Type of 2001

PHOTOGRAVURE

2006, Oct. 6 ***Serpentine Die Cut 11***

Self-Adhesive

4117 A2734 39c multicolored .80 .25

See Nos. 3532, 3674, 4202, 4351, 4416.

Hanukkah Type of 2004

LITHOGRAPHED

Serpentine Die Cut 10¾x11

2006, Oct. 6

Self-Adhesive

4118 A2962 39c multicolored .80 .25
a. Die cutting omitted, pane of 20 —

See Nos. 3880, 4219, 4372.

Kwanzaa Type of 2004

Serpentine Die Cut 11x10¾

2006, Oct. 6

Self-Adhesive

4119 A2963 39c multicolored .80 .25

See Nos. 3881, 4220, 4373.

BLACK HERITAGE SERIES

Ella Fitzgerald (1917-96), Singer — A3143

Serpentine Die Cut 11

2007, Jan. 10

Self-Adhesive

4120 A3143 39c multicolored .80 .25

OKLAHOMA STATEHOOD, 100TH ANNIV.

Cimarron River — A3144

2007, Jan. 11

Self-Adhesive

4121 A3144 39c multicolored .80 .25

LOVE

Hershey's Kiss — A3145

PHOTOGRAVURE

Serpentine Die Cut 10¾x11 on 2, 3 or 4 Sides

2007, Jan. 13

BOOKLET STAMP

Self-Adhesive

4122 A3145 39c multicolored .80 .25
a. Booklet pane of 20 16.00

INTERNATIONAL POLAR YEAR

Souvenir Sheet

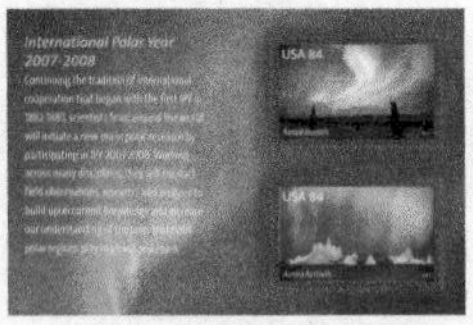

A3146

No. 4123: a, Aurora borealis. b, Aurora australis.

LITHOGRAPHED

Serpentine Die Cut 10¾

2007, Feb. 21

Self-Adhesive

4123 A3146 Pane of 2 4.00
a.-b. 84c Either single 2.00 .50

LITERARY ARTS

Henry Wadsworth Longfellow (1807-82), Poet — A3147

2007, Mar. 15

Self-Adhesive

4124 A3147 39c multicolored .80 .25

Beginning with No. 4125, the United States Postal Service began issuing "Forever" stamps that satisfy the domestic 1-ounce first-class letter rate and the 1-ounce international letter rate regardless of future rate increases. The denomination in parentheses in the catalogue listing represents the face value at the time of issue. The face value increases to the new letter rate whenever rates change.

"FOREVER" STAMP

Liberty Bell — A3148

Large Microprinting (#4125, 4128)

Small Microprinting (#4126)

Medium Microprinting (#4127)

PHOTOGRAVURE

Serpentine Die Cut 11¼x10¾ on 2 or 3 Sides

2007-09

Booklet Stamps

Self-Adhesive

Large Microprinting, Bell 16mm Wide

4125 A3148 (41c) multi, dated "2007," Apr. 12 1.25 .25
a. Booklet pane of 20 25.00
b. (42c) Dated "2008" 1.25 .25
c. Booklet pane of 20 #4125b 25.00
d. As "c," copper ("FOREVER") omitted *1,000.*
e. As "c," copper ("FOREVER") omitted on side with 12 stamps, copper splatters on side with 8 stamps —
f. (44c) Dated "2009" (*'09*) 1.25 .25
g. Booklet pane of 20 #4125f 25.00
h. As No. 4125, copper ("FOREVER") omitted —
i. As No. 4125, die cutting missing, horiz. pair (PS) —
j. As "b," copper ("FOREVER") omitted —

LITHOGRAPHED

Small Microprinting, Bell 16mm Wide

4126 A3148 (41c) multi, dated "2007" 1.25 .25
a. Booklet pane of 20 25.00
b. (42c) Dated "2008" (*'08*) 1.25 .25
c. Booklet pane of 20 #4126b 25.00
d. (44c) Dated "2009" in copper (*'09*) 1.25 .25
e. Booklet pane of 20 #4126d 25.00
f. As "b," copper ("FOREVER") omitted *1,400.*
g. As "c," die cutting omitted —

Medium Microprinting, Bell 15mm Wide

4127 A3148 (41c) multi, dated "2007" (*'07*) 1.25 .25
a. Booklet pane of 20 25.00
b. Booklet pane of 4 5.00
c. Booklet pane of 6 7.50
d. (42c) Dated "2008" (*'08*) 1.25 .25
e. As "d," booklet pane of 20 25.00
f. (42c) Dated "2008," date in smaller type (*'08*) 1.25 .25
g. As "f," booklet pane of 4 5.00
h. As "f," booklet pane of 6 7.50
i. (44c) Dated "2009" in copper (*'09*) 1.25 .25
j. As "i," booklet pane of 20 25.00
k. As "i," die cutting omitted, pair 300.00
l. As No. 4127, copper ("FOREVER") and "USA FIRST-CLASS" missing (PS) —
m. As "e," die cutting omitted *600.00*

PHOTOGRAVURE

Large Microprinting, Bell 16mm Wide

Serpentine Die Cut 8 on 2, 3 or 4 Sides

4128 A3148 (41c) multi, dated "2007" 1.25 .25
a. Booklet pane of 18 22.50
b. (42c) Dated "2009" (*'09*) 1.25 .25
c. As "b," booklet pane of 18 22.50
Nos. 4125-4128 (4) 5.00 1.00

Nos. 4125-4128 were sold for 41c on the day of issue and will be valid for the one ounce first class postage rate after any new rates go into effect. As of May 12, 2008, any "Forever" stamp (Nos. 4125-4128 and 4127d) in stock was sold for 42c. As of May 15, 2009, all "Forever" stamps in stock were sold for 44c, etc.

Nos. 4125a, 4125c, 4126a, 4126c, 4127a, 4127e and 4127j are double-sided booklet panes, with 12 stamps on one side and eight stamps plus a label that serves as a booklet cover on the other side.

Nos. 4127b and 4127c exist with rouletting on backing paper of either gauge 9½ or 13.

See No. 4437.

Flag — A3149

LITHOGRAPHED

2007, Apr. 12 ***Perf. 11¼***

4129 A3149 (41c) multicolored .90 .40

Self-Adhesive

Serpentine Die Cut 11¼x10¾

4130 A3149 (41c) multicolored 1.10 .25

COIL STAMPS

Perf. 9¾ Vert.

4131 A3149 (41c) multicolored 1.10 .40

Self-Adhesive (#4132-4135) With Perpendicular Corners

Serpentine Die Cut 9½ Vert.

4132 A3149 (41c) multicolored 1.20 .25

Serpentine Die Cut 11 Vert.

4133 A3149 (41c) multicolored 1.20 .25
a. Die cutting omitted, pair *1,250.*

Serpentine Die Cut 8½ Vert.

PHOTOGRAVURE

4134 A3149 (41c) multicolored, overall tagging 1.10 .25

With Rounded Corners

Serpentine Die Cut 11 Vert.

4135 A3149 (41c) multicolored 1.25 .75
Nos. 4129-4135 (7) 7.85 2.55

Nos. 4132-4134 are on backing paper as high as the stamp. No. 4135 is on backing paper that is larger than the stamp.

SETTLEMENT OF JAMESTOWN, 400TH ANNIV.

Ships Susan Constant, Godspeed and Discovery — A3150

LITHOGRAPHED

Serpentine Die Cut 10½x10½x10¾

2007, May 11

Self-Adhesive

4136 A3150 41c multicolored 1.10 .25

WILDLIFE

Bighorn Sheep A3151

Florida Panther A3152

LITHOGRAPHED, PHOTOGRAVURE (#4138, 4142)

2007 ***Perf. 11¼x11***

4137 A3152 26c multi .60 .25

Self-Adhesive

Serpentine Die Cut 11

4138 A3151 17c multi .35 .25

Serpentine Die Cut 11¼x11

4139 A3152 26c multi .55 .25

Coil Stamps

Serpentine Die Cut 11 Vert.

4140 A3151 17c multi .35 .25
4141 A3152 26c multi .75 .25
a. Die cutting omitted, pair *350.00*

Booklet Stamp

Serpentine Die Cut 11¼x11 on 3 Sides

4142 A3152 26c multi .55 .25
a. Booklet pane of 10 5.50

Nos. 4137 and 4139 have microprinted "USPS" to the left and above the lower left whisker. No. 4140 has microprinted "USPS" on right horn. No. 4141 has microprinted "USPS" along the right edge of the stamp just above the panther. Nos. 4138 and 4142 lack microprinting.

Issued: Nos. 4137, 4139, 4141, 4142, 5/12; No. 4138, 5/14; No. 4140, 5/21.

PREMIERE OF MOVIE "STAR WARS," 30TH ANNIVERSARY

A3153

No. 4143: a, Darth Vader (40x53mm). b, Millennium Falcon (47x25mm). c, Emperor Palpatine (41x26mm). d, Anakin Skywalker and Obi-Wan Kenobi (41x33mm). e, Luke Skywalker (31x41mm). f, Princess Leia and R2-D2 (41x33mm). g, C-3PO (21x65mm). h, Queen Padmé Amidala (26x48mm). i, Obi-Wan Kenobi (31x48mm). j, Boba Fett (32x40mm). k, Darth Maul (26x41mm). l, Chewbacca and Han Solo (48x31mm). m, X-wing Starfighter (41x26mm). n, Yoda (31x48mm). o, Stormtroopers (41x31mm).

LITHOGRAPHED

2007, May 25 ***Serpentine Die Cut 11***

Self-Adhesive

4143 A3153 Pane of 15 15.00
a.-o. 41c Any single 1.00 .50

PRESIDENTIAL AIRCRAFT

Air Force One — A3154

Marine One — A3155

LITHOGRAPHED & ENGRAVED (#4144), LITHOGRAPHED (#4145)

Serpentine Die Cut 10¾

2007, June 13

Self-Adhesive

4144 A3154 $4.60 multi 9.25 5.00
a. Black (engr.) omitted *200.00*
4145 A3155 $16.25 multi 30.00 16.00

PACIFIC LIGHTHOUSES

Diamond Head Lighthouse, Hawaii A3156

Five Finger Lighthouse, Alaska A3157

Grays Harbor Lighthouse, Washington A3158

Umpqua River Lighthouse, Oregon A3159

St. George Reef Lighthouse, California — A3160

PHOTOGRAVURE

Serpentine Die Cut 11

2007, June 21

Self-Adhesive

4146 A3156 41c multicolored 1.20 .40
4147 A3157 41c multicolored 1.20 .40
4148 A3158 41c multicolored 1.20 .40
4149 A3159 41c multicolored 1.20 .40
4150 A3160 41c multicolored 1.20 .40
a. Horiz. strip of 5, #4146-4150 6.00

WEDDING HEARTS

Heart With Lilac Background A3161

Heart With Pink Background A3162

LITHOGRAPHED (#4151), PHOTOGRAVURE (#4152) BOOKLET STAMP (#4151)

Serpentine Die Cut 10¾ on 2, 3 or 4 Sides

2007, June 27

Self-Adhesive

4151 A3161 41c multicolored 1.00 .25
a. Booklet pane of 20 20.00

Serpentine Die Cut 10¾x11

4152 A3162 58c multicolored 1.25 .25

POLLINATION

Purple Nightshade, Morrison's Bumblebee A3163

Hummingbird Trumpet, Calliope Hummingbird A3164

Saguaro, Lesser Long-nosed Bat — A3165

Prairie Ironweed, Southern Dogface Butterfly — A3166

No. 4153: Type I, Tip of bird wing is directly under center of "U" in "USA," straight edge at left. Type II, Tip of bird wing is directly under the right line of the "U" in "USA," straight edge at right.

No. 4154: Type I, Tip of bird wing is even with the top of denomination, straight edge at right. Type II, Tip of bird wing is well above denomination, straight edge at left.

No. 4155: Type I, Top of "USA" is even with the lower portion of the nearest unopened green saguaro flower bud, straight edge at left. Type II, Top of "USA" is even with the point where the flower and unopened green saguaro bud meet, straight edge at right.

No. 4156: Type I, Bottom of denomination is even with top point of the white triangle found between the bottom of the purple flower and the green leaf below it, straight edge at right. Type II, Bottom of denomination is even with the lower point of the white triangle found between the bottom of the purple flower and the green leaf below it, straight edge at left.

LITHOGRAPHED

Serpentine Die Cut 11 on 2, 3 or 4 Sides

2007, June 29 **Tagged**

Self-Adhesive

Booklet Stamps

4153 A3163 41c multi, Type I .85 .30
a. Type II .85 .30
4154 A3164 41c multi, Type I .85 .30
a. Type II .85 .30
4155 A3165 41c multi, Type I .85 .30
a. Type II .85 .30
4156 A3166 41c multi, Type I .85 .30
a. Type II .85 .30
b. Block of 4, #4153-4156 3.40
c. Block of 4, #4153a-4156a 3.40
d. Booklet pane of 20, 3 each #4153-4156, 2 each #4153a-4156a 17.00

No. 4156d is a double-sided booklet with 12 stamps (2 each #4153-4156, 1 each #4153a-4156a) on one side and 8 stamps plus label (booklet cover) on the other side.

Patriotic Banner — A3167

PHOTOGRAVURE (#4157), LITHOGRAPHED (#4158)

Serpentine Die Cut 11 Vert.

2007, July 4 **Untagged**

Coil Stamps

Self-Adhesive

4157 A3167 (10c) red, gold & blue .30 .25

Serpentine Die Cut 11¾ Vert.

4158 A3167 (10c) red, gold & blue .30 .25

See No. 4385.

MARVEL COMICS SUPERHEROES

A3168

No. 4159: a, Spider-man. b, The Hulk. c, Sub-Mariner. d, The Thing. e, Captain America. f, Silver Surfer. g, Spider-Woman. h, Iron Man. i, Elektra. j, Wolverine. k, Cover of *The Amazing Spider-Man #1.* l, Cover of *The Incredible Hulk #1.* m, Cover of *Sub-Mariner #1.* n, Cover of *The Fantastic Four #3.* o, Cover of *Captain America #100.* p, Cover of *The Silver Surfer #1.* q, Cover of *Marvel Spotlight on The Spider-Woman #32.* r, Cover of *Iron Man #1.* s, Cover of *Daredevil #176 Featuring Elektra.* t, Cover of *The X-Men #1.*

PHOTOGRAVURE

Serpentine Die Cut 10½x10¾

2007, July 26

Self-Adhesive

4159 A3168 Pane of 20 20.00
a.-t. 41c Any single 1.00 .50

VINTAGE MAHOGANY SPEEDBOATS

1915 Hutchinson A3169

1954 Chris-Craft A3170

1939 Hacker-Craft A3171

1931 Gar Wood A3172

LITHOGRAPHED

Serpentine Die Cut 10½

2007, Aug. 4

Self-Adhesive

4160 A3169 41c multicolored .85 .35
4161 A3170 41c multicolored .85 .35
4162 A3171 41c multicolored .85 .35
4163 A3172 41c multicolored .85 .35
a. Horiz. strip of 4, #4160-4163 3.40

Purple Heart Type of 2003

LITHOGRAPHED

Serpentine Die Cut 11¼x10¾

2007, Aug. 7

Self-Adhesive

4164 A2891 41c multicolored .85 .25

See Nos. 3784-3784A, 4032, 4263-4264, 4390.

AMERICAN TREASURES SERIES

Magnolia and Irises, Stained Glass by Louis Comfort Tiffany — A3173

BOOKLET STAMP

Serpentine Die Cut 10¾ on 2 or 3 Sides

2007, Aug. 9

Self-Adhesive

4165 A3173 41c multicolored .85 .25
a. Booklet pane of 20 17.00

No. 4165a is a double-sided booklet pane with 12 stamps on one side and eight stamps plus label (booklet cover) on the other side.

FLOWERS

Iris A3174

Dahlia A3175

Magnolia A3176

Red Gerbera Daisy A3177

Coneflower A3178

Tulip A3179

Water Lily A3180

Poppy A3181

Chrysanthemum A3182

Orange Gerbera Daisy A3183

LITHOGRAPHED

Serpentine Die Cut 9½ Vert.

2007, Aug. 10

COIL STAMPS

Self-Adhesive

4166 A3174 41c multicolored 2.00 .35
4167 A3175 41c multicolored 2.00 .35
4168 A3176 41c multicolored 2.00 .35
4169 A3177 41c multicolored 2.00 .35
4170 A3178 41c multicolored 2.00 .35
4171 A3179 41c multicolored 2.00 .35
4172 A3180 41c multicolored 2.00 .35
4173 A3181 41c multicolored 2.00 .35
4174 A3182 41c multicolored 2.00 .35
4175 A3183 41c multicolored 2.00 .35
a. Strip of 10, #4166-4175 20.00

PHOTOGRAVURE

BOOKLET STAMPS

Serpentine Die Cut 11¼x11½ on 2 or 3 Sides

4176 A3182 41c multicolored 1.25 .35
4177 A3183 41c multicolored 1.25 .35
4178 A3174 41c multicolored 1.25 .35
4179 A3175 41c multicolored 1.25 .35
4180 A3176 41c multicolored 1.25 .35
4181 A3177 41c multicolored 1.25 .35
4182 A3180 41c multicolored 1.25 .35
4183 A3181 41c multicolored 1.25 .35
4184 A3178 41c multicolored 1.25 .35
4185 A3179 41c multicolored 1.25 .35
a. Booklet pane of 20, 2 each #4176-4185 25.00
b. As "a," die cutting missing on Nos. 4178 & 4183 on side with 8 stamps (PS) *1,000.*

No. 4185a is a double-sided booklet pane with 12 stamps on one side (2 each #4176-4177, 1 each #4178-4185) and eight stamps (#4178-4185) plus label (booklet cover) on the other side.

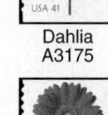

Flag — A3184

LITHOGRAPHED

Serpentine Die Cut 9½ Vert.

2007, Aug. 15

COIL STAMPS

Self-Adhesive

With "USPS" Microprinted on Right Side of Flagpole

With Perpendicular Corners

4186 A3184 41c multicolored 1.20 .25

With "USPS" Microprinted on Left Side of Flagpole

Serpentine Die Cut 11 Vert.

4187 A3184 41c multicolored 1.20 .25

PHOTOGRAVURE

Without "USPS" Microprinting on Flagpole

Serpentine Die Cut 8½ Vert.

4188 A3184 41c multicolored .85 .25

Serpentine Die Cut 11 Vert.

With Rounded Corners

4189 A3184 41c multicolored .85 .25

No. 4188 is on backing paper as high as the stamp. No. 4189 is on backing paper that is larger than the stamp.

LITHOGRAPHED

BOOKLET STAMPS

Serpentine Die Cut 11¼x10¾ on 3 Sides

With "USPS" Microprinted on Right Side of Flagpole

4190 A3184 41c multicolored .85 .25
a. Booklet pane of 10 8.50

With "USPS" Microprinted on Left Side of Flagpole

Serpentine Die Cut 11¼x10¾ on 2 or 3 Sides

4191 A3184 41c multicolored .85 .25
a. Booklet pane of 20 17.00

The microprinting on Nos. 4190 and 4191 is under the ball of the flagpole. The flagpole is light gray on No. 4190 and dark gray on No. 4191. No. 4191a is a double-sided booklet with 12 stamps on one side of the peelable backing and 8 stamps plus label (booklet cover) on the other side.

THE ART OF DISNEY: MAGIC

Mickey Mouse A3185

Peter Pan and Tinker Bell A3186

Dumbo and Timothy Mouse A3187

Aladdin and Genie A3188

PHOTOGRAVURE

Serpentine Die Cut 10½x10¾

2007, Aug. 16

Self-Adhesive

4192 A3185 41c multicolored .85 .30
4193 A3186 41c multicolored .85 .30
4194 A3187 41c multicolored .85 .30
4195 A3188 41c multicolored .85 .30
a. Block or strip of 4, #4192-4195 3.40

CELEBRATE

A3189

LITHOGRAPHED

Serpentine Die Cut 10¾

2007, Aug. 17

Self-Adhesive

4196 A3189 41c multicolored .85 .25

See Nos. 4335, 4407.

LEGENDS OF HOLLYWOOD

James Stewart (1908-97), Actor — A3190

2007, Aug. 17

Self-Adhesive

4197 A3190 41c multicolored 1.00 .25

ALPINE TUNDRA

A3191

No. 4198 — Wildlife: a, Elk. b, Golden eagle, horiz. c, Yellow-bellied marmot. d, American pika. e, Bighorn sheep. f, Magdalena alpine butterfly. g, White-tailed ptarmigan. h, Rocky Mountain parnassian butterfly. i, Melissa arctic butterfly, horiz. j, Brown-capped rosy-finch, horiz.

PHOTOGRAVURE

2007, Aug. 28

Self-Adhesive

4198 A3191 Pane of 10 8.50
a.-j. 41c any single .85 .40

GERALD R. FORD

Gerald R. Ford (1913-2006), 38th President — A3192

LITHOGRAPHED

Serpentine Die Cut 11

2007, Aug. 31

Self-Adhesive

4199 A3192 41c multicolored .85 .25

JURY DUTY

Twelve Jurors — A3193

Serpentine Die Cut 10½

2007, Sept. 12

Self-Adhesive

4200 A3193 41c multicolored .85 .25

MENDEZ v. WESTMINSTER, 60th ANNIV.

A3194

LITHOGRAPHED

Serpentine Die Cut 11

2007, Sept. 14

Self-Adhesive

4201 A3194 41c multicolored .85 .25

Eid Type of 2001

PHOTOGRAVURE

Serpentine Die Cut 11

2007, Sept. 28

Self-Adhesive

4202 A2734 41c multicolored .90 .25

See Nos. 3532, 3674, 4117, 4351, 4416.

AURORAS

Aurora Borealis — A3195

Aurora Australis — A3196

LITHOGRAPHED

Serpentine Die Cut 10¾

2007, Oct. 1

Self-Adhesive

4203 A3195 41c multicolored 1.25 .30
4204 A3196 41c multicolored 1.25 .30
a. Horiz. or vert. pair, #4203-4204 2.50

YODA

A3197

Serpentine Die Cut 10½x10¾

2007, Oct. 25

Self-Adhesive

4205 A3197 41c multicolored 1.00 .25

CHRISTMAS

Madonna of the Carnation, by Bernardino Luini — A3198

LITHOGRAPHED

Serpentine Die Cut 10¾x11 on 2 or 3 Sides

2007, Oct. 25

Self-Adhesive

Booklet Stamps (#4206, 4210b, 4211-4218)

4206 A3198 41c multicolored .85 .25
a. Booklet pane of 20 17.00

No. 4206a is a double-sided booklet pane with 12 stamps on one side and eight stamps plus label that serves as a booklet cover on the other side.

Knit Reindeer A3199

Knit Christmas Tree A3200

Knit Snowman A3201

Knit Bear A3202

Serpentine Die Cut 10¾ on 2, 3 or 4 Sides

4207 A3199 41c multicolored .85 .25
4208 A3200 41c multicolored .85 .25
4209 A3201 41c multicolored .85 .25
4210 A3202 41c multicolored, overall tagging .85 .25
b. Block or vert. strip of 4, #4207-4210 3.40
d. Booklet pane of 20 17.00

No. 4210d is a double-sided booklet pane with 12 stamps on one side and eight stamps plus label that serves as a booklet cover on the other side.

Knit Reindeer A3203

Knit Christmas Tree A3204

Knit Snowman A3205

Knit Bear A3206

Serpentine Die Cut 11¼x11 on 2 or 3 Sides

4211 A3203 41c multicolored 1.25 .25
4212 A3204 41c multicolored 1.25 .25
4213 A3205 41c multicolored 1.25 .25
4214 A3206 41c multicolored 1.25 .25
a. Block of 4, #4211-4214 5.00
b. Booklet pane of 4, #4211-4214 5.00
c. Booklet pane of 6, #4213-4214, 2 each #4211-4212 7.50
d. Booklet pane of 6, #4211-4212, 2 each #4213-4214 7.50

PHOTOGRAVURE

Serpentine Die Cut 8 on 2, 3 or 4 Sides

4215 A3203 41c multicolored 1.50 .25
4216 A3204 41c multicolored 1.50 .25
4217 A3205 41c multicolored 1.50 .25
4218 A3206 41c multicolored 1.50 .25
a. Block or strip of 4, #4215-4218 6.00
b. Booklet pane of 18, 4 each #4215, 4218, 5 each #4216, 4217 27.00
Nos. 4206-4218 (13) 15.25 3.25

Hanukkah Type of 2004

LITHOGRAPHED

Serpentine Die Cut 10¾x11

2007, Oct. 26

Self-Adhesive

4219 A2962 41c multicolored .85 .25

See Nos. 3880, 4118, 4372.

Kwanzaa Type of 2004

LITHOGRAPHED

Serpentine Die Cut 11x10¾

2007, Oct. 26

Self-Adhesive

4220 A2963 41c multicolored .85 .25

See Nos. 3881, 4119, 4373.

CHINESE NEW YEAR

Year of the Rat — A3207

PHOTOGRAVURE

Serpentine Die Cut 10¾

2008, Jan. 9 **Self-Adhesive**

4221 A3207 41c multicolored .85 .25

BLACK HERITAGE SERIES

Charles W. Chesnutt (1858-1932), Writer — A3208

Serpentine Die Cut 11

2008, Jan. 31 **Self-Adhesive**

4222 A3208 41c multicolored .85 .25

LITERARY ARTS SERIES

Marjorie Kinnan Rawlings (1896-1953), Writer — A3209

Serpentine Die Cut 11

2008, Feb. 21

Self-Adhesive

4223 A3209 41c multicolored .85 .25

AMERICAN SCIENTISTS

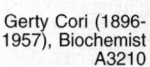

Gerty Cori (1896-1957), Biochemist A3210

Linus Pauling (1901-94), Structural Chemist — A3211

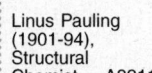

Edwin Hubble (1889-1953), Astronomer A3212

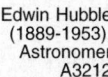

John Bardeen (1908-91), Theoretical Physicist — A3213

2008, Mar. 6

Self-Adhesive

4224 A3210 41c multicolored 1.00 .35
4225 A3211 41c multicolored 1.00 .35
4226 A3212 41c multicolored 1.00 .35
4227 A3213 41c multicolored 1.00 .35
a. Horiz. strip of 4, #4224-4227 4.00

Flag at Dusk A3214

Flag at Night A3215

Flag at Dawn A3216

Flag at Midday A3217

PHOTOGRAVURE

2008, Apr. 18 ***Perf. 9¾ Vert.***

COIL STAMPS

4228 A3214 42c multicolored 2.50 .40
4229 A3215 42c multicolored 2.50 .40
4230 A3216 42c multicolored 2.50 .40
4231 A3217 42c multicolored 2.50 .40
a. Horiz. strip of 4, #4228-4231 10.00 1.60

Self-Adhesive

With Perpendicular Corners

Serpentine Die Cut 9½ Vert.

4232 A3214 42c multicolored 2.25 .25
4233 A3215 42c multicolored 2.25 .25
4234 A3216 42c multicolored 2.25 .25
4235 A3217 42c multicolored 2.25 .25
a. Horiz. strip of 4, #4232-4235 9.00

Serpentine Die Cut 11 Vert.

4236 A3214 42c multicolored 2.50 .25
4237 A3215 42c multicolored 2.50 .25
4238 A3216 42c multicolored 2.50 .25
4239 A3217 42c multicolored 2.50 .25
a. Horiz. strip of 4, #4236-4239 10.00

Serpentine Die Cut 8½ Vert.

4240 A3214 42c multicolored 2.00 .25
4241 A3215 42c multicolored 2.00 .25
4242 A3216 42c multicolored 2.00 .25
4243 A3217 42c multicolored 2.00 .25
a. Horiz. strip of 4, #4240-4243 8.00

Serpentine Die Cut 11 Vert.

With Rounded Corners

4244 A3214 42c multicolored 1.25 .30
4245 A3215 42c multicolored 1.25 .30
4246 A3216 42c multicolored 1.25 .30
4247 A3217 42c multicolored 1.25 .30
a. Horiz. strip of 4, #4244-4247 6.00
Nos. 4228-4247 (20) 42.00 5.80

Nos. 4232-4243 are on backing paper as high as the stamp. Nos. 4244-4247 are on backing paper that is larger than the stamp. Nos. 4232-4235 have "USPS" microprinted on the right side of a white flag stripe. Nos. 4236-4239 have "USPS" micorprinted on red flag stripes. On Nos. 4244-4247, the paper, vignette size and "2008" year date are slightly larger than those features on Nos. 4236-4239.

AMERICAN JOURNALISTS

Martha Gellhorn (1908-98) A3218

John Hersey (1914-93) A3219

George Polk (1913-48) A3220

Ruben Salazar (1928-70) A3221

Eric Sevareid (1912-92) A3222

LITHOGRAPHED

Serpentine Die Cut 10¾x10½

2008, Apr. 22

Self-Adhesive

4248 A3218 42c multicolored 1.40 .40
4249 A3219 42c multicolored 1.40 .40
4250 A3220 42c multicolored 1.40 .40
4251 A3221 42c multicolored 1.40 .40
4252 A3222 42c multicolored 1.40 .40
a. Vert. strip of 5, #4248-4252 7.00

TROPICAL FRUIT

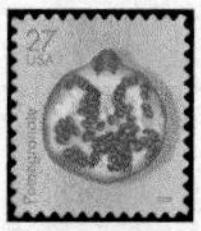

Pomegranate A3223

Star Fruit A3224

Kiwi A3225

Papaya A3226

Guava — A3227

LITHOGRAPHED

Serpentine Die Cut 11¼x10¾

2008, Apr. 25

Self-Adhesive

4253 A3223 27c multicolored 1.25 .25
4254 A3224 27c multicolored 1.25 .25
4255 A3225 27c multicolored 1.25 .25
4256 A3226 27c multicolored 1.25 .25
4257 A3227 27c multicolored 1.25 .25
a. Horiz. strip of 5, #4253-4257 6.25

PHOTOGRAVURE

COIL STAMPS

Serpentine Die Cut 8½ Vert.

4258 A3226 27c multicolored 2.00 .25
4259 A3227 27c multicolored 2.00 .25
4260 A3223 27c multicolored 2.00 .25
4261 A3224 27c multicolored 2.00 .25
4262 A3225 multicolored 2.00 .25
a. Strip of 5, #4258-4262 10.00
b. As No. 4262, light green ("27 USA," "Kiwi" and year date) omitted —
Nos. 4253-4262 (10) 16.25 2.50

Purple Heart Type of 2003

LITHOGRAPHED

2008, Apr. 30 ***Perf. 11¼***

4263 A2891 42c multicolored .90 .25

Self-Adhesive

Serpentine Die Cut 11¼x10¾

4264 A2891 42c multicolored .85 .25

See Nos. 4032, 4164, 4390.

FRANK SINATRA

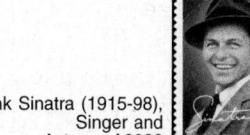

Frank Sinatra (1915-98), Singer and Actor — A3228

Serpentine Die Cut 10¾

2008, May 13

Self-Adhesive

4265 A3228 42c multicolored .85 .25

MINNESOTA STATEHOOD, 150th ANNIV.

Bridge Over Mississippi River Near Winona — A3229

Serpentine Die Cut 10¾

2008, May 17

Self-Adhesive

4266 A3229 42c multicolored .85 .25

WILDLIFE

Dragonfly — A3230

LITHOGRAPHED

Serpentine Die Cut 11¼x11

2008, May 19

Self-Adhesive

4267 A3230 62c multicolored 2.50 .25

AMERICAN LANDMARKS

Mount Rushmore A3231

Hoover Dam — A3232

2008 ***Serpentine Die Cut 10¾x10½***

Self-Adhesive

4268 A3231 $4.80 multi 12.00 5.00
4269 A3232 $16.50 multi 35.00 17.00

Issued: $4.80, 6/6; $16.50, 6/20.

LOVE

Man Carrying Heart — A3233

PHOTOGRAVURE

Serpentine Die Cut 10¾ on 2, 3, or 4 Sides

2008, June 10

Booklet Stamp

Self-Adhesive

4270 A3233 42c multicolored .95 .25
a. Booklet pane of 20 19.00

WEDDING HEARTS

Heart With Light Green Background A3234

Heart With Buff Background A3235

LITHOGRAPHED (#4271), PHOTOGRAVURE (#4272) BOOKLET STAMP (#4271)

Serpentine Die Cut 10¾ on 2, 3 or 4 Sides

2008, June 10

Self-Adhesive

4271 A3234 42c multicolored .90 .25
a. Booklet pane of 20 18.00

Serpentine Die Cut 10¾

4272 A3235 59c multicolored 1.25 .25

FLAGS OF OUR NATION

American Flag and Clouds A3236

Alabama Flag and Shrimp Boat — A3237

Alaska Flag and Humpback Whale A3238

American Samoa Flag and Island Peaks and Trees — A3239

Arizona Flag and Saguaro Cacti — A3240

Arkansas Flag and Wood Duck — A3241

California Flag and Coast — A3242

Colorado Flag and Mountain A3243

Connecticut Flag, Sailboats and Buoy — A3244

Delaware Flag and Beach A3245

PHOTOGRAVURE

Serpentine Die Cut 11 Vert.

2008, June 14

Self-Adhesive

Coil Stamps

4273	A3236	42c multicolored	1.00	.30
4274	A3237	42c multicolored	1.00	.30
4275	A3238	42c multicolored	1.00	.30
4276	A3239	42c multicolored	1.00	.30
4277	A3240	42c multicolored	1.00	.30
a.		Strip of 5, #4273-4277	5.00	
4278	A3241	42c multicolored	1.00	.30
4279	A3242	42c multicolored	1.00	.30
4280	A3243	42c multicolored	1.00	.30
4281	A3244	42c multicolored	1.00	.30
4282	A3245	42c multicolored	1.00	.30
a.		Strip of 5, #4278-4282	5.00	
b.		P # set of 10, #4277a + 4282a	10.00	

No. 4273 always has a plate number. No. 4282b may be collected as one continuous strip, but the item will not fit in any standard album.

District of Columbia Flag and Cherry Tree — A3246

Florida Flag and Anhinga A3247

Georgia Flag, Fence and Lamppost A3248

Guam Flag, Fish and Tropicbird A3249

Hawaii Flag and Ohia Lehua Flowers A3250

Idaho Flag and Rainbow Trout — A3251

Illinois Flag and Windmill A3252

Indiana Flag and Tractor A3253

Iowa Flag, Farm Field and Cornstalks A3254

Kansas Flag and Farm Buildings A3255

2008, Sept. 2

Self-Adhesive

Coil Stamps

4283	A3246	42c multicolored	1.00	.30
4284	A3247	42c multicolored	1.00	.30
4285	A3248	42c multicolored	1.00	.30
4286	A3249	42c multicolored	1.00	.30
4287	A3250	42c multicolored	1.00	.30
a.		Strip of 5, #4283-4287	5.00	
4288	A3251	42c multicolored	1.00	.30
4289	A3252	42c multicolored	1.00	.30
4290	A3253	42c multicolored	1.00	.30
4291	A3254	42c multicolored	1.00	.30
4292	A3255	42c multicolored	1.00	.30
a.		Strip of 5, #4288-4292	5.00	
b.		P # set of 10, #4287a + 4192a	10.00	

No. 4283 always has a plate number. No. 4292b may be collected as one continuous strip, but the item will not fit in any standard album.

Kentucky Flag, Fence and Horses A3256

Louisiana Flag and Brown Pelicans A3257

Maine Flag and Moose A3258

Maryland Flag and Red-winged Blackbird A3259

Massachusetts Flag, Sea Birds and Sailboats A3260

Michigan Flag and Great Lakes Ships — A3261

Minnesota Flag, Swans and Grain Elevator A3262

Mississippi Flag and Black Bears — A3263

Missouri Flag and Paddle Wheeler A3264

American Flag and Wheat A3265

2009, Aug. 6

Self-Adhesive

Coil Stamps

4293	A3256	44c multicolored	1.00	.30
4294	A3257	44c multicolored	1.00	.30
4295	A3258	44c multicolored	1.00	.30
4296	A3259	44c multicolored	1.00	.30
4297	A3260	44c multicolored	1.00	.30
a.		Strip of 5, #4293-4297	5.00	
4298	A3261	44c multicolored	1.00	.30
4299	A3262	44c multicolored	1.00	.30
4300	A3263	44c multicolored	1.00	.30
4301	A3264	44c multicolored	1.00	.30
4302	A3265	44c multicolored	1.00	.30
a.		Strip of 5, #4298-4302	5.00	
b.		P # set of 10, #4297a + 4302a	10.00	

No. 4293 always has a plate number. No. 4302b may be collected as one continuous strip, but the item will not fit in any standard album.

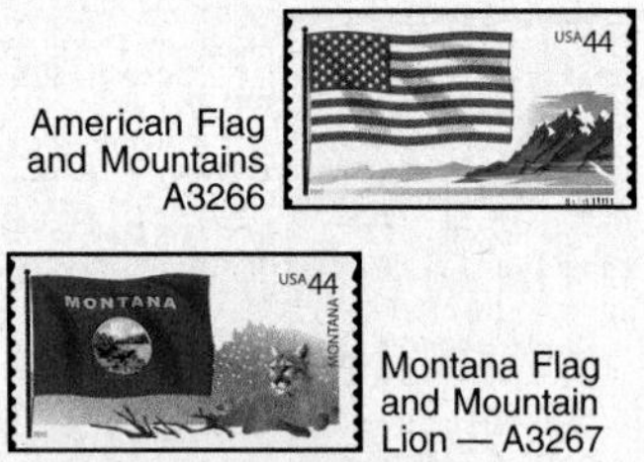

American Flag and Mountains A3266

Montana Flag and Mountain Lion — A3267

Nebraska Flag and Central-pivot Irrigation System A3268

Nevada Flag, Mountains and Ocotillos A3269

New Hampshire Flag and Loon — A3270

New Jersey Flag and Sand Castle A3271

New Mexico Flag, Mountains and Hot Air Balloons A3272

New York Flag, Fireboats and City Skyline A3273

North Carolina Flag, Great Blue Heron and Cape Hatteras Lighthouse A3274

North Dakota Flag and Elk — A3275

2010, Apr. 16

Self-Adhesive

Coil Stamps

4303	A3266	44c multicolored	1.00	.30
4304	A3267	44c multicolored	1.00	.30
4305	A3268	44c multicolored	1.00	.30
4306	A3269	44c multicolored	1.00	.30
4307	A3270	44c multicolored	1.00	.30
a.		Strip of 5, #4303-4307	5.00	
4308	A3271	44c multicolored	1.00	.30
4309	A3272	44c multicolored	1.00	.30
4310	A3273	44c multicolored	1.00	.30
4311	A3274	44c multicolored	1.00	.30
4312	A3275	44c multicolored	1.00	.30
a.		Strip of 5, #4308-4312	5.00	
b.		P # set of 10, #4307a + 4312a	10.00	

No. 4303 always has a plate number. No. 4312b may be collected as one continuous strip, but the item will not fit in any standard album.

Northern Marianas Flag, Beach and Palm Trees — A3276

Ohio Flag, Butterfly, Milkweed Flowers and River — A3277

Oklahoma Flag and Oil Pumps A3278

Oregon Flag, Mount Hood and Camas Lilies — A3279

Pennsylvania Flag and White-tailed Deer — A3280

Puerto Rico Flag and Puerto Rican Tody Bird — A3281

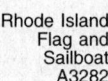

Rhode Island Flag and Sailboat A3282

South Carolina Flag, Marsh and Gazebo A3283

South Dakota Flag and Bison — A3284

Tennessee Flag and Scarlet Tanagers A3285

PHOTOGRAVURE

Serpentine Die Cut 11 Vert.

2011, Aug. 11

Self-Adhesive

Coil Stamps

4313	A3276	(44c) multicolored	1.50	.30
4314	A3277	(44c) multicolored	1.50	.30
4315	A3278	(44c) multicolored	1.50	.30
4316	A3279	(44c) multicolored	1.50	.30
4317	A3280	(44c) multicolored	1.50	.30
a.		Strip of 5, #4313-4317	7.50	
4318	A3281	(44c) multicolored	1.50	.30
4319	A3282	(44c) multicolored	1.50	.30
4320	A3283	(44c) multicolored	1.50	.30
4321	A3284	(44c) multicolored	1.50	.30
4322	A3285	(44c) multicolored	1.50	.30
a.		Strip of 5, #4318-4322	7.50	
b.		P# set of 10, #4317a + 4322a	12.50	

Alternating examples of the five examples of No. 4313 in the roll have a plate number. No. 4322b may be collected as one continuous strip, but the item will not fit in any standard album.

Texas Flag, Cotton Plant and Field — A3286

Utah Flag, Cactus and Rock Arch — A3287

Vermont Flag and Owls — A3288

Virgin Islands Flag, Sailfish and Boat — A3289

Virginia Flag and Replicas of Ships that Carried Settlers to Jamestown A3290

Washington Flag and Evergreen Forest — A3291

West Virginia Flag and Wild Turkeys A3292

Wisconsin Flag and Dairy Cows — A3293

Wyoming Flag and Bighorn Sheep A3294

American Flag and Fruited Plain — A3295

PHOTOGRAVURE

Serpentine Die Cut 11 Vert.

2012, Aug. 16

Self-Adhesive

Coil Stamps

4323 A3286 (45c) multicolored 3.00 .30
4324 A3287 (45c) multicolored 3.00 .30
4325 A3288 (45c) multicolored 3.00 .30
4326 A3289 (45c) multicolored 3.00 .30
4327 A3290 (45c) multicolored 3.00 .30
a. Strip of 5, #4323-4327 15.00
4328 A3291 (45c) multicolored 3.00 .30
4329 A3292 (45c) multicolored 3.00 .30
4330 A3293 (45c) multicolored 3.00 .30
4331 A3294 (45c) multicolored 3.00 .30
4332 A3295 (45c) multicolored 3.00 .30
a. Strip of 5, #4328-4332 15.00
b. P# set of 10, #4327a + 4332a 30.00

Alternating examples of the five examples of No. 4323 in the roll have a plate number. No. 4332b may be collected as one continuous strip, but the item will not fit in any standard album.

CHARLES (1907-78) AND RAY (1912-88) EAMES, DESIGNERS

A3296

No. 4333: a, Christmas card depicting Charles and Ray Eames. b, "Crosspatch" fabric design. c, Stacking chairs. d, Case Study House #8, Pacific Palisades, CA. e, Wire-base table. f, Lounge chair and ottoman. g, Hang-it-all. h, La Chaise. i, Scene from film, "Tops." j, Wire mesh chair. k, Cover of May 1943 edition of *California Arts & Architecture* Magazine. l, House of Cards. m, Molded plywood sculpture. n, Eames Storage Unit. o, Aluminum group chair. p, Molded plywood chair.

PHOTOGRAVURE

Serpentine Die Cut 10¾x10½

2008, June 17

Self-Adhesive

4333 A3296 Pane of 16 + label 18.00
a.-p. 42c Any single 1.10 .50

SUMMER OLYMPIC GAMES, BEIJING, CHINA

Gymnast A3297

LITHOGRAPHED

Serpentine Die Cut 10¾

2008, June 19

Self-Adhesive

4334 A3297 42c multicolored .85 .25

Celebrate Type of 2007

Serpentine Die Cut 10¾

2008, July 10

Self-Adhesive

4335 A3189 42c multicolored .85 .25

VINTAGE BLACK CINEMA

Poster for "Black and Tan" A3298

Poster for "The Sport of the Gods" A3299

Poster for "Prinsesse Tam-Tam" A3300

Poster for "Caldonia" A3301

Poster for "Hallelujah" — A3302

Serpentine Die Cut 10¾

2008, July 16 **Tagged**

Self-Adhesive

4336 A3298 42c multicolored .95 .45
4337 A3299 42c multicolored .95 .45
4338 A3300 42c multicolored .95 .45
4339 A3301 42c multicolored .95 .45
4340 A3302 42c multicolored .95 .45
a. Horiz. strip of 5, #4336-4340 4.75

"TAKE ME OUT TO THE BALLGAME," CENT.

Baseball Players and First Six Notes of Song — A3303

PHOTOGRAVURE

Serpentine Die Cut 11

2008, July 16

Self-Adhesive

4341 A3303 42c multicolored .85 .25

THE ART OF DISNEY: IMAGINATION

Pongo and Pup — A3304

Steamboat Willie — A3305

Princess Aurora, Flora, Fauna and Merryweather A3306

Mowgli and Baloo A3307

Serpentine Die Cut 10½x10¾

2008, Aug. 7

Self-Adhesive

4342 A3304 42c multicolored .85 .30
4343 A3305 42c multicolored .85 .30
4344 A3306 42c multicolored .85 .30
4345 A3307 42c multicolored .85 .30
a. Block or strip of 4, #4342-4345 3.40

AMERICAN TREASURES SERIES

Valley of the Yosemite, by Albert Bierstadt A3308

LITHOGRAPHED

BOOKLET STAMP

Serpentine Die Cut 11 on 2 or 3 Sides

2008, Aug. 14

Self-Adhesive

4346 A3308 42c multicolored .85 .25
a. Booklet pane of 20 17.00

No. 4346a is a double-sided booklet pane with 12 stamps on one side and eight stamps plus label (booklet cover) on the other side.

Sunflower — A3309

BOOKLET STAMP

Serpentine Die Cut 11¼x10¾ on 2 or 3 Sides

2008, Aug. 15

Self-Adhesive

4347 A3309 42c multicolored .85 .25
a. Booklet pane of 20 17.00

No. 4347a is a double-sided booklet pane with 12 stamps on one side and eight stamps plus label (booklet cover) on the other side.

Sea Coast Type of 2002

LITHOGRAPHED

COIL STAMP

Perf. 9¾ Vert.

2008, Sept. 5 **Untagged**

4348 A2853 (5c) multicolored .30 .25

No. 4348 has "2008" year date in black, and microprinted "USPS" at the end of the purple rock to the right of the crashing wave.

See Nos. 3693, 3775, 3785, 3864, 3874-3875.

LATIN JAZZ

Musicians A3310

PHOTOGRAVURE

Serpentine Die Cut 11x10¾

2008, Sept. 8

Self-Adhesive

4349 A3310 42c multicolored .85 .25

LEGENDS OF HOLLYWOOD

Bette Davis (1908-89), Actress — A3311

LITHOGRAPHED

Serpentine Die Cut 10¾

2008, Sept. 18

Self-Adhesive

4350 A3311 42c multicolored 1.00 .25

Eid Type of 2001

PHOTOGRAVURE

Serpentine Die Cut 11

2008, Sept. 23

Self-Adhesive

4351 A2734 42c multicolored .85 .25

GREAT LAKES DUNES

A3312

No. 4352 — Wildlife: a, Vesper sparrow. b, Red fox, vert. c, Piping plover. d, Eastern hog-nose snake. e, Common mergansers. f, Spotted sandpiper, vert. g, Tiger beetle, vert. h, White-footed mouse, vert. i, Piping plover nestlings. j, Red admiral butterfly, vert.

Serpentine Die Cut 10¾

2008, Oct. 2

Self-Adhesive

4352 A3312 Pane of 10 10.00
a.-j. 42c Any single 1.00 .40

AUTOMOBILES OF THE 1950s

1959 Cadillac Eldorado A3313

1957 Studebaker Golden Hawk — A3314

1957 Pontiac Safari — A3315

1957 Lincoln Premiere A3316

1957 Chrysler 300C — A3317

LITHOGRAPHED

2008, Oct. 3

Self-Adhesive

4353 A3313 42c multicolored .85 .45
4354 A3314 42c multicolored .85 .45
4355 A3315 42c multicolored .85 .45
4356 A3316 42c multicolored .85 .45
4357 A3317 42c multicolored .85 .45
a. Vert. strip of 5, #4353-4357 4.25

ALZHEIMER'S DISEASE AWARENESS

A3318

PHOTOGRAVURE

Serpentine Die Cut 10¾

2008, Oct. 17

Self-Adhesive

4358 A3318 42c multicolored .85 .25

CHRISTMAS

Virgin and Child with the Young John the Baptist, by Sandro Botticelli
A3319

Drummer Nutcracker
A3320

Santa Claus Nutcracker
A3321

King Nutcracker
A3322

Soldier Nutcracker — A3323

LITHOGRAPHED

Serpentine Die Cut 10¾x11 on 2 or 3 Sides

2008, Oct. 23

Self-Adhesive

Booklet Stamps

4359 A3319 42c multicolored .85 .25
a. Booklet pane of 20 17.00
b. Die cutting omitted, pair —
4360 A3320 42c multicolored 1.00 .25
4361 A3321 42c multicolored 1.00 .25
4362 A3322 42c multicolored 1.00 .25
4363 A3323 42c multicolored 1.00 .25
a. Block of 4, #4360-4363 4.00
b. Booklet pane of 20, 5 each #4360-4363 20.00

No. 4359a is a double-sided booklet pane with 12 stamps on one side and eight stamps plus label that serves as a booklet cover on the other side. No. 4363b is a double-sided booklet pane with 12 stamps on one side (3 each of Nos. 4360-4363) and eight stamps (2 each of Nos. 4360-4363) plus label that serves as a booklet cover on the other side.

Drummer Nutcracker
A3324

Santa Claus Nutcracker
A3325

King Nutcracker
A3326

Soldier Nutcracker
A3327

Serpentine Die Cut 11¼x11 on 2 or 3 Sides

4364 A3324 42c multicolored 1.25 .25
4365 A3325 42c multicolored 1.25 .25
4366 A3326 42c multicolored 1.25 .25
4367 A3327 42c multicolored 1.25 .25
a. Block of 4, #4364-4367 5.00
b. Booklet pane of 4, #4364-4367 5.00
c. Booklet pane of 6, #4366-4367, 2 each #4364-4365 7.50
d. Booklet pane of 6, #4364-4365, 2 each #4366-4367 7.50

Serpentine Die Cut 8 on 2, 3 or 4 Sides

PHOTOGRAVURE

4368 A3324 42c multicolored 1.25 .25
4369 A3325 42c multicolored 1.25 .25
4370 A3326 42c multicolored 1.25 .25
4371 A3327 42c multicolored 1.25 .25
a. Block or strip of 4, #4368-4371 5.00
b. Booklet pane of 18, 5 each #4368-4369, 4 each #4370-4371 22.50
Nos. 4359-4371 (13) 14.85 3.25

Hanukkah Type of 2004

LITHOGRAPHED

Serpentine Die Cut 10¾x11

2008, Oct. 24

Self-Adhesive

4372 A2962 42c multicolored .85 .25

Kwanzaa Type of 2004

Serpentine Die Cut 11x10¾

2008, Oct. 24

Self-Adhesive

4373 A2963 42c multicolored .85 .25

ALASKA STATEHOOD, 50TH ANNIV.

Dogsledder Near Rainy Pass — A3328

Serpentine Die Cut 10¾

2009, Jan. 3

Self-Adhesive

4374 A3328 42c multicolored .85 .25

CHINESE NEW YEAR

Year of the Ox — A3329

2009, Jan. 8

Self-Adhesive

4375 A3329 42c multicolored .85 .25

OREGON STATEHOOD, 150TH ANNIV.

Pacific Coast of Oregon — A3330

2009, Jan. 14

Self-Adhesive

4376 A3330 42c multicolored .85 .25

EDGAR ALLAN POE

Edgar Allan Poe (1809-49), Writer — A3331

PHOTOGRAVURE

2009, Jan. 16

Self-Adhesive

4377 A3331 42c multicolored .90 .25

AMERICAN LANDMARKS

Redwood Forest — A3332

Old Faithful — A3333

LITHOGRAPHED

Serpentine Die Cut 10¾x10½

2009, Jan. 16

Self-Adhesive

4378 A3332 $4.95 multi 11.00 5.00
4379 A3333 $17.50 multi 40.00 20.00

ABRAHAM LINCOLN (1809-65), 16TH PRESIDENT

Lincoln as Rail-splitter
A3334

Lincoln as Lawyer — A3335

Lincoln as Politician
A3336

Lincoln as President
A3337

Serpentine Die Cut 10¾

2009, Feb. 9

Self-Adhesive

4380 A3334 42c multicolored 1.50 .35
4381 A3335 42c multicolored 1.50 .35
4382 A3336 42c multicolored 1.50 .35
4383 A3337 42c multicolored 1.50 .35
a. Horiz. strip of 4, #4380-4383 6.00

CIVIL RIGHTS PIONEERS

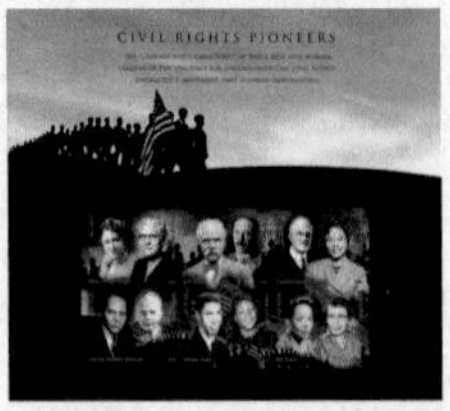

A3338

No. 4384: a, Mary Church Terrell (1863-1954), writer, Mary White Ovington (1865-1951), journalist. b, J. R. Clifford (1848-1933), attorney, Joel Elias Spingarn (1875-1939), educator. c, Oswald Garrison Villard (1872-1949), co-founder of National Association for the Advancement of Colored People (NAACP), Daisy Gatson Bates (1914-99), mentor of black Little Rock Central High School students. d, Charles Hamilton Houston (1895-1950), lawyer, Walter White (1893-1955), chief secretary of NAACP. e, Medgar Evers (1925-63), assassinated Mississippi NAACP field secretary, Fannie Lou Hamer (1917-77), voting rights activist. f, Ella Baker (1903-86), activist, Ruby Hurley (1909-80), NAACP Southeast Regional Director.

PHOTOGRAVURE

2009, Feb. 21

Self-Adhesive

4384 A3338 Pane of 6 9.00
a.-f. 42c Any single 1.50 .40

Patriotic Banner Type of 2007

LITHOGRAPHED

COIL STAMP

Perf. 9¾ Vert.

2009, Feb. 24 **Untagged**

4385 A3167 (10c) multicolored .30 .25

See Nos. 4157-4158.

LITERARY ARTS

Richard Wright (1908-60), Author — A3339

Serpentine Die Cut 10¾

2009, Apr. 9

Self-Adhesive

4386 A3339 61c multicolored 1.25 .25

WILDLIFE

Polar Bear
A3340

Dolphin
A3341

LITHOGRAPHED (#4387), PHOTOGRAVURE

2009 ***Serpentine Die Cut 11¼x11***

Self-Adhesive

4387 A3340 28c multi .75 .25
a. Die cutting omitted, pane of 20 *7,250.*

Serpentine Die Cut 11

4388 A3341 64c multi 1.40 .25

COIL STAMP

Serpentine Die Cut 8½ Vert.

4389 A3340 28c multi .60 .25

Issued: Nos. 4387, 4389, 4/16; No. 4388, 6/12.

Purple Heart Type of 2003

LITHOGRAPHED

Serpentine Die Cut 11¼x10¾

2009, Apr. 28

Self-Adhesive

4390 A2891 44c multicolored .90 .25

See Nos. 3784-3784A, 4032, 4164, 4263-4264.

Flag — A3342

LITHOGRAPHED

2009 ***Perf. 9¾ Vert.***

COIL STAMPS

4391 A3342 44c multi 1.00 1.00

Self-Adhesive

Serpentine Die Cut 11 Vert.

With Pointed Corners

4392 A3342 44c multi 2.00 .25
a. Die cutting omitted, pair *350.00*

Serpentine Die Cut 9½ Vert.

4393 A3342 44c multi 1.50 .25

Serpentine Die Cut 8½ Vert.

PHOTOGRAVURE

4394 A3342 44c multi 1.50 .25

Serpentine Die Cut 11 Vert.

With Rounded Corners

4395 A3342 44c multi 1.25 .25

BOOKLET STAMP

Serpentine Die Cut 11¼x10¾ on 3 Sides

4396 A3342 44c multi .90 .25
a. Booklet pane of 10 9.00

Nos. 4392-4394 are on backing paper as high as the stamp. No. 4395 is on backing paper that is taller than the stamp. No. 4393 has microprinted "USPS" on white stripe below the blue field.

Issued: Nos. 4391, 4395, 5/1; Nos. 4392-4394, 5/8, No. 4396, 6/5.

WEDDINGS

Wedding Rings
A3343

Wedding Cake
A3344

LITHOGRAPHED, PHOTOGRAVURE (#4398)

Serpentine Die Cut 10¾

2009, May 1

Self-Adhesive

4397	A3343	44c multicolored	.90	.25
4398	A3344	61c multicolored	1.40	.25

See Nos. 4521, 4602, 4735, 4867, 5000.

THE SIMPSONS TELEVISION SHOW, 20TH ANNIV.

Homer Simpson
A3345

Marge Simpson
A3346

Bart Simpson
A3347

Lisa Simpson
A3348

Maggie Simpson — A3349

LITHOGRAPHED
BOOKLET STAMPS

Serpentine Die Cut 10¾ on 2, 3 or 4 Sides

2009, May 7

Self-Adhesive

4399	A3345	44c multicolored	1.15	.40
4400	A3346	44c multicolored	1.15	.40
4401	A3347	44c multicolored	1.15	.40
4402	A3348	44c multicolored	1.15	.40
4403	A3349	44c multicolored	1.15	.40
a.		Horiz. strip of 5, #4399-4403	5.75	
b.		Booklet pane of 20, 4 each #4399-4403	23.00	

LOVE

King of Hearts
A3350

Queen of Hearts
A3351

PHOTOGRAVURE
BOOKLET STAMPS

Serpentine Die Cut 10¾ on 2, 3 or 4 Sides

2009, May 8

Self-Adhesive

4404	A3350	44c multicolored	1.15	.25
4405	A3351	44c multicolored	1.15	.25
a.		Horiz. or vert. pair, #4404-4405	2.30	
b.		Booklet pane of 20, 10 each #4404-4405	23.00	

BOB HOPE

Bob Hope (1903-2003), Actor, Comedian — A3352

LITHOGRAPHED

Serpentine Die Cut 10¾

2009, May 29

Self-Adhesive

4406	A3352	44c multicolored	1.00	.25

Celebrate Type of 2007

2009, June 10

Self-Adhesive

4407	A3189	44c multicolored	.90	.25
a.		Die cutting omitted, pair	*175.00*	

See Nos. 4196, 4335.

BLACK HERITAGE

Anna Julia Cooper (c. 1858-1964), Educator — A3353

2009, June 11

Self-Adhesive

4408	A3353	44c multicolored	.90	.25

GULF COAST LIGHTHOUSES

Matagorda Island Lighthouse, Texas
A3354

Sabine Pass Lighthouse, Louisiana
A3355

Biloxi Lighthouse, Mississippi
A3356

Sand Island Lighthouse, Alabama
A3357

Fort Jefferson Lighthouse, Florida — A3358

Serpentine Die Cut 11x10¾

2009, July 23

Self-Adhesive

4409	A3354	44c multicolored	.90	.40
4410	A3355	44c multicolored	.90	.40
4411	A3356	44c multicolored	.90	.40
4412	A3357	44c multicolored	.90	.40
4413	A3358	44c multicolored	.90	.40
a.		Horiz. strip of 5, #4409-4413	4.50	

EARLY TV MEMORIES

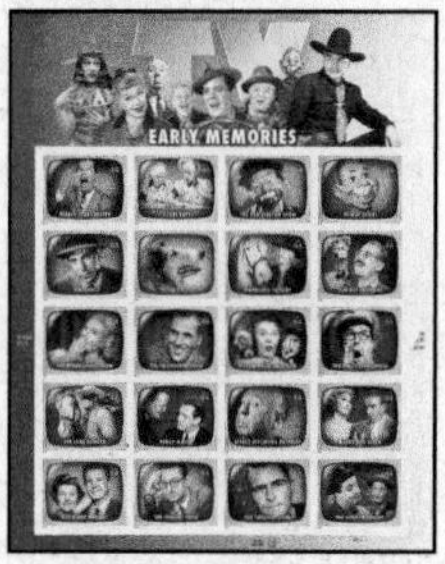

A3359

No. 4414: a, Milton Berle in "Texaco Star Theater." b, Lucille Ball and Vivian Vance in "I Love Lucy." c, Red Skelton in "The Red Skelton Show." d, Marionette Howdy Doody in "Howdy Doody." e, Jack Webb in "Dragnet." f, Lassie in "Lassie." g, William Boyd and horse, Topper, in "Hopalong Cassidy." h, Groucho Marx in "You Bet Your Life." i, Dinah Shore in "The Dinah Shore Show." j, Ed Sullivan in "The Ed Sullivan Show." k, Fran Allison and puppets, Kukla and Ollie in "Kukla, Fran and Ollie." l, Phil Silvers in "The Phil Silvers Show." m, Clayton Moore and horse, Silver, in "The Lone Ranger." n, Raymond Burr and William Talman in "Perry Mason." o, Alfred Hitchcock in "Alfred Hitchcock Presents." p, George Burns and Gracie Allen in "Burns and Allen." q, Ozzie and Harriet Nelson in "Ozzie and Harriet." r, Steve Allen in "The Tonight Show." s, Rod Serling in "The Twilight Zone." t, Jackie Gleason and Art Carney in "The Honeymooners."

Serpentine Die Cut 10¾x10½

2009, Aug. 11

Self-Adhesive

4414	A3359	Pane of 20	20.00	
a.-t.		44c Any single	1.00	.50

HAWAII STATEHOOD, 50TH ANNIV.

Surfer and Outrigger Canoe — A3360

PHOTOGRAVURE

Serpentine Die Cut 11

2009, Aug. 21

Self-Adhesive

4415	A3360	44c multicolored	1.25	.25

Eid Type of 2001

PHOTOGRAVURE

2009, Sept. 3

Self-Adhesive

4416	A2734	44c multicolored	.90	.25

See Nos. 3532, 3674, 4117, 4202, 4351.

THANKSGIVING DAY PARADE

Crowd, Street Sign, Bear Balloon — A3361

Drum Major, Musicians
A3362

Musicians, Balloon, Horse — A3363

Cowboy, Turkey Balloon, Crowd, Television Cameraman
A3364

Serpentine Die Cut 11x10¾

2009, Sept. 9

Self-Adhesive

4417	A3361	44c multicolored	.90	.35
4418	A3362	44c multicolored	.90	.35
4419	A3363	44c multicolored	.90	.35
4420	A3364	44c multicolored	.90	.35
a.		Horiz. strip of 4, #4417-4420	3.60	

LEGENDS OF HOLLYWOOD

Gary Cooper (1901-61), Actor — A3365

Serpentine Die Cut 11

2009, Sept. 10

Self-Adhesive

4421	A3365	44c multicolored	1.00	.25

SUPREME COURT JUSTICES

Souvenir Sheet

A3366

No. 4422: a, Felix Frankfurter (1882-1965). b, William J. Brennan, Jr. (1906-97). c, Louis D. Brandeis (1856-1941). d, Joseph Story (1779-1845).

LITHOGRAPHED

Serpentine Die Cut 11x10½

2009, Sept. 22

Self-Adhesive

4422	A3366	Pane of 4	4.00	
a.-d.		44c Any single	1.00	.30

KELP FOREST

A3367

Wildlife: a, Brown pelican. b, Western gull, southern sea otters, red sea urchin. c, Harbor seal. d, Lion's mane nudibranch, vert. e, Yellowtail rockfish, white-spotted rose anemone. f, Vermilion rockfish. g, Copper rockfish. h, Pacific rock crab, jeweled top snail. i, Northern kelp crab, vert. j, Treefish, Monterey turban snail, brooding sea anemones.

PHOTOGRAVURE

Serpentine Die Cut 10¾

2009, Oct. 1

Self-Adhesive

4423	A3367	Pane of 10	14.00	
a.-j.		44c Any single	1.40	.40

CHRISTMAS

Madonna and Sleeping Child, by Sassoferrato (Giovanni Battista Salvi)
A3368

Reindeer
A3369

Snowman
A3370

Gingerbread Man
A3371

Toy Soldier
A3372

Reindeer
A3373

Snowman
A3374

Gingerbread Man
A3375

Toy Soldier — A3376

LITHOGRAPHED, PHOTOGRAVURE (#4429-4432)

Serpentine Die Cut 10¾x11 on 2 or 3 Sides

2009

Self-Adhesive

Booklet Stamps

4424 A3368 44c multicolored .90 .25
a. Booklet pane of 20 18.00
4425 A3369 44c multicolored 1.10 .25
4426 A3370 44c multicolored 1.10 .25
4427 A3371 44c multicolored 1.10 .25
4428 A3372 44c multicolored 1.10 .25
a. Block of 4, #4425-4428 4.40
b. Booklet pane of 20, 5 each #4425-4428 22.00
c. As "b," die cutting omitted on side with 12 stamps —
d. As "b," die cutting omitted on side with 8 stamps —
e. As "a," die cutting omitted *375.00*

Serpentine Die Cut 8 on 2, 3 or 4 Sides

4429 A3373 44c multicolored 1.25 .25
4430 A3374 44c multicolored 1.25 .25
4431 A3375 44c multicolored 1.25 .25
4432 A3376 44c multicolored 1.25 .25
a. Block or strip of 4, #4429-4432 5.00
b. Booklet pane of 18, 5 each #4429, 4431, 4 each #4430, 4432 22.50
Nos. 4424-4432 (9) 10.30 2.25

No. 4424a is a double-sided booklet pane with 12 stamps on one side and eight stamps plus label that serves as a booklet cover on the other side. No. 4428b is a double-sided booklet pane with 12 stamps on one side (3 each of Nos. 4425-4428) and eight stamps (2 each of Nos. 4425-4428) plus label that serves as a booklet cover on the other side.

HANUKKAH

Menorah — A3377

LITHOGRAPHED

Serpentine Die Cut 10¾x11

2009, Oct. 9

Self-Adhesive

4433 A3377 44c multicolored .90 .25

KWANZAA

Family — A3378

2009, Oct. 9

Self-Adhesive

4434 A3378 44c multicolored .90 .25

CHINESE NEW YEAR

Year of the Tiger — A3379

PHOTOGRAVURE

Serpentine Die Cut 11

2010, Jan. 14 **Tagged**

Self-Adhesive

4435 A3379 44c multicolored 1.10 .25

2010 WINTER OLYMPICS, VANCOUVER

Snowboarder — A3380

PHOTOGRAVURE

Serpentine Die Cut 11

2010, Jan. 22 **Tagged**

Self-Adhesive

4436 A3380 44c multicolored .90 .25

"Forever" Liberty Bell Type of 2007

Serpentine Die Cut 11¼x10¾ on 2, 3 or 4 Sides

2010, Feb. 3 Self-Adhesive Litho.

Booklet Stamp

Medium Microprinting, Bell 16mm Wide

Dated "2009" in Copper

4437 A3148 (44c) multicolored 1.25 .25
a. Booklet pane of 18 22.50

On No. 4437, the "2009" date is smaller than that on No. 4127i, which has a 15mm wide bell. The bell on No. 4437 is also 17mm tall while No. 4127i is 16mm tall. The microprinted "Forever" is on a dotted background on No. 4437 and on a white background on No. 4127i.

See also Nos. 4125, 4128c.

AMERICAN LANDMARKS

Mackinac Bridge, Michigan
A3381

Bixby Creek Bridge, California
A3382

PHOTOGRAVURE

Serpentine Die Cut 10¾x10½

2010, Feb. 3 **Tagged**

Self-Adhesive

4438 A3381 $4.90 multi 11.00 5.00
4439 A3382 $18.30 multi 45.00 18.00

DISTINGUISHED SAILORS

Admiral William S. Sims (1858-1936), Emblem of USS W.S. Sims — A3383

Admiral Arleigh A. Burke (1901-96), Emblem of USS Arleigh Burke — A3384

Lieutenant Commander John McCloy (1876-1945), Emblem of USS McCloy — A3385

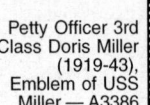

Petty Officer 3rd Class Doris Miller (1919-43), Emblem of USS Miller — A3386

PHOTOGRAVURE

Serpentine Die Cut 10¾x10½

2010, Feb. 4 **Tagged**

Self-Adhesive

4440 A3383 44c multicolored .90 .40
4441 A3384 44c multicolored .90 .40
4442 A3385 44c multicolored .90 .40
4443 A3386 44c multicolored .90 .40
a. Block or horiz. strip of 4, #4440-4443 3.60

ABSTRACT EXPRESSIONISTS

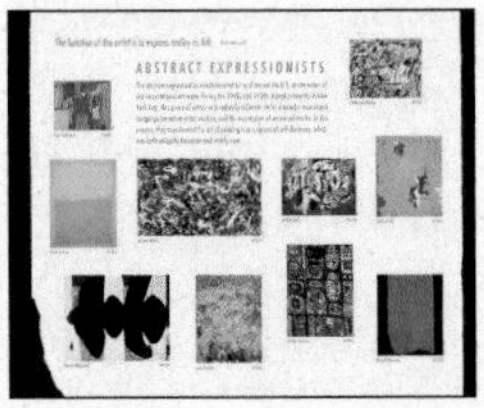
A3387

No. 4444: a, The Golden Wall, by Hans Hofmann (30x30mm). b, Asheville, by Willem de Kooning (38x38mm). c, Orange and Yellow, by Mark Rothko (35x49mm). d, Convergence, by Jackson Pollock (63x43mm). e, The Liver Is the Cock's Comb, by Arshile Gorky (39x32mm). f, 1948-C, by Clyfford Still (35x49mm). g, Elegy to the Spanish Republic No. 34, by Robert Motherwell (54x49mm). h, La Grande Vallée 0, by Joan Mitchell (35x49mm). i, Romanesque Façade, by Adolph Gottlieb (35x49mm). j, Achilles, by Barnett Newman (35x49mm).

LITHOGRAPHED

Serpentine Die Cut 10¾x11, 10¾ (#4444a, 4444b, 4444e), 11x10¾ (#4444d)

2010, Mar. 11 **Tagged**

Self-Adhesive

4444 A3387 Pane of 10 12.50
a.-j. 44c Any single 1.25 .40

BILL MAULDIN (1921-2003), CARTOONIST

A3388

LITHOGRAPHED

Serpentine Die Cut 10¾

2010, Mar. 31 **Tagged**

Self-Adhesive

4445 A3388 44c multicolored .90 .25

COWBOYS OF THE SILVER SCREEN

Roy Rogers (1911-98)
A3389

Tom Mix (1880-1940)
A3390

William S. Hart (1864-1946)
A3391

Gene Autry (1907-98)
A3392

LITHOGRAPHED

Serpentine Die Cut 10½x10¾

2010, Apr. 17

Self-Adhesive

4446 A3389 44c multicolored 1.25 .35
4447 A3390 44c multicolored 1.25 .35
4448 A3391 44c multicolored 1.25 .35
4449 A3392 44c multicolored 1.25 .35
a. Block or strip of 4, #4446-4449 5.00

LOVE

Pansies in a Basket — A3393

PHOTOGRAVURE

Serpentine Die Cut 10¾

2010, Apr. 22

Self-Adhesive

4450 A3393 44c multicolored .90 .25

ANIMAL RESCUE

Wire-haired Jack Russell Terrier
A3394

Maltese
A3395

Calico
A3396

Yellow Labrador Retriever
A3397

Golden Retriever
A3398

Gray, White and Tan Cat
A3399

Black, White and Tan Cat
A3400

Australian Shepherd
A3401

Boston Terrier
A3402

Orange Tabby
A3403

LITHOGRAPHED

Serpentine Die Cut 10¾

2010, Apr. 30

Self-Adhesive

4451 A3394 44c multicolored 1.50 .40
4452 A3395 44c multicolored 1.50 .40
4453 A3396 44c multicolored 1.50 .40
4454 A3397 44c multicolored 1.50 .40
4455 A3398 44c multicolored 1.50 .40
4456 A3399 44c multicolored 1.50 .40
4457 A3400 44c multicolored 1.50 .40
4458 A3401 44c multicolored 1.50 .40
4459 A3402 44c multicolored 1.50 .40
4460 A3403 44c multicolored 1.50 .40
a. Block of 10, #4451-4460 15.00

LEGENDS OF HOLLYWOOD

Katharine Hepburn (1907-2003), Actress — A3404

PHOTOGRAVURE

Serpentine Die Cut 10¾

2010, May 12

Self-Adhesive

4461 A3404 44c black 1.00 .25

MONARCH BUTTERFLY

A3405

PHOTOGRAVURE

Serpentine Die Cut 10½

2010, May 17

Self-Adhesive

4462 A3405 64c multicolored 1.50 .25

KATE SMITH

Kate Smith (1907-86), Singer — A3406

PHOTOGRAVURE

2010, May 27 ***Serpentine Die Cut 11***

Self-Adhesive

4463 A3406 44c multicolored .90 .25

BLACK HERITAGE

Oscar Micheaux (1884-1951), Film Director — A3407

Serpentine Die Cut 11

2010, June 22

Self-Adhesive

4464 A3407 44c multicolored .90 .25

NEGRO LEAGUES BASEBALL

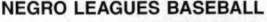

Play at the Plate — A3408

Andrew "Rube" Foster (1879-1930), Founder of Negro National League — A3409

PHOTOGRAVURE

Serpentine Die Cut 11

2010, July 15

Self-Adhesive

4465 A3408 44c multicolored .90 .30
4466 A3409 44c multicolored .90 .30
a. Horiz. pair, #4465-4466 1.80

SUNDAY FUNNIES

Beetle Bailey A3410

Calvin and Hobbes A3411

Archie A3412

Garfield A3413

Dennis the Menace — A3414

LITHOGRAPHED

Serpentine Die Cut 10½x10¾

2010, July 16

Self-Adhesive

4467 A3410 44c multicolored 1.00 .30
4468 A3411 44c multicolored 1.00 .30
4469 A3412 44c multicolored 1.00 .30
4470 A3413 44c multicolored 1.00 .30
4471 A3414 44c multicolored 1.00 .30
a. Horiz. strip of 5, #4467-4471 5.00

BOY SCOUTS OF AMERICA, CENTENNIAL

Boy Scouts — A3415

PHOTOGRAVURE

Serpentine Die Cut 11

2010, July 27

Self-Adhesive

4472 A3415 44c multicolored .90 .25

Boys in a Pasture, by Winslow Homer (1836-1910) A3416

Serpentine Die Cut 10¾

2010, Aug. 12

Self-Adhesive

4473 A3416 44c multicolored 1.00 .25

HAWAIIAN RAIN FOREST

A3417

No. 4474: a, Hawaii 'amakihi, Hawaii 'elepaio, ohi'a lehua. b, 'Akepa, 'ope'ape'a, vert. c, 'I'iwi, haha. d, 'Oma'o, kanawao, 'ohelo kau la'au, vert. e, 'Oha, vert. f, Pulelehua butterfly, kolea lau nui, 'ilihia. g, Koele Mountain damselfly, 'akala, vert. h, 'Apapane, Hawaiian mint, vert. i, Jewel orchid, vert. j, Happyface spider, 'ala'ala wai nui, vert.

LITHOGRAPHED

Serpentine Die Cut 10¾

2010, Sept. 1

Self-Adhesive

4474 A3417 Pane of 10 10.00
a.-j. 44c Any single 1.00 .40

MOTHER TERESA

Mother Teresa (1910-97), Humanitarian, 1979 Nobel Peace Laureate — A3418

PHOTOGRAVURE

2010, Sept. 5 ***Serpentine Die Cut 11***

Self-Adhesive

4475 A3418 44c multicolored .90 .25

LITERARY ARTS

Julia de Burgos (1914-53), Poet — A3419

PHOTOGRAVURE

Serpentine Die Cut 11

2010, Sept. 14

Self-Adhesive

4476 A3419 44c multicolored .90 .25

CHRISTMAS

Angel with Lute, Detail of Fresco by Melozzo da Forli — A3420

PHOTOGRAVURE (#4477), LITHOGRAPHED

Serpentine Die Cut 10¾

2010, Oct. 21 **Tagged**

Self-Adhesive

4477 A3420 44c multi 1.00 .25

Ponderosa Pine A3421

Eastern Red Cedar A3422

Balsam Fir A3423

Blue Spruce A3424

Booklet Stamps

Serpentine Die Cut 11 on 2 or 3 Sides

4478 A3421 (44c) multi 2.50 .25
4479 A3422 (44c) multi 2.50 .25
4480 A3423 (44c) multi 2.50 .25
4481 A3424 (44c) multi 2.50 .25
a. Block of 4, #4478-4481 10.00
b. Booklet pane of 20, 5 each #4478-4481 50.00
c. As "a," die cutting omitted — 500.00
d. As "b," die cutting omitted on side with 12 stamps 400.00
e. As "b," die cutting omitted on side with 8 stamps 450.00
f. As "b," die cutting omitted on side with 12 stamps, die cutting omitted on bottom 4 stamps on side with 8 stamps 950.00

Ponderosa Pine A3425

Eastern Red Cedar A3426

Balsam Fir A3427

Blue Spruce A3428

Serpentine Die Cut 11¼x10¾ on 2, 3 or 4 Sides

4482 A3425 (44c) multi 2.50 .25
4483 A3426 (44c) multi 2.50 .25
4484 A3427 (44c) multi 2.50 .25
4485 A3428 (44c) multi 2.50 .25
a. Block or strip of 4, #4482-4485 10.00
b. Booklet pane of 18, 5 each #4482, 4484, 4 each #4483, 4485 45.00
Nos. 4477-4485 (9) 21.00 2.25

No. 4481b is a double-sided booklet pane with 12 stamps on one side (3 each of Nos. 4478-4481) and eight stamps (2 each of Nos. 4478-4481) plus label that serves as a booklet cover on the other side.

Statue of Liberty A3429

Flag A3430

LITHOGRAPHED (#4486-4489)

Serpentine Die Cut 9½ Vert.

2010, Dec. 1

COIL STAMPS

Self-Adhesive

4486 A3429 (44c) multicolored 1.50 .25
4487 A3430 (44c) multicolored 1.50 .25
a. Pair, #4486-4487 3.00

Serpentine Die Cut 11 Vert.

4488 A3429 (44c) multicolored 1.50 .25
a. Vert. pair, horiz. unslit btwn. —
4489 A3430 (44c) multicolored 1.50 .25
a. Pair, #4488-4489 3.00
b. Block of 4 (one pair each from two different coil rolls), horiz. unslit btwn. 900.00

Serpentine Die Cut 8½ Vert.

4490 A3429 (44c) multicolored 1.50 .25
4491 A3430 (44c) multicolored 1.50 .25
a. Pair, #4490-4491 3.00
Nos. 4486-4491 (6) 9.00 1.50

Microprinting reads "4evR" on Nos. 4486-4487, "4evr" on Nos. 4488-4489, and "4EVR" on Nos. 4490-4491. The microprinting is found above the Statue of Liberty's hair, and at the bottom of the lowest red stripe of the flag.

See Nos. 4518-4519, 4559-4564.

CHINESE NEW YEAR

Year of the Rabbit — A3431

PHOTOGRAVURE

Serpentine Die Cut 11

2011, Jan. 22

Self-Adhesive

4492 A3431 (44c) multicolored 1.25 .25

KANSAS STATEHOOD, 150TH ANNIV.

Windmill and Wind Turbines — A3432

LITHOGRAPHED

Serpentine Die Cut 11

2011, Jan. 27

Self-Adhesive

4493 A3432 (44c) multicolored 1.25 .25

PRES. RONALD REAGAN (1911-2004)

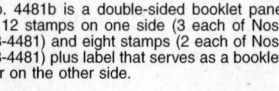

Pres. Ronald Reagan — A3433

PHOTOGRAVURE

Serpentine Die Cut 10½

2011, Feb. 10

Self-Adhesive

4494 A3433 (44c) multicolored 1.25 .25

Art Deco Bird — A3434

LITHOGRAPHED

Serpentine Die Cut 10 Vert.

2011, Feb. 11 **Untagged**

COIL STAMP

Self-Adhesive

4495 A3434 (5c) multicolored .30 .25

Quill and Inkwell — A3435

LITHOGRAPHED

Serpentine Die Cut 11¾ Vert.

2011, Feb. 14

COIL STAMP

Self-Adhesive

4496 A3435 44c multicolored .95 .25

LATIN MUSIC LEGENDS

Tito Puente (1923-2000) A3436

Carmen Miranda (1909-55) A3437

Selena (1971-95) A3438

Carlos Gardel (1890-1935) A3439

Celia Cruz (1925-2003) — A3440

PHOTOGRAVURE

Serpentine Die Cut 10¾

2011, Mar. 16

Self-Adhesive

4497 A3436 (44c) multicolored 1.25 .40
4498 A3437 (44c) multicolored 1.25 .40
4499 A3438 (44c) multicolored 1.25 .40
4500 A3439 (44c) multicolored 1.25 .40
4501 A3440 (44c) multicolored 1.25 .40
a. Horiz. strip of 5, #4497-4501 6.25

CELEBRATE

A3441

PHOTOGRAVURE

Serpentine Die Cut 11x11½

2011, Mar. 25

Self-Adhesive

4502 A3441 (44c) multicolored 1.25 .25

Compare with type A3855.

JAZZ

Musicians — A3442

PHOTOGRAVURE

Serpentine Die Cut 10¾

2011, Mar. 26

Self-Adhesive

4503 A3442 (44c) multicolored 1.25 .25

Statue of Liberty and Flag Types of 2010 and

George Washington — A3443

LITHOGRAPHED (#4504, 4518-4519)

2011 *Serpentine Die Cut 11¼x10¾*

Self-Adhesive

4504 A3443 20c multicolored .40 .25

Oregano A3444

Flax A3445

Foxglove A3446

Lavender A3447

Sage A3448

Oveta Culp Hobby (1905-95), First Health, Education and Welfare Department Secretary A3449

PHOTOGRAVURE (#4505-4510)

Serpentine Die Cut 11

4505 A3444 29c multicolored 1.50 .25
4506 A3445 29c multicolored 1.50 .25
4507 A3446 29c multicolored 1.50 .25
4508 A3447 29c multicolored 1.50 .25
4509 A3448 29c multicolored 1.50 .25
a. Horiz. strip of 5, #4505-4509 7.50
4510 A3449 84c multicolored 1.75 .35

New River Gorge Bridge, West Virginia — A3450

LITHOGRAPHED (#4511)

Serpentine Die Cut 10¾x10½

4511 A3450 $4.95 multicolored 10.00 5.00
Nos. 4504-4511 (7) 17.90 6.50

LITHOGRAPHED (#4512)

Coil Stamps

Serpentine Die Cut 9½ Vert.

4512 A3443 20c multicolored .40 .25

No. 4512a is recorded only on a single cover bearing a strip of 9 and three strips of 10. The editors would welcome reports of unused examples.

LITHOGRAPHED (#4512)

Serpentine Die Cut 8½ Vert.

4513 A3446 29c multicolored 2.00 .25
4514 A3447 29c multicolored 2.00 .25
4515 A3448 29c multicolored 2.00 .25
4516 A3444 29c multicolored 2.00 .25
4517 A3445 29c multicolored 2.00 .25
a. Horiz. strip of 5, #4513-4517 10.00
Nos. 4512-4517 (6) 10.40 1.50

LITHOGRAPHED (#4518-4519)

Booklet Stamps

Thin Paper

Serpentine Die Cut 11¼x10¾ on 2, 3, or 4 Sides

4518 A3429 (44c) multicolored 1.25 .25
4519 A3430 (44c) multicolored 1.25 .25
a. Pair, #4518-4519 2.50
b. Booklet pane of 18, 9 each #4518-4519 22.50

Issued: Nos. 4504, 4511, 4512, 4/11; Nos. 4505-4509, 4513-4517, 4/7; No. 4510, 4/15; Nos. 4518-4519. 4/8.

Wedding Cake Type of 2009 With "USA" in Serifed Type and

Wedding Roses — A3450i

LITHOGRAPHED (#4520), PHOTOGRAVURE (#4521)

2011 *Serpentine Die Cut 11*

Self-Adhesive

4520 A3450i (44c) multicolored 5.00 .25
a. Die cutting omitted, pair *250.00*
4521 A3344 64c multicolored 2.50 .25

CIVIL WAR SESQUICENTENNIAL

Battle of Fort Sumter A3451

First Battle of Bull Run A3452

LITHOGRAPHED

Serpentine Die Cut 11

2011, Apr. 12

Self-Adhesive

4522 A3451 (44c) multicolored 1.25 .30
4523 A3452 (44c) multicolored 1.25 .30
a. Pair, #4522-4523 2.50

GO GREEN

A3453

No. 4524 — Messages: a, Buy local produce, reuse bags. b, Fix water leaks. c, Share rides. d, Turn off lights not in use. e, Choose to walk. f, Go Green, reduce our environmental footprint step by step. g, Compost. h, Let nature do the work. i, Recycle more. j, Ride a bike. k, Plant trees. l, Insulate the home. m, Use public transportation. n, Use efficient light bulbs. o, Adjust the thermostat. p, Maintain tire pressure.

PHOTOGRAVURE

Serpentine Die Cut 10¾

2011, Apr. 14

Self-Adhesive

4524 A3453 Pane of 16 20.00
a.-p. (44c) Any single 1.25 .50

HELEN HAYES

Helen Hayes (1900-93), Actress — A3454

Serpentine Die Cut 11

2011, Apr. 25 **Tagged**

Self-Adhesive

4525 A3454 (44c) multicolored 1.25 .25

LEGENDS OF HOLLYWOOD

Gregory Peck (1916-2003), Actor — A3455

Serpentine Die Cut 10¾

2011, Apr. 28

Self-Adhesive

4526 A3455 (44c) black 1.25 .25

SPACE FIRSTS

Alan B. Shepard, Jr. (1923-98), First American in Space — A3456

Messenger, First Spacecraft to Orbit Mercury — A3457

LITHOGRAPHED

2011, May 4 *Serpentine Die Cut 11*

Self-Adhesive

4527 A3456 (44c) multicolored 1.25 .30
4528 A3457 (44c) multicolored 1.25 .30
a. Horiz. pair, #4527-4528 2.50

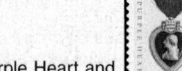

Purple Heart and Ribbon — A3458

Serpentine Die Cut 11¼x10¾

2011, May 5

Self-Adhesive

4529 A3458 (44c) multicolored 1.25 .25

INDIANAPOLIS 500, CENT.

Ray Harroun Driving Marmon Wasp — A3459

LITHOGRAPHED

Serpentine Die Cut 10¾

2011, May 20

Self-Adhesive

4530 A3459 (44c) multicolored 1.25 .25

GARDEN OF LOVE

Pink Flower A3460

Red Flower A3461

Blue Flowers A3462

Butterfly A3463

Green Vine Leaves A3464

Blue Flower A3465

Doves A3466

Orange Red Flowers A3467

Strawberry A3468

Yellow Orange Flowers A3469

Designed by Derry Noyes. Printed by Avery Dennison.

PHOTOGRAVURE

Serpentine Die Cut 10¾

2011, May 23

Self-Adhesive

4531	A3460	(44c)	multicolored	2.00	.40
4532	A3461	(44c)	multicolored	2.00	.40
4533	A3462	(44c)	multicolored	2.00	.40
4534	A3463	(44c)	multicolored	2.00	.40
4535	A3464	(44c)	multicolored	2.00	.40
4536	A3465	(44c)	multicolored	2.00	.40
4537	A3466	(44c)	multicolored	2.00	.40
4538	A3467	(44c)	multicolored	2.00	.40
4539	A3468	(44c)	multicolored	2.00	.40
4540	A3469	(44c)	multicolored	2.00	.40
a.	Block of 10, #4531-4540			20.00	
	Nos. 4531-4540 (10)			20.00	4.00

The two blocks of 10 on the pane are separated by a gutter.

AMERICAN SCIENTISTS

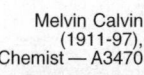

Melvin Calvin (1911-97), Chemist — A3470

Asa Gray (1810-88), Botanist — A3471

Maria Goeppert Mayer (1906-72), Physicist A3472

Severo Ochoa (1905-93), Biochemist A3473

LITHOGRAPHED

Serpentine Die Cut 11

2011, June 16

Self-Adhesive

4541	A3470	(44c)	multicolored	1.25	.50
4542	A3471	(44c)	multicolored	1.25	.50
4543	A3472	(44c)	multicolored	1.25	.50
4544	A3473	(44c)	multicolored	1.25	.50
a.	Horiz. strip of 4, #4541-4544			5.00	
b.	Horiz. strip of 4, die cutting missing on backing paper (from misaligned die-cutting mat)			*375.00*	

LITERARY ARTS

Mark Twain (Samuel L. Clemens) (1835-1910), Writer — A3474

PHOTOGRAVURE

Serpentine Die Cut 11

2011, June 25

Self-Adhesive

4545	A3474	(44c)	multicolored	1.25	.25

PIONEERS OF AMERICAN INDUSTRIAL DESIGN

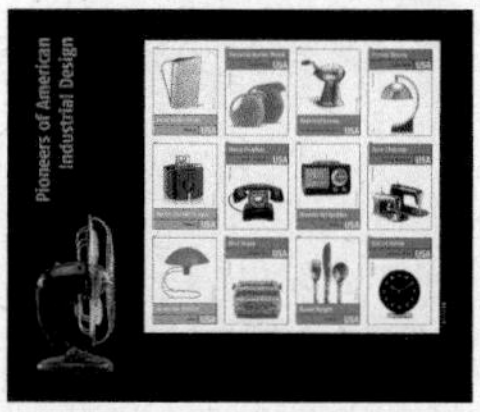

A3475

No. 4546: a, "Normandie" pitcher, designed by Peter Müller-Munk (1904-67). b, Fiesta dinnerware, designed by Frederick Hurten Rhead (1880-1942). c, Streamlined pencil sharpener, designed by Raymond Loewy (1893-1986). d, Table lamp, designed by Donald Deskey (1894-1989). e, Kodak "Baby Brownie" camera, designed by Walter Dorwin Teague (1883-1960). f, Model 302 Bell telephone, designed by Henry Dreyfuss (1904-72). g, Emerson "Patriot" radio, designed by Norman Bel Geddes (1893-1958). h, Streamlined sewing machines, designed by Dave Chapman (1909-78). i, "Anywhere" lamp, designed by Greta von Nessen (1900-74). j, IBM "Selectric" typewriter, designed by Eliot Noyes (1910-77). k, "Highlight/Pinch" flatware, designed by Russel Wright (1904-76). l, Herman Miller electric clock, designed by Gilbert Rohde (1894-1944).

PHOTOGRAVURE

Serpentine Die Cut 10¾

2011, June 29

Self-Adhesive

4546	A3475		Pane of 12	15.00	
a.-l.		(44c)	Any single	1.25	.50

OWNEY, THE POSTAL DOG

Owney, His Medals and Tags — A3476

PHOTOGRAVURE

Serpentine Die Cut 11

2011, July 27

Self-Adhesive

4547	A3476	(44c)	multicolored	1.50	.25

U.S. MERCHANT MARINE

Clipper Ship — A3477

Auxiliary Steamship A3478

Liberty Ship — A3479

Container Ship — A3480

PHOTOGRAVURE

Serpentine Die Cut 11

2011, July 28

Self-Adhesive

4548	A3477	(44c)	multicolored	1.25	.35
4549	A3478	(44c)	multicolored	1.25	.35
4550	A3479	(44c)	multicolored	1.25	.35
4551	A3480	(44c)	multicolored	1.25	.35
a.	Block or horiz. strip of 4, #4548-4551			5.00	

EID

"Eid Mubarak" — A3481

PHOTOGRAVURE

Serpentine Die Cut 11¼

2011, Aug. 12

Self-Adhesive

4552	A3481	(44c)	mar, gray & gold	1.25	.25

CHARACTERS FROM DISNEY-PIXAR FILMS

Send a Hello

Lightning McQueen and Mater from *Cars* A3482

Remy the Rat and Linguini from *Ratatouille* A3483

Buzz Lightyear and Aliens from *Toy Story* — A3484

Carl Fredricksen and Dug the Dog from *Up* — A3485

WALL-E from *WALL-E* — A3486

PHOTOGRAVURE

Serpentine Die Cut 10½

2011, Aug. 19

Self-Adhesive

4553	A3482	(44c)	multicolored	1.25	.40
4554	A3483	(44c)	multicolored	1.25	.40
4555	A3484	(44c)	multicolored	1.25	.40
4556	A3485	(44c)	multicolored	1.25	.40
4557	A3486	(44c)	multicolored	1.25	.40
a.	Horiz. strip of 5, #4553-4557			6.25	

Adjacent horizontal or vertical stamps will have selvage between the stamps.

AMERICAN TREASURES SERIES

The Long Leg, by Edward Hopper (1882-1967) A3487

PHOTOGRAVURE

Serpentine Die Cut 11

2011, Aug. 24

Self-Adhesive

4558	A3487	(44c)	multicolored	1.25	.25

Statue of Liberty and Flag Types of 2010

LITHOGRAPHED (#4559-4562), PHOTOGRAVURE

Serpentine Die Cut 11¼x11 on 2 or 3 Sides

2011, Sept. 14

BOOKLET STAMPS

Self-Adhesive

4559	A3429	(44c)	multicolored	1.50	.25
4560	A3430	(44c)	multicolored	1.50	.25
a.	Pair, #4559-4560			3.00	
b.	Booklet pane of 20, 10 each #4559-4560			30.00	
4561	A3429	(44c)	multicolored	1.50	.25
4562	A3430	(44c)	multicolored	1.50	.25
a.	Pair, #4561-4562			3.00	
b.	Booklet pane of 20, 10 each #4561-4562			30.00	

Serpentine Die Cut 11¼x11½ on 2 or 3 Sides

4563	A3429	(44c)	multicolored	1.25	.25
4564	A3430	(44c)	multicolored	1.25	.25
a.	Pair, #4563-4564			2.50	
b.	Booklet pane of 20, 10 each #4563-4564			25.00	
	Nos. 4559-4564 (6)			8.50	1.50

Microprinting reads "4evR" on Nos. 4559-4560, "4evr" on Nos. 4561-4562, and "4EVR" on Nos. 4563-4564. The microprinting is found above the Statue of Liberty's hair, and at the bottom of the lowest red stripe of the flag. Nos. 4560b, 4562b and 4564b are double-sided booklet panes with 12 stamps one one side (6 each of types A3429-A3430) and 8 stamps (4 each of types A3429-A3430) on the other side. The paper used on Nos. 4561-4562 is thicker than that used on Nos. 4518-4519.

BLACK HERITAGE

Barbara Jordan (1936-96), Congresswoman A3488

LITHOGRAPHED

Serpentine Die Cut 10¾

2011, Sept. 16

Self-Adhesive

4565	A3488	(44c)	multicolored	1.25	.25

ART OF ROMARE BEARDEN (1911-88)

Conjunction A3489

Odysseus: Poseidon, The Sea God - Enemy of Odysseus A3490

Prevalence of Ritual: Conjur Woman A3491

Falling Star A3492

PHOTOGRAVURE

Serpentine Die Cut 10¾

2011, Sept. 28

Self-Adhesive

4566	A3489	(44c)	multicolored	1.25	.40
4567	A3490	(44c)	multicolored	1.25	.40
4568	A3491	(44c)	multicolored	1.25	.40
4569	A3492	(44c)	multicolored	1.25	.40
a.	Horiz. strip of 4, #4566-4569			5.00	

CHRISTMAS

Madonna of the Candelabra, by Raphael — A3493

A3494 A3495

A3496 A3497

LITHOGRAPHED

Serpentine Die Cut 10¾x 11 on 2 or 3 Sides

2011, Oct. 13

Booklet Stamps
Self-Adhesive

4570 A3493 (44c) multicolored 1.25 .25
a. Booklet pane of 20 25.00

With "USPS" Microprinted on Collar of Ornament

4571 A3494 (44c) multicolored 1.50 .25
4572 A3495 (44c) multicolored 1.50 .25
4573 A3496 (44c) multicolored 1.50 .25
4574 A3497 (44c) multicolored 1.50 .25
a. Block of 4, #4571-4574 6.00
b. Booklet pane of 20, 5 each #4571-4574 30.00

Microprinted "USPS" in Places Other Than Collar of Ornament

4575 A3494 (44c) multicolored 1.50 .25
4576 A3495 (44c) multicolored 1.50 .25
4577 A3496 (44c) multicolored 1.50 .25
4578 A3497 (44c) multicolored 1.50 .25
a. Block of 4, #4575-4578 6.00
b. Booklet pane of 20, 5 each #4575-4578 30.00

A3498 A3499

Ornaments
A3500 A3501

Serpentine Die Cut 11¼x11 on 2, 3 or 4 Sides

4579 A3498 (44c) multicolored 1.50 .25
4580 A3499 (44c) multicolored 1.50 .25
4581 A3500 (44c) multicolored 1.50 .25
4582 A3501 (44c) multicolored 1.50 .25
a. Block or strip of 4, #4579-4582 6.00
b. Booklet pane of 18, 5 each #4579, 4582, 4 each #4580-4581 27.50
Nos. 4570-4582 (13) 19.25 3.25

The microprinted "USPS" is to the left of the third stripe on Nos. 4575 and 4579, on the left side of the bottom ribbon of the ribbon cluster above the ornament collar on Nos. 4576 and 4578, below the bottom stripe near the bottom tip on No. 4577, on the vertical ribbon on No. 4580, on a curved ribbon above the collar on No. 4581, and on the left side of the ornament, below the collar, on No. 4582.

No. 4570a is a double-sided booklet with 12 stamps on one side and eight stamps plus a label that serves as a booklet cover on the other side. Nos. 4574b and 4578b are double sided booklets with 12 stamps (3 each of types A3494-A3497) on one side and eight stamps (2 each of types A3494-A3497) plus a label that serves as a booklet cover on the other side.

HANUKKAH

A3502

Serpentine Die Cut 11x10¾

2011, Oct. 14

Self-Adhesive

4583 A3502 (44c) multicolored 1.25 .25

KWANZAA

Family — A3503

Serpentine Die Cut 10¾x11

2011, Oct. 14

Self-Adhesive

4584 A3503 (44c) multicolored 1.25 .25

Eagle — A3504

PHOTOGRAVURE

Serpentine Die Cut 11 Vert.

2012, Jan. 3

Coil Stamps
Self-Adhesive
Color Behind "USA"

4585 A3504 (25c) green .50 .25
4586 A3504 (25c) blue green .50 .25
4587 A3504 (25c) blue .50 .25
4588 A3504 (25c) red violet .50 .25
4589 A3504 (25c) brown orange .50 .25
4590 A3504 (25c) yellow orange .50 .25
a. Strip of 6, #4585-4590 3.00

NEW MEXICO STATEHOOD CENTENNIAL

Sanctuary II, Painting by Doug West — A3505

PHOTOGRAVURE

2012, Jan. 6 ***Serpentine Die Cut 11***

Self-Adhesive

4591 A3505 (44c) multicolored 1.25 .25

ALOHA SHIRTS

Surfers and Palm Trees A3506 — Surfers A3507

Bird of Paradise Flowers A3508 — Kilauea Volcano A3509

Fossil Fish, Shells and Starfish — A3510

PHOTOGRAVURE

Serpentine Die Cut 11

2012, Jan. 19

Self-Adhesive

4592 A3506 32c multicolored 2.00 .30
4593 A3507 32c multicolored 2.00 .30
4594 A3508 32c multicolored 2.00 .30
4595 A3509 32c multicolored 2.00 .30
4596 A3510 32c multicolored 2.00 .30
a. Horiz. strip of 5, #4592-4596 10.00

LITHOGRAPHED
Coil Stamps

Serpentine Die Cut 11 Vert.

4597 A3510 32c multicolored 2.00 .30
4598 A3506 32c multicolored 2.00 .30
4599 A3507 32c multicolored 2.00 .30
4600 A3508 32c multicolored 2.00 .30
4601 A3509 32c multicolored 2.00 .30
a. Strip of 5, #4597-4601 10.00
b. As "a," die cutting omitted 125.00
Nos. 4592-4601 (10) 20.00 3.00

On Nos. 4592-4596, the top of the shirt collars are all higher than the cross line of the "A" in "USA," and on Nos. 4597-4601, they are even with or slightly below the cross line.

See Nos. 4682-4686.

Wedding Cake Type of 2009

LITHOGRAPHED

Serpentine Die Cut 10¾

2012, Jan. 20

Self-Adhesive

4602 A3344 65c multicolored 2.50 .25

See Nos. 4398, 4521, 4735, 4867, 5000.

BALTIMORE CHECKERSPOT BUTTERFLY

A3511

PHOTOGRAVURE

Serpentine Die Cut 10¾

2012, Jan. 20

Self-Adhesive

4603 A3511 65c multicolored 1.50 .25

DOGS AT WORK

Seeing Eye Dog A3512 — Therapy Dog A3513

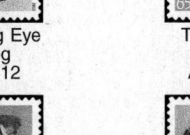

Military Dog A3514 — Rescue Dog A3515

PHOTOGRAVURE

Serpentine Die Cut 10¾

2012, Jan. 20

Self-Adhesive

4604 A3512 65c multicolored 1.30 .30
4605 A3513 65c multicolored 1.30 .30
4606 A3514 65c multicolored 1.30 .30
4607 A3515 65c multicolored 1.30 .30
a. Block or vert. strip of 4, #4604-4607 5.20

BIRDS OF PREY

Northern Goshawk A3516 — Peregrine Falcon A3517

Golden Eagle A3518 — Osprey A3519

Northern Harrier — A3520

LITHOGRAPHED

Serpentine Die Cut 11¼x10¾

2012, Jan. 20

Self-Adhesive

4608 A3516 85c multicolored 1.75 .35
4609 A3517 85c multicolored 1.75 .35
4610 A3518 85c multicolored 1.75 .35
4611 A3519 85c multicolored 1.75 .35
4612 A3520 85c multicolored 1.75 .35
a. Horiz. strip of 5, #4608-4612 8.75

WEATHER VANES

Rooster With Perch A3521 — Cow A3522

Eagle A3523 — Rooster Without Perch A3524

Centaur — A3525

LITHOGRAPHED

Serpentine Die Cut 11¾ Vert.

2012, Jan. 20

Coil Stamps
Self-Adhesive

4613 A3521 45c multicolored 1.50 .30
4614 A3522 45c multicolored 1.50 .30
4615 A3523 45c multicolored 1.50 .30
4616 A3524 45c multicolored 1.50 .30
4617 A3525 45c multicolored 1.50 .30
a. Strip of 5, #4613-4617 7.50

BONSAI

Sierra Juniper A3526 — Black Pine A3527

Banyan A3528 — Trident Maple A3529

Azalea — A3530

LITHOGRAPHED

Serpentine Die Cut 11x10¾ on 2 or 3 Sides

2012, Jan. 23

Booklet Stamps
Self-Adhesive

4618 A3526 (45c) multicolored 2.00 .40
4619 A3527 (45c) multicolored 2.00 .40
4620 A3528 (45c) multicolored 2.00 .40
4621 A3529 (45c) multicolored 2.00 .40
4622 A3530 (45c) multicolored 2.00 .40
a. Vert. strip of 5, #4618-4622 10.00
b. Booklet pane of 20, 4 each #4618-4622 40.00

Stamps in No. 4622a are not adjacent, as rows of selvage are between stamps two and three, and between stamps four and five.

No. 4622b is a double-sided booklet with 12 stamps on one side (3 each #4618, 4621, 2 each #4619, 4620, 4622) and eight stamps (#4618, 4621, 2 each #4619, 4620, 4622) plus label that serves as a booklet cover on the other side.

CHINESE NEW YEAR

Year of the Dragon — A3531

PHOTOGRAVURE

Serpentine Die Cut 11x10¾

2012, Jan. 23

Self-Adhesive

4623 A3531 (45c) multicolored 1.25 .25

BLACK HERITAGE

John H. Johnson (1918-2005), Magazine Publisher — A3532

LITHOGRAPHED

Serpentine Die Cut 10¾

2012, Jan. 31

Self-Adhesive

4624 A3532 (45c) multicolored 1.25 .25

HEART HEALTH

Tree, Man, Sun and Apple — A3533

PHOTOGRAVURE

2012, Feb. 9 ***Serpentine Die Cut 11***

Self-Adhesive

4625 A3533 (45c) multicolored 1.25 .25

LOVE

Ribbons — A3534

LITHOGRAPHED

Serpentine Die Cut 10¾

2012, Feb. 14

Self-Adhesive

4626 A3534 (45c) red 1.25 .25
a. Die cutting omitted, pair *200.00*

Postal Service officials declared on Feb. 2 that No. 4626 could be sold in post offices as of that date to make the stamp available to customers before St. Valentine's Day, but the first day ceremony for the stamp was held Feb. 14 in Colorado Springs, CO. Official first day covers have that date and city.

ARIZONA STATEHOOD CENTENNIAL

Cathedral Rock — A3535

PHOTOGRAVURE

Serpentine Die Cut 11

2012, Feb. 14

Self-Adhesive

4627 A3535 (45c) multicolored 1.25 .25

DANNY THOMAS

Thomas (1912-91), Comedian, and St. Jude's Children's Research Hospital, Memphis A3536

LITHOGRAPHED

Serpentine Die Cut 10¾x10½

2012, Feb. 16

Self-Adhesive

4628 A3536 (45c) multicolored 1.25 .25

Flag and "Equality" A3537

Flag and "Justice" A3538

Flag and "Freedom" A3539

Flag and "Liberty" A3540

PHOTOGRAVURE

Serpentine Die Cut 8½ Vert.

2012, Feb. 22

Coil Stamps
Self-Adhesive

4629 A3537 (45c) multicolored 1.50 .25
4630 A3538 (45c) multicolored 1.50 .25
4631 A3539 (45c) multicolored 1.50 .25
4632 A3540 (45c) multicolored 1.50 .25
a. Strip of 4, #4629-4632 6.00

LITHOGRAPHED (#4633-4648)

Serpentine Die Cut 9½ Vert.

4633 A3537 (45c) multicolored 1.25 .25
4634 A3538 (45c) multicolored 1.25 .25
4635 A3539 (45c) multicolored 1.25 .25
4636 A3540 (45c) multicolored 1.25 .25
b. Strip of 4, #4633-4636 5.00

Serpentine Die Cut 11 Vert.

4637 A3537 (45c) multicolored 1.50 .25
4638 A3538 (45c) multicolored 1.50 .25
4639 A3539 (45c) multicolored 1.50 .25
4640 A3540 (45c) multicolored 1.50 .25
a. Strip of 4, #4637-4640 6.00
b. As "a," die cutting omitted *450.00*
Nos. 4629-4640 (12) 17.00 3.00

Booklet Stamps
Colored Dots in Stars
18½mm From Lower Left to Lower Right Corners of Flag

Serpentine Die Cut 11¼x10¾ on 2 or 3 Sides

4641 A3539 (45c) multicolored 1.25 .25
4642 A3540 (45c) multicolored 1.25 .25
4643 A3537 (45c) multicolored 1.25 .25
4644 A3538 (45c) multicolored 1.25 .25
b. Block of 4, #4641-4644 5.00
c. Booklet pane of 20, 5 each #4641-4644 25.00

Dark Dots Only in Stars
19mm from Lower Left to Lower Right Corners of Flag

4645 A3539 (45c) multicolored 1.50 .25
4646 A3540 (45c) multicolored 1.50 .25
4647 A3537 (45c) multicolored 1.50 .25
4648 A3538 (45c) multicolored 1.50 .25
a. Block of 4, #4645-4648 6.00
b. Booklet pane of 20, 5 each #4645-4648 30.00
Nos. 4641-4648 (8) 11.00 2.00

On Nos. 4641-4644, the blue canton of the flag is made up of blue and red inks. The paper is tagged over each block of 4, with no tagging on the paper between the blocks. The tagging is a dull yellow green under ultraviolet light. The words are slightly longer than those on Nos. 4645-4648.

On Nos. 4645-4648, the blue canton is made up of blue and dull blue inks. The paper is prephosphored with the tagging appearing bright yellow green under ultraviolet light. The words are slightly shorter than those on Nos. 4641-4644.

No. 4644b is a double-sided booklet with 12 stamps on one side (3 each #4641-4644) and eight stamps (2 each #4641-4644) plus label that serves as a booklet cover on the other side.

No. 4648b is a double-sided booklet with 12 stamps on one side (3 each #4645-4648) and eight stamps (2 each #4645-4648) plus label that serves as a booklet cover on the other side.

See Nos. 4673-4676.

AMERICAN LANDMARKS ISSUE

Sunshine Skyway Bridge, Florida — A3541

Carmel Mission, Carmel, CA — A3542

LITHOGRAPHED

Serpentine Die Cut 10¾x10½

2012, Feb. 28

Self-Adhesive

4649 A3541 $5.15 multi 11.00 5.75
4650 A3542 $18.95 multi 42.50 19.00

CHERRY BLOSSOM CENTENNIAL

Cherry Blossoms and Washington Monument A3543

Cherry Blossoms and Jefferson Memorial A3544

LITHOGRAPHED

Serpentine Die Cut 10¾

2012, Mar. 24 **Tagged**

Self-Adhesive

4651 A3543 (45c) multicolored 1.25 .25
4652 A3544 (45c) multicolored 1.25 .25
a. Horiz. pair, #4651-4652 2.50

See Japan No. 3413.

AMERICAN TREASURES SERIES

Flowers, by William H. Johnson (1901-70) — A3545

PHOTOGRAVURE

Serpentine Die Cut 10¾

2012, Apr. 11 **Tagged**

Self-Adhesive

4653 A3545 (45c) multicolored 1.25 .35

TWENTIETH CENTURY POETS

Joseph Brodsky (1940-96) A3546

Gwendolyn Brooks (1917-2000) A3547

William Carlos Williams (1883-1963) A3548

Robert Hayden (1913-80) A3549

Sylvia Plath (1932-63) A3550

Elizabeth Bishop (1911-79) A3551

Wallace Stevens (1879-1955) A3552

Denise Levertov (1923-97) A3553

E. E. Cummings (1894-1962) A3554

Theodore Roethke (1908-63) A3555

LITHOGRAPHED

Sheets of 160 in eight panes of 20

Serpentine Die Cut 10¾x11

2012, Apr. 21 **Tagged**

Self-Adhesive

4654 A3546 (45c) multicolored 2.50 .50
4655 A3547 (45c) multicolored 2.50 .50
4656 A3548 (45c) multicolored 2.50 .50
4657 A3549 (45c) multicolored 2.50 .50
4658 A3550 (45c) multicolored 2.50 .50
4659 A3551 (45c) multicolored 2.50 .50
4660 A3552 (45c) multicolored 2.50 .50
4661 A3553 (45c) multicolored 2.50 .50
4662 A3554 (45c) multicolored 2.50 .50
4663 A3555 (45c) multicolored 2.50 .50
a. Block of 10, #4654-4663 25.00
Nos. 4654-4663 (10) 25.00 5.00

CIVIL WAR SESQUICENTENNIAL

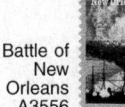

Battle of New Orleans A3556

Battle of Antietam A3557

LITHOGRAPHED

Serpentine Die Cut 11

2012, Apr. 24 **Tagged**

Self-Adhesive

4664 A3556 (45c) multicolored 1.25 .30
4665 A3557 (45c) multicolored 1.25 .30
a. Pair, #4664-4665 2.50

DISTINGUISHED AMERICANS

José Ferrer (1912-92), Actor — A3558

LITHOGRAPHED

Serpentine Die Cut 10¾x11

2012, Apr. 26 **Tagged**

Self-Adhesive

4666 A3558 (45c) multicolored 1.25 .25

LOUISIANA STATEHOOD BICENTENNIAL

Sunset Over Flat Lake — A3559

PHOTOGRAVURE

Serpentine Die Cut 11

2012, Apr. 30 **Tagged**

Self-Adhesive

4667	A3559 (45c) multicolored	1.25	.25

GREAT FILM DIRECTORS

John Ford (1894-1973), Scene From *The Searchers,* Starring John Wayne — A3560

Frank Capra (1897-1991), Scene From *It Happened One Night,* Starring Clark Gable and Claudette Colbert — A3561

Billy Wilder (1906-2002), Scene From *Some Like It Hot,* Starring Marilyn Monroe — A3562

John Huston (1906-87), Scene From *The Maltese Falcon,* Starring Humphrey Bogart — A3563

PHOTOGRAVURE

Serpentine Die Cut 10¾

2012, May 23

Self-Adhesive

4668	A3560 (45c) multicolored	1.25	.40
4669	A3561 (45c) multicolored	1.25	.40
4670	A3562 (45c) multicolored	1.25	.40
4671	A3563 (45c) multicolored	1.25	.40
a.	Block or horiz. strip of 4, #4668-4671	5.00	

WILDLIFE

Bobcat — A3564

LITHOGRAPHED

Serpentine Die Cut 10 Vert.

2012, June 1

Coil Stamp

Self-Adhesive

4672	A3564 1c multicolored	.30	.25
a.	Dated "2015"	.30	.25

Issued: No. 4672a, 2/21/15. Microprinting is on bobcat's ear on No. 4672 and on the bobcat's leg on No. 4672a.

See No. 4802.

Flags Type of 2012

PHOTOGRAVURE

Serpentine Die Cut 11¼x10¾ on 3 Sides

2012, June 1 **Tagged**

Booklet Stamps

Self-Adhesive

Colored Dots in Stars

19¼mm From Lower Left to Lower Right Corners of Flag

4673	A3539 (45c) multicolored	1.25	.25
4674	A3540 (45c) multicolored	1.25	.25
4675	A3537 (45c) multicolored	1.25	.25
4676	A3538 (45c) multicolored	1.25	.25
a.	Block of 4, #4673-4676	5.00	
b.	Booklet pane of 10, 3 each #4673-4674, 2 each #4675-4676	12.50	

Nos. 4673 and No. 4675 have straight edge on left side only. Nos. 4674 and 4676 have straight edge on right side only. Nos. 4641-4648 each have a straight edge at top or bottom. The letters in the "USPS" microprinting on Nos. 4673-4676, found at the right side of the bottom white flag stripe, are printed in a distinct curve, with the tops of the middle letters, "SP," being below the tops of the outside letters, "U" and "S," and the letters can be difficult to distinguish against the shading on the stripe. The letters in the microprinting on Nos. 4641-4648, found in the same place on the stamp, are printed in a straight line, and are printed boldly, making them easily distinguishable from the shading. The lettering on Nos. 4673-4767 has a fuzzier, less distinct appearance under magnification than the lettering on Nos. 4641-4648, which is most evident in the year "2012."

CHARACTERS FROM DISNEY-PIXAR FILMS

Mail a Smile

Flik and Dot From *A Bug's Life* A3565

Bob Parr and Dashiell Parr From *The Incredibles* A3566

Nemo and Squirt From *Finding Nemo* — A3567

Jessie, Woody and Bullseye From *Toy Story 2* — A3568

Boo, Mike Wazowski and James P. "Sulley" Sullivan From *Monsters, Inc.* — A3569

PHOTOGRAVURE

Serpentine Die Cut 10½

2012, June 1

Self-Adhesive

4677	A3565 (45c) multicolored	1.25	.40
4678	A3566 (45c) multicolored	1.25	.40
4679	A3567 (45c) multicolored	1.25	.40
4680	A3568 (45c) multicolored	1.25	.40
4681	A3569 (45c) multicolored	1.25	.40
a.	Horiz. strip of 5, #4677-4681	6.25	

Adjacent horizontal or vertical stamps will have selvage between the stamps.

Aloha Shirts Type of 2012

LITHOGRAPHED

Tagged

Serpentine Die Cut 11¼x10¾ on 3 Sides

2012, June 2

Booklet Stamps

Self-Adhesive

4682	A3506 32c multicolored	8.50	.30
4683	A3508 32c multicolored	8.50	.30
4684	A3510 32c multicolored	8.50	.30
4685	A3507 32c multicolored	8.50	.30
4686	A3509 32c multicolored	8.50	.30
a.	Vert. strip of 5, #4682-4686	42.50	
b.	Booklet pane of 10, 2 each #4682-4686	85.00	

Stamps in No. 4686a are not adjacent, as a row of selvage is between stamps two and three.

See Nos. 4592-4601.

BICYCLING

Child on Bicycle with Training Wheels — A3570

Commuter on Bicycle with Panniers A3571

Road Racer — A3572

BMX Rider — A3573

LITHOGRAPHED

Serpentine Die Cut 10¾

2012, June 7

Self-Adhesive

4687	A3570 (45c) multicolored	1.25	.35
4688	A3571 (45c) multicolored	1.25	.35
4689	A3572 (45c) multicolored	1.25	.35
4690	A3573 (45c) multicolored	1.25	.35
a.	Horiz. strip of 4, #4687-4690	5.00	

GIRL SCOUTS OF AMERICA, CENT.

Girl Scouts — A3574

LITHOGRAPHED

Serpentine Die Cut 10¾

2012, June 9

Self-Adhesive

4691	A3574 (45c) multicolored	1.25	.25
a.	Die cutting omitted, pair	—	

MUSICIANS

Edith Piaf (1915-63), Singer A3575

Miles Davis (1926-91), Jazz Trumpet Player A3576

PHOTOGRAVURE

Serpentine Die Cut 10¾x11

2012, June 12

Self-Adhesive

4692	A3575 (45c) multicolored	1.25	.30
4693	A3576 (45c) multicolored	1.25	.30
a.	Pair, #4692-4693	2.50	

See France Nos. 4256-4257.

Imperforate Uncut Press Sheets

Beginning with Nos. 4694-4697, the United States Postal Service made available for sale imperforate uncut press sheets of selected commemorative and definitive issues. These sheets, along with their corresponding multiples, are described and valued in footnotes following each issue in the Scott *Specialized Catalogue of United States Stamps and Covers.* For descriptions and illustrations of typical press-sheet multiples, see the note after No. 2868 in the Scott U.S. Specialized catalogue.

MAJOR LEAGUE BASEBALL ALL-STARS

Ted Williams (1918-2002) A3577

Larry Doby (1923-2003) A3578

Willie Stargell (1940-2001) A3579

Joe DiMaggio (1914-99) A3580

PHOTOGRAVURE

Serpentine Die Cut 10¾x11

2012, July 20

Self-Adhesive

4694	A3577 (45c) multicolored	1.25	.30
a.	Imperforate	2.50	—
4695	A3578 (45c) multicolored	1.25	.30
a.	Imperforate	2.50	—
4696	A3579 (45c) multicolored	1.25	.30
a.	Imperforate	2.50	—
4697	A3580 (45c) multicolored	1.25	.30
a.	Imperforate	2.50	—
b.	Horiz. strip or block of 4, #4694-4697	5.00	
c.	Imperf. horiz. strip or block of 4, #4694a-4697a	14.00	—

Panes containing 20 of the same stamp were issued on July 21 in Boston, MA (for No. 4694), Cleveland, OH (for No. 4695), Pittsburgh, PA (for No. 4696) and New York, NY (for No. 4697).

INNOVATIVE CHOREOGRAPHERS

Isadora Duncan (1877-1927) A3581

José Limón (1908-72) A3582

Katherine Dunham (1909-2006) A3583

Bob Fosse (1927-87) A3584

LITHOGRAPHED

Serpentine Die Cut 10¾x11

2012, July 28

Self-Adhesive

4698	A3581 (45c) multicolored	1.25	.35
4699	A3582 (45c) multicolored	1.25	.35
4700	A3583 (45c) multicolored	1.25	.35
4701	A3584 (45c) multicolored	1.25	.35
a.	Vert. strip of 4, #4698-4701	5.00	

EDGAR RICE BURROUGHS

Edgar Rice Burroughs (1875-1950), Writer, and Tarzan — A3585

LITHOGRAPHED

Serpentine Die Cut 10¾

2012, Aug. 17

Self-Adhesive

4702	A3585 (45c) multicolored	1.25	.25

WAR OF 1812 BICENTENNIAL

Painting of U.S.S. Constitution, by Michele Felice Corné — A3586

PHOTOGRAVURE

Serpentine Die Cut 10¾x10½

2012, Aug. 18

Self-Adhesive

4703	A3586	(45c) multicolored	1.75	.25
a.		Imperforate	2.75	—

Purple Heart and Ribbon

Purple Heart and Ribbon — A3587

PHOTOGRAVURE

2012, Sept. 4 *Serpentine Die Cut 11*

Self-Adhesive

4704	A3587	(45c) multicolored	1.25	.25
a.		Imperforate	2.50	—
b.		Dated "2014"	1.25	.25

Compare with Type A3458.

LITERARY ARTS

O. Henry (William S. Porter) (1862-1910), New York City Buildings and Elevated Trains — A3588

PHOTOGRAVURE

Serpentine Die Cut 11

2012, Sept. 11

Self-Adhesive

4705	A3588	(45c) multicolored	1.25	.25

Flags Type of 2012

LITHOGRAPHED

Serpentine Die Cut 11¼x10¾ on 2, 3 or 4 Sides

2012, Sept. 22

Booklet Stamps

Self-Adhesive

Colored Dots in Stars

18½mm From Lower Left to Lower Right Corners of Flag

Thin Paper

4706	A3539	(45c) multicolored	1.25	.25
4707	A3540	(45c) multicolored	1.25	.25
4708	A3537	(45c) multicolored	1.25	.25
4709	A3538	(45c) multicolored	1.25	.25
a.		Block or strip of 4, #4706-4709	5.00	
b.		Booklet pane of 18, 5 each #4706-4707, 4 each #4708-4709	25.00	
		Nos. 4706-4709 (4)	5.00	1.00

The overall-tagged paper used for Nos. 4706-4709 is glossier than that used on Nos. 4641-4644. The blue canton of the flag on Nos. 4706-4709 is made up of blue and red inks, similar to Nos. 4641-4644.

EARTHSCAPES

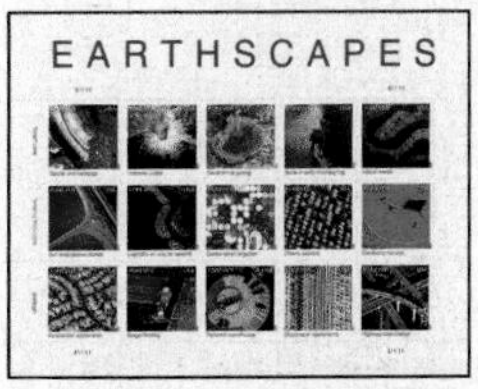

A3589

No. 4710: a, Glacier and icebergs. b, Volcanic crater. c, Geothermal spring. d, Butte in early morning fog. e, Inland marsh. f, Salt evaporation ponds. g, Log rafts on way to sawmill. h, Center-pivot irrigation. i, Cherry orchard. j, Cranberry harvest. k, Residential subdivision. l, Barge fleeting. m, Railroad roundhouse. n, Skyscraper apartments. o, Highway interchange.

LITHOGRAPHED

Serpentine Die Cut 10¾

2012, Oct. 1

Self-Adhesive

4710	A3589	Pane of 15	33.00	
a.-o.		(45c) Any single	1.65	.50
p.		Imperforate pane of 15	75.00	

CHRISTMAS

Holy Family and Donkey A3590

Reindeer in Flight, Moon A3591

Santa Claus and Sleigh A3592

Reindeer Over Roof A3593

Snow-covered Buildings — A3594

LITHOGRAPHED

Serpentine Die Cut 11 on 2 or 3 Sides

2012

Booklet Stamps

Self-Adhesive

4711	A3590	(45c) multi	1.25	.25
a.		Booklet pane of 20	25.00	
b.		Imperforate	1.75	—
c.		Imperforate booklet pane of 20	35.00	

Serpentine Die Cut 11x10¾ on 2 or 3 sides

4712	A3591	(45c) multi	1.50	.25
4713	A3592	(45c) multi	1.50	.25
4714	A3593	(45c) multi	1.50	.25
4715	A3594	(45c) multi	1.50	.25
a.		Block of 4, #4712-4715	6.00	
b.		Booklet pane of 20, 5 each #4712-4715	30.00	
c.		Imperforate block of 4	8.00	—
d.		Imperforate booklet pane of 20	40.00	
		Nos. 4711-4715 (5)	7.25	1.25

Issued: No. 4711, Oct. 10, Nos. 4712-4715, Oct. 13.

No. 4711a is a double-sided booklet with 12 stamps on one side and eight stamps plus a label that serves as a booklet cover on the other side. No. 4715b is a double-sided booklet with 12 stamps on one side (3 each of Nos. 4712-4715) and eight stamps (2 each of Nos. 4712-4715) plus a label that serves as a booklet cover on the other side.

See No. 4813.

LADY BIRD JOHNSON

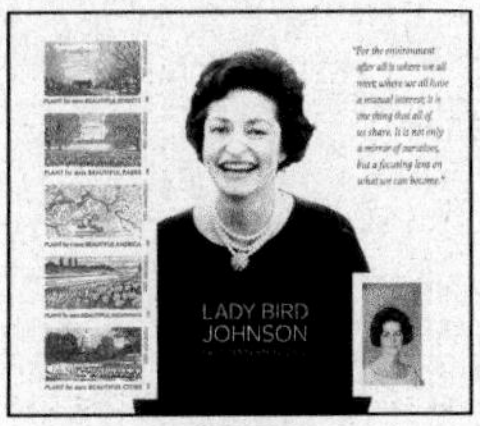

A3595

No. 4716: a, Blooming crab apples lining avenue (Plant for more Beautiful Streets). b, Washington Monument, Potomac River and daffodils (Plant for more Beautiful Parks). c, Jefferson Memorial, Tidal Basin and cherry blossoms (Plant for a more Beautiful America). d, Poppies and lupines along highway (Plant for more Beautiful Highways). e, Capitol, azaleas and tulips (Plant for more Beautiful Cities). f, Lady Bird Johnson (1912-2007), First Lady, vert.

LITHOGRAPHED

Serpentine Die Cut 10¾

2012, Nov. 30

Self-Adhesive

4716	A3595	Pane of 6	9.00	
a.-f.		(45c) Any single	1.50	.40
g.		Imperforate pane of 6	25.00	

WAVES OF COLOR

A3596

A3597

A3598

A3599

LITHOGRAPHED & ENGRAVED

Serpentine Die Cut 11, 10¾ (#4719)

2012, Dec. 1

Self-Adhesive

4717	A3596	$1 multi	4.50	.50
4718	A3597	$2 multi	4.50	1.25
4719	A3598	$5 multi	8.75	2.50
4720	A3599	$10 multi	17.50	9.00
		Nos. 4717-4720 (4)	35.25	13.25

Adjacent horizontal or vertical stamps have selvage between the stamps. Plate blocks have sheet margins on the top or bottom and both sides.

EMANCIPATION PROCLAMATION, 150th ANNIV.

A3600

PHOTOGRAVURE

2013, Jan. 1 *Serpentine Die Cut 11*

Self-Adhesive

4721	A3600	(45c) multicolored	1.25	.25
a.		Imperforate	2.00	—

KALEIDOSCOPE FLOWERS

A3601

A3602

A3603

A3604

LITHOGRAPHED

Serpentine Die Cut 11 Vert.

2013, Jan. 14

Coil Stamps

Self-Adhesive

Color of Large Outer Leaves

4722	A3601	46c yellow orange	1.25	.25
4723	A3602	46c yellow green	1.25	.25
4724	A3603	46c red violet	1.25	.25
4725	A3604	46c red	1.25	.25
a.		Strip of 4, #4722-4725	5.00	
		Nos. 4722-4725 (4)	5.00	1.00

CHINESE NEW YEAR

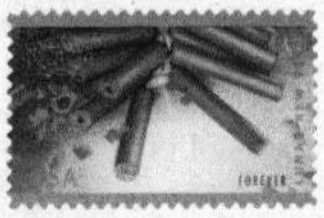

Year of the Snake — A3605

PHOTOGRAVURE

Serpentine Die Cut 11

2013, Jan. 16

Self-Adhesive

4726	A3605	(45c) multicolored	1.25	.25
a.		Imperforate	2.00	—

APPLES

Northern Spy Apple A3606

Golden Delicious Apple A3607

Granny Smith Apple A3608

Baldwin Apple A3609

LITHOGRAPHED

Serpentine Die Cut 11¼x10¾

2013, Jan. 17

Self-Adhesive

4727	A3606	33c multicolored	1.25	.25
4728	A3607	33c multicolored	1.25	.25
4729	A3608	33c multicolored	1.25	.25
4730	A3609	33c multicolored	1.25	.25
a.		Block or strip of 4, #4727-4730	5.00	
b.		Imperforate block or strip of 4	6.50	—

Coil Stamps

Serpentine Die Cut 11 Vert.

4731	A3609	33c multicolored	1.50	.25
4732	A3606	33c multicolored	1.50	.25
4733	A3607	33c multicolored	1.50	.25
4734	A3608	33c multicolored	1.50	.25
a.		Strip of 4, #4731-4734	6.00	
		Nos. 4727-4734 (8)	11.00	2.00

Wedding Cake Type of 2009

LITHOGRAPHED

Serpentine Die Cut 10¾

2013, Jan. 18

Self-Adhesive

4735	A3344	66c multicolored	1.75	.25
a.		Imperforate	3.50	—

See Nos. 4398, 4521, 4602, 4867, 5000.

SPICEBUSH SWALLOWTAIL BUTTERFLY

A3610

PHOTOGRAVURE

Serpentine Die Cut 10¾

2013, Jan. 23

Self-Adhesive

4736	A3610	66c multicolored	1.40	.25
a.		Imperforate	3.00	—

TUFTED PUFFINS

A3611

LITHOGRAPHED

Serpentine Die Cut 11¼x10¾

2013, Jan. 23

"2013" in Orange Red Solid Color in "Tufted Puffins" and "86"

Self-Adhesive

4737 A3611 86c multicolored 1.80 .35
b. Imperforate 4.00 —

"2013" in Black With Dots in "Tufted Puffins" and "86"

4737A A3611 86c multi 5.00 .35

AMERICAN LANDMARKS ISSUE

Arlington Green Bridge, Vermont — A3612

Grand Central Terminal, New York City — A3613

PHOTOGRAVURE

2013 ***Serpentine Die Cut 10¾x10½***

Self-Adhesive

4738 A3612 $5.60 multi 11.00 6.25
4739 A3613 $19.95 multi 40.00 21.00

Earth — A3614

PHOTOGRAVURE

2013, Jan. 28 ***Serpentine Die Cut***

Self-Adhesive

4740 A3614 ($1.10) multi 3.00 .50
a. Imperforate 5.00 —

Unused values are for stamps with surrounding selvage. Adjacent stamps are separated by rouletting.

LOVE

Envelope With Wax Seal — A3615

PHOTOGRAVURE

Serpentine Die Cut 10¾

2013, Jan. 30

Self-Adhesive

4741 A3615 (46c) multicolored 1.25 .25
a. Imperforate 2.00 —

ROSA PARKS

Parks (1913-2005), Civil Rights Pioneer — A3616

PHOTOGRAVURE

Serpentine Die Cut 10¾

2013, Feb. 4

Self-Adhesive

4742 A3616 (46c) multicolored 1.25 .25
a. Imperforate 2.00 —

MUSCLE CARS

1969 Dodge Charger Daytona — A3617

1966 Pontiac GTO — A3618

1967 Ford Mustang Shelby GT 500 — A3619

1970 Chevrolet Chevelle SS — A3620

1970 Plymouth Hemi Barracuda A3621

PHOTOGRAVURE

Serpentine Die Cut 10¾

2013, Feb. 22 **Tagged**

Self-Adhesive

4743 A3617 (46c) multicolored 1.25 .30
4744 A3618 (46c) multicolored 1.25 .30
4745 A3619 (46c) multicolored 1.25 .30
4746 A3620 (46c) multicolored 1.25 .30
4747 A3621 (46c) multicolored 1.25 .30
a. Vert. strip of 5, #4743-4747 6.25
Vert. P# block of 10, 5# + V 12.50
Horiz. P# block of 8, 2 sets of 5# + V 10.00
b. Imperforate vert. strip of 5 10.00 —
Nos. 4743-4747 (5) 6.25 1.50

MODERN ART IN AMERICA

A3622

No. 4748: a, I Saw the Figure 5 in Gold, by Charles Demuth (37x51mm). b, Sunset, Maine Coast, by John Marin (43x43mm). c, House and Street, by Stuart Davis (51x41mm). d, Painting, Number 5, by Marsden Hartley (37x51mm). e, Black Mesa Landscape, New Mexico/Out Back of Marie's II, by Georgia O'Keeffe (51x41mm). f, Noire et Blanche, by Man Ray (43x41mm). g, The Prodigal Son, by Aaron Douglas (34x51mm). h, American Landscape, by Charles Sheeler (43x41mm). i, Brooklyn Bridge, by Joseph Stella (38x47mm). j, Razor, by Gerald Murphy (43x43mm). k, Nude Descending a Staircase, No. 2, by Marcel Duchamp (34x58mm). l, Fog Horns, by Arthur Dove (43x37mm).

PHOTOGRAVURE

Serpentine Die Cut 10½

2013, Mar. 7

Self-Adhesive

4748 A3622 Pane of 12 15.00
a.-l. (46c) Any single 1.25 .50
m. Imperforate pane of 12 70.00

Armory Show, cent.

Patriotic Star — A3623

LITHOGRAPHED

Serpentine Die Cut 10¾ Vert.

2013, Mar. 19

Coil Stamp

Self-Adhesive

4749 A3623 46c multicolored 1.25 .25

LA FLORIDA

A3624 A3625

A3626 A3627

PHOTOGRAVURE

Serpentine Die Cut 10½

2013, Apr. 3

Self-Adhesive

4750 A3624 (46c) multicolored 1.25 .25
4751 A3625 (46c) multicolored 1.25 .25
4752 A3626 (46c) multicolored 1.25 .25
4753 A3627 (46c) multicolored 1.25 .25
a. Block of 4, #4750-4753 5.00
b. Imperforate block of 4 10.00 —
Nos. 4750-4753 (4) 5.00 1.00

Naming of Florida, 500th anniv.

VINTAGE SEED PACKETS

Phlox A3628

Calendula A3629

Digitalis A3630

Linum A3631

Alyssum A3632

Zinnias A3633

Pinks A3634

Cosmos A3635

Aster A3636

Primrose A3637

PHOTOGRAVURE

Serpentine Die Cut 10¾ on 2 or 3 Sides

2013, Apr. 5

Booklet Stamps

Self-Adhesive

4754 A3628 (46c) multicolored 2.50 .25
4755 A3629 (46c) multicolored 2.50 .25
4756 A3630 (46c) multicolored 2.50 .25
4757 A3631 (46c) multicolored 2.50 .25
4758 A3632 (46c) multicolored 2.50 .25
4759 A3633 (46c) multicolored 2.50 .25
4760 A3634 (46c) multicolored 2.50 .25
4761 A3635 (46c) multicolored 2.50 .25
4762 A3636 (46c) multicolored 2.50 .25
4763 A3637 (46c) multicolored 2.50 .25
a. Block of 10, #4754-4763 25.00
b. Booklet pane of 20, 2 each #4754-4763 50.00
Nos. 4754-4763 (10) 25.00 2.50

No. 4763b is a double-sided booklet pane with 12 stamps on one side (2 each #4754, 4759, 1 each #4755-4758, 4760-4763), and eight stamps (1 each #4755-4758, 4760-4763) plus label (booklet cover) on the other side.

WEDDING FLOWERS

Flowers A3638

Flowers and "Yes I Do" A3639

LITHOGRAPHED

Serpentine Die Cut 10¾

2013, Apr. 11

Self-Adhesive

4764 A3638 (46c) multicolored 1.25 .25
a. Dated "2014" 1.25 .25
b. Imperforate 2.50 —
4765 A3639 66c multicolored 1.40 .30
a. Imperforate 3.00 —

Flag in Autumn A3640

Flag in Winter A3641

Flag in Spring A3642

Flag in Summer A3643

PHOTOGRAVURE

2013 ***Serpentine Die Cut 8½ Vert.***

Coil Stamps

Self-Adhesive

4766 A3640 (46c) multicolored 2.25 .25
4767 A3641 (46c) multicolored 2.25 .25
4768 A3642 (46c) multicolored 2.25 .25
4769 A3643 (46c) multicolored 2.25 .25
a. Strip of 4, #4766-4769 9.00

LITHOGRAPHED (#4770-4785)

Serpentine Die Cut 9½ Vert.

4770 A3640 (46c) multicolored 2.25 .25
4771 A3641 (46c) multicolored 2.25 .25
4772 A3642 (46c) multicolored 2.25 .25
4773 A3643 (46c) multicolored 2.25 .25
a. Strip of 4, #4770-4773 9.00

Serpentine Die Cut 11 Vert.

4774 A3641 (46c) multicolored 3.00 .25
4775 A3642 (46c) multicolored 3.00 .25
4776 A3643 (46c) multicolored 3.00 .25
4777 A3640 (46c) multicolored 3.00 .25
a. Strip of 4, #4774-4777 12.00
b. Block of 28 (4x7), #4774-4777, with no horiz. slits —
Nos. 4766-4777 (12) 30.00 3.00

Booklet Stamps

With Microprinted "USPS" at Lower Left Corner of Flag

Serpentine Die Cut 11¼x10¾ on 2 or 3 Sides

4778 A3642 (46c) multicolored 1.25 .25
4779 A3643 (46c) multicolored 1.25 .25
4780 A3640 (46c) multicolored 1.25 .25
4781 A3641 (46c) multicolored 1.25 .25
a. Block of 4, #4778-4781 6.00
b. Booklet pane of 20, 5 each #4778-4781 30.00

With Microprinted "USPS" Near Top of Pole or at Lower Left Corner Near Rope (#4783, 4783b)

Pre-phosphored Paper

4782 A3642 (46c) multicolored 1.25 .25
b. As #4782, dated "2014" 1.25 .25
4783 A3643 (46c) multicolored 1.25 .25
b. As #4783, dated "2014" 1.25 .25
4784 A3640 (46c) multicolored 1.25 .25
b. As #4784, dated "2014" 1.25 .25
c. Tagging omitted —
4785 A3641 (46c) multicolored 1.25 .25
b. As #4785, dated "2014" 1.25 .25
c. Block of 4, #4782-4785 5.00
d. Booklet pane of 20, 5 each #4782-4785 25.00
f. Booklet pane of 10, 3 each #4782a, 4783a, 2 each #4784a, 4785a 12.50

g. Block of 4, #4782b, 4783b, 4784b, 4785b — 5.00
h. Booklet pane of 20, 5 each #4782b, 4783b, 4784b, 4785b — 25.00
i. As "h," die cutting omitted on side with 8 stamps and 3 pairs on side with 12 stamps — 1,800.
Nos. 4778-4785 (8) — 10.00 2.00

Issued: Nos. 4766-4777, 5/3; Nos. 4778-4785, 5/17. No. 4781b is a double-sided booklet with 12 stamps on one side (3 each #4778-4781) and eight stamps (2 each #4778-4781) plus label that serves as a booklet cover on the other side.

No. 4785c is a double-sided booklet with 12 stamps on one side (3 each #4782-4785) and eight stamps (2 each #4782-4785) plus label that serves as a booklet cover on the other side.

A microprinted "USPS" is found on tree trunk to the left of the "F" in "Forever" on No. 4766, on tree trunk near lower left corner of flag on No. 4767, on white flag stripe at lower right on No. 4768, and on the top of the flagpole below the ball on No. 4769. Nos. 4770-4773 are microprinted "USPS" in the same places as on Nos. 4778-4781. Nos. 4774-4777 are microprinted "USPS" in the same places as on Nos. 4782-4785.

No. 4785e comprises stamps printed on paper with overall tagging. For detailed listings, see the *Scott Specialized Catalogue of United States Stamps and Covers.*

See Nos. 4796-4799.

Issued: Nos. 4782b, 4783b, 4784b, 4785b, 3/17/14. Nos. 4782b, 4783b, 4784b and 4785b each sold for 49c on day of issue.

MUSIC ICONS

Lydia Mendoza (1916-2007), Tejano Music Recording Artist — A3644

PHOTOGRAVURE

Serpentine Die Cut 10¾

2013, May 15

Self-Adhesive

4786 A3644 (46c) multicolored — 1.25 .25
a. Imperforate — 1.75 —

Adjacent horizontal or vertical stamps have selvage between the stamps.

CIVIL WAR SESQUICENTENNIAL

Battle of Vicksburg A3645

Battle of Gettysburg A3646

LITHOGRAPHED

2013, May 23 ***Serpentine Die Cut 11***

Self-Adhesive

4787 A3645 (46c) multicolored — 1.25 .30
4788 A3646 (46c) multicolored — 1.25 .30
a. Pair, #4787-4788 — 2.50
b. Imperforate pair, #4787-4788 — 5.50 —

MUSIC ICONS

Johnny Cash (1932-2003), Country Music Recording Artist — A3647

PHOTOGRAVURE

Serpentine Die Cut 10¾

2013, June 5

Self-Adhesive

4789 A3647 (46c) multicolored — 1.25 .25
a. Imperforate — 1.75 —

WEST VIRGINIA STATEHOOD, 150th ANNIV.

Hills in Monongahela National Forest — A3648

PHOTOGRAVURE

Serpentine Die Cut 11

2013, June 20

Self-Adhesive

4790 A3648 (46c) multicolored — 1.25 .25
a. Imperforate — 1.75 —

NEW ENGLAND COASTAL LIGHTHOUSES

Portland Head Lighthouse, Maine A3649

Portsmouth Harbor Lighthouse, New Hampshire A3650

Boston Harbor Lighthouse, Massachusetts A3651

Point Judith Lighthouse, Rhode Island A3652

New London Harbor Lighthouse, Connecticut — A3653

Original

"FOREVER" and "USA" 1mm higher than original

LITHOGRAPHED

Serpentine Die Cut 11x10¾

2013, July 13

Self-Adhesive

4791 A3649 (46c) multicolored — 1.25 .40
a. "FOREVER" and "USA" 1mm higher than normal (pos. 1) — 2.00 1.00
b. Horiz. strip of 5, #4791a, 4792-4795 — 6.50
4792 A3650 (46c) multicolored — 1.25 .40
4793 A3651 (46c) multicolored — 1.25 .40
4794 A3652 (46c) multicolored — 1.25 .40
4795 A3653 (46c) multicolored — 1.25 .40
a. Horiz. strip of 5, #4791-4795 — 6.25
b. Imperforate horiz. strip of 5 — 11.00 —
c. Imperforate horiz. strip of 5, pos. 1 as No. 4791a — 13.00 —
Nos. 4791-4795 (5) — 6.25 2.00

Flag Types of 2013

PHOTOGRAVURE

Serpentine Die Cut 11¼x11½ on 2 or 3 Sides

2013, Aug. 8

Booklet Stamps

Self-Adhesive

4796 A3642 (46c) multicolored — 1.50 .25
4797 A3643 (46c) multicolored — 1.50 .25
4798 A3640 (46c) multicolored — 1.50 .25
4799 A3641 (46c) multicolored — 1.50 .25
a. Block of 4, #4796-4799 — 6.00
b. Booklet pane of 20, 5 each #4796-4799 — 30.00
Nos. 4796-4799 (4) — 6.00 1.00

No. 4799b is a double-sided booklet with 12 stamps on one side (3 each #4796-4799) and eight stamps (2 each #4796-4799) plus label that serves as a booklet cover on the other side. Nos. 4796-4799 are microprinted "USPS" in the same places as Nos. 4766-4769.

EID

"Eid Mubarak" — A3654

LITHOGRAPHED

2013, Aug. 8 ***Serpentine Die Cut 11***

Self-Adhesive

4800 A3654 (46c) dk grn, gray & gold — 1.25 .25
a. Imperforate — 2.00 —

BUILDING A NATION

Airplane Mechanic, Photograph by Lewis Hine — A3655

Derrick Man on Empire State Building, Photograph by Lewis Hine — A3656

Millinery Apprentice, Photograph by Lewis Hine — A3657

Man on Hoisting Ball on Empire State Building, Photograph by Lewis Hine — A3658

Linotype Operator, Photograph by Lewis Hine — A3659

Welder on Empire State Building, Photograph by Lewis Hine — A3660

Coal Miner, by Anonymous Photographer A3661

Riveters on Empire State Building, Photograph by Lewis Hine A3662

Powerhouse Mechanic, Photograph by Lewis Hine — A3663

Railroad Track Walker, Photograph by Lewis Hine — A3664

Textile Worker, Photograph by Lewis Hine — A3665

Man Guiding Beam on Empire State Building, Photograph by Lewis Hine — A3666

PHOTOGRAVURE

Serpentine Die Cut 10½x10¾

2013, Aug. 8

Self-Adhesive

4801 Pane of 12 — 15.00
a. A3655 (46c) black & gray — 1.25 .50
b. A3656 (46c) black & gray — 1.25 .50
c. A3657 (46c) black & gray — 1.25 .50
d. A3658 (46c) black & gray — 1.25 .50
e. A3659 (46c) black & gray — 1.25 .50
f. A3660 (46c) black & gray — 1.25 .50
g. A3661 (46c) black & gray — 1.25 .50
h. A3662 (46c) black & gray — 1.25 .50
i. A3663 (46c) black & gray — 1.25 .50
j. A3664 (46c) black & gray — 1.25 .50
k. A3665 (46c) black & gray — 1.25 .50
l. A3666 (46c) black & gray — 1.25 .50
m. Imperforate pane of 12 — 70.00

No. 4801 was printed with five different sheet margins depicting coal miner from No. 4801g, man on hoisting ball on Empire State Building, man measuring bearings in large gearwheel, man on cable at Empire State Building, and woman welder. Value is for sheet with any margin.

Bobcat Type of 2012

LITHOGRAPHED

2013, Aug. 9 ***Perf. 9¾ Vert.***

Coil Stamp

4802 A3564 1c multicolored — .30 .25

See No. 4672.

BLACK HERITAGE

Althea Gibson (1927-2003), Tennis Player — A3667

PHOTOGRAVURE

Serpentine Die Cut 11

2013, Aug. 23

Self-Adhesive

4803 A3667 (46c) multicolored — 1.25 .25
a. Imperforate — 1.75 —

MARCH ON WASHINGTON, 50th ANNIV.

Marchers and Washington Monument — A3668

PHOTOGRAVURE

Serpentine Die Cut 10¾

2013, Aug. 23

Self-Adhesive

4804	A3668 (46c) multicolored		1.25	.25
a.	Imperforate		1.75	—

WAR OF 1812 BICENTENNIAL

Painting of Battle of Lake Erie, by William Henry Powell — A3669

LITHOGRAPHED

Serpentine Die Cut 10¾

2013, Sept. 10

Self-Adhesive

4805	A3669 (46c) multicolored		1.25	.25
a.	Imperforate		1.75	—

INVERTED JENNY

Miniature Sheet

A3670

LITHOGRAPHED & ENGRAVED

Serpentine Die Cut 10½x11¼

2013, Sept. 22

Self-Adhesive

4806	A3670 multicolored	24.00	
a.	$2 Single stamp	4.00	1.25
b.	Imperforate pane of 6	72.50	—
c.	As "b," single stamp	12.00	—
d.	Pane of 6, airplane right-side up	*70,000.*	
e.	As "d," single stamp	*13,500.*	

No. 4806, along with a piece of white cardboard backing, was placed in a sealed envelope. The envelope, along with a piece of gray cardboard backing, was inside a sealed plastic outerwrap. One hundred panes were produced that contain the airplane right-side up. These panes were included in the same envelope and outerwrap and were distributed randomly. No returns or refunds were offered for any opened packages. Values for No. 4806 are for panes removed from the envelope.

A book containing an unused and a first-day canceled example of No. 4806, along with items that are termed "proofs" and "die wipes" sold for $200.

MUSIC ICONS

Ray Charles (1930-2004), Recording Artist — A3671

LITHOGRAPHED

Serpentine Die Cut 10½

2013, Sept. 23

Self-Adhesive

4807	A3671 (46c) multicolored	1.25	.25
a.	Imperforate	1.75	—

Adjacent horizontal or vertical stamps have selvage between the stamps.

SNOWFLAKES

A3672

A3673

A3674

A3675

A3676

PHOTOGRAVURE

Serpentine Die Cut 11 Vert.

2013, Oct. 1

Coil Stamps
Self-Adhesive

4808	A3672 (10c) lt bl & multi	.30	.25
4809	A3673 (10c) pale bl & multi	.30	.25
4810	A3674 (10c) lt bl & multi	.30	.25
4811	A3675 (10c) pale bl & multi	.30	.25
4812	A3676 (10c) lil & multi	.30	.25
a.	Strip of 5, #4808-4812	1.25	
	Nos. 4808-4812 (5)	1.50	1.25

Holy Family and Donkey Type of 2012 Dated "2013" and

Wreath
A3677

Virgin and Child, by Jan Gossaert
A3678

Poinsettia
A3679

Gingerbread House With Red Door
A3680

Gingerbread House With Blue Door
A3681

Gingerbread House With Green Door
A3682

Gingerbread House With Orange Door
A3683

Poinsettia
A3684

LITHOGRAPHED, PHOTOGRAVURE (#4821)

2013 ***Serpentine Die Cut 11***

Self-Adhesive

4813	A3590 (46c) multicolored	1.25	.25
a.	Imperforate	1.75	—

Serpentine Die Cut

4814	A3677 ($1.10) multicolored	3.00	.50
a.	Imperforate	4.00	—

Booklet Stamps

Serpentine Die Cut 11 on 2 or 3 Sides

4815	A3678 (46c) multicolored	1.25	.25
a.	Booklet pane of 20	25.00	
b.	Imperforate	1.75	—
c.	Imperforate booklet pane of 20	35.00	
4816	A3679 (46c) multicolored	1.25	.25
a.	Booklet pane of 20	25.00	
b.	Dated "2014"	1.25	.25
c.	As #4816a, dated "2014"	25.00	
d.	Imperforate, dated "2013"	1.75	—
e.	Imperforate booklet pane of 20	35.00	
4817	A3680 (46c) multicolored	1.25	.25
4818	A3681 (46c) multicolored	1.25	.25
4819	A3682 (46c) multicolored	1.25	.25
4820	A3683 (46c) multicolored	1.25	.25
b.	Block of 4, #4817-4820	5.00	
c.	Booklet pane of 20, 5 each #4817-4820	25.00	
f.	Imperforate block of 4	8.00	—
g.	Imperforate booklet pane of 20	40.00	

Serpentine Die Cut 8 on 2, 3 or 4 Sides

4821	A3684 (46c) multicolored	1.25	.25
a.	Booklet pane of 18	22.50	
	Nos. 4815-4821 (7)	8.75	1.75

Issued: Nos. 4813, 4815, 10/11; No. 4814, 10/24; Nos. 4816, 4821, 10/10; Nos. 4817-4820, 11/6.

MEDALS OF HONOR

Navy Medal of Honor
A3685

Army Medal of Honor
A3686

LITHOGRAPHED

Serpentine Die Cut 11

2013, Nov. 11

Self-Adhesive

4822	A3685 (46c) multicolored	1.25	.30
a.	Dated "2014"	1.25	.30
b.	Dated "2015"	1.25	.30
4823	A3686 (46c) multicolored	1.25	.30
a.	Dated "2014"	1.25	.30
b.	Dated "2015"	1.25	.30
c.	Pair, #4822-4823	2.50	
d.	Pair, #4822a-4823a	2.50	
e.	Pair, 4822b-4823b	2.50	
f.	Imperf. pair, #4822-4823	4.50	—
g.	Imperf. pair, #4822a-4823a	4.50	—

Issued: Nos. 4822a, 4823a, 7/26/14. Nos. 4822a, 4822b, 4823a and 4823b sold for 49c on day of issue. Folios containing Nos. 4822a and 4823a have different images of Medal of Honor recipients, product numbers (on folio margins) and text on the paper backing than that found on the folios with Nos. 4822 and 4823. Nos. 4822b and 4823b were in a folio with No. 4988.

HANUKKAH

Menorah — A3687

LITHOGRAPHED

Serpentine Die Cut 11

2013, Nov. 19

Self-Adhesive

4824	A3687 (46c) multicolored	1.25	.25
a.	Imperforate	1.75	—

Postal Service officials declared on Nov. 8 that No. 4824 could be sold in post offices on Nov. 9, but the first day ceremony was held on Nov. 19 in New York, NY. Official first day covers have that date and city.

SCENES FROM HARRY POTTER MOVIES

Harry Potter
A3688

Harry Potter and Ron Weasley
A3689

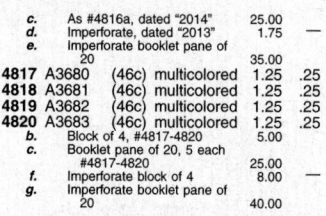

Harry Potter, Ron Weasley, Hermione Granger
A3690

Hermione Granger
A3691

Harry Potter and Fawkes the Phoenix
A3692

Hedwig the Owl
A3693

Dobby the House Elf — A3694

Harry Potter and Buckbeak the Hippogriff — A3695

Headmaster Albus Dumbledore
A3696

Professor Severus Snape
A3697

Rubeus Hagrid
A3698

Professor Minerva McGonagall
A3699

Harry Potter, Ron Weasley, Hermione Granger
A3700

Luna Lovegood
A3701

Fred and George Weasley
A3702

Ginny Weasley
A3703

Draco Malfoy A3704

Harry Potter A3705

Lord Voldemort A3706

Bellatrix Lestrange A3707

LITHOGRAPHED

Serpentine Die Cut 11

2013, Nov. 19

Booklet Stamps

Self-Adhesive

4825 A3688 (46c) multicolored 2.00 .30
4826 A3689 (46c) multicolored 2.00 .30
4827 A3690 (46c) multicolored 2.00 .30
4828 A3691 (46c) multicolored 2.00 .30
a. Booklet pane of 4, #4825-4828, + central label 8.00
b. Imperf. booklet pane of 4 12.50 —
4829 A3692 (46c) multicolored 2.00 .30
4830 A3693 (46c) multicolored 2.00 .30
4831 A3694 (46c) multicolored 2.00 .30
4832 A3695 (46c) multicolored 2.00 .30
a. Booklet pane of 4, #4829-4832, + central label 8.00
b. Imperf. booklet pane of 4 12.50 —
4833 A3696 (46c) multicolored 2.00 .30
4834 A3697 (46c) multicolored 2.00 .30
4835 A3698 (46c) multicolored 2.00 .30
4836 A3699 (46c) multicolored 2.00 .30
a. Booklet pane of 4, #4833-4836, + central label 8.00
b. Imperf. booklet pane of 4 12.50 —
4837 A3700 (46c) multicolored 2.00 .30
4838 A3701 (46c) multicolored 2.00 .30
4839 A3702 (46c) multicolored 2.00 .30
4840 A3703 (46c) multicolored 2.00 .30
a. Booklet pane of 4, #4837-4840, + central label 8.00
b. Imperf. booklet pane of 4 12.50 —
4841 A3704 (46c) multicolored 2.00 .30
4842 A3705 (46c) multicolored 2.00 .30
4843 A3706 (46c) multicolored 2.00 .30
4844 A3707 (46c) multicolored 2.00 .30
a. Booklet pane of 4, #4841-4844, + central label 8.00
b. Imperf. booklet pane of 4 12.50 —
Nos. 4825-4844 (20) 40.00 6.00

KWANZAA

People, Candles and Book — A3708

LITHOGRAPHED

Serpentine Die Cut 11

2013, Nov. 26

Self-Adhesive

4845 A3708 (46c) multicolored 1.25 .25
a. Imperforate 1.75 —

CHINESE NEW YEAR

Year of the Horse — A3709

PHOTOGRAVURE

Serpentine Die Cut 11

2014, Jan. 15

Self-Adhesive

4846 A3709 (46c) multicolored 1.25 .25
a. Imperforate 2.00 —

LOVE

Heart — A3710

PHOTOGRAVURE

Serpentine Die Cut 10¾

2014, Jan. 21

Self-Adhesive

4847 A3710 (46c) multicolored 1.25 .25
a. Imperforate 2.00 —

FERNS

Fortune's Holly Fern A3711

Soft Shield Fern A3712

Autumn Fern A3713

Goldie's Wood Fern A3714

Painted Fern — A3715

PHOTOGRAVURE

Serpentine Die Cut 11 Vert.

2014, Jan. 27

Coil Stamps

Self-Adhesive

4848 A3711 49c multicolored 1.50 .25
4849 A3712 49c multicolored 1.50 .25
4850 A3713 49c multicolored 1.50 .25
4851 A3714 49c multicolored 1.50 .25
4852 A3715 49c multicolored 1.50 .25
a. Strip of 5, #4848-4852 7.50
Nos. 4848-4852 (5) 7.50 1.25

Fort McHenry Flag and Fireworks — A3716

PHOTOGRAVURE

Serpentine Die Cut 8½ Vert.

2014, Jan. 28

Coil Stamps

Self-Adhesive

4853 A3716 (49c) multicolored 1.25 .25
Pair 2.50

LITHOGRAPHED (#4854-4855)

Serpentine Die Cut 9½ Vert.

4854 A3716 (49c) multicolored 1.25 .25
Pair 2.50
a. Die cutting omitted, pair 150.00

Booklet Stamp

Serpentine Die Cut 11¼x10¾ on 2 or 3 Sides

4855 A3716 (49c) multicolored 1.25 .25
a. Booklet pane of 20 25.00

No. 4855a is a double-sided booklet with 12 stamps on one side and eight stamps plus a label that serves as the booklet cover on the other side.

Nos. 4854 and 4855 each have a microprinted "USPS" on the right side of the lowest white stripe of the flag.

See Nos. 4868-4871.

BLACK HERITAGE

Shirley Chisholm (1924-2005), Congresswoman A3717

PHOTOGRAVURE

Serpentine Die Cut 11

2014, Jan. 31

Self-Adhesive

4856 A3717 (49c) multicolored 1.25 .25
a. Imperforate 2.00 —

WILDLIFE ISSUE

Hummingbird — A3718

LITHOGRAPHED

Serpentine Die Cut 11¼x10¾

2014, Feb. 7

Self-Adhesive

4857 A3718 34c multicolored .70 .25

Coil Stamp

Serpentine Die Cut 9½ Vert.

4858 A3718 34c multicolored .70 .25
a. Overall tagging .70 .25
b. As "a," die cutting omitted, pair —

GREAT SPANGLED FRITILLARY BUTTERFLY

A3719

PHOTOGRAVURE

Serpentine Die Cut 10¾

2014, Feb. 10

Self-Adhesive

4859 A3719 70c multicolored 1.50 .25
a. Imperforate 3.25 —

Statue of Abraham Lincoln in Lincoln Memorial — A3720

PHOTOGRAVURE

Serpentine Die Cut 11

2014, Feb. 12

Self-Adhesive

4860 A3720 21c multicolored .45 .25
a. Imperforate 1.25 —

Coil Stamp

Serpentine Die Cut 8½ Vert.

4861 A3720 21c multicolored .45 .25

WINTER FLOWERS

Amaryllis A3721

Cyclamen A3722

Paperwhite A3723

Christmas Cactus A3724

LITHOGRAPHED

Serpentine Die Cut 11 on 2 or 3 Sides

2014, Feb. 14

Booklet Stamps

Self-Adhesive

4862 A3721 (49c) multicolored 1.50 .30
4863 A3722 (49c) multicolored 1.50 .30
4864 A3723 (49c) multicolored 1.50 .30
4865 A3724 (49c) multicolored 1.50 .30
a. Block of 4, #4862-4865 6.00
b. Booklet pane of 20, 5 each #4862-4865 30.00
c. Imperforate block of 4 7.00 —
d. Imperforate booklet pane of 20 35.00
Nos. 4862-4865 (4) 6.00 1.20

No. 4865b is a double-sided booklet pane with 12 stamps on one side (3 each #4862-4865), and eight stamps (2 each #4862-4865) plus label (booklet cover) on the other side.

LITERARY ARTS

Ralph Ellison (1913-94), Buildings in Harlem — A3725

PHOTOGRAVURE

Serpentine Die Cut 11

2014, Feb. 18

Self-Adhesive

4866 A3725 91c multicolored 1.90 .45
a. Imperforate 4.00 —

Wedding Cake Type of 2009

LITHOGRAPHED

Serpentine Die Cut 10¾

2014, Feb. 22

Self-Adhesive

4867 A3344 70c multicolored 2.00 .25

See Nos. 4398, 4521, 4602, 4735, 5000.

Fort McHenry Flag and Fireworks Type of 2014

LITHOGRAPHED

Coil Stamp Self-Adhesive With "USPS" Microprinted in Fireworks Above Flagpole

Serpentine Die Cut 11 Vert.

2014, Mar. 3

4868 A3716 (49c) multicolored 1.25 .25
a. Vert. strip of 3 (one single each from three different coil rolls), horiz. unslit between 60.00
b. Pair, die cutting omitted —

PHOTOGRAVURE (#4869), LITHOGRAPHED (#4870-4871)

Booklet Stamps

Without Microprinted "USPS"

Serpentine Die Cut 11¼x11½ on 2 or 3 Sides

4869 A3716 (49c) multicolored 1.25 .25
a. Booklet pane of 20 25.00

With "USPS" Microprinted in Fireworks Above Flagpole

Serpentine Die Cut 11¼x10¾ on 2 or 3 Sides

4870 A3716 (49c) multicolored 1.25 .25
a. Booklet pane of 20 25.00

The actual design images on Nos. 4855, 4869 and 4870 differ slightly in size. This is easiest seen by measuring the height of the flagpole: No. 4855 is 13mm, No. 4869 is 14mm, and No. 4870 is 12mm.

Thin Paper

Serpentine Die Cut 11¼x11 on 2, 3 or 4 Sides

4871 A3716 (49c) multicolored 1.25 .25
a. Booklet pane of 18 25.00

Nos. 4869a and 4870a are double-sided booklets with 12 stamps on one side and eight stamps plus a label that serves as the booklet cover on the other side.

AMERICAN LANDMARKS ISSUE

Verrazano-Narrows Bridge, New York — A3726

USS Arizona Memorial, Hawaii — A3727

LITHOGRAPHED

2014 ***Serpentine Die Cut 10¾x10½***

Self-Adhesive

4872 A3726 $5.60 multi 11.00 6.25
4873 A3727 $19.99 multi 40.00 21.00
a. Imperforate 55.00 —

Issued: $5.60, 3/4; $19.99, 3/13.

FERNS

Fortune's Holly Fern A3728

Soft Shield Fern A3729

Autumn Fern A3730

Goldie's Wood Fern A3731

Painted Fern — A3732

PHOTOGRAVURE

Serpentine Die Cut 11 Vert.

2014, Mar. 6

Coil Stamps
Self-Adhesive

4874	A3728	(49c)	multicolored	2.00	.25
4875	A3729	(49c)	multicolored	2.00	.25
4876	A3730	(49c)	multicolored	2.00	.25
4877	A3731	(49c)	multicolored	2.00	.25
4878	A3732	(49c)	multicolored	2.00	.25
a.	Strip of 5, #4874-4878			10.00	
	Nos. 4874-4878 (5)			10.00	1.25

DISTINGUISHED AMERICANS

C. Alfred "Chief" Anderson (1907-96), Aviator — A3733

LITHOGRAPHED

Serpentine Die Cut 10¾x11

2014, Mar. 13

Self-Adhesive

4879	A3733	70c	multicolored	1.40	.30
a.	Imperforate			3.00	—

MUSIC ICONS

Jimi Hendrix (1942-70), Rock Guitarist — A3734

PHOTOGRAVURE

2014, Mar. 13 **Tagged**

Self-Adhesive

4880	A3734	(49c)	multicolored	1.25	.25
a.	Imperforate			1.75	—

Adjacent horizontal or vertical stamps have selvage between the stamps. Any stamp on the pane is rotated 90 degrees with respect to any adjacent stamp, so that any block of four has stamps oriented in each of the four directions.

See No. 4765.

Flowers and "Yes I Do" Type of 2013

LITHOGRAPHED

Serpentine Die Cut 10¾

2014, Mar. 21

Self-Adhesive

4881	A3639	70c	multicolored	1.40	.30

See Nos. 4765, 5001.

SONGBIRDS

Western Meadowlark A3735

Mountain Bluebird A3736

Western Tanager A3737

Painted Bunting A3738

Baltimore Oriole A3739

Evening Grosbeak A3740

Scarlet Tanager A3741

Rose-breasted Grosbeak A3742

American Goldfinch A3743

White-throated Sparrow A3744

LITHOGRAPHED

Serpentine Die Cut 10¾ on 2 or 3 Sides

2014, Apr. 5

Booklet Stamps
Self-Adhesive

4882	A3735	(49c)	multicolored	1.50	.40
4883	A3736	(49c)	multicolored	1.50	.40
4884	A3737	(49c)	multicolored	1.50	.40
4885	A3738	(49c)	multicolored	1.50	.40
4886	A3739	(49c)	multicolored	1.50	.40
4887	A3740	(49c)	multicolored	1.50	.40
4888	A3741	(49c)	multicolored	1.50	.40
4889	A3742	(49c)	multicolored	1.50	.40
4890	A3743	(49c)	multicolored	1.50	.40
4891	A3744	(49c)	multicolored	1.50	.40
a.	Block of 10, #4882-4891			15.00	
b.	Booklet pane of 20, 2 each #4882-4891			30.00	
c.	Imperforate block of 10			20.00	—
d.	Imperforate booklet pane of 20			40.00	
	Nos. 4882-4891 (10)			15.00	4.00

No. 4891b is a double-sided booklet pane with 12 stamps on one side (Nos. 4883-4886, 4888-4891, 2 each Nos. 4882, 4887) and eight stamps (Nos. 4883-4886, 4888-4891) plus label (booklet cover) on the other side.

LEGENDS OF HOLLYWOOD

Charlton Heston (1923-2008), Actor — A3745

LITHOGRAPHED

Serpentine Die Cut 11

2014, Apr. 11

Self-Adhesive

4892	A3745	(49c)	multicolored	1.25	.25
a.	Imperforate			1.75	—

Map of Sea Surface Temperatures A3746

LITHOGRAPHED

2014, Apr. 22 ***Serpentine Die Cut***

Self-Adhesive

4893	A3746	($1.15)	multi	3.00	.50
a.	Imperforate			3.50	—

Unused values are for stamps with surrounding selvage. Adjacent stamps are separated by rouletting.

FLAGS

Flag With 5 Full and 3 Partial Stars A3747

Flag With 3 Full Stars A3748

Flag With 4 Full and 2 Partial Stars A3749

Flag With 2 Full and 2 Partial Stars A3750

PHOTOGRAVURE

Serpentine Die Cut 11 Vert.

2014, Apr. 25

Coil Stamps
Self-Adhesive

4894	A3747	(49c)	blue & red	1.25	.25
4895	A3748	(49c)	blue & red	1.25	.25
4896	A3749	(49c)	blue & red	1.25	.25
4897	A3750	(49c)	blue & red	1.25	.25
a.	Strip of 4, #4894-4897			5.00	
	Nos. 4894-4897 (4)			5.00	1.00

CIRCUS POSTERS

Barnum and Bailey Circus Poster With Clown A3751

Sells-Floto Circus Poster — A3752

Ringling Bros. Barnum and Bailey Circus Poster With Dainty Miss Leitzel A3753

Al G. Barnes Wild Animal Circus Poster — A3754

Ringling Bros. Shows Poster With Hillary Long A3755

Barnum and Bailey Circus Poster With Tiger — A3756

Ringling Bros. Barnum and Bailey Circus Poster With Elephant A3757

Carl Hagenbeck-Wallace Circus Poster — A3758

A3758a

LITHOGRAPHED, ENGRAVED (50c), SHEET MARGIN (#4905b)
LITHOGRAPHED WITH FOIL APPLICATION

2014, May 5 ***Serpentine Die Cut 11***

Self-Adhesive

4898	A3751	(49c)	multicolored	1.25	.45
4899	A3752	(49c)	multicolored	1.25	.45
4900	A3753	(49c)	multicolored	1.25	.45
4901	A3754	(49c)	multicolored	1.25	.45
4902	A3755	(49c)	multicolored	1.25	.45
4903	A3756	(49c)	multicolored	1.25	.45
4904	A3757	(49c)	multicolored	1.25	.45
4905	A3758	(49c)	multicolored	1.25	.45
a.	Block of 8, #4898-4905			10.00	
b.	Imperforate block of 8			16.00	—
c.	A3758a Imperforate souvenir sheet of 3, #4905d, 2 #4905c			9.00	—
d.	A1811 50c red, imperforate			2.25	—
e.	$1 multicolored (57x48mm stamp similar to #4898), imperforate			4.50	—
f.	As "c," gold omitted in sheet margin				—
	Nos. 4898-4905 (8)			10.00	3.60

No. 4905c was printed only in press sheets containing 12 souvenir sheets. No. 4905c has die cutting around the souvenir sheet margin, but values for unused examples are for souvenir sheets having the white press sheet margin surrounding the die cutting. Examples of No. 4905c with serpentine die cutting around the three stamps were sold only with the USPS 2014 Stamp Yearbook, which sold for $64.95. The souvenir sheets sold with the yearbook are punched out from the press sheets and lack the white press sheet margin.

HARVEY MILK

Harvey Milk (1930-78), Homosexual Rights Advocate and Politician — A3759

LITHOGRAPHED

Sheets of 240 in 12 panes of 20

Serpentine Die Cut 10¾

2014, May 22

Self-Adhesive

4906 A3759 (49c) multicolored 1.25 .25
a. Imperforate 1.75 —

NEVADA STATEHOOD, 150th ANNIV.

Fire Canyon — A3760

LITHOGRAPHED

Serpentine Die Cut 10¾

2014, May 29

Self-Adhesive

4907 A3760 (49c) multicolored 1.25 .25
a. Imperforate 1.75 —

HOT RODS

Rear of 1932 Ford "Deuce" Roadster A3761

Front of 1932 Ford "Deuce" Roadster A3762

PHOTOGRAVURE

Serpentine Die Cut 11¾x11¼ on 2 or 3 Sides

2014, June 6

Booklet Stamps

Self-Adhesive

4908 A3761 (49c) multicolored 1.25 .25
4909 A3762 (49c) multicolored 1.25 .25
a. Pair, #4908-4909 2.50
b. Booklet pane of 20, 10 each #4908-4909 25.00
c. Imperforate pair 4.00 —
d. Imperforate booklet pane of 20 40.00

No. 4909b is a double-sided booklet pane with 12 stamps on one side (6 each Nos. 4908-4909) and eight stamps (4 each Nos. 4908-4909) plus label (booklet cover) on the other side.

CIVIL WAR SESQUICENTENNIAL

Battle of Petersburg A3763

Battle of Mobile Bay A3764

LITHOGRAPHED

Serpentine Die Cut 11

2014, July 30

Self-Adhesive

4910 A3763 (49c) multicolored 1.25 .35
4911 A3764 (49c) multicolored 1.25 .35
a. Pair, #4910-4911 2.50
b. Imperforate pair 5.00 —

FARMERS MARKETS

Breads A3765

Fruits and Vegetables A3766

Flowers A3767

Plants A3768

LITHOGRAPHED

Serpentine Die Cut 10¾

2014, Aug. 7

Self-Adhesive

4912 A3765 (49c) multicolored 1.25 .30
4913 A3766 (49c) multicolored 1.25 .30
4914 A3767 (49c) multicolored 1.25 .30
4915 A3768 (49c) multicolored 1.25 .30
a. Horiz. strip of 4, #4912-4915 5.00
b. Imperf. horiz. strip of 4 9.00 —
Nos. 4912-4915 (4) 5.00 1.20

MUSIC ICONS

Janis Joplin (1943-70), Rock Singer — A3769

LITHOGRAPHED

Serpentine Die Cut 10½

2014, Aug. 8

Self-Adhesive

4916 A3769 (49c) multicolored 1.25 .25
a. Imperforate 1.75 —

HUDSON RIVER SCHOOL PAINTINGS

Grand Canyon, by Thomas Moran (1837-1926) A3770

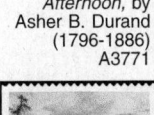

Summer Afternoon, by Asher B. Durand (1796-1886) A3771

Sunset, by Frederic Edwin Church (1826-1900) A3772

Distant View of Niagara Falls, by Thomas Cole (1801-48) A3773

PHOTOGRAVURE

Serpentine Die Cut 10¾ on 2 or 3 Sides

2014, Aug. 21

Booklet Stamps

Self-Adhesive

4917 A3770 (49c) multicolored 1.50 .30
4918 A3771 (49c) multicolored 1.50 .30
4919 A3772 (49c) multicolored 1.50 .30
4920 A3773 (49c) multicolored 1.50 .30
a. Block of 4, #4917-4920 6.00
b. Booklet pane of 20, 5 each #4917-4920 30.00
c. Imperforate block of 4 8.00 —
d. Imperforate booklet pane of 20 40.00
Nos. 4917-4920 (4) 6.00 1.20

No. 4920b is a double-sided booklet pane with 12 stamps on one side (3 each #4917-4920), and eight stamps (2 each #4917-4920) plus label (booklet cover) on the other side.

WAR OF 1812 BICENTENNIAL

Bombardment of Fort McHenry A3774

PHOTOGRAVURE

Serpentine Die Cut 10¾x10½

2014, Sept. 13

Self-Adhesive

4921 A3774 (49c) multicolored 1.25 .25
Pane of 20 25.00
a. Imperforate 1.75 —

CELEBRITY CHEFS

Edna Lewis (1916-2006) A3775

Felipe Rojas-Lombardi (1946-91) A3776

Joyce Chen (1917-94) A3777

James Beard (1903-85) A3778

Julia Child (1912-2004) — A3779

LITHOGRAPHED

Serpentine Die Cut 11x10¾

2014, Sept. 26

Self-Adhesive

4922 A3775 (49c) multicolored 1.25 .45
4923 A3776 (49c) multicolored 1.25 .45
4924 A3777 (49c) multicolored 1.25 .45
4925 A3778 (49c) multicolored 1.25 .45
4926 A3779 (49c) multicolored 1.25 .45
a. Horiz. strip of 5, #4922-4926 6.25
b. Imperf. horiz. strip of 5 8.00 —
Nos. 4922-4926 (5) 6.25 2.25

The gray shading of the inner curve of the dinner plate shown in the margin of the pane continues into the white frames surrounding some of the stamps in the pane's outer rows and columns.

AMERICAN LANDMARKS ISSUE

Glade Creek Grist Mill, West Virginia — A3780

LITHOGRAPHED

Serpentine Die Cut 10¾x10½

2014, Sept. 29

Self-Adhesive

4927 A3780 $5.75 multi 11.50 6.50
a. Imperforate 15.00 —

BATMAN

Bat Signal A3781

Bat Signal A3782

Bat Signal A3783

Bat Signal A3784

Batman A3785

Batman and Bat Signal A3786

Batman and Rope A3787

Batman A3788

LITHOGRAPHED

2014, Oct. 9 ***Serpentine Die Cut***

Self-Adhesive

4928 A3781 (49c) multicolored 3.00 .40
4929 A3782 (49c) multicolored 3.00 .40
4930 A3783 (49c) multicolored 3.00 .40
4931 A3784 (49c) multicolored 3.00 .40

Serpentine Die Cut 11x10¾

4932 A3785 (49c) multicolored 1.25 .40
4933 A3786 (49c) multicolored 1.25 .40
4934 A3787 (49c) multicolored 1.25 .40
4935 A3788 (49c) multicolored 1.25 .40
a. Vert. block of 8, #4928-4935 17.00
b. Imperf. vert. block of 8 20.00 —
Nos. 4928-4935 (8) 17.00 3.20

Silver Bells Wreath — A3789

LITHOGRAPHED

2014, Oct. 23 ***Serpentine Die Cut***

Self-Adhesive

4936 A3789 ($1.15) multicolored 3.00 .50
a. Imperforate 4.00 —

Unused values are for stamps with surrounding selvage. Adjacent stamps are separated by rouletting.

WINTER FUN

Skaters A3790

Child Making Snowman A3791

Cardinal A3792

Child Making Snow Angel A3793

PHOTOGRAVURE

Serpentine Die Cut 10¾x11 on 2 or 3 Sides

2014, Oct. 23

Booklet Stamps
Self-Adhesive

4937	A3790	(49c)	multicolored	1.25	.30
4938	A3791	(49c)	multicolored	1.25	.30
4939	A3792	(49c)	multicolored	1.25	.30
4940	A3793	(49c)	multicolored	1.25	.30
a.	Block of 4, #4937-4940			5.00	
b.	Booklet pane of 20, 5 each #4937-4940			25.00	
c.	Imperforate block of 4			7.00	—
d.	Imperf. booklet pane of 20			35.00	

Skaters A3794

Child Making Snowman A3795

Cardinal A3796

Child Making Snow Angel A3797

LITHOGRAPHED

Serpentine Die Cut 11¼x11 on 2, 3 or 4 Sides

Thin Paper

4941	A3794	(49c)	multicolored	4.00	.30
4942	A3795	(49c)	multicolored	4.00	.30
4943	A3796	(49c)	multicolored	4.00	.30
4944	A3797	(49c)	multicolored	4.00	.30
a.	Block or strip of 4, #4941-4944			16.00	
b.	Booklet pane of 18, 5 each #4941-4942, 4 each #4943-4944			72.00	
	Nos. 4937-4944 (8)			21.00	2.40

CHRISTMAS

Magi A3798

Rudolph, the Red-Nosed Reindeer A3799

Hermey and Rudolph A3800

Santa Claus A3801

Bumble — A3802

LITHOGRAPHED (#4945), PHOTOGRAVURE

Serpentine Die Cut 10¾x11 on 2 or 3 Sides

2014

Booklet Stamps
Self-Adhesive

4945	A3798	(49c)	multi	1.25	.25
a.	Booklet pane of 20			25.00	
b.	Imperforate			1.75	—
c.	Imperf. booklet pane of 20			35.00	

Serpentine Die Cut 11x10¾ on 2 or 3 sides

4946	A3799	(49c)	multi	1.25	.30
4947	A3800	(49c)	multi	1.25	.30
4948	A3801	(49c)	multi	1.25	.30
4949	A3802	(49c)	multi	1.25	.30
a.	Block of 4, #4946-4949			5.00	
b.	Booklet pane of 20, 5 each #4946-4949			25.00	
c.	Imperf. block of 4			7.50	—
d.	Imperf. booklet pane of 20			37.50	
	Nos. 4945-4949 (5)			6.25	1.45

Issued: No. 4945, 11/19; Nos. 4946-4949, 11/6.

Premiere of *Rudolph, the Red-Nosed Reindeer* animated television show, 50th anniv.

No. 4945a is a double-sided booklet with 12 stamps on one side and eight stamps plus a label that serves as a booklet cover on the other side. No. 4949b is a double-sided booklet with 12 stamps on one side (3 each of Nos. 4946-4949) and eight stamps (2 each of Nos. 4946-4949) plus a label that serves as a booklet cover on the other side.

WILT CHAMBERLAIN (1936-99), BASKETBALL PLAYER

Chamberlain in Philadelphia Warriors Uniform A3803

Chamberlain in Los Angeles Lakers Uniform A3804

LITHOGRAPHED

Serpentine Die Cut 11x10¾

2014, Dec. 5

Self-Adhesive

4950	A3803	(49c)	multicolored	1.25	.25
4951	A3804	(49c)	multicolored	1.25	.25
a.	Pair, #4950-4951			2.50	
b.	Imperforate pair			3.50	—

WAR OF 1812 BICENTENNIAL

Battle of New Orleans — A3805

PHOTOGRAVURE

Serpentine Die Cut 10¾x10½

2015, Jan. 8

Self-Adhesive

4952	A3805	(49c)	multicolored	1.25	.25
a.	Imperforate			1.75	—

PATRIOTIC WAVES

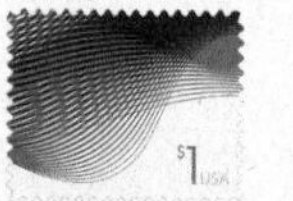
A3806

A3807

LITHOGRAPHED

Serpentine Die Cut 11

2015 **Tagged**

Self-Adhesive

4953	A3806	$1	multicolored	2.00	.50
a.	Imperforate			3.00	—
4954	A3807	$2	multicolored	4.00	1.00
a.	Imperforate			5.00	—

LOVE

A3808

A3809

LITHOGRAPHED

Serpentine Die Cut 11

2015, Jan. 22 **Tagged**

Self-Adhesive

4955	A3808	(49c)	red	1.25	.25
4956	A3809	(49c)	red & gray	1.25	.25
a.	Pair, #4955-4956			2.50	
b.	Imperforate pair			3.50	—

CHINESE NEW YEAR

Year of the Ram — A3810

LITHOGRAPHED

2015, Feb. 7 ***Serpentine Die Cut 11***

Self-Adhesive

4957	A3810	(49c)	multicolored	1.25	.25
a.	Imperforate			1.75	—

BLACK HERITAGE

Robert Robinson Taylor (1868-1942), Architect — A3811

LITHOGRAPHED

Serpentine Die Cut 11

2015, Feb. 12

Self-Adhesive

4958	A3811	(49c)	multicolored	1.25	.25
a.	Imperforate			2.25	—

FLOWERS

Rose and Heart A3812

Tulip and Heart A3813

ENGRAVED

Serpentine Die Cut 10¾x 11

2015, Feb. 14

Self-Adhesive

4959	A3812	(49c)	red & black	5.00	.25
a.	Imperforate			1.75	—
4960	A3813	70c	black & red	3.00	.30
a.	Imperforate			2.50	—

See No. 5002.

FLAGS

Stripes at Left, Stars at Right A3814

Stars and White Stripe A3815

Stars at Left, Stripes at Right — A3816

LITHOGRAPHED

Serpentine Die Cut 11 Vert.

2015, Feb. 27

Coil Stamps
Self-Adhesive

4961	A3814	(10c)	multicolored	.30	.25
4962	A3815	(10c)	multicolored	.30	.25
4963	A3816	(10c)	multicolored	.30	.25
a.	Strip of 3, #4961-4963			.75	
	Nos. 4961-4963 (3)			.90	.75

WATER LILIES

Pale Pink Water Lily A3817

Red Water Lily A3818

Purple Water Lily A3819

White Water Lily A3820

LITHOGRAPHED

Serpentine Die Cut 11x11¼ on 2 or 3 Sides

2015, Mar. 20

Booklet Stamps
Self-Adhesive

4964	A3817	(49c)	multicolored	1.50	.25
4965	A3818	(49c)	multicolored	1.50	.25
4966	A3819	(49c)	multicolored	1.50	.25
4967	A3820	(49c)	multicolored	1.50	.25
a.	Block of 4, #4964-4967			6.00	
b.	Booklet pane of 20, 5 each #4964-4967			30.00	
c.	Imperf. block of 4			7.00	—
d.	Imperf. booklet pane of 20			35.00	
	Nos. 4964-4967 (4)			6.00	1.00

No. 4967b is a double-sided booklet pane with 12 stamps on one side (3 each Nos. 4964-4967) and eight stamps (2 each Nos. 4964-4967) plus label (booklet cover) on the other side.

ART BY MARTIN RAMIREZ (1895-1963)

Untitled (Horse and Rider With Trees), 1954 A3821

Untitled (Man Riding Donkey), c. 1960-63 A3822

Untitled (Trains on Inclined Tracks), c. 1960-63 A3823

Untitled (Deer), c. 1960-63 A3824

Untitled (Tunnel with Cars and Buses), 1954 — A3825

LITHOGRAPHED

Serpentine Die Cut 10¾

2015, Mar. 26

Self-Adhesive

4968	A3821	(49c)	multicolored	1.25	.40
4969	A3822	(49c)	multicolored	1.25	.40
4970	A3823	(49c)	multicolored	1.25	.40
4971	A3824	(49c)	multicolored	1.25	.40
4972	A3825	(49c)	multicolored	1.25	.40
a.	Vert. strip of 5, #4968-4972			6.25	
b.	Imperf. vert. strip of 5			7.50	—

Ferns Type of 2014

LITHOGRAPHED

Serpentine Die Cut 11 Vert.

2015, Mar. 27

Coil Stamps
Self-Adhesive
With Microprinted "USPS"
Dated "2014"

4973	A3729	(49c)	multicolored	1.25	.25
a.	Dated "2015"			1.25	.25
4974	A3730	(49c)	multicolored	1.25	.25
a.	Dated "2015"			1.25	.25
4975	A3731	(49c)	multicolored	1.25	.25
a.	Dated "2015"			1.25	.25
4976	A3732	(49c)	multicolored	1.25	.25
a.	Dated "2015"			1.25	.25
4977	A3728	(49c)	multicolored	1.25	.25
a.	Dated "2015"			1.25	.25
b.	Strip of 5, #4973-4977			5.50	
c.	Strip of 5, #4973a-4977a			5.50	
	Nos. 4973-4977 (5)			6.25	1.25

Nos. 4973a-4977a are from coil rolls containing 3,000 stamps. Nos. 4973-4977 are from coil rolls containing 10,000 stamps. Microprinted "USPS" is near the end of the upper left fern branch on No. 4973 and near the base of the fern's stem on Nos. 4974-

4977. Nos. 4973a-4977a have same microprinting locations as Nos. 4973-4977. Nos. 4874-4878 lack microprinted "USPS."

FROM ME TO YOU

A3826

LITHOGRAPHED
Sheets of 120 in six panes of 20

2015, Apr. 1 ***Serpentine Die Cut 11***
Self-Adhesive

4978 A3826 (49c) multicolored 1.25 .25
a. Imperforate 2.00 —

MAYA ANGELOU (1928-2014), WRITER

Angelou and Quotation A3827

LITHOGRAPHED

2015, Apr. 7 ***Serpentine Die Cut 11***
Self-Adhesive

4979 A3827 (49c) multicolored 1.25 .25
a. Imperforate 1.75 —

The quotation on the stamp is not Angelou's but is similar to a quote by Joan Walsh Anglund.

CIVIL WAR SESQUICENTENNIAL

Battle of Five Forks A3828

Surrender at Appomattox Court House — A3829

LITHOGRAPHED
Double-sided sheets of 72 in six panes of 12 (60 on one side, 12 on other side)

2015, Apr. 9 ***Serpentine Die Cut 11***
Self-Adhesive

4980 A3828 (49c) multicolored 1.25 .30
4981 A3829 (49c) multicolored 1.25 .30
a. Pair, #4980-4981 2.50
b. Imperforate pair *27.50* —

GIFTS OF FRIENDSHIP

Lincoln Memorial and Cherry Blossoms A3830

U.S. Capitol and Dogwood Blossoms A3831

Japanese Diet, Tokyo, and Cherry Blossoms A3832

Clock Tower, Tokyo, and Dogwood Blossoms A3833

LITHOGRAPHED
Sheets of 72 in six panes of 12
Serpentine Die Cut 11

2015, Apr. 10
Self-Adhesive

4982 A3830 (49c) multicolored 1.25 .30
4983 A3831 (49c) multicolored 1.25 .30
a. Horiz. pair, #4982-4983 2.50
b. Imperforate pair 4.50 —
4984 A3832 (49c) multicolored 5.00 .30
4985 A3833 (49c) multicolored 5.00 .30
a. Horiz. pair, #4984-4985 10.00
b. Imperforate pair 12.50 —
Nos. 4982-4985 (4) 12.50 1.20

See Japan No. 3814.

SPECIAL OLYMPICS WORLD GAMES

Emblem — A3834

LITHOGRAPHED
Serpentine Die Cut 10¾

2015, May 9
Self-Adhesive

4986 A3834 (49c) multicolored 1.25 .25
a. Imperforate 1.75 —

HELP FIND MISSING CHILDREN

Forget-me-nots A3835

LITHOGRAPHED
Serpentine Die Cut 10¾

2015, May 18
Self-Adhesive

4987 A3835 (49c) multicolored 1.25 .25
a. Imperforate 1.75 —

MEDAL OF HONOR

Air Force Medal of Honor — A3836

LITHOGRAPHED

2015, May 25 ***Serpentine Die Cut 11***
Self-Adhesive

4988 A3836 (49c) multicolored 1.25 .25
a. Horiz. strip of 3, #4822b, 4823b, 4988 3.75
b. Imperforate strip of 3 6.00 —

WILDLIFE ISSUE

Emperor Penguins — A3837

LITHOGRAPHED
Serpentine Die Cut 11¼x11

2015, June 1
Self-Adhesive

4989 A3837 (22c) multicolored .50 .25
a. Imperforate 1.00 —

Coil Stamp
Serpentine Die Cut 11 Vert.

4990 A3837 (22c) multicolored .50 .25

COASTAL BIRDS

Red Knot A3838

King Eider A3839

Spoonbill A3840

Frigatebird A3841

LITHOGRAPHED
Serpentine Die Cut 11¼x11

2015, June 1
Self-Adhesive

4991 A3838 (35c) multicolored .90 .25
4992 A3839 (35c) multicolored .90 .25
4993 A3840 (35c) multicolored .90 .25
4994 A3841 (35c) multicolored .90 .25
a. Block or vert. strip of 4, #4991-4994 3.60
b. Imperforate block or vert. strip of 4 4.50 —

Coil Stamps
Serpentine Die Cut 9½ Vert.

4995 A3840 (35c) multicolored .90 .25
4996 A3841 (35c) multicolored .90 .25
4997 A3838 (35c) multicolored .90 .25
4998 A3839 (35c) multicolored .90 .25
a. Horiz. strip of 4, #4995-4998 3.60

EASTERN TIGER SWALLOWTAIL BUTTERFLY

A3842

LITHOGRAPHED
Serpentine Die Cut 10½

2015, June 1
Self-Adhesive

4999 A3842 (71c) multicolored 2.00 .25
a. Imperforate 2.50 —

Wedding Cake — A3843

LITHOGRAPHED
Serpentine Die Cut 10¾

2015, June 1
Self-Adhesive

5000 A3843 (71c) multicolored 5.00 .25

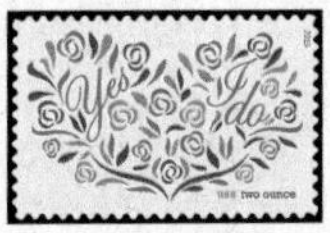
Flowers and "Yes, I Do" — A3844

LITHOGRAPHED
Serpentine Die Cut 10¾

2015, June 1 **Tagged**
Self-Adhesive

5001 A3844 (71c) multicolored 5.00 .25

See Nos. 4765, 4881.

Tulip and Heart — A3845

ENGRAVED

2015, June 1 ***Serpentine Die Cut 11***
Self-Adhesive

5002 A3845 (71c) black & red 6.00 .25

See No. 4960.

LITERARY ARTS

Flannery O'Connor (1925-64), Novelist — A3846

LITHOGRAPHED
Serpentine Die Cut 10¾

2015, June 5
Self-Adhesive

5003 A3846 (93c) multicolored 2.20 .30
a. Imperforate 2.50 —

SUMMER HARVEST

Watermelon A3847

Sweet Corn A3848

Cantaloupes A3849

Tomatoes A3850

LITHOGRAPHED
Serpentine Die Cut 11¼x10¾ on 2 or 3 Sides

2015, July 11
Booklet Stamps
Self-Adhesive

5004 A3847 (49c) multicolored 1.50 .30
5005 A3848 (49c) multicolored 1.50 .30
5006 A3849 (49c) multicolored 1.50 .30
5007 A3850 (49c) multicolored 1.50 .30
a. Block of 4, #5004-5007 6.00
b. Booklet pane of 20, 5 each #5004-5007 30.00
c. As "a," imperforate 7.00 —
d. As "b," imperforate 35.00
Nos. 5004-5007 (4) 6.00 1.20

No. 5007b is a double-sided booklet pane with 12 stamps on one side (3 each #5004-5007), and eight stamps (2 each #5004-5007) plus label (booklet cover) on the other side.

COAST GUARD

MH-65 Dolphin Helicopter and Cutter *Eagle* — A3851

LITHOGRAPHED
Serpentine Die Cut 10¾

2015, Aug. 4 **Tagged**
Self-Adhesive

5008 A3851 (49c) multicolored 1.25 .25
a. Imperforate 1.75 —

MUSIC ICONS

Elvis Presley (1935-77), Singer — A3852

LITHOGRAPHED
Serpentine Die Cut 10½

2015, Aug. 12
Self-Adhesive

5009 A3852 (49c) multicolored 1.25 .25
a. Imperforate 1.75 —

2016 WORLD STAMP SHOW, NEW YORK CITY

Star — A3853

LITHOGRAPHED
Serpentine Die Cut 11

2015, Aug. 20
Self-Adhesive

5010 A3853 (49c) red 1.25 .25
5011 A3853 (49c) blue 1.25 .25
a. Pair, #5010-5011 2.50
b. As "a," imperforate 4.00 —

LEGENDS OF HOLLYWOOD

Ingrid Bergman (1915-82), Actress — A3854

LITHOGRAPHED

Serpentine Die Cut 11

2015, Aug. 20

Self-Adhesive

5012 A3854 (49c) multicolored 1.50 .25
a. Imperforate 1.75 —

See Sweden Nos. 2756-2758.

Eagle Type of 2012

LITHOGRAPHED

Serpentine Die Cut 10¼ Vert.

2015, Sept. 2

Coil Stamps
Self-Adhesive
Color Behind "USA"

5013 A3504 (25c) green .50 .25
5014 A3504 (25c) blue green .50 .25
5015 A3504 (25c) blue .50 .25
5016 A3504 (25c) red violet .50 .25
5017 A3504 (25c) orange .50 .25
5018 A3504 (25c) yellow orange .50 .25
a. Strip of 6, #5013-5018 3.00
Nos. 5013-5018 (6) 3.00 1.50

See Nos. 4585-4590.

CELEBRATE

A3855

LITHOGRAPHED

Serpentine Die Cut 10¾

2015, Sept. 9

Self-Adhesive

5019 A3855 (49c) multicolored 1.25 .25

Compare with type A3441.

Counterfeits exist of No. 5019. See the Postal Counterfeits section of this catalog.

PAUL NEWMAN (1925-2008), ACTOR AND PHILANTHROPIST

A3856

LITHOGRAPHED

Serpentine Die Cut 10¾

2015, Sept. 18

Self-Adhesive

5020 A3856 (49c) multicolored 1.25 .25
a. Imperforate 1.75 —

CHRISTMAS

Charlie Brown Carrying Christmas Tree A3857

Charlie Brown, Pigpen and Dirty Snowman A3858

Snoopy, Lucy, Violet, Sally and Schroeder Skating A3859

Characters, Dog House and Christmas Tree A3860

Linus and Christmas Tree A3861

Charlie Brown Looking in Mailbox A3862

Charlie Brown and Linus Behind Brick Wall — A3863

Charlie Brown, Linus and Christmas Tree — A3864

Charlie Brown Screaming, Snoopy Decorating Dog House A3865

Charlie Brown Hanging Ornament on Christmas Tree A3866

LITHOGRAPHED

Serpentine Die Cut 10¾ on 2 or 3 Sides

2015, Oct. 1

Booklet Stamps
Self-Adhesive

5021 A3857 (49c) multicolored 2.50 .40
5022 A3858 (49c) multicolored 2.50 .40
5023 A3859 (49c) multicolored 2.50 .40
5024 A3860 (49c) multicolored 2.50 .40
5025 A3861 (49c) multicolored 2.50 .40
5026 A3862 (49c) multicolored 2.50 .40
5027 A3863 (49c) multicolored 2.50 .40
5028 A3864 (49c) multicolored 2.50 .40
5029 A3865 (49c) multicolored 2.50 .40
5030 A3866 (49c) multicolored 2.50 .40
a. Block of 10, #5021-5030 25.00
b. Booklet pane of 20, 2 each #5021-5030 50.00
c. As "a," imperforate 17.50 —
d. As "b," imperforate 35.00
Nos. 5021-5030 (10) 25.00 4.00

Premiere of *A Charlie Brown Christmas* animated television show, 50th anniv.

No. 5030b is a double-sided booklet pane with 12 stamps on one side (Nos. 5023-5030, 2 each Nos. 5021-5022) and eight stamps (Nos. 5023-5030) plus label (booklet cover) on the other side.

GEOMETRIC SNOWFLAKES

A3867

A3868

A3869

A3870

LITHOGRAPHED

Serpentine Die Cut 11¼x10¾ on 2 or 3 Sides

2015, Oct. 23

Booklet Stamps
Self-Adhesive
Snowflake Colors

5031 A3867 (49c) purple & lilac 1.25 .30
5032 A3868 (49c) dark blue & blue 1.25 .30
5033 A3869 (49c) dark green & green 1.25 .30
5034 A3870 (49c) crimson & pink 1.25 .30
a. Block of 4, #5031-5034 5.00
b. Booklet pane of 20, 5 each #5031-5034 25.00
c. As "a," imperforate 7.00 —
d. As "b," imperforate 35.00
Nos. 5031-5034 (4) 5.00 1.20

No. 5034b is a double-sided booklet pane with 12 stamps on one side (3 each Nos. 5031-5034), and eight stamps (2 each Nos. 5031-5034) plus label (booklet cover) on the other side.

Purple Heart and Ribbon Type of 2012

LITHOGRAPHED

2015, Oct. ***Serpentine Die Cut 11***

Self-Adhesive
With "USPS" Microprinted At Left of Ribbon

5035 A3587 (49c) multicolored 1.25 .25

See Nos. 4529, 4704.

LOVE

Quilled Paper Heart — A3871

LITHOGRAPHED

Serpentine Die Cut 10¾

2016, Jan. 12

Self-Adhesive

5036 A3871 (49c) multicolored 1.25 .25
a. Imperforate 1.75 —
b. Die cutting omitted, P#B11111 block of 4 *100.00*

No. 5036b was printed from P#B11111 only and may also be collected in plate blocks of 6, half panes of 10 and full panes of 20. Pairs or other multiples without P#B11111 selvage attached cannot be distinguished from No. 5036a, which was printed only from P#S11111.

FRUIT

Albemarle Pippin Apples A3872

Pinot Noir Grapes A3873

Red Pears — A3874

LITHOGRAPHED

Serpentine Die Cut 10 Vert.

2016 **Self-Adhesive**

Coil Stamps

5037 A3872 1c multicolored .30 .25
5038 A3873 5c multicolored .30 .25

Serpentine Die Cut 10¾ Vert.

5039 A3874 10c multicolored .30 .25

See Nos. 5177-5178 for sheet versions of Nos. 5038-5039, also see No. 5201, 5256.

AMERICAN LANDMARKS ISSUE

La Cueva del Indio, Puerto Rico — A3875

Columbia River Gorge — A3876

LITHOGRAPHED

Serpentine Die Cut 10¾x10½

2016, Jan. 17

Self-Adhesive

5040 A3875 $6.45 multi 17.50 7.50
a. Imperforate 17.50 —
5041 A3876 $22.95 multi *75.00* 24.00
a. Imperforate *200.00* —

BOTANICAL ART

Corn Lilies A3877

Tulips A3878

Tulips A3879

Dahlias A3880

Stocks A3881

Roses A3882

Japanese Irises A3883

Tulips A3884

Petunias A3885

Jonquils A3886

LITHOGRAPHED

Serpentine Die Cut 10¾ on 2 or 3 Sides

2016, Jan. 29

Booklet Stamps
Self-Adhesive

5042 A3877 (49c) multicolored 2.50 .40
5043 A3878 (49c) multicolored 2.50 .40
5044 A3879 (49c) multicolored 2.50 .40
5045 A3880 (49c) multicolored 2.50 .40
5046 A3881 (49c) multicolored 2.50 .40
5047 A3882 (49c) multicolored 2.50 .40
5048 A3883 (49c) multicolored 2.50 .40
5049 A3884 (49c) multicolored 2.50 .40
5050 A3885 (49c) multicolored 2.50 .40
5051 A3886 (49c) multicolored 2.50 .40
a. Block of 10, #5042-5051 25.00
b. Booklet pane of 10, #5042-5051 25.00
c. Booklet pane of 20, 2 each #5042-5051 50.00
d. Imperforate block of 10 125.00 —
e. Imperforate booklet pane of 20 225.00
f. As "c," horiz. die cutting missing between all stamps front and reverse —
Nos. 5042-5051 (10) 25.00 4.00

No. 5051c is a double-sided booklet pane with 12 stamps on one side (Nos. 5042-5049, 2 each Nos. 5050-5051) and eight stamps (Nos. 5042-5049) plus label (booklet cover) on the other side.

No. 5051f resulted from a misregistration of the die cutting/pane cutting and the printed web. The horizontal rows are reversed from their normal positions, and horizontal die cutting appears at the top and bottom of the pane.

Flag — A3887

LITHOGRAPHED

Serpentine Die Cut 11 Vert.

2016, Jan. 29

Coil Stamps

Self-Adhesive

Microprinted "USPS" To Right of Pole Under Flag

5052 A3887 (49c) multicolored 1.25 .25
- *a.* Die cutting omitted, pair 200.00
- *b.* As "a," grayish blue (inscription and date) omitted 200.00

Serpentine Die Cut 9½ Vert.

Microprinted "USPS" on Second White Flag Stripe

5053 A3887 (49c) multicolored 1.25 .25

Booklet Stamps

Microprinted "USPS" To Right of Pole Under Flag

Serpentine Die Cut 11¼x10¾ on 2 or 3 Sides

5054 A3887 (49c) multicolored 1.25 .25
- *a.* Booklet pane of 10 12.50
- *b.* Booklet pane of 20 25.00
- *c.* As "b," horiz. die cutting omitted on side with 12 stamps —

Microprinted "USPS" on Second White Flag Stripe

5055 A3887 (49c) multicolored 1.25 .25
- *a.* Booklet pane of 20 25.00

Nos. 5054b and 5055a are double-sided booklets with 12 stamps on one side and eight stamps plus a label that serves as the booklet cover on the other side.

BLACK HERITAGE

Richard Allen (1760-1831), Founder of African Methodist Episcopal Church — A3888

LITHOGRAPHED

Serpentine Die Cut 10¾

2016, Feb. 2

Self-Adhesive

5056 A3888 (49c) multicolored 1.25 .25
- *a.* Imperforate 3.00 —

CHINESE NEW YEAR

Year of the Monkey — A3889

LITHOGRAPHED

Serpentine Die Cut 10¾

2016, Feb. 5

Self-Adhesive

5057 A3889 (49c) multicolored 1.25 .25
- *a.* Imperforate 1.75 —

Moon — A3890

LITHOGRAPHED

2016, Feb. 22 ***Serpentine Die Cut***

Self-Adhesive

5058 A3890 ($1.20) multicolored 3.00 .50

Unused values are for stamps with surrounding selvage. Adjacent stamps are separated by rouletting.

MUSIC ICONS

Sarah Vaughan (1924-90), Singer — A3891

LITHOGRAPHED

Serpentine Die Cut 10½

2016, Mar. 29

Self-Adhesive

5059 A3891 (49c) multicolored 1.25 .25

LEGENDS OF HOLLYWOOD

Shirley Temple (1928-2014), Actress and Diplomat — A3892

LITHOGRAPHED

Serpentine Die Cut 10¾

2016, Apr. 18

Self-Adhesive

5060 A3892 (47c) multicolored 2.00 .25

"USA" and Star — A3893

LITHOGRAPHED

Serpentine Die Cut 10 Vert.

2016, Apr. 28

COIL STAMP

Self-Adhesive

5061 A3893 (5c) multicolored .30 .25

See No. 5172.

2016 WORLD STAMP SHOW, NEW YORK CITY

Star — A3894

ENGRAVED

Serpentine Die Cut 10¾

2016, May 28

Self-Adhesive

5062 A3894 (47c) blue 1.25 .25
5063 A3894 (47c) red 1.25 .25
- *a.* Pair, #5062-5063 2.50

REPEAL OF THE STAMP ACT, 250TH ANNIV.

Man Posting of Notice of Repeal on Tree — A3895

LITHOGRAPHED

Serpentine Die Cut 10¾

2016, May 29

Self-Adhesive

5064 A3895 (47c) multicolored 1.25 .25

SERVICE CROSS MEDALS

Distinguished Service Cross A3896

Navy Cross A3897

Air Force Cross A3898

Coast Guard Cross A3899

LITHOGRAPHED

Serpentine Die Cut 10¾

2016, May 30

Self-Adhesive

5065 A3896 (47c) multicolored 1.25 .30
5066 A3897 (47c) multicolored 1.25 .30
5067 A3898 (47c) multicolored 1.25 .30
5068 A3899 (47c) multicolored 1.25 .30
- *a.* Block or horiz. strip of 4, #5065-5068 5.00

Nos. 5065-5068 (4) 5.00 1.20

VIEWS OF OUR PLANETS

Mercury A3900

Venus A3901

Earth — A3902

Mars — A3903

Jupiter A3904

Saturn A3905

Uranus A3906

Neptune A3907

LITHOGRAPHED

Serpentine Die Cut 10½

2016, May 31

Self-Adhesive

5069 A3900 (47c) multicolored 2.00 .40
5070 A3901 (47c) multicolored 2.00 .40
5071 A3902 (47c) multicolored 2.00 .40
5072 A3903 (47c) multicolored 2.00 .40
5073 A3904 (47c) multicolored 2.00 .40
5074 A3905 (47c) multicolored 2.00 .40
5075 A3906 (47c) multicolored 2.00 .40
5076 A3907 (47c) multicolored 2.00 .40
- *a.* Block of 8, #5069-5076 16.00

Nos. 5069-5076 (8) 16.00 3.20

PLUTO EXPLORED

Pluto A3908

New Horizons Probe A3909

LITHOGRAPHED

Serpentine Die Cut 10½

2016, May 31

Self-Adhesive

5077 A3908 (47c) multicolored 1.25 .25
5078 A3909 (47c) multicolored 1.25 .25
- *a.* Pair, #5077-5078 2.50

CLASSICS FOREVER

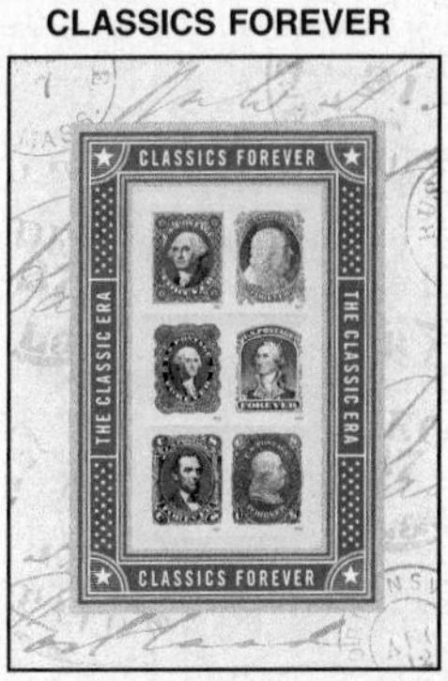

A3910

No. 5079: a, George Washington (redrawn type A16). b, Benjamin Franklin (redrawn type A5). c, Washington (redrawn type A17). d, Washington (redrawn type A19). e, Abraham Lincoln (redrawn type A33). f, Franklin (redrawn type A24).

LITHOGRAPHED & ENGRAVED

Serpentine Die Cut 10¾

2016, June 1

Self-Adhesive

5079 A3910 Pane of 6 7.50
- *a.* (47c) tan & black 1.25 .40
- *b.* (47c) tan & blue 1.25 .40
- *c.* (47c) tan & black 1.25 .40
- *d.* (47c) tan & blue 1.25 .40
- *e.* (47c) tan & black 1.25 .40
- *f.* (47c) tan & blue 1.25 .40

NATIONAL PARK SERVICE, CENT.

A3911

No. 5080: a, Iceberg in Glacier Bay National Park and Preserve, Alaska (48x31mm). b, Mount Rainier National Park (48x31mm). c, *Scenery in the Grand Tetons,* painting by Albert Bierstadt, at Marsh-Billings-Rockefeller National Historic Park, Vermont (24x31mm). d, Bass Harbor Head Lighthouse, Acadia National Park, Maine (48x31mm). e, *The Grand Canyon of Arizona,* painting by Thomas Moran, at Grand Canyon National Park, Arizona (48x31mm). f, Horses at Assateague Island National Seashore, Virginia and Maryland (48x31mm). g, Ship *Balclutha,* at San Francisco Maritime National Historic Park, California (24x31mm). h, Stone arch at Arches National Park, Utah (24x31mm). i, Aerial view of Theodore Roosevelt National Park, North Dakota (24x31mm). j, Water lily at Kenilworth Park and Aquatic Gardens, Washington, D.C. (24x31mm). k, *Administration Building at Frijoles Canyon,* drawing by Helmuth Naumer, Sr., at Bandelier National Monument, New Mexico (48x31mm). l, Everglades National Park, Florida (48x31mm). m, Rainbow at Haleakala National Park, Hawaii (48x31mm). n, Bison at Yellowstone National Park, Idaho, Montana and Wyoming (48x31mm). o, Carlsbad Caverns National Park, New Mexico (48x31mm). p, Heron at Gulf Islands National Seashore, Florida and Mississippi (24x31mm).

LITHOGRAPHED

Serpentine Die Cut 10½x10¾

2016, June 2 **Self-Adhesive**

5080 A3911 Pane of 16 + label 20.00
- *a.-p.* (47c) Any single 1.25 .50

COLORFUL CELEBRATIONS

Bird and Flowers A3912

Birds and Flowers A3913

Flowers A3914 | Flowers A3915

Flowers A3916 | Flowers A3917

Birds and Flower A3918 | Bird and Flower A3919

Flowers A3920 | Birds and Flower A3921

LITHOGRAPHED

Serpentine Die Cut 11 on 2 or 3 Sides

2016, June 3

Booklet Stamps Self-Adhesive

5081 A3912 (47c) lt blue 2.00 .40
5082 A3913 (47c) orange 2.00 .40
5083 A3914 (47c) violet 2.00 .40
5084 A3915 (47c) magneta 2.00 .40
5085 A3916 (47c) lt blue 2.00 .40
5086 A3917 (47c) orange 2.00 .40
5087 A3918 (47c) violet 2.00 .40
5088 A3919 (47c) magneta 2.00 .40
5089 A3920 (47c) magneta 2.00 .40
5090 A3921 (47c) violet 2.00 .40
a. Block of 10, #5081-5090 20.00
b. Booklet pane of 20, 2 each #5081-5090 40.00
Nos. 5081-5090 (10) 20.00 4.00

No. 5090b is a double-sided booklet pane with 12 stamps on one side (Nos. 5083-5090, 2 each Nos. 5081-5082) and eight stamps (Nos. 5083-5090) plus label (booklet cover) on the other side.

INDIANA STATEHOOD, 200th ANNIV.

Corn Field Near Milford — A3922

LITHOGRAPHED

Serpentine Die Cut 10¾

2016, June 7

Self-Adhesive

5091 A3922 (47c) multicolored 1.25 .25

EID

"Eidukum Mubarak" — A3923

LITHOGRAPHED

Serpentine Die Cut 11

2016, June 10

Self-Adhesive

5092 A3923 (47c) multicolored 1.25 .25

SODA FOUNTAIN FAVORITES

Ice Cream Cone A3924 | Egg Cream A3925

Banana Split A3926

Root Beer Float A3927

Hot Fudge Sundae — A3928

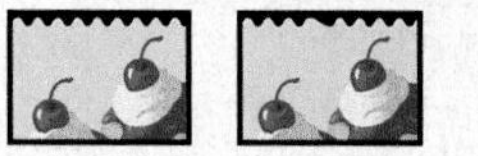

No. 5095 | No. 5095a

LITHOGRAPHED

Serpentine Die Cut 10¾

2016, June 30

Booklet Stamps Self-Adhesive

5093 A3924 (47c) multicolored 1.50 .40
5094 A3925 (47c) multicolored 1.50 .40
5095 A3926 (47c) multicolored (long sloping die cut at bottom) 1.50 .40
a. Long sloping die cut at top 1.50 .40
5096 A3927 (47c) multicolored 1.50 .40
5097 A3928 (47c) multicolored 1.50 .40
a. Horiz. strip of 5, #5093-5097 7.50
b. Horiz. strip of 5, #5093-5094, 5095a, 5096-5097 7.50
c. Booklet pane of 20, 4 each #5093-5094, 5096-5097, 2 each #5095, 5095a 30.00
Nos. 5093-5097 (5) 7.50 2.00

STAR QUILTS

A3929 | A3930

LITHOGRAPHED

Serpentine Die Cut 11 Vert.

2016, July 6

Coil Stamps Self-Adhesive

5098 A3929 (25c) multicolored .50 .25
5099 A3930 (25c) multicolored .50 .25
a. Pair, #5098-5099 1.00

JAIME ESCALANTE

Jaime Escalante (1930-2010), High School Calculus Teacher — A3931

LITHOGRAPHED

Serpentine Die Cut 10¾

2016, July 13

Self-Adhesive

5100 A3931 (47c) multicolored 1.25 .25

Adjacent horizontal or vertical stamps have selvage between the stamps.

PICKUP TRUCKS

1938 International Harvester D-2 A3932 | 1953 Chevrolet A3933

1948 Ford F-1 A3934 | 1965 Ford F-100 A3935

LITHOGRAPHED

Serpentine Die Cut 11 on 2 or 3 Sides

2016, July 15

Booklet Stamps Self-Adhesive

5101 A3932 (47c) multicolored 1.25 .30
5102 A3933 (47c) multicolored 1.25 .30
5103 A3934 (47c) multicolored 1.25 .30
5104 A3935 (47c) multicolored 1.25 .30
a. Block of 4, #5101-5104 5.00
b. Booklet pane of 20, 5 each #5101-5104 25.00
Nos. 5101-5104 (4) 5.00 1.20

No. 5104b is a double-sided booklet pane with 12 stamps on one side (3 each Nos. 5101-5104) and eight stamps (2 each Nos. 5101-5104) plus label (booklet cover) on the other side.

LITERARY ARTS

Henry James (1843-1916), Novelist — A3936

LITHOGRAPHED

Serpentine Die Cut 11

2016, July 31

Self-Adhesive

5105 A3936 (89c) multicolored 2.20 .30

PETS

Puppy A3937 | Betta Fish A3938

Iguana A3939 | Hamster A3940

Goldfish A3941 | Kitten A3942

Rabbit A3943 | Tortoise A3944

Guinea Pig A3945 | Parrot A3946

Corn Snake A3947 | Mouse A3948

Hermit Crab A3949 | Chinchilla A3950

Gerbil A3951 | Gecko A3952

Cat A3953 | Horse A3954

Parakeets A3955 | Dog A3956

LITHOGRAPHED

Serpentine Die Cut 11 on 2 or 3 Sides

2016, Aug. 2

Booklet Stamps Self-Adhesive

5106 A3937 (47c) multicolored 1.50 .50
5107 A3938 (47c) multicolored 1.50 .50
5108 A3939 (47c) multicolored 1.50 .50
5109 A3940 (47c) multicolored 1.50 .50
5110 A3941 (47c) multicolored 1.50 .50
5111 A3942 (47c) multicolored 1.50 .50
5112 A3943 (47c) multicolored 1.50 .50
5113 A3944 (47c) multicolored 1.50 .50
5114 A3945 (47c) multicolored 1.50 .50
5115 A3946 (47c) multicolored 1.50 .50
5116 A3947 (47c) multicolored 1.50 .50
5117 A3948 (47c) multicolored 1.50 .50
5118 A3949 (47c) multicolored 1.50 .50
5119 A3950 (47c) multicolored 1.50 .50
5120 A3951 (47c) multicolored 1.50 .50
5121 A3952 (47c) multicolored 1.50 .50
5122 A3953 (47c) multicolored 1.50 .50
5123 A3954 (47c) multicolored 1.50 .50
5124 A3955 (47c) multicolored 1.50 .50
5125 A3956 (47c) multicolored 1.50 .50
a. Booklet pane of 20, #5106-5125 30.00
Nos. 5106-5125 (20) 30.00 10.00

No. 5125a is a double-sided booklet pane with 12 stamps on one side (Nos. 5106-5117) and eight stamps (Nos. 5118-5125) plus label (booklet cover) on the other side.

SONGBIRDS IN SNOW

Golden-crowned Kinglets A3957 | Cedar Waxwing A3958

Northern Cardinal A3959 | Red-breasted Nuthatches A3960

LITHOGRAPHED

Serpentine Die Cut 10¾ on 2 or 3 Sides

2016, Aug. 4

Booklet Stamps Self-Adhesive

5126 A3957 (47c) multicolored 1.50 .30
5127 A3958 (47c) multicolored 1.50 .30
5128 A3959 (47c) multicolored 1.50 .30
5129 A3960 (47c) multicolored 1.50 .30
a. Block of 4, #5126-5129 6.00
b. Booklet pane of 20, 5 each #5126-5129 30.00
Nos. 5126-5129 (4) 6.00 1.20

No. 5129b is a double-sided booklet pane with 12 stamps on one side (3 each Nos.

5126-5129) and eight stamps (2 each Nos. 5126-5129) plus label (booklet cover) on the other side.

PATRIOTIC SPIRAL

Stars — A3961

LITHOGRAPHED
Serpentine Die Cut 10 Vert.
2016, Aug. 19
Coil Stamp
Self-Adhesive

5130 A3961 (47c) multicolored 1.25 .25

Booklet Stamp
Serpentine Die Cut 11 on 2 or 3 Sides

5131 A3961 (47c) multicolored 1.25 .25
a. Booklet pane of 10 12.50

STAR TREK TELEVISION SHOW, 50TH ANNIV

Starship Enterprise and Starfleet Insignia A3962

Crewman in Transporter A3963

Starship Enterprise and Planet A3964

Starship Enterprise, Planet, Vulcan Hand Salute A3965

LITHOGRAPHED
2016, Sept. 2 *Serpentine Die Cut 11*
Self-Adhesive

5132 A3962 (47c) multicolored 1.25 .30
5133 A3963 (47c) multicolored 1.25 .30
5134 A3964 (47c) multicolored 1.25 .30
5135 A3965 (47c) multicolored 1.25 .30
a. Block or vert. strip of 4, #5132-5135 5.00
Nos. 5132-5135 (4) 5.00 1.20

EASTERN TAILED-BLUE BUTTERFLY

A3966

LITHOGRAPHED
Serpentine Die Cut 10½
2016, Sept. 24
Self-Adhesive

5136 A3966 (68c) multicolored 2.00 .25

JACK-O'-LANTERNS

Four Teeth A3967

Five Teeth A3968

Three Teeth A3969

Nine Teeth A3970

LITHOGRAPHED
Serpentine Die Cut 11x10¾ on 2 or 3 Sides
2016, Sept. 29
Booklet Stamps
Self-Adhesive

5137 A3967 (47c) multicolored 1.25 .30
5138 A3968 (47c) multicolored 1.25 .30
5139 A3969 (47c) multicolored 1.25 .30
5140 A3970 (47c) multicolored 1.25 .30
a. Block of 4, #5137-5140 5.00
b. Booklet pane of 20, 5 each #5137-5140 25.00
Nos. 5137-5140 (4) 5.00 1.20

No. 5140b is a double-sided booklet pane with 12 stamps on one side (3 each Nos. 5137-5140) and eight stamps (2 each Nos. 5137-5140) plus label (booklet cover) on the other side.

KWANZAA

Woman, Fruits and Vegetables — A3971

LITHOGRAPHED
2016, Oct. 1 *Serpentine Die Cut 11*
Self-Adhesive

5141 A3971 (47c) multicolored 1.25 .25

DIWALI

Diya — A3972

LITHOGRAPHED
2016, Oct. 5 *Serpentine Die Cut 11*
Self-Adhesive

5142 A3972 (47c) multicolored 1.25 .25

CHRISTMAS

Madonna and Child, by a Follower of Fra Filippo Lippi and Peselino A3973

Nativity A3974

Candle in Window A3975

Wreath in Window A3976

Star in Window A3977

Christmas Tree in Window A3978

LITHOGRAPHED
Serpentine Die Cut 10¾x11 on 2 or 3 Sides
2016
Booklet Stamps
Self-Adhesive

5143 A3973 (47c) multicolored 1.25 .25
a. Booklet pane of 20 25.00
5144 A3974 (47c) multicolored 1.25 .25
a. Booklet pane of 20 25.00
5145 A3975 (47c) multicolored 1.25 .25
5146 A3976 (47c) multicolored 1.25 .25
5147 A3977 (47c) multicolored 1.25 .25
5148 A3978 (47c) multicolored 1.25 .25
a. Block of 4, #5145-5148 5.00
b. Booklet pane of 20, 5 each #5145-5148 25.00
Nos. 5143-5148 (6) 7.50 1.50

Issued: No. 5143, 10/18; No. 5144, 11/3; Nos. 5145-5148, 10/6. Nos. 5143a and 5144a are double-sided booklet panes with 12 stamps on one side and eight stamps plus label (booklet cover) on the other side. No. 5148b is a double-sided booklet pane with 12 stamps on one side (3 each Nos. 5145-5148) and eight stamps (2 each Nos. 5145-5148) plus label (booklet cover) on the other side.

WONDER WOMAN, 75TH ANNIVERSARY

Modern Age Wonder Woman A3979

Bronze Age Wonder Woman A3980

Silver Age Wonder Woman A3981

Golden Age Wonder Woman A3982

LITHOGRAPHED
2016, Oct. 7 *Serpentine Die Cut 11*
Self-Adhesive

5149 A3979 (47c) multicolored 1.50 .30
5150 A3980 (47c) multicolored 1.50 .30
5151 A3981 (47c) multicolored 1.50 .30
5152 A3982 (47c) multicolored 1.50 .30
a. Vert. strip of 4, #5149-5152 6.00
Nos. 5149-5152 (4) 6.00 1.20

HANUKKAH

Menorah — A3983

LITHOGRAPHED
2016, Nov. 1 *Serpentine Die Cut 11*
Self-Adhesive

5153 A3983 (47c) multicolored 1.25 .25

CHINESE NEW YEAR

Year of the Rooster — A3984

LITHOGRAPHED
Serpentine Die Cut 10¾
2017, Jan. 5
Self-Adhesive

5154 A3984 (47c) multicolored 1.25 .25

LOVE

Airplane and Skywriting — A3985

LITHOGRAPHED
Serpentine Die Cut 11x10¾
2017, Jan. 7
Self-Adhesive

5155 A3985 (47c) light blue 1.25 .25

AMERICAN LANDMARKS ISSUE

Lili'uokalani Gardens, Hilo, Hawaii — A3986

Gateway Arch, St. Louis, Missouri — A3987

LITHOGRAPHED
Serpentine Die Cut 10¾x10½
2017, Jan. 22
Self-Adhesive

5156 A3986 $6.65 multi 17.50 7.75
5157 A3987 $23.75 multi 65.00 25.00

Flag — A3988

LITHOGRAPHED
Serpentine Die Cut 11 Vert.
2017, Jan. 27
Coil Stamps
Self-Adhesive
Microprinted "USPS" On Right End of Fourth Red Stripe

5158 A3988 (49c) multicolored 1.25 .25
a. Die cutting omitted, pair —
b. Vert. pair, unslit between —

Serpentine Die Cut 9½ Vert.
Microprinted "USPS" on Right End of Second White Flag Stripe

5159 A3988 (49c) multicolored 1.25 .25

Booklet Stamps
Microprinted "USPS" on Right End of Fourth Red Stripe
Serpentine Die Cut 11¼x10¾ on 2 or 3 Sides

5160 A3988 (49c) multicolored 1.25 .25
a. Booklet pane of 10 12.50
b. Booklet pane of 20 25.00

Microprinted "USPS" on Right End of Second White Flag Stripe

5161 A3988c (49c) multicolored 1.25 .25
a. Booklet pane of 20 25.00

Microprinted "USPS" on Left End of Second White Flag Stripe Near Blue Field
Thin Paper
Serpentine Die Cut 11¼x10¾ on 2, 3 or 4 Sides

5162 A3988 (49c) multicolored 2.75 .25
a. Booklet pane of 18 50.00
Nos. 5160-5162 (3) 5.25 .75

Nos. 5160b and 5161a are double-sided booklets with 12 stamps on one side and eight stamps plus a label that serves as the booklet cover on the other side.

SHELLS

Queen Conch A3989

Pacific Calico Scallop A3990

Alphabet Cone A3991

Zebra Nerite A3992

LITHOGRAPHED

Serpentine Die Cut 11¼x10¾

2017, Jan. 28

Self-Adhesive

5163 A3989 (34c) multicolored .90 .25
5164 A3990 (34c) multicolored .90 .25
5165 A3991 (34c) multicolored .90 .25
5166 A3992 (34c) multicolored .90 .25
a. Horiz. or vert. strip of 4, #5163-5166 3.60
Nos. 5163-5166 (4) 3.60 1.00

Coil Stamps

Serpentine Die Cut 9¾ Vert.

5167 A3991 (34c) multicolored .90 .25
5168 A3992 (34c) multicolored .90 .25
5169 A3989 (34c) multicolored .90 .25
5170 A3990 (34c) multicolored .90 .25
a. Horiz. strip of 4, #5167-5170 3.60
Nos. 5167-5170 (4) 3.60 1.00

BLACK HERITAGE

Dorothy Height (1912-2010), President of National Council of Negro Women — A3993

LITHOGRAPHED

2017, Feb. 1 ***Serpentine Die Cut 11***

Self-Adhesive

5171 A3993 (49c) multicolored 1.25 .25

"USA" and Star With Blue Frame — A3994

LITHOGRAPHED

Serpentine Die Cut 10 Vert.

2017, Feb. 10

COIL STAMP

Self-Adhesive

5172 A3994 (5c) multicolored .30 .25
a. Red omitted —

The discovery example of No. 5172a is on piece, uncanceled.

OSCAR DE LA RENTA

Oscar de la Renta (1932-2014), Fashion Designer — A3995

A3996

A3997

A3998

A3999

A4000

A4001

A4002

A4003

A4004

A4005

LITHOGRAPHED

Serpentine Die Cut 11x10¾ (No. 5173a), 10¾x11

2017, Feb. 16

Self-Adhesive

5173 Pane of 11 13.75
a. A3995 (49c) multicolored 1.25 .50
b. A3996 (49c) multicolored 1.25 .50
c. A3997 (49c) multicolored 1.25 .50
d. A3998 (49c) multicolored 1.25 .50
e. A3999 (49c) multicolored 1.25 .50
f. A4000 (49c) multicolored 1.25 .50
g. A4001 (49c) multicolored 1.25 .50
h. A4002 (49c) multicolored 1.25 .50
i. A4003 (49c) multicolored 1.25 .50
j. A4004 (49c) multicolored 1.25 .50
k. A4005 (49c) multicolored 1.25 .50

People Wearing Uncle Sam Hats — A4006

LITHOGRAPHED

Serpentine Die Cut 11¼x11

2017, Feb. 18

Self-Adhesive

5174 A4006 (21c) multicolored .50 .25

See No. 5341.

PRES. JOHN F. KENNEDY (1917-63)

Pres. John F. Kennedy — A4007

LITHOGRAPHED

Serpentine Die Cut 10¾

2017, Feb. 20

Self-Adhesive

5175 A4007 (49c) brown 1.25 .25

Fruits Type of 2016

Designs: 5c, Pinot Noir Grapes. 10c, Red Pears.

LITHOGRAPHED

2017 ***Serpentine Die Cut 11¼x11***

Self-Adhesive

5177 A3873 5c multicolored .30 .25

See Nos. 5038, 5039.

5178 A3874 10c multicolored .30 .25

Issued: 5c, 2/24; 10c, 3/23.
See Nos. 5038-5039, 5201, 5256.

NEBRASKA STATEHOOD, 150th ANNIV.

Sandhill Cranes Flying Over Platte River — A4008

LITHOGRAPHED

Serpentine Die Cut 10¾

2017, Mar. 1

Self-Adhesive

5179 A4008 (49c) multicolored 1.25 .25

WORKS PROGRESS ADMINISTRATION (WORK PROJECTS ADMINISTRATION) POSTERS

See America Welcome to Montana Poster A4009

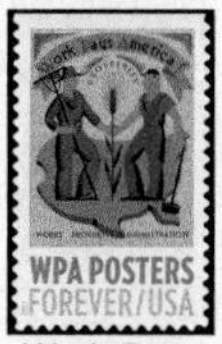

Work Pays America Poster A4010

Field Day Poster A4011

Discover Puerto Rico Poster A4012

City of New York Municipal Airports Poster A4013

Foreign Trade Zone Poster A4014

Visit the Zoo Poster A4015

Work with Care Poster A4016

The National Parks Preserve Wild Life Poster A4017

Hiking Poster A4018

LITHOGRAPHED

Serpentine Die Cut 11 on 2 or 3 Sides

2017, Mar. 7

Booklet Stamps

Self-Adhesive

5180 A4009 (49c) multicolored 1.50 .40
5181 A4010 (49c) multicolored 1.50 .40
5182 A4011 (49c) multicolored 1.50 .40
5183 A4012 (49c) multicolored 1.50 .40
5184 A4013 (49c) multicolored 1.50 .40
5185 A4014 (49c) multicolored 1.50 .40
5186 A4015 (49c) multicolored 1.50 .40
5187 A4016 (49c) multicolored 1.50 .40
5188 A4017 (49c) multicolored 1.50 .40
5189 A4018 (49c) multicolored 1.50 .40
a. Block of 10, #5180-5189 15.00
b. Booklet pane of 20, 2 each #5180-5189 30.00
Nos. 5180-5189 (10) 15.00 4.00

No. 5189b is a double-sided booklet pane with 12 stamps on one side (Nos. 5181-5184, 5186-5189, 2 each Nos. 5180, 5185) and eight stamps (Nos. 5181-5184, 5186-5189) plus label (booklet cover) on the other side.

MISSISSIPPI STATEHOOD, 200th ANNIV.

Guitarist — A4019

LITHOGRAPHED

Serpentine Die Cut 10¾

2017, Mar. 31

Self-Adhesive

5190 A4019 (49c) multicolored 1.25 .25

DISTINGUISHED AMERICANS

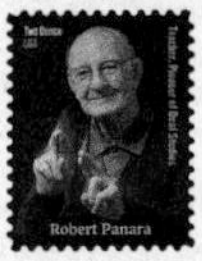

Robert Panara (1920-2014), Educator of the Deaf — A4020

LITHOGRAPHED

Serpentine Die Cut 10¾

2017, Apr. 11 **Tagged**

Self-Adhesive

5191 A4020 (70c) multicolored 1.70 .25

Adjacent horizontal or vertical stamps have selvage between the stamps.

DELICIOSO (LATIN AMERICAN DISHES)

Tamales A4021

Flan A4022

Sancocho A4023

Empanadas A4024

Chile Relleno A4025

Ceviche A4026

LITHOGRAPHED

Serpentine Die Cut 11 on 2 or 3 Sides

2017, Apr. 20 **Tagged**

Booklet Stamps

Self-Adhesive

5192 A4021 (49c) multicolored 1.25 .40
5193 A4022 (49c) multicolored 1.25 .40
5194 A4023 (49c) multicolored 1.25 .40
5195 A4024 (49c) multicolored 1.25 .40
5196 A4025 (49c) multicolored 1.25 .40
5197 A4026 (49c) multicolored 1.25 .40
a. Block of 6, #5192-5197 7.50
b. Booklet pane of 20, 4 each #5192-5193, 3 each #5194-5197 25.00
Nos. 5192-5197 (6) 7.50 2.40

No. 5197b is a double-sided booklet pane with 12 stamps on one side (2 each Nos. 5192-5197) and eight stamps (Nos. 5194-5197, 2 each Nos. 5192-5193) plus label (booklet cover) on the other side.

Echeveria — A4027

LITHOGRAPHED

Serpentine Die Cut

2017, Apr. 28 **Tagged**

Self-Adhesive

5198 A4027 ($1.15) multicolored 3.00 .50

Unused values are for stamps with surrounding selvage. Adjacent stamps are separated by rouletting.

CELEBRATION FLOWERS

Boutonniere A4028 Corsage A4029

LITHOGRAPHED

Serpentine Die Cut 10¾

2017, May 2 **Tagged**

Self-Adhesive

5199 A4028 (49c) multicolored 1.25 .25
5200 A4029 (70c) multicolored 1.70 .25

FRUIT

Strawberries — A4030

LITHOGRAPHED

Serpentine Die Cut 10 Vert.

2017, May 5

Coil Stamps
Self-Adhesive

5201 A4030 3c multicolored .25 .25

HENRY DAVID THOREAU

Henry David Thoreau (1817-62), Writer, and Sumac Leaves — A4031

LITHOGRAPHED

Serpentine Die Cut 10¾

2017, May 23

Self-Adhesive

5202 A4031 (49c) multicolored 1.25 .25

SPORTS BALLS

Football A4032

Volleyball A4033

Soccer Ball — A4034

Golf Ball — A4035

Baseball A4036

Basketball A4037

Tennis Ball A4038

Kickball A4039

LITHOGRAPHED & TYPOGRAPHED

2017, June 14 ***Serpentine Die Cut***

Self-Adhesive

5203	A4032 (49c)	multicolored	1.25	.40
5204	A4033 (49c)	multicolored	1.25	.40
5205	A4034 (49c)	multicolored	1.25	.40
5206	A4035 (49c)	multicolored	1.25	.40
5207	A4036 (49c)	multicolored	1.25	.40
5208	A4037 (49c)	multicolored	1.25	.40
5209	A4038 (49c)	multicolored	1.25	.40
5210	A4039 (49c)	multicolored	1.25	.40
a.	Block of 8, #5203-5210		10.00	
	Nos. 5203-5210 (8)		10.00	3.20

The typographed printing imitates the texture of the ball.

AUGUST 21, 2017, TOTAL SOLAR ECLIPSE

Total Solar Eclipse — A4040

LITHOGRAPHED

Serpentine Die Cut 10½

2017, June 20

Self-Adhesive

5211 A4040 (49c) multicolored 1.25 .25

The moon is covered with a circle of thermochromic ink, which when warmed, allows the moon and the corona of the sun around the moon to be seen.

PAINTINGS BY ANDREW WYETH (1917-2009)

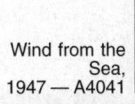

Wind from the Sea, 1947 — A4041

Big Room, 1988 — A4042

Christina's World, 1948 — A4043

Alvaro and Christina, 1968 — A4044

Frostbitten, 1962 — A4045

Sailor's Valentine, 1985 — A4046

Soaring, 1942-50 — A4047

North Light, 1984 — A4048

Spring Fed, 1967 — A4049

The Carry, 2003 — A4050

Young Bull, 1960 — A4051

My Studio, 1974 — A4052

LITHOGRAPHED

Serpentine Die Cut 10¾x10½

2017, July 12

Self-Adhesive

5212	Pane of 12		15.00	
a.	A4041 (49c)	multicolored	1.25	.50
b.	A4042 (49c)	multicolored	1.25	.50
c.	A4043 (49c)	multicolored	1.25	.50
d.	A4044 (49c)	multicolored	1.25	.50
e.	A4045 (49c)	multicolored	1.25	.50
f.	A4046 (49c)	multicolored	1.25	.50
g.	A4047 (49c)	multicolored	1.25	.50
h.	A4048 (49c)	multicolored	1.25	.50
i.	A4049 (49c)	multicolored	1.25	.50
j.	A4050 (49c)	multicolored	1.25	.50
k.	A4051 (49c)	multicolored	1.25	.50
l.	A4052 (49c)	multicolored	1.25	.50

DISNEY VILLAINS

The Queen from *Snow White and the Seven Dwarfs* A4053

Honest John from *Pinocchio* A4054

Lady Tremaine from *Cinderella* A4055

Queen of Hearts from *Alice in Wonderland* A4056

Captain Hook from *Peter Pan* A4057

Maleficent from *Sleeping Beauty* A4058

Cruella De Vil from *One Hundred and One Dalmatians* A4059

Ursula from *The Little Mermaid* A4060

Gaston from *Beauty and the Beast* — A4061

Scar from *The Lion King* — A4062

LITHOGRAPHED

Serpentine Die Cut 10½x10¾

2017, July 15

Self-Adhesive

5213	A4053 (49c)	multicolored	1.25	.40
5214	A4054 (49c)	multicolored	1.25	.40
5215	A4055 (49c)	multicolored	1.25	.40
5216	A4056 (49c)	multicolored	1.25	.40
5217	A4057 (49c)	multicolored	1.25	.40
5218	A4058 (49c)	multicolored	1.25	.40
5219	A4059 (49c)	multicolored	1.25	.40
5220	A4060 (49c)	multicolored	1.25	.40
5221	A4061 (49c)	multicolored	1.25	.40
5222	A4062 (49c)	multicolored	1.25	.40
a.	Block of 10, #5213-5222		12.50	
	Nos. 5213-5222 (10)		12.50	4.00

SHARKS

Mako Shark — A4063

Whale Shark — A4064

Thresher Shark — A4065

Hammerhead Shark — A4066

Great White Shark — A4067

LITHOGRAPHED

Serpentine Die Cut 10¾

2017, July 26

Self-Adhesive

5223	A4063 (49c)	multicolored	1.25	.40
5224	A4064 (49c)	multicolored	1.25	.40
5225	A4065 (49c)	multicolored	1.25	.40
5226	A4066 (49c)	multicolored	1.25	.40
5227	A4067 (49c)	multicolored	1.25	.40
a.	Vert. strip of 5, #5223-5227		6.25	
	Nos. 5223-5227 (5)		6.25	2.00

PROTECT POLLINATORS

Monarch Butterfly on Purple Coneflower A4068

Western Honeybee on Golden Ragwort A4069

Monarch Butterfly on Red Zinnia — A4070

Western Honeybee on Purple New England Aster — A4071

Monarch Butterfly on Goldenrod A4072

LITHOGRAPHED

Serpentine Die Cut 10¾

2017, Aug. 3

Self-Adhesive

5228 A4068 (49c) multicolored 1.25 .40
5229 A4069 (49c) multicolored 1.25 .40
5230 A4070 (49c) multicolored 1.25 .40
5231 A4071 (49c) multicolored 1.25 .40
5232 A4072 (49c) multicolored 1.25 .40
a. Vert. strip of 5, #5228-5232 6.25
Nos. 5228-5232 (5) 6.25 2.00

FLOWERS FROM THE GARDEN

Red Camellias and Yellow Forsythia in Yellow Pitcher A4073

White Peonies and Pink Tree Peonies in Clear Vase A4074

Blue Hydrangeas in Blue Pot A4075

Assorted Flowers in White Vase A4076

Red Camellias and Yellow Forsythia in Yellow Pitcher A4077

Assorted Flowers in White Vase A4078

White Peonies and Pink Tree Peonies in Clear Vase A4079

Blue Hydrangeas in Blue Pot A4080

LITHOGRAPHED

Serpentine Die Cut 10¾ Vert.

2017, Aug. 16

Coil Stamps
Self-Adhesive

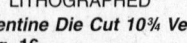

5233 A4073 (49c) multicolored 1.25 .30
5234 A4074 (49c) multicolored 1.25 .30
5235 A4075 (49c) multicolored 1.25 .30
5236 A4076 (49c) multicolored 1.25 .30
a. Strip of 4, #5233-5236 5.00
Nos. 5233-5236 (4) 5.00 1.20

Booklet Stamps

Serpentine Die Cut 11 on 2 or 3 Sides

5237 A4077 (49c) multicolored 1.25 .30
5238 A4078 (49c) multicolored 1.25 .30
5239 A4079 (49c) multicolored 1.25 .30
5240 A4080 (49c) multicolored 1.25 .30
a. Block of 4, #5237-5240 5.00
b. Booklet pane of 20, 5 each #5237-5240 25.00
Nos. 5237-5240 (4) 5.00 1.20

No. 5240b is a double-sided booklet pane with 12 stamps on one side (3 each Nos. 5237-5240) and eight stamps (2 each Nos. 5237-5240) plus label (booklet cover) on the other side.

FATHER THEODORE ("TED") HESBURGH

Hesburgh (1917-2015), President of University of Notre Dame — A4081

LITHOGRAPHED

Serpentine Die Cut 11

2017, Sept. 1 **Tagged**

Self-Adhesive

5241 A4081 (49c) multicolored 1.25 .25

Coil Stamp

Serpentine Die Cut 9½ Horiz.

5242 A4081 (49c) multicolored 1.25 .25

"THE SNOWY DAY," BY EZRA JACK KEATS

Peter Making Snowball A4082

Peter Sliding Down Mountain of Snow A4083

Peter Making Snow Angel A4084

Peter Leaving Footprints in Snow A4085

LITHOGRAPHED

Serpentine Die Cut 10¾ on 2 or 3 Sides

2017, Oct. 4

Booklet Stamps
Self-Adhesive

5243 A4082 (49c) multicolored 1.25 .30
5244 A4083 (49c) multicolored 1.25 .30
5245 A4084 (49c) multicolored 1.25 .30
5246 A4085 (49c) multicolored 1.25 .30
a. Block of 4, #5243-5246 5.00
b. Booklet pane of 20, 5 each #5243-5246 25.00
Nos. 5243-5246 (4) 5.00 1.20

No. 5246b is a double-sided booklet pane with 12 stamps on one side (3 each Nos. 5243-5246), and eight stamps (2 each Nos. 5243-5246) plus label (booklet cover) on the other side.

CHRISTMAS CAROLS

Christmas Lights, Cookies, and Line From "Deck the Halls" A4086

Star of Bethlehem, Lamb, and Line From "Silent Night" A4087

Snowflakes, Horse, and Line From "Jingle Bells" A4088

Child, Santa Claus, and Line From "Jolly Old St. Nicholas" A4089

LITHOGRAPHED

Serpentine Die Cut 10¾ on 2 or 3 Sides

2017, Oct. 5

Booklet Stamps
Self-Adhesive

5247 A4086 (49c) multicolored 1.25 .30
5248 A4087 (49c) multicolored 1.25 .30
5249 A4088 (49c) multicolored 1.25 .30
5250 A4089 (49c) multicolored 1.25 .30
a. Block of 4, #5247-5250 5.00
b. Booklet pane of 20, 5 each #5247-5250 25.00
Nos. 5247-5250 (4) 5.00 1.20

No. 5250b is a double-sided booklet pane with 12 stamps on one side (3 each Nos. 5247-5250), and eight stamps (2 each Nos. 5247-5250) plus label (booklet cover) on the other side.

NATIONAL MUSEUM OF AFRICAN AMERICAN HISTORY AND CULTURE

Museum Building, Washington, D.C. — A4090

LITHOGRAPHED

Serpentine Die Cut 10¾x10½

2017, Oct. 13 **Tagged**

Self-Adhesive

5251 A4090 (49c) multicolored 1.25 .25

HISTORY OF ICE HOCKEY

Player Wearing Helmet and Protective Gear A4091

Player Wearing Hat and Scarf A4092

LITHOGRAPHED

2017, Oct. 20 ***Serpentine Die Cut 11***

Self-Adhesive

5252 A4091 (49c) multicolored 1.25 .25
a. As No. 5252, matte-finish stamp 1.25 .25
5253 A4092 (49c) multicolored 1.25 .25
a. As No. 5253, matte-finish stamp 1.25 .25
b. Vert. pair, #5252-5253 2.50
c. Souvenir sheet of 2, #5252a-5253a 2.50

On Nos. 5253b and 5253c, stamps are printed tete-beche. Stamps from No. 5253b have a glossier finish than those on No. 5253c. Adjacent horizontal stamps have selvage between them.

See Canada Nos. 3039-3041.

CHINESE NEW YEAR

Year of the Dog — A4093

LITHOGRAPHED

Serpentine Die Cut 10¾

2018, Jan. 11

Self-Adhesive

5254 A4093 (49c) multicolored 1.25 .25

LOVE

Flowers — A4094

LITHOGRAPHED

Serpentine Die Cut 11x10¾

2018, Jan. 18

Self-Adhesive

5255 A4094 (49c) multicolored 1.25 .25

FRUIT

Meyer Lemons — A4095

LITHOGRAPHED

Serpentine Die Cut 10¾ Vert.

2018, Jan. 19

Coil Stamp
Self-Adhesive

5256 A4095 2c multicolored .30 .25

AMERICAN LANDMARKS ISSUE

Byodo-In Temple, Kaneohe, Hawaii — A4096

Sleeping Bear Dunes, Michigan A4097

LITHOGRAPHED

Serpentine Die Cut 10¾x10½

2018, Jan. 21

Self-Adhesive

5257 A4096 $6.70 multi 15.00 7.75
5258 A4097 $24.70 multi 60.00 25.00

BLACK HERITAGE

Lena Horne (1917-2010), Singer — A4098

LITHOGRAPHED

Serpentine Die Cut 10¾

2018, Jan. 30

Self-Adhesive

5259 A4098 (50c) multicolored 1.25 .25

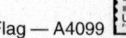

Flag — A4099

LITHOGRAPHED

Serpentine Die Cut 9½ Vert.

2018, Feb. 9

Coil Stamps
Self-Adhesive
Microprinted "USPS" at Left of Flag Fold on Fourth White Stripe

5260 A4099 (50c) multicolored 1.25 .25

Serpentine Die Cut 11 Vert.

Microprinted "USPS" at Right of Flag Fold on Fifth White Stripe

5261 A4099 (50c) multicolored 1.25 .25

Booklet Stamps Microprinted "USPS" at Left of Flag Fold on Fourth Red Stripe

Serpentine Die Cut 11¼x10¾ on 2 or 3 Sides

5262 A4099b(50c) multicolored 1.25 .25
a. Booklet pane of 20 25.00

Microprinted "USPS" at Right of Flag Fold on Fifth White Stripe

5263 A4099 (50c) multicolored 1.25 .25
a. Booklet pane of 20 25.00

Nos. 5262a and 5263a are double-sided booklets with 12 stamps on one side and eight stamps plus a label that serves as the booklet cover on the other side.

BIOLUMINESCENT LIFE

Octopus — A4100

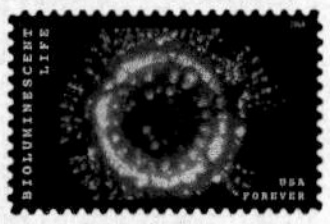

Jellyfish — A4101

Comb Jelly — A4102

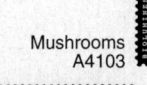

Mushrooms A4103

Firefly — A4104

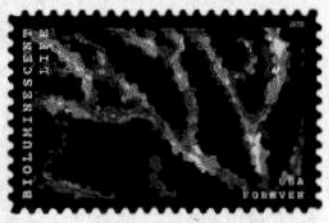

Bamboo Coral — A4105

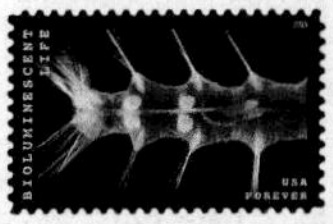

Marine Worm — A4106

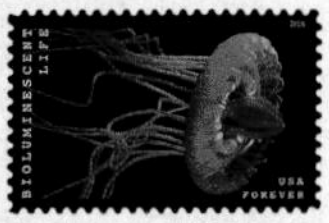

Crown Jellyfish — A4107

Marine Worm — A4108

Sea Pen — A4109

LITHOGRAPHED

Serpentine Die Cut 11

2018, Feb. 22

Self-Adhesive

5264 A4100 (50c) multicolored 1.25 .40
5265 A4101 (50c) multicolored 1.25 .40
5266 A4102 (50c) multicolored 1.25 .40
5267 A4103 (50c) multicolored 1.25 .40
5268 A4104 (50c) multicolored 1.25 .40
5269 A4105 (50c) multicolored 1.25 .40
5270 A4106 (50c) multicolored 1.25 .40
5271 A4107 (50c) multicolored 1.25 .40
5272 A4108 (50c) multicolored 1.25 .40
5273 A4109 (50c) multicolored 1.25 .40
a. Block of 10, #5264-5273 12.50
Nos. 5264-5273 (10) 12.50 4.00

ILLINOIS STATEHOOD, 200TH ANNIV.

Map of Illinois and Sun Rays — A4110

LITHOGRAPHED

2018, Mar. 5 ***Serpentine Die Cut 11***

Self-Adhesive

5274 A4110 (50c) multicolored 1.25 .25

MISTER ROGERS

Fred Rogers (1928-2003), Host of Children's Television Show, *Mister Rogers*, and Puppet, King Friday XIII — A4111

LITHOGRAPHED

Serpentine Die Cut 11

2018, Mar. 23

Self-Adhesive

5275 A4111 (50c) multicolored 1.25 .25

SCIENCE, TECHNOLOGY, ENGINEERING AND MATHEMATICS (STEM) EDUCATION

Head and Symbols of Science Education A4112

Head and Symbols of Technology Education A4113

Head and Symbols of Engineering Education A4114

Head and Symbols of Mathematics Education A4115

LITHOGRAPHED

2018, Apr. 6 ***Serpentine Die Cut 11***

Self-Adhesive

5276 A4112 (50c) multicolored 1.25 .30
5277 A4113 (50c) multicolored 1.25 .30
5278 A4114 (50c) multicolored 1.25 .30
5279 A4115 (50c) multicolored 1.25 .30
a. Vert. strip of 4, #5276-5279 5.00
Nos. 5276-5279 (4) 5.00 1.20

Peace Rose — A4116

LITHOGRAPHED

Serpentine Die Cut 11¼x10¾ on 2 or 3 Sides

2018, Apr. 21

Booklet Stamp
Self-Adhesive

5280 A4116 (50c) multicolored 1.25 .25
a. Booklet pane of 20 25.00

No. 5280a is a double-sided booklet with 12 stamps on one side and eight stamps plus a label that serves as the booklet cover on the other side.

See note after No. 1549.

AIR MAIL, CENT.

Curtiss JN-4H "Jenny" Biplane — A4117

ENGRAVED

2018 ***Serpentine Die Cut 10¾***

Self-Adhesive

5281 A4117 (50c) blue 1.25 .25
5282 A4117 (50c) carmine lake 1.25 .25

Issued: No. 5281, 5/1. No. 5282, 8/11.

SALLY RIDE

Sally Ride (1951-2012), First American Woman in Space, and Space Shuttle Launch — A4118

LITHOGRAPHED

Serpentine Die Cut 10½x10¾

2018, May 23

Self-Adhesive

5283 A4118 (50c) multicolored 1.25 .25

FLAG ACT OF 1818, BICENT.

20-Star Flag — A4119

LITHOGRAPHED

Serpentine Die Cut 10¾

2018, June 9

Self-Adhesive

5284 A4119 (50c) multicolored 1.25 .25

FROZEN TREATS

A4120

A4121

A4122

A4123

A4124

A4125

A4126

A4127

A4128

A4129

LITHOGRAPHED

Serpentine Die Cut 11¼x10¾ on 2 or 3 Sides

2018, June 20

Booklet Stamps
Self-Adhesive

5285 A4120 (50c) multicolored 1.25 .40
5286 A4121 (50c) multicolored 1.25 .40
5287 A4122 (50c) multicolored 1.25 .40
5288 A4123 (50c) multicolored 1.25 .40
5289 A4124 (50c) multicolored 1.25 .40
5290 A4125 (50c) multicolored 1.25 .40
5291 A4126 (50c) multicolored 1.25 .40
5292 A4127 (50c) multicolored 1.25 .40
5293 A4128 (50c) multicolored 1.25 .40
5294 A4129 (50c) multicolored 1.25 .40
a. Block of 10, #5285-5294 12.50
b. Booklet pane of 20, 2 each #5285-5294 25.00
Nos. 5285-5294 (10) 12.50 4.00

Nos. 5294b has a scratch-and-sniff coating with a fruity aroma, and is a double-sided booklet with 12 stamps on one side (Nos. 5286-5289, 5291-5294, 2 each Nos 5285, 5290), and eight stamps (Nos. 5286-5289, 5291-5294) plus a label that serves as the booklet cover on the other side.

STATUE OF FREEDOM

Head of Statue of Freedom on U.S. Capitol Dome — A4130

LITHOGRAPHED & ENGRAVED

Serpentine Die Cut 10¾x10½

2018, June 27

Self-Adhesive

5295 A4130 $1 emer, reddsh pink & blk 2.00 .50
5296 A4130 $2 indigo, reddsh pink & blk 4.00 1.00
5297 A4130 $5 brk red, reddsh pink & blk 10.00 2.50
Nos. 5295-5297 (3) 16.00 4.00

Optically-variable ink was used for the numerals in the denominations.

O BEAUTIFUL

Death Valley National Park, California and Nevada A4131

Three Fingers Mountain, Washington A4132

Double Rainbow Over Field, Kansas A4133

Great Smoky Mountains National Park, North Carolina and Tennessee A4134

Field of Wheat, Wisconsin A4135

Plowed Wheat Fields, Palouse Hills, Washington A4136

Grasslands Wildlife Management Area, Merced County, California A4137

Field of Wheat, Montana A4138

Yosemite National Park, California A4139

Crater Lake National Park, Oregon A4140

Monument Valley Navajo Tribal Park, Arizona and Utah A4141

Maroon Bells, Colorado A4142

Sunrise Near Orinda, California A4143

Pigeon Point, Near Pescadero, California A4144

Edna Valley, San Luis Obispo County, California A4145

Livermore, California A4146

Napali Coast State Wilderness Park, Hawaii A4147

Lone Ranch Beach, Oregon A4148

Canaveral National Seashore, Florida A4149

Bailey Island, Maine A4150

LITHOGRAPHED

Serpentine Die Cut 10½

2018, July 4

Self-Adhesive

5298 Pane of 20 35.00
a. A4131 (50c) multicolored 1.75 .50
b. A4132 (50c) multicolored 1.75 .50
c. A4133 (50c) multicolored 1.75 .50
d. A4134 (50c) multicolored 1.75 .50
e. A4135 (50c) multicolored 1.75 .50
f. A4136 (50c) multicolored 1.75 .50
g. A4137 (50c) multicolored 1.75 .50
h. A4138 (50c) multicolored 1.75 .50
i. A4139 (50c) multicolored 1.75 .50
j. A4140 (50c) multicolored 1.75 .50
k. A4141 (50c) multicolored 1.75 .50
l. A4142 (50c) multicolored 1.75 .50
m. A4143 (50c) multicolored 1.75 .50
n. A4144 (50c) multicolored 1.75 .50
o. A4145 (50c) multicolored 1.75 .50
p. A4146 (50c) multicolored 1.75 .50
q. A4147 (50c) multicolored 1.75 .50
r. A4148 (50c) multicolored 1.75 .50
s. A4149 (50c) multicolored 1.75 .50
t. A4150 (50c) multicolored 1.75 .50

SCOOBY-DOO

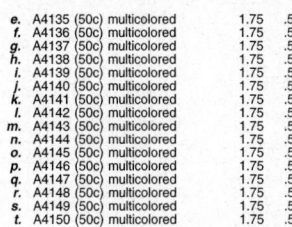

Cartoon Character Scooby-Doo Watering Plant — A4151

LITHOGRAPHED

Serpentine Die Cut 10¾x10½

2018, July 14

Self-Adhesive

5299 A4151 (50c) multicolored 1.25 .25

WORLD WAR I, CENT.

Member of American Expedtionary Force Holding Flag — A4152

LITHOGRAPHED

Serpentine Die Cut 10¾

2018, July 27

Self-Adhesive

5300 A4152 (50c) multicolored 1.25 .25

THE ART OF MAGIC

Rabbit in Hat — A4153

Fortune Teller and Crystal Ball — A4154

Levitating Woman and Hoop — A4155

Empty Bird Cage — A4156

Bird Emerging From Flower — A4157

LITHOGRAPHED (Nos. 5301-5305), TYPOGRAPHED WITH LENTICULAR LENS AFFIXED (No. 5306)

Serpentine Die Cut 10½x10¾

2018, Aug. 7

Self-Adhesive

5301 A4153 (50c) multicolored 1.25 .40
5302 A4154 (50c) multicolored 1.25 .40
5303 A4155 (50c) multicolored 1.25 .40
5304 A4156 (50c) multicolored 1.25 .40
5305 A4157 (50c) multicolored 1.25 .40
a. Horiz. strip of 5, #5301-5305 6.25
Nos. 5301-5305 (5) 6.25 2.00

Souvenir Sheet

5306 A4153 Sheet of 3 #5306a 3.75
a. (50c) Single stamp 1.25 .30
b. As No. 5306, die cutting omitted *800.00*

The printing method used on No. 5306a makes the rabbit in the vignette appear and disappear when the stamp is tilted.

DRAGONS

Green Dragon and Castle A4158

Purple Dragon and Castle A4159

Black Dragon and Ship A4160

Orange Dragon and Pagoda A4161

LITHOGRAPHED WITH FOIL APPLICATION

Serpentine Die Cut 10¾

2018, Aug. 9

Self-Adhesive

5307 A4158 (50c) multicolored 1.25 .30
5308 A4159 (50c) multicolored 1.25 .30
5309 A4160 (50c) multicolored 1.25 .30
5310 A4161 (50c) multicolored 1.25 .30
a. Strip or block of 4, #5307-5310 5.00
b. Horiz. strip of 4, #5307-5310, with die cutting missing (PS) *400.00*
Nos. 5307-5310 (4) 5.00 1.20

Poinsettia — A4162

LITHOGRAPHED

2018, Aug. 26 ***Serpentine Die Cut***

Self-Adhesive

5311 A4162 ($1.15) multicolored 2.80 .50

Unused values are for stamps with surrounding selvage. Adjacent stamps are separated by rouletting.

MUSIC ICONS

John Lennon (1940-80), Rock Musician — A4163

LITHOGRAPHED

Serpentine Die Cut 10¾

2018, Sept. 7

Self-Adhesive

Color of Shoulders

5312 A4163 (50c) red 1.25 .30
5313 A4163 (50c) red lilac 1.25 .30
5314 A4163 (50c) dark violet 1.25 .30
5315 A4163 (50c) blue 1.25 .30
a. Vert. strip of 4, #5312-5315 5.00
b. As "a," die cutting omitted —
Nos. 5312-5315 (4) 5.00 1.20

Adjacent horizontal or vertical stamps have selvage between the stamps.

FIRST RESPONDERS

Firefighter, Paramedic, and Law Enforcement Officer — A4164

LITHOGRAPHED

Serpentine Die Cut 11

2018, Sept. 13

Self-Adhesive

5316 A4164 (50c) multicolored 1.25 .25

BIRDS IN WINTER

Black-capped Chickadee A4165

Northern Cardinal A4166

Red-bellied Woodpecker A4167

Blue Jay A4168

LITHOGRAPHED

Serpentine Die Cut 10¾ on 2 or 3 Sides

2018, Sept. 22

Booklet Stamps

Self-Adhesive

5317 A4165 (50c) multicolored 1.25 .30
5318 A4166 (50c) multicolored 1.25 .30
5319 A4167 (50c) multicolored 1.25 .30
5320 A4168 (50c) multicolored 1.25 .30
a. Block of 4, #5317-5320 5.00
b. Booklet pane of 20, 5 each #5317-5320 25.00
Nos. 5317-5320 (4) 5.00 1.20

No. 5320b is a double-sided booklet pane with 12 stamps on one side (3 each Nos. 5317-5320), and eight stamps (2 each Nos. 5317-5320) plus label (booklet cover) on the other side.

HOT WHEELS TOY CARS, 50TH ANNIV.

Purple Passion — A4169

Rocket-Bye-Baby A4170

Rigor Motor — A4171

Rodger Dodger — A4172

Mach Speeder — A4173

Twin Mill — A4174

Bone Shaker — A4175

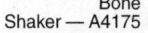

HW40 — A4176

Deora II — A4177

Sharkruiser A4178

LITHOGRAPHED

Serpentine Die Cut 10¾

2018, Sept. 29

Self-Adhesive

5321 A4169 (50c) multicolored 1.25 .40
5322 A4170 (50c) multicolored 1.25 .40
5323 A4171 (50c) multicolored 1.25 .40
5324 A4172 (50c) multicolored 1.25 .40
5325 A4173 (50c) multicolored 1.25 .40
5326 A4174 (50c) multicolored 1.25 .40
5327 A4175 (50c) multicolored 1.25 .40
5328 A4176 (50c) multicolored 1.25 .40
5329 A4177 (50c) multicolored 1.25 .40
5330 A4178 (50c) multicolored 1.25 .40
Nos. 5321-5330 (10) 12.50 4.00

CHRISTMAS

Madonna and Child, by Bachiacca A4179

Head of Santa Claus, by Haddon Sundblom A4180

Santa Claus and Wreath, by Sundblom A4181

Santa Claus and Book, by Sundblom A4182

Santa Claus and Card, by Sundblom — A4183

Santa Claus and Book, by Sundblom — A4184

LITHOGRAPHED

Serpentine Die Cut 10¾x11 on 2 or 3 Sides

2018

Booklet Stamps
Self-Adhesive

5331 A4179 (50c) multicolored 1.25 .25
a. Booklet pane of 20 25.00

5332 A4180 (50c) multicolored 1.25 .30
5333 A4181 (50c) multicolored 1.25 .30
5334 A4182 (50c) multicolored 1.25 .30
5335 A4183 (50c) multicolored 1.25 .30
a. Block of 4, #5332-5335 5.00
b. Booklet pane of 20, 5 each #5332-5335 25.00
c. As "a," die cutting omitted —
Nos. 5331-5335 (5) 6.25 1.45

Souvenir Sheet

Serpentine Die Cut 10¾

5336 A4184 (50c) multicolored 1.25 .30
a. Single stamp 1.25 .30

Issued: No. 5331, 10/3; Nos. 5332-5336, 10/11.

No. 5331a is a double-sided booklet panes with 12 stamps on one side and eight stamps plus label (booklet cover) on the other side. No. 5335b is a double-sided booklet pane with 12 stamps on one side (3 each Nos. 5332-5335) and eight stamps (2 each Nos. 5332-5335) plus label (booklet cover) on the other side.

The three examples of No. 5335c are from a booklet pane missing the stamps on the 8-stamp side.

KWANZAA

Family and Kinara — A4185

LITHOGRAPHED

Serpentine Die Cut 10¾

2018, Oct. 10

Self-Adhesive

5337 A4185 (50c) multicolored 1.25 .25

HANUKKAH

Menorah — A4186

LITHOGRAPHED

Serpentine Die Cut 10¾

2018, Oct. 16

Self-Adhesive

5338 A4186 (50c) multicolored 1.25 .25

See Israel No. 2200.

LOVE

Hearts — A4187

LITHOGRAPHED

Serpentine Die Cut 10¾x11

2019, Jan. 10

Self-Adhesive

5339 A4187 (50c) multicolored 1.25 .25

CHINESE NEW YEAR

Year of the Boar — A4188

LITHOGRAPHED

Serpentine Die Cut 10¾

2019, Jan. 17

Self-Adhesive

5340 A4188 (50c) multicolored 1.25 .25

People Wearing Uncle Sam Hats Type of 2017

LITHOGRAPHED

Serpentine Die Cut 11 Vert.

2019, Jan. 27 **Tagged**

Coil Stamp
Self-Adhesive

5341 A4006 (15c) multicolored .30 .25

See No. 5174.

Flag — A4189

LITHOGRAPHED

Serpentine Die Cut 9½ Horiz.

2019, Jan. 27

Coil Stamps
Self-Adhesive
Microprinted "USPS" at Lower Flag Grommet

5342 A4189 (55c) multicolored 1.25 .25

Serpentine Die Cut 11 Horiz.

Microprinted "USPS" to Right of Sixth Red Flag Stripe

5343 A4189 (55c) multicolored 1.25 .25
a. Die cutting omitted, pair — —

Used example of No. 5343 is single stamp on cover.

Booklet Stamps
Microprinted "USPS" at Upper Left Corner of Flag

Serpentine Die Cut 10¾x11¼ on 2 or 3 Sides

5344 A4189 (55c) multicolored 1.25 .25
a. Booklet pane of 20 25.00

Microprinted "USPS" to Right of Sixth Red Flag Stripe

5345 A4189 (55c) multicolored 1.25 .25
a. Booklet pane of 20 25.00

Nos. 5344a and 5345a are double-sided booklets with 12 stamps on one side and eight stamps plus a label that serves as the booklet cover on the other side.

CALIFORNIA DOGFACE BUTTERFLY

A4190

LITHOGRAPHED

Serpentine Die Cut 10½

2019, Jan. 27

Self-Adhesive

5346 A4190 (70c) multicolored 2.00 .25

AMERICAN LANDMARKS ISSUE

Joshua Tree — A4191

Bethesda Fountain, Central Park, New York City — A4192

LITHOGRAPHED

Serpentine Die Cut 10¾x10½

2019, Jan. 27

Self-Adhesive

5347 A4191 $7.35 multi 17.50 7.50
5348 A4192 $25.50 multi *12.00* 25.00

BLACK HERITAGE

Gregory Hines (1946-2003), Tap Dancer — A4193

LITHOGRAPHED

Serpentine Die Cut 10¾

2019, Jan. 28

Self-Adhesive

5349 A4193 (55c) multicolored 1.25 .25

CACTUS FLOWERS

Opuntia Engelmannii A4194

Rebutia Minuscula A4195

Echinocereus Dasyacanthus A4196

Echinocereus Poselgeri A4197

Echinocereus Coccineus A4198

Pelecyphora Aselliformis A4199

Parodia Microsperma A4200

Echinocactus Horizonthalonius A4201

Thelocactus Heterochromus A4202

Parodia Scopa A4203

LITHOGRAPHED

Serpentine Die Cut 11 on 2 or 3 Sides

2019, Feb. 15

Booklet Stamps
Self-Adhesive

5350 A4194 (55c) multicolored 2.50 .40
5351 A4195 (55c) multicolored 2.50 .40
5352 A4196 (55c) multicolored 2.50 .40
5353 A4197 (55c) multicolored 2.50 .40
5354 A4198 (55c) multicolored 2.50 .40
5355 A4199 (55c) multicolored 2.50 .40
5356 A4200 (55c) multicolored 2.50 .40
5357 A4201 (55c) multicolored 2.50 .40
5358 A4202 (55c) multicolored 2.50 .40
5359 A4203 (55c) multicolored 2.50 .40
a. Block of 10, #5350-5359 25.00
b. Booklet pane of 20, 2 each #5350-5359 50.00
Nos. 5350-5359 (10) 25.00 4.00

No. 5359b is a double-sided booklet pane with 12 stamps on one side (Nos. 5352-5359, 2 each Nos. 5350-5351), and eight stamps (Nos. 5352-5359) plus label (booklet cover) on the other side.

ALABAMA STATEHOOD, BICENT.

Pulpit Rock, Cheaha State Park — A4204

LITHOGRAPHED

Serpentine Die Cut 11x10¾

2019, Feb. 23

Self-Adhesive

5360 A4204 (55c) multicolored 1.25 .25

Star Ribbon — A4205

LITHOGRAPHED

Serpentine Die Cut 11¼x10¾

2019, Mar. 22

Self-Adhesive

5361 A4205 (55c) multicolored 1.25 .25

Coil Stamp

Serpentine Die Cut 10¾ Vert.

5362 A4205 (55c) multicolored 1.25 .25

CORAL REEFS

Elkhorn Coral and French Angelfish A4206

Brain Coral and Spotted Moray Eel A4207

Pillar Coral, Coney Grouper and Neon Gobies A4208

Staghorn Coral and Blue-striped Grunts A4209

LITHOGRAPHED

Serpentine Die Cut 11¼x10¾

2019, Mar. 29

Self-Adhesive

5363 A4206 (35c) multicolored .90 .25
5364 A4207 (35c) multicolored .90 .25
5365 A4208 (35c) multicolored .90 .25
5366 A4209 (35c) multicolored .90 .25
a. Horiz. or vert. strip of 4, #5363-5366 3.60
Nos. 5363-5366 (4) 3.60 1.00

Coil Stamps

Serpentine Die Cut 9½ Vert.

5367 A4208 (35c) multicolored .90 .25
a. Aqua ("POSTCARD") color omitted — —
5368 A4209 (35c) multicolored .90 .25
a. Aqua ("POSTCARD") color omitted —
5369 A4206 (35c) multicolored .90 .25
a. Aqua ("POSTCARD") color omitted —
5370 A4207 (35c) multicolored .90 .25
a. Aqua ("POSTCARD") color omitted — —
b. Horiz. strip of 4, #5367-5370 3.60
Nos. 5367-5370 (4) 3.60 1.00

MUSIC ICONS

Marvin Gaye (1939-84), Singer — A4210

LITHOGRAPHED

Serpentine Die Cut 10½

2019, Apr. 2

Self-Adhesive

5371 A4210 (55c) multicolored 1.25 .25

POST OFFICE MURALS

Piggott, Arkansas Mural *Air Mail,* by Daniel Rhodes A4211

Florence, Colorado Mural, *Antelope,* by Olive Rush A4212

Rockville, Maryland Mural, *Sugarloaf Mountain,* by Judson Smith A4213

Anadarko, Oklahoma Mural, *Kiowas Moving Camp,* by Stephen Mopope, James Auchiah, and Spencer Asah A4214

Deming, New Mexico Mural, *Mountains and Yucca,* by Kenneth Miller Adams A4215

LITHOGRAPHED

Serpentine Die Cut 11½x11

2019, Apr. 10

Self-Adhesive

5372 A4211 (55c) multicolored 1.25 .40
5373 A4212 (55c) multicolored 1.25 .40
5374 A4213 (55c) multicolored 1.25 .40
5375 A4214 (55c) multicolored 1.25 .40
5376 A4215 (55c) multicolored 1.25 .40
a. Vert. strip of 5, #5372-5376 6.25
Nos. 5372-5376 (5) 6.25 2.00

MAUREEN CONNOLLY BRINKER

Maureen "Little Mo" Connolly Brinker (1934-69), Tennis Player — A4216

LITHOGRAPHED

Serpentine Die Cut 10¾

2019, Apr. 23

Self-Adhesive

5377 A4216 (55c) multicolored 1.25 .25

TRANSCONTINENTAL RAILROAD, 150TH ANNIV.

Jupiter Locomotive A4217

Golden Spike A4218

No. 119 Locomotive A4219

LITHOGRAPHED WITH FOIL APPLICATION

Serpentine Die Cut 10¾x10½

2019, May 10

Self-Adhesive

5378 A4217 (55c) multicolored 1.25 .30
5379 A4218 (55c) multicolored 1.25 .30
5380 A4219 (55c) multicolored 1.25 .30
a. Horiz. strip of 3, #5378-5380 3.75
Nos. 5378-5380 (3) 3.75 .90

WILD AND SCENIC RIVERS

A4220

No. 5381: a, Merced River. b, Owyhee River. c, Koyukuk River. d, Niobrara River. e, Snake River. f, Flathead River. g, Missouri River. h, Skagit River. i, Deschutes River. j, Tlikakila River. k, Ontonagon River. l, Clarion River.

LITHOGRAPHED

Serpentine Die Cut 10¾x10½

2019, May 21

Self-Adhesive

5381 A4220 Pane of 12 15.00
a.-l. (55c) Any single 1.25 .50

ART OF ELLSWORTH KELLY (1923-2015)

Yellow White, 1961 — A4221

Colors for a Large Wall, 1951 — A4222

Blue Red Rocker, 1963 — A4223

Spectrum I, 1953 — A4224

South Ferry, 1956 — A4225

Blue Green, 1962 — A4226

Orange Red Relief (for Delphine Seyrig), 1990 — A4227

Meschers, 1951 — A4228

Red Blue, 1964 — A4229

Gaza, 1956 — A4230

LITHOGRAPHED

Serpentine Die Cut 10½x10¾

2019, May 31

Self-Adhesive

5382 A4221 (55c) multicolored 1.25 .40
5383 A4222 (55c) multicolored 1.25 .40
5384 A4223 (55c) multicolored 1.25 .40
5385 A4224 (55c) multicolored 1.25 .40
5386 A4225 (55c) multicolored 1.25 .40
5387 A4226 (55c) multicolored 1.25 .40
5388 A4227 (55c) multicolored 1.25 .40
5389 A4228 (55c) multicolored 1.25 .40
5390 A4229 (55c) multicolored 1.25 .40
5391 A4230 (55c) multicolored 1.25 .40
a. Block of 10, #5382-5391 12.50
Nos. 5382-5391 (10) 12.50 4.00

COMMISSIONING OF U.S.S. MISSOURI, 75th ANNIV.

U.S.S. Missouri — A4231

LITHOGRAPHED

Serpentine Die Cut 10¾

2019, June 11 **Tagged**

Self-Adhesive

5392 A4231 (55c) multicolored 1.25 .25
a. Die cutting omitted, pair —

GEORGE HERBERT WALKER BUSH

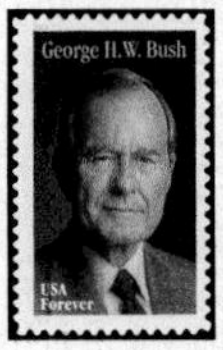

George Herbert Walker Bush (1924-2018), 41st President — A4232

LITHOGRAPHED

Serpentine Die Cut 10¾

2019, June 12 **Tagged**

Self-Adhesive

5393 A4232 (55c) multicolored 1.25 .25
a. Die cutting omitted, pair 500.00

SESAME STREET CHILDREN'S TELEVISION SHOW, 50th ANNIV.

Muppet Characters — A4233

No. 5394: a, Big Bird. b, Ernie. c, Bert. d, Cookie Monster. e, Rosita. f, The Count. g, Oscar the Grouch. h, Abby Cadabby. i, Herry Monster. j, Julia. k, Guy Smiley. l, Snuffleupagus. m, Elmo. n, Telly. o, Grover. p, Zoe.

LITHOGRAPHED

Serpentine Die Cut 10¾

2019, June 22 **Tagged**

Self-Adhesive

5394 A4233 Pane of 16 20.00
a.-p. (55c) Any single 1.25 .50

FROGS

Pacific Tree Frog — A4234

Northern Leopard Frog — A4235

American Green Tree Frog — A4236

Squirrel Tree Frog — A4237

LITHOGRAPHED

Serpentine Die Cut 11x10¾ on 2 or 3 Sides

2019, July 9 **Tagged**

Booklet Stamps

Self-Adhesive

5395 A4234 (55c) multicolored 1.25 .30
5396 A4235 (55c) multicolored 1.25 .30
5397 A4236 (55c) multicolored 1.25 .30
5398 A4237 (55c) multicolored 1.25 .30
a. Block of 4, #5395-5398 5.00
b. Booklet pane of 20, 5 each #5395-5398 25.00
Nos. 5395-5398 (4) 5.00 1.20

FIRST MOON LANDING, 50TH ANNIV.

Astronaut Edwin E. "Buzz" Aldrin, Jr. on Moon A4238

Moon with Landing Site Highlighted A4239

LITHOGRAPHED

Serpentine Die Cut 10¾

2019, July 19

Self-Adhesive

5399 A4238 (55c) multicolored 1.25 .25
5400 A4239 (55c) multicolored 1.25 .25
a. Pair, #5399-5400 2.50

Adjacent horizontal or vertical stamps have selvage between the stamps.

STATE AND COUNTY FAIRS

Farmers Unloading Large Fruits and Vegetables A4240

Girl and Farm Animals A4241

Parents and Children A4242

Child Buying Candy Apple A4243

LITHOGRAPHED

Serpentine Die Cut 10½x10¾

2019, July 25

Self-Adhesive

5401 A4240 (55c) multicolored 1.25 .30
5402 A4241 (55c) multicolored 1.25 .30
5403 A4242 (55c) multicolored 1.25 .30
5404 A4243 (55c) multicolored 1.25 .30
a. Horiz. strip of 4, #5401-5404 5.00
Nos. 5401-5404 (4) 5.00 1.20

Adjacent vertical stamps have selvage between the stamps.

MILITARY WORKING DOGS

German Shepherd A4244

Labrador Retriever A4245

Belgian Malinois A4246

Dutch Shepherd A4247

LITHOGRAPHED

Serpentine Die Cut 10¾x10½ (Nos. 5405, 5408), 10½x10¾ (Nos. 5406-5407)

2019, Aug. 1

Booklet Stamps
Self-Adhesive

5405 A4244 (55c) multicolored 1.25 .30
5406 A4245 (55c) multicolored 1.25 .30
5407 A4246 (55c) multicolored 1.25 .30
5408 A4247 (55c) multicolored 1.25 .30
a. Block of 4, #5405-5408 5.00
b. Booklet pane of 20, 5 each #5405-5408 25.00
Nos. 5405-5408 (4) 5.00 1.20

Adjacent horizontal and vertical stamps have selvage between the stamps. No. 5408b is a double-sided booklet pane with 12 stamps on one side (3 each Nos. 5405-5408), and eight stamps (2 each Nos. 5405-5408) plus label (booklet cover) on the other side.

WOODSTOCK MUSIC FESTIVAL, 50TH ANNIV.

Dove — A4248

TYPOGRAPHED

Serpentine Die Cut 10¾

2019, Aug. 8

Self-Adhesive

5409 A4248 (55c) multicolored 1.25 .25

TYRANNOSAURUS REX

Juvenile Tyrannosaurus Rex, Egg, and Insect — A4249

Adult Tyrannosaurus Rex — A4250

Young Adult Tyrannosaurus Rex and Juvenile Triceratops A4251

Juvenile Tyrannosaurus Rex Chasing Mammal — A4252

TYPOGRAPHED WITH LENTICULAR LENS AFFIXED

Serpentine Die Cut 10¾x10½

2019, Aug. 29

Self-Adhesive

5410 A4249 (55c) multicolored 1.25 .30
5411 A4250 (55c) multicolored 1.25 .30
5412 A4251 (55c) multicolored 1.25 .30
5413 A4252 (55c) multicolored 1.25 .30
a. Block of 4, #5410-5413 5.00
Nos. 5410-5413 (4) 5.00 1.20

Adjacent stamps have selvage between them. Only Nos. 5411 and 5412 show movement in the design when viewed from different positions.

LITERARY ARTS

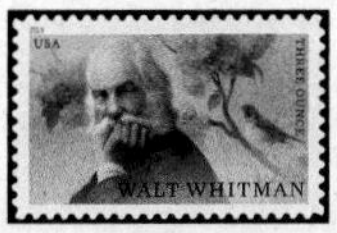

Walt Whitman (1819-92), Poet — A4253

LITHOGRAPHED

Serpentine Die Cut 10¾

2019, Sept. 12

Self-Adhesive

5414 A4253 (85c) multicolored 2.20 .30

WINTER BERRIES

Winterberry A4254

Juniper Berry A4255

Beautyberry A4256

Soapberry A4257

LITHOGRAPHED

Serpentine Die Cut 11¼x10¾ on 2 or 3 Sides

2019, Sept. 17

Booklet Stamps
Self-Adhesive

5415 A4254 (55c) multicolored 1.25 .30
5416 A4255 (55c) multicolored 1.25 .30
5417 A4256 (55c) multicolored 1.25 .30
5418 A4257 (55c) multicolored 1.25 .30
a. Block of 4, #5415-5418 5.00
b. Booklet pane of 20, 5 each #5415-5418 25.00
Nos. 5415-5418 (4) 5.00 1.20

No. 5398b is a double-sided booklet pane with 12 stamps on one side (3 each Nos. 5395-5398), and eight stamps (2 each Nos. 5395-5398) plus label (booklet cover) on the other side.

Purple Heart and Ribbon With Frame — A4258

LITHOGRAPHED

Serpentine Die Cut 11¼x10¾

2019, Oct. 4

Self-Adhesive

5419 A4258 (55c) multicolored 1.25 .25

SPOOKY SILHOUETTES

Cat and Raven A4259

Ghosts A4260

Spider and Web A4261

Bats A4262

TYPOGRAPHED WITH FOIL APPLICATION

Serpentine Die Cut 10¾

2019, Oct. 11

Self-Adhesive
Color of Foil

5420 A4259 (55c) silver 1.25 .30
5421 A4260 (55c) orange 1.25 .30
5422 A4261 (55c) red 1.25 .30
5423 A4262 (55c) violet 1.25 .30
a. Block of 4, #5420-5423 5.00
Nos. 5420-5423 (4) 5.00 1.20

CHRISTMAS WREATHS

Aspidistra Leaf Wreath A4263

Wreath Made of Gilded Pine Cones and Magnolia Pods A4264

Wreath Made of Gilded Hydrangea, Eucalyptus, Nandina and Ribbon A4265

Wreath Made of Woodland Bush Ivy and Red Winterberry A4266

LITHOGRAPHED

Serpentine Die Cut 11¼x10¾ on 2 or 3 Sides

2019, Oct. 25

Booklet Stamps
Self-Adhesive

5424 A4263 (55c) multicolored 1.25 .30
5425 A4264 (55c) multicolored 1.25 .30
5426 A4265 (55c) multicolored 1.25 .30
5427 A4266 (55c) multicolored 1.25 .30
a. Block of 4, #5424-5427 5.00
b. Booklet pane of 20, 5 each #5424-5427 25.00
Nos. 5424-5427 (4) 5.00 1.20

No. 5398b is a double-sided booklet pane with 12 stamps on one side (3 each Nos. 5395-5398), and eight stamps (2 each Nos. 5395-5398) plus label (booklet cover) on the other side.

CHINESE NEW YEAR

Year of the Rat — A4267

LITHOGRAPHED WITH FOIL APPLICATION

Serpentine Die Cut 10¾

2020, Jan. 11

Self-Adhesive

5428 A4267 (55c) multicolored 1.25 .25

AMERICAN LANDMARKS ISSUE

Big Bend National Park, Texas — A4268

Grand Island Ice Caves, Michigan A4269

LITHOGRAPHED

Serpentine Die Cut 10¾x10½

2020, Jan. 18

Self-Adhesive

5429 A4268 $7.75 multi 15.50 7.75
5430 A4269 $26.35 multi 53.00 26.50

LOVE

Hearts — A4270

LITHOGRAPHED

Serpentine Die Cut 10¾

2020, Jan. 23

Self-Adhesive

5431 A4270 (55c) multicolored 1.25 .25

BLACK HERITAGE

Gwen Ifill (1955-2016), Television Newscaster — A4271

LITHOGRAPHED

Serpentine Die Cut 10¾

2020, Jan. 30

Self-Adhesive

5432 A4271 (55c) multicolored 1.25 .25

Star and Stripes — A4272

LITHOGRAPHED

Serpentine Die Cut 10¾ Vert.

2020, Feb. 3

COIL STAMP

Self-Adhesive

5433 A4272 (10c) multicolored .30 .25

CELEBRATE

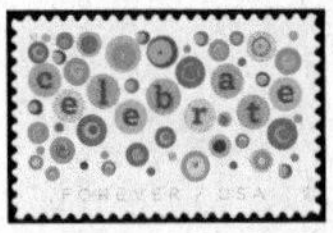

A4273

LITHOGRAPHED WITH FOIL APPLICATION

Serpentine Die Cut 10¾

2020, Feb. 14

Self-Adhesive

5434 A4273 (55c) multicolored 1.25 .25
a. Die cutting omitted, pair —

WILD ORCHIDS

Platanthera Grandiflora A4274

Cyrtopodium Polyphyllum A4275

Calopogon Tuberosus A4276

Spiranthes Odorata A4277

Triphora Trianthophoros A4278

Cypripedium Californicum A4279

Hexalectris Spicata A4280

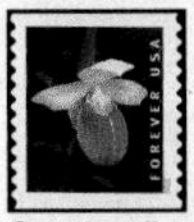

Cypripedium Reginae A4281

Platanthera Leucophaea A4282

Triphora Trianthophoros A4283

Triphora Trianthophoros A4284

Cypripedium Californicum A4285

Hexalectris Spicata A4286

Cypripedium Reginae A4287

Spiranthes Odorata A4288

Platanthera Leucophaea A4289

Triphora Trianthophoros A4290

Platanthera Grandiflora A4291

Cyrtopodium Polyphyllum A4292

Calopogon Tuberosus A4293

LITHOGRAPHED

Serpentine Die Cut 10¾ Vert.

2020, Feb. 21

Coil Stamps

Self-Adhesive

5435 A4274 (55c) multicolored 1.25 .40
5436 A4275 (55c) multicolored 1.25 .40
5437 A4276 (55c) multicolored 1.25 .40
5438 A4277 (55c) multicolored 1.25 .40
5439 A4278 (55c) multicolored 1.25 .40
5440 A4279 (55c) multicolored 1.25 .40
5441 A4280 (55c) multicolored 1.25 .40
5442 A4281 (55c) multicolored 1.25 .40
5443 A4282 (55c) multicolored 1.25 .40
5444 A4283 (55c) multicolored 1.25 .40
a. Horiz. strip of 10, #5435-5444 12.50
Nos. 5435-5444 (10) 12.50 4.00

Booklet Stamps

Serpentine Die Cut 10¾x11 on 2 or 3 Sides

5445 A4284 (55c) multicolored 1.25 .40
5446 A4285 (55c) multicolored 1.25 .40
5447 A4286 (55c) multicolored 1.25 .40
5448 A4287 (55c) multicolored 1.25 .40
5449 A4288 (55c) multicolored 1.25 .40
5450 A4289 (55c) multicolored 1.25 .40
5451 A4290 (55c) multicolored 1.25 .40
5452 A4291 (55c) multicolored 1.25 .40
5453 A4292 (55c) multicolored 1.25 .40
5454 A4293 (55c) multicolored 1.25 .40
a. Block of 10, #5445-5454 12.50
b. Booklet pane of 20, 2 each #5445-5454 25.00
Nos. 5445-5454 (10) 12.50 4.00

Nos. 5454b is a double-sided booklet with 12 stamps on one side (Nos. 5446-5449, 5451-5454, 2 each Nos 5445, 5450), and eight stamps (Nos. 5446-5449, 5451-5454) plus a label that serves as the booklet cover on the other side.

ARNOLD PALMER

Arnold Palmer (1929-2016), Professional Golfer — A4294

LITHOGRAPHED

Serpentine Die Cut 10¾

2020, Mar. 4

Self-Adhesive

5455 A4294 (55c) multicolored 1.25 .25

MAINE STATEHOOD BICENTENARY

Sea at Ogunquit, by Edward Hopper (1882-1967) A4295

LITHOGRAPHED

Serpentine Die Cut 10¾

2020, Mar. 15

Self-Adhesive

5456 A4295 (55c) multicolored 1.25 .25

Boutonniere A4296

Corsage A4297

LITHOGRAPHED

Serpentine Die Cut 10¾x11

2020, Apr. 2

Self-Adhesive

5457 A4296 (55c) multicolored 1.25 .25
5458 A4297 (70c) multicolored 1.70 .25

EARTH DAY, 50th ANNIV.

Stylized Globe — A4298

LITHOGRAPHED

Serpentine Die Cut 11x10¾ on 2 or 3 Sides

2020, Apr. 18

Booklet Stamp

Self-Adhesive

5459 A4298 (55c) multicolored 1.25 .25
a. Booklet pane of 20 25.00

No. 5459a is a double-sided booklet with 12 stamps on one side and eight stamps plus a label that serves as the booklet cover on the other side.

Chrysanthemum A4299

LITHOGRAPHED

Sheets of 90 in nine panes of 10

Serpentine Die Cut

2020, Apr. 24 **Tagged**

Self-Adhesive

5460 A4299 ($1.20) multicolored 3.00 .50

Unused values are for stamps with surrounding selvage. Adjacent stamps are separated by rouletting.

AMERICAN GARDENS

Brooklyn Botanic Garden, New York — A4300

Stan Hywet Hall and Gardens, Ohio — A4301

Dumbarton Oaks, District of Columbia A4302

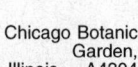

Coastal Maine Botanical Gardens, Maine — A4303

Chicago Botanic Garden, Illinois — A4304

Winterthur Garden, Delaware A4305

Biltmore Estate Gardens, North Carolina — A4306

Alfred B. Maclay Gardens State Park, Florida — A4307

The Huntington Botanical Gardens, California A4308

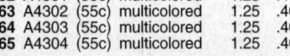

Norfolk Botanical Garden, Virginia — A4309

LITHOGRAPHED

Serpentine Die Cut 10¾x10½

2020, May 13

Self-Adhesive

5461 A4300 (55c) multicolored 1.25 .40
5462 A4301 (55c) multicolored 1.25 .40
5463 A4302 (55c) multicolored 1.25 .40
5464 A4303 (55c) multicolored 1.25 .40
5465 A4304 (55c) multicolored 1.25 .40

5466	A4305	(55c)	multicolored	1.25	.40
5467	A4306	(55c)	multicolored	1.25	.40
5468	A4307	(55c)	multicolored	1.25	.40
5469	A4308	(55c)	multicolored	1.25	.40
5470	A4309	(55c)	multicolored	1.25	.40
a.			Block of 10, #5461-5470	12.50	
			Nos. 5461-5470 (10)	12.50	4.00

Die cut uncut press sheets of Nos. 5461-5470 were made available for sale. Values: cross gutter block of 10, $18; pairs with gutters between, $4.25 each. See note after No. 4693.

See note after No. 1549.

VOICES OF THE HARLEM RENAISSANCE

Nella Larsen (1891-1964), Novelist A4310

Arturo Schomburg (1874-1938), Historian A4311

Anne Spencer (1882-1975), Poet A4312

Alain Locke (1885-1954), Writer A4313

LITHOGRAPHED

Serpentine Die Cut 10¾

2020, May 21

Self-Adhesive

5471	A4310	(55c)	multicolored	1.25	.30
5472	A4311	(55c)	multicolored	1.25	.30
5473	A4312	(55c)	multicolored	1.25	.30
5474	A4313	(55c)	multicolored	1.25	.30
a.			Horiz. or vert. strip of 4, #5471-5474	5.00	
			Nos. 5471-5474 (4)	5.00	1.20

Die cut uncut press sheets of Nos. 5471-5474 were made available for sale. Values: cross gutter block of 8, $16; pairs with gutters between, $4.25 each. See note after No. 4693.

See note after No. 1549.

ENJOY THE GREAT OUTDOORS

Child Building Sandcastle A4314

Canoeing A4315

Hiking — A4316

Bicycling A4317

Cross-country Skiing — A4318

LITHOGRAPHED

Serpentine Die Cut 10¾

2020, June 13

Self-Adhesive

5475	A4314	(55c)	multicolored	1.25	.40
5476	A4315	(55c)	multicolored	1.25	.40
5477	A4316	(55c)	multicolored	1.25	.40
5478	A4317	(55c)	multicolored	1.25	.40
5479	A4318	(55c)	multicolored	1.25	.40
a.			Vert. strip of 5, #5475-5479	6.25	
			Nos. 5475-5479 (5)	6.25	2.00

HIP HOP

MC With Microphone Rapping A4319

B-Boy Dancing A4320

Graffiti Art A4321

DJ at Turntable A4322

LITHOGRAPHED

Serpentine Die Cut 10¾

2020, July 1

Self-Adhesive

5480	A4319	(55c)	multicolored	1.25	.30
5481	A4320	(55c)	multicolored	1.25	.30
5482	A4321	(55c)	multicolored	1.25	.30
5483	A4322	(55c)	multicolored	1.25	.30
a.			Block or vert. strip of 4, #5480-5483	5.00	
			Nos. 5480-5483 (4)	5.00	1.20

FRUITS AND VEGETABLES

Red and Black Plums A4323

Heirloom and Cherry Tomatoes A4324

Carrots A4325

Lemons A4326

Blueberries A4327

Red and Green Grapes A4328

Lettuce A4329

Strawberries A4330

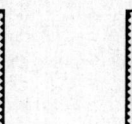

Eggplants A4331

Figs A4332

LITHOGRAPHED

Serpentine Die Cut 10¾x11 on 2 or 3 Sides

2020, July 17

Booklet Stamps

Self-Adhesive

5484	A4323	(55c)	multicolored	1.25	.40
5485	A4324	(55c)	multicolored	1.25	.40
5486	A4325	(55c)	multicolored	1.25	.40
5487	A4326	(55c)	multicolored	1.25	.40
5488	A4327	(55c)	multicolored	1.25	.40
5489	A4328	(55c)	multicolored	1.25	.40
5490	A4329	(55c)	multicolored	1.25	.40
5491	A4330	(55c)	multicolored	1.25	.40
5492	A4331	(55c)	multicolored	1.25	.40
5493	A4332	(55c)	multicolored	1.25	.40
a.			Block of 10, #5484-5493	12.50	
b.			Booklet pane of 20, 2 each #5484-5493	25.00	
			Nos. 5484-5493 (10)	12.50	4.00

Nos. 5493b is a double-sided booklet pane with 12 stamps on one side (Nos. 5485-5488, 5490-5493, 2 each Nos. 5484, 5489) and eight stamps (Nos. 5485-5488, 5490-5493) plus label (booklet cover) on the other side.

BUGS BUNNY, 80th ANNIV.

Bugs Bunny as Barber, From *Rabbit of Seville,* 1950 — A4333

Bugs Bunny as Basketball Player, From *Space Jam,* 1996 — A4334

Bugs Bunny as Hollywood Celebrity, From *A Hare Grows in Manhattan,* 1947 — A4335

Bugs Bunny as Court Jester, From *Knighty Knight Bugs,* 1958 — A4336

Bugs Bunny as Brunhilde, From *What's Opera, Doc?,* 1957 — A4337

Bugs Bunny as Mermaid, From *Hare Ribbin',* 1944 — A4338

Bugs Bunny as Piano Player, From *Rhapsody Rabbit,* 1946 — A4339

Bugs Bunny as Super-Rabbit, From *Super-Rabbit,* 1943 — A4340

Bugs Bunny as Baseball Player, From *Baseball Bugs,* 1946 A4341

Bugs Bunny as Soldier, From World War II Poster A4342

LITHOGRAPHED

Serpentine Die Cut 10½x10¾

2020, July 27

Self-Adhesive

5494	A4333	(55c)	multicolored	1.25	.40
5495	A4334	(55c)	multicolored	1.25	.40
5496	A4335	(55c)	multicolored	1.25	.40
5497	A4336	(55c)	multicolored	1.25	.40
5498	A4337	(55c)	multicolored	1.25	.40
5499	A4338	(55c)	multicolored	1.25	.40
5500	A4339	(55c)	multicolored	1.25	.40
5501	A4340	(55c)	multicolored	1.25	.40
5502	A4341	(55c)	multicolored	1.25	.40
5503	A4342	(55c)	multicolored	1.25	.40
a.			Block of 10, #5494-5503	12.50	
			Nos. 5494-5503 (10)	12.50	4.00

WIRE SCULPTURES BY RUTH ASAWA (1926-2013)

Three Untitled Sculptures From 1958, 1978 and 1959 A4343

Untitled Sculpture From 1959 A4344

Untitled Sculpture From 1958 A4345

Untitled Sculpture From 1955 A4346

Untitled Sculpture From 1955 A4347

Untitled Sculpture From 1980 A4348

Untitled Sculpture From 1978 A4349

Untitled Sculpture From 1952 A4350

Untitled Sculpture From 1954
A4351

Six Untitled Sculptures From Various Years
A4352

LITHOGRAPHED
Serpentine Die Cut 10¾
2020, Aug. 13
Self-Adhesive

5504 A4343 (55c) multicolored 1.25 .40
5505 A4344 (55c) multicolored 1.25 .40
5506 A4345 (55c) multicolored 1.25 .40
5507 A4346 (55c) multicolored 1.25 .40
5508 A4347 (55c) multicolored 1.25 .40
5509 A4348 (55c) multicolored 1.25 .40
5510 A4349 (55c) multicolored 1.25 .40
5511 A4350 (55c) multicolored 1.25 .40
5512 A4351 (55c) multicolored 1.25 .40
5513 A4352 (55c) multicolored 1.25 .40
a. Block of 10, #5504-5513 12.50

INNOVATION

Computing
A4353

Biomedicine
A4354

Genome Sequencing
A4355

Robotics
A4356

Solar Technology — A4357

LITHOGRAPHED WITH FOIL APPLICATION
Sheets of 120 in six panes of 20
Serpentine Die Cut 10¾
2020, Aug. 20
Self-Adhesive

5514 A4353 (55c) multicolored 1.25 .40
5515 A4354 (55c) multicolored 1.25 .40
5516 A4355 (55c) multicolored 1.25 .40
5517 A4356 (55c) multicolored 1.25 .40
5518 A4357 (55c) multicolored 1.25 .40
a. Horiz. strip of 5, #5514-5518 6.25
Nos. 5514-5518 (5) 6.25 2.00

THANK YOU

A4358

A4359

A4360

A4361

TYPOGRAPHED WITH FOIL APPLICATION
Serpentine Die Cut 10¾
2020, Aug. 21
Self-Adhesive

5519 A4358 (55c) rose brown & gold 1.25 .40
5520 A4359 (55c) olive & gold 1.25 .40
5521 A4360 (55c) slate blue & gold 1.25 .40
5522 A4361 (55c) violet & gold 1.25 .40
a. Block of 4, #5519-5522 5.00
Nos. 5519-5522 (4) 5.00 1.60

WOMAN SUFFRAGE CENTENARY

Suffragists Marching for Passage of 19th Amendment — A4362

LITHOGRAPHED
Serpentine Die Cut 10¾
2020, Aug. 22
Self-Adhesive

5523 A4362 (55c) multicolored 1.25 .25

MAYFLOWER IN PLYMOUTH HARBOR, 400th ANNIV.

The Mayflower in Plymouth Harbor and Mayflower
A4363

LITHOGRAPHED & ENGRAVED
Serpentine Die Cut 10¾
2020, Sept. 17
Self-Adhesive

5524 A4363 (55c) multicolored 1.25 .25

A pane of No. 5524, imperforate panes of single-color progressive proofs in cyan, magenta, yellow, and lithographed black, a commemorative book, and a numbered certificate were produced in a quantity of 2,500 and sold as a unit for $59.95.

CHRISTMAS

Our Lady of Guápulo, by Unknown 18th Century Peruvian Artist
A4364

Ornament
A4365

Christmas Tree
A4366

Christmas Stocking
A4367

Reindeer — A4368

LITHOGRAPHED
Serpentine Die Cut 10¾ on 2 or 3 Sides
2020
Booklet Stamps
Self-Adhesive

5525 A4364 (55c) multicolored 1.25 .25
a. Booklet pane of 20 25.00
5526 A4365 (55c) multicolored 1.25 .30
5527 A4366 (55c) multicolored 1.25 .30
5528 A4367 (55c) multicolored 1.25 .30
5529 A4368 (55c) multicolored 1.25 .30
a. Block of 4, #5526-5529 5.00
b. Booklet pane of 20, 5 each #5526-5529 25.00
Nos. 5525-5529 (5) 6.25 1.45

Issued: No. 5525, 10/20; Nos. 5526-5529, 9/24.

No. 5525a is a double-sided booklet pane with 12 stamps on one side, and eight stamps plus label (booklet cover) on the other side.

No. 5529b is a double-sided booklet pane with 12 stamps on one side (3 each Nos. 5526-5529), and eight stamps (2 each Nos. 5526-55290) plus label (booklet cover) on the other side.

HANUKKAH

Children and Menorah — A4369

LITHOGRAPHED
Serpentine Die Cut 10¾
2020, Oct. 6
Self-Adhesive

5530 A4369 (55c) multicolored 1.25 .25

KWANZAA

Woman and Kinara — A4370

LITHOGRAPHED
Serpentine Die Cut 10¾
2020, Oct. 13
Self-Adhesive

5531 A4370 (55c) multicolored 1.25 .25

WINTER SCENES

Two Deer, Photograph by Lisa Carter
A4371

Cardinal, Photograph by Gerald A. DeBoer
A4372

Snowy Morning at Sunrise, Photograph by Lisa Lacasse
A4373

Red Barn with Wreath, Photograph by Lisa Lacasse
A4374

Barred Owl, Photograph by Malachi Ives
A4375

Blue Jay, Photograph by Edgar Lee Espe
A4376

Mackenzie Barn, Woodstock, Vermont, Photograph by Lisa Lacasse
A4377

Rabbit, Photograph by Melani Wright
A4378

After the Snowfall, Photograph by Lisa Lacasse
A4379

Mike and Burt, the Belgian Draft Horses, Photograph by Lisa Lacasse
A4380

LITHOGRAPHED
Serpentine Die Cut 10¾ on 2 or 3 Sides
2020, Oct. 16
Booklet Stamps
Self-Adhesive

5532 A4371 (55c) multicolored 1.25 .40
5533 A4372 (55c) multicolored 1.25 .40
5534 A4373 (55c) multicolored 1.25 .40
5535 A4374 (55c) multicolored 1.25 .40
5536 A4375 (55c) multicolored 1.25 .40
5537 A4376 (55c) multicolored 1.25 .40
5538 A4377 (55c) multicolored 1.25 .40
5539 A4378 (55c) multicolored 1.25 .40
5540 A4379 (55c) multicolored 1.25 .40
5541 A4380 (55c) multicolored 1.25 .40
a. Block of 10, #5532-5541 12.50
b. Booklet pane of 20, 2 each #5532-5541 25.00
Nos. 5532-5541 (10) 12.50 4.00

Nos. 5541b is a double-sided booklet with 12 stamps on one side (Nos. 5533-5536, 5538-5541, 2 each Nos 5532, 5537), and eight stamps (Nos. 5533-5536, 5538-5541) plus a label that serves as the booklet cover on the other side.

DRUG FREE USA

Star and Stripes — A4381

LITHOGRAPHED
Serpentine Die Cut 10¾
2020, Oct. 27
Self-Adhesive

5542 A4381 (55c) multicolored 1.25 .25

LOVE

A4382

LITHOGRAPHED
Serpentine Die Cut 11
2021, Jan. 14
Self-Adhesive

5543 A4382 (55c) multicolored 1.25 .25
a. Imperforate 1.50 —

BRUSH RABBIT

A4383

A4383a

LITHOGRAPHED
Serpentine Die Cut 11¼x11
2021, Jan. 24
Self-Adhesive

5544 A4383 (20c) multicolored .50 .25

Coil Stamp
Serpentine Die Cut 9½ Vert.

5545 A4383 (20c) multicolored .50 .25

BARNS

Round Barn
A4384

Barn With Gambrel Roof, Windmill
A4385

Forebay Barn
A4386

Snow-covered Western Barn
A4387

LITHOGRAPHED

Serpentine Die Cut 11x11¼

2021, Jan. 24

Self-Adhesive

5546 A4384 (36c) multicolored .90 .30
5547 A4385 (36c) multicolored .90 .30
5548 A4386 (36c) multicolored .90 .30
5549 A4387 (36c) multicolored .90 .30
a. Block or horiz. strip of 4, #5546-5549 3.60
Nos. 5546-5549 (4) 3.60 1.20

Counterfeits exist of Nos. 5546-5549. See the Postal Counterfeits section of this catalog.

Coil Stamps

Serpentine Die Cut 11 Horiz.

5550 A4385 (36c) multicolored .90 .30
5551 A4387 (36c) multicolored .90 .30
5552 A4386 (36c) multicolored .90 .30
5553 A4384 (36c) multicolored .90 .30
a. Vert. strip of 4, #5550-5553 3.60

AMERICAN LANDMARKS ISSUE

Castillo de San Marcos, St. Augustine, Florida — A4388

LITHOGRAPHED

Serpentine Die Cut 10¾x10½

2021, Jan. 24

Self-Adhesive

5554 A4388 $7.95 multi 16.00 8.00

BLACK HERITAGE

August Wilson (1945-2005), Playwright — A4389

LITHOGRAPHED

Serpentine Die Cut 11

2021, Jan. 28

Self-Adhesive

5555 A4389 (55c) multicolored 1.25 .25
a. Imperforate 2.00 —

CHINESE NEW YEAR

Year of the Ox — A4390

LITHOGRAPHED & TYPOGRAPHED WITH FOIL APPLICATION

2021, Feb. 2 ***Serpentine Die Cut 11***

Self-Adhesive

5556 A4390 (55c) multi 1.25 .25
a. Imperforate 3.00 —

CHIEN-SHIUNG WU

Dr. Chien-Shiung Wu (1912-97), Nuclear Physicist — A4391

LITHOGRAPHED

Serpentine Die Cut 11

2021, Feb. 11

Self-Adhesive

5557 A4391 (55c) multicolored 1.25 .25
a. Imperforate 6.00 —

GARDEN BEAUTY

Pink Flowering Dogwood
A4392

Orange and Yellow Tulip
A4393

Allium
A4394

Pink Moth Orchid with Mottled Petals
A4395

Magenta Dahlia
A4396

Yellow Moth Orchid with Pink Center
A4397

Pink and White Sacred Lotus
A4398

White Asiatic Lily
A4399

Rose Pink and White Tulip
A4400

Pink American Lotus
A4401

LITHOGRAPHED

Serpentine Die Cut 11 on 2 or 3 Sides

2021, Feb. 23

Booklet Stamps
Self-Adhesive

5558 A4392 (55c) multicolored 1.25 .40
5559 A4393 (55c) multicolored 1.25 .40
5560 A4394 (55c) multicolored 1.25 .40
5561 A4395 (55c) multicolored 1.25 .40
5562 A4396 (55c) multicolored 1.25 .40
5563 A4397 (55c) multicolored 1.25 .40
5564 A4398 (55c) multicolored 1.25 .40
5565 A4399 (55c) multicolored 1.25 .40
5566 A4400 (55c) multicolored 1.25 .40
5567 A4401 (55c) multicolored 1.25 .40
a. Block of 10, #5558-5567 12.50
b. Booklet pane of 20, 2 each #5558-5567 25.00
Nos. 5558-5567 (10) 12.50 4.00

No. 5567b is a double-sided booklet pane with 12 stamps on one side (Nos. 5560-5567, 2 each Nos. 5558-5559), and eight stamps (Nos. 5560-5567) plus label (booklet cover) on the other side.

COLORADO HAIRSTREAK BUTTERFLY

A4402

LITHOGRAPHED

Serpentine Die Cut 10½

2021, Mar. 9

Self-Adhesive

5568 A4402 (75c) multicolored 2.00 .25

ESPRESSO DRINKS

Caffe Latte
A4403

Espresso
A4404

Caffe Mocha
A4405

Cappuccino
A4406

LITHOGRAPHED

Serpentine Die Cut 11¼x10¾ on 2 or 3 Sides

2021, Apr. 9

Booklet Stamps

Self-Adhesive

5569 A4403 (55c) multicolored 1.25 .30
5570 A4404 (55c) multicolored 1.25 .30
5571 A4405 (55c) multicolored 1.25 .30
5572 A4406 (55c) multicolored 1.25 .30
a. Block of 4, #5569-5572 5.00
b. Booklet pane of 20, 5 each #5569-5572 25.00
Nos. 5569-5572 (4) 5.00 1.20

No. 5398b is a double-sided booklet pane with 12 stamps on one side (3 each Nos. 5395-5398), and eight stamps (2 each Nos. 5395-5398) plus label (booklet cover) on the other side.

STAR WARS MOVIE DROIDS

IG-11
A4407

R2-D2
A4408

K-2SO
A4409

D-O
A4410

L3-37
A4411

BB-8
A4412

C-3PO
A4413

Gonk Droid
A4414

2-1B Droid
A4415

Chopper
A4416

LITHOGRAPHED & TYPOGRAPHED

Serpentine Die Cut 10¾

2021, May 4

Self-Adhesive

5573 A4407 (55c) multicolored 1.25 .40
a. Imperforate 6.00 —
5574 A4408 (55c) multicolored 1.25 .40
a. Imperforate 6.00 —
5575 A4409 (55c) multicolored 1.25 .40
a. Imperforate 6.00 —
5576 A4410 (55c) multicolored 1.25 .40
a. Imperforate 6.00 —
5577 A4411 (55c) multicolored 1.25 .40
a. Imperforate 6.00 —
5578 A4412 (55c) multicolored 1.25 .40
a. Imperforate 6.00 —
5579 A4413 (55c) multicolored 1.25 .40
a. Imperforate 6.00 —
5580 A4414 (55c) multicolored 1.25 .40
a. Imperforate 6.00 —
5581 A4415 (55c) multicolored 1.25 .40
a. Imperforate 6.00 —
5582 A4416 (55c) multicolored 1.25 .40
a. Imperforate 6.00 —
b. Block of 10, #5573-5582 12.50
c. Imperforate block of 10, #5573a-5582a 60.00
Nos. 5573-5582 (10) 12.50 4.00

HERITAGE BREEDS

Mulefoot Hog
A4417

Wyandotte Chicken
A4418

Milking Devon Cow
A4419

Narragansett Turkey
A4420

American Mammoth Jackstock Donkey
A4421

Cotton Patch Goose
A4422

San Clemente Island Goat — A4423

American Cream Draft Horse — A4424

Cayuga Duck A4425

Barbados Blackbelly Sheep A4426

LITHOGRAPHED & TYPOGRAPHED

Serpentine Die Cut 10½x10¾

2021, May 17

Self-Adhesive

5583 A4417 (55c) multicolored 1.25 .40
a. Imperforate 6.00 —
5584 A4418 (55c) multicolored 1.25 .40
a. Imperforate 6.00 —
5585 A4419 (55c) multicolored 1.25 .40
a. Imperforate 6.00 —
5586 A4420 (55c) multicolored 1.25 .40
a. Imperforate 6.00 —
5587 A4421 (55c) multicolored 1.25 .40
a. Imperforate 6.00 —
5588 A4422 (55c) multicolored 1.25 .40
a. Imperforate 6.00 —
5589 A4423 (55c) multicolored 1.25 .40
a. Imperforate 6.00 —
5590 A4424 (55c) multicolored 1.25 .40
a. Imperforate 6.00 —
5591 A4425 (55c) multicolored 1.25 .40
a. Imperforate 6.00 —
5592 A4426 (55c) multicolored 1.25 .40
a. Imperforate 6.00 —
b. Block of 10, #5583-5592 12.50
c. Imperforate block of 10, #5583a-5592a 60.00
Nos. 5583-5592 (10) 12.50 4.00

GO FOR BROKE

Japanese-American Soldier of World War II — A4427

LITHOGRAPHED & ENGRAVED

Serpentine Die Cut 10¾

2021, June 3

Self-Adhesive

5593 A4427 (55c) blue & red 1.25 .25
a. Imperforate 2.00 —

PAINTINGS BY EMILIO SANCHEZ (1921-99)

Los Toldos, 1973 — A4428

Ty's Place, 1976 — A4429

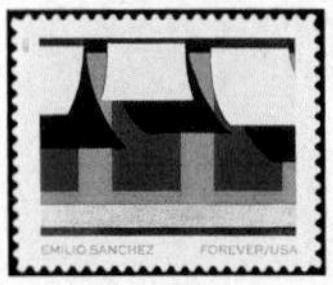

En el Souk, 1972 — A4430

Untitled (Ventanita Entreabierta), 1981 — A4431

LITHOGRAPHED

Serpentine Die Cut 10¾

2021, June 10

Self-Adhesive

5594 A4428 (55c) multicolored 1.25 .30
a. Imperforate 2.00 —
5595 A4429 (55c) multicolored 1.25 .30
a. Imperforate 2.00 —
5596 A4430 (55c) multicolored 1.25 .30
a. Imperforate 2.00 —
5597 A4431 (55c) multicolored 1.25 .30
a. Imperforate 2.00 —
b. Horiz. or vert. strip of 4, #5594-5597 5.00
c. Imperforate horiz. or vert. strip of 4, #5594a-5597a 8.00
Nos. 5594-5597 (4) 5.00 1.20

SUN SCIENCE

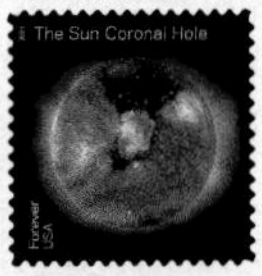

Coronal Hole A4432

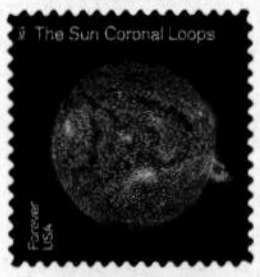

Coronal Loops A4433

Solar Flare — A4434

Active Sun — A4435

Plasma Blast A4436

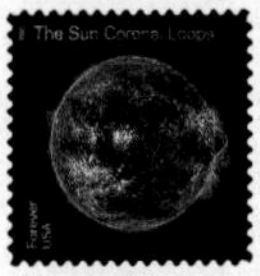
Coronal Loops A4437

Sunspots A4438

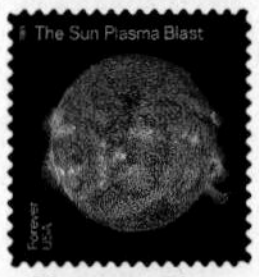

Plasma Blast A4439

Solar Flare — A4440

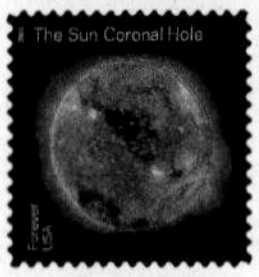

Coronal Hole — A4441

TYPOGRAPHED WITH FOIL APPLICATION

Serpentine Die Cut 10¾x10½

2021, June 18

Self-Adhesive

5598 A4432 (55c) multicolored 1.25 .40
a. Imperforate 5.00 —
5599 A4433 (55c) multicolored 1.25 .40
a. Imperforate 5.00 —
5600 A4434 (55c) multicolored 1.25 .40
a. Imperforate 5.00 —
5601 A4435 (55c) multicolored 1.25 .40
a. Imperforate 5.00 —
5602 A4436 (55c) multicolored 1.25 .40
a. Imperforate 5.00 —
5603 A4437 (55c) multicolored 1.25 .40
a. Imperforate 5.00 —
5604 A4438 (55c) multicolored 1.25 .40
a. Imperforate 5.00 —
5605 A4439 (55c) multicolored 1.25 .40
a. Imperforate 5.00 —
5606 A4440 (55c) multicolored 1.25 .40
a. Imperforate 5.00 —
5607 A4441 (55c) multicolored 1.25 .40
a. Imperforate 5.00 —
b. Block of 10, #5598-5607 12.50
c. Imperforate block of 10, #5598a-5607a 50.00
Nos. 5598-5607 (10) 12.50 4.00

YOGI BERRA

Lawrence Peter "Yogi" Berra (1925-2015), Baseball Player — A4442

LITHOGRAPHED & TYPOGRAPHED

Serpentine Die Cut 10¾

2021, June 24

Self-Adhesive

5608 A4442 (55c) multicolored 1.25 .25
a. Imperforate 2.00 —

TAP DANCE

Max Pollak A4443

Michela Marino Lerman A4444

Derick Grant A4445

Dormeshia Sumbry-Edwards A4446

Ayodele Casel — A4447

LITHOGRAPHED

Serpentine Die Cut 11

2021, July 10

Color of "TAP"

Self-Adhesive

5609 A4443 (55c) buff 1.25 .40
a. Imperforate 3.00 —
5610 A4444 (55c) rose 1.25 .40
a. Imperforate 3.00 —
5611 A4445 (55c) greenish blue 1.25 .40
a. Imperforate 3.00 —
5612 A4446 (55c) light blue 1.25 .40
a. Imperforate 3.00 —
5613 A4447 (55c) bister 1.25 .40
a. Imperforate 3.00 —
b. Horiz. strip of 5, #5609-5613 5.50
c. Imperforate strip of 5, #5609a-5613a 15.00
P# block of 10, 2 sets of 4# + P 11.00
Nos. 5609-5613 (5) 6.25 2.00

MYSTERY MESSAGE

"More Than Meets The Eye" — A4448

LITHOGRAPHED & TYPOGRAPHED

Serpentine Die Cut 10½

2021, July 14

Self-Adhesive

5614 A4448 (55c) multicolored 1.25 .25
a. Imperforate 1.25 —

WESTERN WEAR

Cowboy Hat, Snakes and Roses A4449

Belt Buckle, Roses, Stars and Spurs A4450

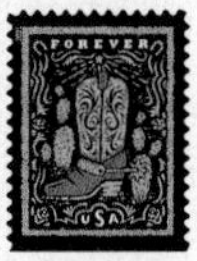
Cowboy Boot With Spur, Roses, Cacti and Star A4451

Western Shirt, Roses, Cacti and Star A4452

LITHOGRAPHED

Serpentine Die Cut 10¾ on 2 or 3 Sides

2021, July 23

Booklet Stamps

Self-Adhesive

5615 A4449 (55c) multicolored 1.25 .30
5616 A4450 (55c) multicolored 1.25 .30
5617 A4451 (55c) multicolored 1.25 .30
5618 A4452 (55c) multicolored 1.25 .30
a. Block of 4, #5615-5618 5.00
b. Booklet pane of 20, 5 each #5615-5618 25.00
Nos. 5615-5618 (4) 5.00 1.20

No. 5618b is a double-sided booklet pane with 12 stamps on one side (3 each Nos. 5615-5618), and eight stamps (2 each Nos. 5615-5618) plus label (booklet cover) on the other side.

LITERARY ARTS

Ursula K. Le Guin (1929-2018), Science Fiction Novelist — A4453

LITHOGRAPHED

Serpentine Die Cut 10¾

2021, July 27

Self-Adhesive

5619 A4453 (95c) multicolored 2.20 .30

RAVEN STORY

Mythological Raven from Stories of Indigenous People of the Northern Northwest Coast — A4454

TYPOGRAPHED WITH FOIL APPLICATION

Serpentine Die Cut 10¾

2021, July 30

Self-Adhesive

5620 A4454 (55c) multicolored 1.25 .25
a. Imperforate *20.00* —

MID-ATLANTIC LIGHTHOUSES

Montauk Point Lighthouse, New York A4455

Navesink Twin Lighthouses, New Jersey A4456

Erie Harbor Lighthouse, Pennsylvania A4457

Harbor of Refuge Lighthouse, Delaware A4458

Thomas Point Shoal Lighthouse, Maryland — A4459

LITHOGRAPHED

Serpentine Die Cut 10¾

2021, Aug. 6

Self-Adhesive

5621 A4455 (55c) multicolored		1.25	.40
a.	Imperforate	1.50	—
5622 A4456 (55c) multicolored		1.25	.40
a.	Imperforate	1.50	—
5623 A4457 (55c) multicolored		1.25	.40
a.	Imperforate	1.50	—
5624 A4458 (55c) multicolored		1.25	.40
a.	Imperforate	1.50	—
5625 A4459 (55c) multicolored		1.25	.40
a.	Imperforate	1.50	—
b.	Horiz. strip of 5, #5621-5625	6.25	
c.	Imperforate strip of 5, #5621a-5625a	7.50	
	Nos. 5621-5625 (5)	6.25	2.00

MISSOURI STATEHOOD BICENTENARY

Bollinger Mill and Burfordville Covered Bridge — A4460

LITHOGRAPHED

Serpentine Die Cut 10¾

2021, Aug. 10

Self-Adhesive

5626 A4460 (55c) multicolored		1.25	.25
a.	Imperforate	1.25	—

BACKYARD GAMES

Horseshoes A4461

Bocce A4462

Flying Disc A4463

Croquet A4464

Pick-up Baseball Variation A4465

Tetherball A4466

Badminton A4467

Cornhole A4468

LITHOGRAPHED

Serpentine Die Cut 10¾

2021, Aug. 12

Self-Adhesive

5627 A4461 (55c) multicolored		1.25	.40
a.	Imperforate	2.00	—
5628 A4462 (55c) multicolored		1.25	.40
a.	Imperforate	2.00	—
5629 A4463 (55c) multicolored		1.25	.40
a.	Imperforate	2.00	—
5630 A4464 (55c) multicolored		1.25	.40
a.	Imperforate	2.00	—
5631 A4465 (55c) multicolored		1.25	.40
a.	Imperforate	2.00	—
5632 A4466 (55c) multicolored		1.25	.40
a.	Imperforate	2.00	—
5633 A4467 (55c) multicolored		1.25	.40
a.	Imperforate	2.00	—
5634 A4468 (55c) multicolored		1.25	.40
a.	Imperforate	2.00	—
b.	Block of 8, #5627-5634	10.00	
c.	Imperforate block of 8, #5627a-5634a	16.00	
	Nos. 5627-5634 (8)	10.00	3.20

HAPPY BIRTHDAY

Birthday Hat, Confetti and Streamers — A4469

LITHOGRAPHED

2021, Sept. 9 ***Serpentine Die Cut 11***

Self-Adhesive

5635 A4469 (58c) multicolored		1.25	.25

MESSAGE MONSTERS

Pink and Red Monster A4470

Four-Armed Monster A4471

Tentacled Monster A4472

Red-Headed Monster A4473

LITHOGRAPHED

Serpentine Die Cut 10½x10¾

2021, Sept. 24

Self-Adhesive

5636 A4470 (58c) multicolored		1.25	.30
a.	Imperforate	2.00	—
5637 A4471 (58c) multicolored		1.25	.30
a.	Imperforate	2.00	—
5638 A4472 (58c) multicolored		1.25	.30
a.	Imperforate	2.00	—
5639 A4473 (58c) multicolored		1.25	.30
a.	Imperforate	2.00	—
b.	Horiz. or vert. strip of 4, #5636-5639	5.00	
c.	Imperforate strip of 4 #5636a-5639a	8.00	
	Nos. 5636-5639 (4)	5.00	1.20

DAY OF THE DEAD

Girl's Skull With Bow — A4474

Man's Skull With Hat — A4475

Woman's Skull With Curled Hair — A4476

Boy's Skull — A4477

LITHOGRAPHED

Serpentine Die Cut 11

2021, Sept. 30

Self-Adhesive

5640 A4474 (58c) multicolored		1.25	.30
a.	Imperforate	1.75	—
5641 A4475 (58c) multicolored		1.25	.30
a.	Imperforate	1.75	—
5642 A4476 (58c) multicolored		1.25	.30
a.	Imperforate	1.75	—
5643 A4477 (58c) multicolored		1.25	.30
a.	Imperforate	1.75	—
b.	Horiz. strip of 4, #5640-5643	5.00	
c.	Imperforate strip of 4, #5640a-5643a	7.00	
	Nos. 5640-5643 (4)	5.00	1.20

CHRISTMAS

Santa Claus on Roof A4478

Santa Claus in Fireplace A4479

Head of Santa Claus A4480

Santa Claus, Sleigh and Reindeer in Flight A4481

LITHOGRAPHED

Serpentine Die Cut 10¾x11 on 2 or 3 Sides

2021, Oct. 7

Booklet Stamps

Self-Adhesive

5644 A4478 (58c) multicolored		1.25	.30
5645 A4479 (58c) multicolored		1.25	.30
5646 A4480 (58c) multicolored		1.25	.30
5647 A4481 (58c) multicolored		1.25	.30
a.	Block of 4, #5644-5647	5.00	
b.	Booklet pane of 20, 5 each #5644-5647	25.00	
	Nos. 5644-5647 (4)	5.00	1.20

No. 5618b is a double-sided booklet pane with 12 stamps on one side (3 each Nos. 5615-5618), and eight stamps (2 each Nos. 5615-5618) plus label (booklet cover) on the other side.

OTTERS IN SNOW

Otter in Water A4482

Otter, Tail at Right A4483

Otter, Tail at Left A4484

Otter in Snow A4485

LITHOGRAPHED

Serpentine Die Cut 10¾x11 on 2 or 3 Sides

2021, Oct. 12

Booklet Stamps

Self-Adhesive

5648 A4482 (58c) multicolored		1.25	.30
5649 A4483 (58c) multicolored		1.25	.30
5650 A4484 (58c) multicolored		1.25	.30
5651 A4485 (58c) multicolored		1.25	.30
a.	Block of 4, #5648-5651	5.00	
b.	Booklet pane of 20, 5 each #5648-5651	25.00	
	Nos. 5648-5651 (4)	5.00	1.20

No. 5618b is a double-sided booklet pane with 12 stamps on one side (3 each Nos. 5615-5618), and eight stamps (2 each Nos. 5615-5618) plus label (booklet cover) on the other side.

FRUIT

Blueberries — A4486

LITHOGRAPHED

Serpentine Die Cut 11¼x11

2022, Jan. 9

Self-Adhesive

5652 A4486 4c multicolored	.30	.25

Coil Stamp

Serpentine Die Cut 10¾ Vert.

5653 A4486 4c multicolored	.30	.25

See note after No. 1549.

Flags — A4487

LITHOGRAPHED

Serpentine Die Cut 11¼x11

2022, Jan. 9

Self-Adhesive

Microprinted "USPS" Above Lower Connector on Flagpole at Left

5654 A4487 (58c) multicolored	1.25	.25

Coil Stamps

Stamps Not Adjacent on Coil Roll Backing Paper Taller Than Stamp

Serpentine Die Cut 10¾ Vert.

5655 A4487 (58c) multicolored	1.25	.25

Serpentine Die Cut 11 Vert.

Stamps Adjacent on Coil Roll Backing Paper Same Height as Stamp

5656 A4487 (58c) multicolored	1.25	.25

Microprinted "USPS" Above Lowest Blue Flag Field

Serpentine Die Cut 9½ Vert.

5657 A4487 (58c) multicolored	1.25	.25
Nos. 5655-5657 (3)	3.75	.75

Booklet Stamps

Microprinted "USPS" Above Lower Connector on Flagpole at Left

Serpentine Die Cut 11¼x10¾ on 2 or 3 Sides

5658 A4487 (58c) multicolored	1.25	.25
a. Booklet pane of 20	25.00	

Microprinted "USPS" Above Lowest Blue Flag Field

5659 A4487 (58c) multicolored	1.25	.25
a. Booklet pane of 20	25.00	

Nos. 5262a and 5263a are double-sided booklets with 12 stamps on one side and eight stamps plus a label that serves as the booklet cover on the other side.

LOVE

A4488

A4489

LITHOGRAPHED

Serpentine Die Cut 11

2022, Jan. 14

Self-Adhesive

Background Color

5660 A4488 (58c) blue gray		1.25	.25
a.	Imperforate	1.25	—
5661 A4489 (58c) pink		1.25	.25
a.	Imperforate	1.25	—
b.	Horiz. or vert. pair, #5660-5661	2.50	
c.	Imperforate horiz. or vert. pair, #5660a-5661a	2.50	

CHINESE NEW YEAR

Year of the Tiger — A4490

LITHOGRAPHED & TYPOGRAPHED WITH FOIL APPLICATION

Serpentine Die Cut 11

2022, Jan. 20

Self-Adhesive

5662 A4490 (58c) multi 1.25 .25
a. Imperforate 1.25 —

BLACK HERITAGE

Edmonia Lewis (c. 1844-1907), Sculptor — A4491

LITHOGRAPHED

Serpentine Die Cut 10¾

2022, Jan. 26

Self-Adhesive

5663 A4491 (58c) multicolored 1.25 .25
a. Imperforate 1.25 —

BUTTERFLY GARDEN FLOWERS

Cosmos A4492

Scabiosas A4493

LITHOGRAPHED

Serpentine Die Cut 10¾ Vert.

2022, Feb. 1

Coil Stamps

Self-Adhesive

5664 A4492 (5c) multicolored .30 .25
5665 A4493 (5c) multicolored .30 .25
a. Pair, #5664-5665 .30

AMERICAN LANDMARKS ISSUE

Monument Valley, Utah — A4494

Palace of Fine Arts, San Francisco, California A4495

LITHOGRAPHED

Serpentine Die Cut 10¾x10½

2022, Feb. 14

Self-Adhesive

5666 A4494 $8.95 multi 18.00 8.00
5667 A4495 $26.95 multi 55.00 27.50

TITLE IX CIVIL RIGHTS LAW, 50TH ANNIV.

Runner A4496

Swimmer A4497

Gymnast A4498

Soccer Player A4499

LITHOGRAPHED

Serpentine Die Cut 10¾

2022, Mar. 3

Self-Adhesive

5668 A4496 (58c) multicolored 1.25 .30
a. Imperforate 1.25 —
5669 A4497 (58c) multicolored 1.25 .30
a. Imperforate 1.25 —
5670 A4498 (58c) multicolored 1.25 .30
a. Imperforate 1.25 —
5671 A4499 (58c) multicolored 1.25 .30
a. Imperforate 1.25 —
b. Block or vert. strip of 4, #5668-5671 5.00
c. Imperforate block or vert. strip of 4 #5668a-5671a 5.00
Nos. 5668-5671 (4) 5.00 1.20

MOUNTAIN FLORA

Wood Lily A4500

Alpine Buttercup A4501

Woods' Rose A4502

Pasqueflower A4503

Pasqueflower A4504

Wood Lily A4505

Alpine Buttercup A4506

Woods' Rose A4507

LITHOGRAPHED

Serpentine Die Cut 10 Vert.

2022, Mar. 14

Coil Stamps

Self-Adhesive

5672 A4500 (58c) multicolored 1.25 .30
5673 A4501 (58c) multicolored 1.25 .30
5674 A4502 (58c) multicolored 1.25 .30
5675 A4503 (58c) multicolored 1.25 .30
a. Horiz. strip of 4, #5672-5675 5.00
Nos. 5672-5675 (4) 5.00 1.20

Booklet Stamps

Serpentine Die Cut 10¾x11 on 2 or 3 Sides

5676 A4504 (58c) multicolored 1.25 .30
5677 A4505 (58c) multicolored 1.25 .30
5678 A4506 (58c) multicolored 1.25 .30
5679 A4507 (58c) multicolored 1.25 .30
a. Block of 4, #5676-5679 5.00
b. Booklet pane of 20, 5 each #5676-5679 25.00
Nos. 5676-5679 (4) 5.00 1.20

Nos. 5679b is a double-sided booklet with 12 stamps on one side (3 each Nos 5676-5679), and eight stamps (2 each Nos. 5676-5679) plus a label that serves as the booklet cover on the other side.

African Daisy — A4508

LITHOGRAPHED

2022, Mar. 14 *Serpentine Die Cut*

Self-Adhesive

5680 A4508 ($1.30) multicolored 3.00 .60

Unused values are for stamps with surrounding selvage. Adjacent stamps are separated by rouletting.

Tulips A4509

Sunflower Bouquet A4510

LITHOGRAPHED

Serpentine Die Cut 11x10¾

2022, Mar. 24

Self-Adhesive

5681 A4509 (58c) multicolored 1.25 .25
a. Die cutting omitted, pair —

Serpentine Die Cut 10¾x11

5682 A4510 (78c) multicolored 1.60 .25

SHEL SILVERSTEIN (1930-99), CHILDREN'S BOOK WRITER

Boy Catching Apple, Illustration From *The Giving Tree*, by Silverstein — A4511

LITHOGRAPHED

2022, Apr. 8 *Serpentine Die Cut 11*

Self-Adhesive

5683 A4511 (58c) multicolored 1.25 .25
a. Imperforate — —

FLAGS ON BARNS

Flag on Red Barn Near Well A4512

Flag on White Barn in Winter A4513

Flag on White Barn With Gambrel Roof A4514

Flag on Barn Near Windmill A4515

LITHOGRAPHED

Serpentine Die Cut 10½ Vert.

2022, Apr. 14

Coil Stamps

Self-Adhesive

5684 A4512 (10c) multicolored .30 .25
5685 A4513 (10c) multicolored .30 .25
5686 A4514 (10c) multicolored .30 .25
5687 A4515 (10c) multicolored .30 .25
a. Strip of 4, #5684-5687 1.20
Nos. 5684-5687 (4) 1.20 1.00

PAINTINGS BY GEORGE MORRISON (1919-2000)

Sun and River, 1949 — A4516

Phenomena Against the Crimson: Lake Superior Landscape, 1985 — A4517

Lake Superior Landscape, 1981 — A4518

Spirit Path, New Day, Red Rock Variation: Lake Superior Landscape, 1990 — A4519

Untitled, 1995 — A4520

LITHOGRAPHED

Serpentine Die Cut 10¾

2022, Apr. 22

Self-Adhesive

5688 A4516 (58c) multicolored 1.25 .40
a. Imperforate — —
5689 A4517 (58c) multicolored 1.25 .40
a. Imperforate — —
5690 A4518 (58c) multicolored 1.25 .40
a. Imperforate — —
5691 A4519 (58c) multicolored 1.25 .40
a. Imperforate — —
5692 A4520 (58c) multicolored 1.25 .40
a. Imperforate — —
b. Vert. strip of 5, #5688-5692 6.25
c. Imperforate strip of 5, #5688a-5692a —
Nos. 5688-5692 (5) 6.25 2.00

EUGENIE CLARK (1922-2015), ICHTHYOLOGIST

Clark and Lemon Shark — A4521

LITHOGRAPHED

Serpentine Die Cut 10¾

2022, May 4

Self-Adhesive

5693 A4521 (58c) multicolored 1.25 .25
a. Imperforate — —

WOMEN'S ROWING

Women Wearing Red Shirts, No Oar Splash — A4522

Women Wearing Red Shirts, Oar Splash at Lower Left — A4523

Women Wearing Blue Shirts, Oar Splash at Center — A4524

Women Wearing Blue Shirts, No Oar Splash — A4525

LITHOGRAPHED

Serpentine Die Cut 10¾

2022, May 13

Self-Adhesive

5694 A4522 (58c) multicolored 1.25 .30
a. Imperforate — —
5695 A4523 (58c) multicolored 1.25 .30
a. Imperforate — —
b. Horiz. pair, #5694-5695 2.50
c. Imperforate horiz. pair, #5694a-5695a —
5696 A4524 (58c) multicolored 1.25 .30
a. Imperforate — —
5697 A4525 (58c) multicolored 1.25 .30
a. Imperforate — —
b. Horiz. pair, #5696-5697 2.50
c. Imperforate horiz. pair, #5696a-5697a —
Nos. 5694-5697 (4) 5.00 1.20

MIGHTY MISSISSIPPI

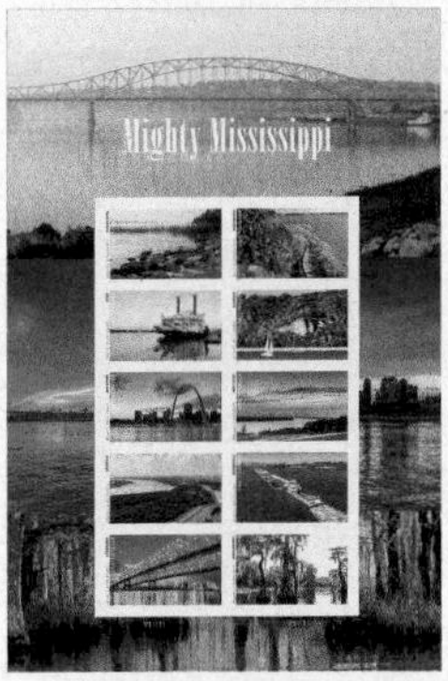

Views of the Mississippi River from States Along its Route — A4526

No. 5698 — Photographs of: a, Headwaters of the Mississippi River, Lake Itasca, Minnesota. b, Great River Road, Wisconsin. c, Steamboat *American Queen,* Iowa. d, Sailboat and limestone cliff, Illinois. e, Gateway Arch and St. Louis skyline, Missouri. f, Mississippi River from Fort Jefferson Hill Park, Wickliffe, Kentucky. g, Curved levee and farmland, Arkansas. h, Towboat pushing barges near Memphis, Tennessee. i, Crescent City Connection Bridges, New Orleans, Louisiana. j, Cypress trees in bayou, Mississippi.

LITHOGRAPHED

Serpentine Die Cut 10¾

2022, May 23

Self-Adhesive

5698	A4526	Pane of 10	12.50	
a.-j.		(58c) Any single	1.25	.50
k.		As #5698, imperforate	—	—
l.		As #5698a, imperforate	—	—
m.		As #5698b, imperforate	—	—
n.		As #5698c, imperforate	—	—
o.		As #5698d, imperforate	—	—
p.		As #5698e, imperforate	—	—
q.		As #5698f, imperforate	—	—
r.		As #5698g, imperforate	—	—
s.		As #5698h, imperforate	—	—
t.		As #5698i, imperforate	—	—
u.		As #5698j, imperforate	—	—

DISTINGUISHED AMERICANS

Katherine Graham (1917-2001), Publisher of the *Washington Post* — A4527

LITHOGRAPHED

Serpentine Die Cut 10¾

2022, June 14

Self-Adhesive

5699	A4527	(78c) multicolored	1.60	.25

Adjacent horizontal or vertical stamps have selvage between the stamps.

FLORAL GEOMETRY

A4528

A4529

LITHOGRAPHED WITH FOIL APPLICATION

Serpentine Die Cut 10¾

2022, June 20

Self-Adhesive

5700	A4528	$2 multicolored	4.00	1.00
5701	A4529	$5 multicolored	10.00	2.50

Adjacent horizontal or vertical stamps have selvage between the stamps.

NANCY REAGAN (1921-2016), ACTRESS AND FIRST LADY

A4530

LITHOGRAPHED

2022, July 6 ***Serpentine Die Cut 11***

Self-Adhesive

5702	A4530	(58c) multicolored	1.25	.25
a.		Imperforate	—	—

MARIACHI

Guitarist and Moon
A4531

Guitarist and Sun
A4532

Violinist and Sun
A4533

Bass Guitarist and Sun
A4534

Trumpet Player and Sun — A4535

LITHOGRAPHED

Serpentine Die Cut 10¾

2022, July 15

5703	A4531	(60c) multicolored	1.25	.40
a.		Imperforate	1.25	—
5704	A4532	(60c) multicolored	1.25	.40
a.		Imperforate	1.25	—
5705	A4533	(60c) multicolored	1.25	.40
a.		Imperforate	1.25	—
5706	A4534	(60c) multicolored	1.25	.40
a.		Imperforate	1.25	—
5707	A4535	(60c) multicolored	1.25	.40
a.		Imperforate	1.25	—
b.		Horiz. strip of 5, #5703-5707	6.25	
c.		Imperforate strip of 5, #5703a-5707a	6.25	
		Nos. 5703-5707 (5)	6.25	2.00

MUSIC ICONS

Pete Seeger (1919-2014), Folk Singer — A4536

LITHOGRAPHED

Serpentine Die Cut 10½

2022, July 21

Self-Adhesive

5708	A4536	(60c) multicolored	1.25	.25
a.		Imperforate	1.25	—

BUZZ LIGHTYEAR

Head in Profile
A4537

Standing With Legs Visible
A4538

Running
A4539

Standing, Feet Not Visible
A4540

LITHOGRAPHED

2022, Aug. 3 ***Serpentine Die Cut 11***

5709	A4537	(60c) multicolored	1.25	.30
a.		Imperforate	1.25	—
5710	A4538	(60c) multicolored	1.25	.30
a.		Imperforate	1.25	—
5711	A4539	(60c) multicolored	1.25	.30
a.		Imperforate	1.25	—
5712	A4540	(60c) multicolored	1.25	.30
a.		Imperforate	1.25	—
b.		Vert. or horiz. strip of 4, #5709-5712	5.00	
c.		Imperforate vert. or horiz. strip of 4, #5709a-5712a	5.00	
		Nos. 5709-5712 (4)	5.00	1.20

NATIONAL MARINE SANCTUARIES

A4541

No. 5713: a, Balloon fish, Florida Keys National Marine Sanctuary (26x26mm). b, Red-footed boobies, Papahanaumokuakea Marine National Monument (26x41mm). c, Humpback whale, Stellwagen Bank National Marine Sanctuary (41x26mm). d, Sea stacks, Olympic Coast National Marine Sanctuary (41x41mm). e, Mallows Bay-Potomac River Marine Sanctuary at sunset (26x41mm). f, Farallon Islands, Greater Farallones National Marine Sanctuary (41x26mm). g, Elkhorn coral, Florida Keys National Marine Sanctuary (26x41mm). h, Hawaiian monk seal, Hawaiian Islands Humpback Whale National Marine Sanctuary (41x26mm). i, Queen angelfish, Flower Garden Banks National Marine Sanctuary (41x26mm). j, Sea otter, Monterey Bay National Marine Sanctuary (26x41mm). k, Young rockfish exploring reef, Cordell Bank National Marine Sanctuary (41x26mm). l, Atlantic sea nettle, Gray's Reef National Marine Sanctuary (26x41mm). m, Sea lions, Channel Islands National Marine Sanctuary (41x41mm). n, Sand tiger shark, Monitor National Marine Sanctuary (41x26mm). o, Corals and fish, Rose Atoll, National Marine Sanctuary of American Samoa (26x41mm). p, Ice on shoreline, Thunder Bay National Marine Sanctuary (26x26mm).

LITHOGRAPHED

2022, Aug. 5 ***Serpentine Die Cut 11***

Self-Adhesive

5713	A4541	Pane of 16 + 2 labels	20.00	
a.-p.		(60c) Any single	1.25	.50
q.		As #5713, imperforate	20.00	—
r.		As #5713a, imperforate	1.25	—
s.		As #5713b, imperforate	1.25	—
t.		As #5713c, imperforate	1.25	—
u.		As #5713d, imperforate	1.25	—
v.		As #5713e, imperforate	1.25	—
w.		As #5713f, imperforate	1.25	—
x.		As #5713g, imperforate	1.25	—
y.		As #5713h, imperforate	1.25	—
z.		As #5713i, imperforate	1.25	—
aa.		As #5713j, imperforate	1.25	—
ab.		As #5713k, imperforate	1.25	—
ac.		As #5713l, imperforate	1.25	—
ad.		As #5713m, imperforate	1.25	—
ae.		As #5713n, imperforate	1.25	—
af.		As #5713o, imperforate	1.25	—
ag.		As #5713p, imperforate	1.25	—

ELEPHANTS

Adult Elephant and Calf — A4542

LITHOGRAPHED

Serpentine Die Cut 11 on 2 or 3 Sides

2022, Aug. 12

Booklet Stamp
Self-Adhesive

5714	A4542	(60c) multicolored	1.25	.25
a.		Booklet pane of 20	25.00	

No. 5459a is a double-sided booklet with 12 stamps on one side and eight stamps plus a label that serves as the booklet cover on the other side.

PONY CARS

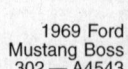

1969 Ford Mustang Boss 302 — A4543

1970 Dodge Challenger R/T — A4544

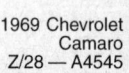

1969 Chevrolet Camaro Z/28 — A4545

1967 Mercury Cougar XR-7 GT — A4546

1969 AMC Javelin SST — A4547

LITHOGRAPHED

Serpentine Die Cut 10¾

2022, Aug. 25

Self-Adhesive

5715 A4543 (60c) multicolored 1.25 .40
a. Imperforate 1.25 —
5716 A4544 (60c) multicolored 1.25 .40
a. Imperforate 1.25 —
5717 A4545 (60c) multicolored 1.25 .40
a. Imperforate 1.25 —
5718 A4546 (60c) multicolored 1.25 .40
a. Imperforate 1.25 —
5719 A4547 (60c) multicolored 1.25 .40
a. Imperforate 1.25 —
b. Vert. strip of 5, #5715-5719 6.25
c. Imperforate strip of 5, #5715a-5719a 6.25
Nos. 5715-5719 (5) 6.25 2.00

JAMES WEBB SPACE TELESCOPE

James Webb Space Telescope A4548

LITHOGRAPHED

2022, Sept. 8 ***Serpentine Die Cut 11***

Self-Adhesive

5720 A4548 (60c) multicolored 1.25 .25
a. Imperforate 1.25 .25

Adjacent horizontal or vertical stamps have selvage between the stamps.

CHRISTMAS

Virgin and Child, by the Master of the Scandicci Lamentation A4549

Elf and Teddy Bear A4550

Elf Tying Ribbon A4551

Elf With Toy Car A4552

Elf With Rocket — A4553

LITHOGRAPHED

Serpentine Die Cut 11 on 2 or 3 Sides

2022

Booklet Stamps
Self-Adhesive

5721 A4549 (60c) multicolored 1.25 .25
a. Booklet pane of 20 25.00
5722 A4550 (60c) multicolored 1.25 .30
5723 A4551 (60c) multicolored 1.25 .30
5724 A4552 (60c) multicolored 1.25 .30
5725 A4553 (60c) multicolored 1.25 .30
a. Block of 4, #5722-5725 5.00
b. Booklet pane of 20, 5 each #5722-5725 25.00
c. As, "a," horiz. imperforate-between (PS) —
d. As, "b," horiz. imperforate-between on 12-stamp side —
Nos. 5721-5725 (5) 6.25 1.45

Issued: No. 5721, 9/22; Nos. 5722-5725, 9/15.

No. 5721a is a double-sided booklet pane with 12 stamps on one side, and eight stamps plus label (booklet cover) on the other side.

No. 5725b is a double-sided booklet pane with 12 stamps on one side (3 each Nos. 5722-5725), and eight stamps (2 each Nos. 5722-5725) plus label (booklet cover) on the other side.

CHARACTERS FROM PEANUTS COMIC STRIP, BY CHARLES M. SCHULZ (1922-2000)

Charlie Brown A4554

Lucy A4555

Franklin A4556

Sally A4557

Pigpen A4558

Linus A4559

Snoopy and Woodstock A4560

Schroeder A4561

Peppermint Patty A4562

Marcie A4563

LITHOGRAPHED

Serpentine Die Cut 11

2022, Sept. 30

Self-Adhesive

5726 Pane of 20, 2 each #5726a-5726j, + central label 25.00
a. A4554 (60c) multicolored 1.25 .40
b. A4555 (60c) multicolored 1.25 .40
c. A4556 (60c) multicolored 1.25 .40
d. A4557 (60c) multicolored 1.25 .40
e. A4558 (60c) multicolored 1.25 .40
f. A4559 (60c) multicolored 1.25 .40
g. A4560 (60c) multicolored 1.25 .40
h. A4561 (60c) multicolored 1.25 .40
i. A4562 (60c) multicolored 1.25 .40
j. A4563 (60c) multicolored 1.25 .40
k. Imperforate sheet of 20, 2 each #5726l-5726u, + central label 25.00 —
l. A4554 (60c) Imperforate 1.25 —
m. A4555 (60c) Imperforate 1.25 —
n. A4556 (60c) Imperforate 1.25 —
o. A4557 (60c) Imperforate 1.25 —
p. A4558 (60c) Imperforate 1.25 —
q. A4559 (60c) Imperforate 1.25 —
r. A4560 (60c) Imperforate 1.25 —
s. A4561 (60c) Imperforate 1.25 —
t. A4562 (60c) Imperforate 1.25 —
u. A4563 (60c) Imperforate 1.25 —

SNOWY BEAUTY

Camellia A4564

Winter Aconite A4565

Crocuses A4566

Hellebore A4567

Winterberry A4568

Pansies A4569

Plum Blossoms A4570

Grape Hyacinths A4571

Daffodils A4572

Ranunculus A4573

LITHOGRAPHED

Serpentine Die Cut 11 on 2 or 3 Sides

2022, Oct. 11

Booklet Stamps
Self-Adhesive

5727 A4564 (60c) multicolored 1.25 .40
5728 A4565 (60c) multicolored 1.25 .40
5729 A4566 (60c) multicolored 1.25 .40
5730 A4567 (60c) multicolored 1.25 .40
5731 A4568 (60c) multicolored 1.25 .40
5732 A4569 (60c) multicolored 1.25 .40
5733 A4570 (60c) multicolored 1.25 .40
5734 A4571 (60c) multicolored 1.25 .40
5735 A4572 (60c) multicolored 1.25 .40
5736 A4573 (60c) multicolored 1.25 .40
a. Block of 10, #5727-5736 12.50
b. Booklet pane of 20, 2 each #5727-5736 25.00
Nos. 5727-5736 (10) 12.50 4.00

No. 5736b is a double-sided booklet pane with 12 stamps on one side (Nos. 5729-5736, 2 each Nos. 5727-5728), and eight stamps (Nos. 5729-5736) plus label (booklet cover) on the other side.

KWANZAA

Girl, Boy and Kinara — A4574

LITHOGRAPHED

Serpentine Die Cut 10¾x11

2022, Oct. 13

Self-Adhesive

5737 A4574 (60c) multicolored 1.25 .25

WOMEN CRYPTOLOGISTS OF WORLD WAR II

Woman and Japanese Purple Code Characters — A4575

LITHOGRAPHED

Serpentine Die Cut 10¾

2022, Oct. 18

Self-Adhesive

5738 A4575 (60c) multicolored 1.25 .25
a. Imperforate 1.25 —

HANUKKAH

Menorah — A4576

LITHOGRAPHED

2022, Oct. 20 ***Serpentine Die Cut 11***

Self-Adhesive

5739 A4576 (60c) multicolored 1.25 .25

SCHOOL BUS AND SCHOOL

A4577

A4578

LITHOGRAPHED

2023, Jan. 5 ***Serpentine Die Cut 11***

Self-Adhesive

5740 A4577 (24c) multicolored .50 .25

Coil Stamp

Serpentine Die Cut 11 Horiz.

5545 A4383 (20c) multicolored .50 .25

RED FOX

A4579

A4579a

LITHOGRAPHED

Serpentine Die Cut 11¼x11

2023, Jan. 5

Self-Adhesive

5742 A4579 40c multicolored .80 .25

Coil Stamp

Serpentine Die Cut 11 Vert.

5545 A4383 (20c) multicolored .80 .25
Pair 1.60
P# strip of 5, #B11111 7.25
P# single, #B11111 — 2.00

See note after No. 1549.

CHINESE NEW YEAR

Year of the Rabbit — A4580

LITHOGRAPHED & TYPOGRAPHED WITH FOIL APPLICATION

Serpentine Die Cut 11

2023, Jan. 12

Self-Adhesive

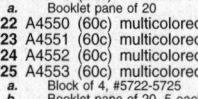

5744 A4580 (60c) multi 1.25 .25
a. Imperforate 1.25 —

SUBJECT INDEX OF REGULAR, COMMEMORATIVE & AIR POST ISSUES

ORDER YOUR 2022 U.S. SUPPLEMENTS TODAY!

SCOTT NATIONAL SERIES

Item No.	Supplement Title	Retail	AA
100S022	National	$26.49	$22.52
101S022	U.S. Booklet Panes	$19.16	$16.29
105S022	U.S. Postal Stationery ***	$14.16	$12.04
110S022	U.S. Postal Cards	$14.16	$12.04
113S022	U.S. Plate Number Coils–Simplified	$14.16	$12.04
114S022	U.S. Plate Number Coils–Comprehensive	$22.25	$18.91
115S022	U.S. Federal & State Duck Stamps	$26.49	$22.52
116S022	U.S. Federal Duck Plate Blocks ***	$11.16	$9.49
117S022	U.S. Plate Number Coil Singles	$22.25	$18.91
118S022	U.S. Small Panes	$39.21	$33.33
119S022	U.S. Official Joint Issues ***	$12.93	$10.99
121S022	U.S. Junior Duck ***	$8.16	$6.94
128S022	U.S. Comprehensive Plate Blocks	$36.03	$30.62
150S022	U.S. Used Singles (Built From National)	$16.16	$13.74
170S022	American	$39.21	$33.33
180S022	Minuteman - Narratives	$26.49	$22.52
181S022	Minuteman–United Nations	$29.67	$25.22
551S022	U.N. Singles & Postal Stationery	$29.67	$25.22
552S022	U.N. Imprint Blocks	$22.25	$18.91

SCOTT-SCHAUBEK HINGELESS

199S022	Platinum	$87.97	$74.77
HUSA2022	Schaubek - HUSA	$86.89	$73.86

MINKUS ALBUM SERIES

MPNC22	U.S. Plate Number Coils	$14.16	$12.04
MUSC22	U.S. Commemoratives	$19.16	$16.29
MUSR22	U.S. Regular Issues	$19.16	$16.29
MNPS22	U.N. Postal Stationery***	$14.16	$12.04
MUN22	U.N. Singles	$29.67	$25.22
MUSP22	U.S. Postal Stationery ***	$14.16	$12.04
MUBK22	U.S. Booklet Panes	$22.25	$18.91
MSPB22	U.S. Plate Blocks	$26.49	$22.52
MUSPC22	U.S. Postal Cards	$14.16	$12.04
MSH22	U.S. Sheetlets	$26.49	$22.52

MINKUS ALL-AMERICAN SERIES

MAA122	Part 1: US Reg Issues & Commems	$26.49	$22.52
MAA222	Part 2: US Postal Stationery ***	$12.99	$11.04
MAA322	Part 3: United Nations	$29.67	$25.22
MAA422	Part 4: US Booklet Panes	$19.16	$16.29
MAA522	Part 5: US Sheetlets	$26.49	$22.52
MAA622	Part 6: US Plate Number Coils	$14.16	$12.04
MAA722	Part 7: US Postal Cards	$12.93	$10.99

PURCHASE A MOUNT SET AND A 2022 SUPPLEMENT TOGETHER AND SAVE OVER 15%!

New U.S. Scott Mount Set For 2022 Supplements!

The U.S. mount packs are designed specifically for the Scott National, Minuteman and Minkus All-American yearly supplement pages. These sturdy custom mounts are easy to use and take the guess work out of selecting the correct mount for your stamps. The U.S. mount packs are available in black or clear. Don't wait because we only offer for a limited quantity.

U.S. MOUNT SET (MOUNTS ONLY)

Item		Retail	AA
2022 B	2022 U.S. Mount Set, Black	$52.49	$44.62
2022 C	2022 U.S. Mount Set, Clear	$52.49	$44.62

BUNDLE UP AND SAVE!
2022 SCOTT MOUNTS AND SUPPLEMENT SET

Item		Retail	AA
180S022BB	2022 Minuteman Supplement + Black Mount Set	$70.98	$60.33
180S022BC	2022 Minuteman Supplement + Clear Mount Set	$70.98	$60.33
100S022BB	2022 National Supplement + Black Mount Set	$70.98	$60.33
100S022BC	2022 National Supplement + Clear Mount Set	$70.98	$60.33
MAA122BB	2022 Minkus All-American Supplement + Black Mount Set	$70.98	$60.33
MAA122BC	2022 Minkus All-American Supplement + Clear Mount Set	$70.98	$60.33

3-RING BINDER & SLIPCASE

With this three ring binder, pages lay flat while the locking mechanism ensures that the rings won't pop open, even when the binder is full.

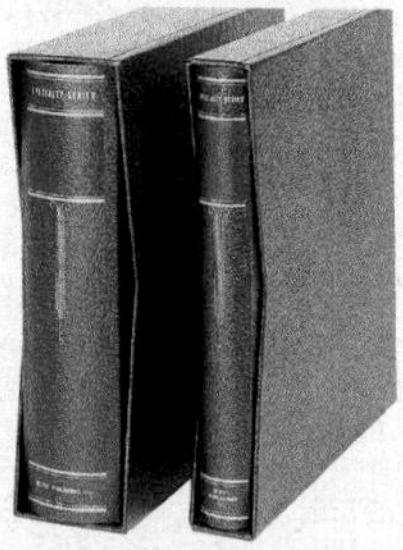

Item		Retail	AA
ACBR01D	Small Metal-Hinged Binder	$46.99	$37.59
ACBR01SET	3-Ring Binder and Slipcase – small	$85.49	$70.32
ACSR01	Small Slipcase	$38.50	$32.73
ACBR03D	Large Metal-Hinged Binder	$46.99	$37.59
ACBR03SET	3-Ring Binder and Slipcase	$85.49	$70.32
ACSR03	Large Slipcase	$38.50	$32.73

SCOTT MINUTEMAN ACCESSORIES

Item		Retail	AA
180BNDR3	Minuteman 3-Ring Binder	$19.99	$15.99
180Z003	Minuteman Blank Pages (20 pages)	$22.25	$18.91

ALL-AMERICAN ALBUM SERIES (2-POST)

Item	Retail	AA
MUSAAP 1847-2001	$272.41	$231.55

ALL-AMERICAN 2-POST BINDER

Item	Retail	AA
MUSAAB	$36.99	$31.44

BLANK PAGES (2-POST)

Item		Retail	AA
MAAUNBL	U.N. Issues Blank Pages	$22.25	$18.91
MAACBL	Commemorative Blank Pages	$22.25	$18.91
MAARBL	Postage Issues Blank Pages	$22.25	$18.91
MUSABL	Commemorative & Postage Issues Blank Pages	$22.25	$18.91

AmosAdvantage.com | 1-800-572-6885

ORDERING INFORMATION: *AA prices apply to paid subscribers of Amos Media titles, or for orders placed online. Prices, terms and product availability subject to change.
SHIPPING & HANDLING: U.S.: Orders total $0-$10.00 charged $4.99 shipping. U.S. Order total $10.01-$74.99 charged $9.99 shipping. Orders totaling $75+ will ship FREE!
Taxes will apply in CA, OH, & IL. Canada: 20% of order total. Minimum charge $19.99 Maximum charge $200.00. Foreign orders are shipped via FedEx Intl. or USPS and billed actual freight.

UNITED STATES

SEMI-POSTAL STAMPS

BREAST CANCER RESEARCH

SP1

PHOTOGRAVURE

Serpentine Die Cut 11

1998, July 29

Self-Adhesive

B1	SP1 (32c+8c) multicolored	1.00	.25

HEROES OF 2001

Firemen Atop World Trade Center Rubble — SP2

LITHOGRAPHED

Serpentine Die Cut 11¼

2002, June 7

Self-Adhesive

B2	SP2 (34c+11c) multicolored	.80	.35

STOP FAMILY VIOLENCE

SP3

PHOTOGRAVURE

2003, Oct. 8 ***Serpentine Die Cut 11***

Self-Adhesive

B3	SP3 (37c+8c) multicolored	.80	.45

SAVE VANISHING SPECIES

Amur Tiger Cub — SP4

PHOTOGRAVURE

Serpentine Die Cut 10¾

2011, Sept. 20

Self-Adhesive

B4	SP4 (44c+11c) multicolored	1.10	.50

The 11c surtax was for the Multinational Species Conservation Funds of the U.S. Fish and Wildlife Service.

Breast Cancer Awareness Type of 1998

LITHOGRAPHED

Design Size: 20x35mm

Serpentine Die Cut 11x10¾

2014, Sept. 30

Dated 2014

Self-Adhesive

B5	SP1 (49c+11c) multicolored	1.10	.50
a.	Imperforate (from uncut press sheet)	2.25	—
b.	Imperf., pair (error, see footnote)		—

Imperforates from imperforate uncut press sheets (No. B5a) do not have die cutting on either the front or the reverse. On the imperforate error (No. B5b), there is die cutting on the reverse.

ALZHEIMER'S DISEASE AWARENESS

SP5

LITHOGRAPHED

Serpentine Die Cut 10½x10¾

2017, Nov. 30

Self-Adhesive

B6	SP5 (49c+11c) multicolored	1.10	.60

The 11c surtax was for the National Institutes of Health.

HEALING POST-TRAUMATIC STRESS DISORDER

Plant Sprout and Fallen Leaves — SP6

LITHOGRAPHED

Serpentine Die Cut 10¾

2019, Dec. 2 **Tagged**

Self-Adhesive

B7	SP6 (55c+10c) multicolored	1.10	.60

The 10c surtax was for the National Center for Post-traumatic Stress Disorder of the Department of Veterans Affairs to assist in treatment of those impacted by post-traumatic stress disorder.

AIR POST

Curtiss Jenny — AP1

FLAT PLATE PRINTINGS

1918 Unwmk. Engr. ***Perf. 11***

C1	AP1 6c orange	55.	30.
	Never hinged	110.	
C2	AP1 16c green	60.	35.
	Never hinged	120.	
C3	AP1 24c car rose & blue	65.	35.
	Never hinged	130.	
a.	Center inverted	*450,000.*	
	Never hinged	*850,000.*	
	Nos. C1-C3 (3)	180.00	100.00
	Nos. C1-C3, never hinged	360.00	

Wooden Propeller and Radiator AP2

Emblem of Air Service AP3

De Havilland Biplane — AP4

1923

C4	AP2 8c dark green	17.50	15.00
	Never hinged	35.00	
C5	AP3 16c dark blue	60.00	30.00
	Never hinged	120.00	
C6	AP4 24c carmine	65.00	30.00
	Never hinged	130.00	
	Nos. C4-C6 (3)	142.50	75.00
	Nos. C4-C6, never hinged	285.00	

Map of U.S. and Two Mail Planes AP5

1926-27

C7	AP5 10c dark blue	2.25	.35
	Never hinged	4.00	
C8	AP5 15c olive brown	2.50	2.50
	Never hinged	4.75	
C9	AP5 20c yellow green	6.50	2.00
	Never hinged	12.50	
	Nos. C7-C9 (3)	11.25	4.85
	Nos. C7-C9, never hinged	21.25	

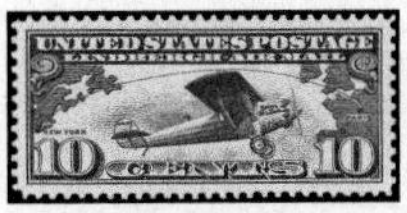

Lindbergh's Airplane "Spirit of St. Louis" — AP6

1927, June 18

C10	AP6 10c dark blue	7.00	2.50
	Never hinged	12.50	
a.	Booklet pane of 3	70.00	*65.00*
	Never hinged	115.00	
b.	Double impression		*16,500.*

Singles from No. C10a are imperf. at sides or imperf. at sides and bottom.

Only one example is recorded of No. C10b.

Beacon on Rocky Mountains — AP7

1928, July 25

C11	AP7 5c carmine and blue	5.50	.85
	Never hinged	10.00	
a.	Vert. pair, imperf. between	*7,000.*	

No. C11a is unique. It is torn and valued thus.

Winged Globe — AP8

1930, Feb. 10

Stamp design: 46½x19mm

C12	AP8 5c violet	9.50	.50
	Never hinged	17.50	
a.	Horiz. pair, imperf. between	*4,500.*	

See Nos. C16-C17, C19.

GRAF ZEPPELIN ISSUE

Zeppelin over Atlantic Ocean AP9

Zeppelin between Continents AP10

Zeppelin Passing Globe AP11

1930, Apr. 19

C13	AP9 65c green	180.	160.
	Never hinged	250.	
C14	AP10 $1.30 brown	375.	360.
	Never hinged	575.	
C15	AP11 $2.60 blue	525.	550.
	Never hinged	850.	
	Nos. C13-C15 (3)	1,080.	1,070.
	Nos. C13-C15, never hinged	1,675.	

ROTARY PRESS PRINTING

1931-32 ***Perf. 10½x11***

Stamp design: 47½x19mm

C16	AP8 5c violet	4.75	.60
	Never hinged	8.50	
C17	AP8 8c olive bister ('32)	2.25	.40
	Never hinged	3.75	

CENTURY OF PROGRESS ISSUE

Airship "Graf Zeppelin" AP12

FLAT PLATE PRINTING

1933, Oct. 2 ***Perf. 11***

C18	AP12 50c green	45.00	47.50
	Never hinged	75.00	

Catalogue values for unused stamps in this section, from this point to the end, are for Never Hinged items.

Type of 1930 Issue

ROTARY PRESS PRINTING

1934, June 30 ***Perf. 10½x11***

C19	AP8 6c dull orange	3.50	.25

TRANSPACIFIC ISSUES

The "China Clipper" over the Pacific — AP13

FLAT PLATE PRINTING

1935, Nov. 22 ***Perf. 11***

C20	AP13 25c blue	1.40	1.00

The "China Clipper" over the Pacific — AP14

1937, Feb. 15

C21	AP14 20c green	10.00	1.75
C22	AP14 50c carmine	10.00	5.00

Eagle Holding Shield, Olive Branch and Arrows — AP15

1938, May 14

C23	AP15 6c dark blue & carmine	.70	.25
a.	Vert. pair, imperf. horiz.	*300.00*	*300.00*
b.	Horiz. pair, imperf. vert.	*12,500.*	
c.	6¢ ultra & car	300.00	*2,000.*
	On cover		*2,250.*

TRANSATLANTIC ISSUE

Winged Globe AP16

1939, May 16

C24	AP16 30c dull blue	11.00	1.50

Twin-Motored Transport Plane — AP17

ROTARY PRESS PRINTING

1941-44 ***Perf. 11x10½***

C25	AP17 6c carmine	.25	.25
a.	Booklet pane of 3	3.50	1.50
b.	Horiz. pair, imperf. between	*2,250.*	

Singles from No. C25a are imperf. at sides or at sides and bottom.

Value of No. C25b is for pair without blue crayon P. O. rejection mark on front. Very fine pairs with crayon mark sell for about $1,500.

C26	AP17 8c olive green	.25	.25
a.	All color omitted	—	

No. C26a has an albino impression and exists as a pair of stamps within a double-paper spliced strip of six stamps.

C27	AP17 10c violet	1.10	.25
C28	AP17 15c brown carmine	2.10	.35
C29	AP17 20c bright green	2.10	.30
C30	AP17 30c blue	2.10	.35
C31	AP17 50c orange	11.00	3.25
	Nos. C25-C31 (7)	18.90	5.00

DC-4 Skymaster AP18

1946, Sept. 25 ***Perf. 11x10½***

C32	AP18 5c carmine	.25	.25

DC-4 Skymaster — AP19

1947, Mar. 26 ***Perf. 10½x11***
C33 AP19 5c carmine .25 .25

Pan American Union Building, Washington, DC — AP20

Statue of Liberty & New York Skyline — AP21

Plane over San Francisco-Oakland Bay Bridge — AP22

1947 ***Perf. 11x10½***
C34 AP20 10c black .25 .25
a. Dry printing .40 .25
C35 AP21 15c bright blue green .35 .25
a. Horiz. pair, imperf. between *1,500.*
b. Dry printing .55 .25
C36 AP22 25c blue .90 .25
a. Dry printing 1.20 .25
Nos. C34-C36 (3) 1.50 .75

See note on wet and dry printings following No. 1029.

No. C35a is valued in the grade of fine.

Type of 1947
ROTARY PRESS COIL STAMP
1948, Jan. 15 ***Perf. 10 Horizontally***
C37 AP19 5c carmine 1.00 .80

NEW YORK CITY ISSUE

Map of Five Boroughs, Circular Band & Planes — AP23

50th anniv. of the consolidation of the five boroughs of New York City.

ROTARY PRESS PRINTING
1948, July 31 ***Perf. 11x10½***
C38 AP23 5c bright carmine .25 .25

Type of 1947
1949 ***Perf. 10½x11***
C39 AP19 6c carmine .25 .25
a. Booklet pane of 6 12.00 5.00
b. Dry printing .50 .25
c. As "a," dry printing 25.00 —

See note on wet and dry printings following No. 1029.

ALEXANDRIA BICENTENNIAL ISSUE

Home of John Carlyle, Alexandria Seal & Gadsby's Tavern — AP24

200th anniv. of the founding of Alexandria, Va.

1949, May 11 ***Perf. 11x10½***
C40 AP24 6c carmine .25 .25

Type of 1947
ROTARY PRESS COIL STAMP
1949, Aug. 25 ***Perf. 10 Horizontally***
C41 AP19 6c carmine 3.00 .25

UNIVERSAL POSTAL UNION ISSUE

Post Office Department Building — AP25

Globe & Doves Carrying Messages AP26

Boeing Stratocruiser & Globe — AP27

ROTARY PRESS PRINTING
1949 ***Perf. 11x10½***
C42 AP25 10c violet .25 .25
C43 AP26 15c ultramarine .30 .25
C44 AP27 25c rose carmine .60 .40
Nos. C42-C44 (3) 1.15 .90

WRIGHT BROTHERS ISSUE

Wilbur & Orville Wright and their Plane — AP28

1949, Dec. 17
C45 AP28 6c magenta .25 .25

Diamond Head, Honolulu, Hawaii — AP29

1952, Mar. 26
C46 AP29 80c bright red violet 4.50 1.25

POWERED FLIGHT, 50th ANNIV.

First Plane and Modern Plane — AP30

1953, May 29
C47 AP30 6c carmine .25 .25

Eagle in Flight — AP31

Issued primarily for use on domestic post cards.

1954, Sept. 3
C48 AP31 4c bright blue .25 .25

AIR FORCE, 50th ANNIV.

B-52 Stratofortress and F-104 Starfighters AP32

1957, Aug. 1
C49 AP32 6c ultra & blue .25 .25

Type of 1954
1958, July 31
C50 AP31 5c red .25 .25

Silhouette of Jet Airliner — AP33

1958, July 31 ***Perf. 10½x11***
C51 AP33 7c blue .25 .25
a. Booklet pane of 6 6.50 5.00
b. Vert. pair, imperf. between (from booklet pane) *4,000.*

No. C51b resulted from a paper foldover after perforating and before cutting into panes. Two or three pairs are believed to exist.

ROTARY PRESS COIL STAMP
Perf. 10 Horizontally
C52 AP33 7c blue 2.00 .25

ALASKA STATEHOOD ISSUE

Big Dipper, North Star & Map of Alaska — AP34

ROTARY PRESS PRINTING
1959, Jan. 3 ***Perf. 11x10½***
C53 AP34 7c dark blue .25 .25

BALLOON JUPITER ISSUE

Balloon & Crowd — AP35

Centenary of the carrying of mail by the balloon Jupiter from Lafayette to Crawfordsville, Ind.

GIORI PRESS PRINTING
1959, Aug. 17 ***Perf. 11***
C54 AP35 7c dark blue & red .30 .25

HAWAII STATEHOOD ISSUE

Alii Warrior, Map of Hawaii & Star of Statehood AP36

ROTARY PRESS PRINTING
1959, Aug. 21 ***Perf. 11x10½***
C55 AP36 7c rose red .25 .25

PAN AMERICAN GAMES ISSUE

Runner Holding Torch — AP37

3rd Pan American Games, Chicago, Aug. 27-Sept. 7, 1959.

GIORI PRESS PRINTING
1959, Aug. 27 ***Perf. 11***
C56 AP37 10c red, white & blue .25 .25

Liberty Bell — AP38

Statue of Liberty — AP39

Abraham Lincoln — AP40

1959-66
C57 AP38 10c black & green ('60) 1.00 .70
C58 AP39 15c black & orange .35 .25
C59 AP40 25c black & maroon ('60) .50 .25
a. Tagged ('66) .60 .30
Nos. C57-C59 (3) 1.85 1.20

Airmail stamps starting with No. C69 are tagged unless otherwise noted.

Type of 1958
ROTARY PRESS PRINTING
1960, Aug. 12 ***Perf. 10½x11***
C60 AP33 7c carmine .25 .25
a. Booklet pane of 6 7.00 6.00
b. Vert. pair, imperf between (from booklet pane) *5,500.*

No. C60b resulted from a paper foldover after perforating and before cutting into panes. Two pairs are known.

Type of 1958
ROTARY PRESS COIL STAMP
1960, Oct. 22 ***Perf. 10 Horizontally***
C61 AP33 7c carmine 4.00 .25

Type of 1959-60 and

Statue of Liberty — AP41

GIORI PRESS PRINTING
1961-67 ***Perf. 11***
C62 AP38 13c black & red .40 .25
a. Tagged ('67) .75 .50
C63 AP41 15c black & orange .30 .25
a. Tagged ('67) .35 .25
b. As "a," horiz. pair, imperf. vert. *15,000.*
c. As "a," horiz. pair, imperf between and at left *2,750.*
d. All color omitted *100.00*

On No. C63d, there is a clear albino plate impression.

Jet Airliner Over Capitol — AP42

ROTARY PRESS PRINTING
1962, Dec. 5 ***Perf. 10½x11***
C64 AP42 8c carmine .25 .25
a. Tagged ('63) .25 .25
b. Booklet pane of 5 + label 6.00 3.00
c. As "b," tagged ('64) 1.75 .75

Nos. C64a and C64c were made by overprinting Nos. C64 and C64b with phosphorescent ink. No. C64a was first issued at Dayton, Ohio, for experiments in high speed mail sorting. The tagging is visible in shortwave ultraviolet light.

COIL STAMP; ROTARY PRESS
Perf. 10 Horizontally
C65 AP42 8c carmine .40 .25
a. Tagged ('64) .35 .25

MONTGOMERY BLAIR ISSUE

Montgomery Blair — AP43

Montgomery Blair (1813-83), Postmaster General (1861-64), who called the 1st Intl. Postal Conf., Paris, 1863, forerunner of the UPU.

GIORI PRESS PRINTING
1963, May 3 ***Perf. 11***
C66 AP43 15c dull red, dark brown & blue .55 .50

Bald Eagle — AP44

Issued primarily for use on domestic post cards.

ROTARY PRESS PRINTING
1963, July 12 ***Perf. 11x10½***
C67 AP44 6c red .25 .25
a. Tagged ('67) 4.00 3.00

AMELIA EARHART ISSUE

Amelia Earhart & Lockheed Electra — AP45

GIORI PRESS PRINTING

1963, July 24 *Perf. 11*
C68 AP45 8c carmine & maroon .25 .25

ROBERT H. GODDARD ISSUE

Robert H. Goddard, Atlas Rocket & Launching Tower, Cape Kennedy — AP46

1964, Oct. 5
C69 AP46 8c blue, red & bister .35 .25

Luminescence

Air Post stamps issued after mid-1964 are tagged.

ALASKA PURCHASE ISSUE

Tlingit Totem, Southern Alaska — AP47

1967, Mar. 30
C70 AP47 8c brown .25 .25

"Columbia Jays," by Audubon — AP48

1967, Apr. 26
C71 AP48 20c multicolored .75 .25

See note over No. 1241.

50-Star Runway — AP49

ROTARY PRESS PRINTING

1968, Jan. 5 *Perf. 11x10½*
C72 AP49 10c carmine .25 .25
b. Booklet pane of 8 2.25 2.00
c. Booklet pane of 5 + label 3.50 1.25
d. Vert. pair, imperf. btwn., in #C72b with foldover 5,000.

No. C72d resulted from a paper foldover after perforating and before cutting into panes. Two pairs are recorded from different panes.

ROTARY PRESS COIL STAMP
Perf. 10 Vertically

C73 AP49 10c carmine .30 .25
a. Imperf., pair 450.00

The $1 Airlift stamp is listed as No. 1341.

50th ANNIVERSARY OF AIR MAIL ISSUE

Curtiss Jenny — AP50

50th anniv. of regularly scheduled air mail service.

LITHOGRAPHED, ENGRAVED (GIORI)

1968, May 15 *Perf. 11*
C74 AP50 10c blue, black & red .25 .25

USA and Jet — AP51

1968, Nov. 22
C75 AP51 20c red, blue & black .35 .25

See No. C81.

MOON LANDING ISSUE

First Man on the Moon AP52

1969, Sept. 9
C76 AP52 10c multicolored .25 .25
a. Rose red (litho.) omitted 500.00 —

On No. C76a, the lithographed rose red is missing from the entire vignette-the dots on top of the yellow areas as well as the flag shoulder patch.

Silhouette of Delta Wing Plane AP53

Silhouette of Jet Airliner AP54

Winged Airmail Envelope AP55

Statue of Liberty AP56

ROTARY PRESS PRINTING

1971-73 *Perf. 10½x11*
C77 AP53 9c red .25 .25

No. C77 issued primarily for use on domestic post cards.

Perf. 11x10½

C78 AP54 11c carmine .25 .25
a. Booklet pane of 4 + 2 labels 1.25 1.00
b. Untagged (Bureau precanceled) .85 .85
C79 AP55 13c carmine ('73) .25 .25
a. Booklet pane of 5 + label ('73) 1.50 1.00
b. Untagged (Bureau precanceled) .85 .85
c. Green instead of red tagging (single from booklet pane) —

No. C78b Bureau precanceled "WASHINGTON D.C." (or "DC" - more valuable thus), No. C79b "WASHINGTON DC" only; both for use of Congressmen, but available to any permit holder.

GIORI PRESS PRINTING
Perf. 11

C80 AP56 17c bluish black, red, & dark green .35 .25

"USA" & Jet Type of 1968

LITHOGRAPHED, ENGRAVED (GIORI)

C81 AP51 21c red, blue & black .40 .25
b. Black (engr.) missing (FO) 2,750.

The two recorded examples of No. C81b are in a single full pane. Catalogue value is for both errors.

COIL STAMPS

ROTARY PRESS PRINTING

1971-73 *Perf. 10 Vertically*
C82 AP54 11c carmine .25 .25
a. Imperf., pair 160.00
C83 AP55 13c carmine ('73) .30 .25
a. Imperf., pair 60.00

NATIONAL PARKS CENTENNIAL ISSUE

City of Refuge, Hawaii

Kii Statue & Temple, City of Refuge, Hawaii — AP57

LITHOGRAPHED, ENGRAVED (GIORI)

1972, May 3 *Perf. 11*
C84 AP57 11c orange & multicolored .25 .25
a. Blue & green (litho.) omitted 400.00 900.00

OLYMPIC GAMES ISSUE

Skiing & Olympic Rings — AP58

11th Winter Olympic Games, Sapporo, Japan, Feb. 3-13, and 20th Summer Olympic Games, Munich, Germany, Aug. 26-Sept. 11.

PHOTOGRAVURE (Andreotti)

1972, Aug. 17 *Perf. 11x10½*
C85 AP58 11c black, blue, red, emerald & yellow .25 .25

ELECTRONICS PROGRESS ISSUE

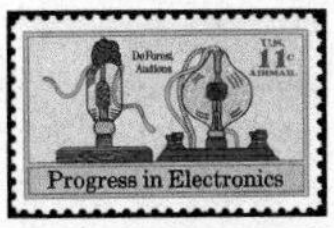

De Forest Audions — AP59

LITHOGRAPHED, ENGRAVED (GIORI)

1973, July 10 *Perf. 11*
C86 AP59 11c multicolored .30 .25
a. Vermilion & olive (litho.) omitted 525.00
c. Olive omitted 800.00

Statue of Liberty — AP60

Mt. Rushmore National Memorial — AP61

GIORI PRESS PRINTING

1974
C87 AP60 18c carmine, black & ultramarine .35 .30
C88 AP61 26c ultramarine, black & carmine .60 .25

Plane & Globes — AP62

Plane, Globes & Flag — AP63

1976, Jan. 2
C89 AP62 25c red, blue & black .50 .25
C90 AP63 31c red, blue & black .60 .25
b. All colors omitted —

On No. C90b, there is a colorless embossed image and a tagging ghost plane visible under UV light.

WRIGHT BROTHERS ISSUE

Orville and Wilbur Wright, Flyer A AP64

Wright Brothers, Flyer A and Shed AP65

LITHOGRAPHED, ENGRAVED (GIORI)

1978, Sept. 23
C91 AP64 31c ultra & multi .65 .30
C92 AP65 31c ultra & multi .65 .30
a. Vert. pair, #C91-C92 1.30 1.20
b. As "a," ultra. & black (engr.) omitted 475.00
c. As "a," black (engr.) omitted 1,750.
d. As "a," black, yellow, magenta, blue & brown (litho.) omitted 1,400.

OCTAVE CHANUTE ISSUE

Chanute & Biplane Hangglider AP66

Biplane Hanggliders & Chanute AP67

1979, Mar. 29
C93 AP66 21c blue & multi .70 .35
C94 AP67 21c blue & multi .70 .35
a. Vert. pair, #C93-C94 1.40 1.20
b. As "a," ultra & black (engr.) omitted 4,000.

WILEY POST ISSUE

Wiley Post & "Winnie Mae" AP68

NR-105 W, Post in Pressurized Suit, Portrait AP69

1979, Nov. 20
C95 AP68 25c blue &multi .90 .45
C96 AP69 25c blue & multi .90 .45
a. Vert. pair, #C95-C96 1.80 1.50

OLYMPIC GAMES ISSUE

High Jump — AP70

PHOTOGRAVURE

1979, Nov. 1
C97 AP70 31c multicolored .70 .30

PHILIP MAZZEI (1730-1816)

Philip Mazzei (1730-1816), Italian-born Political Writer — AP71

1980, Oct. 13
C98 AP71 40c multicolored .80 .25
b. Imperf., pair 2,250.

1982 *Perf. 10½x11¼*
C98A AP71 40c multicolored 5.00 1.50
c. Horiz. pair, imperf. vert. 3,250.

BLANCHE STUART SCOTT

Blanche Stuart Scott (1886-1970) AP72

1980, Dec. 30 ***Perf. 11***

C99 AP72 28c multicolored .60 .25
 a. Imperf., pair *1,850.*

GLENN CURTISS

Glenn Curtiss (1878-1930) AP73

1980, Dec. 30

C100 AP73 35c multicolored .65 .25
 a. Light blue (background) omitted *2,000.*

SUMMER OLYMPICS 1984

Women's Gymnastics AP74

Hurdles AP75

Women's Basketball AP76

Soccer AP77

1983, June 17

C101 AP74 28c multicolored 1.00 .30
C102 AP75 28c multicolored 1.00 .30
C103 AP76 28c multicolored 1.00 .30
C104 AP77 28c multicolored 1.00 .30
 a. Block of 4, #C101-C104 4.25 2.50
 b. As "a," imperf. vert. *5,000.*

Shot Put — AP78

Men's Gymnastics AP79

Women's Swimming AP80

Weight Lifting — AP81

1983, Apr. 8 ***Perf. 11.2 Bullseye***

C105 AP78 40c multicolored .90 .40
C106 AP79 40c multicolored .90 .40
C107 AP80 40c multicolored .90 .40
C108 AP81 40c multicolored .90 .40
 b. Block of 4, #C105-C108 4.25 3.00
 d. Block of 4, imperf. *625.00*

Women's Fencing — AP82

Cycling — AP83

Women's Volleyball — AP84

Pole Vaulting — AP85

1983, Nov. 4 ***Perf. 11***

C109 AP82 35c multicolored .90 .55
C110 AP83 35c multicolored .90 .55
C111 AP84 35c multicolored .90 .55
C112 AP85 35c multicolored .90 .55
 a. Block of 4, #C109-C112 4.00 3.25

AVIATION PIONEERS

Alfred V. Verville — AP86

Lawrence & Elmer Sperry — AP87

1985, Feb. 13 Tagged ***Perf. 11***

C113 AP86 33c multicolored .65 .25
 a. Imperf., pair *500.00*
C114 AP87 39c multicolored .80 .25
 a. Imperf., pair *1,250.*

TRANSPACIFIC AIRMAIL

50th Anniversary

Transpacific Airmail — AP88

1985, Feb. 15

C115 AP88 44c multicolored .85 .25
 a. Imperf., pair *550.00*

FR. JUNIPERO SERRA (1713-1784)

California Missionary

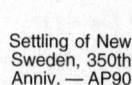

Outline Map of Southern California, Portrait, San Gabriel Mission — AP89

1985, Aug. 22

C116 AP89 44c multicolored 1.00 .35
 a. Imperf., pair *850.00*

SETTLING OF NEW SWEDEN, 350th ANNIV.

Settling of New Sweden, 350th Anniv. — AP90

LITHOGRAPHED AND ENGRAVED

1988, Mar. 29

C117 AP90 44c multicolored 1.00 .25

See Sweden No. 1672 and Finland No. 768.

SAMUEL P. LANGLEY (1834-1906)

Langley and Unmanned Aerodrome No. 5 — AP91

1988, May 14

C118 AP91 45c multicolored 1.00 .25

IGOR SIKORSKY (1889-1972)

Sikorsky and VS300 Helicopter, 1939 — AP92

PHOTOGRAVURE AND ENGRAVED

1988, June 23

C119 AP92 36c multicolored .70 .25
 a. Red, dk blue & black (engraved) omitted *900.00*

Beware of examples with traces of engraved red offered as "red omitted" varieties.

FRENCH REVOLUTION BICENTENNIAL

Liberty, Equality and Fraternity AP93

LITHOGRAPHED AND ENGRAVED

1989, July 14 ***Perf. 11½x11***

C120 AP93 45c multicolored .95 .25

See France Nos. 2143-2145a.

PRE-COLUMBIAN AMERICA ISSUE

UPAE Emblem & *Key Marco Cat* — AP94

PHOTOGRAVURE

1989, Oct. 12 ***Perf. 11***

C121 AP94 45c multicolored .90 .25

20th UPU CONGRESS
Futuristic Mail Delivery

Spacecraft — AP95

Air-suspended Hover Car — AP96

Moon Rover — AP97

Space Shuttle — AP98

LITHOGRAPHED & ENGRAVED

1989, Nov. 27

C122 AP95 45c multicolored 1.00 .50
C123 AP96 45c multicolored 1.00 .50
C124 AP97 45c multicolored 1.00 .50
C125 AP98 45c multicolored 1.00 .50
 a. Block of 4, #C122-C125 4.00 3.00
 b. As "a," light blue (engr.) omitted *475.00*
 c. As "a," tagging omitted —

Souvenir Sheet

LITHOGRAPHED & ENGRAVED

1989, Nov. 24 ***Imperf.***

C126 Sheet of 4 5.00 4.00
 a. AP95 45c multicolored 1.25 .50
 b. AP96 45c multicolored 1.25 .50
 c. AP97 45c multicolored 1.25 .50
 d. AP98 45c multicolored 1.25 .50

PRE-COLUMBIAN AMERICA ISSUE

Tropical Coast — AP99

PHOTOGRAVURE

1990, Oct. 12 ***Perf. 11***

C127 AP99 45c multicolored .90 .25

HARRIET QUIMBY, 1ST AMERICAN WOMAN PILOT

Harriet Quimby, Bleriot Aircraft — AP100

1991, Apr. 27

C128 AP100 50c multicolored 1.00 .25
 a. Vert. pair, imperf. horiz. *800.00*
 b. Perf. 11.2 bullseye, prephosphored uncoated paper ('93) 1.25 .25

WILLIAM T. PIPER, AIRCRAFT MANUFACTURER

William T. Piper, Piper Cub — AP101

1991, May 17

C129 AP101 40c multicolored, shiny gum .80 .25

Blue sky is plainly visible all the way across stamp above Piper's head.
 See No. C132.

ANTARCTIC TREATY, 30TH ANNIVERSARY

Antarctic Treaty, 30th Anniv. — AP102

1991, June 21

C130 AP102 50c multicolored 1.00 .35

PRE-COLUMBIAN AMERICA ISSUE

First Americans Crossed Over From Asia — AP103

1991, Oct. 12

C131 AP103 50c multicolored 1.00 .35

Piper Type of 1991

1993 ***Perf. 11.2 Bullseye***

C132 AP101 40c multicolored, low gloss gum 3.50 .65

Piper's hair touches top edge of design. No selvage inscriptions.

"All LC (Letters and Cards) mail receives First-Class Mail service in the United States, is dispatched by the fastest transportation available, and travels by airmail or priority service in the destination country. All LC mail should be marked 'AIRMAIL' or 'PAR AVION.'" (U.S. Postal Service, Pub. 51).

No. C133 listed below was issued to meet the LC rate to Canada and Mexico and is inscribed with the silhouette of a jet plane next to the denomination indicating the need for airmail service. This is unlike No. 2998, which met the LC rate to other countries, but contained no indication that it was intended for that use.

Future issues that meet a specific international airmail rate and contain the airplane silhouette will be treated by Scott as Air Post stamps. Stamps similar to No. 2998 will be listed in the Postage section.

SCENIC AMERICAN LANDSCAPES

Niagara Falls — AP104

1999, May 12 ***Serpentine Die Cut 11***

Self-Adhesive

C133 AP104 48c multicolored 1.00 .25

Rio Grande — AP105

1999, July 30

Self-Adhesive

C134 AP105 40c multicolored .80 .60

Grand Canyon — AP106

LITHOGRAPHED

Serpentine Die Cut 11¼x11½

2000, Jan. 20

Self-Adhesive

C135 AP106 60c multi 1.25 .25
a. Die cutting omitted, pair 1,150.
b. Vert. pair, die cutting omitted horiz. —
c. Horiz. pair, die cutting omitted between —
d. Horiz. pair, die cutting omitted vert. —

Nine-Mile Prairie, Nebraska AP107

LITHOGRAPHED

2001, Mar. 6

Self-Adhesive

C136 AP107 70c multi 1.40 .30

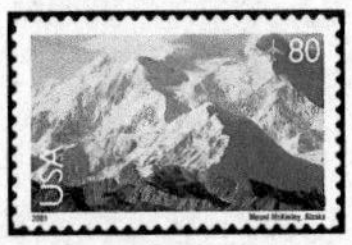
Mt. McKinley AP108

PHOTOGRAVURE

Serpentine Die Cut 11

2001, Apr. 17

Self-Adhesive

C137 AP108 80c multi 1.60 .35

Acadia National Park — AP109

LITHOGRAPHED

Serpentine Die Cut 11.25x11.5

2001-05

Self-Adhesive

C138 AP109 60c multi 1.25 .25
a. Serpentine die cut 11½x11¾ 1.25 .25
b. As "a," with "2005" year date 1.25 .25
c. As "b," printed on back of backing paper, pane of 20 3,500.

Bryce Canyon National Park — AP110

Great Smoky Mountains National Park — AP111

LITHOGRAPHED

Serpentine Die Cut 10¾

2006, Feb. 24

Self-Adhesive

C139 AP110 63c multicolored 1.25 .25
a. Die cutting omitted, pair 450.00
C140 AP111 75c multicolored 1.50 .35
a. Die cutting omitted, pair 500.00

Yosemite National Park — AP112

PHOTOGRAVURE

Serpentine Die Cut 11

C141 AP112 84c multicolored 1.75 .35
Nos. C139-C141 (3) 4.50 .95

Okefenokee Swamp, Georgia and Florida — AP113

Hagatña Bay, Guam — AP114

LITHOGRAPHED (#C142), PHOTOGRAVURE (#C143)

Serpentine Die Cut 10¾

2007, June 1

Self-Adhesive

C142 AP113 69c multicolored 1.40 .30

Serpentine Die Cut 11

C143 AP114 90c multicolored 1.80 .40

13-Mile Woods, New Hampshire AP115

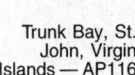

Trunk Bay, St. John, Virgin Islands — AP116

LITHOGRAPHED (#C144), PHOTOGRAVURE (#C145)

Serpentine Die Cut 10¾

2008, May 16

Self-Adhesive

C144 AP115 72c multicolored 1.50 .30

Serpentine Die Cut 11

C145 AP116 94c multicolored 1.90 .45

AP117

AP118

LITHOGRAPHED, PHOTOGRAVURE (#C147)

Serpentine Die Cut 10¾

2009, June 28

Self-Adhesive

C146 AP117 79c multicolored 1.75 .35

Serpentine Die Cut 11

C147 AP118 98c multicolored 2.00 .45

Voyageurs National Park, Minnesota AP119

LITHOGRAPHED

Serpentine Die Cut 10¾

2011, Apr. 11

Self-Adhesive

C148 AP119 80c multicolored 1.60 .25

See note after No. 1549.

Glacier National Park, Montana — AP120

Amish Horse and Buggy on Road, Lancaster County, Pennsylvania — AP121

LITHOGRAPHED

2012 ***Serpentine Die Cut 10¾***

Self-Adhesive

C149 AP120 85c multicolored 1.75 .35
C150 AP121 $1.05 multicolored 2.10 .45
a. Die cutting omitted on front, pair 500.00
b. Silver (airplane silhouette) missing (PS) —

Issued: 85c, 1/19; $1.05, 1/20.

AIR POST SPECIAL DELIVERY STAMPS

To provide for the payment of both the postage and the special delivery fee in one stamp.

Great Seal of United States — APSD1

1934, Aug. 30 **Unwmk.** ***Perf. 11***

CE1 APSD1 16c dark blue .70 .80
Never hinged .90

For imperforate variety see No. 771.

Great Seal of United States — APSD2

1936, Feb. 10

CE2 APSD2 16c red & blue .45 .35
Never hinged .65
a. Horiz. pair, imperf. vert. 4,250.
Never hinged 5,250.

SPECIAL DELIVERY STAMPS

When affixed to any letter or article of mailable matter, secured immediate delivery, between 7 A. M. and midnight, at any post office.

Messenger Running — SD1

Flat Plate Printing

1885 **Unwmk.** ***Perf. 12***

E1 SD1 10c blue 600.00 80.00
Never hinged 1,300.

Messenger Running — SD2

1888, Sept. 6

E2 SD2 10c blue 500.00 45.00
Never hinged 1,150.

COLUMBIAN EXPOSITION ISSUE

Though not issued expressly for the Exposition, No. E3 is considered to be part of that issue.

1893, Jan. 24

E3 SD2 10c orange 300.00 50.00
Never hinged 650.00

Messenger Running — SD3

1894, Oct. 10

Line under "TEN CENTS"

E4 SD3 10c blue 900.00 110.00
Never hinged 2,000.

No. E5a

1895, Aug. 16 **Wmk. 191**

E5 SD3 10c blue 210.00 12.50
Never hinged 475.00
a. Dots in curved frame above messenger (Pl. 882) 400.00 50.00
Never hinged 800.00

Messenger on Bicycle — SD4

1902, Dec. 9

E6 SD4 10c ultramarine 240.00 10.00
Never hinged 500.00
a. 10c blue 300.00 12.50
Never hinged 750.00

Helmet of Mercury and Olive Branch — SD5

1908, Dec. 12

E7 SD5 10c green 65.00 50.00
Never hinged 140.00

1911, Jan. **Wmk. 190** ***Perf. 12***

E8 SD4 10c ultramarine 120.00 10.00
Never hinged 250.00
b. 10c violet blue 160.00 14.00
Never hinged 350.00

1914, Sept. ***Perf. 10***

E9 SD4 10c ultramarine 190.00 12.00
Never hinged 425.00
a. 10c blue 260.00 15.00
Never hinged 575.00

1916, Oct. 19 **Unwmk.** ***Perf. 10***

E10 SD4 10c pale ultramarine 350.00 50.00
Never hinged 750.00
a. 10c blue 400.00 55.00
Never hinged 800.00

1917, May 2 ***Perf. 11***

E11 SD4 10c ultramarine 20.00 .75
Never hinged 45.00
b. 10c gray violet 35.00 3.00
Never hinged 75.00
c. 10c blue 100.00 5.00
Never hinged 210.00
d. Perf. 10 at left —

Postman and Motorcycle SD6

1922, July 12

E12 SD6 10c gray violet 45.00 3.00
Never hinged 95.00
a. 10c deep ultramarine 55.00 3.50
Never hinged 130.00

Post Office Truck — SD7

1925

E13 SD6 15c deep orange	40.00	3.75
Never hinged	75.00	
E14 SD7 20c black	2.00	1.00
Never hinged	4.00	
Nos. E12-E14 (3)	87.00	7.75

Motorcycle Type of 1922
ROTARY PRESS PRINTING

1927-31 *Perf. 11x10½*

E15 SD6 10c gray violet	1.25	.25
Never hinged	2.00	
On cover		.50
a. 10c red lilac	.80	.25
Never hinged	1.40	
b. 10c gray lilac	.90	.25
Never hinged	1.60	
c. Horiz. pair, imperf. btwn., red lilac shade	*350.00*	
Never hinged	*575.00*	
E16 SD6 15c orange ('31)	.60	.25
Never hinged	.90	

Catalogue values for unused stamps in this section, from this point to the end, are for Never Hinged items.

1944-51

E17 SD6 13c blue	.60	.25
E18 SD6 17c orange yellow	3.50	2.50
E19 SD7 20c black ('51)	1.20	.25

Special Delivery Letter, Hand to Hand — SD8

1954, Oct. 13 *Perf. 11x10½*

E20 SD8 20c deep blue	.40	.25

1957, Sept. 3

E21 SD8 30c lake	.50	.25

Arrows — SD9

GIORI PRESS PRINTING

1969, Nov. 21 *Perf. 11*

E22 SD9 45c red & blue	1.20	.25

1971, May 10

E23 SD9 60c blue & red	1.25	.25

From 1885 to the present, special delivery stamps have not been and are not valid for the payment of postage of any description, nor for registry fees.

REGISTRATION STAMP

Issued for the prepayment of registry fees; not usable for postage.

Eagle — RS1

1911, Dec. 1 Wmk. 190 *Perf. 12*

F1 RS1 10c ultramarine	75.00	14.00
Never hinged	160.00	

CERTIFIED MAIL STAMP

For use on first-class mail for which no indemnity value is claimed, but for which proof of mailing and proof of delivery are available at less cost than registered mail.

Catalogue value for the unused stamp in this section is for a Never Hinged item.

Letter Carrier — CM1

ROTARY PRESS PRINTING

1955, June 6 Unwmk. *Perf. 10½x11*

FA1 CM1 15c red	.75	.75

POSTAGE DUE STAMPS

For affixing, by a postal clerk to any piece of mailable matter, to denote the amount to be collected from the addressee because of insufficient prepayment of postage.

D1

Printed by the American Bank Note Co.

Plates of 200 subjects in two panes of 100 each.

1879 Unwmk. Engr. *Perf. 12*

J1 D1 1c brown	100.00	14.00
Never hinged	270.00	
J2 D1 2c brown	450.00	25.00
Never hinged	1,050.	
J3 D1 3c brown	100.00	6.00
Never hinged	280.00	
J4 D1 5c brown	800.00	70.00
Never hinged	1,950.	
J5 D1 10c brown	950.00	70.00
Never hinged	*2,500.*	
a. Imperf., pair	*2,500.*	
J6 D1 30c brown	425.00	65.00
Never hinged	900.00	
J7 D1 50c brown	625.00	90.00
Never hinged	1,600.	
Nos. J1-J7 (7)	3,450.	340.00

Special Printing

J8 D1 1c deep brown	*16,000.*	
Never hinged	—	
No gum	*6,500.*	
J9 D1 2c deep brown	*15,000.*	
No gum	*6,000.*	
J10 D1 3c deep brown	*20,000.*	
No gum	*8,000.*	
J11 D1 5c deep brown	*13,000.*	
No gum	*5,250.*	
J12 D1 10c deep brown	*6,750.*	
No gum	*2,900.*	
J13 D1 30c deep brown	*7,000.*	
No gum	*3,000.*	
J14 D1 50c deep brown	*7,000.*	
No gum	*3,000.*	

1884

J15 D1 1c red brown	70.00	7.00
Never hinged	190.00	
J16 D1 2c red brown	80.00	6.00
Never hinged	225.00	
J17 D1 3c red brown	1,050.	350.00
Never hinged	2,500.	
J18 D1 5c red brown	550.00	50.00
Never hinged	1,300.	
J19 D1 10c red brown	550.00	35.00
Never hinged	1,300.	
J20 D1 30c red brown	225.00	70.00
Never hinged	550.00	
J21 D1 50c red brown	1,900.	250.00
Never hinged	4,000.	
Nos. J15-J21 (7)	4,425.	768.00

1891

J22 D1 1c bright claret	30.00	2.00
Never hinged	85.00	
J23 D1 2c bright claret	32.50	2.00
Never hinged	90.00	
J24 D1 3c bright claret	67.50	16.00
Never hinged	180.00	
J25 D1 5c bright claret	100.00	16.00
Never hinged	290.00	
J26 D1 10c bright claret	165.00	30.00
Never hinged	500.00	
J27 D1 30c bright claret	575.00	225.00
Never hinged	1,700.	
J28 D1 50c bright claret	650.00	225.00
Never hinged	1,750.	
Nos. J22-J28 (7)	1,620.	516.00

Nos. J22-J28 fluoresce orange under longwave ultraviolet light. Nos. J15-J21 do not.

See Die and Plate Proofs in the Scott U.S. Specialized catalog for imperfs. on stamp paper.

The color on Nos. J29-J44 will run when immersed in water. Extreme caution is advised.

D2

Printed by the Bureau of Engraving and Printing.

1894

J29 D2 1c vermilion	2,400.	750.
Never hinged	*6,000.*	
J30 D2 2c vermilion	800.	350.
Never hinged	1,900.	

1894-95

J31 D2 1c deep claret	72.50	12.00
Never hinged	260.00	
b. Vertical pair, imperf. horiz.	—	
J32 D2 2c deep claret	62.50	10.00
Never hinged	240.00	
J33 D2 3c deep claret ('95)	200.00	50.00
Never hinged	575.00	
J34 D2 5c deep claret ('95)	300.00	55.00
Never hinged	850.00	
J35 D2 10c deep claret	350.00	40.00
Never hinged	1,000.	
J36 D2 30c deep claret ('95)	550.00	250.00
Never hinged	1,250.	
a. 30c carmine	675.00	275.00
Never hinged	1,600.	
b. 30c pale rose	450.00	200.00
Never hinged	1,100.	
J37 D2 50c deep claret ('95)	1,800.	800.00
Never hinged	4,250.	
a. 50c pale rose	1,600.	725.00
Never hinged	3,750.	
Nos. J31-J37 (7)	3,335.	1,217.

Shades are numerous in the 1894 and later issues.

See Die and Plate Proofs in the Scott U.S. Specialized catalog for imperfs. on stamp paper.

1895-97 **Wmk. 191**

J38 D2 1c deep claret	13.50	1.00
Never hinged	40.00	
J39 D2 2c deep claret	13.50	1.00
Never hinged	40.00	
J40 D2 3c deep claret	100.00	5.00
Never hinged	225.00	
J41 D2 5c deep claret	110.00	5.00
Never hinged	280.00	
J42 D2 10c deep claret	110.00	7.50
Never hinged	280.00	
J43 D2 30c deep claret ('97)	600.00	80.00
Never hinged	1,500.	
J44 D2 50c deep claret ('96)	375.00	60.00
Never hinged	925.00	
Nos. J38-J44 (7)	1,322.	159.50

1910-12 **Wmk. 190**

J45 D2 1c deep claret	40.00	5.00
Never hinged	115.00	
a. 1c rose carmine	35.00	5.00
Never hinged	105.00	
J46 D2 2c deep claret	40.00	2.00
Never hinged	115.00	
a. 2c rose carmine	35.00	2.00
Never hinged	105.00	
J47 D2 3c deep claret	625.00	60.00
Never hinged	1,600.	
J48 D2 5c deep claret	120.00	12.00
Never hinged	275.00	
a. 5c rose carmine	120.00	12.00
Never hinged	275.00	
J49 D2 10c deep claret	125.00	20.00
Never hinged	280.00	
a. 10c rose carmine	125.00	20.00
Never hinged	280.00	
J50 D2 50c deep claret ('12)	1,100.	200.00
Never hinged	2,900.	
a. 50c rose carmine	1,150.	190.00
Never hinged	*3,000.*	
Nos. J45-J50 (6)	2,050.	299.00

1914 *Perf. 10*

J52 D2 1c carmine lake	80.00	15.00
Never hinged	220.00	
a. 1c dull rose	85.00	15.00
Never hinged	230.00	
J53 D2 2c carmine lake	62.50	1.00
Never hinged	170.00	
a. 2c dull rose	67.50	2.00
Never hinged	180.00	
b. 2c vermilion	67.50	2.00
Never hinged	180.00	
J54 D2 3c carmine lake	1,050.	75.00
Never hinged	3,000.	
a. 3c dull rose	1,000.	75.00
Never hinged	2,900.	
J55 D2 5c carmine lake	50.00	6.00
Never hinged	140.00	
a. 5c dull rose	45.00	4.00
Never hinged	130.00	
J56 D2 10c carmine lake	75.00	4.00
Never hinged	200.00	
a. 10c dull rose	80.00	5.00
Never hinged	210.00	
J57 D2 30c carmine lake	225.00	55.00
Never hinged	525.00	
J58 D2 50c carmine lake	*11,500.*	1,700.
Never hinged	*22,000.*	
Nos. J52-J58 (7)	13,043.	1,856.

No. J58 unused is valued in the grade of fine to very fine.

1916 Unwmk. *Perf. 10*

J59 D2 1c rose 4,000. 750.00
Never hinged 9,000.
J60 D2 2c rose 250.00 75.00
Never hinged 625.00

1917 *Perf. 11*

J61 D2 1c carmine rose 2.75 .25
Never hinged 9.00
a. 1c rose red 2.75 .25
Never hinged 9.00
b. 1c deep claret 2.75 .25
Never hinged 9.00
J62 D2 2c carmine rose 2.75 .25
Never hinged 9.00
a. 2c rose red 2.75 .25
Never hinged 9.00
b. 2c deep claret 2.75 .25
Never hinged 9.00
J63 D2 3c carmine rose 13.50 .80
Never hinged 35.00
a. 3c rose red 13.50 .80
Never hinged 35.00
b. 3c deep claret 13.50 .80
Never hinged 35.00
J64 D2 5c carmine 11.00 .80
Never hinged 32.50
a. 5c rose red 11.00 .80
Never hinged 32.50
b. 5c deep claret 11.00 .80
Never hinged 32.50
J65 D2 10c carmine rose 22.50 1.00
Never hinged 65.00
a. 10c rose red 22.50 1.00
Never hinged 65.00
b. 10c deep claret 22.50 1.00
Never hinged 65.00
J66 D2 30c carmine rose 80.00 2.00
Never hinged 220.00
a. 30c deep claret 80.00 2.00
Never hinged 220.00
b. As "a," perf 10 at top, precanceled *21,000.*

No. J66b is valued with small faults and fine centering, as the two recorded examples are in this condition and grade.

J67 D2 50c carmine rose 140.00 1.00
Never hinged 325.00
a. 50c rose red 140.00 1.00
Never hinged 325.00
b. 50c deep claret 140.00 1.00
Never hinged 325.00
Nos. J61-J67 (7) 272.50 6.10
Nos. J61-J67, never hinged 695.50

1925

J68 D2 ½c dull red 1.00 .25
Never hinged 1.75

D3

D4

1930 *Perf. 11*

J69 D3 ½c carmine 4.25 1.90
Never hinged 9.50
J70 D3 1c carmine 2.75 .35
Never hinged 6.25
J71 D3 2c carmine 3.75 .35
Never hinged 8.50
J72 D3 3c carmine 20.00 2.75
Never hinged 47.50
J73 D3 5c carmine 18.00 5.00
Never hinged 42.50
J74 D3 10c carmine 42.50 2.00
Never hinged 95.00
J75 D3 30c carmine 125.00 4.00
Never hinged 275.00
J76 D3 50c carmine 175.00 2.00
Never hinged 375.00
J77 D4 $1 carmine 32.50 .35
Never hinged 65.00
a. $1 scarlet 27.50 .35
Never hinged 55.00
J78 D4 $5 dull carmine 37.50 .35
Never hinged 85.00
a. scarlet 32.50 .35
Never hinged 70.00

Type of 1930-31 Issue
Rotary Press Printing

1931 *Perf. 11x10½*

J79 D3 ½c dull carmine 1.25 .25
Never hinged 1.80
a. ½c scarlet .90 .25
Never hinged 1.30
P# block of 4 20.00 —
J80 D3 1c dull carmine .40 .25
Never hinged .50
a. scarlet .25 .25
Never hinged .30
J81 D3 2c dull carmine .40 .25
Never hinged .50
a. scarlet .25 .25
Never hinged .30
J82 D3 3c dull carmine .40 .25
Never hinged .50
a. scarlet .30 .25
Never hinged .45
J83 D3 5c dull carmine .75 .25
Never hinged 1.15
a. scarlet .50 .25
Never hinged .75
J84 D3 10c dull carmine 1.60 .25
Never hinged 2.50
a. scarlet 1.25 .25
Never hinged 1.90
J85 D3 30c dull carmine 12.50 .25
Never hinged 20.00
a. 30c scarlet 7.50 .25
Never hinged 11.50
P# block of 4 35.00 —
J86 D3 50c dull carmine 12.50 .25
Never hinged 20.00
a. 50c scarlet 9.00 .25
Never hinged 15.00
P# block of 4 52.50 —

Design measures 22½x19mm

1956 *Perf. 10½x11*

J87 D4 $1 scarlet 30.00 .25
Never hinged 52.50
Nos. J79-J87 (9) 59.80 2.25
Nos. J79-J87, never hinged 99.45

For listings of other color shades and printing varieties see the *Scott Specialized Catalogue of United States Stamps and Covers.*

Catalogue values for unused stamps in this section, from this point to the end, are for Never Hinged items.

D5

Denominations added in black by rubber plates in an operation similar to precanceling.

Rotary Press Printing
Perf. 11x10½

1959, June 19 Unwmk.

Denomination in Black

J88 D5 ½c carmine rose 1.50 1.10
J89 D5 1c carmine rose .25 .25
a. Denomination omitted 150.00
b. Pair, one without "1 CENT" 350.00
J90 D5 2c carmine rose .25 .25
J91 D5 3c carmine rose .25 .25
a. Pair, one without "3 CENTS" *550.00*
J92 D5 4c carmine rose .25 .25
J93 D5 5c carmine rose .25 .25
a. Pair, one without "5 CENTS" *1,500.*
J94 D5 6c carmine rose .25 .25
a. Pair, one without "6 CENTS" *700.00*
J95 D5 7c carmine rose .25 .25
J96 D5 8c carmine rose .25 .25
a. Pair, one without "8 CENTS" *750.00*
J97 D5 10c carmine rose .25 .25
J98 D5 30c carmine rose .70 .25
J99 D5 50c carmine rose 1.10 .25

Straight Numeral Outlined in Black

J100 D5 $1 carmine rose 2.00 .25
J101 D5 $5 carmine rose 9.00 .25
Nos. J88-J101 (14) 16.55 4.35

All single stamps with denomination omitted are catalogued as No. J89a.

1978-85 Denomination in Black

J102 D5 11c carmine rose .25 .25
J103 D5 13c carmine rose .25 .25
J104 D5 17c carmine rose ('85) .40 .35

UNITED STATES OFFICES IN CHINA

Issued for sale by the postal agency at Shanghai, at their surcharged value in local currency. Valid to the prepayment of their original values for the prepayment of postage on mail dispatched from the U.S. postal agency at Shanghai to addresses in the U.S.

Nos. 498-499, 502-504, 506-510, 512, 514-518 Surcharged

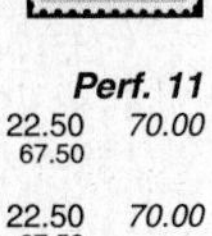

1919 Unwmk. *Perf. 11*

K1 A140 2c on 1c green 22.50 *70.00*
Never hinged 67.50
K2 A140 4c on 2c rose, type I 22.50 *70.00*
Never hinged 67.50
K3 A140 6c on 3c vio, type II 55.00 *140.00*
Never hinged 140.00
K4 A140 8c on 4c brown 55.00 *140.00*
Never hinged 140.00
K5 A140 10c on 5c blue 60.00 *140.00*
Never hinged 160.00
K6 A140 12c on 6c red org 80.00 *210.00*
Never hinged 210.00
K7 A140 14c on 7c black 82.50 *210.00*
Never hinged 215.00
K8 A148 16c on 8c ol bis 65.00 *160.00*
Never hinged 170.00
a. 16c on 8c ol grn 55.00 *140.00*
Never hinged 150.00
K9 A148 18c on 9c sal red 60.00 *175.00*
Never hinged 150.00
K10 A148 20c on 10c org yel 55.00 *140.00*
Never hinged 140.00
K11 A148 24c on 12c brn car 75.00 *160.00*
Never hinged 190.00
a. 24c on 12c cl brn 110.00 *240.00*
Never hinged 275.00
K12 A148 30c on 15c gray 82.50 *230.00*
Never hinged 200.00
K13 A148 40c on 20c deep ultra 120.00 *325.00*
Never hinged 300.00
K14 A148 60c on 30c org red 110.00 *275.00*
Never hinged 260.00
K15 A148 $1 on 50c lt vio 550.00 *1,000.*
Never hinged 1,200.
K16 A148 $2 on $1 vio brn 425.00 *750.00*
Never hinged 925.00
a. Double surcharge *10,500.* *11,500.*
Never hinged *17,500.*
Nos. K1-K16 (16) 1,920. *4,195.*

Fake surcharges exist, but most are rather crudely made.

Nos. 498 and 528B Surcharged

1922, July 3

K17 A140 2c on 1c green 100.00 *225.00*
Never hinged 225.00
K18 A140 4c on 2c car, type VII 100.00 *225.00*
Never hinged 225.00
a. "SHANGHAI" omitted *7,500.*
b. "CHINA" only *16,000.*

OFFICIAL STAMPS

The franking privilege having been abolished, as of July 1, 1873, these stamps were provided for each of the departments of Government for the prepayment of postage on official matter.

Penalty franks were first authorized in 1877, and their expanded use after 1879 reduced the need for official stamps, the use of which was finally abolished on July 5, 1884.

Designs, except Post Office, resemble those illustrated but are not identical. Each bears the name of Department. Portraits are as follows: 1c, Franklin; 2c, Jackson; 3c, Washington; 6c, Lincoln; 7c, Stanton; 10c, Jefferson; 12c, Clay; 15c, Webster; 24c, Scott; 30c, Hamilton; 90c, Perry.

Special printings overprinted "SPECIMEN" follow No. O120.

Printed by the Continental Bank Note Co.

O1

Thin Hard Paper
AGRICULTURE

1873 Engr. Unwmk. *Perf. 12*

O1 O1 1c yellow 300.00 *200.00*
Never hinged *1,000.*
No gum 170.00
O2 O1 2c yellow 275.00 100.00
Never hinged 575.00
No gum 130.00
O3 O1 3c yellow 225.00 17.50
Never hinged 450.00
No gum 105.00
O4 O1 6c yellow 275.00 60.00
Never hinged 575.00
No gum 130.00
O5 O1 10c yellow 525.00 200.00
Never hinged 1,150.
No gum 240.00
O6 O1 12c yellow 450.00 260.00
Never hinged *1,000.*
No gum 250.00
O7 O1 15c yellow 425.00 230.00
Never hinged 950.00
No gum 225.00
O8 O1 24c yellow 425.00 250.00
Never hinged 950.00
No gum 225.00
O9 O1 30c yellow 550.00 280.00
Never hinged 1,200.
No gum 275.00
Nos. O1-O9 (9) 3,450. 1,598.

EXECUTIVE

Franklin—O2

1873

O10 O2 1c carmine 900.00 550.00
Never hinged *3,500.*
No gum 450.00
O11 O2 2c carmine 575.00 260.00
Never hinged 1,400.
No gum 260.00
O12 O2 3c carmine 700.00 225.00
Never hinged 1,600.
No gum 325.00
a. 3c violet rose 1,100. 275.00
Never hinged 2,500.
No gum 500.00
On cover —
O13 O2 6c carmine 900.00 600.00
Never hinged —
No gum 425.00
O14 O2 10c carmine 1,200. 1,000.
Never hinged *2,500.*
No gum 600.00
Nos. O10-O14 (5) 4,275. 2,635.

INTERIOR

O3

1873

O15 O3 1c vermilion 75.00 10.00
Never hinged 170.00
No gum 35.00
O16 O3 2c vermilion 70.00 12.00
Never hinged 160.00
No gum 30.00
O17 O3 3c vermilion 80.00 6.00
Never hinged 175.00
No gum 40.00
O18 O3 6c vermilion 70.00 10.00
Never hinged 160.00
No gum 30.00
O19 O3 10c vermilion 70.00 20.00
Never hinged 160.00
No gum 30.00
O20 O3 12c vermilion 90.00 12.00
Never hinged 200.00
No gum 45.00
O21 O3 15c vermilion 200.00 25.00
Never hinged 450.00
No gum 90.00
O22 O3 24c vermilion 180.00 20.00
Never hinged 400.00
No gum 85.00
a. Double impression —
O23 O3 30c vermilion 290.00 20.00
Never hinged 625.00
No gum 130.00
O24 O3 90c vermilion 325.00 50.00
Never hinged 700.00
No gum 140.00
Nos. O15-O24 (10) 1,450. 185.00

JUSTICE

O4

1873

O25 O4 1c purple 250.00 100.00
Never hinged 550.00
No gum 120.00
O26 O4 2c purple 310.00 110.00
Never hinged 700.00
No gum 135.00
O27 O4 3c purple 300.00 35.00
Never hinged 700.00
No gum 135.00
O28 O4 6c purple 310.00 45.00
Never hinged 700.00
No gum 135.00
O29 O4 10c purple 310.00 100.00
Never hinged *1,250.*
No gum 135.00
O30 O4 12c purple 260.00 75.00
Never hinged *1,500.*
No gum 125.00
O31 O4 15c purple 500.00 200.00
Never hinged *1,500.*
No gum 240.00
O32 O4 24c purple 1,250. 425.00
Never hinged *4,250.*
No gum 600.00
O33 O4 30c purple 1,300. 350.00
Never hinged —
No gum 625.00
O34 O4 90c purple 1,900. 900.00
Never hinged *4,000.*
No gum 900.00
Nos. O25-O34 (10) 6,690. 2,340.

NAVY

O5

1873

O35 O5 1c ultramarine	160.00	50.00
Never hinged	350.00	
No gum	75.00	
a. 1c dull blue	200.00	50.00
Never hinged	400.00	
No gum	87.50	
O36 O5 2c ultramarine	160.00	25.00
Never hinged	350.00	
No gum	75.00	
a. 2c dull blue	200.00	25.00
Never hinged	400.00	
No gum	87.50	
O37 O5 3c ultramarine	170.00	15.00
Never hinged	*1,750.*	
No gum	80.00	
a. 3c dull blue	225.00	15.00
Never hinged	450.00	
No gum	100.00	
O38 O5 6c ultramarine	150.00	25.00
Never hinged	450.00	
No gum	70.00	
a. 6c dull blue	175.00	25.00
Never hinged	385.00	
No gum	82.50	
O39 O5 7c ultramarine	700.00	230.00
Never hinged	*1,600.*	
No gum	325.00	
a. 7c dull blue	750.00	230.00
Never hinged	—	
No gum	325.00	
O40 O5 10c ultramarine	210.00	45.00
Never hinged	*1,000.*	
No gum	95.00	
a. 10c dull blue	225.00	45.00
Never hinged	1,000.	
No gum	110.00	
O41 O5 12c ultramarine	240.00	45.00
Never hinged	*900.00*	
No gum	115.00	
O42 O5 15c ultramarine	425.00	80.00
Never hinged	—	
No gum	200.00	
O43 O5 24c ultramarine	425.00	85.00
Never hinged	*1,750.*	
No gum	200.00	
a. 24c dull blue	425.00	80.00
Never hinged	*1,350.*	
No gum	200.00	
O44 O5 30c ultramarine	350.00	50.00
Never hinged	*3,000.*	
No gum	160.00	
O45 O5 90c ultramarine	1,050.	375.00
Never hinged	*6,000.*	
No gum	500.00	
a. Double impression		*20,000.*
Nos. O35-O45 (11)	4,040.	1,025.

POST OFFICE

Stamps of the Post Office Department are often on paper with a gray surface. This is essentially a wiping problem, caused by an over-milled carbon black pigment that released acid and etched the plates. There is no premium for stamps on paper with a gray surface.

O6

1873

O47 O6 1c black	25.00	12.00
Never hinged	60.00	
No gum	12.00	
O48 O6 2c black	30.00	10.00
Never hinged	75.00	
No gum	14.00	
O49 O6 3c black	10.00	2.00
Never hinged	25.00	
No gum	4.50	
a. Printed on both sides		*7,500.*
b. Double paper	—	—
O50 O6 6c black	30.00	8.00
Never hinged	75.00	
No gum	14.00	
a. Diagonal half used as 3c on cover		*5,000.*
b. Double impression		*3,000.*
O51 O6 10c black	140.00	55.00
Never hinged	325.00	
No gum	65.00	
O52 O6 12c black	120.00	12.00
Never hinged	275.00	
No gum	55.00	
O53 O6 15c black	140.00	20.00
Never hinged	325.00	
No gum	65.00	
O54 O6 24c black	225.00	25.00
Never hinged	500.00	
No gum	105.00	
a. Double paper	—	—
O55 O6 30c black	250.00	25.00
Never hinged	550.00	
No gum	110.00	
O56 O6 90c black	260.00	25.00
Never hinged	575.00	
No gum	120.00	
a. Double paper	—	—
Nos. O47-O56 (10)	1,230.	194.00

STATE

Franklin — O7

Seward — O8

1873

O57 O7 1c dark green	260.00	75.00
Never hinged	575.00	
No gum	125.00	
O58 O7 2c dark green	310.00	100.00
Never hinged	—	
No gum	150.00	
O59 O7 3c dark green	220.00	25.00
Never hinged	500.00	
No gum	105.00	
b. Double paper	—	—
O60 O7 6c dark green	250.00	30.00
Never hinged	550.00	
No gum	120.00	
O61 O7 7c dark green	290.00	65.00
Never hinged	650.00	
No gum	140.00	
O62 O7 10c dark green	250.00	55.00
Never hinged	575.00	
No gum	120.00	
O63 O7 12c dark green	310.00	125.00
Never hinged	700.00	
No gum	150.00	
O64 O7 15c dark green	350.00	90.00
Never hinged	775.00	
No gum	170.00	
O65 O7 24c dark green	550.00	230.00
Never hinged	*1,200.*	
No gum	275.00	
O66 O7 30c dark green	525.00	180.00
Never hinged	*1,150.*	
No gum	260.00	
O67 O7 90c dark green	1,100.	325.00
Never hinged	*2,400.*	
No gum	525.00	
O68 O8 $2 green & black	1,800.	3,000.
Never hinged	*3,750.*	
No gum	850.00	
O69 O8 $5 green & black	8,000.	*13,000.*
Never hinged	—	
No gum	3,750.	
O70 O8 $10 green & black	4,500.	*12,500.*
Never hinged	10,500.	
No gum	2,500.	

Nos. O68-O70 used are valued with neat handstamp cancels. Examples with black smudge or similar nondescript cancels sell for much less.

O71 O8 $20 green & black	5,000.	5,500.
Never hinged	11,500.	
No gum	2,500.	

No. O71 used is valued with a blue or red handstamp favor cancel. Nos. O68-O71 with pen cancels sell for approximately 25-40% of the values shown.

TREASURY

O9

1873

O72 O9 1c brown	120.00	10.00
Never hinged	250.00	
No gum	55.00	
O73 O9 2c brown	125.00	8.00
Never hinged	275.00	
No gum	57.50	
O74 O9 3c brown	110.00	2.00
Never hinged	230.00	
No gum	50.00	
a. Double impression		*5,000.*
b. Double paper	—	
O75 O9 6c brown	120.00	4.00
Never hinged	250.00	
No gum	55.00	
O76 O9 7c brown	250.00	35.00
Never hinged	550.00	
No gum	120.00	
O77 O9 10c brown	240.00	12.00
Never hinged	525.00	
No gum	110.00	
a. Double paper	—	—
O78 O9 12c brown	350.00	10.00
Never hinged	750.00	
No gum	160.00	
O79 O9 15c brown	300.00	12.00
Never hinged	650.00	
No gum	140.00	
O80 O9 24c brown	725.00	100.00
Never hinged	—	
No gum	325.00	
O81 O9 30c brown	400.00	12.00
Never hinged	—	
No gum	180.00	
O82 O9 90c brown	475.00	17.50
Never hinged	950.00	
No gum	225.00	
a. Double paper	—	—
Nos. O72-O82 (11)	3,215.	222.50

WAR

O10

1873

O83 O10 1c rose	240.00	15.00
Never hinged	*850.00*	
No gum	115.00	
O84 O10 2c rose	260.00	15.00
Never hinged	1,200.0	
No gum	125.00	
O85 O10 3c rose	275.00	5.00
Never hinged	650.00	
No gum	135.00	
O86 O10 6c rose	675.00	12.50
Never hinged	1,450.	
No gum	325.00	

Examples of Nos. O114-O117 which bear Continental Bank Note Co. imprints are often mistaken for/offered as Nos. O83-O86. If there are doubts, expert opinions should be requested.

O87 O10 7c rose	175.00	90.00
Never hinged	600.00	
No gum	90.00	
O88 O10 10c rose	140.00	25.00
Never hinged	375.00	
No gum	65.00	
O89 O10 12c rose	275.00	12.00
Never hinged	700.00	
No gum	130.00	
O90 O10 15c rose	85.00	15.00
Never hinged	260.00	
No gum	40.00	
O91 O10 24c rose	85.00	12.00
Never hinged	190.00	
No gum	40.00	
O92 O10 30c rose	130.00	12.00
Never hinged	375.00	
No gum	65.00	
O93 O10 90c rose	225.00	60.00
Never hinged	800.00	
No gum	110.00	
Nos. O83-O93 (11)	2,565.	273.50

Printed by the American Bank Note Co.

1879

Soft Porous Paper

AGRICULTURE

O94 O1 1c yel, no gum	5,750.	
O95 O1 3c yellow	550.00	150.00
Never hinged	1,250.	
No gum	260.00	

INTERIOR

O96 O3 1c vermilion	300.00	*400.00*
Never hinged	550.00	
No gum	150.00	
O97 O3 2c vermilion	10.00	3.00
Never hinged	17.50	
No gum	4.50	
O98 O3 3c vermilion	10.00	3.00
Never hinged	22.50	
No gum	4.50	
O99 O3 6c vermilion	10.00	*12.50*
Never hinged	17.50	
No gum	4.50	
O100 O3 10c vermilion	110.00	75.00
Never hinged	250.00	
No gum	55.00	
O101 O3 12c vermilion	230.00	115.00
Never hinged	525.00	
No gum	115.00	
O102 O3 15c pale vermilion	400.00	500.00
Never hinged	900.00	
No gum	200.00	
O103 O3 24c pale vermilion	4,500.	*6,250.*
Never hinged	10,000.	
No gum	2,200.	
Nos. O96-O103 (8)	5,570.	7,359.

JUSTICE

O106 O4 3c bluish pur	250.00	125.00
Never hinged	575.00	
No gum	120.00	
O107 O4 6c bluish pur	475.00	300.00
Never hinged	1,050.	
No gum	250.00	

POST OFFICE

O108 O6 3c black	30.00	10.00
Never hinged	70.00	
No gum	14.00	

TREASURY

O109 O9 3c brown	80.00	10.00
Never hinged	175.00	
No gum	35.00	
O110 O9 6c brown	200.00	50.00
Never hinged	450.00	
No gum	90.00	
O111 O9 10c brown	275.00	80.00
Never hinged	650.00	
No gum	130.00	
O112 O9 30c brown	2,400.	550.00
Never hinged	—	
No gum	1,200.	
O113 O9 90c brown	10,000.	750.00
Never hinged	—	
No gum	5,000.	
Nos. O109-O113 (5)	12,955.	1,440.

WAR

O114 O10 1c rose red	7.50	4.00
Never hinged	15.00	
No gum	3.50	
O115 O10 2c rose red	15.00	4.00
Never hinged	30.00	
No gum	7.00	
O116 O10 3c rose red	10.00	2.00
Never hinged	20.00	
No gum	3.25	
a. Imperf., pair	*5,000.*	
b. Double impression	*7,500.*	
O117 O10 6c rose red	12.50	3.00
Never hinged	25.00	
No gum	6.00	
O118 O10 10c rose red	75.00	50.00
Never hinged	150.00	
No gum	35.00	
O119 O10 12c rose red	70.00	14.00
Never hinged	140.00	
No gum	35.00	
O120 O10 30c rose red	225.00	100.00
Never hinged	500.00	
No gum	110.00	
Nos. O114-O120 (7)	415.00	177.00

SPECIAL PRINTINGS

Special printings of Official stamps were made in 1875 at the time the other Reprints, Re-issues and Special Printings were printed. They are ungummed.

Although perforated, these stamps were sometimes (but not always) cut apart with scissors. As a result the perforations may be mutilated and the design damaged. Values are for very fine stamps with intact perforations.

All values exist imperforate.

Printed by the Continental Bank Note Co.
Similar to Type D, without period, 11mm long

AGRICULTURE

Overprinted in Block Letters

Thin, hard white paper

Carmine Overprint

1875	*Perf. 12*
O1S D 1c yellow	32.50
a. "Sepcimen" error	*2,500.*
b. Horiz. ribbed paper	37.50
c. As "b," small dotted "i" in "Specimen"	500.00
O2S D 2c yellow	55.00
a. "Sepcimen" error	*3,000.*
O3S D 3c yellow	400.00
a. "Sepcimen" error	*19,000.*
O4S D 6c yellow	400.00
a. "Sepcimen" error	*22,500.*
O5S D 10c yellow	400.00
P# strip of 5, Impt.	—
a. "Sepcimen" error	*19,000.*
O6S D 12c yellow	400.00
a. "Sepcimen" error	*15,000.*
O7S D 15c yellow	400.00
a. "Sepcimen" error	*12,500.*
O8S D 24c yellow	400.00
a. "Sepcimen" error	*12,500.*
O9S D 30c yellow	400.00
a. "Sepcimen" error	*13,500.*
Nos. O1S-O9S (9)	2,888.

EXECUTIVE

Blue Overprint

O10S D 1c carmine	32.50
a. Horiz. ribbed paper	40.00
b. As "a," small dotted "i" in "Specimen"	500.00
O11S D 2c carmine	55.00
O12S D 3c carmine	67.50
O13S D 6c carmine	67.50
O14S D 10c carmine	67.50
Nos. O10S-O14S (5)	290.00

INTERIOR

Blue Overprint

O15S D 1c vermilion	60.00
O16S D 2c vermilion	140.00
a. "Sepcimen" error	—

The existence of a genuine example of No. O16Sa has been questioned by specialists. The editors would like to see authenticated evidence of the existence of the single reported example.

O17S D 3c vermilion	*2,500.*
O18S D 6c vermilion	*2,500.*
O19S D 10c vermilion	*2,500.*
O20S D 12c vermilion	*2,500.*
O21S D 15c vermilion	*2,500.*
O22S D 24c vermilion	*2,500.*
O23S D 30c vermilion	*2,500.*
O24S D 90c vermilion	*2,500.*
Nos. O15S-O24S (10)	*20,200.*

JUSTICE
Blue Overprint

O25S D 1c purple 32.50
a. "Sepcimen" error 2,500.
b. Horiz. ribbed paper 35.00
c. As "b," small dotted "i" in "Specimen" 500.00
O26S D 2c purple 55.00
a. "Sepcimen" error 3,500.
O27S D 3c purple 1,250.
a. "Sepcimen" error 11,000.
O28S D 6c purple 1,250.
O29S D 10c purple 1,250.
a. "Sepcimen" error 21,000.
O30S D 12c purple 1,250.
a. "Sepcimen" error 19,000.
O31S D 15c purple 1,250.
a. "Sepcimen" error 25,000.
O32S D 24c purple 1,250.
a.. "Sepcimen" error 20,000.
O33S D 30c purple 1,250.
a. "Sepcimen" error 15,000.
O34S D 90c purple 1,250.
Nos. O25S-O34S (10) 10,088.

NAVY
Carmine Overprint

O35S D 1c ultramarine 35.00
a. "Sepcimen" error 2,750.
b. Double "Specimen" overprint 1,900.
O36S D 2c ultramarine 75.00
a. "Sepcimen" error 4,500.
O37S D 3c ultramarine 1,750.
O38S D 6c ultramarine 1,750.
O39S D 7c ultramarine 550.00
a. "Sepcimen" error 10,000.
O40S D 10c ultramarine 1,750.
a. "Sepcimen" error 17,500.
O41S D 12c ultramarine 1,750.
a. "Sepcimen" error 21,000.
O42S D 15c ultramarine 1,750.
a. "Sepcimen" error 16,000.
O43S D 24c ultramarine 1,750.
a. "Sepcimen" error 15,000.
O44S D 30c ultramarine 1,750.
a. "Sepcimen" error 17,500.
O45S D 90c ultramarine 1,750.
Nos. O35S-O45S (11) 14,660.

POST OFFICE
Carmine Overprint

O47S D 1c black 45.00
a. "Sepcimen" error 3,250.
b. Inverted overprint 2,500.
O48S D 2c black 325.00
a. "Sepcimen" error 15,000.
O49S D 3c black 1,600.
a. "Sepcimen" error 37,500.
O50S D 6c black 1,600.
O51S D 10c black 1,000.
a. "Sepcimen" error 15,000.
O52S D 12c black 1,600.
O53S D 15c black 1,600.
a. "Sepcimen" error 26,000.
O54S D 24c black 1,600.
a. "Sepcimen" error 22,000.
O55S D 30c black 1,600.
O56S D 90c black 1,600.
a. "Sepcimen" error 25,000.
Nos. O47S-O56S (10) 12,570.

STATE
Carmine Overprint

O57S D 1c bluish green 32.50
a. "Sepcimen" error 2,500.
b. Horiz. ribbed paper 35.00
c. As "b," small dotted "i" in "Specimen" 650.00
d. Double "Specimen" overprint 3,850.
O58S D 2c bluish green 90.00
a. "Sepcimen" error 2,500.
O59S D 3c bluish green 140.00
a. "Sepcimen" error 7,000.
O60S D 6c bluish green 350.00
a. "Sepcimen" error 12,500.
O61S D 7c bluish green 175.00
a. "Sepcimen" error 9,000.
O62S D 10c bluish green 550.00
a. "Sepcimen" error 27,500.
O63S D 12c bluish green 550.00
a. "Sepcimen" error 19,000.
O64S D 15c bluish green 600.00
O65S D 24c bluish green 600.00
a. "Sepcimen" error 25,000.
O66S D 30c bluish green 600.00
a. "Sepcimen" error 27,500.
O67S D 90c bluish green 600.00
a. "Sepcimen" error 27,500.
O68S D $2 green & blk 15,000.
O69S D $5 green & blk 67,500.
O70S D $10 green & blk 100,000.
O71S D $20 green & blk 145,000.
Nos. O57S-O67S (11) 4,288.

TREASURY
Blue Overprint

O72S D 1c dark brown 80.00
O73S D 2c dark brown 450.00
O74S D 3c dark brown 1,600.
O75S D 6c dark brown 1,600.
O76S D 7c dark brown 950.00
O77S D 10c dark brown 1,600.
O78S D 12c dark brown 1,600.
O79S D 15c dark brown 1,600.
O80S D 24c dark brown 1,600.
O81S D 30c dark brown 1,600.
O82S D 90c dark brown 1,650.
Nos. O72S-O82S (11) 14,330.

WAR
Blue Overprint

O83S D 1c deep rose 35.00
a. "Sepcimen" error 3,000.
O84S D 2c deep rose 125.00
a. "Sepcimen" error 3,500.
O85S D 3c deep rose 1,400.
a. "Sepcimen" error 30,000.
O86S D 6c deep rose 1,400.
a. "Sepcimen" error 32,000.
O87S D 7c deep rose 425.00
a. "Sepcimen" error 17,500.
O88S D 10c deep rose 1,400.
a. "Sepcimen" error 27,500.
O89S D 12c deep rose 1,400.
a. "Sepcimen" error 32,000.
O90S D 15c deep rose 1,400.
a. "Sepcimen" error 30,000.
O91S D 24c deep rose 1,400.
a. "Sepcimen" error 30,000.
O92S D 30c deep rose 1,400.
a. "Sepcimen" error 30,000.
O93S D 90c deep rose 1,400.
a. "Sepcimen" error 30,000.
Nos. O83S-O93S (11) 11,785.

EXECUTIVE
Printed by the American Bank Note Co.
Soft Porous Paper

1881 Blue Overprint
O10xS D 1c violet rose 95.00

NAVY
Carmine Overprint

O35xS D 1c gray blue 100.00
a. Double overprint 1,200.

STATE

O57xS D 1c yellow green 180.00

OFFICIAL POSTAL SAVINGS MAIL

These stamps were used to prepay postage on official correspondence of the Postal Savings Division of the POD. Discontinued Sept. 23, 1914.

O11

Printed by the Bureau of Engraving & Printing

1910-11 Engr. Wmk. 191
O121 O11 2c black 17.50 2.00
Never hinged 40.00
O122 O11 50c dark green 175.00 60.00
Never hinged 425.00
O123 O11 $1 ultramarine 200.00 15.00
Never hinged 450.00

Wmk. 190
O124 O11 1c dark violet 12.50 2.00
Never hinged 27.50
O125 O11 2c black 65.00 7.00
Never hinged 150.00
O126 O11 10c carmine 20.00 2.00
Never hinged 50.00
Nos. O121-O126 (6) 490.00 88.00

Catalogue values for unused stamps in this section, from this point to the end, are for Never Hinged items.

Catalogue values for used stamps are for regularly used examples, not for examples removed from first day covers.

From No. O127 onward, all official stamps are tagged unless noted.

OFFICIAL MAIL

O12

Engraved
Unwmk.

1983, Jan. 12-1985 *Perf. 11*
O127 O12 1c red, blue & black .25 .25
O128 O12 4c red, blue & black .25 .25
O129 O12 13c red, blue & black .50 15.00
O129A O12 14c red, blue & black .45 .50
O130 O12 17c red, blue & black .55 .40
O132 O12 $1 red, blue & black 2.25 1.00
O133 O12 $5 red, blue & black 9.50 20.00
Nos. O127-O133 (7) 13.75 37.40

No. O129A does not have a "c" after the "14."

COIL STAMPS
Perf. 10 Vert.

O135 O12 20c red, blue & black 1.75 2.00
a. Imperf., pair 750.00
O136 O12 22c red, blue & blk ('85) 1.00 2.00
b. Imperf, pair 1,750.

Inscribed: Postal Card Rate D

1985, Feb. 4 *Perf. 11*
O138 O12 (14c) red, blue & black 5.00 15.00

Frame line completely around blue design — O13

Inscribed: No. O139, Domestic Letter Rate D; No. O140, Domestic Mail E.

COIL STAMPS
Litho., Engr. (#O139)

1985-88 *Perf. 10 Vert.*
O138A O13 15c red, blue & blk .50 .50
O138B O13 20c red, blue & blk .50 .30
O139 O12 (22c) red, blue & blk 5.25 20.00
O140 O13 (25c) red, blue & blk .75 2.00
O141 O13 25c red, blue & blk .65 .50
a. Imperf., pair 700.00 —
Nos. O138A-O141 (5) 7.65 23.30

Issue dates: 1985; E, Mar. 22, 1988; 15c, June 11; 20c, May 19; 25c, June 11.
See Nos. O143, O145-O151, O153-O156.

Plates of 400 in four panes of 100.

1989, July 5 Litho. *Perf. 11*
O143 O13 1c red, blue & black .25 .25

On No. O143, the denomination is shown as "1". See No. O154.

Type of 1985 and

O14

COIL STAMPS

1991 Litho. *Perf. 10 Vert.*
O144 O14 (29c) red, blue & blk .80 .50
O145 O13 29c red, blue & blk .70 .30

Plates of 400 in four panes of 100.

1991-93 Litho. *Perf. 11*
O146 O13 4c red, blue & blk .25 .30
O146A O13 10c red, blue & blk .30 .30
O147 O13 19c red, blue & blk .40 .50
O148 O13 23c red, blue & blk .50 .30

Perf. 11¼
O151 O13 $1 red, blue & blk 5.00 .75
Nos. O146-O151 (5) 6.45 2.15

Nos. O146A, O151 have a line of microscopic printing below eagle.
See No. O156 for 23c with microscopic text below eagle.
Imperfs of No. O148 are printer's waste.
Issued: No. O146, 4/6; Nos. O147-O148, 5/24; 10c, 10/19/93; No. O151, 9/1993.

COIL STAMPS

Inscribed: No. O152, For U.S. addresses only G.

Perf. 9.8 Vert.
O152 O14 (32c) red, blue & blk .65 .50
O153 O13 32c red, blue & blk 1.50 .50

Nos. O146A, O151, O153 have a line of microscopic text below the eagle.

1995, May 9 Untagged *Perf. 11.2*
O154 O13 1c red, blue & black .25 .50

Denomination on No. O154 has a cent sign. See No. O143.

O155 O13 20c red, blue & black .55 .50
O156 O13 23c red, blue & black .60 .50

COIL STAMP

1999, Oct. 8 *Perf. 9¾ Vert.*
O157 O13 33c red, blue & black 2.25 —

Type of 1985
COIL STAMP

2001, Feb. 27 *Perf. 9¾ Vert.*
O158 O13 34c red, blue & black 2.25 .50

Nos. O154-O158 have a line of microscopic text below the eagle.

Type of 1985
COIL STAMP

2002, Aug. 2 Photo. *Perf. 10 Vert.*
O159 O13 37c red, blue & black .75 .50

Type of 1985
COIL STAMP

2006, Mar. 8 *Perf. 10 Vert.*
O160 O13 39c red, blue & black 1.00 1.00

Type of 1988

2006, Sept. 29 Litho. *Perf. 11¼*
O161 O13 $1 red, blue & black 5.00 1.25

No. O161 has a solid blue background. No. O151 has a background of crosshatched lines.

Type of 1985
COIL STAMP

2007, June 25 *Perf. 9¾*
O162 O13 41c red, blue & black 1.00 1.00

Nos. O159-O162 have solid blue backgrounds. Nos. O138A-O158 have a background of crosshatched lines.

Type of 1985
Serpentine Die Cut 11½x10¾

2009, Feb. 24 Untagged
Self-Adhesive

O163 O13 1c red, blue & black .25 .40

NEWSPAPER STAMPS

For the prepayment of postage on bulk shipments of newspapers and periodicals. From 1875 on, the stamps were affixed to pages of receipt books, sometimes canceled and retained by the post office. Discontinued on July 1, 1898.

Virtually all used stamps of Nos. PR1-PR4 are canceled by blue brush strokes. All are rare. Most used stamps of Nos. PR9-PR32, PR57-PR79 and PR81-PR89 are pen canceled (or uncanceled), with some of Nos. PR9-PR32 also known canceled by a thick blue brush stroke.

Handstamp cancellations on any of these issues are rare and sell for much more than catalogue values which are for pen-canceled examples.

Used values for Nos. PR90-PR125 are for stamps with handstamp cancellations.

Washington — N1

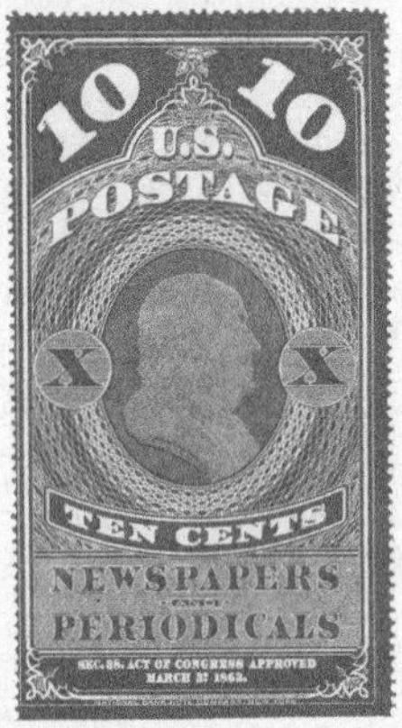

Franklin
N2

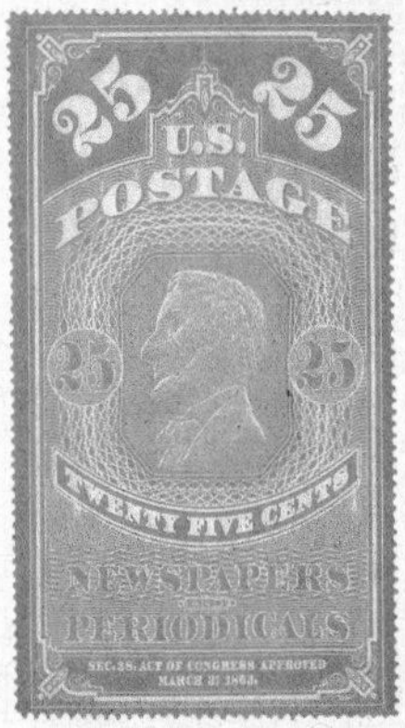

Lincoln
N3

Values for Nos. PR1-PR8 are for examples with perforations on all four sides. Examples with natural straight edges sell for somewhat less. Some panes were fully perforated, while others have natural straight edges either at top or bottom affecting five stamps in the pane of ten.

Printed by the National Bank Note Co.
Thin hard paper, without gum
Size of design: 51x95mm

Typographed and Embossed

1865 Unwmk. ***Perf. 12***

Colored Border

PR1	N1	5c dark blue	750.00	*2,000.*
a.		5c light blue	1,350.	*4,250.*
PR2	N2	10c blue green	300.00	*2,250.*
a.		10c green	300.00	*2,250.*
b.		Pelure paper	400.00	*2,000.*
PR3	N3	25c orange red	400.00	*2,500.*
a.		25c carmine red	475.00	*2,500.*
b.		Pelure paper	500.00	

Nos. PR1-PR3 used are valued with faults.

White Border

Yellowish paper

PR4	N1	5c light blue	900.00	*5,000.*
a.		5c dark blue	900.00	—
b.		Pelure paper	975.00	—
		Nos. PR1-PR4 (4)	2,350.	

No. PR4 used is valued with faults.

REPRINTS of 1865 ISSUE
Printed by the Continental Bank Note Co. using the original National Bank Note Co. plates

1875

Hard white paper, without gum

5c White Border, 10c and 25c Colored Border

PR5	N1	5c dull blue	225.00
a.		Printed on both sides	*5,750.*
PR6	N2	10c dark bluish green	250.00
a.		Printed on both sides	*4,250.*
PR7	N3	25c dark carmine	300.00
		Nos. PR5-PR7 (3)	775.00

The 5c has white border, 10c and 25c have colored borders.

Many fakes exist of Nos. PR1-PR7, some of high quality. Certification is highly recommended.

The Continental Bank Note Co. made another special printing from new plates, which did not have the colored border. These exist imperforate and perforated, but they were not regularly issued. Value, imperf. set $3,250.

Printed by the American Bank Note Co.
Soft porous paper, without gum

1881 **White Border**

PR8	N1	5c dark blue	750.

Statue of Freedom — N4

"Justice"
N5

Ceres
N6

"Victory"
N7

Clio
N8

Minerva
N9

Vesta
N10

"Peace"
N11

"Commerce"
N12

Hebe
N13

Indian Maiden
N14

Values for used examples of Nos. PR9-PR113 are for fine-very fine examples for denominations to $3, and fine for denominations of $5 or higher. Used examples of some Scott numbers might not exist without faults.

Printed by the Continental Bank Note Co.
Size of design: 24x35mm

1875, Jan. 1 **Engr.**

PR9	N4	2c black	350.00	45.00
		No gum	140.00	
PR10	N4	3c black	350.00	50.00
		No gum	140.00	
PR11	N4	4c black	350.00	45.00
		No gum	140.00	
PR12	N4	6c black	350.00	50.00
		No gum	140.00	
PR13	N4	8c black	350.00	75.00
		No gum	140.00	
PR14	N4	9c black	600.00	140.00
		No gum	225.00	
PR15	N4	10c black	375.00	67.50
		No gum	135.00	
PR16	N5	12c rose	800.00	110.00
		No gum	325.00	
PR17	N5	24c rose	1,000.	175.00
		No gum	400.00	
PR18	N5	36c rose	1,000.	200.00
		No gum	400.00	
PR19	N5	48c rose	1,250.	500.00
		No gum	450.00	
PR20	N5	60c rose	1,500.	125.00
		No gum	550.00	
PR21	N5	72c rose	1,500.	450.00
		No gum	550.00	
PR22	N5	84c rose	1,850.	450.00
		No gum	650.00	
PR23	N5	96c rose	*2,250.*	300.00
		No gum	875.00	
PR24	N6	$1.92 dk brn	*2,250.*	300.00
		No gum	825.00	
PR25	N7	$3 ver	2,500.	600.00
		No gum	975.00	
PR26	N8	$6 ultra	*4,250.*	650.00
		No gum	1,700.	
PR27	N9	$9 yel org	4,500.	*2,400.*
		No gum	1,750.	
PR28	N10	$12 bl grn	4,750.	*1,250.*
		No gum	1,850.	
PR29	N11	$24 dk gray vio	4,750.	*1,400.*
		No gum	1,850.	
PR30	N12	$36 brn rose	*5,500.*	*1,600.*
		No gum	2,250.	
PR31	N13	$48 red brn	*7,500.*	*1,800.*
		No gum	2,750.	
PR32	N14	$60 violet	*7,000.*	*2,000.*
		No gum	2,600.	

SPECIAL PRINTING of 1875 ISSUE
Printed by the Continental Bank Note Co.
Hard white paper, without gum

1875

PR33	N4	2c gray black	700.00
a.		Horiz. ribbed paper	500.00
PR34	N4	3c gray black	700.00
a.		Horiz. ribbed paper	550.00
PR35	N4	4c gray black	700.00
		Horiz. ribbed paper	1,000.
PR36	N4	6c gray black	1,000.
PR37	N4	8c gray black	1,100.
PR38	N4	9c gray black	1,200.
PR39	N4	10c gray black	1,500.
PR40	N5	12c pale rose	1,600.
PR41	N5	24c pale rose	2,250.
PR42	N5	36c pale rose	3,000.
PR43	N5	48c pale rose	4,000.
PR44	N5	60c pale rose	4,750.
PR45	N5	72c pale rose	4,500.
PR46	N5	84c pale rose	5,750.
PR47	N5	96c pale rose	*10,000.*
PR48	N6	$1.92 dk brn	*22,500.*
PR49	N7	$3 vermilion	*42,500.*
PR50	N8	$6 ultra	*70,000.*
PR51	N9	$9 yellow org	*350,000.*
PR52	N10	$12 blue green	*225,000.*
PR53	N11	$24 dk gray vio	*500,000.*
PR54	N12	$36 brn rose	*400,000.*
PR55	N13	$48 red brown	—
PR56	N14	$60 violet	—

Nos. PR50 and PR52 are valued in the grade of fine.

Although four examples of No. PR51 were sold, only one is currently documented.

No. PR54 is valued in the grade of fine. Although two stamps were sold, only one is currently documented.

All values of this issue, Nos. PR33 to PR56, exist imperforate but were not regularly issued thus. Value, set $60,000.

Printed by the American Bank Note Co.
Soft porous paper

1879

PR57	N4	2c black	75.00	17.50
		No gum	30.00	
PR58	N4	3c black	85.00	22.50
		No gum	35.00	
PR59	N4	4c black	85.00	22.50
		No gum	35.00	
a.		Double paper	—	
PR60	N4	6c black	125.00	40.00
		No gum	50.00	
PR61	N4	8c black	135.00	40.00
		No gum	55.00	
PR62	N4	10c black	135.00	40.00
		No gum	55.00	
PR63	N5	12c red	500.00	140.00
		No gum	210.00	
PR64	N5	24c red	500.00	140.00
		No gum	210.00	
PR65	N5	36c red	1,000.	375.00
		No gum	475.00	
PR66	N5	48c red	1,000.	350.00
		No gum	450.00	
PR67	N5	60c red	1,250.	325.00
		No gum	550.00	
a.		Imperf., pair	*4,000.*	
PR68	N5	72c red	1,500.	475.00
		No gum	700.00	
PR69	N5	84c red	1,250.	400.00
		No gum	575.00	
PR70	N5	96c red	1,500.	325.00
		No gum	700.00	
PR71	N6	$1.92 pale brn	550.00	200.00
		No gum	225.00	
PR72	N7	$3 red ver	625.00	230.00
		No gum	250.00	
PR73	N8	$6 blue	1,050.	350.00
		No gum	400.00	
PR74	N9	$9 orange	800.00	260.00
		No gum	325.00	
PR75	N10	$12 yel grn	850.00	260.00
		No gum	325.00	
PR76	N11	$24 dk vio	800.00	350.00
		No gum	300.00	
PR77	N12	$36 Indian red	850.00	400.00
		No gum	350.00	
PR78	N13	$48 yel brn	900.00	525.00
		No gum	350.00	
PR79	N14	$60 purple	850.00	450.00
		No gum	350.00	
		Nos. PR57-PR70 (14)	9,140.	2,713.

SPECIAL PRINTING of 1879 ISSUE
Printed by the American Bank Note Co.

Without gum

1883

PR80	N4	2c intense black	1,750.

REGULAR ISSUE
With gum

1885

PR81	N4	1c black, *July 1, 1885*	95.00	14.00
		Never hinged	225.00	
		No gum	42.50	
PR82	N5	12c carmine	200.00	35.00
		Never hinged	450.00	
		No gum	85.00	
PR83	N5	24c carmine	225.00	35.00
		Never hinged	500.00	
		No gum	95.00	
PR84	N5	36c carmine	350.00	65.00
		Never hinged	800.00	
		No gum	145.00	
PR85	N5	48c carmine	425.00	85.00
		Never hinged	975.00	
		No gum	180.00	
PR86	N5	60c carmine	600.00	120.00
		No gum	260.00	
PR87	N5	72c carmine	600.00	130.00
		No gum	260.00	
PR88	N5	84c carmine	900.00	290.00
		No gum	350.00	
PR89	N5	96c carmine	750.00	225.00
		Never hinged	2,250.	
		No gum	300.00	
		Nos. PR81-PR89 (9)	4,145.	999.00

See the Scott U.S. Specialized Catalogue Die and Plate Proof section for imperforates.

Printed by the Bureau of Engraving and Printing

1894

Soft wove paper, with pale, whitish gum

PR90	N4	1c intense blk	400.00	*5,000.*
		Never hinged	900.00	
		No gum	160.00	
PR91	N4	2c intense blk	450.00	—
		Never hinged	1,075.	
		No gum	190.00	

PR92 N4 4c intense blk 550.00 *13,500.*
Never hinged 1,275.
No gum 210.00
PR93 N4 6c intense blk 4,500.
Never hinged *11,500.*
No gum 1,900.
PR94 N4 10c intense blk 1,400. —
Never hinged *2,750.*
No gum 550.00
PR95 N5 12c pink 2,400. *4,500.*
Never hinged *3,500.*
No gum 1,100.
PR96 N5 24c pink 3,750. *8,000.*
Never hinged *8,500.*
No gum 1,850.
PR97 N5 36c pink *50,000.*
PR98 N5 60c pink *40,000.* *16,000.*
PR99 N5 96c pink *50,000.* —
PR100 N7 $3 scarlet *50,000.*
PR101 N8 $6 pale blue *50,000.* —
No gum *25,000.*

The never hinged block of No. PR96 is in the fine grade, and it is valued thus.

Nos. PR90, PR95-PR98 used are valued with fine centering and small faults.

No. PR97 unused is valued in the grade of very good to fine. No. PR98 unused is valued in the grade of fine. Nos. PR99-PR100 unused are valued in the grade of fine-very fine.

Statue of Freedom N15

"Justice" N16

"Victory" N17

Clio N18

Vesta N19

"Peace" N20

"Commerce" N21

Indian Maiden N22

Size of designs: 1c-50c, 21x34mm; $2-$100, 24x35mm

1895, Feb. 1

PR102 N15 1c black 230.00 *125.00*
Never hinged 500.00
No gum 90.00
PR103 N15 2c black 230.00 *125.00*
Never hinged 500.00
No gum 90.00
PR104 N15 5c black 300.00 *300.00*
Never hinged 650.00
No gum 125.00
PR105 N15 10c black 600.00 *600.00*
Never hinged 1,300.
No gum 240.00
PR106 N16 25c car 750.00 *650.00*
Never hinged 1,650.
No gum 300.00
PR107 N16 50c car *2,750.* *800.00*
Never hinged *6,250.*
No gum *875.00*
PR108 N17 $2 scarlet 2,250. *1,100.*
Never hinged *5,000.*
No gum 850.00
PR109 N18 $5 ultra 2,250. *1,750.*
No gum 850.00
PR110 N19 $10 green 2,500. *2,000.*
No gum 900.00
PR111 N20 $20 slate 3,250. *2,500.*
No gum 1,200.
PR112 N21 $50 dull rose 2,750. *950.00*
Never hinged *6,250.*
No gum 1,050.
PR113 N22 $100 purple 3,500. *7,000.*
No gum 1,400.
Nos. PR102-PR113 (12) 21,360. 17,900.

1895-97 Wmk. 191

PR114 N15 1c black 8.00 *25.00*
Never hinged 20.00
No gum 2.75
PR115 N15 2c black 8.00 *25.00*
Never hinged 20.00
No gum 2.75
PR116 N15 5c black 13.00 *40.00*
Never hinged 27.50
No gum 4.25
PR117 N15 10c black 13.00 *25.00*
Never hinged 27.50
No gum 4.25
PR118 N16 25c carmine 20.00 *65.00*
Never hinged 45.00
No gum 7.00
PR119 N16 50c carmine 25.00 *75.00*
Never hinged 55.00
No gum 8.50
PR120 N17 $2 scarlet 30.00 *110.00*
Never hinged 75.00
No gum 10.00
PR121 N18 $5 dark bl 40.00 *175.00*
Never hinged 100.00
No gum 13.50
a. $5 light blue 200.00 *500.00*
Never hinged 500.00
No gum 67.50
PR122 N19 $10 green 42.50 *175.00*
Never hinged 105.00
No gum 14.00
PR123 N20 $20 slate 45.00 *200.00*
Never hinged 110.00
No gum 15.00
PR124 N21 $50 dull rose 75.00 *400.00*
Never hinged 170.00
No gum 27.50
PR125 N22 $100 purple 65.00 *300.00*
Never hinged 150.00
No gum 22.50
Nos. PR114-PR125 (12) 384.50 *1,615.*
Nos. PR114-PR125, never hinged 905.00

In 1899 the Government sold 26,989 sets of these stamps, but, as the stock of high values was not sufficient to make up the required number, an additional printing was made of the $5, $10, $20, $50 and $100. These are virtually indistinguishable from earlier printings.

For overprints, see Nos. R159-R160.

PARCEL POST STAMPS

Issued for the prepayment of postage on parcel post packages only.

Post Office Clerk — PP1

City Carrier — PP2

Railway Postal Clerk — PP3

Rural Carrier — PP4

Mail Train — PP5

Steamship and Mail Tender — PP6

Automobile Service — PP7

Airplane Carrying Mail — PP8

Manufacturing PP9

Dairying PP10

Harvesting PP11

Fruit Growing PP12

1913 Wmk. 190 Engr. *Perf. 12*

Q1 PP1 1c carmine rose 4.25 1.60
Never hinged 12.00
Q2 PP2 2c carmine rose 5.00 1.25
Never hinged 12.50
a. 2c lake *3,750.*
b. 2c carmine lake *350.00*

No. Q2a is valued in the grade of fine-very fine.

Q3 PP3 3c carmine 9.00 6.00
Never hinged 24.00
Q4 PP4 4c carmine rose 27.50 3.00
Never hinged 77.50
Q5 PP5 5c carmine rose 22.50 2.25
Never hinged 62.50
Q6 PP6 10c carmine rose 40.00 3.00
Never hinged 90.00
Q7 PP7 15c carmine rose 60.00 13.50
Never hinged 170.00
Q8 PP8 20c carmine rose 110.00 25.00
Never hinged 260.00
Q9 PP9 25c carmine rose 52.50 8.00
Never hinged 145.00
Q10 PP10 50c carmine rose 210.00 45.00
Never hinged 525.00
Q11 PP11 75c carmine rose 85.00 35.00
Never hinged 190.00
Q12 PP12 $1 carmine rose 260.00 40.00
Never hinged 625.00
Nos. Q1-Q12 (12) 885.75 183.60
Nos. Q1-Q12, never hinged 2,273.

PARCEL POST POSTAGE DUE STAMPS

For affixing by a postal clerk to any parcel post package, to denote the amount to be collected from the addressee because of insufficient prepayment of postage.

PPD1

1913 Wmk. 190 Engr. *Perf. 12*

JQ1 PPD1 1c dark green 8.00 4.00
Never hinged 22.50
JQ2 PPD1 2c dark green 60.00 16.00
Never hinged 160.00
JQ3 PPD1 5c dark green 9.00 4.50
Never hinged 24.00
JQ4 PPD1 10c dark green 110.00 40.00
Never hinged 290.00
JQ5 PPD1 25c dark green 70.00 4.50
Never hinged 185.00
Nos. JQ1-JQ5 (5) 257.00 69.00
Nos. JQ1-JQ5, never hinged 642.50

SPECIAL HANDLING STAMPS

For use on fourth-class mail to secure the same expeditious handling accorded to first-class mail matter.

PP13

1925-28 Engr. Unwmk. *Perf. 11*

QE1 PP13 10c yellow green, wet printing, printed on "special" booklet paper, *1928* (see note before #551) 3.00 1.50
Never hinged 5.25
QE2 PP13 15c yellow green, wet printing, printed on "special" booklet paper, *1928* (see note before #551) 3.25 1.50
Never hinged 5.75
QE3 PP13 20c yellow green, wet printing, printed on "special" booklet paper, *1928* (see note before #551) 4.75 2.50
Never hinged 8.75
QE4 PP13 25c dp grn ('25) 20.00 4.00
Never hinged 37.50
a. yel grn ('28) 16.50 *22.50*
Never hinged 30.00
Nos. QE1-QE4 (4) 31.00 9.50
Nos. QE1-QE4, never hinged 57.25

COMPUTER VENDED POSTAGE

CVP1

CVP2

1989, Aug. 23 Tagged *Guillotined*
Self-Adhesive
Washington, DC, Machine 82
Date Other Than First Day

CVP1 CVP1 25c First Class 6.00 —
a. First day dated, serial Nos. 12501-15500 5.00 —
b. First day dated, serial Nos. 00001-12500 5.00 —
c. First day dated, over No. 27500 — —
CVP2 CVP1 $1 Third Class — —
a. First day dated, serial Nos. 24501-27500 — —
b. First day dated, over No. 27500 — —
CVP3 CVP2 $1.69 Parcel Post — —
a. First day dated, serial Nos. 21501-24500 — —
b. First day dated, over No. 27500 — —
CVP4 CVP1 $2.40 Priority Mail — —
a. First day dated, serial Nos. 18501-21500 — —
b. Priority Mail ($2.74), with bar code (CVP2) *100.00*
c. First day dated, over No. 27500 — —
CVP5 CVP1 $8.75 Express Mail — —
a. First day dated, serial Nos. 15501-18500 — —
b. First day dated, over No. 27500 — —

Washington, DC, Machine 83
Date Other Than First Day

CVP6 CVP1 25c First Class 6.00 —
a. First day dated, serial Nos. 12501-15500 5.00 —
b. First day dated, serial Nos. 00001-12500 5.00 —
c. First day dated, over No. 27500 — —
CVP7 CVP1 $1 Third Class — —
a. First day dated, serial Nos. 24501-27500 — —
b. First day dated, over No. 27500 — —
CVP8 CVP2 $1.69 Parcel Post 15.00 —
a. First day dated, serial Nos. 21501-24500 — —
b. First day dated, over No. 27500 — —
CVP9 CVP1 $2.40 Priority Mail — —
a. First day dated, serial Nos. 18501-21500 — —
b. First day dated, over No. 27500 — —

A Priority Mail $3.25 value also exists unused. A Priority Mail stamp exists on cover with error date 11/17/90 exists, and an unused stamp with error date 11/18/90 exists.

c. Priority Mail ($2.74), with bar code (CVP2) *100.00*

Error date 11/18/90 exists.

CVP10 CVP1 $8.75 Express Mail — —
a. First day dated, serial Nos. 15501-18500 — —
b. First day dated, over No. 27500 — —

Error date 11/17/90 exists.

1989, Sept. 1

Kensington, MD, Machine 82

Date Other Than First Day

CVP11 CVP1 25c First Class 6.00 —
- *a.* First day dated, serial Nos. 12501-15500 5.00 —
- *b.* First day dated, serial Nos. 00001-12500 5.00 —
- *c.* First day dated, over No. 27500 — —

CVP12 CVP1 $1 Third Class — —
- *a.* First day dated, serial Nos. 24501-27500 — —
- *b.* First day dated, over No. 27500 — —

CVP13 CVP2 $1.69 Parcel Post — —
- *a.* First day dated, serial Nos. 21501-24500 — —
- *b.* First day dated, over No. 27500 — —

CVP14 CVP1 $2.40 Priority Mail — —
- *a.* First day dated, serial Nos. 18501-21500 — —
- *b.* First day dated, over No. 27500 — —
- *c.* Priority Mail ($2.74), with bar code (CVP2) *100.00*

CVP15 CVP1 $8.75 Express Mail — —
- *a.* First day dated, serial Nos. 15501-18500 — —
- *b.* First day dated, over No. 27500 — —

Kensington, MD, Machine 83

Date Other Than First Day

CVP16 CVP1 25c First Class 6.00 —
- *a.* First day dated, serial Nos. 12501-15500 5.00 —
- *b.* First day dated, serial Nos. 00001-12500 5.00 —
- *c.* First day dated, over No. 27500 — —

CVP17 CVP1 $1 Third Class — —
- *a.* First day dated, serial Nos. 24501-27500 — —
- *b.* First day dated, over No. 27500 — —

CVP18 CVP2 $1.69 Parcel Post — *12.50*
- *a.* First day dated, serial Nos. 21501-24500 — —
- *b.* First day dated, over No. 27500 — —

CVP19 CVP1 $2.40 Priority Mail — —
- *a.* First day dated, serial Nos. 18501-21500 — —
- *b.* First day dated, over No. 27500 — —
- *c.* Priority Mail ($2.74), with bar code (CVP2) 100.00

CVP20 CVP1 $8.75 Express Mail — —
- *a.* First day dated, serial Nos. 15501-18500 — —
- *b.* First day dated, over No. 27500 — —

1989, Nov.

Washington, DC, Machine 11

CVP21 CVP1 25c First Class *150.00*
- *a.* First Class, with bar code (CVP2) —

Stamps in CVP1 design with $1.10 denominations exist (certified first class) dated 11/20/89. Value, unused, $650. A 45c denomination exists unused (dated 11/22/89) on cover to Europe and on Certificate of Mailing.

CVP22 CVP1 $1 Third Class *500.00*
CVP23 CVP2 $1.69 Parcel Post *500.00*
CVP24 CVP1 $2.40 Priority Mail *500.00*
- *a.* Priority Mail ($2.74), with bar code (CVP2) —

CVP25 CVP1 $8.75 Express Mail *500.00*

Washington, DC, Machine 12

CVP26 CVP1 25c First Class *200.00*

No. CVP26, dated 12/13/89 is known on cover. $1.10 Certified First Class stamps dated 11/20/89 exist on covers.

CVP27 CVP1 $1 Third Class *600.00*

A $1.40 Third Class stamp of type CVP2, dated Dec. 1 is known on a Dec. 2 cover.

CVP28 CVP2 $1.65 Parcel Post *600.00*
CVP29 CVP1 $2.40 Priority Mail *600.00*
- *a.* Priority Mail ($2.74), with bar code (CVP2) —

CVP30 CVP1 $8.75 Express Mail *600.00*

An $8.50 Express Mail stamp, dated Dec. 2, exists on cover.

CVP3 — Type 1

CVP3 — Type II

1992, Aug. 20 Engr. *Perf. 10 Horiz.*

Coil Stamp

CVP31 CVP3 29c red & blue, type I .75 .25
- *c.* 32c Type II ('94) 1.25 .40

No. CVP31 was available in all denominations from 1c to $99.99.

The listing is for the first class rate. Other denominations, se-tenant combinations, or "errors" are not listed.

Type II denomination has large sans-serif numerals preceded by an asterisk measuring 2mm across. No. CVP31 has small numerals with serifs preceded by an asterisk 1½mm across.

CVP4

1994, Feb. 19 Photo. *Perf. 9.9 Vert.*

CVP32 CVP4 29c dark red & dark blue .75 .35

No. CVP32 was available in all denominations from 19c to $99.99.

The listing is for the first class rate at time of issue. Other denominations, se-tenant combinations, or "errors" will not be listed.

1996, Jan. 26

CVP33 CVP4 32c brt red & blue, "1996" below design .75 .25

Letters in "USA" on No. CVP33 are thicker than on No. CVP32. Numerous other design differences exist in the moire pattern and in the bunting. No. CVP33 has "1996" in the lower left corner; No. CVP32 has no date.

For No. CVP33, the 32c value has been listed because it was the first class rate in effect at the time the stamp was issued.

CVP5

1999, June Tagged *Die Cut*

Self-Adhesive

CVP34 CVP5 33c black *50.00* —
- *a.* "Priority Mail" under encryption at LL — —
- *b.* "Express Mail" under encryption at LL — —

No. CVP34 was available from 15 NCR Automated Postal Center machines located in central Florida. Machines could produce values in any denomination required. The backing paper is taller and wider than the stamp.

Sales of No. CVP34 were discontinued in 2000 or 2001.

CVP6

1999, May 7 Tagged *Die Cut*

Self-Adhesive

Size: 77½x39mm

Microprinting Above Red Orange Line

CVP35 CVP6 33c blk & red org, control numbers only at LL, round corners 20.00 —
- *a.* "Priority Mail" at LL, square corners 150.00 —
- *b.* "Priority Mail AS" and text string at LL, square corners 150.00 —

No Microprinting Above Red Orange Line

CVP36 CVP6 33c blk & red org, control numbers only at LL, round corners 9.00 —
- *a.* "Priority Mail" at LL, square corners 125.00 —
- *b.* "Priority Mail AS" and text string at LL, square corners 125.00 —

Size: 73½x42mm

CVP37 CVP6 33c blk & pink, control numbers only at LL 3.75 —
- *a.* "Priority Mail" at LL 5.00 —
- *b.* "Priority Mail AS" and text string at LL 5.00 —

Nos. CVP35-CVP37 were available from 18 IBM Neopost machines located in central Florida, and at least one machine in the Washington, DC area (Merrifield, VA Automated Postal Center). The backing paper is taller than the stamp. Any denomination could be printed up to $99.99.

Simplypostage.com — CVP8

Serpentine Die Cut 8 at Right

2001 Self-Adhesive

Eagle and Stars Background

CVP39 CVP8 34c blk, blue & org, *2001* — —
CVP40 CVP8 34c blk, blue & org, with control number at UL, *2001* — —

Flag Background

CVP41 CVP8 34c blk, blue & org, with control number at UL, *2001* 50.00 —
CVP42 CVP8 34c blk, blue & org, with control number at UL, *2001* 50.00 20.00

Large Flag Design

The item shown was produced by Neopost. It was found that the large flag image hampered the barcode from being scanned. It is believed no examples were actually sold to the public. Five panes of four are believed to exist. Value, pane of 4, $300.

Neopostage.com CVP9

Serpentine Die Cut 8¾ at Right

2002, June Self-Adhesive

CVP43 CVP9 21c blk, blue & org 15.00
- *a.* Booklet pane of 10 200.00

CVP44 CVP9 23c blk, blue & org 10.00 —
- *a.* Booklet pane of 10 120.00

CVP45 CVP9 34c blk, blue & org 20.00 —
- *a.* Booklet pane of 10 250.00

CVP46 CVP9 37c blk, blue & org 12.50 —
- *a.* Booklet pane of 10 150.00

CVP47 CVP9 50c blk, blue & org 15.00 —
- *a.* Booklet pane of 10 180.00

CVP47B CVP9 57c blk, blue & org —
- *a.* Booklet pane of 10 —

CVP48 CVP9 60c blk, blue & org 14.00 —
- *a.* Booklet pane of 10 160.00

CVP49 CVP9 70c blk, blue & org 16.00 —
- *a.* Booklet pane of 10 200.00

CVP50 CVP9 80c blk, blue & org 18.00 —
- *a.* Booklet pane of 10 200.00

CVP51 CVP9 $3.50 blk, blue & org 60.00 —
- *a.* Booklet pane of 1 —
- *b.* Booklet pane of 2 —
- *c.* Booklet pane of 5 —
- *d.* Booklet pane of 10 700.00

CVP52 CVP9 $3.85 blk, blue & org 55.00
- *a.* Booklet pane of 1 —
- *b.* Booklet pane of 2 —
- *c.* Booklet pane of 5 —
- *d.* Booklet pane of 10 600.00

CVP52E CVP9 $12.45 blk, blue & org —
- *a.* Booklet pane of 1 —

CVP53 CVP9 $13.65 blk, blue & org — —
- *a.* Booklet pane of 1 —
- *b.* Booklet pane of 2 —
- *c.* Booklet pane of 5 —
- *d.* Booklet pane of 10 —

Nos. CVP43-CVP53 were printed only with the stated values.

Denominations of 34c, 57c, $3.50 and perhaps others exist with a ICNOVA kiosk location designation. These were produced during pre-issue testing at a location not publicly accessible and are not considered to be valid postage. Stamps from the ICNOVA location have much smaller 2-D bar code squares. The denominations listed above come from other publicly accessible kiosk locations from June 20, 2002, forward. Official sales of these stamps began on June 20, 2002, or later for some denominations.

The 21c, 34c, 57c, $3.50 and $12.45 denominations were only sold from June 21 to June 29, 2002. They are all scarce, and some are rare. The 37c, $3.85 and $13.65 denominations were not sold until June 30, 2002, when the rate change took effect.

While the name on Nos. CVP39-CVP42 reads simplypostage.com and the name on Nos. CVP43-CVP53 reads neopostage.com, both were products of Neopost.

Issued: Nos. CVP43-CVP49, CVP51-CVP53, 6/2002; No. CVP50, 7/2002.

Earliest documented use: Nos. CVP43, CVP47, CVP51-CVP52, not known used; Nos. CVP44, CVP46, CVP48-CVP49, CVP53, 6/30; No. CVP45, 6/21; No. CVP50, 7/3.

CVP10

IBM Pitney Bowes CVP11

2004, Apr. 14 *Die Cut*

Self-Adhesive

CVP54 CVP10 37c black & pink 5.00 —
- *a.* "First Class Mail" under encryption at LL 2.50 —
- *b.* "Priority Mail" under encryption at LL 2.50 —
- *c.* "Parcel Post" under encryption at LL 2.50 —
- *d.* "International" under encryption at LL 2.50 —

CVP55 CVP11 37c black, "US Postage" under encryption at LL 5.00 —
- *a.* "First Class Mail" under encryption at LL 2.50 —
- *b.* "Priority Mail" under encryption at LL 2.50 —

c. "Parcel Post" under encryption at LL 2.50 —
d. "International" under encryption at LL 2.50 —

Nos. CVP54-CVP55 could be printed in any denomination up to $99.99. Catalogue values for Nos. CVP54-CVP54d and CVP55 are for stamps with low denominations. Stamps with denominations appropriate to the service described are valued correspondingly higher.

CVP12

IBM Pitney Bowes CVP13

2004, Nov. 19 ***Die Cut***

Self-Adhesive

Serial Number Under Encryption APC

CVP56 CVP12 37c black 2.50 .45
CVP57 CVP13 37c black & pink 1.25 .45

Nos. CVP56-CVP57 could be printed in any denomination. No. CVP56 could be printed with three different rate inscriptions under the denomination. No. CVP57 could be printed with 18 different rate inscriptions and/or service indicators under the denomination, and with at least 27 different rate inscriptions and or/service indicators under the denomination on stamps with a four-digit code after the zip code.

Blank Under Denomination

"IM" and Numbers Under Encryption

CVP58 CVP13 60c black & pink 3.00 .50
CVP59 CVP13 80c black & pink 3.75 .50

"PM" and Numbers Under Encryption

CVP60 CVP13 $3.85 black & pink 15.00 .50

"EM" and Numbers Under Encryption

CVP61 CVP13 $13.65 black & pink 42.50 1.00

"IB" and Numbers Under Encryption

CVP62 CVP13 $1 black & pink 4.00 .25

Nos. CVP58-CVP61 could only be printed in denominations listed. No. CVP62 could be printed in any denomination above 99c. As of May 12, 2008, it was possible to create stamps with "IB" and numbers under encryption in any denomination. The computer software was later changed to once again only permit stamps of certain denominations to be created with "IB" and numbers under the encryption.

IBM Pitney Bowes Type of 2004

2006 Self-Adhesive ***Die Cut***

Blank Under Denomination

"IM" and Numbers Under Encryption

CVP63 CVP13 48c black & pink 1.50 .40
CVP64 CVP13 63c black & pink 1.75 .50
CVP65 CVP13 84c black & pink 2.25 .50

"PM" and Numbers Under Encryption

CVP66 CVP13 $4.05 black & pink 11.00 .50
CVP66A CVP13 $8.10 black & pink 30.00 1.00

"EM" and Numbers Under Encryption

CVP67 CVP13 $14.40 black & pink 32.50 1.00

Nos. CVP63-CVP67 could only be printed in denominations listed.

IBM Pitney Bowes CVP14

2006 Self-Adhesive ***Die Cut***

No Inscription Under Encryption

Serial Number to Right of "APC"

"Ship To:" Above Destination City

CVP69 CVP14 39c black 2.25 .25

Nos. CVP69 could be printed in any denomination, with 14 different rate inscriptions and/or service indicators under the denomination on stamps having "Ship To:" at the left and no code below the weight, and at least 29 different rate inscriptions and/or service indicators under the denomination on stamps having a four-digit code at the right that is even with the words "Ship To:" and below the weight.

IBM Pitney Bowes Type of 2004

2006(?)-07 Self-Adhesive ***Die Cut***

Blank Under Denomination

"IB" and Numbers Under Encryption

CVP70 CVP13 39c black & pink 1.00 .50
CVP71 CVP13 41c black & pink 1.75 .50
CVP72 CVP13 69c black & pink 2.50 .70

"IM" and Numbers Under Encryption

CVP73 CVP13 61c black & pink 2.25 .50
CVP74 CVP13 90c black & pink 3.50 .95

Nos. CVP70-CVP74 could only be printed in the denominations listed.

Nos. CVP71-CVP74 issued May, 2007. No. CVP70 was issued before the May rate change. As of May 12, 2008, it was possible to create stamps with "IB" and numbers under encryption in any denomination. The computer software was later changed to once again only permit stamps of certain denominations to be created with "IB" and numbers under the encryption. No. CVP70 was available for sale from Nov. 2006 to May 13, 2007. Nos. CVP71-CVP72 were available for sale from May 14, 2007 to May 11, 2008.

Pitney Bowes With Eagle at Right CVP15

2006, Dec. Self-Adhesive ***Die Cut***

CVP75 CVP15 41c blk & pink, no inscription below sold date — —
a. "Mailed From Zip Code ..." on bottom line 35.00 —
b. "Postcard" on bottom line 15.00 —
c. "First-Class Mail" on bottom line 15.00 —
d. "First-Class Mail Intl" on bottom line 15.00 —
e. "Priority" on bottom line 15.00 —
f. "Priority Envelope" on bottom line 15.00 —
g. "Priority Box" on bottom line 15.00 —
h. "Express Mail" on bottom line 30.00 —
i. "Express Envelope" on bottom line 30.00 —
j. "Parcel Post" on bottom line — —
k. "Priority Tube" on bottom line — —
l. "First Class" on bottom line 15.00 —

No. CVP75 was put into service at large companies and universities in Dec. 2006, with the majority of the machines not being available to the general public. Information about this stamp was not made available until 2007. Other rates and inscriptions might be available.

Nos. CVP75a could be printed in any denomination. Nos. CVP75b-CVP75f could be printed only in pre-programmed denominations based on the current rates for the service, or in any denominations at or above the minimum rates for the service. Values are for stamps with low denominations. A stamp with "Priority - Irregular Shape" on the bottom line has been reported to exist but has not been seen by the editors. Inscriptions generated by the software may vary from machine to machine depending on when the software was installed.

Two distinctly different colors of phosphor stripes on labels used in Mail & Go machines are known, with many Mail & Go adhesives appearing in both versions.

Private sector operators of Pitney Bowes "Mail & Go" machines are not bound to use only label paper supplied by Pitney Bowes. Competing label paper producers make and sell labels in the formats required for the machines that dispense Nos. CVP75 and CVP84. Thus, Nos. CVP75 and CVP84 without the Pitney Bowes logo on the reverse are not errors.

IBM Pitney Bowes Type of 2004

2008, May Self-Adhesive ***Die Cut***

Blank Under Denomination

"IM" and Numbers Under Encryption

CVP76 CVP13 94c black & pink 3.00 .60
CVP77 CVP13 $1.20 black & pink 3.75 1.25

Nos. CVP76-CVP77 could only be printed in the denominations listed.

IBM CVP16

Die Cut With Rounded Corners

2008, June 4 Self-Adhesive

CVP78 CVP16 42c black & pink 4.25 —
a. Without "date of sale" inscription, *2009* — —

Die Cut With Perpendicular Corners

CVP79 CVP16 42c black & pink 4.25 —
a. Without "date of sale" inscription, *2009* — —

Nos. CVP78-CVP79 were made available during a pilot study to evaluate a new IBM kiosk at Schaumburg, IL. No. CVP78 could be printed in any denomination from 1c to $25. Each kiosk transaction was limited to $100. Individual panes with 6, 7, 8, 9 or 10 stamps could be purchased as long as the total face value of the pane did not exceed $100. The pane of 10 exists with the vertical pink tagging stripe along the left side of the stamps. The pane of 10 could only be bought with stamps denominated from 1c to $10. Stamps denominated from $10.01 to $16.66 could only be purchased in panes containing fewer than 10 stamps. Stamps denominated from $16.67 to $25 could only be purchased as a single stamp.

IBM Pitney Bowes Type of 2004

2009 Self-Adhesive ***Die Cut***

Blank Under Denomination

"IM" and Numbers Under Encryption

CVP80 CVP13 98c black & pink 2.00 .60
CVP81 CVP13 $1.24 black & pink 2.50 1.25

Nos. CVP80-CVP81 could only be printed in denominations listed.

IBM (Statue of Liberty) CVP17

Illustration reduced.

Die Cut With Rounded Corners

2009, June 5 Self-Adhesive

CVP82 CVP17 44c black & pink 7.50 —
a. Without "date of sale" inscription, *2009* — —

Die Cut With Perpendicular Corners

CVP83 CVP17 44c black & pink 7.50 —
a. Without "date of sale" inscription, *2009* — —

No. CVP82 could be printed in any denomination from 1c to $25. Nos. CVP82-CVP83 were made available during a pilot study to evaluate a new IBM kiosk at Schaumburg, IL. The machine study at Schaumburg was scheduled to end on July 31, 2009. No. CVP82 was created for purchases of one to five individual stamps or any extra stamps beyond multiples of 10 ending in numerals 1 to 5.

INVERTS

Labels used to produce stamps in the dimensions of many items of CVP54 and similar later issues in this format were packaged in a fanfolded strip two labels wide and packaged in boxes that are stored in the machines from which the labels are fed to printers as purchases occur. Nothing prevents the labels from being fed in reverse, which results in inverted paper "errors." Such "inverts" (with phosphor stripe appearing on the opposite edge of the stamp than the intended edge) can be deliberately produced, and therefore are not listed.

SERVICE-INSCRIBED STAMPS

Listings of small label stamps from CVP84 reveal that various service-related abbreviations appear under the denominations of some stamps. From CVP84 onward (including the FOLD HERE varieties), all denominated stamps may be purchased that include service-specific indicators under the denominations (e.g., EXPRESS for a clearly identifiable service as well as abbreviations that are less clear such as EM HFPU FRB). When a machine asks a mailer if any postage is already affixed to an item, the mailer can indicate that all postage but one cent or more is affixed. A customer stating that almost all required postage is already affixed will result in the stamp vending machine dispensing a stamp with a service-specific indicator that has a face value as low as one cent. For this reason, listings no longer include small format vended stamps with service-specific indicators beyond No. CVP84, because the stamps can be produced to show any face value, use not being restricted to the class indicated, and all types may be used on any mail matter.

Flag — CVP18

Serpentine Die Cut 13¼x12½

2011, Oct. 18 Self-Adhesive

CVP84 CVP18 44c multi, date sold only on bottom line — —
a. Date sold and "Postcard" on bottom line — —
b. Date sold and "First-Class" on bottom line — —

No. CVP84 was issued in panes of 10. It was made available at Mail & Go postal stations in Super Target stores in the Dallas, TX area. Panes could be printed in any denomination from 29c to $9.99. Serpentine die cut 9 examples of No. CVP84 with dates earlier than Oct. 18 were produced at Pitney Bowes facilities. This serpentine die cut 9 sticker stock is not known to have been sent out for use in machines that were available for use by the general public. No. CVP84 was made available in 2013 with dozens of images other than the flag shown. These optional images are for various holidays and events, as well as social causes, such as support for breast cancer, education and recycling. One image, for bridal showers, has been made available in two different types.

Pitney Bowes With Eagle at Left — CVP18a

Pitney Bowes Without Eagle — CVP18b

Die Cut With Perpendicular Corners

2011, Oct. 18 **Self-Adhesive**

CVP84C CVP18a 46c black & pink, no inscription below sold date 5.00 —
- *d.* CVP18b 46c With eagle emblem omitted — —
- *e.* "Mailed From Zip Code ..." on bottom line — —
- *f.* "Postcard" on bottom line 7.50 —
- *g.* "First-Class Mail" on bottom line 5.00 —
- *h.* "First-Class Mail Intl" on bottom line — —
- *i.* "Priority Mail" on bottom line — —
- *j.* "Priority Envelope" on bottom line — —
- *k.* "Priority Box" on bottom line — —
- *l.* "Priority Tube" on bottom line — —
- *m.* "Priority - Irregular Shape" on bottom line — —
- *n.* "Express Mail" on bottom line — —

No. CVP84C was made available at Mail & Go postal stations in Super Target stores in the Dallas, TX area, and presumably could be printed in any denomination.

In 2013, twelve Mail & Go machines vending No. CVP84C and the holiday and social cause designs noted under No. CVP84 were installed and operated at thirteen Rite Aid drug stores in central California along the Highway 1 corridor. The machines were installed by the LePages Company (a USPS-licensed manufacturer and wholesaler of USPS-brand mailing supplies). They were placed under the jurisdiction of the Oakland, CA region of the USPS throughout most of 2014-15. Postmasters in the towns supported the machines officially with Priority Mail containers, postal labels and daily mail collection. The locations were listed by the USPS in its online Internet database of self-service post office locations. The machines appear to have been removed between Oct. 2015 and Jan. 2016.

The stamps vended by these machines were officially approved by the USPS and are no different than stamps sold from the same models of machines installed at colleges and universities across the nation. Locations of about 40 other privately supported Mail & Go machines have been recorded. These other machines are installed and operated by Pitney Bowes employees who manage mail rooms the company operates under contracts. At those locations, the mail room staff takes the daily mail to the local post officce, and there is no USPS logistical support.

The USPS regulations classify Mail & Go machines as "third party kiosks." No. CVP84Cd is an error that Pitney Bowes technicians could not explain. It appeared for a short time on a machine in Illinois and at the U.S. Department of Defense Medical HQ facility mailroom in Annandale, Va., and other unidentified locations.

Thermal prints generated by vending machines with too little electrically generated heat tend to fade very quickly.

APC With Vertical Coding at Right of Date CVP19

Die Cut With Rounded Corners

2012, Apr. 12 **Self-Adhesive**

CVP85 CVP19 black & pink 1.50 —
- *a.* Die cut with perpendicular corners, colored bar at left, "Fold Here" at center, 100x38mm — —

No. CVP85 has "APC" reading upwards at right. No. CVP78 has "IBM" reading upwards at right. No. CVP85 was available during a nationwide test of machines, and could be printed in any denomination from 1c to $99.99.

No. CVP85a was produced on label stock normally used for No. CVP87 when machines ran out of label stock to produce orders for Nos. CVP85, CVP85B, and varieties of CVP86.

APC With Vertical Coding At Left of Date — CVP19a

Die Cut With Rounded Corners

2012 **Self-Adhesive**

CVP85B CVP19a black & pink 2.00 —
- *c.* Die cut with perpendicular corners, colored bar at left, "FOLD HERE" at center, 100x38mm 2.00 —

No. CVP85Bc was produced on label stock normally used for No. CVP87 when machines ran out of stock to produce orders for Nos. CVP85, CVP85B, and varieties of CVP86.

APC Variable Vignette Stamp CVP20

Die Cut With Rounded Corners

2012, Apr. 12 **Self-Adhesive**

CVP86 CVP20 (45c) black & pink 2.50 —
- *a.* Die cut with perpendicular corners, colored bar at left, "Fold Here" at center, 100x38mm 3.00 —

No. CVP86 was available during a nationwide test of machines, and could be printed only as "Forever" stamps. The vignette portion of the stamp at left could be chosen from a gallery of six images (Mr. Zip, Heart, Flowers, Flag, Eagle, and Balloons and "Celebrate!", which is depicted). Values are for any vignette, or for any other vignette that may be programmed into the machine at a later date. Each vignette design could be purchased in a quantities ranging from 1 stamp to 100 stamps, but because a $1 minimum purchase was required, at least three examples of the first stamp chosen had to be purchased. A maximum of ten stamps could be printed on a sheet. Sales of stamps that are not in multiples of 10 were printed in strips, smaller-sized sheets containing an even number of stamps, or in sheets having one label inscribed "This Block Is Not Valid Postage" when the sheet contained an odd number of stamps.

No. CVP86a was produced on wide-label stock normally used for No. CVP87 when the small-label printer was defective or the machine had run out of small-label stock.

Examples of No. CVP86 without a printed image at left are the result of machines having their image-printing capability shut off so preprinted label stock for producing No. CVP88 could be substituted for the blank label stock used for Nos. CVP85 and CVP86. See footnote under No. CVP88 for information about examples of No. CVP86 with date of purchase inscriptions to right of "Forever."

APC With Vertical Coding to Right of Date CVP21

Die Cut With Perpendicular Corners

2012, Apr. 12 **Self-Adhesive**

CVP87 CVP21 black & pink — —

No. CVP87 was available during a nationwide test of machines, and could be printed in any denomination from 1c to $99.99. Stamps can be inscribed with a variety of different service inscriptions.

APC With Vertical Coding to Left of Date — CVP21a

Die Cut With Perpendicular Corners

2012 **Self-Adhesive**

CVP87A CVP21a black & pink — —

Labels of type CVP21a with postage indicia inscribed FCM LETTER below the denomination have only a bar code and the Zip code of the destination at the bottom third rather than a USPS TRACKING NUMBER. Labels for which a Certified Mail fee has been paid have a CERTIFIED MAIL bar code. Express Mail labels have POSTAL USE ONLY form at the bottom.

On Nov. 7, 2013, the USPS had distributed and had begun requiring the use of "signalling label" stock with a clear phosphor stripe. The clear stripe appears positioned vertically along the left margin of the labels. Labels with pink stripes along the right margin continued to be used until stocks were exhausted or labels with pre-printed vignettes were issued for use in some machines on Apr. 1, 2014 (CVP90-CVP91).

APC With Vertical Coding at Left of Date And Clear Phosphor Stripe Along Left Margin — CVP21b

Die Cut With Rounded Corners

2013, Nov. 7 **Self-Adhesive**

CVP87B CVP21b black 5.00 —
- *c.* Die cut with perpendicular corners, colored bar at left, "Fold Here" at center, 100x38mm 8.50 —

The Scheduled Delivery and Expected Delivery inscriptions, date and times seen on Nos. CVP89B and CVP89C replaced "THIS BLOCK IS NOT VALID FOR POSTAGE" on labels normally found adjacent to Nos. CVP87B and CVP92A when sold for other than Priority Mail.

Mailbox CVP22

Die Cut With Rounded Corners

2012, Oct. 31 **Self-Adhesive**

CVP88 CVP22 (45c) multicolored 3.50 —

The mailbox vignette is preprinted on No. CVP88. This preprinted stock was placed in machines in November 2012 and was to be removed from machines on December 31, 2012. The earliest known date of sale is Nov. 10, 2012.

Examples of No. CVP88 with the mailbox design covered by images used for Nos. CVP85 and CVP86 were the result of machines having their blank label stock replaced with the pre-printed label stock while the machine's image-printing capability was not shut off to accommodate the preprinted stock.

On No. CVP88, the number of the month and last two digits of the year in which the stamp was purchased, separated by an asterisk, appear to the right of "Forever." If the operator of the machine programmed it to sell No. CVP88 but failed to turn off the vignettes available as No. CVP86 and did not load the preprinted Christmas Mailbox label stock, the resulting vended product would be No. CVP86 with the month and year appearing to the right of "FOREVER."

Labels inscribed "This Block Is Not Valid For Postage" differ from similar labels created with No. CVP86. Various sizes of "Void" overprints on these labels exist.

USPS Emblem — CVP22a

Die Cut With Rounded Corners

2013, Oct. 31 **Self-Adhesive**

CVP88A CVP22a (46c) black & pink 3.00 —
- *b.* Die cut with perpendicular corners, colored bar at left, "Fold Here" at center, 100x38mm 7.50 —

This design was first placed in a few machines in the Washington, DC and Merrifield, VA area on Oct. 31, 2013. Stamps vended with encoded dates prior to Nov. 7, 2013 were test stamps. On Nov. 6, 2013, the USPS declared the test to be successful and the image was released for general use as a fall-back design.

No. CVP88Ab was produced on wide-label stock normally used to produce No. CVP87 when the small-label printer was either defective or machines ran out of stock to produce orders for No. CVP88A. The earliest known sale date of No. CVP88Ab is Nov. 2, 2013.

Examples of CVP88A lacking the eagle vignette could be made if the machine had blank label stock in the feeder but was set to print on pre-printed labels such as No. CVP89. When the machine has pre-printed labels (starting with No. CVP89) in the feeder and is set to print on blank labels, the Eagle vignette will print on top of the preprinted image.

Reindeer CVP23

Die Cut With Rounded Corners

2013, Nov. 7 **Self-Adhesive**

CVP89 CVP23 (46c) multicolored 3.00 2.00

The reindeer vignette is preprinted on No. CVP89. The issue date is the earliest documented sale date.

USPS Emblem With Clear Phosphor Stripe Along Left Margin — CVP23a

Die Cut With Rounded Corners

2014, Jan. 8 **Self-Adhesive**

CVP89A CVP23a (46c) black 3.00 —
- *d.* (50c) Vertical serial number with no leading letter, *2018* 2.50 —

Examples of CVP89A lacking the eagle vignette could be made if the machine had blank label stock in the feeder but was set to print on pre-printed labels such as No. CVP89. When the machine has pre-printed labels (starting with No. CVP89) in the feeder and is set to print on blank labels, the Eagle vignette will print on top of the preprinted image. Examples known include 2018-generation stamps with serial number with no leading letter.

APC With Scheduled Delivery — CVP23b

Die Cut With Perpendicular Corners

2014, Jan. **Self-Adhesive**

CVP89B CVP23b black & pink — —

No. CVP89B is generated when the mailer answers a machine-system prompt with a "no" answer when asked if the full-length label (Type CVP21) will fit on the mailer's item. This is vended only when pre-printed labels are installed in the machine or the small-label printer is defective.

For selected mail service the USPS doesn't track, the field to the right of "FOLD HERE" remains blank (in effect creating No. CVP87Bc).

APC With Expected Delivery — CVP23c

Die Cut With Perpendicular Corners

2014, Jan. **Self-Adhesive**

CVP89C CVP23c black & pink — —

See note after No. CVP89B.

Spiderman CVP24

Die Cut With Rounded Corners

2014, Apr. 1 **Self-Adhesive**

CVP90 CVP24 (49c) multicolored 3.00 1.25

The Spiderman vignette is preprinted on No. CVP90.

Flag — CVP25

Die Cut With Rounded Corners

2014, Apr. 1 **Self-Adhesive**

CVP91 CVP25 (49c) multicolored 3.00 1.25
- *a.* "FOREVER" (only) missing — —
- *b.* (50c) With vertical serial number with no leading letter, *2018* 3.00 1.50

The flag vignette is preprinted on No. CVP91.

Examples of No. CVP91b exist with the USPS Eagle emblem (see illustration at design CVP23a) printed on top of the preprinted flag design label; value, $5. It is theoretically possible that blank labels without a preprinted flag or other preprinted design could be inserted in the new machine, and (likely) be printed without the operator having turned on the thermal-printed USPS logo that machines can produce on-site, leaving an indicia and value printed on a stamp without any pictorial element. Such varieties are products of local operator error that has occurred on all issues from No. CVP88 in 2013 and can be manufactured through illicit cooperation of postal officials.

Rudolph, the Red-Nosed Reindeer CVP26

Die Cut With Rounded Corners

2014, Nov. 6 **Self-Adhesive**

CVP92 CVP26 (49c) multicolored 4.00 1.75

The Rudolph vignette is preprinted on No. CVP92.

From Nov. 14, 2014, Automated Postal Centers (APC) vending machines were renamed by the USPS to be Self Service Kiosks (SSK), and the machines were changed to issue stamps inscribed "SSK" rather than "APC."

SSK With Vertical Coding at Left of Date — CVP27

Die Cut With Rounded Corners

2014, Nov. 14 **Self-Adhesive**

CVP93 CVP27 black & pink — —
- *a.* Black, with vertical transparent stripe at left 1.00 —

No. CVP93 was available at machines that had not yet retired the pink-striped labels.

It was not intended by the USPS that indicia inscribed with SSK would be printed on pink-striped labels. The design was shifted to appear farther to the right, to insure the bar code would remain uncompromised and at a safe distance from the clear phosphor stripe on the newer labels. Almost all examples of this issue will have SSK appearing within the pink stripe.

Value of No. CVP93a is for 49c denomination, current at the time. Other denominations pro-rata.

SSK With Vertical Coding to Left of Date CVP28

Die Cut With Perpendicular Corners

2014, Nov. 14 **Self-Adhesive**

CVP94 CVP28 black & pink 2.50 —
- *a.* Indicia at upper right with no leading letter, various service level indicators, *2018* 2.50 —

Like No. CVP87A, No. CVP94 exists in other denominations inscribed with various mail service inscriptions or with blackened square in place of letters such as "F," above.

SSK With Blank Area at Right of "Fold Here" CVP29

Die Cut With Perpendicular Corners

2014, Nov. 14 **Self-Adhesive**

CVP95 CVP29 black & pink 5.00 —
- *a.* black, vertical serial number with no leading letter, clear phosphor stripe, *2018* 5.00 —

See note below No. CVP89B.

SSK With "Expected Delivery" at Right of "Fold Here" — CVP30

Die Cut With Perpendicular Corners

2014, Nov. 14 **Self-Adhesive**

CVP96 CVP30 black & pink — —
- *a.* black, vertical serial number with no leading letter, various service level indicators, clear phosphor stripe, *2018* 3.00 —

See note below No. CVP89B.

SSK With "Scheduled Delivery" at Right of "Fold Here" — CVP31

Die Cut With Perpendicular Corners

2014, Nov. 14 **Self-Adhesive**

CVP97 CVP31 black & pink — —
- *a.* black, vertical serial number with no leading letter, various sevice level indicators, clear phosphor stripe, *2018* 3.00 —

See note below No. CVP89B.

Charlie Brown Looking in Mailbox CVP32

Die Cut With Rounded Corners

2015, Oct. 20 **Self-Adhesive**

CVP98 CVP32 (49c) multicolored 4.00 1.00

The Charlie Brown vignette is preprinted on No. CVP98. Issue date is earliest recorded sale date. Post offices were authorized to place the labels in machines at the close of business on Oct. 20, which many did prior to the SSK system-wide date change that occurs daily prior to midnight.

mPOS CVP33

Die Cut With Rounded Corners

2015 **Self-Adhesive**

CVP99 CVP33 black — —

No. CVP99 is generated by a mobile hand-held point-of-sale vending machine with integrated thermal postage printer and embedded credit/debit card acceptance processor. Possible denominations are limited to the postage prices applicable to each available pre-printed type of Priority and Express Mail flat rate envelopes and packages (rate determined by scanning the bar code on the package the customer needs). While this indicia is intended to be affixed to mail matter at the time it is presented, postage can be generated and sold in quantities to take away for later use. Labels are generated from vertical coils with blank labels.

Wreath in Window CVP34

Die Cut With Rounded Corners

2016, Oct. 27 **Self-Adhesive**

CVP100 CVP34 (47c) multi 3.00 1.00

The wreath in window vignette is preprinted on No. CVP100. Issue date is earliest recorded sale date.

Christmas Cookies CVP35

Die Cut With Rounded Corners

2017, Oct. 17 **Self-Adhesive**

CVP101 CVP35 (49c) multi 3.00 1.00
- *a.* On 2018-generation stamp with serial number with no leading letter — —

The Christmas cookies vignette is preprinted on No. CVP101. Issue date is earliest recorded sale date.

Flag — CVP36

Die Cut With Rounded Corners

2018, Aug. 23 **Self-Adhesive**

CVP108 CVP36 (50c) multi 3.00 1.00

The flag vignette is preprinted on No. CVP108. Issue date is earliest recorded sale date.

Santa Claus CVP37

Die Cut With Rounded Corners

2018, Oct. 21 **Self-Adhesive**

CVP109 CVP37 (50c) multi 2.50 1.00

The Santa Claus vignette is preprinted on No. CVP109. Issue date is earliest recorded sale date.

Christmas Stocking CVP38

Die Cut With Rounded Corners

2020, Nov. 16 **Self-Adhesive**

CVP110 CVP38 (55c) multi 2.50 1.00

The Christmas stocking vignette is preprinted on No. CVP110.

Santa Claus, Sleigh and Reindeer in Flight CVP39

Die Cut With Rounded Corners

2021, Nov. **Self-Adhesive**

CVP111 CVP39 (58c) multi 2.50 1.00

The Santa Claus vignette is preprinted on No. CVP111.

Elf Tying Ribbon CVP40

Die Cut With Rounded Corners

2022, Nov. **Self-Adhesive**

CVP112 CVP40 (60c) multi 2.50 1.00

The elf vignette is preprinted on No. CVP112.

PERSONAL COMPUTER POSTAGE

Personal computer postage, approved by the US Postal Service, was created by subscribing to Stamps.com, an Internet website. Customers ordered self-adhesive labels showing vignettes, but lacking any franking value. The franking value indicia of the stamps could be printed at the customer's convenience at any computer with an Internet connection, using the customer's access codes. Any postage printed would be charged against the customer's account.

Neopost

CVPA1

2000 ***Serpentine Die Cut 8***

Self-Adhesive

1CVP1 CVPA1 33c black, yellow & pink — —

Stamps.com

Flag and Star — CVPA1a

Serpentine Die Cut 5¾ at Left

2002, July

"Stamps.com" in Lower Case Letters

Identification Code Below Zip Code

No Mail Class Inscribed

1CVP2 CVPA1a 37c black, blue & orange 7.00 3.00

Identification Code Above Zip Code Inscribed "US Postage" only

1CVP2A CVPA1a 37c black, blue & orange 4.00 3.00

a. "First Class" below "US Postage" 2.75 2.00

b. "Priority" below "US Postage" 8.25 2.50

c. "Express" below "US Postage" 25.00 5.00

d. "Media Mail" below "US Postage" 7.75 2.50

e. "Parcel Post" below "US Postage" 7.75 2.50

f. "Bound Printed Matter" below "US Postage" 7.75 2.50

g. "BPM" below "US Postage" 7.75 2.50

See Nos. 1CVP9, 1CVP21.

No. 1CVP2 apparently could be printed in denominations up to and including 37c. The 37c denomination comes with "FIRST-CLASS" between the Zip code and the identification code.

Later versions of the Stamps.com software allow any denomination to be printed, as well as additional or different mail-class inscriptions, on any basic stamp except for No. 1CVP2.

Values for Nos. 1CVP2A and 1CVP3-1CVP42 are for items appropriate to the service described. Stamps with denominations far lower than those appropriate to the service are valued correspondingly lower.

The software changes allow Nos. 1CVP2A and 1CVP3-1CVP37 to be printed with the mail-class inscriptions described for Nos. 1CVP38f-1CVP38p.

Later software changes allow Nos. 1CVP2A, 1CVP3-1CVP42 and 1CVP51-1CVP58 to be printed with mail-class inscriptions "Library Mail," "Intl. First Class," "Intl Priority," "Intl Express," and "M-Bag" with any denomination.

Love — CVPA2

2002 ***Serpentine Die Cut 5¾ at Left***

1CVP3 CVPA2 37c black, blue & orange 4.00 4.00

a. "First Class" below "US Postage" 2.75 2.00

b. "Priority" below "US Postage" 8.25 2.50

c. "Express" below "US Postage" 25.00 5.00

d. "Media Mail" below "US Postage" 7.75 2.50

e. "Parcel Post" below "US Postage" 7.75 2.50

f. "Bound Printed Matter" below "US Postage" 7.75 2.50

g. "BPM" below "US Postage" 7.75 2.50

Statue of Liberty and Flag — CVPA3

Liberty Bell and Flag — CVPA4

Eagle and Flag — CVPA5

George Washington and Flag — CVPA6

Capitol Building and Flag — CVPA7

Serpentine Die Cut 5¾ at Left

2003, June

1CVP4 CVPA3 37c black, blue & orange 3.50 2.00

a. "First Class" below "US Postage" 3.25 2.00

b. "Priority" below "US Postage" 8.00 1.00

c. "Express" below "US Postage" 25.00 3.00

d. "Media Mail" below "US Postage" 7.50 1.00

e. "Parcel Post" below "US Postage" 7.50 1.00

f. "Bound Printed Matter" below "US Postage" 7.50 1.00

g. "BPM" below "US Postage" 7.50 1.00

1CVP5 CVPA4 37c black, blue & orange 3.50 2.00

a. "First Class" below "US Postage" 3.25 2.00

b. "Priority" below "US Postage" 8.00 1.00

c. "Express" below "US Postage" 25.00 3.00

d. "Media Mail" below "US Postage" 7.50 1.00

e. "Parcel Post" below "US Postage" 7.50 1.00

f. "Bound Printed Matter" below "US Postage" 7.50 1.00

g. "BPM" below "US Postage" 7.50 1.00

1CVP6 CVPA5 37c black, blue & orange 3.50 2.00

a. "First Class" below "US Postage" 3.25 2.00

b. "Priority" below "US Postage" 8.00 1.00

c. "Express" below "US Postage" 25.00 3.00

d. "Media Mail" below "US Postage" 7.50 1.00

e. "Parcel Post" below "US Postage" 7.50 1.00

f. "Bound Printed Matter" below "US Postage" 7.50 1.00

g. "BPM" below "US Postage" 7.50 1.00

1CVP7 CVPA6 37c black, blue & orange 3.50 2.00

a. "First Class" below "US Postage" 3.25 .25

b. "Priority" below "US Postage" 8.00 1.00

c. "Express" below "US Postage" 25.00 3.00

d. "Media Mail" below "US Postage" 7.50 1.00

e. "Parcel Post" below "US Postage" 7.50 1.00

f. "Bound Printed Matter" below "US Postage" 7.50 1.00

g. "BPM" below "US Postage" 7.50 1.00

1CVP8 CVPA7 37c black, blue & orange 3.50 2.00

a. "First Class" below "US Postage" 3.25 .45

b. "Priority" below "US Postage" 8.00 1.00

c. "Express" below "US Postage" 25.00 3.00

d. "Media Mail" below "US Postage" 7.50 1.00

e. "Parcel Post" below "US Postage" 7.50 1.00

f. "Bound Printed Matter" below "US Postage" 7.50 1.00

g. "BPM" below "US Postage" 7.50 1.00

h. Strip of 5, #1CVP4-1CVP8 17.50

Flag and Star Type of 2002 Redrawn With "Stamps.com" in Upper Case Letters

Serpentine Die Cut 5¾ at Left

2003, June

Identification Code Above Zip Code

1CVP9 CVPA1a 37c black, blue & orange, "US Postage" only 3.00 1.50

a. "First Class" below "US Postage" 2.00 .45

b. "Priority" below "US Postage" 8.00 1.00

c. "Express" below "US Postage" 25.00 3.00

d. "Media Mail" below "US Postage" 7.50 1.00

e. "Parcel Post" below "US Postage" 7.50 1.00

f. "Bound Printed Matter" below "US Postage" 7.50 1.00

g. "BPM" below "US Postage" 7.50 1.00

Snowman CVPA8

Snowflakes CVPA9

Holly CVPA10

Dove CVPA11

Gingerbread Man and Candy — CVPA12

Serpentine Die Cut 4½ at Left

2003, Dec.

1CVP10 CVPA8 37c black, blue & orange 3.00 1.50

a. "First Class" below "US Postage" 2.00 1.00

b. "Priority" below "US Postage" 8.00 1.00

c. "Express" below "US Postage" 25.00 3.00

d. "Media Mail" below "US Postage" 7.50 1.00

e. "Parcel Post" below "US Postage" 7.50 1.00

f. "Bound Printed Matter" below "US Postage" 7.50 1.00

g. "BPM" below "US Postage" 7.50 1.00

1CVP11 CVPA9 37c black, blue & orange 3.00 1.50

a. "First Class" below "US Postage" 2.00 1.00

b. "Priority" below "US Postage" 8.00 1.00

c. "Express" below "US Postage" 25.00 3.00

d. "Media Mail" below "US Postage" 7.50 1.00

e. "Parcel Post" below "US Postage" 7.50 1.00

f. "Bound Printed Matter" below "US Postage" 7.50 1.00

g. "BPM" below "US Postage" 7.50 1.00

1CVP12 CVPA10 37c black, blue & orange 3.00 1.50

a. "First Class" below "US Postage" 2.00 1.00

b. "Priority" below "US Postage" 8.00 1.00

c. "Express" below "US Postage" 25.00 3.00

d. "Media Mail" below "US Postage" 7.50 1.00

e. "Parcel Post" below "US Postage" 7.50 1.00

f. "Bound Printed Matter" below "US Postage" 7.50 1.00

g. "BPM" below "US Postage" 7.50 1.00

1CVP13 CVPA11 37c black, blue & orange 3.00 1.50

a. "First Class" below "US Postage" 2.00 1.00

b. "Priority" below "US Postage" 8.00 1.00

c. "Express" below "US Postage" 25.00 3.00

d. "Media Mail" below "US Postage" 7.50 1.00

e. "Parcel Post" below "US Postage" 7.50 1.00

f. "Bound Printed Matter" below "US Postage" 7.50 1.00

g. "BPM" below "US Postage" 7.50 1.00

1CVP14 CVPA12 37c black, blue & orange 3.00 1.50

a. "First Class" below "US Postage" 2.00 1.00

b. "Priority" below "US Postage" 8.00 1.00

c. "Express" below "US Postage" 25.00 3.00

d. "Media Mail" below "US Postage" 7.50 1.00

e. "Parcel Post" below "US Postage" 7.50 1.00

f. "Bound Printed Matter" below "US Postage" 7.50 1.00

g. "BPM" below "US Postage" 7.50 1.00

h. Strip of 5, #1CVP10-1CVP14 12.50

Mailbox — CVPA13

Serpentine Die Cut 6½ at Left

2004, Mar.

1CVP15 CVPA13 37c black, blue & orange 25.00 15.00

a. "First Class" below "US Postage" 25.00 15.00

b. "Priority" below "US Postage" — —

c. "Express" below "US Postage" — —

d. "Media Mail" below "US Postage" — —

e. "Parcel Post" below "US Postage" — —

f. "Bound Printed Matter" below "US Postage" — —

g. "BPM" below "US Postage" — —

Blank sheets of No. 1CVP15 were sent free of charge to those who responded to special Stamps.com promotions which offered a fixed amount of free postage as an enticement to new subscribers. The franking portion of the stamps could only be applied after subscribing.

George Washington CVPA14

Thomas Jefferson CVPA15

Abraham Lincoln CVPA16

Theodore Roosevelt CVPA17

John F. Kennedy — CVPA18

Serpentine Die Cut 6½ at Left

2004, Apr.

1CVP16 CVPA14 37c black, blue & orange 2.00 1.00

a. "First Class" below "US Postage" 1.10 .75

b. "Priority" below "US Postage" 5.00 2.50

c. "Express" below "US Postage" 20.00 5.00

d. "Media Mail" below "US Postage" 5.00 2.50

e. "Parcel Post" below "US Postage" 5.00 2.50

f. "Bound Printed Matter" below "US Postage" 5.00 2.50

g. "BPM" below "US Postage" 5.00 2.50

1CVP17 CVPA15 37c black, blue & orange 2.00 1.00

a. "First Class" below "US Postage" 1.10 .75

b. "Priority" below "US Postage" 5.00 2.50

c. "Express" below "US Postage" 20.00 5.00

d. "Media Mail" below "US Postage" 5.00 2.50

e. "Parcel Post" below "US Postage" 5.00 2.50

f. "Bound Printed Matter" below "US Postage" 5.00 2.50
g. "BPM" below "US Postage" 5.00 2.50

1CVP18 CVPA16 37c black, blue & orange 2.00 1.00
a. "First Class" below "US Postage" 1.10 .75
b. "Priority" below "US Postage" 5.00 2.50
c. "Express" below "US Postage" 20.00 5.00
d. "Media Mail" below "US Postage" 5.00 2.50
e. "Parcel Post" below "US Postage" 5.00 2.50
f. "Bound Printed Matter" below "US Postage" 5.00 2.50
g. "BPM" below "US Postage" 5.00 2.50

1CVP19 CVPA17 37c black, blue & orange 2.00 1.00
a. "First Class" below "US Postage" 1.10 .75
b. "Priority" below "US Postage" 5.00 2.50
c. "Express" below "US Postage" 20.00 5.00
d. "Media Mail" below "US Postage" 5.00 2.50
e. "Parcel Post" below "US Postage" 5.00 2.50
f. "Bound Printed Matter" below "US Postage" 5.00 2.50
g. "BPM" below "US Postage" 5.00 2.50

1CVP20 CVPA18 37c black, blue & orange 2.00 1.00
a. "First Class" below "US Postage" 1.10 .75
b. "Priority" below "US Postage" 5.00 2.50
c. "Express" below "US Postage" 20.00 5.00
d. "Media Mail" below "US Postage" 5.00 2.50
e. "Parcel Post" below "US Postage" 5.00 2.50
f. "Bound Printed Matter" below "US Postage" 5.00 2.50
g. "BPM" below "US Postage" 5.00 2.50
h. Horiz. strip of 5, #1CVP16-1CVP20 10.00

Flag and Star Type of 2002 Redrawn With Orange Stars and Text at Left

Serpentine Die Cut 6½ at Left

2004, Apr.

"Stamps.com" in Upper Case Letters

Identification Code Above Zip Code

1CVP21 CVPA1a 37c black, blue & orange 2.00 1.00
a. "First Class" below "US Postage" 1.35 .75
b. "Priority" below "US Postage" 6.00 2.50
c. "Express" below "US Postage" 22.50 5.00
d. "Media Mail" below "US Postage" 6.00 2.50
e. "Parcel Post" below "US Postage" 6.00 2.50
f. "Bound Printed Matter" below "US Postage" 6.00 2.50
g. "BPM" below "US Postage" 6.00 2.50

Bicycling
CVPA19

Running
CVPA20

Swimming
CVPA21

Boxing
CVPA22

Equestrian
CVPA23

Basketball
CVPA24

Judo
CVPA25

Soccer
CVPA26

Gymnastics
CVPA27

Tennis
CVPA28

Serpentine Die Cut 6½ at Left

2004, Apr.

1CVP22 CVPA19 37c black, blue & orange 3.00 2.00
a. "First Class" below "US Postage" 2.50 1.50
b. "Priority" below "US Postage" 8.00 1.00
c. "Express" below "US Postage" 25.00 3.00
d. "Media Mail" below "US Postage" 7.50 1.00
e. "Parcel Post" below "US Postage" 7.50 1.00
f. "Bound Printed Matter" below "US Postage" 7.50 1.00
g. "BPM" below "US Postage" 7.50 1.00

1CVP23 CVPA20 37c black, blue & orange 3.00 2.00
a. "First Class" below "US Postage" 2.50 1.50
b. "Priority" below "US Postage" 8.00 1.00
c. "Express" below "US Postage" 25.00 3.00
d. "Media Mail" below "US Postage" 7.50 1.00
e. "Parcel Post" below "US Postage" 7.50 1.00
f. "Bound Printed Matter" below "US Postage" 7.50 1.00
g. "BPM" below "US Postage" 7.50 1.00

1CVP24 CVPA21 37c black, blue & orange 3.00 2.00
a. "First Class" below "US Postage" 2.50 1.50
b. "Priority" below "US Postage" 8.00 1.00
c. "Express" below "US Postage" 25.00 3.00
d. "Media Mail" below "US Postage" 7.50 1.00
e. "Parcel Post" below "US Postage" 7.50 1.00
f. "Bound Printed Matter" below "US Postage" 7.50 1.00
g. "BPM" below "US Postage" 7.50 1.00

1CVP25 CVPA22 37c black, blue & orange 3.00 2.00
a. "First Class" below "US Postage" 2.50 1.50
b. "Priority" below "US Postage" 8.00 1.00
c. "Express" below "US Postage" 25.00 3.00
d. "Media Mail" below "US Postage" 7.50 1.00
e. "Parcel Post" below "US Postage" 7.50 1.00
f. "Bound Printed Matter" below "US Postage" 7.50 1.00
g. "BPM" below "US Postage" 7.50 1.00

1CVP26 CVPA23 37c black, blue & orange 3.00 2.00
a. "First Class" below "US Postage" 2.50 1.50
b. "Priority" below "US Postage" 8.00 1.00
c. "Express" below "US Postage" 25.00 3.00
d. "Media Mail" below "US Postage" 7.50 1.00
e. "Parcel Post" below "US Postage" 7.50 1.00
f. "Bound Printed Matter" below "US Postage" 7.50 1.00
g. "BPM" below "US Postage" 7.50 1.00
h. Horiz. strip of 5, #1CVP22-1CVP26 15.00

1CVP27 CVPA24 37c black, blue & orange 3.00 2.00
a. "First Class" below "US Postage" 2.50 1.50
b. "Priority" below "US Postage" 8.00 1.00
c. "Express" below "US Postage" 25.00 3.00
d. "Media Mail" below "US Postage" 7.50 1.00
e. "Parcel Post" below "US Postage" 7.50 1.00
f. "Bound Printed Matter" below "US Postage" 7.50 1.00
g. "BPM" below "US Postage" 7.50 1.00

1CVP28 CVPA25 37c black, blue & orange 3.00 2.00
a. "First Class" below "US Postage" 2.50 1.50
b. "Priority" below "US Postage" 8.00 1.00
c. "Express" below "US Postage" 25.00 3.00
d. "Media Mail" below "US Postage" 7.50 1.00
e. "Parcel Post" below "US Postage" 7.50 1.00
f. "Bound Printed Matter" below "US Postage" 7.50 1.00
g. "BPM" below "US Postage" 7.50 1.00

1CVP29 CVPA26 37c black, blue & orange 3.00 2.00
a. "First Class" below "US Postage" 2.50 1.50
b. "Priority" below "US Postage" 8.00 1.00
c. "Express" below "US Postage" 25.00 3.00
d. "Media Mail" below "US Postage" 7.50 1.00
e. "Parcel Post" below "US Postage" 7.50 1.00
f. "Bound Printed Matter" below "US Postage" 7.50 1.00
g. "BPM" below "US Postage" 7.50 1.00

1CVP30 CVPA27 37c black, blue & orange 3.00 2.00
a. "First Class" below "US Postage" 2.50 1.50
b. "Priority" below "US Postage" 8.00 1.00
c. "Express" below "US Postage" 25.00 3.00
d. "Media Mail" below "US Postage" 7.50 1.00
e. "Parcel Post" below "US Postage" 7.50 1.00
f. "Bound Printed Matter" below "US Postage" 7.50 1.00
g. "BPM" below "US Postage" 7.50 1.00

1CVP31 CVPA28 37c black, blue & orange 3.00 2.00
a. "First Class" below "US Postage" 2.50 1.50
b. "Priority" below "US Postage" 8.00 1.00
c. "Express" below "US Postage" 25.00 3.00
d. "Media Mail" below "US Postage" 7.50 1.00
e. "Parcel Post" below "US Postage" 7.50 1.00
f. "Bound Printed Matter" below "US Postage" 7.50 1.00
g. "BPM" below "US Postage" 7.50 1.00
h. Horiz. strip of 5, #1CVP27-1CVP31 15.00

The item pictured above was produced by Stamps.com for a special promotional mailing of its own and was not made available unused to customers.

Leaning Tower of Pisa
CVPA29

Sphinx and Pyramids
CVPA30

Sydney Opera House
CVPA31

Mayan Pyramid
CVPA32

Asian Temple — CVPA33

Serpentine Die Cut 6½ at Left

2004, July

1CVP32 CVPA29 37c black, blue & orange 3.00 2.00
a. "First Class" below "US Postage" 2.30 1.50
b. "Priority" below "US Postage" 8.00 1.00
c. "Express" below "US Postage" 25.00 3.00
d. "Media Mail" below "US Postage" 7.50 1.00
e. "Parcel Post" below "US Postage" 7.50 1.00
f. "Bound Printed Matter" below "US Postage" 7.50 1.00
g. "BPM" below "US Postage" 7.50 1.00

1CVP33 CVPA30 37c black, blue & orange 3.00 2.00
a. "First Class" below "US Postage" 2.30 1.50
b. "Priority" below "US Postage" 8.00 1.00
c. "Express" below "US Postage" 25.00 3.00
d. "Media Mail" below "US Postage" 7.50 1.00
e. "Parcel Post" below "US Postage" 7.50 1.00
f. "Bound Printed Matter" below "US Postage" 7.50 1.00
g. "BPM" below "US Postage" 7.50 1.00

1CVP34 CVPA31 37c black, blue & orange 3.00 2.00
a. "First Class" below "US Postage" 2.30 1.50
b. "Priority" below "US Postage" 8.00 1.00
c. "Express" below "US Postage" 25.00 3.00
d. "Media Mail" below "US Postage" 7.50 1.00
e. "Parcel Post" below "US Postage" 7.50 1.00
f. "Bound Printed Matter" below "US Postage" 7.50 1.00
g. "BPM" below "US Postage" 7.50 1.00

1CVP35 CVPA32 37c black, blue & orange 3.00 2.00
a. "First Class" below "US Postage" 2.30 1.50
b. "Priority" below "US Postage" 8.00 1.00
c. "Express" below "US Postage" 25.00 3.00
d. "Media Mail" below "US Postage" 7.50 1.00
e. "Parcel Post" below "US Postage" 7.50 1.00
f. "Bound Printed Matter" below "US Postage" 7.50 1.00
g. "BPM" below "US Postage" 7.50 1.00

1CVP36 CVPA33 37c black, blue & orange 3.00 2.00
a. "First Class" below "US Postage" 2.30 1.50
b. "Priority" below "US Postage" 8.00 1.00
c. "Express" below "US Postage" 25.00 3.00
d. "Media Mail" below "US Postage" 7.50 1.00
e. "Parcel Post" below "US Postage" 7.50 1.00
f. "Bound Printed Matter" below "US Postage" 7.50 1.00
g. "BPM" below "US Postage" 7.50 1.00
h. Strip of 5, #1CVP32-1CVP36 15.00

Computer and Letters — CVPA34

Serpentine Die Cut 6½ at Left

2005, Mar.

1CVP37 CVPA34 37c black, blue & orange 25.00 15.00
a. "First Class" below "US Postage" 25.00 15.00
b. "Priority" below "US Postage" — —
c. "Express" below "US Postage" — —
d. "Media Mail" below "US Postage" — —
e. "Parcel Post" below "US Postage" — —

f. "Bound Printed Matter" below "US Postage" — —
g. "BPM" below "US Postage" — —

Blank sheets of No. 1CVP37 were sent free of charge to those who responded to special Stamps.com promotions which offered a fixed amount of free postage as an enticement to new subscribers. The franking portion of the stamps could only be applied after subscribing.

Logo — CVPA35

2005, Aug. ***Die Cut Perf. 6½ at Left***

1CVP38 CVPA35 37c black, blue & orange 1.00 .45
a. "Priority" below "US Postage" 8.00 1.00
b. "Express" below "US Postage" 25.00 3.00
c. "Media Mail" below "US Postage" 7.50 1.00
d. "Parcel Post" below "US Postage" 7.50 1.00
e. "BPM" below "US Postage" 7.50 1.00
f. "Aerogramme" below "US Postage" 1.40 1.00
g. "Intl Air Letter" below "US Postage" 1.25 1.00
h. "Intl Eco Letter" (Economy Letter Mail) below "US Postage" 5.50 1.00
i. "GXG" (Global Express Guaranteed) below "US Postage" 50.00 6.00
j. "EMS" (Global Express Mail) below "US Postage" 32.50 4.00
k. "GPM" (Global Priority Mail) below "US Postage" 8.00 1.00
l. "Intl Air Parcel" (Air Parcel Post) below "US Postage" 26.00 3.00
m. "Intl Eco Parcel" (Economy Parcel Post) below "US Postage" 32.50 4.00
n. "M-Bag (Air)" below "US Postage" 35.00 5.00
o. "M-Bag (Economy)" below "US Postage" 18.00 3.00
p. "Mat for Blind" below "US Postage" 1.25 —
q. "Library Mail" 5.00 1.00

Values for lettered varieties on Nos. 1CVP38 are based on the prices set as the minimum values for each service classification in the software available at the time the stamps were issued. In mid-December 2005, the software was changed to allow for a 1c minimum value for any of these lettered varieties.

In 2006, No. 1CVP38 was made available on a coil roll. Value, $1.40.

Snowman CVPA36

Candy Cane CVPA37

Dove CVPA38

Stylized Christmas Tree and Window CVPA39

2005, Nov. ***Die Cut Perf. 6 at Right***

1CVP39 CVPA36 37c multi 1.60 1.00
a. "Priority" below "US Postage" 8.00 1.00
b. "Express" below "US Postage" 25.00 3.00
c. "Media Mail" below "US Postage" 7.50 1.00
d. "Parcel Post" below "US Postage" 7.50 1.00
e. "BPM" below "US Postage" 7.50 1.00
f. "Aerogramme" below "US Postage" 1.40 1.00
g. "Intl Air Letter" below "US Postage" 1.25 1.00
h. "Intl Eco Letter" (Economy Letter Mail) below "US Postage" 5.50 1.00
i. "GXG" (Global Express Guaranteed) below "US Postage" 50.00 6.00
j. "EMS" (Global Express Mail) below "US Postage" 32.50 4.00
k. "GPM" (Global Priority Mail) below "US Postage" 8.00 1.00
l. "Intl Air Parcel" (Air Parcel Post) below "US Postage" 26.00 3.00
m. "Intl Eco Parcel" (Economy Parcel Post) below "US Postage" 32.50 4.00
n. "M-Bag (Air)" below "US Postage" 35.00 5.00
o. "M-Bag (Economy)" below "US Postage" 18.00 3.00
p. "Mat for Blind" below "US Postage" .25 —

1CVP40 CVPA37 37c multi 1.60 1.00
a. "Priority" below "US Postage" 8.00 1.00
b. "Express" below "US Postage" 25.00 3.00
c. "Media Mail" below "US Postage" 7.50 1.00
d. "Parcel Post" below "US Postage" 7.50 1.00
e. "BPM" below "US Postage" 7.50 1.00
f. "Aerogramme" below "US Postage" 1.40 1.00
g. "Intl Air Letter" below "US Postage" 1.25 1.00
h. "Intl Eco Letter" (Economy Letter Mail) below "US Postage" 5.50 1.00
i. "GXG" (Global Express Guaranteed) below "US Postage" 50.00 6.00
j. "EMS" (Global Express Mail) below "US Postage" 32.50 4.00
k. "GPM" (Global Priority Mail) below "US Postage" 8.00 1.00
l. "Intl Air Parcel" (Air Parcel Post) below "US Postage" 26.00 3.00
m. "Intl Eco Parcel" (Economy Parcel Post) below "US Postage" 32.50 4.00
n. "M-Bag (Air)" below "US Postage" 35.00 5.00
o. "M-Bag (Economy)" below "US Postage" 18.00 3.00
p. "Mat for Blind" below "US Postage" .45 —

1CVP41 CVPA38 37c multi 1.60 1.00
a. "Priority" below "US Postage" 8.00 1.00
b. "Express" below "US Postage" 25.00 3.00
c. "Media Mail" below "US Postage" 7.50 1.00
d. "Parcel Post" below "US Postage" 7.50 1.00
e. "BPM" below "US Postage" 7.50 1.00
f. "Aerogramme" below "US Postage" 1.40 1.00
g. "Intl Air Letter" below "US Postage" 1.25 1.00
h. "Intl Eco Letter" (Economy Letter Mail) below "US Postage" 5.50 1.00
i. "GXG" (Global Express Guaranteed) below "US Postage" 50.00 6.00
j. "EMS" (Global Express Mail) below "US Postage" 32.50 4.00
k. "GPM" (Global Priority Mail) below "US Postage" 8.00 1.00
l. "Intl Air Parcel" (Air Parcel Post) below "US Postage" 26.00 3.00
m. "Intl Eco Parcel" (Economy Parcel Post) below "US Postage" 32.50 4.00
n. "M-Bag (Air)" below "US Postage" 35.00 5.00
o. "M-Bag (Economy)" below "US Postage" 18.00 3.00
p. "Mat for Blind" below "US Postage" .45 —

1CVP42 CVPA39 37c multi 1.60 1.00
a. "Priority" below "US Postage" 8.00 1.00
b. "Express" below "US Postage" 25.00 3.00
c. "Media Mail" below "US Postage" 7.50 1.00
d. "Parcel Post" below "US Postage" 7.50 1.00
e. "BPM" below "US Postage" 7.50 1.00
f. "Aerogramme" below "US Postage" 1.40 1.00
g. "Intl Air Letter" below "US Postage" 1.25 1.00
h. "Intl Eco Letter" (Economy Letter Mail) below "US Postage" 5.50 1.00
i. "GXG" (Global Express Guaranteed) below "US Postage" 50.00 6.00
j. "EMS" (Global Express Mail) below "US Postage" 32.50 4.00
k. "GPM" (Global Priority Mail) below "US Postage" 8.00 1.00
l. "Intl Air Parcel" (Air Parcel Post) below "US Postage" 26.00 3.00
m. "Intl Eco Parcel" (Economy Parcel Post) below "US Postage" 32.50 4.00
n. "M-Bag (Air)" below "US Postage" 35.00 5.00
o. "M-Bag (Economy)" below "US Postage" 18.00 3.00
p. "Mat for Blind" below "US Postage" .45 —
q. Vert. strip, 2 each #1CVP39-1CVP42 6.00

Values for lettered varieties on Nos. 1CVP39-1CVP42 are based on the prices set as the minimum values for each service classification in the software available at the time the stamps were issued. In mid-December 2005, the software was changed to allow for a 1c minimum value for any of these lettered varieties.

Endicia.com

CVPA40

CVPA41

2005-06 ***Serpentine Die Cut 10¼***

1CVP43 CVPA40 24c black & bright rose 10.00 4.00
a. 39c "First Class" under "US Postage" 2.00 .50
b. 63c "Intl. Mail" under "US Postage" 3.25 2.50
c. $4.05 "Priority Mail" under "US Postage" 12.00 2.50

Coil Stamps

Serpentine Die Cut 10½x10¼ on 2 Sides

1CVP44 CVPA41 24c black & pink 11.00 4.00
a. 39c "First Class" under "US Postage" 2.25 .50
b. 63c "Intl. Mail" under "US Postage" 3.50 2.50
c. $4.05 "Priority Mail" under "US Postage" 12.50 2.50

Issued: Nos. 1CVP43, Nov. 2005; Nos. 1CVP44, Jan. 2006.

Originally, face values of 2c, 52c, 63c, 87c, $1.11, $1.35, $1.59, $1.83, $2.07, $2.31, $2.55, $2.79, $3.03, and $3.27 could also be printed on stamps with the "First class" inscription. Additionally, an 84c face value could be printed on stamps with the "Intl. Mail" inscription, and a $8.10 face value could be printed on stamps with the "Priority Mail" inscription. Values for Nos. 1CVP43-1CVP44 are for stamps with the listed face values and mail-class inscription. Values for stamps with lower or higher face values are correspondingly lower or higher.

In 2007, software changes permitted Nos. 1CVP43 and 1CVP44 to be printed with mail class inscriptions "Media Mail," "BPM," "Parcel Post," "Library Mail," and "Express Mail," as well as any face value for any mail-class inscription.

Nos. 1CVP43 and 1CVP44 printed after the software changes are inscribed "First Class" under "US Postage" and sell for considerably less than the values shown. Stamps printed before the software changes are inscribed "Postcard" under "US Postage," as shown in the illustrations.

Stamps.com

Flag and Mount Rushmore CVPA42

Flag and Eagle CVPA43

Flag and Statue of Liberty CVPA44

Flag and Liberty Bell CVPA45

2006, Mar. ***Die Cut Perf. 6 at Right***

1CVP51 CVPA42 39c multi 1.25 1.00
1CVP52 CVPA43 39c multi 1.25 1.00
1CVP53 CVPA44 39c multi 1.25 1.00
1CVP54 CVPA45 39c multi 1.25 1.00
a. Vert. strip of 8, 2 each #1CVP51-1CVP54 8.00

Other service inscriptions with any possible face value can be printed on Nos. 1CVP51-1CVP54.

Stamps.com

Leaning Tower of Pisa CVPA46

Taj Mahal CVPA47

Eiffel Tower CVPA48

Parthenon CVPA49

2006 ***Die Cut Perf 6 at Right***

1CVP55 CVPA46 39c multi 1.25 1.00
1CVP56 CVPA47 39c multi 1.25 1.00
1CVP57 CVPA48 39c multi 1.25 1.00
1CVP58 CVPA49 39c multi 1.25 1.00
a. Vert. strip, 2 each #1CVP55-1CVP58 8.00

With the introduction of the new software in December 2005, any stamp could have any denomination 1c and above, and any service classification.

Pitney Bowes Stamp Expressions

CVPA50

2006 ***Die Cut Perf. 6 Horiz.***

Inscribed "pitneybowes.com/se" at Right

1CVP59 CVPA50 39c black + label 1.35 .80

The stamp and label are separated by vertical roulettes. Users could create their own label images on the Pitney Bowes Stamp Expressions website (which required approval of the image from Pitney Bowes before it could be used), or download various pre-approved label images from the website into their personal computers. Stamps could be printed without label images. Stamps were printed on rolls of tagged thermal paper from a device that could be operated without a direct connection to the personal computer. See No. 1CVT1.

Stamps.com

CVPA51

Personalizable Images — CVPA52

2006, Sept. ***Die Cut Perf. 6 at Right***

1CVP60	CVPA51 39c multi		1.50	.95
a.	Numerals in denomination 2½mm high, thicker text		1.50	.95

Perf. Die Cut Perf. 6 at Top

1CVP61	CVPA52 39c multi		1.50	.95
a.	Numerals in denomination 2½mm high, thicker text		1.50	.95

Users could requisition sheets of Nos. 1CVP60 and 1CVP61 with images of their choice from Stamps.com at $4.99 per sheet of 24. Priority and Express service classifications could also be printed on Nos. 1CVP60-1CVP61 with any denomination. Stamps exist with slightly larger die cutting (60x30mm and 30x60mm) in both squared and rounded corners. The denomination type shown on Nos. 1CVP60-1CVP61 can be placed on label types CVPA36-CVPA39, CVPA42-CVPA49, CVPA53-CVPA60 and any later stamps.com labels of this size.

Numerals in denomination are 3mm tall on Nos. 1CVP60-1CVP61. Serial numbers on Nos. 1CPVP60-1CVP61 lack periods and have small bank-check style numerals.

Autumn Leaves
CVPA53

Pumpkins
CVPA54

Basket of Apples, Sheaf of Wheat, Falling Leaves and Pumpkins
CVPA55

Leaves and Carved Pumpkin
CVPA56

2006 ***Die Cut Perf. 6 at Right***

1CVP62	CVPA53 39c multi		1.25	1.00
1CVP63	CVPA54 39c multi		1.25	1.00
1CVP64	CVPA55 39c multi		1.25	1.00
1CVP65	CVPA56 39c multi		1.25	1.00
a.	Vert. strip, 2 each #1CVP62-1CVP65		10.00	

See note after No. 1CVP58.

"Season's Greetings"
CVPA57

Christmas Trees
CVPA58

Snowman
CVPA59

Dove
CVPA60

2006 ***Die Cut Perf. 6 at Right***

1CVP66	CVPA57 39c multi		1.25	.45
1CVP67	CVPA58 39c multi		1.25	.45
1CVP68	CVPA59 39c multi		1.25	.45
1CVP69	CVPA60 39c multi		1.25	.45
a.	Vert. strip, 2 each #1CVP66-1CVP69		10.00	

See note after No. 1CVP58.

Flag
CVPA61

Statue of Liberty and Flag
CVPA62

Bald Eagle and Flag
CVPA63

Flag Painted on Building
CVPA64

2008 ***Die Cut Perf. 5½ at Right***

Serial Number With Period, Large Letters and Numerals

1CVP70	CVPA61 42c multi		1.25	1.00
1CVP71	CVPA62 42c multi		1.25	1.00
1CVP72	CVPA63 42c multi		1.25	1.00
1CVP73	CVPA64 42c multi		1.25	1.00

On Nos. 1CVP70-1CVP105, and perhaps on other stamps, placement of the stamp serial number and the stamps.com logo might differ on various printings of the label stock. Descriptive text outside the frame might also vary or not be present on these various printings.

Autumn
CVPA65

Designs: No. 1CVP74, Oak leaves. No. 1CVP75, Pumpkin patch. No. 1CVP76, Autumn reflection. No. 1CVP77, Pumpkins and gourds.

2008

Serial Number With Period, Large Letters and Numerals

1CVP74	CVPA65 42c multi		2.00	1.00
1CVP75	CVPA65 42c multi		2.00	1.00
1CVP76	CVPA65 42c multi		2.00	1.00
1CVP77	CVPA65 42c multi		2.00	1.00

Flowers
CVPA66

Designs: No. 1CVP78, Sunflowers. No. 1CVP79, Daisies. No. 1CVP80, Sunflower sky. No. 1CVP81, Treasure flowers.

2008

Serial Number With Period, Large Letters and Numerals

1CVP78	CVPA66 42c multi		1.25	1.00
1CVP79	CVPA66 42c multi		1.25	1.00
1CVP80	CVPA66 42c multi		1.25	1.00
1CVP81	CVPA66 42c multi		1.25	1.00

Endangered Animals — CVPA67

Designs: No. 1CVP82, Bengal tiger. No. 1CVP83, Hawksbill turtle. No. 1CVP84, Panda. No. 1CVP85, African rhino.

2008

Serial Number With Period, Large Letters and Numerals

1CVP82	CVPA67 42c multi		2.00	1.00
1CVP83	CVPA67 42c multi		2.00	1.00
1CVP84	CVPA67 42c multi		2.00	1.00
1CVP85	CVPA67 42c multi		2.00	1.00

Parks
CVPA68

Designs: No. 1CVP86, Grand Canyon National Park, Arizona. No. 1CVP87, Yosemite National Park, California. No. 1CVP88, Niagara Falls. No. 1CVP89, Arches National Park, Utah.

2008

Serial Number With Period, Large Letters and Numerals

1CVP86	CVPA68 42c multi		1.25	1.00
1CVP87	CVPA68 42c multi		1.25	1.00
1CVP88	CVPA68 42c multi		1.25	1.00
1CVP89	CVPA68 42c multi		1.25	1.00

City Skylines
CVPA69

Designs: No. 1CVP90, New York City. No. 1CVP91, St. Louis. No. 1CVP92, Chicago. No. 1CVP93, San Francisco.

2008

Serial Number With Period, Large Letters and Numerals

1CVP90	CVPA69 42c multi		2.00	1.00
1CVP91	CVPA69 42c multi		2.00	1.00
1CVP92	CVPA69 42c multi		2.00	1.00
1CVP93	CVPA69 42c multi		2.00	1.00

Presidential Memorials — CVPA70

Designs: No. 1CVP94, Washington Monument. No. 1CVP95, Lincoln Memorial. No. 1CVP96, Jefferson Memorial. No. 1CVP97, Mount Rushmore.

2008

Serial Number With Period, Large Letters and Numerals

1CVP94	CVPA70 42c multi		1.25	1.00
1CVP95	CVPA70 42c multi		1.25	1.00
1CVP96	CVPA70 42c multi		1.25	1.00
1CVP97	CVPA70 42c multi		1.25	1.00

Christmas
CVPA71

Designs: No. 1CVP98, Ornament, "Happy Holidays." No. 1CVP99, Gingerbread men, "Season's Greetings." No. 1CVP100, Snowflake, "Happy Holidays." No. 1CVP101, Christmas tree, "Season's Greetings."

2008

Serial Number With Period, Large Letters and Numerals

Without Year or Text at Left

1CVP98	CVPA71 42c multi		2.00	1.00
1CVP99	CVPA71 42c multi		2.00	1.00
1CVP100	CVPA71 42c multi		2.00	1.00
1CVP101	CVPA71 42c multi		2.00	1.00

Love
CVPA72

"Love" and: No. 1CVP102, Rose. No. 1CVP103, Small hearts. No. 1CVP104, Large heart. No. 1CVP105, Hearts on curtain.

2009

Serial Number With Period, Large Letters and Numerals

Without Year or Text at Left

1CVP102	CVPA72 42c multi		1.25	1.00
1CVP103	CVPA72 42c multi		1.25	1.00
1CVP104	CVPA72 42c multi		1.25	1.00
1CVP105	CVPA72 42c multi		1.25	1.00

Wavy Lines — CVPA73

2009 ***Die Cut Perf 6½ at Right***

1CVP106	CVPA73 44c multi		1.25	.45

White Label — CVPA73a

Clear Label — CVPA73b

2020? ***Die Cut Perf 6½ at Right***

1CVP106A	CVPA73a 53c multi		1.25	.45
1CVP106B	CVPA73b 53c multi		1.25	.45

Endicia.com

Globe — CVPA74

Globe — CVPA74a

2009 ***Serpentine Die Cut 10¼x10½***

1CVP107	CVPA74 44c org & blk		1.25	.45
1CVP107A	CVPA74a 45c org & blk		—	—

Software allowed for six other inscriptions below "US Postage" (Priority Mail, Media Mail, Parcel Post, Library Mail, Express Mail and Intl Mail) and any face value for any mail-class inscription.

No. 1CVP107 with space between denomination and "US POSTAGE". No. 1CVP107A with no space between denomination and "US POSTAGE".

Stamps.com

Thank You For Your Business
CVPA75

Text: No. 1CVP108, On billboard. No. 1CVP109, And building. No. 1CVP110, On red background. No. 1CVP111, And two people shaking hands.

2009 ***Die Cut Perf. 5½ at Right***

Serial Number With Period, Large Letters and Numerals

Without Year or Text at Left

1CVP108	CVPA75 44c multi		1.25	1.00
1CVP109	CVPA75 44c multi		1.25	1.00
1CVP110	CVPA75 44c multi		1.25	1.00
1CVP111	CVPA75 44c multi		1.25	1.00

We're Moving
CVPA76

Text: No. 1CVP112, Stack of three boxes, green background. No. 1CVP113, Eleven boxes, orange background. No. 1CVP114,

Four boxes, green background. No. 1CVP115, Four boxes, red background.

2009

Serial Number With Period, Large Letters and Numerals

Without Year or Text at Left

1CVP112	CVPA76 44c multi		1.25	1.00
1CVP113	CVPA76 44c multi		1.25	1.00
1CVP114	CVPA76 44c multi		1.25	1.00
1CVP115	CVPA76 44c multi		1.25	1.00

Special Invitation CVPA77

Text: No. 1CVP116, And pen nib. No. 1CVP117, And circled "15" on calendar. No. 1CVP118, On card on envelope. No. 1CVP119, On wax seal.

2009

Serial Number With Period, Large Letters and Numerals

Without Year or Text at Left

1CVP116	CVPA77 44c multi	1.25	1.00
1CVP117	CVPA77 44c multi	1.25	1.00
1CVP118	CVPA77 44c multi	1.25	1.00
1CVP119	CVPA77 44c multi	1.25	1.00

US Flag CVPA78

Flag: No. 1CVP120, On flagpole. No. 1CVP121, Behind Statue of Liberty. No. 1CVP122, Behind bald eagle. No. 1CVP123, On United States map.

2009

Serial Number With Period, Large Letters and Numerals

Without Year or Text at Left

1CVP120	CVPA78 44c multi	2.00	1.00
1CVP121	CVPA78 44c multi	2.00	1.00
1CVP122	CVPA78 44c multi	2.00	1.00
1CVP123	CVPA78 44c multi	2.00	1.00

Patriotic Symbols CVPA79

Designs: No. 1CVP124, Statue of Liberty. No. 1CVP125, Flag. No. 1CVP126, Bald eagle.

2010 ***Die Cut Perf. 5½ Vert.***

1CVP124	CVPA79 44c multi	1.25	1.00
1CVP125	CVPA79 44c multi	1.25	1.00
1CVP126	CVPA79 44c multi	1.25	1.00

Jewish Symbols CVPA80

Designs: No. 1CVP127, Menorah. No. 1CVP125, Dreidel. No. 1CVP126, Star of David.

2010 ***Die Cut Perf. 5½ Vert.***

1CVP127	CVPA80 44c multi	1.25	1.00
1CVP128	CVPA80 44c multi	1.25	1.00
1CVP129	CVPA80 44c multi	1.25	1.00

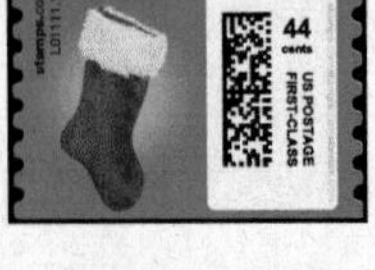

Christmas CVPA81

Designs: No. 1CVP130, Christmas stocking. No. 1CVP131, Christmas tree. No. 1CVP132, Santa Claus.

2010 ***Die Cut Perf. 5½ Vert.***

1CVP130	CVPA81 44c multi	1.25	1.00
1CVP131	CVPA81 44c multi	1.25	1.00
1CVP132	CVPA81 44c multi	1.25	1.00

Valentine's Day — CVPA82

Designs: No. 1CVP133, Hearts. No. 1CVP134, Rose. No. 1CVP135, Candy hearts.

2011 ***Die Cut Perf. 5½ Vert.***

1CVP133	CVPA82 44c multi	2.00	1.00
1CVP134	CVPA82 44c multi	2.00	1.00
1CVP135	CVPA82 44c multi	2.00	1.00

Christian Symbols CVPA83

Designs: No. 1CVP136, Cross. No. 1CVP137, Fish. No. 1CVP138, Rosary beads.

2011 ***Die Cut Perf. 5½ Vert.***

1CVP136	CVPA83 44c multi	1.25	1.00
1CVP137	CVPA83 44c multi	1.25	1.00
1CVP138	CVPA83 44c multi	1.25	1.00

Thank You — CVPA84

2020 ***Die Cut Perf. 5½ at Right***

1CVP139	CVPA84 53c multi	2.00	1.00

Star Spangled Banner — CVPA85

2021 ***Die Cut Perf. 5½ at Right***

1CVP140	CVPA85 53c multi	2.00	1.00

Flowers CVPA86

Designs: No. 1CVP141, "sunflower sky." No. 1CVP142, "treasure flowers." No. 1CVP143, "spring honey bee." No. 1CVP144, "summer flower." No. 1CVP145, "spring blossoms." No. 1CVP146, "dandelion wishes." No. 1CVP147, "pink cosmos."

2021 ***Die Cut Perf. 5½ at Right***

1CVP141	CVPA86 53c multi	2.00	1.00
1CVP142	CVPA86 53c multi	2.00	1.00
1CVP143	CVPA86 53c multi	2.00	1.00
1CVP144	CVPA86 53c multi	2.00	1.00
1CVP145	CVPA86 53c multi	2.00	1.00
1CVP146	CVPA86 53c multi	2.00	1.00
1CVP147	CVPA86 53c multi	2.00	1.00

Cherry Blossoms — CVPA87

Designs: No. 1CVP148, Jefferson Memorial with cherry blossoms. No. 1CVP149, cherry trees.

2022 ***Die Cut Perf. 5½ at Right***

1CVP148	CVPA87 53c multi	2.00	1.00
1CVP149	CVPA87 53c multi	2.00	1.00

Fall CVPA88

Designs: No. 1CVP150, "fall river." No. 1CVP151, pumpkins.

2022 ***Die Cut Perf. 5½ at Right***

1CVP150	CVPA88 53c multi	2.00	1.00
1CVP151	CVPA88 53c multi	2.00	1.00

Winter CVPA89

Designs: No. 1CVP152, "snowman hugs." No. 1CVP153, "holiday treats." No. 1CVP154, "warm wishes" hot cocoa. No. 1CVP155, "frosty hot cocoa." No. 1CVP156, "let it snow!" No. 1CVP157, snowflake ornaments.

2022 ***Die Cut Perf. 5½ at Right***

1CVP152	CVPA89 53c multi	2.00	1.00
1CVP153	CVPA89 53c multi	2.00	1.00
1CVP154	CVPA89 53c multi	2.00	1.00
	On cover		2.50
1CVP155	CVPA89 53c multi	2.00	1.00
1CVP156	CVPA89 53c multi	2.00	1.00
1CVP157	CVPA89 53c multi	2.00	1.00

Dog With Sunglasses — CVPA90

2022 ***Die Cut Perf. 5½ at Right***

1CVP158	CVPA90 53c multi	2.00	1.00

Hawksbill Turtle CVPA91

2022 ***Die Cut Perf. 5½ at Right***

1CVP159	CVPA91 53c multi	2.00	1.00

OFFICAL STAMPS PRINTED TO ORDER

1CVPO1

1CVPO2

2002-06 ***Serpentine Die Cut 10.6***

Self-Adhesive

1CVPO1	1CVPO1	37c	blk, red & blu-ish gray	—	—

No denomination below vignette.

1CVPO2	1CVPO2	37c	blk, red & blue	—	—

Denomination below vignette.

1CVPO3	1CVPO2	39c	blk, red & blue	—	—

Denomination below vignette.

1CVPO5	1CVPO2	$4.05	blk, red & blue	—	—

Denomination below vignette.

Endicia filled federal agency orders for stamps to be limited for use by government officials. Nos. 1CVPO1 and 1CVPO2 were printed in sheets of 10. 39c and 41c denominations are thought to exist.

NON-PERSONALIZABLE POSTAGE

Stamps.com

These stamps, approved by the USPS, were non-personalizable stamps that could be purchased directly from private manufacturers, which shipped them to the customer. Other non-personalizable stamps have been created by a variety of companies, all sold at excessive amounts over face value as "collectibles". Such items are not listed here. Most items created that sold for excessive amounts over face value have vignettes that are licensed images, usually depicting sport team emblems or other sports-related themes, or celebrities.

Personalized postage stamps, first available in 2004, created by a variety of different companies, and heretofore listed with Scott numbers having a "2CVP" prefix, are no longer listed. Personalized stamps, though valid for postage, are not sold at any U.S. Postal Service post office. They are available only by on-line ordering through the company's website. Stamps are only available from the companies in full panes of 20. Each pane is sold at a significant premium above the stated face value to cover the costs of personalization, shipping and handling.

In recent years, there has been a steadily increasing number of private companies, either directly licensed by the USPS or created as spinoff companies of these licensees, creating distinctly different personalized stamps. None of the companies has issued fewer than seven stamps for each rate change, with one issuing as many as 42 different stamps. Because mailing rates set by the USPS are expected to change yearly, the collective output of distinctly different, rate-based stamps from these various companies likely will increase. There are no restrictions in place to prevent more firms from bringing personalized stamps to the marketplace, or to keep stamp producers from offering even more customer options. Some personalized stamps do not differ in any appreciable manner from some of the non-personalizable stamps sold as collectibles and not listed here.

CVPC1

CVPC2

2007, May *Die Cut*

Self-Adhesive

3CVP1 CVPC1 2c black & gray green 1.00 1.00
a. Inscribed "US Postag" — —

Die Cut Perf. 5¼ at Right

3CVP2 CVPC2 2c multicolored 1.00 1.00
a. Tagged *2.00 2.00*

2008 *Die Cut*

Self-Adhesive

3CVP3 CVPC1 1c black & gray 1.00 1.00

No. 3CVP1 was printed in sheets of 40 stamps. Stamps with serial numbers ending in "06" are No. 3CVP1a. Sheets were sold for face value plus a shipping charge and were obtainable through the stamps.com website.

No. 3CVP2 was printed in sheets of 20. Full sheets were given free of charge to first-time stamps.com customers, but the full sheets were available for sale to other customers at face value plus a shipping charge through the stamps.com website.

Stamps.com Type of 2007

2019 *Die Cut*

Self-Adhesive

3CVP4 CVPC1 5c black & gray 1.00 1.00

No. 3CVP4 was printed in sheets of 40 stamps that were sold for face value plus a shipping charge and were obtainable through the stamps.com website.

CARRIERS' STAMPS

GENERAL ISSUE CARRIER STAMPS

Issued by the U.S. Government to facilitate payment of fees for delivering and collecting letters.

Franklin — OC1

1851 Engr. Unwmk. ***Imperf.***

LO1 OC1 (1c) dull blue, *rose* *7,000. 8,000.*

U.S.P.O. Despatch

Eagle — OC2

1851

LO2 OC2 1c blue (shades) 50.00 *80.00*

1875 ***Imperf.***

LO3 OC1 (1c) blue, *rose* 60.

Perf. 12

LO4 OC1 (1c) blue *16,000.*

No. LO4 is valued in the grade of average to fine.

Eagle Reprints

Imperf.

LO5 OC2 1c blue 25.

Perf. 12

LO6 OC2 1c blue 175.

Reprints of the Franklin Carrier are printed in dark blue, instead of the dull blue or deep blue of the originals. Two reprintings of 10,000 each were made in 1875 on the same rose paper as the originals. A third reprinting of 5,000 in 1881 is on soft wove paper.

The first two reprintings of 10,000 each of the Eagle carrier are on hard white paper, ungummed and sometimes perforated. A third reprinting of 10,000 stamps in 1881 is on soft wove paper. Originals are on yellowish paper with brown gum.

No. LO6 is valued with the perfs cutting slightly into the design.

CITY CARRIER DEPARTMENT STAMPS

Issued by officials or employees of the U.S. Government for the purpose of securing or indicating payment of carriers' fees.

All are imperforate.

Baltimore, Md.

C1

1850-55 **Typo.**

Settings of 10 (2x5) varieties

1LB1 C1 1c red, *bluish* 180. 160.
1LB2 C1 1c blue, *bluish* 200. 150.
a. Bluish laid paper — —
1LB3 C1 1c blue 160. 100.
a. Laid paper 200. 150.
b. Block of 14 containing three tete-beche gutter pairs (unique) *6,250.*
1LB4 C1 1c green — 1,000.
1LB5 C1 1c red 2,250. 1,750.

C2

1856 **Typo.**

1LB6 C2 1c blue (shades) 130. 90.
1LB7 C2 1c red (shades) 130. 90.

C3

The sheet consisted of at least four panes of 10 placed horizontally, the two center panes tete beche. This makes possible five horizontal tete beche gutter pairs.

Plate of 10 (2x5); 10 Varieties

1857

1LB8 C3 1c black (shades) 65. 50.
a. "SENT" 100. 75.
b. Short rays 100. 75.
1LB9 C3 1c red 100. 90.
a. "SENT" 140. 110.
b. Short rays 140. 110.
c. As "b," double impression *800.*

Boston, Mass.

C6

Several Varieties

1849-50 Pelure Paper Typeset

3LB1 C6 1c blue 375. 180.
a. Wrong ornament at left *400.*

C7

Several Varieties

1851

Wove Paper Colored Through

3LB2 C7 1c blue (shades), *slate* 190. 100.

Charleston, S. C.

Honour's City Express

C8

1849 **Typo.**

Wove Paper Colored Through

4LB1 C8 2c blk, *brn rose* *10,000.*
Cut to shape *4,000. 4,000.*
4LB2 C8 2c blk, *yel,* cut to shape —

No. 4LB1 unused is a unique uncanceled stamp on piece. The used cut-to-shape stamp is also unique. In addition two covers exist bearing No. 4LB1.

No. 4LB2 unused (uncanceled) off cover is unique; three known on cover.

See the Scott U.S. Specialized Catalogue.

4LB2A C8 2c blk, *bl gray,* on cover, cut to shape —

No. 4LB2A is unique.

C10

1854 Wove Paper Typeset

4LB3 C10 2c black *1,500.*

C11

Several Varieties

1849-50

Wove Paper Colored Through

4LB5 C11 2c black, *bluish,* pelure *750. 500.*
a. "Ceuts" *5,750.*
4LB7 C11 2c black, *yellow* *750. 1,000.*
a. "Ccnts," ms. tied on cover *14,500.*

No. 4LB5a is unique. It is without gum and is valued thus. No. 4LB7a also is unique.

C13

C14

C15

Several varieties of each type

1851-58

Wove Paper Colored Through

4LB8 C13 2c black, *bluish* 350. 175.
a. Period after "PAID" 500. 250.
b. "Cens" 700. *900.*
c. "Conours" and "Bents" —

The No. 4LB8 with No. 2 combination cover is unique. It is a cover front only and is valued thus.

No. 4LB8a on cover with 5c No. 1 is unique.

4LB9 C13 2c black, *bluish,* pelure *850. 950.*
4LB10 C13 2c black, *pink,* pelure, on cover *7,000.*
4LB11 C14 (2c) black, *bluish* — 375.
4LB12 C14 (2c) black, *bluish,* pelure — —
4LB13 C15 (2c) black, *bluish* ('58) 750. 400.
a. Comma after "PAID" *1,100.*
b. No period after "Post" *1,400.*

Kingman's City Post

C16

C17

Several varieties of each

Wove Paper Colored Through

1851(?)-58(?)

4LB14 C16 2c black, *bluish* *1,400. 900.*
a. "Kingman's" erased *5,000.*
4LB15 C17 2c black, *bluish* *800. 800.*
a. "Kingman's" erased, on cover with 3c #11, tied by pen cancel (unique) *4,500.*

Martin's City Post

C18

Several Varieties

1858 Typeset

Wove Paper Colored Through

4LB16 C18 2c black, *bluish* *8,000.*

Beckman's City Post

C19

1860

4LB17 C19 2c black, on cover —

No. 4LB17 is unique.

Steinmeyer's City Post

C19a

C20

Several varieties of Type C19

Type C20 printed from plate of 10 (2x5) varieties

1859 Typeset

Wove Paper Colored Through

4LB18 C19a 2c black, *bluish* *21,000.*
4LB19 C20 2c black, *bluish* *4,500.* —
4LB20 C20 2c black, *pink* *200.* —
4LB21 C20 2c black, *yellow* 200.

Cincinnati, Ohio

Williams' City Post

C20a

1854 Wove Paper Litho.

9LB1 C20a 2c brown — *4,000.*

Cleveland, Ohio

Bishop's City Post

C20b

C20c

1854 Wove Paper Litho.

10LB1 C20b blue *5,000. 4,000.*

Vertically Laid Paper

10LB2 C20c 2c black, *bluish* *4,000. 6,000.*

No. 10LB2 unused is unique. It is cut in at bottom and without gum, and is valued thus.

Louisville, Ky.

Wharton's U.S.P.O. Despatch

C21

1857 Lithographed

5LB1 C21 (2c) bluish green (shades) 125.

Brown & McGill's U. S. P. O. Despatch

C22

1858, Nov.-1860 Lithographed

5LB2 C22 (2c) blue (shades) 250. *750.*

1858, Feb.-Aug.

5LB3 C22 (2c) black *4,500. 15,000.*
On cover, not tied, with 3c #26 *17,500.*

The value for No. 5LB3 used refers to the finer of the two known used (canceled) examples; it is extremely fine and on a piece with a 3c #26.

New York, N. Y.

United States City Despatch Post

C23

Wove Paper Colored Through

1842 **Engr.**

6LB1 C23 3c black, *grayish* 2,000.

Used examples are Carriers' stamps only when canceled with the regular government cancellation "U.S." in octagonal frame (see illustration), "U.S.CITY DESPATCH POST," or New York circular postmark.

When canceled "FREE" in frame they were used as local stamps. See No. 40L1 in the Scott Specialized Catalogue of United States Stamps.

C24

Wove Paper (unsurfaced) Colored Through

1842-45

6LB2 C24 3c black, *rosy buff* 5,000.

6LB3 C24 3c black, *light blue* 1,500. 750.

6LB4 C24 3c black, *green* 11,500.

a. 3c black, *apple green* —

Some authorities consider No. 6LB2 to be an essay, and No. 6LB4 a color changeling. No. 6LB2 unused is valued without gum.

Glazed Paper, Surface Colored

6LB5 C24 3c black, *blue green* (shades) 200. 175.

a. Double impression 1,500.
On cover 4,500.

b. 3c black, *blue* 650. 300.

c. As "b," double impression 1,000.

d. 3c black, *green* 1,250. 750.
black, *apple green* 2,000.
Pair 2,750.

e. As "d," double impression —

6LB6 C24 3c black, *pink*, on cover front 14,500.

No. 6LB6 is unique.

No. 6LB5 Surcharged in Red

1846

6LB7 C24 2c on 3c black, *bluish grn*, on cover 14,000.
On cover, not tied, with certificate 70,000.

The City Despatch 2c red is listed in the Scott U.S. Specialized Catalogue as a Local stamp.

U.S. MAIL

C27

1849 **Typo.**

Wove Paper, Colored Through

6LB9 C27 1c black, *rose* 100. 100.

1849-50 **Glazed Surface Paper**

6LB10 C27 1c black, *yellow* 100. 100.

6LB11 C27 1c black, *buff* 100. 100.

a. Pair, one stamp sideways 2,850.

Philadelphia, Pa.

C28

Several Varieties
Thick Wove Paper Colored Through

1849-50 **Typeset**

7LB1 C28 1c black, *rose* (with "L P") 450.

7LB2 C28 1c black, *rose* (with "S") 3,000.

7LB3 C28 1c black, *rose* (with "H") 275.

7LB4 C28 1c black, *rose* (with "L S") 400. 500.

7LB5 C28 1c black, *rose* (with "J J") 7,500.

The used No. 7LB5 also is unique and is an uncanceled stamp on a cover front.

C29

Several Varieties

7LB6 C29 1c black, *rose* 300. 250.

7LB7 C29 1c black, *blue*, glazed 1,000.

7LB8 C29 1c blk, *ver*, glazed 700.

7LB9 C29 1c blk, *yel*, glazed 2,750. 2,250.

Cancellations on Nos. 7LB1-7LB9: Normally these stamps were left uncanceled on the letter, but occasionally were accidentally tied by the Philadelphia town postmark which was normally struck in blue ink.

A 1c black on buff (unglazed) of type C29 is believed to be a color changeling.

C30

Settings of 25 (5x5) varieties (Five basic types)

1850-52 **Litho.**

7LB11 C30 1c gold, *black*, glazed 175. 110.

7LB12 C30 1c blue 400. 275.

7LB13 C30 1c black 750. 550.

25 varieties of C30.

C31

Handstamped

7LB14 C31 1c blue, *buff* 3,250.

1855(?)

7LB16 C31 1c black 5,000.

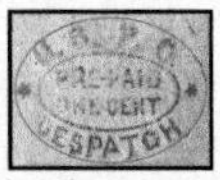

C32

1856(?) **Handstamped**

7LB18 C32 1c black 1,250. 2,000.

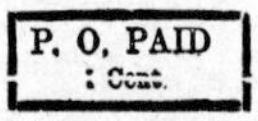

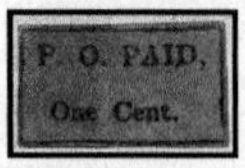

Labels of these designs are believed by most specialists not to be carrier stamps. Those seen are uncanceled, either off cover or affixed to stampless covers of the early 1850s. Some students believe they should be given carrier status.

St. Louis, Mo.

C36

C37

Illustrations enlarged to show details of the two types (note upper corners especially). Sizes of actual designs are 17 1/2x22mm.

1849 **White Wove Paper** **Litho.**
Two Types

8LB1 C36 2c black 7,000. 3,000.

8LB2 C37 2c black 6,000. —

Cancellation on Nos. 8LB1-8LB2: Black town.

C38

1857 **Litho.**

8LB3 C38 2c blue 22,500.

The used example off cover is unique. Five covers are recorded.

Cancellations on No. 8LB3: Black boxed "1ct," "Paid" in arc, black pen.

STAMPED ENVELOPES & WRAPPERS

VALUES

Unless otherwise noted, values are for cut squares in a grade of very fine.

Very fine cut squares will have the design well centered within moderately large margins. Precanceled cut squares must include the entire precancellation.

Values for unused entires are for those without printed or manuscript address. Values for letter sheets are for folded entires. Unfolded examples sell for more. A "full corner" includes back and side flaps and commands a premium.

Entire envelopes and wrappers are listed in the Scott U.S. Specialized Catalogue.

Wrappers are listed with envelopes of corresponding designs, and indicated by prefix letter "W" instead of "U."

An ALBINO impression is where two or more envelope blanks are fed into the printing press. The one adjacent to the printing die receives the color and the embossing, while the others are embossed only. Albinos are printing errors and are sometimes worth more than normal, inked impressions. Because of the nature of the printing process, many albinos were produced, and most collectors will not pay much, or any, premium for most of them. Albinos of earlier issues, canceled while current, are scarce.

The papers of these issues vary greatly in texture, and in color from yellowish to bluish white and from amber to dark buff.

"+" Some authorities claim that Nos. U37, U48, U49, U110, U124, U125, U130, U133A, U137A, U137B, U137C, W138, U145, U162, U178A, U185, U220, U285, U286, U298, U299, UO3, UO32, UO38, UO45 and UO45A (each with "+" before number) were not regularly issued and are not known to have been used.

U1

"THREE" in short label with curved ends; 13mm wide at top. Twelve varieties.

Washington — U2

"THREE" in short label with straight ends; 15½mm wide at top. Three varieties.

U3

"THREE" in short label with octagonal ends. Two varieties.

U4

"THREE" in wide label with straight ends; 20mm wide at top.

U5

"THREE" in medium wide label with curved ends; 14½mm wide at top. Ten varieties. A sub-variety shows curved lines at either end of label omitted; both T's have longer cross stroke; R is smaller (20 varieties).

U6

Four varieties.

U7

"TEN" in short label; 15½mm wide at top.

U8

"TEN" in wide label; 20mm wide at top.

1853-55

On Diagonally Laid Paper (Early printings of No. U1 on Horizontally Laid Paper)

U1	U1	3c red	350.00	35.00
U2	U1	3c red, *buff*	90.00	30.00
U3	U2	3c red	950.00	50.00
U4	U2	3c red, *buff*	425.00	45.00
U5	U3	3c red ('54)	5,750.	500.00
U6	U3	3c red, *buff* ('54)	3,750.	100.00
U7	U4	3c red	5,000.	150.00
U8	U4	3c red, *buff*	*8,250.*	175.00
U9	U5	3c red ('54)	40.00	4.00
U10	U5	3c red, *buff* ('54)	20.00	4.00
U11	U6	6c red	275.00	90.00
U12	U6	6c red, *buff*	145.00	90.00
U13	U6	6c green	260.00	150.00
U14	U6	6c green, *buff*	200.00	125.00
U15	U7	10c green ('55)	400.00	100.00
U16	U7	10c green, *buff* ('55)	175.00	90.00
a.		10c pale green, *buff*	135.00	70.00
U17	U8	10c green ('55)	375.00	140.00
a.		10c pale green	275.00	125.00
U18	U8	10c green, *buff* ('55)	375.00	100.00
a.		10c pale green, *buff*	350.00	100.00

Earliest documented uses: No. U1, July 6, 1853; No. U2, July 12, 1853 (Nesbitt seal); No. U3, July 7, 1853 (Nesbitt seal); No. U4, July 7, 1853 (flap missing); No. U5, Feb. 18, 1854; No. U6, Feb. 24, 1854; No. U7, Oct. 6, 1853; No. U8, Nov. 9, 1853; No. U9, May 30, 1854; No. U10, Mar. 24, 1854; No. U11, Mar. 25, 1855; No. U12, Feb. 22, 1855; No. U13, Nov. 29, 1853; No. U14, Nov. 10, 1853; No. U15, Oct. 15, 1856; No. U16, May 15, 1857 (cut square), June 15, 1857 (entire); No. U16a, Dec. 19, 1856 (cut square), June 4, 1857 (entire); No. U17, no dates documented; No. U17a, Nov. 14, 1855; No. U18, June 1, 1855; No. U18a, Sept. 4, 1855.

Nos. U9, U10, U11, U12, U13, U14, U17, and U18 have been reprinted on white and buff papers, wove or vertically laid, and are not known entire. The originals are on diagonally laid paper. Value, set of 8 reprints on laid, $225. Reprints on wove sell for more.

The first printings of Nos. U1, U2, U3, U4 and U7 have G.F. Nesbitt crests printed on the envelope flaps. These sell for a premium. Such examples of Nos. U1-U4 with 1853 year-dated cancels sell for a very large premium.

No. U1 with watermark having a space between lines and on horizontally laid paper sells for a substantial premium.

U9

Period after "POSTAGE." (Eleven varieties.)

Franklin, Period after "POSTAGE." — U10

Bust touches inner frame-line at front and back.

No period after "POSTAGE" — U11

No period after "POSTAGE." (Two varieties.)

Washington — U12

Nine varieties of type U12.

Envelopes are on diagonally laid paper.

Wrappers on vertically or horizontally laid paper, or on unwatermarked wove paper (Nos. U21A, W22, W25)

1860-61

W18B	U9	1c blue ('61)	*5,500.*	
U19	U9	1c blue, *buff*	35.00	12.50
W20	U9	1c bl, *buff* ('61)	65.00	50.00
W21	U9	1c bl, *man* ('61)	55.00	45.00
U21A	U9	1c bl, *org*	*950.00*	*325.00*
W22	U9	1c bl, *org* ('61)	*3,000.*	
U23	U10	1c bl, *org*	500.00	350.00
U24	U11	1c bl, *amb*	350.00	110.00
W25	U11	1c bl, *man* ('61)	*6,750.*	*1,500.*
U26	U12	3c red	25.00	17.50
U27	U12	3c red, *buff*	22.50	12.50
U28	U12+U9	3c +1c red & bl	250.00	225.00
U29	U12+U9	3c +1c red & bl, *buff*	250.00	250.00
U30	U12	6c red	1,800.	1,500.
U31	U12	6c red, *buff*	3,500.	1,450.
U32	U12	10c green	1,250.	450.00
U33	U12	10c green, *buff*	1,250.	400.00

Nos. U26, U27, U30 to U33 have been reprinted on the same vertically laid paper as the reprints of the 1853-55 issue, and are not known entire. Value, Nos. U26-U27, $75 each; Nos. U30-U33, $75 each.

U13

U14

U15

Washington — U16

Envelopes are on diagonally laid paper.

U36 and U45 come on vertically or horizontally laid paper.

1861

U34	U13	3c pink	27.50	5.00
U35	U13	3c pink, *buff*	32.50	6.00
U36	U13	3c pink, *blue* (Letter Sheet)	65.00	65.00
+U37	U13	3c pink, *orange*	*2,750.*	
U38	U14	6c pink	100.00	80.00
U39	U14	6c pink, *buff*	60.00	60.00
U40	U15	10c yellow green	40.00	30.00
a.		10c blue green	40.00	30.00
U41	U15	10c yel grn, *buff*	40.00	30.00
a.		10c blue green, *buff*	40.00	30.00
U42	U16	12c red & brn, *buff*	180.00	180.00
a.		12c lake & brown, *buff*	*1,250.*	
U43	U16	20c red & bl, *buff*	250.00	225.00
U44	U16	24c red & grn, *buff*	225.00	210.00
a.		24c lake & green, *salmon*	275.00	225.00
U45	U16	40c blk & red, *buff*	325.00	400.00

Nos. U38 and U39 have been reprinted on the same papers as the reprints of the 1853-55 issue, and are not known entire. Value, set of 2 reprints, $60.

Jackson — U17

"U.S. POSTAGE" above. Downstroke and tail of "2" unite near the point (seven varieties).

Jackson — U18

"U.S. POSTAGE" above. The downstroke and tail of the "2" touch but do not merge.

Jackson — U19

"U.S. POST" above. Stamp 24-25mm wide (Sixteen varieties).

Jackson — U20

"U.S. POST" above. Stamp 25½-26¼mm wide. (Twenty-five varieties.)

Envelopes are on diagonally laid paper. Wrappers on vertically or horizontally laid paper.

Envelopes are on diagonally laid paper.

Wrappers on vertically or horizontally laid paper.

1863-64

U46	U17	2c black, *buff*	50.00	24.00
W47	U17	2c black, *dark manila*	75.00	65.00
+U48	U18	2c black, *buff*	*2,250.*	
+U49	U18	2c black, *orange*	1,750.	
U50	U19	2c black, *buff* ('64)	17.50	11.00
W51	U19	2c black, *buff* ('64)	425.00	275.00
U52	U19	2c black, *orange* ('64)	20.00	11.00
W53	U19	2c black, *dark manila* ('64)	42.50	40.00
U54	U20	2c black, *buff* ('64)	17.50	9.50
W55	U20	2c black, *buff* ('64)	95.00	65.00
U56	U20	2c black, *orange* ('64)	17.50	10.00
W57	U20	2c black, *light manila* ('64)	22.50	14.00

Washington — U21

79 varieties for Nos. U58-U61; 2 varieties for Nos. U63-U65.

Washington — U22

1864-65

U58	U21	3c pink	8.00	1.60
U59	U21	3c pink, *buff*	7.50	1.25
U60	U21	3c brown ('65)	60.00	40.00
U61	U21	3c brown, *buff* ('65)	50.00	30.00
U62	U21	6c pink	75.00	29.00
U63	U21	6c pink, *buff*	35.00	27.50
U64	U21	6c purple ('65)	50.00	26.00
U65	U21	6c purple, *buff* ('65)	40.00	20.00
U66	U22	9c lemon, *buff* ('65)	375.00	250.00
U67	U22	9c orange, *buff* ('65)	125.00	90.00
a.		9c orange yellow, *buff*	150.00	90.00
U68	U22	12c brown, *buff* ('65)	275.00	275.00
U69	U22	12c red brown, *buff* ('65)	125.00	55.00
U70	U22	18c red, *buff* ('65)	70.00	95.00
U71	U22	24c blue, *buff* ('65)	70.00	95.00
U72	U22	30c green, *buff* ('65)	80.00	80.00
a.		30c yellow green, *buff*	75.00	75.00
U73	U22	40c rose, *buff* ('65)	80.00	*250.00*

Printed by George H. Reay, Brooklyn, N. Y.

The engravings in this issue are finely executed.

Franklin — U23

Bust points to the end of the "N" of "ONE."

Jackson — U24

Bust narrow at back. Small, thick figures of value.

Washington — U25

Queue projects below bust.

Lincoln — U26

Neck very long at the back.

Stanton — U27

Bust pointed at the back; figures "7" are normal.

Jefferson — U28

Queue forms straight line with the bust.

Clay — U29

Ear partly concealed by hair, mouth large, chin prominent.

Webster — U30

Has side whiskers.

Scott — U31

Straggling locks of hair at top of head; ornaments around the inner oval end in squares.

Hamilton — U32

Back of bust very narrow, chin almost straight; labels containing figures of value are exactly parallel.

Perry — U33

Front of bust very narrow and pointed; inner lines of shields project very slightly beyond the oval.

1870-71

U74	U23	1c blue	32.50	30.00
a.		1c ultramarine	60.00	35.00
U75	U23	1c blue, *amber*	25.00	27.50
a.		1c ultramarine, *amber*	55.00	30.00
U76	U23	1c blue, *orange*	17.00	15.00
W77	U23	1c blue, *manila*	35.00	35.00
U78	U24	2c brown	35.00	16.00
U79	U24	2c brown, *amber*	14.00	10.00
U80	U24	2c brown, *orange*	8.00	6.50
W81	U24	2c brown, *manila*	25.00	20.00
U82	U25	3c green	7.00	1.00
a.		3c brown (error), entire	*9,000.*	
U83	U25	3c green, *amber*	6.00	2.00
U84	U25	3c green, *cream*	8.00	4.50
U85	U26	6c dark red	17.50	16.00
a.		6c vermilion	17.50	16.00
U86	U26	6c dark red, *amber*	30.00	20.00
a.		6c vermilion, *amber*	30.00	20.00
U87	U26	6c dark red, *cream*	30.00	25.00
a.		6c vermilion, *cream*	25.00	20.00
U88	U27	7c vermilion, *amber* ('71)	55.00	175.00
U89	U28	10c olive black	650.00	900.00
U90	U28	10c olive black, *amber*	625.00	800.00
U91	U28	10c brown	82.50	70.00
U92	U28	10c brown, *amber*	85.00	52.50
a.		10c dark brown, *amber*	85.00	75.00
U93	U29	12c plum	100.00	82.50
U94	U29	12c plum, *amber*	110.00	100.00
U95	U29	12c plum, *cream*	225.00	200.00
U96	U30	15c red orange	75.00	75.00
a.		15c orange	75.00	
U97	U30	15c red orange, *amber*	160.00	275.00
a.		15c orange, *amber*	170.00	
U98	U30	15c red orange, *cream*	325.00	375.00
a.		15c orange, *cream*	325.00	
U99	U31	24c purple	110.00	125.00
U100	U31	24c purple, *amber*	180.00	300.00
U101	U31	24c purple, *cream*	225.00	450.00
U102	U32	30c black	60.00	120.00
U103	U32	30c black, *amber*	180.00	450.00
U104	U32	30c black, *cream*	150.00	450.00
U105	U33	90c carmine	125.00	300.00
U106	U33	90c carmine, *amber*	350.00	900.00
U107	U33	90c carmine, *cream*	175.00	*2,250.*

Printed by Plimpton Manufacturing Co.

The profiles in this issue are inferior to the fine engraving of the Reay issue.

U34

Bust forms an angle at the back near the frame. Lettering poorly executed. Distinct circle in "O" of "Postage."

U35

Lower part of bust points to the end of the "E" in "ONE." Head inclined downward.

U36

Bust narrow at back. Thin numerals. Head of "P" narrow. Bust broad at front, ending in sharp corners.

U37

Bust broad. Figures of value in long ovals.

U38

Similar to U37 but the figure "2" at the left touches the oval.

U39

Similar to U37 but the "O" of "TWO" has the center netted instead of plain and the "G" of "POSTAGE" and the "C" of "CENTS" have diagonal crossline.

U40

Bust broad: numerals in ovals short and thick.

U41

Similar to U40 but the ovals containing the numerals are much heavier. A diagonal line runs from the upper part of the "U" to the white frame-line.

U42

Similar to U40 but the middle stroke of "N" in "CENTS" is as thin as the vertical strokes.

U43

Bottom of bust cut almost semi-circularly.

U44

Thin lettering, long thin figures of value.

U45

Thick lettering, well-formed figures of value, queue does not project below bust.

U46

Top of head egg-shaped; knot of queue well marked and projects triangularly.

Taylor — U47

Die 1- Figures of value with thick, curved tops

Die 2- Figures of value with long, thin tops

U48

Neck short at back.

U49

Figures of value turned up at the ends.

U50

Very large head.

U51

Knot of queue stands out prominently.

U52

Ear prominent, chin receding.

U53

No side whiskers, forelock projects above head.

U54

Hair does not project; ornaments around the inner oval end in points.

U55

Back of bust rather broad, chin slopes considerably; labels containing figures of value are not exactly parallel.

U56

Front of bust sloping; inner lines of shields project considerably into the inner oval.

1874-86 Design U34

U108	1c dark blue	175.00	60.00
a.	1c light blue	175.00	60.00
U109	1c dk bl, *amb*	150.00	75.00
+U110	1c dk blue, *cr*	1,000.	
U111	1c dk blue, *org*	15.00	15.00
a.	dk blue, *org*	12.50	12.50
W112	1c dk blue, *man*	62.50	40.00

Design U35

U113	1c light blue	2.25	1.00
a.	1c dark blue	6.50	6.50
U114	1c lt blue, *amb*	3.25	3.25
a.	dk blue, *amb*	17.50	10.00
U115	1c blue, *cr*	4.25	4.25
a.	dk blue, *cr*	17.50	8.50
U116	1c lt blue, *org*	.75	.40
a.	dk blue, *org*	4.00	2.50
U117	1c lt bl, *bl* ('80)	6.50	5.00
U118	1c lt bl, *fawn* ('79)	7.00	5.00

U119	1c lt bl, *man* ('86)	8.00	3.25
W120	1c lt bl, *man*	1.25	1.10
a.	dk bl, *man*	8.00	7.00
U121	1c lt bl, *amb man*	17.50	10.00

Design U36

U122	2c brown	140.00	65.00
U123	2c brown, *amb*	67.50	40.00
+U124	2c brn, *crm*	1,000.	
+U125	2c brn, *org*	*18,000.*	
W126	2c brn, *man*	125.00	85.00
W127	2c ver, *man*	2,500.	500.00

Design U37

U128	2c brown	60.00	35.00
U129	2c brn, *amb*	80.00	45.00
+U130	2c brn, *cr*	*35,000.*	
W131	2c brn, *man*	17.50	15.00

Design U38

U132	2c brown	70.00	27.50
U133	2c brn, *amb*	325.00	70.00
+U133A	2c brn, *cr*	*70,000.*	

Design U39

U134	2c brown	800.00	160.00
U135	2c brn, *amb*	425.00	150.00
U136	2c brn, *org*	50.00	27.50
W137	2c brn, *man*	75.00	40.00
+U137A	2c ver	*32,500.*	
+U137B	2c ver, *amb*	*30,000.*	
+U137C	2c ver, *org*	*70,000.*	
+W138	2c ver, *man*	*25,000.*	

Design U40

U139	2c brn ('75)	57.50	37.50
U140	2c brn,*amb* ('75)	85.00	62.50
+U140A	2c reddish brn, *org* ('75)	*17,500.*	
W141	2c brn, *man* ('75)	32.50	25.00
U142	2c ver ('75)	8.00	5.00
a.	2c pink	8.00	5.00
U143	2c ver, *amb* ('75)	9.00	5.00
U144	2c ver, *cr* ('75)	17.50	7.00
+U145	2c ver, *org* ('75)	*35,000.*	
U146	2c ver, *bl* ('80)	110.00	40.00
U147	2c ver, *fawn* ('75)	7.00	5.00
W148	2c ver, *man* ('75)	4.00	3.50

Design U41

U149	2c ver ('78)	45.00	25.00
a.	2c pink	52.50	27.00
U150	2c ver, *amb* ('78)	45.00	15.00
U151	2c ver, *bl* ('80)	10.00	8.00
a.	2c pink, *blue*	11.00	8.00
U152	2c ver, *fawn* ('78)	10.00	4.00

Design U42

U153	2c ver ('76)	75.00	30.00
U154	2c ver, *amb* ('76)	300.00	90.00
W155	2c ver, *man* ('76)	20.00	10.00

Design U43

U156	2c ver ('81)	1,250.	175.00
U157	2c ver, *amb* ('81)	*42,500.*	*27,500.*
W158	2c ver, *man* ('81)	90.00	55.00

Design U44

U159	3c green	35.00	10.00
U160	3c grn, *amb*	35.00	10.00
U161	3c grn, *cr*	35.00	12.00
+U162	3c grn, *bl*	*75,000.*	

Design U45

U163	3c green	1.40	.30
U164	3c grn, *amb*	1.50	.70
U165	3c grn, *cr*	8.50	6.50
U166	3c grn, *bl*	7.50	6.00
U167	3c grn, *fawn* ('75)	4.75	3.50

Design U46

U168	3c grn ('81)	1,000.	80.00
U169	3c grn, *amb*	450.00	140.00
U170	3c grn, *bl* ('81)	*11,500.*	*2,750.*
U171	3c grn, *fawn* ('81)	*40,000.*	*2,750.*

Design U47

U172	5c bl, die I ('75)	10.00	10.00
U173	5c bl, die I, *amb* ('75)	12.50	11.00
U174	5c bl, die I, *cr* ('75)	95.00	45.00
U175	5c bl, die I, *bl* ('75)	22.50	17.50
U176	5c bl, die I, *fawn* ('75)	150.00	65.00
U177	5c bl, die 2 ('75)	11.00	9.00
U178	5c bl, die 2, *amb* ('75)	8.00	8.00
+U178A	5c bl, die 2, *cr* ('76)	*10,000.*	
U179	5c bl, die 2, *bl* ('75)	20.00	12.50
U180	5c bl, die 2, *fawn* ('75)	125.00	50.00

Design U48

U181	6c red	8.00	6.50
a.	6c vermilion	8.00	6.50
U182	6c red, *amber*	12.50	6.50
a.	6c ver, *amb*	12.50	6.50
U183	6c red, *cream*	50.00	17.50
a.	6c ver, *cr*	45.00	15.00
U184	6c red, *fawn* ('75)	17.50	12.50

Design U49

+U185	7c vermilion	*1,200.*	
U186	7c ver, *amb*	125.00	75.00

Design U50

U187	10c brown	40.00	20.00
U188	10c brn, *amb*	75.00	35.00

Design U51

U189	10c choc ('75)	6.00	4.00
a.	10c bister brown	7.00	5.00
b.	10c yellow ocher	*3,000.*	
U190	10c choc, *amb* ('75)	7.00	6.00
a.	10c bis brn, *amb*	7.00	6.00
b.	10c yel ocher, *amb*	*3,000.*	
U191	10c brn, *oriental buff* ('86)	12.50	8.75
U192	10c brn, *bl* ('86)	12.50	8.00
a.	10c gray blk, *bl*	12.50	7.50
b.	10c red brn, *bl*	12.50	7.50
U193	10c brn, *man* ('86)	12.50	10.00
a.	10c red brn, *man*	12.50	10.00
U194	10c brn, *amb man* ('86)	17.50	9.00
a.	10c red brn, *amb man*	17.50	9.00

Design U52

U195	12c plum	250.00	100.00
U196	12c plum, *amb*	200.00	160.00
U197	12c plum, *cr*	450.00	130.00

Design U53

U198	15c orange	50.00	35.00
U199	15c org, *amb*	140.00	130.00
U200	15c org, *cr*	550.00	300.00

Design U54

U201	24c purple	175.00	150.00
U202	24c pur, *amb*	180.00	100.00
U203	24c pur, *cr*	375.00	100.00

Design U55

U204	30c black	55.00	25.00
U205	30c blk, *amb*	70.00	60.00
U206	30c blk, *cr* ('75)	300.00	325.00
U207	30c blk, *oriental buff* ('81)	90.00	80.00
U208	30c blk, *bl* ('81)	90.00	80.00
U209	30c blk, *man* ('81)	80.00	70.00
U210	30c blk, *amb man* ('86)	190.00	100.00

Design U56

U211	90c car ('75)	80.00	75.00
U212	90c car, *amb* ('75)	175.00	250.00
U213	90c car, *cr* ('75)	1,000.	
U214	90c car, *oriental buff* ('86)	140.00	250.00
U215	90c car, *bl* ('86)	160.00	250.00
U216	90c car, *man* ('86)	120.00	225.00
U217	90c car, *amb man* ('86)	140.00	*200.00*

Note: No. U206 has watermark #2; No. U207 watermark #6 or #7. No U213 has watermark #2; No. U214 watermark #7. These envelopes cannot be positively identified except by the watermark.

Single line under "POSTAGE" — U57

Double line under "POSTAGE" — U58

1876

U218	U57 3c red	30.00	25.00
U219	U57 3c green	30.00	17.50
+U220	U58 3c red	*27,500.*	
U221	U58 3c green	30.00	25.00

Cent. of the U.S., and the World's Fair at Philadelphia.

Used examples of Nos. U218-U221 with exposition cancels and/or typed addresses sell for a premium.

See No. U582.

Garfield — U59

1882-86

U222	U59 5c brown	5.00	3.00
U223	U59 5c brn, *amb*	5.25	3.50
+U224	U59 5c brn, *oriental buff* ('86)	130.00	
+U225	U59 5c brn, *bl*	75.00	
U226	U59 5c brn, *fawn*	300.00	

Washington — U60

1883, October

U227	U60 2c red	5.50	2.25
a.	2c brown (error), entire	*3,000.*	
U228	U60 2c red, *amb*	6.50	2.75
U229	U60 2c red, *blue*	8.00	5.00
U230	U60 2c red, *fawn*	9.00	5.25

Wavy lines fine and clear — U61

1883, November

Four Wavy Lines in Oval

U231	U61 2c red	5.00	2.50
U232	U61 2c red, *amb*	6.00	3.75
U233	U61 2c red, *blue*	10.00	7.50
U234	U61 2c red, *fawn*	7.50	4.75
W235	U61 2c red, *man*	18.00	6.25

Wavy lines thick and blurred — U62

Retouched die.

1884, June

U236	U62 2c red	15.00	4.00
U237	U62 2c red, *amber*	20.00	10.00
U238	U62 2c red, *blue*	29.00	12.00
U239	U62 2c red, *fawn*	20.00	11.00

See Nos. U260-W269.

3½ links over left "2" — U63

U240	U63 2c red	90.00	45.00
U241	U63 2c red, *amb*	550.00	300.00
U242	U63 2c red, *fawn*		*25,000.*

2 links below right "2" — U64

U243	U64 2c red	110.00	75.00
U244	U64 2c red, *amb*	250.00	100.00
U245	U64 2c red, *blue*	275.00	125.00
U246	U64 2c red, *fawn*	275.00	175.00

Round "O" in "TWO." White lines above "WO" of "TWO" joined to form thick white dash. — U65

U247	U65 2c red	1,500.	400.00
U248	U65 2c red, *amb*	2,500.	750.00
U249	U65 2c red, *fawn*	750.	500.00

See Nos. U270-U276.

Jackson — U66

Die 1- Numeral at left is 2 ¾ mm wide

Die 2- Numeral at left is 3 ¼ mm wide

1883-86

U250	U66 4c green, die 1	4.00	3.50
U251	U66 4c grn, die 1, *amb*	5.00	3.50
U252	U66 4c grn, die 1, *oriental buff* ('86)	13.00	9.00
U253	U66 4c green, die 1, *blue* ('86)	11.00	6.50
U254	U66 4c grn, die 1, *man* ('86)	16.00	7.50
U255	U66 4c grn, die 1, *amb man* ('86)	22.50	10.00
U256	U66 4c green, die 2	8.00	5.00
U257	U66 4c grn, die 2, *amb*	12.50	7.00
U258	U66 4c grn, die 2, *man* ('86)	12.50	7.50
U259	U66 4c grn, die 2, *amb man* ('86)	12.50	7.50

1884, May

U260	U61 2c brown	17.50	5.75
U261	U61 2c brown, *amber*	17.50	6.50
U262	U61 2c brown, *blue*	17.50	10.00
U263	U61 2c brown, *fawn*	15.00	9.25
W264	U61 2c brown, *manila*	15.00	11.50

1884, June

Retouched Die

U265	U62 2c brown	15.00	6.50
U266	U62 2c brn, *amb*	60.00	40.00
U267	U62 2c brown, *blue*	22.50	9.00
U268	U62 2c brown, *fawn*	15.00	11.00
W269	U62 2c brn, *man*	25.00	15.00

2 Links Below Right "2"

U270	U64 2c brown	115.00	50.00
U271	U64 2c brn, *amb*	425.00	125.00
U272	U64 2c brown, *fawn*	*7,000.*	*2,000.*

Round "O" in "Two"

U273	U65 2c brown	225.00	100.00
U274	U65 2c brn, *amb*	225.00	100.00
U275	U65 2c brown, *blue*		*10,000.*
U276	U65 2c brown, *fawn*	700.00	750.00

U67

Extremity of bust below the queue forms a point.

Washington — U68

Extremity of bust is rounded.

Similar to U61
Two wavy lines in oval

1884-86

U277	U67 2c brown	.50	.25
a.	2c brown lake, die 1	22.50	21.00
U278	U67 2c brn, *amb*	.65	.50
a.	2c brown lake, *amber*	35.00	25.00
U279	U67 2c brn, *oriental buff* ('86)	6.00	2.10
U280	U67 2c brown, *blue*	3.00	2.10
U281	U67 2c brown, *fawn*	3.75	2.40

U282	U67	2c brn, *man* ('86)	12.00	4.00
W283	U67	2c brn, *man*	8.00	5.00
U284	U67	2c brn, *amb man* ('86)	7.00	5.75
+U285	U67	2c red	600.00	
+U286	U67	2c red, *blue*	225.00	
W287	U67	2c red, *manila*	150.00	
U288	U68	2c brown	325.00	50.00
U289	U68	2c brn, *amb*	20.00	13.00
U290	U68	2c brown, *blue*	850.00	325.00
U291	U68	2c brown, *fawn*	25.00	25.00
W292	U68	2c brn, *man*	30.00	19.00

Gen. U.S. Grant — US1

Letter Sheet, 160x271mm

1886 Creamy White Paper

U293	US1	2c green, entire	30.00	20.00

See the Scott U.S. Specialized Catalogue for perforation and inscription varieties.

Franklin — U69

Washington U70

Bust points between third and fourth notches of inner oval "G" of "POSTAGE" has no bar.

U71

Bust points between second and third notches of inner oval; "G" of "POSTAGE" has a bar; ear is indicated by one heavy line; one vertical line at corner of mouth.

U72

Frame same as U71; upper part of head more rounded; ear indicated by two curved lines with two locks of hair in front; two vertical lines at corner of mouth.

Jackson U73

Grant U74

There is a space between the beard and the collar of the coat. A button is on the collar.

U75

The collar touches the beard and there is no button.

1887-94 Design U69

U294	1c blue	.55	.25
U295	1c dk bl ('94)	6.50	2.50
U296	1c bl, *amb*	3.25	1.25
U297	1c dk bl, *amb* ('94)	40.00	22.50
+U298	1c bl, *oriental buff*	7,000.	—
+U299	1c bl, *bl*	10,000.	
U300	1c bl, *man*	.65	.35
W301	1c bl, *man*	.45	.30
U302	1c dk bl, *man* ('94)	27.50	12.50
W303	1c DK bl, *man* ('94)	12.50	10.00
U304	1c bl, *amb man*	12.50	5.00

Design U70

U305	2c green	15.00	10.00
U306	2c grn, *amb*	40.00	17.50
U307	2c grn, *oriental buff*	80.00	40.00
U308	2c grn, *bl*	12,500.	4,250.
U309	2c grn, *man*	10,000.	1,000.
U310	2c grn, *amb man*	28,000.	4,000.

Design U71

U311	2c green	.30	.25
a.	2c dark green ('94)	.45	.30
b.	Double impression, entire	375.00	
U312	2c grn, *amb*	.40	.25
a.	Double impression	90.00	
b.	2c dk grn, *amb* ('94)	.55	.35
U313	2c grn, *oriental buff*	.55	.25
a.	2c dk grn, *oriental buff* ('94)	2.00	1.00
b.	Double impression	150.00	
U314	2c grn, *bl*	.60	.30
a.	2c dk grn, *bl* ('94)	.80	.40
U315	2c grn, *man*	2.00	.50
a.	2c dk grn, *man* ('94)	2.75	.75
W316	2c grn, *man*	3.50	2.50
U317	2c grn, *amb man*	2.50	1.90
a.	2c dk grn, *amb man* ('94)	3.50	3.00

Design U72

U318	2c green	110.00	12.50
U319	2c grn, *amb*	160.00	27.50
U320	2c grn, *oriental buff*	125.00	40.00
U321	2c grn, *bl*	150.00	70.00
U322	2c grn, *man*	225.00	70.00
U323	2c grn, *amb man*	400.00	100.00

Design U73

U324	4c carmine	3.25	2.00
a.	4c lake	3.50	2.00
b.	4c scarlet ('94)	3.50	2.00
U325	4c car, *amb*	3.50	3.50
a.	4c lake, *amber*	3.50	3.50
b.	4c scarlet, *amber* ('94)	4.00	3.75
U326	4c car, *oriental buff*	6.00	3.50
a.	4c lake, *oriental buff*	7.00	3.50
U327	4c car, *bl*	5.50	4.00
a.	4c lake, *blue*	6.00	4.00
U328	4c car, *man*	8.00	7.00
a.	4c lake, *manila*	8.00	6.00
b.	4c pink, *manila*	15.00	10.00
U329	4c car, *amb man*	6.00	3.25
a.	4c lake, *amb man*	6.00	3.25
b.	4c pink, *amb man*	15.00	10.00

Design U74

U330	5c blue	3.75	4.00
U331	5c bl, *amb*	6.00	2.50
a.	Double impression, entire	—	
U332	5c bl, *oriental buff*	6.50	4.00
U333	5c blue, *blue*	7.00	6.00

Design U75

U334	5c blue ('94)	20.00	12.50
U335	5c bl, *amb* ('94)	11.00	7.50

Design U55

U336	30c red brn	40.00	45.00
a.	30c yellow brown	40.00	45.00
b.	30c chocolate	40.00	45.00
U337	30c red brn, *amb*	40.00	45.00
a.	30c yel brn, *amb*	40.00	45.00
b.	30c choc, *amb*	40.00	45.00
U338	30c red brn, *oriental buff*	40.00	45.00
a.	30c yel brn, *oriental buff*	40.00	45.00
U339	30c red brn, *bl*	40.00	45.00
a.	30c yel brn, *bl*	40.00	45.00
U340	30c red brn, *man*	40.00	45.00
a.	30c brown, *manila*	40.00	45.00
U341	30c red brn, *amb man*	40.00	45.00
a.	30c yel brn, *amb man*	40.00	45.00

Design U56

U342	90c purple	55.00	85.00
U343	90c pur, *amb*	70.00	85.00
U344	90c pur, *oriental buff*	75.00	85.00
U345	90c pur, *bl*	75.00	85.00
U346	90c pur, *man*	80.00	85.00
U347	90c pur, *amb man*	80.00	85.00

Columbus and Liberty — U76

1893

U348	U76	1c deep blue	2.00	1.25
U349	U76	2c violet	1.50	.50
a.		2c dark slate (error)	*1,500.*	
U350	U76	5c chocolate	6.50	7.00
a.		5c slate brown (error)	*700.00*	*1,400.*
U351	U76	10c slate brown	25.00	27.50
		Nos. U348-U351 (4)	35.00	36.25

Franklin — U77

Bust points to fourth notch of inner circle.

Washington — U78

Bust points to first notch of inner oval and is only slightly concave below.

U79

Bust points to middle of second notch of inner oval and is quite hollow below. Queue has ribbon around it.

U80

Same as die 2, but hair flowing. No ribbon on queue.

Lincoln — U81

Bust pointed but not draped.

U82

Bust broad and draped.

U83

Head larger, inner oval has no notches.

Grant — U84

Similar to design of 1887-95 but smaller.

1899

U352	U77	1c green	2.75	.25
U353	U77	1c green, *amber*	5.00	1.50
U354	U77	1c green, *oriental buff*	10.00	2.75
U355	U77	1c green, *blue*	10.00	7.50
U356	U77	1c green, *manila*	2.50	.95
W357	U77	1c green, *manila*	2.75	1.10
U358	U78	2c carmine	3.00	1.75
U359	U78	2c car, *amb*	15.00	12.50
U360	U78	2c carmine, *oriental buff*	17.50	11.00
U361	U78	2c carmine, *blue*	55.00	35.00
U362	U79	2c carmine	.35	.25
a.		2c dark lake	30.00	30.00
U363	U79	2c car, *amb*	1.75	.25
U364	U79	2c carmine, *oriental buff*	1.20	.25
U365	U79	2c carmine, *blue*	1.50	.55
W366	U79	2c car, *man*	9.00	3.25
U367	U80	2c carmine	5.00	2.75
U368	U80	2c car, *amb*	8.00	6.50
U369	U80	2c carmine, *oriental buff*	17.50	12.50
U370	U80	2c carmine, *blue*	11.00	10.00
U371	U81	4c brown	15.00	12.50
U372	U81	4c brown, *amber*	15.00	12.50
U373	U82	4c brown	*6,500.*	1,000.
U374	U83	4c brown	10.00	8.00
U375	U83	4c brown, *amber*	60.00	25.00
W376	U83	4c brown, *manila*	12.50	12.50
U377	U84	5c blue	9.00	9.00
U378	U84	5c blue, *amber*	10.00	10.00

Franklin U85

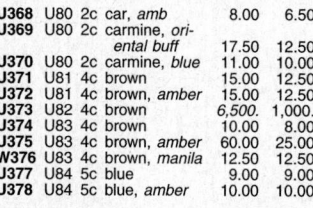

Washington U86

"D" of "UNITED" contains vertical line at right that parallels the left vertical line. One short and two long vertical lines at the right of "CENTS."

Grant — U87

Lincoln — U88

1903

U379	U85	1c green	.75	.25
U380	U85	1c green, *amber*	10.00	2.00
U381	U85	1c green, *oriental buff*	12.50	2.50
U382	U85	1c green, *blue*	15.00	2.50
U383	U85	1c green, *manila*	3.50	.90
W384	U85	1c green, *manila*	2.50	.40
a.		Double impression, entire letter sheet	*275.00*	
U385	U86	2c carmine	.40	.25
a.		2c pink	2.00	1.50
b.		2c red	2.00	1.50
U386	U86	2c carmine, *amber*	2.00	.50
a.		2c pink, *amber*	5.50	3.00
b.		2c red, *amber*	12.50	7.00
U387	U86	2c carmine, *oriental buff*	2.00	.30
a.		2c pink, *oriental buff*	3.50	2.00
b.		2c red, *oriental buff*	4.00	2.25
U388	U86	2c carmine, *blue*	1.75	.50
a.		2c pink, *blue*	17.50	14.00
b.		2c red, *blue*	17.50	14.00
W389	U86	2c carmine, *manila*	15.00	9.00
U390	U87	4c choc	17.50	11.00
U391	U87	4c choc, *amber*	17.50	11.00
W392	U87	4c choc, *manila*	20.00	12.50
U393	U88	5c blue	15.00	11.00
U394	U88	5c blue, *amber*	15.00	11.00

U89

Re-cut die — "D" of "UNITED" is well rounded at right. The three lines at the right of "CENTS" and at the left of "TWO" are usually all short; the lettering is heavier and the ends of the ribbons slightly changed.

1904 Re-cut Die

U395	U89	2c carmine	.75	.25
a.		2c pink	5.00	2.50
U396	U89	2c carmine, *amber*	7.50	1.00
a.		2c pink, *amber*	8.50	3.00
U397	U89	2c carmine, *oriental buff*	5.00	1.10
a.		2c pink, *oriental buff*	6.50	2.75
U398	U89	2c carmine, *blue*	3.75	.90
a.		2c pink, *blue*	5.00	2.50
W399	U89	2c carmine, *manila*	12.50	8.00
a.		2c pink, *manila*	25.00	17.50
b.		Double impression, entire	*375.00*	

Franklin — U90

Die 1

Die 2

Die 3

Die 4

Die 1 — Wide "D" in "UNITED."
Die 2 — Narrow "D" in "UNITED."
Die 3 — Wide "S-S" in "STATES" (1910).
Die 4 — Sharp angle at back of bust, "N" and "E" of "ONE" are parallel (1912).

1907-16 **Die 1**

U400	U90 1c green	.35	.25
a.	Die 2	.85	.25
b.	Die 3	.85	.55
c.	Die 4	.85	.25
U401	U90 1c green, *amber*	2.00	.40
a.	Die 2	2.50	1.00
b.	Die 3	3.25	3.00
c.	Die 4	2.00	1.00
U402	U90 1c green, *oriental buff*	9.00	.75
a.	Die 2	12.50	1.50
b.	Die 3	14.00	1.50
c.	Die 4	3.50	.75
U403	U90 1c green, *blue*	9.00	.75
a.	Die 2	12.50	3.00
b.	Die 3	11.50	3.00
c.	Die 4	.75	.65
U404	U90 1c green, *manila*	2.00	1.90
a.	Die 3	4.50	3.00
W405	U90 1c green, *manila*	.65	.25
a.	Die 2	60.00	25.00
b.	Die 3	11.00	4.00

Washington — U91 — brown red

Die 1, Washington — U91 — carmine

Die 2

Die 3

Die 4

Die 5

Die 6

Die 7

Die 8

Die 1 — Oval "O" in "TWO" and "C" in "CENTS." Front of bust broad.
Die 2 — Similar to 1 but hair re-cut in two distinct locks at top of head.
Die 3 — Round "O" in "TWO" and "C" in "CENTS," coarse lettering.
Die 4 — Similar to 3 but lettering fine and clear, hair lines clearly embossed. Inner oval thin and clear.
Die 5 — All "S's" wide (1910).
Die 6 — Similar to 1 but front of bust narrow (1913).
Die 7 — Similar to 6 but upper corner of front of bust cut away (1916).
Die 8 — Similar to 7 but lower stroke of "S" in "CENTS" is a straight line. Hair as in Die 2 (1916).

Die 1

U406	U91 2c brown red	.90	.25
a.	Die 2	40.00	7.00
b.	Die 3	.80	.25
U407	U91 2c brown red, *amber*	6.50	2.00
a.	Die 2	350.00	65.00
b.	Die 3	4.50	1.25
U408	U91 2c brown red, *oriental buff*	8.75	1.50
a.	Die 2	275.00	125.00
b.	Die 3	7.50	2.50
U409	U91 2c brn red, *blue*	5.75	2.00
a.	Die 2	375.00	200.00
b.	Die 3	5.75	1.75
W410	U91 2c brn red, *man*	35.00	35.00
U411	U91 2c carmine	.35	.25
a.	Die 2	.75	.25
b.	Die 3	.75	.25
c.	Die 4	.65	.25
d.	Die 5	.65	.30
e.	Die 6	.60	.25
f.	Die 7	3.00	3.00
g.	Die 8	37.50	25.00
h.	#U411 with added impression of #U400, entire	475.00	
i.	#U411 with added impression of #U416a, entire	475.00	
k.	As No. U411, double impression, entire	175.00	
U412	U91 2c carmine, *amb*	.50	.25
a.	Die 2	1.00	.25
b.	Die 3	2.25	2.00
c.	Die 4	.55	.25
d.	Die 5	.90	.35
e.	Die 6	.70	.25
f.	Die 7	35.00	25.00
U413	U91 2c car, *oriental buff*	.55	.25
a.	Die 2	2.00	.45
b.	Die 3	9.00	3.00
c.	Die 4	.55	1.00
d.	Die 5	3.50	1.25
e.	Die 6	1.00	.70
f.	Die 7	100.00	45.00
g.	Die 8	25.00	17.50
U414	U91 2c carmine, *blue*	.55	.25
a.	Die 2	1.00	1.00
b.	Die 3	2.75	2.00
c.	Die 4	.50	.50
d.	Die 5	1.00	.45
e.	Die 6	.65	.30
f.	Die 7	37.50	25.00
g.	Die 8	37.50	25.00
W415	U91 2c car, *manila*	5.00	2.00
a.	Die 2	5.50	1.25
b.	Die 5	5.50	2.50
c.	Die 7	120.00	97.50

U90 4c Die 1

U90 4c Die 2

Die 1 — "F" close to (1mm) left "4."

Die 2 — "F" far from (1¾mm) left "4."

U416	U90 4c black, die 2, laid paper	2.00	1.50
a.	Die 1	1.50	2.00
U417	U90 4c black, *amb,* die 2	7.50	2.50
a.	Die 1	.75	2.00

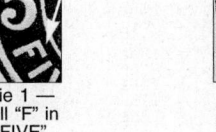

Die 1 — Tall "F" in "FIVE"

Die 2 — Short "F" in "FIVE"

U418	U91 5c Die 2	1.50	1.50
a.	Die 1	7.00	2.25
b.	5c blue, *buff,* die 2 (error)	*3,250.*	
c.	5c blue, *blue,* die 2 (error)	*3,000.*	
d.	As "c," die 1 (error), entire	*6,250.*	
U419	U91 5c blue, *amber,* die 2, laid paper	1.00	.75
a.	Die 1	15.00	12.00

Franklin — U92

Die 1

Die 2

Die 3

Die 4

Die 5

(The 1c and 4c dies are the same except for figures of value.)
Die 1 — UNITED nearer inner circle than outer circle.
Die 2 — Large U; large NT closely spaced.
Die 3 — Knob of hair at back of neck. Large NT widely spaced.
Die 4 — UNITED nearer outer circle than inner circle.
Die 5 — Narrow oval C, (also O and G).

1915-32 **Die 1**

U420	U92 1c green ('17)	.25	.25
a.	Die 2	100.00	55.00
b.	Die 3	.35	.25
c.	Die 4	.55	.40
d.	Die 5	.45	.35
U421	U92 1c grn, *amber* ('17)	.55	.30
a.	Die 2	400.00	175.00
b.	Die 3	1.40	.65
c.	Die 4	1.90	.85
d.	Die 5	1.10	.55
U422	U92 1c grn, *oriental buff* ('17)	2.40	.90
a.	Die 4	5.50	1.25
U423	U92 1c grn, *bl* ('17)	.50	.35
a.	Die 3	.80	.45
b.	Die 4	1.40	.65
c.	Die 5	.85	.35
U424	U92 1c grn, *manila* (unglazed) ('16)	6.50	4.00
W425	U92 1c grn, *manila* (unglazed) ('16)	.30	.25
a.	Die 3	175.00	125.00
U426	U92 1c grn, *brown* (glazed) ('20)	45.00	16.00
W427	U92 1c grn, *brown* (glazed) ('20)	65.00	35.00
a.	Printed on unglazed side	*400.00*	
	Entire	*750.00*	
b.	Unglazed on both sides		*150.00*
U428	U92 1c grn, *brown* (unglazed) ('20)	12.50	7.50
W428A	U92 1c grn, *brown* (unglazed) ('20)		*3,000.*

Washington — U93

Die 1

Die 2

Die 3

Die 4

Die 5

Die 6

Die 7

Die 8

Die 9

(The 1½c, 2c, 3c, 5c, and 6c dies are the same except for figures of value.)
Die 1 — Letters broad. Numerals vertical. Large head (9¼mm). from tip of nose to back of neck. E closer to inner circle than N of cents.
Die 2 — Similar to 1; but U far from left circle.
Die 3 — Similar to 2; but all inner circles very thin (Rejected die).
Die 4 — Large head as in Die 1. C of CENTS close to circle. Baseline of right numeral "2" slants downward to right. Left numeral "2" is larger.
Die 5 — Small head (8¾mm) from tip of nose to back of neck. T and S of CENTS close at bottom.
Die 6 — Similar to 5; but T and S of CENTS far apart at bottom. Left numeral slopes to right.
Die 7 — Large head. Both numerals slope to right. Clean cut lettering. All letters T have short top strokes.
Die 8 — Similar to 7; but all letters T have long top strokes.
Die 9 — Narrow oval C (also O and G).

1915-32 **Die 1**

U429 U93 2c carmine .25 .25
- *a.* Die 2 15.00 7.00
- *b.* Die 3 40.00 50.00
- *c.* Die 4 25.00 15.00
- *d.* Die 5 .55 .35
- *e.* Die 6 .65 .30
- *f.* Die 7 .70 .25
- *g.* Die 8 .50 .25
- *h.* Die 9 .50 .25
- *i.* 2c green (error), die 1, entire *12,500.*
- *j.* #U429 with added impression of #U420 600.00
- *k.* #U429 with added impression of #U416a, entire *3,500.*
- *l.* #U429 with added impression of #U400, entire 950.00
- *m.* #U429, double impression, entire 1,500.
- *n.* As "f," double impression, entire *750.00*
- *o.* As "e," triple impression —
- *p.* As "m," second impression on side flap, entire *250.00*

U430 U93 2c car, *amber* ('16) .30 .25
- *a.* Die 2 20.00 12.50
- *b.* Die 4 50.00 25.00
- *c.* Die 5 1.60 .35
- *d.* Die 6 1.25 .40
- *e.* Die 7 .75 .35
- *f.* Die 8 .70 .30
- *g.* Die 9 .65 .25
- *h.* As No. U430, with added impression of 4c black (#U416a), entire *600.00*
- *i.* As "g," with added impression of 2c car. die 1 on side flap, entire —

U431 U93 2c car, *oriental buff* ('16) 2.25 .65
- *a.* Die 2 180.00 75.00
- *b.* Die 4 75.00 60.00
- *c.* Die 5 3.50 2.00
- *d.* Die 6 3.50 2.00
- *e.* Die 7 3.50 2.00

U432 U93 2c car, *blue* ('16) .30 .25
- *b.* Die 2 35.00 25.00
- *c.* Die 3 130.00 90.00
- *d.* Die 4 60.00 50.00
- *e.* Die 5 1.10 .30
- *f.* Die 6 1.10 .40
- *g.* Die 7 .85 .35
- *h.* Die 8 .65 .25
- *i.* Die 9 1.00 .30
- *j.* 2c purple (error), die 9 —
- *k.* Double impression 650.00

U432A U93 2c car, *manila*, die 7, entire *50,000.*

W433 U93 2c car, *manila*, ('16) .25 .25

W434 U93 2c car, *brn* (glazed) ('20) 70.00 45.00

W435 U93 2c car, *brn* (unglazed) ('20) 90.00 60.00

U436 U93 3c purple ('32) .30 .25
- *a.* 3c dark violet, die 1 ('17) .60 .25
- *b.* 3c dark violet, die 5 ('17) 1.75 .75
- *c.* 3c dark violet, die 6 ('17) 2.10 1.40
- *d.* 3c dark violet, die 7 ('17) 1.50 .95
- *e.* 3c purple, die 7 ('32) .70 .30
- *f.* 3c purple, die 9 ('32) .45 .25
- *g.* 3c carmine (error), die 1 35.00 35.00
- *h.* 3c carmine (error), die 5 27.50 —
- *i.* #U436 with added impression of #U420, entire 900.00
- *j.* #U436 with added impression of #U429, entire 900.00 950.00
- *k.* As "f," double impression, preprinted, entire *600.00*

U437 U93 3c purple, *amb* ('32) .35 .25
- *a.* 3c dk vio, die 1 ('17) 5.50 1.25
- *b.* 3c dk vio, die 5 ('17) 8.50 2.50
- *c.* 3c dk vio, die 6 ('17) 8.50 2.50
- *d.* 3c dk vio, die 7 ('17) 8.50 2.25
- *e.* 3c pur, die 7 ('32) .75 .25
- *f.* 3c pur, die 9 ('32) .55 .25
- *g.* 3c carmine (error), die 5 375.00 400.00
- *h.* 3c black (error), die 1 190.00 —

U438 U93 3c dk vio, *oriental buff* ('17) 22.50 5.50
- *a.* Die 5 22.50 5.50
- *b.* Die 6 30.00 8.00
- *c.* Die 7 30.00 10.00

U439 U93 3c purple, *bl* ('32) .35 .25
- *a.* 3c dark violet, die 1 ('17) 7.00 2.00
- *b.* 3c dark violet, die 5 ('17) 7.50 6.00
- *c.* 3c dark violet, die 6 ('17) 7.50 6.00
- *d.* 3c dark violet, die 7 ('17) 10.00 6.00
- *e.* 3c purple, die 7 ('32) .75 .25
- *f.* 3c purple, die 9 ('32) .60 .25
- *g.* 3c carmine (error), die 5 225.00 300.00

U440 U92 4c black ('18) 1.75 .60
- *a.* With added impression of 2c carmine (#U429), die 1, entire 450.00

U441 U92 4c black, *amb* ('18) 3.00 .85
- *a.* 4c black, *amb*, with added impression of 2c car (#U429), die 1 175.00

U442 U92 4c blk, *bl* ('21) 3.25 .85

U443 U93 5c blue ('18) 3.25 2.75

U444 U93 5c blue, *amber* ('18) 4.00 1.60

U445 U93 5c bl, *blue* ('21) 3.25 3.25

For 1½c and 6c see Nos. U481-W485, U529-U531.

Double or triple surcharge listings of 1920-25 are for examples with surcharge directly or partly upon the stamp.

Surcharged on 1874-1920 Envelopes indicated by Numbers in Parentheses

Type 1

1920-21 **Surcharged in Black**

U446 U93 2c on 3c dark vio (U436a, die 1) 11.00 10.00
- *a.* On No. U436b (die 5) 11.00 10.00
- *b.* As U446, double surcharge 140.00

Surcharged

Type 2

Rose Surcharge

U447 U93 2c on 3c dark vio (U436a, die 1) 8.00 7.50
- *b.* On No. U436c (die 6) 10.00 8.50

Black Surcharge

U447A U92 2c on 1c green (U420, die 1) Entire *3,000.*

U447C U93 2c on 2c carmine (U429, die 1) —

U447D U93 2c on 2c car, *amb* (U430, die 1) 12,000.

U448 U93 2c on 3c dark vio (U436a, die 1) 2.75 2.00
- *a.* On No. U436b (die 5) 2.75 2.00
- *b.* On No. U436c (die 6) 3.50 2.00
- *c.* On No. U436d (die 7) 2.75 2.00

U449 U93 2c on 3c dk vio, *amb* (U437a, die 1) 6.50 6.00
- *a.* On No. U437b (die 5) 13.00 7.50
- *b.* On No. U437c (die 6) 9.50 6.00
- *c.* On No. U437d (die 7) 8.50 6.50

U450 U93 2c on 3c dk vio, *oriental buff* (U438, die 1) 12.50 15.00
- *a.* On No. U438a (die 5) 15.00 15.00
- *b.* On No. U438b (die 6) 15.00 15.00
- *c.* On No. U438c (die 7) 130.00 90.00

U451 U93 2c on 3c dk vio, *blue* (U439a, die 1) 11.00 10.50
- *b.* On No. U439b (die 5) 11.00 10.50
- *c.* On No. U439c (die 6) 11.00 10.50
- *d.* On No. U439d (die 7) 22.50 22.50

Surcharged

Type 3

Bars 2mm apart, 25 to 26mm in length from outer edges of end bars

U451A U90 2c on 1c green (U400, die 1) *25,000.*

U452 U92 2c on 1c green (U420, die 1) 1,750.
- *a.* On No. U420b (die 3) 3,000.
- *b.* As No. U452, double surcharge 3,750.

U453 U91 2c on 2c car (U411b, die 3) 3,500.
- *a.* On No. U411 (die 1) 3,250.

U453B U91 2c on 2c car, *bl* (U414e, die 6) 1,250. 750.00

U453C U91 2c on 2c car, *oriental buff* (U413e, die 6) 1,400. *750.00*
- *d.* On No. U413 (die 1) 1,400.

U454 U93 2c on 2c car (U429e, die 6) 125.00
- *a.* On No. U429 (die 1) 300.00
- *b.* On No. U429d (die 5) 500.00
- *c.* On No. U429f (die 7) 125.00

U455 U93 2c on 2c car, *amb* (U430, die 1) 1,250.
- *a.* On No. U430d (die 6) 1,500.
- *b.* On No. U430e (die 7) 1,500.

U456 U93 2c on 2c car, *oriental buff* (U431a, die 2) 225.00
- *a.* On No. U431c (die 5) 225.00
- *b.* On No. U431e (die 7) 800.00
- *c.* As No. U456, double surcharge 700.00

U457 U93 2c on 2c car, *bl* (U432f, die 6) 325.00
- *a.* On No. U432e (die 5) 275.00
- *b.* On No. U432g (die 7) 650.00

U458 U93 2c on 3c dark vio (U436a, die 1) .50 .35
- *a.* On No. U436b (die 5) .50 .40
- *b.* On No. U436c (die 6) .50 .35
- *c.* On No. U436d (die 7) .50 .35
- *d.* As #U458, double surcharge 25.00 7.50
- *e.* As #U458, triple surcharge 90.00
- *f.* As #U458, dbl. surch., 1 in magenta 90.00
- *g.* As #U458, dbl. surch., types 2 & 3 140.00
- *h.* As "a," double surcharge 27.50 15.00
- *i.* As "a," triple surcharge 110.00
- *j.* As "a," double surch., both magenta 110.00
- *k.* As "b," double surcharge 25.00 8.00
- *l.* As "c," double surcharge 25.00 8.00
- *m.* As "c," triple surcharge 110.00
- *n.* Double impression of indicia, single surcharge, entire 450.00

U459 U93 2c on 3c dk vio, *amb* (U437c, die 6) 3.00 1.00
- *a.* On No. U437a (die 1) 4.00 1.00
- *b.* On No. U437b (die 5) 4.00 1.00
- *c.* On No. U437d (die 7) 3.00 1.00
- *d.* As #U459, double surcharge 35.00
- *e.* As "a," double surcharge 35.00
- *f.* As "b," double surcharge 35.00
- *g.* As "b," double surcharge, types 2 & 3 125.00
- *h.* As "c," double surcharge 35.00

U460 U93 2c on 3c dk vio, *oriental buff* (U438a, die 5) 3.50 2.00
- *a.* On No. U438 (die 1) 3.50 2.00
- *b.* On No. U438b (die 6) 4.00 2.00
- *c.* As #U460, double surcharge 20.00
- *d.* As "a," double surcharge 20.00
- *e.* As "b," double surcharge 20.00
- *f.* As "b," triple surcharge 150.00

U461 U93 2c on 3c dk vio, *bl* (U439a, die 1) 6.00 1.00
- *a.* On No. U439b (die 5) 6.00 1.00
- *b.* On No. U439c (die 6) 6.00 2.50
- *c.* On No. U439d (die 7) 12.50 7.50
- *d.* As #U461, double surcharge 17.50
- *e.* As "a," double surcharge 17.50
- *f.* As "b," double surcharge 17.50
- *g.* As "c," double surcharge 17.50

U462 U87 2c on 4c choc (U390) 475.00 260.00

U463 U87 2c on 4c choc, *amb* (U391) 750.00 350.00

U463A U90 2c on 4c black (U416, die 2) 800.00 400.00

U464 U93 2c on 5c blue (U443) 850.00

Surcharged

Type 4

Bars 1 mm apart, 21 to 23 mm in length from outer edges of end bars

U465 U92 2c on 1c green (U420, die 1) 900.00
- *a.* On No. U420b (die 3) 1,100.

U466 U91 2c on 2c car (U411e, die 6), entire 22,500.

U466A U93 2c on 2c carmine (U429, die 1) 700.00
- *c.* On No. U429d (die 5) 900.00
- *d.* On No. U429e (die 6) 900.00
- *e.* On No. U429f (die 7) 750.00

U466B U93 2c on 2c car, *amb* (U430) *15,000.*

U466C U93 2c on 2c car, *oriental buff* (U431), entire *15,000.*

U466D U25 2c on 3c green, die 2 (U82) *9,500.*

U467 U45 2c on 3c green, die 2 (U163) 325.00

U468 U93 2c on 3c dark vio (U436a, die 1) .70 .45
- *a.* On No. U436b (die 5) .70 .50
- *b.* On No. U436c (die 6) .70 .50
- *c.* On No. U436d (die 7) .70 .50
- *d.* As #U468, double surcharge 20.00
- *e.* As #U468, triple surcharge 90.00
- *f.* As #U468, dbl. surch., types 2 & 4 125.00
- *g.* As "a," double surcharge 20.00
- *h.* As "b," double surcharge 20.00
- *i.* As "c," double surcharge 20.00
- *j.* As "c," triple surcharge 100.00
- *k.* As "c," inverted surcharge 75.00
- *l.* 2c on 3c carmine (error), (U436h) 600.00
- *m.* As #U468, triple surcharge, one inverted, entire *700.00*

U469 U93 2c on 3c dk vio, *amb* (U437a, die 1) 3.75 2.25
- *a.* On No. U437b (die 5) 3.75 2.25
- *b.* On No. U437c (die 6) 3.75 2.25
- *c.* On No. U437d (die 7) 3.75 2.25
- *d.* As #U469, double surcharge 30.00
- *e.* As "a," double surcharge 30.00
- *f.* As "a," double surcharge, types 2 & 4 100.00
- *g.* As "b," double surcharge 30.00
- *h.* As "c," double surcharge 30.00

U470 U93 2c on 3c dk vio, *oriental buff* (U438, die 1) 6.00 2.50
- *a.* On No. U438a (die 5) 6.00 2.50
- *b.* On No. U438b (die 6) 6.00 2.50
- *c.* On No. U438c (die 7) 42.50 32.50
- *d.* As #U470, double surcharge 25.00
- *e.* As #U470, double surch., types 2 & 4 80.00
- *f.* As "a," double surcharge 25.00
- *g.* As "b," double surcharge 25.00

U471 U93 2c on 3c dk vio, *bl* (U439a, die 1) 6.00 1.75
- *a.* On No. U439b (die 5) 7.00 1.75
- *b.* On No. U439c (die 6) 7.00 1.75
- *c.* On No. U439d (die 7) 10.00 10.00
- *d.* As #U471, double surcharge 25.00
- *e.* As #U471, double surch., types 2 & 4 160.00
- *f.* As "a," double surcharge 25.00
- *g.* As "b," double surcharge 25.00

U471A U83 2c on 4c brown, (U374), entire 625.00

U472 U87 2c on 4c choc (U390) 11.00 11.00
a. Double surcharge 150.00
U473 U87 2c on 4c choc, *amb* (U391) 17.00 10.00

Surcharged

Double Surcharge, Type 4 and 1c as above

U474 U93 2c on 1c on 3c dark violet (U436a, die 1) 175. *500.*
a. On No. U436b (die 5) 200.
b. On No. U436d (die 7) 850.
U475 U93 2c on 1c on 3c dk vio, *amb* (U437a, die 1) 150.

Surcharged

Type 5

U476 U93 2c on 3c dk vio, *amb* (U437a, die 1) 200.
a. On No. U437c (die 6) 700.
b. As #U476, double surcharge —

Surcharged

Type 6

U477 U93 2c on 3c dark vio (U436a, die 1) 120.
a. On No. U436b (die 5) 250.
b. On No. U436c (die 6) 250.
c. On No. U436d (die 7) 250.
U478 U93 2c on 3c dk vio, *amb* (U437a, die 1) 250.

Handstamped Surcharge in Black or Violet — Type 7

U479 U93 2c on 3c dark violet (Bk) (U436a, die 1) 240. —
a. On No. U436b (die 5) 625.
b. On No. U436d (die 7) 425.
U480 U93 2c on 3c dark violet (V) (U436d, die 7) *4,500.*
a. Double overprint —

Expertization by competent authorities is required for Nos. U476-U480.

Type of 1916-32 Issue

1925-34 **Die 1**

U481 U93 1½c brown .25 .25
a. Die 8 .70 .25
b. 1½c purple, die 1 (error) ('34) 55.00
U482 U93 1½c brown, *amber* .90 .40
a. Die 8 1.75 .75
U483 U93 1½c brown, *bl* 1.60 .95
a. Die 8 2.40 1.25
U484 U93 1½c brown, *manila* 5.00 3.00
W485 U93 1½c brown, *manila* .85 .25
a. With added impression of #W433 120.00 —

Surcharged Type 8

1925 **On Envelopes of 1887**

U486 U71 1½c on 2c grn (U311) 500.00
U487 U71 1½c on 2c green, *amb* (U312) 900.00
U488 U77 1½c on 1c green (U352) 500.00
U489 U77 1½c on 1c grn, *amb* (U353) 110.00 60.
U490 U90 1½c on 1c green (U400, die 1) 6.25 3.50
a. On No. U400a (die 2) 15.00 9.00
b. On No. U400b (die 3) 35.00 17.50
c. On No. U400c (die 4) 9.00 2.50
U491 U90 1½c on 1c grn, *amb* (U401c, die 4) 7.00 3.00
a. On No. U401 (die 1) 12.50 3.50
b. On No. U401a (die 2) 110.00 70.00
c. On No. U401b (die 3) 60.00 50.00
U492 U90 1½c on 1c grn, *oriental buff* (U402a, die 2) 500.00 150.00
a. On No. U402c (die 4) 700.00 250.00
U493 U90 1½c on 1c grn, *bl* (U403c, die 4) 100.00 65.00
a. On No. U403a (die 2) 100.00 67.50
U494 U90 1½c on 1c grn, *man* (U404, die 1) 250.00 100.00
a. On No. U404a (die 3) 950.00
U495 U92 1½c on 1c green (U420, die 1) .80 .25
a. On No. U420a (die 2) 80.00 52.50
b. On No. U420b (die 3) 2.10 .70
c. On No. U420c (die 4) 2.10 .85
d. As #U495, double surcharge 10.00 3.00
e. As "b," double surcharge 10.00 3.00
f. As "c," double surcharge 10.00 3.00
U496 U92 1½c on 1c grn, *amb* (U421, die 1) 15.00 12.50
a. On No. U421b (die 3) 725.00
b. On No. U421c (die 4) 15.00 12.50
U497 U92 1½c on 1c grn, *oriental buff* (U422, die 1) 3.75 1.90
a. On No. U422b (die 4) 67.50
U498 U92 1½c on 1c grn, *bl* (U423c, die 4) 1.40 .75
a. On No. U423 (die 1) 2.40 1.50
b. On No. U423b (die 3) 1.75 1.50
U499 U92 1½c on 1c grn, *man* (U424) 8.00 6.00
U500 U92 1½c on 1c grn, *brn* (unglazed) (U428) 60.00 30.00
U501 U92 1½c on 1c grn, *brn* (glazed) (U426) 65.00 30.00
U502 U93 1½c on 2c car (U429, die 1) 200.00 —
a. On No. U429d (die 5) 250.00
b. On No. U429f (die 7) 250.00
c. On No. U429e (die 6) 325.00
d. On No. U429g (die 8) 450.00
U503 U93 1½c on 2c car, *oriental buff* (U431c, die 5) 200.00 —
a. Double surcharge —
b. Double surcharge, one inverted *700.00*
U504 U93 1½c on 2c car, *bl* (U432, die 1) 300.00 —
a. On No. U432g (die 7) 300.00
b. As "a," double surcharge, entire *350.00*
c. On No. U432f (die 6), entire *400.00*
U505 U93 1½c on 1½c brn (U481, die 1) 300.00
a. On No. U481a (die 8) 400.00
b. As No. U505, double surcharge, entire *2,000.*
U506 U93 1½c on 1½c brn, *bl* (U483a, die 8) 200.00
a. On No. U483 (die 1) 300.00

The paper of No. U500 is not glazed and appears to be the same as that used for the wrappers of 1920.

Surcharged Type 9

Black Surcharge

U507 U69 1½c on 1c blue (U294) 1,750.
U507B U69 1½c on 1c blue, *manila* (U300) 3,500.
U508 U77 1½c on 1c grn, *amb* (U353) 55.00
U508A U85 1½c on 1c grn (U379) 2,750.
U509 U85 1½c on 1c grn, *amb* (U380) 12.50 10.00
a. Double surcharge 75.00
U509B U85 1½c on 1c green, *oriental buff* (U381) 40.00 40.00
U510 U90 1½c on 1c green (U400, die 1) 2.75 1.25
b. On No. U400a (die 2) 9.00 4.00
c. On No. U400b (die 3) 37.50 8.00
d. On No. U400c (die 4) 3.50 1.25
e. As No. U510, double surcharge 25.00
U511 U90 1½c on 1c grn, *amb* (U401, die 1) 200.00 100.00
U512 U90 1½c on 1c grn, *oriental buff* (U402, die 1) 7.00 4.00
a. On No. U402c (die 4) 21.00 14.00
U513 U90 1½c on 1c grn, *bl* (U403, die 1) 6.00 4.00
a. On No. U403c (die 4) 6.00 4.00
U514 U90 1½c on 1c grn, *man* (U404, die 1) 30.00 9.00
a. On No. U404a (die 3) 77.50 40.00
U515 U92 1½c on 1c green (U420, die 1) .40 .25
a. On No. U420a (die 2) 15.00 15.00
b. On No. U420b (die 3) .40 .25
c. On No. U420c (die 4) .40 .25
d. As #U515, double surcharge 10.00
e. As #U515, inverted surcharge 15.00
f. As #U515, triple surcharge 15.00
g. As #U515, dbl. surch., one invtd., entire —
h. As "b," double surcharge 10.00
i. As "b," inverted surcharge 15.00
j. As "b," triple surcharge 25.00
k. As "c," double surcharge 10.00
l. As "c," inverted surcharge 15.00
U516 U92 1½c on 1c grn, *amb* (U421c, die 4) 50.00 27.50
a. On No. U421 (die 1) 55.00 32.50
U517 U92 1½c on 1c grn, *oriental buff* (U422, die 1) 6.25 1.25
a. On No. U422a (die 4) 7.25 1.50
U518 U92 1½c on 1c grn, *bl* (U423b, die 4) 5.00 1.50
a. On No. U423 (die 1) 8.25 4.50
b. On No. U423a (die 3) 27.50 7.50
c. As "a," double surcharge 30.00
U519 U92 1½c on 1c grn, *man* (U424, die 1) 25.00 12.00
a. Double surcharge 100.00
U520 U93 1½c on 2c car (U429, die 1) 300.00 —
a. On No. U429d (die 5) 275.00
b. On No. U429e (die 6) 275.00
c. On No. U429f (die 7) 275.00
U520D U93 1½c on 2c car, *amber* (U430c, die 5), entire —
U520E U92 1½c on 4c black (U440, die 1), entire —

Magenta Surcharge

U521 U92 1½c on 1c grn (U420b, die 3) 4.25 3.50
a. Double surcharge 75.00

Sesquicentennial Exposition Issue

150th anniversary of the Declaration of Independence.

Liberty Bell — U94

Die 1. The center bar of "E" of "postage" is shorter than top bar.
Die 2. The center bar of "E" of "postage" is of same length as top bar.

1926, July 27

U522 U94 2c carmine, die 1 1.00 .50
a. Die 2 5.50 3.75

Washington Bicentennial Issue

200th anniversary of the birth of George Washington.

Mount Vernon — U95

2c Die 1 — "S" of "Postage" normal.
2c Die 2 — "S" of "Postage" raised.

1932

U523 U95 1c olive green 1.00 .80
U524 U95 1½c chocolate 2.00 1.50
U525 U95 2c car, die 1 .40 .25
a. 2c carmine, die 2 60.00 20.00
b. 2c carmine, *blue*, die 1 (error) entire *30,000.*
U526 U95 3c violet 1.75 .35
U527 U95 4c black 15.00 17.50
U528 U95 5c dark blue 3.50 3.50
Nos. U523-U528 (6) 23.65 23.90

Type of 1916-32 Issue

1932, Aug. 18

U529 U93 6c orange, die 7 6.00 4.00
U530 U93 6c orange, *amber*, die 7 10.00 10.00
U531 U93 6c orange, *blue*, die 7 10.00 10.00

Franklin — U96

Die 1

Die 2

Die 3

Die 1 — Short (3½mm) and thick "l" in thick circle.
Die 2 — Tall (4½mm) and thin "1" in thin circle; upper and lower bars of E in ONE long and 1mm from circle.
Die 3 — As in Die 2, but E normal and 1½mm from circle.

1950

U532 U96 1c green, die 1 5.00 1.75
a. Die 2 6.50 3.00
b. Die 3 6.50 3.00
Precanceled, die 3 1.25

Washington — U97

Die 1

Die 2

Die 3

Die 4

Die 1 — Thick "2" in thick circle; toe of "2" is acute angle.

Die 2 — Thin "2" in thin circle; toe of "2" is almost right angle; line through left stand of "N" in UNITED and stand of "E" in POSTAGE goes considerably below tip of chin; "N" of UNITED is tall; "O" of TWO is high.

Die 3 — Figure "2" as in Die 2. Short UN in UNITED thin crossbar in A of STATES.

Die 4 — Tall UN in UNITED; thick crossbar in A of STATES; otherwise like Die 3.

U533	U97 2c carmine, die 3	.70	.25
a.	Die 1	.80	.30
b.	Die 2	1.40	.85
c.	Die 4	1.30	.60

Die 1

Die 2

Die 3

Die 4

Die 5

Die 1 — Thick and tall (4½mm) "3" in thick circle; long top bars and short stems in T's of STATES.

Die 2 — Thin and tall (4½mm) "3" in medium circle; short top bars and long stems in T's of STATES.

Die 3 — Thin and short (4mm) "3" in thin circle; lettering wider than Dies 1 and 2; line from left stand of N to stand of E is distinctly below tip of chin.

Die 4 — Figure and letters as in Die 3. Line hits tip of chin; short N in UNITED and thin crossbar in A of STATES.

Die 5 — Figure, letter and chin line as in Die 4; but tall N in UNITED and thick crossbar in A of STATES.

U534	U97 3c dark violet, die 4	.35	.25
a.	Die 1	1.90	.70
b.	Die 2	.75	.50
c.	Die 3	.55	.25
d.	Die 5	.75	.45
e.	As "c," double impression	*300.00*	

Washington — U98

1952

U535	U98 1½c brown	4.50	3.50
	Precanceled		1.25

Die 1

Die 2

Die 3

Die 1 — Head high in oval (2mm below T of STATES). Circle near (1mm) bottom of colored oval.

Die 2 — Head low in oval (3mm). Circle 1½mm from edge of oval. Right leg of A in POSTAGE shorter than left. Short leg on P.

Die 3 — Head centered in oval (2½mm). Circle as in Die 2. Legs of A of POSTAGE about equal. Long leg on P.

1958

U536	U96 4c red violet, die 1	.75	.25
a.	Die 2	.90	.25
b.	Die 3	.90	.25

Nos. U429, U429f, U429h, U533, U533a-U533c Surcharged in Red at Left of Stamp

1958

U537	U93 2c + 2c carmine, die 1	3.25	1.50
a.	Die 7	10.00	7.00
b.	Die 9	4.75	5.00
U538	U97 2c + 2c carmine, die 1	.70	.80
a.	Die 2	.90	1.00
b.	Die 3	.70	.70
c.	Die 4	.70	1.00

Nos. U436a, U436e-U436f, U534, U534b-U534d Surcharged in Green at Left of Stamp

U539	U93 3c + 1c purple, die 1	12.50	9.00
a.	Die 7	11.00	7.50
b.	Die 9	17.50	15.00
U540	U97 3c + 1c dark violet, die 3	.40	1.00
a.	Die 2, entire	*3,500.*	—
b.	Die 4	.65	1.00
c.	Die 5	.70	1.00

Benjamin Franklin — U99

George Washington — U100

Die 1

Die 2

Dies of 1¼c

Die 1 — The "4" is 3mm high. Upper leaf in left cluster is 2mm from "U."

Die 2 — The "4" is 3½mm high. Leaf clusters are larger. Upper leaf at left is 1mm from "U."

1960

U541	U99 1¼c turquoise, die 1	.65	.50
	Die 1, precanceled		.25
a.	Die 2, precanceled		1.25
U542	U100 2½c dull blue	.80	.50
	Precanceled		.25

Precanceled cut squares
Precanceled envelopes do not normally receive another cancellation. Since the lack of a cancellation makes it impossible to distinguish between cut squares from used and unused envelopes, they are valued here as used only.

Pony Express Centennial Issue

Pony Express Rider — U101

Envelope White Outside, Blue Inside.

1960

U543	U101 4c brown	.55	.30

Abraham Lincoln — U102

Die 1

Die 2

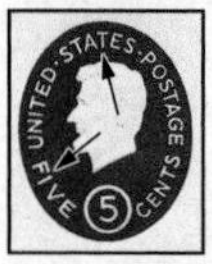

Die 3

Die 1 — Center bar of E of POSTAGE is above the middle. Center bar of E of STATES slants slightly upward. Nose sharper, more pointed. No offset ink specks inside envelope on back of die impression.

Die 2 — Center bar of E of POSTAGE in middle. P of POSTAGE has short stem. Ink specks on back of die impression.

Die 3 — Fl of FIVE closer than Die 1 or 2. Second T of STATES seems taller than ES. Ink specks on back of die impression.

1962

U544	U102 5c dark blue, die 2	.80	.25
a.	Die 1	.80	.25
b.	Die 3	.85	.35
c.	Die 2 with albino impression of 4c (#U536)	50.00	—
d.	Die 3 with albino impression of 4c (#U536), entire	*125.00*	—
e.	Die 3 on complete impression of 4c (#U536), cut square		*125.00*

No. U536 Surcharged in Green at left of Stamp

Two types of surcharge:

Type I — "U.S. POSTAGE" 18½mm high. Serifs on cross of T both diagonal. Two lines of shading in C of CENT.

Type II — "U.S. POSTAGE" 17½mm high. Right serif on cross of T is vertical. Three shading lines in C.

1962

U545	U96 4c + 1c red vio, die 1, type I	1.25	1.10
a.	Type II	1.25	1.10

Values for used envelopes are for examples used within the period of issue. Envelopes used much later sell at substantially reduced prices.

New York World's Fair Issue

Issued to publicize the New York World's Fair, 1964-65.

Globe with Satellite Orbit — U103

1964

U546	U103 5c maroon	.55	.40

Liberty Bell U104

Old Ironsides U105

Eagle U106

Head of Statue of Liberty U107

1965-69

U547	U104	1¼c brown		.50
U548	U104	1⁴⁄₁₀c brown ('68)		.50
U548A	U104	1⁶⁄₁₀c orange ('69)		.50
b.		1⁶⁄₁₀c brown (error), entire	*5,000.*	
U549	U105	4c bright blue	.90	.25
U550	U106	5c bright purple	.75	.25
a.		Bar tagged ('67)	3.00	1.00

Tagged

U551	U107	6c lt green ('68)	.70	.25
a.		6c dark gray green, entire	200.00	—

Nos. U549-U550 Surcharged in Red or Green at Left of Stamp

1968, Feb. 5

U552	U105 4c + 2c bright blue (R)	3.25	2.00
U553	U106 5c + 1c bright purple (G)	3.00	2.75
a.	Tagged	3.00	2.75
b.	With 2c surcharge type "b" (error)		400.00

Tagged
Envelopes from No. U554 onward are tagged, except for bulk-rate and non-profit envelopes, which are untagged. The tagging element is in the ink through No. 608 unless otherwise noted. From No. 611 on, envelopes have bar or block tagging unless otherwise noted.

Herman Melville Issue

Issued to honor Herman Melville (1819-1891), writer, and the whaling industry.

Moby Dick — U108

1970, Mar. 7
U554 U108 6c blue .50 .25

Youth Conference Issue

Issued to publicize the White House Conference on Youth, Estes Park, Colo., Apr. 18-22.

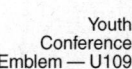

Youth Conference Emblem — U109

1971, Feb. 24
U555 U109 6c light blue .70 1.00

Liberty Bell Type of 1965 and

Eagle — U110

1971
U556 U104 1 7/10c deep lilac, untagged .35
U557 U110 8c ultramarine .40 .25

Nos. U551 and U555 Surcharged in Green at Left of Stamp

1971, May 16
U561 U107 6c + (2c) light green .90 1.25
a. Inverted surcharge, entire *275.00*
U562 U109 6c + (2c) light blue 2.00 2.50
a. Inverted surcharge printed on reverse, entire —

Bowling Issue

Issued as a salute to bowling and in connection with the 7th World Tournament of the International Bowling Federation, Milwaukee, Wis.

Bowling Ball and Pin — U111

1971, Aug. 21
U563 U111 8c rose red .60 .25

Aging Conference Issue

White House Conference on Aging, Washington, D.C., Nov. 28-Dec. 2, 1971.

Conference Symbol — U112

1971, Nov. 15
U564 U112 8c light blue .50 .25

International Transportation Exhibition Issue

U.S. International Transportation Exhibition, Dulles International Airport, Washington, D.C., May 27-June 4.

Transportation Exhibition Emblem — U113

1972, May 2
U565 U113 8c ultramarine & rose red .50 .25

No. U557 Surcharged in Ultramarine at Left of Stamp

1973, Dec. 1
U566 U110 8c + 2c brt. ultra .40 1.25

Liberty Bell — U114

1973, Dec. 5
U567 U114 10c emerald .40 .25

"Volunteer Yourself" — U115

1974, Aug. 23
Untagged
U568 U115 1 8/10c blue green .25

Tennis Centenary Issue

Centenary of tennis in the United States.

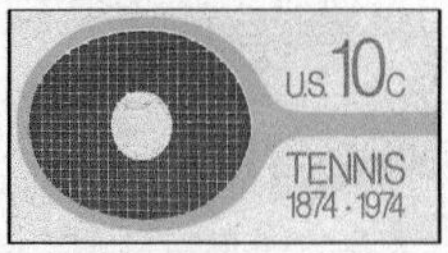

Tennis Racquet — U116

1974, Aug. 31 **Block Tagged**
U569 U116 10c yellow, brt. blue & light green .55 .25

Bicentennial Era Issue

The Seafaring Tradition — Compass Rose — U118

The American Homemaker — Quilt Pattern — U119

The American Farmer — Sheaf of Wheat — U120

The American Doctor — U121

The American Craftsman — Tools, c. 1750 — U122

Designs (in brown on left side of envelope): 10c, Norwegian sloop Restaurationen. No. U572, Spinning wheel. No. U573, Plow. No. U574, Colonial era medical instruments and bottle. No. U575, Shaker rocking chair.

1975-76 **Embossed**
Light Brown Diagonally Laid Paper
U571 U118 10c brown & blue .30 .25
a. Brown ("10c/USA," etc.) omitted, entire *125.00*
U572 U119 13c brn & blue grn .35 .25
a. Brown ("13c/USA," etc.) omitted, entire *125.00*
U573 U120 13c brn & brt grn .35 .25
a. Brown ("13c/USA," etc.) omitted, entire *125.00*
U574 U121 13c brn & org .35 .25
a. Brown ("13c/USA," etc.) omitted, entire *125.00*
U575 U122 13c brn & car .35 .25
a. Brown ("13c/USA," etc.) omitted, entire *125.00*
Nos. U571-U575 (5) 1.70 1.25

Liberty Tree, Boston, 1646 — U123

1975, Nov. 8 **Embossed**
U576 U123 13c orange brown .30 .25

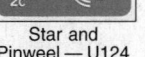

Star and Pinweel — U124

U125

U126

Eagle — U127

"Uncle Sam" — U128

1976-78 **Embossed**
U577 U124 2c red, untagged .25
U578 U125 2.1c grn, untagged .25
U579 U126 2.7c grn, untagged .25
U580 U127 (15c) orange .40 .25
U581 U128 15c red, ink tagged .40 .25
a. Bar tagged *7.00* 7.00

For No. U581 with surcharge, see No. U586b.

Bicentennial Issue

Centennial Envelope, 1876 — U129

1976, Oct. 15 **Embossed**
U582 U129 13c emerald .35 .25

Golf Issue

Golf Club in Motion and Golf Ball U130

Photogravure and Embossed
1977, Apr. 7
U583 U130 13c blk, blue & yel grn .65 .25
a. Black omitted, entire *500.00*
b. Black & blue omitted, entire *500.00*
c. Black, blue & yellow green omitted, entire *500.00*

On No. U583c, the embossing is present.

Energy Issue

Conservation and development of national resources.

Energy Conservation U131

Energy Development U132

1977, Oct. 20 **Photo.**
Bar Tagged
U584 U131 13c blk, red & yel .45 .25
a. Red, yellow & tagging omitted, entire *190.00*
b. Yellow & tagging omitted, entire *150.00*
c. Black omitted, entire *135.00*
d. Black & red omitted, entire *350.00*
U585 U132 13c blk, red & yel .45 .25

Olive Branch and Star — U133

1978, July 28 **Embossed**
Black Surcharge
U586 U133 15c on 16c blue .40 .25
a. Surcharge omitted, entire 225.00 1,000.
b. Surcharge on No. U581, entire 260.00
c. As "a," with surcharge printed on envelope flap 175.00 —
d. Surcharge inverted (in lower left corner), entire 200.00 —

Auto Racing Issue

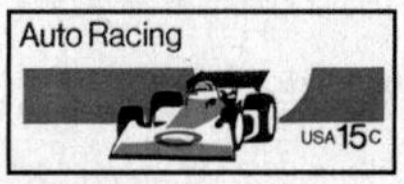

Indianapolis 500 Racing Car — U134

1978, Sept. 2 **Embossed**
U587 U134 15c red, blue & black .45 .25
a. Black omitted, entire 100.00
b. Black & blue omitted, entire *170.00*
c. Red & tagging omitted, entire 100.00
d. Red, blue & tagging omitted, entire *170.00*
e. Tagging bar inverted at LL, entire 100.00
f. Tagging bar on reverse, entire —

No. U576 Surcharged

1978, Nov. 28 **Embossed**

U588 U123 15c on 13c org brn .40 .25
a. Surcharge inverted (in lower left corner), entire 450.00

U135

Embossed

1979, May 18 **Untagged**

U589 U135 3.1c ultramarine .35

Weaver Violins — U136

1980, June 23 **Untagged**

U590 U136 3.5c purple .35
a. 3.5c violet, tagged (in ink), error of color and tagging using ink intended for No. U592, entire *300.00* *500.00*

U137

1982, Feb. 17 **Untagged**

U591 U137 5.9c brown .35

Eagle — U138

1981, Mar. 15

U592 U138 (18c) violet .45 .25

Star — U139

1981, Apr. 2

U593 U139 18c dark blue .45 .25

Eagle — U140

1981, Oct. 11

U594 U140 (20c) brown .45 .25

Veterinary Medicine Issue

Seal of Veterinarians U141

Design at left side of envelope shows 5 animals and bird in brown, "Veterinary Medicine" in gray.

1979, July 24

U595 U141 15c brown & gray .50 .25
a. Gray omitted, entire *425.00*
b. Brown omitted, entire *500.00*
c. Gray & brown omitted, tagging omitted, entire *325.00*

On No. U595c, the embossing of the seal is present.

Olympic Games Issue

22nd Olympic Games, Moscow, July 19-Aug. 3, 1980.

U142

Design (multicolored on left side of envelope) shows two soccer players with ball.

1979, Dec. 10

U596 U142 15c red, grn & blk .60 .25
a. Red & green omitted, tagging omitted, entire *150.00*
b. Black omitted, tagging omitted, entire *150.00*
c. Black & green omitted, entire *150.00*
d. Red omitted, tagging omitted, entire *325.00*
e. All colors omitted *250.00*
f. Tagging omitted, entire 125.00
g. Black omitted, tagged, entire —

No. U596c exists with a portion of the green present in the Olympics 1980 design at the lower left corner of the envelope.

On No. U596e, the blind embossing of "USA 15c" remains.

Highwheeler Bicycle U143

Design (blue on left side of envelope) shows racing bicycle.

1980, May 16

U597 U143 15c blue & rose claret .40 .25
a. Blue ("15c USA") omitted, entire 100.00

Racing Yacht — U144

1980, Sept. 15

U598 U144 15c blue & red .40 .25

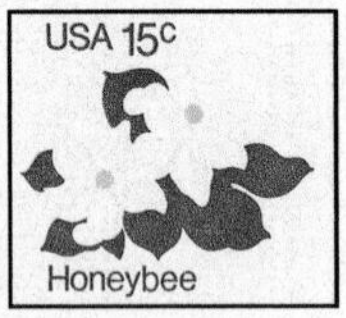

Italian Honeybee and Orange Blossoms U145

Bee and petals colorless embossed.

Photogravure and Embossed

1980, Oct. 10

U599 U145 15c brn, grn & yel .35 .25
a. Brown ("USA 15c") omitted, entire *100.00*
b. Green omitted, entire *100.00*

No. U599b also has almost all of the brown color missing.

U146

Hand and braille colorless embossed.

1981, Aug. 13 **Embossed**

U600 U146 18c blue & red .45 .25
a. Blue omitted, entire *300.00*
b. Red omitted, entire *210.00*

Capitol Dome — U147

1981, Nov. 13

U601 U147 20c dp mag, ink tagged .45 .25
a. Bar tagged 4.50 1.50

U148

1982, June 15

U602 U148 20c dk blue, blk & mag .45 .25
a. Dark blue omitted, entire *175.00*
b. Dark blue & magenta omitted, entire *175.00*
c. All colors omitted, entire *175.00*

On No. 602c, the colorless embossed impression of the Great Seal is present.

U149

1982, Aug. 6

U603 U149 20c purple & black .75 .25
a. Black omitted, entire *80.00*
b. Purple omitted, entire *200.00*

U150

1983, Mar. 21 **Untagged**

U604 U150 5.2c orange .90

U151

1983, Aug. 3

U605 U151 20c red, blue & black .45 .25
a. Red omitted, entire *260.00*
b. Blue omitted, entire *260.00*
c. Red & black omitted, entire *125.00*
d. Blue & black omitted, entire *125.00*
e. Black omitted, entire *230.00*

U152

Design shows storefronts at lower left. Stamp and design continue on back of envelope.

1984, May 7 **Photo.**

U606 U152 20c multi .50 .25

U153

1985, Feb. 1 **Embossed**

U607 U153 (22c) deep green .55 .30

American Buffalo — U154

1985, Feb. 25

U608 U154 22c vio brn, ink tagged .55 .25
a. Untagged, 3 blue precancel lines, unwmk'd ('86) .25
b. Bar tagged 2.00 1.00

Frigate U.S.S. Constitution, "Old Ironsides" — U155

1985, May 3 **Untagged**

U609 U155 6c green blue .35

Mayflower — U156

1986, Dec. 4 **Untagged**

Precanceled

U610 U156 8.5c black & gray .65

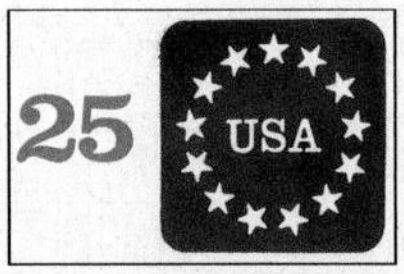

Stars — U157

1988, Mar. 26 **Typo. & Embossed**

U611 U157 25c dark red & deep blue .60 .25
a. Dark red (25) omitted, tagging omitted 50.00 —
c. Dark red (25) omitted, tagging not omitted *60.00*

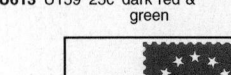

Sea Gulls, Frigate USS Constellation — U158

1988, Apr. 12 **Untagged**

Precanceled

U612 U158 8.4c blk & brt blue .65
a. Black omitted, entire *500.00*

Snowflake U159

"Holiday Greetings!" inscribed in lower left.

1988, Sept. 8 **Typo.**

U613 U159 25c dark red & green 1.25 *20.00*

Stars and "*Philatelic Mail*" Continuous in Dark Red Below Vignette U160

"Philatelic Mail" and asterisks in dark red below vignette; continuous across envelope face and partly on reverse.

1989, Mar. 10

U614 U160 25c dark red & deep blue .50 .25
- *b.* Red omitted, entire 125.00

"USA" and Stars — U161

1989, July 10 **Unwmk.**

U615 U161 25c dark red & deep blue .50 .25
- *a.* Dark red omitted, entire *425.00*

Lined with a blue design to provide security for enclosures.

Love — U162

Litho. & Typo.

1989, Sept. 22 **Unwmk.**

U616 U162 25c dk red & brt blue .50 .75
- *a.* Dark red and bright blue omitted, entire 150.00
- *b.* Bright blue omitted, entire 150.00

No. U616 has light blue lines printed diagonally over the entire surface of the envelope.

Shuttle Docking at Space Station U163

1989, Dec. 3 **Typo.** **Unwmk.**
Die Cut

U617 U163 25c ultramarine .90 .60
- *a.* Ultramarine omitted, entire *400.00*

A hologram, visible through the die cut window to the right of "USA 25," is affixed to the inside of the envelope.

See Nos. U625, U639.

Vince Lombardi Trophy, Football Players U164

1990, Sept. 9 **Unwmk.** ***Die Cut***

U618 U164 25c vermilion .90 .60

A hologram, visible through the die cut window to the right of "USA 25," is affixed to the inside of the envelope.

Star — U165

Typo. & Embossed

1991, Jan. 24 **Wmk.**

U619 U165 29c ultra & rose .60 .30
- *a.* Ultramarine omitted, entire *300.00*
- *b.* Rose omitted, tagged, entire *250.00*
- *c.* Rose omitted, tagging omitted, entire *275.00*

See No. U623.

Birds — U166

Stamp and design continue on back of envelope.

1991, May 3 **Typo.** **Wmk.**
Untagged, Precanceled

U620 U166 11.1c blue & red — .90
- *a.* Blue omitted, entire

Love U167

1991, May 9 **Litho.** **Unwmk.**

U621 U167 29c lt blue, pur & brt rose .60 .60
- *a.* Bright rose omitted, entire *200.00*
- *b.* Purple omitted, entire *400.00*

Magazine Industry, 250th Anniv. — U168

Photo. & Typo.

1991, Oct. 7 **Unwmk.**

U622 U168 29c multicolored .70 1.00

The photogravure vignette, visible through the die cut window to the right of "USA 29", is affixed to the inside of the envelope.

Star — U169

Stamp and design continue on back of envelope.

1991, July 20 **Typo.** **Unwmk.**

U623 U169 29c ultra & rose .60 .30
- *a.* Ultra omitted, entire *350.00*
- *b.* Rose omitted, entire *200.00*

Lined with a blue design to provide security for enclosures.

Country Geese — U170

1991, Nov. 8 **Litho. & Typo.** **Wmk.**

U624 U170 29c blue gray & yel .60 .60

Space Shuttle Type of 1989
Unwmk.

1992, Jan. 21 **Typo.** ***Die Cut***

U625 U163 29c yellow green .80 .50

A hologram, visible through the die cut window to the right of "USA 29," is affixed to the inside of the envelope.

U171

Typo. & Litho.

1992, Apr. 10 ***Die Cut***

U626 U171 29c multicolored .60 1.00

The lithographed vignette, visible through the die cut window to the right of "USA 29," is affixed to the inside of the envelope.

Hillebrandia — U172

1992, Apr. 22

U627 U172 29c multicolored .65 1.00

The lithographed vignette, visible through the die cut window to the right of "29 USA," is affixed to the inside of the envelope.

U173

Typo. & Embossed

1992, May 19 **Precanceled**
Untagged

U628 U173 19.8c red & blue .40

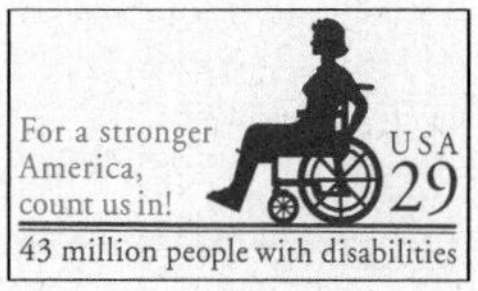

U174

1992, July 22 **Typo.**

U629 U174 29c red & blue .60 .30

U175

1993, Oct. 2 **Typo. & Litho.** ***Die Cut***

U630 U175 29c multicolored 1.10 1.10

The lithographed vignette, visible through the die cut window to the right of "USA 29," is affixed to the inside of the envelope.

U176

Typo. & Embossed

1994, Sept. 17

U631 U176 29c brn & blk .70 1.25
- *a.* Black ("29/USA") omitted, entire *325.00*

Liberty Bell — U177

1995, Jan. 3 **Typo. & Embossed**

U632 U177 32c grnsh blue & blue .65 .30
- *a.* Greenish blue omitted *120.00*
- *b.* Blue ("USA 32") omitted 90.00
- *c.* All colors omitted, entire —

A colorless embossed design is present on No. U632c.

See No. U638.

U178

Design sizes: 49x38mm (#U633), 53x44mm (U634). Stamp and design continue on back of envelope.

1995 **Typo.**

U633 U178 (32c) blue & red 1.25 2.00
U634 U178 (32c) blue & red 1.25 2.00
- *a.* Red & tagging omitted, entire *325.00*
- *b.* Blue omitted, entire *325.00*

Originally, Nos. U633-U634 were only available through the Philatelic Fullfillment Center after their announcement 1/12/95.

U179

Stamp and design continue on back of envelope.

1995, Mar. 10
Precanceled, Untagged

U635 U179 (5c) grn & red brn .40

Graphic Eagle U180

1995, Mar. 10
Precanceled, Untagged

U636 U180 (10c) dk car & blue 1.50

Spiral Heart — U181

1995, May 12

U637 U181 32c red, *light blue* .65 .30
- *a.* Red omitted, entire *200.00*

Liberty Bell Type of 1995

1995, May 16

U638 U177 32c greenish blue & blue .70 .30
- *a.* Greenish blue omitted, entire *175.00*

Space Shuttle Type of 1989

1995, Sept. 22 ***Die Cut***

U639 U163 32c carmine rose .75 .35

A hologram, visible through the die cut window to the right of "USA 32," is affixed to the inside of the envelope.

U182

Typo. & Litho.

1996, Apr. 20 ***Die Cut***

U640 U182 32c multicolored .70 .30

The lithographed vignette, visible through the die cut window to the right of "USA 32c," is affixed to the inside of the envelope.

U183

1996, May 2

U641 U183 32c multicolored .70 .30
- *a.* Blue & red omitted, entire *260.00*
- *b.* Blue & gold omitted, entire *550.00*
- *c.* Red omitted, entire *260.00*
- *d.* Black & red omitted, entire *450.00*
- *e.* Blue omitted, entire *300.00*

U184

U184a

1999, Jan. 11 Typo. & Embossed

U642 U184 33c yellow, blue & red, tagging bar to left of design 1.00 .30
- *a.* Tagging bar to right of design 7.50 3.00
- *b.* As "a," blue omitted, entire 200.00
- *c.* As "a," yellow omitted, entire 175.00
- *d.* As "a," yellow and blue omitted, entire 175.00
- *e.* As "a," blue and red omitted, entire 175.00
- *f.* As "a," all colors omitted, entire 175.00
- *g.* As No. U642, red omitted, entire 450.00
- *h.* As No. U642, yellow and red omitted, entire —
- *i.* As No. U642, blue and red omitted, entire —
- *j.* Tagging omitted —

On No. U642f, the distinctive tagging bar is present. Expertization is required.

1999, Jan. 11 Typo.

U643 U184a 33c blue & red 1.00 .30
- *a.* Tagging bar to right of design 10.00 5.00

U185

1999, Jan. 28 Litho.

U644 U185 33c violet .65 .30
- *a.* Tagging bar to right of design .65 .30

Lincoln — U186

1999, June 5 Typo. & Litho.

U645 U186 33c blue & black .65 .30

Eagle — U187

2001, Jan. 7 Typo.

U646 U187 34c blue gray & gray .70 .30
- *a.* Blue gray omitted 175.00

Many color shades known.

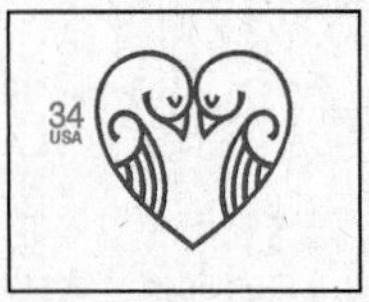

Lovebirds U188

2001, Feb. 14 Litho.

U647 U188 34c rose & dull violet .70 .30

Community Colleges, Cent. U189

2001, Feb. 20 Typo.

U648 U189 34c dk blue & org brn .70 .30

Ribbon Star — U190

2002, June 7

U649 U190 37c red, blue & gray .75 .35
- *a.* Gray omitted, entire —
- *b.* Blue and gray omitted, entire —

All No. U649 were printed on recycled paper. It was also produced using a different blue-gray recycled paper starting in 2002.

Type of 1995 Inscribed "USA / Presorted / Standard"

2002, Aug. 8 Untagged

Precanceled

U650 U180 (10c) dk car & blue .25

Nurturing Love — U191

2003, Jan. 25

U651 U191 37c ol grn & yel org .80 .35

Jefferson Memorial Type

2003, Dec. 29

U652 A2818 $3.85 multicolored 12.50 6.25

On No. U652, the stamp indicia is printed on the flap of the envelope.

Disney Type of 2004

2004, June 23 Letter Sheet Litho.

U653 A2949 37c multicolored 2.50 2.25
U654 A2950 37c multicolored 2.50 2.25
U655 A2951 37c multicolored 2.50 2.25
- *a.* All color missing on reverse, entire —

U656 A2952 37c multicolored 2.50 2.25
- *a.* Booklet of 12 letter sheets, 3 each #U653-U656 30.00

No. U656a sold for $14.95.

White Lilacs and Pink Roses Type of 2004

2005, Mar. 3 Letter Sheet

U657 A2931 37c multicolored 3.00 2.50

No. U657 was sold in pads of 12 for $14.95.

Computer-generated Study of an X-Plane — U192

2006, Jan. 5 Typo.

U658 U192 $4.05 multicolored 10.00 9.00

Benjamin Franklin — U193

2006, Jan. 9

U659 U193 39c blue green & black .80 .40
- *a.* All color omitted, entire —
- *b.* Tagging omitted, entire 45.00

On No. 659a, the tagging bar and the blue green printing on the reverse are present.

Air Force One — U194

2007, May 6

U660 U194 $4.60 multicolored 12.50 10.00

Marine One — U195

2007, May 6

U661 U195 $16.25 multicolored 35.00 20.00

Horses U196

2007, May 12

U662 U196 41c reddish brown & black .85 .40

Elk — U197

2008, May 2

U663 U197 42c green & black, tagging bar 20mm tall .85 .40
- *a.* Tagging bar 26mm tall .85 .40
- *b.* As No. U663, litho., tagging bar 19mm tall .85 .40

No. U663 was printed by National Envelope for Ashton-Potter (USA) Ltd. No. U663a was printed by Westvaco.

No. U663b was printed by Ashton-Potter (USA) Ltd. The lithographed impressions of No. U663b are slightly sharper (some tree branches are slightly thinner and more distinct) than the typographed impressions on Nos. U663 and U663a, but because of the nature of the design are nonetheless difficult to distinguish without measuring the tagging bar.

Mount Rushmore U198

2008, May 12

U664 U198 $4.80 multicolored 12.50 10.00

Sunflower Type of 2008 Letter Sheet

2008, Aug. 15 Litho.

U665 A3309 42c multicolored 4.00 3.00

No. U665 was sold in packs of 10 for $14.95.

Redwood Forest Type of 2009

2009, Jan. 16 Typo.

U666 A3332 $4.95 multicolored 10.00 7.50

U199

2009-11 Litho.

U667 U199 (44c) multicolored .90 .90
- *a.* As #U667, typographed .90 .45
- *b.* As #U667, dated "2011," "FOREVER" multicolored (with color dots) .90 .90
- *c.* As #U667b, "FOREVER" in brown (solid color) .90 .90

Issued: No. U667, 5/11; No. U667a, 8/16; Nos. U667b, U667c, 1/3/11.

No. U667 had a franking value of 44c on the day of issue and will be valid for the one ounce first class postage rate after any new rates go into effect.

The typographed version (No. U667a) can be distinguished from No. U667 by the position of the recycle logo on the back. On the litho. version it is to the right of the recycle text; on the typo. version it is to the left of the text.

U200

2009, May 11

U668 U200 44c multicolored .90 .45
- *a.* As #U668, typographed .90 .45
- *b.* As No. U668, triple impression of black, entire —

On No. U668a, the screened blue dots cover the entire area between the "S" and the "C" on No. U668, but appear more random on No. U668a. The pattern of blue dots running towards the shoulder under the head and neck of the horse is long and distinct on No. U668, but barely noticeable, with only a few dots showing, on No. U668a.

See second paragraph of No. U667 footnote, which also applies to Nos. U668 and U668a.

Gulf Coast Lighthouses Type of 2009

2009, July 23 Litho.

U669 A3354 44c multicolored 3.75 3.00
U670 A3355 44c multicolored 3.75 3.00
U671 A3356 44c multicolored 3.75 3.00
U672 A3357 44c multicolored 3.75 3.00
U673 A3358 44c multicolored 3.75 3.00
Nos. U669-U673 (5) 18.75 15.00

Pack of ten, containing two of each letter sheet, sold for $15.95.

Mackinac Bridge — U201

2010, Jan. 4 Typo. Unwmk.

U674 U201 $4.90 multicolored 12.50 10.00

No. U674 was sold only in packs of 5.

New River Gorge Bridge, West Virginia — U202

2011, Jan. 3 Typo. Unwmk.

U675 U202 $4.95 multicolored 12.50 10.00

No. U675 was sold only in packs of 5.

Sunshine Skyway Bridge, Florida — U203

2012, Jan. 3 Typo. Unwmk.

U676 U203 $5.15 multicolored 12.50 10.00

No. U676 was sold only in packs of 5.

Purple Martin U204

2012, Jan. 23 Litho. Unwmk.

Design Size: 48x33mm

U677 U204 (45c) multicolored 1.50 .50

Design Size: 50x35mm

U678 U204 (45c) multicolored 1.50 .50

No. U677 was from No. 6¾ size envelopes only. No. U678 was from No. 9 and No. 10 size envelopes.

No. U678 was reprinted in June 2012 without the 'Cradle to Cradle' recycling logo on the back.

Arlington Green Bridge Type of 2013

2013, Jan. 25 Typo. Unwmk.

U679 A3612 $5.60 multicolored 11.00 8.00

No. U679 was sold only in packs of 5.

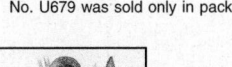

Bank Swallows — U205

2013, Mar. 1 Litho. Unwmk.

Design Size: 38x35mm

U680 U205 (46c) multicolored 1.50 .50

Design Size: 41x38mm

U681 U205 (46c) multicolored 1.50 .50

No. U680 is from No. 6¾ size envelopes only. No. U681 is from No. 9 and No. 10 size envelopes.

Eagle, Shield and Flags — U206

2013, Aug. 9 Litho. Unwmk.

U682 U206 (46c) multicolored .95 .50
- *a.* Double impression of magenta, entire —
- *b.* Triple impression of light blue, entire —
- *c.* Blurry microprinting 4.00 5.00
  Entire — —

Verrazano-Narrows Bridge Type of 2014

2014, Mar. 4 Typo. Unwmk.

U683 A3726 $5.60 multicolored 12.50 8.00

No. U683 was sold only in packs of 5, 10 or 25.

Poinsettia U207

Snowflake U208

Snowflake U209

Cardinal U210

Child Making Snowman — U211

2014, Oct. 1 Litho. Unwmk.

U684 U207 (49c) multicolored 2.50 1.50
U685 U208 (49c) multicolored 2.50 1.50
U686 U209 (49c) multicolored 2.50 1.50
U687 U210 (49c) multicolored 2.50 1.50
U688 U211 (49c) multicolored 2.50 1.50
Nos. U684-U688 (5) 12.50 7.50

Packs of 10 No. U684 and 10 self-adhesive stickers sold for $9.95. Packs containing 5 each of Nos. U685 and U686 and 10 self-adhesive stickers sold for $9.95. Packs containing 5 each of Nos. U687 and U688 and 10 self-adhesive stickers sold for $9.95. Nos. U684-U688 were available only as No. 10 size envelopes.

Glade Creek Grist Mill Type of 2014

2015, Jan. 12 Typo. Unwmk.

U689 A3780 $5.75 multicolored 11.50 8.25

No. U689 was sold only in packs of 5.

Red Water Lily — U212

White Water Lily — U213

2015, Apr. 17 Litho. Unwmk.

U690 U212 (49c) multicolored 2.50 1.75
U691 U213 (49c) multicolored 2.50 1.75

Nos. U690 and U691 were only sold in packets of 10 containing five of each envelope and 10 stickers for $9.95. Nos. U690 and U691 were only available in #10 size with self-adhesive flap.

Forget-me-nots U214

2015, May 18 Litho. Unwmk.

U692 U214 (49c) multicolored 2.50 1.75

No. U692 was sold only in packets of 10 + 10 stickers for $9.95. It was only available in #10 size with self-adhesive flap.

La Cueva del Indio Type of 2016

2016, Jan. 17 Typo. Unwmk.

U693 A3875 $6.45 multicolored 13.00 9.50

No. U693 was sold only in packs of 5.

Northern Cardinal — U215

Designed by Derry Noyes.

2016, Nov. 3 Litho. Unwmk.

U694 U215 (47c) multicolored 1.75 1.75

No. U694 was sold only in packets of 12 + 12 stickers for $9.95. It was only available in #10 size with self-adhesive flap. Packets of No. U694 were sold in post offices in Ohio and Puerto Rico (and perhaps elsewhere) in late December, prior to the acknowledgment of the existence of the envelope by USPS Stamp Services. The packets were not offered for sale by USPS Stamp Fulfillment Services until Jan. 4, 2017. In late January, the packet was made available for direct order on the USPS Stamp Fulfillment Services website, which then noted that the day of issue was Jan. 8, 2017, even though the packets could be ordered on Jan. 4. The official first day of issue was announced as Nov. 3, 2016 in the Feb. 16, 2017 *Postal Bulletin,* but no indication was given that any first day cancels would be made available for this issue. The earliest documented use is postmarked Jan. 3, 2017.

Lili'uokalani Gardens Type of 2017

2017, Jan. 22 Typo. Unwmk.

U695 A3986 $6.65 multicolored 13.50 9.75

No. U695 was sold only in packs of 5.

Barn Swallows U216

2017, Mar. 3 Litho. Unwmk.

U696 U216 (49c) multicolored 1.25 .50

Byodo-In Temple Type of 2018

2018, Jan. 21 Typo. Unwmk.

U697 A4096 $6.70 multicolored 13.50 9.75

No. U697 was sold only in packs of 5.

Joshua Tree Type of 2019

2019, Jan. 27 Typo. Unwmk.

U698 A4191 $7.35 multicolored 15.00 10.00

No. U698 was sold only in packs of 5 or 10.

Big Bend National Park Type of 2020

Designed by Greg Breeding.

2020, Jan. 18 Typo. Unwmk.

U699 A4268 $7.75 multicolored 15.50 10.50

No. U699 was sold only in packs of 5 or 10.

Flag and Stars — U217

2020, June 15 Litho. Unwmk.

U700 U217 (55c) multicolored 1.40 .50

Castillo de San Marcos Type of 2021

2021, Jan. 24 Typo. Unwmk.

U701 A4388 $7.95 multicolored 16.00 11.00

No. U701 was sold only in packs of 5, 10 or 25.

AIR POST STAMPED ENVELOPES & AIR LETTER SHEETS

UC1

5c — Vertical rudder is not semi-circular but slopes down to the left. The tail of the plane projects into the G of POSTAGE.

UC2

Die 2 (5c and 8c): Vertical rudder is semi-circular. The tail of the plane touches but does not project into the G of POSTAGE.

Die 2 (6c) — Same as UC2 except three types of numeral.

2a — The numeral "6" is 6½mm wide.
2b — The numeral "6" is 6mm wide.
2c — The numeral "6" is 5½mm wide.

Die 3 (6c): Vertical rudder leans forward. S closer to O than to T of POSTAGE. E of POSTAGE has short center bar. Border types b and d, also without border.

1929-44

UC1 UC1 5c blue 3.00 2.00
- *a.* Orange and blue border, type b 375.00 *450.00*

UC2 UC2 5c blue, die 2 9.00 5.00
UC3 UC2 6c orange, die 2a ('34) 1.25 .40
- *a.* With added impression of 3c purple (#U436a), entire without border *4,000.*
- *b.* Double impression of indicium, entire, with bicolored border —

UC4 UC2 6c orange, die 2b ('42) 3.00 2.00
  Entire, without border 4.50 2.50
UC5 UC2 6c orange, die 2c ('44) .70 .30
UC6 UC2 6c orange, die 3 ('42) 1.00 .35
- *a.* 6c orange, *blue,* die 3 (error) Entire, without border *15,000.* *10,000.*
- *b.* Double impression, entire *400.00*

UC7 UC2 8c olive green, die 2 ('32) 10.00 3.50

Surcharged in Black on Envelopes Indicated by Number in Parenthesis

1945

UC8 U93 6c on 2c carmine (U429, die 1) 1.25 .65
- *a.* On U429f, die 7 2.25 1.50
- *b.* On U429g, die 8 1.90 1.10
- *c.* On U429h, die 9 8.00 7.50
- *d.* 6c on 1c green (error) (U420) *1,750.*
- *e.* 6c on 3c dk violet (error) (U436a) *2,000.*
- *f.* 6c on 3c dk violet (error), *amber* (U437a) *3,000.*
- *g.* 6c on 3c violet (error) (U526) *3,000.*

UC9 U95 6c on 2c carmine (U525) 40.00 35.00

Surcharged in Black

Surcharged on 6c orange air post envelopes without borders.

1946

UC10 UC2 5c on 6c orange, die 2a 2.75 1.50
- *a.* Double surcharge 75.00

UC11 UC2 5c on 6c orange, die 2b 8.00 5.50
UC12 UC2 5c on 6c orange, die 2c .75 .50
- *a.* Double surcharge 75.00 *900.00*

UC13 UC2 5c on 6c orange, die 3 .70 .60
- *a.* Double surcharge 75.00 50.00
- *c.* Double surcharge, one on reverse —

UC13B U93 5c on 6c (UC8a), entire —

The 6c borderless envelopes and the revalued envelopes were issued primarily for use to and from members of the armed forces. The 5c rate came into effect Oct. 1, 1946.

DC-4 Skymaster — UC3

Die 1 — The end of the wing at the right is a smooth curve. The juncture of the front end of the plane and the engine forms an acute angle. The first T of STATES and the E's of UNITED STATES lean to the left.

Die 2 — The end of the wing at the right is a straight line. The juncture of the front end of the plane and the engine is wide open. The first T of STATES and the E's of UNITED STATES lean to the right.

1946

UC14 UC3 5c carmine, die 1 .75 .25
UC15 UC3 5c carmine, die 2 .75 .25

See Nos. UC18, UC26.

DC-4 Skymaster — UC4

1947-55 **Typo.**

Letter Sheets for Foreign Postage

UC16 UC4 10c brt red, *pale bl*, entire 8.50 7.00
- *e.* Blue omitted, entire 400.00
- *f.* Overlay omitted front & back, entire *100.00*
- *g.* Overlay omitted from front only, entire *500.00*
- *a.* "Air Letter" on face, 4-line inscription on back ('51), entire 17.50 10.00
- *b.* As "a," 10c chocolate, *pale bl*, entire 450.00
- *c.* "Air Letter" and "Aerogramme" on face, 4-line inscription on back ('53), entire 45.00 12.50
- *d.* As "c," 3-line inscription on back ('55), entire 9.00 8.00

Postage Stamp Centenary Issue

Centenary of the first postage stamps issued by the United States Government.

Washington & Franklin, Early and Modern Mail-carrying Vehicles — UC5

Two dies: Rotary, design measures 22¼mm high; and flat bed press, design 21¾mm high.

Embossed, Rotary Press Printing

1947, May 21

For Domestic Postage

UC17 UC5 5c carmine (rotary) .50 .30
- *a.* Flat plate printing .50 .30

Type of 1946

Type I: 6's lean to right.
Type II: 6's upright.

1950 , Sept. 22

UC18 UC3 6c carmine, type I .75 .25
- *a.* Type II .90 .25

Several other types differ slightly from the two listed.

Nos. UC14, UC15, UC18 Surcharged in Red Left of Stamp

1951

UC19 UC3 6c on 5c carmine, die 1 .85 1.50
- *a.* Surcharge inverted at lower left, entire —

UC20 UC3 6c on 5c carmine, die 2 .85 1.50
- *a.* 6c on 6c carmine (error) entire *1,500.*
- *b.* Double surcharge *975.00* —

To qualify as No. UC20b, both surcharges must be to the left of the indicia.

Nos. UC14-UC15 Surcharged in Red at Left of Stamp

1952

UC21 UC3 6c on 5c carmine, die 1 25.00 20.00
- *a.* Double surcharge, entire *600.00*

UC22 UC3 6c on 5c carmine, die 2 3.75 2.50
- *a.* Double surcharge 250.00
- *b.* Triple surcharge, entire 275.00

To qualify as Nos. UC22a or UC22b, all surcharges must be to the left of the indicia.

No. UC17 Surcharged in Red

UC23 UC5 6c on 5c carmine *850.*

The 6c on 4c black (No. U440) is believed to be a favor printing.

Fifth International Philatelic Exhibition Issue

FIPEX, the Fifth International Philatelic Exhibition, New York, N.Y., Apr. 28-May 6, 1956.

Eagle in Flight — UC6

1956, May 2

UC25 UC6 6c red .75 .50

Two types exist, differing slightly in the clouds at top.

Skymaster Type of 1946

1958, July 31

UC26 UC3 7c blue .65 .50

Nos. UC3-UC5, UC18 and UC25 Surcharged in Green at Left of Stamp

1958

UC27 UC2 6c + 1c orange, die 2a 250.00 *300.00*

UC28 UC2 6c + 1c orange, die 2b 65.00 80.00

UC29 UC2 6c + 1c orange, die 2c 30.00 55.00

UC30 UC3 6c + 1c carmine, type I 1.00 .50
- *a.* Type II 1.00 .50

UC31 UC6 6c + 1c red 1.00 .50

Jet Airliner — UC7

Type I: Back inscription in 3 lines.
Type II: Back inscription in 2 lines.

Letter Sheet for Foreign Postage

Typographed, Without Embossing

1958-59

UC32 UC7 10c blue & red, *blue*, II ('59), entire 6.00 5.00
- *a.* Type I ('58), entire 10.00 5.00
- *b.* Red omitted, II, entire *625.00*
- *c.* Blue omitted, II, entire *600.00*
- *d.* Red omitted, I, entire *700.00*

Silhouette of Jet Airliner — UC8

1958, Nov. 21 **Embossed**

UC33 UC8 7c blue .60 .25

1960, Aug. 18

UC34 UC8 7c carmine .60 .25

Jet Plane and Globe — UC9

Letter Sheet for Foreign Postage

Typographed, Without Embossing

1961, June 16

UC35 UC9 11c red & blue, *blue*, entire 3.00 3.50
- *a.* Red omitted, entire *750.00*
- *b.* Blue omitted, entire *950.00*

UC10

1962, Nov. 17 **Embossed**

UC36 UC10 8c red .55 .25

UC11

1965-67

UC37 UC11 8c red .45 .25
- *a.* Tagged 3.50 .30

No. UC37a has a 8x24mm panel at left of stamp that glows orange red under ultraviolet light.

Pres. John F. Kennedy and Jet Plane — UC12

Letter Sheets for Foreign Postage

Typographed, Without Embossing

1965, May 29

UC38 UC12 11c red & dark blue, *blue*, entire 3.75 4.00

1967, May 29

UC39 UC12 13c red & dark blue, *blue*, entire 3.25 4.00
- *a.* Red omitted, entire *600.00*
- *b.* Dark blue omitted, entire *500.00*

UC13

1968, Jan. 8 **Tagged** **Embossed**

UC40 UC13 10c red .50 .25

No. UC37 Surcharged in Red at Left of Stamp

1968, Feb. 5

UC41 UC11 8c + 2c red .65 .25

Tagging

Envelopes and Letter Sheets from No. UC42 onward are tagged unless otherwise noted.

Human Rights Year Issue

Issued for International Human Rights Year, and to commemorate the 20th anniversary of the United Nations' Declaration of Human Rights.

Globes and Flock of Birds UC14

Letter Sheet for Foreign Postage

1968, Dec. 3 **Photo.**

UC42 UC14 13c gray, brown, orange & black, *blue*, entire 8.00 7.50
- *a.* Orange omitted, entire *800.00*
- *b.* Brown omitted, entire *375.00*
- *c.* Black omitted, entire *700.00*
- *d.* Gray and black omitted, entire —
- *e.* Tagging omitted, entire 150.00

No. UC42 has a luminescent panel ⅜x1 inch on the right globe. The panel glows orange red under ultraviolet light.

UC15

1971, May 6 **Embossed (Plane)**

UC43 UC15 11c red & blue .50 *1.75*

Birds in Flight and "usa" UC16

Letter Sheet for Foreign Postage

1971 **Photo.**

UC44 UC16 15c gray, red, white & blue, *blue*, entire 1.50 *7.50*
- *a.* "AEROGRAMME" added to inscription, entire 1.50 *7.50*
- *b.* As #UC44, red omitted, entire *300.00*
- *c.* As "a," red omitted, entire —

Folding instructions (2 steps) in capitals on No. C44; (4 steps) in upper and lower case on No. UC44a.

On Nos. UC44-UC44a the white rhomboid background of "USA postage 15c" is luminescent. No. UC44 is inscribed: "VIA AIR MAIL-PAR AVION". "postage 15c" is in gray. See No. UC46.

No. UC40 Surcharged in Green at Left of Stamp

1971, June 28 **Embossed**

UC45 UC13 10c + (1c) red 1.50 .75

HOT AIR BALLOONING CHAMPIONSHIPS ISSUE

Hot Air Ballooning World Championships, Albuquerque, N.M., Feb. 10-17, 1973.

"usa" Type of 1971

Design: Three balloons and cloud at left in address section; no birds beside stamp. Inscribed "INTERNATIONAL HOT AIR BALLOONING." "postage 15c" in blue.

Letter Sheet for Foreign Postage

1973, Feb. 10

UC46 UC16 15c red, white & blue, *blue*, entire 1.00 *7.50*

Folding instructions as on No. UC44a. See notes after No. UC44.

Bird in Flight — UC17

1973, Dec. 1 **Luminescent Ink**

UC47 UC17 13c rose red .30 .25

Beginning with No. UC48, all listings are letter sheets for foreign postage.

UC18

1974, Jan. 4 **Photo.**

UC48 UC18 18c red & blue, *blue*, entire 1.00 *6.00*
a. Red omitted, entire *200.00*

25TH ANNIVERSARY OF NATO ISSUE

UC19

Design: "NATO" and NATO emblem at left in address section.

1974, Apr. 4

UC49 UC19 18c red & blue, *blue*, entire 1.00 *6.00*
Die cutting reversed, entire *100.00*

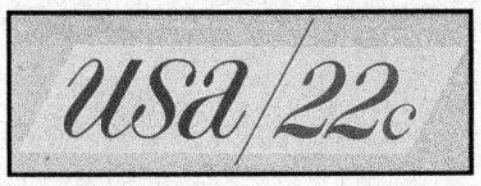

UC20

1976, Jan. 16

UC50 UC20 22c red & blue, *blue*, entire 1.00 *6.00*
a. Red color missing due to foldover and die cutting —

UC21

1978, Nov. 3

UC51 UC21 22c blue, *blue*, entire 1.00 *3.00*

22nd OLYMPIC GAMES, MOSCOW, JULY 19-AUG. 3, 1980.

UC22

Design (multicolored in bottom left corner) shows discus thrower.

1979, Dec. 5

UC52 UC22 22c red, black & green, *bluish*, entire 1.50 *6.00*

UC23

Design (brown on No. UC53, green and brown on No. UC54): lower left, Statue of Liberty. Inscribed "Tour the United States." Folding area shows tourist attractions.

1980, Dec. 29

UC53 UC23 30c blue, red & brown, *blue*, entire .85 *6.00*
a. Red (30) omitted, entire 70.00

1981, Sept. 21

UC54 UC23 30c yellow, magenta, blue & black, *blue*, entire .65 *6.00*

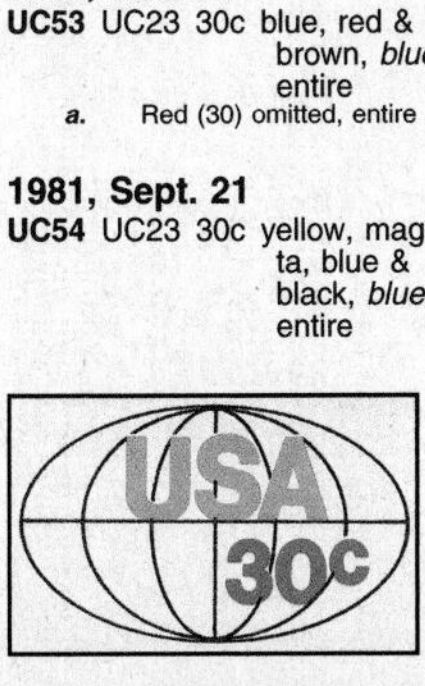

UC24

Design: "Made in USA . . . world's best buys!" on flap, ship, tractor in lower left. Reverse folding area shows chemicals, jet silhouette, wheat, typewriter and computer tape disks.

1982, Sept. 16

UC55 UC24 30c multi, *blue*, entire .80 *6.00*

WORLD COMMUNICATIONS YEAR

World Map Showing Locations of Satellite Tracking Stations UC25

Design: Reverse folding area shows satellite, tracking station.

1983, Jan. 7

UC56 UC25 30c multi, *blue*, entire .90 *8.00*

1984 OLYMPICS

UC26

Indicia in black, multicolor design of woman equestrian at lower left with montage of competitive events on reverse folding area.

1983, Oct. 14

UC57 UC26 30c black & multi, *light blue*, entire .85 *8.00*

WEATHER SATELLITES, 25TH ANNIV.

UC27

Design: Landsat orbiting the earth at lower left with three Landsat photographs on reverse folding area. Inscribed: "Landsat views the Earth."

1985, Feb. 14

UC58 UC27 36c multi, *blue*, entire 1.25 *12.50*

NATIONAL TOURISM WEEK

Urban Skyline — UC28

Design: Inscribed "Celebrate America" at lower left and "Travel. . . the perfect freedom" on folding area. Skier, Indian chief, cowboy, jazz trumpeter and pilgrims on reverse folding area.

1985, May 21

UC59 UC28 36c multi, *blue*, entire 1.25 *12.50*
a. Black omitted, entire *600.00* —

MARK TWAIN AND HALLEY'S COMET

Comet Tail Viewed from Space — UC29

Design: Portrait of Twain at lower left and inscribed "I came in with Halley's Comet in 1835. It is coming again next year, and I expect to go out with it. It will be the greatest disappointment of my life if I don't go out with Halley's Comet." "1835 . Mark Twain . 1910 . Halley's Comet . 1985" and Twain, Huckleberry Finn, steamboat and comet on reverse folding areas.

1985, Dec. 4

UC60 UC29 36c multi, entire 2.00 *12.50*

UC30

1988, May 9 **Litho.**

UC61 UC30 39c multi, entire 1.25 *12.50*
a. Tagging bar to left of design ('89) 1.25 *1.50*

On No. UC61, the tagging bar is between "USA" and "39."

MONTGOMERY BLAIR, POSTMASTER GENERAL 1861-64

Montgomery Blair and Pres. Lincoln — UC31

Design: Mail bags and "Free city delivery," "Railway mail service" and "Money order system" at lower left. Globe, locomotive, bust of Blair, UPU emblem and "The Paris conference of 1863, initiated by Postmaster General Blair, led, in 1874, to the founding of the Universal Postal Union" contained on reverse folding area.

1989, Nov. 20

UC62 UC31 39c multicolored, entire 1.40 *16.00*
a. Double impression —
b. Triple impression —
c. Quadruple impression —

UC32

1991, May 17

UC63 UC32 45c gray, red & blue, *blue*, entire 1.40 *16.00*
a. White paper, entire 1.00 *16.00*

Thaddeus Lowe (1832-1913), Balloonist — UC33

1995, Sept. 23

UC64 UC33 50c multicolored, *blue*, entire 1.50 *20.00*

Voyageurs Natl. Park, Minnesota UC34

1999, May 15

UC65 UC34 60c multicolored, *blue*, entire 1.75 *12.50*

No. UC65 used is often found with additional postage affixed.

OFFICIAL STAMPED ENVELOPES

By the Act of Congress, January 31, 1873, the franking privilege of officials was abolished as of July 1, 1873 and the Postmaster General was authorized to prepare official envelopes. At the same time official stamps were prepared for all Departments. Department envelopes became obsolete July 5, 1884. After that, government offices began to use franked envelopes of varied design. These indicate no denomination and lie beyond the scope of this Catalogue.

Post Office Department

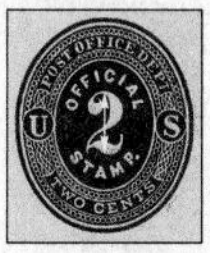
"2" 9mm high — UO1

"3" 9mm high — UO2

"6" 9½mm high — UO3

1873

UO1	UO1 2c black, *lemon*	25.00	10.00
UO2	UO2 3c black, *lemon*	12.50	6.50
+UO3	UO2 3c black	*17,500.*	
UO4	UO3 6c black, *lemon*	25.00	17.50

"2" 9¼mm high — UO4

"3" 9¼mm high — UO5

"6" 10½mm high — UO6

1874-79

UO5	UO4 2c black, *lemon*	8.00	4.25
UO6	UO4 2c black	120.00	37.50
UO7	UO5 3c black, *lemon*	2.75	.75
UO8	UO5 3c black	1,750.	1,200.
UO9	UO5 3c black, *amber*	120.00	37.50
UO10	UO5 3c black, *blue*		—
UO11	UO5 3c blue, *blue* ('75)	*20,000.*	
UO12	UO6 6c black, *lemon*	12.50	6.50
UO13	UO6 6c black	1,250.	1,750.

Fakes exist of Nos. UO3, UO8 and UO13.

Postal Service

UO7

1877

UO14	UO7	black	6.00	4.50
UO15	UO7	black, *amber*	125.00	42.50
UO16	UO7	blue, *amber*	125.00	40.00
UO17	UO7	blue, *blue*	7.50	6.75

War Department

Franklin — UO8

Bust points to the end of "N" of "ONE".

Jackson — UO9

Bust narrow at the back.

Washington — UO10

Queue projects below the bust.

Lincoln — UO11

Neck very long at the back.

Jefferson — UO12

Queue forms straight line with bust.

Clay — UO13

Ear partly concealed by hair, mouth large, chin prominent.

Webster — UO14

Has side whiskers.

Scott UO15

Hamilton UO16

Back of bust very narrow; chin almost straight; the labels containing the letters "U S" are exactly parallel.

Reay Issue

1873

UO18	UO8	1c dk red	350.00	200.00
WO18A	UO8	1c dk red, *man,* entire		—
UO19	UO9	2c dk red	1,000.	—
UO20	UO10	3c dk red	12.50	30.00
UO21	UO10	3c dk red, *amb*	*27,500.*	
UO22	UO10	3c dk red, *cr*	500.00	250.00
UO23	UO11	6c dk red	250.00	100.00
UO24	UO11	6c dk red, *cr*	4,000.	425.00
UO25	UO12	10c dk red	*7,500.*	
UO26	UO13	12c dk red	90.00	
UO27	UO14	15c dk red	125.00	55.00
UO28	UO15	24c dk red	100.00	40.00
UO29	UO16	30c dk red	250.00	150.00
UO30	UO8	1c ver	200.00	
WO31	UO8	1c ver, *man*	17.50	14.00
+UO32	UO9	2c ver	400.00	
WO33	UO9	2c ver, *man*	250.00	
UO34	UO10	3c ver	75.00	40.00
UO35	UO10	3c ver, *amb*	85.00	40.00
UO36	UO10	3c ver, *cr*	12.50	12.50
UO37	UO11	6c ver	75.00	
+UO38	UO11	6c ver, *cr*	400.00	
UO39	UO12	10c ver	300.00	
UO40	UO13	12c ver	130.00	
UO41	UO14	15c ver	200.00	
UO42	UO15	24c ver	300.00	
UO43	UO16	30c ver	250.00	

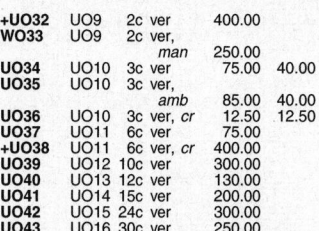

UO17

Bottom serif on "S" is thick and short; bust at bottom below hair forms a sharp point.

UO18

Bottom serif on "S" is thick and short; front part of bust is rounded.

UO19

Bottom serif on "S" is short; queue does not project below bust.

UO20

Neck very short at the back.

UO21

Knot of queue stands out prominently.

UO22

Ear prominent, chin receding. No "dot" uner "T" of "Dept."

UO23

Has no side whiskers; forelock projects above head.

UO24

Back of bust rather broad; chin slopes considerably; the label containing letters "U S" are not exactly parallel.

Plimpton Issue

1875

UO44	UO17	1c red	175.00	85.00
+UO45	UO17	1c red, *amb*	600.00	
+UO45A	UO17	1c red, *org*	*32,500.*	
WO46	UO17	1c red, *man*	4.50	2.75
UO47	UO18	2c red	90.00	—
UO48	UO18	2c red, *amber*	12.50	17.50
UO49	UO18	2c red, *orange*	12.50	17.50
WO50	UO18	2c red, *manila*	90.00	40.00
UO51	UO19	3c red	11.00	10.00
UO52	UO19	3c red, *amber*	12.50	10.00
UO53	UO19	3c red, *cream*	5.00	3.75
UO54	UO19	3c red, *blue*	3.00	2.00
UO55	UO19	3c red, *fawn*	6.00	5.00
UO56	UO20	6c red	45.00	30.00
UO57	UO20	6c red, *amber*	65.00	40.00
UO58	UO20	6c red, *cream*	175.00	85.00
UO59	UO21	10c red	180.00	80.00
UO60	UO21	10c red, *amber*	650.00	
UO61	UO22	12c red	25.00	25.00
UO62	UO22	12c red, *amber*	400.00	
UO63	UO22	12c red, *cream*	450.00	
UO64	UO23	15c red	200.00	125.00
UO65	UO23	15c red, *amber*	650.00	
UO66	UO23	15c red, *cream*	525.00	
UO67	UO24	30c red	150.00	140.00
UO68	UO24	30c red, *amber*	550.00	
UO69	UO24	30c red, *cream*	675.00	

POSTAL SAVINGS ENVELOPES

UO25

1911

UO70	UO25	1c green	75.00	25.00
UO71	UO25	1c green, *oriental buff*	175.00	85.00
UO72	UO25	2c carmine	12.50	4.00
a.		2c carmine, *manila* (error)	*1,200.*	*1,000.*

Used Values

Catalogue values for regularly used entires. Those with first-day cancels generally sell for much less.

Tagged
Envelopes from No. UO73 onward are tagged unless otherwise noted.

OFFICIAL MAIL

UO26

1983, Jan. 12 — Typo. & Embossed

UO73	UO26	20c blue, entire	1.00	*10.00*

UO27

1985, Feb. 26 — Typo. & Embossed

UO74	UO27	22c blue, entire	.90	*5.00*

UO28

1987, Mar. 2 — Typo.

UO75	UO28	22c blue, entire	1.50	*25.00*

Used exclusively to mail U.S. Savings Bonds.

UO29

1988, Mar. 22

UO76	UO29	(25c) black & blue, entire	1.25	*15.00*

Used exclusively to mail U.S. Savings Bonds.

UO30

UO31

1988, Apr. 11 — Typo. & Embossed

UO77	UO30	25c black & blue, entire	.85	*6.00*
a.		Denomination & lettering as on No. UO78, entire	*5.00*	*6.00*

Nos. UO77 and UO77a used to mail U.S. Savings Bonds and also occasionally used by the director of admissions at the U.S. Air Force Academy and by Air Force recruiting stations for intra-agency correspondence.

Typo.

UO78	UO31	25c black & blue, entire	1.00	*35.00*
a.		Denomination & lettering as on No. UO77, entire	1.00	*35.00*

Used to mail U.S. Savings Bonds. Also used by the Department of Agriculture.

Used Values

Postally used examples of Nos. UO79-UO94 seldom appear in the marketplace and thus cannot be valued with as much certainty as the editors would like. They must show evidence of postal usage. Clear cancels are valued even higher. The editors would like to have records of sales of examples of these used envelopes. If a value exists, it is based on a known transaction(s) or consultation with experts.

1990, Mar. 17

Stars and "E Pluribus Unum" illegible. "Official" is 13mm, "USA" is 16mm long.

UO79	UO31	45c black & blue, entire	1.25	*80.00*
UO80	UO31	65c black & blue, entire	1.75	*100.00*

Used exclusively to mail U.S. passports.

UO32

Stars and "E Pluribus Unum" clear and sharply printed. "Official" is 14½mm, "USA" is 17mm long.

1990, Aug. 10 — Litho.

UO81	UO32	45c black & blue, entire	1.25	*100.00*
UO82	UO32	65c black & blue, entire	1.75	*160.00*

Used exclusively to mail U.S. passports.

UO33

1991, Jan. 22 — Typo. — Wmk.

UO83	UO33	(29c) black & blue, entire	1.00	*20.00*

Used exclusively to mail U.S. Savings Bonds.

UO34

Litho. & Embossed

1991, Apr. 6 **Wmk.**

UO84 UO34 29c black & blue, entire .70 *5.00*
- *a.* Unwatermarked paper, entire 7.50 *4.00*

No. UO84a has a "recycled" imprint under the flap.

UO35

1991, Apr. 17 **Wmk.**

UO85 UO35 29c black & blue, entire .70 *20.00*

Used exclusively to mail U.S. Savings Bonds.

Consular Service, Bicent. — UO36

1992, July 10 **Litho.** **Unwmk.**

UO86 UO36 52c blue & red, entire 6.00 *20.00*
- *a.* 52c blue & red, *blue-white,* entire 1.50 *20.00*

UO87 UO36 75c blue & red, entire 11.00 *30.00*
- *a.* 75c blue & red, *blue-white,* entire 2.50 *30.00*

Used exclusively to mail U.S. passports. Available only in 4⅜ inch x 8⅞ inch size with self-adhesive flap.

UO37

1995-99 **Typo. & Embossed**

UO88 UO37 32c blue & red, entire .90 *7.00*

UO89 UO37 33c blue & red, entire .90 *8.00*

Type of 1995

2001, Feb. 27

UO90 UO37 34c blue & red, entire 1.00 *10.00*

Type of 1995

2002, Aug. 2

UO91 UO37 37c blue & red, type I, entire 1.00 *15.00*
- *a.* Type II, entire 1.00 *35.00*

Type I has 29x28mm blue panel, top of "USA" even with the bottom of the eagle's neck and is made with "100% recycled paper" as noted on reverse. Type II has a 27½x27½mm blue panel, top of "USA" even with the highest arrow, and has no mention of "100% recycled paper" on reverse.

Type of 1995

2006, Jan. 9

UO92 UO37 39c blue & red, entire 2.00 *12.50*

Type of 1995

2007, May 12

UO93 UO37 41c blue & red, entire 2.00 *25.00*

Type of 1995

2008, June 20 **Typo.**

UO94 UO37 42c blue & red, entire 2.00 *25.00*

REVENUE STAMPS

Nos. R1-R102 were used to pay taxes on documents and proprietary articles including playing cards. Until Dec. 25, 1862, the law stated that a revenue stamp could be used only for payment of the tax upon the particular instrument or article specified on its face. After that date stamps, except the Proprietary, could be used indiscriminately.

Values quoted are for pen-canceled stamps. Stamps with handstamped cancellations sell at higher prices. Stamps canceled with cuts, punches or holes sell for less. See the Scott U.S. Specialized Catalogue.

General Issue
First Issue

Head of Washington in Oval. Various Frames as Illustrated.

Nos. R1b to R42b, part perforate, occur perforated sometimes at sides only and sometimes at top and bottom only. The higher values, part perforate, are perforated at sides only. Imperforate and part perforate revenues often bring much more in pairs or blocks than as single stamps. Part perforate revenues with an asterisk (*) after the value exist imperforate horizontally or vertically.

The experimental silk paper is a variety of the old paper and has only a very few minute fragments of fiber.

Some of the stamps were in use eight years and were printed several times. Many color variations occurred, particularly when unstable pigments were used and the color was intended to be purple or violet, such as the 4c Proprietary, 30c and $2.50 stamps. Before 1868 dull colors predominate on these and the early red stamps. In later printings of the 4c Proprietary, 30c and $2.50 stamps, red predominates in the mixture, and on the dollar values the red is brighter. The early $1.90 stamp is dull purple, imperf. or perforated. In a later printing, perforated only, the purple is darker.

R1

George Washington — R2

Old Paper

1862-71 **Engr.** ***Perf. 12***

R1 R1 1c Express, red
- *a.* Imperf. 125.00
- *b.* Part perf. 75.00*
- *c.* Perf. 1.50
- *d.* As No. R1c, silk paper *450.00*
- *e.* As No. R1c, vertical pair, imperf. between *200.00*

R2 R1 1c Playing Cards, red
- *a.* Imperf. 4,500.
- *b.* Part perf. 2,500.
- *c.* Perf. 250.00

R3 R1 1c Proprietary, red
- *a.* Imperf. 1,800.
- *b.* Part perf. 350.00*
- *c.* Perf. .50
- *d.* As No. R3c, silk paper 75.00

R4 R1 1c Telegraph, red
- *a.* Imperf. 1,000.
- *c.* Perf. 20.00

R5 R2 2c Bank Check, blue
- *a.* Imperf. 1.50
- *b.* Part perf. 5.50*
- *c.* Perf. .50
- *e.* As No. R5c, Double impression *1,500.*
- *f.* As No. R5c, pair imperf between 500.00

R6 R2 2c Bank Check, orange
- *b.* Part perf. 60.00*
- *c.* Perf. .45
- *d.* As No. R6c, silk paper 275.00
- *e.* As No. R6c, orange, *green* 1,000.

R7 R2 2c Certificate, blue
- *a.* Imperf. 20.00
- *c.* Perf. 32.50

R8 R2 2c Certificate, orange
- *c.* Perf. 50.00

R9 R2 2c Express, blue
- *a.* Imperf. 15.00
- *b.* Part perf. 35.00*
- *c.* Perf. .40

R10 R2 2c Express, orange
- *b.* Part perf. *3,250.*
- *c.* Perf. 14.00
- *d.* As No. R10c, silk paper 500.00

R11 R2 2c Playing Cards, blue
- *a.* Imperf. *1,750.*
- *b.* Part perf. 325.00
- *c.* Perf. 4.50

R12 R2 2c Playing Cards, org
- *c.* Perf. 55.00

R13 R2 2c Proprietary, blue
- *a.* Imperf. 2,000.
- *b.* Part perf. 250.
- *c.* Perf. .40
- *d.* As No. R13c, silk paper 350.00
- Double transfer (T13a) 500.00
- *e.* ultramarine 400.00

R14 R2 2c Proprietary, orange
- *c.* Perf. 70.00

R15 R2 2c U.S. Internal Revenue, orange ('64)
- *c.* Perf. .25
- *d.* As No. R15c, silk paper 1.00
- *e.* As No. R15c, orange, *green* *2,500.*

R3

R16 R3 3c Foreign Exchange, green
- *b.* Part perf. 1,750.*
- *c.* Perf. 5.00
- *d.* As No. R16c, silk paper 250.00

R17 R3 3c Playing Cards, green ('63)
- *a.* Imperf. *27,500.*
- *c.* Perf. 200.00

R18 R3 3c Proprietary, green
- *b.* Part perf. 1,250.
- *c.* Perf. 9.00
- *d.* As No. R18c, silk paper 300.00
- *e.* As No. R18c, double impression *1,750.*
- *f.* As No. R18c, printed on both sides *4,000.*

R19 R3 3c Telegraph, green
- *a.* Imperf. 100.00
- *b.* Part perf. 30.00
- *c.* Perf. 3.00

R20 R3 4c Inland Exchange, brown ('63)
- *c.* Perf. 2.25
- *d.* As No. R20c, silk paper 190.00

R21 R3 4c Playing Cards, slate ('63)
- *c.* Perf. 700.00

R22 R3 4c Proprietary, purple
- *a.* Imperf. —
- *b.* Part perf. 500.00
- *c.* Perf. 8.50
- *d.* As No. R22c, silk paper 350.00

There are shade and color variations of Nos. R21-R22.

R23 R3 5c Agreement, red
- *c.* Perf. .50
- *d.* As No. R23c, silk paper 4.50

R24 R3 5c Certificate, red
- *a.* Imperf. 4.00
- *b.* Part perf. 15.00
- *c.* Perf. .50
- *d.* As No. R24c, silk paper 1.10
- *f.* As No. R24d, impression of No. R3 on back *3,000.*

R25 R3 5c Express, red
- *a.* Imperf. 8.00
- *b.* Part perf. 8.00*
- *c.* Perf. .40

R26 R3 5c Foreign Exchange, red
- *b.* Part perf. *2,500.*
- *c.* Perf. .50
- *d.* As No. R26c, silk paper 850.00

R27 R3 5c Inland Exchange, red
- *a.* Imperf. 10.00
- *b.* Part perf. 6.75
- *c.* Perf. .60
- *d.* As No. R27c, silk paper 17.50
- *e.* As No. R27c, double impression *3,500.*

R28 R3 5c Playing Cards, red ('63)
- *c.* Perf. 40.00
- *e.* Double impression *2,000.*

R29 R3 5c Proprietary, red ('64)
- *c.* Perf. 30.00
- *d.* As No. R29c, silk paper 400.00

R30 R3 6c Inland Exchange, orange ('63)
- *b.* Part perf. (imperf. vert.), on document —
- *c.* Perf. 2.25
- *d.* As No. R30c, silk paper 350.00

R31 R3 6c Proprietary, orange ('71)
- *c.* Perf. *1,800.*

Nearly all examples of No. R31 are faulty or repaired and poorly centered. The catalogue value is for a fine centered stamp with minor faults which do not detract from its appearance.

R32 R3 10c Bill of Lading, blue
- *a.* Imperf. 90.00
- *b.* Part perf. 600.00*
- *c.* Perf. 1.75

R33 R3 10c Certificate, blue
- *a.* Imperf. 400.00
- *b.* Part perf. 850.00*
- *c.* Perf. .35
- *d.* As No. R33c, silk paper 6.00

R34 R3 10c Contract, blue
- *b.* Part perf. 700.00*
- *be.* As No. R34b, ultramarine 1,000.
- *c.* Perf. .50
- *ce.* As No. R34c, ultramarine 1.00
- *d.* As No. R34c, silk paper 4.25

R35 R3 10c Foreign Exchange, blue
- *c.* Perf. 14.00
- *d.* As No. R35c, silk paper —
- *e.* As No. R35c, ultramarine 20.00

R36 R3 10c Inland Exchange, blue
- *a.* Imperf. 500.00
- *b.* Part perf. 4.50*
- *c.* Perf. .30
- *d.* As No. R36c, silk paper 125.00

R37 R3 10c Power of Attorney, blue
- *a.* Imperf. 1,000.
- *b.* Part perf. 30.00
- *c.* Perf. 1.00

R38 R3 10c Proprietary, blue ('64)
- *c.* Perf. 19.00

R39 R3 15c Foreign Exchange, brown ('63)
- *c.* Perf. 35.00
- *e.* Double impression *1,750.*

R40 R3 15c Inland Exchange, brown
- *a.* Imperf. 45.00
- *b.* Part perf. 14.00
- *c.* Perf. 2.00
- *e.* As No. R40b, double impression *2,250.*
- *f.* As No. R40c, double impression *1,000.*

R41 R3 20c Foreign Exchange, red
- *a.* Imperf. 100.00
- *c.* Perf. 80.00
- *d.* As No. R41c, silk paper 650.00

R42 R3 20c Inland Exchange, red
- *a.* Imperf. 17.00
- *b.* Part perf. 22.50
- *c.* Perf. .45
- *d.* As No. R42c, silk paper —

R4

R5

R43 R4 25c Bond, red
- *a.* Imperf. 300.00
- *b.* Part perf. 6.75
- *c.* Perf. 3.75

R44 R4 25c Certificate, red
- *a.* Imperf. 11.00
- *b.* Part perf. 6.75*
- *c.* Perf. .50
- *d.* As No. R44c, silk paper 2.75
- *e.* As No. R44c, printed on both sides *3,500.*
- *f.* As No. R44c, impression of No. R48 on back *6,000.*

R45 R4 25c Entry of Goods, red
- *a.* Imperf. 22.50
- *b.* Part perf. 500.00*
- *c.* Perf. 1.50
- *d.* As No. R45c, silk paper 200.00

R46 R4 25c Insurance, red
- *a.* Imperf. 12.50
- *b.* Part perf. 19.00
- *c.* Perf. .30
- *d.* As No. R46c, silk paper 7.00
- *e.* As No. R46c, double impression *1,000.*

R47 R4 25c Life Insurance, red
- *a.* Imperf. 50.00
- *b.* Part perf. 1,250.
- *c.* Perf. 11.00

R48 R4 25c Power of Attorney, red
- *a.* Imperf. 10.00
- *b.* Part perf. 45.00
- *c.* Perf. 1.00
- *d.* As No. R48c, silk paper *1,750.*

R49 R4 25c Protest, red
- *a.* Imperf. 35.00
- *b.* Part perf. 1,000.
- *c.* Perf. 10.00

R50 R4 25c Warehouse Receipt, red
- *a.* Imperf. 55.00
- *b.* Part perf. 1,300.
- *c.* Perf. 45.00

R51 R4 30c Foreign Exchange, lilac
- *a.* Imperf. 200.00
- *b.* Part perf. *11,000.*
- *c.* Perf. 60.00
- *d.* As No. R51c, silk paper *675.00*

R52 R4 30c Inland Exchange, lilac
- *a.* Imperf. 75.00
- *b.* Part perf. 90.00
- *c.* Perf. 8.50
- *d.* As No. R52c, silk paper *1,750.*

R53 R4 40c Inland Exchange, brown
- *a.* Imperf. *2,500.*
- *b.* Part perf. 9.00
- *c.* Perf. 8.00
- *d.* As No. R53c, silk paper 550.00
- *f.* As No. R53c, double impression *2,000.*

R54 R5 50c Conveyance, blue
- *a.* Imperf. 20.00
- *b.* Part perf. 3.50
- *c.* Perf. .35
- *ce.* As No. R54c, ultramarine .50
- *d.* As No. R54c, silk paper, blue 3.00
- *de.* As No. R54d, ultramarine —

R55 R5 50c Entry of Goods, blue
b. Part perf. 17.50
c. Perf. .60
d. As No. R55c, silk paper 150.00

R56 R5 50c Foreign Exchange, blue
a. Imperf. 75.00
b. Part perf. 125.00*
c. Perf. 7.50
e. As No. R56c, double impression *1,000.*

R57 R5 50c Lease, blue
a. Imperf. 35.00
b. Part perf. 250.00
c. Perf. 10.00

R58 R5 50c Life Insurance, blue
a. Imperf. 45.00
b. Part perf. 200.00
c. Perf. 1.75
e. As No. R58c, double impression *1,100.*

R59 R5 50c Mortgage, blue
a. Imperf. 22.50
b. Part perf. 5.00
c. Perf. .70
d. As No. R59c, silk paper —
e. As No. R59a, double impression —
f. As No. R59c, double impression —

R60 R5 50c Original Process, blue
a. Imperf. 5.50
b. Part perf. *5,000.*
c. Perf. 1.00
d. As No. R60c, silk paper 7.50

R61 R5 50c Passage Ticket, blue
a. Imperf. 140.00
b. Part perf. 750.00*
c. Perf. 2.25

R62 R5 50c Probate of Will, blue
a. Imperf. 55.00
b. Part perf. 250.00
c. Perf. 22.50

R63 R5 50c Surety Bond, blue
a. Imperf. 400.00
b. Part perf. 2.75
c. Perf. .30
e. As No. R63c, ultramarine .75

R64 R5 60c Inland Exchange, orange
a. Imperf. 120.00
b. Part perf. 90.00
c. Perf. 9.00
d. As No. R64c, silk paper 85.00

R65 R5 70c Foreign Exchange, green
a. Imperf. 750.00
b. Part perf. 200.00
c. Perf. 14.00
d. As No. R65c, silk paper 75.00

R6

R7

R66 R6 $1 Conveyance, red
a. Imperf. 27.50
b. Part perf. *4,500.*
c. Perf. 27.50
d. As No. R66c, silk paper 200.00

R67 R6 $1 Entry of Goods, red
a. Imperf. 50.00
c. Perf. 2.75
d. As No. R67c, silk paper 180.00

R68 R6 $1 Foreign Exchange, red
a. Imperf. 125.00
c. Perf. .75
d. As No. R68c, silk paper 150.00

R69 R6 $1 Inland Exchange, red
a. Imperf. 17.00
b. Part perf. *6,000.**
c. Perf. .70
d. As No. R69c, silk paper 6.00
e. As No. R69c, horiz. pair, imperf. vert. —

No. R69e is an error from a pane of stamps that was intended to be issued fully perforated. It can be differentiated from No. R69b by the color, paper and date of cancel. Expertization is strongly recommended and some specialists doubt the existence of No. R69b.

R70 R6 $1 Lease, red
a. Imperf. 50.00
c. Perf. 4.50

R71 R6 $1 Life Insurance, red
a. Imperf. 300.00
c. Perf. 10.00
d. As No. R71c, silk paper *1,000.*

R72 R6 $1 Manifest, red
a. Imperf. 47.50
c. Perf. 40.00

R73 R6 $1 Mortgage, red
a. Imperf. 27.50
c. Perf. 300.00

R74 R6 $1 Passage Ticket, red
a. Imperf. 350.00
c. Perf. 350.00

R75 R6 $1 Power of Attorney, red
a. Imperf. 100.00
c. Perf. 2.75

R76 R6 $1 Probate of Will, red
a. Imperf. 100.00
c. Perf. 55.00

R77 R7 $1.30 Foreign Exchange, orange ('63)
a. Imperf. *11,000.*
c. Perf. 120.00

R78 R7 $1.50 Inland Exchange, blue
a. Imperf. 32.50
c. Perf. 7.00

R79 R7 $1.60 Foreign Exchange, green ('63)
a. Imperf. 1,400.
c. Perf. 180.00

R80 R7 $1.90 Foreign Exchange, purple ('63)
a. Imperf. *12,500.*
c. Perf. 200.00
d. As No. R80c, silk paper 650.00

R8

R81 R8 $2 Conveyance, red
a. Imperf. 250.00
b. Part perf. 5,500.
c. Perf. 4.00
d. As No. R81c, silk paper 40.00

R82 R8 $2 Mortgage, red
a. Imperf. 200.00
c. Perf. 7.00
d. As No. R82c, silk paper 60.00

R83 R8 $2 Probate of Will, red ('63)
a. Imperf. *5,500.*
c. Perf. 90.00

R84 R8 $2.50 Inland Exchange, purple ('63)
a. Imperf. *10,000.*
c. Perf. 22.50
d. As No. R84c, silk paper 40.00
e. As No. R84c, double impression *2,000.*

There are many shade and color variations of Nos. R84c and R84d.

R85 R8 $3 Charter Party, green
a. Imperf. 250.00
c. Perf. 11.00
d. As No. R85c, silk paper 175.00
e. As No. R85c, printed on both sides *7,000.*
g. As No. R85c, impression of No. RS208 on back *17,000.*

R86 R8 $3 Manifest, green
a. Imperf. 250.00
c. Perf. 55.00

R87 R8 $3.50 Inland Exchange, blue ('63)
a. Imperf. *8,500.*
c. Perf. 70.00
e. As No. R87c, printed on both sides *4,000.*

The $3.50 has stars in upper corners.

R9

R10

R88 R9 $5 Charter Party, red
a. Imperf. 350.00
c. Perf. 10.00
d. As No. R88c, silk paper 170.00

R89 R9 $5 Conveyance, red
a. Imperf. 50.00
c. Perf. 11.00
d. As No. R89c, silk paper 160.00

R90 R9 $5 Manifest, red
a. Imperf. 250.00
c. Perf. 120.00

R91 R9 $5 Mortgage, red
a. Imperf. 200.00
c. Perf. 25.00

R92 R9 $5 Probate of Will, red
a. Imperf. 750.00
c. Perf. 27.50

R93 R9 $10 Charter Party, green
a. Imperf. 900.00
c. Perf. 37.50

R94 R9 $10 Conveyance, green
a. Imperf. 175.00
c. Perf. 77.50

R95 R9 $10 Mortgage, green
a. Imperf. 800.00
c. Perf. 40.00

R96 R9 $10 Probate of Will, green
a. Imperf. *3,500.*
c. Perf. 45.00

R97 R10 $15 Mortgage, blue
a. Imperf. 4,500.
c. Perf. 300.00
e. As No. R97c, ultramarine 500.00
f. As No. R97c, milky blue 525.00

R98 R10 $20 Conveyance, orange
a. Imperf. 150.00
c. Perf. 110.00
d. As No. R98c, silk paper 175.00

R99 R10 $20 Probate of Will, orange
a. Imperf. 2,500.
c. Perf. 3,000.

R100 R10 $25 Mortgage, red ('63)
a. Imperf. 3,250.
c. Perf. 250.00
d. As No. R100c, silk paper 300.00
e. As No. R100c, horiz. pair, imperf. between *6,000.*

R101 R10 $50 U.S. Internal Revenue, green ('63)
a. Imperf. 325.00
c. Perf. 210.00

R11

R102 R11 $200 U.S. Int. Rev., green & red ('64)
a. Imperf. 2,500.
c. Perf. 750.00

DOCUMENTARY STAMPS
Second Issue

After release of the First Issue revenue stamps, the Bureau of Internal Revenue received many reports of fraudulent cleaning and re-use. The Bureau ordered a Second Issue with new designs and colors, using a patented "chameleon" paper which is usually violet or pinkish, with silk fibers.

While designs are different from those of the first issue, stamp sizes and make up of the plates are the same as for corresponding denominations.

R12

R12a

George Washington
Various Frames and Numeral Arrangements

1871 ***Perf. 12***

R103 R12 1c blue & black 100.00
Cut cancel 40.00
a. Inverted center *2,000.*
Cut cancel *750.00*

R104 R12 2c blue & black 2.75
Cut cancel .30
a. Inverted center *6,000.*
Cut cancel *3,500.*

R105 R12a 3c blue & black 75.00
Cut cancel 30.00

R106 R12a 4c blue & black 160.00
Cut cancel 65.00

R107 R12a 5c blue & black 2.00
Cut cancel .50
a. Inverted center *5,000.*
Cut cancel *2,500.*

R108 R12a 6c blue & black 300.00
Cut cancel 100.00

R109 R12a 10c blue & black 1.50
Cut cancel .30
a. Inverted center *2,500.*
Cut cancel *1,250.*
b. Double impression of center —

No. R109a is valued in the grade of fine.

R110 R12a 15c blue & black 100.00
Cut cancel 35.00

R111 R12a 20c blue & black 10.00
Cut cancel 4.00
a. Inverted center *8,000.*

No. R111a is valued in the grade of fine and with small faults, as almost all examples have faults.

R13

R13a

R112 R13 25c blue & black 1.50
Cut cancel .30
a. Inverted center *13,000.*
Cut cancel *6,500.*
b. Imperf. —

R113 R13 30c blue & black 175.00
Cut cancel 70.00

R114 R13 40c blue & black 150.00
Cut cancel 50.00

R115 R13a 50c blue & black 1.40
Cut cancel .35
a. Inverted center 1,050.
Cut cancel 650.00
Punch cancel 275.00

R116 R13a 60c blue & black 250.00
Cut cancel 80.00

R117 R13a 70c blue & black 100.00
Cut cancel 35.00
a. Inverted center *4,000.*
Cut cancel *1,750.*

R13b

R118 R13b $1 blue & black 10.00
Cut cancel 2.25
a. Inverted center *6,000.*
Cut cancel *1,500.*
Punch cancel *1,150.*

R119 R13b $1.30 blue & black 750.00
Cut cancel 175.00

R120 R13b $1.50 blue & black 22.50
Cut cancel 9.00

R121 R13b $1.60 blue & black 750.00
Cut cancel 325.00

R122 R13b $1.90 blue & black 500.00
Cut cancel 150.00

R13c

R123 R13c $2 blue & black 25.00
Cut cancel 10.00

R124 R13c $2.50 blue & black 60.00
Cut cancel 30.00

R125 R13c $3 blue & black 75.00
Cut cancel 35.00

R126 R13c $3.50 blue & black 500.00
Cut cancel 250.00

R13d

R127 R13d $5 blue & black 40.00
Cut cancel 15.00
a. Inverted center *3,000.*
Cut cancel *1,500.*
Punch cancel *1,100.*

R128 R13d $10 blue & black 260.00
Cut cancel 90.00

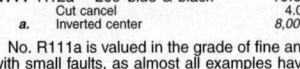

R13e

R129 R13e $20 blue & black 800.00
Cut cancel 275.00
R130 R13e $25 blue & black 750.00
Cut cancel 275.00
R131 R13e $50 blue & black 900.00
Cut cancel 325.00

R13f

R132 R13f $200 red, blue & black *8,500.*
Cut cancel *3,500.*

Printed in sheets of one.

R13g

R133 R13g $500 red org, grn & blk *17,500.*
Cut cancel *8,500.*

Printed in sheets of one.

Value for No. R133 is for a very fine appearing example with a light circular cut cancel or with minor flaws.

Inverted Centers: Fraudulently produced inverted centers exist, some excellently made.

Confusion resulting from the fact that all 1c through $50 denominations of the Second Issue were uniform in color, caused the ordering of a new printing with values in distinctive colors.

Plates used were those of the preceding issue.

Third Issue

Various Frames and Numeral Arrangements.

Violet "Chameleon" Paper with Silk Fibers.

1871-72 ***Perf. 12***

R134 R12 1c claret & black ('72) 65.00
Cut cancel 30.00
R135 R12 2c orange & black .40
Cut cancel .25
a. 2c vermilion & black (error) *900.00*
b. Inverted center 425.00
Cut cancel 300.00
c. Imperf., pair —
d. As No. R135, double impression of frame *2,500.*
e. As No. R135, frame printed on both sides *1,800.*
f. As No. R135, double impression of center *150.00*

R136 R12a 4c brown & black ('72) 110.00
Cut cancel 45.00
R137 R12a 5c orange & black .35
Cut cancel .25
a. Inverted center *6,500.*
Cut cancel *3,750.*

No. R137a is valued in the grade of fine.

R138 R12a 6c orange & black ('72) 125.00
Cut cancel 50.00
R139 R12a 15c brown & black ('72) 27.50
Cut cancel 10.00
a. Inverted center *16,000.*
Cut cancel *9,000.*
R140 R13 30c orange & black ('72) 50.00
Cut cancel 15.00
a. Inverted center *3,500.*
Cut cancel *1,750.*
R141 R13 40c brown & black ('72) 110.00
Cut cancel 35.00
R142 R13a 60c orange & black ('72) 140.00
Cut cancel 55.00
R143 R13a 70c green & black ('72) 90.00
Cut cancel 30.00
R144 R13b $1 green & black ('72) 3.00
Cut cancel .80
a. Inverted center *12,500.*
Cut cancel *10,000.*

No. R144a is valued in the grade of fine.

R145 R13c $2 vermilion & black ('72) 65.00
Cut cancel 25.00
R146 R13c $2.50 claret & black ('72) 125.00
Cut cancel 35.00
a. Inverted center *25,000.*
Cut cancel *17,000.*
R147 R13c $3 green & black ('72) 125.00
Cut cancel 35.00
R148 R13d $5 vermilion & black ('72) 50.00
Cut cancel 20.00
R149 R13d $10 green & black ('72) 400.00
Cut cancel 85.00
R150 R13e $20 orange & black ('72) 900.00
Cut cancel 350.00
a. $20 vermilion & black (error) 1,250.
Cut cancel 700.00

See note on Inverted Centers after No. R133.

1874 ***Perf. 12***

R151 R12 2c orange & black, *green* .25
Cut cancel .25
a. Inverted center 800.00
Cut cancel 375.00

Liberty — R14

1875-78 ***Perf. 12***

R152 R14 2c blue, *blue*
a. silk paper 3.00 .45
b. Wmk. 191R ('78) 2.00 .35
c. Wmk. 191R, rouletted 6 125.00 32.50
d. As "a," vert. pair, imperf. horiz. 525.00
e. As "b," imperf., pair *350.00*
f. As "b," vert. pair, imperf. horiz. 350.00

The watermarked paper came into use in 1878. The rouletted stamps probably were introduced in 1881.

Nos. 279, 267a, 267, 279Bg, 279B, 272-274 Overprinted in Red or Blue

a

b

1898 **Wmk. 191** ***Perf. 12***

For Nos. R153-R160, values in the first column are for unused examples, values in the second column are for used.

R153 A87(a) 1c deep grn (R) 5.00 2.75
R154 A87(b) 1c green (R) .35 .35
a. Overprint inverted 45.00 30.00
b. Overprint on back instead of face, inverted *4,000.*
c. Pair, one without overprint *10,000.*

R155 A88(b) 2c pink, III (Bl) .30 .25
b. 2c **carmine,** type III (Bl) .35 .25
c. As No. R155, overprint inverted 10.00 7.50
d. Vertical pair, one without overprint *1,750.*
e. Horiz. pair, one without overprint —
f. As No. R155, overprint on back instead of face, inverted 350.00
i. Double ovt., one split *850.00*
R155A A88(b) 2c pink, IV (Bl) .25 .25
g. 2c **carmine,** type IV (Bl) .25 .25
h. As No. R155A, overprint inverted 2.75 2.00

Handstamped Type "b" or Type "c" in Magenta

c

R156 A93(b) 8c violet brown *5,250.*
R157 A94(b) 10c dark green *4,000.*
a. As No. R157, handstamped type "c" — —
R158 A95(b) 15c dark blue *6,250.*

Nos. R156-R158 were emergency provisionals, privately prepared, not officially issued.

Privately Prepared Provisionals

No. 285 Overprinted in Red

1898 **Wmk. 191** ***Perf. 12***

R158A A100 1c dark yellow green *15,000.* *12,500.*

No. R158A is valued in sound condition and in the grade of fine to very fine. Most examples have faults, and such examples sell for less.

No. 285 Ovptd. "I.R./P.I.D. & Son" in Red

R158B A100 1c dark yellow green *25,000.* *30,000.*

No. R158B is valued with small faults as each of the four recorded examples have faults.

Nos. R158A-R158B were overprinted with federal government permission by the Purvis Printing Co. upon order of Capt. L. H. Chapman of the Chapman Steamboat Line. Both the Chapman Line and P. I. Daprix & Son operated freight-carrying steamboats on the Erie Canal. The Chapman Line touched at Syracuse, Utica, Little Falls and Fort Plain; the Daprix boat ran between Utica and Rome. Overprintings of 250 of each stamp were made.

Dr. Kilmer & Co. provisional overprints and St. Louis provisional proprietary stamps are listed under "Private Die Medicine Stamps" in the Scott U.S. Specialized Catalogue.

Newspaper Stamp No. PR121 Srchd. Vertically in Red

1898 ***Perf. 12***

R159 N18 $5 dark blue, surcharge reading down 550.00 325.00
R160 N18 $5 dark blue, surcharge reading up 150.00 140.00

Battleship — R15

Inscribed: "Series of 1898" and "Documentary."

There are 2 styles of rouletting for the 1898 proprietary and documentary stamps, an ordinary roulette 5½ and one where small rectangles of the paper are cut out, called hyphen hole perf. 7.

1898 **Wmk. 191R** ***Rouletted 5½***

R161 R15 ½c orange 5.00 *25.00*
R162 R15 ½c dark gray .30 .25
a. Vert. pair, imperf. horiz. 125.00
R163 R15 1c pale blue .25 .25
a. Vert. pair, imperf. horiz. 8.00
b. Imperf., pair *600.00*
R164 R15 2c car rose .30 .30
a. Vert. pair, imperf. horiz. 125.00
b. Imperf., pair 400.00
c. Horiz. pair, imperf. vert. 375.00
R165 R15 3c dark blue 3.50 .35
R166 R15 4c pale rose 2.50 .35
a. Vert. pair, imperf. horiz. 250.00
R167 R15 5c lilac .65 .35
a. Pair, imperf. horiz. or vert. 350.00 175.00
b. Horiz. pair, imperf. btwn. *650.00*
R168 R15 10c dark brown 2.00 .25
a. Vert. pair, imperf. horiz. 40.00 35.00
b. Horiz. pair, imperf. vert. —
R169 R15 25c pur brown 7.50 .50
R170 R15 40c blue lilac 125.00 1.50
Cut cancellation .35
R171 R15 50c slate violet 35.00 .25
a. Imperf., pair *450.00*
b. Horiz. pair, imperf. btwn. *550.00*
R172 R15 80c bister 125.00 .50
Cut cancellation .25

No. R167b may not be genuine.

Hyphen Hole Perf. 7

R163p	1c	.30	.25
R164p	2c	.35	.25
R165p	3c	40.00	1.40
R166p	4c	17.50	1.60
R167p	5c	17.50	.35
R168p	10c	10.00	.25
R169p	25c	20.00	.50
R170p	40c	210.00	35.00
	Cut cancellation		12.50
R171p	50c	75.00	1.00
b.	Horiz. pair, imperf. btwn.	—	*250.00*
R172p	80c	250.00	60.00
	Cut cancellation		20.00

Commerce — R16

1898 ***Rouletted 5½***

R173 R16 $1 dark green 35.00 .25
a. Vert. pair, imperf. horiz. 800.00
b. Horiz. pair, imperf. vert. — 325.00
p. Hyphen hole perf. 7 37.50 2.00
Cut cancel .75
R174 R16 $3 dark brown 65.00 1.25
Cut cancellation .30
a. Horiz. pair, imperf. vert. 500.00
p. Hyphen hole perf. 7 110.00 3.50
Cut cancellation .40
R175 R16 $5 orange red 115.00 2.00
Cut cancellation .30
R176 R16 $10 black 190.00 3.50
Cut cancellation .65
a. Horiz. pair, imperf. vert. —
R177 R16 $30 red 750.00 175.00
Cut cancellation 47.50
R178 R16 $50 gray brown 400.00 7.00
Cut cancellation 2.50

See Nos. R182-R183.

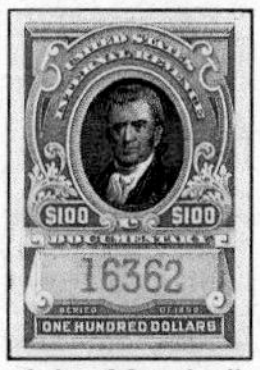
John Marshall R17

Alexander Hamilton R18

James Madison — R19

1899 ***Imperf.***

Without Gum

R179 R17 $100 yel brn & blk 400.00 40.00
Cut cancel 22.50

R180 R18 $500 car lake & blk 2,500. 1,000.
Cut cancel 350.00
R181 R19 $1000 grn & blk 1,750. 350.00
Cut cancel 150.00

1900 ***Hyphen-hole perf. 7***

Allegorical Figure of Commerce

R182 R16 $1 carmine 60.00 .55
Cut cancel .30
R183 R16 $3 lake (fugitive ink) 400.00 60.00
Cut cancel 10.00

Warning: The ink on No. R183 will run in water.

a 

Surcharged type "a"

1900

R184 R16 $1 gray 50.00 .40
Cut cancel .30
a. Horiz. pair, imperf. vert —
b. Surcharge omitted 140.00
As "b," cut cancel 82.50
R185 R16 $2 gray 50.00 .40
Cut cancel .25
R186 R16 $3 gray 200.00 15.00
Cut cancel 6.00
R187 R16 $5 gray 110.00 11.00
Cut cancel 1.60
R188 R16 $10 gray 275.00 25.00
Cut cancel 4.50
R189 R16 $50 gray 2,750. 575.00
Cut cancel 140.00

b 

Surcharged type "b"

Warning: If Nos. R190-R194 are soaked, the center part of the surcharged numeral may wash off. Before the surcharging, a square of soluble varnish was applied to the middle of some stamps.

1902

R190 R16 $1 green 70.00 3.50
Cut cancel .30
a. Inverted surcharge *190.00*
R191 R16 $2 green 70.00 2.50
Cut cancel .45
a. Surcharged as No. R185 150.00 90.00
b. Surcharged as No. R185, in violet *2,000.* —
c. As "a," double surcharge *150.00*
d. As "a," triple surcharge *2,500.*
e. Pair, Nos. R191c and R191d *5,000.*
R192 R16 $5 green 325.00 42.50
Cut cancel 5.00
a. Surcharge omitted 400.00
b. Pair, one without surcharge *700.00*
R193 R16 $10 green 525.00 225.00
Cut cancel 80.00
R194 R16 $50 green 3,000. 1,250.
Cut cancel 500.00

R20

Inscribed "Series of 1914"

Offset Printing

1914 **Wmk. 190** ***Perf. 10***

R195 R20 ½c rose 16.00 5.00
R196 R20 1c rose 3.50 .30
R197 R20 2c rose 5.00 .30
R198 R20 3c rose 125.00 40.00
R199 R20 4c rose 35.00 2.50
R200 R20 5c rose 12.00 .40
R201 R20 10c rose 10.00 .25
R202 R20 25c rose 60.00 .60
R203 R20 40c rose 40.00 3.00
R204 R20 50c rose 15.00 .35
R205 R20 80c rose 250.00 17.00
Nos. R195-R205 (11) 571.50 69.70

Wmk. 191R

R206 R20 ½c rose 1.60 .50
R207 R20 1c rose .25 .25
R208 R20 2c rose .30 .25
R209 R20 3c rose 1.50 .25
R210 R20 4c rose 4.50 .50
R211 R20 5c rose 2.00 .35
R212 R20 10c rose .80 .25
R213 R20 25c rose 10.00 1.50
R214 R20 40c rose 150.00 15.00
Cut cancel .50
R215 R20 50c rose 35.00 .40
Cut cancel .25
R216 R20 80c rose 225.00 35.00
Cut cancel 1.25
Nos. R206-R216 (11) 430.95 54.25

Liberty — R21

Inscribed "Series 1914"

Engr.

R217 R21 $1 green 100.00 .55
Cut cancel .25
a. $1 yellow green 85.00 .25
R218 R21 $2 carmine 175.00 1.00
Cut cancel .25
R219 R21 $3 purple 200.00 5.00
Cut cancel .80
R220 R21 $5 blue 140.00 4.50
Cut cancel .65
R221 R21 $10 yel org 400.00 7.50
Cut cancel 1.10
R222 R21 $30 vermilion 1,000. 21.00
Cut cancel 2.25
R223 R21 $50 violet 2,000. 1,250.
Cut cancel 600.00

See Nos. R240-R245, R257-R259, R276-R281.

Portrait Types of 1899 Inscribed "Series of 1915" (#R224), or "Series of 1914"
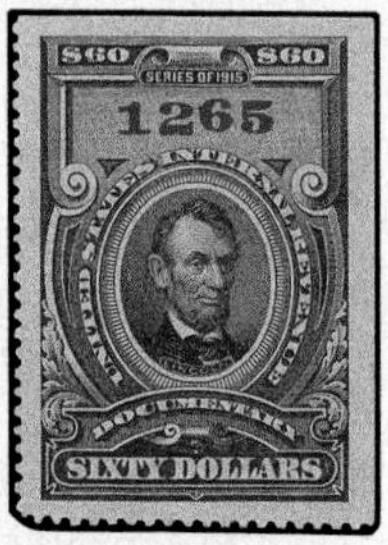

1914-15 **Without Gum** ***Perf. 12***

R224 R19 $60 brown *(Lincoln)* 300. 150.00
Cut cancel 70.00
R225 R17 $100 green *(Washington)* 90. 45.00
Cut cancel 16.00
R226 R18 $500 blue *(Hamilton)* 13,000. 650.00
Cut cancel 275.00
R227 R19 $1000 orange *(Madison)* — 750.00
Cut cancel 325.00

The stamps of types R17, R18 and R19 in this and subsequent issues were issued in vertical strips of 4 which are imperforate at the top, bottom and right side; therefore, single stamps are always imperforate on one or two sides.

R22

Offset Printing

1917 **Wmk. 191R** ***Perf. 11***

R228 R22 1c carmine rose .35 .25
R229 R22 2c carmine rose .25 .25
R230 R22 3c carmine rose 1.75 .40
R231 R22 4c carmine rose .75 .25
R232 R22 5c carmine rose .30 .25
R233 R22 8c carmine rose 3.00 .35
R234 R22 10c carmine rose .40 .25
R235 R22 20c carmine rose .75 .25
R236 R22 25c carmine rose 1.75 .25
R237 R22 40c carmine rose 2.25 .50
R238 R22 50c carmine rose 2.50 .25
R239 R22 80c carmine rose 9.00 .35
Nos. R228-R239 (12) 23.05 3.60

Liberty Type of 1914 without "Series 1914"

1917-33 **Engr.**

R240 R21 $1 yellow green 15.00 .30
a. $1 green 9.50 .25
R241 R21 $2 rose 25.00 .25
R242 R21 $3 violet 90.00 1.50
Cut cancel .30
R243 R21 $4 yellow brown ('33) 60.00 2.00
Cut cancel .30
R244 R21 $5 dark blue 40.00 .35
Cut cancel .25
R245 R21 $10 orange 90.00 1.40
Cut cancel .30

Portrait Types of 1899 without "Series of" and Date
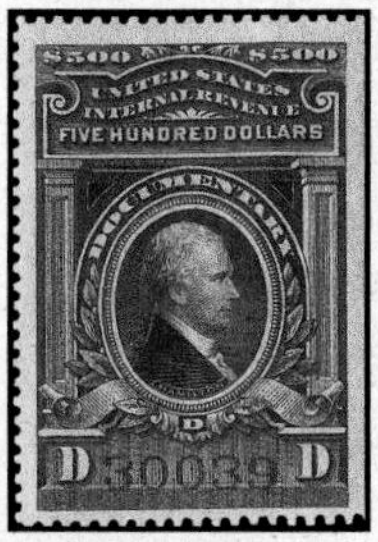

Portraits: $30, Grant. $60, Lincoln. $100, Washington. $500, Hamilton. $1,000, Madison.

1917 **Without Gum** ***Perf. 12***

R246 R17 $30 dp org, green numerals 65.00 13.00
Cut cancel 2.25
a. As "b," imperf. pair *1,000.*
b. Numerals in blue 150.00 3.50
Cut cancel 1.50
R247 R19 $60 brown 75.00 8.00
Cut cancel .85
R248 R17 $100 green 55.00 2.00
Cut cancel .50
R249 R18 $500 blue, red numerals 350.00 50.00
Cut cancel 15.00
a. Numerals in orange 425.00 65.00
Cut cancel 20.00
R250 R19 $1000 orange 200.00 20.00
Cut cancel 7.50
a. Imperf., pair *2,000.*

See note after No. R227.

1928-29 **Offset Printing** ***Perf. 10***

R251 R22 1c carmine rose 2.10 1.60
R252 R22 2c carmine rose .60 .30
R253 R22 4c carmine rose 7.00 4.00
R254 R22 5c carmine rose 1.75 .55
R255 R22 10c carmine rose 2.75 1.25
R256 R22 20c carmine rose 6.00 4.50

Engr.

R257 R21 $1 green 200.00 45.00
Cut cancel 5.00
R258 R21 $2 rose 90.00 5.00
R259 R21 $10 orange 325.00 75.00
Cut cancel 30.00

1929 **Offset Printing** ***Perf. 11x10***

R260 R22 2c carmine rose ('30) 3.00 2.75
R261 R22 5c carmine rose ('30) 2.00 1.90
R262 R22 10c carmine rose 9.25 6.75
R263 R22 20c carmine rose 15.00 8.25

Used values for Nos. R264-R734 are for stamps which are neither cut nor perforated with initials. Examples with cut cancellations or perforated initials are valued in the Scott U. S. Specialized Catalogue.

Types of 1917-33 Overprinted in Black

SERIES 1940

Offset Printing

1940 **Wmk. 191R** ***Perf. 11***

R264 R22 1c rose pink 3.75 2.40
R265 R22 2c rose pink 5.00 2.25
R266 R22 3c rose pink 11.00 5.00
R267 R22 4c rose pink 5.00 .80
R268 R22 5c rose pink 5.00 1.25
R269 R22 8c rose pink 22.50 17.00
R270 R22 10c rose pink 2.50 .65
R271 R22 20c rose pink 3.25 .80
R272 R22 25c rose pink 8.00 1.50
R273 R22 40c rose pink 6.75 .90
R274 R22 50c rose pink 11.00 .55
R275 R22 80c rose pink 14.00 1.75

Engr.

R276 R21 $1 green 80.00 1.25
R277 R21 $2 rose 80.00 2.00
R278 R21 $3 violet 115.00 37.50
b. Vert. pair, imperf. horiz. *750.00*

Only one example of No. R278b is recorded. It is thinned and is valued thus.

R279 R21 $4 yellow brown 210.00 35.00
R280 R21 $5 dark blue 100.00 20.00
R281 R21 $10 orange 275.00 50.00

Types of 1917 Handstamped "Series 1940" like R264-R281

1940 **Wmk. 191R** ***Perf. 12***

Without Gum

R282 R17 $30 vermilion (B, G) 1,250.
a. With black 2-line handstamp in larger type *25,000.*
R283 R19 $60 brown (B, G) 2,400.
a. As #R282a, cut cancel *12,500.*
R284 R17 $100 green (B) 4,500.
R285 R18 $500 blue (V) 3,000.
a. As #R282a *3,250.* *4,000.*
R286 R19 $1000 orange (B, G) 1,250.
b. Double overprint, cut cancel —

Types of 1917 Handstamped with black 2-line "Series 1941" in larger type.

1941

R287 R17 $30 vermilion *35,000.*
R287A R19 $60 brown 35,000.

Alexander Hamilton R23

Levi Woodbury R24

Overprinted in Black SERIES 1940

Various Portraits: 2c, Oliver Wolcott, Jr. 3c, Samuel Dexter. 4c, Albert Gallatin. 5c. G. W. Campbell. 8c, Alexander Dallas. 10c, William H. Crawford. 20c, Richard Rush. 25c, S. D. Ingham. 40c. Louis McLane. 50c, William J. Duane. 80c, Roger B. Taney. $2, Thomas Ewing. $3, Walter Forward. $4, J. C. Spencer. $5, G. M. Bibb. $10, R. J. Walker. $20, William M. Meredith.

1940 **Engr.** **Wmk. 191R** ***Perf. 11***

R288 R23 1c carmine 5.75 4.50
a. Imperf, pair, without gum *250.00*
R289 R23 2c carmine 8.50 4.00
a. Imperf, pair, without gum *250.00*
R290 R23 3c carmine 30.00 12.00
a. Imperf, pair, without gum *250.00*
R291 R23 4c carmine 62.50 27.50
a. Imperf, pair, without gum *250.00*
R292 R23 5c carmine 4.75 .80
a. Imperf, pair, without gum *250.00*
R293 R23 8c carmine 85.00 60.00
a. Imperf, pair, without gum *250.00*
R294 R23 10c carmine 4.25 .60
a. Imperf, pair, without gum *250.00*
R295 R23 20c carmine 5.50 4.25
a. Imperf, pair, without gum *250.00*
R296 R23 25c carmine 5.00 .75
a. Imperf, pair, without gum *250.00*
R297 R23 40c carmine 75.00 30.00
a. Imperf, pair, without gum *250.00*
R298 R23 50c carmine 8.00 .60
a. Imperf, pair, without gum *250.00*
R299 R23 80c carmine 200.00 110.00
a. Imperf, pair, without gum *475.00*

R300 R24 $1 carmine 50.00 .60
a. Imperf, pair, without gum *250.00*
R301 R24 $2 carmine 100.00 .90
a. Imperf, pair, without gum —
R302 R24 $3 carmine 190.00 95.00
a. Imperf, pair, without gum *1,400.*
R303 R24 $4 carmine 150.00 50.00
a. Imperf, pair, without gum —
R304 R24 $5 carmine 85.00 3.00
a. Imperf, pair, without gum —
R305 R24 $10 carmine 150.00 10.00
R305A R24 $20 carmine *3,000.* 1,750.
b. Imperf, pair, without gum *700.00*

Thomas Corwin — R25

Various Frames and Portraits: $50, James Guthrie. $60, Howell Cobb. $100, P. F. Thomas. $500, J. A. Dix, $1,000, S. P. Chase.

Perf. 12

Without Gum

R306	R25	$30 car	350.00	75.00
R306A	R25	$50 car	—	*8,500.*
R307	R25	$60 car	450.00	100.00
a.		Vert. pair, imperf. btwn.	*2,750.*	*1,500.*
R308	R25	$100 car	375.00	100.00
R309	R25	$500 car	—	5,000.
R310	R25	$1000 car	—	

The $30 to $1,000 denominations in this and following similar issues, and the $2,500, $5,000 and $10,000 stamps of 1952-58 have straight edges on one or two sides. They were issued without gum through No. R723.

Editors would like to see a used uncut example of No. R310.

Nos. R288-R310 Overprinted

SERIES 1941

1941		Wmk. 191R		*Perf. 11*
R311	R23	1c carmine	5.00	2.75
R312	R23	2c carmine	5.25	1.10
R313	R23	3c carmine	10.00	4.25
R314	R23	4c carmine	7.50	1.75
R315	R23	5c carmine	1.50	.40
R316	R23	8c carmine	21.00	8.50
R317	R23	10c carmine	2.00	.35
R318	R23	20c carmine	4.75	.65
R319	R23	25c carmine	2.40	.65
R320	R23	40c carmine	16.00	3.25
R321	R23	50c carmine	3.50	.30
R322	R23	80c carmine	65.00	12.00
R323	R24	$1 carmine	15.00	.30
R324	R24	$2 carmine	20.00	.50
R325	R24	$3 carmine	32.50	3.50
R326	R24	$4 carmine	47.50	27.50
R327	R24	$5 carmine	60.00	1.10
R328	R24	$10 carmine	100.00	6.00
R329	R24	$20 carmine	850.00	500.00

Perf. 12

Without Gum

R330	R25	$30 car	275.00	55.00
R331	R25	$50 car	1,500.	1,000.
R332	R25	$60 car	275.00	87.50
R333	R25	$100 car	140.00	37.50
R334	R25	$500 car	—	375.00
R335	R25	$1000 car	1,500.	225.00

Nos. R288-R310 Overprinted

SERIES 1942

1942		Wmk. 191R		*Perf. 11*
R336	R23	1c carmine	2.00	.60
R337	R23	2c carmine	2.00	.60
R338	R23	3c carmine	2.00	.80
R339	R23	4c carmine	3.00	1.10
R340	R23	5c carmine	.60	.35
R341	R23	8c carmine	9.50	4.75
R342	R23	10c carmine	1.75	.35
R343	R23	20c carmine	4.50	.60
R344	R23	25c carmine	3.00	.55
R345	R23	40c carmine	6.50	1.75
R346	R23	50c carmine	4.00	.35
R347	R23	80c carmine	27.50	13.00
R348	R24	$1 carmine	12.50	.25
R349	R24	$2 carmine	15.00	.30
R350	R24	$3 carmine	27.50	3.25
R351	R24	$4 carmine	35.00	7.50
R352	R24	$5 carmine	37.50	1.50
R353	R24	$10 carmine	85.00	3.75
R354	R24	$20 carmine	300.00	45.00
a.		Imperf., perf. initials		—

Perf. 12

Without Gum

R355	R25	$30 carmine	125.00	42.50
R356	R25	$50 carmine	2,250.	1,400.
R357	R25	$60 carmine	*5,000.*	1,500.
R358	R25	$100 carmine	325.00	175.00
R359	R25	$500 carmine	*2,000.*	275.00
R360	R25	$1000 carmine	6,500.	175.00

Nos. R288-R310 Overprinted

1943		Wmk. 191R		*Perf. 11*
R361	R23	1c carmine	.80	.65
R362	R23	2c carmine	.65	.55
R363	R23	3c carmine	3.75	3.50
R364	R23	4c carmine	1.60	1.50
R365	R23	5c carmine	.70	.45
R366	R23	8c carmine	6.00	4.00
R367	R23	10c carmine	.85	.30
R368	R23	20c carmine	2.50	.80
R369	R23	25c carmine	2.75	.50
R370	R23	40c carmine	7.50	4.00
R371	R23	50c carmine	2.00	.30
R372	R23	80c carmine	27.50	8.00
R373	R24	$1 carmine	9.00	.35
R374	R24	$2 carmine	18.00	.35
R375	R24	$3 carmine	30.00	3.00
R376	R24	$4 carmine	55.00	10.00
R377	R24	$5 carmine	52.50	.75
R378	R24	$10 carmine	85.00	5.00
R379	R24	$20 carmine	350.00	60.00

Perf. 12

Without Gum

R380	R25	$30 carmine	225.00	25.00
R381	R25	$50 carmine	250.00	75.00
R382	R25	$60 carmine	375.00	125.00
R383	R25	$100 carmine	50.00	22.50
R384	R25	$500 carmine	*800.00*	325.00
R385	R25	$1000 carmine	*800.00*	200.00

Nos. R288-R310 Overprinted

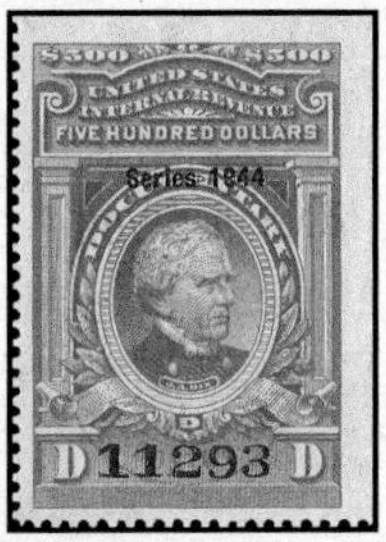

1944		Wmk. 191R		*Perf. 11*
R386	R23	1c carmine	.50	.45
R387	R23	2c carmine	.65	.55
R388	R23	3c carmine	.65	.40
R389	R23	4c carmine	.75	.65
R390	R23	5c carmine	.40	.25
R391	R23	8c carmine	2.25	1.75
R392	R23	10c carmine	.50	.25
R393	R23	20c carmine	1.10	.35
R394	R23	25c carmine	2.00	.30
R395	R23	40c carmine	3.75	.80
R396	R23	50c carmine	4.00	.35
R397	R23	80c carmine	21.00	5.50
R398	R24	$1 carmine	10.00	.30
R399	R24	$2 carmine	15.00	.45
R400	R24	$3 carmine	25.00	2.40
R401	R24	$4 carmine	32.50	11.50
R402	R24	$5 carmine	32.50	.50
R403	R24	$10 carmine	65.00	1.60
R404	R24	$20 carmine	275.00	19.00

Perf. 12

Without Gum

R405	R25	$30 carmine	110.00	35.00
R406	R25	$50 carmine	50.00	22.50
R407	R25	$60 carmine	350.00	75.00
R408	R25	$100 carmine	70.00	12.50
R409	R25	$500 carmine	—	*3,250.*
R410	R25	$1000 carmine	*4,000.*	500.00

Nos. R288-R310 Overprinted

1945		Wmk. 191R		*Perf. 11*
R411	R23	1c carmine	.40	.30
R412	R23	2c carmine	.40	.30
R413	R23	3c carmine	.75	.50
R414	R23	4c carmine	.45	.35
R415	R23	5c carmine	.45	.30
R416	R23	8c carmine	6.25	2.75
R417	R23	10c carmine	1.25	.25
R418	R23	20c carmine	8.00	1.50
R419	R23	25c carmine	1.75	.30
R420	R23	40c carmine	9.00	1.25
R421	R23	50c carmine	4.00	.25
R422	R23	80c carmine	26.00	14.00
R423	R24	$1 carmine	13.50	.30
R424	R24	$2 carmine	13.50	.40
R425	R24	$3 carmine	27.50	3.00
R426	R24	$4 carmine	35.00	4.25
R427	R24	$5 carmine	35.00	.50
R428	R24	$10 carmine	65.00	2.50
R429	R24	$20 carmine	200.00	16.00

Perf. 12

Without Gum

R430	R25	$30 carmine	250.00	40.00
R431	R25	$50 carmine	230.00	45.00
R432	R25	$60 carmine	450.00	80.00
R433	R25	$100 carmine	50.00	20.00
R434	R25	$500 carmine	750.00	325.00
R435	R25	$1000 carmine	500.00	125.00

Nos. R288-R310 Overprinted

Series 1946

1946		Wmk. 191R		*Perf. 11*
R436	R23	1c carmine	.30	.30
R437	R23	2c carmine	.45	.35
R438	R23	3c carmine	.55	.40
R439	R23	4c carmine	.80	.65
R440	R23	5c carmine	.45	.30
R441	R23	8c carmine	2.50	2.00
R442	R23	10c carmine	1.10	.30
R443	R23	20c carmine	1.75	.50
R444	R23	25c carmine	6.00	.35
R445	R23	40c carmine	4.50	.85
R446	R23	50c carmine	6.00	.30
R447	R23	80c carmine	17.50	5.00
R448	R24	$1 carmine	16.00	.30
R449	R24	$2 carmine	19.00	.30
R450	R24	$3 carmine	27.50	5.00
R451	R24	$4 carmine	60.00	20.00
R452	R24	$5 carmine	40.00	.50
R453	R24	$10 carmine	72.50	1.75
R454	R24	$20 carmine	200.00	16.00

Perf. 12

Without Gum

R455	R25	$30 carmine	75.00	17.50
R456	R25	$50 carmine	65.00	12.50
R457	R25	$60 carmine	110.00	22.50
R458	R25	$100 carmine	90.00	12.50
R459	R25	$500 carmine	*1,750.*	150.00
R460	R25	$1000 carmine	*750.00*	160.00

Nos. R288-R310 Overprinted

Series 1947

1947		Wmk. 191R		*Perf. 11*
R461	R23	1c carmine	.85	.55
R462	R23	2c carmine	.75	.55
R463	R23	3c carmine	.85	.55
R464	R23	4c carmine	.90	.75
R465	R23	5c carmine	.55	.40
R466	R23	8c carmine	1.75	.80
R467	R23	10c carmine	1.40	.30
R468	R23	20c carmine	2.25	.55
R469	R23	25c carmine	3.00	.70
R470	R23	40c carmine	5.50	1.10
R471	R23	50c carmine	3.75	.40
R472	R23	80c carmine	12.00	8.00
R473	R24	$1 carmine	8.25	.35
R474	R24	$2 carmine	14.00	.65
R475	R24	$3 carmine	17.50	6.00
R476	R24	$4 carmine	19.00	5.00
R477	R24	$5 carmine	27.50	.60
R478	R24	$10 carmine	67.50	3.00
R479	R24	$20 carmine	110.00	14.00

Perf. 12

Without Gum

R480	R25	$30 carmine	180.00	27.50
R481	R25	$50 carmine	150.00	17.50
R482	R25	$60 carmine	250.00	60.00
R483	R25	$100 carmine	85.00	15.00
R484	R25	$500 carmine	*900.00*	250.00
R485	R25	$1000 carmine	*550.00*	100.00

Nos. R288-R310 Overprinted

1948		Wmk. 191R		*Perf. 11*
R486	R23	1c carmine	.35	.30
R487	R23	2c carmine	.50	.45
R488	R23	3c carmine	.60	.40
R489	R23	4c carmine	.55	.40
R490	R23	5c carmine	.50	.25
R491	R23	8c carmine	1.00	.50
R492	R23	10c carmine	1.00	.25
R493	R23	20c carmine	2.50	.40
R494	R23	25c carmine	2.25	.30
R495	R23	40c carmine	7.00	1.75
R496	R23	50c carmine	2.50	.30
R497	R23	80c carmine	12.00	8.00
R498	R24	$1 carmine	10.50	.30
R499	R24	$2 carmine	18.00	.40
R500	R24	$3 carmine	24.00	3.50
R501	R24	$4 carmine	35.00	4.00
R502	R24	$5 carmine	30.00	.50
R503	R24	$10 carmine	70.00	1.50
a.		Pair, one dated "1946"		—
R504	R24	$20 carmine	400.00	18.00

Perf. 12

Without Gum

R505	R25	$30 carmine	150.00	35.00
R506	R25	$50 carmine	180.00	27.50
a.		Vert. pair, imperf. btwn.	*2,500.*	
R507	R25	$60 carmine	300.00	75.00
a.		Vert. pair, imperf. btwn.	*4,250.*	
R508	R25	$100 carmine	140.00	20.00
a.		Vert. pair, imperf. btwn.	*2,000.*	

No. R508a is known as four used singles, all four positions from a single pane of four, clearly imperf. horiz. before being separated.

R509	R25	$500 carmine	1,500.	200.00
R510	R25	$1000 carmine	450.00	125.00

Nos. R288-R310 Overprinted

Series 1949

1949		Wmk. 191R		*Perf. 11*
R511	R23	1c carmine	.40	.35
R512	R23	2c carmine	.75	.45
R513	R23	3c carmine	.60	.50
R514	R23	4c carmine	.80	.60
R515	R23	5c carmine	.55	.30
R516	R23	8c carmine	1.00	.70
R517	R23	10c carmine	.60	.35
R518	R23	20c carmine	1.75	.75
R519	R23	25c carmine	2.25	.85
R520	R23	40c carmine	6.50	2.75
R521	R23	50c carmine	5.00	.40
R522	R23	80c carmine	15.00	7.50
R523	R24	$1 carmine	13.50	.85
R524	R24	$2 carmine	17.00	2.50
R525	R24	$3 carmine	27.50	8.00
R526	R24	$4 carmine	30.00	8.00
R527	R24	$5 carmine	32.50	4.25
R528	R24	$10 carmine	72.50	5.25
R529	R24	$20 carmine	150.00	15.00

Perf. 12

Without Gum

R530	R25	$30 carmine	200.00	35.00
R531	R25	$50 carmine	210.00	60.00
R532	R25	$60 carmine	350.00	70.00
R533	R25	$100 carmine	100.00	21.00
R534	R25	$500 carmine	*1,250.*	260.00
R535	R25	$1000 carmine	*1,000.*	160.00

Nos. R288-R310 Overprinted

Series 1950

1950		Wmk. 191R		*Perf. 11*
R536	R23	1c carmine	.40	.25
R537	R23	2c carmine	.40	.35
R538	R23	3c carmine	.50	.40
R539	R23	4c carmine	.70	.50
R540	R23	5c carmine	.45	.35
R541	R23	8c carmine	1.75	.80
R542	R23	10c carmine	.80	.30
R543	R23	20c carmine	1.40	.45
R544	R23	25c carmine	2.00	.45
R545	R23	40c carmine	6.00	2.10
R546	R23	50c carmine	8.00	.35
R547	R23	80c carmine	15.00	8.50
R548	R24	$1 carmine	15.00	.40
R549	R24	$2 carmine	17.50	2.75
R550	R24	$3 carmine	20.00	6.00
R551	R24	$4 carmine	27.50	7.50
R552	R24	$5 carmine	35.00	1.00
R553	R24	$10 carmine	70.00	10.00
R554	R24	$20 carmine	150.00	15.00

Perf. 12
Without Gum

R555	R25	$30 carmine	150.00	70.00
R556	R25	$50 carmine	125.00	22.50
a.		Vert. pair, imperf. horiz.		—
R557	R25	$60 carmine	260.00	75.00
R558	R25	$100 carmine	100.00	22.50
R559	R25	$500 carmine	*1,250.*	125.00
R560	R25	$1000 carmine	*900.00*	95.00

Nos. R288-R310 Overprinted

Series 1951

1951 Wmk. 191R *Perf. 11*

R561	R23	1c carmine	.30	.25
R562	R23	2c carmine	.30	.35
R563	R23	3c carmine	.30	.35
R564	R23	4c carmine	.30	.35
R565	R23	5c carmine	.30	.35
R566	R23	8c carmine	1.25	.45
R567	R23	10c carmine	.30	.35
R568	R23	20c carmine	.30	.55
R569	R23	25c carmine	.30	.50
R570	R23	40c carmine	3.75	1.60
R571	R23	50c carmine	3.00	.60
R572	R23	80c carmine	10.00	3.25
R573	R24	$1 carmine	16.00	.30
R574	R24	$2 carmine	21.00	.55
R575	R24	$3 carmine	16.00	4.00
R576	R24	$4 carmine	20.00	12.50
R577	R24	$5 carmine	10.00	.70
R578	R24	$10 carmine	18.00	2.50
R579	R24	$20 carmine	55.00	16.00

Perf. 12
Without Gum

R580	R25	$30 carmine	150.00	25.00
a.		Imperf., pair	*2,500.*	*2,000.*
R581	R25	$50 carmine	300.00	45.00
R582	R25	$60 carmine	375.00	75.00
R583	R25	$100 carmine	90.00	25.00
R584	R25	$500 carmine	*900.00*	175.00
R585	R25	$1000 carmine	*750.00*	150.00

No. R583 is known imperf horizontally. It exists as a reconstructed used vertical strip of 4 that was separated into single stamps.

Documentary Stamps and Types of 1940 Overprinted in Black

Series 1952

Designs: 55c, $1.10, $1.65, $2.20, $2.75, $3.30, L. J. Gage; $2500, William Windom; $5000, C. J. Folger; $10,000, W. Q. Gresham.

1952 Wmk. 191R *Perf. 11*

R586	R23	1c carmine	.35	.30
R587	R23	2c carmine	.50	.35
R588	R23	3c carmine	.40	.35
R589	R23	4c carmine	.45	.30
R590	R23	5c carmine	.35	.30
R591	R23	8c carmine	.90	.60
R592	R23	10c carmine	.50	.30
R593	R23	20c carmine	1.25	.40
R594	R23	25c carmine	2.50	.45
R595	R23	40c carmine	6.00	1.75
R596	R23	50c carmine	3.50	.30
R597	R23	55c carmine	.60	15.00
R598	R23	80c carmine	19.00	4.00
R599	R24	$1 carmine	7.00	1.50
R600	R24	$1.10 carmine	25.00	30.00
R601	R24	$1.65 carmine	175.00	62.50
R602	R24	$2 carmine	17.00	.90
R603	R24	$2.20 carmine	160.00	70.00
R604	R24	$2.75 carmine	190.00	70.00
R605	R24	$3 carmine	32.50	6.00
a.		Horiz. pair, imperf. btwn.	*1,300.*	
R606	R24	$3.30 carmine	225.00	90.00
R607	R24	$4 carmine	37.50	6.00
R608	R24	$5 carmine	32.50	1.25
R609	R24	$10 carmine	60.00	1.25
R610	R24	$20 carmine	92.50	16.00

Perf. 12
Without Gum

R611	R25	$30 carmine	90.00	27.50
R612	R25	$50 carmine	95.00	35.00
R613	R25	$60 carmine	600.00	70.00
R614	R25	$100 carmine	110.00	10.00
R615	R25	$500 carmine	*750.00*	160.00
R616	R25	$1000 carmine	*325.00*	75.00
R617	R25	$2500 carmine	*1,250.*	275.00
R618	R25	$5000 carmine	—	*5,000.*
R619	R25	$10,000 carmine	*1,750.*	*1,400.*

Documentary Stamps and Types of 1940 Overprinted in Black

Series 1953

1953 Wmk. 191R *Perf. 11*

R620	R23	1c carmine	.40	.35
R621	R23	2c carmine	.40	.30
R622	R23	3c carmine	.45	.35
R623	R23	4c carmine	.60	.45
R624	R23	5c carmine	.50	.30
a.		Vert. pair, imperf. horiz.		*1,150.*
R625	R23	8c carmine	1.10	.85
R626	R23	10c carmine	.65	.35
R627	R23	20c carmine	1.50	.50
R628	R23	25c carmine	1.75	.65
R629	R23	40c carmine	2.50	.90
R630	R23	50c carmine	3.00	.35
R631	R23	55c carmine	7.00	2.00
a.		Horiz. pair, imperf. vert.	*550.00*	
R632	R23	80c carmine	10.00	2.10
R633	R24	$1 carmine	5.25	.35
R634	R24	$1.10 carmine	12.00	2.50
a.		Horiz. pair, imperf. vert.	*700.00*	
b.		Imperf. pair	*850.00*	
R635	R24	$1.65 carmine	12.00	4.50
R636	R24	$2 carmine	9.00	.75
R637	R24	$2.20 carmine	20.00	6.00
R638	R24	$2.75 carmine	1.75	7.00
R639	R24	$3 carmine	17.00	4.00
R640	R24	$3.30 carmine	50.00	17.50
R641	R24	$4 carmine	40.00	15.00
R642	R24	$5 carmine	27.50	1.25
R643	R24	$10 carmine	60.00	2.25
R644	R24	$20 carmine	140.00	22.50

Perf. 12
Without Gum

R645	R25	$30 car	175.00	40.00
R646	R25	$50 car	175.00	50.00
R647	R25	$60 car	1,000.	425.00
R648	R25	$100 car	70.00	15.00
R649	R25	$500 car	*3,500.*	175.00
R650	R25	$1000 car	800.00	80.00
R651	R25	$2500 car	2,000.	1,750.
R652	R25	$5000 car	—	*7,500.*
R653	R25	$10,000 car	—	*4,250.*

In 1955, the BEP began printing flat plate documentary stamps Nos. R654-R681 using the dry-printing method. This method used paper with a 5-10% moisture content versus the 15-35% moisture content for the wet printing. The dry-printed stamps from the same plates are .25-.75mm larger than the wet-printed examples. Four sub-varieties are known: (1) wet printing with ridged yellow gum, (2) wet printing with smooth yellow gum, (3) dry printing with smooth yellow gum, and (4) dry printing with smooth white gum.

Types of 1940
Without Overprint

1954 Wmk. 191R *Perf. 11*

R654	R23	1c carmine	.25	.25
a.		Horiz. pair, imperf. vert.	*1,500.*	
R655	R23	2c carmine	.25	.30
R656	R23	3c carmine	.25	.30
R657	R23	4c carmine	.25	.30
R658	R23	5c carmine	.25	.25
a.		Vert. pair, imperf. horiz.	—	
R659	R23	8c carmine	.25	.25
R660	R23	10c carmine	.25	.25
R661	R23	20c carmine	.30	.40
R662	R23	25c carmine	.35	.45
R663	R23	40c carmine	.75	.60
R664	R23	50c carmine	1.00	.25
a.		Horiz. pair, imperf. vert.	900.00	
R665	R23	55c carmine	.90	1.25
R666	R23	80c carmine	1.50	1.90
R667	R24	$1 carmine	.90	.35
R668	R24	$1.10 carmine	2.00	2.50
R669	R24	$1.65 carmine	25.00	25.00
R670	R24	$2 carmine	1.00	.45
R671	R24	$2.20 carmine	2.25	3.75
R672	R24	$2.75 carmine	25.00	55.00
R673	R24	$3 carmine	2.00	2.00
R674	R24	$3.30 carmine	3.50	5.00
R675	R24	$4 carmine	2.75	4.00
R676	R24	$5 carmine	3.25	.50
R677	R24	$10 carmine	5.00	1.50
R678	R24	$20 carmine	10.00	6.50

Documentary Stamps & Type of 1940 Ovptd. in Black

1954 Wmk. 191R *Perf. 12*
Without Gum

R679	R25	$30 carmine	55.00	17.50
a.		Booklet pane of 4	*225.00*	
R680	R25	$50 carmine	55.00	29.00
a.		Booklet pane of 4	*225.00*	
R681	R25	$60 carmine	55.00	30.00
a.		Booklet pane of 4	*225.00*	
R682	R25	$100 carmine	55.00	7.50
a.		Booklet pane of 4	*225.00*	
R683	R25	$500 carmine	*150.00*	87.50
a.		Booklet pane of 4	*600.00*	
R684	R25	$1000 carmine	200.00	90.00
a.		Booklet pane of 4	*1,200.*	
R685	R25	$2500 carmine	*250.00*	350.00
a.		Booklet pane of 4	*1,400.*	
R686	R25	$5000 carmine	*1,750.*	*2,750.*
a.		Booklet pane of 4	*7,000.*	
R687	R25	$10,000 carmine	*1,000.*	*2,250.*
a.		Booklet pane of 4	*7,000.*	

Documentary Stamps and Type of 1940 Overprinted in Black

1955 Wmk. 191R *Perf. 12*
Without Gum

R688	R25	$30 carmine	110.00	17.50
R689	R25	$50 carmine	125.00	30.00
R690	R25	$60 carmine	200.00	45.00
R691	R25	$100 carmine	160.00	20.00
R692	R25	$500 carmine	1,250.	200.00
R693	R25	$1000 carmine	*1,800.*	80.00
R694	R25	$2500 carmine	*1,250.*	275.00
R695	R25	$5000 carmine	*4,000.*	*2,000.*
R696	R25	$10,000 carmine	—	1,250.

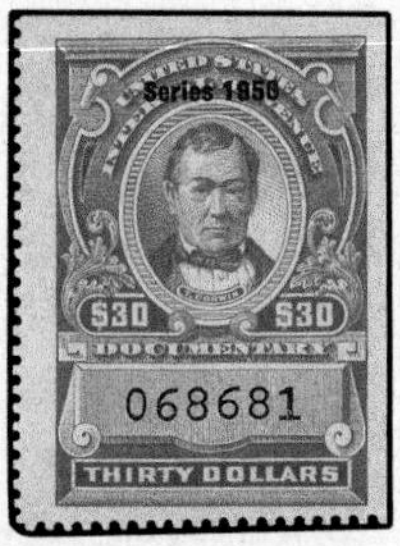

Documentary Stamps and Type of 1940 Overprinted

1956 Wmk. 191R *Perf. 12*
Without Gum

R697	R25	$30 carmine	180.00	20.00
R698	R25	$50 carmine	300.00	27.50
R699	R25	$60 carmine	250.00	60.00
R700	R25	$100 carmine	125.00	15.00
R701	R25	$500 carmine	*1,500.*	150.00
R702	R25	$1000 carmine	*1,750.*	100.00
R703	R25	$2500 carmine	—	750.00
R704	R25	$5000 carmine	—	2,000.
R705	R25	$10,000 carmine	—	750.00

Documentary Stamps and Type of 1940 Overprinted

1957 Wmk. 191R *Perf. 12*
Without Gum

R706	R25	$30 carmine	275.00	60.00
R707	R25	$50 carmine	160.00	47.50
R708	R25	$60 carmine	*1,500.*	400.00
R709	R25	$100 carmine	140.00	20.00
R710	R25	$500 carmine	900.00	200.00
R711	R25	$1000 carmine	*4,000.*	100.00
R712	R25	$2500 carmine	—	1,200.
R713	R25	$5000 carmine	*4,250.*	1,800.
R714	R25	$10,000 carmine	—	650.00

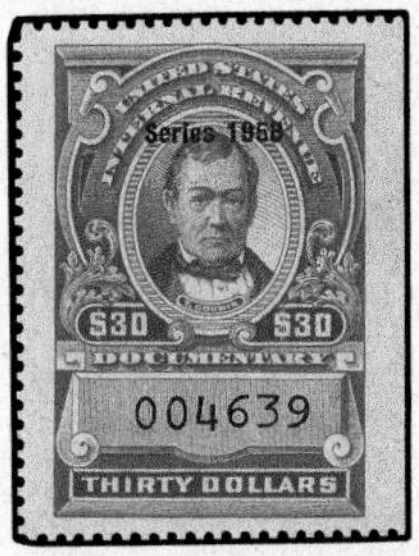

Documentary Stamps and Type of 1940 Overprinted in Black

1958 Wmk. 191R *Perf. 12*
Without Gum

R715	R25	$30 carmine	140.00	27.50
R716	R25	$50 carmine	190.00	35.00
R717	R25	$60 carmine	210.00	42.50
R718	R25	$100 carmine	225.00	15.00
R719	R25	$500 carmine	600.00	125.00
R720	R25	$1000 carmine	*2,750.*	90.00
R721	R25	$2500 carmine	—	1,500.
R722	R25	$5000 carmine	—	*4,250.*
R723	R25	$10,000 carmine	—	2,750.

Documentary Stamps and Type of 1940 Without Overprint

1958 Wmk. 191R *Perf. 12*
With Gum

R724	R25	$30 carmine	11.00	7.00
a.		Booklet pane of 4	*57.50*	
b.		Vert. pair, imperf. horiz.	*3,000.*	
R725	R25	$50 carmine	12.00	7.00
a.		Booklet pane of 4	*60.00*	
b.		Vert. pair, imperf. horiz.		*3,500.*
R726	R25	$60 carmine	17.50	21.00
a.		Booklet pane of 4	*90.00*	
R727	R25	$100 carmine	13.00	4.75
a.		Booklet pane of 4	*65.00*	
R728	R25	$500 carmine	17.50	26.00
a.		Booklet pane of 4	*90.00*	
R729	R25	$1000 carmine	16.00	21.00
a.		Booklet pane of 4	*80.00*	
b.		Vert. pair, imperf. horiz.		*1,750.*
c.		Vert. pair, imperf. btwn.	*1,500.*	
R730	R25	$2500 carmine	*125.00*	175.00
a.		Booklet pane of 4	*600.00*	
R731	R25	$5000 carmine	200.00	175.00
a.		Booklet pane of 4	*850.00*	
R732	R25	$10,000 carmine	*200.00*	140.00
a.		Booklet pane of 4	*850.00*	

Internal Revenue Building, Washington, DC — R26

Centenary of the Internal Revenue Service.

Giori Press Printing

1962, July 2 Unwmk. *Perf. 11*

R733	R26	10c violet blue & bright green	1.00	.40
		Never hinged	1.25	

1963

"Established 1862" Removed

R734	R26	10c violet blue & bright green	3.00	.70
		Never hinged	5.00	

Documentary revenue stamps were no longer required after Dec. 31, 1967.

PROPRIETARY STAMPS

Stamps for use on proprietary articles were included in the first general issue of 1862-71. They are Nos. R3, R13-R14, R18, R22, R29, R31, R38.

Washington — RB1

RB1a

Various Frame Designs

1871-74 Engr. *Perf. 12*

RB1 RB1 1c grn & blk
a. Violet paper ('71) 8.00
b. Green paper ('74) 14.00
c. As "a," Imperf. 80.00
d. As "a," Inverted center *5,250.*
RB2 RB1 2c grn & blk
a. Violet paper ('71) 8.75
b. Green paper ('74) 30.00
c. As "a," Invtd. center *40,000.*
d. As "b," Invtd. center *8,000.*
e. As "b," vert. half used as 1c on document —

Only three examples recorded of the inverted center on violet paper, No. RB2c. Value is for example with very good to fine centering and very small faults.

RB2d is valued with fine centering and small faults.

RB3 RB1a 3c grn & blk
a. Violet paper ('71) 32.50
b. Green paper ('74) 67.50
c. As "a," privately perforated, sewing machine perfs 800.00
d. As "a," inverted center *14,000.*

No. RB3d is valued with small faults because all of the 8 recorded examples have faults.

RB4 RB1a 4c grn & blk
a. Violet paper ('71) 16.00
b. Green paper ('74) 25.00
c. As "a," inverted center *15,000.*
d. As "b," vert. half used as 2c on document —

No. RB4c is valued with small faults as all seven of the recorded examples have faults.

RB5 RB1a 5c grn & blk
a. Violet paper ('71) 175.00
b. Green paper ('74) 250.00
c. As "a," inverted center *155,000.*

No. RB5c is unique. Value represents price realized in 2000 auction sale.

RB6 RB1a 6c grn & blk
a. Violet paper ('71) 57.50
b. Green paper ('74) 140.00
RB7 RB1a 10c grn & blk ('73)
a. Violet paper ('71) 300.00
b. Green paper ('74) 65.00

RB1b

RB8 RB1b 50c grn & blk ('73)
a. Violet paper ('71) 1,000.
b. Green paper ('74) 850.00
RB9 RB1b $1 grn & blk ('73)
a. Violet paper ('71) *3,500.*
b. Green paper ('74) *12,500.*

RB1c

RB10 RB1c $5 grn & blk ('73)
a. Violet paper ('71) *11,000.*
b. Green paper ('74) *75,000.*

No. RB10b is valued with small faults.

Washington — RB2

RB2a

Various Frame Designs
Green Paper

1875-81 *Perf. 12*

Unmwkd. (Silk Paper), Wmk. 191R

RB11 RB2 1c green
a. Silk paper 2.25
b. Wmk 191R .50
c. Rouletted 6 200.00
d. As No. RB11b, vert. pair, imperf btwn. *400.00*
RB12 RB2 2c brown
a. Silk paper 3.25
b. Wmk 191R 2.00
c. Rouletted 6 225.00
RB13 RB2a 3c orange
a. Silk paper 14.00
b. Wmk 191R 4.00
c. Rouletted 6 160.00
d. As No. RB13c, horiz. pair, imperf. between *2,500.*
e. As No. RB13c, vert. pair, imperf. between *2,500.*
f. Privately perforated, sewing machine perfs —
RB14 RB2a 4c red brown
a. Silk paper 10.00
b. Wmk 191R 9.00
c. Rouletted 6 *22,000.*
RB15 RB2a 4c red
b. Wmk 191R 6.00
c. Rouletted 6 450.00
RB16 RB2a 5c black
a. Silk paper 200.00
b. Wmk 191R 125.00
c. Rouletted 6 *1,850.*
RB17 RB2a 6c violet blue
a. Silk paper 35.00
b. Wmk 191R 25.00
c. Rouletted 6 *1,100.*
Pair —
RB18 RB2a 6c violet
b. Wmk 191R 35.00
c. Rouletted 6 *2,500.*
RB19 RB2a 10c blue ('81)
b. Wmk 191R 400.00

Many fraudulent roulettes exist.

Battleship — RB3

Inscribed "Series of 1898." and "Proprietary."

See note on rouletting preceding No. R161.

Rouletted 5½

1898 Wmk. 191R Engr.

RB20 RB3 ⅛c yel grn .25 .25
a. Vert. pair, imperf. horiz. —
b. Vert. pair, imperf. btwn. *1,100.*
RB21 RB3 ¼c brown .25 .25
a. ¼c red brown .25 .25
b. ¼c yellow brown .25 .25
c. ¼c orange brown .25 .25
d. ¼c bister .25 .25
e. Vert. pair, imperf. horiz. — —
f. Printed on both sides —
RB22 RB3 ⅜c dp org .30 .30
a. Horiz. pair, imperf. vert. 12.50
b. Vert. pair, imperf. horiz. —
RB23 RB3 ⅝c deep ultra .25 .25
a. Vert. pair, imperf. horiz. 85.00 —
b. Horiz. pair, imperf. btwn. *450.00* *400.00*
RB24 RB3 1c dark green 2.25 .50
a. Vert. pair, imperf. horiz. *600.00*
RB25 RB3 1¼c violet .35 .25
a. 1¼c brown violet .25 .25
b. Vert. pair, imperf. btwn. —
RB26 RB3 1⅞c dull blue 15.00 2.00
RB27 RB3 2c violet brown 1.40 .35
a. Horiz. pair, imperf. vert. 60.00
RB28 RB3 2½c lake 5.00 .35
a. Vert. pair, imperf. horiz. 400.00
RB29 RB3 3¾c olive gray 42.50 15.00
RB30 RB3 4c purple 16.00 1.50
RB31 RB3 5c brn org 15.00 1.50
a. Vert. pair, imperf. horiz. — *400.00*
b. Horiz. pair, imperf. vert. — *750.00*
Nos. RB20-RB31 (12) 98.55 22.50

Hyphen Hole Perf. 7

RB20p ⅛c .30 .25
RB21p ¼c .25 .25
b. ¼c yellow brown .25 .25
c. ¼c orange brown .25 .25
d. ¼c bister .25 .25
RB22p ⅜c .50 .35
RB23p ⅝c .30 .25
RB24p 1c 30.00 15.00
RB25p 1¼c .30 .30
a. 1¼c brown violet .25 .25
RB26p 1⅞c 40.00 9.00
RB27p 2c 10.00 1.00
RB28p 2½c 7.50 .40
RB29p 3¾c 100.00 27.50
RB30p 4c 70.00 22.50
RB31p 5c 85.00 25.00

See note before No. R161.

RB4

Inscribed "Series of 1914"

Offset Printing

1914 Wmk. 190 *Perf. 10*

RB32 RB4 ⅛c black .25 .35
RB33 RB4 ¼c black 4.00 1.50
RB34 RB4 ⅜c black .35 .35
RB35 RB4 ⅝c black 10.00 3.00
RB36 RB4 1¼c black 7.50 1.75
RB37 RB4 1⅞c black 80.00 22.50
RB38 RB4 2½c black 19.00 3.50
RB39 RB4 3⅛c black 230.00 67.50
RB40 RB4 3¾c black 75.00 27.50
RB41 RB4 4c black 110.00 45.00
RB42 RB4 4⅜c black *3,000.* —
RB43 RB4 5c black 200.00 110.00
Nos. RB32-RB41,RB43 (11) 736.10 282.95

Wmk. 191R

RB44 RB4 ⅛c black .35 .30
RB45 RB4 ¼c black .25 .25
RB46 RB4 ⅜c black .75 .45
RB47 RB4 ½c black 4.25 3.75
RB48 RB4 ⅝c black .30 .25
RB49 RB4 1c black 5.50 5.50
RB50 RB4 1¼c black .65 .40
RB51 RB4 1½c black 4.25 3.00
RB52 RB4 1⅞c black 1.35 .90
RB53 RB4 2c black 7.50 6.00
RB54 RB4 2½c black 2.00 1.40
RB55 RB4 3c black 6.00 4.00
RB56 RB4 3⅛c black 10.00 5.00
RB57 RB4 3¾c black 22.50 11.00
RB58 RB4 4c black .50 .30
RB59 RB4 4⅜c black 22.50 11.00
RB60 RB4 5c black 6.00 3.75
RB61 RB4 6c black 90.00 52.50
RB62 RB4 8c black 30.00 16.00
RB63 RB4 10c black 20.00 11.00
RB64 RB4 20c black 40.00 24.00
Nos. RB44-RB64 (21) 274.65 160.75

RB5

1919 Offset Printing *Perf. 11*

RB65 RB5 1c dark blue .25 .25
RB66 RB5 2c dark blue .35 .25
RB67 RB5 3c dark blue 1.50 .75
RB68 RB5 4c dark blue 2.25 .75
RB69 RB5 5c dark blue 3.00 1.25
RB70 RB5 8c dark blue 27.50 20.00
RB71 RB5 10c dark blue 12.50 5.00
RB72 RB5 20c dark blue 20.00 7.50
RB73 RB5 40c dark blue 75.00 25.00
Nos. RB65-RB73 (9) 142.35 60.75

FUTURE DELIVERY STAMPS

Issued to facilitate the collection of a tax upon each sale, agreement of sale or agreement to sell any products or merchandise at any exchange or board of trade, or other similar place for future delivery.

Documentary Stamps of 1917 Overprinted in Black or Red

Documentary Stamps Nos. R228-R250 Overprinted in Black or Red

Offset Printing

1918-34 Wmk. 191R *Perf. 11*

Overprint Horizontal (Lines 8mm apart)

Left Value — Unused With Gum

Right Value — Used

RC1 R22 2c carmine rose 8.75 .25
RC2 R22 3c carmine rose ('34) 47.50 37.50
Cut cancel 20.00
RC3 R22 4c carmine rose 17.50 .25
b. Double impression of stamp 10.00
RC3A R22 5c carmine rose ('33) 100.00 7.50
RC4 R22 10c carmine rose 24.00 .35
a. Double overprint — 5.25
b. "FUTURE" omitted — *500.00*
c. "DELIVERY FUTURE" 37.50
RC5 R22 20c carmine rose 40.00 .25
a. Double overprint 21.00
RC6 R22 25c carmine rose 85.00 .60
Cut cancel .30
RC7 R22 40c carmine rose 110.00 1.25
Cut cancel .35
RC8 R22 50c carmine rose 27.50 .35
a. "DELIVERY" omitted — *110.00*
RC9 R22 80c carmine rose 190.00 15.00
Cut cancel 4.00
a. Double overprint 37.50

Engr.

Overprint Vertical, Reading Up (Lines 2mm apart)

RC10 R21 $1 green (R) 75.00 .35
Cut cancel .25
a. Overprint reading down *450.00*
b. Black overprint —
Cut cancel 125.00
RC11 R21 $2 rose 85.00 .45
Cut cancel .25
RC12 R21 $3 violet (R) 270.00 3.50
Cut cancel .30
a. Overprint reading down — 52.50
RC13 R21 $5 dark blue (R) 150.00 .60
Cut cancel .25
RC14 R21 $10 orange 180.00 1.35
Cut cancel .30
a. "DELIVERY FUTURE" *110.00*
RC15 R21 $20 olive bister 450.00 9.00
Cut cancel .80

Overprint Horizontal (Lines 11½mm apart)

Perf. 12

Without Gum

RC16 R17 $30 vermilion, green numerals 150.00 5.50
Cut cancel 1.75
a. Numerals in blue 160.00 4.75
Cut cancel 2.00
b. Imperf., blue numerals *175.00*
RC17 R19 $50 olive green *(Cleveland)* 125.00 3.00
Cut cancel .90
a. $50 olive bister 125.00 2.75
Cut cancel .25
RC18 R19 $60 brown 160.00 9.00
Cut cancel 1.20
a. Vert. pair, imperf. horiz. *950.00*
RC19 R17 $100 yellow green ('34) 260.00 37.50
Cut cancel 9.00
RC20 R18 $500 blue, red numerals (R) 325.00 25.00
Cut cancel 9.00
a. Numerals in orange — 70.00
Cut cancel 20.00
RC21 R19 $1000 orange 230.00 7.50
Cut cancel 2.00
a. Vert. pair, imperf. horiz. *1,350.*

See note after No. R227.

1923-24 Offset Printing *Perf. 11*

Overprint Horizontal (Lines 2mm apart)

RC22 R22 1c carmine rose 1.25 .25
RC23 R22 80c carmine rose 200.00 3.50
Cut cancel .70

Documentary Stamps of 1917 Overprinted in Black or Red

1925-34 Engr.

RC25 R21 $1 green (R) 100.00 2.00
Cut cancel .45
RC26 R21 $10 orange (Bk) ('34) 260.00 29.00
Cut cancel 18.00

Overprint Type I

1928-29 Offset Printing *Perf. 10*

RC27 R22 10c carmine rose *5,000.*
RC28 R22 20c carmine rose *5,000.*

STOCK TRANSFER STAMPS

Issued to facilitate the collection of a tax on all sales or agreements to sell, or memoranda of sales or delivery of, or transfers of legal title to shares or certificates of stock.

Documentary Stamps Nos. R228-R259 Overprinted in Black or Red

Offset Printing
1918-22 Wmk. 191R *Perf. 11*

Overprint Horizontal (Lines 8mm apart)

RD1 R22 1c carmine rose 1.00 .25
a. Double overprint — —
RD2 R22 2c carmine rose .25 .25
a. Double overprint — 15.00
Double overprint, cut cancel 7.50
RD3 R22 4c carmine rose .25 .25
a. Double overprint — 4.25
Double overprint, cut cancel 2.10
b. "STOCK" omitted 10.50
d. Ovpt. lines 10mm apart —
RD4 R22 5c carmine rose .30 .25
RD5 R22 10c carmine rose .30 .25
a. Double overprint — 5.25
Double overprint, cut cancel 2.75
b. "STOCK" omitted —
RD6 R22 20c carmine rose .55 .25
a. Double overprint 6.25
b. "STOCK" double —
RD7 R22 25c carmine rose 2.25 .30
Cut cancel .25
RD8 R22 40c carmine rose ('22) 2.25 .25
RD9 R22 50c carmine rose .80 .25
a. Double overprint —
RD10 R22 80c carmine rose 10.00 .45
Cut cancel .25

Engr.
Overprint Vertical, Reading Up (Lines 2mm apart)

RD11 R21 $1 green (R) 225.00 40.00
Cut cancel 10.00
a. Overprint reading down 300.00 60.00
Overprint reading down, cut cancel 20.00
RD12 R21 $1 green (Bk) 3.00 .30
a. Pair, one without overprint — 180.00
b. Overprinted on back instead of face, inverted — 150.00
c. Overprint reading down — 7.50
d. $1 yellow green 3.00 .25
RD13 R21 $2 rose 3.00 .25
a. Overprint reading down 11.50
Overprint reading down, cut cancel 1.50
b. Vert. pair, imperf. horiz. 800.00
RD14 R21 $3 violet (R) 35.00 6.00
Cut cancel .30
RD15 R21 $4 yellow brown 15.00 .30
Cut cancel .25
RD16 R21 $5 dark blue (R) 10.00 .30
Cut cancel .25
a. Overprint reading down 42.50 1.35
Overprint reading down, cut cancel .25
RD17 R21 $10 orange 37.50 .45
Cut cancel .25
RD18 R21 $20 olive bister ('21) 150.00 18.00
Cut cancel 4.50
a. Overprint reading down —

Overprint Horizontal (Lines 11½mm apart)
1918 Without Gum *Perf. 12*

RD19 R17 $30 ver, grn numerals 55.00 6.50
Cut cancel 2.25
a. Numerals in blue 200.00 75.00
RD20 R19 $50 ol grn, *Cleveland* 160.00 70.00
Cut cancel 27.50
RD21 R19 $60 brown 350.00 30.00
Cut cancel 12.00
RD22 R17 $100 green 50.00 7.50
Cut cancel 3.00
RD23 R18 $500 blue (R) 625.00 160.00
Cut cancel 75.00
a. Numerals in orange 175.00
RD24 R19 $1,000 orange 500.00 110.00
Cut cancel 35.00

See note after No. R227.

1928 Offset Printing *Perf. 10*
Overprint Horizontal (Lines 8mm apart)

RD25 R22 2c carmine rose 5.50 .30
RD26 R22 4c carmine rose 5.50 .30
RD27 R22 10c carmine rose 5.50 .30
a. Inverted overprint 1,400.
b. Ovpt. lines 9½mm apart —
RD28 R22 20c carmine rose 6.50 .35
RD29 R22 50c carmine rose 10.00 .50

Engr.
Overprint Vertical, Reading Up (Lines 2mm apart)

RD30 R21 $1 green 60.00 .35
a. $1 yellow green 60.00 .50
RD31 R21 $2 carmine rose 55.00 .35
a. Pair, one without overprint 225.00 190.00
RD32 R21 $10 orange 60.00 .50

Overprinted Horiz. in Black

1920 Offset Printing *Perf. 11*

RD33 R22 2c carmine rose 12.50 1.00
RD34 R22 10c carmine rose 3.00 .35
b. Inverted overprint 2,250. 1,250.
RD35 R22 20c carmine rose 5.75 .25
a. Horiz. pair, one without overprint 950.00
d. Inverted overprint (perf. initials) —
RD36 R22 50c carmine rose 5.00 .30

Engr.
RD37 R21 $1 green 85.00 17.50
RD38 R21 $2 rose 100.00 17.50

Offset Printing
Perf. 10
RD39 R22 2c carmine rose 13.00 1.10
RD40 R22 10c carmine rose 5.25 .55
RD41 R22 20c carmine rose 6.00 .25

Used values for Nos. RD42-RD372 are for stamps which are neither cut nor perforated with initials. Stamps with cut cancellations or perforated initials are valued in the Scott U.S. Specialized Catalogue.

Documentary Stamps of 1917-33 Overprinted in Black

1940 *Perf. 11*

RD42 R22 1c rose pink 4.50 .65
a. "Series 1940" inverted (pos. 31LR) 1,000. 600.00

No. RD42a always comes with a natural straight edge at left.

RD43 R22 2c rose pink 6.00 .65
RD45 R22 4c rose pink 7.50 .35
RD46 R22 5c rose pink 8.00 .25
RD48 R22 10c rose pink 14.00 .35
RD49 R22 20c rose pink 17.00 .35
RD50 R22 25c rose pink 17.00 1.10
RD51 R22 40c rose pink 11.00 1.00
RD52 R22 50c rose pink 12.50 .35
RD53 R22 80c rose pink 280.00 110.00

Engr.
RD54 R21 $1 green 50.00 .60
RD55 R21 $2 rose 55.00 1.00
RD56 R21 $3 violet 350.00 18.00
RD57 R21 $4 yellow brown 125.00 1.60
RD58 R21 $5 dark blue 100.00 2.00
RD59 R21 $10 orange 275.00 10.00
RD60 R21 $20 olive bister 500.00 150.00

Nos. RD19-RD24 Handstamped in Blue "Series 1940"
1940 *Perf. 12*
Without Gum

RD61 R17 $30 ver 2,000. 1,500.
RD62 R19 $50 ol grn 2,500. 2,500.
a. Double ovpt., perf. initial 1,400.
RD63 R19 $60 brown 5,500. 3,000.
RD64 R17 $100 green 5,000. 850.00
RD65 R18 $500 blue 4,250.
RD66 R19 $1,000 orange
Cut cancel 5,000.

Alexander Hamilton ST1

Levi Woodbury ST2

Overprinted in Black SERIES 1940

Same Portraits as Nos. R288-R310.

1940 Engr. *Perf. 11*

RD67 ST1 1c brt grn 17.50 3.25
a. Imperf, pair, without gum 250.00
RD68 ST1 2c brt grn 10.00 1.75
a. Imperf, pair, without gum 250.00
RD70 ST1 4c brt grn 19.00 4.50
a. Imperf, pair, without gum 250.00
RD71 ST1 5c brt grn 12.00 1.75
a. Imperf, pair, without gum 250.00
b. Without overprint, cut cancel 850.00
RD73 ST1 10c brt grn 16.00 2.10
a. Imperf, pair, without gum 250.00
RD74 ST1 20c brt grn 19.00 2.40
a. Imperf, pair, without gum 250.00
RD75 ST1 25c brt grn 60.00 10.50
a. Imperf, pair, without gum 250.00
RD76 ST1 40c brt grn 125.00 50.00
a. Imperf, pair, without gum 250.00
RD77 ST1 50c brt grn 16.00 2.10
a. Imperf, pair, without gum 250.00
RD78 ST1 80c brt grn 180.00 75.00
a. Imperf, pair, without gum 250.00
RD79 ST2 $1 brt grn 75.00 4.25
a. Without overprint, perf. initial 750.00
RD80 ST2 $2 brt grn 75.00 12.00
a. Imperf, pair, without gum 250.00
RD81 ST2 $3 brt grn 110.00 15.00
a. Imperf, pair, without gum 250.00
RD82 ST2 $4 brt grn 1,000. 300.00
a. Imperf, pair, without gum 250.00
RD83 ST2 $5 brt grn 110.00 16.00
a. Imperf, pair, without gum 250.00
RD84 ST2 $10 brt grn 250.00 60.00
a. Imperf, pair, without gum 250.00
RD85 ST2 $20 brt grn 1,250. 125.00
a. Imperf, pair, without gum 250.00

Nos. RD67-RD85 exist imperforate, without overprint. Value, set of pairs, $750.

Thomas Corwin — ST3

Overprinted "SERIES 1940"

Various frames and portraits as Nos. R306-R310.

Perf. 12
Without Gum

RD86 ST3 $30 brt grn 6,000. 200.00
RD87 ST3 $50 brt grn 3,250. 900.00
RD88 ST3 $60 brt grn 5,000. 2,250.
RD89 ST3 $100 brt grn 3,000. 450.00
RD90 ST3 $500 brt grn —
RD91 ST3 $1,000 brt grn 4,000.

Nos. RD86-RD91 exist as unfinished imperforates with complete receipt tabs, without overprints or serial numbers. Known in singles, pairs (Nos. RD86-RD88 and Nos. RD90-RD91, value $300 per pair; No. RD89, value $150 per pair), panes of four with plate number, uncut sheets of four panes (with two plate numbers), cross gutter blocks of eight, and blocks of four with vertical gutter between and plate number.

Stock Transfer Stamps and Type of 1940 Overprinted in Black
Nos. RD67-RD91 Overprinted SERIES 1941 Instead:

1941 *Perf. 11*

RD92 ST1 1c brt grn .80 .55
RD93 ST1 2c brt grn .60 .30
RD95 ST1 4c brt grn .65 .25
RD96 ST1 5c brt grn .60 .25
RD98 ST1 10c brt grn 1.10 .25
RD99 ST1 20c brt grn 2.40 .30
RD100 ST1 25c brt grn 2.40 .45
RD101 ST1 40c brt grn 3.75 .75
RD102 ST1 50c brt grn 5.00 .35
RD103 ST1 80c brt grn 35.00 10.00
RD104 ST2 $1 brt grn 25.00 .25
RD105 ST2 $2 brt grn 27.50 .30
RD106 ST2 $3 brt grn 40.00 1.50
RD107 ST2 $4 brt grn 65.00 8.50
RD108 ST2 $5 brt grn 65.00 .65
RD109 ST2 $10 brt grn 140.00 5.50
RD110 ST2 $20 brt grn 500.00 110.00

Perf. 12
Without Gum

RD111 ST3 $30 brt grn 2,250. 500.00
RD112 ST3 $50 brt grn 1,250. 750.00
RD113 ST3 $60 brt grn 2,500. 1,000.
RD114 ST3 $100 brt grn 500.00 210.00
RD115 ST3 $500 brt grn 4,000. 3,500.
RD116 ST3 $1,000 brt grn — 4,000.

Stock Transfer Stamps and Type of 1940 Overprinted in Black
Nos. RD67-RD91 overprinted SERIES 1942 instead:

1942 *Perf. 11*

RD117 ST1 1c brt grn .75 .30
RD118 ST1 2c brt grn .65 .35
RD119 ST1 4c brt grn 3.50 1.10
RD120 ST1 5c brt grn .70 .25
a. Overprint inverted 1,000.
RD121 ST1 10c brt grn 2.25 .25
RD122 ST1 20c brt grn 2.75 .25
RD123 ST1 25c brt grn 2.50 .25
RD124 ST1 40c brt grn 5.75 .40
RD125 ST1 50c brt grn 6.50 .25
RD126 ST1 80c brt grn 30.00 6.00
RD127 ST2 $1 brt grn 27.50 .40
RD128 ST2 $2 brt grn 45.00 .40
RD129 ST2 $3 brt grn 50.00 1.10
RD130 ST2 $4 brt grn 65.00 24.00
RD131 ST2 $5 brt grn 60.00 .40
a. Double overprint, perf. initial 2,500.
RD132 ST2 $10 brt grn 125.00 9.50
RD133 ST2 $20 brt grn 350.00 65.00

Perf. 12
Without Gum

RD134 ST3 $30 brt grn 900.00 175.00
RD135 ST3 $50 brt grn 950.00 400.00
RD136 ST3 $60 brt grn 2,500. 350.00
RD137 ST3 $100 brt grn 900.00 110.00
RD138 ST3 $500 brt grn 15,000.
RD139 ST3 $1,000 brt grn — 2,750.

Stock Transfer Stamps and Type of 1940 Overprinted in Black
Nos. RD67-RD91 overprinted SERIES 1943 instead

1943 *Perf. 11*

RD140 ST1 1c brt grn .55 .30
RD141 ST1 2c brt grn .60 .40
RD142 ST1 4c brt grn 2.10 .25
RD143 ST1 5c brt grn .60 .25
RD144 ST1 10c brt grn 1.50 .25
RD145 ST1 20c brt grn 2.25 .25
RD146 ST1 25c brt grn 6.75 .35
RD147 ST1 40c brt grn 6.25 .30
RD148 ST1 50c brt grn 5.75 .30
RD149 ST1 80c brt grn 35.00 7.50
RD150 ST2 $1 brt grn 27.50 .25

RD151 ST2 $2 brt grn 30.00 .50
RD152 ST2 $3 brt grn 35.00 2.50
RD153 ST2 $4 brt grn 85.00 30.00
RD154 ST2 $5 brt grn 90.00 .60
RD155 ST2 $10 brt grn 140.00 7.50
RD156 ST2 $20 brt grn 450.00 90.00

Perf. 12

Without Gum

RD157 ST3 $30 brt grn 2,500. 750.00
RD158 ST3 $50 brt grn 2,500. 450.00
RD159 ST3 $60 brt grn *4,000.* *2,750.*
RD160 ST3 $100 brt grn 225.00 90.00
RD161 ST3 $500 brt grn — 2,250.
RD162 ST3 $1,000 brt grn 2,500. 2,000.

Stock Transfer Stamps and Type of 1940 Overprinted in Black

Series 1944

1944 ***Perf. 11***

RD163 ST1 1c brt grn .90 .75
RD164 ST1 2c brt grn .70 .25
RD165 ST1 4c brt grn .70 .35
RD166 ST1 5c brt grn .65 .25
RD167 ST1 10c brt grn 1.00 .30
RD168 ST1 20c brt grn 2.25 .25
RD169 ST1 25c brt grn 3.25 .90
RD170 ST1 40c brt grn 17.50 8.00
RD171 ST1 50c brt grn 5.50 .30
RD172 ST1 80c brt grn 17.50 6.25
RD173 ST2 $1 brt grn 17.50 .50
RD174 ST2 $2 brt grn 60.00 .75
RD175 ST2 $3 brt grn 55.00 2.00
RD176 ST2 $4 brt grn 95.00 17.50
RD177 ST2 $5 brt grn 65.00 3.50
RD178 ST2 $10 brt grn 150.00 7.25
RD179 ST2 $20 brt grn 425.00 25.00

Perf. 12

Without Gum

Designs: $2,500, William Windom. $5,000, C. J. Folger. $10,000, W. Q. Gresham.

RD180 ST3 $30 brt grn 850.00 125.00
RD181 ST3 $50 brt grn 1,000. 150.00
RD182 ST3 $60 brt grn *4,750.* 750.00
RD183 ST3 $100 brt grn 3,250. 100.00
RD184 ST3 $500 brt grn *2,500.* *2,250.*
RD185 ST3 $1,000 brt grn *3,000.* 2,500.
RD185A ST3 $2,500 brt grn —
RD185B ST3 $5,000 brt grn *65,000.*
RD185C ST3 $10,000 brt grn, cut cancel *45,000.*
Perf. initial *35,000.*

Stock Transfer Stamps and Type of 1940 Overprinted in Black

Series 1945

1945 ***Perf. 11***

RD186 ST1 1c brt grn .45 .25
RD187 ST1 2c brt grn .45 .35
RD188 ST1 4c brt grn .50 .35
RD189 ST1 5c brt grn .45 .25
RD190 ST1 10c brt grn 1.25 .35
RD191 ST1 20c brt grn 2.25 .45
RD192 ST1 25c brt grn 3.50 .40
RD193 ST1 40c brt grn 5.00 .25
RD194 ST1 50c brt grn 11.00 .45
RD195 ST1 80c brt grn 17.50 4.75
RD196 ST2 $1 brt grn 20.00 .30
RD197 ST2 $2 brt grn 37.50 .90
RD198 ST2 $3 brt grn 65.00 1.75
RD199 ST2 $4 brt grn 65.00 4.25
RD200 ST2 $5 brt grn 40.00 1.00
RD201 ST2 $10 brt grn 95.00 12.00
RD202 ST2 $20 brt grn 375.00 25.00

Perf. 12

Without Gum

RD203 ST3 $30 brt grn 300.00 90.00
RD204 ST3 $50 brt grn 275.00 70.00
RD205 ST3 $60 brt grn 1,750. 500.00
RD206 ST3 $100 brt grn 600.00 75.00
RD207 ST3 $500 brt grn — 1,400.
RD208 ST3 $1,000 brt grn *3,250.* 2,250.
RD208A ST3 $2,500 brt grn, perf. initial *20,000.*
RD208B ST3 $5,000 brt grn, cut cancel *45,000.*
RD208C ST3 $10,000 brt grn, cut cancel *45,000.*

Stock Transfer Stamps and Type of 1940 Overprinted in Black

Series 1946

1946 ***Perf. 11***

RD209 ST1 1c brt grn .50 .35
a. Pair, one dated "1945" *850.00*
RD210 ST1 2c brt grn .50 .25
RD211 ST1 4c brt grn .50 .25
RD212 ST1 5c brt grn .55 .25
RD213 ST1 10c brt grn 1.25 .25
RD214 ST1 20c brt grn 2.50 .30
RD215 ST1 25c brt grn 3.00 .40
RD216 ST1 40c brt grn 6.50 1.25
RD217 ST1 50c brt grn 6.75 .25
RD218 ST1 80c brt grn 24.00 9.50
RD219 ST2 $1 brt grn 17.50 .90
RD220 ST2 $2 brt grn 19.00 1.00
RD221 ST2 $3 brt grn 35.00 2.25
RD222 ST2 $4 brt grn 35.00 9.00
RD223 ST2 $5 brt grn 60.00 2.25
RD224 ST2 $10 brt grn 100.00 4.25
RD225 ST2 $20 brt grn 550.00 75.00

Perf. 12

Without Gum

RD226 ST3 $30 brt grn 350.00 62.50
RD227 ST3 $50 brt grn 450.00 75.00
RD228 ST3 $60 brt grn 1,250. 250.00
RD229 ST3 $100 brt grn 225.00 90.00
RD230 ST3 $500 brt grn *2,500.* 350.00
RD231 ST3 $1,000 brt grn 2,000. 300.00
RD232 ST3 $2,500 brt grn *25,000.*
RD233 ST3 $5,000 brt grn, cut cancel *17,500.*
RD234 ST3 $10,000 brt grn, cut cancel *22,500.*

Stock Transfer Stamps and Type of 1940 Overprinted in Black

Series 1947

1947 ***Perf. 11***

RD235 ST1 1c bright green 2.75 .90
RD236 ST1 2c bright green 2.75 .90
RD237 ST1 4c bright green 2.00 .70
RD238 ST1 5c bright green 2.00 .60
RD239 ST1 10c bright green 2.00 .90
RD240 ST1 20c bright green 3.75 .90
RD241 ST1 25c bright green 6.00 .90
RD242 ST1 40c bright green 6.00 1.40
RD243 ST1 50c bright green 7.50 .35
RD244 ST1 80c bright green 32.50 14.00
RD245 ST2 $1 bright green 25.00 1.00
RD246 ST2 $2 bright green 35.00 1.25
RD247 ST2 $3 bright green 50.00 2.50
RD248 ST2 $4 bright green 70.00 9.50
RD249 ST2 $5 bright green 50.00 3.25
RD250 ST2 $10 bright green 225.00 11.00
RD251 ST2 $20 bright green 300.00 50.00

Perf. 12

Without Gum

RD252 ST3 $30 brt grn 2,000. 85.00
RD253 ST3 $50 brt grn 1,500. 325.00
RD254 ST3 $60 brt grn 2,750. 250.00
RD255 ST3 $100 brt grn 175.00 70.00
RD256 ST3 $500 brt grn 2,500. 850.00
RD257 ST3 $1,000 brt grn 2,750. 140.00
RD258 ST3 $2,500 brt grn *3,000.*
Cut cancel 400.00
RD259 ST3 $5,000 brt grn 2,500.
Cut cancel 600.00
RD260 ST3 $10,000 brt grn —
Cut cancel 75.00
a. Vert. pair, imperf. horiz., cut cancel —

Stock Transfer Stamps and Type of 1940 Overprinted in Black

Series 1948

1948 ***Perf. 11***

RD261 ST1 1c bright green .45 .35
RD262 ST1 2c bright green .45 .35
RD263 ST1 4c bright green .80 .45
RD264 ST1 5c bright green .45 .25
RD265 ST1 10c bright green .55 .35
RD266 ST1 20c bright green 1.60 .40
RD267 ST1 25c bright green 1.90 .55
RD268 ST1 40c bright green 5.00 1.00
RD269 ST1 50c bright green 7.00 .45
RD270 ST1 80c bright green 30.00 9.50
RD271 ST2 $1 bright green 17.50 .50
RD272 ST2 $2 bright green 35.00 1.00
RD273 ST2 $3 bright green 60.00 10.00
RD274 ST2 $4 bright green 70.00 20.00
RD275 ST2 $5 bright green 80.00 5.00
RD276 ST2 $10 bright green 90.00 7.25
RD277 ST2 $20 bright green 400.00 30.00

Perf. 12

Without Gum

RD278 ST3 $30 brt grn 350.00 100.00
RD279 ST3 $50 brt grn 400.00 95.00
RD280 ST3 $60 brt grn 2,000. 350.00
RD281 ST3 $100 brt grn 175.00 30.00
RD282 ST3 $500 brt grn 2,500. 375.00
RD283 ST3 $1,000 brt grn 2,500. 125.00
RD284 ST3 $2,500 brt grn 2,500. 1,750.
RD285 ST3 $5,000 brt grn 2,500. 1,750.
RD286 ST3 $10,000 brt grn

Stock Transfer Stamps and Type of 1940 Overprinted in Black

Series 1949

1949 ***Perf. 11***

RD287 ST1 1c bright green 2.25 .70
RD288 ST1 2c bright green 2.25 .75
RD289 ST1 4c bright green 2.50 .75
RD290 ST1 5c bright green 3.00 .75
RD291 ST1 10c bright green 7.50 1.00
RD292 ST1 20c bright green 12.00 1.00
RD293 ST1 25c bright green 13.00 1.25
RD294 ST1 40c bright green 30.00 3.25
RD295 ST1 50c bright green 35.00 .45
RD296 ST1 80c bright green 45.00 10.00
RD297 ST2 $1 bright green 32.50 1.00
RD298 ST2 $2 bright green 60.00 1.75
RD299 ST2 $3 bright green 110.00 10.00
RD300 ST2 $4 bright green 110.00 20.00
RD301 ST2 $5 bright green 85.00 3.00
RD302 ST2 $10 bright green 150.00 12.50
RD303 ST2 $20 bright green 325.00 22.50

Perf. 12

Without Gum

RD304 ST3 $30 brt grn 3,000. 150.00
RD305 ST3 $50 brt grn 2,250. 300.00
RD306 ST3 $60 brt grn 2,500. 400.00
RD307 ST3 $100 brt grn 225.00 70.00
RD308 ST3 $500 brt grn *1,500.* 300.00
RD309 ST3 $1,000 brt grn *1,500.* 85.00
RD310 ST3 $2,500 brt grn
RD311 ST3 $5,000 brt grn
RD312 ST3 $10,000 brt grn 475.00
a. Pair, one without ovpt., cut cancel *8,000.*

No. RD312a is unique.

Stock Transfer Stamps and Type of 1940 Overprinted in Black

Series 1950

1950 ***Perf. 11***

RD313 ST1 1c bright green .80 .40
RD314 ST1 2c bright green .70 .35
RD315 ST1 4c bright green .65 .40
RD316 ST1 5c bright green .75 .25
RD317 ST1 10c bright green 3.25 .30
RD318 ST1 20c bright green 5.00 .80
RD319 ST1 25c bright green 10.00 1.00
RD320 ST1 40c bright green 15.00 1.50
RD321 ST1 50c bright green 19.00 .50
RD322 ST1 80c bright green 27.50 7.25
RD323 ST2 $1 bright green 27.50 .55
RD324 ST2 $2 bright green 40.00 1.25
RD325 ST2 $3 bright green 70.00 8.50
RD326 ST2 $4 bright green 85.00 20.00
RD327 ST2 $5 bright green 70.00 3.25
RD328 ST2 $10 bright green 210.00 12.50
RD329 ST2 $20 bright green 300.00 60.00

Perf. 12

Without Gum

RD330 ST3 $30 brt grn 600.00 250.00
RD331 ST3 $50 brt grn 800.00 225.00
RD332 ST3 $60 brt grn 1,000. 250.00
RD333 ST3 $100 brt grn 150.00 55.00
a. Vert. pair, imperf. btwn. 2,000. *1,750.*
RD334 ST3 $500 brt grn — 350.00
RD335 ST3 $1,000 brt grn 275.00 85.00
RD336 ST3 $2,500 brt grn 5,500. 2,500.
RD337 ST3 $5,000 brt grn 5,500. 2,500.
RD338 ST3 $10,000 brt grn 5,500. 1,500.

Stock Transfer Stamps and Type of 1940 Overprinted in Black

Series 1951

1951 ***Perf. 11***

RD339 ST1 1c bright green 3.00 .75
RD340 ST1 2c bright green 2.50 .50
RD341 ST1 4c bright green 3.00 .75
RD342 ST1 5c bright green 2.25 .55
RD343 ST1 10c bright green 3.00 .35
RD344 ST1 20c bright green 10.00 1.25
RD345 ST1 25c bright green 12.00 1.50
RD346 ST1 40c bright green 50.00 12.50
RD347 ST1 50c bright green 20.00 1.50
RD348 ST1 80c bright green 40.00 14.00
RD349 ST2 $1 bright green 40.00 1.25
RD350 ST2 $2 bright green 55.00 1.75
RD351 ST2 $3 bright green 70.00 14.00
RD352 ST2 $4 bright green 350.00 25.00
RD353 ST2 $5 bright green 90.00 4.00
RD354 ST2 $10 bright green 170.00 11.00
RD355 ST2 $20 bright green 400.00 35.00

Perf. 12

Without Gum

RD356 ST3 $30 brt grn *2,500.* 200.00
RD357 ST3 $50 brt grn *2,500.* 250.00
RD358 ST3 $60 brt grn *2,500.* *1,600.*
RD359 ST3 $100 brt grn 250.00 100.00
RD360 ST3 $500 brt grn *2,500.* 550.00
RD361 ST3 $1,000 brt grn 275.00 125.00
RD362 ST3 $2,500 brt grn *4,250.*
RD363 ST3 $5,000 brt grn — *3,250.*
RD364 ST3 $10,000 brt grn *2,000.* 250.00

Stock Transfer Stamps and Type of 1940 Overprinted in Black

1952 ***Perf. 11***

RD365 ST1 1c brt grn 42.50 27.50
RD366 ST1 10c brt grn 45.00 27.50
RD367 ST1 20c brt grn 400.00 —
RD368 ST1 25c brt grn 550.00 —
RD369 ST1 40c brt grn 140.00 55.00
RD370 ST2 $4 brt grn *1,500.* 1,250.
RD371 ST2 $10 brt grn *3,500.* —
RD372 ST2 $20 brt grn *6,000.* —

Stock Transfer Stamps were discontinued in 1952.

Catalogue values for all unused stamps in this section are for stamps with never-hinged original gum. Minor natural gum skips and bends are normal on Nos. RW1-RW20. No-gum stamps are without signature or other cancel.

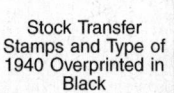

HUNTING PERMIT STAMPS

Catalogue values for all unused stamps in this section are for stamps with never-hinged original gum. Hinged examples from No. RW13 to present usually sell for 40%-60% of the values of never-hinged examples. Minor natural gum skips and bends are normal on Nos. RW1-RW20. No-gum stamps are without signature or other cancel.
Nos. RW1-RW12 were issued in panes of 28, of which 10 stamps have a straight edge on one or two sides. Such examples sell for 20%-30% less than the values shown.

Department of Agriculture
Various Designs Inscribed
"U. S. Department of Agriculture"

Mallards Alighting — HP1

Engraved: Flat Plate Printing

1934 Unwmk. *Perf. 11*
Inscribed "Void after June 30, 1935"
RW1 HP1 $1 blue 775. 175.
Hinged 300.
No gum 175.

Used value is for stamp with handstamp or manuscript cancel.
It is almost certain that examples of No. RW1 offered as imperforate vertical pairs or as vertical pairs imperforate horizontally are from printer's waste. Additionally, it is almost certain that all imperforate vertical pairs are pairs imperforate horizontally that have had the vertical perforations trimmed off. No horizontal imperforate pairs are known. All recorded pairs are vertical, with narrow side margins. Most examples exist without gum and with faults. Some pairs have gum on the front (which in some cases appears to have been removed).
The stamps imperforate horizontally are recorded as a unique vertical block of eight, with the other recorded varieties being the manufactured imperforate vertical pairs.

Canvasbacks Taking to Flight — HP2

1935
Inscribed "Void after June 30, 1936"
RW2 HP2 $1 rose lake 700. 160.
deep rose lake —
Hinged 375.
No gum 175.

Canada Geese in Flight — HP3

1936
Inscribed "Void after June 30, 1937"
RW3 HP3 $1 brown black 325. 100.
Hinged 150.
No gum 90.

Scaup Ducks Taking to Flight — HP4

1937
Inscribed "Void after June 30, 1938"
RW4 HP4 $1 light green 300. 65.
Hinged 140.
No gum 85.

Pintail Drake and Hen Alighting HP5

1938
Inscribed "Void after June 30, 1939"
RW5 HP5 $1 light violet 425. 75.
Hinged 200.
No gum 85.

Department of the Interior
Various Designs Inscribed
"U. S. Department of the Interior"

Green-Winged Teal — HP6

1939
Inscribed "Void after June 30, 1940"
RW6 HP6 $1 chocolate 250. 50.
Hinged 115.
No gum 60.

Black Mallards HP7

1940
Inscribed "Void after June 30, 1941"
RW7 HP7 $1 sepia 250. 50.
Hinged 115.
No gum 60.

1941
Inscribed "Void after June 30, 1942"
RW8 HP8 $1 brown carmine 225. 50.
Hinged 95.
No gum 45.

1942
Inscribed "Void after June 30, 1943"
RW9 HP9 $1 violet brown 225. 45.
Hinged 95.
No gum 45.

1943
Inscribed "Void After June 30, 1944"
RW10 HP10 $1 deep rose 120. 35.
Hinged 55.
No gum 35.

1944
Inscribed "Void after June 30, 1945"
RW11 HP11 $1 red orange 125. 35.
Hinged 45.
No gum 35.

1945
Inscribed "Void after June 30, 1946"
RW12 HP12 $1 black 100. 25.
Hinged 45.
No gum 35.

1946
Inscribed "Void after June 30, 1947"
RW13 HP13 $1 red brown 50.00 12.50
No gum 15.00

The previously listed No. RW13a in a bright rose pink shade has been determined to be a chemically induced changeling.

1947
Inscribed "Void after June 30, 1948"
RW14 HP14 $1 black 55.00 15.00
No gum 18.00

1948
Inscribed "Void after June 30, 1949"
RW15 HP15 $1 bright blue 60.00 12.00
No gum 15.00

Goldeneye Ducks — HP16

1949
Inscribed "Void after June 30, 1950"
RW16 HP16 $2 bright green 70.00 15.00
No gum 20.00

1950
Inscribed "Void after June 30, 1951"
RW17 HP17 $2 violet 90.00 15.00
No gum 20.00

1951
Inscribed "Void after June 30, 1952"
RW18 HP18 $2 gray black 90.00 15.00
No gum 20.00

1952
Inscribed "Void after June 30, 1953"
RW19 HP19 $2 dp ultra 90.00 15.00
No gum 20.00

1953
Inscribed "Void after June 30, 1954"
RW20 HP20 $2 dp rose brn 90.00 15.00
No gum 20.00

No. RW21 and following issues are printed on dry, pregummed paper and the back inscription is printed on top of the gum, except for the self-adhesive stamp issues starting in 1998.

1954
Inscribed "Void after June 30, 1955"
RW21 HP21 $2 black 85.00 15.00
No gum 20.00

1955
Inscribed "Void after June 30, 1956"
RW22 HP22 $2 dark blue 85.00 12.50
No gum 20.00
a. Back inscription inverted *5,500. 4,500.*

1956
Inscribed "Void after June 30, 1957"
RW23 HP23 $2 black 85.00 12.50
No gum 20.00

1957
Inscribed "Void after June 30, 1958"
RW24 HP24 $2 emerald 85.00 12.50
No gum 20.00
a. Back inscription inverted *7,500.*

1958
Inscribed "Void after June 30, 1959"
RW25 HP25 $2 black 85.00 12.50
No gum 20.00
a. Back inscription inverted —

Labrador Retriever Carrying Mallard Drake — HP26

Giori Press Printing

1959
Inscribed "Void after June 30, 1960"
RW26 HP26 $3 multi 130.00 12.50
No gum 45.00
a. Back inscription inverted *15,000. 12,500.*

Redhead Ducks — HP27

1960
Inscribed "Void after June 30, 1961"
RW27 HP27 $3 multi 95.00 12.50
No gum 30.00

1961
Inscribed "Void after June 30, 1962"
RW28 HP28 $3 multicolored 95.00 12.50
No gum 30.00

Pintail Drakes — HP29

1962
Inscribed "Void after June 30, 1963"
RW29 HP29 $3 multicolored 110.00 12.50
No gum 35.00
a. Back inscription omitted —

1963
Inscribed "Void after June 30, 1964"
RW30 HP30 $3 multicolored 100.00 12.50
No gum 35.00

1964
Inscribed "Void after June 30, 1965"
RW31 HP31 $3 multicolored 100.00 12.50
No gum 35.00

1965
Inscribed "Void after June 30, 1966"
RW32 HP32 $3 multicolored 100.00 12.50
No gum 40.00

Whistling Swans — HP33

1966
Inscribed "Void after June 30, 1967"
RW33 HP33 $3 multi 100.00 12.50
No gum 40.00

1967
Inscribed "Void after June 30, 1968"
RW34 HP34 $3 multicolored 100.00 12.50
No gum 40.00

1968
Inscribed "Void after June 30, 1969"
RW35 HP35 $3 multicolored 65.00 12.50
No gum 20.00
a. Back inscription omitted —

White-winged Scoters — HP36

1969
Inscribed "Void after June 30, 1970"
RW36 HP36 $3 multi 65.00 8.00
No gum 20.00

1970 Engraved & Lithographed
Inscribed "Void after June 30, 1971"
RW37 HP37 $3 multi 65.00 8.00
No gum 20.00

1971
Inscribed "Void after June 30, 1972"
RW38 HP38 $3 multi 42.50 8.00
No gum 15.00

1972
Inscribed "Void after June 30, 1973"
RW39 HP39 $5 multi 30.00 6.00
No gum 8.00

1973
Inscribed "Void after June 30, 1974"
RW40 HP40 $5 multi 18.00 6.00
No gum 7.00

1974
Inscribed "Void after June 30, 1975"
RW41 HP41 $5 multi 18.00 5.00
No gum 6.00
a. Back inscription missing, but printed vertically on face of stamp and selvage, from foldover *4,750.*

1975
Inscribed "Void after June 30, 1976"
RW42 HP42 $5 multi 15.00 5.00
No gum 7.00

1976 **Engr.**
Inscribed "Void after June 30, 1977"
RW43 HP43 $5 grn & blk 12.50 5.00
No gum 7.00

1977 **Litho. & Engr.**
Inscribed "Void after June 30, 1978"
RW44 HP44 $5 multi 10.00 5.00
No gum 7.00

Hooded Merganser — HP45

1978
Inscribed "Void after June 30, 1979"
RW45 HP45 $5 multicolored 10.00 5.00
No gum 7.00

1979
Inscribed "Void after June 30, 1980"
RW46 HP46 $7.50 multi 12.50 6.00
No gum 8.00

1980
Inscribed "Void after June 30, 1981"
RW47 HP47 $7.50 multi 12.50 6.00
No gum 8.00

1981
Inscribed "Void after June 30, 1982"
RW48 HP48 $7.50 multi 12.50 6.00
No gum 8.00

1982
Inscribed "Void after June 30, 1983"
RW49 HP49 $7.50 multi 15.00 7.00
No gum 9.00
a. Orange and violet omitted *10,000.*

A certificate from a recognized expertization committee is required for No. RW49a.

1983
Inscribed "Void after June 30, 1984"
RW50 HP50 $7.50 multi 15.00 7.00
No gum 7.00

1984
Inscribed "Void after June 30, 1985"
RW51 HP51 $7.50 multi 12.50 7.00
No gum 7.00

1985
Inscribed "Void after June 30, 1986"
RW52 HP52 $7.50 multi 15.00 8.00
No gum 7.00
a. Light blue (litho.) omitted *20,000.*

The omitted color on No. RW52a coincides with a double paper splice affecting the top row of five stamps from the sheet and top ⅓ of stamps in the second row. There is also a color changeling of the brownish red ducks and their reflections in the water to yellow and yellow orange, respectively, on the error stamps. This error currently exists as three vertical strips of 6 (top stamp the error) and a plate number block of 12 (2x6, top two stamps the error).

1986
Inscribed "Void after June 30, 1987"
RW53 HP53 $7.50 multi 15.00 8.00
No gum 9.00
a. Black omitted *1,450.*

1987 ***Perf. 11½x11***
Inscribed "Void after June 30, 1988"
RW54 HP54 $10 multi 17.50 8.00
No gum 8.00

1988
Inscribed "Void after June 30, 1989"
RW55 HP55 $10 multicolored 17.50 8.00
No gum 8.00

1989
Inscribed "Void after June 30, 1990"
RW56 HP56 $12.50 multi 21.50 8.00
No gum 9.00

1990
Inscribed "Void after June 30, 1991"
RW57 HP57 $12.50 multi 20.00 8.00
No gum 9.00
a. Back inscription omitted *300.00*

The back inscription is normally on top of the gum so beware of examples with gum removed offered as No. RW57a. Full original gum must be intact on No. RW57a. Used examples of No. RW57a cannot exist.

King Eiders — HP58

1991
Inscribed "Void after June 30, 1992"
RW58 HP58 $15 multi 30.00 8.00
No gum 15.00
a. Black (engr.) omitted *20,000.*

1992
Inscribed "Void after June 30, 1993"
RW59 HP59 $15 multi 30.00 10.00
No gum 15.00

1993
Inscribed "Void after June 30, 1994"
RW60 HP60 $15 multi 27.50 9.00
No gum 15.00
a. Black (engr.) omitted *1,750.* *1,500.*

1994 ***Perf. 11¼x11***
Inscribed "Void after June 30, 1995"
RW61 HP61 $15 multi 27.50 10.00
No gum 15.00

1995
Inscribed "Void after June 30, 1996"
RW62 HP62 $15 multi 32.50 12.00
No gum 15.00

1996
Inscribed "Void after June 30, 1997"
RW63 HP63 $15 multi 32.50 12.00
No gum 12.50

1997
Inscribed "Void after June 30, 1998"
RW64 HP64 $15 multi 27.50 12.00
No gum 15.00

1998 ***Perf. 11¼***
Inscribed "Void after June 30, 1999"
RW65 HP65 $15 multi 45.00 22.50
No gum 22.50

Self-Adhesive
Die Cut Perf. 10
RW65A HP65 $15 multi 30.00 15.00
No gum 15.00

Nos. RW65 and later issues were sold in panes of 30 (RW65 and RW66) or 20 (RW67 and later issues), with four plate numbers per pane. The self-adhesives starting with No. RW65A were sold in panes of 1. The self-adhesives are valued unused as complete panes and used as single stamps.

1999 ***Perf. 11¼***
Inscribed "Void after June 30, 2000"
RW66 HP66 $15 multi 40.00 20.00
No gum 22.50

Self-Adhesive
Die Cut Perf. 10
RW66A HP66 $15 multi 30.00 12.00
No gum 15.00

2000 ***Perf. 11¼***
Inscribed "Void after June 30, 2001"
RW67 HP67 $15 multi 35.00 15.00
No gum 17.50

Self-Adhesive
Die Cut Perf. 10
RW67A HP67 $15 multi 30.00 14.00
No gum 17.50

2001 ***Perf. 11¼***
Inscribed "Void after June 30, 2002"
RW68 HP68 $15 multi 35.00 18.00
No gum 17.50

Self-Adhesive
Die Cut Perf. 10
RW68A HP68 $15 multi 30.00 14.00
No gum 15.00

2002 ***Perf. 11¼***
Inscribed "Void after June 30, 2003"
RW69 HP69 $15 multi 35.00 16.00
No gum 17.50

Self-Adhesive
Serpentine Die Cut 11x10¾
RW69A HP69 $15 multi 30.00 12.00
No gum 15.00

2003 ***Perf. 11***
Inscribed "Void after June 30, 2004"
RW70 HP70 $15 multi 35.00 16.00
No gum 17.50
b. Imperf, pair *5,000.*
c. Back inscription omitted *4,500.*

Self-Adhesive
Serpentine Die Cut 11x10¾
RW70A HP70 $15 multi 30.00 12.00
No gum 15.00

2004 ***Perf. 11***
Inscribed "Void after June 30, 2005"
RW71 HP71 $15 multicolored 35.00 16.00
No gum 17.00

Self-Adhesive
Serpentine Die Cut 11x10¾
RW71A HP71 $15 multicolored 30.00 12.00
No gum 15.00

2005 **Litho. & Engr.** ***Perf. 11***
Inscribed "Void after June 30, 2006"
RW72 HP72 $15 multi, type I 30.00 16.00
No gum 16.00
b. Souvenir sheet of 1 *1,950.*
c. Type II 30.00 16.00
No gum 16.00
d. As "b," without artist's signature (error) *3,250.*

There are two types of RW72: type I has no frame lines; type II has gray frame lines at top, right and bottom edges of design. No. RW72c, the type II stamp, is any stamp from the right two panes of the sheet of four panes. No. RW72, the Type I stamp, is any stamp from the left two panes.

No. RW72b sold for $20. 1,000 No. RW72b were issued. Approximately 750 were signed by the artist in black, value $1,950 as shown. Approximately 150 were signed in blue ink, value $2,500. Approximately 100 were signed in gold ink, value $3,000. Most examples of No. RW72b are in the grade of F-VF. Catalogue values are for Very Fine examples.

The Duck Stamp Office never announced the existence of No. RW72b to the public through a press release or a website announcement during the time the sheet was on sale, apparently because it was not clear beforehand that the souvenir sheet could be produced successfully and on time. No. RW72b sold out before a public announcement of the item's existence could be made.

Self-Adhesive
Litho. & Debossed
Serpentine Die Cut 11x10¾
RW72A HP72 $15 multi 27.50 11.00
No gum 15.00

Ross's Goose — HP73

2006 **Litho. & Engr.** ***Perf. 11***
Inscribed "Void after June 30, 2007"
RW73 HP73 $15 multi 25.00 11.00
No gum 15.00
b. Souvenir sheet of 1 95.00 —
c. As "b," without artist's signature (error) *2,500.*

No. RW73b sold for $25. All examples of No. RW73b have a black signature of the artist on a designated line in the sheet margin. Ten thousand were issued.

The sheet margin has a line designated for the signature of the engraver, Piotr Naszarkowski, but no sheets were sold with his signature. Naszarkowski signed approximately 2,500 sheets during three days at the Washington 2006 World Philatelic Exhibition, and he signed another 2,500 or more after the conclusion of the exhibition. Value $150.

An example of No. RW73c is known with the engraver↔s signature.

Self-Adhesive
Serpentine Die Cut 11x10¾
RW73A HP73 $15 multi 25.00 11.00
No gum 15.00

Ring-necked Ducks — HP74

2007 **Litho.** ***Perf. 11***
Inscribed "Void after June 30, 2008"
RW74 HP74 $15 multi 35.00 11.00
No gum 16.00
b. Souvenir sheet of 1 140.00
c. As "b", without artist's signature (error) *2,750.*

No. RW74b sold for $25 plus a shipping fee. The artist signed No. RW74b on a designated line in the sheet margin. Ten thousand were issued. There is no back inscription on No. RW74b.

Self-Adhesive
Serpentine Die Cut 11x10¾
RW74A HP74 $15 multi 27.50 11.00
No gum 15.00

Northern Pintails — HP75

2008 Litho. *Perf. 13¼*
Inscribed "Void after June 30, 2009"

RW75 HP75 $15 multi 35.00 11.00
No gum 16.00
b. Souvenir sheet of 1 70.00 —
c. As "b," without artist's signature (error) *500.00*

Self-Adhesive
Serpentine Die Cut 10¾

RW75A HP75 $15 multi 35.00 11.00
No gum 25.00

2009 Litho. *Perf. 13¼*
Inscribed "Void after June 30, 2010"

RW76 HP76 $15 multi 30.00 11.00
No gum 16.00
b. Souvenir sheet of 1 60.00
c. As "b," without artist's signature (error) *400.00*

No. RW76b sold for $30 plus a shipping fee. The artist signed No. RW76b on a designated line in the sheet margin. Ten thousand were prepared.

Self-Adhesive
Serpentine Die Cut 11x10¾

RW76A HP76 $15 multi 30.00 11.00
No gum 20.00

2010 Litho. *Perf. 11¼x11*
Inscribed "Void after June 30, 2011"

RW77 HP77 $15 multi 30.00 11.00
No gum 16.00
b. Souvenir sheet of 1, perf. 13¼ 55.00
c. As "b," without artist's signature (error) *200.00*

No. RW77b was sold for $30 plus a shipping fee. The artist signed No. RW77b on a designated line in the sheet margin. Ten thousand were prepared. There is no back inscription on No. RW77b, and the stamp on the sheet is tagged.

Self-Adhesive
Serpentine Die Cut 11x10¾

RW77A HP77 $15 multi 30.00 11.00
No gum 20.00

White-fronted Geese — HP78

2011 Litho. *Perf. 13¼*
Inscribed "Void after June 30, 2012"

RW78 HP78 $15 multi 37.50 11.00
No gum 16.00
b. Souvenir sheet of 1 60.00
c. As "b," without artist's signature (error) *175.00*

No. RW78b was sold for $25 plus a shipping fee. The artist signed No. RW78b on a designated line in the sheet margin. Ten thousand were prepared.

Self-Adhesive
Serpentine Die Cut 11x10¾

RW78A HP78 $15 multi 40.00 11.00
No gum 20.00

Wood Duck — HP79

2012 Litho. *Perf. 13¼*
Inscribed "Void after June 30, 2013"

RW79 HP79 $15 multi 37.50 11.00
No gum 16.00
b. Souvenir sheet of 1 60.00
c. As "b," without artist's signature (error) *1,750.*

No. RW79b was sold for $25 plus a shipping fee. The artist signed No. RW79b on a designated line in the sheet margin. There is a back inscription on No. RW79b. Five thousand were prepared.

One No. RW79b was signed in red ink as a "surprise" for a random buyer. This was not authorized.

Self-Adhesive
Serpentine Die Cut 11x10¾

RW79A HP79 $15 multi 40.00 11.00
No gum 20.00

Common Goldeneye — HP80

2013 Litho. *Perf. 13¼*
Inscribed "Void after June 30, 2014"

RW80 HP80 $15 multi 37.50 11.00
No gum 16.00
b. Souvenir sheet of 1 80.00
c. As "b," without artist's signature (error) *1,250.*

No. RW80b was sold for $25 plus a shipping fee. The artist signed No. RW80b on a designated line in the sheet margin. There is a back inscription on No. RW80b. Five thousand were prepared.

Self-Adhesive
Serpentine Die Cut 11x10¾

RW80A HP80 $15 multi 35.00 11.00
No gum 20.00

Canvasbacks — HP81

2014 Litho. *Perf. 13¼*
Inscribed "Void after June 30, 2015"

RW81 HP81 $15 multi 40.00 11.00
No gum 16.00

Self-Adhesive
Serpentine Die Cut 11x10¾

RW81A HP81 $15 multi 40.00 12.50
No gum 20.00

Ruddy Ducks — HP82

2015 Litho. *Perf. 13¼*
Inscribed "Void after June 30, 2016"

RW82 HP82 $25 multi 55.00 12.00
No gum 25.00

Self-Adhesive
Serpentine Die Cut 11x10¾

RW82A HP82 $25 multi 55.00 12.50
No gum 32.50

Trumpeter Swans — HP83

2016 Litho. *Perf. 13¼*
Inscribed "Void after June 30, 2017"

RW83 HP83 $25 multi 90.00 15.00
No gum 40.00

Self-Adhesive
Serpentine Die Cut 11x10¾

RW83A HP83 $25 multi 65.00 12.50
No gum 32.50

Canada Geese — HP84

2017 Litho. *Perf. 13¼*
Inscribed "Void after June 30, 2018"

RW84 HP84 $25 multi 45.00 12.50
No gum 25.00

Self-Adhesive
Serpentine Die Cut 11x10¾

RW84A HP84 $25 multi 40.00 12.50
No gum 32.50

Mallards — HP85

Serpentine Die Cut 11x10¾
2018 Litho.
Inscribed "Void after June 30, 2019"
Self-Adhesive

RW85 HP85 $25 multi 55.00 12.50
No gum 25.00
b. Souvenir sheet of 4 200.00

Sheet of 1

RW85A HP85 $25 multi 50.00 12.50
No gum 32.50

Inscriptions on the backing paper differ for Nos. RW85, RW85A, and RW85b. Once removed from the backing paper, used examples are considered to be No. RW85.

Wood Duck and Decoy — HP86

Serpentine Die Cut 11x10¾
2019 Litho.
Inscribed "Void after June 30, 2020"
Self-Adhesive

RW86 HP86 $25 multi 45.00 12.50
No gum 25.00

Sheet of 1

RW86A HP86 $25 multi 45.00 12.50
No gum 32.50

Inscriptions on the backing paper differ for Nos. RW86 and RW86A. Once removed from the backing paper, used examples are considered to be No. RW86.

Black-bellied Whistling Ducks — HP87

Serpentine Die Cut 11x10¾
2020 Litho.
Inscribed "Void after June 30, 2021"
Self-Adhesive

RW87 HP87 $25 multi 37.50 12.50
No gum 25.00

Sheet of 1

RW87A HP87 $25 multi 37.50 12.50
No gum 32.50

Inscriptions on the backing paper differ for Nos. RW87 and RW87A. Once removed from the backing paper, used examples are considered to be No. RW87.

Lesser Scaup — HP88

Serpentine Die Cut 11x10¾
2021 Litho.
Inscribed "Void after June 30, 2022"
Self-Adhesive

RW88 HP88 $25 multi 37.50 12.50
No gum 25.00

Sheet of 1

RW88A HP88 $25 multi 37.50 12.50

Inscriptions on the backing paper differ for Nos. RW88 and RW88A. Once removed from the backing paper, used examples are considered to be No. RW88.

Redheads — HP89

Printed by Banknote Corporation of America.

Serpentine Die Cut 11x10¾
Litho., Engr. & Embossed
2022 Tagged
Inscribed "Void after June 30, 2023"
Self-Adhesive

RW89 HP89 $25 multi 37.50 12.50
No gum 25.00
P# block of 4 160.00

Sheet of 1

RW89A HP89 $25 multi 37.50 12.50

Inscriptions on the backing paper differ for Nos. RW89 and RW89A. Once removed from the backing paper, used examples are considered to be No. RW89.

CONFEDERATE STATES OF AMERICA

3¢ 1861 POSTMASTERS' PROVISIONALS

With the secession of South Carolina from the Union on Dec. 20, 1860, a new era began in U.S. history as well as its postal history. Other Southern states quickly followed South Carolina's lead, which in turn led to the formation of the provisional government of the Confederate States of America on Feb. 4, 1861.

President Jefferson Davis' cabinet was completed Mar. 6, 1861, with the acceptance of the position of Postmaster General by John H. Reagan of Texas. The provisional government had already passed regulations that required payment for postage in cash and that effectively carried over the U.S. 3c rate until the new Confederate Post Office Department took over control of the system.

Soon after entering on his duties, Reagan directed the postmasters in the Confederate States and in the newly seceded states to "continue the performance of their duties as such, and render all accounts and pay all moneys (sic) to the order of the Government of the U.S. as they have heretofore done, until the Government of the Confederate States shall be prepared to assume control of its postal affairs."

As coinage was becoming scarce, postal patrons began having problems buying individual stamps or paying for letters individually, especially as stamp stocks started to run short in certain areas. Even though the U.S. Post Office Department was technically in control of the postal system and southern postmasters were operating under Federal authority, the U.S.P.O. was hesitant in re-supplying seceded states with additional stamps and stamped envelopes.

The U.S. government had made the issuance of postmasters' provisionals illegal many years before, but the southern postmasters had to do what they felt was necessary to allow patrons to pay for postage and make the system work. Therefore, a few postmasters took it upon themselves to issue provisional stamps in the 3c rate then in effect.

Interestingly, these were stamps and envelopes that the U.S. government did not recognize as legal, but they did do postal duty unchallenged in the Confederate States. Yet the proceeds were to be remitted to the U.S. government in Washington! Six authenticated postmasters' provisionals in the 3c rate have been recorded.

On May 13, 1861, Postmaster General Reagan issued his proclamation "assuming control and direction of postal service within the limits of the Confederate States of America on and after the first day of June," with new postage rates and regulations.

The Federal government suspended operations in the Confederate States (except for western Virginia and the seceding state of Tennessee) by a proclamation issued by Postmaster General Montgomery Blair on May 27, 1861, effective from May 31, 1861, and June 10 for western and middle Tennessee.

As Tennessee did not join the Confederacy until July 2, 1861, the unissued 3c Nashville provisional was produced in a state that was in the process of seceding, while the other provisionals were used in the Confederacy before the June 1 assumption of control of postal service by the Confederate States of America.

Illustrations are reduced in size.

XU numbers are envelope entires.

DARLINGTON C.H., S. C.

E1

Handstamped Envelope

8AXU1 E1 3c black *3,500.*

One example of No. 8AXU1 is recorded, used under a pair of C.S.A. No. 7. To be a provisional, the 3¢ marking must be unused or used under Confederate stamps.

FORT VALLEY, GA.

E1

E2

Handstamped Envelope

7AXU1 E1 3c black —

HILLSBORO, N.C.

A1

Handstamped Adhesive

1AX1 A1 3c bluish black, on cover *11,500.*

No. 1AX1 is unique. This is the same handstamp as used for No. 39X1. 3c usage is determined from the May 27, 1861 circular date stamp.

JACKSON, MISS.

E1

Handstamped Envelope

2AXU1 E1 3c black *3,000.*

See Nos. 43XU1-43XU4.

No. 2AXU1 is unique. It is on a southern patriotic cover.

MADISON COURT HOUSE, FLA.

A1

"CNETS"

Typeset Adhesive

3AX1 A1 3c gold — *20,000.*
a. "CNETS" *22,500.*

No. 3AX1a is unique.

See No. 137XU1.

NASHVILLE, TENN.

A1

Typeset Adhesive (5 varieties)

4AX1 A1 3c carmine 400.

For more than 150 years, it has been believed that No. 4AX1 was prepared by Postmaster McNish with the U.S. rate, but it was not issued. Recent research and historical evidence indicate that this "stamp" most likely is a fantasy rather than a genuine stamp.

See Nos. 61X2-61XU2.

SELMA, ALA.

E1

Handstamped Envelope

5AXU1 E1 3c black *1,950.*

See Nos. 77XU1-77XU3.

TUSCUMBIA, ALA.

E1

Handstamped Envelope, impression at upper right

6AXU1 E1 3c dull red, *buff* *30,000.*

Dangerous forgeries exist of No. 6AXU1.

See Nos. 84XU1-84XU3.

For later additions, listed out of numerical sequence, see:
#*7AXU1*, Fort Valley, Ga.
#*8AXU1*, Darlington, C.H., S.C.

POSTMASTERS' PROVISIONAL ISSUES

These stamps and envelopes were issued by individual postmasters generally between June 1, 1861, when the use of U.S. stamps stopped in the Confederacy, and Oct. 16, 1861, when the 1st Confederate Government stamps were issued.

They were occasionally issued at later periods, especially in Texas, when regular issues of Government stamps were unavailable.

Canceling stamps of the post offices were often used to produce envelopes, some of which were supplied in advance by private citizens.

These envelopes and other stationery therefore may be found in a wide variety of papers, colors, sizes & shapes, including patriotic and semi-official types.

It is often difficult to determine whether the impression made by the canceling stamp indicates provisional usage or merely postage paid at the time the letter was deposited in the post office. Occasionally the same mark was used for both purposes.

The *press-printed* provisional envelopes are in a different category. They were produced in quantity, using envelopes procured in advance by the postmaster, such as those of Charleston, Lynchburg, Memphis, etc.

The press-printed envelopes are listed and valued on all known papers.

The handstamped provisional envelopes are listed and valued according to type and variety of handstamp, but not according to paper. Many exist on such a variety of papers that they defy accurate, complete listing.

The value of a handstamped provisional envelope is determined *primarily* by the clarity of the markings and its overall condition and attractiveness, rather than type of paper.

All handstamped provisional envelopes, when used, should also show the postmark of the town of issue.

Most handstamps are impressed at top right, although they exist from some towns in other positions.

Illustrations in this section are reduced in size.

XU numbers are envelope entires.

ABERDEEN, MISS.

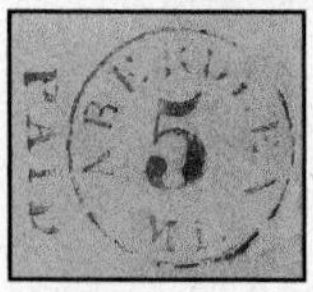

E1

Handstamped Envelopes

1XU1 E1 5c black — *5,500.*
a. 10c (ms.) on 5c black — *9,000.*

No. 1XU1a is unique.

ABINGDON, VA.

E1

Handstamped Envelopes

2XU1 E1 2c black — *12,500.*
a. 5c (ms.) on 2c black — *15,000.*
2XU2 E1 5c black — *1,500.*
2XU3 E1 10c black — *2,200.* *3,500.*

No. 2XU1 is unique. No. 2XU3 unused and used are each unique.

ALBANY, GA.

E1

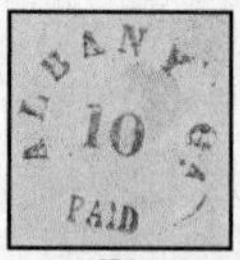

E2

E3

E4

Handstamped Envelopes

3XU1 E1 5c greenish blue — 1,000.
3XU2 E2 10c greenish blue — *1,750.*
a. 10c on 5c greenish blue — *3,500.*
3XU5 E3 5c greenish blue — —
3XU6 E4 10c greenish blue — *3,500.*

Only one example each recorded of Nos. 3XU2, 3XU2a and 3XU6. No. 3XU2 is a cover front only and is valued as such. No. 3XU2a is the unique Confederate example of one provisional marking revaluing another.

The existence of No. 3XU5 is in question. The editors would like to see an authenticated example of this marking.

ANDERSON COURT HOUSE, S.C.

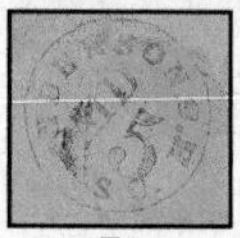

E1

E2

E3

Handstamped Envelopes

4XU1 E1 5c black — 1,000. *2,750.*
4XU2 E2 10c (ms.) black — *2,500.*
4XU3 E3 (2c) black, denomination omitted (circular rate) — *2,250.*

ATHENS, GA

A1 — Type I

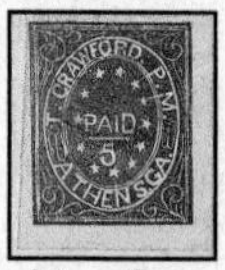

A1 — Type II

E1

Typographed Adhesives (from woodcuts of two types)

Pairs, both horizontal and vertical, always show one of each type.

5X1 A1 5c purple (shades) — 1,000. 1,400.
a. Tete beche pair (vertical) — *7,500.*
5X2 A1 5c red, type II — 5,750. 3,000.

The colorless ornaments in the four corners of No. 5X2 were recut making them wider than those in No. 5X1.

Dangerous fakes exist of Nos. 5X1 and 5X2. Certificates of authenticity from recognized committees are strongly recommended.

No. 5X2 is unique.

Handstamped Envelopes

5XU1 E1 10c black, on patriotic cover — *2,500.*

The markings on No. 5XU1 are the same as those used on stampless envelopes. On the unique listed example of No. 5XU1, there is a handwritten note on the inside of the flap: 'Andrew had these envelopes stamped & I am obliged to use them or loose the postage.' Two or more similar covers from the same correspondence are known, but without the note under the flap. While these also may be provisional use, it cannot be proven, and these covers are considered handstamp paid covers.

ATLANTA, GA.

E1

E2

E3

E4

Handstamped Envelopes

6XU1 E1 5c red — *5,000.*
6XU2 E1 5c black — 160. 700.
a. 10c on 5c black — *2,500.*
6XU4 E3 2c black — *2,750.*
6XU5 E3 5c black — 1,250.
a. 10c on 5c black — *2,500.*
6XU6 E4 10c black — 600.

Only one example recorded of No. 6XU1.

E3

Handstamped Envelopes

6XU8 E3 5c black — 3,500.
6XU9 E3 10c black ("10" upright) — 3,000.

Only one example recorded of No. 6XU8.

AUSTIN, MISS.

E1

Press-printed Envelope (typeset)

8XU1 E1 5c red, *amber* — *75,000.*

One example recorded.

AUSTIN, TEX.

E1a

Handstamped Adhesive

9X1 E1a 10c black, *white* or *buff* — —

Handstamped Envelope

9XU1 E1a 10c black — 2,500.

AUTAUGAVILLE, ALA.

E1

E2

Handstamped Envelopes

10XU1 E1 5c black — *20,000.*
10XU2 E2 5c black — *20,000.*

No. 10XU2 is unique.

BALCONY FALLS, VA.

E1

Handstamped Envelope

122XU1 E1 10c blue — *2,000.*

The use of No. 122XU1 as a provisional marking is in question. The editors would like to see authenticated evidence of its use as a provisional.

BARNWELL COURT HOUSE, S. C.

E1

Handstamped Envelope

123XU1 E1 5c black — *3,000.*

These are two separate handstamps.

All recorded uses are on addressed covers without postmarks.

BATON ROUGE, LA.

A1

A2

Typeset Adhesives

Ten varieties of each

11X1 A1 2c green — *8,250.* *5,000.*
a. "McCcrmick" — *35,000.* *35,000.*
11X2 A2 5c **green & carmine** — 1,500. 1,400.
a. "McCcrmick" — *10,000.* *3,500.*

Only one example each is recorded of No. 11X1a unused, used and on cover.

A3

A4

Ten varieties of each

11X3 A3 5c green & carmine — *10,000.* *4,000.*
a. "McCcrmick" — *32,500.*
11X4 A4 10c blue — *50,000.*

BEAUFORT, S. C.

E1

Handstamped Envelope

150XU1 E1 5c black — — *3,500.*

To be the No. 150XU1 provisional, the cover must be unused, used under a Confederate stamp, or used from another town. Two examples are recorded.

BEAUMONT, TEX.

A1

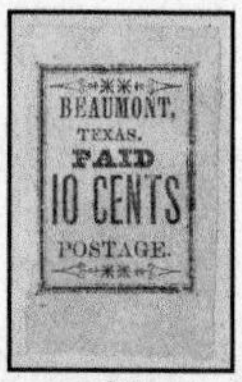

A2

Typeset Adhesives

Several varieties of each

12X1 A1 10c black, *yellow* — *65,000.*
12X2 A1 10c black, *pink* — *40,000.*
12X3 A2 10c black, *yellow*, on cover — *250,000.*

One example recorded of No. 12X3. Value represents auction realization in 2019.

BLUFFTON, S. C.

E1

Handstamped Envelope

124XU1 E1 5c black — *4,750.*

Only one example recorded of No. 124XU1.

BRIDGEVILLE, ALA.

A1

Handstamped Adhesive in black within red pen-ruled squares

13X1 A1 5c black & red, pair on cover — *20,000.*

CAMDEN, S. C.

E1

E2

Handstamped Envelopes

125XU1 E1 5c black — *2,500.*
125XU2 E2 10c black — *750.*

No. 125XU2 unused was privately carried and is addressed but has no postal markings. No. 125XU2 is indistinguishable from a handstamp paid cover when used.

CANTON, MISS.

E1

"P" in star is initial of Postmaster William Priestly.

Handstamped Envelopes

14XU1 E1 5c black — *2,000.*
  a. 10c (ms.) on 5c black — *4,500.*

CAROLINA CITY, N. C.

E1

Handstamped Envelope

118XU1 E1 5c black — *5,000.*

CARTERSVILLE, GA.

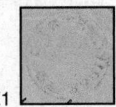

E1

Handstamped Envelope

126XU1 E1 (5c) red — *1,500.*

CHAPEL HILL, N. C.

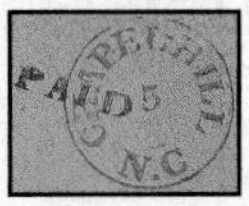

E1

Handstamped Envelope

15XU1 E1 5c black — *4,500.*

CHARLESTON, S. C.

A1

E1

E2

Lithographed Adhesive

16X1 A1 5c blue — 1,400. 800.

Values are for stamps showing parts of the outer frame lines on at least 3 sides. The vast majority of this stamp small faults and are valued thus. Completely sound examples are scarce and sell for more.

Press-printed Envelopes (typographed from woodcut)

16XU1 E1 5c blue — 1,250. *1,750.*
16XU2 E1 5c blue, *amber* — 1,250. *2,250.*
16XU3 E1 5c blue, *orange* — 1,250. *2,250.*
16XU4 E1 5c blue, *buff* — 1,250. *1,500.*
16XU5 E1 5c blue, *blue* — 1,250. *2,250.*
16XU6 E2 10c blue, *orange* — *55,000.*

The No. 16XU6 used entire is unique; value based on 2022 auction sale.
Beware of fakes of the E1 design.

Handstamped Cut Square

16XU7 E2 10c black — *2,000.*

There is only one example of No. 16XU7. It is a cutout, not an entire. It may not have been mailed from Charleston, and it may not have paid postage.

CHARLOTTE, N. C.

E1

146XU1 E1 5c blue, "5" in circle and straight line "PAID" — *3,500.*

CHARLOTTESVILLE, VA.

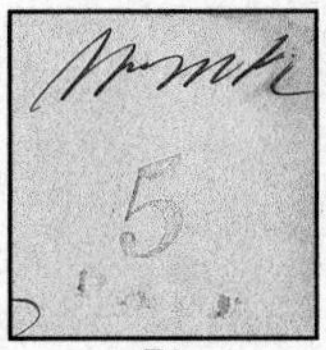

E1

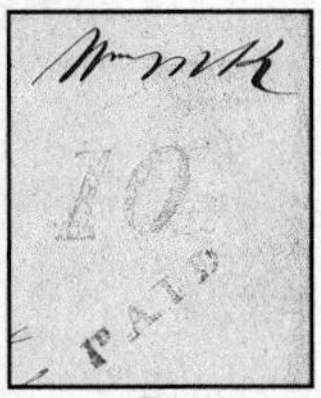

E2

Handstamped Envelopes, Manuscript Initials "WmMK"

127XU1 E1 5c blue — *2,250.*
127XU2 E2 10c blue — *2,250.*

The control initials appear at the upper right on the front of the envelope.

CHATTANOOGA, TENN.

E1

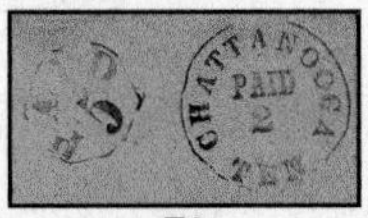

E2

Handstamped Envelopes

17XU2 E1 5c black — 1,900.
17XU3 E2 5c on 2c black — *5,000.*

No. 17XU3 is unique.

CHRISTIANSBURG, VA.

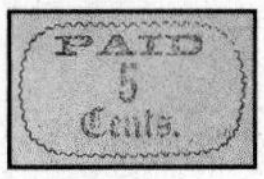

E1

Handstamped Envelopes

Impressed at top right

99XU1 E1 5c black — *2,250.*
99XU2 E1 5c blue — *2,000.*
99XU4 E1 5c green on U.S. envelope No. U27 — *4,250.*
99XU5 E1 10c blue — *3,500.*

The absence of 5c and 10c handstamped paid markings from this town suggests that Nos. 99XU1-99XU5 were used as both provisional and handstamped paid markings.

COLAPARCHEE, GA.

E1

Control

Handstamped Envelope

119XU1 E1 5c black — *3,500.*

There are only two recorded examples of No. 119XU1, and both are used from Savannah with a general issue stamp.
The control appears on the front of the envelope.

COLUMBIA, S. C.

Oval Control

Circular Control

E1

E2

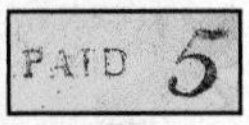

E3

E4

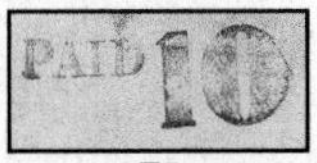

E5

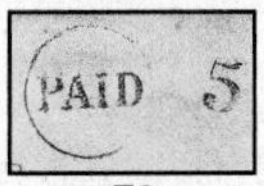

E6

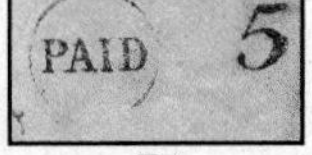

E7

E8

Handstamped Envelopes

18XU1 E1 5c blue — 550. *1,500.*
  a. 10c on 5c blue — *3,500.*
18XU4 E2 5c blue, oval control on front — *2,500.*
  a. Oval control on back — *1,100.*
18XU7 E3 5c blue, oval control on back — 1,000.
18XU8 E4 5c blue oval control on back — 1,000.
  a. Circular control on back — 2,000.
18XU9 E4 10c blue oval control on back — 1,250.
18XU10 E5 10c blue oval control on back — 1,500.
18XU11 E6 5c blue oval control on front — *2,500.*
18XU12 E6 10c blue oval control on back — 1,250.
18XU13 E7 5c blue oval control on back — 1,000.
  a. Circular control on back — 2,000.
18XU14 E8 5c blue oval control on back — 1,000.
  a. No control (unused) — —

COLUMBIA, TENN.

E1

Handstamped Envelope

113XU1 E1 5c red — *6,000.*

One example recorded.

COLUMBUS, GA.

E1

Handstamped Envelopes

19XU1 E1 5c blue — *900.*
19XU2 E1 10c red — *3,250.*

COURTLAND, ALA.

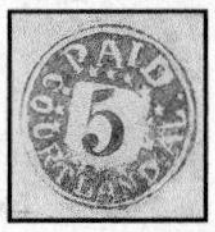

E1

Handstamped Envelopes (from woodcut)

103XU1 E1 5c red — *32,500.*

One example recorded.

CUTHBERT, GA

E1

Handstamped Envelope

95XU1 E1 10c black — *1,000.*

The unique example of No. 95XU1 was used by having a C.S.A. 10c #12c placed over it.

DALTON, GA

E1

Handstamped Envelopes

20XU1 E1 5c black — *750.*
  a. Denomination omitted (5c rate) — *875.*
  b. 10c (ms.) on 5c black — 1,500.
  c. 20c (ms.) on 5c black — —
20XU2 E1 10c black — 1,100.

DANVILLE, VA.

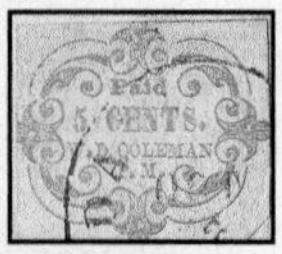
A1

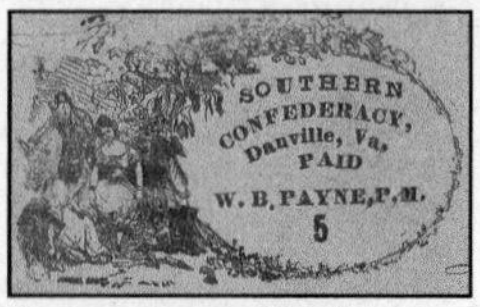
Design measures 60x37mm — E1

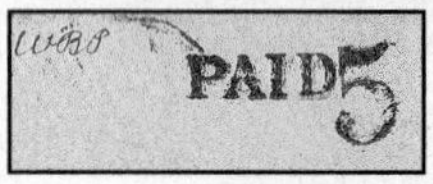
E2

E3

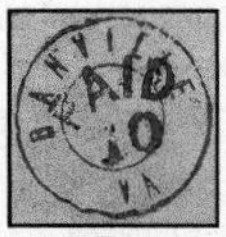
E4

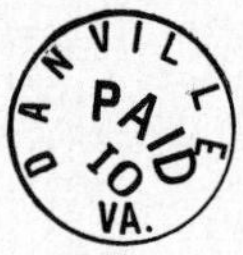
E5

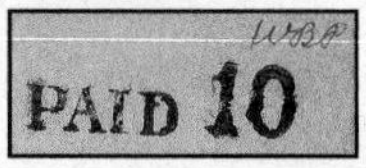
E6

Typeset Adhesive
Wove Paper

21X1 A1 5c red *7,500.*

Two varieties known.

Laid Paper

21X2 A1 5c red *10,000.*

No. 21X2 is unique.

Press-printed Envelopes (typographed)

Two types: "SOUTHERN" in straight or curved line

Impressed (usually) at top left

21XU1 E1 5c black *5,000.*
21XU2 E1 5c black, *light yellowish* *5,000.*
21XU3 E1 5c black, *dark buff* *5,000.*

Unissued 10c envelopes (type E1, in red) are known. All recorded examples are envelopes that show evidence of added stamps being torn off.

Dangerous forgeries exist of No. 21XU1.

Handstamped Envelopes

21XU3A E2 5c black (ms "WBP" initials) *1,000.*
21XU3B E3 5c black (ms "WPB" initials) *8,500.*
21XU4 E4 10c black *2,500.*
21XU6 E5 10c black *2,750.*
21XU7 E6 10c black (ms "WBP" initials) —

Types E4 and E5 both exist on one cover.

On No. 21XU3B, the "PAID 5 Cents" handstamp is to the left, and the "PAID" and ms. "5" are toward the right. It is unique.

DEMOPOLIS, ALA.

E1

Handstamped Envelopes, Signature in ms.

22XU1 E1 5c black ("Jno. T. Hall") *3,500.*
22XU2 E1 5c black ("J. T. Hall") *3,500.*
22XU3 E1 5c (ms.) black ("J. T. Hall") *4,000.*

EATONTON, GA.

E1

E2

Handstamped Envelopes

23XU1 E1 5c black *3,000.*
a. 10 (ms) on 5c black —
23XU2 E2 5c + 5c black *5,500.*

EMORY, VA.

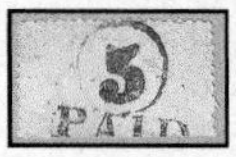
A1

Handstamped Adhesives ("PAID" and "5" in circle on selvage of U.S. 1c 1857 issue)

Perf. 15 on three sides

24X1 A1 5c blue, on cover, tied *27,500.*
On cover, not tied *22,500.*

Also known with "5" above "PAID."

E1

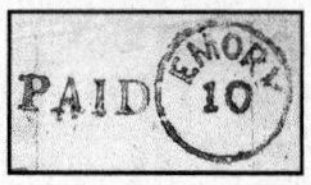
E2

Handstamped Envelopes

24XU1 E1 5c blue *4,000.*
24XU2 E2 10c blue *5,000.*

One example each recorded of Nos. 24XU1 and 24XU2.

FINCASTLE, VA.

E1

Press-printed Envelope (typeset)

Impressed at top right

104XU1 E1 10c black *20,000.*

One example recorded of No. 104XU1.

FORSYTH, GA.

E1

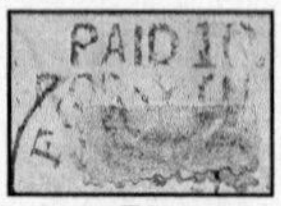
E2

Handstamped Envelope

120XU1 E1 10c black *2,000.*
120XU2 E2 10c black *1,250.*

Only one example each recorded of Nos. 120XU1 and 120XU2.

FORT VALLEY, GA.

E1

E2

Handstamped Envelope

148XU1 E1 5c on 3c black *3,250.*

Black circle control on front of envelope. Unique.

FRANKLIN, N. C.

E1

E2

Press-printed Envelope (typeset) (No. 25XU1)

Impressed at top right

25XU1 E1 5c blue, *buff* *30,000.*
25XU2 E2 5c black, large "5" woodcut in 31mm circular town mark *2,500.*

The one known No. 25XU1 envelope shows black circular Franklin postmark with manuscript date.

FRAZIERSVILLE, S. C.

E1

Handstamped Envelope, "5" manuscript

128XU1 E1 5c black *5,000.*

Only one example recorded of No. 128XU1.

FREDERICKSBURG, VA.

A1

Sheets of 20, two panes of 10 varieties each

Typeset Adhesives
Thin bluish paper

26X1 A1 5c blue, *bluish* *1,000.* *2,000.*
26X2 A1 10c red (shades), *bluish* *2,250.*

GAINESVILLE, ALA.

E1

E2

E3

Handstamped Envelopes

27XU1 E1 5c black *4,500.*
27XU2 E2 5c black *5,000.*
27XU3 E3 10c ("01") black *12,000.*

GALVESTON, TEX.

E1

Handstamped Envelopes

98XU1 E1 5c black 500. *1,500.*
98XU2 E1 10c black *2,500.*

E2

E3

Handstamped Envelopes

98XU3 E2 10c black 550. *2,750.*
98XU4 E2 20c black *3,500.*
98XU5 E3 5c black *4,500.*

GASTON, N. C.

E1

Handstamped Envelope

129XU1 E1 5c black *6,000.*

Only one example recorded of No. 129XU1.

GEORGETOWN, S. C.

E1

Control

E2

Handstamped Envelopes

28XU1 E1 5c black *1,000.*
28XU2 E2 5c black, separate "5" and straightline "PAID" handstamps, control on reverse — *1,750.*

GOLIAD, TEX.

A1

A2

Typeset Adhesives

29X1 A1 5c black *16,500.*
29X2 A1 5c black, *gray* *11,500.*
29X3 A1 5c black, *rose* *12,000.*
29X4 A1 10c black — *25,000.*
29X5 A1 10c black, *rose* *12,000.*

Type A1 stamps are signed "Clarke-P.M." vertically in black or red.

29X6 A2 5c black, *gray* *22,500.*
a. "GOILAD" *12,000.*
29X7 A2 10c black, *bluish gray* *12,000.*
a. "GOILAD" *15,000.*
29X8 A2 5c black, *dark blue,* on cover *18,000.*
29X9 A2 10c black, *dark blue* *27,500.*

GONZALES, TEX.

Colman & Law were booksellers when John B. Law (of the firm) was appointed Postmaster. The firm used a small lithographed label on drugs and on the front or inside of books they sold.

A1

Lithographed Adhesives on colored glazed paper

30X1 A1 (5c) gold, *dark blue,* pair on cover, *1861* — *15,000.*
30X2 A1 (10c) gold, *garnet,* on cover, *1864* — *80,000.*
30X3 A1 (10c) gold, *black,* on cover, *1865* — *35,000.*

No. 30X1 must bear double-circle town cancel as validating control. The control was applied to the labels in the sheet before their sale as stamps. When used, the stamps bear an additional Gonzales double-circle postmark.

GREENSBORO, ALA.

E1

E2

E3

Handstamped Envelopes

31XU1 E1 5c black — *3,250.*
31XU2 E1 10c black — *3,750.*
31XU3 E2 10c black — *6,000.*
31XU4 E3 10c on 5c black — *3,000.*

GREENSBORO, N. C.

E1

Handstamped Envelope

32XU1 E1 10c red — 1,250.

GREENVILLE, ALA.

A1

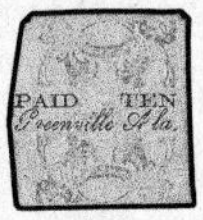

A2

Typeset Adhesives On pinkish surface-colored glazed paper.

33X1 A1 5c blue & red — *28,000.*
33X2 A2 10c red & blue, on cover — *47,500.*

Two used examples each are known of Nos. 33X1-33X2, and all are on covers. Covers bear a postmark but it was not used to cancel the stamps.

The former No. 33X1a has been identified as a fake.

GREENVILLE, TENN.

E1

144XU1 E1 5c black — *5,000.*

Only one example of No. 144XU1 is recorded.

GREENVILLE COURT HOUSE, S. C.

E1

E2

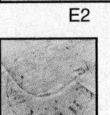

Control A

Control B

Control C

Handstamped Envelopes (Several types)

34XU1 E1 5c black — *2,000.*
34XU2 E2 10c black — *2,000.*
a. 20c (ms.) on 10c black — *3,000.*

Envelopes must bear one of three different postmark controls on the back. When the control postmark is dated, the date must be the same or prior to the date of the postmark on the front of the envelope.

GREENWOOD DEPOT, VA.

A1

"PAID" Handstamped Adhesive ("PAID" with value and signature in ms.) Laid Paper

35X1 A1 10c black, *gray blue,* on cover — *40,000.*

GRIFFIN, GA.

E1

Handstamped Envelopes

102XU1 E1 5c black — 2,000.
102XU2 E1 10c black — *5,000.*

No. 102XU2 is on a large piece of an envelope with July 25 postmark at left. It is unique.

GROVE HILL, ALA.

A1

Handstamped Adhesive (from woodcut)

36X1 A1 5c black — *125,000.*

Two examples are recorded. One is on cover tied by the postmark. The other is canceled by magenta pen on a cover front. Value is for the complete cover.

HALLETTSVILLE, TEX.

A1

Handstamped Adhesive Ruled Letter Paper

37X1 A1 10c black, *gray blue,* on cover — *10,000.*

One example known.

HAMBURGH, S. C.

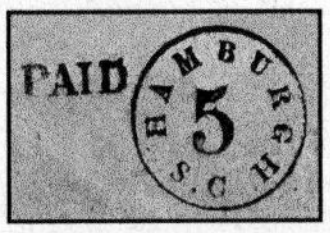

E1

Handstamped Envelope

112XU1 E1 5c black — *8,000.*

HARRISBURGH (Harrisburg), TEX.

E1

E2

Handstamped Envelope

130XU1 E1 5c black — *5,500.*
130XU2 E2 10c black — —

The unused 5c entire is the only example recorded of No. 130XU1

HELENA, TEX.

A1

Typeset Adhesives
Several varieties

38X1 A1 5c black, *buff* — *22,500.* *20,000.*
38X2 A1 10c black, *gray* — *40,000.*

On 10c "Helena" is in upper and lower case italics.

Used examples are valued with small faults or repairs, as all recorded have faults.

HILLSBORO, N. C.

A1

Handstamped Adhesive

39X1 A1 5c black, on cover — *10,000.*

See 3c 1861 Postmaster's Provisional No. 1AX1.

No. 39X1 is unique.

Ms./Handstamped Envelope

39XU1 E1 10c "paid 10" in manuscript with undated blue town cancel as control on face — *2,250.*

No. 39XU1 is unique.

HOLLANDALE, TEX.

E1

Handstamped Envelope

132XU1 E1 5c black — —

HOUSTON, TEX.

E1

No. 40XU1a

Handstamped Envelopes

40XU1 E1 5c red — — 800.
a. 10c (ms.) on 5c red — *6,500.*
40XU2 E1 10c red — — *1,750.*
40XU3 E1 10c black — *6,750.*
40XU4 E1 5c +10c red — *2,500.*
40XU5 E1 10c +10c red — *2,500.*

Nos. 40XU2-40XU5 show "TEX" instead of "TXS."

HUNTSVILLE, TEX.

E1

Control

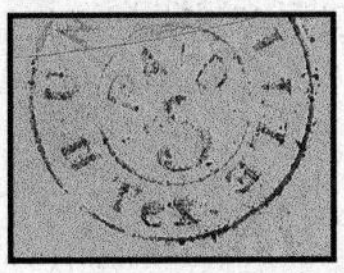

E2

E3

Handstamped Envelope

92XU1 E1 5c black — *5,000.*
92XU2 E2 5c black — —
92XU3 E3 10c black — —

INDEPENDENCE, TEX.

A1

A2

Handstamped Adhesives

41X1 A1 10c black, *buff,* on cover, uncanceled, cut to shape — *20,000.*
41X2 A1 10c black, *dull rose,* on cover — —

With small "10" and "Pd" in manuscript

41X3 A2 10c black, *buff,* on cover, uncanceled, cut to shape — *20,000.*

No. 41X1 is unique.

All known examples of Nos. 41X1-41X3 are uncanceled on covers with black "INDEPENDANCE TEX." (sic) postmark.

The existence of No. 41X2 has been questioned by specialists. The editors would like to see authenticated evidence of the existence of this item.

ISABELLA, GA.

E1

Handstamped Envelope, Manuscript "5"

133XU1 E1 5c black *5,000.*

Only one example recorded of No. 133XU1.

IUKA, MISS.

E1

Handstamped Envelope

42XU1 E1 5c black *1,750.*

JACKSON, MISS.

E1

Handstamped Envelopes

Two types of numeral

43XU1 E1 5c black 900.
a. 10c on 5c black *2,750.*
b. 5c on 3c black *1,500.*
43XU2 E1 10c black *2,000.*
a. 5c on 10c black *3,750.*
43XU4 E1 10c on 5c blue *2,750.*

The 5c also exists on a lettersheet.

See 3c 1861 Postmaster's Provisional No. 2AXU1.

JACKSONVILLE, ALA.

E1

Handstamped Envelope

110XU1 E1 5c black — *3,000.*

JACKSONVILLE, FLA.

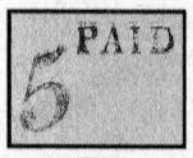

E1

Control

Handstamped Envelope

134XU1 E1 5c black *4,000.*

Undated double circle postmark control on reverse. No. 134XU1 is unique.

JETERSVILLE, VA.

A1

Handstamped Adhesive ("5" with ms. "AHA." initials)

Laid Paper

44X1 A1 5c black, vertical pair on cover, uncanceled *16,000.*

JONESBORO, TENN.

E1

Handstamped Envelopes

45XU1 E1 5c black *6,000.*
45XU2 E1 5c dark blue *5,000.*

KINGSTON, GA.

E1

E2

E3

E4

Typeset Envelopes

(design types E1-E2, E4 are handstamps; typeset design E3 probably impressed by hand but possibly press printed)

46XU1 E1 5c black 3,000.
46XU2 E2 5c black *10,000.*
a. Without "CS" at sides of "5" *3,500.*
46XU4 E3 5c black *12,500.*
46XU5 E4 5c black *2,000.*

There is only one recorded example of No. 46XU4.

KNOXVILLE, TENN.

A1

Typographed Adhesives (stereotype from woodcut)

Grayish Laid Paper

47X1 A1 5c brick red *1,750.* 1,400.
47X2 A1 5c carmine *2,750.* *2,250.*
47X3 A1 10c green, on cover *57,750.*

The #47X3 cover is unique. Value is based on 1997 auction sale.

E1

E2

Press-printed Envelopes (typographed)

47XU1 E1 5c blue *2,500.*
47XU2 E1 5c blue, *orange* *5,000.*
47XU3 E1 10c red (cut to shape) *7,000.*
47XU4 E1 10c red, *orange* (cut to shape) *6,000.*

Only one example each recorded of Nos. 47XU3 and 47XU4.

Dangerous fakes exist of Nos. 47XU1 and 47XU2.

Handstamped Envelopes

47XU5 E2 5c black *1,400.*
a. 10c on 5c black *3,500.*

Type E2 exists with "5" above or below "PAID."

LA GRANGE, TEX.

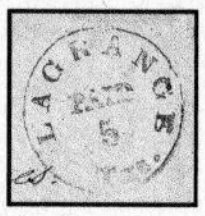

E1

Handstamped Envelopes

48XU1 E1 5c black — 3,250.
48XU2 E1 10c black 3,250.

LAKE CITY, FLA.

E1

Control Type A

Control Type B

Handstamped Envelope

96XU1 E1 10c black *4,000.*

Envelopes have black circle control mark, or printed name of E. R. Ives, postmaster, on back.

LAURENS COURT HOUSE, S. C.

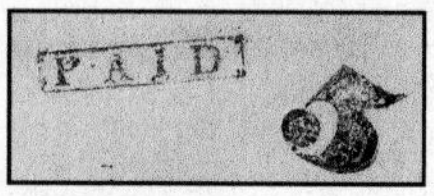

E1

E2

Control

Handstamped Envelopes

116XU1 E1 5c black *2,000.*
116XU2 E2 5c black *2,000.*

Envelopes have a 25mm undated control mark on reverse. No. 116XU1 is unique.

LENOIR, N. C.

A1

A2

E1

Handstamped Adhesive (from woodcut)

White wove paper with cross-ruled orange lines

49X1 A1 5c blue & orange *7,250.* *6,750.*

Handstamped Envelopes

49XU1 A1 5c blue *4,000.*
49XU2 A2 10c (5c+5c) blue *25,000.*
49XU3 E1 5c blue *4,500.*
49XU4 E1 5c black *4,500.*

No. 49XU2 is unique.

LEXINGTON, MISS.

E1

Handstamped Envelopes

50XU1 E1 5c black *3,750.*
50XU2 E1 10c black *5,000.*

Only one example is recorded of No. 50XU2.

LEXINGTON, VA.

E1

Handstamped Envelopes

135XU1 E1 5c blue *350.*
135XU2 E1 10c blue *350.*

Nos. 135XU1-135XU2 by themselves are indistinguishable from stampless covers when used.

LIBERTY, VA. (and Salem, Va.)

A1

Typeset Adhesive (probably impressed by hand)

Laid Paper

74X1 A1 5c black, on cover, uncanceled *25,000.*

Two known on covers with Liberty, Va. postmark; one cover known with the nearby Salem, Va. office postmark.

LIMESTONE SPRINGS, S. C.

A1

Handstamped Adhesive

121X1 A1 5c black, *light blue*, on cover *10,000.*
121X2 A1 5c black, *white*, two on cover *32,500.*

Stamps are cut round or rectangular. Covers are not postmarked. The No. 121X2 cover bears the only two recorded examples of this stamp.

LIVINGSTON, ALA.

A1

Lithographed Adhesive

51X1 A1 5c blue *10,000.*

LYNCHBURG, VA.

A1

E1

Typographed Adhesive (stereotype from woodcut)

52X1 A1 5c blue (shades) *1,800.* *1,500.*

Press-printed Envelopes (typographed)

Impressed at top right or left

52XU1 E1 5c black *700.00* *3,000.*
52XU2 E1 5c black, *amber* *3,000.*
52XU3 E1 5c black, *buff* *3,000.*
52XU4 E1 5c black, *brown* *3,000.*

MACON, GA.

A1

A2

A3

A4

Typeset Adhesives
Several varieties of type A1, 10 of A2, 5 of A3

Wove Paper

53X1 A1 5c black, *light blue green* (shades) 1,250. 1,000.

Warning: Dangerous forgeries exist of the normal variety and the Comma after "OFFICE" variety. Certificates of authenticity from recognized committees are strongly recommended.

53X3 A2 5c black, *yellow* 2,500. 1,250.
53X4 A3 5c black, *yellow* (shades) 3,000. 3,000.
a. Vertical tête bêche pair, on cover *60,000.*
53X5 A4 2c black, *gray green* —

Laid Paper

53X6 A2 5c black, *yellow* *6,000.* *6,000.*
53X7 A3 5c black, *yellow* *6,000.*
53X8 A1 5c black, *light blue green* 1,750. *2,250.*

No. 53X4a is unique.

E1

Handstamped Envelope

Two types: "PAID" over "5," "5" over "PAID"

53XU1 E1 5c black 250. 650.

Values are for "PAID" over "5" variety. "5" over "PAID" is much scarcer.

MADISON, GA.

E1

Handstamped Envelope

136XU1 E1 5c red *600.*

No. 136XU1 is indistinguishable from a handstamp paid cover when used.

MADISON COURT HOUSE, FLA.

E1

Typeset Envelope

137XU1 E1 5c black, *yellow* *35,000.*

No. 137XU1 is unique.

See 3c 1861 Postmaster's Provisional No. 3AX1.

MARIETTA, GA.

E1

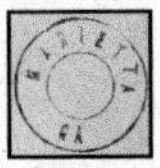
Control

E2

Handstamped Envelopes

54XU1 E1 5c black 500.
a. 10c on 5c black *1,750.*

With Double Circle Control

54XU3 E1 10c black
54XU4 E2 5c black *2,000.*

The existence of No. 54XU3 has been questioned by specialists. The editors would like to see authenticated evidence that verifies this listing.

MARION, VA.

A1

Adhesives with Typeset frame and Handstamped numeral in center

55X1 A1 5c black *6,500.*
55X2 A1 10c black *10,000.* *10,000.*
55X2A A1 10c 10c black, *bluish,* tied on cover *15,000.*
55X3 A1 5c black, *bluish,* laid paper — —
55X4 A1 5c black, *bluish,* tied on cover 6,000.

The 2c, 3c, 15c and 20c are believed to be bogus items printed later using the original typeset frame.

MARS BLUFF, S. C.

E1

145XU1 E1 5c black *2,000.*

The No. 145XU1 marking is a provisional only when unused, used from another town or used under a general issue.

MEMPHIS, TENN.

A1

56X1a Partial Print

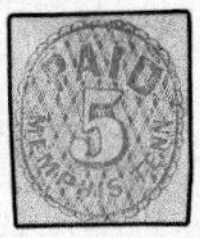
A2

Typographed Adhesives (stereotyped from woodcut)

56X1 A1 2c blue (shades) 100. *1,250.*
a. Partial print 250. —
56X2 A2 5c red (shades) 150. *250.*
a. Tête bêche pair *1,500.*
b. Pair, one sideways 2,500.
c. Pelure paper — —

Press-printed Envelopes (typographed)

56XU1 A2 5c red (shades) *3,000.*
56XU2 A2 5c red, *amber* *3,000.*
56XU3 A2 5c red, *orange* *2,500.*
56XU4 A2 5c red, *cream* *5,750.*

Only one example of No. 56XU4 is recorded. It is on a cover on which a C.S.A. No. 11 is affixed over the provisional to pay the postage.

MICANOPY, FLA.

E1

Handstamped Envelope

105XU1 E1 5c black *11,500.*

Two examples are recorded.

MILLEDGEVILLE, GA.

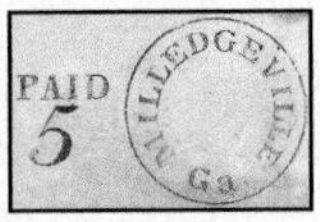
E1

E2

E3

Handstamped Envelopes

Two types of No. 57XU5: Type I, tall, thin "1" and "0" of "10"; Type II, short, fat "1" and "0" of "10."

57XU1 E1 5c black 800.
a. Wide spacing between "I" and "D" of "PAID" 900.
b. 10c on 5c black 1,250.
57XU2 E1 5c blue 800.
57XU4 E2 10c black 375. 1,200.
a. Wide spacing between "I" and "D" of "PAID" 1,200.
57XU5 E3 10c black, type I 450. 950.
a. Type II 1,500.

On No. 57XU4, the "PAID/10" virtually always falls outside the Milledgeville control marking (as in illustration E1).

The existence of No. 57XU2 as a provisional has been questioned by specialists. The editors would like to see authenticated evidence of provisional use of this marking.

MILTON, N. C.

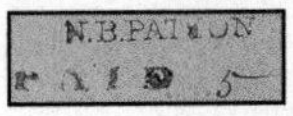
E1

Handstamped Envelope, "5" Manuscript

138XU1 E1 5c black *3,750.*

MOBILE, ALA.

A1

Lithographed Adhesives

58X1 A1 2c black 2,250. 1,200.
58X2 A1 5c blue 350. 450.

MONTGOMERY, ALA.

E1

E1a

Handstamped Envelopes

59XU1 E1 5c red *1,000.*
a. 10c on 5c red *2,750.*
59XU2 E1 5c blue 400. *1,000.*
59XU3 E1a 10c red *900.*
59XU4 E1a 10c blue *1,250.*
59XU5 E1a 10c black 850.

E2

E3

59XU7 E2 2c red *2,500.*
59XU7A E2 2c blue *3,500.*
59XU8 E2 5c black *2,000.*
59XU9 E3 10c black *2,000.*
59XU10 E3 10c red *1,750.*

The existence of No. 59XU10 is in question. The editors would like to see an authenticated example of this marking.

MOUNT LEBANON, LA.

A1

Woodcut Adhesive (mirror image of design)

60X1 A1 5c red brown, on cover *255,000.*

One example known. Value represents sale price at 2009 auction.

MOUNT PLEASANT, N. C.

E1

Handstamped Envelope

151XU1 E1 10c blue *3,500.*

One example of No. 151XU1 is recorded, posted in January 1866 and covered by a U.S. 3¢ stamp subsequently removed to reveal the provisional.

NASHVILLE, TENN.

A2

E1

Typographed Adhesives (stereotyped from woodcut)

Gray Blue Ribbed Paper

61X2 A2 5c carmine (shades) 1,000. 800.
a. Vertical tête bêche pair *4,000.*
61X3 A2 5c brick red (shades) 900. 850.
a. Vertical tête bêche pair *3,000.*
61X4 A2 5c gray (shades) 1,250. 1,500.
61X5 A2 5c violet brown (shades) 1,250. 750.
a. Vertical tete beche pair *5,000.* *7,500.*
61X6 A2 10c green — *3,750.*

Handstamped Envelopes

61XU1 E1 5c blue 900.
61XU2 E1 10c on 5c blue *2,750.*

See 3c Postmaster's Provisional No. 4AX1.

NEW ORLEANS, LA.

A1

A2

Typographed Adhesives (stereotyped from woodcut)

62X1 A1 2c blue 225. *800.*
a. Printed on both sides, on cover *10,500.*

62X2 A1 2c red (shades) 190. *1,000.*
62X3 A2 5c brown, *white* 300. 275.
a. Printed on both sides *3,750.*
b. 5c ocher 700. 625.
62X4 A2 5c red brn, *bluish* 325. 200.
a. Printed on both sides *3,000.*
62X5 A2 5c yel brn, *off-white* 160. *250.*
62X6 A2 5c red (shades) — *14,000.*
62X7 A2 5c red (shades), *bluish* *15,000.*

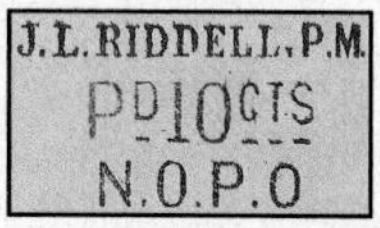

E1

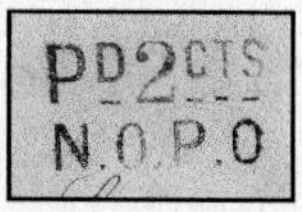

E2

Handstamped Envelopes

62XU1 E1 5c black 4,500.
62XU2 E1 10c black *11,500.*

"J. L. RIDDELL, P. M." omitted

62XU3 E2 2c black *8,500.*

Some authorities question the use of No. 62XU3 as a provisional.

NEW SMYRNA, FLA.

A1

Handstamped Adhesive

On white paper with blue ruled lines

63X1 A1 10c ("O1") on 5c black *50,000.*

One example known. It is uncanceled on a postmarked patriotic cover.

NORFOLK, VA.

E1

E2

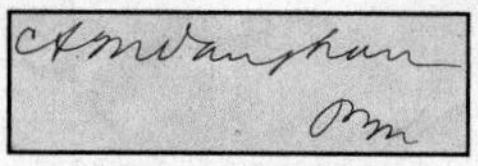
Manuscript Signature

Handstamped Envelopes

Ms Signature on Back

139XU1 E1 5c blue 1,000. *1,750.*
139XU2 E2 10c blue *1,750.*

OAKWAY, S. C.

A1

Handstamped Adhesive (from woodcut)

115X1 A1 5c black, on cover *60,000.*

Two used examples of No. 115X1 are recorded, both on cover. Value represents 2012 auction realization for the cover on which the stamp is tied by manuscript "Paid."

OXFORD, N. C.

E1

Handstamped Envelope

152XU1 E1 10c black *3,500.*

One example of No. 152XU1 is recorded, covered by a C.S.A. 10¢ No. 12 that paid the postage.

PATTERSON, N. C.

E1

E2

Control

Handstamped Envelopes

149XU1 E1 5c black *750.*
149XU2 E2 10c black *2,500.*

Nos. 149XU1 and 149XU2 must have an undated postmark on the cover as a control.

PENSACOLA, FLA.

E1

Handstamped Envelopes

106XU1 E1 5c black *5,000.*
a. 10c (ms.) on 5c black *5,250.*

PETERSBURG, VA.

A1

Typeset Adhesive

Ten varieties

65X1 A1 5c red (shades) *2,250.* 500.

PITTSYLVANIA COURT HOUSE, VA.

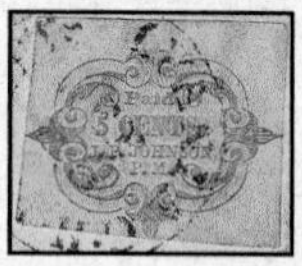
A1

Typeset Adhesives

66X1 A1 5c dull red, wove paper *7,500.* *9,000.*
66X2 A1 5c dull red, laid paper *5,500.*

PLAINS OF DURA, GA.

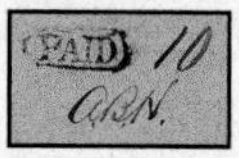
E1

Handstamped Envelopes, Ms. Initials

140XU1 E1 5c black —
140XU2 E1 10c black *5,000.*

No. 140XU2 is unique.

PLEASANT SHADE, VA.

A1

Typeset Adhesive

Five varieties

67X1 A1 5c blue *8,000.* *15,000.*

PLUM CREEK, TEX.

E1

Manuscript Adhesive

141X1 E1 10c black, *blue,* on cover *6,500.*

The stamps have ruled lines with the value "10" in manuscript. Size and shape vary.

PORT GIBSON, MISS.

E1

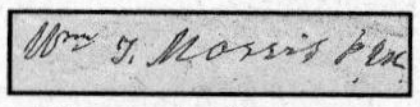
Manuscript Signature

Handstamped Envelope, Ms Signature

142XU1 E1 5c black —

PORT LAVACA, TEX.

A1

Typeset Adhesive

107X1 A1 10c black, on cover *27,000.*

One example known. It is uncanceled on a postmarked cover.

RALEIGH, N. C.

E1

Handstamped Envelopes

68XU1 E1 5c red 500.
68XU2 E1 5c blue *4,000.*

RHEATOWN, TENN.

A1

Typeset Adhesive

Three varieties

69X1 A1 5c red *6,000.* *6,500.*

RICHMOND, TEX.

E1

Handstamped Envelopes or Letter Sheets

70XU1 E1 5c red 2,250.
a. 10c on 5c red *11,750.*
70XU2 E1 10c red 2,000.
a. 15c (ms.) on 10c red *5,000.*

RINGGOLD, GA.

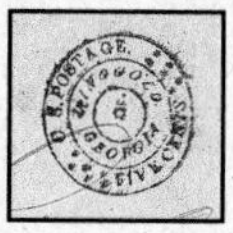
E1

Handstamped Envelope

71XU1 E1 5c blue black *8,500.*

RUTHERFORDTON, N. C.

A1

Handstamped Adhesive, Ms. "Paid 5cts"

72X1 A1 5c black, cut round, on cover (uncanceled) *60,000.*

No. 72X1 is unique.

SALEM, N. C.

"Paid 5" in Ms. — E1

"Paid 5" Handstamped — E2

Handstamped Envelopes

73XU1 E1 5c black 1,500.
73XU2 E1 10c black *3,500.*
73XU3 E2 5c black *2,250.*
a. 10c on 5c black *2,800.*

Reprints exist on various papers. They either lack the "Paid" and value or have them counterfeited.

Salem, Va.
See No. 74X1 under Liberty, Va.

SALISBURY, N. C.

E1

Press-printed Envelope (typeset)

Impressed at top left

75XU1 E1 5c black, *greenish* *15,000.*

One example known. Part of the envelope was torn away (now repaired), leaving part of design missing.

SAN ANTONIO, TEX.

E1

E2

Control

Handstamped Envelopes

76XU1 E1 10c black 500. *2,000.*
76XU1A E2 5c black *13,000.*
76XU2 E2 10c black *2,500.*

Black circle control mark is on front or back.
One example of No. 76XU1A is recorded.

SAVANNAH, GA.

E1

Control

E2

Handstamped Envelopes

101XU1 E1 5c black 450.
a. 10c on 5c black 1,500.
101XU2 E2 5c black 600.
a. 20c on 5c black *2,000.*
101XU3 E1 10c black 750.
101XU4 E2 10c black 750.

Envelopes must have octagonal control mark. One example is known of No.101XU2a.

SELMA, ALA.

E1

Handstamped Envelopes; Signature in Ms.

77XU1 E1 5c black *1,250.*
a. 10c on 5c black *3,000.*
77XU2 E1 10c black *2,500.*

Signature is that of Postmaster William H. Eagar.

See 3c 1861 Postmaster's Provisional No. 5AX1.

SPARTA, GA.

E1

Handstamped Envelopes

93XU1 E1 5c red — 2,250.
93XU2 E1 10c red *5,000.*

Only one example recorded of No. 93XU2.

SPARTANBURG, S. C.

A1

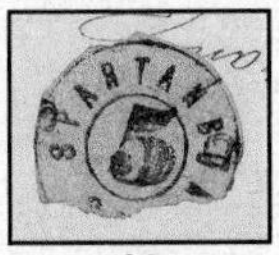
A2

Handstamped Adhesives
(on ruled or plain wove paper)

78X1 A1 5c black, cut to shape —
a. "Paid" instead of denomination, revalued to 5c with "PAID" and "5" in small circle handstamps, on cover *6,000.*

78X2 A2 5c black, *bluish,* on cover *9,000.*
78X3 A2 5c black, *brown* *4,000.*

Most examples of Nos. 78X1-78X3 are cut round. Cut square examples in sound condition are worth much more.

No. 78X1a is unique. Also, only one example of No. 78X2 is recorded; part of the stamp is missing, and the cover is valued thus.

E1

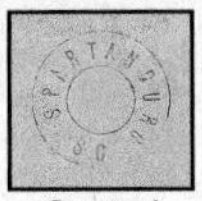
Control

Handstamped Envelopes

78XU1 E1 10c black (control on reverse) *5,000.*

STATESVILLE, N. C.

E1

Handstamped Envelopes

79XU1 E1 5c black *1,500.*
a. 10c on 5c black, handstamped "10" 3,000.
b. 10c on 5c black, manuscript "10" 2,500.

There are four identifiable varieties of No. 79XU1.

Unused examples of No. 79XU1 are reprints.

SUMTER, S. C.

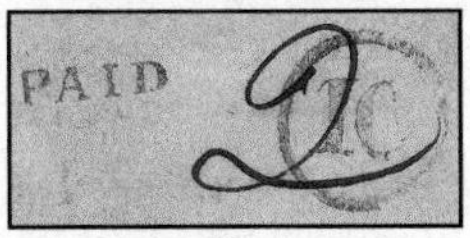

E1

Handstamped Envelopes

80XU1 E1 5c black 500.
a. 10c on 5c black *900.*
80XU2 E1 10c black 600.
a. 2c (ms.) on 10c black *1,100.*

Used examples of Nos. 80XU1-80XU2 are indistinguishable from handstamped "Paid" covers.

TALBOTTON, GA.

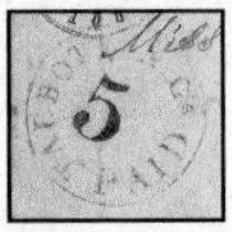

E1

Handstamped Envelopes

94XU1 E1 5c black 900.
a. 10c on 5c black 2,000.
94XU2 E1 10c black 1,250.

TALLADEGA, ALA.

E1

Handstamped Envelopes

143XU1 E1 5c black *1,500.* —
143XU2 E1 10c black *1,500.* —

These same markings were used on handstamped "Paid" covers.

TELLICO PLAINS, TENN.

A1

Typeset Adhesives
Laid Paper

81X1 A1 5c red *2,000.* *10,000.*
81X2 A1 10c red *3,750.*

THOMASVILLE, GA.

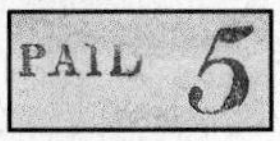

E1

Control

Handstamped Envelopes

82XU1 E1 5c black 750.

On No. 82XU1, the control is on the reverse of the cover. The dated control is known with five different dates, including June 1, June 13, June 21, and August 23. The patriotic envelope is unique.

E2

82XU2 E2 5c black 1,000.

TULLAHOMA, TENN.

E1

Control

Handstamped Envelope

111XU1 E1 10c black *5,000.*

The control appears either on the front or the back of the envelope.

TUSCALOOSA, ALA.

E1

Handstamped Envelopes

83XU1 E1 5c black 250.
83XU2 E1 10c black 250.

Used examples of Nos. 83XU1-83XU2 are indistinguishable from handstamped "Paid" covers.

TUSCUMBIA, ALA.

E1

Handstamped Envelopes

84XU1 E1 5c black *2,750.*
84XU2 E1 5c red *5,000.*
84XU3 E1 10c black *5,250.*

See 3c 1861 Postmaster's Provisional No. 6AXU1.

UNIONTOWN, ALA.

A1

Typeset Adhesives
(settings of 4 (2x2), 4 varieties of each value)
Laid Paper

86X1 A1 2c dark blue, *gray blue,* on cover *65,000.*
86X2 A1 2c dark blue, sheet of 4 *30,000.*
86X3 A1 5c green, *gray blue* *4,000.* *3,250.*
86X4 A1 5c green *4,000.* *3,250.*
86X5 A1 10c red, *gray blue* *10,000.*

Two examples known of No. 86X1, both on cover (drop letters), one uncanceled and one pen canceled.

The only recorded examples of No. 86X2 are in a unique sheet of 4.

The item listed as No. 86X5 used is an uncanceled stamp on a large piece with part of addressee's name in manuscript. The value for the stamp on cover is for the cover with the stamp pen canceled.

UNIONVILLE, S. C.

A1

Handstamped Adhesive
"PAID" and "5" applied separately
Paper with Blue Ruled Lines

87X1 A1 5c black, *grayish* *3,500.*

VALDOSTA, GA.

E1

Control

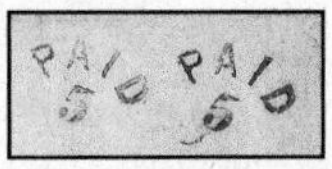

E2

Handstamped Envelopes

100XU1 E1 10c black *9,000.*
100XU2 E2 5c +5c black —

The black circle control must appear on front of the No. 100XU2 envelope and on the back of the No. 100XU1 envelope.

There is one recorded cover each of Nos. 100XU1-100XU2.

VICTORIA, TEX.

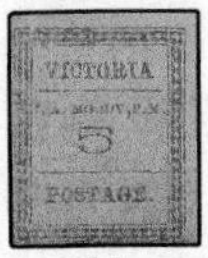

A1

A2

Typeset Adhesives
Surface colored paper

88X1 A1 5c red brown, *green* *17,500.*
88X2 A1 10c red brown, *green* *22,500.*
88X3 A2 10c red brown, *green,* pelure paper *30,000.* *30,000.*

WALTERBOROUGH, S. C.

E1

Handstamped Envelopes

108XU1 E1 10c black, *buff* —
108XU2 E1 10c carmine *4,000.*

The existence of No. 108XU1 is in question. The editors would like to see authenticated evidence of its existence.

WARRENTON, GA.

E1

Handstamped Envelopes

89XU1 E1 5c black *1,500.*
a. 10c (ms.) on 5c black *900.*

Fakes of the Warrenton provisional marking based on the illustration shown are known on addressed but postally unused covers.

WASHINGTON, GA.

E1 

Handstamped Envelope

117XU1 E1 10c black *2,000.*

Envelopes must have black circle postmark control on the back. Examples with the undated control on the front are not considered provisional unless a dated postmark is also present.

WEATHERFORD, TEX.

E1

Handstamped Envelopes (woodcut with "PAID" inserted in type)

109XU1 E1 5c black *2,000.*
109XU2 E1 5c +5c black *11,000.*

One example is known of No. 109XU2.

WILKESBORO, N. C.

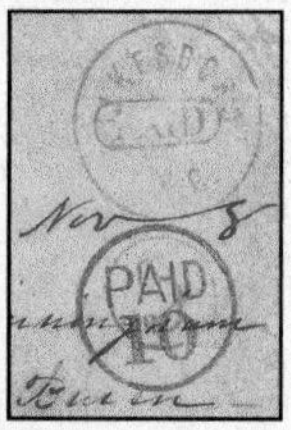

E1

Handstamped Envelope

147XU1 E1 5c black, revalued to 10c *3,500.*

No. 147XU1 is unique.

WILLISTON, S.C.

E1

Handstamped Envelopes

153XU1 E1 10c brown *1,250.*

No. 153XU1 is unique. Value is based on 2020 auction sale. This cover must be either unused (as the one recorded example is) or covered by a C.S.A. stamp.

WINNSBOROUGH, S. C.

E1

E2

Control

Handstamped Envelopes

97XU1 E1 5c black *2,000.*
97XU2 E2 10c black *1,000. 2,500.*

Envelopes must have black circle control on front or back.

WYTHEVILLE, VA.

E1

Control

Handstamped Envelope

114XU1 E1 5c black 900.

For later additions, listed out of numerical sequence, see:

- *#74X1*, **Liberty, Va.**
- *#92XU1*, **Huntsville, Tex.**
- *#92XU2*, **Huntsville, Tex.**
- *#92XU3*, **Huntsville, Tex.**
- *#93XU1*, **Sparta, Ga.**
- *#94XU1*, **Talbotton, Ga.**
- *#95XU1*, **Cuthbert, GA**
- *#96XU1*, **Lake City, Fla.**
- *#97XU1*, **Winnsborough, S.C.**
- *#98XU1*, **Galveston, Tex.**
- *#99XU1*, **Christiansburg, Va.**
- *#100XU1*, **Valdosta, Ga.**
- *#101XU1*, **Savannah, Ga.**
- *#102XU1*, **Griffin, Ga.**
- *#103XU1*, **Courtland, Ala.**
- *#104XU1*, **Fincastle, Va.**
- *#105XU1*, **Micanopy, Fla.**
- *#106XU1*, **Pensacola, Fla.**
- *#107X1*, **Port Lavaca, Tex.**
- *#108XU1*, **Walterborough, S.C.**
- *#109XU1*, **Weatherford, Tex.**
- *#110XU1*, **Jacksonville, Ala.**
- *#111XU1*, **Tullahoma, Tenn.**
- *#112XU1*, **Hamburgh, S.C.**
- *#113XU1*, **Columbia, Tenn.**
- *#114XU1*, **Wytheville, Va.**
- *#115X1*, **Oakway, S.C.**
- *#116XU1*, **Laurens Court House, S.C.**
- *#117XU1*, **Washington, Ga.**
- *#118XU1*, **Carolina City, N.C.**
- *#119XU1*, **Colaparchee, Ga.**
- *#120XU1*, **Forsyth, Ga.**
- *#121XU1*, **Limestone Springs, S.C.**
- *#122XU1*, **Balcony Falls, Va.**
- *#123XU1*, **Barnwell Court House, S.C.**
- *#124XU1*, **Bluffton, S.C.**
- *#125XU1*, **Camden, S.C.**
- *#126XU1*, **Cartersville, Ga.**
- *#127XU1*, **Charlottesville, Va.**
- *#128XU1*, **Fraziersville, S.C.**
- *#129XU1*, **Gaston, N.C.**
- *#130XU1*, **Harrisburgh, Tex.**
- *#132XU1*, **Hollandale, Tex.**
- *#133XU1*, **Isabella, Ga.**
- *#134XU1*, **Jacksonville, Fla.**
- *#135XU1*, **Lexington, Va.**
- *#136XU1*, **Madison, Ga.**
- *#137XU1*, **Madison Court House, Fla.**
- *#138XU1*, **Milton, N.C.**
- *#139XU1*, **Norfolk, Va.**
- *#140XU1*, **Plains of Dura, Ga.**
- *#141X1*, **Plum Creek, Tex.**
- *#142XU1*, **Port Gibson, Miss.**
- *#143XU1*, **Talladega, Ala.**
- *#144XU1*, **Greenville, Tenn.**
- *#145XU1*, **Mars Bluff, S.C.**
- *#146XU1*, **Charlotte, N.C.**
- *#147XU1*, **Wilkesboro, N.C.**
- *#148XU1*, **Fort Valley, Ga.**
- *#149XU1*, **Patterson, N.C.**
- *#150XU1*, **Beaufort, S.C.**
- *#151XU1*, **Mount Pleasant, N.C.**
- *#152XU1*, **Oxford, N.C.**
- *#153XU1*, **Williston, S.C.**

GENERAL ISSUES

Due to its tendency to damage the paper and color of the stamps, the gum on most (but not all) Confederate States stamps very often is removed. Except for the De La Rue-printed Nos. 6 and 14, which are valued both with original gum and without gum, unused values for all Confederate States stamps are for stamps without gum. Stamps with original gum sell for about the same prices, if the gum has not deteriorated and damaged the paper or stamp color.

Jefferson Davis — A1

1861 Unwmk. Litho. ***Imperf.***

Soft Porous Paper

1 A1 5c green (shades) 300. 175.
a. 5c light green 275. 175.
b. 5c dark green 375. 250.
c. 5c olive green 425. 250.

Thomas Jefferson — A2

1861-62

2 A2 10c blue 275. 180.
a. 10c light blue 300. 200.
b. 10c dark blue 700. 300.
c. 10c indigo *5,000.* *7,500.*
d. Printed on both sides *1,750.*
e. light milky blue 1,250. 325.

Specialists have questioned the existence of No. 2bd, the Hoyer & Ludwig printed on both sides. The editors would like to see authenticated evidence of its existence.

The earliest printings of No. 2 were made by Hoyer & Ludwig, the later ones by J. T. Paterson & Co.

Stamps of the later printings usually have a small colored dash below the lowest point of the upper left spandrel.

Andrew Jackson — A3

1862

3 A3 2c green 1,000. 750.
a. 2c bright yellow green *2,000.* —

4 A1 5c blue 225. 125.
a. 5c dark blue 275. 175.
b. 5c light milky blue 350. 200.

5 A2 10c rose (shades) 2,400. 400.
a. 10c carmine *3,750.* *1,900.*

Jefferson Davis — A4

Typo.

6 A4 5c light blue 20. 30.
No gum 10.

7 A4 5c blue (De La Rue thin paper) 22. 22.
a. 5c deep blue 28. 35.
b. Printed on both sides *2,500.* *1,400.*

No. 6 has fine, clear impression. No. 7 has coarser impression and the color is duller and often blurred.

Both 2c and 10c stamps, types A4 and A10, were privately printed in various colors.

Andrew Jackson — A5

1863 **Engr.**

8 A5 2c brown red 75. *350.*
a. 2c pale red 90. *450.*

A6

Thick or Thin Paper

9 A6 10c blue 950. 500.
a. 10c milky blue (first printing) 1,050. 550.
b. 10c gray blue 1,050. 600.

Jefferson Davis — A6a

10 A6a 10c blue (with dividing lines) 5,500. 2,500.
a. 10c milky blue 5,500. 2,500.
b. 10c greenish blue 6,000. 2,500.
c. 10c dark blue 6,000. 2,500.

Values of Nos. 10, 10a, 10b and 10c are for examples showing parts of lines on at least three sides. Used stamps showing 4 complete lines sell for approximately 3 to 4 times the values given. Unused stamps showing 4 complete lines are exceedingly rare (only two recorded), and the one sound example is valued at $35,000.

A7

There are many slight differences between A7 and A8, the most noticeable being the additional line outside the ornaments at the four corners of A8.

1863-64

11 A7 10c blue 18. *20.*
a. 10c milky blue 55. 60.
b. 10c dark blue 25. 30.
c. 10c greenish blue 30. 50.
d. 10c green 100. *80.*
e. Officially perforated 12½ (Archer & Daly printing) 450. 350.

A8

12 A8 10c blue 22. 25.
a. 10c milky blue 55. 60.
b. 10c light blue 21. 22.
c. 10c greenish blue 40. *50.*
d. 10c dark blue 24. 25.
e. 10c green 150. 140.
f. Officially perforated 12½ (Archer & Daly printing) 450. 375.

The paper of Nos. 11 and 12 varies from thin hard to thick soft. The stamp that sometimes is offered as "laid paper" is actually normal paper with thick, streaky gum.

George Washington — A9

1863

13 A9 20c green 45. *400.*
a. 20c yellow green 80. *450.*
b. 20c dark green 65. *500.*
c. 20c bluish green 100. —
d. Diagonal half used as 10c on cover *1,400.*
e. Horizontal half used as 10c on cover *2,500.*

John C. Calhoun — A10

1862 **Typo.**

14 A10 1c orange	110.	
No gum	60.	
a. 1c deep orange	145.	
No gum	85.	

No. 14 was never put in use.

CANAL ZONE

kə-ˈnal ˈzōn

LOCATION — A strip of land 10 miles wide, extending through the Republic of Panama, between the Atlantic and Pacific Oceans.

GOVT. — From 1904-79 a U.S. Government Reservation; from 1979-99 under joint control of the Republic of Panama and the U.S.

AREA — 552.8 sq. mi.

POP. — 41,800 (est. 1976)

The Canal Zone, site of the Panama Canal, was leased in perpetuity to the U.S. for a cash payment of $10,000,000 and a yearly rental. Treaties between the two countries provided for joint jurisdiction by the U.S. and Panama, 1979-1999, with Panama handling postal service. At the end of 1999, the canal, in its entirety, reverted to Panama.

100 Centavos = 1 Peso
100 Centesimos = 1 Balboa
100 Cents = 1 Dollar

Catalogue values for unused stamps in this country are for Never Hinged items, beginning with Scott 118 in the regular postage section and Scott C6 in the air post section.

Watermarks

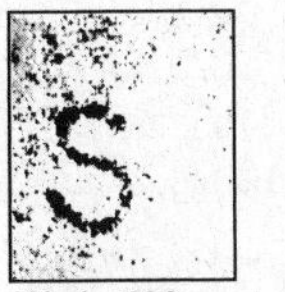

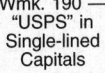

Wmk. 190 — "USPS" in Single-lined Capitals

Wmk. 191 — Double-lined "USPS" in Capitals

Panama Nos. 72, 72a-72c, 78-79 Handstmped in Violet to Violet-Blue

On the 2c "PANAMA" is normally 13mm long. On the 5c and 10c it measures about 15mm.

On the 2c, "PANAMA" reads up on the upper half of the sheet and down on the lower half. On the 5c and 10c, "PANAMA" reads up at left and down at right on each stamp.

On the 2c only, varieties exist with inverted "V" for "A," accent on "A," inverted "N," etc., in "PANAMA."

Unwmk.

1904, June 24 **Engr.** ***Perf. 12***

1 A3 2c rose, both "PANAMA" reading up or down	650.	400.
a. "CANAL ZONE" inverted	*1,000.*	850.
b. "CANAL ZONE" double	*4,250.*	2,000.
c. "CANAL ZONE" double, both inverted	*20,000.*	
d. "PANAMA" reading down and up	750.	650.
e. As "d," "CANAL ZONE" invtd.	*9,000.*	*9,000.*
f. Vert. pair, "PANAMA" reading up on top 2c, down on other	*2,100.*	*2,100.*
g. As "f," "CANAL ZONE" inverted	*20,000.*	
2 A3 5c blue	300.	190.
a. "CANAL ZONE" inverted	775.	600.
b. "CANAL ZONE" double	2,250.	1,500.
c. Pair, one without "CANAL ZONE" overprint	*5,000.*	*5,000.*
d. "CANAL ZONE" overprint diagonal, reading down to right	800.	700.
3 A3 10c yellow	400.	210.
a. "CANAL ZONE" inverted	775.	600.
b. "CANAL ZONE" double		*14,000.*
c. Pair, one without "CANAL ZONE" overprint	*6,000.*	*5,000.*
Nos. 1-3 (3)	1,350.	800.00

Cancellations consist of town and/or bars in magenta or black, or a mixture of both colors.

Nos. 1-3 were withdrawn July 17, 1904.

Forgeries of the "Canal Zone" overprint and cancellations are numerous.

United States Nos. 300, 319, 304, 306 & 307 Ovptd. in Black

1904, July 18 **Wmk. 191**

4 A115 1c blue green	35.00	22.50
5 A129 2c carmine	25.00	25.00
a. 2c scarlet	32.50	30.00
6 A119 5c blue	85.00	60.00
7 A121 8c violet black	130.00	85.00
8 A122 10c pale red brown	120.00	80.00
Nos. 4-8 (5)	395.00	272.50

Beware of fake overprints.

Stamps of Panama Overprinted in Black

12ovpt

CANAL ZONE Regular Type — CANAL ZONE Antique Type

1904-06 **Unwmk.**

9 A5 1c green	2.50	2.00
a. "CANAL" in antique type	90.00	90.00
b. "ZONE" in antique type	60.00	60.00
c. Inverted overprint	*7,500.*	*6,000.*
d. Double overprint	*2,750.*	*2,000.*
10 A5 2c rose	4.00	2.50
a. Inverted overprint	225.00	275.00
b. "L" of "CANAL" sideways	*2,000.*	*2,250.*

"PANAMA" (15mm long) reading up at left, down at right

Overprint "CANAL ZONE" in Black, "PANAMA" and Bar in Red

11 A3 2c rose	6.50	4.50
a. "ZONE" in antique type	175.00	175.00
b. "PANAMA" overprint inverted, bar at bottom	600.00	*675.00*
12 A3 5c blue	7.50	2.75
a. "CANAL" in antique type	75.00	65.00
b. "ZONE" in antique type	75.00	65.00
c. "CANAL ZONE" double	800.00	800.00
d. "PANAMA" double	1,100.	1,000.
e. "PANAMA" inverted, bar at bottom	1,000.	1,250.
f. "PANAAM" at right	*950.00*	*850.00*
13 A3 10c yellow	17.00	12.00
a. "CANAL" in antique type	180.00	180.00
b. "ZONE" in antique type	175.00	160.00
c. "PANAMA" ovpt. double	650.00	650.00
d. "PANAMA" overprint in red brown	27.50	22.50
Nos. 11-13 (3)	31.00	19.25

With Added Surcharge in Red

a

14 A3 8c on 50c bister brown	25.00	25.00
a. "ZONE" in antique type	1,150.	1,150.
b. "CANAL ZONE" inverted	450.00	425.00
c. "PANAMA" overprint in rose brown	35.00	35.00
d. As "c," "CANAL" in antique type	*1,750.*	*850.00*
e. As "c," "ZONE" in antique type	*1,750.*	
f. As "c," "8 cts" double	*1,100.*	
g. As "c," "8" omitted	*4,500.*	
h. As "c," "cts 8"		—

Nos. 11-14 are overprinted or surcharged on Panama Nos. 77, 77e, 78, 78c, 78d, 78f, 78g, 78h, 79 79c, 79e, 79g and 81 respectively.

On No. 14 with original gum, the gum is almost always disturbed. Unused stamps are valued thus.

Panama No. 74a, 74b Overprinted "CANAL ZONE" in Regular Type in Black and Surcharged Type "a" in Red

Both "PANAMA" (13mm long) Reading Up

15 A3(a) 8c on 50c bister brown	2,000.	*4,750.*
a. "PANAMA" reading down and up	*6,000.*	—

On No. 15 with original gum, the gum is almost always disturbed. Unused stamps are valued thus.

Panama Nos. 19 and 21 Surcharged in Black

a

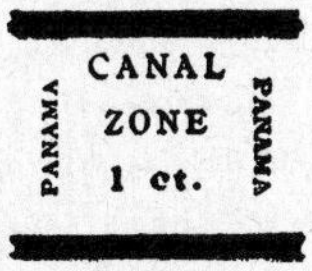

b

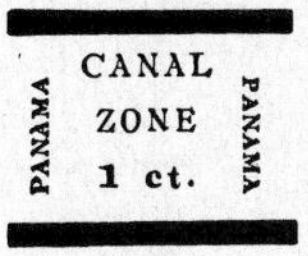

c

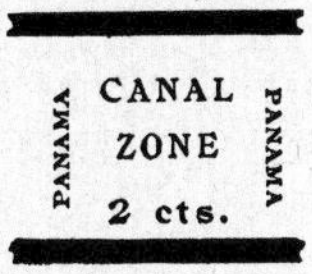

d

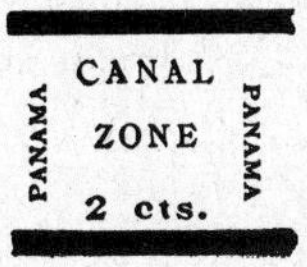

e

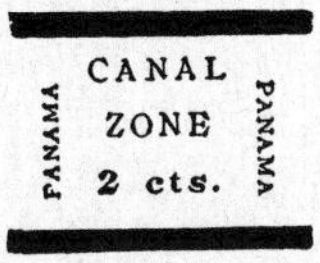

f

There were three printings of each denomination, differing principally in the relative position of the various parts of the surcharges. Varieties occur with inverted "V" for the final "A" in "PANAMA," "CA" spaced, "ZO" spaced, "2c" spaced, accents in various positions, and with bars shifted so that two bars appear on top or bottom of the stamp (either with or without the corresponding bar on top or bottom) and sometimes with only one bar at top or bottom.

1906

16 A4 1c on 20c violet, type a	1.90	1.60
a. Type b	1.90	1.60
b. Type c	1.90	1.50
c. As No. 16, double surcharge		*2,000.*
17 A4 2c on 1p lake, type d	2.25	2.25
a. Type e	2.25	2.25
b. Type f	20.00	20.00

Panama Nos. 74, 74a and 74b Overprinted "CANAL ZONE" in Regular Type in Black and Surcharged in Red

b

c

1905-06

Both "PANAMA" Reading Up

18 A3(b) 8c on 50c bister brown	45.00	45.00
a. "ZONE" in antique type	200.00	180.00
b. "PANAMA" reading down and up	160.00	150.00
19 A3(c) 8c on 50c bister brown	45.00	37.50
a. "CANAL" in antique type	210.00	180.00
b. "ZONE" in antique type	210.00	180.00
c. "8 cts" double	*1,100.*	*1,100.*
d. "PANAMA" reading down and up	110.00	90.00

On Nos. 18-19 with original gum, the gum is usually disturbed. Unused stamps are valued thus.

Panama No. 81 Overprinted "CANAL ZONE" in Regular Type in Black and Surcharged in Red Type "c" plus Period

"PANAMA" reading up and down

20 A3(c) 8c on 50c bister brown	35.00	37.50
a. "CANAL" antique type	200.00	180.00
b. "ZONE" in antique type	200.00	180.00
c. "8 cts" omitted	800.00	800.00
d. "8 cts" double	*1,500.*	
e. "cts 8"		—

Nos. 14 and 18-20 exist without CANAL ZONE overprint but were not regularly issued and are considered printer's waste. Forgeries of the overprint varieties of Nos. 9-15 and 18-20 are known.

On No. 20 with original gum, the gum is usually disturbed. Unused stamps are valued thus.

Francisco Hernandez de Cordoba
A5

Vasco Nunez de Balboa
A6

Fernández de Córdoba
A7

Justo Arosemena
A8

Manuel J. Hurtado
A9

Jose de Obaldia
A10

Stamps of Panama Overprinted in Black

1906-07 ***Perf. 12***

Overprint Reading Up

21 A5 2c red & black	25.00	25.00
a. "CANAL" only	*4,000.*	

Overprint Reading Down

22 A6 1c green & black	2.00	.90
a. Horiz. pair, imperf. btwn.	1,100.	1,100.
b. Vert. pair, imperf. btwn.	*2,000.*	*2,000.*
c. Vert. pair, imperf. horiz.	*2,250.*	*1,750.*
d. Inverted overprint reading up	550.00	550.00
e. Double overprint	275.00	275.00
f. Double overprint, one inverted	1,750.	1,600.
g. Invtd. center, ovpt. reading up	*3,500.*	*4,500.*
h. Horiz. pair, imperf vert.	*5,000.*	
23 A7 2c red & black	3.00	1.00
a. Horizontal pair, imperf. between	2,000.	2,000.
b. Vertical pair, one without overprint	2,500.	2,500.
c. Double overprint	600.00	700.00
d. Double overprint, one diagonal	800.00	800.00
e. Double overprint, one diagonal, in pair with normal	2,500.	
f. 2c carmine red & black	5.00	2.75
g. As "f," inverted center and overprint reading up		*14,000.*
h. As "d," one "ZONE CANAL"	*4,000.*	
i. "CANAL" double	*6,500.*	
24 A8 5c ultramarine & black	5.75	2.00
c. Double overprint	500.00	400.00
d. "CANAL" only	*7,000.*	
e. "ZONE CANAL"	*5,000.*	
25 A9 8c purple & black	20.00	8.00
a. Horizontal pair, imperf. between and at left margin	*1,600.*	*4,000.*
26 A10 10c violet & black	20.00	7.00
a. Dbl. ovpt., one reading up	*5,000.*	
b. Overprint reading up	*5,500.*	
Nos. 22-26 (5)	50.75	18.90

Nos. 22-25 occur with "CA" of "CANAL" spaced ½mm further apart on position No. 50 of the setting.

The used pair of No. 25a is unique.

Cordoba
A11

Arosemena
A12

Hurtado
A13

Jose de Obaldia
A14

1909

Overprint Reading Down

27 A11 2c vermilion & black 12.00 5.00
a. Horizontal pair, one without overprint *2,500.*
b. Vert. pair, one without ovpt. *3,250.*
c. Vert. pair, one without "ZONE" —
28 A12 5c deep blue & black 40.00 12.50
29 A13 8c violet & black 37.50 14.00
30 A14 10c violet & black 40.00 14.00
a. Horizontal pair, one with "ZONE" omitted *3,000.*
b. Vertical pair, one without overprint *4,000.*
Nos. 27-30 (4) 129.50 45.50

Nos. 27-30 occur with "CA" spaced (position 50).

Do not confuse No. 27 with Nos. 39d or 53a.

On No. 30a, the stamp with "ZONE" omitted is also missing most of "CANAL."

For designs A11-A14 with overprints reading up, see Nos. 32-35, 39-41, 47-48, 53-54, 56-57.

Black Overprint Reading Up

Vasco Nunez de Balboa — A15

Type I

Type I Overprint: "C" with serifs both top and bottom. "L," "Z" and "E" with slanting serifs.

Compare Type I overprint with Types II to V illustrated before Nos. 38, 46, 52 and 55.

1909-10

31 A15 1c dark green & black 4.25 1.25
a. Inverted center and overprint reading down *22,500.*
c. Bklt. pane of 6, handmade, perf. margins *500.00*
32 A11 2c vermilion & black 4.50 1.25
a. Vert. pair, imperf. horiz. 1,000. 1,000.
c. Bklt. pane of 6, handmade, perf. margins *800.00*
d. Double overprint (I) *6,000.*
33 A12 5c deep blue & black 17.00 3.50
a. Double overprint 375.00 375.00
34 A13 8c violet & black 11.00 5.00
a. Vertical pair, one without overprint *1,750.*
35 A14 10c violet & black 47.50 20.00
Nos. 31-35 (5) 84.25 31.00

No. 32d is unique and has small faults.
See Nos. 38, 46, 52, 55.

A16

A17

Black Surcharge

1911, Jan. 14

36 A16 10c on 13c gray 6.00 2.00
a. "10 cts" inverted 325.00 325.00
b. "10 cts" omitted 300.00

Many used stamps offered as No. 36b are merely No. 36 from which the surcharge has been chemically removed.

1914, Jan. 6

37 A17 10c gray 47.50 11.00

Black Overprint Reading Up

Type II: "C" with serif at top only. "L" and "E" with vertical serifs. "O" tilts to left

1912-16

38 A15 1c green & black 10.00 3.00
a. Vertical pair, one without overprint 1,750. 1,750.
b. Booklet pane of 6, imperf. margins 575.00
c. Booklet pane of 6, handmade, perf. margins *1,000.*
39 A11 2c vermilion & black 8.00 1.10
a. Horiz. pair, right stamp without overprint *1,250.*
b. Horiz. pair, left stamp without overprint *1,500.*
c. Booklet pane of 6, imperf. margins 550.00
d. Overprint reading down 200.00
e. As "d," inverted center 600.00 *750.00*
f. As "e," booklet pane of 6, handmade, perf. margins *8,000.*
g. As "c," handmade, perf. margins 900.00 800.00
h. As No. 39, "CANAL" only (1) *2,500.*
40 A12 5c deep blue & black 20.00 2.50
a. With Cordoba portrait of 2c *12,500.*
41 A14 10c violet & black 60.00 7.50
Nos. 38-41 (4) 98.00 14.10

Map of Panama Canal — A18

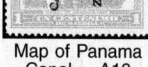

Balboa Takes Possession of the Pacific Ocean — A19

Gatun Locks — A20

Culebra Cut — A21

1915, Mar. 1

Blue Overprint, Type II

42 A18 1c dark green & black 8.75 6.50
43 A19 2c carmine & black 12.00 4.25
44 A20 5c blue & black 10.00 5.75
45 A21 10c orange & black 19.00 11.00
Nos. 42-45 (4) 49.75 27.50

Black Overprint Reading Up

Type III Overprint: Similar to Type I but letters appear thinner, particularly the lower bar of "L," "Z" and "E." Impressions are often light, rough and irregular, and not centered.

1915-20

46 A15 1c green & black 175.00 125.00
a. Overprint reading down 375.00
b. Double overprint 225.00
c. "ZONE" double *6,500.*
d. Double overprint, one reads "ZONE CANAL" 2,000.
47 A11 2c orange vermilion & black 2,750. 60.00
48 A12 5c deep blue & black 425.00 130.00
Nos. 46-48 (3) 3,350. 315.00

Spacing between words of overprint on Nos. 46-48 is 9¼mm; spacing varieties are not known. This should not be confused with a fairly common 9¼mm spacing of the 2c value of type I, nor with an uncommon 9¼mm spacing variety of the 5c of type I.

S.S. "Panama" in Culebra Cut — A22

S.S. "Panama" in Culebra Cut — A23

S.S. "Cristobal" in Gatun Locks — A24

1917, Jan. 23

Blue Overprint, Type II

49 A22 12c purple & black 17.50 5.25
50 A23 15c bright blue & black 50.00 17.50
51 A24 24c yellow brown & black 35.00 13.00
Nos. 49-51 (3) 102.50 35.75

Black Overprint Reading Up

Type IV: "C" thick at bottom, "E" with center bar same length as top and bottom bars

1918-20

52 A15 1c green & black 32.50 10.00
a. Overprint reading down 175.00 —
b. Booklet pane of 6 600.00
c. Booklet pane of 6, left vertical row of 3 without overprint *7,500.*
d. Booklet pane of 6, right vertical row of 3 with double overprint *7,500.*
e. Horiz. bklt. pair, left stamp without overprint *3,000.*
f. Horiz. bklt. pair, right stamp with double overprint *3,000.*
g. Double overprint, booklet single 3,000.
h. "CANAL" omitted —
53 A11 2c vermilion & black 110.00 6.00
a. Overprint reading down 150.00 150.00
b. Horiz. pair, right stamp without ovpt. (from misregistered overprints) 2,000.
c. Booklet pane of 6 1,050.
d. Booklet pane of 6, left vertical row of 3 without overprint *15,000.*
e. Horiz. bklt. pair, left stamp without overprint *3,000.*
f. Horiz. sheet pair, left stamp without overprint (2) *1,750.*
54 A12 5c deep blue & black 150.00 32.50
Nos. 52-54 (3) 292.50 48.50

No. 53e used is unique and is on cover.

Black Overprint Reading Up

Type V: Smaller block type 1¾mm high. "A" with flat top

1920-21

55 A15 1c light green & black 22.50 3.25
a. Overprint reading down 300.00 225.00
b. Horiz. pair, right stamp without ovpt. *1,750.*
c. Horiz. pair, left stamp without ovpt. 1,100.
d. "ZONE" only *4,000.* —
e. Booklet pane of 6 *2,250.*
f. As No. 55, "CANAL" double *1,750.*
g. Vert. pair, one without overprint (2) 3,000.
h. Vert. pair,one "ZONE" only, one without overprint (1) *4,000.*
56 A11 2c orange vermilion & black 8.50 1.75
a. Double overprint 500.00
b. Double overprint, one reading down 600.00
c. Horiz. pair, right stamp without overprint 1,400.
d. Horiz. pair, left stamp without overprint 1,000.
e. Vertical pair, one without overprint 1,500.
f. "ZONE" double 900.00
g. Booklet pane of 6 900.00
h. As No. 56, "CANAL" double 800.00
57 A12 5c deep blue & black 300.00 45.00
a. Horiz. pair, right stamp without overprint *2,000.*
b. Horiz. pair, left stamp without overprint *2,000.*
Nos. 55-57 (3) 331.00 50.00

Drydock at Balboa — A25

Ship in Pedro Miguel Locks — A26

1920, Sept.

Black Overprint Type V

58 A25 50c orange & black 250.00 160.00
59 A26 1b dark violet & black 175.00 50.00

Jose Vallarino
A27

The "Land Gate"
A28

Bolivar's Tribute — A29

Municipal Building in 1821 and 1921 — A30

Statue of Balboa
A31

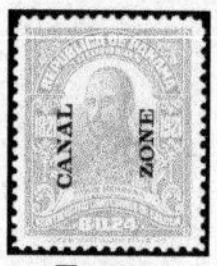
Tomas Herrera
A32

Jose de Fabrega — A33

Type V overprint in black, reading up, on all values except the 5c which is overprinted with larger type in red

1921, Nov. 13

60 A27 1c green 3.75 1.50
a. "CANAL" double *1,900.*
b. Booklet pane of 6 *900.00*
61 A28 2c carmine 2.75 1.00
a. Overprint reading down 200.00 *225.00*
b. Double overprint 900.00
c. Vertical pair, one without overprint *3,500.*
d. "CANAL" double *1,900.*
e. "ZONE" only (1) *4,000.*
f. Booklet pane of 6 *2,000.*
62 A29 5c blue (R) 10.00 3.00
a. Overprint reading down (R) 65.00
63 A30 10c violet 18.00 7.50
a. Overprint, reading down 90.00
64 A31 15c light blue 47.50 17.50
65 A32 24c black brown 67.50 22.50
66 A33 50c black 145.00 85.00
Nos. 60-66 (7) 294.50 138.00

Experts question the status of the 5c with a small type V overprint in red or black.

Type III overprint in black, reading up

1924, Jan. 28

67 A27 1c green 500. 200.
a. "ZONE CANAL" reading down 800.
b. "ZONE" only, reading down *1,900.*
c. Se-tenant pair, #67a and 67b *2,750.*

Coat of Arms — A34

1924, Feb.

68 A34 1c dark green 10.00 4.50
69 A34 2c carmine 7.00 2.75

The 5c to lb values were prepared but never issued. See listing in the Scott U.S. specialized catalogue.

United States Nos. 551-554, 557, 562, 564-566, 569, 570 and 571 Overprinted in Red (No. 70) or Black (all others)

Type A: Letters "A" with Flat Tops

Type A

Letters "A" with Flat Tops

1924-25 Unwmk. *Perf. 11*

70 A154 ½c olive brown .25 .70
Never hinged .40
71 A155 1c deep green 1.40 1.00
Never hinged 2.50
a. Inverted overprint 500.00 500.00
b. "ZONE" inverted 350.00 325.00
c. "CANAL" only 1,150.
d. "ZONE CANAL" 400.00
e. Booklet pane of 6 80.00 —
f. Se-tenant pair, #71c and 71d *1,750.*
72 A156 1½c yellow brown 2.00 1.70
Never hinged 3.25
73 A157 2c carmine 6.75 1.70
Never hinged 10.50
a. Booklet pane of 6 175.00
74 A160 5c dark blue 16.00 7.00
Never hinged 25.00
75 A165 10c orange 40.00 20.00
Never hinged 65.00
76 A167 12c brown violet 32.50 30.00
Never hinged 62.50
a. "ZONE" inverted *3,750.* *3,000.*
77 A168 14c dark blue 27.50 22.50
Never hinged 45.00
78 A169 15c gray 45.00 37.50
Never hinged 70.00
79 A172 30c olive brown 32.50 20.00
Never hinged 52.50
80 A173 50c lilac 75.00 45.00
Never hinged 150.00
81 A174 $1 violet brown 225.00 95.00
Never hinged 400.00
Nos. 70-81 (12) 503.90 282.10

Normal spacing between words of the overprint is 9¼mm. Minor spacing variations are known.

All examples of Nos. 71b and 76a have a natural straight edge at right.

Type B: Letters "A" with Sharp Pointed Tops

Type B

1925-28

84 A157 2c carmine 27.50 8.00
Never hinged 45.00
a. "CANAL" only *2,250.*
b. "ZONE CANAL" 425.00
c. Horizontal pair, one without overprint *3,500.*
d. Booklet pane of 6 175.00
e. Se-tenant pair, #84a and 84b *3,000.*
85 A158 3c violet 3.75 3.00
Never hinged 6.00
a. "ZONE ZONE" 550.00 550.00
86 A160 5c dark blue 3.50 2.75
Never hinged 6.00
a. "ZONE ZONE" (LR18) 1,000.
b. "CANAL" inverted (LR7) 950.00
c. Inverted overprint 500.00
d. Horizontal pair, one without overprint *3,250.*
e. Overprinted "ZONE CANAL" 350.00
f. "ZONE" only *2,000.*
g. Vertical pair, one without overprint, other overprint inverted *2,000.*
h. "CANAL" only *2,000.*
i. Se-tenant pair, #86e and 86f *2,500.*
87 A165 10c orange 35.00 12.00
Never hinged 52.50
a. "ZONE ZONE" (LR18) *3,000.*
b. "ZONE" only (1) *4,000.*
88 A167 12c brown violet 20.00 12.50
Never hinged 34.00
a. "ZONE ZONE" (LR18) *5,000.*
89 A168 14c dark blue 27.50 15.00
Never hinged 45.00
90 A169 15c gray 7.50 4.50
Never hinged 12.00
a. "ZONE ZONE" (LR18) *5,500.*
91 A187 17c black 4.50 2.75
Never hinged 7.50
a. "ZONE" only 1,000.
b. "CANAL" only *(11)* 1,900.
c. "ZONE CANAL" 275.00
d. Se-tenant pair, #91a and 91c *1,400.*
92 A170 20c carmine rose 7.25 3.25
Never hinged 12.00
a. "CANAL" inverted (UR48) *6,500.*
b. "ZONE" inverted (LL76) *4,750.*
c. "ZONE CANAL" (LL91) *4,750.*
93 A172 30c olive brown 5.75 3.75
Never hinged 9.00
94 A173 50c lilac 230.00 165.00
Never hinged 120.00
95 A174 $1 violet brown 120.00 55.00
Never hinged 250.00
Nos. 84-95 (12) 492.25 287.50

Overprint Type B on U.S. No. 627

1926

96 A188 2c carmine rose 4.50 3.75
Never hinged 7.00

On this stamp there is a space of 5mm instead of 9mm between the two words of the overprint.

Overprint Type B in Black on U.S. Nos. 583, 584, 591

1926-27 *Perf. 10*

97 A157 2c carmine 45.00 11.00
Never hinged 75.00
a. Pair, one without overprint *2,250.*
b. Booklet pane of 6 500.00
c. "CANAL" only *2,000.*
d. "ZONE" only *2,750.*
98 A158 3c violet 7.50 4.25
Never hinged 11.00
99 A165 10c orange 18.00 7.50
Never hinged 27.50
Nos. 97-99 (3) 70.50 22.75

No. 97d is valued in the grade of fine. Very fine examples are not known.

Overprint Type B in Black on U.S. Nos. 632, 634 (Type I), 635, 637, 642

1927-31 *Perf. 11x10½*

100 A155 1c green 1.75 1.40
Never hinged 2.60
a. Vertical pair, one without overprint *3,250.*
101 A157 2c carmine 1.75 1.00
Never hinged 2.50
a. Booklet pane of 6 200.00
102 A158 3c violet 4.25 2.75
Never hinged 6.25
a. Booklet pane of 6, handmade, perf. margins *6,500.*
103 A160 5c blue 25.00 10.00
Never hinged 45.00
104 A165 10c orange 17.50 10.00
Never hinged 26.00
Nos. 100-104 (5) 50.25 25.15

> Wet and Dry Printings
>
> Canal Zone stamps printed by both the "wet" and "dry" process are Nos. 105, 108-109, 111-114, 117, 138-140, C21-C24, C26, J25, J27. Starting with Nos. 147 and C27, the Bureau of Engraving and Printing used the "dry" method exclusively. Late dry printings of Nos. 105, 108, 112-114, 117, 138 and 152 also exist with dull gum.
>
> See note on Wet and Dry Printings following U.S. No. 1029.

Maj. Gen. William Crawford Gorgas A35

Maj. Gen. George Washington Goethals A36

Gaillard Cut A37

Maj. Gen. Harry Foote Hodges A38

Lt. Col. David DuB. Gaillard A39

Maj. Gen. William L. Sibert A40

Jackson Smith A41

Rear Adm. Harry H. Rousseau A42

Col. Sydney B. Williamson A43

J.C.S. Blackburn A44

1928-40 *Perf. 11*

105 A35 1c green .25 .25
Never hinged .25
106 A36 2c carmine .25 .25
Never hinged .30
a. Booklet pane of 6 15.00 *20.00*
Never hinged 22.50
107 A37 5c blue 1.00 .40
Never hinged 1.30
108 A38 10c orange .25 .25
Never hinged .25
109 A39 12c brown violet .75 .60
Never hinged 1.00
110 A40 14c blue .85 .85
Never hinged 1.20
111 A41 15c gray black .40 .35
Never hinged .55
112 A42 20c dark brown .60 .25
Never hinged .80
113 A43 30c black .80 .70
Never hinged 1.10
114 A44 50c rose lilac 1.50 .65
Never hinged 2.00
Nos. 105-114 (10) 6.65 4.55

For surcharges and overprints, see Nos. J21-J24, O1-O8.

Coils are listed as Nos. 160-161.

United States Nos. 720 and 695 Overprinted type B

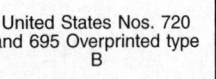

1933, Jan. 14 *Perf. 11x10½*

115 A226 3c deep violet 2.75 .25
Never hinged 4.00
b. "CANAL" only *2,600.*
c. Booklet pane of 6, handmade, perf. margins 80.00 —
d. Vertical pair, one without overprint —
116 A168 14c dark blue 4.50 3.50
Never hinged 7.00
a. "ZONE CANAL" *1,500.*

Gen. George Washington Goethals — A45

20th anniversary of the opening of the Panama Canal.

1934 *Perf. 11*

117 A45 3c red violet .25 .25
Never hinged .30
a. Booklet pane of 6 *12.50* *32.50*
b. As "a," handmade, perf. margins 160.00 —

Coil is listed as No. 153.

> **Catalogue values for unused stamps in this section, from this point to the end, are for Never Hinged items.**

United States Nos. 803 and 805 Overprinted in Black

1939, Sept. 1 *Perf. 11x10½*

118 A275 ½c red orange .25 .25
119 A277 1½c bister brown .25 .25

Panama Canal Anniversary Issue

Balboa-Before A46

Balboa-After A47

Gaillard Cut-Before — A48

Gaillard Cut-After — A49

Bas Obispo-Before A50

Bas Obispo-After A51

Gatun Locks-Before A52

Gatun Locks-After — A53

Canal Channel-Before — A54

Canal Channel-After A55

Gamboa- Before A56

Gamboa-After A57

Pedro Miguel Locks-Before A58

Pedro Miguel Locks-After — A59

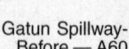

Gatun Spillway-Before — A60

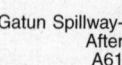

Gatun Spillway-After A61

25th anniversary of the opening of the Panama Canal.

1939, Aug. 15

120 A46 1c yellow green .60 .30
121 A47 2c rose carmine .70 .35
122 A48 3c purple .70 .25
123 A49 5c dark blue 2.00 1.25
124 A50 6c red orange 4.50 3.00
125 A51 7c black 4.75 3.00
126 A52 8c green 7.00 3.25
127 A53 10c ultramarine 5.50 5.00
128 A54 11c blue green 11.00 8.00
129 A55 12c brown carmine 11.00 7.50
130 A56 14c dark violet 11.00 7.00
131 A57 15c olive green 14.00 5.75
132 A58 18c rose pink 15.00 8.50
133 A59 20c brown 17.50 7.00
134 A60 25c orange 27.50 15.00
135 A61 50c violet brown 30.00 6.00
Nos. 120-135 (16) 162.75 81.15

Maj. Gen. George W. Davis A62

Gov. Charles E. Magoon A63

Theodore Roosevelt A64

John F. Stevens A65

John F. Wallace — A66

1946-49

Size: 19x22mm

136 A62 ½c bright red .40 .25
137 A63 1½c chocolate .40 .25
138 A64 2c light rose carmine .25 .25
139 A65 5c dark blue .35 .25
140 A66 25c green .85 .55
Nos. 136-140 (5) 2.25 1.55

See Nos. 155, 162, 164. For overprint, see No. O9.

Map of Biological Area and Coati-Mundi A67

25th anniversary of the establishment of the Canal Zone Biological Area on Barro Colorado Island.

1948, Apr. 17

141 A67 10c black 1.75 1.00

"Forty-niners" Arriving at Chagres A68

Journey by "Bungo" to Las Cruces A69

Las Cruces Trail to Panama A70

Departure for San Francisco A71

Centenary of the California Gold Rush.

1949, June 1

142 A68 3c blue .65 .25
143 A69 6c violet .65 .30
144 A70 12c bright blue green 1.75 .90
145 A71 18c deep red lilac 2.00 1.50
Nos. 142-145 (4) 5.05 2.95

Workers in Culebra Cut — A72

Contribution of West Indian laborers in the construction of the Panama Canal.

1951, Aug. 15

146 A72 10c carmine 3.50 1.50

Centenary of the completion of the Panama Railroad and the first transcontinental railroad trip in the Americas.

Early Railroad Scene — A73

1955, Jan. 28

147 A73 3c violet 1.00 .60

Gorgas Hospital and Ancon Hill — A74

75th anniversary of Gorgas Hospital.

1957, Nov. 17

148 A74 3c black, *dull blue grn* .45 .35

S.S. Ancon — A75

1958, Aug. 30

149 A75 4c greenish blue .40 .30

Roosevelt Medal and Map — A76

Centenary of the birth of Theodore Roosevelt (1858-1919).

1958, Nov. 15

150 A76 4c brown .60 .30

Boy Scout Badge — A77

50th anniversary of the Boy Scouts of America.

1960, Feb. 8 Giori Press Printing

151 A77 4c dark blue, red & bister .55 .40

Administration Building — A78

1960, Nov. 1

152 A78 4c rose lilac .25 .25

Types of 1934, 1960 and 1946 Coil Stamps

1960-62 Unwmk. *Perf. 10 Vertically*

153 A45 3c deep violet .25 .25

Perf. 10 Horizontally

154 A78 4c dull rose lilac .25 .25

Perf. 10 Vertically

155 A65 5c deep blue .25 .25
Nos. 153-155 (3) .75 .75

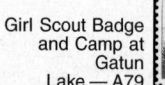

Girl Scout Badge and Camp at Gatun Lake — A79

50th anniversary of the Girl Scouts.

Giori Press Printing

1962, Mar. 12 ***Perf. 11***

156 A79 4c blue, dark green & bister .40 .30

Thatcher Ferry Bridge and Map of Western Hemisphere A80

Opening of the Thatcher Ferry Bridge, spanning the Panama Canal.

Giori Press Printing

1962, Oct. 12

157 A80 4c black & silver .35 .25
a. Silver (bridge) omitted *(50)* 8,000.
Hinged 6,000.

Goethals Memorial, Balboa A81

Fort San Lorenzo A82

1968-71 Giori Press Printing

158 A81 6c green & ultra. .30 .30
159 A82 8c slate green, blue, dark brown & ocher .35 .25

Types of 1928, 1932 and 1948 Coil Stamps

1975, Feb. 14 ***Perf. 10 Vertically***

160 A35 1c green .25 .25
161 A38 10c orange .70 .40
162 A66 25c yellow green 2.75 2.75
Nos. 160-162 (3) 3.70 3.40

Dredge Cascadas — A83

Giori Press Printing

1976, Feb. 23

163 A83 13c multicolored .35 .25
a. Booklet pane of 4 3.00 —

No. 163a exists with and without staple holes in selvage tab.

Stevens Type of 1946

1977 ***Perf. 11x10½***

Size: 19x22½mm

164 A65 5c deep blue .60 .85
a. Tagged, dull gum 12.00 15.00

No. 164 exists with both shiny gum and dull gum. Stamps with dull gum exist with and without tagging.

No. 164a exists even though there was no equipment in the Canal Zone to detect tagging.

Value for No. 164a on cover is for covers postmarked prior to Sept. 30, 1979.

Towing Locomotive, Ship in Lock — A84

1978, Oct. 25 ***Perf. 11***

165 A84 15c dp grn & bl grn .35 .25

AIR POST STAMPS

Nos. 105-106 Surcharged in Dark Blue

Type I - Flag of "Five" pointing up

Type II - Flag of "5" curved

1929-31 Engr. Unwmk. *Perf. 11*

C1 A35 15c on 1c green, type I 7.50 4.75
Never hinged 11.50
C2 A35 15c on 1c yellow green, type II 60.00 47.50
Never hinged 120.00
C3 A36 25c on 2c carmine 3.50 2.00
Never hinged 5.25
Nos. C1-C3 (3) 71.00 54.25

Nos. 114 and 106 Surcharged

1929, Dec. 31

C4 A44 10c on 50c lilac 8.00 5.75
Never hinged 12.00
C5 A36 20c on 2c carmine 4.50 1.25
Never hinged 7.50
a. Dropped "2" in surcharge 85.00 60.00

Catalogue values for unused stamps in this section, from this point to the end, are for Never Hinged items.

Gaillard Cut — AP1

1931-49

C6 AP1 4c red violet .75 .65
C7 AP1 5c yellow green .60 .30
C8 AP1 6c yellow brown .75 .35
C9 AP1 10c orange 1.00 .35
C10 AP1 15c blue 1.25 .30
C11 AP1 20c red violet 2.00 .25
C12 AP1 30c rose lake 7.50 1.50
C13 AP1 40c yellow 3.50 1.10
C14 AP1 $1 black 10.00 1.60
Nos. C6-C14 (9) 27.35 6.40

For overprints, see Nos. CO1-CO14.

Douglas Plane over Sosa Hill — AP2

Planes and Map of Central America — AP3

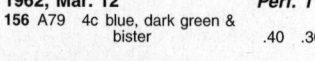

Pan American Clipper and Scene near Fort Amador — AP4

Pan American Clipper at Cristobal Harbor — AP5

Pan American Clipper over Gaillard Cut — AP6

Pan American Clipper Landing — AP7

10th anniversary of Air Mail service and the 25th anniversary of the opening of the Panama Canal.

1939, July 15

C15	AP2	5c greenish black	3.75	2.25
C16	AP3	10c dull violet	3.50	3.00
C17	AP4	15c light brown	5.00	1.00
C18	AP5	25c blue	17.50	8.00
C19	AP6	30c rose carmine	17.50	6.00
C20	AP7	$1 green	45.00	27.50
		Nos. C15-C20 (6)	92.25	47.75

Globe and Wing — AP8

1951, July 16

C21	AP8	4c lt red violet	.75	.35
C22	AP8	6c lt brown	.50	.25
C23	AP8	10c lt red orange	.90	.35
C24	AP8	21c lt blue	8.00	4.00
C25	AP8	31c cerise	9.50	3.75
a.		Horiz. pair, imperf. vert.	1,000.	—
C26	AP8	80c lt gray black	6.00	1.50
		Nos. C21-C26 (6)	25.65	10.20

Flat Plate Printing

1958, Aug. 16 Unwmk. *Perf. 11*

C27	AP8	5c yellow green	1.00	.60
C28	AP8	7c olive	1.00	.45
C29	AP8	15c brown violet	4.50	2.75
C30	AP8	25c orange yellow	12.50	2.75
C31	AP8	35c dark blue	9.00	2.75
		Nos. C27-C31 (5)	28.00	9.30
		Nos. C21-C31 (11)	53.65	19.50

See No. C34.

Emblem of U.S. Army Caribbean School — AP9

US Army Caribbean School for Latin America at Fort Gulick.

1961, Nov. 21

C32	AP9	15c red & blue	1.60	.75

Malaria Eradication Emblem and Mosquito — AP10

World Health Organization drive to eradicate malaria.

1962, Sept. 24

C33	AP10	7c yellow & black	.50	.40

Globe-Wing Type of 1951

1963, Jan. 7 *Perf. 10½x11*

C34	AP8	8c carmine	.75	.30

Alliance Emblem — AP11

2nd anniv. of the Alliance for Progress, which aims to stimulate economic growth and raise living standards in Latin America.

1963, Aug. 17 *Perf. 11*

C35	AP11	15c gray, grn & dk ultra	1.50	.85

Jet over Canal Zone Views — AP12

50th anniversary of the opening of the Panama Canal.

Designs: 6c, Cristobal. 8c, Gatun Locks. 15c, Madden Dam. 20c, Gaillard Cut. 30c, Miraflores Locks. 80c, Balboa.

1964, Aug. 15

C36	AP12	6c green & black	.60	.35
C37	AP12	8c rose red & black	.60	.35
C38	AP12	15c blue & black	1.25	.75
C39	AP12	20c rose lilac & black	1.60	1.00
C40	AP12	30c reddish brown & black	2.75	2.25
C41	AP12	80c olive bister & black	4.75	3.00
		Nos. C36-C41 (6)	11.55	7.70

Seal and Jet Plane — AP13

1965, July 15

C42	AP13	6c green & black	.50	.30
C43	AP13	8c rose red & black	.45	.25
C44	AP13	15c blue & black	.75	.25
C45	AP13	20c lilac & black	.80	.30
C46	AP13	30c redsh brn & blk	1.10	.30
		On cover, single franking, to Australasia, Asia or sub-Sahara Africa		25.00
C47	AP13	80c bister & black	2.50	.75
		Nos. C42-C47 (6)	6.10	2.15

1968-76

C48	AP13	10c dull orange & black	.35	.25
a.		Booklet pane of 4	4.25	—
C49	AP13	11c olive & black	.35	.25
a.		Booklet pane of 4	3.50	—
C50	AP13	13c emerald & black	.85	.25
a.		Booklet pane of 4	6.00	—
C51	AP13	22c vio & blk	1.10	*2.00*
C52	AP13	25c pale yellow & black	.80	.70
C53	AP13	35c salmon & black	1.25	*2.00*
		Nos. C48-C53 (6)	4.70	*5.45*

AIR POST OFFICIAL STAMPS

Beginning in March 1915, stamps for use on official mail were identified by a large "P" perforated through each stamp. These were replaced by overprinted issues in 1941. The use of official stamps was discontinued December 31, 1951. During their currency, they were not for sale in mint condition and were sold to the public only when canceled with a parcel post rotary canceler reading "Balboa Heights, Canal Zone" between two wavy lines.

After having been withdrawn from use, mint stamps (except Nos. CO8-CO12 and O3, O8) were made available to the public at face value for three months beginning Jan. 2, 1952. **Values for used examples of Nos. CO1-CO7, CO14, O1-O2, O4-O9, are for canceled-to-order stamps with original gum, postally used stamps being worth more.**

Nos. C7, C9-C14 Overprinted in Black

Two types of overprint

Type I — "PANAMA CANAL" 19-20mm long

1941-42 Unwmk. *Perf. 11*

CO1	AP1	5c yellow green	6.50	1.50
CO2	AP1	10c orange	8.50	1.75
CO3	AP1	15c blue	11.00	1.75
CO4	AP1	20c red violet	13.00	4.00
CO5	AP1	30c rose lake	17.50	5.00
CO6	AP1	40c yellow	17.50	7.50
CO7	AP1	$1 black	20.00	10.00
		Nos. CO1-CO7 (7)	94.00	31.50

Overprint varieties occur on Nos. CO1-CO7 and CO14: "O" of "OFFICIAL" over "N" of "PANAMA" (entire third row). "O" of "OFFICIAL" broken at top (position 31). "O" of "OFFICIAL" over second "A" of "PANAMA" (position 45). First "F" of "OFFICIAL" over second "A" of "PANAMA" (position 50).

Type II — "PANAMA CANAL" 17mm long

1941, Sept. 22

CO8	AP1	5c yellow green	—	150.00
CO9	AP1	10c orange	*1,100.*	260.00
CO10	AP1	20c red violet	—	160.00
CO11	AP1	30c rose lake	*900.*	60.00
CO12	AP1	40c yellow	—	170.00
		Nos. CO8-CO12 (5)		800.00

Type I — "PANAMA CANAL" 19-20mm long

1947, Nov.

CO14	AP1	6c yellow brown	13.00	5.50
a.		Inverted overprint *(50)*		*2,000.*

POSTAGE DUE STAMPS

Prior to 1914, many of the postal issues were handstamped "Postage Due" and used as postage due stamps.

Postage Due Stamps of the U.S. Nos. J45a, J46a and J49a Overprinted in Black

1914, Mar. Wmk. 190 *Perf. 12*

J1	D2	1c rose carmine	85.00	15.00
J2	D2	2c rose carmine	250.00	42.50
J3	D2	10c rose carmine	900.00	40.00
		Nos. J1-J3 (3)	1,235.	97.50

Blue Overprint, Type II, on Postage Due Stamps of Panama

Castle Gate (See footnote) — D1

Statue of Columbus D2

Pedro J. Sosa D3

1915, Mar. Unwmk.

J4	D1	1c olive brown	11.00	5.00
J5	D2	2c olive brown	225.00	17.50
J6	D3	10c olive brown	50.00	10.00
		Nos. J4-J6 (3)	286.00	32.50

Type D1 was intended to show a gate of San Lorenzo Castle, Chagres, and is so labeled. By error the stamp actually shows the main gate of San Geronimo Castle, Portobelo.

Surcharged in Red

1915, Nov.

J7	D1	1c on 1c olive brown	110.00	14.00
J8	D2	2c on 2c olive brown	22.50	7.50
J9	D3	10c on 10c olive brown	22.50	5.00
		Nos. J7-J9 (3)	155.00	26.50

Columbus Statue D4

Capitol, Panama City D5

1919, Dec.

Surcharged in Carmine by Panama Canal Press, Mount Hope, C. Z.

"Canal Zone" Type III

J10	D4	2c on 2c olive brown	40.00	12.50
J11	D5	4c on 4c olive brown	45.00	15.00
a.		"ZONE" omitted	*9,250.*	
b.		"4" omitted	*8,500.*	

Blue Overprint, Type V, on Postage Due Stamp of Panama

1922

J11C	D1	1c dark olive brown	—	5.00
d.		"CANAL ZONE" reading down		200.00

United States Postage Due Stamps Nos. J61, J62b and J65b Overprinted

Type A
Letters "A" with Flat Tops

1924, July 1 *Perf. 11*

J12	D2	1c carmine rose	110.00	27.50
J13	D2	2c deep claret	55.00	15.00
J14	D2	10c deep claret	250.00	50.00
		Nos. J12-J14 (3)	415.00	92.50

U.S. Postage Stamps Nos. 552, 554 and 562 Overprinted Type A and additional Overprint in Red or Blue

1925, Feb.

J15	A155	1c deep green (R)	90.00	15.00
J16	A157	2c carmine (Bl)	22.50	7.00
J17	A165	10c orange (R)	55.00	11.00
a.		"POSTAGE DUE" double	800.00	
b.		"E" of "POSTAGE" omitted	750.00	
c.		As "b," "POSTAGE DUE" double	*3,250.*	
		Nos. J15-J17 (3)	167.50	33.00

On U.S. Postage Due Stamps Nos. J61, J62, J65, J65a

Overprinted Type B
Letters "A" with Sharp Pointed Tops

1925, June 24

J18	D2	1c carmine rose	8.00	2.75
a.		"ZONE ZONE" (LR18)	1,500.	
J19	D2	2c carmine rose	15.00	2.75
a.		"ZONE ZONE" (LR18)	1,500.	
J20	D2	10c carmine rose	150.00	20.00
a.		Vert. pair, one without ovpt.	*3,000.*	
b.		10c rose red	*250.00*	150.00
c.		As "b," double overprint	*450.00*	—
		Nos. J18-J20 (3)	173.00	25.50

Regular Issue of 1928-29 Surcharged

1929-30

J21 A37 1c on 5c blue 3.75 1.75
Never hinged 7.50
a. "POSTAGE DUE" missing *5,500.*
J22 A37 2c on 5c blue 6.50 2.50
Never hinged 13.00
J23 A37 5c on 5c blue 6.50 2.75
Never hinged 13.00
J24 A37 10c on 5c blue 6.50 2.75
Never hinged 13.00
Nos. J21-J24 (4) 23.25 9.75

On No. J23 the three short horizontal bars in the lower corners of the surcharge are omitted.

Canal Zone Seal — D6

1932-41

J25 D6 1c claret .25 .25
Never hinged .30
J26 D6 2c claret .25 .25
Never hinged .30
J27 D6 5c claret .35 .25
Never hinged .50
J28 D6 10c claret 1.75 1.50
Never hinged 2.25
J29 D6 15c claret 1.25 1.00
Never hinged 1.60
Nos. J25-J29 (5) 3.85 3.25

OFFICIAL STAMPS

See note at beginning of Air Post Official Stamps

Regular Issues of 1928-34 Overprinted in Black

Type 1

Type 2

Type 1 — "PANAMA" 10mm long
Type 1a — "PANAMA" 9mm long
Type 2 — "PANAMA CANAL" 19-20mm long

Unwmk.

1941, Mar. 31 Engr. *Perf. 11*

O1 A35 1c yellow green, type 1 2.00 .40
O2 A45 3c deep violet, type 1 3.75 .75
O3 A37 5c blue, type 2 *1,000.* 25.00
O4 A38 10c orange, type 1 7.50 1.90
O5 A41 15c gray black, type 1 15.00 2.25
O6 A42 20c olive brown, type 1 17.50 2.75
O7 A44 50c lilac, type 1 42.50 5.50
O8 A44 50c rose lilac, type 1a 550.00
Nos. O1-O2,O4-O7 (6) 88.25 13.55

No. 139 Overprinted in Black

1947, Feb.

O9 A65 5c deep blue, type 1 12.50 3.75

CUBA

ˈkyü-bə

LOCATION — The largest island of the West Indies; south of Florida.
GOVT. — socialist; under US military governor 1899-1902 and US provisional governor 1906-1909.
AREA — 44,206 sq. mi.
POP. — 9,710,000 (1981)
CAPITAL — Havana

Formerly a Spanish possession, Cuba's attempts to gain freedom led to US intervention in 1898. Under Treaty of Paris of that year, Spain relinquished the island to US trust. In 1902, a republic was established and Cuban Congress took over government from US military authorities.

100 Cents = 1 Dollar

Watermark

Wmk. 191 — Double-lined "USPS" in Capitals

The basic stamps used for overprinting at Puerto Principe are normally poorly centered. Values for Nos. 176-220 are for stamps with fine centering, as typically found. Furthermore, values are for stamps accompanied by certificates issued by competent experts. Convincing fakes and counterfeits are plentiful.

Values for Nos. 221-J4 are for very fine examples.

Issued under Administration of the United States

Puerto Principe Issue

Issues of Cuba of 1898 and 1896 Surcharged

a

b

Black Surcharge on Nos. 156-158, 160

Types a, c, d, e, f, g and h are 17½mm high, the others are 19½mm high.

1898-99

176 A19 (a) 1c on 1m org brn 100.00 60.00
177 A19 (b) 1c on 1m org brn 600.00 115.00
a. Broken figure "1" *3,000.* 275.00
b. Inverted surcharge *500.00*
d. As "a," inverted *1,500.*

c

d

178 A19 (c) 2c on 2m org brn 65.00 62.50
a. Inverted surcharge 500.00 100.00
179 A19 (d) 2c on 2m org brn 82.50 77.50
a. Inverted surcharge — *500.00*

k

l

179B A19 (k) 3c on 1m org brn 300. 175.
c. Double surcharge — *3,000.*

An unused example is known with "cents" omitted.

179D A19 (l) 3c on 1m org brn *1,350. 675.00*

e

f

179F A19 (e) 3c on 2m org brn *1,500.*

Value is for examples with minor faults.

179G A19 (f) 3c on 2m org brn — *2,000.*

Value is for examples with minor faults.

180 A19 (e) 3c on 3m org brn 150. *100.*
a. Inverted surcharge 375.
181 A19 (f) 3c on 3m org brn 600. 400.
a. Inverted surcharge *750.*

g

h

i

j

182 A19 (g) 5c on 1m org brn 1,000. 165.
a. Inverted surcharge — *1,000.*
183 A19 (h) 5c on 1m org brn *1,500. 1,000.*
a. Inverted surcharge — *1,500.*
184 A19 (g) 5c on 2m org brn 1,000. 275.
185 A19 (h) 5c on 2m org brn 1,500. 600.
186 A19 (g) 5c on 3m org brn 1,500. 350.
a. Inverted surcharge 1,200. 700.
187 A19 (h) 5c on 3m org brn — 1,000.
a. Inverted surcharge — *1,000.*
188 A19 (g) 5c on 5m org brn 145. 230.
a. Inverted surcharge — 750.
b. Double surcharge — —
189 A19 (h) 5c on 5m org brn 3,000. 425.
a. Inverted surcharge *3,000. 900.*
b. Double surcharge — —

The 2nd printing of Nos. 188-189 has shiny ink. Values are for the 1st printing.

189C A19 (i) 5c on 5m org brn *7,500.*

No. 191

Black Surcharge on No. P25

190 N2 (g) 5c on ½m bl grn 375. 115.
a. Inverted surcharge 1,000. 210.
b. Pair, one without surcharge 500.

Value for 190b is for pair with unsurcharged stamp at right. Also exists with unsurcharged stamp at left.

191 N2 (h) 5c on ½m bl grn 1,000. 275.
a. Inverted surcharge *1,000.*
192 N2 (i) 5c on ½m bl grn 3,000. 100.
a. Dbl. surch., one diagonal *3,500.* —
193 N2 (j) 5c on ½m bl grn 900. 500.

Red Surcharge on No. 161

196 A19 (k) 3c on 1c blk vio 150. 125.
a. Inverted surcharge 500.
197 A19 (l) 3c on 1c blk vio 250. 200.
a. Inverted surcharge *1,500.*
198 A19 (i) 5c on 1c blk vio 92.50 72.50
a. Inverted surcharge 500.
b. Surcharge vert. reading up —
c. Double surcharge *600. 2,750.*
d. Double invtd. surch. — —

Value for No. 198b is for surcharge reading up. One example is known with surcharge reading down.

199 A19 (j) 5c on 1c blk vio 150. 115.
a. Inverted surcharge *3,000.*
b. Vertical surcharge — —
c. Double surcharge *3,000. 3,000.*

m

200 A19 (m) 10c on 1c blk vio 62.50 *92.50*
a. Broken figure "1" 160.00 *225.00*

Black Surcharge on Nos. P26-P30

201 N2 (k) 3c on 1m bl grn 350. 350.
a. Inverted surcharge 450.
b. "EENTS" 600. 450.
c. As "b", inverted 850.
202 N2 (l) 3c on 1m bl grn 1,000. 400.
a. Inverted surcharge 850.
203 N2 (k) 3c on 2m bl grn 1,650. 400.
a. "EENTS" 1,650. 500.
b. Inverted surcharge 1,500.
c. As "a," inverted *2,750.*
204 N2 (l) 3c on 2m bl grn 2,750. 600.
a. Inverted surcharge *1,500.*
205 N2 (k) 3c on 3m bl grn 900. 400.
a. Inverted surcharge 750.
b. "EENTS" 1,250. 450.
c. As "b," inverted *2,750.*
206 N2 (l) 3c on 3m bl grn 1,500. 550.
a. Inverted surcharge *1,000.*
211 N2 (i) 5c on 1m bl grn 1,800.
a. "EENTS" — 3,000.
212 N2 (j) 5c on 1m bl grn — 2,250.
213 N2 (i) 5c on 2m bl grn 3,000. 1,800.
a. "EENTS" 3,000. 3,000.
214 N2 (j) 5c on 2m bl grn 3,250. 1,750.
215 N2 (i) 5c on 3m bl grn 550.
a. "EENTS" 1,000.
216 N2 (j) 5c on 3m bl grn 3,000. 1,000.
217 N2 (i) 5c on 4m bl grn *3,000.* 900.
a. "EENTS" *3,000.* 1,500.
b. Inverted surcharge *2,000.*
c. As "a," inverted *3,000.*
218 N2 (j) 5c on 4m bl grn 3,000. *1,500.*
a. Inverted surcharge *2,000.*
219 N2 (i) 5c on 8m bl grn *2,500.* 1,250.
a. Inverted surcharge 1,500.
b. "EENTS" 3,000. 2,750.
c. As "b," inverted 2,500.
220 N2 (j) 5c on 8m bl grn 2,000.
a. Inverted surcharge 2,500.

Beware of forgeries of the Puerto Principe issue. Obtaining expert opinions is recommended.

United States Stamps Nos. 279, 267, 267b, 279Bf, 279Bh, 268, 281, 282C and 283 Surcharged in Black

1899 Wmk. 191 *Perf. 12*

221 A87 1c on 1c yel grn 4.50 .40
Never hinged 11.50
222 A88 2c on 2c reddish car, III 10.00 .75
Never hinged 25.00
b. 2c on 2c vermilion, type III 10.00 .75
222A A88 2c on 2c reddish car, IV 6.00 .40
Never hinged 15.00
c. 2c on 2c vermilion, IV 6.00 .40
d. As No. 222A, inverted surcharge *5,500. 4,000.*
223 A88 2½c on 2c reddish car, III 6.00 .80
Never hinged 15.00
b. 2½c on 2c vermilion, III 6.00 .80
223A A88 2½c on 2c reddish car, IV 3.50 .50
Never hinged 8.75
c. 2½c on 2c vermilion, IV 3.50 .50
224 A89 3c on 3c purple 12.00 1.75
Never hinged 30.00
a. Period between "B" and "A" 40.00 35.00
225 A91 5c on 5c blue 12.50 2.00
Never hinged 30.00
226 A94 10c on 10c brn, I 25.00 6.00
Never hinged 70.00
b. "CUBA" omitted *7,000. 4,000.*
226A A94 10c on 10c brn, II *6,000.*
Nos. 221-226 (8) 79.50 12.60

The 2½c was sold and used as a 2c stamp. Excellent counterfeits of this and the preceding issue exist, especially inverted and double surcharges.

Issues of the Republic under US Military Rule

Statue of Columbus A20

Royal Palms A21

"Cuba"
A22

Ocean Liner
A23

Cane Field — A24

1899 Wmk. US-C (191C) *Perf. 12*

227	A20 1c yellow green	3.50	.25
	Never hinged	8.75	
228	A21 2c carmine	3.50	.25
	Never hinged	8.75	
a.	scarlet	3.50	.25
b.	Booklet pane of 6	5,500.	
229	A22 3c purple	3.50	.30
	Never hinged	8.75	
230	A23 5c blue	4.50	.30
	Never hinged	11.00	
231	A24 10c brown	11.00	.80
	Never hinged	27.50	
	Nos. 227-231 (5)	26.00	1.90

No. 228b was issued by the Republic.

See Nos. 233-237 in Scott Standard Catalogue Vol 2. For surcharge see No. 232.

SPECIAL DELIVERY STAMPS

Issued under Administration of the United States

US No. E5 Surcharged in Red

1899 Wmk. 191 *Perf. 12*

E1	SD3 10c blue	130.	100.
	Never hinged	300.	
a.	No period after "CUBA"	575.	400.

Issue of the Republic under US Military Rule

Special Delivery Messenger — SD2

Printed by the US Bureau of Engraving and Printing

1899 Wmk. US-C (191C)

Inscribed: "Immediata"

E2	SD2 10c orange	52.50	15.00
	Never hinged	120.00	

POSTAGE DUE STAMPS

Issued under Administration of the United States

Postage Due Stamps of the United States Nos. J38, J39, J41 and J42 Srchd. in Black Like Nos. 221-226A

1899 Wmk. 191 *Perf. 12*

J1	D2 1c dp claret	45.00	5.25
	Never hinged	110.00	
J2	D2 2c dp claret	45.00	5.25
	Never hinged	110.00	
a.	Inverted surcharge		4,000.
J3	D2 5c dp claret	42.50	5.25
	Never hinged	105.00	
J4	D2 10c dp claret	25.00	2.50
	Never hinged	60.00	
	Nos. J1-J4 (4)	157.50	18.25

DANISH WEST INDIES AND UNITED STATES VIRGIN ISLANDS

ˈdā-nish ˈwest ˈin-dēs

LOCATION — Group of islands in the West Indies, lying east of Puerto Rico

GOVT. — Danish colony

AREA — 132 sq. mi.

POP. — 27,086 (1911)

CAPITAL — Charlotte Amalie

The US bought these islands in 1917 and they became the US Virgin Islands, using US stamps and currency.

100 Cents = 1 Dollar

100 Bit = 1 Franc (1905)

Wmk. 111 — Small Crown

Wmk. 112 — Crown

Wmk. 113 — Crown

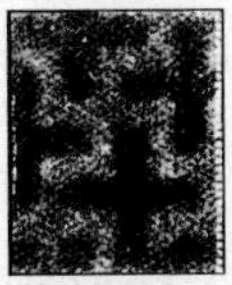

Wmk. 114 — Multiple Crosses

Coat of Arms — A1

Yellowish Paper

Yellow Wavy-line Burelage, UL to LR

1856 Typo. Wmk. 111 *Imperf.*

1	A1 3c dark carmine, brown gum	210.	*235.*
a.	3c dark carmine, yellow gum	350.	*375.*
b.	3c carmine, white gum	*3,750.*	*3,750.*

No. 228b was issued by the Republic.The brown and yellow gums were applied locally.

Reprint: 1981, carmine, back-printed across two stamps ("Reprint by Dansk Post og Telegrafmuseum 1978"), value, pair, $10.

White Paper

1866

Yellow Wavy-line Burelage UR to LL

2	A1 3c rose	42.50	*50.*

No. 2 reprints, unwatermarked: 1930, carmine, value $100. 1942, rose carmine, back-printed across each row ("Nytryk 1942 G. A. Hagemann Danmark og Dansk Vestindiens Frimaerker Bind 2"), value $50.

1872 *Perf. 12½*

3	A1 3c rose	130.	*320.*

1873 Without Burelage

4	A1 4c dull blue	325.	*700.*
a.	Imperf., pair	775.	
b.	Horiz. pair, imperf. vert.	575.	

The 1930 reprint of No. 4 is ultramarine, unwatermarked and imperf., value $100.

The 1942 4c reprint is blue, unwatermarked, imperf. and has printing on back (see note below No. 2), value $60.

A2

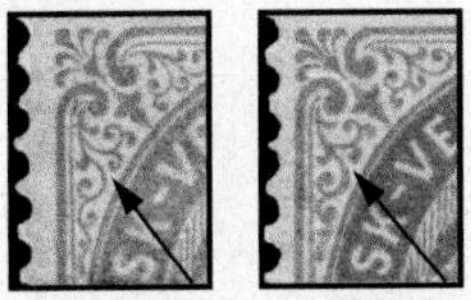

Normal Frame Inverted Frame

The arabesques in the corners have a main stem and a branch. When the frame is in normal position, in the upper left corner the branch leaves the main stem half way between two little leaflets. In the lower right corner the branch starts at the foot of the second leaflet. When the frame is inverted the corner designs are, of course, transposed.

Values for inverted frames, covers and blocks are for the cheapest variety.

White Wove Paper

Varying from Thin to Thick

1874-79 Wmk. 112 *Perf. 14x13½*

5	A2 1c green & brown red	35.00	*32.50*
a.	1c green & rose lilac, thin paper	160.00	*190.00*
b.	1c green & red violet, medium paper	50.00	*65.00*
c.	1c green & claret, thick paper	32.50	*26.00*
e.	As "c," inverted frame	40.00	*26.00*
f.	As "a," inverted frame	*900.00*	1,900.

No. 5 exists with a surcharge similar to the surcharge on No. 15, with 10 CENTS value and 1895 date. This stamp is an essay.

6	A2 3c blue & carmine	35.00	18.00
a.	3c light blue & rose carmine, thin paper	45.00	35.00
b.	3c deep blue & dark carmine, medium paper	45.00	25.00
c.	3c greenish blue & lake, thick paper	29.00	18.00
d.	Imperf., pair	325.00	—
e.	Inverted frame, thick paper	45.00	35.00
f.	As "a," inverted frame	*800.00*	1,200.
7	A2 4c brown & dull blue	23.00	*22.50*
b.	4c brown & ultramarine, thin paper	290.00	*250.00*
c.	Diagonal half used as 2c on cover		165.00
d.	As "b," inverted frame	*1,450.*	*2,400.*
8	A2 5c grn & gray ('76)	45.00	29.00
a.	5c yellow green & dark gray, thin paper	85.00	45.00
b.	Inverted frame, thick paper	37.50	26.00
9	A2 7c lilac & orange	40.00	*135.00*
a.	7c lilac & yellow	120.00	*130.00*
b.	Inverted frame	65.00	*220.00*
10	A2 10c blue & brn ('76)	57.50	34.00
a.	10c dark blue & black brown, thin paper	85.00	47.50
b.	Period between "t" & "s" of "cents"	72.50	47.50
c.	Inverted frame	26.00	*27.50*
11	A2 12c red lil & yel grn ('77)	60.00	*170.00*
a.	12c lilac & deep green	230.00	*240.00*
12	A2 14c lilac & green	1,050.	*1,750.*
a.	Inverted frame	*4,000.*	*4,800.*
13	A2 50c vio, thin paper ('79)	260.00	*390.00*
a.	50c gray violet, thick paper	310.00	*525.00*
	Nos. 5-13 (9)	1,606.	2,581.

The central element in the fan-shaped scrollwork at the outside of the lower left corner of Nos. 5a and 7b looks like an elongated diamond.

See Nos. 16-20. For surcharges see Nos. 14-15, 23-28, 40.

No. 9 Surcharged in Black

a

1887

14	A2 (a) 1c on 7c lilac & orange	140.00	*275.00*
b.	1c on 7c lilac & yellow	190.00	*300.00*
d.	Inverted frame	175.00	*525.00*

No. 13 Surcharged in Black

b

1895

15	A2 (b) 10c on 50c violet, thin paper	45.00	*72.50*

The "b" surcharge also exists on No. 5, with "10" found in two sizes. These are essays.

Type of 1874-79

1896-1901 *Perf. 13*

16	A2 1c grn & red vio, inverted frame ('98)	26.00	*36.50*
a.	Normal frame	590.00	*735.00*
17	A2 3c blue & lake, inverted frame ('98)	15.50	*17.00*
a.	Normal frame	400.00	*600.00*
18	A2 4c bister & dull blue ('01)	21.50	13.50
a.	Diagonal half used as 2c on cover		67.50
b.	Inverted frame	85.00	*110.00*
c.	As "b," diagonal half used as 2c on cover		425.00
19	A2 5c green & gray, inverted frame	47.50	42.50
a.	Normal frame	1,375.	*1,700.*
20	A2 10c blue & brn ('01)	110.00	*145.00*
a.	Inverted frame	1,550.	*2,925.*
b.	Period between "t" and "s" of "cents"	155.00	180.00
	Nos. 16-20 (5)	220.50	*254.50*

Arms — A5

1900

21	A5 1c light green	2.60	2.25
22	A5 5c light blue	17.00	*25.00*

See Nos. 29-30. For surcharges see Nos. 41-42.

Nos. 6, 17, 20 Surcharged

c

Surcharge "c" in Black

1902 *Perf. 14x13½*

23	A2 2c on 3c blue & carmine, inverted frame	1,075.	*1,450.*
a.	"2" in date with straight tail	1,200.	*1,600.*
b.	Normal frame	—	

Perf. 13

24	A2 2c on 3c blue & lake, inverted frame	11.50	*32.00*
a.	"2" in date with straight tail	30.00	*50.00*
b.	Dated "1901"	1,000.	1,000.
c.	Normal frame	320.00	*825.00*
d.	Dark green surcharge	3,000.	—
e.	As "d" & "a"	—	
f.	As "d" & "c"	—	

The overprint on No. 24b exists in two types: with "1901" measuring 2.5 mm or 2.2 mm high.

Only one example of No. 24f can exist.

25 A2 8c on 10c blue & brown 26.00 *55.00*
a. "2" with straight tail 35.00 *65.00*
b. On No. 20b 55.00 *85.00*
c. Inverted frame 300.00 *675.00*

d

Surcharge "d" in Black

1902 ***Perf. 13***

27 A2 2c on 3c blue & lake, inverted frame 15.75 *63.00*
a. Normal frame 415.00 *720.00*
28 A2 8c on 10c blue & brown 14.00 15.00
a. On No. 20b 26.00 *32.00*
b. Inverted frame 415.00 *675.00*
Nos. 23-28 (5) 1,142. 1,615.

1903 **Wmk. 113**

29 A5 2c carmine 9.50 *25.00*
30 A5 8c brown 36.00 *62.00*

King Christian IX — A8

St. Thomas Harbor — A9

1905 **Typo.** ***Perf. 13***

31 A8 5b green 4.75 3.00
32 A8 10b red 4.75 3.00
33 A8 20b green & blue 9.50 8.00
34 A8 25b ultramarine 9.50 *8.00*
35 A8 40b red & gray 9.50 *7.00*
36 A8 50b yellow & gray 14.00 11.00

Perf. 12

Wmk. Two Crowns (113)

Frame Typographed, Center Engraved

37 A9 1fr green & blue 17.50 *50.00*
38 A9 2fr orange red & brown 32.50 *67.50*
39 A9 5fr yellow & brown 85.00 *315.00*
Nos. 31-39 (9) 187.00 *472.50*

Favor cancels exist on Nos. 37-39. Value 25% less.

Nos. 18, 22 and 30 Surcharged in Black

1905 **Wmk. 112**

40 A2 5b on 4c bister & dull blue 17.50 *70.00*
a. Inverted frame 110.00 *190.00*
41 A5 5b on 5c light blue 13.00 *64.00*

Wmk. 113

42 A5 5b on 8c brown 13.00 *75.00*
Nos. 40-42 (3) 43.50 209.00

Favor cancels exist on Nos. 40-42. Value 25% less.

Frederik VIII — A10

Frame Typographed, Center Engraved

1908

43 A10 5b green 2.75 1.90
44 A10 10b red 2.75 1.90
45 A10 15b violet & brown 5.00 *5.75*
46 A10 20b green & blue 32.50 27.50
47 A10 25b blue & dark blue 2.25 *2.50*
48 A10 30b claret & slate 67.50 *60.00*
49 A10 40b vermilion & gray 8.00 *11.50*
50 A10 50b yellow & brown 8.50 *10.00*
Nos. 43-50 (8) 129.25 121.05

Christian X — A11

1915 **Wmk. 114** ***Perf. 14x14½***

51 A11 5b yellow green 5.25 *6.25*
52 A11 10b red 5.25 *110.00*
53 A11 15b lilac & red brown 5.25 *110.00*
54 A11 20b green & blue 5.25 *110.00*
55 A11 25b blue & dark blue 5.25 *16.00*
56 A11 30b claret & black 5.25 *200.00*
57 A11 40b orange & black 5.25 *200.00*
58 A11 50b yellow & brown 5.25 *200.00*
Nos. 51-58 (8) 42.00 *952.25*

Forged and favor cancellations exist.

POSTAGE DUE STAMPS

Royal Cipher, "Christian 9 Rex" — D1

1902 **Litho.** **Unwmk.** ***Perf. 11½***

J1 D1 1c dark blue 8.25 *45.00*
J2 D1 4c dark blue 20.00 *45.00*
J3 D1 6c dark blue 40.00 *87.50*
J4 D1 10c dark blue 40.00 *87.50*
Nos. J1-J4 (4) 108.25 *265.00*

There are five types of each value. On the 4c they may be distinguished by differences in the figure "4"; on the other values differences are minute.

Used values of Nos. J1-J8 are for canceled stamps. Uncanceled stamps without gum have probably been used. Value 60% of unused.

Excellent counterfeits of Nos. J1-J4 exist.

Numeral of value — D2

1905-13 ***Perf. 13***

J5 D2 5b red & gray 6.50 *8.00*
J6 D2 20b red & gray 11.50 *14.50*
J7 D2 30b red & gray 9.50 *14.50*
J8 D2 50b red & gray 9.00 *36.00*
a. Perf. 14x14½ ('13) 75.00 *290.00*
b. Perf. 11½ 475.00
Nos. J5-J8 (4) 36.50 *73.00*

All values of this issue are known imperforate, but were not regularly issued.

Used values of Nos. J5-J8 are for canceled stamps. Uncanceled examples without gum have probably been used. Value 60% of unused.

No. J8b is valued in the grade of fine.

Counterfeits of Nos. J5-J8 exist.

Danish West Indies stamps were replaced by those of the U.S. in 1917, after the U.S. bought the islands.

GUAM

'gwäm

LOCATION — One of the Mariana Islands in the Pacific Ocean, about 1450 miles east of the Philippines
GOVT. — United States Possession
AREA — 206 sq. mi.
POP. — 9,000 (est. 1899)
CAPITAL — Agaña

Formerly a Spanish possession, Guam was ceded to the United States in 1898 following the Spanish-American War. Stamps overprinted "Guam" were superseded by the regular postage stamps of the United States in 1901.

100 Cents = 1 Dollar

United States Nos. 279, 279B, 279Bc, 268, 280a, 281, 282, 272, 282C, 283, 284, 275, 275a, 276 and 276A Overprinted

1899 **Wmk. 191** ***Perf. 12***

Black Overprint

1 A87 1c deep green 20.00 *25.00*
Never hinged 40.00

A bogus inverted overprint exists.

2 A88 2c red, type IV 17.50 *25.00*
Never hinged 35.00
a. rose carmine, type IV 30.00 30.00
Never hinged 60.00
3 A89 3c purple 140.00 *175.00*
Never hinged 275.00
4 A90 4c lilac brown 125.00 *175.00*
Never hinged 250.00
5 A91 5c blue 32.50 *45.00*
Never hinged 65.00
6 A92 6c lake 125.00 *190.00*
Never hinged 250.00
7 A93 8c violet brown 125.00 *160.00*
Never hinged 275.00
8 A94 10c brown, type I 45.00 *55.00*
Never hinged 90.00
9 A94 10c brown, type II *2,750.* —
Never hinged *5,500.*
10 A95 15c olive green 150.00 140.00
Never hinged 300.00
11 A96 50c orange 350.00 *400.00*
Never hinged 700.00
a. 50c red orange 550.00 —
Never hinged 1,100.

Red Overprint

12 A97 $1 black, type I 350.00 *400.00*
Never hinged 700.00
13 A97 $1 black, type II *3,750.*
Never hinged —
Nos. 1-8,10-12 (11) 1,480. *1,790.*

Counterfeits of the overprint exist.
No. 13 exists only in the special printing.

SPECIAL DELIVERY STAMP

United States No. E5 Overprinted in Red

1899 **Wmk. 191** ***Perf. 12***

E1 SD3 10c blue 150. *200.00*
Never hinged 275.
a. Dots in curved frame above messenger (Plate 882) 200.
Never hinged 400.

Counterfeits of the overprint exist.

The special stamps for Guam were replaced by the regular issues of the United States.

Guam Guard Mail stamps of 1930 are listed in the Scott U.S. specialized catalogue.

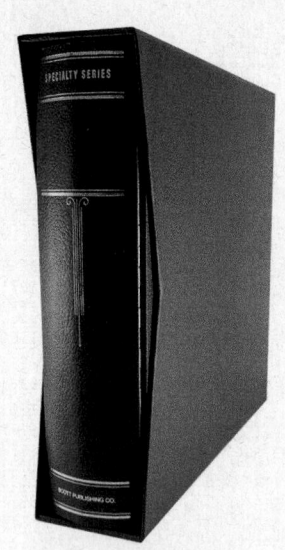

HAWAII

hə-'wä-yē

LOCATION — Group of 20 islands in the Pacific Ocean, about 2,000 miles southwest of San Francisco.
GOVT. — Former Kingdom and Republic
AREA — 6,435 sq. mi.
POP. — 150,000 (est. 1899)
CAPITAL — Honolulu

Until 1893 an independent kingdom, from 1893 to 1898 a republic, the Hawaiian Islands were annexed to the US in 1898. The Territory of Hawaii achieved statehood in 1959.

100 Cents = 1 Dollar

Values for Nos. 1-4 are for examples with minor damage that has been skillfully repaired.

Values of Hawaii stamps vary considerably according to condition. For Nos. 1-4, values are for examples with minor damage that has been skillfully repaired.

A1

A2

A3

1851-52 Unwmk. Typeset *Imperf.*
Pelure Paper

1 A1 2c blue 625,000. 250,000.
2 A1 5c blue 55,000. 45,000.
3 A2 13c blue 37,000. 32,500.
4 A3 13c blue 52,500. 42,500.

Nos. 1-4 are known as the "Missionaries."
Two varieties of each. Nos. 1-4, off cover, are almost invariably damaged.
No. 1 unused is unique.

Values for Nos. 5-82 are for very fine examples. Extremely fine to superb stamps sell at much higher prices, and inferior or poor stamps sell at reduced prices, depending on the condition of the individual example.

King Kamehameha III

A4

A5

Printed in Sheets of 20 (4x5)

1853 Engr.
Thick White Wove Paper

5 A4 5c blue 1,900. 1,900.
a. Line through "Honolulu" (Pos. 2) 3,000. 3,000.
6 A5 13c dark red 900. 1,700.

See Nos. 8-11.

A6

1857

7 A6 5c on 13c dark red 7,000. 10,000.

Beware of fake manuscript surcharges. Expertization is strongly recommended.

1857 Thin White Wove Paper

8 A4 5c blue 700. 750.
a. Line through "Honolulu" (Pos. 2) 1,350. 1,350.
b. Double impression 4,250. 4,750.

1861 Thin Bluish Wove Paper

9 A4 5c blue 400. 400.
a. Line through "Honolulu" (Pos. 2) 950. 1,000.

RE-ISSUE

1868 Ordinary White Wove Paper

10 A4 5c blue 27.50
a. Line through "Honolulu" (Pos. 2) 80.
11 A5 13c dull rose 325.

Remainders of Nos. 10 and 11 were overprinted "SPECIMEN." See Nos. 10S-11Sb in the Scott U.S. Specialized Catalogue.

Nos. 10 and 11 were never placed in use but stamps (both with and without overprint) were sold at face value at the Honolulu post office.

REPRINTS (Official Imitations)

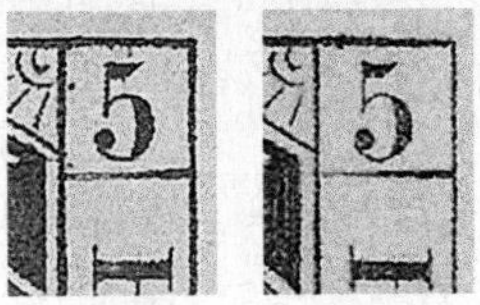
Original Reprint

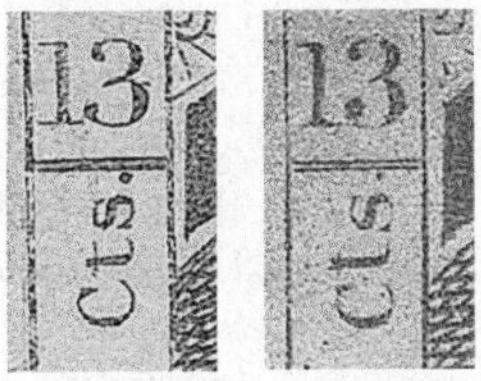
Original Reprint

5c — *Originals have two small dots near the left side of the square in the upper right corner. These dots are missing in the reprints.*

13c — *The bottom of the 3 of 13 in the upper left corner is flattened in the originals and rounded in the reprints. The "t" of "Cts" on the left side is as tall as the "C" in the reprints, but shorter in the originals.*

1889

10R A4 5c blue 65.
11R A5 13c orange red 300.

On August 19, 1892, the remaining supply of reprints was overprinted in black "REPRINT." The reprints (both with and without overprint) were sold at face value. See the Scott U.S. Specialized Catalogue.

Values for the Numeral stamps, Nos. 12-26, are for examples with four reasonably large margins. Unused values are for stamps without gum.

A7

A8

A9

1859-62 Typeset

12 A7 1c light blue, *bluish white* 15,000. 15,000.
a. "1 Ce" omitted 22,500.
b. "nt" omitted — —

No. 12a is unique.

13 A7 2c light blue, *bluish white* 6,250. 5,000.
a. 2c dark blue, *grayish white* 6,750. 5,000.
b. Comma after "Cents" — 6,750.
c. No period after "LETA" — —
14 A7 2c black, *greenish blue* ('62) 8,000. 6,000.
a. "2-Cents." —

1859-63

15 A7 1c black, *grayish* ('63) 650. 2,750.
a. Tête bêche pair 9,000.
b. "NTER" —
c. Period omitted after "Postage" 850.
d. 1c black, *bluish gray* 850.
16 A7 2c black, *grayish* 1,000. 850.
a. "2" at top of rectangle 3,750. 3,750.
b. Printed on both sides — 21,000.
c. "NTER" 3,250. 6,500.
d. 2c black, *grayish white* 1,000. 850.
e. Period omitted after "Cents" —
f. Overlapping impressions — —
g. "TAGE" —
17 A7 2c dark blue, *bluish* ('63) 12,000. 8,750.
a. "ISL" — —
18 A7 2c black, *blue gray* ('63) 3,250. 6,000.

1864-65

19 A7 1c black 625. 10,000.
20 A7 2c black 775. 1,500.
21 A8 5c blue, *blue* ('65) 900. 700.
a. Tête bêche pair 10,500.
b. 5c bluish black, *grayish white* 11,000. 3,750.

No. 21b unused is unique. No. 21b used is also unique but defective.

22 A9 5c blue, *blue* ('65) 575. 900.
a. Tête bêche pair 18,000.
b. 5c blue, *grayish white* —
c. Overlapping impressions —

1864 Laid Paper

23 A7 1c black 300. 2,500.
a. "HA" instead of "HAWAIIAN" 3,500.
b. Tête bêche pair 6,000.
c. Tête bêche pair, Nos. 23, 23a 18,000.
24 A7 2c black 350. 1,050.
a. "NTER" 3,250.
b. "S" of "POSTAGE" omitted 1,500.
c. Tête bêche pair 7,000.

A10

1865 Wove Paper

25 A10 1c dark blue 350.
a. Double impression —
b. With inverted impression of No. 21 on face 18,500.
26 A10 2c dark blue 350.

Nos. 12 to 26 were typeset and were printed in settings of ten, each stamp differing from the others.

King Kamehameha IV — A11

1861-63 Litho.
Horizontally Laid Paper

27 A11 2c pale rose 350. 350.
a. 2c carmine rose ('63) 3,000. 2,850.

Vertically Laid Paper

28 A11 2c pale rose 325. 325.
a. 2c carmine rose ('63) 400. 450.

RE-ISSUE

1869 Engr. Thin Wove Paper

29 A11 2c red 45.00 —

No. 29 was not issued for postal purposes although canceled examples are known. It was sold only at the Honolulu post office, at first without overprint and later with overprint "CANCELLED." See No. 29S in the Scott U.S. Specialized Catalogue.

See Nos. 50-51 and note following No. 51.

Princess Victoria Kamamalu — A12

King Kamehameha IV — A13

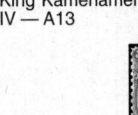

King Kamehameha V — A14

King Kamehameha V — A15

Mataio Kekuanaoa — A16

1864-86 Engr. *Perf. 12*
Wove Paper

30 A12 1c purple ('86) 11.00 8.00
Never hinged 25.00
a. 1c mauve ('71) 60.00 20.00
Never hinged 95.00
b. 1c violet ('78) 20.00 10.00
Never hinged 45.00
31 A13 2c rose vermilion 65.00 12.50
Never hinged 150.00
a. 2c vermilion ('86) 55.00 17.50
Never hinged 130.00
b. Half used as 1c on cover with #32 7,500.
32 A14 5c blue ('66) 175.00 30.00
Never hinged 375.00

33 A15 6c yellow green ('71) 45.00 10.00
Never hinged 100.00
a. 6c bluish green ('78) 35.00 10.00
Never hinged 85.00
b. As "a," horiz. pair, imperf. *2,250.*
34 A16 18c dull rose ('71) 100.00 45.00
Never hinged 220.00
Nos. 30-34 (5) 396.00 105.50
Set, never hinged 860.00

No. 32 has traces of rectangular frame lines surrounding the design. Nos. 39 and 52C have no such frame lines.

For overprints see Nos. 53, 58-60, 65, 66C, 71.

King David Kalakaua A17

Prince William Pitt Leleiohoku A18

1875

35 A17 2c brown 9.00 3.00
Never hinged 22.00
36 A18 12c black 75.00 32.50
Never hinged 165.00

See Nos. 38, 43, 46. For overprints see Nos. 56, 62-63, 66, 69.

Princess Likelike A19

King David Kalakaua A20

Queen Kapiolani — A21

Statue of King Kamehameha I — A22

King William Lunalilo A23

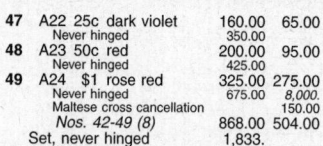

Queen Emma Kaleleonalani A24

1882

37 A19 1c blue 11.00 6.00
Never hinged 27.50
38 A17 2c lilac rose 125.00 47.50
Never hinged 275.00
39 A14 5c ultramarine 15.00 3.00
Never hinged 35.00
a. Vert. pair, imperf. horiz. *5,000.* *6,000.*
40 A20 10c black 50.00 25.00
Never hinged 115.00
41 A21 15c red brown 70.00 27.50
Never hinged 150.00
Nos. 37-41 (5) 271.00 109.00
Set, never hinged 602.50

1883-86

42 A19 1c green 3.00 2.00
Never hinged 7.00
43 A17 2c rose ('86) 5.00 1.00
Never hinged 11.00
a. 2c dull red 65.00 22.50
Never hinged 140.00
44 A20 10c red brown ('84) 40.00 12.00
Never hinged 90.00
45 A20 10c vermilion 45.00 14.00
Never hinged 100.00
46 A18 12c red lilac 90.00 40.00
Never hinged 225.00
47 A22 25c dark violet 160.00 65.00
Never hinged 350.00
48 A23 50c red 200.00 95.00
Never hinged 425.00
49 A24 $1 rose red 325.00 275.00
Never hinged 675.00 *8,000.*
Maltese cross cancellation 150.00
Nos. 42-49 (8) 868.00 504.00
Set, never hinged 1,833.

Other fiscal cancellations exist on No. 49.

Nos. 48-49 are valued used with postal cancels. Canceled-to-order cancels exist and are worth less.

REPRODUCTION and REPRINT

Yellowish Wove Paper

1886-89 Engr. *Imperf.*

50 A11 2c orange vermilion 170.00
Never hinged 275.00
51 A11 2c carmine ('89) 35.00
Never hinged 50.00

In 1885, the Postmaster General wished to have on sale complete sets of Hawaii's portrait stamps, but was unable to find either the stone from which Nos. 27 and 28 were printed, or the plate from which No. 29 was printed. He therefore sent an example of No. 29 to the American Bank Note Company, with an order to engrave a new plate like it and print 10,000 stamps therefrom, of which 5000 were overprinted "SPECIMEN" in blue.

The original No. 29 was printed in sheets of fifteen (5x3), but the plate of these "Official Imitations" was made up of fifty stamps (10x5). Later, in 1887, the original die for No. 29 was discovered, and, after retouching, a new plate was made and 37,500 stamps were printed (No. 51). These, like the originals, were printed in sheets of fifteen. They were delivered during 1889 and 1890. In 1892, all remaining unsold in the Post Office were overprinted "Reprint".

No. 29 is red in color, and printed on very thin white wove paper. No. 50 is orange vermilion in color, on medium, white to buff paper. In No. 50 the vertical line on the left side of the portrait touches the horizontal line over the label "Elua Keneta", while in the other two varieties, Nos. 29 and 51, it does not touch the horizontal line by half a millimeter. In No. 51 there are three parallel lines on the left side of the King's nose, while in No. 29 and No. 50 there are no such lines. No. 51 is carmine in color and printed on thick, yellowish to buff, wove paper.

It is claimed that both Nos. 50 and 51 were available for postage, although not made to fill a postal requirement. They exist with favor cancellation. No. 51 also is known postally used. See Nos. 50S-51S in the Scott U.S. specialized catalogue.

Queen Liliuokalani — A25

1890-91 *Perf. 12*

52 A25 2c dull violet ('91) 15.00 1.50
Never hinged 25.00
a. Vert. pair, imperf. horiz. *3,750.*
52C A14 5c deep indigo 125.00 150.00
Never hinged 280.00

Stamps of 1864-91 Overprinted in Red

Three categories of double overprints:
I. Both overprints heavy.
II. One overprint heavy, one of moderate strength.
III. One overprint heavy, one of light or weak strength.

1893 Overprinted in Red

53 A12 1c violet 9.00 13.00
Never hinged 20.00
a. "189" instead of "1893" 600.00 —
b. No period after "GOVT" *275.00* *275.00*
f. Double overprint (III) *600.00*
54 A19 1c blue 9.00 *15.00*
Never hinged 21.00
b. No period after "GOVT" *140.00* *150.00*
e. Double overprint (II) *1,500.*
f. Double overprint (III) *400.00*
55 A19 1c green 2.00 *3.00*
Never hinged 4.00
d. Double overprint (I) *650.00* *650.00*
f. Double overprint (III) *250.00* *250.00*
g. Pair, one without ovpt. *10,000.*
56 A17 2c brown 12.50 *20.00*
Never hinged 27.50
b. No period after "GOVT" *325.00* —
57 A25 2c dull violet 2.00 1.50
Never hinged 3.00
a. "18 3" instead of "1893" *900.00* *900.00*
d. Double overprint (I) *1,300.* *1,000.*
f. Double overprint (III) *190.00* *190.00*
g. Inverted overprint *4,000.* *4,750.*
58 A14 5c deep indigo 15.00 *30.00*
Never hinged 32.00
b. No period after "GOVT" *275.00* *275.00*
f. Double overprint (III) *1,250.* *675.00*
59 A14 5c ultramarine 7.00 3.00
Never hinged 15.00
d. Double overprint (I) *6,500.*
e. Double overprint (II) *3,750.* *3,750.*
f. Double overprint (III) *600.00*
g. Inverted overprint *1,500.* *1,500.*
60 A15 6c green 17.50 *25.00*
Never hinged 40.00
e. Double overprint (II) *1,100.*
61 A20 10c black 14.00 *20.00*
Never hinged 30.00
e. Double overprint (II) *1,000.* *900.00*
f. Double overprint (III) *225.00*
61B A20 10c red brown *15,000.* *29,000.*
Never hinged *25,000.*
62 A18 12c black 14.00 *20.00*
Never hinged 30.00
d. Double overprint (I) *1,500.*
e. Double overprint (II) *1,100.*
f. Double overprint (III) —
63 A18 12c red lilac 175.00 *250.00*
Never hinged 400.00
64 A22 25c dark violet 35.00 *45.00*
Never hinged 70.00
b. No period after "GOVT" *350.00* *350.00*
Never hinged *600.00*
f. Double overprint (III) *1,250.*
Nos. 53-61,62-64 (12) 312.00 *445.50*
Nos. 53-61, 62-64 never hinged 692.75

Virtually all known examples of No. 61B are cut in at the top.

Overprinted in Black

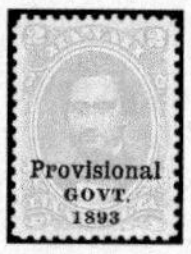

65 A13 2c vermilion 85.00 *90.00*
Never hinged 200.00
b. No period after "GOVT" *300.00* *300.00*
66 A17 2c rose 2.50 *2.50*
Never hinged 3.75
b. No period after "GOVT" 70.00 70.00
d. Double overprint (I) *4,000.*
e. Double overprint (II) *2,750.*
f. Double overprint (III) *300.00*
66C A15 6c green *15,000.* *29,000.*
67 A20 10c vermilion 22.50 *30.00*
Never hinged 45.00
f. Double overprint (III) *1,250.*
68 A20 10c red brown 12.00 *13.00*
Never hinged 24.00
f. Double overprint (III) *4,000.*
69 A18 12c red lilac 350.00 *500.00*
Never hinged 575.00
70 A21 15c red brown 27.50 *35.00*
Never hinged 55.00
e. Double overprint (II) *2,000.*
71 A16 18c dull rose 40.00 40.00
Never hinged 80.00
a. "18 3" instead of "1893" *525.00* *525.00*
b. No period after "GOVT" *350.00* *350.00*
d. Double overprint (I) *650.00*
f. Double overprint (III) *275.00* —
g. Pair, one without ovpt. *3,500.*
h. As "b," double overprint (II) *1,750.*
72 A23 50c red 90.00 *120.00*
Never hinged 180.00
b. No period after "GOVT" *500.00* *500.00*
Never hinged *775.00*
f. Double overprint (III) *1,000.*
73 A24 $1 rose red 160.00 *190.00*
Never hinged 325.00
b. No period after "GOVT" *525.00* 500.00
Nos. 65-66,67-73 (9) 789.50 *1,021.*
Nos. 65-66, 67-73 never hinged 1,485.

Coat of Arms A26

View of Honolulu A27

Statue of Kamehameha I — A28

Stars and Palms A29

S. S. "Arawa" A30

Pres. Sanford Ballard Dole — A31

1894

74 A26 1c yellow 2.00 1.50
Never hinged 4.00
75 A27 2c brown 2.00 .60
Never hinged 4.00
76 A28 5c rose lake 5.00 2.00
Never hinged 11.00
77 A29 10c yellow green 8.00 5.00
Never hinged 18.00
78 A30 12c blue 17.50 *20.00*
Never hinged 37.50
79 A31 25c deep blue 22.50 17.50
Never hinged 47.50
Nos. 74-79 (6) 57.00 *46.60*
Set, never hinged 122.50

Numerous double transfers exist on Nos. 75 and 81.

"CENTS" Added — A32

1899

80 A26 1c dark green 2.00 1.50
Never hinged 4.50
81 A27 2c rose 1.50 1.00
Never hinged 3.50
a. 2c salmon 1.50 1.50
Never hinged 3.50
b. Vert. pair, imperf. horiz. *4,250.*
82 A32 5c blue 8.00 4.00
Never hinged 20.00
Nos. 80-82 (3) 11.50 6.50
Set, never hinged 28.00

OFFICIAL STAMPS

Lorrin Andrews Thurston — O1

1896 Engr. Unwmk. *Perf. 12*

O1 O1 2c green 45.00 20.00
Never hinged 90.00
O2 O1 5c black brown 45.00 20.00
Never hinged 90.00
O3 O1 6c deep ultramarine 45.00 20.00
Never hinged 90.00
O4 O1 10c bright rose 45.00 20.00
Never hinged 90.00
O5 O1 12c orange 55.00 22.50
Never hinged 110.00
O6 O1 25c gray violet 65.00 22.50
Never hinged 130.00
Nos. O1-O6 (6) 300.00 125.00
Set, never hinged 600.00

Used values for Nos. O1-O6 are for stamps canceled-to-order "FOREIGN OFFICE/HONOLULU H.I." in double circle without date. Values of postally used stamps: Nos. O1-O2, O4, $50 each; No. O3, $125; No. O5, $160; No. O6, $200.

The stamps of Hawaii were replaced by those of the United States.

PHILIPPINES

ˌfi-lə-ˈpēnz

LOCATION — Group of 7,100 islands and islets in the Malay Archipelago, north of Borneo, in the North Pacific Ocean
GOVT. — US Admin., 1898-1946
AREA — 115,748 sq. mi.
POP. — 16,971,100 (est. 1941)
CAPITAL — Quezon City

The islands were ceded to the US by Spain in 1898. On Nov. 15, 1935, they were given their independence, subject to a transition period which ended July 4, 1946. On that date the Commonwealth became the "Republic of the Philippines."

100 Cents = 1 Dollar (1899)
100 CENTAVOS = 1 PESO (1906)

Wmk. 191PI — Double-lined PIPS

Wmk. 190PI — Single-lined PIPS

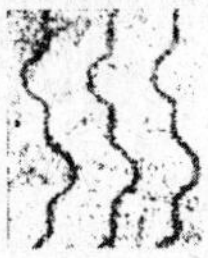

Wmk. 257 — Curved Wavy Lines

Issued under U.S. Administration

Regular Issues of the United States Overprinted in Black

1899-1901 Unwmk. *Perf. 12*

On U.S. Stamp No. 260

212	A96 50c orange	300.	225.
	Never hinged	775.	

On U.S. Stamps Nos. 279, 279B, 279Bd, 279Bj, 279Bf, 279Bc, 268, 281, 282C, 283, 284, 275, 275a

Regular Issues of the United States Overprinted in Black

Wmk. Double-lined USPS (191)

213	A87 1c yellow green	3.50	.60
	Never hinged	10.00	
a.	Inverted overprint	*77,500.*	
214	A88 2c red, type IV	1.75	.60
	Never hinged	4.25	
a.	2c orange red, type IV, ('01)	1.75	.60
	Never hinged	4.25	
b.	Bklt. pane of 6, red, type IV ('00)	200.00	*300.00*
	Never hinged	450.00	
c.	2c reddish carmine, type IV	2.50	1.00
	Never hinged	6.00	
d.	2c rose carmine, type IV	3.00	1.10
	Never hinged	7.25	
215	A89 3c purple	9.00	1.25
	Never hinged	21.50	
216	A91 5c blue	9.00	1.00
	Never hinged	21.50	
a.	Inverted overprint		*6,500.*

No. 216a is valued in the grade of fine.

217	A94 10c brown, type I	35.00	4.00
	Never hinged	80.00	
217A	A94 10c org brn, type II	110.00	27.50
	Never hinged	275.00	

No. 217A was overprinted on U.S. No. 283a, vertical watermark. The watermark on No. 217 is horizontal.

218	A95 15c olive green	40.00	8.00
	Never hinged	95.00	
219	A96 50c orange	125.00	37.50
	Never hinged	300.00	
a.	50c red orange	250.00	55.00
	Never hinged	600.00	
	Nos. 213-219 (8)	333.25	80.45

Regular Issue

U.S. Stamps Nos. 280b, 282 and 272 Overprinted in Black

1901, Aug. 30

220	A90 4c orange brown	35.00	5.00
	Never hinged	80.00	
221	A92 6c lake	40.00	7.00
	Never hinged	95.00	
222	A93 8c purple brown	40.00	7.50
	Never hinged	95.00	
	Nos. 220-222 (3)	115.00	19.50

Same Overprint in Red On U.S. Stamps Nos. 276, 276A, 277a and 278

223	A97 $1 black, type I	300.00	200.00
	Never hinged	1,000.	
223A	A97 $1 black, type II	1,500.	750.00
	Never hinged	5,000.	
224	A98 $2 dark blue	350.00	325.00
	Never hinged	1,150.	
225	A99 $5 dark green	500.00	*900.00*
	Never hinged	1,600.	

U.S. Stamps Nos. 300-310 and Shades Overprinted in Black

Regular Issue

1903-04

226	A115 1c blue green	7.00	.40
	Never hinged	15.50	
227	A116 2c carmine	9.00	1.10
	Never hinged	20.00	
228	A117 3c bright violet	67.50	12.50
	Never hinged	150.00	
229	A118 4c brown	80.00	22.50
	Never hinged	175.00	
a.	4c orange brown	80.00	20.00
	Never hinged	175.00	
230	A119 5c blue	17.50	1.00
	Never hinged	40.00	
231	A120 6c brnsh lake	85.00	22.50
	Never hinged	190.00	
232	A121 8c violet black	50.00	15.00
	Never hinged	125.00	
233	A122 10c pale red brn	35.00	2.25
	Never hinged	80.00	
a.	10c red brown	35.00	3.00
	Never hinged	80.00	
b.	Pair, one without overprint		*1,500.*
234	A123 13c purple black	35.00	17.50
	Never hinged	80.00	
a.	13c brown violet	35.00	17.50
	Never hinged	80.00	
235	A124 15c olive green	60.00	15.00
	Never hinged	135.00	
236	A125 50c orange	125.00	35.00
	Never hinged	275.00	
	Nos. 226-236 (11)	571.00	144.75
	Set, never hinged	1,285.	

Same Overprint in Red On U.S. Stamps Nos. 311, 312 and 313

237	A126 $1 black	300.00	200.00
	Never hinged	800.00	
238	A127 $2 dark blue	550.00	*800.00*
	Never hinged	1,500.	
239	A128 $5 dark green	800.00	*2,750.*
	Never hinged	2,000.	

Same Overprint in Black On U.S. Stamp Nos. 319 and 319c

240	A129 2c carmine	8.00	2.25
	Never hinged	17.50	
a.	Booklet pane of 6	*1,500.*	
b.	2c scarlet	8.00	2.75
	Never hinged	19.00	
c.	As "b," booklet pane of 6	—	

José Rizal A40

Arms of City of Manila A41

Designs: 4c, McKinley. 6c, Ferdinand Magellan. 8c, Miguel Lopez de Legaspi. 10c, Gen. Henry W. Lawton. 12c, Lincoln. 16c, Adm. William T. Sampson. 20c, Washington. 26c, Francisco Carriedo. 30c, Franklin. 2p-10p, Arms of City of Manila.

Wmk. Double-lined PIPS (191PI)

1906, Sept. 8 *Perf. 12*

241	A40 2c deep green	.40	.25
	Never hinged	1.00	
a.	2c yellow green ('10)	.60	.25
	Never hinged	1.50	
b.	Booklet pane of 6	750.00	*800.00*
	Never hinged	*1,500.*	
242	A40 4c carmine	.50	.25
	Never hinged	1.25	
a.	4c carmine lake ('10)	1.00	.25
	Never hinged	2.50	
b.	Booklet pane of 6	*650.00*	*700.00*
	Never hinged	*1,250.*	
243	A40 6c violet	2.50	.25
	Never hinged	6.25	
244	A40 8c brown	4.50	.90
	Never hinged	11.00	
245	A40 10c blue	3.50	.30
	Never hinged	8.75	
a.	10c dark blue	3.50	.30
	Never hinged	8.75	
246	A40 12c brown lake	9.00	2.50
	Never hinged	22.50	
247	A40 16c violet black	6.00	.35
	Never hinged	15.00	
248	A40 20c org brn	7.00	.35
	Never hinged	17.50	
249	A40 26c vio brn	11.00	3.00
	Never hinged	27.50	
250	A40 30c olive green	6.50	1.75
	Never hinged	16.00	
251	A41 1p orange	55.00	17.50
	Never hinged	130.00	
252	A41 2p black	50.00	1.75
	Never hinged	130.00	
253	A41 4p dark blue	160.00	20.00
	Never hinged	375.00	
254	A41 10p dark green	225.00	80.00
	Never hinged	575.00	
	Nos. 241-254 (14)	540.90	129.15
	Set, never hinged	1,316.	

1909-13 Change of Colors

255	A40 12c red orange	11.00	3.00
	Never hinged	27.50	
256	A40 16c olive green	6.00	.75
	Never hinged	15.00	
257	A40 20c yellow	9.00	1.25
	Never hinged	22.50	
258	A40 26c blue green	3.50	1.25
	Never hinged	8.75	
259	A40 30c ultramarine	13.00	3.50
	Never hinged	32.50	
260	A41 1p pale violet	45.00	5.00
	Never hinged	110.00	
260A	A41 2p vio brn ('13)	100.00	12.00
	Never hinged	250.00	
	Nos. 255-260A (7)	187.50	26.75
	Set, never hinged	466.25	

Wmk. Single-lined PIPS (190PI)

1911

261	A40 2c green	.75	.25
	Never hinged	1.80	
a.	Booklet pane of 6	*800.00*	*900.00*
	Never hinged	*1,400.*	
262	A40 4c carmine lake	3.00	.25
	Never hinged	6.75	
a.	4c carmine	—	—
b.	Booklet pane of 6	*600.00*	*700.00*
	Never hinged	*1,100.*	
263	A40 6c deep violet	3.00	.25
	Never hinged	6.75	
264	A40 8c brown	9.50	.50
	Never hinged	21.50	
265	A40 10c blue	4.00	.25
	Never hinged	9.00	
266	A40 12c orange	4.00	.45
	Never hinged	9.00	
267	A40 16c olive green	4.50	.40
	Never hinged	10.00	
a.	16c pale olive green	4.50	.50
	Never hinged	10.00	
268	A40 20c yellow	3.50	.25
	Never hinged	7.75	
a.	20c orange	4.00	.30
	Never hinged	9.00	
269	A40 26c blue green	6.00	.30
	Never hinged	13.50	
270	A40 30c ultramarine	6.00	.50
	Never hinged	13.50	
271	A41 1p pale violet	27.50	.60
	Never hinged	62.50	
272	A41 2p violet brown	45.00	1.00
	Never hinged	100.00	
273	A41 4p deep blue	550.00	110.00
	Never hinged	1,100.	
274	A41 10p deep green	200.00	30.00
	Never hinged	400.00	
	Nos. 261-274 (14)	866.75	145.00
	Set, never hinged	1,862.	

1914

275	A40 30c gray	12.00	.50
	Never hinged	27.50	

1914 *Perf. 10*

276	A40 2c green	3.00	.25
	Never hinged	7.00	
a.	Booklet pane of 6	*600.00*	*800.00*
	Never hinged	*1,250.*	
277	A40 4c carmine	4.00	.30
	Never hinged	9.00	
a.	Booklet pane of 6	*600.00*	
	Never hinged	*1,300.*	
278	A40 6c light violet	45.00	9.50
	Never hinged	100.00	
a.	6c deep violet	50.00	6.25
	Never hinged	110.00	
279	A40 8c brown	55.00	10.50
	Never hinged	125.00	
280	A40 10c dark blue	30.00	.25
	Never hinged	67.50	
281	A40 16c olive green	100.00	5.00
	Never hinged	225.00	
282	A40 20c orange	40.00	1.00
	Never hinged	85.00	
283	A40 30c gray	60.00	4.50
	Never hinged	130.00	
284	A41 1p pale violet	150.00	3.75
	Never hinged	350.00	
	Nos. 276-284 (9)	487.00	35.05
	Set, never hinged	1,020.	

Wmk. Single-lined PIPS (190PI)

1918 *Perf. 11*

285	A40 2c green	21.00	4.25
	Never hinged	40.00	
a.	Booklet pane of 6	*600.00*	*800.00*
	Never hinged	*1,100.*	
286	A40 4c carmine	26.00	6.00
	Never hinged	55.00	
a.	Booklet pane of 6	*1,350.*	*2,000.*
287	A40 6c deep violet	40.00	6.00
	Never hinged	90.00	
287A	A40 8c light brown	220.00	25.00
	Never hinged	400.00	
288	A40 10c dark blue	60.00	3.00
	Never hinged	140.00	
289	A40 16c olive green	110.00	10.00
	Never hinged	250.00	
289A	A40 20c orange	175.00	12.00
	Never hinged	400.00	
289C	A40 30c gray	95.00	18.00
	Never hinged	215.00	
289D	A41 1p pale violet	100.00	25.00
	Never hinged	225.00	
	Nos. 285-289D (9)	847.00	109.25
	Set, never hinged	1,815.	

1917 Unwmk. *Perf. 11*

290	A40 2c yellow green	.25	.25
	Never hinged	.55	
	Never hinged	140.00	
a.	2c dark green	.30	.25
	Never hinged	.65	
b.	Vert. pair, imperf. horiz.	*2,750.*	
c.	Horiz. pair, imperf. between	*1,500.*	—
d.	Vertical pair, imperf. btwn.	*1,750.*	*1,000.*
e.	Booklet pane of 6	27.50	*30.00*
	Never hinged	60.00	
291	A40 4c carmine	.30	.25
	Never hinged	.65	
a.	4c light rose	.30	.25
	Never hinged	.65	
b.	Booklet pane of 6	20.00	*22.50*
	Never hinged	35.00	
292	A40 6c deep violet	.35	.25
	Never hinged	.70	
a.	6c lilac	.40	.25
	Never hinged	.80	
b.	6c red violet	.40	.25
	Never hinged	.70	
c.	Booklet pane of 6	*550.00*	*800.00*
	Never hinged	*900.00*	
293	A40 8c yellow brown	.30	.25
	Never hinged	.50	
a.	8c orange brown	.30	.25
	Never hinged	.50	
294	A40 10c deep blue	.30	.25
	Never hinged	.65	
295	A40 12c red orange	.35	.25
	Never hinged	.75	
296	A40 16c light olive green	65.00	.25
	Never hinged	130.00	
a.	16c olive bister	65.00	.50
	Never hinged	130.00	
297	A40 20c orange yellow	.35	.25
	Never hinged	.75	
298	A40 26c green	.50	.45
	Never hinged	1.10	
a.	26c blue green	.60	.25
	Never hinged	1.35	
299	A40 30c gray	.55	.25
	Never hinged	1.35	
300	A41 1p pale violet	40.00	2.00
	Never hinged	90.00	
a.	1p red lilac	40.00	2.50
	Never hinged	90.00	
b.	1p pale rose lilac	40.00	1.10
	Never hinged	90.00	
301	A41 2p violet brown	35.00	1.00
	Never hinged	77.50	
302	A41 4p blue	32.50	.50
	Never hinged	72.50	
a.	4p dark blue	35.00	.55
	Never hinged	77.50	
	Nos. 290-302 (13)	175.75	6.20
	Set, never hinged	377.00	

1923-26

Design: 16c, Adm. George Dewey.

303	A40 16c olive bister	1.00	.25
	Never hinged	2.25	
a.	16c olive green	1.25	.25
	Never hinged	2.75	
304	A41 10p dp grn ('26)	50.00	20.00
	Never hinged	110.00	

Legislative Palace — A42

1926, Dec. 20 *Perf. 12*

319	A42 2c green & black	.50	.25
	Never hinged	1.25	
a.	Horiz. pair, imperf. between	*275.00*	—
b.	Vert. pair, imperf. between	*375.00*	
320	A42 4c car & blk	.55	.40
	Never hinged	1.20	
a.	Horiz. pair, imperf. between	*350.00*	—
b.	Vert. pair, imperf. between	*400.00*	
321	A42 16c ol grn & blk	1.00	.65
	Never hinged	2.25	
a.	Horiz. pair, imperf. between	*250.00*	—
b.	Vert. pair, imperf. between	*425.00*	—
c.	Double impression of center	*675.00*	
322	A42 18c lt brn & blk	1.10	.50
	Never hinged	2.50	
a.	Double impression of center	*850.00*	
b.	Vertical pair, imperf. between	*475.00*	
323	A42 20c orange & black	2.00	1.00
	Never hinged	4.50	
a.	20c orange & brown	*600.00*	—
b.	As No. 323, imperf., pair	*575.00*	*575.00*
c.	As "a," imperf., pair	*1,750.*	—
d.	Vert. pair, imperf. between	*500.00*	
324	A42 24c gray & black	1.00	.55
	Never hinged	2.25	
a.	Vert. pair, imperf. between	*500.00*	
325	A42 1p rose lil & blk	47.50	50.00
	Never hinged	70.00	
a.	Vert. pair, imperf. between	*500.00*	
	Nos. 319-325 (7)	53.65	53.35
	Set, never hinged	83.95	

Opening of the Legislative Palace.
No. 322a is valued in the grade of fine.
For overprints, see Nos. O1-O4.

Rizal Type of 1906
Coil Stamp

1928 *Perf. 11 Vertically*

326	A40 2c green	7.50	*12.50*
	Never hinged	19.00	

Types of 1906-1923

1925-31 *Imperf.*

340	A40 2c yel green ('31)	.50	.50
	Never hinged	.90	
a.	2c green ('25)	.80	.75
	Never hinged	1.80	
341	A40 4c car rose ('31)	.50	*1.00*
	Never hinged	1.00	
a.	4c carmine ('25)	1.20	1.00
	Never hinged	2.75	
342	A40 6c violet ('31)	3.00	3.75
	Never hinged	5.00	
a.	6c deep violet ('25)	12.00	8.00
	Never hinged	26.00	
343	A40 8c brown ('31)	2.00	*5.00*
	Never hinged	4.00	
a.	8c yellow brown ('25)	13.00	8.00
	Never hinged	26.00	
344	A40 10c blue ('31)	5.00	*7.50*
	Never hinged	12.00	
a.	10c deep blue ('25)	45.00	20.00
	Never hinged	100.00	
345	A40 12c dp orange ('31)	8.00	10.00
	Never hinged	15.00	
a.	12c red orange ('25)	60.00	35.00
	Never hinged	135.00	
346	A40 16c olive green	6.00	7.50
	Never hinged	11.00	
a.	16c bister green ('25)	42.50	18.00
	Never hinged	100.00	
347	A40 20c dp yel org ('31)	5.00	*7.50*
	Never hinged	11.00	
a.	20c yellow orange ('25)	45.00	20.00
	Never hinged	100.00	
348	A40 26c green ('31)	6.00	*9.00*
	Never hinged	11.00	
a.	26c blue green ('25)	45.00	25.00
	Never hinged	110.00	
349	A40 30c light gray ('31)	8.00	10.00
	Never hinged	16.00	
a.	30c gray ('25)	45.00	25.00
	Never hinged	110.00	
350	A41 1p light violet ('31)	10.00	*15.00*
	Never hinged	20.00	
a.	1p violet ('25)	200.00	100.00
	Never hinged	425.00	
351	A41 2p brn vio ('31)	30.00	*45.00*
	Never hinged	80.00	
a.	2p violet brown ('25)	400.00	400.00
	Never hinged	675.00	
352	A41 4p blue ('31)	80.00	90.00
	Never hinged	150.00	
a.	4p deep blue ('25)	2,200.	1,100.
	Never hinged	3,500.	
353	A41 10p green ('31)	175.00	*225.00*
	Never hinged	300.00	
a.	10p deep green ('25)	2,750.	*2,950.*
	Never hinged	4,250.	
	Nos. 340-353 (14)	339.00	436.75
	Set, never hinged	636.90	
	Nos. 340a-353a (14)	5,860.	4,711.

Nos. 340a-353a were the original post office issue. These were reprinted twice in 1931 for sale to collectors (Nos. 340-353).

Mount Mayon, Luzon — A43

Post Office, Manila — A44

Pier No. 7, Manila Bay A45

(See footnote) A46

Rice Planting — A47

Rice Terraces — A48

Baguio Zigzag — A49

1932, May 3 *Perf. 11*

354	A43 2c yellow green	.75	.30
	Never hinged	1.25	
355	A44 4c rose carmine	.75	.30
	Never hinged	1.25	
356	A45 12c orange	.90	.75
	Never hinged	1.30	
357	A46 18c red orange	45.00	15.00
	Never hinged	72.50	
358	A47 20c yellow	1.00	.75
	Never hinged	1.60	
359	A48 24c deep violet	1.60	1.00
	Never hinged	2.75	
360	A49 32c olive brown	1.60	1.00
	Never hinged	2.75	
	Nos. 354-360 (7)	51.60	19.10
	Set, never hinged	83.40	

The 18c vignette was intended to show Pagsanjan Falls in Laguna, central Luzon, and is so labeled. Through error the stamp pictures Vernal Falls in Yosemite National Park, California.

For overprints see #C29-C35, C47-C51, C63.

Nos. 302, 302a Surcharged in Orange or Red

1932

368	A41 1p on 4p blue (O)	6.00	1.00
	Never hinged	9.75	
a.	1p on 4p dark blue (O)	6.00	1.00
	Never hinged	9.25	
	P# block of 10, Impt.	140.00	
	Never hinged	175.00	
369	A41 2p on 4p dark blue (R)	9.00	1.50
	Never hinged	15.00	
	P# block of 10, Impt.	160.00	
	Never hinged	200.00	
a.	2p on 4p blue (R)	9.00	1.00
	Never hinged	15.00	

Far Eastern Championship

Issued in commemoration of the Tenth Far Eastern Championship Games.

Baseball Players — A50

Tennis Player — A51

Basketball Players — A52

1934, Apr. 14 *Perf. 11½*

380	A50 2c yellow brown	1.50	.80
	Never hinged	2.25	
381	A51 6c ultramarine	.25	.25
	Never hinged	.30	
a.	Vertical pair, imperf. between	*700.00*	
	Never hinged	*1,100.*	
382	A52 16c violet brown	.50	.50
	Never hinged	.75	
a.	Vert. pair, imperf. horiz.	*950.00*	
	Never hinged	*1,500.*	
	Nos. 380-382 (3)	2.25	1.55
	Set, never hinged	3.30	

José Rizal A53

Woman and Carabao A54

La Filipina A55

Pearl Fishing A56

Fort Santiago — A57

Salt Spring — A58

Magellan's Landing, 1521 A59

"Juan de la Cruz" A60

Rice Terraces — A61

"Blood Compact," 1565 — A62

Barasoain Church, Malolos — A63

Battle of Manila Bay, 1898 — A64

Montalban Gorge A65

George Washington A66

1935, Feb. 15 *Perf. 11*

383	A53 2c rose	.25	.25
	Never hinged	.25	
384	A54 4c yellow green	.25	.25
	Never hinged	.25	
385	A55 6c dark brown	.25	.25
	Never hinged	.35	
386	A56 8c violet	.25	.25
	Never hinged	.35	
387	A57 10c rose carmine	.30	.25
	Never hinged	.45	
388	A58 12c black	.35	.25
	Never hinged	.50	
389	A59 16c dark blue	.35	.25
	Never hinged	.55	
390	A60 20c light olive green	.35	.25
	Never hinged	.45	
391	A61 26c indigo	.40	.40
	Never hinged	.60	
392	A62 30c orange red	.40	.40
	Never hinged	.60	
393	A63 1p red org & blk	2.00	1.25
	Never hinged	3.00	
394	A64 2p bis brn & blk	12.00	2.00
	Never hinged	16.00	
395	A65 4p blue & black	12.00	4.00
	Never hinged	16.00	
396	A66 5p green & black	25.00	5.00
	Never hinged	50.00	
	Nos. 383-396 (14)	54.15	15.05
	Set, never hinged	74.45	

For overprints & surcharges see Nos. 411-424, 433-446, 449, 463-466, 468, 472-474, 478-484, 485-494, C52-C53, O15-O36, O38, O40-O43, N2-N9, N28, NO2-NO6.

Issues of the Commonwealth

Issued to commemorate the inauguration of the Philippine Commonwealth, Nov. 15, 1935.

The Temples of Human Progress A67

1935, Nov. 15

397	A67 2c carmine rose	.25	.25
	Never hinged	.35	
398	A67 6c deep violet	.25	.25
	Never hinged	.35	

399 A67 16c blue .25 .25
Never hinged .40
400 A67 36c yellow green .40 .30
Never hinged .65
401 A67 50c brown .70 .55
Never hinged 1.00
Nos. 397-401 (5) 1.85 1.60
Set, never hinged 2.75

Jose Rizal Issue

75th anniversary of the birth of Jose Rizal (1861-1896), national hero of the Filipinos.

Jose Rizal — A68

1936, June 19 ***Perf. 12***
402 A68 2c yellow brown .25 .25
Never hinged .25
403 A68 6c slate blue .25 .25
Never hinged .25
a. Imperf. vertically, pair *1,000.*
Never hinged *1,500.*
404 A68 36c red brown .50 *.70*
Never hinged .75
Nos. 402-404 (3) 1.00 1.20
Set, never hinged 1.25

Commonwealth Anniversary Issue

Issued in commemoration of the first anniversary of the Commonwealth.

President Manuel L. Quezon — A69

1936, Nov. 15 ***Perf. 11***
408 A69 2c orange brown .25 .25
Never hinged .30
409 A69 6c yellow green .25 .25
Never hinged .30
410 A69 12c ultramarine .25 .25
Never hinged .30
Nos. 408-410 (3) .75 .75
Set, never hinged .90

Stamps of 1935 Overprinted in Black

a

b

1936-37
411 A53(a) 2c rose .25 .25
Never hinged .25
a. Bklt. pane of 6 ('37) 2.50 2.00
Never hinged 4.00
b. Hyphen omitted 125.00 100.00
412 A54(b) 4c yel grn ('37) .45 *4.00*
Never hinged .70
P# block of 6 35.00
Never hinged 45.00
413 A55(a) 6c dark brown .25 .25
Never hinged .25
414 A56(b) 8c violet ('37) .25 .25
Never hinged .35
415 A57(b) 10c rose carmine .25 .25
Never hinged .25
a. "COMMONWEALT" 20.00 —
Never hinged 30.00
416 A58(b) 12c black ('37) .25 .25
Never hinged .30
417 A59(b) 16c dark blue .25 .25
Never hinged .40
418 A60(a) 20c lt ol grn ('37) .90 .40
Never hinged 1.50
419 A61(b) 26c indigo ('37) .80 .35
Never hinged 1.40
420 A62(b) 30c orange red .45 .25
Never hinged .75
421 A63(b) 1p red org & blk .90 .25
Never hinged 1.50
422 A64(b) 2p bis brn & blk ('37) 12.50 4.00
Never hinged 21.00
423 A65(b) 4p bl & blk ('37) 45.00 8.00
Never hinged 72.50
424 A66(b) 5p grn & blk ('37) 12.50 *25.00*
Never hinged 21.00
Nos. 411-424 (14) 75.00 43.75
Set, never hinged 122.15

Eucharistic Congress Issue

Issued to commemorate the 33rd International Eucharistic Congress held at Manila, Feb. 3-7, 1937.

Map of Philippines — A70

1937, Feb. 3
425 A70 2c yellow green .25 .25
Never hinged .25
426 A70 6c light brown .25 .25
Never hinged .25
427 A70 12c sapphire .25 .25
Never hinged .25
428 A70 20c deep orange .30 .25
Never hinged .50
429 A70 36c deep violet .55 .40
Never hinged .80
430 A70 50c carmine .70 .35
Never hinged 1.10
Nos. 425-430 (6) 2.30 1.75
Set, never hinged 3.15

Arms of Manila — A71

1937, Aug. 27
431 A71 10p gray 5.00 2.00
Never hinged 7.25
P# block of 6 67.50
Never hinged 85.00
432 A71 20p henna brown 4.00 1.40
Never hinged 6.50

Stamps of 1935 Overprinted in Black

a

b

1938-40
433 A53(a) 2c rose ('39) .25 .25
Never hinged .25
P# block of 6 8.00
Never hinged 10.00
a. Booklet pane of 6 3.50 3.50
Never hinged 5.50
b. As "a," lower left-hand stamp overprinted "WEALTH COMMON-" *2,000.*
Never hinged *3,250.*
c. Hyphen omitted 100.00 50.00
434 A54(b) 4c yel grn ('40) 3.00 *30.00*
Never hinged 4.75
P# block of 6 35.00
Never hinged 45.00
435 A55(a) 6c dk brn ('39) .25 .25
Never hinged .40
a. 6c golden brown .25 .25
Never hinged .40
P# block of 6 5.50
Never hinged 7.00
436 A56(b) 8c violet ('39) .25 *1.75*
Never hinged .25
P# block of 6 8.00
Never hinged 10.00
a. "COMMONWEALT" (LR 31) 90.00
Never hinged 140.00
437 A57(b) 10c rose car ('39) .25 .25
Never hinged .25
P# block of 6 8.00
Never hinged 10.00
a. "COMMONWEALT" (LR 31) 65.00 —
Never hinged 100.00
438 A58(b) 12c black ('40) .25 *1.00*
Never hinged .25
P# block of 6 8.00
Never hinged 10.00
439 A59(b) 16c dark blue .25 .25
Never hinged .25
P# block of 6 16.00
Never hinged 20.00
440 A60(a) 20c lt ol grn ('39) .25 .25
Never hinged .25
P# block of 6 12.00
Never hinged 15.00
441 A61(b) 26c indigo ('40) 1.00 *2.50*
Never hinged 1.50
P# block of 6 16.00
Never hinged 20.00
442 A62(b) 30c org red ('39) 3.00 .70
Never hinged 5.00
P# block of 6 22.50
Never hinged 35.00
443 A63(b) 1p red org & blk .60 .25
Never hinged 1.00
444 A64(b) 2p bis brn & blk ('39) 10.00 1.00
Never hinged 15.00
P# block of 4 87.50
Never hinged 110.00
445 A65(b) 4p bl & blk ('40) 150.00 250.00
Never hinged 325.00
446 A66(b) 5p grn & blk ('40) 20.00 8.00
Never hinged 35.00
P# block of 4 200.00
Never hinged 250.00
Nos. 433-446 (14) 189.35 *296.45*
Set, never hinged 414.15

Overprint "b" measures 18½x1¾mm.

No. 433b occurs in booklet pane, No. 433a, position 5; all examples are straight-edged, left and bottom.

First Foreign Trade Week Issue
Nos. 384, 298a and 432 Surcharged in Red, Violet or Black

a

b

c

1939, July 5
449 A54(a) 2c on 4c yel grn (R) .25 .25
Never hinged .35
450 A40(b) 6c on 26c blue grn (V) .25 .50
Never hinged .35
a. 6c on 26c green 3.00 1.00
Never hinged 5.00
451 A71(c) 50c on 20p henna brn (Bk) 1.25 1.00
Never hinged 2.00 5.00
Nos. 449-451 (3) 1.75 1.75
Set, never hinged 2.70

Commonwealth 4th Anniversary Issue (#452-460)

Triumphal Arch — A72

1939, Nov. 15
452 A72 2c yellow green .25 .25
Never hinged .25
453 A72 6c carmine .25 .25
Never hinged .25
454 A72 12c bright blue .25 .25
Never hinged .25
Nos. 452-454 (3) .75 .75
Set, never hinged .75

For overprints see Nos. 469, 476.

Malacañan Palace — A73

1939, Nov. 15
455 A73 2c green .25 .25
Never hinged .25
456 A73 6c orange .25 .25
Never hinged .25
457 A73 12c carmine .25 .25
Never hinged .25
Nos. 455-457 (3) .75 .75
Set, never hinged .75

For overprint, see No. 470.

Pres. Quezon Taking Oath of Office — A74

1940, Feb. 8
458 A74 2c dark orange .25 .25
Never hinged .25
459 A74 6c dark green .25 .25
Never hinged .25
460 A74 12c purple .25 .25
Never hinged .30
Nos. 458-460 (3) .75 .75
Set, never hinged .80

For overprints, see Nos. 471, 477.

José Rizal — A75

ROTARY PRESS PRINTING

1941, Apr. 14 ***Perf. 11x10½***
Size: 19x22½mm
461 A75 2c apple green .25 *.50*
Never hinged .25

FLAT PLATE PRINTING

1941, Nov. 14 ***Perf. 11***
Size: 18¾x22¼mm
462 A75 2c pale apple green 1.00 —
Never hinged 1.25
a. Booklet pane of 6 6.00 —
Never hinged 7.50

No. 461 was issued only in sheets. No. 462 was issued only in booklet panes on Nov. 14, 1941, just before the war, and only a few used stamps and covers exist. All examples have one or two straight edges. Mint booklets reappeared after the war. In August 1942, the booklet pane was reprinted in a darker shade (apple green). However, the apple green panes were available only to U.S. collectors during the war years, so no war-period used stamps from the Philippines exist. Value of apple green booklet pane, never hinged, $6.

For type A75 overprinted, see Nos. 464, O37, O39, N1 and NO1.

Philippine Stamps of 1935-41, Handstamped in Violet

1944 ***Perf. 11, 11x10½***
463 A53 2c rose (On 411) *1,250. 650.00*
a. Booklet pane of 6 *12,500.*
463B A53 2c rose (On 433) *2,000. 1,750.*
464 A75 2c apple grn (On 461) 12.50 10.00
Never hinged 22.50
a. Pair, one without ovpt. — —
465 A54 4c yel grn (On 384) 47.50 *50.00*
Never hinged 80.00
466 A55 6c dk brn (On 385) *3,250. 2,000.*
467 A69 6c yel grn (On 409) 300.00 *150.00*
Never hinged *525.00*
468 A55 6c dk brn (On 413) *4,000. 825.00*
469 A72 6c car (On 453) *350.00 125.00*
470 A73 6c org (On 456) *1,750. 725.00*
471 A74 6c dk grn (On 459) *500.00 225.00*
472 A56 8c vio (On 436) 17.50 *30.00*
Never hinged 30.00
473 A57 10c car rose (On 415) *350.00 150.00*
474 A57 10c car rose (On 437) *275.00 200.00*
Never hinged *475.00*
475 A69 12c ultra (On 410) *1,100. 400.00*
476 A72 12c brt bl (On 454) *7,000. 2,500.*
477 A74 12c pur (On 460) *500.00 275.00*
478 A59 16c dk bl (On 389) *3,000.* —
479 A59 16c dk bl (On 417) *1,500. 1,000.*
480 A59 16c dk bl (On 439) *500.00 200.00*
481 A60 20c lt ol grn (On 440) 140.00 35.00
Never hinged 230.00
482 A62 30c org red (On 420) *450.00 1,500.*
483 A62 30c org red (On 442) *800.00 375.00*
484 A63 1p red org & blk (On 443) *6,250. 4,500.*

Nos. 463-484 are valued in the grade of fine to very fine.

No. 463 comes only from the booklet pane. All examples have one or two straight edges.

Types of 1935-37 Overprinted

a

b

Nos. 431-432 Overprinted in Black — c

1945 *Perf. 11*

485	A53(a) 2c rose	.25	.25
	Never hinged	.25	
486	A54(b) 4c yellow green	.25	.25
	Never hinged	.25	
487	A55(a) 6c golden brown	.25	.25
	Never hinged	.25	
488	A56(b) 8c violet	.25	.25
	Never hinged	.25	
489	A57(b) 10c rose carmine	.25	.25
	Never hinged	.25	
490	A58(b) 12c black	.25	.25
	Never hinged	.25	
491	A59(b) 16c dark blue	.25	.25
	Never hinged	.30	
492	A60(a) 20c lt olive green	.30	.25
	Never hinged	.40	
493	A62(b) 30c orange red	.50	.35
	Never hinged	.75	
494	A63(b) 1p red org & blk	1.10	.25
	Never hinged	1.60	
495	A71(c) 10p gray	55.00	13.50
	Never hinged	90.00	
496	A71(c) 20p henna brown	50.00	15.00
	Never hinged	75.00	
	Nos. 485-496 (12)	108.65	31.10
	Set, never hinged	169.55	

José Rizal — A76

1946, May 28 *Perf. 11x10½*

497	A76 2c sepia	.25	.25
	Never hinged	.25	

For overprints see Nos. 503, O44.

Catalogue values for unused stamps in this section, from this point to the end of the section, are for Never Hinged items.

Later issues, released by the Philippine Republic on July 4, 1946, and thereafter, are listed in Scott's Standard Postage Stamp Catalogue, Vol. 5A.

AIR POST STAMPS

Madrid-Manila Flight Issue

Issued to commemorate the flight of Spanish aviators Gallarza and Loriga from Madrid to Manila.

Regular Issue of 1917-26 Overprinted in Red or Violet

Designs: Nos. C7-C8, Adm. William T. Sampson. No. C9, Adm. George Dewey.

1926, May 13 **Unwmk.** *Perf. 11*

C1	A40 2c green (R)	20.00	25.00
	Never hinged	45.00	
C2	A40 4c carmine (V)	30.00	35.00
	Never hinged	55.00	
a.	Inverted overprint	*2,600.*	—
C3	A40 6c lilac (R)	60.00	90.00
	Never hinged	125.00	
C4	A40 8c org brn (V)	60.00	85.00
	Never hinged	125.00	
C5	A40 10c deep blue (R)	80.00	85.00
	Never hinged	140.00	
C6	A40 12c red org (V)	70.00	95.00
	Never hinged	150.00	
C7	A40 16c lt ol grn (V)	*2,800.*	*3,250.*
C8	A40 16c ol bister (R)	*5,000.*	*5,000.*
C9	A40 16c ol grn (V)	90.00	125.00
	Never hinged	160.00	
C10	A40 20c org ye (V)	90.00	125.00
	Never hinged	160.00	
C11	A40 26c blue grn (V)	90.00	125.00
	Never hinged	160.00	
C12	A40 30c gray (V)	90.00	125.00
	Never hinged	160.00	
C13	A41 2p vio brn (R)	500.00	600.00
	Never hinged	1,100.	
C14	A41 4p dk blue (R)	800.00	900.00
	Never hinged	1,300.	
C15	A41 10p dp grn (V)	1,000.	1,350.

Same Overprint on No. 269
Wmk. Single-lined PIPS (190)
Perf. 12

C16	A40 26c blue grn (V)	*5,000.*	

Same Overprint on No. 284
Perf. 10

C17	A41 1p pale violet (V)	300.00	250.00
	Never hinged	450.00	

London-Orient Flight Issue

Issued Nov. 9, 1928, to celebrate the arrival of a British squadron of hydroplanes.

Regular Issue of 1917-25 Overprinted in Red

1928, Nov. 9 *Perf. 11*

C18	A40 2c green	1.00	1.00
	Never hinged	2.00	
C19	A40 4c carmine	1.25	1.50
	Never hinged	2.00	
C20	A40 6c violet	5.00	3.00
	Never hinged	10.00	
C21	A40 8c orange brown	5.00	3.00
	Never hinged	10.00	
C22	A40 10c deep blue	5.00	3.00
	Never hinged	10.00	
C23	A40 12c red orange	8.00	4.00
	Never hinged	12.00	
C24	A40 16c ol grn (No. 303a)	8.00	4.00
	Never hinged	12.00	
C25	A40 20c orange yellow	8.00	4.00
	Never hinged	12.00	
C26	A40 26c blue green	20.00	8.00
	Never hinged	35.00	
C27	A40 30c gray	20.00	8.00
	Never hinged	35.00	

Same Overprint on No. 271
Wmk. Single-lined PIPS (190)
Perf. 12

C28	A41 1p pale violet	55.00	30.00
	Never hinged	90.00	
	Nos. C18-C28 (11)	136.25	69.50
	Set, never hinged	230.00	

Von Gronau Issue

Commemorating the visit of Capt. Wolfgang von Gronau's airplane on its round-the-world flight.

Nos. 354-360 Overprinted

1932, Sept. 27 **Unwmk.** *Perf. 11*

C29	A43 2c yellow green	.90	.60
	Never hinged	1.40	
C30	A44 4c rose carmine	.90	.40
	Never hinged	1.40	
C31	A45 12c orange	1.25	.65
	Never hinged	2.00	
C32	A46 18c red orange	5.00	5.00
	Never hinged	8.00	
C33	A47 20c yellow	3.50	3.50
	Never hinged	5.75	
C34	A48 24c deep violet	3.50	4.00
	Never hinged	5.75	
C35	A49 32c olive brown	3.50	3.00
	Never hinged	5.75	
	Nos. C29-C35 (7)	18.55	17.15
	Set, never hinged	31.55	

Rein Issue

Commemorating the flight from Madrid to Manila of the Spanish aviator Fernando Rein y Loring.

Regular Issue of 1917-25 Overprinted

1933, Apr. 11

C36	A40 2c green	.75	.45
	Never hinged	1.10	
C37	A40 4c carmine	.90	.45
	Never hinged	1.40	
C38	A40 6c deep violet	1.10	.80
	Never hinged	1.75	
C39	A40 8c orange brown	3.75	2.00
	Never hinged	5.75	
	P# block of 10, Impt.	120.00	
	Never hinged	150.00	
C40	A40 10c dark blue	3.75	2.25
	Never hinged	5.75	
	P# block of 10, Impt.	120.00	
	Never hinged	150.00	
C41	A40 12c orange	3.75	2.00
	Never hinged	5.75	
	P# block of 10, Impt.	120.00	
	Never hinged	150.00	
C42	A40 16c olive green	3.50	2.00
	Never hinged	5.25	
	P# block of 6	160.00	
	Never hinged	200.00	
C43	A40 20c yellow	3.75	2.00
	Never hinged	5.75	
	P# block of 10, Impt.	160.00	
	Never hinged	200.00	
C44	A40 26c green	3.75	2.75
	Never hinged	5.75	
a.	26c blue green	4.00	2.00
	Never hinged	6.00	
C45	A40 30c gray	4.00	3.00
	Never hinged	6.00	
	Nos. C36-C45 (10)	29.00	17.70
	Set, never hinged	44.25	

No. 290a Overprinted

Printed by the Philippine Bureau.

1933, May 26

C46	A40 2c green	.65	.40
	Never hinged	1.00	
	P# block of 6	12.00	
	Never hinged	15.00	

Regular Issue of 1932 Overprinted

C47	A44 4c rose carmine	.30	.25
	Never hinged	.45	
	P# block of 6	16.00	
	Never hinged	20.00	
C48	A45 12c orange	.60	.25
	Never hinged	.90	
	P# block of 6	20.00	
	Never hinged	25.00	
C49	A47 20c yellow	.60	.25
	Never hinged	.90	
	P# block of 6	20.00	
	Never hinged	25.00	
C50	A48 24c deep violet	.65	.25
	Never hinged	1.00	
	P# block of 6	24.00	
	Never hinged	30.00	
C51	A49 32c olive brown	.85	.35
	Never hinged	1.40	
	Nos. C46-C51 (6)	3.65	1.75
	Set, never hinged	5.65	

Transpacific Issue

Issued to commemorate the China Clipper flight from Manila to San Francisco, Dec. 2-5, 1935.

Nos. 387, 392 Overprinted in Gold

1935, Dec. 2

C52	A57 10c rose carmine	.40	.25
	Never hinged	.60	
C53	A62 30c orange red	.60	.35
	Never hinged	.90	

Manila-Madrid Flight Issue

Issued to commemorate the Manila-Madrid flight by aviators Antonio Arnaiz and Juan Calvo.

Regular Issue of 1917-25 Surcharged in Various Colors

1936, Sept. 6

C54	A40 2c on 4c carmine (Bl)	.25	.25
	Never hinged	.25	
C55	A40 6c on 12c red org (V)	.25	.25
	Never hinged	.30	
C56	A40 16c on 26c blue grn (Bk)	.25	.25
	Never hinged	.40	
a.	16c on 26c green	2.00	.70
	Never hinged	3.00	
	Nos. C54-C56 (3)	.75	.75
	Set, never hinged	.95	

Air Mail Exhibition Issue

Issued to commemorate the first Air Mail Exhibition, held Feb. 17-19, 1939.

Regular Issue of 1917-37 Surcharged in Black or Red

1939, Feb. 17

C57	A40 8c on 26c blue grn (Bk)	2.00	2.00
	Never hinged	4.00	
a.	8c on 26c green (Bk)	10.00	4.00
	Never hinged	16.00	
C58	A71 1p on 10p gray (R)	8.00	4.00
	Never hinged	12.00	

Moro Vinta and Clipper — AP1

1941, June 30

C59	AP1 8c carmine	2.00	.60
	Never hinged	2.75	
C60	AP1 20c ultramarine	3.00	.50
	Never hinged	4.00	
C61	AP1 60c blue green	3.00	1.00
	Never hinged	4.00	
C62	AP1 1p sepia	.70	.50
	Never hinged	1.00	
	Nos. C59-C62 (4)	8.70	2.60
	Set, never hinged	11.75	

For overprint see No. NO7. For surcharges see Nos. N10-N11, N35-N36.

No. C47 Hstmpd. in Violet

1944, Dec. 3

C63	A44 4c rose carmine	*3,750.*	*2,750.*

SPECIAL DELIVERY STAMPS

United States No. E5 Overprinted in Red

Wmk. Double-lined USPS (191)

1901, Oct. 15 *Perf. 12*

E1	SD3 10c dark blue	100.	80.
	Never hinged	185.	
a.	Dots in curved frame above messenger (Pl. 882)	*175.*	*160.*

Special Delivery Messenger SD2

Wmk. Double-lined PIPS (191PI)

1906, Sept. 8

E2	SD2 20c deep ultra	45.00	8.00
	Never hinged	90.00	
b.	20c pale ultramarine	35.00	8.00
	Never hinged	70.00	

See Nos. E3-E6. For overprints see Nos. E7-E10, EO1.

SPECIAL PRINTING

U.S. No. E6 Overprinted in Red

Wmk. Double-lined USPS (191)

1907

E2A	SD4 10c ultramarine	*3,250.*	

Wmk. Single-lined PIPS (190PI)

1911, Apr.

E3	SD2 20c deep ultra	22.00	1.75
	Never hinged	42.00	

1916 *Perf. 10*

E4	SD2 20c deep ultra	175.00	150.00
	Never hinged	275.00	

1919 **Unwmk.** *Perf. 11*

E5	SD2 20c ultramarine	.60	.25
	Never hinged	.90	
a.	20c pale blue	.75	.25
	Never hinged	1.00	
b.	20c dull violet	.60	.25
	Never hinged	.90	

Type of 1906 Issue

1925-31 *Imperf.*

E6	SD2 20c dull violet ('31)	27.50	*75.00*
	Never hinged	40.00	
a.	20c violet blue ('25)	50.00	—
	Never hinged	80.00	

Type of 1919 Overprinted in Black

1939, Apr. 27 *Perf. 11*

E7	SD2 20c blue violet	.25	.25
	Never hinged	.40	

Nos. E5b and E7, Hstmpd. in Violet

1944

E8 SD2 20c dull violet (On E5b) *1,400.* *550.00*
On cover —
Block of 4 *6,000.*
E9 SD2 20c blue violet (On E7) *550.00* *250.00*

Type SD2 Overprinted

1945, May 1

E10 SD2 20c blue violet .70 .55
Never hinged 1.10
a. "IC" close together 3.25 2.75
Never hinged 4.75

SPECIAL DELIVERY OFFICIAL STAMP

Type of 1906 Issue Overprinted

1931 Unwmk. *Perf. 11*

EO1 SD2 20c dull violet 3.00 *75.00*
Never hinged 4.50
P# block of 6 150.00
Never hinged 190.00
a. No period after "B" 50.00 *250.00*
Never hinged 75.00
b. Double overprint —

It is strongly recommended that expert opinion be acquired for Nos. EO1 and EO1a used.

POSTAGE DUE STAMPS

U.S. Nos. J38-J44 Overprinted in Black

Wmk. Double-lined USPS (191)

1899, Aug. 16 *Perf. 12*

J1 D2 1c deep claret 7.50 2.50
Never hinged 15.00
J2 D2 2c deep claret 7.50 2.50
Never hinged 15.00
J3 D2 5c deep claret 15.00 2.50
Never hinged 30.00
J4 D2 10c deep claret 19.00 5.50
Never hinged 37.50
J5 D2 50c deep claret 250.00 100.00
Never hinged 425.00

No. J1 was used to pay regular postage Sept. 5-19, 1902.

1901, Aug. 31

J6 D2 3c deep claret 17.50 7.00
Never hinged 35.00
J7 D2 30c deep claret 250.00 110.00
Never hinged 415.00
Nos. J1-J7 (7) 566.50 230.00
Set, never hinged 882.50

Post Office Clerk — D3

1928, Aug. 21 Unwmk. *Perf. 11*

J8 D3 4c brown red .25 .25
Never hinged .25
P# block of 6 14.00
Never hinged 17.50
J9 D3 6c brown red .30 .75
Never hinged .45
P# block of 6 14.00
Never hinged 17.50
J10 D3 8c brown red .25 .75
Never hinged .35
P# block of 6 14.00
Never hinged 17.50
J11 D3 10c brown red .30 .75
Never hinged .45
P# block of 6 14.00
Never hinged 17.50
J12 D3 12c brown red .25 .75
Never hinged .35
P# block of 6 14.00
Never hinged 17.50
J13 D3 16c brown red .30 .75
Never hinged .45
P# block of 6 14.00
Never hinged 17.50
J14 D3 20c brown red .30 .75
Never hinged .45
P# block of 6 14.00
Never hinged 17.50
Nos. J8-J14 (7) 1.95 4.75
Set, never hinged 2.75

No. J8 Surcharged in Blue

1937, July 29 Unwmk. *Perf. 11*

J15 D3 3c on 4c brown red .25 .25
Never hinged .35

See note after No. NJ1.

Nos. J8 to J14 Handstamped in Violet

1944, Dec. 3

J16 D3 4c brown red *150.00* —
J17 D3 6c brown red *100.00* —
J18 D3 8c brown red *110.00* *350.00*
J19 D3 10c brown red *100.00* —
J20 D3 12c brown red *100.00* —
J21 D3 16c brown red *100.00* 350.00
a. Pair, one without ovpt. —
J22 D3 20c brown red *110.00* —
Nos. J16-J22 (7) *770.00*

OFFICIAL STAMPS

Official Handstamped Overprints

"Officers purchasing stamps for government business may, if they so desire, surcharge them with the letters O.B. either in writing with black ink or by rubber stamps but in such a manner as not to obliterate the stamp that postmasters will be unable to determine whether the stamps have been previously used." C.M. Cotterman, Director of Posts, December 26, 1905.

Beginning January 1, 1906, all branches of the Insular Government used postage stamps to prepay postage instead of franking them as before. Some officials used manuscript, some utilized the typewriting machines but by far the larger number provided themselves with rubber stamps. The majority of these read "O.B." but other forms were: "OFFICIAL BUSINESS" or "OFFICIAL MAIL" in two lines, with variations on many of these.

These "O.B." overprints are known on U.S. 1899-1901 stamps; on 1903-06 stamps in red and blue; on 1906 stamps in red, blue, black, yellow and green.

"O.B." overprints were also made on the centavo and peso stamps of the Philippines, per order of May 25, 1907.

Beginning in 1926 the Bureau of Posts issued press-printed official stamps, but many government offices continued to handstamp ordinary postage stamps "O.B." The press-printed "O.B." overprints are listed below.

During the Japanese occupation period 1942-45, the same system of handstamped official overprints prevailed, but the handstamp usually consisted of "K.P.", initials of the Tagalog words, "Kagamitang Pampamahalaan" (Official Business), and the two Japanese characters used in the printed overprint on Nos. NO1 to NO4.

Regular Issue of 1926 Ovptd. in Red

1926, Dec. 20 Unwmk. *Perf. 12*

O1 A42 2c green & black 3.00 1.00
Never hinged 4.50
O2 A42 4c car & blk 3.00 1.25
Never hinged 4.50
a. Vertical pair, imperf. between 550.00
O3 A42 18c lt brn & blk 8.00 4.00
Never hinged 12.00
O4 A42 20c org & blk 7.75 1.75
Never hinged 11.50
Nos. O1-O4 (4) 21.75 8.00
Set, never hinged 32.50

Opening of the Legislative Palace.

Regular Issue of 1917-26 Overprinted by the U.S. Bureau of Engraving and Printing

1931 *Perf. 11*

O5 A40 2c green .40 .25
Never hinged .65
P# block of 6 20.00
Never hinged 25.00
a. No period after "B" 17.50 17.50
Never hinged 27.50
b. No period after "O" 40.00 30.00
O6 A40 4c carmine .45 .25
Never hinged .70
P# block of 6 20.00
Never hinged 25.00
a. No period after "B" 40.00 20.00
Never hinged 60.00
O7 A40 6c deep violet .75 .25
Never hinged 1.25
P# block of 10, Impt. 40.00
Never hinged 50.00
O8 A40 8c yellow brown .75 .25
Never hinged 1.25
P# block of 6 32.00
Never hinged 40.00
P# block of 10, Impt. 40.00
Never hinged 50.00
O9 A40 10c deep blue 1.20 .25
Never hinged 1.90
P# block of 10, Impt. 32.00
Never hinged 40.00
O10 A40 12c red orange 2.00 .25
Never hinged 3.00
P# block of 6 65.00
Never hinged 80.00
P# block of 10, Impt. 80.00
Never hinged 95.00
a. No period after "B" 80.00 80.00
Never hinged 120.00
O11 A40 16c lt ol grn 1.00 .25
Never hinged 1.50
P# block of 6 24.00
Never hinged 30.00
a. 16c olive bister 2.00 .25
Never hinged 3.00
P# block of 6 20.00
Never hinged 25.00
O12 A40 20c orange yellow 1.25 .25
Never hinged 1.90
P# block of 10, Impt. 75.00
Never hinged 95.00
a. No period after "B" 80.00 80.00
Never hinged 120.00
O13 A40 26c green 2.00 1.00
Never hinged 3.25
P# block of 6 120.00
Never hinged 150.00
a. 26c blue green 2.50 1.50
Never hinged 4.00
P# block of 6 130.00
Never hinged 165.00
O14 A40 30c gray 2.00 .25
Never hinged 3.25
P# block of 10, Impt. 80.00
Never hinged 100.00
Nos. O5-O14 (10) 11.80 3.25
Set, never hinged 18.65

Many collectors prefer to collect the plate blocks of 6 of Nos. O5-O6, O8, O10-O11a and O14 as blocks of 10 so they fit aesthetically with the other plate blocks of 10 with imprints.

Overprinted on Nos. 383-392

1935

O15 A53 2c rose .25 .25
Never hinged .30
P# block of 6 4.75
Never hinged 6.00
a. No period after "B" 15.00 10.00
Never hinged 22.50
b. No period after "O" — —
O16 A54 4c yellow green .25 .25
Never hinged .30
P# block of 6 4.00
Never hinged 5.00
a. No period after "B" 15.00 *40.00*
Never hinged 22.50
O17 A55 6c dark brown .25 .25
Never hinged .40
P# block of 6 8.00
Never hinged 10.00
a. No period after "B" 35.00 35.00
Never hinged 52.50
O18 A56 8c violet .30 .25
Never hinged .45
P# block of 6 9.50
Never hinged 12.00
O19 A57 10c rose carmine .30 .25
Never hinged .45
P# block of 6 8.00
Never hinged 10.00
O20 A58 12c black .75 .25
Never hinged 1.10
P# block of 6 8.00
Never hinged 10.00
O21 A59 16c dark blue .55 .25
Never hinged .85
P# block of 6 8.00
Never hinged 10.00
O22 A60 20c light olive green .60 .25
Never hinged .90
P# block of 6 12.00
Never hinged 15.00
O23 A61 26c indigo .90 .25
Never hinged 1.50
P# block of 6 20.00
Never hinged 25.00
O24 A62 30c orange red .80 .25
Never hinged 1.20
P# block of 6 20.00
Never hinged 25.00
Nos. O15-O24 (10) 4.95 2.50
Set, never hinged 7.40

Nos. 411 and 418 with Additional Overprint in Black

1937-38

O25 A53 2c rose .25 .25
Never hinged .30
a. No period after "B" 25.00 25.00
Never hinged 45.00
b. Period after "B" raised (UL 4) 150.00
O26 A60 20c lt ol grn ('38) .70 .50
Never hinged 1.10
P# block of 6 20.00
Never hinged 25.00

Regular Issue of 1935 Overprinted In Black

a

b

1938-40

O27 A53(a) 2c rose .25 .25
Never hinged .30
P# block of 6 4.75
Never hinged 6.00
a. Hyphen omitted 10.00 10.00
Never hinged 15.00
b. No period after "B" 20.00 *30.00*
Never hinged 30.00
O28 A54(b) 4c yellow green .75 1.00
Never hinged 1.10
P# block of 6 24.00
Never hinged 30.00
O29 A55(a) 6c dark brown .30 .25
Never hinged .45
P# block of 6 12.00
Never hinged 15.00
O30 A56(b) 8c violet .75 .85
Never hinged 1.10
P# block of 6 9.50
Never hinged 12.00
O31 A57(b) 10c rose carmine .25 .25
Never hinged .30
P# block of 6 16.00
Never hinged 20.00
a. No period after "O" 50.00 40.00
Never hinged 75.00
O32 A58(b) 12c black .30 .25
Never hinged .45
P# block of 6 12.00
Never hinged 15.00
O33 A59(b) 16c dark blue .30 .25
Never hinged .45
P# block of 6 16.00
Never hinged 20.00
O34 A60(a) 20c lt ol grn ('40) .55 .85
Never hinged .85
P# block of 6 16.00
Never hinged 20.00
O35 A61(b) 26c indigo 1.50 *2.00*
Never hinged 2.25
P# block of 6 12.00
Never hinged 15.00
O36 A62(b) 30c orange red .75 .85
Never hinged 1.10
P# block of 6 16.00
Never hinged 20.00
Nos. O27-O36 (10) 5.70 6.80
Set, never hinged 8.25

No. 461 Overprinted in Black — c

1941, Apr. 14 *Perf. 11x10½*

O37 A75(c) 2c apple green .25 *.40*
Never hinged .30

Official Stamps Handstamped in Violet

1944 *Perf. 11, 11x10½*

O38 A53 2c rose (On O27) *375.00* *200.00*
Never hinged *750.00*
O39 A75 2c apple grn (On O37) 15.00 *20.00*
Never hinged 20.00
O40 A54 4c yel grn (On O16) 45.00 *30.00*
Never hinged 80.00
O40A A55 6c dk brn (On O29) *8,000.* —
O41 A57 10c rose car (On O31) *500.00*
a. No period after "O" *4,000.*

O42 A60 20c lt ol grn (On O22) *8,000.*
O43 A60 20c lt ol grn (On O26) *1,750.*

No. 497 Overprinted Type "c" in Black

1946, June 19 ***Perf. 11x10½***
O44 A76 2c sepia .25 .25
Never hinged .25
a. Vertical pair, bottom stamp without ovpt. —

OCCUPATION STAMPS

Issued Under Japanese Occupation

No. 461 Overprinted in Black

No. 438 Overprinted in Black

No. 439 Overprinted in Black

1942-43 **Unwmk.** ***Perf. 11x10½, 11***
N1 A75 2c apple green .25 *1.00*
Never hinged .30
a. Pair, one without overprint —
N2 A58 12c black ('43) .25 *2.00*
Never hinged .40
P# block of 6 12.00
Never hinged 15.00
N3 A59 16c dark blue 5.00 3.75
Never hinged 7.50
P# block of 6 37.50
Never hinged 55.00
Nos. N1-N3 (3) 5.50 6.75
Set, never hinged 8.20

Nos. 435a, 435, 442, 443, and 423 Surcharged in Black

a

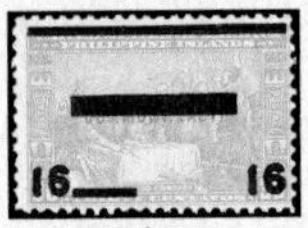

b

c

d

Type I

Type II

Two types of 50c surcharge
Type I: Center of "A" is a triangle.
Type II: Center of "A" is a pin hole.

1942-43 ***Perf. 11***
N4 A55(a) 5(c) on 6c golden brown .25 *.75*
Never hinged .35
a. Top bar shorter and thinner .25 *1.00*
Never hinged .35
P# block of 6 50.00
Never hinged 60.00
b. 5(c) on 6c dark brown .25 *.85*
Never hinged .35
c. As "b," top bar shorter and thinner .25 *1.00*
Never hinged .35
d. Double surcharge, on cover —
N5 A62(b) 16(c) on 30c org red ('43) .25 *.60*
Never hinged .45
N6 A63(c) 50c on 1p red org & blk ('43) .75 *1.25*
Never hinged 1.10
P# block of 4, 2 P# 16.00
Never hinged 20.00
a. Double surcharge *300.00*
b. Type I surcharge 100.00 90.00
Never hinged 125.00
P# block of 4 500.00
Never hinged 600.00
N7 A65(d) 1p on 4p bl & blk ('43) 100.00 *150.00*
Never hinged 155.00
Nos. N4-N7 (4) 101.25 152.60
Set, never hinged 156.90

On Nos. N4 and N4b, the top bar measures 1½x22½mm. On Nos. N4a and N4c, the top bar measures 1x21mm and the "5" is smaller and thinner.

The used value for No. N7 is for postal cancellation. Used stamps exist with first day cancellations. They are worth somewhat less.

No. 384 Surcharged in Black

1942, May 18
N8 A54 2(c) on 4c yellow green 4.00 5.00
Never hinged 8.75

Issued to commemorate Japan's capture of Bataan and Corregidor. The American-Filipino forces finally surrendered May 7, 1942. No. N8 exists with "R" for "B" in BATAAN.

No. 384 Surcharged in Black

1942, Dec. 8
N9 A54 5(c) on 4c yellow green .50 *1.00*
Never hinged .75

1st anniversary of the "Greater East Asia War."

Nos. C59 and C62 Surcharged in Black

1943, Jan. 23
N10 AP1 2(c) on 8c carmine .25 *1.00*
Never hinged .35
P# block of 6 20.00
Never hinged 25.00
N11 AP1 5c on 1p sepia .50 *1.50*
Never hinged .75

1st anniv. of the Philippine Executive Commission.

Nipa Hut
OS1

Rice Planting
OS2

Mt. Mayon and Mt. Fuji
OS3

Moro Vinta
OS4

The "c" currency is indicated by four Japanese characters, "p" currency by two.

Engraved; Typographed (2c, 6c, 25c)

1943-44 **Wmk. 257** ***Perf. 13***
N12 OS1 1c dp orange .25 .40
Never hinged .30
Margin block of 6, inscription 2.40
Never hinged 3.00
N13 OS2 2c brt green .25 .40
Never hinged .30
Margin block of 6, inscription 2.40
Never hinged 3.00
N14 OS1 4c slate green .25 .40
Never hinged .30
Margin block of 6, inscription 2.40
Never hinged 3.00
N15 OS3 5c orange brown .25 .40
Never hinged .30
Margin block of 6, inscription 2.40
Never hinged 3.00
N16 OS2 6c red .25 .60
Never hinged .30
Margin block of 6, inscription 2.40
Never hinged 3.00
N17 OS3 10c blue green .25 .40
Never hinged .30
Margin block of 6, inscription 2.40
Never hinged 3.00
N18 OS4 12c steel blue 1.00 1.50
Never hinged 1.50
Margin block of 6, inscription 11.00
Never hinged 14.00
N19 OS4 16c dk brown .25 .40
Never hinged .30
Margin block of 6, inscription 2.40
Never hinged 3.00
N20 OS1 20c rose violet 1.25 1.75
Never hinged 1.90
Margin block of 6, inscription 15.00
Never hinged 19.00
N21 OS3 21c violet .25 .40
Never hinged .35
Margin block of 6, inscription 2.40
Never hinged 3.00
N22 OS2 25c pale brown .25 .40
Never hinged .35
Margin block of 6, inscription 2.40
Never hinged 3.00
N23 OS3 1p dp carmine .75 1.25
Never hinged 1.15
Margin block of 6, inscription 9.50
Never hinged 12.00
N24 OS4 2p dull violet 6.50 6.50
Never hinged 10.00
N25 OS4 5p dark olive 16.00 18.00
Never hinged 25.00
Nos. N12-N25 (14) 27.75 32.80
Set, never hinged 42.00

Issued: Nos. N13, N15, 4/1; Nos. N12, N14, N23, 6/7; Nos. N16-N19, 7/14; Nos. N20-N22, 8/16; No. N24, 9/16; No. N25, 4/1/44.

For surcharges see Nos. NB5-NB7.

OS5

1943, May 7 **Photo.** **Unwmk.**
N26 OS5 2c carmine red .25 *.75*
Never hinged .30
Margin block of 6, inscription 4.00
Never hinged 5.00
N27 OS5 5c bright green .25 *1.00*
Never hinged .35
Margin block of 6, inscription 6.50
Never hinged 8.00

1st anniversary of the fall of Bataan and Corregidor.

No. 440 Surcharged in Black

1943, June 20 **Engr.** ***Perf. 11***
N28 A60 12(c) on 20c light olive green .25 *.75*
Never hinged .35
a. Double surcharge —

350th anniversary of the printing press in the Philippines. "Limbagan" is Tagalog for "printing press."

Rizal Monument, Filipina and Philippine Flag — OS6

1943, Oct. 14 **Photo.** ***Perf. 12***
N29 OS6 5c light blue .25 *.90*
Never hinged .30
a. Imperf. .25 .90
N30 OS6 12c orange .25 *.90*
Never hinged .30
a. Imperf. .25 *.90*
N31 OS6 17c rose pink .25 *.90*
Never hinged .30
a. Imperf. .25 *.90*
Nos. N29-N31 (3) .75 2.70
Set, never hinged .90

"Independence of the Philippines." Japan granted "independence" Oct. 14, 1943, when the puppet republic was founded.

The imperforate stamps were issued without gum.

José Rizal
OS7

Rev. José Burgos
OS8

Apolinario Mabini — OS9

1944, Feb. 17 **Litho.**
N32 OS7 5c blue .25 *1.00*
Never hinged .30
a. Imperf. .25 *2.00*
Never hinged .35
N33 OS8 12c carmine .25 *1.00*
Never hinged .30
a. Imperf. .25 *2.00*
Never hinged .35
N34 OS9 17c deep orange .25 *1.00*
Never hinged .30
a. Imperf. .25 *2.00*
Never hinged .35
Nos. N32-N34 (3) .75 *3.00*
Set, never hinged .90

See No. NB8.

Nos. C60 and C61 Surcharged in Black

1944, May 7 ***Perf. 11***
N35 AP1 5(c) on 20c ultra .50 1.00
Never hinged .75
P# block of 6 32.50
Never hinged 40.00
N36 AP1 12(c) on 60c blue green 1.75 1.75
Never hinged 2.50
P# block of 6 42.50
Never hinged 52.50

2nd anniversary of the fall of Bataan and Corregidor.

OS10

1945, Jan. 12 **Litho.** ***Imperf.***
Without Gum
N37 OS10 5c dull violet brown .25 *.50*
Never hinged .30
N38 OS10 7c blue green .25 *.50*
Never hinged .30
N39 OS10 20c chalky blue .25 *.50*
Never hinged .30
Nos. N37-N39 (3) *.75* *1.50*
Set, never hinged .90

Issued belatedly on Jan. 12, 1945, to commemorate the first anniversary of the puppet Philippine Republic, Oct. 14, 1944. "S" stands for "sentimos."

OCCUPATION SEMI-POSTAL STAMPS

Woman, Farming and Cannery — OSP1

Unwmk.

1942, Nov. 12 Litho. *Perf. 12*

NB1 OSP1 2c + 1c pale violet .25 *.60*
Never hinged .30
NB2 OSP1 5c + 1c brt grn .25 *1.00*
Never hinged .30
NB3 OSP1 16c + 2c orange 25.00 *32.50*
Never hinged 42.00
Nos. NB1-NB3 (3) 25.50 34.10
Set, never hinged 42.60

Issued to promote the campaign to produce and conserve food. The surtax aided the Red Cross.

Souvenir Sheet

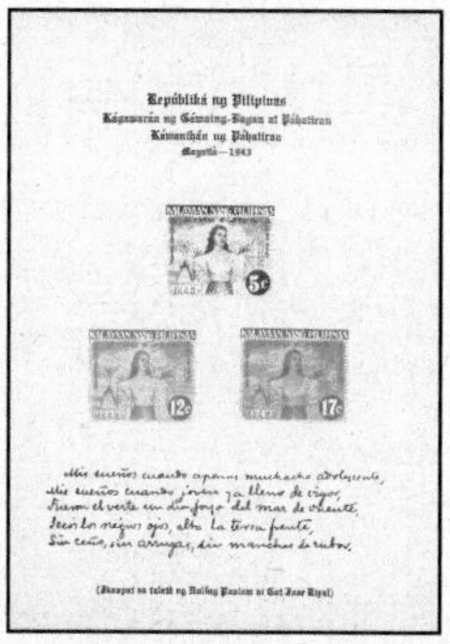

OSP2

1943, Oct. 14 Without Gum *Imperf.*

NB4 OSP2 Sheet of 3 60.00 *17.50*

"Independence of the Philippines."

No. NB4 contains one each of Nos. N29a-N31a. Marginal inscription is from Rizal's "Last Farewell." Sold for 2.50p.

The value of No. NB4 used is for a sheet from a first day cover. Commercially used sheets are extremely scarce and worth much more.

Nos. N18, N20 and N21 Surcharged in Black

1943, Dec. 8 Wmk. 257 *Perf. 13*

NB5 OS4 12c + 21c steel blue .25 *1.50*
Never hinged .30
Margin block of 6, inscription 4.00
Never hinged 5.00
NB6 OS1 20c + 36c rose violet .25 *1.50*
Never hinged .30
Margin block of 6, inscription 4.00
Never hinged 5.00
NB7 OS3 21c + 40c violet .25 *2.00*
Never hinged .30
Margin block of 6, inscription 4.75
Never hinged 6.00
Nos. NB5-NB7 (3) .75 5.00
Set, never hinged .90

The surtax was for the benefit of victims of a Luzon flood. "Baha" is Tagalog for "flood."

Souvenir Sheet

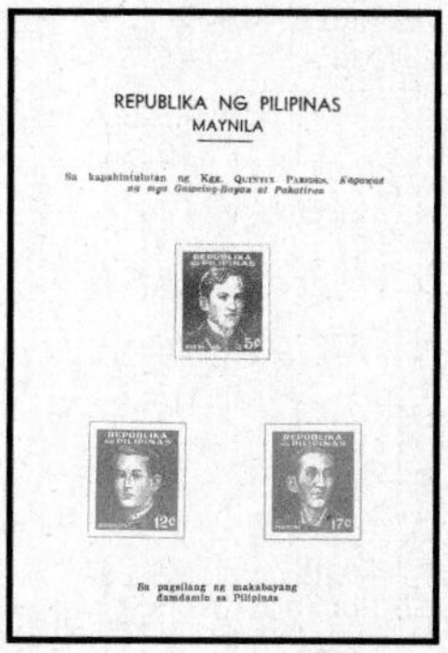

OSP3

Unwmk.

1944, Feb. 9 Litho. *Imperf.*

Without Gum

NB8 OSP3 Sheet of 3 6.50 3.50

No. NB8 contains 1 each of Nos. N32a-N34a.

Sheet sold for 1p, surtax going to a fund for the care of heroes' monuments.

The value for No. NB8 used is for a stamp from a first day cover. Commercially used examples are worth much more.

OCCUPATION POSTAGE DUE STAMP

No. J15 Overprinted in Blue

1942, Oct. 14 Unwmk. *Perf. 11*

NJ1 D3 3c on 4c brown red 25.00 *35.00*
Never hinged 37.50

On examples of No. J15, two lines were drawn in India ink with a ruling pen across "United States of America" by employees of the Short Paid Section of the Manila Post Office to make a provisional 3c postage due stamp which was used from Sept. 1, 1942 (when the letter rate was raised from 2c to 5c) until Oct. 14 when No. NJ1 went on sale. Value on cover, $175.

Bottom plate blocks of 6 of No. NJ1 are much scarcer than the right side plate blocks. Value $325 hinged, $450 never hinged.

OCCUPATION OFFICIAL STAMPS

Nos. 461, 413, 435, 435a and 442 Ovptd. or Srchd. in Black with Bars and

1943-44 Unwmk. *Perf. 11x10½, 11*

NO1 A75 2c apple green .25 *.75*
Never hinged .30
a. Double overprint *400.00*
Never hinged *600.00*
NO2 A55 5(c) on 6c dk brn (On No. 413) ('44) 40.00 *45.00*
Never hinged 55.00
NO3 A55 5(c) on 6c golden brn (On No. 435a) .25 *.90*
Never hinged .35
P# block of 6 14.00
Never hinged 17.50
a. Narrower spacing between bars .25 *.90*
Never hinged .35
b. 5(c) on 6c dark brown (On No. 435) .25 *.90*
Never hinged .35
c. As "b," narrower spacing between bars .25 *.90*
Never hinged .35
d. Double overprint —
NO4 A62 16(c) on 30c org red .30 *1.25*
Never hinged .45
P# block of 6 20.00
Never hinged 25.00
a. Wider spacing between bars .30 *1.25*
Never hinged .45
Nos. NO1-NO4 (4) 40.80 47.90
Set, never hinged 56.10

On Nos. NO3 and NO3b the bar deleting "United States of America" is 9¾ to 10mm above the bar deleting "Common." On Nos. NO3a and NO3c, the spacing is 8 to 8½mm.

On No. NO4, the center bar is 19mm long, 3½mm below the top bar and 6mm above the Japanese characters. On No. NO4a, the center bar is 20½mm long, 9mm below the top bar and 1mm above the Japanese characters.

"K.P." stands for Kagamitang Pampamahalaan, "Official Business" in Tagalog.

Nos. 435 & 435a Surcharged in Black

1944, Aug. 28 *Perf. 11*

NO5 A55 (5c) on 6c gldn brn .30 *.40*
Never hinged .45
P# block of 6 20.00
Never hinged 25.00
a. 5(c) on 6c dark brown .30 *.40*
Never hinged .45
P# block of 6 20.00
Never hinged 25.00

Nos. O34 and C62 Overprinted in Black

a

b

NO6 A60(a) 20c light olive green .40 *.50*
Never hinged .60
P# block of 6 12.00
Never hinged 15.00
NO7 AP1(b) 1p sepia .90 *1.00*
Never hinged 1.45
P# block of 6 20.00
Never hinged 25.00
Nos. NO5-NO7 (3) 1.60 1.90
Set, never hinged 2.05

PUERTO RICO

ˌpwer-tə-ˈrē-ˌₒkō

(Porto Rico)

LOCATION — Large island in the West Indies, east of Hispaniola
GOVT. — Former Spanish possession
AREA — 3,435 sq. mi.
POP. — 953,243 (1899)
CAPITAL — San Juan

The island was ceded to the US by the Treaty of 1898.

Spanish issues of 1855-73 used in both Puerto Rico and Cuba are listed as Cuba Nos. 1-4, 9-14, 18-21, 32-34, 35A-37, 39-41, 43-45, 47-49, 51-53, 55-57.

Spanish issues of 1873-1898 for Puerto Rico only are listed in Vol. 4 of this Catalogue.

100 Cents = 1 Dollar (1898)

Issued under U.S. Administration

LOCAL ISSUES

Ponce Issue

A11

Handstamped

1898 Unwmk. *Imperf.*

200 A11 5c violet —

No. 200 is a violet handstamp and control mark used on envelopes. Some examples have no control mark. There are three types of circular markings known, and two control marks. Uses on 2¢ U.S. stamps on cover were strictly as a cancellation, not as local postage. Because genuine usage is extremely difficult to authenticate with certainty, certification by competent authorities is essential.

Coamo Issue

A12

Typeset, setting of 10

1898, Aug.

201 A12 5c black 700. *1,250.*

See the Scott U.S. Specialized Catalogue for more detailed listings.

The stamps bear the control mark "F. Santiago" in violet. About 500 were issued.

Dangerous forgeries exist.

Regular Issue

United States Nos. 279, 279Bf, 281, 272 and 282C Overprinted in Black at 36 degree angle

1899 Wmk. 191 *Perf. 12*

210 A87 1c yellow green 6.00 1.40
Never hinged 13.00
a. Overprint at 25 degree angle 8.00 2.25
Never hinged 17.50
211 A88 2c redsh car, type IV 5.00 1.25
Never hinged 11.00
a. Overprint at 25 degree angle, *Mar. 15* 6.50 2.25
Never hinged 14.00
212 A91 5c blue 12.50 2.50
Never hinged 27.50
213 A93 8c violet brown 40.00 17.50
Never hinged 90.00
a. Overprint at 25 degree angle 45.00 19.00
Never hinged 100.00
c. "PORTO RIC" 150.00 110.00
214 A94 10c brown, type I 22.50 6.00
Never hinged 50.00
Nos. 210-214 (5) 86.00 28.65

Misspellings of the overprint on Nos. 210-214 (PORTO RICU, PORTU RICO, FORTO RICO) are actually broken letters.

United States Nos. 279 and 279B Overprinted Diagonally in Black

1900

215 A87 1c yellow green 7.50 1.40
Never hinged 17.50
216 A88 2c red, type IV 5.50 2.00
Never hinged 12.50
b. Inverted overprint *12,500.*

POSTAGE DUE STAMPS

United States Nos. J38, J39 and J42 Overprinted in Black at 36 degree angle

1899 Wmk. 191 *Perf. 12*

J1 D2 1c deep claret 22.50 5.50
Never hinged 50.00
a. Overprint at 25 degree angle 22.50 7.50
Never hinged 50.00
J2 D2 2c deep claret 20.00 6.00
Never hinged 45.00
a. Overprint at 25 degree angle 20.00 7.00
Never hinged 45.00
J3 D2 10c deep claret 180.00 55.00
Never hinged 375.00
a. Overprint at 25 degree angle 160.00 75.00
Never hinged 330.00
Nos. J1-J3 (3) 222.50 66.50

Stamps of Puerto Rico were replaced by those of the United States.

RYUKYU ISLANDS

rē-ˈyü-ˌₑkyü ˈī-lənds

LOCATION — Chain of 63 islands between Japan and Formosa, separating the East China Sea from the Pacific Ocean.
GOVT. — Semi-autonomous under United States administration.
AREA — 848 sq. mi.
POP. — 945,465 (1970)
CAPITAL — Naha, Okinawa

The Ryukyus were part of Japan until American forces occupied them in 1945. The islands reverted to Japan May 15, 1972.

Before the general issue of 1948, a number of provisional stamps were used. These included a mimeographed-handstamped adhesive for Kume Island, and various current stamps of Japan handstamped with chops by the postmasters of Okinawa, Amami, Miyako and Yaeyama. Although authorized by American authorities, these provisionals were local in nature, so are omitted in the listings that follow. They are listed in the *Scott United States Specialized Catalogue.*

100 Sen = 1 Yen
100 Cents = 1 Dollar (1958)

Catalogue values for unused stamps in this country are for Never Hinged items.

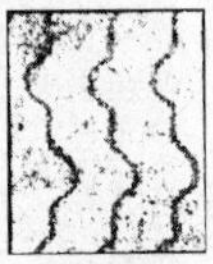
Wmk. 257

Cycad
A1

Lily
A2

Sailing Ship
A3

Farmer
A4

1948-49 Typo. Wmk. 257 *Perf. 13*
Second Printing, July 18, 1949

1	A1	5s magenta	2.00	2.00
2	A2	10s yellow green	5.00	5.00
3	A1	20s yellow green	3.00	3.00
4	A3	30s vermilion	1.25	1.25
5	A2	40s magenta	1.25	1.25
6	A3	50s ultramarine	5.00	*4.00*
7	A4	1y ultramarine	5.00	5.00
		Nos. 1-7 (7)	22.50	21.50

First Printing, July 1, 1948

1a	A1	5s magenta	3.00	*3.50*
2a	A2	10s yellow green	2.00	*2.00*
3a	A1	20s yellow green	2.00	*2.00*
4a	A3	30s vermilion	4.00	*3.50*
5a	A2	40s magenta	50.00	50.00
6a	A3	50s ultramarine	4.00	4.00
7a	A4	1y ultramarine	400.00	325.00
		Nos. 1a-7a (7)	465.00	390.00

First printing: thick yellow gum, dull colors, rough perforations, grayish paper. Second printing: white gum, sharp colors, clean-cut and rough perforations, white paper. Third printing (Sept. 28, 1950): 5s to 50s denominations, white gum, clean-cut perforations, cream paper (same values as second printings).

Tile Rooftop and Shishi — A5

Designs: 50s, Tile rooftop and Shisa. 1y, Ryukyuan girl. 2y, Main hall of Shuri Castle. 3y, Female dragonhead statue. 4y, Two women. 5y, Sea shells.

Perf. 13x13¼
1950, Jan. 21 Photo. Unwmk.
Off-white Paper

8	A5	50s dark carmine rose	.25	.25
a.		White paper, third printing, *Sept. 6, 1958*	.50	.50
b.		"White Sky" variety (pos. 76)	3.50	3.50
9	A5	1y deep blue	3.25	3.00
10	A5	2y rose violet	9.00	6.00
11	A5	3y carmine rose	22.50	11.00
12	A5	4y greenish gray	11.00	11.00
13	A5	5y blue green	6.50	6.00
		Nos. 8-13 (6)	52.50	37.25

The original first two printings (No. 8) were printed on off-white paper with yellowish gum and a 5-character imprint in the sheet margin. The first printing is a deep carmine red or dark red, and the second printing a dark carmine rose. The first printing was issued Jan. 21, 1950; the second printing received in Naha Sept. 22, 1950; and the third printing (No. 8a) Sept. 6, 1958. Quantities: first printing: 300,000; second printing: 3,000,000; and third printing: 300,000. The first printing unused is much scarcer than the second printing because most of the first printing was used as postage.

No. 8a has colorless gum and an 8-character imprint in the sheet margin. The color is a deep red.

For No. 8b, a defect in position 76 of the plates used resulted in the sky above the roof being predominantly white in the second printing, whereas in the first printing the 'white sky' is not as pronounced. The master negative and plate were reworked for the third printing, so position 76 in this printing does not have the "white sky" variety.

For surcharges see Nos. 16-17.

Ryukyu University and Female Dragonhead Statue — A6

1951, Feb. 12 *Perf. 13½x13¼*

14	A6	3y red brown	45.00	25.00

Opening of Ryukyu University, Feb. 12.

Ryukyuan Pine Tree — A7

1951, Feb. 19 *Perf. 13¼*

15	A7	3y dark green	40.00	22.50

Reforestation Week, Feb. 18-24.

No. 8 surcharged in Black

Type I

Type II

Type III

There are three types of 10y surcharge:

Type I: narrow-spaced rules, "10" normal spacing, "Kai Tei" characters in 9-point type. First printing, Jan. 1, 1952.

Type II: wide-spaced rules, "10" normal spacing, "Kai Tei" characters in 9-point type. Second printing, June 5, 1952.

Type III: rules and "10" both wide-spaced, "Kai Tei" characters in 8-point type. Third printing, Dec. 8, 1952.

Both eight and nine point type were used in overprinting Nos. 16-17. In the varieties listed below, the first number indicates the size of the "Kai" character, and the second number is the size of the "Tei" character.

1952 *Perf. 13½x13*

16	A5	10y on 50s dark carmine rose (II)	8.00	8.00
c.		8/8 point Kai Tei	8.00	8.00
d.		9/8 point Kai Tei	80.00	80.00
f.		Surcharge transposed	900.00	—
g.		Legend of surcharge only (no obliteration bars)	1,200.	
h.		Wrong font for "0" (pos. 59)	150.00	150.00
i.		Wrong font for "Yen" symbol (pos. 69)	150.00	150.00
j.		Surcharge on "white sky" variety (No. 8b) (pos. 76)	150.00	150.00

On No. 16e, the entire obliteration-bars portion of the surcharge normally under the 10 Yen must be visible at the top of the stamp. Ten examples of No. 16e exist (pos. 91-100) with the full obliteration bars also in the bottom selvage.

Forgeries to defraud the Postal Agency of revenue are known, used only, at the Gusikawa Post Office. Two types. Value, $500 each.

16A	A5	10y on 50s dark carmine rose (I)	30.00	30.00
a.		8/8 point Kai Tei	30.00	30.00
b.		Bottom two bars inverted (pos. 17)	150.00	150.00
c.		Wrong font for "0" (pos. 73)	250.00	250.00
d.		Surcharge on "white sky" variety (No. 8b) (pos. 76)	250.00	250.00
e.		Wide spaced obliterating bars (pos. 72)	150.00	150.00
f.		Wide spaced bottom obliterating bars (pos. 86, 95)	80.00	80.00
16B	A5	10y on 50s dark carmine rose (III)	45.00	35.00
a.		Wrong font for "Yen" symbol (pos. 25, 35, 85)	200.00	200.00
b.		Wrong font for "Tei" (pos. 26)	350.00	350.00
c.		Asterisk missing (pos. 54)	—	—
d.		"Kai Tei" 1.25mm above asterisk (pos. 54)	350.00	350.00
e.		"Kai" omitted (pos. 71)	—	
f.		Narrow spaced "10" (pos. 96)	350.00	350.00
g.		Surcharge on "white sky" variety (No. 8b)	350.00	350.00
h.		Extra wide spaced "10" (pos. 60)	200.00	200.00
i.		Asterisk within 2.0mm of "Kai Tei" (pos. 87)	200.00	200.00

The Kai Tei of the third printing measures the same as the 8-point type in the earlier printings but has differing characteristics. The Top curved line of the Kai is shorter and the lower curved line is also much shorter.

No. 10 surcharged 100y in black

17	A5	100y on 2y rose violet, Kai Tei characters in 9/9-point type, June 16, 1952	2,000.	1,400.
a.		8/8 point Kai Tei	2,000.	1,400.
b.		9/8 point Kai Tei	3,250.	3,250.
c.		Center "0" in wrong font, stamp with 9/9 Kai Tei (pos. 42)	4,000.	4,000.
d.		Center "0" in wrong font, stamp with 8/8 Kai Tei (pos. 67, 86)	3,500.	3,500.
e.		Center "0" in wrong font, stamp with 9/8 Kai Tei (pos. 53)	5,000.	5,000.
f.		Wrong font for last "0" (pos. 59)	5,000.	5,000.
g.		Wrong font for "yen" symbol (pos. 69)	5,000.	5,000.
h.		"Tei" in wrong font (pos. 9)	*4,000.*	*4,000.*

Varieties of shifted and damaged surcharge characters exist, most notably a damaged ("clipped") Kai (pos. 26, 85).

The "Tei" on No. 17h is the character used on Nos. 16 and 16A.

See note after 16B to differentiate between 8-point and 9-point characters.

Surcharge forgeries are known. Authentication by competant experts is recommended.

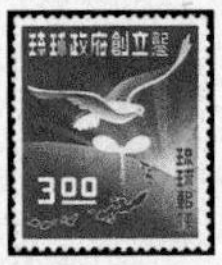
Dove, Bean Sprout and Map — A8

1952, Apr. 1 *Perf. 13¼*

18	A8	3y deep plum	80.00	40.00

Establishment of the Government of the Ryukyu Islands (GRI), April 1, 1952.

Madanbashi Bridge — A9

Designs: 2y, Main Hall, Shuri Castle. 3y, Shureimon Gate. 6y, Stone Gate, Sogen-ji Temple, Naha. 10y, Benzaiten-do Temple. 30y, Sonohyan Utaki (altar) at Shuri Castle. 50y, Tamaudun (royal mausoleum). Shuri. 100y, Stone Bridge, Hojo Pond, Enkaku Temple.

1952-53 *Perf. 13x13¼*

19	A9	1y red	.30	.30
20	A9	2y green	.40	.40
21	A9	3y aquamarine	.50	.50
22	A9	6y blue	2.00	2.00
23	A9	10y crimson rose	2.50	1.00
24	A9	30y olive green	9.00	7.50
a.		30y light olive green, *1958*	50.00	
25	A9	50y rose violet	12.50	9.00
26	A9	100y claret	15.00	5.00
		Nos. 19-26 (8)	42.20	25.70

Issued: 1y, 2y and 3y, 11/20/52. Others,1/20/53.

Reception at Shuri Castle — A10

Perry and American Fleet in Naha Port — A11

1953, May 26 *Perf. 13x13¼*

27	A10	3y deep magenta	12.00	6.50
28	A11	6y chalky blue	1.25	1.50

Centenary of the arrival of Commodore Matthew Calbraith Perry at Naha, Okinawa.

Chofu Ota and Pencil-shaped Matrix — A12

1953, Oct. 1 *Perf. 13¼x13*

29	A12	4y orange brown	11.00	5.00

Third Newspaper Week, Oct. 1-7.

Shigo Toma and Pen — A13

1954, Oct. 1

30	A13	4y blue	10.00	7.50

Fourth Newspaper Week, Oct. 1-7.

Ryukyu Pottery — A14

Designs: 4y, Dachibin (sake or water flask). 15y, Tsuikin lacquerware tray. 20y, Kajimayaa pattern on Kijoka-bashofu textile.

1954-55 Photo. *Perf. 13x13¼*

31	A14	4y	brown	.90	.50
32	A14	15y	vermilion	3.50	3.50
33	A14	20y	yellow orange	2.25	2.25
			Nos. 31-33 (3)	6.65	6.25

For surcharges see Nos. C19, C21, C23.

Noguni Shrine and Sweet Potato Plant — A15

1955, Nov. 26 *Perf. 13¼*

34 A15 4y blue 10.00 7.00

350th anniv. of the introduction of the sweet potato to the Ryukyu Islands.

Stylized Trees — A16

1956, Feb. 18 *Perf. 13*

35 A16 4y blue green 10.00 6.00

Arbor Week, Feb. 18-24.

Yanaji (Willow) Dance — A17

8y, Munjuru (Straw Hat) Dance. 14y, Nido Tichiuchi Dance.

1956, May 1 *Perf. 13x13¼*

36	A17	5y	rose lilac	1.00	.60
37	A17	8y	dk vio blue	2.00	2.00
38	A17	14y	reddish brown	2.50	2.50
			Nos. 36-38 (3)	5.50	5.10

For surcharges see Nos. C20, C22.

Telephone A18

1956, June 8

39 A18 4y violet blue 12.50 8.00

Establishment of dial telephone system.

Garland of Pine, Bamboo and Plum — A19

1956, Dec. 1 *Perf. 13¼*

40 A19 2y multicolored 1.60 1.60

New Year, 1957.

Map of Okinawa and Pencil Rocket — A20

1957, Oct. 1 Photo. *Perf. 13*

41 A20 4y deep violet blue 1.00 1.00

Seventh Newspaper Week, Oct. 1-7.

Phoenix — A21

1957, Dec. 1 *Perf. 13x13¼*

42 A21 2y multicolored .25 .25

New Year, 1958.

Ryukyu Stamps A22

1958, July 1 *Perf. 13½*

43 A22 4y multicolored .80 .80

10th anniv. of 1st Ryukyu stamps.

Yen Symbol and Dollar Sign — A23

Perf. 10.3, 10.8, 11.1 & Compound

1958, Sept. 16 Typo.

Without Gum

44	A23	½c orange	.80	.80
a.		Imperf., pair	*1,500.*	
b.		Horiz. pair, imperf. between	225.00	
c.		Vert. pair, imperf. between	575.00	
d.		Vert. strip of 4, imperf. between	800.00	
45	A23	1c yellow green	1.25	1.25
a.		Horiz. pair, imperf. between	200.00	
b.		Vert. pair, imperf. between	150.00	
c.		Vert. strip of 3, imperf. between	650.00	
d.		Vert. strip of 4, imperf. between	800.00	
e.		Block of 4, imperf. btwn. vert. & horiz.	*10,000.*	
46	A23	2c gray blue	2.00	2.00
a.		Horiz. pair, imperf. between	200.00	
b.		Vert. pair, imperf. between	*2,200.*	
c.		Horiz. strip of 3, imperf. between	450.00	
d.		Horiz. strip of 4, imperf. between	700.00	
47	A23	3c deep carmine	1.50	1.50
a.		Horiz. pair, imperf. between	200.00	
b.		Vert. pair, imperf. between	150.00	
c.		Vert. strip of 3, imperf. between	400.00	
d.		Vert. strip of 4, imperf. between	750.00	
e.		Block of 4, imperf. btwn. vert. & horiz.	*10,000.*	
48	A23	4c lt blue grn	2.00	2.00
a.		Horiz. pair, imperf. between	*400.00*	
b.		Vert. pair, imperf. between	175.00	
49	A23	5c orange brown	4.00	3.75
a.		Horiz. pair, imperf. between	200.00	
b.		Vert. pair, imperf. between	*850.00*	
50	A23	10c aquamarine	5.25	4.75
a.		Horiz. pair, imperf. between	200.00	
b.		Vert. pair, imperf. between	150.00	
c.		Vert. strip of 3, imperf. between	750.00	
51	A23	25c bright violet blue	7.50	6.00
a.		Gummed paper, perf. 10.3 ('61)	15.00	15.00
b.		Horiz. pair, imperf. between	*2,200.*	
c.		Vert. pair, imperf. between	*5,000.*	
d.		Vert. strip of 3, imperf. between	900.00	
52	A23	50c gray	15.00	10.00
a.		Gummed paper, perf. 10.3 ('61)	15.00	15.00
b.		Horiz. pair, imperf. between	*1,750.*	
53	A23	$1 reddish purple	11.00	5.50
a.		Horiz. pair, imperf. between	450.00	
b.		Vert. pair, imperf. between	*2,250.*	
		Nos. 44-53 (10)	50.30	37.55

Printed locally. Perforation, paper and shade varieties exist. Nos. 51a and 52a are on off-white paper and perf 10.3.

Gate of Courtesy A24

1958, Oct. 15 Photo. *Perf. 13x13¼*

54 A24 3c multicolored 1.25 1.25

Restoration of Shureimon, Gate of Courtesy, on road leading to Shuri City.

Imitations of this stamp were distributed in 1972 to discourage speculation in Ryukyuan stamps. The imitations were printed without gum and have a lengthy message in light blue printed on the back. A second type exists, with printed black perforations and three Japanese characters on the back ("Mozo Hin" — imitation) in black. Value, sheet of 10 $15.

Lion Dance — A25

1958, Dec. 10 *Perf. 13¼x13*

55 A25 1½c multicolored .30 .30

New Year, 1959.

Trees and Mountains — A26

1959, Apr. 30 *Perf. 13¼*

56 A26 3c blue, yellow green, green & red .70 .60

"Make the Ryukyus Green" movement.

Yonaguni Moth — A27

1959, July 23 Photo. *Perf. 13x13¼*

57 A27 3c multicolored 1.20 1.00

Meeting of the Japanese Biological Education Society in Okinawa.

Hibiscus — A28

琉球郵便

Inscribed

Designs: 3c, Fish (Moorish idol). 8c, Sea shell (Phalium bandatum). 13c, Butterfly (Kallinia inachus eucerca), denomination at left, butterfly going up. 17c, Jellyfish (Dactylometra pacifera Goette).

1959, Aug. 10 *Perf. 12¾x13*

58	A28	½c	multicolored	.30	.25
59	A28	3c	multicolored	.75	.40
60	A28	8c	light ultramarine, black & ocher	10.00	5.50
61	A28	13c	light blue, gray & orange	1.75	1.75
62	A28	17c	dp ultra, org red & yel	20.00	9.00
			Nos. 58-62 (5)	32.80	16.90

Four-character inscription measures 10x2mm on ½c; 12x3mm on 3c, 8c; 8½x2mm on 13c, 17c. See Nos. 76-80.

Toy (Yakaji) — A29

1959, Dec. 1 *Perf. 13x13¼*

63 A29 1½c gold & multi .55 .45

New Year, 1960.

University Badge — A30

1960, May 22 Photo.

64 A30 3c multicolored .95 .75

10th anniv. opening of Ryukyu University.

Straw Hat Folk Dancer — A31

Designs: 2½c, Nufwabushi. 5c, Hatumabushi. 10c, Hanafu.

1960, Nov. 1 Photo. *Perf. 13¼*

Dark Gray Background

65	A31	1c	yel, red & vio	2.00	.80
66	A31	2½c	crim, blue & yel	3.00	1.00
67	A31	5c	dk blue, yel & red	1.00	.50
68	A31	10c	dk blue, yel & red	1.00	.70
			Nos. 65-68 (4)	7.00	3.00

See Nos. 81-87, 220.

Torch and Nago Bay — A32

Runners at Starting Line — A33

1960, Nov. 8 Litho. *Perf. 13x13¼*

72	A32	3c	lt blue, dp bluish grn & ver	5.00	3.00
73	A33	8c	org & dp bluish grn	1.00	.75

8th Kyushu Inter-Prefectural Athletic Meet, Nago, Northern Okinawa, Nov. 6-7.

Little Egret and Rising Sun — A34

1960, Dec. 1 Photo.

74 A34 3c reddish brown 5.00 3.50

National census.

Okinawa Bull Fight — A35

1960, Dec. 10

75 A35 1½c bister, dark blue & red brown 1.50 1.50

New Year, 1961.

Type of 1959 With Japanese Inscription Redrawn

A28a

1960-61 **Photo.**

76	A28a	½c multicolored	.60	.45
77	A28a	3c multicolored	1.00	.35
78	A28a	8c lt ultra, blk & ocher	1.25	.80
79	A28a	13c lt blue & multi	1.50	.90
80	A28a	17c dp ultra, brn rose & yel	12.50	6.00
		Nos. 76-80 (5)	16.85	8.50

Size of Japanese inscription on Nos. 78-80 is 10½x1½mm. On No.79 the denomination is at right, butterfly going down.

Issued: Nos. 78-80, 7/1/60; No. 77, 8/23/61; No. 76, 10/61.

Dancer Type of 1960 with "RYUKYUS" Added in English

Designs: 20c, Shudun. 25c, Haodori. 50c, Nubui Kuduchi. $1, Koteibushi.

1961-64 ***Perf. 13¼***

81	A31	1c multicolored	.25	.25
82	A31	2½c multicolored	.25	.25
83	A31	5c multicolored	.25	.25
84	A31	10c multicolored	.45	.40
84A	A31	20c multicolored	3.00	1.40
85	A31	25c multicolored	1.00	.90
86	A31	50c multicolored	2.50	1.40
87	A31	$1 multicolored	5.50	.25
		Nos. 81-87 (8)	13.20	5.10

Issued: Nos. 86-87, 9/1/61; No. 81, 12/5/61; No. 85, 2/1/62; Nos. 82-84, 6/20/62; No. 84A, 1/20/64.

Pine Tree — A36

1961, May 1 **Litho.**

88	A36	3c yel grn & red	1.75	1.25

"Make the Ryukyus Green" movement.

Naha, Steamer and Sailboat — A37

1961, May 20 **Photo.**

89	A37	3c aquamarine	2.25	1.50

40th anniv. of Naha.

White Silver Temple — A38

Perf. 10¾, 10¾x10¼

1961, Oct. 1 **Typo.** **Unwmk.**

90	A38	3c red brown	2.50	2.00
a.		Horiz. pair, imperf. between	*1,000.*	
b.		Vert. pair, imperf. between	*700.00*	

Merger of townships Takamine, Kanegushiku and Miwa with Itoman.

A 3-cent stamp to commemorate the merger of two cities, Shimoji-cho and Hirara-shi of Miyako Island, was scheduled to be issued on Oct. 30, 1961. However, the merger was called off and the stamp was never issued. It features a white chaplet on Kiyako linen on a blue background.

Books and Bird — A39

1961, Nov. 12 **Litho.** ***Perf. 13¼***

91	A39	3c multicolored	1.10	.90

Book Week, 10th anniversary.

Rising Sun and Eagles — A40

1961, Dec. 10 **Photo.**

92	A40	1½c gold, ver & blk	2.00	2.00

New Year, 1962.

Symbolic Steps, Trees and Government Building — A41

Design: 3c, Government Building.

1962, Apr. 1 ***Perf. 13½***

93	A41	1½c multicolored	.60	.60
94	A41	3c brt grn, red & gray	.80	.80

10th anniv. of the Government of the Ryukyu Islands (GRI).

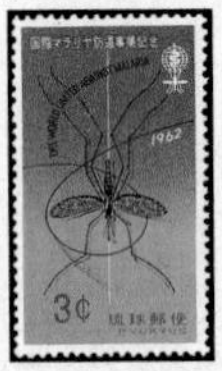

Anopheles Hyrcanus Sinensis — A42

Design: 8c, Malaria eradication emblem and Shurei gate.

1962, Apr. 7 ***Perf. 13¼x13***

95	A42	3c multicolored	.60	.60
96	A42	8c multicolored	.90	.75

World Health Organization drive to eradicate malaria.

Dolls and Toys — A43

1962, May 5 ***Perf. 13x13¼***

97	A43	3c red, black, blue & buff	1.10	1.00

Children's Day, 1962.

Linden or Sea Hibiscus — A44

Flowers: 3c, Deigo tree (Erythrina variegata var. orientealis). 8c, Iju (Schima liukiuensis Nakal). 13c, Touch-me-not (Impatiens balsamina). 17c, Shell flower (Alpinia speciosa).

1962, June 1 **Photo.** ***Perf. 13¼***

98	A44	½c multicolored	.35	.25
99	A44	3c multicolored	.30	.25
100	A44	8c multicolored	.55	.45
101	A44	13c multicolored	.75	.60
102	A44	17c multicolored	1.25	.80
		Nos. 98-102 (5)	3.20	2.35

See Nos. 107 and 114 for 1½c and 15c flower stamps. For surcharge see No. 190.

Akae (Earthenware) A45

1962, July 5

103	A45	3c multicolored	3.50	2.50

Philatelic Week, July 5-12.

Japanese Fencing (Kendo) — A46

1962, July 25 ***Perf. 13¼x13***

104	A46	3c multicolored	3.50	2.50

All-Japan Kendo Meeting in Okinawa, July 24-25, 1962.

Rabbit Playing near Water, Bingata Cloth Design — A47

1962, Dec. 10 ***Perf. 13¼***

105	A47	1½c gold & multi	1.00	.80

New Year, 1963.

Young Man and Woman, Stone Relief — A48

1963, Jan. 15 **Photo.**

106	A48	3c gold, black & blue	.90	.80

Adult Day.

Gooseneck Cactus (Epiphyllum strictum) — A49

1963, Apr. 5 ***Perf. 13x13¼***

107	A49	1½c dark blue green, yellow & pink	.25	.25

Trees and Wooded Hills — A50

1963, Mar. 25 ***Perf. 13¼***

108	A50	3c ultra, grn & red brn	1.00	.80

"Make the Ryukyus Green" movement.

Map of Okinawa — A51

1963, Apr. 30

109	A51	3c multicolored	1.25	1.00

Opening of the Round Road on Okinawa.

Hawks over Islands — A52

1963, May 10 **Photo.**

110	A52	3c multicolored	1.10	.95

Bird Day, May 10.

Shioya Bridge — A53

1963, June 5

111	A53	3c multicolored	1.10	.95

Opening of Shioya Bridge over Shioya Bay.

Tsuikin-wan Lacquerware Bowl — A54

1963, July 1 ***Perf. 13¼***

112	A54	3c multicolored	2.75	2.50

Philatelic Week.

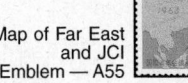

Map of Far East and JCI Emblem — A55

1963, Sept. 16 **Photo.**

113	A55	3c multicolored	.70	.70

Meeting of the International Junior Chamber of Commerce (JCI), Naha, Okinawa, Sept. 16-19.

Hamaomoto (Crinum asiaticum var. japonica) — A56

1963, Oct. 15 ***Perf. 13x13¼***

114	A56	15c multicolored	1.25	.80

Site of Nakagusuku Castle — A57

1963, Nov. 1 ***Perf. 13¼***

115	A57	3c multicolored	.60	.60

Protection of national cultural treasures.

Flame — A58

1963, Dec. 10

116	A58	3c red, dark blue & yellow	.65	.60

15th anniv. of the Universal Declaration of Human Rights.

Dragon — A59

1963, Dec. 10 **Photo.**

117	A59	1½c multicolored	.55	.50

New Year, 1964.

Carnation — A60

1964, May 10 ***Perf. 13¼***

118	A60	3c blue, yel, blk & car	.40	.35

Mothers Day.

Pineapples and Sugar Cane — A61

1964, June 1

119 A61 3c multicolored .40 .35

Agricultural census.

Minsah Obi (Sash Woven of Kapok) — A62

1964, July 1 ***Perf. 13¼***

120 A62 3c deep blue, magenta & ocher .50 .50
a. 3c deep blue, deep carmine & ocher .65 .65

Philatelic Week.

Girl Scout and Emblem — A63

1964, Aug. 31 **Photo.**

121 A63 3c multicolored .45 .40

10th anniv. of Ryukyuan Girl Scouts.

Shuri Relay Station A64

Parabolic Antenna and Map A65

1964, Sept. 1 **Unwmk.**

Black Overprint

122 A64 3c deep green .65 .65
a. Figure "1" inverted 30.00 30.00
b. Overprint inverted *1,500.*
c. Overprint missing *3,500.*
d. Overprint inverted and figure "1" inverted *5,000.*
123 A65 8c ultramarine 1.25 1.25
a. Overprint missing *3,500.*

Opening of the Ryukyu Islands-Japan microwave system carrying telephone and telegraph messages. The overprints indicate the system was not actually opened until 1964.

Many of the stamps with overprint errors listed above are damaged. The values listed here are for stamps in very fine condition.

Gate of Courtesy, Olympic Torch and Emblem — A66

1964, Sept. 7 **Photo.** ***Perf. 13¼***

124 A66 3c ultra, yel & red .30 .25

Relaying the Olympic torch on Okinawa en route to Tokyo.

"Naihanchi," Karate Stance — A67

"Makiwara," Strengthening Hands and Feet — A68

"Kumite," Simulated Combat — A69

1964-65 **Photo.**

125 A67 3c dull clar, yel & blk .50 .45
126 A68 3c yel & multi .40 .40
127 A69 3c gray, red & blk .40 .40
Nos. 125-127 (3) 1.30 1.25

Karate, Ryukyuan self-defense sport. Issued: No. 125, 10/5/64; No. 126, 2/5/65; No. 127, 6/5/65.

Miyara Dunchí — A70

1964, Nov. 1

128 A70 3c multicolored .30 .25

Protection of national cultural treasures. Miyara Dunchi was built as a residence by Peichin Miyara Touen in 1819.

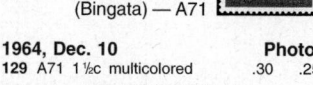

Snake and Iris (Bingata) — A71

1964, Dec. 10 **Photo.**

129 A71 1½c multicolored .30 .25

New Year, 1965.

Boy Scouts — A72

1965, Feb. 6 ***Perf. 13¼***

130 A72 3c light blue & multi .45 .40

10th anniv. of Ryukyuan Boy Scouts.

Main Stadium, Onoyama — A73

1965, July 1 ***Perf. 13x13¼***

131 A73 3c multicolored .25 .25

Inauguration of the main stadium of the Onoyama athletic facilities.

Samisen of King Shoko — A74

1965, July 1 **Photo.** ***Perf. 13¼***

132 A74 3c buff & multi .45 .40

Philatelic Week.

Kin Power Plant — A75

1965, July 1

133 A75 3c green & multi .25 .25

Completion of Kin power plant.

ICY Emblem, Ryukyu Map — A76

1965, Aug. 24 **Photo.**

134 A76 3c multicolored .25 .25

20th anniv. of the UN and International Cooperation Year, 1964-65.

Naha City Hall — A77

1965, Sept. 18

135 A77 3c blue & multi .35 .25

Completion of Naha City Hall.

Chinese Box Turtle (Cyclemys flavomarginata) A78

Turtles: No. 137, Hawksbill turtle (Eretochelys imbricata bissa) (denomination at top, country name at bottom). No. 138, Asian terrapin (Geoemyda japonica) (denomination and country name at top).

1965-66 **Photo.** ***Perf. 13¼***

136 A78 3c golden brown & multi .30 .30
137 A78 3c multi .30 .30
138 A78 3c multicolored .30 .30
Nos. 136-138 (3) .90 .90

Issued: No. 136, 10/20/65; No. 137, 1/20/66; No. 138, 4/20/66.

Horse (Bingata) — A79

1965, Dec. 10 **Photo.**

139 A79 1½c multicolored .25 .25
a. Gold omitted *2,000.* *2,000.*

New Year, 1966.

There are 92 unused and 2 used examples of No. 139a known.

Noguchi's Okinawa Woodpecker (Dendrocopus noguchii) A80

Sika Deer (Cervus nippon var. keramae) A81

Design: No. 142, Dugong (Dugong dugong).

1966 **Photo.**

140 A80 3c blue green & multi .25 .25
141 A81 3c bl, red, blk, brn & grn .25 .25
142 A81 3c bl, yel grn, blk & red .25 .25
Nos. 140-142 (3) .75 .75

Nature Conservation. Issued No. 140, 2/15; No. 141, 3/15; No. 142, 4/20.

Ryukyu Bungalow Swallow (Hirundo tahitica) — A82

1966, May 10 **Photo.** ***Perf. 13¼***

143 A82 3c sky blue, black & brown .25 .25

4th Bird Week, May 10-16.

Lilies and Ruins — A83

1966, June 23 ***Perf. 13***

144 A83 3c multicolored .25 .25

Memorial Day, end of the Battle of Okinawa, June 23, 1945.

University of the Ryukyus — A84

1966, July 1

145 A84 3c multicolored .25 .25

Transfer of the University of the Ryukyus from U.S. authority to the Ryukyu Government.

Chinkin Ukuhan Lacquerware, 18th Century — A85

1966, Aug. 1 ***Perf. 13¼***

146 A85 3c gray & multicolored .25 .25

Philatelic Week.

Tile-Roofed House and UNESCO Emblem — A86

1966, Sept. 20 **Photo.**

147 A86 3c multicolored .25 .25

20th anniv. of UNESCO.

Government Museum and Dragon Statue — A87

1966, Oct. 6

148 A87 3c multicolored .25 .25

Completion of the GRI (Government of the Ryukyu Islands) Museum, Shuri.

Tomb of Nakasone-Toyomiya Genga, Ruler of Miyako — A88

1966, Nov. 1 **Photo.**

149 A88 3c multicolored .25 .25

Protection of national cultural treasures.

Ram in Iris Wreath (Bingata) — A89

1966, Dec. 10 **Photo.** ***Perf. 13¼***

150 A89 1½c dark blue & multi .25 .25

New Year, 1967.

Clown Fish (Amphiprion frenatus) — A90

Fish: No. 152, Young boxfish (Ostracion cubicus) (white numeral at lower left). No. 153, Forceps fish (Forcipiger longirostris) (pale buff numeral at lower right). No. 154, Spotted trig-gerfish (Balistoides conspicillum) (orange numeral at upper right). No. 155, Saddleback butterflyfish (Chaetodon ephippium) (carmine numeral, lower left).

1966-67

151	A90	3c orange red & multi	.25	.25
152	A90	3c org yel & multi	.25	.25
153	A90	3c multicolored	.40	.25
154	A90	3c multicolored	.35	.25
155	A90	3c multicolored	.30	.25
		Nos. 151-155 (5)	1.55	1.25

Issued No. 151, 12/20/66; No. 152, 1/10/67; No. 153, 4/10/67; No. 154, 5/25/67; No. 155, 6/10/67.

A 3-cent stamp to commemorate Japanese-American-Ryukyuan Joint Arbor Day was scheduled for release on March 16, 1967. However, it was not released. The stamp in light blue and white features American and Japanese flags joined by a shield containing a tree.

Tsuboya Urn — A91

1967, Apr. 20

156 A91 3c yellow & multicolored .25 .25

Philatelic Week.

Episcopal Miter (Mitra mitra) — A92

Seashells: No. 158, Venus comb murex (Murex pecten). No. 159, Chiragra spider (Lambis chiragra). No. 160, Green turban (Turbo marmoratus). No. 161, Bubble conch (Euprotomus bulla).

1967-68 Photo. *Perf. 13¼*

157	A92	3c light green & multi	.25	.25
158	A92	3c grnsh bl & multi	.25	.25
159	A92	3c brt grn & multi	.25	.25
160	A92	3c light blue & multi	.30	.25
161	A92	3c bright blue & multi	.60	.50
		Nos. 157-161 (5)	1.65	1.50

Issued: No. 157, 6/20/67; No. 159, 1/18/68; No. 160, 2/20/68; No. 161, 6/5/68; No. 158, 8/30/68.

Red-tiled Roofs and ITY Emblem — A93

1967, Sept. 11 Photo.

162 A93 3c multicolored .25 .25

International Tourist Year.

Mobile TB Clinic — A94

1967, Oct. 13 Photo.

163 A94 3c lilac & multicolored .25 .25

15th anniv. of the Anti-Tuberculosis Society.

Hojo Bridge, Enkaku Temple, 1498 — A95

1967, Nov. 1

164 A95 3c blue green & multi .25 .25

Protection of national cultural treasures.

Monkey (Bingata) — A96

1967, Dec. 11 Photo. *Perf. 13¼*

165 A96 1½c silver & multi .25 .25

New Year, 1968.

TV Tower and Map — A97

1967, Dec. 22

166 A97 3c multicolored .25 .25

Opening of Miyako and Yaeyama television stations.

Dr. Kijin Nakachi and Helper — A98

1968, Mar. 15 Photo.

167 A98 3c multicolored .30 .25

120th anniv. of the first vaccination in the Ryukyu Islands, by Dr. Kijin Nakachi.

Pill Box (Inro) — A99

1968, Apr. 18

168 A99 3c gray & multicolored .45 .45

Philatelic Week.

Young Man, Library, Book and Map of Ryukyu Islands — A100

1968, May 13

169 A100 3c multicolored .30 .25

10th International Library Week.

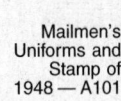

Mailmen's Uniforms and Stamp of 1948 — A101

1968, July 1 Photo. *Perf. 13¼*

170 A101 3c multicolored .30 .25

First Ryukyuan postage stamps, 20th anniv.

Main Gate, Enkaku Temple — A102

1968, July 15 Photo. & Engr.

171 A102 3c multicolored .30 .25

Restoration of the main gate Enkaku Temple, built 1492-1495, destroyed during World War II.

Old Man's Dance — A103

1968, Sept. 15 Photo.

172 A103 3c gold & multicolored .30 .25

Old People's Day.

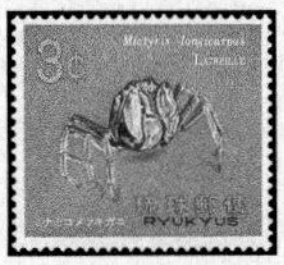

Mictyris Longicarpus — A104

Crabs: No. 174, Uca dubia stimpson. No. 175, Baptozius vinosus. No. 176, Cardisoma carnifex. No. 177, Ocypode ceratophthalma pallas.

1968-69 Photo. *Perf. 13¼*

173	A104	3c blue, ocher & black	.30	.25
174	A104	3c lt bl grn & multi	.35	.30
175	A104	3c light green & multi	.35	.30
176	A104	3c light ultra & multi	.45	.40
177	A104	3c gray blue & multi	.45	.40
		Nos. 173-177 (5)	1.90	1.65

Issued: No. 173, 10/10/68; No. 174, 2/5/69; No. 175, 3/5/69; No. 176, 5/15/69; No. 177, 6/2/69.

Saraswati Pavilion (Benzaitan-do Temple) — A105

1968, Nov. 1 Photo.

178 A105 3c multicolored .30 .25

Restoration of the Sarawati Pavilion (in front of Enkaku Temple), destroyed during World War II.

Tennis Player — A106

1968, Nov. 23 Photo.

179 A106 3c green & multi .40 .35

35th All-Japan East-West Men's Soft-ball Tennis Tournament, Naha City, Nov. 23-24.

Cock and Iris (Bingata) — A107

1968, Dec. 10

180 A107 1½c orange & multi .25 .25

New Year, 1969.

Boxer — A108

1969, Jan. 3

181 A108 3c gray & multi .40 .30

20th All-Japan Amateur Boxing Championships held at the University of the Ryukyus, Jan. 3-5.

Ink Slab Screen — A109

1969, Apr. 17 Photo. *Perf. 13¼x13*

182 A109 3c salmon, indigo & red .40 .35

Philatelic Week.

Box Antennas and Map of Radio Link — A110

1969, July 1 Photo.

183 A110 3c multicolored .30 .25

Opening of the UHF (radio) circuit system between Okinawa and the outlying Miyako-Yaeyama Islands.

Gate of Courtesy and Emblems — A111

1969, Aug. 1 Photo.

184 A111 3c Prussian blue, gold & vermilion .30 .25

22nd All-Japan Formative Education Study Conf., Naha, Aug. 1-3.

Tug of War Festival — A112

Hari Boat Race — A113

Izaiho Ceremony, Kudaka Island — A114

Mortar Drum Dance (Ushideiku) A115

Sea God Dance (Ungami) A116

1969-70 Photo. *Perf. 13¼x13*

185	A112	3c multicolored	.30	.25
186	A113	3c multicolored	.35	.30
187	A114	3c multicolored	.35	.30
188	A115	3c multicolored	.50	.45
189	A116	3c multicolored	.50	.45
		Nos. 185-189 (5)	2.00	1.75

Folklore. Issued, No. 185, 8/1/69; No. 186, 9/5/69; No. 187, 10/3/69; No. 188, 1/20/70; No. 189, 2/27/70.

No. 99 Surcharged

1969, Oct. 15 Photo. *Perf. 13¼*
190 A44 ½c on 3c multicolored 1.00 1.00
a. "1/2c" only surcharge 950.00

No. 190a are right margin stamps from a pane with a leftward misregistration of the surcharging plate.

Nakamura-ke Farm House, Built 1713-51 — A117

1969, Nov. 1 Photo. *Perf. 13¼x13*
191 A117 3c multicolored .25 .25

Protection of national cultural treasures.

Statue of Kyuzo Toyama, Maps of Hawaiian and Ryukyu Islands — A118

1969, Dec. 5 Photo. *Perf. 13¼*
192 A118 3c light ultra & multi .50 .50
a. Without overprint *3,000.*
b. Wide-spaced bars *700.00 500.00*

70th anniv. of Ryukyu-Hawaii emigration led by Kyuzo Toyama.
The overprint "1969" at lower left and bars across "1970" at upper right was applied before No. 192 was issued.

Dog and Flowers (Bingata) — A119

1969, Dec. 10 *Perf. 13¼x13*
193 A119 1½c pink & multi .25 .25

New Year, 1970.

Sake Flask Made from Coconut (Yashi-gwa) — A120

1970, Apr. 15 Photo. *Perf. 13¼*
194 A120 3c multicolored .25 .25

Philatelic Week, 1970.

"The Bell" (Shushin Kaneiri) A121

Child and Kidnapper (Chunusudu) A122

Robe of Feathers (Mekarushi) A123

Vengeance of Two Young Sons (Nidotichiuchi) A124

The Virgin and the Dragon (Kokonomaki) A125

1970 Photo. *Perf. 13¼*
195 A121 3c dull blue & multi .60 .40
a. Souvenir sheet of 4 4.00 4.00
196 A122 3c light blue & multi .60 .40
a. Souvenir sheet of 4 4.00 4.00
197 A123 3c bluish grn & multi .60 .40
a. Souvenir sheet of 4 4.00 4.00
198 A124 3c dull bl grn & multi .60 .40
a. Souvenir sheet of 4 4.00 4.00
199 A125 3c multicolored .60 .40
a. Souvenir sheet of 4 4.00 4.00
Nos. 195-199 (5) 3.00 2.00
Nos. 195a-199a (5) 20.00 20.00

Classic Opera. Issued No. 195, 4/28; No. 196, 5/29; No. 197, 6/30; No. 198, 7/30; No. 199, 8/25.

Underwater Observatory and Tropical Fish — A126

1970, May 22
200 A126 3c blue green & multi .30 .25

Completion of the underwater observatory of Busena-Misaki, Nago.

Noboru Jahana (1865-1908), Politician — A127

Portraits: No. 202, Saion Gushichan Bunjaku (1682-1761), statesman. No. 203, Choho Giwan (1823-1876), regent and poet.

1970-71 Engr.
201 A127 3c rose claret .50 .45
202 A127 3c dull blue green .75 .65
203 A127 3c black .50 .45
Nos. 201-203 (3) 1.75 1.55

Issued: No. 201, 9/25.70; No. 202, 12/22/70; No. 203, 1/22/71.

Map of Okinawa and People — A128

1970, Oct. 1 Photo.
204 A128 3c red & multicolored .25 .25

Oct. 1, 1970 census.

Great Cycad of Une — A129

1970, Nov. 2 Photo. *Perf. 13¼*
205 A129 3c gold & multicolored .25 .25

Protection of national treasures.

Japanese Flag, Diet and Map of Ryukyus — A130

1970, Nov. 15 Photo.
206 A130 3c ultra & multi .80 .75

Citizen's participation in national administration to Japanese law of Apr. 24, 1970.

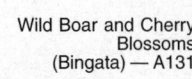

Wild Boar and Cherry Blossoms (Bingata) — A131

1970, Dec. 10 *Perf. 13¼x13*
207 A131 1½c multicolored .25 .25

New Year, 1971.

Low Hand Loom (Jibata) A132

Farmer Wearing Palm Bark Raincoat (Shurunnui) and Kuba Leaf Hat (Kubagasa) A133

Fisherman's Wooden Box (Yutui) and Scoop (Umi-fujo) — A134

Designs: No. 209, Woman running a filature (reel). No. 211, Woman hulling rice with cylindrical "Shiri-ushi."

1971 Photo. *Perf. 13¼*
208 A132 3c light blue & multi .30 .25
209 A132 3c pale grn & multi .30 .25
210 A133 3c pale blue & multi .35 .30
211 A132 3c yellow & multi .40 .35
212 A134 3c gray & multi .35 .30
Nos. 208-212 (5) 1.70 1.45

Issued: No. 208, 2/16; No. 209, 3/16; No. 210, 4/30; No. 211, 5/20; No. 212, 6/15.

Water Carrier (Taku) — A135

1971, Apr. 15 Photo.
213 A135 3c blue grn & multi .35 .30

Philatelic Week.

Old and New Naha, and City Emblem — A136

1971, May 20 *Perf. 13¼x13*
214 A136 3c ultra & multi .25 .25

50th anniv. of Naha as a municipality.

Madder (Sandanka) — A137

Design: 3c, Ogocho (Caesalpinia pulcherrima).

1971 Photo. *Perf. 13¼*
215 A137 2c gray blue & multi .25 .25
216 A137 3c gray grn & multi .25 .25

Issued No. 216, 5/10; No. 215, 9/30.

View from Mabuni Hill — A138

Mt. Arashi from Haneji Sea — A139

Yabuchi Island from Yakena Port — A140

1971-72
217 A138 3c green & multi .25 .25
218 A139 3c blue & multi .25 .25
219 A140 4c multicolored .25 .25
Nos. 217-219 (3) .75 .75

Government parks. Issued: No. 217, 7/30/71; No. 218, 8/30/71; No. 219, 1/20/72.

For the 4-cent unissued "stamp" picturing Iriomote Park, originally planned for issue in 1971 but never released, see the note after No. RQ8 in the Scott U.S. Specialized catalogue.

Dancer (Nu-fwa-bushi) — A141

1971, Nov. 1 Photo. *Perf. 13¼*
220 A141 4c Prussian blue & multicolored .25 .25

Deva King (Misshaku Kongo), Torin-ji Temple — A142

1971, Dec. 1
221 A142 4c dp blue & multi .25 .25

Protection of national cultural treasures.

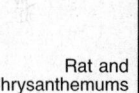

Rat and Chrysanthemums A143

1971, Dec. 10 *Perf. 13¼x13*
222 A143 2c brown orange & multi .25 .25

New Year, 1972.

Student Nurse — A144

1971, Dec. 24 *Perf. 13¼*
223 A144 4c dp mauve & multi .25 .25

Nurses' training, 25th anniversary.

Birds on Seashore A145

Sun over Islands A147

Coral Reef — A146

1972 Photo.
224 A145 5c brt blue & multi .40 .35
225 A146 5c multi .40 .35
226 A147 5c ocher & multi .40 .35
Nos. 224-226 (3) 1.20 1.05

Issued: No. 226, 3/21; No. 225, 3/30; No. 224, 4/14.

Dove, US and Japanese Flags — A148

1972, Apr. 17 Photo.
227 A148 5c bright blue & multi .80 .80

Ratification of Ryukya Islands Reversion Agreement.

Antique Sake Container (Yushibin) — A149

1972, Apr. 20

228 A149 5c ultra & multi .60 .60

Philatelic Week.

Ryukyu stamps were replaced by those of Japan after May 15, 1972.

AIR POST STAMPS

Catalogue values for all unused stamps in this section are for Never Hinged items.

Dove and Map of Ryukyus — AP1

Perf. 13x13¼

1950, Feb. 15 Photo. Unwmk.

C1 AP1 8y bright blue 110.00 40.00
C2 AP1 12y lt green 17.50 17.50
C3 AP1 16y rose carmine 9.00 9.00
Nos. C1-C3 (3) 136.50 66.50

Heavenly Maiden — AP2

1951-54 ***Perf. 13¼x13***

C4 AP2 13y chalky blue 2.00 2.00
C5 AP2 18y green 3.00 3.00
C6 AP2 30y cerise 4.50 1.50
C7 AP2 40y purple 6.50 6.50
C8 AP2 50y orange red 7.50 7.50
Nos. C4-C8 (5) 23.50 20.50

Issued: Nos. C4-C6, 10/1/51; Nos. C7-C8, 8/16/54.

Heavenly Maiden Playing Flute — AP3

1957, Aug. 1 Engr. ***Perf. 13x13¼***

C9 AP3 15y deep blue green 7.50 4.00
C10 AP3 20y scarlet 9.00 7.00
C11 AP3 35y yellow green 10.00 8.00
a. 35y light yellow green, 1958 125.00
C12 AP3 45y reddish brown 14.00 10.00
C13 AP3 60y gray & blk 16.00 12.00
Nos. C9-C13 (5) 56.50 41.00

On one printing of No. C10, position 49 shows an added spur on the right side of the second character from the left. Value unused, $175.

Surcharged in Scarlet, Light Ultramarine & Carmine Red

1959, Dec. 20 Engr.

C14 AP3 9c on 15y blue green (S) 2.50 2.00
a. Inverted surcharge 800.00
b. Pair, one without surcharge 25,000.
C15 AP3 14c on 20y scarlet (L.U.) 3.00 3.25
C16 AP3 19c on 35y yellow green (CR) 7.00 6.00
C17 AP3 27c on 45y reddish brown (L.U.) 12.50 6.00
C18 AP3 35c on 60y gray (CR) 11.00 9.00
Nos. C14-C18 (5) 36.00 26.25

No. C15 is found with the variety described below No. C13. Value unused, $125.

Nos. 31-33, 36 and 38 Surcharged in Black, Brown, Red, Blue or Green

1960, Aug. 3 Photo.

C19 A14 9c on 4y brown 2.50 1.00
a. Surcharge inverted and transposed 12,500. 12,500.
b. Inverted surcharge (legend only) 10,000.
c. Surcharge transposed 800.00
d. Legend of surcharge only 3,500.
e. Vert. pair, one without surcharge 11,000.

Nos. C19c and C19d are from a single sheet of 100 with surcharge shifted downward. Ten examples of No. C19c exist with "9c" also in bottom selvage. No. C19d is from the top row of the sheet.

No. C19e is unique, pos. 100, caused by paper foldover.

C20 A17 14c on 5y rose lilac (Br) 3.00 3.00
C21 A14 19c on 15y vermilion (R) 2.50 3.00
C22 A17 27c on 14y reddish brown (Bl) 7.00 2.50
C23 A14 35c on 20y yellow orange (G) 5.00 5.00
Nos. C19-C23 (5) 20.00 14.50

Wind God — AP4

Designs: 9c, Heavenly Maiden (as on AP2). 14c, Heavenly Maiden (as on AP3). 27c, Wind God at right. 35c, Heavenly Maiden over treetops.

1961, Sept. 21 ***Perf. 13¼***

C24 AP4 9c multicolored .30 .25
C25 AP4 14c multicolored .60 .75
C26 AP4 19c multicolored .70 .85
C27 AP4 27c multicolored 3.00 .60
C28 AP4 35c multicolored 2.00 1.25
Nos. C24-C28 (5) 6.60 3.70

Jet over Gate of Courtesy AP5

Jet Plane AP6

1963, Aug. 28 ***Perf. 13x13¼***

C29 AP5 5½c multicolored .25 .25
C30 AP6 7c multicolored .30 .30

SPECIAL DELIVERY STAMP

Catalogue value for the unused stamp in this section is for a Never Hinged item.

Sea Horse and Map of Ryukyus — SD1

Perf. 13¼

1950, Feb. 15 Unwmk. Photo.

E1 SD1 5y bright blue 25.00 17.50

UNITED NATIONS, OFFICES IN NEW YORK

yu-ˌnī-təd ˈnā-shənz

United Nations stamps are used on UN official mail sent from UN Headquarters in New York City, the UN European Office in Geneva, Switzerland, or from the Donaupark Vienna International Center or Atomic Energy Agency in Vienna, Austria to points throughout the world. They may be used on private correspondence sent through the UN post offices and are valid only at the individual UN post offices.

The UN stamps issued for use in Geneva and Vienna are listed in separate sections. Geneva issues were denominated in centimes and francs and Vienna issues in schillings (now cents and euros) and are valid only in Geneva or Vienna. The UN stamps issued for use in New York, denominated in cents and dollars, are valid only in New York.

Letters bearing Nos. 170-174 provide an exception as they were carried by the Canadian postal system.

See Switzerland Nos. 7O1-7O39 in Volume 6 of the Scott *Standard Postage Stamp Catalogue* for stamps issued by the Swiss Government for official use of the UN European Office and other UN affiliated organizations. See France official stamp listings for stamps issued by the French Government for official use of UNESCO.

Catalogue values for all unused stamps in this section are for Never Hinged items. Values for used UN stamps are for postally used stamps with contemporaneous cancels. Used stamps soaked off of first day covers sell for less.

Stamps are inscribed in English, French, or Spanish or are multilingual.

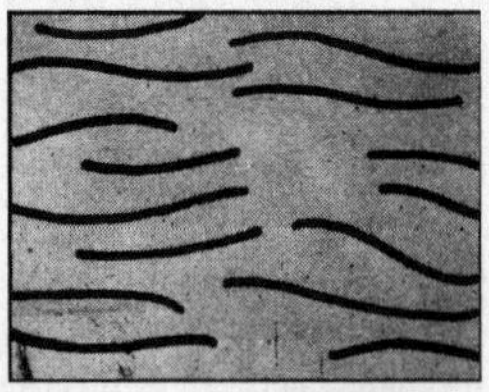

Wmk. 309 — Wavy Lines

Peoples of the World A1

UN Headquarters Building A2

"Peace, Justice, Security" A3

UN Flag A4

UN Children's Fund — A5

World Unity — A6

Perf. 13x12½, 12½x13

1951 Engr. and Photo. Unwmk.

1 A1 1c magenta .25 .25
2 A2 1½c blue green .25 .25
3 A3 2c purple .25 .25
4 A4 3c magenta & blue .25 .25
5 A5 5c blue .25 .25
6 A1 10c chocolate .25 .25
7 A4 15c violet & blue .25 .25
8 A6 20c dark brown .30 .25
9 A4 25c olive gray & blue .35 .25
10 A2 50c indigo 3.00 1.50
11 A3 $1 red 1.25 .90
Nos. 1-11 (11) 6.65 4.65

Veteran's War Memorial Building, San Francisco — A7

7th anniversary of the signing of the United Nations Charter.

1952, Oct. 24 ***Perf. 12***

12 A7 5c blue .50 .35

Globe and Encircled Flame — A8

4th anniversary of the adoption of the Universal Declaration of Human Rights.

1952, Dec. 10 ***Perf. 13½x14***

13 A8 3c deep green .45 .35
14 A8 5c blue .55 .40

Refugee Family — A9

Issued to publicize "Protection for Refugees."

1953, Apr. 24 ***Perf. 12½x13***

15 A9 3c dark red brown & rose brown .25 .25
16 A9 5c indigo & blue .45 .40

Envelope, UN Emblem and Map — A10

Issued to honor the UPU.

1953, June 12 ***Perf. 13***

17 A10 3c black brown .40 .40
18 A10 5c dark blue 1.25 1.00

Gearwheels and UN Emblem — A11

UN activities in the field of technical assistance.

1953, Oct. 24 ***Perf. 13x12½***

19 A11 3c dark gray .25 .25
20 A11 5c dark green .40 .45

Hands Reaching Toward Flame — A12

Human Rights Day.

1953, Dec. 10 *Perf. 12½x13*

21	A12	3c bright blue	.30	.30
22	A12	5c rose red	1.00	1.00

Ear of Wheat — A13

Issued to honor the FAO.

1954, Feb. 11 *Perf. 12½x13*

23	A13	3c dark green & yellow	.30	.25
24	A13	8c indigo & yellow	.75	.50

UN Emblem and Anvil — A14

Issued to honor the ILO.

1954, May 10 *Perf. 12½x13*

25	A14	3c brown	.25	.25
26	A14	8c magenta	1.00	.85

UN European Office, Geneva — A15

Issued on the occasion of UN Day.

1954, Oct. 25 *Perf. 14*

27	A15	3c dark blue violet	1.25	1.00
28	A15	8c red	.35	.30

Mother and Child — A16

Human Rights Day.

1954, Dec. 10 *Perf. 14*

29	A16	3c red orange	3.50	2.50
30	A16	8c olive green	.75	.35

Symbol of Flight — A17

International Civil Aviation Organization.

1955, Feb. 9 *Perf. 13½x14*

31	A17	3c blue	1.00	.75
32	A17	8c rose carmine	.60	.50

UNESCO Emblem — A18

Issued to honor the UN Educational, Scientific and Cultural Organization.

1955, May 11 *Perf. 13½x14*

33	A18	3c lilac rose	.35	.30
34	A18	8c light blue	.30	.30

UN Charter — A19

10th anniversary of the United Nations.

1955, Oct. 24 *Perf. 13½x14*

35	A19	3c deep plum	.90	.55
36	A19	4c dull green	.50	.35
37	A19	8c bluish black	.35	.25
		Nos. 35-37 (3)	1.75	1.15

Souvenir Sheet

1955, Oct. 24 **Wmk. 309** *Imperf.*

38 A19	Sheet of 3	50.00	18.00
a.	3c deep plum	7.00	3.00
b.	4c dull green	7.00	3.00
c.	8c bluish black	7.00	3.00
d.	As No. 38, corrected plates (see footnote)	55.00	27.50

Two printings were made of the sheet: No. 38 (200,000) and No. 38d (50,000). No. 38 may be distinguished by the broken lines in the background shading on the 8c. It leaves a small white spot below the left leg of the "n" of "Unies." On No. 38d, the broken line was retouched, eliminating the white spot. The 4c was also retouched.

Nos. 38 and 38d used are valued with first day of issue cancels. Postally used examples are worth substantially more.

Hand Holding Torch — A20

Issued in honor of Human Rights Day.

1955, Dec. 9 **Unwmk.** *Perf. 14x13½*

39	A20	3c ultramarine	.30	.30
40	A20	8c green	.40	.30

Symbols of Telecommunication — A21

Honoring the International Telecommunication Union.

1956, Feb. 17 *Perf. 14*

41	A21	3c turquoise blue	.25	.25
42	A21	8c deep carmine	.30	.30

Globe & Caduceus — A22

Issued in honor of the World Health Organization.

1956, Apr. 6 *Perf. 14*

43	A22	3c bright greenish blue	.25	.25
44	A22	8c golden brown	.25	.25

General Assembly — A23

Issued to commemorate UN Day.

1956, Oct. 24 *Perf. 14*

45	A23	3c dark blue	.25	.25
46	A23	8c gray olive	.25	.25

Flame and Globe — A24

Issued to publicize Human Rights Day.

1956, Dec. 10 *Perf. 14*

47	A24	3c plum	.25	.25
48	A24	8c dark blue	.25	.25

Weather Balloon — A25

Issued to honor the World Meterological Organization.

1957, Jan. 28 *Perf. 14*

49	A25	3c violet blue	.25	.25
50	A25	8c dark carmine rose	.25	.25

Badge of UN Emergency Force — A26

Issued in honor of the UN Emergency Force.

1957, Apr. 8 *Perf. 14x12½*

51	A26	3c light blue	.25	.25
52	A26	8c rose carmine	.25	.25

Nos. 51-52 Re-engraved

1957, Apr.-May *Perf. 14x12½*

53	A26	3c blue	.25	.25
54	A26	8c rose carmine	.35	.25

On Nos. 53-54 the background within and around the circles is shaded lightly, giving a halo effect. The lettering is more distinct with a line around each letter.

UN Emblem and Globe — A27

Issued to honor the Security Council.

1957, Oct. 24 *Perf. 12½x13*

55	A27	3c orange brown	.25	.25
56	A27	8c dark blue green	.25	.25

Flaming Torch — A28

Issued in honor of Human Rights Day.

1957, Dec. 10 *Perf. 14*

57	A28	3c red brown	.25	.25
58	A28	8c black	.25	.25

Atom & UN Emblem — A29

Issued in honor of the International Atomic Energy Agency.

1958, Feb. 10 *Perf. 12*

59	A29	3c olive	.25	.25
60	A29	8c blue	.25	.25

Central Hall, Westminster — A30

Central Hall, Westminster, London, was the site of the first session of the United Nations General Assembly, 1946.

1958, Apr. 14 *Perf. 12*

61	A30	3c blue	.25	.25
62	A30	8c rose claret	.25	.25

UN Seal — A31

Engraved and printed by Bradbury, Wilkinson & Co., Ltd., England. Panes of 50. Designed by Herbert M. Sanborn.

1958, Oct. 24 *Perf. 13½x14*

63	A31	4c red orange	.25	.25

1958, June 2 *Perf. 13x14*

64	A31	8c bright blue	.25	.25

Issue dates: 4c, Oct. 24; 8c, June 2.

Gearwheels — A32

Issued to honor the Economic and Social Council.

1958, Oct. 24 Unwmk. *Perf. 12*

65	A32 4c blue green	.25	.25
66	A32 8c vermilion	.25	.25

Hands Upholding Globe — A33

Human Rights Day and to commemorate the 10th anniversary of the signing of the Universal Declaration of Human Rights.

1958, Dec. 10 Unwmk. *Perf. 12*

67	A33 4c yellow green	.25	.25
68	A33 8c red brown	.25	.25

New York City Building, Flushing Meadows — A34

Site of many General Assembly meetings, 1946-50.

1959, Mar. 30 Unwmk. *Perf. 12*

69	A34 4c light lilac rose	.25	.25
70	A34 8c aquamarine	.25	.25

UN Emblems and Symbols of Agriculture, Industry and Trade — A35

Issued to honor the Economic Commission for Europe.

1959, May 18 Unwmk. *Perf. 12*

71	A35 4c blue	.25	.25
72	A35 8c red orange	.25	.25

Figure Adapted from Rodin's "Age of Bronze" — A36

Issued to honor the Trusteeship Council.

1959, Oct. 23 Unwmk. *Perf. 12*

73	A36 4c bright red	.25	.25
74	A36 8c dark olive green	.25	.25

World Refugee Year Emblem — A37

World Refugee Year, July 1, 1959-June 30, 1960.

1959, Dec. 10 Unwmk. *Perf. 12*

75	A37 4c ol brn & red	.25	.25
76	A37 8c ol brn & brt grnsh blue	.25	.25

Chaillot Palace, Paris — A38

Chaillot Palace in Paris was the site of General Assembly meetings in 1948 and 1951.

1960, Feb. 29 Unwmk. *Perf. 14*

77	A38 4c rose lilac & blue	.25	.25
78	A38 8c dull green & brown	.25	.25

Map of Far East and Steel Beam — A39

Honoring the Economic Commission for Asia and the Far East (ECAFE).

Perf. 13x13½

1960, Apr. 11 Photo. Unwmk.

79	A39 4c dp clar, blue grn & dull yel	.25	.25
80	A39 8c ol grn, blue & rose	.25	.25

Tree, FAO and UN Emblems — A40

Fifth World Forestry Congress, Seattle, Washington, Aug. 29-Sept. 10.

Perf. 13½

1960, Aug. 29 Photo. Unwmk.

81	A40 4c dk blue, grn & org	.25	.25
82	A40 8c yel grn, blk & org	.25	.25

UN Headquarters and Preamble to UN Charter — A41

Issued to commemorate the 15th anniversary of the United Nations.

1960, Oct. 24 Unwmk. *Perf. 11*

83	A41 4c blue	.25	.25
84	A41 8c gray	.25	.25

Souvenir Sheet

Imperf

85	Sheet of 2	1.25	1.25
a.	A41 4c blue	.55	.55
b.	A41 8c gray	.55	.55

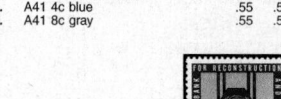

Block and Tackle — A42

Honoring the International Bank for Reconstruction and Development.

Perf. 13½x13

1960, Dec. 9 Photo. Unwmk.

86	A42 4c multicolored	.25	.25
87	A42 8c multicolored	.25	.25

Scales of Justice — A43

Issued to honor the International Court of Justice.

Perf. 13½x13

1961, Feb. 13 Photo. Unwmk.

88	A43 4c yel, org brn & blk	.25	.25
89	A43 8c yel, grn & blk	.25	.25

Seal of International Monetary Fund — A44

Issued to honor the International Monetary Fund.

Perf. 13x13½

1961, Apr. 17 Photo. Unwmk.

90	A44 4c bright bluish green	.25	.25
91	A44 7c terra cotta & yellow	.25	.25

Abstract Group of Flags — A45

Perf. 11½

1961, June 5 Photo. Unwmk.

92	A45 30c multicolored	.45	.30

See UN Offices in Geneva No. 10.

Cogwheel and Map of Latin America — A46

Issued to honor the Economic Commission for Latin America.

Perf. 13½

1961, Sept. 18 Photo. Unwmk.

93	A46 4c blue, red & citron	.25	.25
94	A46 11c grn, lilac & org ver	.25	.25

Africa House, Addis Ababa, and Map — A47

Issued to honor the Economic Commission for Africa.

Perf. 11½

1961, Oct. 24 Photo. Unwmk.

95	A47 4c ultramarine, orange, yellow & brown	.25	.25
96	A47 11c emerald, orange, yellow & brown	.25	.25

Mother Bird Feeding Young and UNICEF Seal — A48

15th anniversary of the United Nations Children's Fund.

Perf. 11½

1961, Dec. 4 Photo. Unwmk.

97	A48 3c brown, gold, orange & yellow	.25	.25
98	A48 4c brown, gold, blue & emerald	.25	.25
99	A48 13c deep green, gold, purple & pink	.25	.25
	Nos. 97-99 (3)	.75	.75

Family and Symbolic Buildings — A49

UN program for housing and urban development,

Perf. 14½x14

1962, Feb. 28 Photo. Unwmk.

Central design multicolored

100	A49 4c bright blue	.25	.25
a.	Black omitted	200.00	
b.	Yellow omitted	—	
c.	Brown omitted	—	
101	A49 7c orange brown	.25	.25
a.	Red omitted	—	
b.	Black omitted	—	
c.	Gold omitted	—	

"The World Against Malaria" — A50

Issued in honor of the WHO and to call attention to the international campaign to eradicate malaria from the world.

Perf. 14x14½

1962, Mar. 30 Photo. Unwmk.

Word frame in gray

102	A50 4c orange, yellow, brown, green & black	.25	.25
103	A50 11c green, yellow, brown & indigo	.25	.25

"Peace" A51

UN Flag A52

Hands Combining "UN" and Globe — A53

UN Emblem over Globe — A54

Photo.; Engr. (5c)

Perf. 14x14½

1962, May 25 Unwmk.

104	A51 1c vermilion, blue, black & gray	.25	.25
105	A52 3c light green, Prussian blue, yellow & gray	.25	.25
	Perf. 12		
106	A53 5c dark carmine rose	.25	.25
	Perf. 12½		
107	A54 11c dark & light blue & gold	.25	.25
	Nos. 104-107 (4)	1.00	1.00

See #167 and UN Offices in Geneva #2, 6. Compare A51 with A76.

Flag at Half-mast and UN Headquarters — A55

Issued on the 1st anniversary of the death of Dag Hammarskjold, Secretary General of the United Nations 1953-61, in memory of those who died in the service of the United Nations.

Perf. 11½

1962, Sept. 17 Photo. Unwmk.

108	A55 5c black, light blue & blue	.25	.25
109	A55 15c black, gray olive & blue	.25	.25

World Map Showing Congo — A56

Issued to commemorate the United Nations Operation in the Congo.

Perf. 11½

1962, Oct. 24 Photo. Unwmk.

110	A56 4c olive, orange, black & yellow	.25	.25
111	A56 11c blue green, orange, black & yellow	.25	.25

Globe in Universe and Palm Frond — A57

Issued to honor the Committee on Peaceful Uses of Outer Space.

Perf. 14x13½

1962, Dec. 3 Engr. Unwmk.

112 A57 4c violet blue .25 .25
113 A57 11c rose claret .25 .25

Development Decade Emblem — A58

UN Development Decade and UN Conference on the Application of Science and Technology for the Benefit of the Less Developed Areas, Geneva, Feb. 4-20.

Perf. 11½

1963, Feb. 4 Photo. Unwmk.

114 A58 5c pale green, maroon, dark blue & Prussian blue .25 .25
115 A58 11c yellow, maroon, dark blue & Prussian blue .25 .25

Stalks of Wheat — A59

Issued for the "Freedom from Hunger" campaign of the Food and Agriculture Organization.

Perf. 11½

1963, Mar. 22 Photo. Unwmk.

116 A59 5c vermilion, green & yellow .25 .25
117 A59 11c vermilion, deep claret & yellow .25 .25

Bridge over Map of New Guinea — A60

1st anniversary of the United Nations Temporary Executive Authority (UNTEA) in West New Guinea (West Irian).

Perf. 11½

1963, Oct. 1 Photo. Unwmk.

118 A60 25c blue, green & gray .50 .40

General Assembly Building, New York — A61

Since October 1955 all sessions of the General Assembly have been held in the General Assembly Hall, UN Headquarters, NY.

Unwmk.

1963, Nov. 4 Photo. *Perf. 13*

119 A61 5c violet blue, blue, yellow green & red .25 .25
120 A61 11c green, yellow green, blue, yellow & red .25 .25

Flame — A62

15th anniversary of the signing of the Universal Declaration of Human Rights.

Unwmk.

1963, Dec. 10 Photo. *Perf. 13*

121 A62 5c green, gold, red & yellow .25 .25
122 A62 11c carmine, gold, blue & yellow .25 .25

Ships at Sea and IMCO Emblem — A63

Issued to honor the Intergovernmental Maritime Consultative Organization.

Perf. 11½

1964, Jan. 13 Photo. Unwmk.

123 A63 5c blue, olive, ocher & yellow .25 .25
124 A63 11c dark blue, dark green, emerald & yellow .25 .25

Map of the World A64

UN Emblem A65

Three Men United Before Globe — A66

Stylized Globe and Weather Vane — A67

1964-71 Photo. Unwmk. *Perf. 14*

125 A64 2c light & dark blue, orange & yellow green .25 .25
a. Perf. 13x13½ .25 .25

Perf. 11½

126 A65 7c dark blue, orange brown & black .25 .25
127 A66 10c blue green, olive green & black .25 .25
128 A67 50c multicolored .55 .45
Nos. 125-128 (4) 1.30 1.20

Issued: 2c, 7c, May 29; 50c, Mar. 6.
See UN Offices in Geneva Nos. 3, 12.

Arrows Showing Global Flow of Trade — A68

Issued to commemorate the UN Conference on Trade and Development, Geneva, Mar. 23-June 15.

Unwmk.

1964, June 15 Photo. *Perf. 13*

129 A68 5c black, red & yellow .25 .25
130 A68 11c black, olive & yellow .25 .25

Poppy Capsule and Hands — A69

Honoring international efforts and achievements in the control of narcotics.

Unwmk.

1964, Sept. 21 Engr. *Perf. 12*

131 A69 5c rose red & black .25 .25
132 A69 11c emerald & black .25 .25

Padlocked Atomic Blast — A70

Signing of the nuclear test ban treaty pledging an end to nuclear explosions in the atmosphere, outer space and under water.

Litho. and Engr.

Perf. 11x11½

1964, Oct. 23 Unwmk.

133 A70 5c dark red & dark brown .25 .25

"Education for Progress" — A71

Issued to publicize the UNESCO world campaign for universal literacy and for free compulsory primary education.

Perf. 12½

1964, Dec. 7 Photo. Unwmk.

134 A71 4c orange, red, bister, green & blue .25 .25
135 A71 5c bister, red, dark & light blue .25 .25
136 A71 11c green, light blue, black & rose .25 .25
Nos. 134-136 (3) .75 .75

Progress Chart, Key & Globe — A72

Issued to publicize the Special Fund program to speed economic growth and social advancement in low-income countries.

Perf. 13½x13

1965, Jan. 25 Photo. Unwmk.

137 A72 5c dull blue, dark blue, yellow & red .25 .25
138 A72 11c yellow green, dark blue, yellow & red .25 .25
a. Black omitted (UN emblem on key) —

Leaves & View of Cyprus — A73

Issued to honor the United Nations Peacekeeping Force on Cyprus.

Perf. 11½

1965, Mar. 4 Photo. Unwmk.

139 A73 5c orange, olive & black .25 .25
140 A73 11c yellow green, blue green & black .25 .25

"From Semaphore to Satellite" — A74

Centenary of the International Telecommunication Union.

Perf. 11½

1965, May 17 Photo. Unwmk.

141 A74 5c aquamarine, orange, blue & purple .25 .25
142 A74 11c light violet, red orange, bister & bright green .25 .25

ICY Emblem — A75

20th anniversary of the United Nations and International Cooperation Year.

Perf. 14x13½

1965, June 26 Engr. Unwmk.

143 A75 5c dark blue .25 .25
144 A75 15c lilac rose .25 .25

Souvenir Sheet

145 A75 Sheet of two .35 .35

"Peace" A76

Opening Words, UN Charter A77

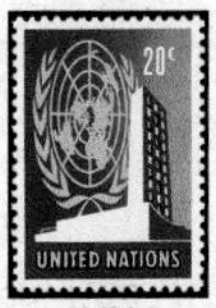

UN Headquarters, Emblem A78

UN Emblem A79

UN Emblem — A80

Perf. 13½x13

1965-66 Photo. Unwmk.

146 A76 1c vermilion, blue, black & gray .25 .25

Perf. 14

147 A77 15c olive bister, dull yellow, black & deep claret .25 .25

Perf. 12

148 A78 20c dark blue, blue, red & yellow .25 .25
a. Yellow omitted —

Litho. and Embossed

Perf. 14

149 A79 25c light & dark blue .30 .25
a. 25c light & dark blue, new dk blue plate/cylinder (see footnote) .30 .25
b. As "a," tagged 10.00 10.00

Photo.

Perf. 11½

150 A80 $1 aquamarine & sapphire 1.60 1.60
Nos. 146-150 (5) 2.65 2.60

Issued: 1c, No. 149, 9/20/65; No. 149a, 11/5/65; 15c, 20c, 10/25/65; $1, 3/25/66.

On No. 149, the dark blue "halo" of the U.N. emblem is large, overlapping the "25c." On No. 149a, a new dark blue plate/cylinder was used, making the "halo" of the U.N. emblem smaller.

See UN Offices in Geneva Nos. 5, 9, 11.

Fields & People — A81

Design: 11c, French inscription.

Issued to emphasize the importance of the world's population growth and its problems and to call attention to population trends and development.

Unwmk.

1965, Nov. 29 Photo. *Perf. 12*

151 A81 4c multicolored .25 .25
152 A81 5c multicolored .25 .25
153 A81 11c multicolored .25 .25
Nos. 151-153 (3) .75 .75

Globe & Flags of UN Members — A82

Design: 11c, French inscription.

Issued to honor the World Federation of United Nations Associations.

Perf. 11½

1966, Jan. 31 Photo. Unwmk.

154 A82 5c multicolored .25 .25
155 A82 15c multicolored .25 .25

WHO Headquarters, Geneva — A83

Design: 11c, French inscription.
Issued to commemorate the opening of the World Health Organization Headquarters, Geneva.

1966, May 26 Photo. *Perf. 12½x12*
Granite Paper

156 A83 5c lt & dk blue, orange, green & bister .25 .25
157 A83 11c orange, lt & dark blue, green & bister .25 .25

Coffee — A84

Design: 11c, Spanish inscription.
Issued to commemorate the International Coffee Agreement of 1962.

1966, Sept. 19 Photo. *Perf. 13½x13*

158 A84 5c orange, lt blue, green, red & dk brown .25 .25
159 A84 11c lt blue, yellow, green, red & dk brown .25 .25

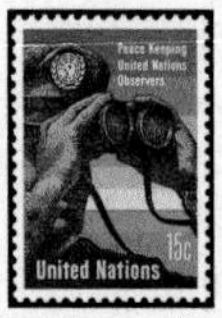

UN Observer — A85

Issued to honor the Peace Keeping United Nation Observers.
Printed by Courvoisier, S.A. Panes of 50. Designed by Ole S. Hamann.

1966, Oct. 24 Photo. *Perf. 11½*
Granite Paper

160 A85 15c steel blue, orange, black & green .25 .25

Children of Various Races — A86

20th anniversary of the United Nations Children's Fund (UNICEF).

1966, Nov. 28 Litho. *Perf. 13x13½*

161 A86 4c pink & multi .25 .25
162 A86 5c pale green & multi .25 .25
a. Yellow omitted — —
163 A86 11c light ultramarine & multi .25 .25
b. Dark blue omitted —
Nos. 161-163 (3) .75 .75

Hand Rolling up Sleeve & Chart Showing Progress — A87

Design: 11c, French inscription.
United Nations Development Program.

1967, Jan. 23 Photo. *Perf. 12½*

164 A87 5c green, yellow, purple & orange .25 .25
165 A87 11c blue, chocolate, light green & orange .25 .25

Type of 1962 and

UN Headquarters, New York & World Map — A88

1967 Photo. *Perf. 11½*

166 A88 1½c ultramarine, black, orange & ocher .25 .25

Size: 33x23mm

167 A53 5c red brown, brown & orange yellow .25 .25

Issue dates: 1½c, Mar. 17; 5c, Jan. 23.
See UN Offices in Geneva No. 1.

Fireworks — A89

Design: 11c, French inscription.
Issued to honor all nations which gained independence since 1945.

1967, Mar. 17 Photo. *Perf. 14x14½*

168 A89 5c dark blue & multi .25 .25
169 A89 11c brown lake & multi .25 .25

"Peace" A90

UN Pavilion, EXPO '67 A91

EXPO '67, International Exhibition, Montreal, Apr. 28-Oct. 27, 1967.

Engr. & Litho.

1967, Apr. 28 *Perf. 11*

170 A90 4c red & red brown .25 .25
171 A90 5c blue & red brown .25 .25

Litho.

172 A91 8c multicolored .25 .25

Engr. and Litho.

173 A90 10c green & red brown .25 .25
174 A90 15c dark brown & red brown .25 .25
Nos. 170-174 (5) 1.25 1.25

Nos. 170-174 were issued in Canadian dollars.

Luggage Tags and UN Emblem — A92

Issued to publicize International Tourist Year, 1967.

1967, June 19 Litho. *Perf. 14*

175 A92 5c reddish brown & multi .25 .25
176 A92 15c ultramarine & multi .25 .25

Quotation from Isaiah 2:4 — A93

Design: 13c, French inscription.
Issued to publicize the UN General Assembly's resolutions on general and complete disarmament and for suspension of nuclear and thermonuclear tests.

1967, Oct. 24 Photo. *Perf. 14*

177 A93 6c ultramarine, yellow, gray & brown .25 .25
178 A93 13c magenta, yellow, gray & brown .25 .25

Art at UN Issue
Miniature Sheet

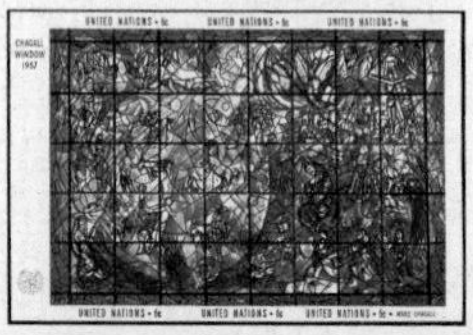

Memorial Window A94

"The Kiss of Peace" — A95

1967, Nov. 17 Litho. *Rouletted 9*

179 A94 6c Sheet of 6, #a.-f. .40 .40

Perf. 13x13½

180 A95 6c multicolored .25 .25

No. 179 contains six 6c stamps, each rouletted on 3 sides, imperf. on fourth side. Size: 124x80mm. On Nos. 179a-179c, "United Nations 6c" appears at top; on Nos. 179d-179f, at bottom. No. 179f includes name "Marc Chagall."

Globe and Major UN Organs — A96

Design: 13c, French inscription.
Issued to honor the United Nations Secretariat.

1968, Jan. 16 Photo. *Perf. 11½*

181 A96 6c multicolored .25 .25
182 A96 13c multicolored .25 .25

Art at UN Issue

Statue by Henrik Starcke — A97

1968, Mar. 1 Photo. *Perf. 11½*

183 A97 6c blue & multi .25 .25
184 A97 75c rose lake & multi 1.10 .90

The 6c is part of the "Art at the UN" series. The 75c belongs to the regular definitive series. The teakwood Starcke statue, which stands in the Trusteeship Council Chamber, represents mankind's search for freedom and happiness.
See UN Offices in Geneva No. 13.

Factories and Chart — A98

Design: 13c, French inscription ("ONUDI," etc.).
Issued to publicize the UN Industrial Development Organization.

1968, Apr. 18 Litho. *Perf. 12*

185 A98 6c greenish blue, lt greenish blue, black & dull claret .25 .25
186 A98 13c dull red brown, light red brown, black & ultra .25 .25

UN Headquarters — A99

1968, May 31 Litho. *Perf. 12x13½*

187 A99 6c green, blue, black & gray .25 .25

Radarscope and Globes — A100

Design: 20c, French inscription.

Issued to publicize World Weather Watch, a new weather system directed by the World Meteorological Organization.

1968, Sept. 19 Photo. *Perf. 13x13½*

188 A100 6c green, black, ocher, red & blue .25 .25
189 A100 20c lilac, black, ocher, red & blue .30 .25

Human Rights Flame — A101

Design: 13c, French inscription.
Issued for International Human Rights Year, 1968.

Photo.; Foil Embossed

1968, Nov. 22 *Perf. 12½*

190 A101 6c bright blue, deep ultra & gold .25 .25
191 A101 13c rose red, dark red & gold .25 .25

Books and UN Emblem — A102

Design: 13c, French inscription in center, denomination panel at bottom.
United Nations Institute for Training and Research (UNITAR).

1969, Feb. 10 Litho. *Perf. 13½*

192 A102 6c yellow green & multi .25 .25
193 A102 13c bluish lilac & multi .25 .25

UN Building, Santiago, Chile — A103

Design: 15c, Spanish inscription.
The UN Building in Santiago, Chile, is the seat of the UN Economic Commission for Latin America and of the Latin American Institute for Economic and Social Planning.

1969, Mar. 14 Litho. *Perf. 14*

194 A103 6c light blue, violet blue & light green .25 .25
195 A103 15c pink, cream & red brown .25 .25

"UN" and UN Emblem — A104

1969, Mar. 14 Photo. *Perf. 13½*

196 A104 13c bright blue, black & gold .25 .25

See UN Offices in Geneva No. 7.

UN Emblem and Scales of Justice — A105

Design: 13c, French inscription.
20th anniversary session of the UN International Law Commission.

Granite Paper

1969, Apr. 21 Photo. *Perf. 11½*

197 A105 6c bright green, ultra & gold .25 .25
198 A105 13c crimson, lilac & gold .25 .25

Allegory of Labor, Emblems of UN and ILO — A106

Design: 20c, French inscription.
Issued to publicize "Labor and Development" and to commemorate the 50th anniversary of the International Labor Organization.

1969, June 5 Photo. *Perf. 13*

199 A106 6c blue, deep blue, yellow & gold .25 .25
200 A106 20c orange vermilion, magenta, yellow & gold .25 .25

Art at UN Issue

Ostrich, Tunisian Mosaic, 3rd Century — A107

Design: 13c, Pheasant; French inscription.

1969, Nov. 21 Photo. *Perf. 14*

201 A107 6c blue & multi .25 .25
202 A107 13c red & multi .25 .25

Art at UN Issue

Peace Bell, Gift of Japanese — A108

Design: 25c, French inscription.
The Peace Bell was a gift of the people of Japan in 1954, cast from donated coins and metals. It is housed in a Japanese cypress structure at UN Headquarters, New York.

1970, Mar. 13 Photo. *Perf. 13½x13*

203 A108 6c violet blue & multi .25 .25
204 A108 25c claret & multi .30 .25

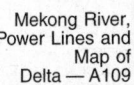

Mekong River, Power Lines and Map of Delta — A109

Design: 13c, French inscription.
Issued to publicize the Lower Mekong Basin Development project under UN auspices.

1970, Mar. 13 *Perf. 14*

205 A109 6c dark blue & multi .25 .25
206 A109 13c deep plum & multi .25 .25

"Fight Cancer" — A110

Design: 13c, French inscription.
Issued to publicize the fight against cancer in connection with the 10th International Cancer Congress of the International Union Against Cancer, Houston, Texas, May 22-29.

1970, May 22 Litho. *Perf. 14*

207 A110 6c blue & black .25 .25
208 A110 13c olive & black .25 .25

UN Emblem and Olive Branch A111

UN Emblem A112

Design: 13c, French inscription.
25th anniv. of the UN. First day covers were postmarked at UN Headquarters, NY, and at San Francisco.

1970, June 26 Photo. *Perf. 11½*

209 A111 6c red, gold, dark & light blue .25 .25
210 A111 13c dark blue, gold, green & red .25 .25

Perf. 12½

211 A112 25c dark blue, gold & light blue .35 .25
Nos. 209-211 (3) .85 .75

Souvenir Sheet

Imperf

212 Sheet of 3 .80 .80
a. A111 6c red, gold & multicolored .25 .25
b. A111 13c violet blue, gold & multi .25 .25
c. A112 25c violet blue, gold & light blue .30 .30

Scales, Olive Branch, Progress Symbol — A113

Design: 13c, French inscription.
Issued to publicize "Peace, Justice and Progress" in connection with the 25th anniversary of the United Nations.

1970, Nov. 20 Photo. *Perf. 13½*

213 A113 6c gold & multi .25 .25
214 A113 13c silver & multi .25 .25

Sea Bed, Fish, Underwater Research — A114

Issued to publicize peaceful uses of the sea bed.

Photo. & Engr.

1971, Jan. 25 *Perf. 13*

215 A114 6c blue & multi .25 .25

See UN Offices in Geneva No. 15.

Refugees, Sculpture by Kaare K. Nygaard — A115

International support for refugees.

1971, Mar. 2 Litho. *Perf. 13x12½*

216 A115 6c brown, ocher & black .25 .25
217 A115 13c ultramarine, greenish blue & black .25 .25

See UN Offices in Geneva No. 16.

Wheat and Globe — A116

Publicizing the UN World Food Program.

1971, Apr. 13 Photo. *Perf. 14*

218 A116 13c red & multicolored .25 .25

See UN Offices in Geneva No. 17.

UPU Headquarters, Bern — A117

Opening of new Universal Postal Union Headquarters, Bern.

1971, May 28 Photo. *Perf. 11½*

219 A117 20c brown orange & multi .30 .25

See UN Offices in Geneva No. 18.

"Eliminate Racial Discrimination" — A118

A119

International Year Against Racial Discrimination.

1971, Sept. 21 Photo. *Perf. 13½*

220 A118 8c yellow green & multi .25 .25
221 A119 13c blue & multi .25 .25

See UN Offices in Geneva Nos. 19-20.

UN Headquarters, New York — A120

UN Emblem and Symbolic Flags — A121

1971, Oct. 22 Photo. *Perf. 13½*

222 A120 8c violet blue & multi .25 .25

Perf. 13

223 A121 60c ultra & multi .80 .80

Maia by Pablo Picasso — A122

To publicize the UN International School.

1971, Nov. 19 Photo. *Perf. 11½*

224 A122 8c olive & multi .25 .25
225 A122 21c ultra & multi .25 .25

Letter Changing Hands — A123

1972, Jan. 5 Litho. *Perf. 14*

226 A123 95c carmine & multi 1.30 1.10

"No More Nuclear Weapons" A124

To promote non-proliferation of nuclear weapons.

1972, Feb. 14 Photo. *Perf. 13½x14*

227 A124 8c dull rose, black, blue & gray .25 .25

See UN Offices in Geneva No. 23.

Proportions of Man (c. 1509), by Leonardo da Vinci — A125

World Health Day, Apr. 7.

Litho. & Engr.

1972, Apr. 7 *Perf. 13x13½*

228 A125 15c black & multi .25 .25

See UN Offices in Geneva No. 24.

"Human Environment" — A126

UN Conf. on Human Environment, Stockholm, June 5-16, 1972.

Litho. & Embossed

1972, June 5 *Perf. 12½x14*

229 A126 8c red, buff, green & blue .25 .25
230 A126 15c blue green, buff, green & blue .25 .25

See UN Offices in Geneva Nos. 25-26.

"Europe" and UN Emblem — A127

Economic Commission for Europe, 25th anniversary.

1972, Sept. 11 Litho. *Perf. 13x13½*

231 A127 21c yellow brown & multi .30 .30

See UN Offices in Geneva No. 27.

Art at UN Issue

The Five Continents, by José Maria Sert — A128

1972, Nov. 17 Photo. *Perf. 12x12½*

232 A128 8c gold, brown & golden brown .25 .25
233 A128 15c gold, blue green & brown .25 .25

See UN Offices in Geneva Nos. 28-29.

Olive Branch and Broken Sword — A129

Disarmament Decade, 1970-79.

1973, Mar. 9 Litho. *Perf. 13½x13*

234 A129 8c blue & multi .25 .25
235 A129 15c lilac rose & multi .25 .25

See UN Offices in Geneva Nos. 30-31.

Poppy Capsule and Skull — A130

Fight against drug abuse.

1973, Apr. 13 Photo. *Perf. 13½*

236 A130 8c deep orange & multi .25 .25
237 A130 15c pink & multi .25 .25

See UN Offices in Geneva No. 32.

Honeycomb — A131

5th anniversary of the United Nations Volunteer Program.

1973, May 25 Photo. *Perf. 14*

238	A131	8c olive bister & multi	.25	.25
239	A131	21c gray blue & multi	.30	.30

See UN Offices in Geneva No. 33.

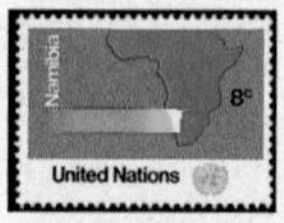

Map of Africa with Namibia — A132

To publicize Namibia (South-West Africa) for which the UN General Assembly ended the mandate of South Africa and established the UN Council for Namibia to administer the territory until independence.

1973, Oct. 1 Photo. *Perf. 14*

240	A132	8c emerald & multi	.25	.25
241	A132	15c bright rose & multi	.25	.25

See UN Offices in Geneva No. 34.

UN Emblem, Human Rights Flame — A133

25th anniversary of the adoption and proclamation of the Universal Declaration of Human Rights.

1973, Nov. 16 Photo. *Perf. 13½*

242	A133	8c deep carmine & multi	.25	.25
243	A133	21c blue green & multi	.25	.25

See UN Offices in Geneva Nos. 35-36.

ILO Headquarters, Geneva — A134

New Headquarters of International Labor Organization.

1974, Jan. 11 Photo. *Perf. 14*

244	A134	10c ultra & multi	.25	.25
245	A134	21c blue green & multi	.30	.25

See UN Offices in Geneva Nos. 37-38.

Post Horn Encircling Globe — A135

Centenary of Universal Postal Union.

1974, Mar. 22 Litho. *Perf. 12½*

246	A135	10c gold & multi	.25	.25

See UN Offices in Geneva Nos. 39-40.

Art at UN Issue

Peace Mural, by Candido Portinari — A136

The mural, a gift of Brazil, is in the Delegates' Lobby, General Assembly Building.

1974, May 6 Photo. *Perf. 14*

247	A136	10c gold & multi	.25	.25
248	A136	18c ultra & multi	.35	.30

See UN Offices in Geneva Nos. 41-42.

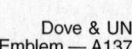

Dove & UN Emblem — A137

UN Headquarters A138

Globe, UN Emblem, Flags A139

1974, June 10 Photo. *Perf. 14*

249	A137	2c dark & light blue	.25	.25
250	A138	10c multicolored	.25	.25
251	A139	18c multicolored	.25	.25
		Nos. 249-251 (3)	.75	.75

Children of the World — A140

World Population Year.

1974, Oct. 18 Photo. *Perf. 14*

252	A140	10c light blue & multi	.25	.25
253	A140	18c lilac & multi	.35	.25

See UN Offices in Geneva Nos. 43-44.

Law of the Sea — A141

Declaration of UN General Assembly that the sea bed is common heritage of mankind, reserved for peaceful purposes.

1974, Nov. 22 Photo. *Perf. 14*

254	A141	10c green & multi	.25	.25
255	A141	26c orange red & multi	.35	.30

See UN Offices in Geneva No. 45.

Satellite and Globe — A142

Peaceful uses (meteorology, industry, fishing, communications) of outer space.

1975, Mar. 14 Litho. *Perf. 13*

256	A142	10c multicolored	.25	.25
257	A142	26c multicolored	.35	.30

See UN Offices in Geneva Nos. 46-47.

Equality Between Men and Women — A143

International Women's Year.

1975, May 9 Litho. *Perf. 15*

258	A143	10c multicolored	.25	.25
259	A143	18c multicolored	.35	.30

See UN Offices in Geneva Nos. 48-49.

UN Flag and "XXX" — A144

30th anniversary of the United Nations.

1975, June 26 Litho. *Perf. 13*

260	A144	10c olive bister & multi	.25	.25
261	A144	26c purple & multi	.40	.35

Souvenir Sheet

Imperf

262	Sheet of 2	.60	.50
a.	A144 10c olive bister & multicolored	.25	.25
b.	A144 26c purple & multicolored	.35	.25

See Offices in Geneva Nos. 50-52.

Hand Reaching up over Map of Africa & Namibia — A145

"Namibia-United Nations direct responsibility." See note after No. 241.

1975, Sept. 22 Photo. *Perf. 13½*

263	A145	10c multicolored	.25	.25
264	A145	18c multicolored	.30	.30

See UN Offices in Geneva Nos. 53-54.

Wild Rose Growing from Barbed Wire — A146

United Nations Peace-keeping Operations.

1975, Nov. 21 Engr. *Perf. 12½*

265	A146	13c ultramarine	.25	.25
266	A146	26c rose carmine	.40	.40

See UN Offices in Geneva Nos. 55-56.

Symbolic Flags Forming Dove A147

UN Emblem A149

People of All Races A148

UN Flag A150

Dove and Rainbow — A151

1976 Litho. *Perf. 13x13½, 13½x13*

267	A147	3c multicolored	.25	.25
268	A148	4c multicolored	.25	.25

Photo.

Perf. 14

269	A149	9c multicolored	.25	.25

Litho.

Perf. 13x13½

270	A150	30c blue, emerald & black	.35	.35
271	A151	50c yellow green & multi	.65	.65
		Nos. 267-271 (5)	1.75	1.75

Issue dates: 3c, 4c, 30c, 50c, Jan. 6; 9c, Nov. 19.

See UN Offices in Vienna No. 8.

Interlocking Bands — A152

World Federation of United Nations Associations.

1976, Mar. 12 Photo. *Perf. 14*

272	A152	13c car & multi	.25	.25
273	A152	26c blk & multi	.35	.30

See UN Offices in Geneva No. 57.

Cargo, Globe and Graph — A153

UN Conference on Trade and Development (UNCTAD), Nairobi, Kenya, May 1976.

1976, Apr. 23 Photo. *Perf. 11½*

274	A153	13c deep magenta & multi	.25	.25
275	A153	31c dull blue & multi	.40	.30

See UN Offices in Geneva No. 58.

Houses Around Globe — A154

Habitat, UN Conference on Human Settlements, Vancouver, Canada, May 31-June 11.

1976, May 28 Photo. *Perf. 14*

276	A154	13c red brown & multi	.25	.25
277	A154	25c green & multi	.40	.30

See UN Offices in Geneva Nos. 59-60.

Magnifying Glass, Sheet of Stamps, UN Emblem — A155

United Nations Postal Administration, 25th anniversary.

1976, Oct. 8 Photo. *Perf. 11½*

278	A155	13c blue & multi	.25	.25
279	A155	31c green & multi	1.00	1.00

See UN Offices in Geneva Nos. 61-62.

Grain — A156

World Food Council.

1976, Nov. 19 Litho. *Perf. 14½*

280	A156	13c multicolored	.25	.25

See UN Offices in Geneva No. 63.

WIPO Headquarters, Geneva — A157

World Intellectual Property Organization (WIPO).

1977, Mar. 11 Photo. *Perf. 14*

281	A157	13c citron & multi	.25	.25
282	A157	31c bright green & multi	.45	.35

See UN Offices in Geneva No. 64.

Drops of Water Falling into Funnel — A158

UN Water Conference, Mar del Plata, Argentina, Mar. 14-25.

1977, Apr. 22 Photo. *Perf. 13½x13*

283 A158 13c yellow & multi .25 .25
284 A158 25c salmon & multi .40 .35

See UN Offices in Geneva Nos. 65-66.

Burning Fuse Severed — A159

UN Security Council.

1977, May 27 Photo. *Perf. 14*

285 A159 13c purple & multi .25 .25
286 A159 31c dark blue & multi .45 .30

See UN Offices in Geneva Nos. 67-68.

"Combat Racism" — A160

Fight against racial discrimination.

1977, Sept. 19 Litho. *Perf. 13½x13*

287 A160 13c black & yellow .25 .25
288 A160 25c black & vermilion .40 .30

See UN Offices in Geneva Nos. 60-70.

Atom, Grain, Fruit and Factory — A161

Peaceful uses of atomic energy.

1977, Nov. 18 Photo. *Perf. 14*

289 A161 13c yellow bister & multi .25 .25
290 A161 18c dull green & multi .30 .25

See UN Offices in Geneva Nos. 71-72.

Opening Words of UN Charter — A162

"Live Together in Peace" — A163

People of the World — A164

1978, Jan. 27 Litho. *Perf. 14½*

291 A162 1c gold, brown & red .25 .25
292 A163 25c multicolored .35 .30
293 A164 $1 multicolored 1.25 1.25
Nos. 291-293 (3) 1.85 1.80

See UN Offices in Geneva No. 73.

Smallpox Virus — A165

Global eradication of smallpox.

1978, Mar. 31 Photo. *Perf. 12x11½*

294 A165 13c rose & black .25 .25
295 A165 31c blue & black .40 .40

See UN Offices in Geneva Nos. 74-75.

Open Handcuff — A166

Liberation, justice and cooperation for Namibia.

1978, May 5 Photo. *Perf. 12*

296 A166 13c multicolored .25 .25
297 A166 18c multicolored .30 .25

See UN Offices in Geneva No. 76.

Multicolored Bands and Clouds — A167

International Civil Aviation Organization for "Safety in the Air."

1978, June 12 Photo. *Perf. 14*

298 A167 13c multicolored .25 .25
299 A167 25c multicolored .35 .30

See UN Offices in Geneva Nos. 77-78.

General Assembly — A168

1978, Sept. 15 Photo. *Perf. 13½*

300 A168 13c multicolored .25 .25
301 A168 18c multicolored .35 .30

See UN Offices in Geneva Nos. 79-80.

Hemispheres as Cogwheels — A169

Technical Cooperation Among Developing Countries Conference, Buenos Aires, Argentina, Sept. 1978.

1978, Nov. 17 Photo. *Perf. 14*

302 A169 13c multicolored .25 .25
303 A169 31c multicolored .50 .40

See UN Offices in Geneva No. 81.

Hand Holding Olive Branch A170

Tree of Various Races A171

Globe, Dove with Olive Branch A172

Birds and Globe A173

1979, Jan. 19 Photo. *Perf. 14*

304 A170 5c multicolored .25 .25
305 A171 14c multicolored .25 .25
306 A172 15c multicolored .25 .25
307 A173 20c multicolored .30 .25
Nos. 304-307 (4) 1.05 1.00

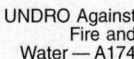

UNDRO Against Fire and Water — A174

Office of the UN Disaster Relief Coordinator (UNDRO).

1979, Mar. 9 Photo. *Perf. 14*

308 A174 15c multicolored .25 .25
309 A174 20c multicolored .35 .30

See UN Offices in Geneva Nos. 82-83.

Child and ICY Emblem — A175

International Year of the Child.

1979, May 4 Photo. *Perf. 14*

310 A175 15c multicolored .25 .25
311 A175 31c multicolored .35 .35

See UN Offices in Geneva Nos. 84-85.

Map of Namibia, Olive Branch — A176

For a free and independent Namibia.

1979, Oct. 5 Litho. *Perf. 13½*

312 A176 15c multicolored .25 .25
313 A176 31c multicolored .30 .35

See UN Offices in Geneva No. 86.

Scales and Sword of Justice — A177

International Court of Justice, The Hague, Netherlands.

1979, Nov. 9 Litho. *Perf. 13x13½*

314 A177 15c multicolored .25 .25
315 A177 20c multicolored .30 .35

See UN Offices in Geneva Nos. 87-88.

Graph of Economic Trends A178

Key A179

New International Economic Order.

1980, Jan. 11 Litho. *Perf. 15x14½*

316 A178 15c multicolored .25 .25
317 A179 31c multicolored .45 .35

See UN Offices in Geneva No. 89; Vienna No. 7.

Women's Year Emblems — A180

United Nations Decade for Women.

1980, Mar. 7 Litho. *Perf. 14½x15*

318 A180 15c multicolored .25 .25
319 A180 20c multicolored .30 .25

See UN Offices in Geneva Nos. 90-91; Vienna Nos. 9-10.

UN Emblem and "UN" on Helmet — A181

Arrows and UN Emblem — A182

United Nations Peace-keeping Operations.

1980, May 16 Litho. *Perf. 14x13*

320 A181 15c blue & black .25 .25
321 A182 31c multicolored .40 .40

See UN Offices in Geneva No. 92; Vienna No. 11.

"35" and Flags A183

Globe and Laurel A184

35th Anniversary of the United Nations.

1980, June 26 Litho. *Perf. 13x13½*

322 A183 15c multicolored .25 .25
323 A184 31c multicolored .40 .35

Souvenir Sheet
Imperf

324 Sheet of 2 .65 .65
a. A183 15c multicolored .25 .25
b. A184 31c multicolored .40 .40

See UN Offices in Geneva Nos. 93-95; Vienna Nos. 12-14.

Flag of Turkey — A185

1980, Sept. 26 Litho. *Perf. 12*

Granite Paper

325 A185 15c shown .25 .25
326 A185 15c Luxembourg .25 .25
327 A185 15c Fiji .25 .25
328 A185 15c Viet Nam .25 .25
a. Se-tenant block of 4, #325-328 1.00 1.00
329 A185 15c Guinea .25 .25
330 A185 15c Surinam .25 .25
331 A185 15c Bangladesh .25 .25
332 A185 15c Mali .25 .25
a. Se-tenant block of 4, #329-332 1.00 1.00
333 A185 15c Yugoslavia .25 .25
334 A185 15c France .25 .25
335 A185 15c Venezuela .25 .25
336 A185 15c El Salvador .25 .25
a. Se-tenant block of 4, #333-336 1.00 1.00
337 A185 15c Madagascar .25 .25
338 A185 15c Cameroon .25 .25
339 A185 15c Rwanda .25 .25
340 A185 15c Hungary .25 .25
a. Se-tenant block of 4, #337-340 1.00 1.00
Nos. 325-340 (16) 4.00 4.00

Issued in 4 panes of 16. Each pane contains 4 blocks of 4 (Nos. 325-328, 329-332, 333-336, 337-340). A se-tenant block of 4 designs centers each pane.

See Nos. 350-365, 374-389, 399-414, 425-440, 450-465, 477-492, 499-514, 528-543, 554-569, 690-697, 719-726, 744-751, 795-802, 921-924, 1063-1066, 1083-1086.

Symbolic Flowers — A186

Symbols of Progress — A187

1980, Nov. 21 Litho. *Perf. 13½x13*

341 A186 15c multicolored .25 .25
342 A187 20c multicolored .40 .35

See UN Offices in Geneva, Nos. 96-97; Vienna Nos. 15-16.

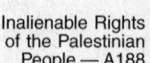

Inalienable Rights of the Palestinian People — A188

1981, Jan. 30 Photo. *Perf. 12x11½*

343 A188 15c multicolored .30 .25

See UN Offices in Geneva No. 98; Vienna No. 17.

Interlocking Puzzle Pieces A189

Stylized Person A190

International Year of the Disabled.

1981, Mar. 6 Photo. *Perf. 14*

344 A189 20c multicolored .25 .25
345 A190 35c black & orange .40 .45

See UN Offices in Geneva Nos. 99-100; Vienna Nos. 18-19.

Art at UN Issue

Divislava and Sebastocrator Kaloyan, Bulgarian Mural, 1259, Boyana Church, Sofia — A191

1981, Apr. 15 Photo. *Perf. 11½*
Granite Paper

346 A191 20c multicolored .25 .25
347 A191 31c multicolored .40 .45

See UN Offices in Geneva No. 101; Vienna No. 20.

Solar Energy — A192

Conference Emblem — A193

Conference on New and Renewable Sources of Energy, Nairobi, Aug. 10-21.

1981, May 29 Litho. *Perf. 13*

348 A192 20c multicolored .25 .25
349 A193 40c multicolored .50 .50

See UN Offices in Geneva No. 102; Vienna No. 21.

Flag Type of 1980

1981, Sept. 25 Litho.
Granite Paper

350 A185 20c Djibouti .25 .25
351 A185 20c Sri Lanka .25 .25
352 A185 20c Bolivia .25 .25
353 A185 20c Equatorial Guinea .25 .25
a. Se-tenant block of 4, #350-353 1.00 1.00
354 A185 20c Malta .25 .25
355 A185 20c Czechoslovakia .25 .25
356 A185 20c Thailand .25 .25
357 A185 20c Trinidad & Tobago .25 .25
a. Se-tenant block of 4, #354-357 1.00 1.00
358 A185 20c Ukrainian SSR .25 .25
359 A185 20c Kuwait .25 .25
360 A185 20c Sudan .25 .25
361 A185 20c Egypt .25 .25
a. Se-tenant block of 4, #358-361 1.00 1.00
362 A185 20c US .25 .25
363 A185 20c Singapore .25 .25
364 A185 20c Panama .25 .25
365 A185 20c Costa Rica .25 .25
a. Se-tenant block of 4, #362-365 1.00 1.00
Nos. 350-365 (16) 4.00 4.00

See note after No. 340.

Seedling and Tree Cross Section — A194

"10" and Symbols of Progress — A195

United Nations Volunteers Program, 10th anniv.

1981, Nov. 13 Litho.

366 A194 18c multicolored .25 .25
367 A195 28c multicolored .55 .55

See UN Offices in Geneva Nos. 103-104; Vienna Nos. 22-23.

Respect for Human Rights A196

Independence of Colonial Countries and People A197

Second Disarmament Decade — A198

1982, Jan. 22 *Perf. 11½x12*

368 A196 17c multicolored .25 .25
369 A197 28c multicolored .45 .40
370 A198 40c multicolored .75 .70
Nos. 368-370 (3) 1.45 1.35

A199

A200

10th Anniversary of United Nations Environment Program.

1982, Mar. 19 Litho. *Perf. 13½x13*

371 A199 20c multicolored .25 .25
372 A200 40c multicolored .65 .65

See UN Offices in Geneva Nos. 107-108; Vienna Nos. 25-26.

UN Emblem and Olive Branch in Outer Space — A201

Exploration and Peaceful Uses of Outer Space.

1982, June 11 Litho. *Perf. 13x13½*

373 A201 20c multicolored .45 .45

See UN Offices in Geneva Nos. 109-110; Vienna No. 27.

Flag Type of 1980

1982, Sept. 24 Litho. *Perf. 12*
Granite Paper

374 A185 20c Austria .25 .25
375 A185 20c Malaysia .25 .25
376 A185 20c Seychelles .25 .25
377 A185 20c Ireland .25 .25
a. Se-tenant block of 4, #374-377 1.50 1.50
378 A185 20c Mozambique .25 .25
379 A185 20c Albania .25 .25
380 A185 20c Dominica .25 .25
381 A185 20c Solomon Islnads .25 .25
a. Se-tenant block of 4, #378-381 1.50 1.50
382 A185 20c Philippines .25 .25
383 A185 20c Swaziland .25 .25
384 A185 20c Nicaragua .25 .25
385 A185 20c Burma .25 .25
a. Se-tenant block of 4, #382-385 1.50 1.50
386 A185 20c Cape Verde .25 .25
387 A185 20c Guyana .25 .25
388 A185 20c Belgium .25 .25
389 A185 20c Nigeria .25 .25
a. Se-tenant block of 4, #386-389 1.50 1.50
Nos. 374-389 (16) 4.00 4.00

See note after No. 340.

Conservation and Protection of Nature — A202

1982, Nov. 19 Photo. *Perf. 14*

390 A202 20c Leaf .30 .30
391 A202 28c Butterfly .55 .50

See UN Offices in Geneva Nos. 111-112; Vienna Nos. 28-29.

A203

World Communications Year — A204

World Communications Year.

1983, Jan. 28 Litho. *Perf. 13*

392 A203 20c multicolored .25 .25
393 A204 40c multicolored .65 .65

See UN Offices in Geneva No. 113; Vienna No. 30.

A205

Safety at Sea — A206

Safety at Sea.

1983, Mar. 18 Litho. *Perf. 14½*

394 A205 20c multicolored .25 .25
395 A206 37c multicolored .60 .55

See UN Offices in Geneva Nos. 114-115; Vienna Nos. 31-32.

World Food Program — A207

1983, Apr. 22 Engr. *Perf. 13½*

396 A207 20c rose lake .35 .35

See UN Offices in Geneva No. 116; Vienna Nos. 33-34.

A208

Trade and Development — A209

UN Conference on Trade and Development.

1983, June 6 Litho. *Perf. 14*

397 A208 20c multicolored .25 .35
398 A209 28c multicolored .70 .65

See UN Offices in Geneva Nos. 117-118; Vienna Nos. 35-36.

Flag Type of 1980

1983, Sept. 23 Photo. *Perf. 12*
Granite Paper

399 A185 20c Great Britain .25 .25
400 A185 20c Barbados .25 .25
401 A185 20c Nepal .25 .25
402 A185 20c Israel .25 .25
a. Se-tenant block of 4, #399-402 1.50 1.50
403 A185 20c Malawi .25 .25
404 A185 20c Byelorussian SSR .25 .25
405 A185 20c Jamaica .25 .25
406 A185 20c Kenya .25 .25
a. Se-tenant block of 4, #403-406 1.50 1.80
407 A185 20c People's Republic of China .25 .25
408 A185 20c Peru .25 .25
409 A185 20c Bulgaria .25 .25
410 A185 20c Canada .25 .25
a. Se-tenant block of 4, #407-410 1.50 1.80
411 A185 20c Somalia .25 .25
412 A185 20c Senegal .25 .25
413 A185 20c Brazil .25 .25
414 A185 20c Sweden .25 .25
a. Se-tenant block of 4, #411-414 1.50 1.80
Nos. 399-414 (16) 4.00 4.00

See note after No. 340.

A210

35th Anniv. of the Universal Declaration of Human Rights — A211

35th Anniversary of the Universal Declaration of Human Rights.

Photo. & Engr.

1983, Dec. 9 *Perf. 13½*

415 A210 20c multicolored .30 .25
416 A211 40c multicolored .70 .65

See UN Offices in Geneva Nos. 119-120; Vienna Nos. 37-38.

Intl. Population Conference — A212

1984, Feb. 3 Litho. *Perf. 14*

417 A212 20c multicolored .25 .25
418 A212 40c multicolored .65 .65

See UN Offices in Geneva No. 121; Vienna No. 39.

Tractor Plowing — A213

Rice Paddy — A214

World Food Day, Oct. 16.

1984, Mar. 15 Litho. *Perf. 14½*

419 A213 20c multicolored .30 .30
420 A214 40c multicolored .60 .60

See UN Offices in Geneva Nos. 122-123; Vienna Nos. 40-41.

Grand Canyon — A215

Ancient City of Polonnaruwa, Sri Lanka — A216

World Heritage.

1984, Apr. 18 Litho. *Perf. 14*

421 A215 20c multicolored .25 .25
422 A216 50c multicolored .75 .75

See Nos. 601-602, UN Offices in Geneva Nos. 124-125, 211-212; Vienna Nos. 42-43, 125-126.

A217

A218

Future for Refugees.

1984, May 29 Photo. *Perf. 11½*

423 A217 20c multicolored .30 .30
424 A218 50c multicolored .90 .90

See UN Offices in Geneva Nos. 126-127; Vienna Nos. 44-45.

Flag Type of 1980

1984, Sept. 21 Photo. *Perf. 12*

Granite Paper

425 A185 20c Burundi .25 .25
426 A185 20c Pakistan .25 .25
427 A185 20c Benin .25 .25
428 A185 20c Italy .25 .25
a. Se-tenant block of 4, #425-428 1.80 1.80
429 A185 20c Tanzania .25 .25
430 A185 20c United Arab Emirates .25 .25
431 A185 20c Ecuador .25 .25
432 A185 20c Bahamas .25 .25
a. Se-tenant block of 4, #429-432 1.80 1.80
433 A185 20c Poland .25 .25
434 A185 20c Papua New Guinea .25 .25
435 A185 20c Uruguay .25 .25
436 A185 20c Chile .25 .25
a. Se-tenant block of 4, #433-436 1.80 1.80
437 A185 20c Paraguay .25 .25
438 A185 20c Bhutan .25 .25
439 A185 20c Central African Republic .25 .25
440 A185 20c Australia .25 .25
a. Se-tenant block of 4, #437-440 1.80 1.80
Nos. 425-440 (16) 4.00 4.00

See note after No. 340.

Intl. Youth Year — A219

1984, Nov. 15 Litho. *Perf. 13½*

441 A219 20c multicolored .35 .35
442 A219 35c multicolored .85 .85

See UN Offices in Geneva No. 128; Vienna Nos. 46-47.

ILO Turin Center — A220

Printed by the Government Printing Bureau, Japan. Panes of 50. Engraved by Mamoru Iwakuni and Hiroshi Ozaki, Japan.

1985, Feb. 1 Engr. *Perf. 13½*

443 A220 23c blue .45 .45

See UN Offices in Geneva Nos. 129-130; Vienna No. 48.

UN University A221

50c, Farmer plowing, discussion group.

1985, Mar. 15 Photo. *Perf. 11½*

444 A221 50c multi .95 .95

See UN Offices in Geneva Nos. 131-132; Vienna No. 49.

Peoples of the World — A222

Painting UN Emblem — A223

1985, May 10 Litho. *Perf. 14*

445 A222 22c multicolored .30 .30
446 A223 $3 multicolored 3.75 1.50

See UN Offices in Geneva Nos. 133-134; Vienna Nos. 50-51.

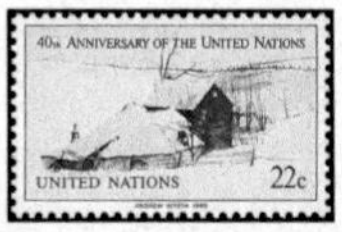
The Corner — A224

Alvaro Raking Hay — A225

UN 40th anniversary. Oil paintings (details) by American artist Andrew Wyeth (b. 1917).

Perf. 12 x 11½

1985, June 26 Photo.

447 A224 22c multicolored .35 .35
448 A225 45c multicolored 1.00 1.00

Souvenir Sheet

Imperf

449 Sheet of 2 1.10 1.30
a. A224 22c multicolored .40 .50
b. A225 45c multicolored .70 .80

See UN Offices in Geneva Nos. 135-137; Vienna Nos. 52-54.

Flag Type of 1980

1985, Sept. 20 Photo. *Perf. 12*

Granite Paper

450 A185 22c Grenada .30 .30
451 A185 22c Federal Republic of Germany .30 .30
452 A185 22c Saudi Arabia .30 .30
453 A185 22c Mexico .30 .30
a. Se-tenant block of 4, #450-453 2.75 3.00
454 A185 22c Uganda .30 .30
455 A185 22c St. Thomas & Prince .30 .30
456 A185 22c USSR .30 .30
457 A185 22c India .30 .30
a. Se-tenant block of 4, #454-457 2.75 3.00
458 A185 22c Liberia .30 .30
459 A185 22c Mauritius .30 .30
460 A185 22c Chad .30 .30
461 A185 22c Dominican Republic .30 .30
a. Se-tenant block of 4, #458-461 2.75 3.00
462 A185 22c Sultanate of Oman .30 .30
463 A185 22c Ghana .30 .30
464 A185 22c Sierra Leone .30 .30
465 A185 22c Finland .30 .30
a. Se-tenant block of 4, #462-465 2.75 3.00
Nos. 450-465 (16) 4.80 4.80

See note after 340.

A226

UNICEF Child Survival Campaign.

Photo. & Engr.

1985, Nov. 22 *Perf. 13½*

466 A226 22c Asian Toddler .30 .30
467 A226 33c Breastfeeding .65 .65

See UN Offices in Geneva Nos. 138-139; Vienna Nos. 55-56.

A227

Africa in Crisis, campaign against hunger.

1986, Jan. 31 Photo. *Perf. 11½x12*

468 A227 22c multicolored .40 .40

See UN Offices in Geneva No. 140; Vienna No. 57.

Water Resources — A228

1986, Mar. 14 Photo. *Perf. 13½*

469 A228 22c Dam .50 .50
470 A228 22c Irrigation .50 .50
471 A228 22c Hygiene .50 .50
472 A228 22c Well .50 .50
a. Block of 4, #469-472 2.00 2.00

UN Development Program. No. 472a has continuous design. See UN Offices in Geneva Nos. 141-144; Vienna Nos. 58-61.

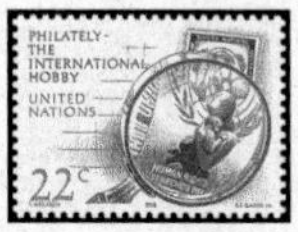
Human Rights Stamp of 1954 — A229

Stamp collecting: 44c, Engraver.

1986, May 22 Engr. *Perf. 12½*

473 A229 22c dk vio & brt blue .25 .25
474 A229 44c brn & emer grn .75 .75

See UN Offices in Geneva Nos. 146-147; Vienna Nos. 62-63.

Birds Nest in Tree A230

Peace in Seven Languages A231

Photo. & Embossed

1986, June 20 *Perf. 13½*

475 A230 22c multicolored .50 .50
476 A231 33c multicolored 1.25 1.25

International Peace Year.

See UN Offices in Geneva Nos. 148-149; Vienna Nos. 64-65.

Flag Type of 1980

1986, Sept. 19 Photo. *Perf. 12*

Granite Paper

477 A185 22c New Zealand .30 .30
478 A185 22c Lao PDR .30 .30
479 A185 22c Burkina Faso .30 .30
480 A185 22c Gambia .30 .30
a. Se-tenant block of 4, #477-480 2.75 3.00
481 A185 22c Maldives .30 .30
482 A185 22c Ethiopia .30 .30
483 A185 22c Jordan .30 .30
484 A185 22c Zambia .30 .30
a. Se-tenant block of 4, #481-484 2.75 3.00
485 A185 22c Iceland .30 .30
486 A185 22c Antigua & Barbuda .30 .30
487 A185 22c Angola .30 .30
488 A185 22c Botswana .30 .30
a. Se-tenant block of 4, #485-488 2.75 3.00
489 A185 22c Romania .30 .30
490 A185 22c Togo .30 .30
491 A185 22c Mauritania .30 .30
492 A185 22c Colombia .30 .30
a. Se-tenant block of 4, #489-492 2.75 3.00
Nos. 477-492 (16) 4.80 4.80

See note after No. 340.

Souvenir Sheet

World Federation of UN Associations, 40th Anniv. — A232

22c, Mother Earth, by Edna Hibel, U.S. 33c, Watercolor by Salvador Dali (b. 1904), Spain. 39c, New Dawn, by Dong Kingman, U.S. 44c, Watercolor by Chaim Gross, U.S.

1986, Nov. 14 Litho. *Perf. 13x13½*

493 A232 Sheet of 4 2.50 2.50
a. 22c multicolored .30 .40
b. 33c multicolored .40 .40
c. 39c multicolored .60 .50
d. 44c multicolored .90 .75

See UN Offices in Geneva No. 150; Vienna No. 66.

Trygve Halvdan Lie (1896-1968), 1st Secretary-General A233

Photo. & Engr.

1987, Jan. 30 *Perf. 13½*

494 A233 22c multicolored .75 .75

See Offices in Geneva No. 151; Vienna No. 67.

Intl. Year of Shelter for the Homeless A234

22c, Surveying and blueprinting. 44c, Cutting lumber.

Perf. 13½x12½

1987, Mar. 13 Litho.

495 A234 22c multicolored .35 .35
496 A234 44c multicolored .90 .90

See Offices in Geneva Nos. 154-155; Vienna Nos. 68-69.

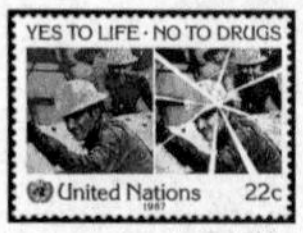
Fight Drug Abuse — A235

22c, Construction. 33c, Education.

1987, June 12 Litho. *Perf. 14½x15*

497 A235 22c multicolored .45 .45
498 A235 33c multicolored .90 .90

See Offices in Geneva Nos. 156-157; Vienna Nos. 70-71.

Flag Type of 1980

1987, Sept. 18 Photo. *Perf. 12*

Granite Paper

499 A185 22c Comoros .30 .35
500 A185 22c Yemen PDR .30 .35
501 A185 22c Mongolia .30 .35
502 A185 22c Vanuatu .30 .35
a. Se-tenant block of 4, #499-502 3.25 3.25
503 A185 22c Japan .30 .35
504 A185 22c Gabon .30 .35
505 A185 22c Zimbabwe .30 .35
506 A185 22c Iraq .30 .35
a. Se-tenant block of 4, #503-506 3.25 3.25
507 A185 22c Argentina .30 .35
508 A185 22c Congo .30 .35
509 A185 22c Niger .30 .35
510 A185 22c St. Lucia .30 .35
a. Se-tenant block of 4, #507-510 3.25 3.25
511 A185 22c Bahrain .30 .35
512 A185 22c Haiti .30 .35
513 A185 22c Afghanistan .30 .35
514 A185 22c Greece .30 .35
a. Se-tenant block of 4, #511-514 3.25 3.25
Nos. 499-514 (16) 4.80 5.60

See note after No. 340.

UN Day — A236

Multinational people in various occupations.

1987, Oct. 23 Litho. *Perf. 14½x15*

515 A236 22c multicolored .35 .35
516 A236 39c multicolored .55 .55

See Offices in Geneva Nos. 158-159; Vienna Nos. 74-75.

Immunize Every Child — A237

22c, Measles. 44c, Tetanus.

1987, Nov. 20 Litho. ***Perf. 15x14½***
517 A237 22c multicolored .75 .75
518 A237 44c multicolored 1.50 1.50

See Offices in Geneva Nos. 160-161; Vienna Nos. 76-77.

Intl. Fund for Agricultural Development (IFAD) — A238

22c, Fishing. 33c, Farming.

1988, Jan. 29 Litho. ***Perf. 13½***
519 A238 22c multicolored .35 .35
520 A238 33c multicolored .75 .75

See Offices in Geneva Nos. 162-163; Vienna Nos. 78-79.

A239

1988, Jan. 29 Photo. ***Perf. 13½x14***
521 A239 3c multicolored .25 .25

Survival of the Forests — A240

Tropical rain forest: 25c, Treetops. 44c, Ground vegetation and tree trunks. Printed se-tenant in a continuous design.

1988, Mar. 18 Litho. ***Perf. 14x15***
522 A240 25c multicolored .75 .75
523 A240 44c multicolored 1.00 1.00
a. Pair, #522-523 2.00 *3.00*

See Offices in Geneva Nos. 165-166; Vienna Nos. 80-81.

Intl. Volunteer Day — A241

25c, Edurahon. 50c, Vocational training, horiz.

Perf. 13x14, 14x13

1988, May 6 Litho.
524 A241 25c multicolored .45 .45
525 A241 50c multicolored .95 .95

See Offices in Geneva Nos. 167-168; Vienna Nos. 82-83.

Health in Sports — A242

25c, Cycling, vert. 35c, Marathon.

Perf. 13½x13, 13x13½

1988, June 17 Litho.
526 A242 25c multicolored .45 .45
527 A242 38c multicolored 1.00 1.00

See Offices in Geneva Nos. 169-170; Vienna Nos. 84-85.

Flag Type of 1980

1988, Sept. 15 Photo. ***Perf. 12***

Granite Paper

528 A185 25c Spain .45 .45
529 A185 25c St. Vincent & Grenadines .45 .45
530 A185 25c Ivory Coast .45 .45
531 A185 25c Lebanon .45 .45
a. Se-tenant block of 4, #528-531 3.00 3.00
532 A185 25c Yemen (Arab Republic) .45 .45
533 A185 25c Cuba .45 .45
534 A185 25c Denmark .45 .45
535 A185 25c Libya .45 .45
a. Se-tenant block of 4, #532-535 3.00 3.00
536 A185 25c Qatar .45 .45
537 A185 25c Zaire .45 .45
538 A185 25c Norway .45 .45
539 A185 25c German Democratic Republic .45 .45
a. Se-tenant block of 4, #536-539 3.00 3.00
540 A185 25c Iran .45 .45
541 A185 25c Tunisia .45 .45
542 A185 25c Samoa .45 .45
543 A185 25c Belize .45 .45
a. Se-tenant block of 4, #540-543 3.00 3.00
Nos. 528-543 (16) 7.20 7.20

See note after No. 340.

A243

Photo. & Engr.

1988, Dec. 9 ***Perf. 11x11½***
544 A243 25c multicolored .45 .45

Souvenir Sheet

545 A243 $1 multicolored 1.00 1.00

Universal Declaration of Human Rights, 40th anniv.

See Offices in Geneva Nos. 171-172; Vienna Nos. 86-87.

A244

1989, Jan. 27 Litho. ***Perf. 13x14***
546 A244 25c Energy and nature .60 .60
547 A244 45c Agriculture 1.10 1.10

World Bank. See Offices in Geneva Nos. 173-174; Vienna Nos. 88-89.

UN Peace-Keeping Force, 1988 Nobel Peace Prize Winner — A245

UN Peace-Keeping Force, awarded 1988 Nobel Peace Prize.

1989, Mar. 17 Litho. ***Perf. 14x13½***
548 A245 25c multicolored .45 .45

See Offices in Geneva No. 175; Vienna No. 90.

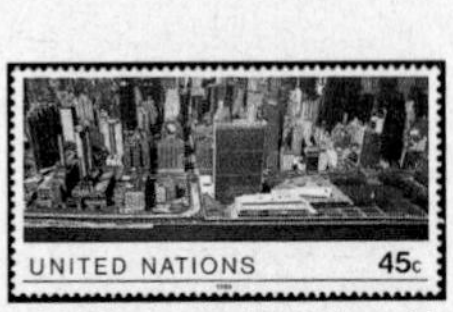

Aerial Photograph of New York Headquarters — A246

1989, Mar. 17 Litho. ***Perf. 14½x14***
549 A246 45c multicolored .65 .65

World Weather Watch, 25th Anniv. (in 1988) — A247

Satellite photographs: 25c, Storm system off the U.S. east coast. 36c, Typhoon Abby in the north-west Pacific.

1989, Apr. 21 Litho. ***Perf. 13x14***
550 A247 25c multicolored .50 .50
551 A247 36c multicolored 1.10 1.10

See Offices in Geneva Nos. 176-177; Vienna Nos. 91-92.

A248

A249

Photo. & Engr., Photo. (90c)

1989, Aug. 23 ***Perf. 14***
552 A248 25c multicolored 1.25 1.25
553 A249 90c multicolored 2.50 2.50

See Offices in Geneva Nos. 178-179; Vienna Nos. 93-94.

Flag Type of 1980

1989, Sept. 22 Photo. ***Perf. 12***

Granite Paper

554 A185 25c Indonesia .60 .55
555 A185 25c Lesotho .60 .55
556 A185 25c Guatemala .60 .55
557 A185 25c Netherlands .60 .55
a. Se-tenant block of 4, #554-557 4.00 4.00
558 A185 25c South Africa .60 .55
559 A185 25c Portugal .60 .55
560 A185 25c Morocco .60 .55
561 A185 25c Syrian Arab Republic .60 .55
a. Se-tenant block of 4, #558-561 4.00 4.00
562 A185 25c Honduras .60 .55
563 A185 25c Kampuchea .60 .55
564 A185 25c Guinea-Bissau .60 .55
565 A185 25c Cyprus .60 .55
a. Se-tenant block of 4, #562-565 4.00 4.00
566 A185 25c Algeria .60 .55
567 A185 25c Brunei .60 .55
568 A185 25c St. Kitts and Nevis .60 .55
569 A185 25c United Nations .60 .55
a. Se-tenant block of 4, #566-569 4.00 4.00
Nos. 554-569 (16) 9.60 8.80

See note after No. 340.

Declaration of Human Rights, 40th Anniv. (in 1988) — A250

Paintings: 25c, The Table of Universal Brotherhood, by Jose Clemente Orozco. 45c, Study for Composition II, by Vassily Kandinsky.

1989, Nov. 17 Litho. ***Perf. 13½***
570 A250 25c multicolored .35 .35
571 A250 45c multicolored .80 .80

Panes of 12+12 se-tenant labels containing Articles 1 (25c) or 2 (45c) inscribed in English, French or German.

See Nos. 582-583, 599-600, 616-617, 627-628; Offices in Geneva Nos. 180-181, 193-194, 209-210, 224-225, 234-235; Vienna Nos. 95-96, 108-109, 123-124, 139-140, 150-151.

Intl. Trade Center — A251

1990, Feb. 2 Litho. ***Perf. 14½x15***
572 A251 25c multicolored 1.00 1.00

See Offices in Geneva No. 182; Vienna No. 97.

Fight AIDS Worldwide A252

40c, Shadow over crowd.

Perf. 13½x12½

1990, Mar. 16 Litho.
573 A252 25c multicolored .35 .35
574 A252 40c multicolored 1.15 1.15

See Offices in Geneva Nos. 184-185, Vienna Nos. 99-100.

Medicinal Plants — A253

25c, Catharanthus roseus. 90c, Panax quinquefolium.

1990, May 4 Photo. ***Perf. 11½***

Granite Paper

575 A253 25c multi .45 .45
576 A253 90c multi 1.40 1.40

See Offices in Geneva Nos. 186-187, Vienna Nos. 101-102.

United Nations, 45th Anniv. — A254

45c, "45," emblem.

1990, June 26 Litho. ***Perf. 14½x13***
577 A254 25c multicolored .50 .50
578 A254 45c multicolored 1.90 1.90

Souvenir Sheet

579 Sheet of 2, #577-578 3.50 3.50

See Offices in Geneva Nos. 188-190; Vienna Nos. 103-105.

Crime Prevention — A255

1990, Sept. 13 Photo. ***Perf. 14***
580 A255 25c Crimes of youth .65 .65
581 A255 36c Organized crime 1.25 1.25

See Offices in Geneva Nos. 191-192; Vienna Nos. 106-107.

Human Rights Type of 1989

25c, Fragment from the sarcophagus of Plotinus, c. 270 A.D. 45c, Combined Chambers of the High Court of Appeal by Charles Paul Renouard.

1990, Nov. 16 Litho. ***Perf. 13½***
582 A250 25c black, gray & tan .35 .35
583 A250 45c black & brown .65 .65

See Offices in Geneva Nos. 193-194; Vienna Nos. 108-109.

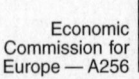

Economic Commission for Europe — A256

1991, Mar. 15 Litho. ***Perf. 14***
584 A256 30c Two storks .85 .85
585 A256 30c Woodpecker, ibex .85 .85
586 A256 30c Capercaille, plover .85 .85
587 A256 30c Falcon, marmot .85 .85
a. Block of 4, #584-587 3.75 3.75

See Offices in Geneva Nos. 195-198; Vienna Nos. 110-113.

Namibian Independence A257

1991, May 10 Litho. *Perf. 14*

588 A257 30c Dunes, Namib Desert .50 .50
589 A257 50c Savanna 1.10 1.00

See Offices in Geneva Nos. 199-200; Vienna Nos. 114-115.

A258

The Golden Rule by Norman Rockwell — A259

UN Headquarters, New York — A260

1991 Litho. *Perf. 13½*

590 A258 30c multi .60 .60

Photo.

Perf. 12x11½

591 A259 50c multi 1.00 1.00

Engr.

592 A260 $2 dark blue 2.75 2.75

Rights of the Child — A261

1991, June 14 Litho. *Perf. 14½*

593 A261 30c Children, globe 1.00 1.00
594 A261 70c House, rainbow 2.00 2.00

See Offices in Geneva Nos. 203-204; Vienna Nos. 117-118.

Banning of Chemical Weapons A262

90c, Hand holding back chemical drums.

1991, Sept. 11 Litho. *Perf. 13½*

595 A262 30c multicolored .75 .75
596 A262 90c multicolored 2.25 2.25

See Offices in Geneva Nos. 205-206; Vienna Nos. 119-120.

UN Postal Administration, 40th Anniv. — A263

1991, Oct. 24 Litho. *Perf. 14x15*

597 A263 30c No. 1 .65 .65
598 A263 40c No. 3 .85 .85

See Offices in Geneva Nos. 207-208; Vienna Nos. 121-122.

Human Rights Type of 1989

30c, The Last of England, by Ford Madox Brown. 40c, The Emigration to the East, by Tito Salas.

1991, Nov. 20 Litho. *Perf. 13½*

599 A250 30c multicolored .35 .35
600 A250 50c multicolored .80 1.00

See Offices in Geneva Nos. 209-210; Vienna Nos. 123-124.

World Heritage Type of 1984

30c, Uluru Natl. Park, Australia. 50c, The Great Wall of China.

1992, Jan. 24 Litho. *Perf. 13*

Size: 35x28mm

601 A215 30c multicolored .55 .55
602 A215 50c multicolored .90 .90

See Offices in Geneva Nos. 211-212; Vienna Nos. 125-126.

Clean Oceans — A264

1992, Mar. 13 Litho. *Perf. 14*

603 A264 29c Ocean surface .45 .50
604 A264 29c Ocean bottom .45 .50
a. Pair, #603-604 .90 1.10

See Offices in Geneva Nos. 214-215, Vienna Nos. 127-128.

Earth Summit — A265

No. 605, Globe at LR. No. 606, Globe at LL. No. 607, Globe at UR. No. 608, Globe at UL.

1992, May 22 Photo. *Perf. 11½*

605 A265 29c multicolored .65 .65
606 A265 29c multicolored .65 .65
607 A265 29c multicolored .65 .65
608 A265 29c multicolored .65 .65
a. Block of 4, #605-608 4.00 3.50

See Offices in Geneva Nos. 216-219, Vienna Nos. 129-132.

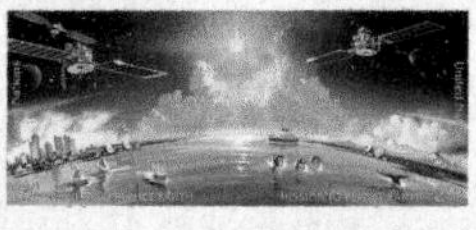
Mission to Planet Earth A266

No. 609, Satellites over city, sailboats, fishing boat. No. 610, Satellite over coast, passenger liner, dolphins, whale, volcano.

1992, Sept. 4 Photo. *Rouletted 8*

Granite Paper

609 29c multicolored 1.50 1.50
610 29c multicolored 1.50 1.50
a. A266 Pair, #609-610 3.00 3.00

See Offices in Geneva Nos. 220-221, Vienna Nos. 133-134.

Science and Technology for Development A267

50c, Animal, man drinking.

1992, Oct. 2 Litho. *Perf. 14*

611 A267 29c multicolored .40 .40
612 A267 50c multicolored .70 .70

UN University Building, Tokyo — A268

UN Headquarters A269

40c, UN University Building, Tokyo, diff.

Perf. 14, 13½x13 (29c)

1992, Oct. 2 Litho.

613 A268 4c multicolored .25 .25
614 A269 29c multicolored .50 .50
615 A268 40c multicolored .65 .65
Nos. 613-615 (3) 1.40 1.40

Human Rights Type of 1989

29c, Lady Writing a Letter with her Maid, by Vermeer. 50c, The Meeting, by Ester Almqvist.

1992, Nov. 20 Litho. *Perf. 13½*

616 A250 29c multicolored .40 .40
617 A250 50c multicolored .60 .60

See Offices in Geneva Nos. 224-225; Vienna Nos. 139-140.

Aging With Dignity — A270

29c, Elderly couple, family. 52c, Old man, physician, woman holding fruit basket.

1993, Feb. 5 Litho. *Perf. 13*

618 A270 29c multicolored .45 .45
619 A270 52c multicolored 1.00 1.00

See Offices in Geneva Nos. 226-227; Vienna Nos. 141-142.

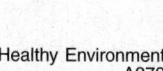

Endangered Species — A271

No. 620, Hairy-nosed wombat. No. 621, Whooping crane. No. 622, Giant clam. No. 623, Giant sable antelope.

1993, Mar. 2 Litho. *Perf. 13x12½*

620 A271 29c multicolored .45 .45
621 A271 29c multicolored .45 .45
622 A271 29c multicolored .45 .45
623 A271 29c multicolored .45 .45
a. Block of 4, #620-623 2.00 2.00

See Nos. 639-642, 657-660, 674-677, 700-703, 730-733, 757-760, 773-776; Offices in Geneva Nos. 228-231, 246-249, 264-267, 280-283, 298-301, 318-321, 336-339, 352-355; Vienna Nos. 143-146, 162-165, 180-183, 196-199, 214-217, 235-238, 253-256, 269-272.

Healthy Environment A272

29c, Personal. 50c, Family.

1993, May 7 Litho. *Perf. 15x14½*

624 A272 29c Man .50 .50
625 A272 50c Family .90 .90

See Offices in Geneva Nos. 232-233; Vienna Nos. 147-148.

A273

1993, May 7 Litho. *Perf. 15x14*

626 A273 5c multicolored .25 .25

Human Rights Type of 1989

29c, Shucking Corn, by Thomas Hart Benton. 35c, The Library, by Jacob Lawrence.

1993, June 11 Litho. *Perf. 13½*

627 A250 29c multicolored .40 .40
628 A250 35c multicolored .45 .45

See Offices in Geneva Nos. 234-235; Vienna Nos. 150-151.

Intl. Peace Day — A274

Denomination at: #629, UL. #630, UR. #631, LL. #632, LR.

Rouletted 12½

1993, Sept. 21 Litho. & Engr.

629 A274 29c blue & multi .75 .75
630 A274 29c blue & multi .75 .75
631 A274 29c blue & multi .75 .75
632 A274 29c blue & multi .75 .75
a. Block of 4, #629-632 4.00 4.00

See Offices in Geneva Nos. 236-239; Vienna Nos. 152-155.

Environment-Climate A275

No. 633, Chameleon. No. 634, Palm trees, top of funnel cloud. No. 635, Bottom of funnel cloud, deer, antelope. No. 636, Bird of paradise.

1993, Oct. 29 Litho. *Perf. 14½*

633 A275 29c multicolored .75 .75
634 A275 29c multicolored .75 .75
635 A275 29c multicolored .75 .75
636 A275 29c multicolored .75 .75
a. Strip of 4, #633-636 4.00 4.00

See Offices in Geneva Nos. 240-243; Vienna Nos. 156-159.

Intl. Year of the Family — A276

29c, Mother holding child, two children, woman. 45c, People tending crops.

1994, Feb. 4 Litho. *Perf. 13.1*

637 A276 29c green & multi .70 .70
638 A276 45c blue & multi .90 .90

See Offices in Geneva Nos. 244-245; Vienna Nos. 160-161.

Endangered Species Type of 1993

No. 639, Chimpanzee. No. 640, St. Lucia Amazon. No. 641, American crocodile. No. 642, Dama gazelle.

1994, Mar. 18 Litho. *Perf. 12.7*

639 A271 29c multicolored .45 .45
640 A271 29c multicolored .45 .45
641 A271 29c multicolored .45 .45
642 A271 29c multicolored .45 .45
a. Block of 4, #639-642 2.00 2.00

See Offices in Geneva Nos. 246-249; Vienna Nos. 162-165.

Protection for Refugees — A277

1994, Apr. 29 Litho. *Perf. 14.3x14.8*

643 A277 50c multicolored .90 .90

See Offices in Geneva No. 250; Vienna No. 166.

Dove of Peace — A278

Sleeping Child, by Stanislaw Wyspianski A279

Mourning Owl, by Vanessa Isitt A280

1994, Apr. 29 Litho. *Perf. 12.9*

644 A278 10c multicolored .25 .25
645 A279 19c multicolored .30 .30

Engr.
Perf. 13.1

646 A280 $1 red brown 1.50 1.50
Nos. 644-646 (3) 2.05 2.05

Intl. Decade for Natural Disaster Reduction — A281

Earth seen from space, outline map of: #647, North America. #648, Eurasia. #649, South America, #650, Australia and South Asia.

1994, May 27 Litho. *Perf. 13.9x14.2*

647 A281 29c multicolored 1.75 1.75
648 A281 29c multicolored 1.75 1.75
649 A281 29c multicolored 1.75 1.75
650 A281 29c multicolored 1.75 1.75
a. Block of 4, #647-650 7.50 7.50

See Offices in Geneva Nos. 251-254; Vienna Nos. 170-173.

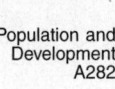

Population and Development A282

29c, Children playing. 52c, Family with house, car, other possessions.

1994, Sept. 1 Litho. *Perf. 13.2x13.6*

651 A282 29c multicolored .40 .40
652 A282 52c multicolored .80 .80

See Offices in Geneva Nos. 258-259; Vienna Nos. 174-175.

UNCTAD, 30th Anniv. — A283

1994, Oct. 28

653 A283 29c multicolored .40 .40
654 A283 50c multi, diff. .80 .80

See Offices in Geneva Nos. 260-261; Vienna Nos. 176-177.

UN, 50th Anniv. — A284

Litho. & Engr.
1995, Jan. 1 *Perf. 13.4*

655 A284 32c multicolored .90 .90

See Offices in Geneva No. 262; Vienna No. 178.

Social Summit, Copenhagen — A285

656 A285 50c multicolored 1.00 1.00

See Offices in Geneva No. 263; Vienna No. 179.

Endangered Species Type of 1993

No. 657, Giant armadillo. No. 658, American bald eagle. No. 659, Fijian/Tongan banded iguana. No. 660, Giant panda.

1995, Mar. 24 Litho. *Perf. 13x12½*

657 A271 32c multicolored .40 .40
658 A271 32c multicolored .40 .40
659 A271 32c multicolored .40 .40
660 A271 32c multicolored .40 .40
a. Block of 4, 657-660 2.25 2.25

See Offices in Geneva Nos. 264-267; Vienna Nos. 180-183.

Intl. Youth Year, 10th Anniv. — A286

32c, Seated child. 55c, Children cycling.

1995, May 26 Litho. *Perf. 14.4x14.7*

661 A286 32c multicolored .55 .55
662 A286 55c multicolored .95 .95

See Offices in Geneva Nos. 268-269; Vienna Nos. 184-185.

UN, 50th Anniv. — A287

32c, Hand with pen signing UN Charter, flags. 50c, Veterans' War Memorial, Opera House, San Francisco.

Perf. 13.3x13.6
1995, June 26 Engr.

663 A287 32c black .55 .55
664 A287 50c maroon 1.00 1.00

Souvenir Sheet
Litho. & Engr.
Imperf

665 Sheet of 2, #663-664 3.00 3.00
a. A287 32c black 1.25 1.25
b. A287 50c maroon 1.50 1.50

No. 665 exists with gold China 1996 overprint. Value $20.

See Offices in Geneva Nos. 270-272; Vienna Nos. 186-188.

4th World Conference on Women, Beijing — A288

32c, Mother and child. 40c, Seated woman, cranes flying above.

1995, Sept. 5 Photo. *Perf. 12*

666 A288 32c multicolored .50 .50

Size: 28x50mm

667 A288 40c multicolored .85 .85

See Offices in Geneva Nos. 273-274; Vienna Nos. 189-190.

UN Headquarters A289

1995, Sept. 5 Litho. *Perf. 15*

668 A289 20c multicolored .35 .35

Miniature Sheet

United Nations, 50th Anniv. — A290

1995, Oct. 24 Litho. *Perf. 14*

669 A290 Sheet of 12 5.00 5.00
a.-l. 32c any single .40 .40
670 Souvenir booklet 5.50
a. A290 32c Booklet pane of 3, vert. strip of 3 from UL of sheet 1.35 1.35
b. A290 32c Booklet pane of 3, vert. strip of 3 from UR of sheet 1.35 1.35
c. A290 32c Booklet pane of 3, vert. strip of 3 from LL of sheet 1.35 1.35
d. A290 32c Booklet pane of 3, vert. strip of 3 from LR of sheet 1.35 1.35

See Offices in Geneva Nos. 275-276; Vienna Nos. 191-192.

WFUNA, 50th Anniv. — A291

1996, Feb. 2 Litho. *Perf. 13x13½*

671 A291 32c multicolored .50 .50

See Offices in Geneva No. 277; Vienna No. 193.

Mural, by Fernand Leger — A292

1996, Feb. 2 Litho. *Perf. 14½x15*

672 A292 32c multicolored .45 .45
673 A292 60c multi, diff. .95 .95

Endangered Species Type of 1993

No. 674, Masdevallia veitchiana. No. 675, Saguaro cactus. No. 676, West Australian pitcher plant. No. 677, Encephalartos horridus.

1996, Mar. 14 Litho. *Perf. 12½*

674 A271 32c multicolored .45 .45
675 A271 32c multicolored .45 .45
676 A271 32c multicolored .45 .45
677 A271 32c multicolored .45 .45
a. Block of 4, #674-677 2.25 2.25

See Offices in Geneva Nos. 280-283; Vienna Nos. 196-199.

City Summit (Habitat II) — A293

No. 678, Deer. No. 679, Man, child, dog sitting on hill, overlooking town. No. 680, People walking in park, city skyline. No. 681, Tropical park, Polynesian woman, boy. No. 682, Polynesian village, orchids, bird.

1996, June 3 Litho. *Perf. 14x13½*

678 A293 32c multicolored .80 .80
679 A293 32c multicolored .80 .80
680 A293 32c multicolored .80 .80
681 A293 32c multicolored .80 .80
682 A293 32c multicolored .80 .80
a. Strip of 5, #678-682 7.00 7.00

See Offices in Geneva Nos. 284-288; Vienna Nos. 200-204.

Sport and the Environment — A294

32c, Men's basketball. 50c, Women's volleyball, horiz.

Perf. 14x14½, 14½x14
1996, July 19 Litho.

683 A294 32c multicolored .65 .65
684 A294 50c multicolored 1.40 1.40

Souvenir Sheet

685 A294 Sheet of 2, #683-684 2.50 2.50

See Offices in Geneva Nos. 289-291; Vienna Nos. 205-207.

1996 Summer Olympic Games, Atlanta, GA.

Plea for Peace — A295

32c, Doves. 60c, Stylized dove.

1996, Sept. 17 Litho. *Perf. 14½x15*

686 A295 32c multicolored .50 .50
687 A295 60c multicolored .90 .90

See Offices in Geneva Nos. 292-293; Vienna Nos. 208-209.

UNICEF, 50th Anniv. — A296

Fairy Tales: 32c, Yeh-Shen, China. 60c, The Ugly Duckling, by Hans Christian Andersen.

1996, Nov. 20 Litho. *Perf. 14½x15*

688 A296 32c multicolored .45 .45
689 A296 60c multicolored 1.10 1.10

See Offices in Geneva Nos. 294-295; Vienna Nos. 210-211.

Flag Type of 1980
1997, Feb. 12 Photo. *Perf. 12*
Granite Paper

690 A185 32c Tadjikistan .75 1.00
691 A185 32c Georgia .75 1.00
692 A185 32c Armenia .75 1.00
693 A185 32c Namibia .75 1.00
a. Block of 4, #690-693 10.00 13.00
694 A185 32c Liechtenstein .75 1.00
695 A185 32c Republic of Korea .75 1.00
696 A185 32c Kazakhstan .75 1.00
697 A185 32c Latvia .75 1.00
a. Block of 4, #694-697 10.00 13.00

See note after No. 340.

Cherry Blossoms, UN Headquarters A297

Peace Rose A298

1997, Feb. 12 Litho. *Perf. 14½*

698 A297 8c multicolored .25 .25
699 A298 55c multicolored .90 .90

Endangered Species Type of 1993

No. 700, African elephant. No. 701, Major Mitchell's cockatoo. No. 702, Black-footed ferret. No. 703, Cougar.

1997, Mar. 13 Litho. *Perf. 12½*

700 A271 32c multicolored .40 .40
701 A271 32c multicolored .40 .40
702 A271 32c multicolored .40 .40
703 A271 32c multicolored .40 .40
a. Block of 4, #700-703 2.25 2.25

See Offices in Geneva Nos. 298-301; Vienna Nos. 214-217.

Earth Summit, 5th Anniv. — A299

No. 704, Sailboat. No. 705, Three sailboats. No. 706, Two people watching sailboat, sun. No. 707, Person, sailboat.
$1, Combined design similar to Nos. 704-707.

1997, May 30 Photo. *Perf. 11.5*

Granite Paper

704 A299 32c multicolored .90 .90
705 A299 32c multicolored .90 .90
706 A299 32c multicolored .90 .90
707 A299 32c multicolored .90 .90
a. Block of 4, #704-707 5.00 5.00

Souvenir Sheet

708 A299 $1 multicolored 3.25 3.25
a. Ovptd. in sheet margin *17.50 17.50*

See Offices in Geneva Nos. 302-306; Vienna Nos. 218-222.
No. 708 contains one 60x43mm stamp. Overprint in sheet margin of No. 708a reads "PACIFIC 97 / World Philatelic Exhibition / San Francisco, California / 29 May - 8 June 1997".

Transportation — A300

Ships: No. 709, Clipper ship. No. 710, Paddle steamer. No. 711, Ocean liner. No. 712, Hovercraft. No. 713, Hydrofoil.

1997, Aug. 29 Litho. *Perf. 14x14½*

709 A300 32c multicolored .65 .65
710 A300 32c multicolored .65 .65
711 A300 32c multicolored .65 .65
712 A300 32c multicolored .65 .65
713 A300 32c multicolored .65 .65
a. Strip of 5, #709-713 4.25 4.25

See Offices in Geneva Nos. 307-311; Vienna Nos. 223-227.
No. 713a has continuous design.

Philately — A301

32c, No. 473. 50c, No. 474.

1997, Oct. 14 Litho. *Perf. 13½x14*

714 A301 32c multicolored .60 .60
715 A301 50c multicolored 1.50 1.50

See Offices in Geneva Nos. 312-313; Vienna Nos. 228-229.

World Heritage Convention, 25th Anniv. — A302

Terracotta warriors of Xian: 32c, Single warrior. 60c, Massed warriors. No. 718a, like #716. No. 718b, like #717. No. 718c, like Geneva #314. No. 718d, like Geneva #315. No. 718e, like Vienna #230. No. 718f, like Vienna #231.

1997, Nov. 19 Litho. *Perf. 13½*

716 A302 32c multicolored .75 .75
717 A302 60c multicolored 1.25 1.25
718 Souvenir booklet 8.50
a.-f. A302 8c any single .35 .35
g. Booklet pane of 4 #718a 1.40 1.40
h. Booklet pane of 4 #718b 1.40 1.40
i. Booklet pane of 4 #718c 1.40 1.40
j. Booklet pane of 4 #718d 1.40 1.40
k. Booklet pane of 4 #718e 1.40 1.40
l. Booklet pane of 4 #718f 1.40 1.40

See Offices in Geneva Nos. 314-316; Vienna Nos. 230-232.

Flag Type of 1980

Printed by Helio Courvoisier, S.A., Switzerland. Designed by Oliver Corwin, and Robert Stein, US. Each pane contains 4 blocks of 4 (Nos. 719-722, 723-726). A se-tenant block of 4 designs centers each pane.

1998, Feb. 13 Photo. *Perf. 12*

Granite Paper

719 A185 32c Micronesia .80 .80
720 A185 32c Slovakia .80 .80
721 A185 32c Deocratic People's Republic of Korea .80 .80
722 A185 32c Azerbaijan .80 .80
a. Block of 4, #719-722 12.50 12.50
723 A185 32c Uzbekistan .80 .80
724 A185 32c Monaco .80 .80
725 A185 32c Czech Republic .80 .80
726 A185 32c Estonia .80 .80
a. Block of 4, #723-726 12.50 12.50
Nos. 719-726 (8) 6.40 6.40

A303

A304

A305

Perf. 14½x15, 15x14½

1998, Feb. 13 Litho.

727 A303 1c multicolored .25 .25
728 A304 2c multicolored .25 .25
729 A305 21c multicolored .40 .40
Nos. 727-729 (3) .90 .90

Endangered Species Type of 1993

No. 730, Lesser galago. No. 731, Hawaiian goose. No. 732, Golden birdwing. No. 733, Sun bear.

1998, Mar. 13 Litho. *Perf. 12½*

730 A271 32c multicolored .45 .45
731 A271 32c multicolored .45 .45
732 A271 32c multicolored .45 .45
733 A271 32c multicolored .45 .45
a. Block of 4, #730-733 2.25 2.25

See Offices in Geneva Nos. 318-321; Vienna Nos. 235-238.

Intl. Year of the Ocean A306

1998, May 20 Litho. *Perf. 13x13½*

734 A306 Sheet of 12 12.50 12.50
a.-l. 32c any single 1.00 1.00

See Offices in Geneva No. 322; Vienna No. 239.

Rain Forests — A307

1998, June 19 Litho. *Perf. 13x13½*

735 A307 32c Jaguar .50 .50

Souvenir Sheet

736 A307 $2 like #735 3.00 3.00

See Offices in Geneva Nos. 323-324; Vienna Nos. 240-241.

U.N. Peacekeeping Forces, 50th Anniv. — A308

33c, Commander with binoculars. 40c, Two soldiers on vehicle.

1998, Sept. 15 Photo. *Perf. 12*

737 A308 33c multicolored .50 .50
738 A308 40c multicolored .75 .75

See Offices in Geneva Nos. 325-326; Vienna Nos. 242-243.

Universal Declaration of Human Rights, 50th Anniv. — A309

Stylized people: 32c, Carrying flag. 55c, Carrying pens.

Litho. & Photo.

1998, Oct. 27 *Perf. 13*

739 A309 32c multicolored .45 .45
740 A309 55c multicolored .90 .90

See Offices in Geneva Nos. 327-328; Vienna Nos. 244-245.

Schönnbrun Palace, Vienna — A310

33c, #743f, The Gloriette. 60c, #743b, Wall painting on fabric (detail), by Johann Wenzl Bergl, vert. No. 743a, Blue porcelain vase, vert. No. 743c, Porcelain stove, vert. No. 743d, Palace. No. 743e, Great Palm House (conservatory).

1998, Dec. 4 Litho. *Perf. 14*

741 A310 33c multicolored .55 .55
742 A310 60c multicolored 1.25 1.00

Souvenir Booklet

743 Booklet 19.50
a.-c. A310 11c any single .35 .35
d.-f. A310 15c any single 1.40 1.40
g. Booklet pane of 4 #743d 5.50 5.50
h. Booklet pane of 3 #743a 1.00 1.00
i. Booklet pane of 3 #743b 1.00 1.00
j. Booklet pane of 3 #743c 1.00 1.00
k. Booklet pane of 4 #743e 5.50 5.50
l. Booklet pane of 4 #743f 5.50 5.50

See Offices in Geneva Nos. 329-331; Vienna Nos. 246-248.

Flag Type of 1980

1999, Feb. 5 Photo. *Perf. 12*

744 A185 33c Lithuania .75 .75
745 A185 33c San Marino .75 .75
746 A185 33c Turkmenistan .75 .75
747 A185 33c Marshall Islands .75 .75
a. Block of 4, #744-747 8.00 8.00
748 A185 33c Moldova .75 .75
749 A185 33c Kyrgyzstan .75 .75
750 A185 33c Bosnia & Herzegovina .75 .75
751 A185 33c Eritrea .75 .75
a. Block of 4, #748-751 8.00 8.00
Nos. 744-751 (8) 6.00 6.00

See note after No. 340.

Flags and Globe A311

Roses A312

1999, Feb. 5 Litho. *Perf. 14x13½*

752 A311 33c multicolored .50 .50

Photo.

Granite Paper

Perf. 11½x12

753 A312 $5 multicolored 6.00 6.00

World Heritage Sites, Australia — A313

33c, #756f, Willandra Lakes region. 60c, #756b, Wet tropics of Queensland. No. 756a, Tasmanian wilderness. No. 756c, Great Barrier Reef. No. 756d, Uluru-Kata Tjuta Natl. Park. No. 756e, Kakadu Natl. Park.

1999, Mar. 19 Litho. *Perf. 13*

754 A313 33c multicolored .60 .60
755 A313 60c multicolored 1.25 1.25

Souvenir Booklet

756 Booklet 35.00
a.-c. A313 5c any single .70 .70
d.-f. A313 15c any single 1.50 1.50
g. Booklet pane of 4, #756a 2.80 2.80
h. Booklet pane of 4, #756d 6.00 6.00
i. Booklet pane of 4, #756b 2.80 2.80
j. Booklet pane of 4, #756e 6.00 6.00
k. Booklet pane of 4, #756c 2.80 2.80
l. Booklet pane of 4, #756f 6.00 6.00

See Offices in Geneva Nos. 333-335; Vienna Nos. 250-252.

Endangered Species Type of 1993

No. 757, Tiger. No. 758, Secretary bird. No. 759, Green tree python. No. 760, Long-tailed chinchilla.

1999, Apr. 22 Litho. *Perf. 12½*

757 A271 33c multicolored .60 .60
758 A271 33c multicolored .60 .60
759 A271 33c multicolored .60 .60
760 A271 33c multicolored .60 .60
a. Block of 4, #757-760 3.00 3.00

See Offices in Geneva Nos. 336-339; Vienna Nos. 253-256.

UNISPACE III, Vienna — A314

No. 761, Probe on planet's surface. No. 762, Planetary rover. No. 763, Composite of #761-762.

1999, July 7 Photo. *Rouletted 8*

761 A314 33c multicolored .50 .50
762 A314 33c multicolored .50 .50
a. Pair, #761-762 1.75 1.75

Souvenir Sheet

Perf. 14½

763 A314 $2 multicolored 4.00 4.00
a. Ovptd. in sheet margin 15.00 15.00

No. 763a was issued 7/7/00 and is overprinted in violet blue "WORLD STAMP EXPO 2000 / ANAHEIM, CALIFORNIA / U.S.A./ 7-16 JULY 2000."
See Offices in Geneva Nos. 340-342; Vienna Nos. 257-259.

UPU, 125th Anniv. — A315

Various people, 19th century methods of mail transportation, denomination at: No. 764, UL. No. 765, UR. No. 766, LL. No. 767, LR.

1999, Aug. 23 Photo. *Perf. 11¾*

764 A315 33c multicolored .45 .45
765 A315 33c multicolored .45 .45
766 A315 33c multicolored .45 .45
767 A315 33c multicolored .45 .45
a. Block of 4, #764-767 2.50 2.50

See Offices in Geneva Nos. 343-346; Vienna Nos. 260-263.

In Memoriam — A316

Designs: 33c, $1, UN Headquarters. Size of $1 stamp: 34x63mm.

1999, Sept. 21 Litho. *Perf. 14½x14*

768 A316 33c multicolored .80 .80

Souvenir Sheet

Perf. 14

769 A316 $1 multicolored 2.00 2.00

Education, Keystone to the 21st Century A317

Perf. 13½x13¾

1999, Nov. 18 Litho.

770 A317 33c Two readers .50 .50
771 A317 60c Heart 1.00 1.00

See Offices in Geneva Nos. 349-350, Vienna Nos. 266-267.

International Year of Thanksgiving — A318

2000, Jan. 1 Litho. *Perf. 13¼x13½*

772 A318 33c multicolored .50 .50

On No. 772 parts of the design were applied by a thermographic process producing a shiny, raised effect. See Offices in Geneva No. 351, Vienna No. 268.

Endangered Species Type of 1993

No. 773, Brown bear. No. 774, Black-bellied bustard. No. 775, Chinese crocodile lizard. No. 776, Pygmy chimpanzee.

2000, Apr. 6 Litho. *Perf. 12¾x12½*

773 A271 33c multicolored .50 .50
774 A271 33c multicolored .50 .50
775 A271 33c multicolored .50 .50
776 A271 33c multicolored .50 .50
a. Block of 4, #773-776 2.50 2.50

See Offices in Geneva Nos. 352-355; Vienna Nos. 269-272.

Our World 2000 — A319

Winning artwork in Millennium painting competition: 33c, Crawling Toward the Millennium, by Sam Yeates, US. 60c, Crossing, by Masakazu Takahata, Japan, vert.

Perf. 13x13½, 13½x13

2000, May 30 Litho.

777 A319 33c multicolored .60 .60
778 A319 60c multicolored 1.00 1.00

See Offices in Geneva No. 356-357, Vienna No. 273-274.

UN, 55th Anniv. — A320

33c, Workmen removing decorative discs in General Assembly Hall, 1956. 55c, UN Building in 1951.

2000, July 7 Litho. *Perf. 13¼x13*

779 A320 33c multicolored .55 .55
780 A320 55c multicolored .95 .95

Souvenir Sheet

781 A320 Sheet of 2, #779-780 3.00 3.00

See Offices in Geneva No. 358-360, Vienna No. 275-277.

International Flag of Peace — A321

2000, Sept. 15 Litho. *Perf. 14½x14*

782 A321 33c multicolored .65 .65

The UN in the 21st Century A322

No. 783: a, Farmers, animals in rice paddy. b, Vehicle chassis being lifted. c, People voting. d, Baby receiving inoculation. e, Woman, man at pump. f, Mason, construction workers.

2000, Sept. 15 Litho. *Perf. 14*

783 A322 Sheet of 6 7.50 7.50
a.-f. 33c any single 1.25 1.25

See Offices in Geneva No. 361; Vienna No. 278.

World Heritage Sites, Spain A323

Nos. 784, 786a, Alhambra, Generalife and Albayzin, Granada. Nos. 785, 786d, Amphitheater of Mérida. #786b, Walled Town of Cuenca. #786c, Aqueduct of Segovia. #786e, Toledo. #786f, Güell Park, Barcelona.

2000, Oct. 6 Litho. *Perf. 14¾x14½*

784 A323 33c multicolored .55 .55
785 A323 60c multicolored 1.10 1.10

Souvenir Booklet

786 Booklet 15.00
a.-c. A323 5c any single .45 .45
d.-f. A323 15c any single .80 .80
g. Booklet pane of 4, #786a 1.80 1.80
h. Booklet pane of 4, #786d 3.20 3.20
i. Booklet pane of 4, #786b 1.80 1.80
j. Booklet pane of 4, #786e 3.20 3.20
k. Booklet pane of 4, #786c 1.80 1.80
l. Booklet pane of 4, #786f 3.20 3.20

See Offices in Geneva Nos. 362-364, Vienna Nos. 279-281.

Respect for Refugees — A324

2000, Nov. 9 Litho. *Perf. 13¼x12¾*

787 A324 33c multicolored .75 .75

Souvenir Sheet

788 A324 $1 multicolored 2.00 2.00

See Offices in Geneva Nos. 365-366, Vienna Nos. 282-283.

Endangered Species Type of 1993

No. 789, Common spotted cuscus. No. 790, Resplendent quetzal. No. 791, Gila monster. No. 792, Guereza.

2001, Feb. 1 Litho. *Perf. 12¾x12½*

789 A271 34c multicolored .60 .60
790 A271 34c multicolored .60 .60
791 A271 34c multicolored .60 .60
792 A271 34c multicolored .60 .60
a. Block of 4, #789-792 3.00 3.00

See Offices in Geneva Nos. 367-370; Vienna Nos. 284-287.

Intl. Volunteers Year — A325

Paintings by: 34c, Jose Zaragoza, Brazil. 80c, John Terry, Australia.

2001, Mar. 29 Litho. *Perf. 13¼*

793 A325 34c multicolored .65 .65
794 A325 80c multicolored 1.60 1.60

See Offices in Geneva Nos. 371-372; Vienna Nos. 288-289.

Flag Type of 1980

Printed by Helio Courvoisier, Switzerland. Designed by Ole Hamann. Issued in panes of 16; each contains 4 blocks of 4 (Nos. 795-798, 799-802). A se-tenant block of 4 designs centers each pane.

2001, May 25 Photo. *Perf. 12*

Granite Paper

795 A185 34c Slovenia 1.25 1.25
796 A185 34c Palau 1.25 1.25
797 A185 34c Tonga 1.25 1.25
798 A185 34c Croatia 1.25 1.25
a. Block of 4, #795-798 15.00 15.00
799 A185 34c Former Yugoslav Republic of Macedonia 1.25 1.25
800 A185 34c Kiribati 1.25 1.25
801 A185 34c Andorra 1.25 1.25
802 A185 34c Nauru 1.25 1.25
a. Block of 4, #799-802 15.00 15.00
Nos. 795-802 (8) 10.00 10.00

Sunflower A326

Rose A327

2001, May 25 Litho. *Perf. 13¼x13¾*

803 A326 7c multicolored .25 .25
804 A327 34c multicolored .60 .60

World Heritage Sites, Japan A328

34c, #807a, Kyoto. 70c, #807d, Shirakawa-Go and Gokayama. #807b, Nara. #807c, Himeji-Jo. #807e, Itsukushima Shinto Shrine. #807f, Nikko.

2001, Aug. 1 Litho. *Perf. 12¾x13¼*

805 A328 34c multicolored .60 .60
806 A328 70c multicolored 1.25 1.25

Souvenir Booklet

807 Booklet 14.00
a.-c. A328 5c any single .40 .40
d.-f. A328 20c any single .75 .75
g. Booklet pane of 4, #807a 1.60 1.60
h. Booklet pane of 4, #807d 3.00 3.00
i. Booklet pane of 4, #807b 1.60 1.60
j. Booklet pane of 4, #807e 3.00 3.00
k. Booklet pane of 4, #807c 1.60 1.60
l. Booklet pane of 4, #807f 3.00 3.00

See Offices in Geneva Nos. 373-375, Vienna Nos. 290-292.

Dag Hammarskjöld (1905-61), UN Secretary General — A329

2001, Sept. 18 Engr. *Perf. 11x11¼*

808 A329 80c blue 1.50 1.50

See Offices in Geneva No. 376, Vienna No. 293.

A330

UN Postal Administration, 50th Anniv. — A331

2001, Oct. 18 Litho. *Perf. 13½*

809 A330 34c Stamps, streamers .55 .55
810 A330 80c Stamps, gifts 1.50 1.50

Souvenir Sheet

811 A331 Sheet of 2 #811a 8.00 8.00
a. $1 blue & light blue, 38mm diameter 4.00 4.00

See Offices in Geneva Nos. 377-379, Vienna Nos. 294-296.

Climate Change — A332

No. 812, Canada geese, greenhouses, butterfly, thistle. No. 813, Canada geese, iceberg, penguins, tomato plant. No. 814, Palm tree, solar collector. No. 815, Hand planting ginkgo cutting.

2001, Nov. 16 Litho. *Perf. 13¼*

812 A332 34c multicolored 1.00 1.00
813 A332 34c multicolored 1.00 1.00
814 A332 34c multicolored 1.00 1.00
815 A332 34c multicolored 1.00 1.00
a. Horiz. strip, #812-815 4.50 4.50

See Offices in Geneva Nos. 380-383, Vienna Nos. 297-300.

Awarding of Nobel Peace Prize to Secretary General Kofi Annan and UN — A333

2001, Dec. 10 Litho. *Perf. 13¼*

816 A333 34c multicolored .70 .70

See Offices in Geneva Nos. 384, Vienna Nos. 301.

Children and Stamps — A334

2002, Mar. 1 Litho. *Perf. 13¾*

817 A334 80c multicolored 1.40 1.40

Endangered Species Type of 1993

No. 818, Hoffmann's two-toed sloth. No. 819, Bighorn sheep. No. 820, Cheetah. No. 821, San Esteban Island chuckwalla.

2002, Apr. 4 Litho. *Perf. 12¾x12½*

818 A271 34c multicolored .80 .80
819 A271 34c multicolored .80 .80
820 A271 34c multicolored .80 .80
821 A271 34c multicolored .80 .80
a. Block of 4, #818-821 3.25 3.25

See Offices in Geneva Nos. 386-389; Vienna 308-311.

Independence of East Timor — A335

34c, Wooden ritual mask. 57c, Decorative door panel.

2002, May 20 Litho. *Perf. 14x14½*

822 A335 34c multicolored .70 .70
823 A335 57c multicolored 1.20 1.20

See Offices in Geneva Nos. 390-391; Vienna Nos. 312-313.

Intl. Year of Mountains A336

No. 824, Khan Tengri, Kyrgyzstan. No. 825, Mt. Kilimanjaro, Tanzania. No. 826, Mt. Foraker, US. No. 827, Paine Grande, Chile.

2002, May 24 Litho. *Perf. 13x13¼*

824 A336 34c multicolored .75 .75
825 A336 34c multicolored .75 .75
826 A336 80c multicolored 1.25 1.50
827 A336 80c multicolored 1.25 1.50
a. Vert. strip or block of four, #824-827 8.00 10.00

See Offices in Geneva Nos. 392-395; Vienna Nos. 314-317.

World Summit on Sustainable Development, Johannesburg A337

No. 828, Sun, Earth, planets, stars. No. 829, Three women. No. 830, Sailboat. No. 831, Three faceless people.

2002, June 27 Litho. *Perf. 14½x14*

828 A337 37c multicolored .75 .75
829 A337 37c multicolored .75 .75
830 A337 60c multicolored 1.25 1.25
831 A337 60c multicolored 1.25 1.25
a. Vert. strip or block of four, #828-831 8.00 10.00

See Offices in Geneva Nos. 396-399; Vienna Nos. 318-321.

World Heritage Sites, Italy — A338

37c, #834d, Florence. 70c, #834a, Amalfi Coast. #834b, Aeolian Islands. #834c, Rome. #834e, Pisa. #834f, Pompeii.

Perf. 13½x13¼

2002, Aug. 30 Litho.

832 A338 37c multicolored .70 .70
833 A338 70c multicolored 1.40 1.40

Souvenir Booklet

834 Booklet 16.00
a.-c. A338 5c any single .40 .40
d.-f. A338 15c any single .90 .90
g. Booklet pane of 4, #834d 3.60 3.60
h. Booklet pane of 4, #834a 1.60 1.60
i. Booklet pane of 4, #834e 3.60 3.60
j. Booklet pane of 4, #834b 1.60 1.60
k. Booklet pane of 4, #834f 3.60 3.60
l. Booklet pane of 4, #834c 1.60 1.60

See Offices in Geneva Nos. 400-402, Vienna Nos. 322-324.
See Italy Nos. 2506-2507.

AIDS Awareness — A339

2002, Oct. 24 Litho. *Perf. 13½*

835 A339 70c multicolored 1.50 1.50

See No. B1, Offices in Geneva Nos. 403, B1, Vienna Nos. 325, B1.

Indigenous Art A340

No. 836: a, Detail of Paracas textile, Peru. b, Sinu culture anthropo-zoomorphic pendant, Colombia. c, Hicholi Indian embroidery, Mexico. d, Rigpaktsa back ornament, Brazil. e, Wool crafts, Chile. f, Huari feathered woven hat, Bolivia.

2003, Jan. 31 Litho. *Perf. 14¼*

836 A340 Sheet of 6 8.50 8.50
a.-f. 37c Any single 1.40 1.40

See Offies in Geneva No. 405; Vienna No. 326.

Clasped Hands A341

UN Emblem A342

UN Headquarters A343

2003, Mar. 28 Litho. *Perf. 14¼*

837 A341 23c multicolored .40 .40

Litho. with Foil Application

838 A342 37c gold & multicolored .60 .60

Litho. with Hologram

Perf. 13¼x12¾

839 A343 70c multicolored 1.40 1.40

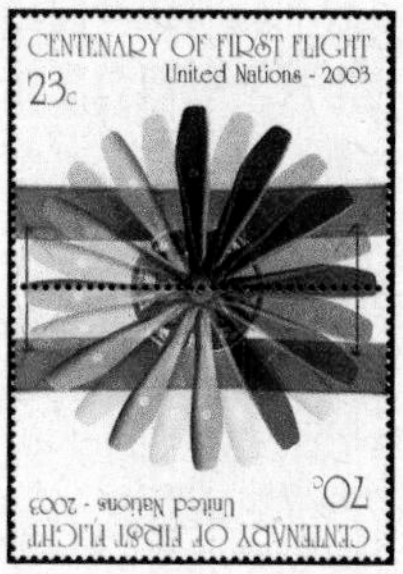

Powered Flight, Cent. A344

Perf. 13½x13¾

2003, Mar. 28 Litho.

840 23c multicolored 1.00 1.00
841 70c multicolored 1.75 1.75
a. A344 Tete beche pair, #840-841 3.00 3.00

Endangered Species Type of 1993

No. 842, Great hornbill. No. 843, Scarlet ibis. No. 844, Knob-billed goose. No. 845, White-faced whistling duck.

2003, Apr. 3 Litho. *Perf. 12¾x12½*

842 A271 37c multicolored .80 .80
843 A271 37c multicolored .80 .80
844 A271 37c multicolored .80 .80
845 A271 37c multicolored .80 .80
a. Block of 4, #842-845 3.25 3.25

See Offices in Geneva Nos. 407-410; Vienna 329-332.

Intl. Year of Freshwater — A345

Perf. 14¼x14½

2003, June 20 Litho.

846 A345 23c Wildlife, garbage 1.50 1.50
847 A345 37c Trees, canoe 2.00 2.00
a. Horiz. pair, #846-847 7.50 7.50

See Offices in Geneva, Nos. 411-412; Vienna Nos. 333-334.

Ralph Bunche (1903-71), Diplomat — A346

Litho. With Foil Application

2003, Aug. 7 *Perf. 13½x14*

848 A346 37c blue & multi .80 .80

See Offices in Geneva No. 413; Vienna No. 336.

In Memoriam of Victims of Aug. 19 Bombing of UN Complex in Baghdad, Iraq — A347

2003, Oct. 24 Litho. *Perf. 13¼x13*

849 A347 60c multicolored 1.25 1.25

See Offices in Geneva No. 414, Vienna No. 337.

World Heritage Sites, United States — A348

37c, #852a, Yosemite National Park. 60c, #852d, Hawaii Volcanoes National Park. #852b, Great Smoky Mountains National Park. #852c, Olympic National Park. #852e, Everglades National Park. #852f, Yellowstone National Park.

2003, Oct. 24 Litho. *Perf. 14½x14¼*

850 A348 37c multicolored .90 .90
851 A348 60c multicolored 1.50 1.50

Souvenir Booklet

852 Booklet 15.00
a.-c. A348 10c any single .35 .35
d.-f. A348 20c any single .70 .70
g. Booklet pane of 4 #852a 1.40 1.40
h. Booklet pane of 4 #852d 2.80 2.80
i. Booklet pane of 4 #852b 1.40 1.40
j. Booklet pane of 4 #852e 2.80 2.80
k. Booklet pane of 4 #852c 1.40 1.40
l. Booklet pane of 4 #852f 2.80 2.80

See Offices in Geneva Nos. 415-417, Vienna Nos. 338-340.

UN Security Council A349

UN Emblem A350

UN General Assembly A351

Flags A352

UN Headquarters — A353

2003, Nov. 26 Litho. *Perf. 13¼*

853 A349 37c multi + label 12.50 12.50
854 A350 37c multi + label 12.50 12.50
855 A351 37c multi + label 12.50 12.50
856 A352 37c multi + label 12.50 12.50
857 A353 37c multi + label 12.50 12.50
a. Vert. strip of 5, #853-857, + 5 labels 65.00 65.00

The full sheet sold for $14.95 with or without personalized labels. The personalization of labels was available only at UN Headquarters, and not through mail order.

One thousand full sheets with sheet margins inscribed "Hong Kong Stamp Expo" were sold only at that venue. Value $135. Also exists with sheet margins inscribed "Essen." Value $125.

A sheet containing two strips of five stamps similar to Nos. 853-857 but dated "2005" and ten labels sold for $4.95. These sheets were only available canceled. Value $100. An imperforate error of this sheet is known.

Endangered Species Type of 1993

No. 858, American black bear. No. 859, Musk deer. No. 860, Golden snub-nosed monkey. No. 861, Wild yak.

2004, Jan. 29 Litho. *Perf. 12¾x12½*

858 A271 37c multicolored .90 .90
859 A271 37c multicolored .90 .90
860 A271 37c multicolored .90 .90
861 A271 37c multicolored .90 .90
a. Block of 4, #858-861 4.00 4.00

See Offices in Geneva Nos. 418-421; Vienna Nos. 342-345.

Indigenous Art Type of 2003

No. 862: a, Viking wood carving depicting Saga of Sigurd Favnesbane, Norway. b, Stele, Italy. c, Detail of matador's suit, Spain. d, Amphora, Greece. e, Bronze figurine of bull, Czech Republic. f, Detail of lacquer box illustration depicting scene from "On the Seashore," by Alexander Pushkin, Russia.

2004, Mar. 4 Litho. *Perf. 13¼*

862 A340 Sheet of 6 6.00 6.00
a.-f. 37c Any single 1.00 1.00

See Offices in Geneva No. 422; Vienna No. 346.

Road Safety — A354

Road map art with: 37c, Automobile with road signs, city skyline. 70c, Automobile, hand, vert.

Perf. 13x13¼, 13¼x13

2004, Apr. 7 **Litho.**
863 A354 37c multicolored .85 .85
864 A354 70c multicolored 1.40 1.40

See Offices in Geneva Nos. 423-424, Vienna Nos. 347-348.

Japanese Peace Bell, 50th Anniv. A355

Litho. & Engr.

2004, June 3 ***Perf. 13¼x13***
865 A355 80c multicolored 1.25 1.25

See Offices in Geneva No. 425; Vienna No. 349.

World Heritage Sites, Greece A356

No. 866, Acropolis, Athens. Nos. 867, 868e, Delos. No. 868a, Delphi. No. 868b, Pythagoreion and Heraion of Samos. No. 868c, Olympia. No. 868d, Mycenae and Tiryns.

2004, Aug. 12 **Litho.** ***Perf. 14x13¼***
866 A356 37c multicolored .70 .70
a. Booklet pane of 4 3.00 —
867 A356 60c multicolored 1.10 1.10

Souvenir Booklet

868 Booklet, #866a, 868f-868j 15.00
a.-d. A356 23c any single .55 .55
e. A356 37c multi .90 .90
f. Booklet pane of 4 #868a 2.20 2.20
g. Booklet pane of 4 #868b 2.20 2.20
h. Booklet pane of 4 #868c 2.20 2.20
i. Booklet pane of 4 #868d 2.20 2.20
j. Booklet pane of 4 #868e 3.60 3.60

See Offices in Geneva Nos. 426-428, Vienna Nos. 350-352. No. 868 sold for $7.20.

My Dream for Peace — A357

Winning designs of Lions Club International children's global peace poster contest by: 37c, Sittichok Pariyaket, Thailand. 80c, Bayan Fais Abu Bial, Israel.

2004, Sept. 21 **Litho.** ***Perf. 14***
869 A357 37c multicolored .60 .60
870 A357 80c multicolored 1.40 1.40

See Offices in Geneva Nos. 429-430, Vienna Nos. 353-354.

A358

Human Rights — A359

2004, Oct. 14 **Litho.** ***Perf. 11¼***
871 A358 37c multicolored .75 .75
872 A359 70c multicolored 1.40 1.40

See Offices in Geneva Nos. 431-432, Vienna Nos. 355-356.

Disarmament A360

2004, Oct. 15 **Litho.** ***Perf. 13¾***
873 A360 37c multicolored .80 .80

United Nations, 60th Anniv. A361

Litho. & Engr.

2005, Feb. 4 ***Perf. 11x11¼***
874 A361 80c multicolored 1.50 1.50

Souvenir Sheet

Litho.

Imperf

875 A361 $1 multicolored 17.50 17.50

See Offices in Geneva Nos. 434-435; Vienna Nos. 357-358.

Endangered Species Type of 1993

Designs: No. 876, Blue orchid. No. 877, Swan orchid. No. 878, Christmas orchid. No. 879, Aerangis modesta.

2005, Mar. 3 **Litho.** ***Perf. 12¾x12½***
876 A271 37c multicolored 1.10 1.10
877 A271 37c multicolored 1.10 1.10
878 A271 37c multicolored 1.10 1.10
879 A271 37c multicolored 1.10 1.10
a. Block of 4, #876-879 4.50 4.50

See Offices in Geneva Nos. 436-439; Vienna Nos. 360-363.

Non-Violence, Sculpture by Carl Fredrik Reuterswärd, New York — A362

Armillary Sphere, Sculpture by Paul Manship, Geneva A363

Terra Cotta Warriors, Vienna A364

Single Form, Sculpture by Barbara Hepworth, New York A365

Sphere Within a Sphere, Sculpture by Arnaldo Pomodoro, New York A366

2005, Mar. 3 **Litho.** ***Perf. 13¼***
880 A362 80c multi + label *35.00 35.00*
881 A363 80c multi + label *35.00 35.00*
882 A364 80c multi + label *35.00 35.00*
883 A365 80c multi + label *35.00 35.00*
884 A366 80c multi + label *35.00 35.00*
a. Vert. strip of 5, #880-884, + 5 labels *175.00 175.00*
b. Sheet of 10, both #884 37c (error) *3,250.*
c. Vert. strip of 5, #884 37c (error) *1,450.*

The full sheet sold for $14.95 with or without personalized labels. The personalization of labels was available only at UN Headquarters, and not through mail order.

The full sheet exists with sheet margins and labels commemorating the Riccione 2005 Philatelic Exhibition. This sheet went on sale 8/20/05 and was also sold for $14.95. Value $175.

Nature's Wisdom A367

37c, Ice climber, Norway. 80c, Egret, Japan.

2005, Apr. 21 **Litho.** ***Perf. 13½x13¼***
885 A367 37c multicolored .65 .65
886 A367 80c multicolored 1.50 1.50

See Offices in Geneva Nos. 440-441, Vienna Nos. 364-365.

Intl. Year of Sport — A368

2005, June 3 **Litho.** ***Perf. 13x13¼***
887 A368 37c Sailing .65 .65
888 A368 70c Running 1.25 1.25

See Offices in Geneva Nos. 442-443; Vienna Nos. 366-367.

World Heritage Sites, Egypt A369

Nos. 889, 891a, Memphis and its Necropolis. Nos. 890, 891d, Ancient Thebes. No. 891b, Philae. No. 891c, Abu Mena. No. 891e, Islamic Cairo. No. 891f, St. Catherine area.

2005, Aug. 4 **Litho.** ***Perf. 14x13¼***
889 A369 37c multicolored .60 .60
890 A369 80c multicolored 1.40 1.40

Souvenir Booklet

891 Booklet, #891g-891l 15.00
a.-c. A369 23c any single .50 .50
d.-f. A369 37c any single .75 .75
g. Booklet pane of 4 #891a 2.00 2.00
h. Booklet pane of 4 #891b 2.00 2.00
i. Booklet pane of 4 #891c 2.00 2.00
j. Booklet pane of 4 #891d 3.00 3.00
k. Booklet pane of 4 #891e 3.00 3.00
l. Booklet pane of 4 #891f 3.00 3.00

See Offices in Geneva Nos. 444-446, Vienna Nos. 368-370.

My Dream for Peace Type of 2004

Winning designs of Lions Club International children's global peace poster contest by: 37c, Vittoria Sansebastiano, Italy. 80c, Jordan Harris, US.

2005, Sept. 21 **Litho.** ***Perf. 14***
892 A357 37c multicolored .60 .60
893 A357 80c multicolored 1.40 1.40

See Offices in Geneva Nos. 447-448, Vienna Nos. 371-372.

Food for Life — A370

37c, Oats, children and adults. 80c, Wheat, mothers breastfeeding babies.

2005, Oct. 20 **Litho.** ***Perf. 13¾***
894 A370 37c multicolored .60 .60
895 A370 80c multicolored 1.40 1.40

See Offices in Geneva Nos. 449-450; Vienna Nos. 373-374.

Stylized Flags in Heart and Hands — A371

2006, Feb. 3 **Litho.** ***Perf. 13x13¼***
896 A371 25c multicolored .75 .75

Indigenous Art Type of 2003

No. 897 — Musical instruments: a, Drum, Ivory Coast. b, Drum, Tunisia. c, Stringed instruments, Morocco. d, Drums, Sudan. e, Instruments, Cameroun. f, Harp, Congo.

2006, Feb. 3 **Litho.** ***Perf. 13¼***
897 A340 Sheet of 6 10.00 10.00
a.-f. 37c Any single 1.50 1.50

See Offices in Geneva No. 452; Vienna No. 375.

UN Symbols Type of 2003

2006, Mar. 6 **Litho.** ***Perf. 13¼***
898 A349 39c multi + label 5.00 5.00
899 A350 39c multi + label 5.00 5.00
900 A351 39c multi + label 5.00 5.00
901 A352 39c multi + label 5.00 5.00
902 A353 39c multi + label 5.00 5.00
a. Vert. strip of 5, #898-902, + 5 labels 25.00 25.00

The full sheet sold for $14.95 with or without personalized labels. The personalization of labels was available only at UN Headquarters, and not through mail order.

Sculpture Type of 2005

2006, Mar. 6 **Litho.** ***Perf. 13¼***
903 A362 84c multi + label 12.00 12.00
a. Perf. 14½x14 + label 16.00 16.00
904 A363 84c multi + label 12.00 12.00
a. Perf. 14½x14 + label 16.00 16.00
905 A364 84c multi + label 12.00 12.00
a. Perf. 14½x14 + label 16.00 16.00
906 A365 84c multi + label 12.00 12.00
a. Perf. 14½x14 + label 16.00 16.00
907 A366 84c multi + label 12.00 12.00
a. Perf. 14½x14 + label 16.00 16.00
b. Vert. strip of 5, #903-907, + 5 labels *60.00 60.00*
c. Vert. strip of 5, #903a-907a, + 5 labels *80.00 80.00*

The full sheet sold for $14.95 with or without personalized labels. The personalization of labels was available only at UN Headquarters, and not through mail order.

Nos. 903a-907a issued 9/21/06. Nos. 903a-907a were from sheet for 2006 Berlin Stamp Show. The year "2006" is slightly smaller on Nos. 903a-907a than on Nos. 903-907.

Full sheets with different margins were sold at the Washington 2006 World Philatelic Exhibition, where the labels could be personalized. These are worth slightly more than the generic No. 907b sheet.

Endangered Species Type of 1993

No. 908, Golden mantella. No. 909, Panther chameleon. No. 910, Peruvian rainbow boa. No. 911, Dyeing poison frog.

Perf. 12¾x12½

2006, Mar. 16 **Litho.**
908 A271 39c multicolored .90 .90
909 A271 39c multicolored .90 .90
910 A271 39c multicolored .90 .90
911 A271 39c multicolored .90 .90
a. Block of 4, #908-911 4.00 4.00

See Offices in Geneva Nos. 453-456; Vienna Nos. 376-379.

Dove Between War and Peace A372

2006, Apr. 10 Litho. *Perf. 13¼*
912 A372 75c multi + label 3.75 3.75

The full sheet sold for $14.95 with or without personalized labels. The personalization of labels was available only at UN Headquarters, and not through mail order.

Intl. Day of Families — A373

39c, Family harvesting grapes. 84c, Children playing with toy sailboats.

2006, May 27 Litho. *Perf. 14x13½*
913 A373 39c multicolored .70 .70
914 A373 84c multicolored 1.50 1.50

See Offices in Geneva Nos. 457-458; Vienna Nos. 380-381.

World Heritage Sites, France A374

Eiffel Tower and: Nos. 915, 917a, Banks of the Seine. Nos. 916, 917d, Roman Aqueduct. No. 917b, Provins. No. 917c, Carcasonne. No. 917e, Mont Saint-Michel. No. 917f, Chateau de Chambord.

Litho. & Embossed with Foil Application

2006, June 17 *Perf. 13½x13¼*
915 A374 39c multicolored .75 .75
916 A374 84c multicolored 1.75 1.75

Souvenir Booklet

917 Booklet, #917g-917l 16.00
a.-c. A374 24c any single .50 .50
d.-f. A374 39c any single .80 .80
g. Booklet pane of 4 #917a 2.00 2.00
h. Booklet pane of 4 #917b 2.00 2.00
i. Booklet pane of 4 #917c 2.00 2.00
j. Booklet pane of 4 #917d 3.25 3.25
k. Booklet pane of 4 #917e 3.25 3.25
l. Booklet pane of 4 #917f 3.25 3.25

See Offices in Geneva Nos. 459-461, Vienna Nos. 382-384.

My Dream for Peace Type of 2004

Winning designs of Lions Club International children's global peace poster contest by: 39c, Cheuk Tat Li, Hong Kong. 84c, Kosshapan Paitoon, Thailand.

2006, Sept. 21 Litho. *Perf. 13½x13*
918 A357 39c multicolored .80 .80
919 A357 84c multicolored 1.75 1.75

See Offices in Geneva Nos. 462-463; Vienna Nos. 385-386.

Flags and Coins — A375

No. 920 — Flag of: a, People's Republic of China, 1 yuan coin. b, Australia, 1 dollar coin. c, Ghana, 50 cedi coin. d, Israel, 10 agorot coin. e, Russia, 1 ruble coin. f, Mexico, 10 peso coin. g, Japan, 10 yen coin. h, Cambodia, 200 riel coin.

2006, Oct. 5 Litho. *Perf. 13¼x13*
920 Sheet of 8 7.00 7.00
a.-h. A375 39c Any single .75 .75

A column of rouletting in the middle of the sheet separates it into two parts. See Nos. 930, 953, 998, 1022, 1039, 1078, 1103; Offices in Geneva Nos. 464, 469, 484, 512, 532, 546, 576, 594; Vienna Nos. 387, 392, 421, 459, 483, 507, 539, 558.

Flag Type of 1980

2007, Feb. 2 Litho. *Perf. 14*
921 A185 39c Tuvalu 1.10 1.10
922 A185 39c Switzerland 1.10 1.10
923 A185 39c Timor-Leste 1.10 1.10
924 A185 39c Montenegro 1.10 1.10
a. Block of 4, #921-924 12.50 12.50
Nos. 921-924 (4) 4.40 4.40

Endangered Species Type of 1993

No. 925, Drill. No. 926, Common squirrel monkey. No. 927, Ring-tailed lemur. No. 928, Collared mangabey.

Perf. 12¾x12½

2007, Mar. 15 Litho.
925 A271 39c multicolored .85 .85
926 A271 39c multicolored .85 .85
927 A271 39c multicolored .85 *.85*
928 A271 39c multicolored .85 .85
a. Block of 4, #925-928 3.50 3.50

See Offices in Geneva Nos. 465-468; Vienna Nos. 388-391.

UN Emblem A376

2007, Feb. 5 Litho. *Perf. 14½x14*
929 A376 84c dk blue + label *17.50 10.00*

The full sheet sold for $14.95. The sheet has two each of five different labels that could not be personalized. The sheet was distributed to members of the Japanese mission on Sept. 21, 2006, but it was not sold to the public until 2007. The sheet's availability to the public was not announced through press releases or on the UNPA website prior to the day of issue or afterward. It was sent to standing order customers in May 2007.
Compare with Type A377.

Flags and Coins Type of 2006

No. 930 — Flag of: a, Brazil, 50 centavo coin. b, Thailand, 1 baht coin. c, Viet Nam, 5,000 dong coin. d, Ecuador, 10 centavo coin. e, India, 5 rupee coin. f, South Africa, 5 cent coin. g, Barbados, 25 cent coin. h, Republic of Korea, 500 won coin.

2007, May 3 Litho. *Perf. 13¼x13*
930 Sheet of 8 8.00 8.00
a.-h. A375 39c Any single .75 .75

A column of rouletting in the middle of the sheet separates it into two parts. See Offices in Geneva No. 469; Vienna No. 392.

UN Emblem A377

2007, June 1 Litho. *Perf. 13¼*
931 A377 84c blue + label *4.50 4.50*

The full sheet sold for $14.95. The sheet has two each of five different labels that could not be personalized.
Compare with Type A376.

Peaceful Visions — A378

39c, "Nest." 84c, "Sisters Weave the Olive Branch."

2007, June 1 Litho. *Perf. 13x12½*
932 A378 39c multicolored .90 .90
933 A378 84c multicolored 1.80 1.80

See Offices in Geneva Nos. 470-471; Vienna Nos. 398-399.

UN Symbols Type of 2003

2007, May 14 Litho. *Perf. 13¼*
934 A349 41c multi + label 3.25 3.25
935 A350 41c multi + label 3.25 3.25
936 A351 41c multi + label 3.25 3.25
937 A352 41c multi + label 3.25 3.25
938 A353 41c multi + label 3.25 3.25
a. Vert. strip of 5, #934-938, + 5 labels 17.00 17.00

The full sheet sold for $14.95 with or without personalized labels. The personalization of labels was available only at UN Headquarters, and not through mail order.

UN Flag A379

2007, May 14 Litho. *Perf. 13¼*
939 A379 90c blue + label *5.00 6.00*

The full sheet sold for $14.95. The sheet has two each of five different labels that could not be personalized.
A second printing of No. 939 has the "U" and "N" more closely spaced, and it has different labels and different pane borders. Value about the same.

Helmet of UN Peacekeeper — A380

2007, Aug. 9 Litho. *Perf. 12½x13¼*
940 A380 90c multicolored 1.90 1.90

World Heritage Sites, South America A381

No. 941, Galapagos Islands, Ecuador. Nos. 942, 943a, Rapa Nui, Chile. No. 943b, Cueva de las Manos, Argentina. No. 943c, Machu Picchu, Peru. No. 943d, Tiwanaku, Bolivia. No. 943e, Iguaçu National Park, Brazil.

2007, Aug. 9 Litho. *Perf. 13¼x13*
941 A381 41c multicolored .85 .85
a. Booklet pane of 4 3.40 —
942 A381 90c multicolored 1.90 1.90

Souvenir Booklet

943 Booklet, #941a, 943f-943j 17.00
a.-c. A381 26c Any single .60 .60
d.-e. A381 41c Either single 1.00 1.00
f. Booklet pane of 4 #943a 2.40 2.40
g. Booklet pane of 4 #943b 2.40 2.40
h. Booklet pane of 4 #943c 2.40 2.40
i. Booklet pane of 4 #943d 4.00 4.00
j. Booklet pane of 4 #943e 4.00 4.00

See Offices in Geneva Nos. 472-474, Vienna Nos. 400-402. No. 943 sold for $8.50.

Humanitarian Mail — A382

2007, Sept. 6 Litho. *Perf. 12½x13¼*
944 A382 90c multicolored 1.90 1.90

See Offices in Geneva No. 475, Vienna No. 403, Switzerland No. 9O21.

Space for Humanity — A383

41c, Space Shuttle. 90c, Astronauts spacewalking.
$1, International Space Station.

2007, Oct. 25 Litho. *Perf. 13½x14*
945 A383 41c multicolored .85 .85
946 A383 90c multicolored 1.90 1.90

Souvenir Sheet

947 A383 $1 multicolored 2.50 2.50
a. With World Space Week emblem in margin 3.00 3.00

See Offices in Geneva Nos. 476-478, Vienna Nos. 409-411.

Intl. Holocaust Remembrance Day — A384

2008, Jan. 27 Litho. *Perf. 13*
948 A384 41c multicolored .85 .85

See Offices in Geneva No. 479, Vienna No. 412, Israel No. 1715.

Endangered Species Type of 1993

No. 949, South African fur seal. No. 950, Orange cup coral. No. 951, Longsnout seahorse. No. 952, Gray whale.

2008, Mar. 6 Litho. *Perf. 12¾x12½*
949 A271 41c multicolored 1.00 1.00
950 A271 41c multicolored 1.00 1.00
941 A271 41c multicolored 1.00 1.00
952 A271 41c multicolored 1.00 1.00
a. Block of 4, #949-952 4.50 4.50

See Offices in Geneva Nos. 480-483; Vienna Nos. 417-420.

Flags and Coins Type of 2006

No. 953 — Flag of: a, United Kingdom, 2 pound coin. b, Singapore, 5 dollar coin. c, Colombia, 500 peso coin. d, Sri Lanka, 10 rupee coin. e, Philippines, 1 peso coin. f, Indonesia, 500 rupiah coin. g, United Arab Emirates, 1 dirham coin. h, Libya, 50 dinar coin.

2008, May 8 Litho. *Perf. 13¼x13*
953 Sheet of 8 7.00 7.00
a.-h. A375 41c Any single .85 .85

A column of rouletting in the middle of the sheet separates it into two parts. See Offices in Geneva No. 484; Vienna No. 421.

Sculpture and Flags A385

UN Flag A386

UN General Assembly A387

Flags A388

UN Headquarters — A389

2008, May 12 Litho. *Perf. 13¼*
954 A385 42c multi + label *3.50 3.50*
955 A386 42c multi + label *3.50 3.50*
956 A387 42c multi + label *3.50 3.50*
957 A388 42c multi + label *3.50 3.50*
958 A389 42c multi + label *3.50 3.50*
a. Vert. strip of 5, #954-958, + 5 labels *17.50 17.50*

The full sheet sold for $14.95 with or without personalized labels. The personalization of labels was available only at UN Headquarters, and not through mail order.

UN Emblem A390

2008, May 12 Litho. *Perf. 13¼*

959 A390 94c blue + label *4.50 4.50*

The full sheet sold for $14.95 with or without labels that could be personalized. There are five non-personalized labels. The personalization of labels was available only at UN Headquarters, and not through mail order.

Wheelchair Accessibility Symbol A391

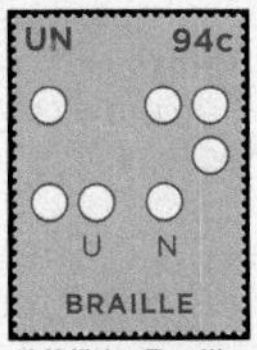

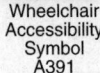

"UN" in Braille A392

Litho. & Embossed

2008, June 6 *Perf. 14x13¼*

960 A391 42c blue & yellow .85 .85
961 A392 94c yellow & blue 1.90 1.90

Convention on the Rights of Persons with Disabilities. See Offices in Geneva Nos. 485-486, Vienna Nos. 427-428.

Sport for Peace A393

42c, $1.25, Sprinter. 94c, Hurdler.

2008, Aug. 8 Litho. *Perf. 14½*

962 A393 42c multicolored .85 .85
963 A393 94c multicolored 1.90 1.90

Souvenir Sheet

Perf. 12¾x13¼

964 A393 $1.25 multicolored 6.00 6.00

2008 Summer Olympics, Beijing. See Offices in Geneva Nos. 487-489, Vienna Nos. 429-431.

Sport for Peace A394

2008, Aug. 8 Litho. *Perf. 13¼*

965 A394 94c multi + label *3.75 3.75*

2008 Summer Olympics, Beijing. The full pane sold for $14.95 with or without personalized labels. There are two non-personalized labels. The personalization of labels was available only at UN Headquarters, and not through mail order.

No. 965 is often collected as a single stamp with the two different labels attached; value thus $6.50.

"We Can End Poverty" A395

Winning designs in children's art contest by: 42c, Grace Tsang, Hong Kong. 94c, Bryan Jevoncia, Indonesia, vert.

Perf. 12¾x12½

2008, Sept. 18 Litho.

966 A395 42c multicolored .85 .85

Perf. 12½x12¾

967 A395 94c multicolored 1.90 1.90

See Offices in Geneva Nos. 490-491, Vienna Nos. 432-433.

Climate Change Types of Geneva and Vienna and

A396

Climate Change A397

No. 968 — Parched ground and snail shell with quarter of Earth in: a, LR. b, LL. c, UR. d, UL.

No. 969 — Coral reef with quarter of Earth in: a, LR. b, LL. c, UR. d, UL.

No. 970: a, Like #969a. b, Like #969b. c, Like #969c. d, Like #969d. e, Like Geneva #493a. f, Like Geneva #493b. g, Like Geneva #493c. h, Like Geneva #493d. i, Like Vienna #434a. j, Like Vienna #434b. k, Like Vienna #434c. l, Like Vienna #434d. m, Like Geneva #492a. n, Like Geneva #492b. o, Like Geneva #492c. p, Like Geneva #492d. q, Like Vienna #435a. r, Like Vienna #435b. s, Like Vienna #435c. t, Like Vienna #435d.

All stamps have blue panels inscribed "Climate Change."

2008, Oct. 23 Litho. *Perf. 13¼x13*

968 Sheet of 4 4.75 4.75
a.-d. A396 42c Any single 1.10 1.10
e. Booklet pane of 4, #968a-968d 6.00 6.00
969 Sheet of 4 10.00 10.00
a.-d. A397 94c Any single 2.50 2.50

Souvenir Booklet

970 Booklet, #968e, 970u-970y 20.00
a.-d. A397 27c Any single .75 .75
e.-h. G77 27c Any single .75 .75
i.-l. V72 27c Any single .75 .75
m.-p. G76 42c Any single 1.00 1.00
q.-t. V73 42c Any single 1.00 1.00
u. Booklet pane of 4, #970a-970d 3.00 3.00
v. Booklet pane of 4, #970e-970h 3.00 3.00
w. Booklet pane of 4, #970i-970l 3.00 3.00
x. Booklet pane of 4, #970m-970p 4.00 4.00
y. Booklet pane of 4, #970q-970t 4.00 4.00

No. 970 sold for $9. See Offices in Geneva Nos. 492-494, Vienna Nos. 434-436.

A398

Designs: 1c, Cielo rosado. 9c, Rosa de sangre. 10c, Espíritu de mujer.

2009, Feb. 6 Litho. *Perf. 13¼*

971 A398 1c multicolored .30 .30
972 A398 9c multicolored .30 .30
973 A398 10c multicolored .30 .30
Nos. 971-973 (3) .90 .90

A399

Litho. With Foil Application

2009, Feb. 6 *Perf. 14x13½*

974 A399 94c purple & multi 2.00 2.00

See Offices in Geneva No. 495, Vienna No. 437.

Endangered Species Type of 1993

No. 975, Emperor dragonfly. No. 976, Southern wood ant. No. 977, Rosalia longicorn. No. 978, Apollo butterfly.

2009, Apr. 16 Litho. *Perf. 12¾x12½*

975 A271 42c multicolored 1.25 1.25
976 A271 42c multicolored 1.25 1.25
977 A271 42c multicolored 1.25 1.25
978 A271 42c multicolored 1.25 1.25
a. Block of 4, #975-978 5.50 5.50
b. Pane of 16, imperf. *5,000.*

See Offices in Geneva Nos. 496-499; Vienna Nos. 438-441.

A400

Nos. 979, 981a, Town Hall and Roland on the Marketplace, Bremen. Nos. 980, 981d, Aachen Cathedral. No. 981b, Wartburg Castle. No. 981c, Palaces and Parks of Potsdam and Berlin. No. 981e, Luther Memorials in Eisleben and Wittenberg. No. 981f, Monastic Island of Reichenau.

2009, May 7 Litho. *Perf. 14x13½*

979 A400 44c multicolored .90 .90
980 A400 98c multicolored 2.00 2.00

Souvenir Booklet

981 Booklet, #981g-981l 20.00
a.-c. A400 27c any single .60 .60
d.-f. A400 42c any single 1.00 1.00
g. Booklet pane of 4 #981a 2.40 2.40
h. Booklet pane of 4 #981b 2.40 2.40
i. Booklet pane of 4 #981c 2.40 2.40
j. Booklet pane of 4 #981d 4.00 4.00
k. Booklet pane of 4 #981e 4.00 4.00
l. Booklet pane of 4 #981f 4.00 4.00

See Offices in Geneva Nos. 500-502, Vienna Nos. 442-444.

UN Flag A401

Let Us Beat Swords Into Plowshares, Sculpture by Evgeny Vuchetich — A402

Single Form, Sculpture by Barbara Hepworth A403

Window Cleaner A404

UN Headquarters — A405

2009, June 5 *Perf. 13¼*

982 A401 44c multi + label *2.00 2.00*
a. Perf. 11¼x11 + label *10.00 10.00*
b. Perf. 14¼x14½ + label *1.80 1.80*
983 A402 44c multi + label *2.00 2.00*
a. Perf. 11¼x11 + label *10.00 10.00*
b. Perf. 14¼x14½ + label *1.80 1.80*
984 A403 44c multi + label *2.00 2.00*
a. Perf. 11¼x11 + label *10.00 10.00*
b. Perf. 14¼x14½ + label *1.80 1.80*
985 A404 44c multi + label *2.00 2.00*
a. Perf. 11¼x11 + label *10.00 10.00*
b. Perf. 14¼x14½ + label *1.80 1.80*
986 A405 44c multi + label *2.00 2.00*
a. Perf. 11¼x11 + label *10.00 10.00*
b. Perf. 14¼x14½ + label *1.80 1.80*
c. Vert. strip of 5, #982-986, + 5 labels *10.00 10.00*
d. Vert. strip of 5, #982a-986a, + 5 labels *50.00 50.00*
e. Vert. strip of 5, #982b-986b, + 5 labels *9.00 7.50*

The full sheets sold for $14.95 with or without personalized labels. The personalization of labels was available only at UN Headquarters, and not through mail order. The sheet of No. 986d has "ver. 2" in the lower right selvage. The sheet of No. 986e has "Ver. 3" in the lower right selvage.

Flags and UN Headquarters — A406

Single Form, Sculpture by Barbara Hepworth A407

UN Flag A408

Sphere Within a Sphere, Sculpture by Arnaldo Pomodoro A409

UN Headquarters and Chrysler Building — A410

2009, June 5

987 A406 98c multi + label *4.00 4.00*
a. Perf. 11¼x11 + label *9.00 9.00*
b. Perf. 14¼x14½ + label *3.50 3.50*
988 A407 98c multi + label *4.00 4.00*
a. Perf. 11¼x11 + label *9.00 9.00*
b. Perf. 14¼x14½ + label *3.50 3.50*
989 A408 98c multi + label *4.00 4.00*
a. Perf. 11¼x11 + label *9.00 9.00*
b. Perf. 14¼x14½ + label *3.50 3.50*
990 A409 98c multi + label *4.00 4.00*
a. Perf. 11¼x11 + label *9.00 9.00*
b. Perf. 14¼x14½ + label *3.50 3.50*
991 A410 98c multi + label *4.00 4.00*
a. Perf. 11¼x11 + label *9.00 9.00*
b. Perf. 14¼x14½ + label *3.50 3.50*
c. Vert. strip of 5, #987-991, + 5 labels *20.00 20.00*
d. Vert. strip of 5, #987a-991a, + 5 labels *45.00 45.00*
e. Vert. strip of 5, #987b-991b, + 5 labels *17.50 17.50*

The full sheets sold for $14.95 with or without personalized labels. The personalization of labels was available only at UN Headquarters, and not through mail order. The sheet of No. 991d has "ver. 2" in the lower right selvage. The sheet of No. 991e has "VER. 3" in the lower right selvage.

Economic and Social Council A411

Designs: 44c, Water and sanitation. 98c, Traditional medicines.

2009, Aug. 6 *Perf. 12¾x12½*

992 A411 44c multicolored 2.00 .90
993 A411 98c multicolored 5.00 2.00

See Offices in Geneva Nos. 503-504, Vienna Nos. 450-451.

UN Emblem A412

2009, Sept. 22 ***Perf. 13¼***

994 A412 98c multi + label *5.50 5.50*
a. Perf. 11¼x11 + label *5.00 5.00*

The full sheets sold for $14.95 with or without personalized labels. There are five different non-personalized labels. The personalization of labels was available only at UN Headquarters, and not through mail order. The sheet of No. 994a has "ver. 2" in the lower right selvage.

Miniature Sheet

Millennium Development Goals — A413

No. 995: a, Bowl of hot food. b, Pencil. c, Female symbol. d, Teddy bear. e, Pregnant woman, heart. f, Medicine bottle. g, Stylized tree. h, Conjoined people.

2009, Sept. 25

995 A413 Sheet of 8 8.50 8.50
a.-h. 44c Any single 1.20 1.20

See Offies in Geneva No. 505; Vienna No. 457.

Mohandas K. Gandhi — A414

2009, Oct. 2

996 A414 $1 multicolored 2.25 2.25

Miniature Sheet

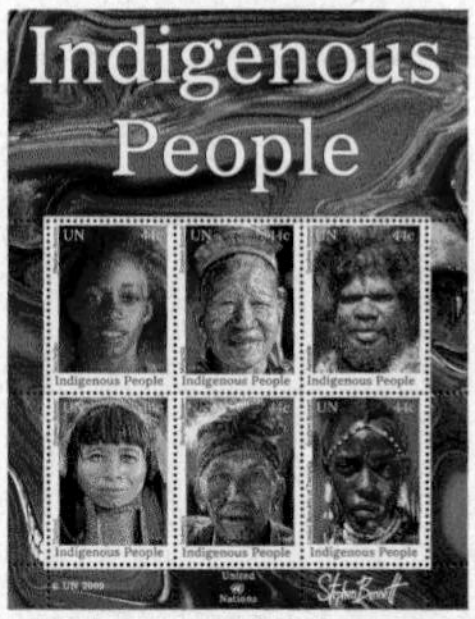

Indigenous People — A415

No. 997 — Portraits of person from: a, Seychelles. b, Malaysia. c, Australia. d, Thailand. e, Indonesia. f, Tanzania.

2009, Oct. 8 ***Perf. 12½***

997 A415 Sheet of 6 7.00 7.00
a.-f. 44c Any single 1.15 1.15

See Offices in Geneva No. 511, Vienna No. 458.

Flags and Coins Type of 2006

No. 998 — Flag of: a, Bahamas, 10 cent coin. b, Jamaica, 20 dollar coin. c, Honduras, 50 centavo coin. d, Kuwait, 100 fils coin. e, Panama, 1 cuarto de Balboa coin. f, Guatemala, 50 centavo coin. g, St. Lucia, 1 cent coin. h, Yemen, 20 rial coin.

2010, Feb. 5 Litho. ***Perf. 13¼x13***

998 Sheet of 8 9.75 9.75
a.-h. A375 44c Any single 1.20 1.20

A column of rouletting in the middle of the sheet separates it into two parts. See Offices in Geneva No. 512; Vienna No. 459.

Endangered Species Type of 1993

No. 999, Monkey puzzle tree. No. 1000, Quiver tree. No. 1001, Bristlecone pine tree. No. 1002, Scarlet ball cactus.

2010, Apr. 15 Litho. ***Perf. 12¾x12½***

999 A271 44c multicolored 1.25 1.25
1000 A271 44c multicolored 1.25 1.25
1001 A271 44c multicolored 1.25 1.25
1002 A271 44c multicolored 1.25 1.25
a. Block of 4, #999-1002 5.50 5.50

See Offices in Geneva Nos. 513-516; Vienna Nos. 465-468.

The stamp pictured above was printed in limited quantities and sold for far more than face value. The label attached to the stamp could not be personalized. Value for stamp and label, $3. A similar stamp dated "2011" with a different label attached exists.

One Planet, One Ocean Types of Geneva and Vienna and

A416

One Planet, One Ocean A417

No. 1003: a, Turtle at top, eel at left, fish at LR. b, Fish at LL, turtle's flipper at bottom. c, Fish at left, yellow sponge at LR, Lobster at right. d, Lobster at left, turtle at right.

No. 1004: a, Octopus at left, fish at LR. b, Fish at left and right, turtle's head at bottom. c, Lobster at left. fish at LL and LR. d, Fish at LL and LR, turtle's body at UR.

No. 1005: a, Like #1003a. b, Like #1003b, c, Like #1003c, d, Like #1003d. e, Like Vienna #471a. f, Like Vienna #471b. g, Like Vienna #471c, h, Like Vienna #471d. i, Like Geneva #519a. j, Like Geneva #519b, k, Like Geneva #519c. l, Like Geneva #519d. m, Like #1004a. n, Like #1004b. o, Like #1004c, p, Like #1004d. q, Like Vienna #472a. r, Like Vienna #472b. s, Like Vienna #472c. t, Like Vienna #472d. u, Like Geneva #520a. v, Like Geneva #520b. w, Like Geneva #520c. x, Like Geneva #520d.

2010, May 6 Litho. ***Perf. 14x13¼***

1003 A416 Sheet of 4 3.60 3.60
a.-d. 44c Any single .90 .90
1004 A417 Sheet of 4 8.00 8.00
a.-d. 98c Any single 2.00 2.00

Souvenir Booklet

Perf. 13¼x13

1005 Booklet, #1005y-1005z, 1005aa-1005ad 18.00
a.-d. A416 28c any single .60 .60
e.-h. V91 28c any single .60 .60
i.-l. G85 28c any single .60 .60
m.-p. A417 44c any single .90 .90
q.-t. V92 44c any single .90 .90
u.-x. G86 44c any single .90 .90
y. Booklet pane of 4 #1005a-1005d 2.40 2.40
z. Booklet pane of 4 #1005e-1005h 2.40 2.40
aa. Booklet pane of 4 #1005i-1005l 2.40 2.40
ab. Booklet pane of 4 #1005m-1005p 3.60 3.60
ac. Booklet pane of 4 #1005q-1005t 3.60 3.60
ad. Booklet pane of 4 #1005u-1005x 3.60 3.60

Intl. Oceanographic Commission, 50th anniv. See Offices in Geneva Nos. 519-521, Vienna Nos. 471-473.

People of Different Cultures A418

People of Different Cultures as New York Buildings A419

2010, June 4 Litho. ***Perf. 13***

1006 A418 3c multicolored .25 .25
1007 A419 4c multicolored .25 .25

UN Headquarters and New York Skyline A420

Shanghai Skyline A421

2010, June 4 Litho. ***Perf. 13¼***

1008 A420 98c multicolored 3.00 3.00
1009 A421 98c multicolored 3.00 3.00
a. Horiz. pair, #1008-1009 6.00 6.00

Expo 2010, Shanghai. Nos. 1008-1009 were sold only in full panes for $14.95.

United Nations, 65th Anniv. — A422

Litho. With Foil Application

2010, June 28 ***Perf. 13¼***

1010 A422 98c light blue & gold 2.25 2.25

Souvenir Sheet

1011 Sheet of 2 #1011a 5.00 5.00
a. A422 98c dark blue & gold 2.50 2.50

See Offices in Geneva No. 522, Vienna No. 474.

A423

A424

A425

A426

United Nations Sea Transport — A427

2010, Sept. 2 Litho. ***Perf. 13¼x13***

1012 A423 44c multicolored .90 .90
1013 A424 44c multicolored .90 .90
1014 A425 44c multicolored .90 .90
1015 A426 44c multicolored .90 .90
1016 A427 44c multicolored .90 .90
a. Horiz. strip of 5, #1012-1016 5.00 5.00

See Offices in Geneva Nos. 523-527, Vienna Nos. 475-479.

Intl. Year of Biodiversity — A428

Drawings from Art Forms from Nature, by Ernst Heinrich: 15c, Hummingbird. $1.50, Liverwort.

2010, Oct. 18 Litho. ***Perf. 13***

1017 A428 15c multicolored .30 .30
1018 A428 $1.50 multicolored 3.00 3.00

See Offices in Geneva Nos. 517-518; Vienna Nos. 469-470.

Miniature Sheet

Indigenous People — A429

No. 1019 — Portraits of person from: a, Thailand. b, French Polynesia (woman, denomination in black). c, Papua New Guinea. d, French Polynesia (man, denomination in white). e, Australia (child). f, Australia (old man with headband).

2010, Oct. 21 Litho. ***Perf. 13***

1019 A429 Sheet of 6 6.00 6.00
a.-f. 44c Any single 1.00 1.00

See Offices in Geneva No. 529; Vienna No. 480.

United Nations Headquarters, New York — A430

United Nations Headquarters: 11c, Aerial view. $5, Ground-level view.

2011, Feb. 4 Litho. ***Perf. 13***

1020 A430 11c multicolored .25 .25
1021 A430 $5 multicolored 9.00 9.00

See Offices in Geneva Nos. 530-531; Vienna Nos. 481-482.

Flags and Coins Type of 2006

No. 1022 — Flag of: a, Mauritius, 1 rupee coin. b, Guyana, 10 dollar coin. c, Timor, 5 cent coin. d, Iceland, 100 krónur coin. e, Chile, 1 peso coin. f, Norway, 20 kroner coin. g, Fiji, 50 cent coin. h, Comoro Islands, 100 franc coin.

2011, Mar. 3 Litho. ***Perf. 13¼x13***

1022 Sheet of 8 8.75 8.75
a.-h. A375 44c Any single 1.10 1.10

A column of rouletting in the middle of the sheet separates it into two parts. See Offices in Geneva No. 532; Vienna No. 483.

UN Emblem A431

2011, Apr. 7 Litho. ***Perf. 14¾***

1023 A431 98c blue + label *4.00 4.00*

Printed in sheets of 10 + 10 different labels which are not personalizable. The full sheet sold for $14.95

Human Space Flight, 50th Anniv. A432

No. 1024: Various parts of outer space scene.
No. 1025: a, Cosmonaut and rocket. b, Astronaut on ladder of Lunar Module.

2011, Apr. 12 Litho. *Perf. 13x13¼*

1024	A432	Sheet of 16	16.00	16.00
a.-p.		44c any single	1.00	1.00

Souvenir Sheet

1025	A432	Sheet of 2	15.00	15.00
a.		44c multi	4.50	4.50
b.		98c multi	11.50	11.50

See Offices in Geneva Nos. 533-534; Vienna Nos. 484-485. No. 1024 contains two 40x48mm stamps that were printed as part of a larger sheet of six stamps, Vienna No. 485c, which was broken up into its component two-stamp souvenir sheets, and also sold as one unit. Value $90, complete unit.

UNESCO World Heritage Sites in Nordic Countries A433

Designs: 44c, Surtsey Volcanic Island, Iceland. 98c, Drottningholm Castle, Sweden.

2011, May 5 Litho. *Perf. 14x13½*

1026	A433	44c multicolored	.90	.90
1027	A433	98c multicolored	2.00	2.00

See Offices in Geneva Nos. 535-536; Vienna Nos. 496-497.

AIDS Ribbon — A434

2011, June 3 Litho. *Die Cut*

Self-Adhesive

1028	A434	44c red & blue	1.75	1.75

See Offices in Geneva No. 537; Vienna No. 498.

Economic and Social Council (ECOSOC) A435

2011, July 1 Litho. *Perf. 14¼*

1029	A435	44c multicolored	1.50	1.50
1030	A435	98c multicolored	3.50	3.50

See Offices in Geneva Nos. 538-539; Vienna Nos. 499-500.

Endangered Species Type of 1993

Designs: No. 1031, Bali starling. No. 1032, California condor. No. 1033, Japanese crane. No. 1034, Black-fronted piping-guan.

2011, Sept. 7 *Perf. 12¾x12½*

1031	A271	44c multicolored	1.10	1.10
1032	A271	44c multicolored	1.10	1.10
1033	A271	44c multicolored	1.10	1.10
1034	A271	44c multicolored	1.10	1.10
a.		Block of 4, #1031-1034	5.00	5.00

See Offices in Geneva Nos. 540-543; Vienna Nos. 501-504.

Intl. Year of Forests — A436

Designs: 44c, Tree with wildlife, man with mask. 98c, Tree roots.

Litho. With Foil Application

2011, Oct. 13 *Perf. 12½*

1035	44c multicolored	1.25	1.25
1036	98c multicolored	2.50	2.50
a.	A436 Vert. pair, #1035-1036	3.75	3.75

See Offices in Geneva Nos. 544-545; Vienna Nos. 505-506.

UN Emblem A437

2012, Jan. 23 Litho. *Perf. 14¾*

1037	A437	$1.05 blue + label	*2.75*	*2.75*
		Sheet of 10 + 10 labels	*27.50*	—

The full sheet sold for $14.95. The generic label exists as shown, and with dragon in yellow against red background. Labels could be personalized. The personalization of labels was available only at UN Headquarters, and not through mail order.

A438

No. 1038: a, Desk in lobby. b, Sculpture of Jesus holding lamb. c, Stained-glass window. d, Meeting room. e, Guided tour. f, Flags in front of United Nations buildings. g, United Nations Peacekeepers helmet in showcase. h, Gift shop. i, View of curved floors above lobby. j, Street signs.

2012, Jan. 23 Litho. *Perf. 14¾*

1038	A438	Sheet of 10	*30.00*	*30.00*
a.-j.		$1.05 Any single + label	*3.00*	*3.00*

The full sheet sold for $14.95. The generic labels are shown. Labels could be personalized. The personalization of labels was available only at UN Headquarters, and not through mail order.

Flags and Coins Type of 2006

No. 1039 — Flag of: a, Nepal, 1 rupee coin. b, Bahrain, 100 fils coin. c, Paraguay, 1000 guarani coin. d, Ethiopia, 25 cent coin. e, Peru, 1 sol coin. f, Solomon Islands, 20 cent coin. g, Dominican Republic, 1 peso coin. h, Canada, 1 dollar coin.

2012, Feb. 3 Litho. *Perf. 13¼x13*

1039		Sheet of 8	7.25	7.25
a.-h.		A375 45c Any single	.90	.90

A column of rouletting in the middle of the sheet separates it into two parts. See Offices in Geneva No. 546; Vienna No. 507.

A439

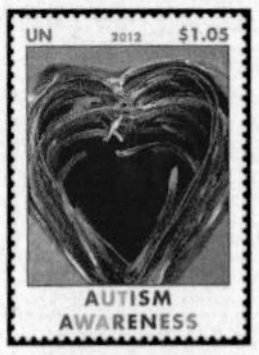

Autism Awareness — A440

Drawings by autistic people: No. 1040, An Abstract Garden II, by Trent Altman, U.S. No. 1041, Crazy Love, by Hannah Kandel, U.S.

2012, Apr. 2 Litho. *Perf. 14x13½*

1040	A439	$1.05 multicolored	2.10	2.10
1041	A440	$1.05 multicolored	2.10	2.10
a.		Pair, #1040-1041	4.20	4.20

See Offices in Geneva Nos. 547-548; Vienna Nos. 508-509.

Endangered Species Type of 1993

Designs: No. 1042, Giant panda. No. 1043, Short-horned chameleon. No. 1044, Oncilla. No. 1045, Cotton-headed tamarin.

2012, Apr. 19 Litho. *Perf. 12¾x12½*

1042	A271	45c multicolored	1.10	1.10
1043	A271	45c multicolored	1.10	1.10
1044	A271	45c multicolored	1.10	1.10
1045	A271	45c multicolored	1.10	1.10
a.		Block of 4, #1042-1045	5.00	5.00

See Offices in Geneva Nos. 549-552; Vienna Nos. 511-514.

Tinker Bell A441

Tinker Bell A442

2012, June 1 Litho. *Perf. 14¾*

1046	A441	$1.05 multi + label	*3.00*	*3.00*
1047	A442	$1.05 multi + label	*3.00*	*3.00*
a.		Vert. pair, #1046-1047, + 2 labels	*6.00*	*6.00*
		Sheet of 10, 5 each #1046-1047, + 10 labels	*30.00*	*30.00*

The full sheet sold for $14.95. The generic labels are shown. Labels could be personalized. The personalization of labels was available only at UN Headquarters, and not through mail order.

Rio + 20 Conference on Sustainable Development, Rio de Janeiro — A443

2012, June 1 Litho. *Perf. 13x13¼*

1048	A443	$1.05 multicolored	2.10	2.10

See Offices in Geneva No. 553; Vienna No. 515.

Sport for Peace A444

2012 Paralympics events: 45c, Goalball. $1.05, Sitting volleyball.

Litho. With Foil Application

2012, Aug. 17 *Perf. 14½*

1049	A444	45c multicolored	.90	.90
1050	A444	$1.05 multicolored	2.10	2.10
a.		Souvenir sheet of 1	3.50	3.50

See Offices in Geneva Nos. 554-555; Vienna Nos. 516-517.

UNESCO World Heritage Sites in Africa — A445

Designs: 45c, Kilamanjaro National Park, Tanzania. $1.05, Old Towns of Djenné, Mali.

2012, Sept. 5 Litho. *Perf. 13¼*

1051	A445	45c multicolored	.90	.90
1052	A445	$1.05 multicolored	2.10	2.10

See Offices in Geneva Nos. 556-557; Vienna Nos. 518-519.

Miniature Sheet

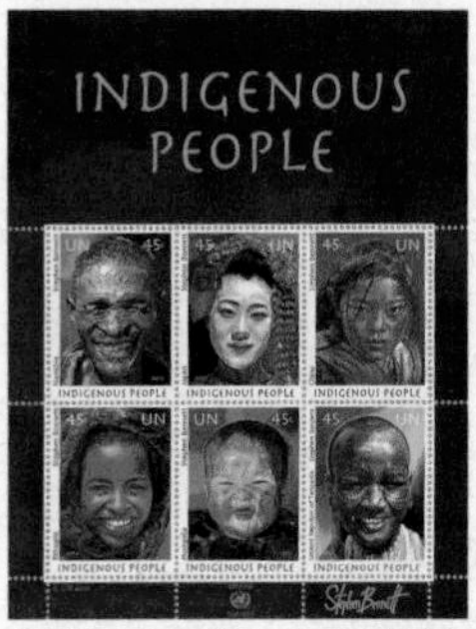

Indigenous People — A446

No. 1053 — Portrait of person from: a, Namibia. b, Japan. c, China. d, Ethiopia. e, Mongolia. f, Tanzania.

2012, Oct. 11 Litho. *Perf. 13¼x13*

1053	A446	Sheet of 6	5.50	5.50
a.-f.		45c Any single	.90	.90

See Offices in Geneva No. 558; Vienna No. 520.

UN Emblem A447

2013, Jan. 28 Litho. *Perf. 14¾*

1054	A447	$1.10 multi + label	*4.00*	*4.00*
		Sheet of 10 + 10 labels	*40.00*	—

The full sheet sold for $14.95. The generic label exists as shown, and with snake against red background. Labels could be personalized. The personalization of labels was available only at UN Headquarters, and not through mail order.

A448

No. 1055: a, Flags in front of Secretariat Building, brown panel at right. b, Aerial view of headquarters and East River, yellow orange panel at left. c, Secretariat Building and wall of General Assembly building, yellow orange panel at left. d, Headquarters and East River, brown panel at right. e, General Asembly and Secretariat Buildings, flags at right, brown panel at right. f, Sculpture and fountain at night, yellow orange panel at left. g, Secretariat Building and cherry blossoms, yellow orange panel at left. h, Secretariat Building, trees without leaves, flags at left, brown panel at right. i, Aerial view of headquarters at night, brown panel at right. j, Headquarters, yellow panel at left.

2013, Jan. 28 Litho. *Perf. 14¾*

1055	A448	Sheet of 10	*30.00*	*30.00*
a.-j.		$1.10 Any single + label	*3.00*	*3.00*

The full sheet sold for $14.95. The generic labels are shown. Labels could be personalized. The personalization of labels was available only at UN Headquarters, and not through mail order.

World Radio Day — A449

Designs: 46c, Radio antenna. $1.10, Audrey Hepburn at microphone.

2013, Feb. 13 Litho. *Perf. 13¼x13*

1056 A449 46c multicolored .95 .95
1057 A449 $1.10 multicolored 2.25 2.25

See Offices in Geneva Nos. 559-560; Vienna Nos. 521-522.

Circle of People A450

United Nations Headquarters A451

2013, Mar. 5 Litho. *Perf. 14x13½*

1058 A450 $1.10 multicolored 2.25 2.25

Perf. 13½x14

1059 A451 $3 multicolored 6.00 6.00

See Offices in Geneva Nos. 561-562; Vienna Nos. 523-524.

World Heritage Sites, China A452

Designs: Nos. 1060, 1062a, Mogao Caves. Nos. 1061, 1062d, Imperial Palace, Beijing. No. 1062b, Potala Palace, Lhasa. No. 1062c, Great Wall of China. No. 1062e, Mount Huangshan. No. 1062f, Mausoleum of the First Qing Emperor.

2013, Apr. 11 Litho. *Perf. 14x13½*

1060 A452 46c multicolored .95 .95
1061 A452 $1.10 multicolored 2.25 2.25

Souvenir Booklet

1062 Booklet, #1062g-1062l 20.00
a.-c. A452 33c any single .70 .70
d.-f. A452 46c any single .95 .95
g. Booklet pane of 4 #1062a 2.80 —
h. Booklet pane of 4 #1062b 2.80 —
i. Booklet pane of 4 #1062c 2.80 —
j. Booklet pane of 4 #1062d 3.80 —
k. Booklet pane of 4 #1062e 3.80 —
l. Booklet pane of 4 #1062f 3.80 —

See Offices in Geneva Nos. 563-565, Vienna Nos. 525-527.

Flag Type of 1980

Printed by Lowe Martin Group, Canada. Designed by Rorie Katz, US. Issued in panes of 16; each pane contains 4 blocks of 4. A se-tenant block of 4 designs centers each pane.

2013, May 2 Litho. *Perf. 13*

1063 A185 $1.10 Myanmar 2.25 2.25
1064 A185 $1.10 Russian Federation 2.25 2.25
1065 A185 $1.10 South Sudan 2.25 2.25
1066 A185 $1.10 Cape Verde 2.25 2.25
a. Block of 4, #1063-1066 12.00 12.00
Nos. 1063-1066 (4) 9.00 9.00

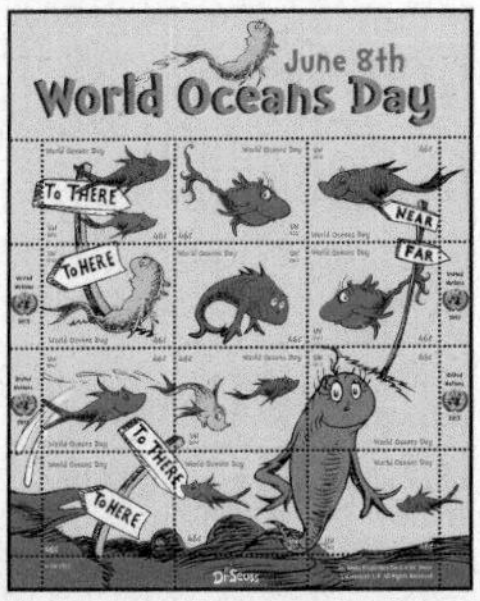

World Oceans Day A453

No. 1067 — Fish from *One Fish, Two Fish, Red Fish, Blue Fish*, by Dr. Seuss: a, Green fish, red fish, sign. b, Red fish facing right. c, Green fish facing left, sign. d, Yellow fish, sign. e, Blue fish. f, Red fish facing left, sign. g, Red fish facing right, water droplets, tail of yellow and red fish, sign. h, Yellow and red fish, green fish, side of blue fish. i, Head of blue fish, sign post. j, Sign and wave. k, Sign, red fish, side and tail of blue fish, wave. l, Side of blue fish, green fish, wave.

2013, May 31 Litho. *Perf. 13*

1067 A453 Sheet of 12 11.50 11.50
a.-l. 46c any single .95 .95

See Offices in Geneva No. 566; Vienna No. 528.

Nebulae — A454

Designs: No. 1068, V838 Mon. No. 1069, WR 25, Tr16-244.
46c, 30 Doradus.

2013, Aug. 9 Litho. *Perf. 13¼*

1068 A454 $1.10 multicolored 2.25 2.25
1069 A454 $1.10 multicolored 2.25 2.25
a. Pair, #1068-1069 4.50 4.50

Souvenir Sheet

1070 A454 46c multicolored 2.50 2.50

No. 1070 contains one 44x44mm stamp. See Offices in Geneva Nos. 567-569; Vienna Nos. 529-531.

World Humanitarian Day — A455

No. 1071 — "The World Needs More" in speech balloon in: a, Somali (Uduunku. . .). b, Thai. c, Arabic (people in background). d, Portuguese (O Mundo. . .). e, Russian. f, Korean. g, Swahili (Mahitaji. . .). h, Chinese. i, Urdu (aerial view of village in background). j, English.

2013, Aug. 19 Litho. *Perf. 14¾*

1071 A455 Sheet of 10 *30.00 30.00*
a.-j. $1.10 Any single + label *3.00 3.00*

The full sheet sold for $14.95. The generic labels are shown. Labels could be personalized. The personalization of labels was available only at UN Headquarters, and not through mail order.

Works of Disabled Artists — A456

Designs: 46c, Self-portrait II by Chuck Close, U.S. $1.10, Tears and Laughter, by Josephine King, United Kingdom.

2013, Sept. 20 Litho. *Perf. 13¼x13*

1072 A456 46c multicolored .95 .95
1073 A456 $1.10 multicolored 2.25 2.25

See Offices in Geneva Nos. 570-571; Vienna Nos. 532-533.

Endangered Species Type of 1993

Designs: No. 1074, Asian tapir. No. 1075, Mongoose lemur. No. 1076, Flat-headed cat. No. 1077, Aye-aye.

2013, Oct. 10 Litho. *Perf. 12¾x12½*

1074 A271 $1.10 multicolored 2.50 2.50
1075 A271 $1.10 multicolored 2.50 2.50
1076 A271 $1.10 multicolored 2.50 2.50
1077 A271 $1.10 multicolored 2.50 2.50
a. Block of 4, #1074-1077 11.00 11.00

See Offices in Geneva Nos. 572-575; Vienna Nos. 534-537.

Flags and Coins Type of 2006

No. 1078 — Flag of: a, Montenegro, 20 cent coin. b, Grenada, 5 cent coin. c, United States, 25 cent coin. d, Gabon, 100 franc coin. e, Palau, 1 cent coin. f, Niger, 100 franc coin. g, Saint Kitts and Nevis, 5 cent coin. h, Venezuela, 1 bolivar coin.

2013, Nov. 6 Litho. *Perf. 13¼x13*

1078 Sheet of 8 7.75 7.75
a.-h. A375 46c Any single .95 .95

A column of rouletting in the middle of the sheet separates it into two parts. See Offices in Geneva No. 576; Vienna No. 539.

UN Emblem A457

2014, Jan. 28 Litho. *Perf. 14¾*

1079 A457 $1.15 multi + label *3.00 3.00*

A458

No. 1080: a, The Golden Rule, mosaic by Norman Rockwell, dark green panel at right. b, Renovated Delegate's Lounge, yellow green panel at left. c, Renovated ECOSOC Chamber, red brown panel at left. d, Dag Hammarskjold Library, dark blue panel at right. e, Helmet of United Nations Peacekeeper and United Nations Flag, dark blue panel at right. f, United Nations Headquarters, dark green panel at left. g, Renovated Security Council Chamber, yellow green panel at left. h, Flags of member nations, red brown panel at right. i, Mankind's Struggle for Lasting Peace, by José Vela-Zanetti, dark blue panel at right. j, Relational Painting No. 90, by Fritz Glarner, yellow green panel at left.

2014, Jan. 28 Litho. *Perf. 14¾*

1080 A458 Sheet of 10 *30.00 30.00*
a.-j. $1.15 Any single + label *3.00 3.00*

The full sheet sold for $14.95. The generic labels are shown. Labels could be personalized. The personalization of labels was available only at UN Headquarters, and not through mail order.

International Day of Happiness — A459

Designs: 47c, Woman smiling, photograph by Mario Castello, "Happy." $1.15, People kissing on beach, photograph by Henryk T. Kaiser, "Feliz."

2014, Mar. 17 Litho. *Perf. 13¼x13*

1081 A459 47c multicolored .95 .95
1082 A459 $1.15 multicolored 2.40 2.40

See Offices in Geneva Nos. 577-578; Vienna Nos. 540-541.

Flag Type of 1980

Printed by Lowe Martin Group, Canada. Designed by Rorie Katz, U.S. Issued in panes of 16; each pane contains 4 blocks of 4. A se-tenant block of 4 designs centers each pane.

2014, Mar. 27 Litho. *Perf. 13x13¼*

1083 A185 $1.15 Afghanistan 3.00 3.00
1084 A185 $1.15 Serbia 3.00 3.00
1085 A185 $1.15 Cambodia 3.00 3.00
1086 A185 $1.15 Democratic Republic of the Congo 3.00 3.00
a. Block of 4, #1083-1086 15.00 15.00
Nos. 1083-1086 (4) 12.00 12.00

Miniature Sheet

International Year of Jazz — A460

No. 1087: a, Trumpeter with cap and mute in trumpet. b, Silhouette of trumpeter in tan. c, Saxophone. d, Trumpet. e, Silhouette of trumpeter in lilac. f, Saxophonist wearing hat. g, Man with hat holding trombone. h, Green saxophone. i, Saxophonist without hat. j, Trombone. k, Trumpeter wearing hat. l, Microphone.

2014, Apr. 30 Litho. *Perf. 13x13¼*

1087 A460 Sheet of 12 12.00 12.00
First day cover 15.00
a.-l. 49c Any single 1.00 1.00

See Offices in Geneva No. 579; Vienna No. 542.

A461

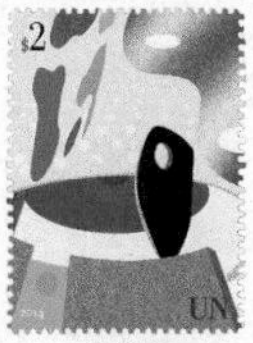

A462

Printed by Lowe-Martin Group, Canada. Panes of 20. Designed by Sergio Baradat, U.S.

2014, June 6 Litho. *Perf. 13¼x13*

1088 A461 33c multicolored .70 .70
1089 A462 $2 multicolored 4.00 4.00

See Offices in Geneva Nos. 580-581; Vienna Nos. 544-545.

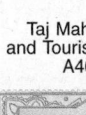

Taj Mahal and Tourists A463

Taj Mahal and Pink Sky — A464

Taj Mahal and Sun — A465

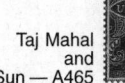

Taj Mahal and Reflecting Pool — A466

Taj Mahal and Camel A467

Taj Mahal and Elephant A468

2014, July 16 Engr. *Perf. 13¼x13*

1090 A463 49c multicolored 1.00 1.00
1091 A464 $1.15 multicolored 2.40 2.40

Souvenir Booklet

1092	Booklet, #1092g-1092l	20.50	
a.	A463 34c multi	.70	.70
b.	A465 34c multi	.70	.70
c.	A466 34c multi	.70	.70
d.	A464 49c multi	1.00	1.00
e.	A467 49c multi	1.00	1.00
f.	A468 49c multi	1.00	1.00
g.	Booklet pane of 4 #1092a	2.80	—
h.	Booklet pane of 4 #1092b	2.80	—
i.	Booklet pane of 4 #1092c	2.80	—
j.	Booklet pane of 4 #1092d	4.00	—
k.	Booklet pane of 4 #1092e	4.00	—
l.	Booklet pane of 4 #1092f	4.00	—

See Offices in Geneva Nos. 582-584, Vienna Nos. 546-548.

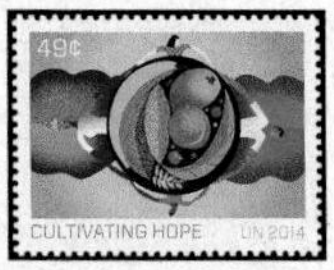

International Year of Family Farming — A469

2014, Aug. 21 Litho. *Perf. 13x13¼*

1093 A469 49c multicolored 1.00 1.00
1094 A469 $1.15 multicolored 2.40 2.40

See Offices in Geneva Nos. 585-586; Vienna Nos. 549-550.

Global Education First Initiative — A470

Designs: $1.15, Teacher and students in forest. $1.50, Chemistry teacher and student.

2014, Sept. 18 Litho. *Perf. 13x13¼*

1095 A470 $1.15 multicolored 2.40 2.40

Souvenir Sheet

Perf. 12½

1096 A470 $1.50 multicolored 6.00 5.00

No. 1096 contains one 32x32mm stamp. See Offices in Geneva Nos. 588-589; Vienna Nos. 551-552.

Endangered Species — A471

Maps and: No. 1097, Denise's pygmy seahorses. No. 1098, Whale shark. No. 1099, Scalloped hammerhead shark. No. 1100, Asian arowana.

2014, Oct. 23 Litho. *Perf. 12¾x12½*

1097 A471 $1.15 multicolored 2.40 2.40
1098 A471 $1.15 multicolored 2.40 2.40
1099 A471 $1.15 multicolored 2.40 2.40
1100 A471 $1.15 multicolored 2.40 2.40
a. Block of 4, #1097-1100 9.75 9.75

See Offices in Geneva Nos. 590-593; Vienna Nos. 553-556.

A472

No. 1101: a, United Nations emblem in gray, bottom panel in blue. b, Aerial view of United Nations Headquarters, bottom panel in red, year date at left. c, View of United Nations Headquarters from across East River, bottom panel in red, year date at right. d, Interior balconies, bottom panel in blue. e, Crowd in lobby, bottom panel in blue. f, Sun reflecting off United Nations Building, street lights, bottom panel in red. g, United Nations emblem in brown, bottom panel in red. h, Woman and two men near General Assembly Building, bottom panel in blue. i, United Nations Building, flags, trees without leaves, bottom panel in blue. j, General Assembly and United Nations Buildings, bottom panel in red.

2014, Oct. 23 Litho. *Perf. 14¾*

1101 A472 Sheet of 10 *32.50 32.50*
a.-j. $1.15 Any single + label *3.00 3.00*

The full sheet sold for $14.95. The generic labels are shown. Labels could be personalized. The personalization of labels was available only at UN Headquarters, and not through mail order.

UN Emblem A473

2015, Jan. 23 Litho. *Perf. 14¾*

1102 A473 $1.15 multi + label *3.00 3.00*
Sheet of 10 + 10 labels *30.00* —

The full sheet sold for $14.95. The generic label exists as shown, with ram on deep bister background. Labels could be personalized. The personalization of labels was available only at UN Headquarters, and not through mail order.

Flags and Coins Type of 2006

No. 1103 — Flag of: a, Kiribati, 10 cent coin. b, Tonga, 2 seniti coin. c, Costa Rica, 10 centimos coin. d, Bhutan, 25 chetrum coin. e, Zimbabwe, 5 dollar coin. f, Angola, 1 kwanza coin. g, Congo Democratic Republic, 1 franc coin. h, Liberia, 25 cent coin.

2015, Feb. 6 Litho. *Perf. 13¼x13*

1103 Sheet of 8 8.00 8.00
a.-h. A375 49c Any single 1.00 1.00

A column of rouletting in the middle of the sheet separates it into two parts. See Offices in Geneva No. 594; Vienna No. 558.

Miniature Sheets

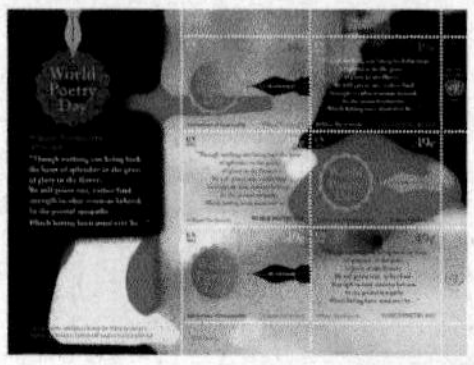

A474

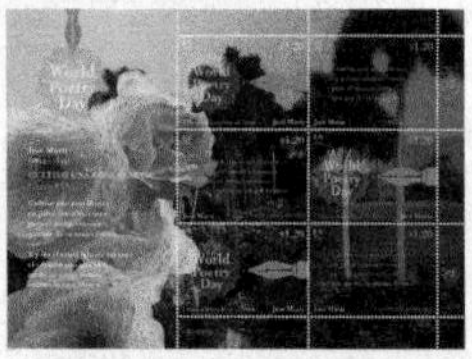

World Poetry Day A475

No. 1104: a, Black pen, denomination in red brown. b, William Wordsworth quotation in white, denomination in red. c, Wordsworth quotation in red brown, denomination in white. d, Gold pen, denomination in white. e, Black pen, denomination in white. f, Wordsworth quotation in black, denomination in red brown.

No. 1105: a, Gold pen, denomination in white, tree top and rose in background. b, José Martí quotation, denomination in lilac, tree tops in background. c, Martí quotation, denomination in white, tree top and rose in background. d, Gold pen, denomination in lilac, tree trunks and tree top in background. e, Gold pen, denomination in lilac, tree trunks and rose in background. f, Martí quotation, denomination in lilac, tree trunks in background.

Perf. 14½x14¼

2015, Mar. 20 Litho.

1104 A474 Sheet of 6 6.00 6.00
a.-f. 49c Any single 1.00 1.00
1105 A475 Sheet of 6 14.50 14.50
a.-f. $1.20 Any single 2.40 2.40

See Offices in Geneva Nos. 595-596; Vienna Nos. 559-560.

Endangered Species — A476

Designs: No. 1106, King bird-of-paradise. No. 1107, Blue bird-of-paradise. No. 1108, Princess Stephanie's bird-of-paradise. No. 1109, Carola's parotia.

2015, Apr. 16 Litho. *Perf. 12½x12¾*

1106 A476 $1.20 multicolored 2.40 2.40
1107 A476 $1.20 multicolored 2.40 2.40
1108 A476 $1.20 multicolored 2.40 2.40
1109 A476 $1.20 multicolored 2.40 2.40
a. Block of 4, #1106-1109 9.75 9.75
Nos. 1106-1109 (4) 9.60 9.60

See Offices in Geneva Nos. 597-600; Vienna Nos. 561-564.

A477 A478

2015, May 7 Litho. *Perf. 13¼x13*

1110 A477 35c multicolored .70 .70
1111 A478 40c multicolored .80 .80

See Offices in Vienna Nos. 565-566.

Miniature Sheet

A479

No. 1112: a, United Nations Headquarters and flags, panel at right. b, Flags, panel at left. c, Stairway and pillars, panel at left. d, Reflection of buildings in windows, panel at right. e, Circular meeting room, panel at right. f, United Nations Headquarters, panel at left. g, Trees and United Nations Building, panel at left. h, Let Us Beat Swords Into Plowshares statue, panel at right. i, General Assembly Building, flags and street, panel at right. j, Arrival sculpture, panel at left.

2015, May 7 Litho. *Perf. 14¾*

1112 A479 Sheet of 10 *30.00 30.00*
a.-j. $1.20 Any single + label *3.00 3.00*

The full sheet sold for $14.95. The generic labels are shown. The personalization of labels was available only at UN Headquarters, and not through mail order.

World Heritage Sites, Southeast Asia — A480

Designs: Nos. 1113, 1115a, Luang Prabang, Laos. Nos. 1114, 1115d, Borobodur Temple, Indonesia. No. 1115b, Angkor Wat, Cambodia. No. 1115c, Ayutthaya, Thailand. No. 1115e, Cordillera, Philippines. No. 1115f, Hué Monuments, Viet Nam.

2015, June 5 Litho. *Perf. 14x13½*

1113 A480 49c multicolored 1.00 1.00
1114 A480 $1.20 multicolored 2.40 2.40

Souvenir Booklet

1115	Booklet, #1115g-1115l	20.50	
a.-c.	A480 35c any single	.70	.70
d.-f.	A480 49c any single	1.00	1.00
g.	Booklet pane of 4 #1115a	2.80	—
h.	Booklet pane of 4 #1115b	2.80	—
i.	Booklet pane of 4 #1115c	2.80	—
j.	Booklet pane of 4 #1115d	4.00	—
k.	Booklet pane of 4 #1115e	4.00	—
l.	Booklet pane of 4 #1115f	4.00	—

See Offices in Geneva Nos. 601-603, Vienna Nos. 567-569.

End Violence Against Children A481

Designs: 49c, Armed violence reduction. $1.20, Sexual violence against children.

Perf. 14½x14¼

2015, Aug. 20 Litho.

1116 A481 49c multicolored 1.00 1.00
1117 A481 $1.20 multicolored 2.40 2.40

See Offices in Geneva Nos. 604-605; Vienna Nos. 570-571.

United Nations, 70th Anniv. A482

Designed by Sergio Baradat, U.S.

2015, Sept. 25 Litho. *Perf. 14¾*

1118 A482 $1.20 multi + label *3.00 3.00*
Sheet of 10 + 10 labels *30.00* —

The full sheet sold for $14.95. The generic label exists as shown, depicting Pope Francis. Labels could be personalized. The personalization of labels was available only at UN Headquarters, and not through mail order. On Sept. 27, No. 1118 was issued in a sheet of 10 + 10 labels depicting Chinese characters.

See Vienna No. 577.

General Assembly Hall — A483

Visitors Lobby — A484

Security Council — A485

Woodrow Wilson Reading Room of Dag Hammarskjöld Library — A486

General Assembly Hall — A487

Printed by Cartor Security Printing, France. Panes of 6. Designed by Rorie Katz, U.S.

2015, Oct. 25 Litho. *Perf. 13¾*

1119 A483 49c multicolored 1.00 1.00
1120 A484 49c multicolored 1.00 1.00
a. Pair, #1119-1120 2.00 2.00

1121 A485 $1.20 multicolored 2.40 2.40
1122 A486 $1.20 multicolored 2.40 2.40
a. Pair, #1121-1122 4.80 4.80
Nos. 1119-1122 (4) 6.80 6.80

Souvenir Sheet

Perf. 13½

1123 A487 $1.20 multicolored 4.00 4.00

United Nations, 70th anniv. See Offices in Geneva Nos. 607-611; Vienna Nos. 572-576.

United Nations Educational, Scientific and Cultural Organization (UNESCO), 70th Anniv. — A488

2015, Nov. 5 Litho. *Perf. 14¾*
1124 A488 $1.20 multi + label *3.50 3.50*
Sheet of 10 + 10 labels *35.00* —

The full sheet sold for $14.95. Ten different generic labels, one of which is shown, are on the sheet. Labels could be personalized. The personalization of labels was available only at UN Headquarters, and not through mail order.

21st United Nations Climate Change Conference, Paris — A489

2015, Nov. 24 Litho. *Perf. 13¼*
1125 A489 $1.20 multicolored 2.40 2.40

Values are for stamps with surrounding selvage. See Offices in Geneva No. 612; Vienna No. 578.

UN Emblem A490

2016, Jan. 8 Litho. *Perf. 14¾*
1126 A490 $1.20 multicolored + label *3.00 3.00*
Sheet of 10 + 10 labels *30.00* —

The full sheet sold for $14.95. The generic label, with monkey on red background, is shown. A sheet of 10 No. 1126 + 10 labels depicting M. S. Subbulaskshmi was issued on Oct. 2, 2016. Labels could be personalized. The personalization of labels was available only at UN Headquarters, and not through mail order. See Nos. 1231, 1263.

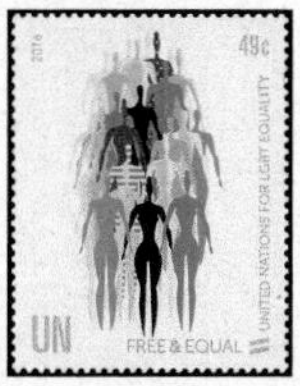

Free and Equal — A491

Designs: 49c, Group of stylized people. $1.20, Woman with butterfly wings.

2016, Feb. 5 Litho. *Perf. 13½x13¼*
1127 A491 49c multicolored 1.00 1.00
1128 A491 $1.20 multicolored 2.40 2.40

See Offices in Geneva Nos. 613-614; Vienna Nos. 579-580.

HeForShe Movement — A492

Designs: 49c, Man, green background. $1.20, Woman, yellow background.

2016, Mar. 8 Litho. *Perf. 12½x13*
1129 A492 49c multicolored 1.00 1.00
1130 A492 $1.20 multicolored 2.40 2.40

See Offices in Geneva Nos. 615-616; Vienna Nos. 581-582.

Miniature Sheet

Angry Birds A493

No. 1131: a, Red, the Pigs, double-decker bus. b, Red with wing extended. c, Red and five Hatchlings. d, Red, New York City skyscrapers. e, Red, Eiffel Tower, recycling container. f, Red in jungle. g, Earth, Hatchlings, Chuck, Red, Bomb, Stella and Matilda. h, Red turning faucet, Pigs in tub. i, Red drinking from squirt bottle, Lower Manhattan skyline. j, Red with shovel, Pyramids.

2016, Apr. 22 Litho. *Perf. 14¾*
1131 A493 Sheet of 10 *30.00 30.00*
a.-j. $1.15 Any single + label *3.00 3.00*

The full sheet sold for $14.95. The generic labels are shown. Labels could be personalized. The personalization of labels was available only at UN Headquarters, and not through mail order.

Miniature Sheets

A494

International Dance Day — A495

No. 1132 — Illustration of Chinese dancers by Marcos Chin: a, Woman with arm extended upward. b, Two women, denomination in magenta. c, Woman facing left with arm extended outward. d, Two women, denomination in white. e, Woman with closed eyes. f, Woman with closed eyes with two pale yellow lines touching flower.

No. 1133 — Illustration of Thai dancers by Chin: a, Back of dancer's head, hand of another dancer. b, Dancer wearing mask, leg and arm of other dancers. c, Dancer with costume with blue shoulders, dancer with arm extended. d, Dancer with arm extended, leg and arm of other dancers. e, Two dancers with green and yellow costumes. f, Dancer with green and yellow costume.

2016, Apr. 29 Litho. *Perf. 13¼x13*
1132 A494 Sheet of 6 5.75 5.75
a.-f. 47c Any single .95 .95
1133 A495 Sheet of 6 14.50 14.50
a.-f. $1.15 Any single 2.40 2.40
g. As #1133, with "Thailand 2018 / World Stamp Exhibition / 28 Nov. - 3 Dec." overprinted in sheet margin *65.00 65.00*

Issued: No. 1133g, 11/28/18. See Offices in Geneva Nos. 617-618; Vienna Nos. 583-584.

International Day of United Nations Peacekeepers — A496

Designs: 47c, Peacekeeper saluting. $1.15, Man disabling landmine.

Litho. With Foil Application

2016, May 29 *Perf. 13¼x13*
1134 A496 47c multicolored .95 .95
1135 A496 $1.15 multicolored 2.40 2.40

See Offices in Geneva Nos. 619-620; Vienna Nos. 586-587.

Miniature Sheet

United Nations Postal Administration, 65th Anniv. — A497

No. 1136 — Old United Nations stamps: a, New York #1. b, New York #127. c, Vienna #86. d, New York #415. e, New York #301. f, New York #548. g, New York #474. h, Vienna #100. i, New York #476. j, Vienna #122.

2016, May 30 Litho. *Perf. 14¾*
1136 A497 Sheet of 10 *30.00 30.00*
a.-j. $1.15 Any single + label *3.00 3.00*

The full sheet sold for $14.95. The generic labels are shown. Labels could be personalized. The personalization of labels was available only at UN Headquarters, and not through mail order.

Sport for Peace A498

Olympic rings and: No. 1137, Shot put, high jump. No. 1138, Runner, javelin. No. 1139, Dove facing left. No. 1140, Dove facing right.

2016, July 22 Litho. *Perf. 14¼*
1137 A498 47c multicolored .95 .95
1138 A498 47c multicolored .95 .95
a. Pair, #1137-1138 1.90 1.90
1139 A498 $1.15 multicolored 2.40 2.40
1140 A498 $1.15 multicolored 2.40 2.40
a. Pair, #1139-1140 4.80 4.80
Nos. 1137-1140 (4) 6.70 6.70

See Offices in Geneva Nos. 621-624; Vienna Nos. 588-591.

Souvenir Sheet

United Nations Economic and Social Commission for Asia and the Pacific Building, Bangkok — A499

No. 1141: a, Left third of building, b, Center third of building, c, Right third of building.

2016, Aug. 10 Litho. *Perf. 13¼x13*
1141 A499 Sheet of 3 24.00 24.00
a. $1.15 multi 5.00 5.00
b. 2fr multi 9.50 9.50
c. €1.70 multi 8.50 8.50

32nd Asian International Stamp Exhibition. No. 1141 sold for $6.

World Heritage Sites, Czech Republic A500

Designs: Nos. 1142, 1144a, Historic Center of Prague. Nos. 1143, 1144d, Holy Trinity Column, Olomouc. No. 1144b, Gardens and Castle at Kromeriz. No. 1144c, Historic Town Center of Kutná Hora. No. 1144e, Lednice-Valtice Cultural Landscape. No. 1144f, Historic Center of Cesky Krumlov.

2016, Sept. 8 Litho. *Perf. 14¼*
1142 A500 47c multicolored .95 .95
1143 A500 $1.15 multicolored 2.40 2.40

Souvenir Booklet

1144 Booklet, #1144g-1144l 20.00
a.-c. A500 34c any single .70 .70
d.-f. A500 47c any single .95 .95
g. Booklet pane of 4 #1144a 2.80 —
h. Booklet pane of 4 #1144b 2.80 —
i. Booklet pane of 4 #1144c 2.80 —
j. Booklet pane of 4 #1144d 3.80 —
k. Booklet pane of 4 #1144e 3.80 —
l. Booklet pane of 4 #1144f 3.80 —

See Offices in Geneva Nos. 625-627; Vienna Nos. 592-594, Czech Republic Nos. 3683-3684.

Miniature Sheet

World Wildlife Conference, Johannesburg — A501

No. 1145 — Part of map of Africa and: a, Addax. b, White rhinoceros. c, African lion. d, Disa uniflora.

2016, Sept. 24 Litho. *Perf. 13x13½*
1145 A501 Sheet of 4 9.75 9.75
a.-d. $1.15 Any single 2.40 2.40

See Offices in Geneva No. 628; Vienna No. 596.

Miniature Sheet

World Post Day A502

No. 1146 — Mail box from: a, Japan. b, Spain. c, Germany. d, Brazil. e, China. f, Denmark. g, India. h, Austria. i, England. j, United States.

2016, Oct. 6 Litho. *Perf. 14¾*
1146 A502 Sheet of 10 *30.00 30.00*
a.-j. $1.15 Any single + label *3.00 3.00*

The full sheet sold for $14.95. The generic labels are shown. Labels could be personalized. The personalization of labels was available only at UN Headquarters, and not through mail order.

Sustainable Development Goals — A503

No. 1147 — Inscription: a, 1 No poverty. b, 2 Zero hunger. c, 3 Good health and well-being. d, 4 Quality education. e, 5 Gender equality. f, 6 Clean water and sanitation. g, 7 Affordable and clean energy. h, 8 Decent work and economic growth. i, 9 Industry, innovation and infrastructure. j, 10 Reduced inequalities. k, 11 Sustainable cities and communities. l, 12 Responsible consumption and production. m, 13 Climate action. n, 14 Life below water. o, 15

Life on land. p, 16 Peace, justice and strong institutions. q, 17 Partnerships for the goals.

2016, Oct. 24 Litho. *Perf. 13¼*

1147 A503 Sheet of 17 + label 17.00 17.00
a.-q. 47c Any single 1.00 1.00

See Offices in Geneva No. 629; Vienna No. 597.

Souvenir Sheet

Monkey King From Chinese Novel *Journey to the West* A504

No. 1148 — Various depictions of Monkey King with inscriptions in: a, English. b, French. c, German.

Litho. With Foil Application

2016, Dec. 2 *Perf. 12*

1148 A504 Sheet of 3 20.00 20.00
a. $1.15 multi 4.00 4.00
b. 2fr multi 7.00 7.00
c. €1.70 multi 6.75 6.75

33rd Asian International Stamp Exhibition, Nanning, People's Republic of China. No. 1148 sold for $6.

United Nations Emblem Type of 2014 Dated "2017" in Purple

2017, Jan. 13 Litho. *Perf. 14¾*

1149 A457 $1.15 multi + label *3.00 3.00*
Sheet of 10 + 10 labels *30.00* —

The full sheet sold for $14.95. The generic label exists as shown, with rooster on red background. Labels could be personalized. The personalization of labels was available only at UN Headquarters, and not through mail order.

Flag Type of 1980

Printed by Lowe Martin Company, Inc., Canada. Designed by Sergio Baradat, U.S. Issued in panes of 16; each pane contains 4 blocks of 4. A se-tenant block of 4 designs centers each pane.

2017, Feb. 3 Litho. *Perf. 13x13¼*

1150 A185 $1.15 Albania 2.40 2.40
1151 A185 $1.15 Benin 2.40 2.40
1152 A185 $1.15 Bulgaria 2.40 2.40
1153 A185 $1.15 Comoros 2.40 2.40
a. Block of 4, #1150-1153 12.00 12.00
1154 A185 $1.15 Congo Republic 2.40 2.40
1155 A185 $1.15 Ethiopia 2.40 2.40
1156 A185 $1.15 Georgia 2.40 2.40
1157 A185 $1.15 Iraq 2.40 2.40
a. Block of 4, #1154-1157 12.00 12.00
Nos. 1150-1157 (8) 19.20 19.20

Miniature Sheet

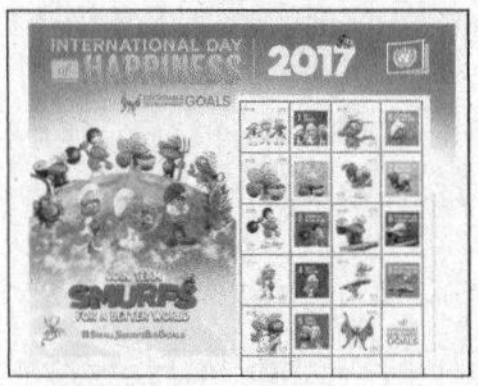

A505

No. 1158: a, Three Smurfs. b, Smurf holding glass of water. c, Smurf holding fruit. d, Smurf with backpack with solar panels. e, Smurf lifting dumbbell. f, Smurf carrying mallet. g, Smurf holding book. h, Two Smurfs with ladder. i, Male and female Smurfs. j, Butterfly.

2017, Mar. 20 Litho. *Perf. 14¾*

1158 A505 Sheet of 10 *30.00 30.00*
a.-j. $1.15 Any single + label *3.00 3.00*

The full sheet sold for $14.95. The generic labels are shown. Labels could be personalized. The personalization of labels was available only at UN Headquarters, and not through mail order.

Miniature Sheets

A506

International Dance — A507

No. 1159 — Illustration of Polynesian dancers by Pascal Campion: a, Woman with arms raised, denomination at LR. b, Woman with arms raised, denomination at UL. c, Two women wearing head coverings, red necklace, denomination at UR. d, One woman wearing head covering and red necklace, denomination at UR. e, Woman with feathered headdress, green necklace, hair of another woman at right, denomination at UR. f, Woman wearing feathered headdress and green necklace, denomination at UR.

No. 1160 — Illustration of Native American tribal dancers by Campion: a, Dancer facing right, denomination in blue at UL. b, Dancer, denomination in orange at UL. c, Back of dancer, denomination in gray lilac at UR. d, Dancer looking downward, denomination in gray lilac at UL. e, Dancer with headband over eyebrows, denomination in orange red at UR, "International Dance" in white. f, Dancer, denomination in orange red at UR, "International Dance" in light blue.

2017, Mar. 23 Litho. *Perf. 13¼x13*

1159 A506 Sheet of 6 6.00 6.00
a.-f. 49c Any single 1.00 1.00
1160 A507 Sheet of 6 14.50 14.50
a.-f. $1.15 Any single 2.40 2.40

See Offices in Geneva Nos. 630-631; Vienna Nos. 599-600.

Souvenir Sheet

Australian Animals — A508

No. 1161: a, Koalas. b, Kangaroos. c, Emu.

Litho. With Foil Application

2017, Mar. 30 *Perf. 13¼x13*

1161 A508 Sheet of 3 12.00 12.00
a. $1.15 multi 4.00 4.00
b. 2fr multi 4.00 4.00
c. €1.70 multi 4.00 4.00

2017 FIAP International Stamp Exhibition, Melbourne, Australia. No. 1161 sold for $6.

Endangered Species — A509

Designs: No. 1162, Masobe gecko. No. 1163, Thresher shark. No. 1164, Clarion angelfish. No. 1165, Blaine's fishhook cactus.

2017, May 11 Litho. *Perf. 12¾x12½*

1162 A509 $1.15 multicolored 2.40 2.40
1163 A509 $1.15 multicolored 2.40 2.40
1164 A509 $1.15 multicolored 2.40 2.40
1165 A509 $1.15 multicolored 2.40 2.40
a. Block of 4, #1162-1165 9.75 9.75
Nos. 1162-1165 (4) 9.60 9.60

See Offices in Geneva Nos. 632-635; Vienna Nos. 601-604.

World Environment Day — A510

Designs: 49c, Hopewell Rocks, New Brunswick, Canada. $1.15, Polar bear, Baffin Island, Nunavut, Canada.

2017, June 5 Litho. *Perf. 13¼*

1166 A510 49c multicolored 1.00 1.00
1167 A510 $1.15 multicolored 2.40 2.40

See Offices in Geneva Nos. 636-637; Vienna Nos. 605-606.

Miniature Sheet

International Day of Yoga — A511

No. 1168: a, Orange woman on stomach holding her legs. b, Dark blue man siting with legs raised. c, Blue woman with arms extended. d, Beige man sitting with legs crossed and arms raised. e, Purple man with arms extended leaning backward to touch toes. f, Light blue woman bent backward with feet and hands on ground. g, Blue violet woman bent backward to touch raised leg. h, Red woman on one knee. i, Pale blue woman with arms extended touching raised leg. j, Orange man bent over with hands on ground.

2017, June 21 Litho. *Perf. 14¾*

1168 A511 Sheet of 10 *30.00 30.00*
a.-j. $1.15 Any single + label *3.00 3.00*

The full sheet sold for $14.95. The generic labels are shown. Labels could be personalized. The personalization of labels was available only at UN Headquarters, and not through mail order.

World Heritage Sites Along the Silk Roads A512

Designs: Nos. 1169, 1171a, Longmen Grottoes, People's Republic of China. Nos. 1170, 1171d, Sulaiman-Too Sacred Mountain, Kyrgyzstan. No. 1171b, Historic Center of Bukhara, Uzbekistan. No. 1171c, Tabriz Historic Bazaar Complex, Iran. No. 1171e, Kunya-Urgench, Turkmenistan. No. 1171f, Safranbolu, Turkey.

2017, Aug. 3 Litho. *Perf. 14¼*

1169 A512 49c multicolored 1.00 1.00
1170 A512 $1.15 multicolored 2.40 2.40

Souvenir Booklet

1171 Booklet, #1115g-1115l 22.50
a.-c. A512 34c any single .75 .75
d.-f. A512 49c any single 1.10 1.10
g. Booklet pane of 4 #1171a 3.00 —
h. Booklet pane of 4 #1171b 3.00 —
i. Booklet pane of 4 #1171c 3.00 —
j. Booklet pane of 4 #1171d 4.50 —
k. Booklet pane of 4 #1171e 4.50 —
l. Booklet pane of 4 #1171f 4.50 —

Complete booklet sold for $11. See Offices in Geneva Nos. 638-640; Vienna Nos. 607-609.

Doves A513

Moths A514

Doves A515

Printed by Johann Enschedé and Sons, the Netherlands. Panes of 20. Designed by Stranger and Stranger, U.S.

2017, Sept. 21 Litho. *Perf. 14x14¼*

1172 A513 49c multicolored 1.00 1.00
1173 A514 $1.15 multicolored 2.40 2.40

Souvenir Sheet

Perf. 14¼x13¾

1174 A515 $1.15 multicolored 2.40 2.40

International Day of Peace. See Offices in Geneva Nos. 641-643; Vienna Nos. 611-613.

World Food Day — A516

Designs: 49c, Vegetables. $1.15, Bowls of food, jar of oil.

2017, Oct. 16 Litho. *Perf. 13¼x14*

1175 A516 49c multicolored 1.00 1.00
1176 A516 $1.15 multicolored 2.40 2.40

See Offices in Geneva Nos. 644-645; Vienna Nos. 614-615.

Souvenir Sheet

Universal Declaration of Human Rights — A517

No. 1177 — Text of Universal Declaration of Human Rights in: a, English. b, French. c, German.

Litho. With Foil Application

2017, Oct. 27 *Perf. 14x13¼*

1177 A517 Sheet of 3 12.00 12.00
a. $1.15 multi 4.00 4.00
b. 2fr multi 4.00 4.00
c. €1.70 multi 4.00 4.00

United Nations Expo 2017, Bellefonte, Pennsylvania. No. 1177 sold for $6.

Souvenir Sheet

Landmarks in Paris — A518

No. 1178: a, Fame of Louis XVI, statue by Antoine Coysevox. b, Fontaines de la Concorde. c, Gargolye on Notre Dame Cathedral.

2017, Nov. 9 Litho. *Perf. 13¼x14*

1178	A518 Sheet of 3	12.00	12.00
a.	$1.15 multi	4.00	4.00
b.	2fr multi	4.00	4.00
c.	€1.70 multi	4.00	4.00

Autumn Philatelic Show, Paris. No. 1178 sold for $6.

Flag Type of 1980

Printed by Lowe Martin Group, Canada. Designed by Rorie Katz, U.S. Issued in panes of 16; each pane contains 4 blocks of 4. A se-tenant block of 4 designs centers each pane.

2018, Jan. 12 Litho. *Perf. 13x13¼*

1179	A185 $1.15 Lesotho	2.40	2.40
1180	A185 $1.15 Libya	2.40	2.40
1181	A185 $1.15 Mozambique	2.40	2.40
1182	A185 $1.15 Romania	2.40	2.40
a.	Block of 4, #1179-1182	12.00	12.00
1183	A185 $1.15 Rwanda	2.40	2.40
1184	A185 $1.15 Seychelles	2.40	2.40
1185	A185 $1.15 South Africa	2.40	2.40
1186	A185 $1.15 Ukraine	2.40	2.40
a.	Block of 4, #1183-1186	12.00	12.00
	Nos. 1179-1186 (8)	19.20	19.20

United Nations Emblem Type of 2014 Dated "2018" in Purple

2018, Feb. 2 Litho. *Perf. 14¾*

1187	A457 $1.15 multi + label	*3.00*	*3.00*
	Sheet of 10 + 10 labels	*30.00*	—

The full sheet sold for $14.95. The generic label depicts a dog. Labels could be personalized. The personalization of labels was available only at UN Headquarters, and not through mail order.

Endangered Species — A519

Designs: No. 1188, Red-crested turaco. No. 1189, Andean hairy armadillo. No. 1190, Lurestan newt. No. 1191, Goldenseal.

2018, Mar. 2 Litho. *Perf. 12¾x12½*

1188	A519 $1.15 multicolored	2.40	2.40
1189	A519 $1.15 multicolored	2.40	2.40
1190	A519 $1.15 multicolored	2.40	2.40
1191	A519 $1.15 multicolored	2.40	2.40
a.	Block of 4, #1188-1191	9.75	9.75
	Nos. 1188-1191 (4)	9.60	9.60

See Offices in Geneva Nos. 646-649; Vienna Nos. 616-619.

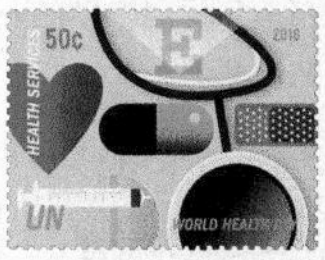

World Health Day — A520

Designs: 50c, Heart, pill, bandage, letter from eye chart, syringe and stethoscope. $1.15, Head with gears, heart, clock, stylized people, circle with arrows.

2018, Apr. 6 Litho. *Perf. 13x13¼*

1192	A520 50c multicolored	1.00	1.00
1193	A520 $1.15 multicolored	2.40	2.40

See Offices in Geneva Nos. 650-651; Vienna Nos. 620-621.

Universal Declaration of Human Rights, 70th Anniv. A521

2018, May 3 Litho. *Perf. 13¼*

1194	A521 $2.50 multicolored	5.00	5.00

United Nations Headquarters A522

2018, May 29 Litho. *Perf. 13¼*

1195	A522 65c multicolored	1.40	1.40

UNISPACE + 50 Conferences A523

Designs: 50c, Milky Way Galaxy. No. 1197, International Space Station and Space Shuttle Endeavour.

No. 1198, Astronaut Scott Kelly during spacewalk.

2018, June 20 Litho. *Perf. 14x14¼*

1196	A523 50c multicolored	1.00	1.00
1197	A523 $1.15 multicolored	2.40	2.40

Souvenir Sheet

Perf. 13¾

1198	A523 $1.15 multicolored	3.00	3.00

No. 1198 contains one 45x45mm stamp. See Offices in Geneva Nos. 653-655; Vienna Nos. 623-625.

World Heritage Sites in the United Kingdom A524

Designs: Nos. 1199, 1201a, Giant's Causeway. Nos. 1200, 1201d, Palace of Westminster. No. 1201b, Stonehenge. No. 1201c, Conwy Castle. No. 1201e, Edinburgh. No. 1201f, Maritime Greenwich.

2018, Aug. 15 Litho. *Perf. 14¼*

1199	A524 50c multicolored	1.00	1.00
1200	A524 $1.15 multicolored	2.40	2.40

Souvenir Booklet

1201	Booklet, #1115g-1115l	22.50	
a.-c.	A524 35c any single	.75	.75
d.-f.	A524 50c any single	1.10	1.10
g.	Booklet pane of 4 #1201a	3.00	—
h.	Booklet pane of 4 #1201b	3.00	—
i.	Booklet pane of 4 #1201c	3.00	—
j.	Booklet pane of 4 #1201d	4.50	—
k.	Booklet pane of 4 #1201e	4.50	—
l.	Booklet pane of 4 #1201f	4.50	—

Complete booklet sold for $11. See Offices in Geneva Nos. 657-659; Vienna Nos. 626-628.

Miniature Sheet

Thomas the Tank Engine A525

No. 1202: a, Thomas and four people. b, Reg lifting bicycle. c, Thomas, conductor holding potted plant. d, Ashima and Thomas. e, Thomas and Nia. f, Passenger car, children and tuba. g, Thomas and giraffe. h, Monkeys on Thomas. i, Water splashing on grimy Thomas. j, Nia, Thomas and ring of colors.

2018, Sept. 12 Litho. *Perf. 14¾*

1202	A525 Sheet of 10	*30.00*	*30.00*
a.-j.	$1.15 Any single + label	*3.00*	*3.00*

The full sheet sold for $14.95. The generic labels are shown. Labels could be personalized. The personalization of labels was available only at UN Headquarters, and not through mail order.

Souvenir Sheet

Characters From Cantonese Opera *Hua Mulan* — A526

No. 1203: a, Baozhen. b, Guanyu. c, Mulan.

2018, Sept. 21 Litho. *Perf. 13¼x13*

1203	A526 Sheet of 3	13.00	13.00
a.	$1.15 multi	4.25	4.25
b.	2fr multi	4.25	4.25
c.	€1.80 multi	4.25	4.25

Macao 2018 Asian International Stamp Exhibition. The vignettes are laser cut. No. 1203 sold for $6.30.

Miniature Sheet

International Music Day — A527

No. 1204: a, Trombone. b, Flute and clarinet. c, Cornet. d, Tuba, bell at right. e, Tuba, bell at left, red in background. f, French horn, red in background. g, Trumpet, bell at UR. h, Baritone horn. i, Saxophone. j, French horn, blue in background. k, Trumpet, bell at LR. l, Tuba, bell at left, blue in background.

2018, Oct. 1 Litho. *Perf. 14x13¼*

1204	A527 Sheet of 12	12.00	12.00
a.-l.	50c Any single	1.00	1.00

See Offices in Geneva No. 660; Vienna No. 629.

Non-Violence, Sculpture by Carl Fredrik Reuterswärd — A528

Printed by Johann Enschedé Stamps BV, the Netherlands. Panes of 50. Designed by Martin Mörck, Norway.

2018, Oct. 2 Litho. *Perf. 13¼x14*

1205	A528 1c multicolored	.25	.25

See Offices in Vienna Nos. 630-631.

Diwali Candles A529

Diwali Candles A530

2018, Oct. 19 Litho. *Perf. 14¾*

1206	A529 $1.15 multi + label	*3.00*	*3.00*
1207	A530 $1.15 multi + label	*3.00*	*3.00*
a.	Vert. pair, #1206-1207, + 2 labels	*6.00*	*6.00*
	Sheet of 10, 5 each #1206-1207, + 10 labels	*30.00*	*30.00*

The full sheet sold for $14.95. The generic labels are shown. Labels could be personalized. The personalization of labels was available only at UN Headquarters, and not through mail order.

Souvenir Sheet

Arena di Verona A531

No. 1208: a, Left side of Arena. b, Central portion of Arena with four upper-tier arches. c, Right side of Arena.

2018, Nov. 23 Litho. *Perf. 13¼x13*

1208	A531 Sheet of 3	13.00	13.00
a.	$1.15 multi	4.25	4.25
b.	2fr multi	4.25	4.25
c.	€1.80 multi	4.25	4.25

Veronafil 2018 Stamp Exhibition, Verona, Italy. No. 1208 sold for $6.30.

United Nations Emblem Type of 2014 Dated "2019" in Purple

2019, Jan. 11 Litho. *Perf. 14¾*

1209	A457 $1.15 multi + label	*3.00*	*3.00*
	Sheet of 10 + 10 labels	*30.00*	—

The full sheet sold for $14.95. The generic label depicts a pig. Labels could be personalized. The personalization of labels was available only at UN Headquarters, and not through mail order.

Miniature Sheet

World Languages — A532

No. 1210 — Word bubbles with word for "Hello" in: a, Chinese and Portuguese (Olá). b, Swahili (Habari) and Persian. c, Italian (Ciao). d, Bengali. e, English. f, Thai and Czech or Slovak (Ahoj).

2019, Feb. 21 Litho. *Perf. 13¼x13*

1210	A532 Sheet of 6	6.75	6.75
a.-f.	55c Any single	1.10	1.10

See Offices in Geneva No. 661; Vienna No. 632.

Stop Sexual Exploitation and Abuse — A533

Printed by Lowe-Martin Group, Canada. Panes of 20. Designed by Chris Gash, U.S.

2019, Mar.15 Litho. *Perf. 13¼x13*

1211	A533 85c multicolored	1.75	1.75

Endangered Species — A534

Designs: No. 1212, Hawksbill turtle. No. 1213, Queen conch. No. 1214, Mushroom coral. No. 1215, Humpback whale.

2019, Apr. 26 Litho. *Perf. 12¾x12½*

1212	A534 $1.15 multicolored	2.40	2.40
1213	A534 $1.15 multicolored	2.40	2.40
1214	A534 $1.15 multicolored	2.40	2.40
1215	A534 $1.15 multicolored	2.40	2.40
a.	Block of 4, #1212-1215	9.75	9.75

See Offices in Geneva Nos. 663-666; Vienna Nos. 634-637.

Souvenir Sheet

Diphaglossine Bee and Corydalis Flavula — A535

Litho. With Foil Application

2019, May 20 *Perf. 13*

1216	A535 $3 multicolored	7.50	7.50

World Bee Day. See Offices in Geneva No. 667; Vienna No. 638.

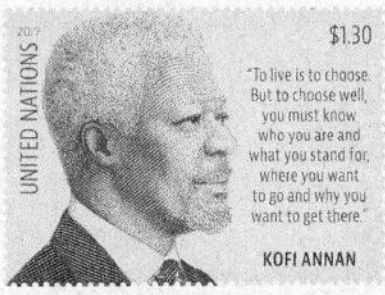

Kofi Annan (1938-2018), Seventh United Nations Secretary-General — A536

2019, May 31 Litho. *Perf. 14x14¼*

1217	A536 $1.30 gray blue & black	2.60	2.60

Souvenir Sheet

Pandas A537

No. 1218: a, Qiqia. b,Qiqi and Diandian. c, Diandian.

2019, June 11 Litho. *Perf. 13½x13*

1218	A537 Sheet of 3	13.00	13.00
a.	$1.15 multi	4.25	4.25
b.	2fr multi	4.25	4.25
c.	€1.80 multi	4.25	4.25

China 2019 World Stamp Exhibition, Wuhan, People's Republic of China. On July 31, 2019, a sheet containing Nos. 1218a-1218c with a different sheet margin was issued for Singpex 2019 International Stamp Exhibition, with a printing quantity of 21,000 sheets. No. 1218 and the sheet issued in July each sold for $6.30.

A538

A539

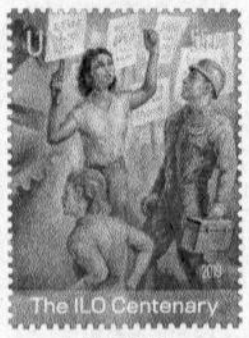

A540

A541

International Labor Organization, Cent. — A542

2019, June 28 Litho. *Perf. 13½x14*

1219	A538 55c multicolored	1.10	1.10
1220	A539 55c multicolored	1.10	1.10
1221	A540 55c multicolored	1.10	1.10
1222	A541 55c multicolored	1.10	1.10
1223	A542 55c multicolored	1.10	1.10
a.	Horiz. strip of 5, #1219-1223	5.50	5.50
	Nos. 1219-1223 (5)	5.50	5.50

See Offices in Geneva Nos. 668-672, Vienna Nos. 639-643.

Climate Change A543

Designs: 55c, Mountain. No. 1225, Fish. No. 1226, Polar bear.

2019, Sept. 23 Litho. *Perf. 14¼*

1224	A543 55c multicolored	1.10	1.10
1225	A543 $1.15 multicolored	2.40	2.40

Souvenir Sheet

Perf.

1226	A543 $1.15 multicolored	2.40	2.40

2019 United Nations Climate Change Conference, Madrid. No. 1226 contains one 47mm diameter stamp. See Offices in Geneva Nos. 673-675; Vienna Nos. 649-651.

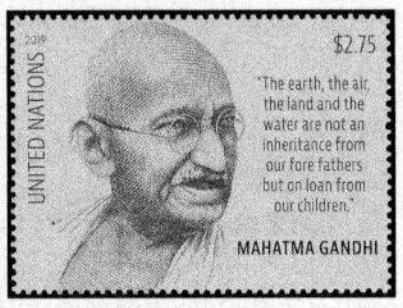

Mohandas K. Gandhi (1869-1948), Indian Nationalist Leader A544

Printed by Johann Enschedé Stamps BV, the Netherlands. Panes of 20. Designed by Rorie Katz, U.S.

2019, Oct. 2 Litho. *Perf. 14¼*

1227	A544 $2.75 pink & black	5.50	5.50

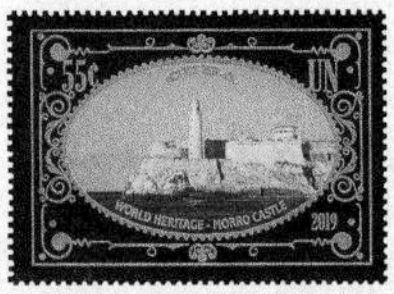

World Heritage Sites in Cuba — A545

Designs: Nos. 1228, 1230a, Morro Castle. Nos. 1229, 1230d, Vinales Valley. No. 1230b, Trinidad. No. 1230c, Camagüey. No. 1230e, Cienfuegos. No. 1230f, San Pedro de la Rosa Castle.

Litho. With Foil Application

2019, Oct. 24 *Perf. 14¼*

1228	A545 55c multicolored	1.10	1.10
1229	A545 $1.15 multicolored	2.40	2.40

Souvenir Booklet

1230	Booklet, #1115g-1115l	24.00	
a.-c.	A545 35c Any single	.75	.75
d.-f.	A545 55c Any single	1.25	1.25
g.	Booklet pane of 4 #1230a	3.00	—
h.	Booklet pane of 4 #1230b	3.00	—
i.	Booklet pane of 4 #1230c	3.00	—
j.	Booklet pane of 4 #1230d	5.00	—
k.	Booklet pane of 4 #1230e	5.00	—
l.	Booklet pane of 4 #1230f	5.00	—

Complete booklet sold for $12. See Offices in Geneva Nos. 677-679; Vienna Nos. 652-654.

United Nations Emblem Type of 2016 Dated "2020" in Purple

2020, Jan. 10 Litho. *Perf. 14¾*

1231	A490 $1.20 multi + label	*3.00*	*3.00*
	Sheet of 10 + 10 labels	*30.00*	—

The full sheet sold for $14.95. The generic label has a rat on red background. The personalization of labels was available only at UN Headquarters, and not through mail order.

Endangered Species — A546

Designs: No. 1232, Great hammerhead shark. No. 1233, Egyptian vulture. No. 1234, Andean flamingo. No. 1235, Argali sheep.

Perf. 12¾x12½

2020, Feb. 17 Litho.

1232	A546 $1.20 multicolored	2.40	2.40
1233	A546 $1.20 multicolored	2.40	2.40
1234	A546 $1.20 multicolored	2.40	2.40
1235	A546 $1.20 multicolored	2.40	2.40
a.	Block of 4, #1232-1235	9.75	9.75

See Offices in Geneva Nos. 680-683; Vienna Nos. 655-658.

Blank Stamp On Which Stickers Can Be Applied A547

Designs: No. 1212, Hawksbill turtle. No. 1213, Queen conch. No. 1214, Mushroom coral. No. 1215, Humpback whale.

2020, Mar. 19 Litho. *Die Cut*

Self-Adhesive

1236	A547 $1.20 multi with rounded corners	2.40	2.40
a.	With perpendicular corners and black frame line	2.40	2.40
b.	Booklet pane of 6 #1236a	14.50	

No. 1236 was issued as a souvenir sheet having two different sheet margins, each with different stickers. No. 1236a was issued in a booklet containing six panes of one stamp, with each pane having different margins and stickers. Each booklet pane contained one sticker depicting Hello Kitty, a color wheel with Hello Kitty at the center, one of six different Sustainable Development Goal emblems, along with a variety of other stickers. The two souvenir sheets had the same sheet margin and stickers found on two of the panes of No. 1236b. No. 1236b was sold folded, without any means of separation between the individual panes.

Miniature Sheet

Act Now Climate Action Campaign — A548

No. 1237: a, Man in shower. b, Hand on light switch. c, Bicyclist. d, Electric plug and socket. e, Knife, fork, vegetables. f, Hand, container and recycling arrow. g, Produce stand. h, Clothing on clothes hanger. i, Man placing bottle in recycling bin. j, Man carrying reusable shopping bag.

2020, Mar. 27 Litho. *Perf. 14¾*

1237	A548 Sheet of 10 + 10 labels	*30.00*	*30.00*
a.-j.	$1.20 Any single + label	*3.00*	*3.00*

The full sheet sold for $14.95. The generic labels are shown. Labels could be personalized. The personalization of labels was available only at UN Headquarters, and not through mail order.

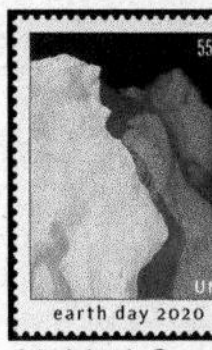

Linblad Cove, Antarctica, Drawing by Zaria Forman A549

Our Changing Seas IV, Glazed Stoneware and Porcelain Item by Courtney Mattison A550

2020, Apr. 22 Litho. *Perf. 13¼*

1238	A549 55c multicolored	1.10	1.10
1239	A550 $1.20 multicolored	2.40	2.40

Earth Day, 50th anniv. Because of the COVID-19 pandemic, Nos. 1238-1239 were not available for sale on day of issue stated on the first-day covers as they had not yet been printed and delivered. See Offices in Geneva Nos. 685-686; Vienna Nos. 660-661.

United Nations Peacekeeping Vehicles — A551

United Nations Peacekeepers — A552

Two Female United Nations Peacekeepers and Helicopter — A553

United Nations Peacekeeping Vehicles — A554

Helmet and Knapsacks of United Nations Peacekeepers — A555

2020, May 29 Litho. *Perf. 14¾*

1240	A551 $1.20 multi + label	*3.00*	*3.00*
1241	A552 $1.20 multi + label	*3.00*	*3.00*
1242	A553 $1.20 multi + label	*3.00*	*3.00*
1243	A554 $1.20 multi + label	*3.00*	*3.00*
1244	A555 $1.20 multi + label	*3.00*	*3.00*
a.	Vert. strip of 5, #1240-1244, + 5 labels	*15.00*	*15.00*

International Day of United Nations Peacekeepers. The full sheet sold for $14.95. The generic labels are shown. Labels could be personalized. The personalization of labels was available only at UN Headquarters, and not through mail order.

Flag Type of 1980

2020, Aug. 20 Litho. *Perf. 14x13¼*

1245	A185 $1.20 Bahrain	2.40	2.40
1246	A185 $1.20 Belarus	2.40	2.40
1247	A185 $1.20 Brazil	2.40	2.40
1248	A185 $1.20 Cyprus	2.40	2.40
a.	Block of 4, #1245-1248	9.60	9.60
1249	A185 $1.20 Dominica	2.40	2.40
1250	A185 $1.20 Mauritania	2.40	2.40
1251	A185 $1.20 Mongolia	2.40	2.40
1252	A185 $1.20 Paraguay	2.40	2.40
a.	Block of 4, #1249-1252	9.60	9.60
	Nos. 1245-1252 (8)	19.20	19.20

World Heritage Sites in Russia A556

Designs: Nos. 1253, 1255a, Lake Baikal. Nos. 1254, 1255d, Kremlin and Red Square, Moscow. No. 1255b, Kazan Kremlin. No. 1255c, Novodevichy Convent. No. 1255e, Saint Petersburg. No. 1255f, Kizhi Pogost.

Perf. 14½x14¼

2020, Sept. 11 Litho.

1253	A556	55c multicolored	1.10	1.10
1254	A556	$1.20 multicolored	2.40	2.40

Souvenir Booklet

1255	Booklet, #1115g-1115l	24.00	
a.-c.	A556 35c any single	.75	.75
d.-f.	A556 55c any single	1.25	1.25
g.	Booklet pane of 4 #1255a	3.00	—
h.	Booklet pane of 4 #1255b	3.00	—
i.	Booklet pane of 4 #1255c	3.00	—
j.	Booklet pane of 4 #1255d	5.00	—
k.	Booklet pane of 4 #1255e	5.00	—
l.	Booklet pane of 4 #1255f	5.00	—

Complete booklet sold for $12. See Offices in Geneva Nos. 688-690; Vienna Nos. 663-665.

Souvenir Sheet

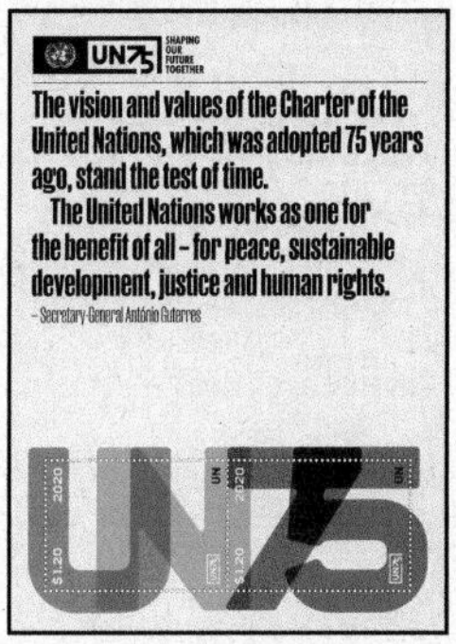

United Nations, 75th Anniv. A557

No. 1256: a, Pink "U," yellow "N." b, Green "7," red "5."

2020, Oct. 24 Litho. *Perf. 13¼*

1256	A557	Sheet of 2	4.80	4.80
a.-b.		$1.20 Either single	2.40	2.40

See Offices in Geneva No. 691; Vienna No. 667.

Souvenir Sheet

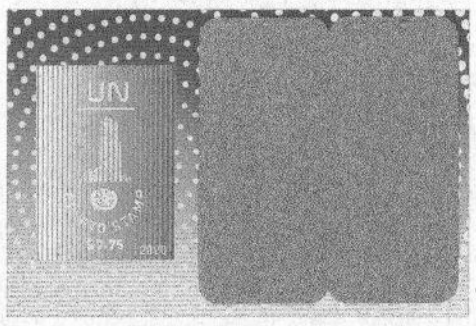

United Nations Building and Emblem A558

Litho. With Foil Application

2020, Nov. 24 *Die Cut Perf. 11½*

Self-Adhesive

1257	A558	$7.75 multicolored	15.50	15.50

Crypto stamp. Unused value is for sheets with unscratched panels at right. See Offices in Geneva No. 692; Vienna No. 668.

Fish A559

Grain Stalk A560

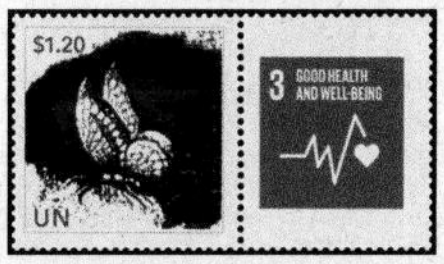

Butterfly A561

Elephants A562

Tree A563

2020, Dec. 5 Litho. *Perf. 14¾*

1258	A559	$1.20 multi + label	*3.00*	*3.00*
1259	A560	$1.20 multi + label	*3.00*	*3.00*
1260	A561	$1.20 multi + label	*3.00*	*3.00*
1261	A562	$1.20 multi + label	*3.00*	*3.00*
1262	A563	$1.20 multi + label	*3.00*	*3.00*
a.		Vert. strip of 5, #1258-1262, + 5 labels	*15.00*	*15.00*
		Sheet of 10, 2 each #1258-1262, + 10 labels	*30.00*	*30.00*
		Nos. 1258-1262 (5)	*15.00*	*15.00*

World Soil Day. The full sheet sold for $14.95. The generic labels are shown. Labels could be personalized. The personalization of labels was available only at UN Headquarters, and not through mail order.

United Nations Emblem Type of 2016 Dated "2021" in Purple

2021, Jan. 22 Litho. *Perf. 14¾*

1263	A490	$1.20 multicolored + label	*3.00*	*3.00*
		Sheet of 10 + 10 labels	*30.00*	—

The full sheet sold for $14.95. The generic label has an ox on red background. The personalization of labels was available only at UN Headquarters, and not through mail order.

International Day for the Elimination of Racial Discrimination — A564

2021, Mar. 19 Litho. *Perf. 13¼x13*

1264	A564	$1.20 multicolored	2.40	2.40

See Offices in Geneva No. 693; Vienna Nos. 669.

Endangered Species — A565

Designs: No. 1265, Waigeo cuscus. No. 1266, Helmeted honeyeater. No. 1267, Venus flytrap. No. 1268, American alligator.

2021, Apr. 7 Litho. *Perf. 12¾x12½*

1265	A565	$1.20 multicolored	2.40	2.40
1266	A565	$1.20 multicolored	2.40	2.40
1267	A565	$1.20 multicolored	2.40	2.40
1268	A565	$1.20 multicolored	2.40	2.40
a.		Block of 4, #1265-1268	9.75	9.75
		Nos. 1265-1268 (4)	9.60	9.60

See Offices in Geneva Nos. 694-697; Vienna Nos. 670-673.

Miniature Sheet

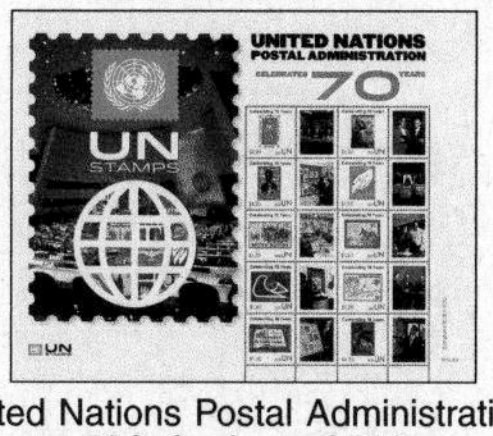

United Nations Postal Administration, 70th Anniv. — A566

No. 1269 — United Nations stamps: a, #171. b, #548. c, #873. d, #5. e, #268. f, #1. g, #249. h, #310. i, #35. j, #160.

2021, Apr. 30 Litho. *Perf. 14¾*

1269	A566	Sheet of 10	*30.00*	*30.00*
a.-j.		$1.20 Any single + label	*3.00*	*3.00*

The full sheet sold for $14.95. The generic labels are shown. Labels could be personalized. The personalization of labels was available only at UN Headquarters, and not through mail order.

Sailors in Sailboat and Bird — A567

Sailors in Sailboat — A568

Sailors in Sailboat and Bird — A569

Batter, Catcher and Umpire — A570

Batter and Baseball A571

Pitcher and Baseball A572

Olympic Gold Medalist and Dove A573

2021, July 23 Litho. *Perf. 13½*

1270	A567	55c multicolored	1.10	1.10
1271	A568	55c multicolored	1.10	1.10
1272	A569	55c multicolored	1.10	1.10
a.		Horiz. strip of 3, #1270-1272	3.30	3.30
1273	A570	$1.20 multicolored	2.40	2.40
1274	A571	$1.20 multicolored	2.40	2.40
1275	A572	$1.20 multicolored	2.40	2.40
a.		Horiz. strip of 3, #1273-1275	7.20	7.20
		Nos. 1270-1275 (6)	10.50	10.50

Souvenir Sheet

1276	A573	$1.20 multicolored	2.40	2.40

Sports for Peace, 2020 Summer Olympics, Tokyo. The 2020 Summer Olympics were postponed until 2021 because of the COVID-19 pandemic. See Offices in Geneva Nos. 698-704, Vienna Nos. 674-680.

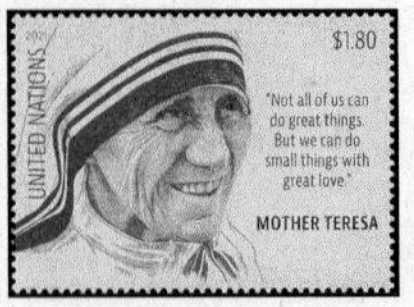

Mother Teresa (1910-97), Humanitarian A574

2021, Aug. 12 Litho. *Perf. 14¼*

1277	A574	$1.80 dark blue & black		3.75	3.75

Waterway, Railway and Bridges World Heritage Sites — A575

Designs: Nos. 1278, 1280a, Rideau Canal, Canada. Nos. 1279, 1280d, Grand Canal, People's Republic of China. No. 1280b, Rhaetian Railway, Switzerland and Italy. No. 1280c, Forth Bridge, Scotland. No. 1280e, Darjeeling Himalayan Railway, India. No. 1280f, Old Bridge, Mostar, Bosnia and Herzegovina.

2021, Aug. 25 Litho. *Perf. 14¼*

1278	A575	55c	multicolored	1.10	1.10
1279	A575	$1.20	multicolored	2.40	2.40

Souvenir Booklet

1280	Booklet, #1280g-1280l	24.00	
a.-c.	A575 35c any single	.75	.75
d.-f.	A575 55c any single	1.25	1.25
g.	Booklet pane of 4 #1280a	3.00	—
h.	Booklet pane of 4 #1280b	3.00	—
i.	Booklet pane of 4 #1280c	3.00	—
j.	Booklet pane of 4 #1280d	5.00	—
k.	Booklet pane of 4 #1280e	5.00	—
l.	Booklet pane of 4 #1280f	5.00	—

Complete booklet sold for $12. See Offices in Geneva Nos. 705-707; Vienna Nos. 681-683.

Souvenir Sheet

Expo 2020, Dubai A576

No. 1281: a, Mobility Pavilion. b, Opportunity Pavilion. c, Sustainability Pavilion.

2021, Oct. 1 Litho. *Perf. 13½x13*

1281	A576 Sheet of 3		14.50	14.50
a.	$1.30 multi		4.75	4.75
b.	2fr multi		4.75	4.75
c.	€1.80 multi		4.75	4.75

Expo 2020 was postponed until 2021 because of the COVID-19 pandemic. No. 1281 sold for $7.04.

Souvenir Sheet

United Nations Biodiversity Conference, Kunming, People's Republic of China — A577

No. 1282: a, Flower. b, Insect. c, Bird.

2021, Oct. 11 Litho. *Perf. 13½x13*

1282	A577 Sheet of 3	14.50	14.50
a.	$1.30 multi	4.75	4.75
b.	2fr multi	4.75	4.75
c.	€1.80 multi	4.75	4.75

No. 1282 sold for $7.04.

Miniature Sheet

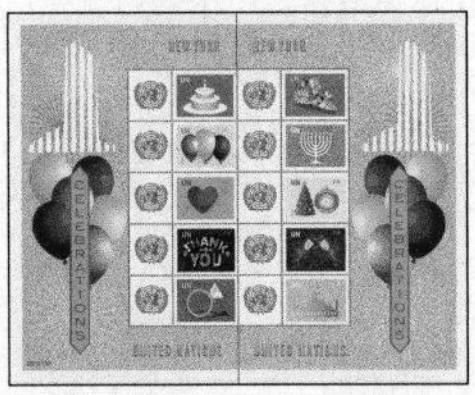

Celebrations — A578

No. 1283: a, Birthday cake. b, Flower bouquet. c, Three balloons. d, Menorah. e, Heart and arrow. f, Christmas tree and ornament. g, "Thank you." h, Champagne flutes. i, Diamond ring. j, Mosque.

2021, Nov. 4 Litho. *Perf. 14¼*

1283	A578 Sheet of 10	*32.50*	*32.50*
a.-j.	$1.30 Any single + label	*3.25*	*3.25*

The full sheet sold for $15.95. The generic labels are shown. Labels could be personalized. The personalization of labels was available only at UN Headquarters, and not through mail order.

World Toilet Day — A579

2021, Nov. 19 Litho. *Perf. 14¼*

1284	A579	58c multicolored	1.25	1.25

Miniature Sheet

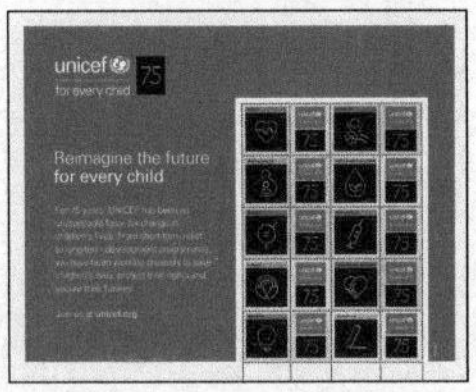

UNICEF, 75th Anniv. A580

No. 1285 — Inscription: a, Health. b, Disability. c, Mental Health. d, Water Sanitation Hygiene. e, Gender. f, Vaccination. g, Climate. h, Humanitarian Response. i, Nutrition. j, Education.

2021, Dec. 11 Litho. *Perf. 14½*

1285	A580 Sheet of 10	*32.50*	*32.50*
a.-j.	$1.30 Any single + label	*3.25*	*3.25*

The full sheet sold for $15.95. The generic labels are shown. Labels could be personalized. The personalization of labels was available only at UN Headquarters, and not through mail order.

Ice Hockey Player and Goaltender A581

Three Ice Hockey Players and Puck — A582

Snowboarder With Yellow Green Vest — A583

Snowboarder in Air With Orange Vest — A584

2022, Jan. 14 Litho. *Perf. 14¼*

1286	A581 58c multicolored	1.25	1.25
1287	A582 58c multicolored	1.25	1.25
a.	Horiz. pair, #1286-1287	2.50	2.50
1288	A583 $1.30 multicolored	2.60	2.60
1289	A584 $1.30 multicolored	2.60	2.60
a.	Horiz. pair, #1288-1289	5.20	5.20
	First day cover, #1288-1289		9.50
	Inscription block of 4	10.50	—
	Pane of 6	16.00	—
	Nos. 1286-1289 (4)	7.70	7.70

Sports for Peace, 2022 Winter Olympics, Beijing. See Offices in Geneva Nos. 710-713; Vienna Nos. 687-690.

Tiger Facing Right A585

Tiger Facing Left A586

2022, Jan. 21 Litho. *Perf. 14¼*

1290	A585 $1.30 multi + label	*3.25*	*3.25*
1291	A586 $1.30 multi + label	*3.25*	*3.25*
a.	Horiz. pair, #1290-1291, + 2 labels	*6.50*	*6.50*
	Sheet of 10, 5 each #1290-1291, + 10 labels	*32.50*	*32.50*

New Year 2022 (Year of the Tiger). The full sheet sold for $15.95. The generic labels are shown. Labels could be personalized. The personalization of labels was available only at UN Headquarters, and not through mail order.

Biggie, Mr. Dinkles, Fruits and Vegetables A587

Guy Diamond, Tiny Diamond, Fruits and Vegetables A588

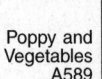

Poppy and Vegetables A589

Branch, Fruits and Vegetables A590

Prince Darnell, Cooper, Fruits and Vegetables A591

2022, Feb. 22 Litho. *Perf. 14¾*

1292	A587 $1.30 multi + label	*3.25*	*3.25*
1293	A588 $1.30 multi + label	*3.25*	*3.25*
1294	A589 $1.30 multi + label	*3.25*	*3.25*
1295	A590 $1.30 multi + label	*3.25*	*3.25*
1296	A591 $1.30 multi + label	*3.25*	*3.25*
a.	Vert. strip of 5, #1292-1296, + 5 labels	*16.25*	*16.25*
	Sheet of 10, 2 each #1292-1296, + 10 labels	*32.50*	*32.50*
	Nos. 1292-1296 (5)	16.25	16.25

Trolls Food Heroes Campaign. The full sheet sold for $15.95. The generic labels are shown. Labels could be personalized. The personalization of labels was available only at UN Headquarters, and not through mail order.

Endangered Species — A592

Designs: No. 1297, Pygmy three-toed sloth. No. 1298, Andean condor. No. 1299, Keel-billed toucan. No. 1300, Jaguar.

Perf. 12¾x12½

2022, Mar. 18 Litho.

1297	A592 $1.30 multicolored	2.60	2.60
1298	A592 $1.30 multicolored	2.60	2.60
1299	A592 $1.30 multicolored	2.60	2.60
1300	A592 $1.30 multicolored	2.60	2.60
a.	Block of 4, #1297-1300	10.50	10.50
	Nos. 1297-1300 (4)	10.40	10.40

See Offices in Geneva Nos. 714-717; Vienna Nos. 691-694.

Exploration of Mars — A593

Designs: 58c, Proctor Crater. No. 1302, Mars Perseverence Rover.

No. 1303, Mars Ingenuity Helicopter.

2022, Apr. 24 Litho. *Perf. 13¼x13*

1301	A593 58c multicolored	1.25	1.25
1302	A593 $1.30 multicolored	2.60	2.60

Souvenir Sheet

Perf. 13½

1303	A593 $1.30 multicolored	2.60	2.60

No. 1303 contains one 44x44mm stamp. See Offices in Geneva Nos. 718-720; Vienna Nos. 696-698.

European Spa Town World Heritage Sites — A594

Designs: Nos. 1304, 1306a, Karlovy Vary, Czech Republic. Nos. 1305, 1306d, Montecatini Terme, Italy. No. 1306b, Spa, Belgium. No. 1306c, Baden-Baden, Germany. No. 1306e, Vichy, France. No. 1306f, Baden bei Wien, Austria.

2022, Sept. 9 Litho. *Perf. 14½x14¼*

1304	A594 60c multicolored	1.25	1.25
1305	A594 $1.40 multicolored	3.00	3.00

Souvenir Booklet

1306	Booklet, #1115g-1115l	28.00	
a.-c.	A594 44c any single	1.00	1.00
d.-f.	A594 60c any single	1.30	1.30
g.	Booklet pane of 4 #1306a	4.00	—
h.	Booklet pane of 4 #1306b	4.00	—
i.	Booklet pane of 4 #1306c	4.00	—
j.	Booklet pane of 4 #1306d	5.25	—
k.	Booklet pane of 4 #1306e	5.25	—
l.	Booklet pane of 4 #1306f	5.25	—

Complete booklet sold for $14. See Offices in Geneva Nos. 722-724; Vienna Nos. 700-702.

Miniature Sheet

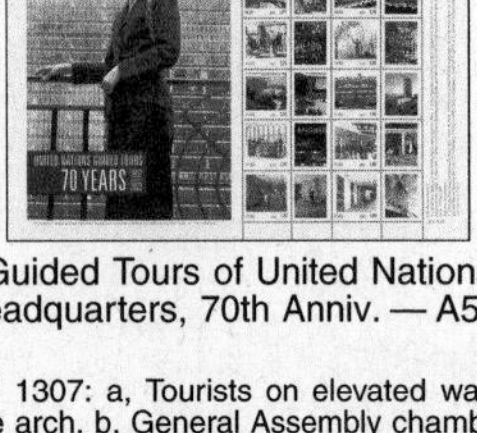

Guided Tours of United Nations Headquarters, 70th Anniv. — A595

No. 1307: a, Tourists on elevated walkway above arch. b, General Assembly chamber. c, Tourists standing in lobby. d, Tour guide touching tree branch. e, Security Council chamber. f, Tour guide standing in aisle, tourists seated in chamber. g, Children and adults at tour information counter in lobby. h, Tourists standing near circular pillars in lobby. i, Tour guide and tourists in front of mural. j, Tourists exiting doorway.

2022, Nov. 1 Litho. *Perf. 14½*

1307 A595 Sheet of 10 *34.00 34.00*
a.-j. $1.40 Any single + label *3.25 3.25*

The full sheet sold for $16.95. The generic labels are shown. Labels could be personalized. The personalization of labels was available only at UN Headquarters, and not through mail order.

Souvenir Sheet

Hands Reaching for Olive Branch — A596

Litho. With Foil Application
2022, Nov. 18 *Die Cut Perf. 11½*
Self-Adhesive

1308 A596 $4.50 multicolored 9.00 9.00

Crypto stamp. Unused value is for sheets with unscratched panels at right. See Offices in Geneva No. 725; Vienna No. 703.

SEMI-POSTAL STAMPS

Souvenir Sheet

AIDS Awareness — SP1

2002, Oct. 24 Litho. *Perf. 14½*

B1 SP1 37c + 6c multicolored 3.50 3.50

See Offices in Geneva No. B1, Vienna No. B1.

Miniature Sheet

Campaign Against COVID-19 Pandemic — SP2

No. B2: a, Hand washing. b, Question mark in speech bubble. c, Social distancing. d, Smiling face. e, Cross in broken circle. f, Hands making heart shape.

2020, Aug. 11 Litho. *Perf. 13¼*

B2 SP2 Sheet of 6 21.00 21.00
a. 55c+50c multi 2.10 2.10
b. $1.20+50c multi 3.50 3.50
c. 1fr+50c multi 3.50 3.50
d. 1.50fr+50c multi 4.50 4.50
e. 85c+50c multi 3.50 3.50
f. €1+50c multi 3.75 3.75

Surtax for World Health Organization COVID Solidarity Response Fund.

SP3

Photograph of John Lennon (1940-80), by Bob Gruen — SP4

2021, Sept. 21 Litho. *Perf. 14¼*

B3 SP3 $1.30 multicolored 3.75 3.75

Souvenir Sheet
Litho. With Foil Application

B4 SP4 $2.60 multicolored 7.25 7.25

International Day of Peace. Surtax for United Nations peacekeeping efforts.

World Humanitarian Day — SP5

2022, Aug. 19 Litho. *Perf. 13¼x13*

B5 SP5 $1.40 multicolored 4.00 4.00

Surtax for United Nations Central Emergency Response Fund. See Offices in Geneva No. B4; Vienna No. B4.

AIR POST STAMPS

Plane and Gull — AP1

Swallows and UN Emblem — AP2

1951, Dec. 14 Unwmk. *Perf. 14*

C1 AP1 6c henna brown .25 .25
C2 AP1 10c brt blue grn .30 .30
C3 AP2 15c deep ultra .40 .40
a. 15c Prussian blue 65.00
C4 AP2 25c gray black .85 .85
Nos. C1-C4 (4) 1.80 1.80

Airplane Wing and Globe — AP3

1957, May 27 *Perf. 12½x14*

C5 AP3 4c maroon .25 .25

Type of 1957 and

UN Flag and Plane — AP4

Perf. 12½x13½

1959, Feb. 9 Unwmk.

C6 AP3 5c rose red .25 .25

Perf. 13½x14

C7 AP4 7c ultramarine .25 .25

Outer Space AP5

UN Emblem AP6

Bird of Laurel Leaves — AP7

Perf. 11½

1963, June 17 Photo. Unwmk.

C8 AP5 6c blk, blue & yel grn .25 .25
C9 AP6 8c yel, ol grn & red .25 .25

Perf. 12½x12

C10 AP7 13c ultra, aquamarine, gray & carmine .25 .25

"Flight Across Globe" AP8

Jet Plane and Envelope AP9

Perf. 11½x12, 12x11½

1964, May 1 Photo. Unwmk.

C11 AP8 15c vio, buff, gray & pale grn .30 .30
a. Gray omitted *225.00*
C12 AP9 25c yel, org, gray, blue & red .50 .50
Nos. C8-C12 (5) 1.55 1.55

See UN Offices in Geneva No. 8.

Jet Plane and UN Emblem — AP10

1968, Apr. 18 Litho. *Perf. 13*

C13 AP10 20c multicolored .35 .35

Wings, Envelopes and UN Emblem — AP11

1969, Apr. 21 Litho. *Perf. 13*

C14 AP11 10c org ver, org, yel & blk .25 .25

UN Emblem and Stylized Wing AP12

Birds in Flight AP13

Clouds — AP14

"UN" and Plane — AP15

Litho. & Engr.

1972, May 1 *Perf. 13x13½*

C15 AP12 9c lt blue, dk red & vio blue .25 .25

Photo.

Perf. 14x13½

C16 AP13 11c blue & multi .25 .25

Perf. 13½x14

C17 AP14 17c yel, red & org .25 .25

Perf. 13

C18 AP15 21c silver & multi .25 .25
Nos. C15-C18 (4) 1.00 1.00

Globe and Jet — AP16

Pathways Radiating from UN Emblem — AP17

Bird in Flight, UN Headquarters AP18

Perf. 13, 12½x13 (18c)

1974, Sept. 16 Litho.

C19 AP16 13c multicolored .25 .25
C20 AP17 18c gray olive & multi .25 .25
C21 AP18 26c blue & multi .35 .35
Nos. C19-C21 (3) .85 .85

Winged Airmail Letter AP19

Symbolic Globe and Plane AP20

1977, June 27 Photo. *Perf. 14*

C22 AP19 25c greenish blue & multi .35 .35
C23 AP20 31c magenta .45 .45

OFFICES IN GENEVA, SWITZERLAND

For use only on mail posted at the Palais des Nations (UN European Office), Geneva. Inscribed in French unless otherwise stated.

100 Centimes = 1 Franc

Catalogue values for all unused stamps in this country are for Never Hinged items.

Types of United Nations Issues 1961-69 and

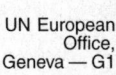

UN European Office, Geneva — G1

Designs: 5c, UN Headquarters, New York, and world map. 10c, UN flag. 20c, Three men united before globe. 50c, Opening words of UN Charter. 60c, UN emblem over globe. 70c, "un" and UN emblem. 75c, "Flight Across Globe." 80c, UN Headquarters and emblem. 90c, Abstract group of flags. 1fr, UN emblem. 2fr, Stylized globe and weather vane. 3fr, Statue by Henrik Starcke. 10fr, "Peace, Justice, Security."

The 20c, 80c and 90c are inscribed in French. The 75c and 10fr carry French inscription at top, English at bottom.

1969-70 Photo. Unwmk.
Perf. 13 (5c, 70c, 90c); 12½x12 (10c);

1 A88 5c purple & multi .25 .30
a. Green omitted —
2 A52 10c salmon & multi .25 .30

Perf. 11½ (20c-60c, 3fr)

3 A66 20c black & multi .25 .30
4 G1 30c dark blue & multi .25 .30
5 A77 50c ultra & multi .25 .30
6 A54 60c dark brown, salmon & gold .25 .30
7 A104 70c red, black & gold .30 .35

Perf. 11½x12 (75c)

8 AP8 75c carmine rose & multi .35 .40

Perf. 13½x14 (80c)

9 A78 80c blue green, red & yellow .35 .40
10 A45 90c blue & multi .40 .45

Litho. & Embossed
Perf. 14 (1fr)

11 A79 1fr light & dark green .40 .45

Photo.
Perf. 12x11½ (2fr)

12 A67 2fr blue & multi .75 .85
13 A97 3fr olive & multi 1.00 1.10

Engr.
Perf. 12 (10fr)

14 A3 10fr dark blue 3.50 3.75
Nos. 1-14 (14) 8.55 9.55

Sea Bed Type of UN
Photo. & Engr.

1971, Jan. 25 ***Perf. 13***
15 A114 30c green & multi .25 .30

Refugee Type of UN

1971, Mar. 12 Litho. ***Perf. 13x12½***
16 A115 50c dp car, dp org & blk .25 .30

World Food Program Type of UN

1971, Apr. 13 Photo. ***Perf. 14***
17 A116 50c dark vio & multi .25 .30

UPU Headquarters Type of UN

1971, May 28 Photo. ***Perf. 11½***
18 A117 75c green & multi .35 .40

Eliminate Racial Discrimination Types of UN

1971, Sept. 21 Photo. ***Perf. 13½***
19 A118 30c blue & multi .25 .30
20 A119 50c yellow grn & multi .25 .30

Picasso Type of UN

1971, Nov. 19 Photo. ***Perf. 11½***
21 A122 1.10fr multicolored .75 .80

Palais des Nations, Geneva — G2

1972, Jan. 5 Photo. ***Perf. 11½***
22 G2 40c ol, blue, sal & dk grn .25 .30

Nuclear Weapons Type of UN

1972, Feb. 14 Photo. ***Perf. 13½x14***
23 A124 40c yel, grn, blk, rose & gray .25 .30

World Health Day Type of UN
Litho. & Engr.

1972, Apr. 7 ***Perf. 13x13½***
24 A125 80c black & multi .45 .50

Human Environment Type of UN
Lithographed & Embossed

1972, June 5 ***Perf. 12½x14***
25 A126 40c ol, lemon, grn & blue .25 .30
26 A126 80c ultra, pink, grn & blue .45 .50

Economic Commission for Europe Type of UN

1972, Sept. 11 Litho. ***Perf. 13x13½***
27 A127 1.10fr red & multi 1.00 1.10

Art at UN (Sert) Type of UN

1972, Nov. 17 Photo. ***Perf. 12x12½***
28 A128 40c gold, red & brn .30 .35
29 A128 80c gold, brn & olive .60 .65

Disarmament Decade Type of UN

1973, Mar. 9 Litho. ***Perf. 13½x13***
30 A129 60c vio & multi .40 .45
31 A129 1.10fr olive & multi .85 .90

Drug Abuse Type of UN

1973, Apr. 13 Photo. ***Perf. 13½***
32 A130 60c blue & multi .45 .50

Volunteers Type of UN

1973, May 25 Photo. ***Perf. 14***
33 A131 80c gray grn & multi .35 .40

Namibia Type of UN

1973, Oct. 1 Photo. ***Perf. 13½***
34 A132 60c red & multi .35 .40

Human Rights Type of UN

1973, Nov. 16 Photo. ***Perf. 13½***
35 A133 40c ultra & multi .30 .35
36 A133 80c olive & multi .50 .55

ILO Headquarters Type of UN

1974, Jan. 11 Photo. ***Perf. 14***
37 A134 60c violet & multi .45 .50
38 A134 80c brown & multi .65 .70

Centenary of UPU Type of UN

1974, Mar. 22 Litho. ***Perf. 12½***
39 A135 30c gold & multi .25 .30
40 A135 60c gold & multi .60 .65

Art at UN (Portinari) Type of UN

1974, May 6 Photo. ***Perf. 14***
41 A136 60c dark red & multi .40 .45
42 A136 1fr green & multi .70 .75

World Population Year Type of UN

1974, Oct. 18 Photo. ***Perf. 14***
43 A140 60c brt grn & multi .50 .55
44 A140 80c brown & multi .70 .75

Law of the Sea Type of UN

1974, Nov. 22 Photo. ***Perf. 14***
45 A141 1.30fr blue & multi 1.00 1.10

Outer Space Type of UN

1975, Mar. 14 Litho. ***Perf. 13***
46 A142 60c multicolored .50 .55
47 A142 90c multicolored .75 .80

International Women's Year Type of UN

1975, May 9 Litho. ***Perf. 15***
48 A143 60c multicolored .40 .45
49 A143 90c multicolored .70 .75

30th Anniversary Type of UN

1975, June 26 Litho. ***Perf. 13***
50 A144 60c green & multi .40 .45
51 A144 90c violet & multi .70 .75

Souvenir Sheet
Imperf

52 Sheet of 2 1.00 1.10
a. A144 60c green & multicolored .30 .35
b. A144 90c violet & multicolored .60 .65

Namibia Type of UN

1975, Sept. 22 Photo. ***Perf. 13½***
53 A145 50c multicolored .30 .35
54 A145 1.30fr multicolored .85 .90

Peace-keeping Operations Type of UN

1975, Nov. 21 Engr. ***Perf. 12½***
55 A146 60c greenish blue .35 .40
56 A146 70c bright violet .65 .65

WFUNA Type of UN

1976, Mar. 12 Photo. ***Perf. 14***
57 A152 90c multicolored .90 .95

UNCTAD Type of UN

1976, Apr. 23 Photo. ***Perf. 11½***
58 A153 1.10fr sepia & multi .90 .95

Habitat Type of UN

1976, May 28 Photo. ***Perf. 14***
59 A154 40c dull blue & multi .25 .30
60 A154 1.50fr violet & multi .75 .80

UN Emblem, Post Horn and Rainbow — G3

UN Postal Administration, 25th anniversary.

1976, Oct. 8 Photo. ***Perf. 11½***
61 G3 80c tan & multi .50 .55
62 A3 1.10fr lt grn & multi 1.60 1.75

World Food Council Type of UN

1976, Nov. 19 Litho. ***Perf. 14½***
63 A156 70c multicolored .50 .55

WIPO Type of UN

1977, Mar. 11 Photo. ***Perf. 14***
64 A157 80c red & multi .60 .65

Drop of Water and Globe — G4

UN Water Conference, Mar del Plata, Argentina, Mar. 14-25.

1977, Apr. 22 Photo. ***Perf. 13½x13***
65 G4 80c ultra & multi .50 .55
66 G4 1.10fr dark car & multi .80 .85

Hands Protecting UN Emblem — G5

UN Security Council.

1977, May 27 Photo. ***Perf. 11***
67 G5 80c blue & multi .50 .55
68 G5 1.10fr emerald & multi .80 .85

Colors of Five Races Spun into One Firm Rope — G6

Fight against racial discrimination.

1977, Sept. 19 Litho. ***Perf. 13½x13***
69 G6 40c multicolored .25 .30
70 G6 1.10fr multicolored .65 .70

Atomic Energy Turning Partly into Olive Branch — G7

Peaceful uses of atomic energy.

1977, Nov. 18 Photo. ***Perf. 14***
71 G7 80c dark car & multi .55 .60
72 G7 1.10fr Prussian blue & multi .75 .80

"Tree" of Doves — G8

1978, Jan. 27 Litho. ***Perf. 14½***
73 G8 35c multicolored .25 .30

Globes with Smallpox Distribution — G9

Global eradication of smallpox.

1978, Mar. 31 Photo. ***Perf. 12x11½***
74 G9 80c yel & multi .60 .65
75 G9 1.10fr lt grn & multi .90 .95

Namibia Type of UN

1978, May 5 Photo. ***Perf. 12***
76 A166 80c multicolored .85 .90

Jets and Flight Patterns — G10

International Civil Aviation Organization for "Safety in the Air."

1978, June 12 Photo. ***Perf. 14***
77 G10 70c multicolored .40 .45
78 G10 80c multicolored .70 .75

General Assembly, Flags and Globe — G11

1978, Sept. 15 Photo. ***Perf. 13½***
79 G11 70c multicolored .45 .50
80 G11 1.10fr multicolored .85 .90

Technical Cooperation Type of UN

1978, Nov. 17 Photo. ***Perf. 14***
81 A169 80c multicolored .70 .75

Seismograph Recording Earthquake — G12

Office of the UN Disaster Relief Coordinator (UNDRO).

1979, Mar. 9 Photo. ***Perf. 14***
82 G12 80c multicolored .50 .55
83 G12 1.50fr multicolored .80 .85

Children and Rainbow — G13

International Year of the Child.

1979, May 4 Photo. ***Perf. 14***
84 G13 80c multicolored .35 .40
85 G13 1.10fr multicolored .65 .70

Namibia Type of UN

1979, Oct. 5 Litho. *Perf. 13½*
86 A176 1.10fr multicolored .60 .65

International Court of Justice, Scales — G14

International Court of Justice, The Hague, Netherlands.

1979, Nov. 9 Litho. *Perf. 13x13½*
87 G14 80c multicolored .40 .45
88 G14 1.10fr multicolored .60 .65

New Economic Order Type of UN

1980, Jan. 11 Litho. *Perf. 15x14½*
89 A179 80c multicolored .85 .90

Women's Year Emblem — G15

United Nations Decade for Women.

1980, Mar. 7 Litho. *Perf. 14½x15*
90 G15 40c multicolored .30 .35
91 G15 70c multicolored .70 .75

Peace-keeping Operations Type of UN

1980, May 16 Litho. *Perf. 14x13*
92 A181 1.10fr blue & green .85 .90

Dove and "35" — G16

35th Anniversary of the United Nations.

1980, June 26 Litho. *Perf. 13x13½*
93 G16 40c blue grn & blk .35 .35
94 A183 70c multicolored .65 .70

Souvenir Sheet
Imperf
95 Sheet of 2 1.10 1.20
a. G16 40c blue green & black .30 .35
b. A183 70c multicolored .80 .85

ECOSOC Type of UN and

Family Climbing Line Graph — G17

1980, Nov. 21 Litho. *Perf. 13½x13*
96 A186 40c multicolored .30 .35
97 G17 70c multicolored .60 .65

Palestinian Rights

1981, Jan. 30 Photo. *Perf. 12x11½*
98 A188 80c multicolored .55 .60

International Year of the Disabled.

1981, Mar. 6 Photo. *Perf. 14*
99 A190 40c black & blue .25 .30
100 V4 1.50fr black & red 1.00 1.10

Art Type of UN

1981, Apr. 15 Photo. *Perf. 11½*
Granite Paper
101 A191 80c multicolored .80 .85

Energy Type of 1981

1981, May 29 Litho. *Perf. 13*
102 A192 1.10fr multicolored .75 .80

Volunteers Program Type and

Volunteers Program Type and Symbols of Science, Agriculture and Industry — G18

1981, Nov. 13 Litho.
103 A194 40c multicolored .45 .50
104 G18 70c multicolored .90 .95

Fight Against Apartheid G19

Flower of Flags G20

1982, Jan. 22 *Perf. 11½x12*
105 G19 30c multicolored .25 .30
106 G20 1fr multicolored .80 .85

Human Environment Type of UN and

Human Environment — G21

10th Anniversary of United Nations Environment Program.

1982, Mar. 19 Litho. *Perf. 13½x13*
107 G21 40c multicolored .30 .35
108 A199 1.20fr multicolored 1.10 1.40

Outer Space Type of UN and

Satellite Applications of Space Technology — G22

Exploration and Peaceful Uses of Outer Space.

1982, June 11 Litho. *Perf. 13x13½*
109 A201 80c multicolored .60 .65
110 G22 1fr multicolored .80 .85

Conservation & Protection of Nature

1982, Nov. 19 Photo. *Perf. 14*
111 A202 40c Bird .45 .50
112 A202 1.50fr Reptile 1.10 1.20

World Communications Year

1983, Jan. 28 Litho. *Perf. 13*
113 A204 1.20fr multicolored 1.25 1.40

Safety at Sea Type of UN and

Life Preserver and Radar — G23

1983, Mar. 18 Litho. *Perf. 14½*
114 A205 40c multicolored .40 .45
115 G23 80c multicolored .80 .85

World Food Program

1983, Apr. 22 Engr. *Perf. 13½*
116 A207 1.50fr blue 1.25 1.40

Trade Type of UN and

G24

1983, June 6 Litho. *Perf. 14*
117 A208 80c multicolored .50 .55
118 G24 1.10fr multicolored .90 .95

G25

35th Anniv. of the Universal Declaration of Human Rights — G26

Photo. & Engr.
1983, Dec. 9 *Perf. 13½*
119 G25 40c multicolored .45 .50
120 G26 1.20fr multicolored .95 1.00

International Conference on Population Type

1984, Feb. 3 Litho. *Perf. 14*
121 A212 1.20fr multicolored .90 .95

Fishing — G27

Women Farm Workers, Africa — G28

World Food Day, Oct. 16

1984, Mar. 15 Litho. *Perf. 14½*
122 G27 50c multicolored .30 .35
123 G28 80c multicolored .60 .65

Valletta, Malta — G29

Los Glaciares Natl. Park, Argentina — G30

World Heritage

1984, Apr. 18 Litho. *Perf. 14*
124 G29 50c multicolored .60 .65
125 G30 70c multicolored .85 .90

G31

G32

Future for Refugees

1984, May 29 Photo. *Perf. 11½*
126 G31 35c multicolored .30 .35
127 G32 1.50fr multicolored 1.10 1.20

International Youth Year — G33

1984, Nov. 15 Litho. *Perf. 13½*
128 G33 1.20fr multicolored 1.25 1.40

ILO Type of UN and

Turin Center — G34

1985, Feb. 1 Engr. *Perf. 13½*
129 A220 80c dull red .70 .75
130 G34 1.20fr U Thant Pavilion 1.10 1.20

UN University Type

50c, Pastoral scene, advanced communications.

1985, Mar. 15 Photo. *Perf. 11½*
131 A221 50c multicolored .60 .65
132 A221 80c like No. 131 1.00 1.10

Postman — G35

Doves — G36

1985, May 10 Litho. *Perf. 14*
133 G35 20c multicolored .25 .30
134 G36 1.20fr multicolored 1.25 1.40

40th Anniversary Type

Perf. 12 x 11½
1985, June 26 Photo.
135 A224 50c multicolored .60 .65
136 A225 70c multicolored .90 .95

Souvenir Sheet
Imperf
137 Sheet of 2 2.25 2.40
a. A224 50c multicolored .85 .90
b. A225 70c multicolored 1.10 1.20

UNICEF Child Survival Campaign Type

Photo. & Engr.
1985, Nov. 22 *Perf. 13½*
138 A226 50c Three girls .40 .45
139 A226 1.20fr Infant drinking 1.10 1.20

Africa in Crisis Type

1986, Jan. 31 Photo. *Perf. 11½x12*
140 A227 1.40fr Mother, hungry children 1.25 1.40

UN Development Program Type

Forestry.

1986, Mar. 14 Photo. *Perf. 13½*
141 A228 35c Erosion control 1.60 1.75
142 A228 35c Logging 1.60 1.75
143 A228 35c Lumber transport 1.60 1.75
144 A228 35c Nursery 1.60 1.75
a. Block of 4, #141-144 6.50 7.50

Doves and Sun — G37

1986, Mar. 14 Litho. *Perf. 15x14½*
145 G37 5c multicolored .25 .30

Stamp Collecting Type

Designs: 50c, UN Human Rights stamp. 80c, UN stamps.

1986, May 22 Engr. *Perf. 12½*
146 A229 50c dark grn & hen brn .60 .65
147 A229 80c dark grn & yel org .90 .95

Flags and Globe as Dove — G38

Peace in French — G39

International Peace Year.

Photo. & Embossed
1986, June 20 *Perf. 13½*
148 G38 45c multicolored .60 .65
149 G39 1.40fr multicolored 1.25 1.40

WFUNA Anniversary Type

Souvenir Sheet

Designs: 35c, Abstract by Benigno Gomez, Honduras. 45c, Abstract by Alexander Calder (1898-1976), US. 50c, Abstract by Joan Miro (b. 1893), Spain. 70c, Sextet with Dove, by Ole Hamann, Denmark.

1986, Nov. 14 Litho. *Perf. 13x13½*

150 Sheet of 4 3.75 4.00
a. A232 35c multicolored .50 .55
b. A232 45c multicolored .70 .75
c. A232 50c multicolored .90 1.00
d. A232 70c multicolored 1.25 1.40

No. 150 has inscribed margin picturing UN and WFUNA emblems.

Trygve Lie Type

Photo. & Engr.

1987, Jan. 30 *Perf. 13½*

151 A233 1.40fr multicolored 1.10 1.20

Sheaf of Colored Bands, by Georges Mathieu G40

Armillary Sphere, Palais des Nations G41

Photo., Photo. & Engr. (#153)

1987, Jan. 30 *Perf. 11½x12, 13½*

152 G40 90c multicolored .65 .70
153 G41 1.40fr multicolored 1.25 1.40

Shelter for the Homeless Type

Designs: 50c, Cement-making and brick-making. 90c, Interior construction and decorating.

Perf. 13½x12½

1987, Mar. 13 Litho.

154 A234 50c multicolored .50 .55
155 A234 90c multicolored 1.00 1.10

Fight Drug Abuse Type

Designs: 80c, Mother and child. 1.20fr, Workers in rice paddy.

1987, June 12 Litho. *Perf. 14½x15*

156 A235 80c multicolored .50 .55
157 A235 1.20fr multicolored 1.00 1.10

UN Day Type

Designs: Multinational people in various occupations.

1987, Oct. 23 Litho. *Perf. 14½x15*

158 A236 35c multicolored .55 .60
159 A236 50c multicolored .80 .85

Immunize Every Child Type

Designs: 90c, Whooping cough. 1.70fr, Tuberculosis.

1987, Nov. 20 Litho. *Perf. 15x14½*

160 A237 90c multicolored 1.50 1.65
161 A237 1.70fr multicolored 2.75 3.00

IFAD Type

Designs: 35c, Flocks, dairy products. 1.40fr, Fruit.

1988, Jan. 29 Litho. *Perf. 13½*

162 A238 35c multicolored .35 .40
163 A238 1.40fr multicolored 1.40 1.50

For A Better World — G42

1988, Jan. 29 Photo. *Perf. 14*

164 G42 50c multicolored .80 .85

Survival of the Forests Type

Pine forest: 50c, Treetops, mountains. 1.10fr, Lake, tree trunks. Printed se-tenant in a continuous design.

1988, Mar. 18 Litho. *Perf. 14x15*

165 A240 50c multicolored 1.25 1.40
166 A240 1.10fr multicolored 3.50 3.75
a. Pair, #165-166 5.50 6.00

Intl. Volunteer Day Type

Designs: 80c, Agriculture, vert. 90c, Veterinary medicine.

Perf. 13x14, 14x13

1988, May 6 Litho.

167 A241 80c multicolored .80 .85
168 A241 90c multicolored 1.00 1.10

Health in Sports Type

Paintings by LeRoy Neiman, American sports artist: 50c, Soccer, vert. 1.40fr, Swimming.

Perf. 13½x13, 13x13½

1988, June 17 Litho.

169 A242 50c multicolored .40 .45
170 A242 1.40fr multicolored 1.40 1.50

Universal Declaration of Human Rights 40th Anniv. Type

Photo. & Engr.

1988, Dec. 9 *Perf. 12*

171 A243 90c multicolored .70 .75

Souvenir Sheet

172 A243 2fr multicolored 2.75 3.00

World Bank Type

80c, Telecommunications. 1.40fr, Industry.

1989, Jan. 27 Litho. *Perf. 13x14*

173 A244 80c multicolored 1.00 1.10
174 A244 1.40fr multicolored 2.00 2.20

Peace-Keeping Force Type

1989, Mar. 17 *Perf. 14x13½*

175 A245 90c multicolored 1.25 1.40

World Weather Watch Type

Satellite photographs: 90c, Europe under the influence of Arctic air. 1.10fr, Surface temperatures of sea, ice and land surrounding the Kattegat between Denmark and Sweden.

1989, Apr. 21 Litho. *Perf. 13x14*

176 A247 90c multicolored 1.25 1.40
177 A247 1.10fr multicolored 2.00 2.20

G43

G44

Photo., Photo. & Engr. (2fr)

1989, Aug. 23 *Perf. 14*

178 G43 50c multicolored .75 1.10
179 G44 2fr multicolored 2.50 3.75

Offices in Vienna, 10th anniv.

Human Rights Type of 1989

Artwork: 35c, Young Mother Sewing, by Mary Cassatt. 80c, The Unknown Slave, sculpture by Albert Mangones.

1989, Nov. 17 Litho. *Perf. 13½*

180 A250 35c multicolored .35 .40
181 A250 80c multicolored 1.00 1.10

Printed in panes of 12+12 se-tenant labels containing Articles 3 (35c) or 4 (80c) inscribed in English, French or German.

See Nos. 193-194, 209-210,34-235.

Intl. Trade Center Type

1990, Feb. 2 Litho. *Perf. 14½x15*

182 A251 1.50fr multicolored 2.25 2.50

G45

1990, Feb. 2 Photo. *Perf. 14x13½*

183 G45 5fr multicolored 4.75 5.25

G46

Fight AIDS Worldwide — G46a

Fight AIDS Type

Designs: 50c, "SIDA." 80c, Proportional drawing of man like the illustration by Leonardo da Vinci.

Perf. 13½x12½

1990, Mar. 16 Litho.

184 G46 50c multicolored 1.00 1.10
185 G46a 80c multicolored 1.75 1.90

Medicinal Plants Type

1990, May 4 Photo. *Perf. 11½*

Granite Paper

186 A253 90c Plumeria rubra 1.00 1.10
187 A253 1.40fr Cinchona officinalis 2.00 2.20

UN 45th Anniv. Type

"45," emblem and: 90c, Symbols of clean environment, transportation and industry. 1.10fr, Dove in silhouette.

1990, June 26 Litho. *Perf. 14½x13*

188 A254 90c multicolored 1.10 1.20
189 A254 1.10fr multicolored 2.25 2.50

Souvenir Sheet

190 Sheet of 2, #188-189 6.00 6.50

Crime Prevention Type

1990, Sept. 13 Photo. *Perf. 14*

191 A255 50c Official corruption 1.25 1.40
192 A255 2fr Environmental crime 3.00 3.25

Human Rights Type of 1989

Artwork: 35c, The Prison Courtyard by Vincent Van Gogh. 90c, Katho's Son Redeems the Evil Doer From Execution by Albrecht Durer.

1990, Nov. 16 Litho. *Perf. 13½*

193 A250 35c multicolored .45 .50
194 A250 90c blk & brn 1.25 1.40

Economic Commission for Europe Type

1991, Mar. 15 Litho. *Perf. 14*

195 A256 90c Owl, gull 1.40 1.60
196 A256 90c Bittern, otter 1.40 1.60
197 A256 90c Swan, lizard 1.40 1.60
198 A256 90c Great crested grebe 1.40 1.60
a. Block of 4, #195-198 5.60 6.50

Namibian Independence Type

1991, May 10 Litho. *Perf. 14*

199 A257 70c Mountains 1.00 1.10
200 A257 90c Baobab tree 2.00 2.20

Ballots Filling Ballot Box G47

UN Emblem G48

1991, May 10 Litho. *Perf. 15x14½*

201 G47 80c multicolored .75 .80
202 G48 1.50fr multicolored 2.00 2.20

G49

Rights of the Child — G50

1991, June 14 Litho. *Perf. 14½*

203 G49 80c Hands holding infant 1.00 1.10
204 G50 1.10fr Children, flowers 2.00 2.20

G51

Banning of Chemical Weapons — G52

1991, Sept. 11 Litho. *Perf. 13½*

205 G51 80c multicolored 2.00 2.20
206 G52 1.40fr multicolored 3.00 3.25

UN Postal Administration, 40th Anniv. Type

1991, Oct. 24 *Perf. 14x15*

207 A263 50c UN NY No. 7 .80 .85
208 A263 1.60fr UN NY No. 10 2.20 2.40

Human Rights Type of 1989

Artwork: 50c, Early Morning in Rio...1925, by Paul Klee. 90c, Marriage of Giovanni (?) Arnolfini and Giovanna Cenami (?), by Jan Van Eyck.

1991, Nov. 20 Litho. *Perf. 13½*

209 A250 50c multicolored .75 .80
210 A250 90c multicolored 1.25 1.40

Panes of 12+12 se-tenant labels containing Articles 15 (50c) or 16 (90c) inscribed in French, German or English.

World Heritage Type of 1984

Designs: 50c, Sagarmatha Natl. Park, Nepal. 1.10fr, Stonehenge, United Kingdom.

1992, Jan. 24 Litho. *Perf. 13*

Size: 35x28mm

211 G29 50c multicolored .80 .85
212 G29 1.10fr multicolored 1.90 2.10

G53

1992, Jan. 24 Litho. *Perf. 15x14½*

213 G53 3fr multicolored 3.00 3.25

Clean Oceans Type

1992, Mar. 13 Litho. *Perf. 14*

214 A264 80c Ocean surface, diff. .90 .95
215 A264 80c Ocean bottom, diff. .90 .95
a. Pair, #214-215 1.80 *2.10*

Earth Summit Type

Designs: No. 216, Rainbow. No. 217, Two clouds shaped as faces. No. 218, Two sailboats. No. 219, Woman with parasol, boat, flowers.

1992, May 22 Photo. *Perf. 11½*

216 A265 75c multicolored 1.50 1.60
217 A265 75c multicolored 1.50 1.60
218 A265 75c multicolored 1.50 1.60
219 A265 75c multicolored 1.50 1.60
a. Block of 4, #216-219 6.00 6.50

Mission to Planet Earth Type

Designs: No. 220, Space station. No. 221, Probes near Jupiter.

1992, Sept. 4 Photo. *Rouletted 8*

Granite Paper

220 A266 1.10fr multicolored 2.40 2.60
221 A266 1.10fr multicolored 2.40 2.60
a. Pair, #220-221 5.00 5.25

Science and Technology Type of 1992

Designs: 90c, Doctor, nurse. 1.60fr, Graduate seated before computer.

1992, Oct. 2 Litho. *Perf. 14*

222 A267 90c multicolored 1.25 1.40
223 A267 1.60fr multicolored 3.00 3.25

Human Rights Type of 1989

Artwork: 50c, The Oath of the Tennis Court, by Jacques Louis David. 90c, Rocking Chair I, by Henry Moore.

1992, Nov. 20 Litho. *Perf. 13½*

224 A250 50c multicolored .75 .80
225 A250 90c multicolored 1.25 1.40

Panes of 12+12 se-tenant labels containing Articles 21 (50c) and 22 (90c) inscribed in French, German or English.

Aging With Dignity Type

Designs: 50c, Older man coaching soccer. 1.60fr, Older man working at computer terminal.

1993, Feb. 5 Litho. *Perf. 13*
226 A270 50c multicolored .50 .55
227 A270 1.60fr multicolored 1.50 1.65

Endangered Species Type

Designs: No. 228, Pongidae (gorilla). No. 229, Falco peregrinus (peregrine falcon). No. 230, Trichechus inunguis (Amazonian manatee). No. 231, Panthera uncia (snow leopard).

1993, Mar. 2 Litho. *Perf. 13x12½*
228 A271 80c multicolored 1.10 1.20
229 A271 80c multicolored 1.10 1.20
230 A271 80c multicolored 1.10 1.20
231 A271 80c multicolored 1.10 1.20
a. Block of 4, #228-231 4.50 4.80

Healthy Environment Type

1993, May 7 Litho. *Perf. 15x14½*
232 A272 60c Neighborhood .75 .80
233 A272 1fr Urban skyscrapers 1.75 1.90

Human Rights Type of 1989

Artwork: 50c, Three Musicians, by Pablo Picasso. 90c, Voice of Space, by Rene Magritte.

1993, June 11 Litho. *Perf. 13½*
234 A250 50c multicolored .75 .80
235 A250 90c multicolored 1.75 1.90

Printed in panes of 12 + 12 se-tenant labels containing Article 27 (50c) and 28 (90c) inscribed in French, German or English.

Intl. Peace Day Type

Denomination at: No. 236, UL. No. 237, UR. No. 238, LL. No. 239, LR.

Roulette 12½
1993, Sept. 21 Litho. & Engr.
236 A274 60c purple & multi 2.00 2.20
237 A274 60c purple & multi 2.00 2.20
238 A274 60c purple & multi 2.00 2.20
239 A274 60c purple & multi 2.00 2.20
a. Block of 4, #236-239 8.00 9.00

Environment-Climate Type

1993, Oct. 29 Litho. *Perf. 14½*
240 A275 1.10fr Polar bears 2.40 2.40
241 A275 1.10fr Whale sounding 2.40 2.40
242 A275 1.10fr Elephant seal 2.40 2.40
243 A275 1.10fr Penguins 2.40 2.40
a. Strip of 4, #240-243 9.75 10.75

Intl. Year of the Family Type of 1993

Designs: 80c, Parents teaching child to walk. 1fr, Two women and child picking plants.

1994, Feb. 4 Litho. *Perf. 13.1*
244 A276 80c rose vio & multi 1.00 1.10
245 A276 1fr brown & multi 1.40 1.50

Endangered Species Type of 1993

Designs: No. 246, Mexican prairie dog. No. 247, Jabiru. No. 248, Blue whale. No. 249, Golden lion tamarin.

1994, Mar. 18 Litho. *Perf. 12.7*
246 A271 80c multicolored 1.10 1.20
247 A271 80c multicolored 1.10 1.20
248 A271 80c multicolored 1.10 1.20
249 A271 80c multicolored 1.10 1.20
a. Block of 4, #246-249 4.50 5.00

Protection for Refugees Type of 1994

Design: 1.20fr, Hand lifting figure over chasm.

1994, Apr. 29 Litho. *Perf. 14.3x14.8*
250 A277 1.20fr multicolored 2.25 2.40

Intl. Decade for Natural Disaster Reduction Type of 1994

Earth seen from space, outline map of: No. 251, North America. No. 252, Eurasia. No. 253, South America. No. 254, Australia and South Pacific region.

1994, May 27 Litho. *Perf. 13.9x14.2*
251 A281 60c multicolored 1.75 1.90
252 A281 60c multicolored 1.75 1.90
253 A281 60c multicolored 1.75 1.90
254 A281 60c multicolored 1.75 1.90
a. Block of 4, #251-254 7.00 7.75

Palais des Nations, Geneva — G54

Creation of the World, by Oili Maki — G55

1994, Sept. 1 Litho. *Perf. 14.3x14.6*
255 G54 60c multicolored .75 .80
256 G55 80c multicolored 1.00 1.10
257 G54 1.80fr multi, diff. 2.25 2.50
Nos. 255-257 (3) 4.00 4.40

Population and Development Type of 1994

Designs: 60c, People shopping at open-air market. 80c, People on vacation crossing bridge.

1994, Sept. 1 Litho. *Perf. 13.2x13.6*
258 A282 60c multicolored 1.00 1.10
259 A282 80c multicolored 1.25 1.40

UNCTAD Type of 1994

1994, Oct. 28
260 A283 80c multi, diff. 1.10 1.20
261 A283 1fr multi, diff. 1.50 1.65
a. Grayish green omitted —

UN 50th Anniv. Type of 1995

Litho. & Engr.
1995, Jan. 1 *Perf. 13.4*
262 A284 80c multicolored 1.10 1.20

Social Summit Type of 1995

Photo. & Engr.
1995, Feb. 3 *Perf. 13.6x13.9*
263 A285 1fr multi, diff. 1.25 1.40

Endangered Species Type of 1993

Designs: No. 264, Crowned lemur, Lemur coronatus. No. 265, Giant Scops owl, Otus gurneyi. No. 266, Zetek's frog, Atelopus varius zeteki. No. 267, Wood bison, Bison bison athabascae.

1995, Mar. 24 Litho. *Perf. 13x12½*
264 A271 80c multicolored 1.10 1.20
265 A271 80c multicolored 1.10 1.20
266 A271 80c multicolored 1.10 1.20
267 A271 80c multicolored 1.10 1.20
a. Block of 4, 264-267 4.50 5.00

Intl. Youth Year Type of 1995

Designs: 80c, Farmer on tractor, fields at harvest time. 1fr, Couple standing by fields at night.

1995, May 26 Litho. *Perf. 14.4x14.7*
268 A286 80c multicolored 1.25 1.40
269 A286 1fr multicolored 2.00 2.20

UN, 50th Anniv. Type of 1995

Designs: 60c, Like No. 663. 1.80fr, Like No. 664.

Perf. 13.3x13.6
1995, June 26 Engr.
270 A287 60c maroon .80 .85
271 A287 1.80fr green 3.00 3.25

Souvenir Sheet
Litho. & Engr.
Imperf
272 Sheet of 2, #270-271 4.25 4.50
a. A287 60c maroon 1.00 1.10
b. A287 1.80fr green 3.25 3.40

Conference on Women Type of 1995

Designs: 60c, Black woman, cranes flying above. 1fr, Women, dove.

1995, Sept. 5 Photo. *Perf. 12*
273 A288 60c multicolored 1.00 1.10

Size: 28x50mm
274 A288 1fr multicolored 2.00 2.20

UN People, 50th Anniv. Type of 1995

1995, Oct. 24 Litho. *Perf. 14*
275 Sheet of 12 14.00 15.00
a.-l. A290 30c each 1.20 1.20
276 Souvenir booklet 15.00
a. A290 30c Booklet pane of 3, vert. strip of 3 from UL of sheet 3.75 3.75
b. A290 30c Booklet pane of 3, vert. strip of 3 from UR of sheet 3.75 3.75
c. A290 30c Booklet pane of 3, vert. strip of 3 from LL of sheet 3.75 3.75
d. A290 30c Booklet pane of 3, vert. strip of 3 from LR of sheet 3.75 3.75

WFUNA, 50th Anniv. Type

Design: 80c, Fishing boat, fish in net.

1996, Feb. 2 Litho. *Perf. 13x13½*
277 A291 80c multicolored 1.25 1.40

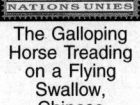

The Galloping Horse Treading on a Flying Swallow, Chinese Bronzework, Eastern Han Dynasty (25-220 A.D.) — G56

Palais des Nations, Geneva — G57

1996, Feb. 2 Litho. *Perf. 14½x15*
278 G56 40c multicolored .50 .55
279 G57 70c multicolored ..90 .95

Endangered Species Type of 1993

Designs: No. 280, Paphiopedilum delenatii. No. 281, Pachypodium baronii. No. 282, Sternbergia lutea. No. 283, Darlingtonia californica.

1996, Mar. 14 Litho. *Perf. 12½*
280 A271 80c multicolored 1.00 1.10
281 A271 80c multicolored 1.00 1.10
282 A271 80c multicolored 1.00 1.10
283 A271 80c multicolored 1.00 1.10
a. Block of 4, #280-283 4.00 4.50

City Summit Type of 1996

Designs: No. 284, Asian family. No. 285, Oriental garden. No. 286, Fruit, vegetable vendor, mosque. No. 287, Boys playing ball. No. 288, Couple reading newspaper.

1996, June 3 Litho. *Perf. 14x13½*
284 A293 70c multicolored 1.50 1.65
285 A293 70c multicolored 1.50 1.65
286 A293 70c multicolored 1.50 1.65
287 A293 70c multicolored 1.50 1.65
288 A293 70c multicolored 1.50 1.65
a. Strip of 5, #284-288 7.50 8.25

Sport and the Environment Type

Designs: 70c, Cycling, vert. 1.10fr, Sprinters.

Perf. 14x14½, 14½x14
1996, July 19 Litho.
289 A294 70c multicolored 1.00 1.10
290 A294 1.10fr multicolored 1.50 1.65

Souvenir Sheet
291 A294 Sheet of 2, #289-290 3.00 3.25

Plea for Peace Type

Designs: 90c, Tree filled with birds, vert. 1.10fr, Bouquet of flowers in rocket tail vase, vert.

1996, Sept. 17 Litho. *Perf. 15x14½*
292 A295 90c multicolored 1.25 1.40
293 A295 1.10fr multicolored 1.50 1.65

UNICEF Type

Fairy Tales: 70c, The Sun and the Moon, South America. 1.80fr, Ananse, Africa.

1996, Nov. 20 Litho. *Perf. 14½x15*
294 A296 70c multicolored .80 .85
295 A296 1.80fr multicolored 2.00 2.20

UN Flag — G58

Palais des Nations Under Construction, by Massimo Campigli — G59

1997, Feb. 12 Litho. *Perf. 14½*
296 G58 10c multicolored .25 .30
297 G59 1.10fr multicolored 1.25 1.40

Endangered Species Type of 1993

Designs: No. 298, Ursus maritimus (polar bear). No. 299, Goura cristata (blue-crowned pigeon). No. 300, Amblyrhynchus cristatus (marine iguana). No. 301, Lama guanicoe (guanaco).

1997, Mar. 13 Litho. *Perf. 12½*
298 A271 80c multicolored .90 .95
299 A271 80c multicolored .90 .95
300 A271 80c multicolored .90 .95
301 A271 80c multicolored .90 .95
a. Block of 4, #298-301 3.60 3.90

Earth Summit Anniv. Type

Designs: No. 302, Person flying over mountain. No. 303, Mountain, person's face. No. 304, Person standing on mountain, sailboats. No. 305, Person, mountain, trees.

1.10fr, Combined design similar to Nos. 302-305.

1997, May 30 Photo. *Perf. 11½*
Granite Paper
302 A299 45c multicolored 1.00 1.10
303 A299 45c multicolored 1.00 1.10
304 A299 45c multicolored 1.00 1.10
305 A299 45c multicolored 1.00 1.10
a. Block of 4, #302-305 4.00 4.50

Souvenir Sheet
306 A299 1.10fr multicolored 4.00 4.25

Transportation Type of 1997

Air transportation: No. 307, Zeppelin, Fokker tri-motor. No. 308, Boeing 314 Clipper, Lockheed Constellation. No. 309, DeHavilland Comet. No. 310, Boeing 747, Illyushin jet. No. 311, Concorde.

1997, Aug. 29 Litho. *Perf. 14x14½*
307 A300 70c multicolored 1.00 1.10
308 A300 70c multicolored 1.00 1.10
309 A300 70c multicolored 1.00 1.10
310 A300 70c multicolored 1.00 1.10
311 A300 70c multicolored 1.00 1.10
a. Strip of 5, #307-311 5.00 5.50

Philately Type

Designs: 70c, No. 146. 1.10fr, No. 147.

1997, Oct. 14 Litho. *Perf. 13½x14*
312 A301 70c multicolored .80 .85
313 A301 1.10fr multicolored 1.50 1.65

World Heritage Convention Type

Terracotta warriors of Xian: 45c, Single warrior. 70c, Massed warriors. No. 316a, like NY No. 716. No. 316b, like NY No. 717. No. 316c, like Geneva No. 314. No. 316d, like Geneva No. 315. No. 316e, like Vienna No. 230. No. 316f, like Vienna No. 231.

1997, Nov. 19 Litho. *Perf. 13½*
314 A302 45c multicolored 1.25 1.40
315 A302 70c multicolored 2.25 2.50
316 Souvenir booklet 12.00
a.-f. A302 10c any single .45 .50
g. Booklet pane of 4 #316a 2.00 2.00
h. Booklet pane of 4 #316b 2.00 2.00
i. Booklet pane of 4 #316c 2.00 2.00
j. Booklet pane of 4 #316d 2.00 2.00
k. Booklet pane of 4 #316e 2.00 2.00
l. Booklet pane of 4 #316f 2.00 2.00

Palais des Nations, Geneva — G60

1998, Feb. 13 Litho. *Perf. 14½x15*
317 G60 2fr multicolored 1.50 1.65

Endangered Species Type of 1993

Designs: No. 318, Macaca thibetana (short-tailed Tibetan macaque). No. 319, Phoenicopterus ruber (Caribbean flamingo). No. 320, Ornithoptera alexandrae (Queen Alexandra's birdwing). No. 321, Dama mesopotamica (Persian fallow deer).

1998, Mar. 13 Litho. *Perf. 12½*
318 A271 80c multicolored 1.00 1.10
319 A271 80c multicolored 1.00 1.10
320 A271 80c multicolored 1.00 1.10
321 A271 80c multicolored 1.00 1.10
a. Block of 4, #318-321 4.00 4.50

Intl. Year of the Ocean G61

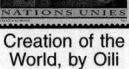

1998, May 20 Litho. *Perf. 13x13½*
322 G61 Pane of 12 11.00 12.00
a.-l. 45c any single .90 1.00

Rain Forests Type

1998, June 19 *Perf. 13x13½*
323 A307 70c Orangutans .90 1.00

Souvenir Sheet

324 A307 3fr like #323 4.00 *7.50*

Peacekeeping Type

Designs: 70c, Soldier with two children. 90c, Two soldiers, children.

1998, Sept. 15 Photo. *Perf. 12*
325 A308 70c multicolored .85 .90
326 A308 90c multicolored 1.40 1.50

Declaration of Human Rights Type of 1998

Designs: 90c, Stylized birds. 1.80fr, Stylized birds flying from hand.

Litho. & Photo.

1998, Oct. 27 *Perf. 13*
327 A309 90c multicolored .95 1.05
328 A309 1.80fr multicolored 2.00 2.20

Schönbrunn Palace Type

Designs: 70c, No. 331b, Great Palm House. 1.10fr, No. 331d, Blue porcelain vase, vert. No. 331a, Palace. No. 331c, The Gloriette (archway). No. 331e, Wall painting on fabric (detail), by Johann Wenzl Bergl, vert. No. 331f, Porcelain stove, vert.

1998, Dec. 4 Litho. *Perf. 14*
329 A310 70c multicolored .90 1.00
330 A310 1.10fr multicolored 1.20 1.30

Souvenir Booklet

331 Booklet 21.50
a.-c. A310 10c any single .55 .55
d.-f. A310 30c any single 1.65 1.65
g. Booklet pane of 4 #331a 2.20 2.20
h. Booklet pane of 3 #331d 5.00 5.00
i. Booklet pane of 3 #331e 5.00 5.00
k. Booklet pane of 4 #331b 2.20 2.20
l. Booklet pane of 4 #331c 2.20 2.20

Palais Wilson, Geneva — G62

1999, Feb. 5 Photo. *Perf. 11½*

Granite Paper

332 G62 1.70fr brown red 1.75 1.90

World Heritage, Australia Type

Designs: 90c, No. 335e, Kakadu Natl. Park. 1.10fr, No. 335c, Great Barrier Reef. No. 335a, Tasmanian Wilderness. No. 335b, Wet tropics of Queensland. No. 335d, Uluru-Kata Tjuta Natl. Park. No. 335f, Willandra Lakes region.

1999, Mar. 19 Litho. *Perf. 13*
333 A313 90c multicolored 1.25 1.40
334 A313 1.10fr multicolored 1.50 1.65

Souvenir Booklet

335 Booklet 16.50
a.-c. A313 10c any single .45 .50
d.-f. A313 20c any single .90 1.00
g. Booklet pane of 4, #335a 1.80 2.00
h. Booklet pane of 4, #335d 3.60 4.00
i. Booklet pane of 4, #335b 1.80 2.00
j. Booklet pane of 4, #335e 3.60 4.00
k. Booklet pane of 4, #335c 1.80 2.00
l. Booklet pane of 4, #335f 3.60 4.00

Endangered Species Type of 1993

Designs: No. 336, Equus hemionus (Asiatic wild ass). No. 337, Anodorhynchus hyacinthinus (hyacinth macaw). No. 338, Epicrates subflavus (Jamaican boa). No. 339, Dendrolagus bennettianus (Bennetts' tree kangaroo).

1999, Apr. 22 Litho. *Perf. 12½*
336 A271 90c multicolored 1.00 1.10
337 A271 90c multicolored 1.00 1.10
338 A271 90c multicolored 1.00 1.10
339 A271 90c multicolored 1.00 1.10
a. Block of 4, #336-339 4.00 4.50

UNISPACE III Type

Designs: No. 340, Farm, satellite dish. No. 341, City, satellite in orbit. No. 342, Composite of Nos. 340-341.

1999, July 7 Photo. *Rouletted 8*
340 A314 45c multicolored .90 1.00
341 A314 45c multicolored .90 1.00
a. Pair, #340-341 2.00 2.20

Souvenir Sheet

Perf. 14½

342 A314 2fr multicolored 4.50 5.00
a. Ovptd. in sheet margin 9.50 10.50

UPU Type

Various people, early 20th century methods of mail transportation, denomination at: No. 343, UL. No. 344, UR. No. 345, LL. No. 346, LR.

1999, Aug. 23 Photo. *Perf. 11¾*
343 A315 70c multicolored .90 1.00
344 A315 70c multicolored .90 1.00
345 A315 70c multicolored .90 1.00
346 A315 70c multicolored .90 1.00
a. Block of 4, #343-346 3.60 4.00

In Memoriam Type

Designs: 1.10fr, 2fr, Armillary sphere, Palais de Nations. Size of 2fr stamp: 34x63mm.

1999, Sept. 21 Litho. *Perf. 14½x14*
347 A316 1.10fr multicolored 1.25 1.40

Souvenir Sheet

Perf. 14

348 A316 2fr multicolored 3.00 3.25

Education Type

90c, Rainbow over globe. 1.80fr, Fish, tree, globe, book.

Perf. 13½x13¾

1999, Nov. 18 Litho.
349 A317 90c multi .75 .80
350 A317 1.80fr multi 1.75 1.90

Intl. Year Of Thanksgiving Type

2000, Jan 1 Litho. *Perf. 13¼x13½*
351 A318 90c multicolored 1.00 1.10

On No. 351 portions of the design were applied by a thermographic process producing a shiny, raised effect.

Endangered Species Type of 1993

Designs: No. 352, Hippopotamus amphibius (hippopotamus). No. 353, Coscoroba coscoroba (Coscoroba swan). No. 354, Varanus prasinus (emerald monitor). No. 355, Enhydra lutris (sea otter).

2000, Apr. 6 Litho. *Perf. 12¾x12½*
352 A271 90c multicolored 1.25 1.40
353 A271 90c multicolored 1.25 1.40
354 A271 90c multicolored 1.25 1.40
355 A271 90c multicolored 1.25 1.40
a. Block of 4, #352-355 5.00 5.75

Our World 2000 Type

Winning artwork in Millennium painting competition: 90c, The Embrace, by Rita Adaimy, Lebanon. 1.10fr, Living Single, by Richard Kimanthi, Kenya, vert.

Perf. 13x13½, 13½x13

2000, May 30 Litho.
356 A319 90c multicolored 1.00 1.10
357 A319 1.10fr multicolored 1.25 1.40

55th Anniversary Type

Designs: 90c, Trygve Lie, Harry S Truman, workers at cornerstone dedication ceremony, 1949. 1.40fr, Window cleaner on Secretariat Building, General Assembly Hall under construction, 1951.

2000, July 7 Litho. *Perf. 13¼x13*
358 A320 90c multicolored 1.00 1.10
359 A320 1.40fr multicolored 1.50 1.65

Souvenir Sheet

360 A320 Sheet of 2, #358-359 3.50 3.75

The UN in the 21st Century G63

No. 361: a, Two people, terraced rice paddy. b, Man carrying bricks on head. c, UN Peacekeeper with binoculars. d, Dam, doves. e, Men with shovels. f, People working on irrigation system.

2000, Sept. 15 Litho. *Perf. 14*
361 G63 Pane of 6 9.00 10.00
a.-f. 50c any single 1.50 1.65

World Heritage, Spain Type

Designs: Nos. 362, 364b, Walled Town of Cuenca. Nos. 363, 364e, Toledo. No. 364a, Alhambra, Generalife and Albayzin, Granada. No. 364c, Aqueduct of Segovia. No. 364d, Amphitheater of Mérida. No. 364f, Güell Park, Barcelona.

2000, Oct. 6 Litho. *Perf. 14¾x14½*
362 A323 1fr multicolored 1.40 1.50
363 A323 1.20fr multicolored 1.60 1.75

Souvenir Booklet

364 Booklet 11.00
a.-c. A323 10c any single .30 .35
d.-f. A323 20c any single .60 .65
g. Booklet pane of 4, #364a 1.20 1.40
h. Booklet pane of 4, #364d 2.40 2.60
i. Booklet pane of 4, #364b 1.20 1.40
j. Booklet pane of 4, #364e 2.40 2.60
k. Booklet pane of 4, #364c 1.20 1.40
l. Booklet pane of 4, #364f 2.40 2.60

Respect for Refugees Type

Designs: 80c, 1.80fr, Refugee with cane, four other refugees.

2000, Nov. 9 Litho. *Perf. 13¼x12¾*
365 A324 80c multicolored 1.25 1.40

Souvenir Sheet

366 A324 1.80fr multicolored 2.50 2.75

Endangered Species Type of 1993

Designs: No. 367, Felis lynx canadensis (North American lynx). No. 368, Pavo muticus (green peafowl). No. 369, Geochelone elephantopus (Galapagos giant tortoise). No. 370, Lepilemur spp. (sportive lemur).

2001, Feb. 1 Litho. *Perf. 12¾x12½*
367 A271 90c multicolored 1.25 1.40
368 A271 90c multicolored 1.25 1.40
369 A271 90c multicolored 1.25 1.40
370 A271 90c multicolored 1.25 1.40
a. Block of 4, #367-370 5.00 5.75

Intl. Volunteers Year — G64

Paintings by: 90c, Ernest Pignon-Ernest, France. 1.30fr, Paul Siché, France.

2001, Mar. 29 Litho. *Perf. 13¼*
371 G64 90c multicolored 1.10 1.20
372 G64 1.30fr multicolored 1.60 1.75

World Heritage, Japan Type

Designs: 1.10fr, No. 375b, Nara. 1.30fr, No. 375e, Itsukushima Shinto Shrine. No. 375a, Kyoto. No. 375c, Himeji-Jo. No. 375d, Shirakawa-Go and Gokayama. No. 375f, Nikko.

2001, Aug. 1 Litho. *Perf. 12¾x13¼*
373 A328 1.10fr multicolored 1.30 1.40
374 A328 1.30fr multicolored 1.50 1.65

Souvenir Booklet

375 Booklet 15.00
a.-c. A328 10c any single .50 .55
d.-f. A328 30c any single .75 .80
g. Booklet pane of 4, #375a 2.00 2.20
h. Booklet pane of 4, #375d 3.00 3.20
i. Booklet pane of 4, #375b 2.00 2.20
j. Booklet pane of 4, #375e 3.00 3.20
k. Booklet pane of 4, #375c 2.00 2.20
l. Booklet pane of 4, #375f 3.00 3.20

Dag Hammarskjöld Type

2001, Sept. 18 Engr. *Perf. 11x11¼*
376 A329 2fr car lake 2.50 2.75

UN Postal Administration, 50th Anniv. Types

2001, Oct. 18 Litho. *Perf. 13½*
377 A330 90c Stamps, globe 1.00 1.10
378 A330 1.30fr Stamps, horns 1.75 1.90

Souvenir Sheet

379 A331 Sheet of 2 12.50 13.50
a. 1.30fr red & light blue, 38mm diameter 5.00 5.50
b. 1.80fr red & light blue, 38mm diameter 7.50 8.00

Climate Change Type

Designs: No. 380, Lizard, flowers, shoreline. No. 381, Windmills, construction workers. No. 382, Non-polluting factory. No. 383, Solar oven, city, village, picnickers.

2001, Nov. 16 Litho. *Perf. 13¼*
380 A332 90c multicolored 1.10 1.20
381 A332 90c multicolored 1.10 1.20
382 A332 90c multicolored 1.10 1.20
383 A332 90c multicolored 1.10 1.20
a. Horiz. strip, #380-383 4.50 5.00

Nobel Peace Prize Type

2001, Dec. 10 Litho. *Perf. 13¼*
384 A333 90c multicolored 1.10 1.20

Palais des Nations — G65

2002, Mar. 1 Litho. *Perf. 13¾*
385 G65 1.30fr multicolored 1.40 1.50

Endangered Species Type of 1993

Designs: No. 386, Cacajao calvus (white uakari). No. 387, Mellivora capensis (honey badger). No. 388, Otocolobus manul (manul). No. 389, Varanus exantematicus (Bosc's monitor).

2002, Apr. 4 Litho. *Perf. 12¾x12½*
386 A271 90c multicolored 1.50 1.65
387 A271 90c multicolored 1.50 1.65
388 A271 90c multicolored 1.50 1.65
389 A271 90c multicolored 1.50 1.65
a. Block of 4, #386-389 6.00 6.75

Independence of East Timor Type

Designs: 90c, Wooden statue of male figure. 1.30fr, Carved wooden container.

2002, May 20 Litho. *Perf. 14x14½*
390 A335 90c multicolored 1.25 1.40
391 A335 1.30fr multicolored 1.75 1.90

Intl. Year of Mountains Type

Designs: No. 392, Weisshorn, Switzerland. No. 393, Mt. Fuji, Japan. No. 394, Vinson Massif, Antarctica. No. 395, Mt. Kamet, India.

2002, May 24 Litho. *Perf. 13x13¼*
392 A336 70c multicolored 1.00 1.10
393 A336 70c multicolored 1.00 1.10
394 A336 1.20fr multicolored 1.75 1.90
395 A336 1.20fr multicolored 1.75 1.90
a. Vert. strip or block of four, #392-395 8.50 9.50

World Summit on Sustainable Development (Peter Max) Type

Designs: No. 396, Sun, birds, flowers, heart. No. 397, Three faceless people, diff. No. 398, Three women, diff. No. 399, Sailboat, mountain.

2002, June 27 Litho. *Perf. 14½x14*
396 A337 90c multicolored 1.25 1.40
397 A337 90c multicolored 1.25 1.40
398 A337 1.80fr multicolored 2.50 2.75
399 A337 1.80fr multicolored 2.50 2.75
a. Vert. strip or block of four, #396-399 10.00 11.00

World Heritage, Italy Type

Designs: 90c, No. 402e, Pisa. 1.30fr, No. 402b, Aeolian Islands. No. 402a, Amalfi Coast. No. 402c, Rome. No. 402d, Florence. No. 402f, Pompeii.

Perf. 13½x13¼

2002, Aug. 30 Litho.
400 A338 90c multicolored 1.25 1.40
401 A338 1.30fr multicolored 2.00 2.20

Souvenir Booklet

402 Booklet 29.00
a.-c. A338 10c any single .60 .80
d.-f. A338 20c any single 1.75 2.00
g. Booklet pane of 4, #402d 7.00 8.00
h. Booklet pane of 4, #402a 2.40 2.75
i. Booklet pane of 4, #402e 7.00 8.00
j. Booklet pane of 4, #402b 2.40 2.75
k. Booklet pane of 4, #402f 7.00 8.00
l. Booklet pane of 4, #402c 2.40 2.75

AIDS Awareness Type

2002, Oct. 24 Litho. *Perf. 13½*
403 A339 1.30fr multicolored 2.00 2.20

Entry of Switzerland into United Nations — G66

2002, Oct. 24 Litho. *Perf. 14½x14¾*
404 G66 3fr multicolored 3.50 3.75

Indigenous Art — G67

No. 405: a, Detail of Inca poncho, Peru. b, Bahia culture seated figure, Brazil. c, Blanket, Ecuador. d, Mayan stone sculpture, Belize. e, Embroidered fabric, Guatemala. f, Colima terra-cotta dog sculpture, Mexico.

2003, Jan. 31 Litho. *Perf. 14¼*

405 G67 Pane of 6 7.50 8.50
a.-f. 90c Any single 1.25 1.35

New Inter-Parliamentary Union Headquarters, Geneva — G68

2003, Feb. 20 Litho. *Perf. 14½x14*

406 G68 90c multicolored 1.75 1.75

Endangered Species Type of 1993

Designs: No. 407, Branta ruficollis (red-breasted goose). No. 408, Geronticus calvus (bald ibis). No. 409, Dendrocygna bicolor (fulvous whistling duck). No. 410, Ramphastos vitellinus (channel-billed toucan).

2003, Apr. 3 Litho. *Perf. 12¾x12½*

407 A271 90c multicolored 1.25 1.25
408 A271 90c multicolored 1.25 1.25
409 A271 90c multicolored 1.25 1.25
410 A271 90c multicolored 1.25 1.25
a. Block of 4, #407-410 5.00 5.00

International Year of Freshwater Type of 2003

Perf. 14¼x14½

2003, June 20 Litho.

411 A345 70c Waterfall 1.25 1.25
412 A345 1.30fr People, mountain 2.25 2.25
a. Horiz. pair, #411-412 5.00 5.00

Ralph Bunche Type

Litho. With Foil Application

2003, Aug. 7 *Perf. 13½x14*

413 A346 1.80fr brn red & multi 2.75 2.75

In Memoriam Type of 2003

2003, Oct. 24 Litho. *Perf. 13¼x13*

414 A347 85c multicolored 1.50 1.50

World Heritage Sites, United States Type

Designs: 90c, No. 417b, Great Smoky Mountains National Park. 1.30fr, No. 417f, Yellowstone National Park. No. 417a, Yosemite National Park. No. 417c, Olympic National Park. No. 417d, Hawaii Volcanoes National Park. No. 417e, Everglades National Park.

2003, Oct. 24 Litho. *Perf. 14½x14¼*

415 A348 90c multicolored 1.50 1.50
416 A348 1.30fr multicolored 2.25 2.25

Souvenir Booklet

417 Booklet 12.00
a.-c. A348 10c any single .30 .30
d.-f. A348 30c any single .65 .65
g. Booklet pane of 4 #417a 1.20 1.20
h. Booklet pane of 4 #417d 2.60 2.60
i. Booklet pane of 4 #417b 1.20 1.20
j. Booklet pane of 4 #417e 2.60 2.60
k. Booklet pane of 4 #417c 1.20 1.20
l. Booklet pane of 4 #417f 2.60 2.60

Endangered Species Type of 1993

Designs: No. 418, Ursus thibetanus (Asiatic black bear). No. 419, Hippocamelus antisensis (Northern Andean deer). No. 420, Macaca silenus (Lion-tailed macaque). No. 421, Bos gaurus (Gaur).

2004, Jan. 29 Litho. *Perf. 12¾x12½*

418 A271 1fr multicolored 1.60 1.60
419 A271 1fr multicolored 1.60 1.60
420 A271 1fr multicolored 1.60 1.60
421 A271 1fr multicolored 1.60 1.60
a. Block of 4, #418-421 6.50 6.50

Indigenous Art Type of 2003

No. 422: a, Decoration for cows, Switzerland. b, Stone Age terra cotta sculpture of seated woman, Romania. c, Butter stamps, France. d, Detail of herald's tabard, United Kingdom. e, Woodcut print of medieval Cologne, Germany. f, Mesolithic era terra cotta sculpture of mother and child, Serbia and Montenegro.

2004, Mar. 4 Litho. *Perf. 13¼*

422 G67 Sheet of 6 7.50 7.50
a.-f. 1fr Any single 1.25 1.25

Road Safety Type

Road map art with: 85c, Man on hand. 1fr, Person, seat belt, vert.

Perf. 13x13¼, 13¼x13

2004, Apr. 7 Litho.

423 A354 85c multicolored 1.40 1.40
424 A354 1fr multicolored 1.75 1.75

See France No. 3011.

Japanese Peace Bell, 50th Anniv. Type

Litho. & Engr.

2004, June 3 *Perf. 13¼x13*

425 A355 1.30fr multicolored 2.00 2.00

World Heritage Sites, Greece Type

Designs: 1fr, No. 428b, Delphi. 1.30fr, No. 428e, Pythagoreion and Heraion of Samos. No. 428a, Acropolis, Athens. No. 428c, Olympia. No. 428d, Delos. No. 428f, Mycenae and Tiryns.

2004, Aug. 12 Litho. *Perf. 14x13¼*

426 A356 1fr multicolored 1.50 1.50
427 A356 1.30fr multicolored 2.00 2.00

Souvenir Booklet

428 Booklet 13.50
a.-c. A356 20c any single .30 .30
d.-f. A356 50c any single .80 .80
g. Booklet pane of 4 #428a 1.25 1.25
h. Booklet pane of 4 #428b 1.25 1.25
i. Booklet pane of 4 #428c 1.25 1.25
j. Booklet pane of 4 #428d 3.25 3.25
k. Booklet pane of 4 #428e 3.25 3.25
l. Booklet pane of 4 #428f 3.25 3.25

My Dream for Peace Type

Winning designs of Lions Club International children's global peace poster contest by: 85c, Anggun Sita Rustinya, Indonesia. 1.20fr, Amanda Nunez, Belize.

2004, Sept. 21 Litho. *Perf. 14*

429 A357 85c multicolored 1.40 1.40
430 A357 1.20fr multicolored 2.00 2.00

G69

Human Rights — G70

2004, Oct. 14 Litho. *Perf. 11¼*

431 G69 85c multicolored 1.25 1.25
432 G70 1.30fr multicolored 2.25 2.25

Sports — G71

2004, Nov. 23 Litho. *Perf. 13x13½*

433 G71 180c multicolored 3.25 3.25

See Switzerland No. 1196.

United Nations, 60th Anniv. Type of 2005

Litho. & Engr.

2005, Feb. 4 *Perf. 11x11¼*

434 A361 1.30fr multicolored 2.50 2.50

Souvenir Sheet

Litho.

Imperf

435 A361 3fr multicolored 7.50 7.50

Endangered Species Type of 1993

Designs: No. 436, Laelia milleri. No. 437, Psygmorchis pusilla. No. 438, Dendrobium cruentum. No. 439, Orchis purpurea.

2005, Mar. 3 Litho. *Perf. 12¾x12½*

436 A271 1fr multicolored 2.00 2.00
437 A271 1fr multicolored 2.00 2.00
438 A271 1fr multicolored 2.00 2.00
439 A271 1fr multicolored 2.00 2.00
a. Block of 4, #436-439 8.00 8.00

Nature's Wisdom G72

Designs: 1fr, Children collecting water, India. 80c, Ruby brittle star, Bahamas.

2005, Apr. 21 Litho. *Perf. 13½x13¼*

440 G72 1fr multicolored 1.75 1.75
441 G72 1.30fr multicolored 2.00 2.00

Intl. Year of Sport Type

2005, June 3 Litho. *Perf. 13x13¼*

442 A368 1fr Wheelchair racing 1.75 1.75
443 A368 1.30fr Cycling 2.25 2.25

World Heritage Sites, Egypt Type

Designs: Nos. 444, 446b, Philae. Nos. 445, 446e, Islamic Cairo. No. 446a, Memphis and its Necropolis. No. 446c, Abu Mena. No. 446d, Ancient Thebes. No. 446f, St. Catherine area.

2005, Aug. 4 Litho. *Perf. 14x13¼*

444 A369 1fr multicolored 2.00 2.00
445 A369 1.30fr multicolored 2.50 2.50

Souvenir Booklet

446 Booklet, #446g-446l 16.50
a.-c. A369 20c any single .40 .40
d.-f. A369 50c any single .90 .90
g. Booklet pane of 4 #446a 1.60 1.60
h. Booklet pane of 4 #446b 1.60 1.60
i. Booklet pane of 4 #446c 1.60 1.60
j. Booklet pane of 4 #446d 3.75 3.75
k. Booklet pane of 4 #446e 3.75 3.75
l. Booklet pane of 4 #446f 3.75 3.75

My Dream for Peace Type

Winning designs of Lions Club International children's global peace poster contest by: 1fr, Marisa Harun, Indonesia. 1.30fr, Carlos Javier Parramón Teixidó, Spain.

2005, Sept. 21 Litho. *Perf. 14*

447 A357 1fr multicolored 1.75 1.75
448 A357 1.30fr multicolored 2.00 2.00

Food for Life Type

Designs: 1fr, Rye, airplane dropping parcels, camel caravan. 1.30fr, Sorghum, people carrying grain sacks, trucks.

2005, Oct. 20 Litho. *Perf. 13¾*

449 A370 1fr multicolored 1.90 1.90
450 A370 1.30fr multicolored 2.40 2.40

Armillary Sphere, Palais des Nations — G73

Litho. with Hologram

2006, Feb. 3 *Perf. 13¼x13½*

451 G73 1.30fr multicolored 2.25 2.25

Indigenous Art Type of 2003

No. 452 — Musical instruments: a, Bell, Benin. b, Drum, Swaziland. c, Sanza, Congo. d, Stringed instruments, Cape Verde. e, Caixixi, Ghana. f, Bells, Central Africa.

2006, Feb. 3 Litho. *Perf. 13¼*

452 G67 Pane of 6 12.00 12.00
a.-f. 1.20fr Any single 2.00 2.00

Endangered Species Type of 1993

Designs: No. 453, Dyscophus antongilii. No. 454, Chamaeleo dilepsis. No. 455, Corallus caninus. No. 456, Phyllobates vittatus.

Perf. 12¾x12½

2006, Mar. 16 Litho.

453 A271 1fr multicolored 1.75 1.75
454 A271 1fr multicolored 1.75 1.75
455 A271 1fr multicolored 1.75 1.75
456 A271 1fr multicolored 1.75 1.75
a. Block of 4, #453-456 7.00 7.00

Intl. Day of Families Type

Designs: 1fr, Family reading together. 1.30fr, Family on motorcycle.

2006, May 27 Litho. *Perf. 14x13½*

457 A373 1fr multicolored 1.25 1.25
458 A373 1.30fr multicolored 1.75 1.75

World Heritage Sites, France Type

Eiffel Tower and: Nos. 459, 461b, Provins. Nos. 460, 461e, Mont Saint-Michel. No. 461a, Banks of the Seine. No. 461c, Carcasonne. No. 461d, Roman Aqueduct. No. 446f, Chateau de Chambord.

Litho. & Embossed with Foil Application

2006, June 17 *Perf. 13½x13¼*

459 A374 1fr multicolored 1.75 1.75
460 A374 1.30fr multicolored 2.25 2.25

Souvenir Booklet

461 Booklet, #461g-461l 15.00
a.-c. A374 20c any single .35 .35
d.-f. A374 50c any single .85 .85
g. Booklet pane of 4 #461a 1.40 1.40
h. Booklet pane of 4 #461b 1.40 1.40
i. Booklet pane of 4 #461c 1.40 1.40
j. Booklet pane of 4 #461d 3.50 3.50
k. Booklet pane of 4 #461e 3.50 3.50
l. Booklet pane of 4 #461f 3.50 3.50

See France Nos. 3219-3220.

My Dream for Peace Type of 2004

Winning designs of Lions Club International children's global peace poster contest by: 85c, Ariam Boaglio, Italy. 1.20fr, Sierra Spicer, US.

2006, Sept. 21 Litho. *Perf. 13½x13*

462 A357 85c multicolored 1.60 1.60
463 A357 1.20fr multicolored 2.25 2.25

Flags and Coins Type

No. 464 — Flag of: a, Uganda, 500 shilling coin. b, Luxembourg, 1 euro coin. c, Cape Verde, 20 escudo coin. d, Belgium, 1 euro coin. e, Italy, 1 euro coin. f, New Zealand, 1 dollar coin. g, Switzerland, 2 franc coin. h, Lebanon, 500 pound coin.

2006, Oct. 5 Litho. *Perf. 13¼x13*

464 Pane of 8 15.00 15.00
a.-h. A375 85c Any single 1.50 1.50

A column of rouletting in the middle of the pane separates it into two parts.

Endangered Species Type of 1993

Designs: No. 465, Theropithecus gelada. No. 466, Cercopithecus neglectus. No. 467, Varecia variegata. No. 468, Hylobates moloch.

Perf. 12¾x12½

2007, Mar. 15 Litho.

465 A271 1fr multicolored 1.75 1.75
466 A271 1fr multicolored 1.75 1.75
467 A271 1fr multicolored 1.75 1.75
468 A271 1fr multicolored 1.75 1.75
a. Block of 4, #465-468 7.00 7.00

Flags and Coins Type of 2006

No. 469 — Flag of: a, Burkina Faso, 500 franc coin. b, France, 50 cent coin. c, Moldova, 50 bani coin. d, Papua New Guinea, 1 kina coin. e, Bolivia, 1 boliviano coin. f, Myanmar, 100 kyat coin. g, Mali, 500 franc coin. h, Tunisia, 5 dinar coin.

2007, May 3 Litho. *Perf. 13¼x13*

469 Sheet of 8 12.50 12.50
a.-h. A375 85c Any single 1.50 1.50

A column of rouletting in the middle of the sheet separates it into two parts.

Peaceful Visions Type of 2007

Designs: 1.20fr, "Harvest for All." 1.80fr, "This Dream Has Wings."

2007, June 1 Litho. *Perf. 13x12½*

470 A378 1.20fr multicolored 2.25 2.25
471 A378 1.80fr multicolored 3.25 3.25

World Heritage Sites, South America Type

Designs: Nos. 472, 474a, Tiwanaku, Bolivia. Nos. 473, 474f, Machu Picchu, Peru. No. 474b, Iguaçu National Park, Brazil. No. 474c, Galapagos Islands, Ecuador. No. 474d, Rapa Nui, Chile. No. 474e, Cueva de las Manos, Argentina.

2007, Aug. 9 Litho. *Perf. 13¼x13*

472 A381 1fr multicolored 1.90 1.90
473 A381 1.80fr multicolored 3.25 3.25

Souvenir Booklet

474 Booklet, #474g-474l 16.00
a.-c. A381 20c Any single .40 .40
d.-f. A381 50c Any single .90 .90
g. Booklet pane of 4 #474a 1.60 1.60
h. Booklet pane of 4 #474b 1.60 1.60

i. Booklet pane of 4 #474c 1.60 1.60
j. Booklet pane of 4 #474d 3.60 3.60
k. Booklet pane of 4 #474e 3.60 3.60
l. Booklet pane of 4 #474f 3.60 3.60

Humanitarian Mail Type

2007, Sept. 6 Litho. *Perf. 12½x13¼*
475 A382 1.80fr multicolored 3.00 3.00

Space for Humanity Type

Designs: 1fr, Astronaut spacewalking. 1.80fr, International Space Station, space probe, Jupiter.
3fr, Astronauts spacewalking.

2007, Oct. 25 Litho. *Perf. 13½x14*
476 A383 1fr multicolored 1.90 1.90
477 A383 1.80fr multicolored 3.25 3.25

Souvenir Sheet

478 A383 3fr multicolored 7.50 7.50

Intl. Holocaust Remembrance Day Type

2008, Jan. 27 Litho. *Perf. 13*
479 A384 85c multicolored 3.00 3.00

Endangered Species Type of 1993

Designs: No. 480, Odobenus rosmarus. No. 481, Platygyra daedalea. No. 482, Hippocampus bargibanti. No. 483, Delphinapterus leucas.

2008, Mar. 6 Litho. *Perf. 12¾x12½*
480 A271 1fr multicolored 2.00 2.00
481 A271 1fr multicolored 2.00 2.00
482 A271 1fr multicolored 2.00 2.00
483 A271 1fr multicolored 2.00 2.00
a. Block of 4, #480-483 8.00 8.00

Flags and Coins Type of 2006

No. 484 — Flag of: a, Madagascar, 1 ariary coin. b, Rwanda, 50 franc coin. c, Benin, 10 franc coin. d, Iran, 500 rial coin. e, Namibia, 5 dollar coin. f, Maldives, 1 rufiyaa coin. g, Albania, 10 lek coin. h, Turkey, 1 lira coin.

2008, May 8 Litho. *Perf. 13¼x13*
484 Sheet of 8 15.00 15.00
a.-h. A375 85c Any single 1.75 1.75

A column of rouletting in the middle of the sheet separates it into two parts.

Handshake G74

Sign Language G75

Litho. & Embossed

2008, June 6 *Perf. 14x13¼*
485 G74 1fr org & red 2.25 2.25
486 G75 1.80fr red & org 4.00 4.00

Convention on the Rights of Persons with Disabilities.

Sport for Peace Type of 2008

Designs: 1fr, 3fr, Gymnast. 1.80fr, Tennis player.

2008, Aug. 8 Litho. *Perf. 14½*
487 A393 1fr multicolored 2.25 2.25
488 A393 1.80fr multicolored 4.00 4.00

Souvenir Sheet
Perf. 12¾x13¼

489 A393 3fr multicolored 9.00 9.00

2008 Summer Olympics, Beijing.

"We Can End Poverty" Type of 2008

Winning designs in children's art contest by: 1fr, Ranajoy Banerjee, India, vert. 1.80fr, Elizabeth Elaine Chun Nig Au, Hong Kong, vert.

Perf. 12½x12¾
2008, Sept. 18 Litho.
490 A395 1fr multicolored 2.25 2.25
491 A395 1.80fr multicolored 3.75 3.75

Climate Change Types of New York and Vienna and

G76

Climate Change G77

No. 492 — Polar bear with quarter of Earth in: a, LR. b, LL. c, UR. d, UL.
No. 493 — Ship and sea ice with quarter of Earth in: a, LR. b, LL. c, UR. d, UL.
No. 494: a, Like New York #969a. b, Like New York #969b. c, Like New York #969c. d, Like New York #969d. e, Like Geneva #493a. f, Like Geneva #493b. g, Like Geneva #493c. h, Like Geneva #493d. i, Like Vienna #434a. j, Like Vienna #434b. k, Like Vienna #434c. l, Like Vienna #434d. m, Like New York #968a. n, Like New York #968b, o, Like New York #968c, p, Like New York #968d. q, Like Geneva #492a. r, Like Geneva #492b. s, Like Geneva #492c. t, Like Geneva #492d. u, Like Vienna #435a. v, Like Vienna #435b. w, Like Vienna #435c. x, Like Vienna #435d.
All stamps have red panels inscribed "Changement de climat."

2008, Oct. 23 Litho. *Perf. 13¼x13*
492 Sheet of 4 10.50 10.50
a.-d. G76 1.20fr Any single 2.60 2.60
493 Sheet of 4 15.50 15.50
a.-d. G77 1.80fr Any single 3.75 3.75

Souvenir Booklet

494 Booklet, #494y-494ad 25.00
a.-d. A397 35c Any single .75 .75
e.-h. G77 35c Any single .75 .75
i.-l. V72 35c Any single .75 .75
m.-p. A396 50c Any single 1.00 1.00
q.-t. G76 50c Any single 1.00 1.00
u.-x. V73 50c Any single 1.00 1.00
y. Booklet pane of 4, #494a-494d 3.00 3.00
z. Booklet pane of 4, #494e-494h 3.00 3.00
aa. Booklet pane of 4, #494i-494l 3.00 3.00
ab. Booklet pane of 4, #494m-494p 4.25 4.25
ac. Booklet pane of 4, #494q-494t 4.25 4.25
ad. Booklet pane of 4, #494u-494x 4.25 4.25

U Thant Type of 2009

Litho. With Foil Application

2009, Feb. 6 *Perf. 14x13½*
495 A399 1.30fr red & multi 3.25 3.25

Endangered Species Type of 1993

No. 496, Maculinea arion. No. 497, Dolomedes plantarius. No. 498, Cerambyx cerdo. No. 499, Coenagrion mercuriale.

2009, Apr. 16 Litho. *Perf. 12¾x12½*
496 A271 1fr multicolored 1.90 1.90
497 A271 1fr multicolored 1.90 1.90
498 A271 1fr multicolored 1.90 1.90
499 A271 1fr multicolored 1.90 1.90
a. Block of 4, #496-499 7.75 7.75
b. Pane of 16, imperf. *5,000.*

World Heritage Sites, Germany Type of 2009

Designs: Nos. 500, 502b, Wartburg Castle. Nos. 501, 502f, Monastic Island of Reichenau. No. 502a, Town Hall and Roland on the Marketplace, Bremen. No. 502c, Palaces and Parks of Potsdam and Berlin. No. 502d, Aachen Cathedral. No. 502e, Luther Memorials in Eisleben and Wittenberg.

2009, May 7 Litho. *Perf. 14x13½*
500 A400 1fr multicolored 2.25 2.25
501 A400 1.30fr multicolored 2.75 2.75

Souvenir Booklet

502 Booklet, #502g-502l 18.00
a.-c. A400 30c any single .55 .55
d.-f. A400 50c any single .90 .90
g. Booklet pane of 4 #502a 2.25 2.25
h. Booklet pane of 4 #502b 2.25 2.25
i. Booklet pane of 4 #502c 2.25 2.25
j. Booklet pane of 4 #502d 3.75 3.75
k. Booklet pane of 4 #502e 3.75 3.75
l. Booklet pane of 4 #502f 3.75 3.75

Economic and Social Council (ECOSOC) Type of 2009

Designs: 85c, Improving maternal health. 1.80fr, Access to essential medicines.

2009, Aug. 6 *Perf. 12¾x12½*
503 A411 85c multicolored 2.00 2.00
504 A411 1.80fr multicolored 4.00 4.00

Millennium Development Goals Type of 2009

Miniature Sheet

No. 505: a, Bowl of hot food. b, Pencil. c, Female symbol. d, Teddy bear. e, Pregnant woman, heart. f, Medicine bottle. g, Stylized tree. h, Conjoined people.

2009, Sept. 25 *Perf. 13¼*
505 A413 Sheet of 8 18.00 18.00
a.-h. 1.10fr Any single 2.25 2.25

Palais des Nations G78

Palais des Nations G79

Flags of United Nations and Switzerland — G80

Meeting Room G81

Armillary Sphere G82

2009, Oct. 2 *Perf. 13¼*
506 G78 1fr multi + label *6.00 6.00*
a. Perf. 11¼x11 + label *5.00 5.00*
507 G79 1fr multi + label *6.00 6.00*
a. Perf. 11¼x11 + label *5.00 5.00*
508 G80 1fr multi + label *6.00 6.00*
a. Perf. 11¼x11 + label *5.00 5.00*
509 G81 1fr multi + label *6.00 6.00*
a. Perf. 11¼x11 + label *5.00 5.00*
510 G82 1fr multi + label *6.00 6.00*
a. Perf. 11¼x11 + label *5.00 5.00*
b. Vert. strip of 5, #506-510, + 5 labels *30.00 30.00*
c. Vert. strip of 5, #506a-510a, + 5 labels *25.00 25.00*

United Nations Postal Administration in Geneva, 40th anniv. The full sheets sold for €19.90 or $14.95. Labels could not be personalized. The sheet of No. 510c has "VER. 2" in the lower right selvage.

Miniature Sheet

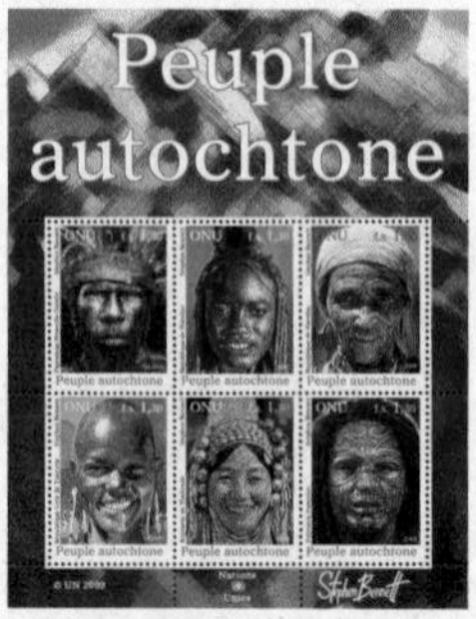

Indigenous People — G83

No. 511 — Portraits of person from: a, Papua New Guinea. b, Namibia (young woman). c, Namibia (old man). d, Tanzania. e, Thailand. f, French Polynesia.

2009, Oct. 8 *Perf. 12½*
511 G83 Sheet of 6 16.00 16.00
a.-f. 1.30fr Any single 2.60 2.60

Flags and Coins Type of 2006

No. 512 — Flag of: a, Equatorial Guinea, 100 franc coin. b, Laos, 20 kip coin. c, Seychelles, 5 rupee coin. d, Mauritania, 1 ougiya coin. e, Argentina, 1 peso coin. f, Morocco, 1 dirham coin. g, Sudan, 20 piaster coin. h, Brunei, 50 cent coin.

2010, Feb. 5 Litho. *Perf. 13¼x13*
512 Sheet of 8 15.00 15.00
a.-h. A375 85c Any single 1.75 1.75

A column of rouletting in the middle of the sheet separates it into two parts.

Endangered Species Type of 1993

No. 513, Fouquieria columnaris. No. 514, Aloe arborescens. No. 515, Galanthus krasnovii. No. 516, Dracaena draco.

2010, Apr. 15 Litho. *Perf. 12¾x12½*
513 A271 1fr multicolored 2.25 2.25
514 A271 1fr multicolored 2.25 2.25
515 A271 1fr multicolored 2.25 2.25
516 A271 1fr multicolored 2.25 2.25
a. Block of 4, #513-516 9.00 9.00

Intl. Year of Biodiversity — G84

Drawings from Art Forms from Nature, by Ernst Heinrich: 1.60fr, Arachnid. 1.90fr, Starfish.

2010, Apr. 15 Litho. *Perf. 13*
517 G84 1.60fr multicolored 3.75 3.75
518 G84 1.90fr multicolored 4.25 4.25

One Planet, One Ocean Types of New York and Vienna and

G85

G86

No. 519: a, Turtles at left and top, fish at bottom. b, Hammerhead shark. c, Fish at left and center, corals. d, Fish at left, coral.
No. 520: a, Dolphins. b, Shark, head of fish at right, small fish in background. c, Ray and fish. d, Fish at bottom, coral and sponges.
No. 521: a, Like New York #1003a. b, Like New York #1003b, c, Like New York #1003c, d, Like New York #1003d. e, Like Vienna #471a. f, Like Vienna #471b. g, Like Vienna #471c, h, Like Vienna #471d. i, Like #519a. j, Like #519b, k, Like #519c. l, Like #519d. m, Like New York #1004a. n, Like New York #1004b. o, Like New York #1004c, p, Like New York #1004d. q, Like Vienna #472a. r, Like Vienna #472b. s, Like Vienna #472c. t, Like Vienna #472d. u, Like #520a. v, Like #520b. w, Like #520c. x, Like #520d.

2010, May 6 Litho. *Perf. 14x13¼*
519 G85 Sheet of 4 8.00 8.00
a.-d. 85c Any single 2.00 2.00
520 G86 Sheet of 4 10.00 10.00
a.-d. 1fr Any single 2.50 2.50

Souvenir Booklet
Perf. 13¼x13

521 Booklet, #521y-521z, 521aa-521ad 22.00
a.-d. A416 30c any single .70 .70
e.-h. V91 30c any single .70 .70
i.-l. G85 30c any single .70 .70
m.-p. A417 50c any single 1.10 1.10
q.-t. V92 50c any single 1.10 1.10
u.-x. G86 50c any single 1.10 1.10
y. Booklet pane of 4 #521a-521d 2.80 2.80
z. Booklet pane of 4 #521e-521h 2.80 2.80
aa. Booklet pane of 4 #521i-521l 2.80 2.80
ab. Booklet pane of 4 #521m-521p 4.40 4.40
ac. Booklet pane of 4 #521q-521t 4.40 4.40
ad. Booklet pane of 4 #521u-521x 4.40 4.40

Intl. Oceanographic Commission, 50th anniv.

United Nations, 65th Anniv. Type of 2010

Litho. With Foil Application

2010, June 28 ***Perf. 13¼***
522 A422 1.90fr red & gold 4.00 4.00
a. Souvenir sheet of 2 8.00 8.00

G87

G88

G89

G90

United Nations Land Transport — G91

2010, Sept. 2 Litho. ***Perf. 13¼x13***
523 G87 1fr multicolored 1.80 1.80
524 G88 1fr multicolored 1.80 1.80
525 G89 1fr multicolored 1.80 1.80
526 G90 1fr multicolored 1.80 1.80
527 G91 1fr multicolored 1.80 1.80
a. Horiz. strip of 5, #523-527 9.00 9.00

Miniature Sheet

Campaign Against Child Labor — G92

No. 528: a, Child, buildings, road, burning can. b, Child with full basket on back, children playing in background. c, Child working, children on school bus. d, Child with mining helmet, three other children. e, Child near tubs, children working, child being beaten. f, Child with hoe. g, Marionette, traffic light. h, Child carrying basket on head. i, Children on rock field near hills. j, Child holding bags in road.

2010, Sept. 2 Litho. ***Perf. 14¾***
528 G92 Sheet of 10 + 10 labels 32.50 32.50
a.-j. 1.90fr Any single + label 3.25 3.25

No. 528 sold for $14.95, 15fr and €11.46, each of which was far lower than the level at which 19fr, the total face value of the stamps on the sheet, was worth on the day of issue. Labels could not be personalized.

Miniature Sheet

Indigenous People — G93

No. 529 — Portraits of person from: a, Australia. b, Brunei. c, Tanzania (girl with bald head). d, French Polynesia (man with headdress of leaves). e, Tanzania (man with headdress). f, French Polynesia (man with white headdress).

2010, Oct. 21 Litho. ***Perf. 13***
529 G93 Pane of 6 14.50 14.50
a.-f. 1.30fr Any single 2.40 2.40

United Nations Headquarters, Geneva — G94

United Nations Headquarters, Geneva: 10c, Aerial view. 50c, Ground-level view.

2011, Feb. 4 Litho. ***Perf. 13***
530 G94 10c multicolored .35 .35
531 G94 50c multicolored 1.25 1.25

Flags and Coins Type of 2006

No. 532 — Flag of: a, Mongolia, 500 tugrik coin. b, Senegal, 500 franc coin. c, Egypt, 100 piaster coin. d, Congo, 100 franc coin. e, Nicaragua, 1 Córdoba coin. f, Central African Republic, 100 franc coin. g, Algeria, 5 dinar coin. h, Ukraine, 5 hryvnia coin.

2011, Mar. 3 Litho. ***Perf. 13¼x13***
532 Sheet of 8 15.00 15.00
a.-h. A375 85c Any single 1.75 1.75

A column of rouletting in the middle of the sheet separates it into two parts.

Human Space Flight, 50th Anniv. G95

No. 533: Various parts of outer space scene.

No. 534, vert.: a, International Space Station. b, International Space Station, diff.

2011, Apr. 12 Litho. ***Perf. 13x13¼***
533 G95 Sheet of 16 18.00 18.00
a.-p. 50c any single 1.10 1.10

Souvenir Sheet

534 G95 Sheet of 2 15.00 15.00
a. 85c multi 6.50 6.50
b. 1fr multi 8.50 8.50

No. 534 contains two 40x48mm stamps that were printed as part of a larger sheet of six stamps, Vienna No. 485c, which was broken up into its component two-stamp souvenir sheets, and also sold as one unit. Value, $90, complete unit.

UNESCO World Heritage Sites in Nordic Countries Type of 2011

Designs: 85c, Kronborg Castle, Denmark. 1fr, Suomenlinna Fortress, Finland.

2011, May 5 Litho. ***Perf. 14x13½***
535 A433 85c multicolored 1.90 1.90
536 A433 1fr multicolored 2.25 2.25

AIDS Ribbon Type of 2011

2011, June 3 Litho. ***Die Cut***

Self-Adhesive

537 A434 1.30fr red & orange 5.00 5.00

ECOSOC Type of 2011

2011, July 1 Litho. ***Perf. 14¼***
538 A435 1fr multicolored 3.00 3.00
539 A435 1.30fr multicolored 4.00 4.00

Endangered Species Type of 1993

Designs: No. 540, Strigops habroptilus (Kakapo). No. 541, Lophophorus impejanus (Himalayan monal). No. 542, Ciconia nigra (Black stork). No. 543, Pithecophaga jeffreyi (Philippine eagle).

2011, Sept. 7 Litho. ***Perf. 12¾x12½***
540 A271 1fr multicolored 2.60 2.60
541 A271 1fr multicolored 2.60 2.60
542 A271 1fr multicolored 2.60 2.60
543 A271 1fr multicolored 2.60 2.60
a. Block of 4, #540-543 10.40 10.40

Intl. Year of Forests Type of 2011

Designs: 85c, Birds and butterflies, tree tops. 1.40fr, Fish and coral.

Litho. With Foil Application

2011, Oct. 13 ***Perf. 12½***
544 85c multicolored 2.25 2.25
545 1.40fr multicolored 3.75 3.75
a. A436 Vert. pair, #544-545 6.00 6.00

Flags and Coins Type of 2006

No. 546 — Flag of: a, Saudi Arabia, 100 halala coin. b, Georgia, 2 lari coin. c, Democratic People's Republic of Korea, 50 won coin. d, Lesotho, 50 lisente coin. e, Serbia, 5 dinar coin. f, Djibouti, 20 franc coin. g, Belize, 1 dollar coin. h, Liechtenstein, 20 centime coin.

2012, Feb. 3 Litho. ***Perf. 13¼x13***
546 Sheet of 8 16.50 16.50
a.-h. A375 85c Any single 2.00 2.00

A column of rouletting in the middle of the sheet separates it into two parts.

G96

Autism Awareness — G97

Drawings by autistic people: No. 547, Victory, by J.A Tan, Canada. No. 548, Untitled drawing, by Michael Augello, U.S.

2012, Apr. 2 Litho. ***Perf. 14x13½***
547 G96 1.40fr multicolored 3.50 3.50
548 G97 1.40fr multicolored 3.50 3.50
a. Pair, #547-548 7.00 7.00

Endangered Species Type of 1993

Designs: No. 549, Panthera tigris altaica. No. 550, Psitacella picta. No. 551, Iguana iguana. No. 552, Propithecus tattersalli.

2012, Apr. 19 Litho. ***Perf. 12¾x12½***
549 A271 1fr multicolored 2.40 2.40
550 A271 1fr multicolored 2.40 2.40
551 A271 1fr multicolored 2.40 2.40
552 A271 1fr multicolored 2.40 2.40
a. Block of 4, #549-552 9.75 9.75

Rio + 20 Type of 2012

2012, June 1 Litho. ***Perf. 13x13¼***
553 A443 1.40fr multicolored 4.00 4.00

Sport for Peace Type of 2012

2012 Paralympics events: 1fr, Track. 1.40fr, Archery.

Litho. With Foil Application

2012, Aug. 17 ***Perf. 14½***
554 A444 1fr multicolored 2.40 2.40
555 A444 1.40fr multicolored 3.50 3.50
a. Souvenir sheet of 1 3.50 3.50

UNESCO World Heritage Sites in Africa Type of 2012

Designs: 85c, Virunga National Park, Congo Democratic Republic. 1fr, Amphitheater of El Jem, Tunisia.

2012, Sept. 5 Litho. ***Perf. 13¼***
556 A445 85c multicolored 2.00 2.00
557 A445 1fr multicolored 2.40 2.40

Miniature Sheet

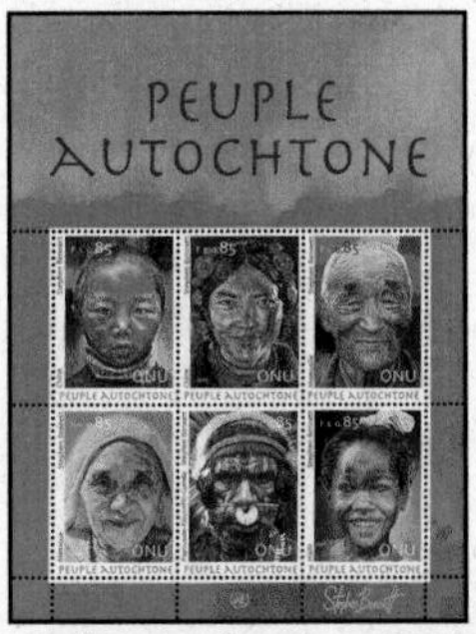

Indigenous People — G98

No. 558 — Portrait of person from: a, China. b, Tibet, China. c, Mongolia. d, Mexico. e, Papua New Guinea. f, Haiti.

2012, Oct. 11 Litho. ***Perf. 13¼x13***
558 G98 Sheet of 6 13.50 13.50
a.-f. 85c Any single 2.25 2.25

World Radio Day Type of 2013

Designs: 1.40fr, Reporter with microphone and tape recorder. 1.90fr, Engineers in studio.

2013, Feb. 13 Litho. ***Perf. 13¼x13***
559 A448 1.40fr multicolored 3.50 3.50
560 A448 1.90fr multicolored 4.50 4.50

Person on Leaf G99

Dove and People G100

2013, Mar. 5 Litho. ***Perf. 14x13½***
561 G99 1fr multicolored 2.40 2.40

Perf. 13½x14

562 G100 1.40fr multicolored 3.50 3.50

World Heritage Sites, China, Type of 2013

Designs: Nos. 563, 565b, Potala Palace, Lhasa. Nos. 564, 565e, Mount Huangshan. No. 565a, Mogao Caves. No. 565c, Great Wall of China. No. 565d, Imperial Palace, Beijing. No. 565f, Mausoleum of the First Qing Emperor.

2013, Apr. 11 Litho. ***Perf. 14x13½***
563 A452 1.40fr multicolored 3.50 3.50
564 A452 1.90fr multicolored 4.50 4.50

Souvenir Booklet

565 Booklet, #565g-565l 24.00
a.-c. A452 30c any single .75 .75
d.-f. A452 50c any single 1.25 1.25
g. Booklet pane of 4 #565a 3.00 —
h. Booklet pane of 4 #565b 3.00 —
i. Booklet pane of 4 #565c 3.00 —
j. Booklet pane of 4 #565d 5.00 —
k. Booklet pane of 4 #565e 5.00 —
l. Booklet pane of 4 #565f 5.00 —

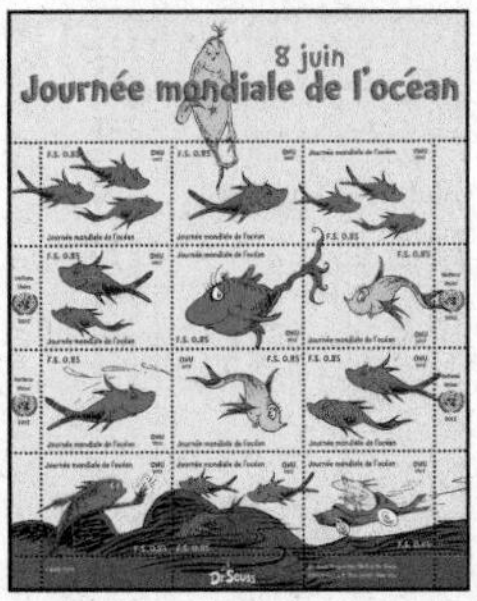

World Oceans Day G101

No. 566 — Fish from *One Fish, Two Fish, Red Fish, Blue Fish*, by Dr. Seuss: a, Three red fish facing right. b, Green fish, tail of yellow fish. c, Three red fish facing right, part of tail of red fish. d, Two entire green fish facing left, tail of bottom fish ends above "n" in "océan." e, Red fish with eye open facing left. f, Tail of red fish, yellow and red fish facing left. g, Red fish facing right, water droplets. h, Yellow and red fish facing right. i, Two green fish facing left, tail of bottom fish ends to right of "océan." j, Red fish and wave. k, Two green fish, red fish, wave. l, Yellow fish in car, wave.

2013, May 31 Litho. ***Perf. 13***
566 G101 Sheet of 12 20.00 20.00
a.-l. 85c any single 1.60 1.60

Nebulae Type of 2013

Designs: No. 567, NGC 2346. No. 568, Sh 2-106.

1fr, Messier 16.

2013, Aug. 9 Litho. ***Perf. 13¼***
567 A454 1.40fr multicolored 3.50 3.50
568 A454 1.40fr multicolored 3.50 3.50
a. Pair, #567-568 7.00 7.00

Souvenir Sheet

569 A454 1fr multicolored 2.40 2.40

No. 569 contains one 44x44mm stamp.

Works of Disabled Artists Type of 2013

Designs: 1.40fr, See the Girl with the Red Dress On, by Sargy Mann, United Kingdom. 1.90fr, Performers in China Disabled People's Performing Art Troupe, People's Republic of China.

2013, Sept. 20 Litho. ***Perf. 13¼x13***

570 A456 1.40fr multicolored 3.50 3.50
571 A456 1.90fr multicolored 4.50 4.50

Endangered Species Type of 1993

Designs: No. 572, Smutsia temminckii. No. 573, Perodicticus potto. No. 574, Tarsius syrichta. No. 575, Pteropus livingstonii.

2013, Oct. 10 Litho. ***Perf. 12¾x12½***

572 A271 1.40fr multicolored 3.25 3.25
573 A271 1.40fr multicolored 3.25 3.25
574 A271 1.40fr multicolored 3.25 3.25
575 A271 1.40fr multicolored 3.25 3.25
a. Block of 4, #572-575 13.00 13.00

Flags and Coins Type of 2006

No. 576 — Flag of: a, Ivory Coast, 100 franc coin. b, Marshall Islands, 10 cent coin. c, Andorra, 20 cent coin. d, Guinea-Bissau, 100 franc coin. e, Kenya, 20 shilling coin. f, Antigua and Barbuda, 5 cent coin. g, Tajikistan, 50 diram coin. h, Micronesia, 5 cent coin.

2013, Nov. 6 Litho. ***Perf. 13¼x13***

576 Sheet of 8 26.00 26.00
a.-h. A375 1.40fr Any single 3.25 3.25

A column of rouletting in the middle of the sheet separates it into two parts.

International Day of Happiness Type of 2014

Designs: 1fr, A Sweet Dog's Muzzle, photograph by Jaymi Heimbuch, "Heureux." 1.40fr, Two women making heart with hands, photograph by Glow Images, Chinese characters for "Happy."

2014, Mar. 17 Litho. ***Perf. 13¼x13***

577 A459 1fr multicolored 2.50 2.50
578 A459 1.40fr multicolored 3.50 3.50

Miniature Sheet

International Year of Jazz — G102

No. 579: a, Woman behind microphone. b, Saxophone. c, Silhouette of pianist at grand piano. d, Cymbal and silhouette of man holding trumpet. e, Cymbal and clarinet. f, Clarinet and drum. g, Hi-hat. h, Silhouette of drummer and drum set. i, Trumpeter with hat. j, Microphone and cymbal stands. k, Clarinetist. l, Bass player.

2014, Apr. 30 Litho. ***Perf. 13x13¼***

579 G102 Sheet of 12 29.50 29.50
First day cover 31.00
a.-l. 1fr Any single 2.40 2.40

G103

G104

2014, June 6 Litho. ***Perf. 13¼x13***

580 G103 2.20fr multicolored 5.50 5.50
581 G104 2.60fr multicolored 6.50 6.50

Taj Mahal Types of 2014

2014, July 16 Engr. ***Perf. 13¼x13***

582 A465 1.40fr multicolored 3.50 3.50
583 A467 1.90fr multicolored 4.75 4.75

Souvenir Booklet

584 Booklet, #584g-584l 20.00
a. A463 30c multi .75 .75
b. A465 30c multi .75 .75
c. A466 50c multi 1.25 1.25
d. A464 50c multi 1.25 1.25
e. A467 30c multi .75 .75
f. A468 50c multi 1.25 1.25
g. Booklet pane of 4 #584a 2.50 —
h. Booklet pane of 4 #584b 2.50 —
i. Booklet pane of 4 #584c 2.50 —
j. Booklet pane of 4 #584d 4.00 —
k. Booklet pane of 4 #584e 4.00 —
l. Booklet pane of 4 #584f 4.00 —

International Year of Family Farming — G105

2014, Aug. 21 Litho. ***Perf. 13x13¼***

585 G105 1.30fr multicolored 3.25 3.25
586 G105 1.60fr multicolored 4.00 4.00

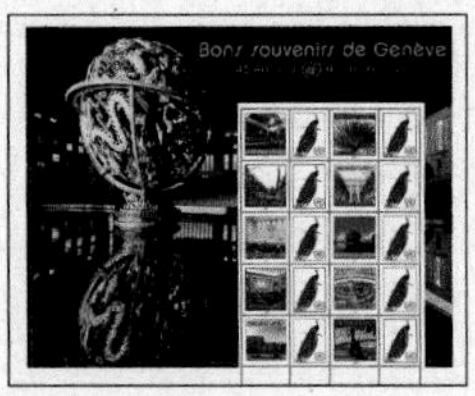

G106

No. 587: a, Room with painted ceiling. b, Peacock with spread tail. c, Rows of flags, brown panel at bottom. d, Rows of flags near Palais des Nations, tan panel at top. e, Meeting hall with United nations emblem on rear wall. f, Armillary sphere and Palais des Nations. g, Meeting hall with movie screen on rear wall. h, Circular meeting hall. i, Farm animals on grass near buildings. j, Peacock with tail down.

2014, Sept. 12 Litho. ***Perf. 14¾***

587 G106 Sheet of 10 *35.00 35.00*
a.-j. 1.30fr Any single + label *3.50 3.50*

The full sheet sold for 14.95fr. The generic labels are shown. Labels could be personalized.

Global Education First Initiative Type of 2014

Designs: No. 588, Students in art museum. No. 589, Student in library.

2014, Sept. 18 Litho. ***Perf. 13x13¼***

588 A470 1.90fr multicolored 4.75 4.75

Souvenir Sheet

Perf. 12½

589 A470 1.90fr multicolored 4.75 4.75

No. 589 contains one 32x32mm stamp.

Endangered Species Type of 2014

Maps and: No. 590, Arapaima gigas. No. 591, Cetorhinus maximus. No. 592, Pristis pristis. No. 593, Acipenser baerii.

2014, Oct. 23 Litho. ***Perf. 12¾x12½***

590 A471 1.40fr multicolored 3.50 3.50
591 A471 1.40fr multicolored 3.50 3.50
592 A471 1.40fr multicolored 3.50 3.50
593 A471 1.40fr multicolored 3.50 3.50
a. Block of 4, #590-593 14.00 14.00

Flags and Coins Type of 2006

No. 594 — Flag of: a, Vanuatu, 10 vatu coin. b, Nauru, 1 dollar coin. c, Eritrea, 100 cent coin. d, El Salvador, 1 colon coin. e, Mozambique, 50 centavo coin. f, Burundi, 1 franc coin. g, Turkmenistan, 10 tenge coin. h, Guinea, 1 franc coin.

2015, Feb. 6 Litho. ***Perf. 13¼x13***

594 Sheet of 8 16.50 16.50
a.-h. A375 90c Any single 2.00 2.00

A column of rouletting in the middle of the sheet separates it into two parts.

Miniature Sheets

G107

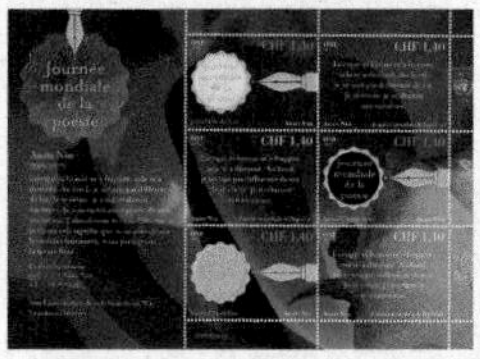

World Poetry Day G108

No. 595: a, Pen and gray circle. b, Li Bai quotation in Chinese, denomination in light blue green. c, Li Bai quotation in Chinese, denomination in red. d, Pen and red circle. e, Pen and orange circle. f, Li Bai quotation in Chinese, denomination in white.

No. 596: a, Pen and light green circle. b, Anais Nin quotation, denomination and "Journée mondiale de poésie" in light blue. c, As "b," with "Journée mondiale de poésie" in white, dark blue area below and to left of date. d, Pen and black circle. e, Pen and lilac circle. f, As "c," with dark blue area below and to right of date.

Perf. 14½x14¼

2015, Mar. 20 Litho.

595 G107 Sheet of 6 14.00 14.00
a.-f. 1fr Any single 2.25 2.25
596 G108 Sheet of 6 19.50 19.50
a.-f. 1.40fr Any single 3.25 3.25

Endangered Species Type of 2015

Designs: No. 597, Diphyllodes respublica. No. 598, Ptiloris paradiseus. No. 599, Semioptera wallacii. No. 600, Paradisaea decora.

2015, Apr. 16 Litho. ***Perf. 12½x12¾***

597 A476 1.40fr multicolored 3.25 3.25
598 A476 1.40fr multicolored 3.25 3.25
599 A476 1.40fr multicolored 3.25 3.25
600 A476 1.40fr multicolored 3.25 3.25
a. Block of 4, #597-600 13.00 13.00
Nos. 597-600 (4) 13.00 13.00

World Heritage Sites, Southeast Asia, Type of 2015

Designs: Nos. 601, 603b, Angkor Wat, Cambodia. Nos. 602, 603e, Cordillera, Philippines. No. 603a, Luang Prabang, Laos. No. 603c, Ayutthaya, Thailand. No. 565d, Borobudur Temple, Indonesia. No. 603f, Hué Monuments, Viet Nam.

2015, June 5 Litho. ***Perf. 14x13½***

601 A480 1.40fr multicolored 3.25 3.25
602 A480 1.90fr multicolored 4.50 4.50

Souvenir Booklet

603 Booklet, #603g-603l 23.50
a.-c. A480 30c any single .70 .70
d.-f. A480 50c any single 1.25 1.25
g. Booklet pane of 4 #603a 2.80 —
h. Booklet pane of 4 #603b 2.80 —
i. Booklet pane of 4 #603c 2.80 —
j. Booklet pane of 4 #603d 5.00 —
k. Booklet pane of 4 #603e 5.00 —
l. Booklet pane of 4 #603f 5.00 —

End Violence Against Children Type of 2015

Designs: 1fr, Child marriage. 1.40fr, Child trafficking.

Perf. 14½x14¼

2015, Aug. 20 Litho.

604 A481 1fr multicolored 2.40 2.40
605 A481 1.40fr multicolored 3.25 3.25

Miniature Sheet

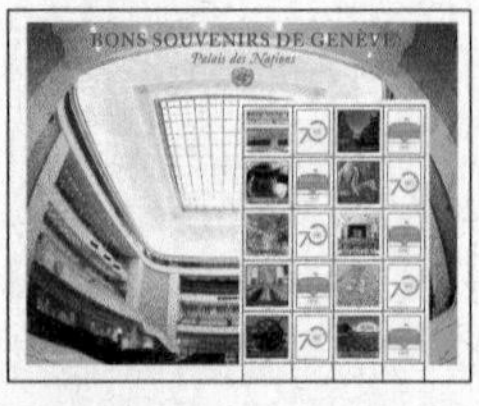

G109

No. 606: a, Balcony above auditorium seats. b, Flags. c, Spiral staircase. d, Stylized horned mammal. e, Painting of trees. f, Auditorium seats facing stage with dais. g, Side view of auditorium seats, painting on wall. h, United Nations emblem. i, Armillary Sphere. j, Palais des Nations and flowers.

2015, Sept. 3 Litho. ***Perf. 14¾***

606 G109 Sheet of 10 + 10 labels *35.00 35.00*
a.-j. 1.40fr Any single + label *3.50 3.50*

The full sheet sold for $18.39 or 14.95fr. The generic labels are shown. Labels could be personalized. The personalization of labels was available only at UN Headquarters, and not through mail order.

Visitors Lobby — G110

ECOSOC Chamber G111

Façade of Secretariat G112

Chairs in ECOSOC Chamber G113

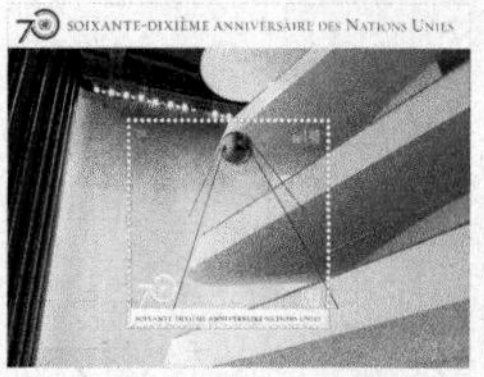

Visitors Lobby G114

Printed by Cartor Security Printing, France. Panes of 6. Designed by Rorie Katz, U.S.

2015, Oct. 25 Litho. ***Perf. 13¾***

607 G110 1fr multicolored 2.40 2.40
608 G111 1fr multicolored 2.40 2.40
a. Pair, #607-608 4.80 4.80
609 G112 1.90fr multicolored 4.50 4.50
610 G113 1.90fr multicolored 4.50 4.50
a. Pair, #609-610 9.00 9.00
Nos. 607-610 (4) 13.80 13.80

Souvenir Sheet

Perf. 13½

611 G114 1.40fr multicolored 4.50 4.50

United Nations, 70th anniv.

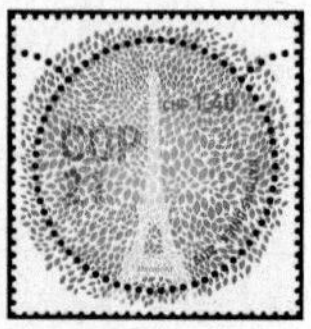

21st United Nations Climate Change Conference, Paris — G115

2015, Nov. 24 Litho. ***Perf. 13¼***

612 G115 1.40fr multicolored 3.25 3.25

Values are for stamps with surrounding selvage.

Free and Equal Type of 2016

Designs: 1fr, Lesbians. 1.50fr, Gay family.

2016, Feb. 5 Litho. ***Perf. 13½x13¼***

613 A491 1fr multicolored 2.25 2.25
614 A491 1.50fr multicolored 3.50 3.50

HeForShe Type of 2016

Designs: 1fr, Man, blue background. 2fr, Woman, mauve background.

2016, Mar. 8 Litho. ***Perf. 12½x13***

615 A492 1fr multicolored 2.25 2.25
616 A492 2fr multicolored 4.50 4.50

Miniature Sheets

G116

International Dance Day — G117

No. 617 — Illustration of Swedish dancers by Karin Römark: a, Two male dancers. b, Male dancer on one knee with female dancer. c, Male dancer with yellow cap and female dancer. d, Male dancer with red cap and vest with female dancer. e, Three dancers, with woman with red skirt at LR. f, Three dancers, with woman with blue skirt at LR.

No. 618 — Illustration of African dancers by Rönmark: a, Four dancers with sticks. b, Three dancers with sticks. c, Dancers without sticks. d, Dancer with blue and white mask. e, Two masked dancers with sticks. f, Masked dancer with two sticks.

2016, Apr. 29 Litho. *Perf. 13¼x13*

617	G116	Sheet of 6	13.50	13.50
a.-f.		1fr Any single	2.25	2.25
618	G117	Sheet of 6	20.00	20.00
a.-f.		1.50fr Any single	3.25	3.25

International Day of United Nations Peacekeepers Type of 2016

Designs: 1fr, Helmeted peacekeepers. 1.50fr, Peacekeeper with African women.

Litho. With Foil Application

2016, May 29 *Perf. 13¼x13*

619	A496	1fr multicolored	2.25	2.25
620	A496	1.50fr multicolored	3.50	3.50

Sport for Peace Type of 2016

Olympic rings and: No. 621, Rowers, denomination at UR. No. 622, Rowers, denomination at UL. No. 623, Rhythmic gymnast facing forward, eyes open. No. 624, Rhythmic gymnast facing left, eyes closed.

2016, July 22 Litho. *Perf. 14¼*

621	A498	1fr multicolored	2.25	2.25
622	A498	1fr multicolored	2.25	2.25
a.		Pair, #621-622	4.50	4.50
623	A498	2fr multicolored	4.50	4.50
624	A498	2fr multicolored	4.50	4.50
a.		Pair, #623-624	9.00	9.00
		Nos. 621-624 (4)	13.50	13.50

Souvenir sheets of three bearing three stamps, one from each office are listed under United Nations, Offices in New York as Nos. 1141, 1161, 1177-1178, 1203, and 1208.

World Heritage Sites, Czech Republic Type of 2016

Designs: Nos. 625, 627b, Gardens and Castle at Kromeríz. Nos. 626, 627e, Lednice-Valtice Cultural Landscape. No. 627a, Historic Center of Prague. No. 627d, Holy Trinity Column, Olomouc. No. 627c, Historic Town Center of Kutná Hora. No. 627f, Historic Center of Cesky Krumlov.

2016, Sept. 8 Litho. *Perf. 14¼*

625	A500	1fr multicolored	2.25	2.25
626	A500	1.50fr multicolored	3.50	3.50

Souvenir Booklet

627		Booklet, #627g-627l	22.00	
a.-c.	A500	30c any single	.65	.65
d.-f.	A500	50c any single	1.10	1.10
g.		Booklet pane of 4 #627a	2.75	—
h.		Booklet pane of 4 #627b	2.75	—
i.		Booklet pane of 4 #627c	2.75	—
j.		Booklet pane of 4 #627d	4.50	—
k.		Booklet pane of 4 #627e	4.50	—
l.		Booklet pane of 4 #627f	4.50	—

Miniature Sheet

World Wildlife Conference, Johannesburg — G118

No. 628 — Part of map of Africa and: a, Grue royale (gray-crowned crane). b, Mantella madagascariensis. c, Gorille des montagnes (mountain gorilla). d, Avonia quinaria.

2016, Sept. 24 Litho. *Perf. 13x13½*

628	G118	Sheet of 4	18.00	18.00
a.-d.		2fr Any single	4.50	4.50

Sustainable Development Goals Type of 2016

No. 629 — Inscription: a, 1 Pas de pauvreté. b, 2 Faim "zéro." c, 3 Bonne santé et bien-être. d, 4 Education de qualité. e, 5 Egalité entre les sexes. f, 6 Eau propre et assainissement. g, 7 Energie propre et d'un coût abordable. h, 8 Travail décent et croissance économique. i, 9 Industrie, innovation et infrastructure. j, 10 Inégalités réduites. k, 11 Villes et communautés durables. l, 12 Consommation et production responsables. m, 13 Mesures relatives à la lutte contre les changements climatiques. n, 14 Vie aquatique. o, 15 Vie terrestre. p, 16 Paix, justice et institutions efficaces. q, 17 Partneriats pour la réalisation des objectifs.

2016, Oct. 24 Litho. *Perf. 13¼*

629		Sheet of 17 + label	39.00	39.00
a.-q.	A503	1fr Any single	2.25	2.25

Miniature Sheets

G119

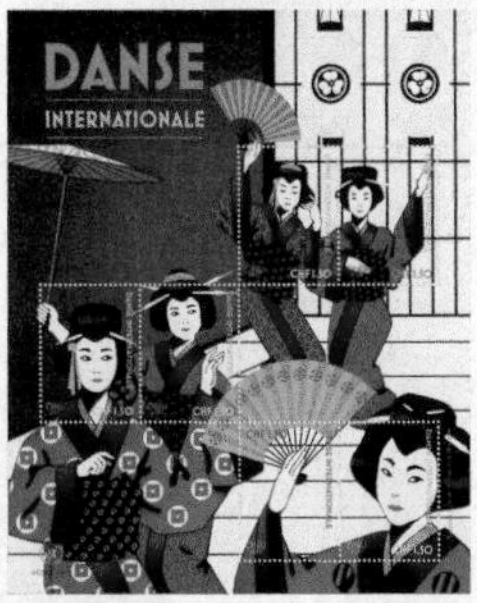

International Dance — G120

No. 630 — Illustration of Quadrille dancers by Jean François Martin: a, Female dancer wearing red mask facing right, striped pole. b, Male dancer wearing brown mask, harlequin costume, facing right. c, Masked male dancer with red mask facing right. d, Female dancer with brown mask facing left. e, Woman holding black mask facing right. f, Man wearing tan mask facing left.

No. 631 — Illustration of Japanese fan dancers by Martin: a, Dancer holding fan and other hand near her hair. b, Dancer with arm upraised at UR. c, Head of dancer, hand of dancer holding umbrella. d, Dancer, part of fan at LR, e, Dancer's hand holding fan. f, Face of dancer, no hands visible.

2017, Mar. 23 Litho. *Perf. 13¼x13*

630	G119	Sheet of 6	13.00	13.00
a.-f.		1fr Any single	2.10	2.10
631	G120	Sheet of 6	19.50	19.50
a.-f.		1.50fr Any single	3.25	3.25

Endangered Species Type of 2017

Designs: No. 632, Rhampholeon spp. No. 633, Mobula spp. No. 634, Adansonia grandidieri. No. 635, Scaphiophryne marmorata.

2017, May 11 Litho. *Perf. 12¾x12½*

632	A509	1.50fr multicolored	3.25	3.25
633	A509	1.50fr multicolored	3.25	3.25
634	A509	1.50fr multicolored	3.25	3.25
635	A509	1.50fr multicolored	3.25	3.25
a.		Block of 4, #632-635	13.00	13.00
		Nos. 632-635 (4)	13.00	13.00

World Environment Day Type of 2017

Designs: 1fr, Snowy owl, Quebec, Canada. 2fr, Red maple and aspen trees, Canada.

2017, June 5 Litho. *Perf. 13¼*

636	A510	1fr multicolored	2.25	2.25
637	A510	2fr multicolored	4.50	4.50

World Heritage Sites Along the Silk Roads Type of 2017

Designs: Nos. 638, 640b, Historic Center of Bukhara, Uzbekistan. Nos. 639, 640e, Kunya-Urgench, Turkmenistan. No. 640a, Longmen Grottoes, People's Republic of China. No. 640c, Tabriz Historic Bazaar Complex, Iran. No. 640d, Sulaiman-Too Sacred Mountain, Kyrgyzstan. No. 640f, Safranbolu, Turkey.

2017, Aug. 3 Litho. *Perf. 14¼*

638	A512	1fr multicolored	2.40	2.40
639	A512	1.50fr multicolored	3.50	3.50

Souvenir Booklet

640		Booklet, #640g-640l	26.50	
a.-c.	A512	30c any single	.80	.80
d.-f.	A512	50c any single	1.40	1.40
g.		Booklet pane of 4 #640a	3.20	—
h.		Booklet pane of 4 #640b	3.20	—
i.		Booklet pane of 4 #640c	3.20	—
j.		Booklet pane of 4 #640d	5.60	—
k.		Booklet pane of 4 #640e	5.60	—
l.		Booklet pane of 4 #640f	5.60	—

Hare, Fox and Dove — G121

Heads and Flowers — G122

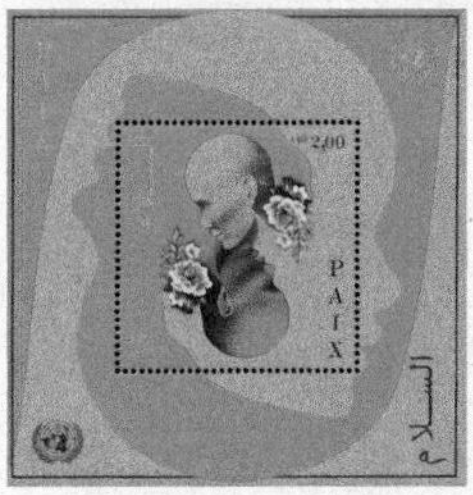

Heads and Flowers G123

Designs: 1fr, Snowy owl, Quebec, Canada. 2fr, Red maple and aspen trees, Canada.

2017, Sept. 21 Litho. *Perf. 14¼x14*

641	G121	1fr multicolored	2.40	2.40
642	G122	2fr multicolored	4.75	4.75

Souvenir Sheet

Perf. 14¼x13¾

643	G123	2fr multicolored	4.75	4.75

International Day of Peace.

World Food Day Type of 2017

Designs: 1fr, Milk, yogurt and cheeses. 1.50fr, Fruits.

2017, Oct. 16 Litho. *Perf. 13¼x14*

644	A516	1fr multicolored	2.40	2.40
645	A516	1.50fr multicolored	3.50	3.50

Endangered Species Type of 2018

Designs: No. 646, Saiga tatarica. No. 647, Uncarina grandidieri. No. 648, Polymita picta. No. 649, Carcharhinus falciformis.

2018, Mar. 2 Litho. *Perf. 12¾x12½*

646	A519	1.50fr multicolored	3.50	3.50
647	A519	1.50fr multicolored	3.50	3.50
648	A519	1.50fr multicolored	3.50	3.50
649	A519	1.50fr multicolored	3.50	3.50
a.		Block of 4, #646-649	14.00	14.00
		Nos. 646-649 (4)	14.00	14.00

World Health Day Type of 2018

Designs: 1fr, Microbes and microscope. 2fr, Child, apple, pencil, triangle, numbers, glass of milk.

2018, Apr. 6 Litho. *Perf. 13x13¼*

650	A520	1fr multicolored	2.25	2.25
651	A520	2fr multicolored	4.50	4.50

Miniature Sheet

G124

No. 652: a, Cathedral of St. Lawrence belltower and buildings on hillside. b, Bank with curved glass facade. c, Table and chairs along footpath in city. d, Villa Saroli (yellow building). e, People near door of Santa Maria degli Angioli Church. f, Lugano Arts and Cultural Center (building with four large windows). g, Storefronts along hill on Via Cattedrale. h, Gates of Villa Ciani. i, Arches along Via della Posta. j, William Tell Monument.

2018, May 17 Litho. *Perf. 14¾*

652	G124	Sheet of 10 + 10 labels	*38.50*	*38.50*
a.-j.		1.50fr Any single + label	*3.75*	*3.75*

The full sheet sold for $19.06 or 16.95fr. The generic labels are shown. Labels could be personalized. The personalization of labels was available only at UN Headquarters, and not through mail order.

UNISPACE + 50 Conferences Type of 2018

Designs: 1fr, View of Earth from space. 1.50fr, Launch of Tiangong 1.

2fr, Widefield Infrared Survey Explorer photograph of Comet 65P/Gunn.

2018, June 20 Litho. *Perf. 14x14¼*

653	A523	1fr multicolored	2.25	2.25
654	A523	1.50fr multicolored	3.50	3.50

Souvenir Sheet

Perf. 13¾

655	A523	2fr multicolored	4.50	4.50

No. 655 contains one 45x45mm stamp.

Nelson Mandela (1918-2013), President of South Africa G125

Printed by Lowe-Martin Group, Canada. Panes of 20. Designed by Martin Morck, Norway.

2018, July 18 Litho. *Perf. 13¼*

656	G125	2fr buff & black	4.50	4.50

World Heritage Sites in the United Kingdom Type of 2016

Designs: Nos. 657, 659b, Stonehenge. Nos. 658, 659e, Edinburgh. No. 659a, Giant's Causeway. No. 659c, Conwy Castle. No. 659d, Palace of Westminster. No. 659f, Maritime Greenwich.

2018, Aug. 15 Litho. *Perf. 14¼*

657	A524	1fr multicolored	2.25	2.25
658	A524	1.50fr multicolored	3.50	3.50

Souvenir Booklet

659		Booklet, #659g-659l	23.50	
a.-c.	A524	30c any single	.75	.75
d.-f.	A524	50c any single	1.10	1.10
g.		Booklet pane of 4 #659a	3.00	—
h.		Booklet pane of 4 #659b	3.00	—
i.		Booklet pane of 4 #659c	3.00	—
j.		Booklet pane of 4 #659d	4.75	—
k.		Booklet pane of 4 #659e	4.75	—
l.		Booklet pane of 4 #659f	4.75	—

Miniature Sheet

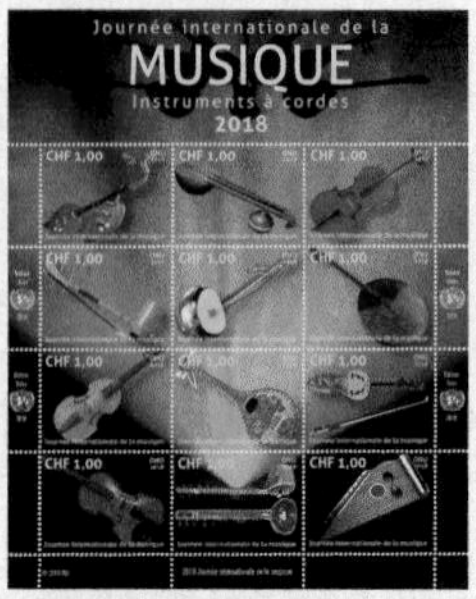

International Music Day — G126

No. 660: a, Electric guitars with carved necks. b, Veena. c, Cello. d, Erhu. e, Ektara. f, Domra. g, Viola da gamba. h, Bazouki. i, Stringed instrument with bow. j, Violin with chin rest. k, Sitars. l, Zither.

2018, Oct. 1 Litho. *Perf. 14x13¼*

660 G126 Sheet of 12 27.00 27.00
a.-l. 1fr Any single 2.25 2.25

Miniature Sheet

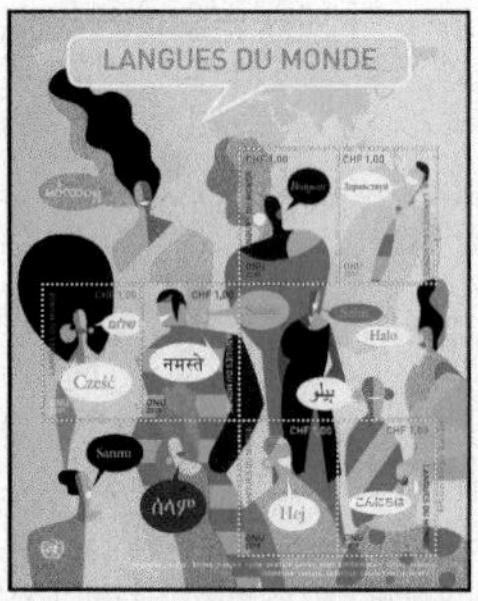

World Languages — G127

No. 661 — Word bubbles with word for "Hello" in: a, French (Bonjour). b, Russian ("Langues du Monde" in lilac). c, Hebrew and Polish (Czesc), d, Hindi ("Langues du Monde" in white). e, Danish or Swedish (Hej). f, Japanese ("Langues du Monde" in dark gray).

2019, Feb. 21 Litho. *Perf. 13¼x13*

661 G127 Sheet of 6 13.50 13.50
a.-f. 1fr Any single 2.25 2.25

Gender Equality — G128

Printed by Lowe-Martin Group, Canada. Panes of 20. Designed by Chris Gash, U.S.

2019, Mar.15 Litho. *Perf. 13¼x13*

662 G128 1.50fr multicolored 3.50 3.50

Endangered Species Type of 2019

Designs: No. 663, Hippocampus kuda. No. 664, Dugong dugon. No. 665, Stylophora pistillata. No. 666, Lamna nasus.

2019, Apr. 26 Litho. *Perf. 12¾x12½*

663 A534 1.50fr multicolored 3.25 3.25
664 A534 1.50fr multicolored 3.25 3.25
665 A534 1.50fr multicolored 3.25 3.25
666 A534 1.50fr multicolored 3.25 3.25
a. Block of 4, #663-666 13.50 13.50
Nos. 663-666 (4) 13.00 13.00

Souvenir Sheet

Bumblebee and Lobelia Cardinalis — G129

Litho. With Foil Application

2019, May 20 *Perf. 13*

667 G129 2.60fr multicolored 6.00 6.00

World Bee Day.

G130

G131

G132

G133

International Labor Organization, Cent. — G134

2019, June 28 Litho. *Perf. 13½x14*

668 G130 1fr multicolored 2.25 2.25
669 G131 1fr multicolored 2.25 2.25
670 G132 1fr multicolored 2.25 2.25
671 G133 1fr multicolored 2.25 2.25
672 G134 1fr multicolored 2.25 2.25
a. Horiz. strip of 5, #668-672 11.25 11.25
Nos. 668-672 (5) 11.25 11.25

Climate Change Type of 2019

Designs: 1fr, Fruit tree and burnt forest. 1.50fr, Field of flowers and traffic jam. 2fr, Clouds.

2019, Sept. 23 Litho. *Perf. 14¼*

673 A543 1fr multicolored 2.25 2.25
674 A543 1.50fr multicolored 3.50 3.50

Souvenir Sheet

Perf.

675 A543 2fr multicolored 4.50 4.50

2019 United Nations Climate Change Conference, Madrid. No. 675 contains one 47mm diameter stamp.

Miniature Sheet

United Nations Postal Administration in Geneva, 50th Anniv. — G135

No. 676: a, Palais des Nations and Armillary Sphere, green panels. b, Palais des Nations and flags, gray panels. c, Assembly Hall, Palais des Nations, violet blue panels. d, Meeting room of Human Rights Council, light blue panels. e, Armillary Sphere in reflecting pond and Lake Geneva, violet black panels. f, Palais des Nations and flags, red panels. g, Palais des Nations and flags, orange yellow panels. h, Palais des Nations and United Nations flag, dark green panels. i, Peacock, blue green panels. j, Council Chamber, blue gray panels.

2019, Oct. 18 Litho. *Perf. 14¾*

676 G135 Sheet of 10 + 10 labels *38.00 38.00*
a.-j. 1.50fr Any single + label *3.75 3.75*

The full sheet sold for $18.80 or 16.95fr. The generic labels are shown. Labels could be personalized. The personalization of labels was available only at UN Headquarters, and not through mail order.

World Heritage Sites in Cuba Type of 2019

Designs: Nos. 677, 679b, Trinidad. Nos. 678, 679e, Cienfuegos. No. 679a, Morro Castle. No. 679c, Camagüey. No. 679d, Vinales Valley. No. 679f, San Pedro de la Rosa Castle.

Litho. With Foil Application

2019, Oct. 24 *Perf. 14¼*

677 A545 1fr multicolored 2.25 2.25
678 A545 1.50fr multicolored 3.50 3.50

Souvenir Booklet

679 Booklet, #679g-679l 24.50
a.-c. A545 30c Any single .75 .75
d.-f. A545 50c Any single 1.25 1.25
g. Booklet pane of 4 #679a 3.00 —
h. Booklet pane of 4 #679b 3.00 —
i. Booklet pane of 4 #679c 3.00 —
j. Booklet pane of 4 #679d 5.00 —
k. Booklet pane of 4 #679e 5.00 —
l. Booklet pane of 4 #679f 5.00 —

Complete booklet sold for $12.20.

Endangered Species Type of 2020

Designs: No. 680, Leucogeranus leucogeranus. No. 681, Addax nasomaculatus. No. 682, Falco cherrug. No. 683, Monodon monoceros.

Perf. 12¾x12½

2020, Feb. 17 Litho.

680 A546 1.50fr multicolored 3.50 3.50
681 A546 1.50fr multicolored 3.50 3.50
682 A546 1.50fr multicolored 3.50 3.50
683 A546 1.50fr multicolored 3.50 3.50
a. Block of 4, #680-683 14.00 14.00
Nos. 680-683 (4) 14.00 14.00

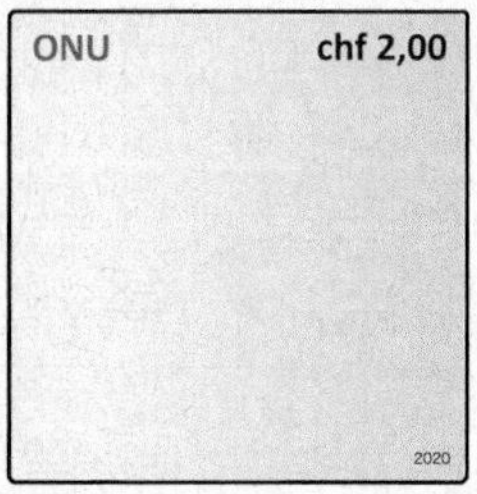

Blank Stamp On Which Stickers Can Be Applied G136

Designs: No. 1212, Hawksbill turtle. No. 1213, Queen conch. No. 1214, Mushroom coral. No. 1215, Humpback whale.

2020, Mar. 19 Litho. *Die Cut*

Self-Adhesive

684 G136 2fr multicolored with rounded corners 4.75 4.75
a. With perpendicular corners and black frame line 4.75 4.75
b. Booklet pane of 6 #1236a 28.50

No. 684 was issued as a souvenir sheet having two different sheet margins, each with different stickers. No. 684a was issued in a booklet containing six panes of one stamp, with each pane having different margins and stickers. Each booklet pane contained one sticker depicting Hello Kitty, a color wheel with Hello Kitty at the center, one of six different Sustainable Development Goal emblems, along with a variety of other stickers. The two souvenir sheets had the same sheet margin and stickers found on two of the panes of No. 684b. No. 684b was sold folded, without any means of separation between the individual panes.

Terre, Artwork by Mathilde Roussel G137

Mermaids Hate Plastic, Photograph by Benjamin Von Wong G138

2020, Apr. 22 Litho. *Perf. 13¼*

685 G137 1fr multicolored 2.25 2.25
686 G138 2fr multicolored 4.50 4.50

Earth Day, 50th anniv. Because of the COVID-19 pandemic, Nos. 685-686 were not available for sale on day of issue stated on the first-day covers as they had not yet been printed and delivered.

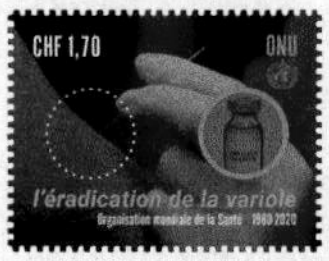

Eradication of Smallpox, 40th Anniv. — G139

Printed by Cartor Security Printing, France. Panes of 20. Designed by Sergio Baradat, U.S., and World Health Organization.

2020, May 8 Litho. *Perf. 13x13¼*

687 G139 1.70fr multicolored 4.00 4.00

World Heritage Sites in Russia Type of 2020

Designs: Nos. 688, 690b, Kazan Kremlin. Nos. 689, 690e, Saint Petersburg. No. 690a, Lake Baikal. No. 690c, Novodevichy Convent. No. 690d, Kremlin and Red Square, Moscow. No. 690f, Kizhi Pogost.

Perf. 14½x14¼

2020, Sept. 11 Litho.

688 A556 1fr multicolored 2.40 2.40
689 A556 1.50fr multicolored 3.75 3.75

Souvenir Booklet

690 Booklet, #690g-690l 28.00
a.-c. A556 30c any single .85 .85
d.-f. A556 50c any single 1.40 1.40
g. Booklet pane of 4 #690a 3.50 —
h. Booklet pane of 4 #690b 3.50 —
i. Booklet pane of 4 #690c 3.50 —
j. Booklet pane of 4 #690d 5.75 —
k. Booklet pane of 4 #690e 5.75 —
l. Booklet pane of 4 #690f 5.75 —

Complete booklet sold for $13.21 or 11fr.

Souvenir Sheet

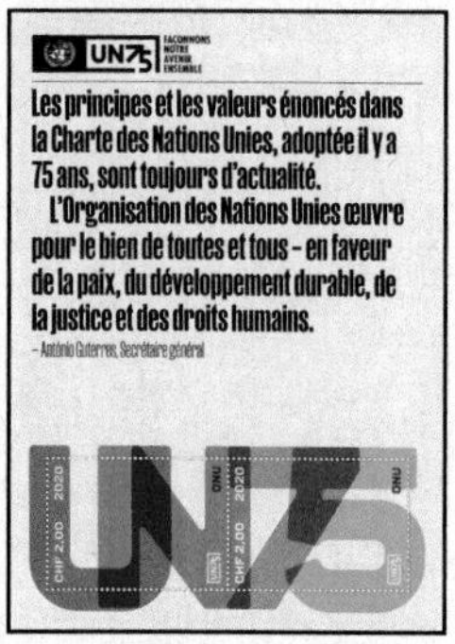

United Nations, 75th Anniv. G140

No. 691: a, Green "U," pink "N." b, Blue "7," yellow "5."

2020, Oct. 24 Litho. *Perf. 13¼*

691 G140 Sheet of 2 10.00 10.00
a.-b. 2fr Either single 5.00 5.00

Souvenir Sheet

Palais des Nations and Emblem G141

Litho. With Foil Application

2020, Nov. 24 *Die Cut Perf. 11½*

Self-Adhesive

692 G141 8fr multicolored 19.50 19.50

Crypto stamp. Unused value is for sheets with unscratched panels at right.

International Day for the Elimination of Racial Discrimination — G142

2021, Mar. 19 Litho. *Perf. 13¼x13*

693 G142 2fr multicolored 5.00 5.00

Endangered Species Type of 2021

Designs: No. 694, Leontopithecus chrysomelas. No. 695, Macrotis lagotis. No. 696, Lemur catta. No. 697, Caladenia huegelii.

2021, Apr. 7 Litho. ***Perf. 12¾x12½***

694 A565 1.50fr multicolored 3.75 3.75
695 A565 1.50fr multicolored 3.75 3.75
696 A565 1.50fr multicolored 3.75 3.75
697 A565 1.50fr multicolored 3.75 3.75
a. Block of 4, #694-697 15.00 15.00
Nos. 694-697 (4) 15.00 15.00

Two Judokas — G143

Judoka in Blue Judogi — G144

Judoka in White Judogi — G145

Female Diver — G146

Diver on Platform G147

Diver Spinning G148

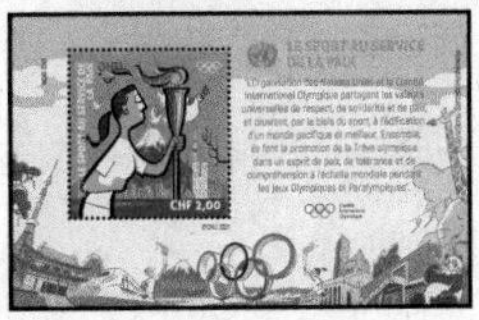

Athlete Carrying Olympic Torch G149

2021, July 23 Litho. ***Perf. 13½***

698 G143 1fr multicolored 2.50 2.50
699 G144 1fr multicolored 2.50 2.50
700 G145 1fr multicolored 2.50 2.50
a. Horiz. strip of 3, #698-700 7.50 7.50
701 G146 1.50fr multicolored 3.75 3.75
702 G147 1.50fr multicolored 3.75 3.75
703 G148 1.50fr multicolored 3.75 3.75
a. Horiz. strip of 3, #701-703 11.25 11.25
Nos. 698-703 (6) 18.75 18.75

Souvenir Sheet

704 G149 2fr multicolored 5.00 5.00

Sports for Peace, 2020 Summer Olympics, Tokyo. The 2020 Summer Olympics were postponed until 2021 because of the COVID-19 pandemic.

Waterways, Railways and Bridges World Heritage Sites Type of 2020

Designs: Nos. 705, 707b, Rhaetian Railway, Switzerland and Italy. Nos. 706, 707e, Darjeeling Himalayan Railway, India. No. 707a, Rideau Canal, Canada. No. 707c, Forth Bridge, Scotland. No. 707d, Grand Canal, People's Republic of China. No. 707f, Old Bridge, Mostar, Bosnia and Herzegovina.

2021, Aug. 25 Litho. ***Perf. 14¼***

705 A575 1fr multicolored 2.50 2.50
706 A575 1.50fr multicolored 3.75 3.75
First day cover 6.00

Souvenir Booklet

707 Booklet, #707g-707l 28.00
a.-c. A575 30c any single .85 .85
d.-f. A575 50c any single 1.40 1.40
g. Booklet pane of 4 #707a 3.50 —
h. Booklet pane of 4 #707b 3.50 —
i. Booklet pane of 4 #707c 3.50 —
j. Booklet pane of 4 #707d 5.75 —
k. Booklet pane of 4 #707e 5.75 —
l. Booklet pane of 4 #707f 5.75 —

Complete booklet sold for $13.21 or 10.95fr.

Miniature Sheet

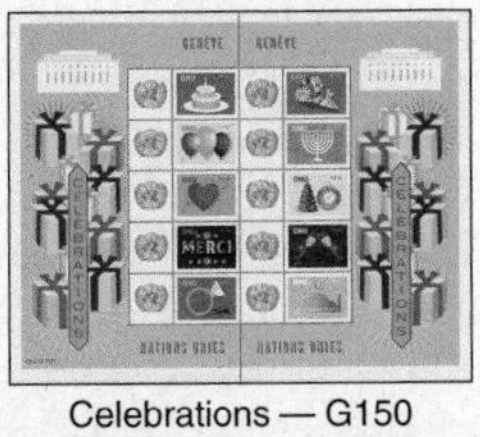

Celebrations — G150

No. 708: a, Birthday cake. b, Flower bouquet. c, Three balloons. d, Menorah. e, Heart and arrow. f, Christmas tree and ornament. g, "Merci." h, Champagne flutes. i, Diamond ring. j, Mosque.

2021, Nov. 4 Litho. ***Perf. 14¼***

708 G150 Sheet of 10 *41.00 41.00*
a.-j. 1.50fr Any single + label *4.00 4.00*

The full sheet sold for $20.28. The generic labels are shown. Labels could be personalized. The personalization of labels was available only at UN Headquarters, and not through mail order.

World Toilet Day — G151

2021, Nov. 19 Litho. ***Perf. 14¼***

709 G151 1fr multicolored 2.40 2.40

Feet of Figure Skater G152

Figure Skaters G153

Four-man Bobsled G154

Monobob G155

2022, Jan. 14 Litho. ***Perf. 14¼***

710 G152 1.10fr multicolored 2.25 2.25
711 G153 1.10fr multicolored 2.25 2.25
a. Horiz. pair, #710-711 5.50 5.50
712 G154 2fr multicolored 5.00 5.00
713 G155 2fr multicolored 5.00 5.00
a. Horiz. pair, #712-713 10.00 10.00
Nos. 710-713 (4) 14.50 14.50

Sports for Peace, 2022 Winter Olympics, Beijing.

Endangered Species Type of 2022

Designs: No. 714, Acropora cervicornis. No. 715, Gonatodes daudini. No. 716, Mobula munkiana. No. 717, Oophaga arborea.

Perf. 12¾x12½

2022, Mar. 18 Litho.

714 A592 1.50fr multicolored 3.75 3.75
715 A592 1.50fr multicolored 3.75 3.75
716 A592 1.50fr multicolored 3.75 3.75
717 A592 1.50fr multicolored 3.75 3.75
a. Block of 4, #714-717 15.00 15.00
Nos. 714-717 (4) 15.00 15.00

Exploration of Mars Type of 2022

Designs: 58c, Proctor Crater. No. 1302, Mars Perseverence Rover.
No. 1303, Mars Ingenuity Helicopter.

2022, Apr. 24 Litho. ***Perf. 13¼x13***

718 A593 1.10fr multicolored 2.75 2.75
719 A593 1.50fr multicolored 3.75 3.75

Souvenir Sheet

Perf. 13½

720 A593 2fr multicolored 5.00 5.00

No. 720 contains one 44x44mm stamp.

Miniature Sheet

World Bicycle Day G156

No. 721: a, Three cyclists on road. b, Two cyclists near water, facing right. c, Two bicycles in front of store. d, Cyclist on dirt path. e, Two cyclists transporting flowers. f, Cyclist wearing hat, facing left. g, Row of identical bicycles. h, Backs of two cyclists near water. i, Cyclist and grass. j, Bicycles leaning on bridge railing.

2022, June 3 Litho. ***Perf. 14¼***

721 G156 Sheet of 10 + 10 labels *45.00 45.00*
a.-j. 1.50fr Any single + label *4.50 4.50*

The full sheet sold for $22.12 or €18.40. The generic labels are shown. Labels could be personalized.

European Spa Town World Heritage Sites Type of 2022

Designs: Nos. 722, 724b, Spa, Belgium. Nos. 723, 724e, Vichy, France. No. 724a, Karlovy Vary, Czech Republic. No. 724c, Baden-Baden, Germany. No. 724d, Montecatini Terme, Italy. No. 724f, Baden bei Wien, Austria.

2022, Sept. 9 Litho. ***Perf. 14½x14¼***

722 A594 1.10fr multicolored 2.60 2.60
723 A594 1.50fr multicolored 3.50 3.50

Souvenir Booklet

724 Booklet, #690g-690l 25.50
a.-c. A594 30c any single .80 .80
d.-f. A594 50c any single 1.30 1.30
g. Booklet pane of 4 #724a 3.25 —
h. Booklet pane of 4 #724b 3.25 —
i. Booklet pane of 4 #724c 3.25 —
j. Booklet pane of 4 #724d 5.25 —
k. Booklet pane of 4 #724e 5.25 —
l. Booklet pane of 4 #724f 5.25 —

Complete booklet sold for $12.63 or 11fr.

Souvenir Sheet

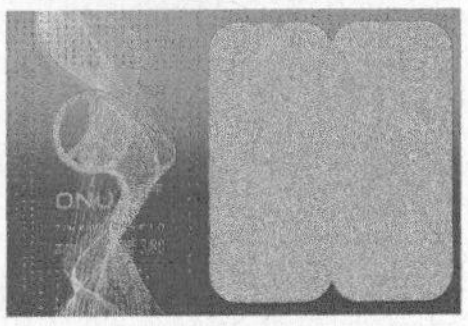

Peace Sign G157

Litho. With Foil Application

2022, Nov. 18 ***Die Cut Perf. 11½***

Self-Adhesive

725 G157 3.80fr multicolored 8.75 8.75

Crypto stamp. Unused value is for sheets with unscratched panels at right.

SEMI-POSTAL STAMPS

AIDS Awareness Semi-postal Type

Souvenir Sheet

2002, Oct. 24 Litho. ***Perf. 14½***

B1 GSP1 90c + 30c multicolored 4.00 4.00

GSP2

Photograph of John Lennon (1940-80), by Iain Macmillan — GSP3

2021, Sept. 21 Litho. ***Perf. 14¼***

B2 GSP2 1.50fr multicolored 5.00 5.00

Souvenir Sheet

Litho. With Foil Application

B3 GSP3 2.60fr multicolored 8.75 8.75

International Day of Peace. Surtax for United Nations peacekeeping efforts.

World Humanitarian Day — GSP4

2022, Aug. 19 Litho. ***Perf. 13¼x13***

B4 GSP4 2fr multicolored 6.00 6.00

Surtax for United Nations Central Emergency Response Fund.

OFFICES IN VIENNA, AUSTRIA

For use only on mail posted at the Vienna International Center for the UN and the International Atomic Energy Agency.

100 Groschen = 1 Schilling
100 Cents = 1 Euro (2002)

Catalogue values for all unused stamps in this country are for Never Hinged items.

Type of Geneva, 1978, UN Types of 1961-72 and

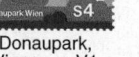

Donaupark, Vienna — V1

Aerial View — V2

1979, Aug. 24 Photo. *Perf. 11½*
Granite Paper

1	G8	50g multicolored	.25	.30
2	A52	1s multicolored	.25	.30
3	V1	4s multicolored	.25	.30
4	AP13	5s multicolored	.30	.35
5	V2	6s multicolored	.35	.35
6	A45	10s multicolored	.60	.70
		Nos. 1-6 (6)	2.00	2.30

No. 6 has no frame.

New Economic Order Type of UN

1980, Jan. 11 Litho. *Perf. 15x14½*

7	A178	4s multicolored	.60	.70

Dove Type of UN

1980, Jan. 11 Litho. *Perf. 14x13½*

8	A147	2.50s multicolored	.25	.30

Women's Year Emblem on World Map — V3

United Nations Decade for Women

1980, Mar. 7 Litho. *Perf. 14½x15*

9	V3	4s light green & dark green	.40	.45
10	V3	6s bister brown	.75	.85

Peace-keeping Operations Type of UN

1980, May 16 Litho. *Perf. 14x13*

11	A182	6s multicolored	.40	.45

35th Anniversary Types of Geneva and UN

1980, June 26 Litho. *Perf. 13x13½*

12	G16	4s carmine rose & black	.35	.40
13	A184	6s multicolored	.60	.65

Souvenir Sheet
Imperf

14		Sheet of 2	.90	1.00
a.		G16 4s carmine rose & black	.25	.30
b.		A184 6s multicolored	.65	.30

ECOSOC Types of UN and Geneva

1980, Nov. 21 Litho. *Perf. 13½x13*

15	A187	4s multicolored	.30	.35
16	G17	6s multicolored	.60	.30

Palestinian Rights Type of UN

1981, Jan. 30 Photo. *Perf. 12x11½*

17	A188	4s multicolored	.45	.50

Disabled Type of UN and

Interlocking Stitches — V4

1981, Mar. 6 Photo. *Perf. 14*

18	A189	4s multicolored	.40	.45
19	V4	6s black & orange	.60	.70

Art Type of UN

1981, Apr. 15 Photo. *Perf. 11½*
Granite Paper

20	A191	6s multicolored	.75	.85

Energy Type of UN

1981, May 29 Litho. *Perf. 13*

21	A193	7.50s multicolored	.70	.80

Volunteers Program Types

1981, Nov. 13 Litho.

22	A195	5s multicolored	.40	.45
23	G18	7s multicolored	.90	1.00

"For a Better World" — V5

1982, Jan. 22 *Perf. 11½x12*

24	V5	3s multicolored	.35	.40

Human Environment Types of UN and Geneva

1982, Mar. 19 Litho. *Perf. 13½x13*

25	A200	5s multicolored	.40	.45
26	G21	7s multicolored	.80	.90

Outer Space Type of Geneva

1982, June 11 Litho. *Perf. 13x13½*

27	G22	5s multicolored	.60	.70

Conservation & Protection of Nature Type

1982, Nov. 16 Photo. *Perf. 14*

28	A202	5s Fish	.50	.60
29	A202	7s Animal	.70	.80

World Communications Year Type

1983, Jan. 28 Litho. *Perf. 13*

30	A203	4s multicolored	.40	.45

Safety at Sea Types of Geneva and UN

1983, Mar. 18 Litho. *Perf. 14½*

31	G23	4s multicolored	.40	.45
32	A206	6s multicolored	.65	.75

World Food Program Type

1983, Apr. 22 Engr. *Perf. 13½*

33	A207	5s green	.45	.50
34	A207	7s brown	.70	.80

UN Conference on Trade and Development Types of Geneva and UN

1983, June 6 Litho. *Perf. 14*

35	G24	4s multicolored	.30	.35
36	A209	8.50s multicolored	.75	.85

V6

35th Anniv. of the Universal Declaration of Human Rights — V7

Photo. & Engr.
1983, Dec. 9 *Perf. 13½*

37	V6	5s multicolored	.40	.45
38	V7	7s multicolored	.65	.75

International Conference on Population Type

1984, Feb. 3 Litho. *Perf. 14*

39	A212	7s multicolored	.65	.75

Field Irrigation — V8

Harvesting Machine — V9

World Food Day, Oct. 16

1984, Mar. 15 Litho. *Perf. 14½*

40	V8	4.50s multicolored	.40	.45
41	V9	6s multicolored	.65	.75

Serengeti Park, Tanzania — V10

Ancient City of Shiban, People's Democratic Rep. of Yemen — V11

World Heritage

1984, Mar. 15 Litho. *Perf. 14*

42	V10	3.50s multicolored	.25	.30
43	V11	15s multicolored	1.25	1.40

V12

V13

Future for Refugees

1984, May 29 Photo. *Perf. 11½*

44	V12	4.50s multicolored	.45	.50
45	V13	8.50s multicolored	1.25	1.40

International Youth Year — V14

1984, Nov. 15 Litho. *Perf. 13½*

46	V14	3.50s multicolored	.45	.50
47	V14	6.50s multicolored	.70	.80

ILO Type of Geneva

1985, Feb. 1 Engr. *Perf. 13½*

48	G34	7.50s U Thant Pavilion	.75	.85

UN University Type

1985, Mar. 15 Photo. *Perf. 11½*

49	A221	8.50s Rural scene, lab researcher	.75	.85

Ship of Peace V15

Sharing Umbrella V16

1985, May 10 Litho. *Perf. 14*

50	V15	4.50s multicolored	.30	.35
51	V16	15s multicolored	2.00	2.25

40th Anniversary Type

Perf. 12 x 11½
1985, June 26 Photo.

52	A224	6.50s multicolored	.90	1.00
53	A225	8.50s multicolored	1.40	1.60

Souvenir Sheet
Imperf

54		Sheet of 2	2.50	2.75
a.		A224 6.50s multi	1.00	1.10
b.		A225 8.50s multi	1.40	1.50

UNICEF Child Survival Campaign Type

4s, Spoonfeeding children. 6s, Mother hugging infant.

Photo. & Engr.
1985, Nov. 22 *Perf. 13½*

55	A226	4s multicolored	.75	.85
56	A226	6s multicolored	1.40	1.60

Africa in Crisis Type

1986, Jan. 31 Photo. *Perf. 11½x12*

57	A227	8s multicolored	.80	.90

UN Development Program Type

Agriculture: No. 58, Developing crop strains. No. 59, Animal husbandry. No. 60, Technical instruction. No. 61, Nutrition education.

1986, Mar. 14 Photo. *Perf. 13½*

58	A228	4.50s multicolored	1.40	1.60
59	A228	4.50s multicolored	1.40	1.60
60	A228	4.50s multicolored	1.40	1.60
61	A228	4.50s multicolored	1.40	1.60
a.		Block of 4, #58-61	6.25	7.00

No. 61a has a continuous design.

Stamp Collecting Type

Designs: 3.50s, UN stamps. 6.50s, Engraver.

1986, May 22 Engr. *Perf. 12½*

62	A229	3.50s dk ultra & dk brown	.40	.45
63	A229	6.50s int blue & brt rose	.90	1.00

Olive Branch, Rainbow, Earth — V17

Photogravure & Embossed
1986, June 20 *Perf. 13½*

64	V17	5s shown	.75	.85
65	V17	6s Doves, UN emblem	1.00	1.10

WFUNA Anniversary Type
Souvenir Sheet

Designs: 4s, White stallion by Elisabeth von Janota-Bzowski, Germany. 5s, Surrealistic landscape by Ernst Fuchs, Austria. 6s, Geometric abstract by Victor Vasarely (b. 1908), France. 7s, Mythological abstract by Wolfgang Hutter (b. 1928), Austria.

1986, Nov. 14 Litho. *Perf. 13x13½*

66		Sheet of 4	4.00	4.25
a.		A232 4s multicolored	.75	.80
b.		A232 5s multicolored	.85	.90
c.		A232 6s multicolored	1.00	1.10
d.		A232 7s multicolored	1.25	1.40

No. 66 has inscribed margin picturing UN and WFUNA emblems.

Trygve Lie Type
Photogravure & Engraved

1987, Jan. 30 *Perf. 13½*

67	A233	8s multicolored	.70	.80

Shelter for the Homeless Type

Designs: 4s, Family and homes. 9.50s, Family entering home.

Perf. 13½x12½
1987, Mar. 13 Litho.

68	A234	4s multicolored	.50	.55
69	A234	9.50s multicolored	1.10	1.25

Fight Drug Abuse Type

Designs: 5s, Soccer players. 8s, Family.

1987, June 12 Litho. *Perf. 14½x15*

70	A235	5s multicolored	.40	.45
71	A235	8s multicolored	.90	1.00

Donaupark, Vienna — V18

Peace Embracing the Earth — V19

1987, June 12 Litho. *Perf. 14½x15*

72	V18	2s multicolored	.30	.35
73	V19	17s multicolored	1.60	1.75

UN Day Type

Designs: Multinational people in various occupations.

1987, Oct. 23 Litho. *Perf. 14½x15*

74 A236 5s multicolored .75 .85
75 A236 6s multicolored .90 1.00

Immunize Every Child Type

Designs: 4s, Poliomyelitis. 9.50s, Diphtheria.

1987, Nov. 20 Litho. *Perf. 15x14½*

76 A237 4s multicolored .75 .85
77 A237 9.50s multicolored 2.00 2.25

IFAD Type

Designs: 4s, Grains. 6s, Vegetables.

1988, Jan. 29 Litho. *Perf. 13½*

78 A238 4s multicolored .40 .45
79 A238 6s multicolored .90 1.00

Survival of the Forests Type

Deciduous forest in fall: 4s, Treetops, hills and dales. 5s, Tree trunks. Printed se-tenant in a continuous design.

1988, Mar. 18 Litho. *Perf. 14x15*

80 A240 4s multicolored 2.25 2.40
81 A240 5s multicolored 3.00 3.25
a. Pair, #80-81 5.25 5.75

Intl. Volunteer Day Type

Designs: 6s, Medical care, vert. 7.50s, Construction.

Perf. 13x14, 14x13

1988, May 6 Litho.

82 A241 6s multicolored .75 .85
83 A241 7.50s multicolored 1.00 1.10

Health in Sports Type

Paintings by LeRoy Neiman, American Sports artist: 6s, Skiing, vert. 8s, Tennis.

Perf. 13½x13, 13x13½

1988, June 17 Litho.

84 A242 6s multicolored .90 1.00
85 A242 8s multicolored 1.40 1.60

Universal Declaration of Human Rights 40th Anniv. Type

Photo. & Engr.

1988, Dec. 9 *Perf. 11½*

86 A243 5s multicolored .50 .55

Souvenir Sheet

87 A243 11s multicolored 1.25 1.40

No. 87 has multicolored decorative margin inscribed with preamble to the human rights declaration in German.

World Bank Type

1989, Jan. 27 Litho. *Perf. 13x14*

88 A244 5.50s Transportation 1.10 1.25
89 A244 8s Health care, education 1.75 1.90

Peace-Keeping Force Type

1989, Mar. 17 *Perf. 14x13½*

90 A245 6s multicolored .85 .95

World Weather Watch Type

Satellite photograph and radar image: 4s, Helical cloud formation over Italy, the eastern Alps, and parts of Yugoslavia. 9.50s, Rainfall in Tokyo, Japan.

1989, Apr. 21 Litho. *Perf. 13x14*

91 A247 4s multicolored 1.00 1.10
92 A247 9.50s multicolored 2.10 2.25

V20

V21

Photo. & Engr., Photo. (7.50s)

1989, Aug. 23 *Perf. 14*

93 V20 5s multicolored 1.25 1.50
94 V21 7.50s multicolored 1.25 1.50

Human Rights Type of 1989

Paintings: 4s, The Prisoners, by Kathe Kollwitz. 6s, Justice, by Raphael.

1989, Nov. 17 Litho. *Perf. 13½*

95 A250 4s multicolored .50 .55
96 A250 6s multicolored .75 .85

See Nos. 108-109, 123-124, 150-151.

Intl. Trade Center Type

1990, Feb. 2 Litho. *Perf. 14½x15*

97 A251 12s multicolored 1.25 1.40

Painting by Kurt Regschek — V22

1990, Feb. 2 Litho. *Perf. 13x13½*

98 V22 1.50s multicolored .30 .35

V23

Designs: 5s, "SIDA." 11s, Stylized figures, ink blot.

Perf. 13½x12½

1990, Mar. 16 Litho.

99 V23 5s multicolored 1.00 1.10
100 V23 11s multicolored 2.25 2.40

Medicinal Plants Type

1990, May 4 Photo. *Perf. 11½*

Granite Paper

101 A253 4.50s Bixa orellana 1.25 1.40
102 A253 9.50s Momordica charantia 2.50 2.75

UN 45th Anniv. Type

Designs: 7s, 9s, "45" and emblem.

1990, June 26 Litho. *Perf. 14½x13*

103 A254 7s multicolored 1.40 1.60
104 A254 9s multicolored, diff. 2.40 2.75

Souvenir Sheet

105 Sheet of 2, #103-104 5.00 5.50

Crime Prevention Type

1990, Sept. 13 Photo. *Perf. 14*

106 A255 6s Domestic violence 1.00 1.10
107 A255 8s Crimes against cultural heritage 2.25 2.50

Human Rights Type of 1989

Paintings: 4.50s, Before the Judge, by Sandor Bihari. 7s, Young Man Greeted by a Woman Writing a Poem, by Suzuki Harunobu.

1990, Nov. 16 Litho. *Perf. 13½*

108 A250 4.50s multicolored .30 .35
109 A250 7s multicolored .90 1.00

Economic Commission for Europe Type

1991, Mar. 15 Litho. *Perf. 14*

110 A256 5s Weasel, hoopoe 1.40 1.60
111 A256 5s Warbler, swans 1.40 1.60
112 A256 5s Badgers, squirrel 1.40 1.60
113 A256 5s Fish 1.40 1.60
a. Block of 4, #110-113 5.60 6.50

Namibian Independence Type

1991, May 10 Litho. *Perf. 14*

114 A257 6s Mountains, clouds 1.00 1.25
115 A257 9.50s Dune, Namib Desert 2.25 2.50

V24

1991, May 10 Litho. *Perf. 15x14½*

116 V24 20s multicolored 1.75 2.00

V25

Rights of the Child — V26

1991, June 14 Litho. *Perf. 14½*

117 V25 7s Stick drawings 1.00 1.25
118 V26 9s Child, clock, fruit 1.50 1.75

V27

Banning of Chemical Weapons — V28

1991, Sept. 11 Litho. *Perf. 13½*

119 V27 5s multicolored .75 .90
120 V28 10s multicolored 1.75 2.00

UN Postal Administration, 40th Anniv. Type

1991, Oct. 24 Litho. *Perf. 14x15*

121 A263 5s UN NY No. 8 .75 .90
122 A263 8s UN NY No. 5 1.50 1.75

Human Rights Type of 1989

Artwork: 4.50s, Pre-columbian Mexican pottery. 7s, Windows, by Robert Delaunay.

1991, Nov. 20 Litho. *Perf. 13½*

123 A250 4.50s black & brown .50 .55
124 A250 7s multicolored .80 .90

World Heritage Type of 1984

Designs: 5s, Iguacu Natl. Park, Brazil. 9s, Abu Simbel, Egypt.

1992, Jan. 24 Litho. *Perf. 13*

Size: 35x28mm

125 V10 5s multicolored .75 .90
126 V10 9s multicolored 1.60 1.80

Clean Oceans Type

1992, Mar. 13 Litho. *Perf. 14*

127 A264 7s Ocean surface, diff. 1.00 1.10
128 A264 7s Ocean bottom, diff. 1.00 1.10
a. Pair, #127-128 2.25 2.50

Earth Summit Type

1992, May 22 Photo. *Perf. 11½*

129 A265 5.50s Man in space 1.30 1.50
130 A265 5.50s Sun 1.30 1.50
131 A265 5.50s Man fishing 1.30 1.50
132 A265 5.50s Sailboat 1.30 1.50
a. Block of 4, #129-132 5.50 6.00

Mission to Planet Earth Type

Designs: No. 133, Satellite, person's mouth. No. 134, Satellite, person's ear.

1992, Sept. 4 Photo. *Rouletted 8*

Granite Paper

133 A266 10s multicolored 3.00 3.25
134 A266 10s multicolored 3.00 3.25
a. Pair, #133-134 6.00 6.50

Science and Technology Type of 1992

Designs: 5.50s, Woman emerging from computer screen. 7s, Green thumb growing flowers.

1992, Oct. 2 Litho. *Perf. 14*

135 A267 5.50s multicolored .75 .85
136 A267 7s multicolored 1.40 1.60

V29

Intl. Center, Vienna — V30

1992, Oct. 2 Litho. *Perf. 13x13½*

137 V29 5.50s multicolored .90 1.00

Perf. 13½x13

138 V30 7s multicolored 1.25 1.40

Human Rights Type of 1989

Artwork: 6s, Les Constructeurs, by Fernand Leger. 10s, Sunday Afternoon on the Island of Le Grande Jatte, by Georges Seurat.

1992, Nov. 20 Litho. *Perf. 13½*

139 A250 6s multicolored .75 .85
140 A250 10s multicolored 1.25 1.40

Aging With Dignity Type

Designs: 5.50s, Elderly couple, family working in garden. 7s, Older woman teaching.

1993, Feb. 5 Litho. *Perf. 13*

141 A270 5.50s multicolored .75 .85
142 A270 7s multicolored 1.40 1.60

Endangered Species Type

Designs: No. 143, Equus grevyi (Grevy's zebra). No. 144, Spheniscus humboldti (Humboldt's penguins). No. 145, Varanus griseus (desert monitor). No. 146, Canis lupus (gray wolf).

1993, Mar. 2 Litho. *Perf. 13x12½*

143 A271 7s multicolored .90 1.00
144 A271 7s multicolored .90 1.00
145 A271 7s multicolored .90 1.00
146 A271 7s multicolored .90 1.00
a. Block of 4, #143-146 3.60 4.00

Healthy Environment Type

1993, May 7 Litho. *Perf. 15x14½*

147 A272 6s Wave in ocean 1.25 1.40
148 A272 10s Globe 2.00 2.25

V31

1993, May 7 Photo. *Perf. 11½*

Granite Paper

149 V31 13s multicolored 2.00 2.25

Human Rights Type of 1989

Artwork: 5s, Lower Austrian Peasants' Wedding, by Ferdinand G. Waldmuller. 6s, Outback, by Sally Morgan.

1993, June 11 Litho. *Perf. 13½*

150 A250 5s multicolored .80 .90
151 A250 6s multicolored 1.00 1.10

Intl. Peace Day Type

Denomination at: No. 152, UL. No. 153, UR. No. 154, LL. No. 155, LR.

Rouletted 12½

1993, Sept. 21 Litho. & Engr.

152 A274 5.50s green & multi 1.80 2.00
153 A274 5.50s green & multi 1.80 2.00
154 A274 5.50s green & multi 1.80 2.00
155 A274 5.50s green & multi 1.80 2.00
a. Block of 4, #152-155 7.25 8.25

Environment-Climate Type

Designs: No. 156, Monkeys. No. 157, Bluebird, industrial pollution, volcano. No. 158, Volcano, nuclear power plant, tree stumps. No. 159, Cactus, tree stumps, owl.

1993, Oct. 29 Litho. *Perf. 14½*

156 A275 7s multicolored 2.50 2.75
157 A275 7s multicolored 2.50 2.75
158 A275 7s multicolored 2.50 2.75
159 A275 7s multicolored 2.50 2.75
a. Strip of 4, #156-159 10.00 11.00

Intl. Year of the Family Type of 1993

Designs: 5.50s, Adults, children holding hands. 8s, Two adults, child planting crops.

1994, Feb. 4 Litho. *Perf. 13.1*

160 A276 5.50s blue green & multi 1.00 1.10
161 A276 8s red & multi 1.25 1.40

Endangered Species Type of 1993

Designs: No. 162, Ocelot. No. 163, White-breasted silver-eye. No. 164, Mediterranean monk seal. No. 165, Asian elephant.

1994, Mar. 18 Litho. *Perf. 12.7*

162 A271 7s multicolored 1.00 1.10
163 A271 7s multicolored 1.00 1.10
164 A271 7s multicolored 1.00 1.10
165 A271 7s multicolored 1.00 1.10
a. Block of 4, #162-165 4.00 4.40

Protection for Refugees Type

Design: 12s, Protective hands surround group of refugees.

1994, Apr. 29 Litho. *Perf. 14.3x14.8*
166 A277 12s multicolored 1.50 1.75

V32

V33

V34

1994, Apr. 29 Litho. *Perf. 12.9*
167 V32 50g multicolored .25 .30
168 V33 4s multicolored .40 .45
169 V34 30s multicolored 4.00 4.50
Nos. 167-169 (3) 4.65 5.25

Intl. Decade for Natural Disaster Reduction Type

Earth seen from space, outline map of: No. 170, North America. No. 171, Eurasia. No. 172, South America. No. 173, Australia and South Asia.

1994, May 27 Litho. *Perf. 13.9x14.2*
170 A281 6s multicolored 1.75 1.90
171 A281 6s multicolored 1.75 1.90
172 A281 6s multicolored 1.75 1.90
173 A281 6s multicolored 1.75 1.90
a. Block of 4, #170-173 7.00 7.75

Population and Development Type

Designs: 5.50s, Women teaching, running machine tool, coming home to family. 7s, Family on tropical island.

1994, Sept. 1 Litho. *Perf. 13.2x13.6*
174 A282 5.50s multicolored .90 1.00
175 A282 7s multicolored 1.50 1.75

UNCTAD Type

1994, Oct. 28
176 A283 6s multi, diff. .90 1.00
177 A283 7s multi, diff. 1.50 1.75

UN 50th Anniv. Type

Litho. & Engr.

1995, Jan. 1 *Perf. 13.4*
178 A284 7s multicolored 1.25 1.40

Social Summit Type

Photo. & Engr.

1995, Feb. 3 *Perf. 13.6x13.9*
179 A285 14s multi, diff. 2.00 2.25

Endangered Species Type of 1993

Designs: No. 180, Black rhinoceros, Diceros bicornis. No. 181, Golden conure, Aratinga guarouba. No. 182, Douc langur, Pygathrix nemaeus. No. 183, Arabian oryx, Oryx leucoryx.

1995, Mar. 24 Litho. *Perf. 13x12½*
180 A271 7s multicolored 1.00 1.10
181 A271 7s multicolored 1.00 1.10
182 A271 7s multicolored 1.00 1.10
183 A271 7s multicolored 1.00 1.10
a. Block of 4, 180-183 4.00 4.50

Intl. Youth Year Type

Designs: 6s, Village in winter. 7s, Teepees.

1995, May 26 Litho. *Perf. 14.4x14.7*
184 A286 6s multicolored .80 .90
185 A286 7s multicolored 1.00 1.10

UN, 50th Anniv. Type

Designs: 7s, Like No. 663. 10s, Like No. 664.

Perf. 13.3x13.6

1995, June 26 Engr.
186 A287 7s green 1.20 1.30
187 A287 10s black 1.75 1.90

Souvenir Sheet

Litho. & Engr.

Imperf

188 Sheet of 2, #186-187 2.75 3.10
a. A287 7s green 1.10 1.25
b. A287 10s black 1.60 1.80

Conference on Women Type

Designs: 5.50s, Women amid tropical plants. 6s, Woman reading, swans on lake.

1995, Sept. 5 Photo. *Perf. 12*
189 A288 5.50s multicolored .80 .90

Size: 28x50mm

190 A288 6s multicolored 1.20 1.30

UN People, 50th Anniv. Type

1995, Oct. 24 Litho. *Perf. 14*
191 Sheet of 12 9.00 10.00
a.-l. A290 3s any single .75 .85
192 Souvenir booklet 9.00
a. A290 3s Booklet pane of 3, vert. strip of 3 from UL of sheet 2.25 2.75
b. A290 3s Booklet pane of 3, vert. strip of 3 from UR of sheet 2.25 2.75
c. A290 3s Booklet pane of 3, vert. strip of 3 from LL of sheet 2.25 2.75
d. A290 3s Booklet pane of 3, vert. strip of 3 from LR of sheet 2.25 2.75

WFUNA, 50th Anniv. Type

Design: 7s, Harlequin holding dove.

1996, Feb. 2 Litho. *Perf. 13x13½*
193 A291 7s multicolored 1.00 1.10

UN Flag V35

Abstract, by Karl Korab V36

1996, Feb. 2 Litho. *Perf. 15x14½*
194 V35 1s multicolored .25 .30
195 V36 10s multicolored 1.60 1.75

Endangered Species Type of 1993

Designs: No. 196, Cypripedium calceolus. No. 197, Aztekium ritteri. No. 198, Euphorbia cremersii. No. 199, Dracula bella.

1996, Mar. 14 Litho. *Perf. 12½*
196 A271 7s multicolored .75 .85
197 A271 7s multicolored .75 .85
198 A271 7s multicolored .75 .85
199 A271 7s multicolored .75 .85
a. Block of 4, #196-199 3.00 3.40

City Summit Type

Designs: No. 200, Arab family selling fruits, vegetables. No. 201, Women beside stream, camels. No. 202, Woman carrying bundle on head, city skyline. No. 203, Woman threshing grain, yoke of oxen in field. No. 204, Native village, elephant.

1996, June 3 Litho. *Perf. 14x13½*
200 A293 6s multicolored 1.50 1.75
201 A293 6s multicolored 1.50 1.75
202 A293 6s multicolored 1.50 1.75
203 A293 6s multicolored 1.50 1.75
204 A293 6s multicolored 1.50 1.75
a. Strip of 5, #200-204 7.50 9.00

Sport and the Environment Type

6s, Men's parallel bars (gymnastics), vert. 7s, Hurdles.

Perf. 14x14½, 14½x14

1996, July 19 Litho.
205 A294 6s multicolored .80 .90
206 A294 7s multicolored .90 1.00

Souvenir Sheet

207 A294 Sheet of 2, #205-206 1.75 1.90

Plea for Peace Type

Designs: 7s, Dove and butterflies. 10s, Stylized dove, diff.

1996, Sept. 17 Litho. *Perf. 14½x15*
208 A295 7s multicolored .80 .90
209 A295 10s multicolored 1.20 1.40

UNICEF Type

Fairy Tales: 5.50s, Hansel and Gretel, by the Brothers Grimm. 8s, How Maui Stole Fire from the Gods, South Pacific.

1996, Nov. 20 Litho. *Perf. 14½x15*
210 A296 5.50s multicolored .90 1.00
211 A296 8s multicolored 1.40 1.60

V37

Phoenixes Flying Down (Detail), by Sagenji Yoshida — V38

1997, Feb. 12 Litho. *Perf. 14½*
212 V37 5s multicolored .80 .90
213 V38 6s multicolored .90 1.00

Endangered Species Type of 1993

Designs: No. 214, Macaca sylvanus (Barbary macaque). No. 215, Anthropoides paradisea (blue crane). No. 216, Equus przewalskii (Przewalski horse). No. 217, Myrmecophaga tridactyla (giant anteater).

1997, Mar. 13 Litho. *Perf. 12½*
214 A271 7s multicolored .75 .85
215 A271 7s multicolored .75 .85
216 A271 7s multicolored .75 .85
217 A271 7s multicolored .75 .85
a. Block of 4, #214-217 3.00 3.40

Earth Summit Anniv. Type

Designs: No. 218, Person running. No. 219, Hills, stream, trees. No. 220, Tree with orange leaves. No. 221, Tree with pink leaves.

11s, Combined design similar to Nos. 218-221.

1997, May 30 Photo. *Perf. 11.5*

Granite Paper

218 A299 3.50s multicolored 1.50 1.75
219 A299 3.50s multicolored 1.50 1.75
220 A299 3.50s multicolored 1.50 1.75
221 A299 3.50s multicolored 1.50 1.75
a. Block of 4, #218-221 6.00 7.00

Souvenir Sheet

222 A299 11s multicolored 2.40 2.60

Transportation Type

Ground transportation: No. 223, 1829 Rocket, 1901 Darraque. No. 224, Steam engine from Vladikawska Railway, trolley. No. 225, Double-decker bus. No. 226, 1950s diesel locomotive, semi-trailer. No. 227, High-speed train, electric car.

1997, Aug. 29 Litho. *Perf. 14x14½*
223 A300 7s multicolored 1.25 1.40
224 A300 7s multicolored 1.25 1.40
225 A300 7s multicolored 1.25 1.40
226 A300 7s multicolored 1.25 1.40
227 A300 7s multicolored 1.25 1.40
a. Strip of 5, #223-227 6.25 7.00

No. 227a has continuous design.

Philately Type

Designs: 6.50s, No. 62. 7s, No. 63.

1997, Oct. 14 Litho. *Perf. 13½x14*
228 A301 6.50s multicolored .80 .90
229 A301 7s multicolored .90 1.00

World Heritage Convention Type

Terracotta warriors of Xian: 3s, Single warrior. 6s, Massed warriors. No. 232a, like No. 716. No. 232b, like No. 717. No. 232c, like Geneva No. 314. No. 232d, like Geneva No. 315. No. 232e, like Vienna No. 230. No. 232f, like Vienna No. 231.

1997, Nov. 19 Litho. *Perf. 13½*
230 A302 3s multicolored 1.00 1.10
231 A302 6s multicolored 2.00 2.25
232 Souvenir booklet 12.00
a.-f. A302 1s any single .50 .55
g. Booklet pane of 4 #232a 2.00 2.25
h. Booklet pane of 4 #232b 2.00 2.25
i. Booklet pane of 4 #232c 2.00 2.25
j. Booklet pane of 4 #232d 2.00 2.25
k. Booklet pane of 4 #232e 2.00 2.25
l. Booklet pane of 4 #232f 2.00 2.25

Japanese Peace Bell, Vienna V39

Vienna Subway, Vienna Intl. Center V40

1998, Feb. 13 Litho. *Perf. 15x14½*
233 V39 6.50s multicolored .80 .90
234 V40 9s multicolored 1.00 1.10

Endangered Species Type of 1993

Designs: No. 235, Chelonia mydas (green turtle). No. 236, Speotyto cunicularia (burrowing owl). No. 237, Trogonoptera brookiana (Rajah Brooke's birdwing). No. 238, Ailurus fulgens (lesser panda).

1998, Mar. 13 Litho. *Perf. 12½*
235 A271 7s multicolored .75 .85
236 A271 7s multicolored .75 .85
237 A271 7s multicolored .75 .85
238 A271 7s multicolored .75 .85
a. Block of 4, #235-238 3.00 3.40

Intl. Year of the Ocean V41

1998, May 20 Litho. *Perf. 13x13½*
239 V41 Sheet of 12 9.50 10.75
a.-l. 3.50s any single .80 .90

Rain Forests Type

1998, June 19 *Perf. 13x13½*
240 A307 6.50s Ocelot .90 1.00

Souvenir Sheet

241 A307 22s like #240 3.00 3.25

Peacekeeping Type of 1998

Designs: 4s, Soldier passing out relief supplies. 7.50s, UN supervised voting.

1998, Sept. 15 Photo. *Perf. 12*
242 A308 4s multicolored .50 .60
243 A308 7.50s multicolored 1.00 1.10

Declaration of Human Rights Type

Designs: 4.50s, Stylized person. 7s, Gears.

Litho. & Photo.

1998, Oct. 27 *Perf. 13*
244 A309 4.50s multicolored .80 .90
245 A309 7s multicolored 1.25 1.40

Schönbrunn Palace Type

Designs: 3.50s, No. 248d, Palace. 7s, No. 248c, Porcelain stove, vert. No. 248a, Blue porcelain vase, vert. No. 248b, Wall painting on fabric (detail), by Johann Wenzl Bergl, vert. No. 248e, Great Palm House (conservatory). No. 248f, The Gloriette (archway).

1998, Dec. 4 Litho. *Perf. 14*
246 A310 3.50s multicolored .60 .70
247 A310 7s multicolored 1.10 1.25

Souvenir Booklet

248 Booklet 20.00
a.-c. A310 1s any single .60 .70
d.-f. A310 2s any single 1.20 1.30
g. Booklet pane of 4 #248d 4.80 5.25
h. Booklet pane of 3 #248a 1.80 2.00
i. Booklet pane of 3 #248b 1.80 2.00
j. Booklet pane of 3 #248c 1.80 2.00
k. Booklet pane of 4 #248e 4.80 5.25
l. Booklet pane of 4 #248f 4.80 5.25

Volcanic Landscape — V42

1999, Feb. 5 Litho. *Perf. 13x13½*
249 V42 8s multicolored 1.25 1.40

World Heritage, Australia Type

Designs: 4.50s, No. 252d, Uluru-Kata Tjuta Natl. Park. 6.50s, No. 252a, Tasmanian Wilderness. No. 252b, Wet tropics of Queensland. No. 252c, Great Barrier Reef. No. 252e, Kakadu Natl. Park. No. 252f, Willandra Lakes region.

1999, Mar. 19 Litho. *Perf. 13*
250 A313 4.50s multicolored .75 .85
251 A313 6.50s multicolored 1.10 1.25

Souvenir Booklet

252 Booklet 12.00
a.-c. A313 1s any single .35 .40
d.-f. A313 2s any single .65 .70
g. Booklet pane of 4, #252a 1.40 1.60
h. Booklet pane of 4, #252d 2.60 2.80
i. Booklet pane of 4, #252b 1.40 1.60
j. Booklet pane of 4, #252e 2.60 2.80
k. Booklet pane of 4, #252c 1.40 1.60
l. Booklet pane of 4, #252f 2.60 2.80

Endangered Species Type of 1993

Designs: No. 253, Pongo pygmaeus (orangutan). No. 254, Pelecanus crispus (Dalmatian pelican). No. 255, Eunectes notaeus (yellow anaconda). No. 256, Caracal.

1999, Apr. 22 Litho. *Perf. 12½*
253 A271 7s multicolored .75 .85
254 A271 7s multicolored .75 .85
255 A271 7s multicolored .75 .85
256 A271 7s multicolored .75 .85
a. Block of 4, #253-256 3.00 3.40

UNISPACE III Type

Designs: No. 257, Satellite over ships. No. 258, Satellite up close. No. 259, Composite of Nos. 257-258.

1999, July 7 Photo. *Rouletted 8*
257 A314 3.50s multicolored .75 .85
258 A314 3.50s multicolored .75 .85
a. Pair, #257-258 1.60 1.70

Souvenir Sheet

Perf. 14½

259 A314 13s multicolored 4.50 5.00

UPU Type

Various people, late 20th century methods of mail transportation, denomination at: No. 260, UL. No. 261, UR. No. 262, LL. No. 263, LR.

1999, Aug. 23 Photo. *Perf. 11¾*
260 A315 6.50s multicolored 1.00 1.10
261 A315 6.50s multicolored 1.00 1.10
262 A315 6.50s multicolored 1.00 1.10
263 A315 6.50s multicolored 1.00 1.10
a. Block of 4, #260-263 4.00 4.50

In Memoriam Type

Designs: 6.50s, 14s, Donaupark. Size of 14s stamp: 34x63mm.

1999, Sept. 21 Litho. *Perf. 14½x14*
264 A316 6.50s multicolored .90 1.00

Souvenir Sheet

Perf. 14

265 A316 14s multicolored 3.00 3.25

Education Type

Perf. 13½x13¾

1999, Nov. 18 Litho.
266 A317 7s Boy, girl, book .75 .85
267 A317 13s Group reading 1.75 1.90

Intl. Year of Thanksgiving Type

2000, Jan. 1 Litho. *Perf. 13¼x13½*
268 A318 7s multicolored .80 .90

On No. 268 parts of the design were applied by a thermographic process producing a shiny, raised effect.

Endangered Species Type of 1993

Designs: No. 269, Panthera pardus (leopard). No. 270, Platalea leucorodia (white spoonbill). No. 271, Hippocamelus bisulcus (huemal). No. 272, Orcinus orca (killer whale).

2000, Apr. 6 Litho. *Perf. 12¾x12½*
269 A271 7s multicolored 1.10 1.25
270 A271 7s multicolored 1.10 1.25
271 A271 7s multicolored 1.10 1.25
272 A271 7s multicolored 1.10 1.25
a. Block of 4, #269-272 4.50 5.00

Our World 2000 Type

Winning artwork in Millennium painting competition: 7s, Tomorrow's Dream, by Voltaire Perez, Philippines. 8s, Remembrance, by Dimitris Nalbandis, Greece, vert.

Perf. 13x13½, 13½x13

2000, May 30 Litho.
273 A319 7s multicolored .60 .70
274 A319 8s multicolored .75 .85

55th Anniversary Type

Designs: 7s, Secretariat Building, unfinished dome of General Assembly Hall, 1951. 9s, Trygve Lie and Headquraters Advisory Committee at topping-out ceremony, 1949.

2000, July 7 Litho. *Perf. 13¼x13*
275 A320 7s multicolored .90 1.00
276 A320 9s multicolored 1.25 1.40

Souvenir Sheet

277 A320 Sheet of 2, #275-276 2.75 3.25

The UN in the 21st Century V43

No. 278: a, Farm machinery. b, UN Peacekeepers and children. c, Oriental farm workers. d, Peacekeepers searching for mines. e, Medical research. f, Handicapped people.

2000, Sept. 15 Litho. *Perf. 14*
278 V43 Sheet of 6 7.50 8.50
a.-f. 3.50s any single 1.25 1.40

World Heritage, Spain Type

Designs: Nos. 279, 281c, Aqueduct of Segovia. Nos. 280, 281f, Güell Park, Barcelona. No. 281a, Alhambra, Generalife and Albayzin, Granada. No. 281b, Walled Town of Cuenca. No. 281d, Amphitheater of Mérida. No. 281e, Toledo.

2000, Oct. 6 Litho. *Perf. 14¾x14½*
279 A323 4.50s multicolored .80 .90
280 A323 6.50s multicolored 1.20 1.40

Souvenir Booklet

281 Booklet 9.00
a.-c. A323 1s any single .25 .30
d.-f. A323 2s any single .50 .55
g. Booklet pane of 4, #281a 1.00 1.10
h. Booklet pane of 4, #281d 2.00 2.25
i. Booklet pane of 4, #281b 1.00 1.10
j. Booklet pane of 4, #281e 2.00 2.25
k. Booklet pane of 4, #281c 1.00 1.10
l. Booklet pane of 4, #281f 2.00 2.25

Respect for Refugees Type

Designs: 7s, 25s, Refugee with hat, three other refugees.

2000, Nov. 9 Litho. *Perf. 13¼x12¾*
282 A324 7s multicolored 1.10 1.25

Souvenir Sheet

283 A324 25s multicolored 3.75 4.25

Endangered Species Type of 1993

Designs: No. 284, Tremarctos ornatus (spectacled bear). No. 285, Anas laysanensis (Laysan duck). No. 286, Proteles cristatus (aardwolf). No. 287, Trachypithecus cristatus (silvered leaf monkey).

2001, Feb. 1 Litho. *Perf. 12¾x12½*
284 A271 7s multicolored 1.10 1.25
285 A271 7s multicolored 1.10 1.25
286 A271 7s multicolored 1.10 1.25
287 A271 7s multicolored 1.10 1.25
a. Block of 4, #284-287 4.50 5.00

Intl. Volunteers Year — V44

Paintings by: 10s, Nguyen Thanh Chuong, Viet Nam. 12s, Ikko Tanaka, Japan.

2001, Mar. 29 Litho. *Perf. 13¼*
288 V44 10s multicolored 1.40 1.60
289 V44 12s multicolored 1.75 1.90

World Heritage, Japan Type

Designs: 7s, No. 290c, Himeji-Jo. 15s, No. 291f, Nikko. No. 292a, Kyoto. No. 292b, Nara. No. 292d, Shirakawa-Go and Gokayama. No. 292e, Itsukushima Shinto Shrine.

2001, Aug. 1 Litho. *Perf. 12¾x13¼*
290 A328 7s multicolored 1.00 1.10
291 A328 15s multicolored 2.10 2.25

Souvenir Booklet

292 Booklet 11.50
a.-c. A328 1s any single .30 .35
d.-f. A328 2s any single .60 .70
g. Booklet pane of 4, #292a 1.20 1.40
h. Booklet pane of 4, #292d 2.40 2.75
i. Booklet pane of 4, #292b 1.20 1.40
j. Booklet pane of 4, #292e 2.40 2.75
k. Booklet pane of 4, #292c 1.20 1.40
l. Booklet pane of 4, #292f 2.40 2.75

Dag Hammarskjöld Type

2001, Sept. 18 Engr. *Perf. 11x11¼*
293 A329 7s green 1.00 1.10

UN Postal Administration, 50th Anniv. Types

2001, Oct. 18 Litho. *Perf. 13½*
294 A330 7s Stamps, balloons 1.00 1.10
295 A330 8s Stamps, cake 1.10 1.25

Souvenir Sheet

296 A331 Sheet of 2 7.50 8.00
a. 7s green & light blue, 38mm diameter 2.50 2.75
b. 21s green & light blue, 38mm diameter 5.00 5.50

Climate Change Type

Designs: No. 297, Solar panels, automobile at pump. No. 298, Blimp, bicyclists, horse and rider. No. 299, Balloon, sailboat, lighthouse, train. No. 300, Bird, train, traffic signs.

2001, Nov. 16 Litho. *Perf. 13¼*
297 A332 7s multicolored 1.00 1.10
298 A332 7s multicolored 1.00 1.10
299 A332 7s multicolored 1.00 1.10
300 A332 7s multicolored 1.00 1.10
a. Horiz. strip, #297-300 5.00 5.50

Nobel Peace Prize Type

2001, Dec. 10 Litho. *Perf. 13¼*
301 A333 7s multicolored 1.00 .55

100 Cents = 1 Euro (€)

Austrian Tourist Attractions — V45

Designs: 7c, Semmering Railway. 51c, Pferdschwemme, Salzburg. 58c, Aggstein an der Donau Ruins. 73c, Hallstatt. 87c, Melk Abbey. €2.03, Kapitelschwemme, Salzburg.

2002, Mar. 1 Litho. *Perf. 14½x14*
302 V45 7c multicolored .25 .30
303 V45 51c multicolored .90 1.25
304 V45 58c multicolored 1.00 1.10
305 V45 73c multicolored 1.25 1.40
306 V45 87c multicolored 1.75 2.00
307 V45 €2.03 multicolored 3.50 3.75
Nos. 302-307 (6) 8.65 9.80

Endangered Species Type of 1993

Designs: No. 308, Hylobates syndactylus (siamang). No. 309, Spheniscus demersus (jackass penguin). No. 310, Prionodon linsang (banded linsang). No. 311, Bufo retiformis (Sonoran green toad).

2002, Apr. 4 Litho. *Perf. 12¾x12½*
308 A271 51c multicolored 1.25 1.25
309 A271 51c multicolored 1.25 1.25
310 A271 51c multicolored 1.25 1.25
311 A271 51c multicolored 1.25 1.25
a. Block of 4, #308-311 5.00 5.00

Independence of East Timor Type

Designs: 51c, Deer horn container with carved wooden stopper. €1.09, Carved wooden tai weaving loom.

2002, May 20 Litho. *Perf. 14x14½*
312 A335 51c multicolored 1.00 1.00
313 A335 €1.09 multicolored 2.25 2.25

Intl. Year of Mountains Type

Designs: No. 314, Mt. Cook, New Zealand. No. 315, Mt. Robson, Canada. No. 316, Mt. Rakaposhi, Pakistan. No. 317, Mt. Everest (Sagarmatha), Nepal.

2002, May 24 Litho. *Perf. 13x13¼*
314 A336 22c multicolored .40 .40
315 A336 22c multicolored .40 .40
316 A336 51c multicolored 1.00 1.00
317 A336 51c multicolored 1.00 1.00
a. Vert. strip or block of four, #314-317 12.50 12.50

World Summit on Sustainable Development (Peter Max) Type

Designs: No. 318, Rainbow. No. 319, Three women, diff. No. 320, Three faceless people. No. 321, Birds, wave.

2002, June 27 Litho. *Perf. 14½x14*
318 A337 51c multicolored 1.00 1.00
319 A337 51c multicolored 1.00 1.00
320 A337 58c multicolored 1.25 1.25
321 A337 58c multicolored 1.25 1.25
a. Vert. strip or block of four, #318-321 10.00 8.50

World Heritage, Italy Type

Designs: 51c, No. 324f, Pompeii. 58c, No. 324c, Rome. No. 324a, Amalfi Coast. No. 324b, Aeolian Islands. No. 324d, Florence. No. 324e, Pisa.

Perf. 13½x13¼

2002, Aug. 30 Litho.
322 A338 51c multicolored 1.10 1.10
323 A338 58c multicolored 1.25 1.25

Souvenir Booklet

324 Booklet 15.00
a.-c. A338 7c any single .40 .40
d.-f. A338 15c any single .85 .85
g. Booklet pane of 4, #324d 3.40 3.40
h. Booklet pane of 4, #324a 1.60 1.60
i. Booklet pane of 4, #324e 3.40 3.40
j. Booklet pane of 4, #324b 1.60 1.60
k. Booklet pane of 4, #324f 3.40 3.40
l. Booklet pane of 4, #324c 1.60 1.60

AIDS Awareness Type

2002, Oct. 24 Litho. *Perf. 13½*
325 A339 €1.53 multicolored 2.50 2.75

Indigenous Art — V46

No. 326: a, Mola, Panama. b, Mochican llama-shaped spouted vessel, Peru. c, Tarabuco woven cloth, Bolivia. d, Masks, Cuba. e, Aztec priest's feather headdress, Mexico. f, Bird-shaped staff head, Colombia.

2003, Jan. 31 Litho. *Perf. 14¼*
326 V46 Sheet of 6 7.50 7.50
a.-f. 51c Any single 1.25 1.25

Austrian Tourist Attractions Type of 2002

Designs: 25c, Kunsthistorisches Museum, Vienna. €1, Belvedere Palace, Vienna.

2003, Mar. 28 Litho. *Perf. 14½x14*
327 V45 25c multicolored .55 .55
328 V45 €1 multicolored 2.25 2.25

Endangered Species Type of 1993

Designs: No. 329, Anas formosa (Baikal teal). No. 330, Bostrychia hagedash (Hadada ibis). No. 331, Ramphastos toco (toco toucan). No. 332, Alopochen aegyptiacus (Egyptian goose).

2003, Apr. 3 Litho. *Perf. 12¾x12½*
329 A271 51c multicolored 1.25 1.25
330 A271 51c multicolored 1.25 1.25
331 A271 51c multicolored 1.25 1.25
332 A271 51c multicolored 1.25 1.25
a. Block of 4, #329-332 5.00 5.00

International Year of Freshwater Type of 2003

Perf. 14¼x14½

2003, June 20 **Litho.**
333 A345 55c Bridge, bird 3.00 3.00
334 A345 75c Horse, empty river 5.00 5.00
a. Horiz. pair, #333-334 8.00 8.00

Austrian Tourist Attractions Type of 2002

Design: 4c, Schloss Eggenberg, Graz.

2003, Aug. 7 **Litho.** ***Perf. 14x13¼***
335 V45 4c multicolored .45 .45

Ralph Bunche Type
Litho. With Foil Application

2003, Aug. 7 ***Perf. 13½x14***
336 A346 €2.10 olive green & multicolored 3.50 3.50

In Memoriam Type of 2003

2003, Oct. 24 **Litho.** ***Perf. 13¼x13***
337 A347 €2.10 multicolored 5.00 5.00

World Heritage Sites, United States Type

Designs: 55c, No. 340c, Olympic National Park. 75c, No. 340e, Everglades National Park. No. 340a, Yosemite National Park. No. 340b, Great Smoky Mountains National Park. No. 340d, Hawaii Volcanoes National Park. No. 340f, Yellowstone National Park.

2003, Oct. 24 **Litho.** ***Perf. 14½x14¼***
338 A348 55c multicolored 1.50 .75
339 A348 75c multicolored 2.00 1.00

Souvenir Booklet

340 Booklet 14.50
a.-c. A348 15c any single .55 .55
d.-f. A348 20c any single .65 .65
g. Booklet pane of 4 #340a 2.10 2.10
h. Booklet pane of 4 #340d 2.60 2.60
i. Booklet pane of 4 #340b 2.10 2.10
j. Booklet pane of 4 #340e 2.60 2.60
k. Booklet pane of 4 #340c 2.10 2.10
l. Booklet pane of 4 #340f 2.60 2.60

Austrian Tourist Attractions Type of 2002

Design: 55c, Schloss Schönbrunn, Vienna.

2004, Jan. 29 **Litho.** ***Perf. 13x13¼***
341 V45 55c multicolored 1.50 1.50

Endangered Species Type of 1993

Designs: No. 342, Melursus ursinus (Sloth bear). No. 343, Cervus eldi (Eld's deer). No. 344, Cercocebus torquatus (Cherry-crowned mangabey). No. 345, Bubalus arnee (Wild water buffalo).

2004, Jan. 29 **Litho.** ***Perf. 12¾x12½***
342 A271 55c multicolored 1.50 1.50
343 A271 55c multicolored 1.50 1.50
344 A271 55c multicolored 1.50 1.50
345 A271 55c multicolored 1.50 1.50
a. Block of 4, #342-345 6.00 6.00

Indigenous Art Type of 2003

No. 346: a, Illuminated illustration from the Book of Kells, Ireland. b, Easter eggs, Ukraine. c, Venus of Willendorf, Paleolithic age limestone statue, Austria. d, Flatatunga panel, Iceland. e, Neolithic era idol, Hungary. f, Illuminated illustration from medical treatise, Portugal.

2004, Mar. 4 **Litho.** ***Perf. 13¼***
346 V46 Sheet of 6 12.00 12.00
a.-f. 55c Any single 2.00 2.00

Road Safety Type

Road map art with: 55c, Automobile, alcohol bottles. 75c, Road, clouds in traffic light colors, vert.

Perf. 13x13¼, 13¼x13

2004, Apr. 7 **Litho.**
347 A354 55c multicolored 1.25 1.25
348 A354 75c multicolored 1.75 1.75

Japanese Peace Bell, 50th Anniv. Type
Litho. & Engr.

2004, June 3 ***Perf. 13¼x13***
349 A355 €2.10 multicolored 4.50 4.50

World Heritage Sites, Greece Type

Designs: 55c, No. 352f, Mycenae and Tiryns. 75c, No. 352e, Olympia. No. 352a, Acropolis, Athens. No. 352b, Delos. No. 352c, Delphi. No. 352d, Pythagoreion and Heraion of Samos.

2004, Aug. 12 **Litho.** ***Perf. 14x13¼***
350 A356 55c multicolored 1.75 1.75
351 A356 75c multicolored 2.25 2.25

Souvenir Booklet

352 Booklet 16.00
a.-d. A356 25c any single .60 .60
e.-f. A356 30c either single .70 .70
g. Booklet pane of 4 #352a 2.40 2.40
h. Booklet pane of 4 #352b 2.40 2.40
i. Booklet pane of 4 #352c 2.40 2.40
j. Booklet pane of 4 #352d 2.40 2.40
k. Booklet pane of 4 #352e 2.80 2.80
l. Booklet pane of 4 #352f 2.80 2.80

My Dream for Peace Type

Winning designs of Lions Club International children's global peace poster contest by: 55c, Henry Ulfe Renteria, Peru. €1, Michelle Fortaliza, Philippines.

2004, Sept. 21 **Litho.** ***Perf. 14***
353 A357 55c multicolored 1.40 1.40
354 A357 €1 multicolored 2.50 2.50

V47

Human Rights — V48

2004, Oct. 14 **Litho.** ***Perf. 11¼***
355 V47 55c multicolored 1.00 1.00
356 V48 €1.25 multicolored 3.00 3.00

United Nations, 60th Anniv. Type of 2005
Litho. & Engr.

2005, Feb. 4 ***Perf. 11x11¼***
357 A361 55c multicolored 2.50 2.50

Souvenir Sheet
Litho.
Imperf

358 A361 €2.10 multicolored 6.50 6.50

International Center, Vienna V49

Litho. with Hologram

2005, Feb. 4 ***Perf. 13½x13¼***
359 V49 75c multicolored 2.25 2.25

Endangered Species Type of 1993

Designs: No. 360, Ansellia africana. No. 361, Phragmipedium kovachii. No. 362, Cymbidium ensifolium. No. 363, Renanthera imschootiana.

2005, Mar. 3 **Litho.** ***Perf. 12¾x12½***
360 A271 55c multicolored 1.40 1.40
361 A271 55c multicolored 1.40 1.40
362 A271 55c multicolored 1.40 1.40
363 A271 55c multicolored 1.40 1.40
a. Block of 4, #360-363 6.00 6.00

Nature's Wisdom V50

Designs: 55c, Desert landscape, China. 80c, Cheetah family, Africa.

2005, Apr. 21 **Litho.** ***Perf. 13½x13¼***
364 V50 55c multicolored 1.60 1.60
365 V50 75c multicolored 2.25 2.25

Intl. Year of Sport Type

2005, June 3 **Litho.** ***Perf. 13x13¼***
366 A368 55c Equestrian 1.60 1.60
367 A368 €1.10 Soccer 3.25 3.25

World Heritage Sites, Egypt Type

Designs: Nos. 368, 370c, Abu Mena. Nos. 369, 370f, St. Catherine area. No. 370a, Memphis and its Necropolis. No. 370b, Philae. No. 370d, Ancient Thebes. No. 370e, Islamic Cairo.

2005, Aug. 4 **Litho.** ***Perf. 14x13¼***
368 A369 55c multicolored 1.60 1.60
369 A369 75c multicolored 2.25 2.25

Souvenir Booklet

370 Booklet, #370g-370l 19.50
a.-c. A369 25c any single .75 .75
d.-f. A369 30c any single .85 .85
g. Booklet pane of 4 #370a 3.00 3.00
h. Booklet pane of 4 #370b 3.00 3.00
i. Booklet pane of 4 #370c 3.00 3.00
j. Booklet pane of 4 #370d 3.50 3.50
k. Booklet pane of 4 #370e 3.50 3.50
l. Booklet pane of 4 #370f 3.50 3.50

No. 370 sold for €6.80.

My Dream for Peace Type

Winning designs of Lions Club International children's global peace poster contest by: 55c, Lee Min Gi, Republic of Korea. €1, Natalie Chan, US.

2004, Sept. 21 **Litho.** ***Perf. 14***
371 A357 55c multicolored 1.60 1.60
372 A357 €1 multicolored 2.75 2.75

Food for Life Type

Designs: 55c, Corn, people with food bowls, teacher and students. €1.25, Rice, helicopter dropping food, elephant caravan.

2005, Oct. 20 **Litho.** ***Perf. 13¾***
373 A370 55c multicolored 1.60 1.60
374 A370 €1.25 multicolored 3.50 3.50

Indigenous Art Type of 2003

No. 375 — Musical instruments: a, Drum, Guinea. b, Whistle, Congo. c, Horn, Botswana. d, Drums, Burundi. e, Harp, Gabon. f, Bell, Nigeria.

2006, Feb. 3 **Litho.** ***Perf. 13¼***
375 V46 Sheet of 6 12.00 12.00
a.-f. 55c Any single 2.00 2.00

Endangered Species Type of 1993

Designs: No. 376, Dendrobates pumilio. No. 377, Furcifer lateralis. No. 378, Corallus hortulanus. No. 379, Dendrobates leucomelas.

Perf. 12¾x12½

2006, Mar. 16 **Litho.**
376 A271 55c multicolored 1.50 1.50
377 A271 55c multicolored 1.50 1.50
378 A271 55c multicolored 1.50 1.50
379 A271 55c multicolored 1.50 1.50
a. Block of 4, #376-379 6.00 6.00

Intl. Day of Families Type

Designs: 55c, Family at water pump. €1.25, Family preparing food.

2006, May 27 **Litho.** ***Perf. 14x13½***
380 A373 55c multicolored 1.25 1.25
381 A373 €1.25 multicolored 2.50 2.50

World Heritage Sites, France Type

Eiffel Tower and: Nos. 382, 384c, Carcasonne. Nos. 383, 384f, Chateau de Chambord. No. 384a, Banks of the Seine. No. 384b, Provins. No. 384d, Roman Aqueduct. No. 384e, Mont Saint-Michel.

Litho. & Embossed with Foil Application

2006, June 17 ***Perf. 13½x13¼***
382 A374 55c multicolored 1.50 1.50
383 A374 75c multicolored 2.00 2.00

Souvenir Booklet

384 Booklet, #384g-384l 18.00
a.-c. A374 25c any single .65 .65
d.-f. A374 30c any single .80 .80
g. Booklet pane of 4 #384a 2.60 2.60
h. Booklet pane of 4 #384b 2.60 2.60
i. Booklet pane of 4 #384c 2.60 2.60
j. Booklet pane of 4 #384d 3.25 3.25
k. Booklet pane of 4 #384e 3.25 3.25
l. Booklet pane of 4 #384f 3.25 3.25

No. 384 sold for €6.80.

My Dream for Peace Type of 2004

Winning designs of Lions Club International children's global peace poster contest by: 55c, Klara Thein, Germany. €1, Laurensia Levina, Indonesia.

2006, Sept. 21 **Litho.** ***Perf. 13½x13***
385 A357 55c multicolored 1.60 1.60
386 A357 €1 multicolored 3.00 3.00

Flags and Coins Type

No. 387 — Flag of: a, Gambia, 1 dalasi coin. b, Pakistan, 1 rupee coin. c, Afghanistan, 2 afghani coin. d, Austria, 1 euro coin. e, Germany, 50 cent coin. f, Haiti, 50 centimes coin. g, Denmark, 20 krone coin. h, Netherlands, 1 euro coin.

2006, Oct. 5 **Litho.** ***Perf. 13¼x13***
387 Sheet of 8 14.00 14.00
a.-h. A375 55c Any single 1.75 1.75

A column of rouletting in the middle of the sheet separates it into two parts.

Endangered Species Type of 1993

Designs: No. 388, Chlorocebus aethiops. No. 389, Nasalis larvatus. No. 390, Papio hamadryas. No. 391, Erythrocebus patas.

Perf. 12¾x12½

2007, Mar. 15 **Litho.**
388 A271 55c multicolored 1.60 1.60
389 A271 55c multicolored 1.60 1.60
390 A271 55c multicolored 1.60 1.60
391 A271 55c multicolored 1.60 1.60
a. Block of 4, #388-391 6.40 6.40

Flags and Coins Type of 2006

No. 392 — Flag of: a, Trinidad and Tobago, 50 cent coin. b, Sierra Leone, 10 cent coin. c, Hungary, 100 forint coin. d, San Marino, 2 euro coin. e, Croatia, 1 kuna coin. f, Spain, 1 euro coin. g, Kazakhstan, 100 tenge coin. h, Ireland, 5 cent coin.

2007, May 3 **Litho.** ***Perf. 13¼x13***
392 Sheet of 8 13.00 13.00
a.-h. A375 55c Any single 1.60 1.60

A column of rouletting in the middle of the sheet separates it into two parts.

Five 55c stamps depicting views of the Vienna International Center and the United Nations flag were released May 3, 2007. The editors have reason to believe that these stamps were not sold at the UN Post Office in Vienna. Value, strip of 5 with labels $45, sheet of 10 $90.

Peaceful Visions Type of 2007

Designs: 55c, "The Sowers." €1.25, "We All Thrive Under the Same Sky."

2007, June 1 **Litho.** ***Perf. 13x12½***
398 A378 55c multicolored 1.60 1.60
399 A378 €1.25 multicolored 3.75 3.75

World Heritage Sites, South America Type

Designs: Nos. 400, 402e, Iguaçu National Park, Brazil. Nos. 401, 402b, Cueva de las Manos, Argentina. No. 402a, Rapa Nui, Chile. No. 402c, Machu Picchu, Peru. No. 402d, Tiwanaku, Bolivia. No. 474f, Galapagos Islands, Ecuador.

2007, Aug. 9 **Litho.** ***Perf. 13¼x13***
400 A381 55c multicolored 2.00 2.00
401 A381 75c multicolored 2.75 2.75

Souvenir Booklet

402 Booklet, #402g-402l 20.00
a.-c. A381 25c Any single .75 .75
d.-f. A381 30c Any single .90 .90
g. Booklet pane of 4 #402a 3.00 3.00
h. Booklet pane of 4 #402b 3.00 3.00
i. Booklet pane of 4 #402c 3.00 3.00
j. Booklet pane of 4 #402d 3.60 3.60
k. Booklet pane of 4 #402e 3.60 3.60
l. Booklet pane of 4 #402f 3.60 3.60

Humanitarian Mail Type

2007, Sept. 6 **Litho.** ***Perf. 12½x13¼***
403 A382 75c multicolored 2.25 2.25

Five 65c stamps depicting the International Space Station, astronauts and planets were released Oct. 1, 2007. The editors have reason to believe that these stamps were not sold at the UN Post Office in Vienna. Value, strip of 5 with labels $35, sheet of 10 $65.

Space for Humanity Type

Designs: 65c, Space stations. €1.15, Space Station.
€2.10, Space probe, Jupiter.

2007, Oct. 25 **Litho.** ***Perf. 13½x14***
409 A383 65c multicolored 2.00 2.00
410 A383 €1.15 multicolored 3.50 3.50

Souvenir Sheet

411 A383 €2.10 multicolored 8.00 8.00

Intl. Holocaust Remembrance Day Type

2008, Jan. 27 **Litho.** ***Perf. 13***
412 A384 65c multicolored 3.00 3.00

Johann Strauss Memorial, Vienna — V61

Pallas Athene Fountain, Vienna — V62

Pegasus Fountain, Salzburg — V63

Statue, Belvedere Palace Gardens, Vienna — V64

2008, Jan. 28 Litho. *Perf. 13½x14*

413 V61 10c black .35 .35

Perf. 14x13½

414 V62 15c black .50 .50
415 V63 65c black 2.25 2.25
416 V64 €1.40 black 4.75 4.75
Nos. 413-416 (4) 7.85 7.85

Endangered Species Type of 1993

Designs: No. 4170, Mirounga angustirostris. No. 418, Millepora alcicornis. No. 419, Hippocampus histrix. No. 420, Physeter catodon.

2008, Mar. 6 Litho. *Perf. 12¾x12½*

417 A271 65c multicolored 2.50 2.50
418 A271 65c multicolored 2.50 2.50
419 A271 65c multicolored 2.50 2.50
420 A271 65c multicolored 2.50 2.50
a. Block of 4, #417-420 10.00 10.00

Flags and Coins Type of 2006

No. 421 — Flag of: a, Poland, 5 zloty coin. b, Latvia, 1 lat coin. c, Portugal, 1 euro coin. d, Armenia, 500 dram coin. e, Sweden, 1 krona coin. f, Cyprus, 1 euro coin. g, Slovakia, 1 koruna coin. h, Qatar, 50 dirham coin.

2008, May 8 Litho. *Perf. 13¼x13*

421 Sheet of 8 18.00 18.00
a.-h. A375 65c Any single 2.25 2.25

A column of rouletting in the middle of the sheet separates it into two parts.

Five 65c stamps depicting the Vienna International Center and its artwork were released May 12, 2008. The editors have reason to believe that these stamps were not sold at the UN Post Office in Vienna. Value, strip of 5 with labels $30, sheet of 10 $60.

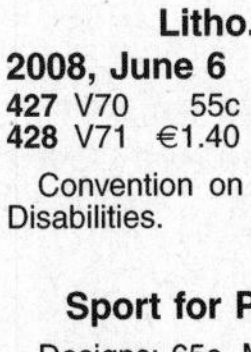

Graduate V70

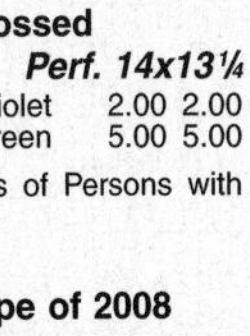

Stylized Person, Heart, Brain, Hands V71

Litho. & Embossed

2008, June 6 *Perf. 14x13¼*

427 V70 55c green & violet 2.00 2.00
428 V71 €1.40 violet & green 5.00 5.00

Convention on the Rights of Persons with Disabilities.

Sport for Peace Type of 2008

Designs: 65c, Man on rings. €1.30, €2.10, Swimmer.

2008, Aug. 8 Litho. *Perf. 14½*

429 A393 65c multicolored 2.25 2.25
430 A393 €1.30 multicolored 4.50 4.50

Souvenir Sheet

Perf. 12¾x13¼

431 A393 €2.10 multicolored 9.00 9.00
a. Overprinted in sheet margin 10.00 10.00

2008 Summer Olympics, Beijing. No. 431a is overprinted in black "Peking 2008" and medals with UN emblem.

"We Can End Poverty" Type of 2008

Winning designs in children's art contest: 65c, By Mariam Marukian, Armenia. 75c, By Rufaro Duri, Zimbabwe, vert.

Perf. 12¾x12½

2008, Sept. 18 Litho.

432 A395 65c multicolored 2.25 2.25

Perf. 12½x12¾

433 A395 75c multicolored 2.60 2.60

Five €1.40 stamps depicting views of the Vienna International Center and its artwork were released Sept. 18, 2008. The editors have reason to believe that these stamps were not sold at the UN Post Office in Vienna. Value, strip of 5 with labels $40, sheet of 10 $80.

Climate Change Types of New York and Geneva and

V72

Climate Change V73

No. 434 — Smokestacks with quarter of Earth in: a, LR. b, LL. c, UR. d, UL.

No. 435 — Cut trees with quarter of Earth in: a, LR. b, LL. c, UR. d, UL.

No. 436: a, Like New York #969a. b, Like New York #969b. c, Like New York #969c. d, Like New York #969d. e, Like Geneva #493a. f, Like Geneva #493b. g, Like Geneva #493c. h, Like Geneva #493d. i, Like Vienna #434a. j, Like Vienna #434b. k, Like Vienna #434c. l, Like Vienna #434d. m, Like New York #968a. n, Like New York #968b, o, Like New York #968c, p, Like New York #968d. q, Like Geneva #492a. r, Like Geneva #492b. s, Like Geneva #492c. t, Like Geneva #492d. u, Like Vienna #435a. v, Like Vienna #435b. w, Like Vienna #435c. x, Like Vienna #435d.

All stamps have green panels inscribed "Klimawandel."

2008, Oct. 23 Litho. *Perf. 13¼x13*

434 Sheet of 4 9.00 9.00
a.-d. V72 65c Any single 2.25 2.25
435 Sheet of 4 16.00 16.00
a.-d. V73 €1.15 Any single 4.00 4.00

Souvenir Booklet

436 Booklet, #436y-436ad 27.00
a.-d. A397 30c Any single 1.00 1.00
e.-h. G77 30c Any single 1.00 1.00
i.-l. V72 30c Any single 1.00 1.00
m.-p. A396 35c Any single 1.10 1.10
q.-t. G76 35c Any single 1.10 1.10
u.-x. V73 35c Any single 1.10 1.10
y. Booklet pane of 4, #436a-436d 4.25 4.25
z. Booklet pane of 4, #436e-436h 4.25 4.25
aa. Booklet pane of 4, #436i-436l 4.25 4.25
ab. Booklet pane of 4, #436m-436p 4.75 4.75
ac. Booklet pane of 4, #436q-436t 4.75 4.75
ad. Booklet pane of 4, #436u-436x 4.75 4.75

U Thant Type of 2009
Litho. With Foil Application

2009, Feb. 6 *Perf. 14x13½*

437 A399 €1.15 green & multi 4.50 4.50

Endangered Species Type of 1993

Designs: No. 438, Trogonoptera brookiana. No. 439, Pandinus imperator. No. 440, Carabus intricatus. No. 441, Brachypelma smithi.

2009, Apr. 16 Litho. *Perf. 12¾x12½*

438 A271 65c multicolored 2.00 2.00
439 A271 65c multicolored 2.00 2.00
440 A271 65c multicolored 2.00 2.00
441 A271 65c multicolored 2.00 2.00
a. Block of 4, #438-441 8.00 8.00

World Heritage Sites, Germany Type of 2009

Designs: Nos. 442, 444c, Palaces and Parks of Potsdam and Berlin. Nos. 443, 444e, Luther Memorials in Eisleben and Wittenberg. No. 444a, Town Hall and Roland on the Marketplace, Bremen. No. 444b, Wartburg Castle. No. 444d, Aachen Cathedral. No. 444f, Monastic Island of Reichenau.

2009, May 7 Litho. *Perf. 14x13½*

442 A400 65c multicolored 1.90 1.90
443 A400 €1.40 multicolored 4.00 4.00

Souvenir Booklet

444 Booklet, #444g-444l 20.00
a.-c. A400 30c any single .75 .75
d.-f. A400 35c any single .90 .90
g. Booklet pane of 4 #444a 3.00 3.00
h. Booklet pane of 4 #444b 3.00 3.00
i. Booklet pane of 4 #444c 3.00 3.00
j. Booklet pane of 4 #444d 3.60 3.60
k. Booklet pane of 4 #444e 3.60 3.60
l. Booklet pane of 4 #444f 3.60 3.60

Memorial Plaza, Vienna International Center — V74

The First Swallows, Sculpture by Juozas Mikenas V75

Conference Building, Vienna International Center — V76

Butterfly Tree, by Rudolf Hausner V77

Flags in Memorial Plaza V78

2009, May 7 *Perf. 13¼*

445 V74 65c multi + label 5.00 5.00
a. Perf. 11¼x11 10.00 10.00
446 V75 65c multi + label 5.00 5.00
a. Perf. 11¼x11 10.00 10.00
447 V76 65c multi + label 5.00 5.00
a. Perf. 11¼x11 10.00 10.00
448 V77 65c multi + label 5.00 5.00
a. Perf. 11¼x11 10.00 10.00
449 V78 65c multi + label 5.00 5.00
a. Perf. 11¼x11 10.00 10.00
b. Vert. strip of 5, #445-449, + 5 labels 25.00 25.00
c. Vert. strip of 5, #445a-449a, + 5 labels 50.00 50.00

The sheet of No. 449c has "ver. 2" in the lower right selvage.

Economic and Social Council (ECOSOC) Type of 2009

Designs: 55c, Combat HIV/AIDS, malaria and other diseases. 65c, Reduce child mortality.

2009, Aug. 6 Litho. *Perf. 12¾x12½*

450 A411 55c multicolored 2.25 2.25
451 A411 65c multicolored 3.50 3.50

V79

V80

V81

V82

Vienna International Center, 30th Anniv. — V83

2009, Aug. 24 *Perf. 13¼*

452 V79 €1.40 multi + label 6.00 6.00
a. Perf. 11¼x11 20.00 20.00
453 V80 €1.40 multi + label 6.00 6.00
a. Perf. 11¼x11 20.00 20.00
454 V81 €1.40 multi + label 6.00 6.00
a. Perf. 11¼x11 20.00 20.00
455 V82 €1.40 multi + label 6.00 6.00
a. Perf. 11¼x11 20.00 20.00
456 V83 €1.40 multi + label 6.00 6.00
a. Perf. 11¼x11 20.00 20.00
b. Vert. strip of 5, #452-456, + 5 labels 30.00 30.00
c. Vert. strip of 5, #452a-456a, + 5 labels 100.00 100.00

The sheet of No. 456c has "ver. 2" in the lower right selvage.

Millennium Development Goals Type of 2009
Miniature Sheet

No. 457: a, Bowl of hot food. b, Pencil. c, Female symbol. d, Teddy bear. e, Pregnant woman, heart. f, Medicine bottle. g, Stylized tree. h, Conjoined people.

2009, Sept. 25

457 A413 Sheet of 8 16.00 16.00
a.-h. 65c Any single 2.00 2.00

Miniature Sheet

Indigenous People — V84

No. 458 — Portraits of person from: a, Tanzania. b, Australia. c, Namibia (small child). d, Indonesia. e, Namibia (young girl). f, Untied Arab Emirates.

2009, Oct. 8 *Perf. 12½*

458 V84 Sheet of 6 12.00 12.00
a.-f. 65c Any single 2.00 2.00

Flags and Coins Type of 2006

No. 459 — Flag of: a, Romania, 1 ban coin. b, Slovenia, 5 cent coin. c, Azerbaijan, 10 giapik coin. d, Bangladesh, 5 taka coin. e, Belarus, 1 ruble coin. f, Malta, 1 euro coin. g, Swaziland, 1 lilangeni coin. h, Jordan, 10 piaster coin.

2010, Feb. 5 Litho. *Perf. 13¼x13*

459 Sheet of 8 16.00 16.00
a.-h. A375 65c Any single 2.00 2.00

A column of rouletting in the middle of the sheet separates it into two parts.

People Pulling Rope V85

Person With Hands Over Eyes V86

Woman Touching Her Shoulder V87

Man With Wheelbarrow — V88

Blue Heart V89

Designed by Rorie Katz, US.

2010, Feb. 5 Litho. *Perf. 11¼x11*

460 V85 65c multi + label *4.50 4.50*
461 V86 65c multi + label *4.50 4.50*
462 V87 65c multi + label *4.50 4.50*
463 V88 65c multi + label *4.50 4.50*
464 V89 65c multi + label *4.50 4.50*
a. Vert. strip of 5, #460-464, + 5 labels *22.50 22.50*

The full sheet sold for $14.95 or €19.90. The labels could not be personalized.

Endangered Species Type of 1993

Designs: No. 465, Mammillaria zeilmanniana. No. 466, Hoodia gordonii. No. 467, Welwitschia mirabilis. No. 468, Euphorbia milii.

2010, Apr. 15 Litho. *Perf. 12¾x12½*

465 A271 65c multicolored 2.25 2.25
466 A271 65c multicolored 2.25 2.25
467 A271 65c multicolored 2.25 2.25
468 A271 65c multicolored 2.25 2.25
a. Block of 4, #465-468 9.00 9.00

Intl. Year of Biodiversity — V90

Drawings from Art Forms from Nature, by Ernst Heinrich: 5c, Colonial algae. 20c, Boxfish.

2010, Apr. 15 Litho. *Perf. 13*

469 V90 5c multicolored .25 .25
470 V90 20c multicolored .70 .70

One Planet, One Ocean Types of New York and Geneva and

V91

V92

No. 471: a, Dolphin at left, fish at right. b, Fish at top, shark in center. c, Dolphin at left, fish at right and bottom. d, Fish at left, top and right.

No. 472: a, Dolphins. b, Shark and fish at center, ray at bottom. c, Fish at left, turtle at bottom. d, Fish and coral.

No. 473: a, Like New York #1003a. b, Like New York #1003b, c, Like New York #1003c, d, Like New York #1003d. e, Like #471a. f, Like #471b. g, Like #471c, h, Like #471d. i, Like Geneva #519a. j, Like Geneva #519b, k, Like Geneva #519c. l, Like Geneva #519d. m, Like New York #1004a. n, Like New York #1004b. o, Like New York #1004c, p, Like New York #1004d. q, Like #472a. r, Like #472b. s, Like #472c. t, Like #472d. u, Like Geneva #520a. v, Like Geneva #520b. w, Like Geneva #520c. x, Like Geneva #520d.

2010, May 6 Litho. *Perf. 14x13¼*

471 V91 Sheet of 4 7.75 7.75
a.-d. 55c Any single 1.90 1.90
472 V92 Sheet of 4 9.00 9.00
a.-d. 65c Any single 2.25 2.25

Souvenir Booklet

Perf. 13¼x13

473 Booklet, #473y-473z, 473aa-473ad 27.00
a.-d. A416 30c any single 1.00 1.00
e.-h. V91 30c any single 1.00 1.00
i.-l. G85 30c any single 1.00 1.00
m.-p. A417 35c any single 1.25 1.25
q.-t. V92 35c any single 1.25 1.25
u.-x. G86 35c any single 1.25 1.25
y. Booklet pane of 4 #473a-473d 4.00 4.00
z. Booklet pane of 4 #473e-473h 4.00 4.00
aa. Booklet pane of 4 #473i-473l 4.00 4.00
ab. Booklet pane of 4 #473m-473p 5.00 5.00
ac. Booklet pane of 4 #473q-473t 5.00 5.00
ad. Booklet pane of 4 #473u-473x 5.00 5.00

Intl. Oceanographic Commission, 50th anniv.

United Nations, 65th Anniv. Type of 2010

Litho. With Foil Application

2010, June 28 *Perf. 13¼*

474 A422 75c green & gold 3.00 3.00
a. Souvenir sheet of 2 6.00 6.00

V93

V94

V95

V96

V97

2010, Sept. 2 Litho. *Perf. 13¼x13*

475 V93 65c multicolored 1.90 1.90
476 V94 65c multicolored 1.90 1.90
477 V95 65c multicolored 1.90 1.90
478 V96 65c multicolored 1.90 1.90
479 V97 65c multicolored 1.90 1.90
a. Horiz. strip of 5, #475-479 9.50 9.50

Miniature Sheet

Indigenous People — V98

No. 480 — Portraits of person from: a, French Polynesia (denomination in white). b, Tanzania (child with cloth head covering). c, Malaysia. d, French Polynesia (denomination in white and green). e, Namibia. f, Tanzania (man with band around forehead).

2010, Oct. 21 Litho. *Perf. 13*

480 V98 Pane of 6 11.50 11.50
a.-f. 65c Any single 1.90 1.90

United Nations Headquarters, Vienna — V99

United Nations Headquarters, Geneva: €1.25, Aerial view. €2.85, Ground-level view.

2011, Feb. 4 Litho. *Perf. 13*

481 V99 €1.25 multicolored 3.75 3.75
482 V99 €2.85 multicolored 8.25 8.25

Flags and Coins Type of 2006

No. 483 — Flag of: a, Lithuania, 2 lita coin. b, Greece, 1 euro coin. c, Kyrgyzstan, 50 tyiyn coin. d, Oman, 100 baisa coin. e, Estonia, 2 euro coin. f, Czech Republic, 5 koruna coin. g, Uzbekistan, 100 som coin. h, Monaco, 1 euro coin.

2011, Mar. 3 Litho. *Perf. 13¼x13*

483 Sheet of 8 15.00 15.00
a.-h. A375 65c Any single 1.75 1.75

A column of rouletting in the middle of the sheet separates it into two parts.

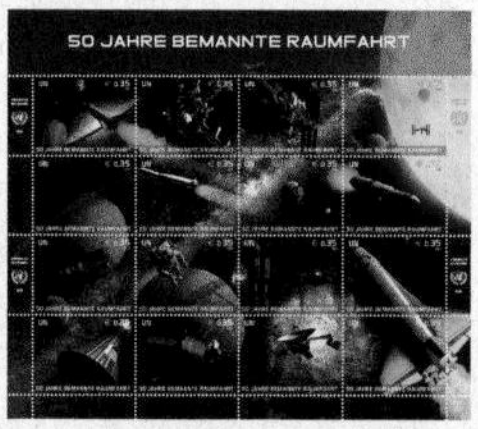

Human Space Flight, 50th Anniv. V100

No. 484: Various parts of outer space scene.

No. 485, vert.: a, Space Shuttle. b, Space Station.

2011, Apr. 12 Litho. *Perf. 13x13¼*

484 V100 Sheet of 16 16.50 16.50
a.-p. 35c any single 1.00 1.00

Souvenir Sheet

485 V100 Sheet of 2 12.00 12.00
a. 55c multi 5.50 5.50
b. 65c multi 6.50 6.50
c. Souvenir sheet of 6, New York #1025a-1025b, Geneva #534a-b, Vienna #485a-485b 42.50 42.50

No. 485 contains two 40x48mm stamps that were printed as part of a larger sheet of six stamps, No. 485c, which was broken up into its component two-stamp souvenir sheets, and also sold as one unit. Value $90, complete unit.

Vienna International Center and Flagpoles — V101

Fish-eye View of Vienna International Center and Flagpole — V102

Vienna International Center and Train — V103

Aerial View of Vienna International Center — V104

Vienna International Center and Water — V105

Detail From La Pioggia, Stadt Unter de Regen, by Friedensreich Hundertwasser — V106

Hand in Hand, by Hans Dietrich V107

The Scholars Pavilion V108

Detail From Grupo Expectante, by Alfredo Sosabravo — V109

Yes to Life, No to Drugs, by Sami Burhan V110

2011, May 1 Litho. *Perf. 14¾*

486 V101 62c multi + label *2.50 2.50*
487 V102 62c multi + label *2.50 2.50*
488 V103 62c multi + label *2.50 2.50*
489 V104 62c multi + label *2.50 2.50*
490 V105 62c multi + label *2.50 2.50*
a. Vert. strip of 5, #486-490, + 5 labels *15.00 15.00*
491 V106 70c multi + label *3.00 3.00*
492 V107 70c multi + label *3.00 3.00*
493 V108 70c multi + label *3.00 3.00*
494 V109 70c multi + label *3.00 3.00*
495 V110 70c multi + label *3.00 3.00*
a. Vert. strip of 5, #491-495, + 5 labels *17.50 17.50*
Nos. 486-495 (10) *25.50 25.50*

The full sheet of Nos. 486-490 sold for $21.45 or €12.40. The full sheet of Nos. 491-495 sold for $14.26 or €9.90. The labels could be personalized.

UNESCO World Heritage Sites in Nordic Countries Type of 2011

Designs: 62c, Urnes Stave Church, Norway. 1fr, Struve Geodetic Arc, Norway, Finland and Sweden.

2011, May 5 Litho. *Perf. 14x13½*

496 A433 62c multicolored 1.90 1.90
497 A433 70c multicolored 2.10 2.10

AIDS Ribbon Type of 2011

2011, June 3 Litho. *Die Cut*

Self-Adhesive

498 A434 70c red & green 2.40 2.40

ECOSOC Type of 2011

2011, July 1 Litho. *Perf. 14¼*

499 A435 62c multicolored 3.00 3.00
500 A435 70c multicolored 4.00 4.00

Endangered Species Type of 1993

Designs: No. 501, Cyanoramphus novaezelandiae (Red-fronted parakeet). No. 502, Haliaeetus albicilla (White-tailed eagle). No. 503, Probosciger aterrimus (Black palm cockatoo). No. 504, Caloenas nicobarica (Nicobar pigeon).

2011, Sept. 7 Litho. *Perf. 12¾x12½*

501 A271 70c multicolored 2.50 2.50
502 A271 70c multicolored 2.50 2.50
503 A271 70c multicolored 2.50 2.50
504 A271 70c multicolored 2.50 2.50
a. Block of 4, #501-504 10.00 10.00

Intl. Year of Forests Type of 2011

Designs: 62c, Tree top, crosses, circles and ovals. 70c, Stylized people and trees.

Litho. With Foil Application

2011, Oct. 13 *Perf. 12½*

505 62c multicolored 2.00 2.00
506 70c multicolored 2.25 2.25
a. A436 Vert. pair, #505-506 4.25 4.25

Flags and Coins Type of 2006

No. 507 — Flag of: a, Cameroun, 100 franc coin. b, Samoa, 2 tala coin. c, Surinam, 5 cent coin. d, Macedonia, 50 denar coin. e, Bulgaria, 50 stotinka coin. f, Tanzania, 100 shilling coin. g, Finland, 1 euro coin. h, Cuba, 1 peso coin.

2012, Feb. 3 Litho. *Perf. 13¼x13*

507 Sheet of 8 16.50 16.50
a.-h. A375 70c Any single 2.00 2.00

A column of rouletting in the middle of the sheet separates it into two parts.

V111

Autism Awareness — V112

Drawings by autistic people: No. 508, The Path, by Ryan Smoluk, Canada. No. 509, Untitled drawing, by Colm Isherwood, Ireland.

2012, Apr. 2 Litho. *Perf. 14x13½*

508 V111 70c multicolored 2.25 2.25
509 V112 70c multicolored 2.25 2.25
a. Pair, #508-509 4.50 4.50

UN Emblem V113

2012, Apr. 12 Litho. *Perf. 14½*

510 V113 70c pur, blk + label *3.50 3.50*
Sheet of 10 + 10 labels *35.00 35.00*

The full sheet sold for $14.52 or €9.90. The labels could be personalized.

Endangered Species Type of 1993

Designs: No. 511, Panthera uncia. No. 512, Polyplectron schleiermacheri. No. 513, Tyto novaehollandiae. No. 514, Ambystoma mexicanum.

2012, Apr. 19 Litho. *Perf. 12¾x12½*

511 A271 70c multicolored 2.25 2.25
512 A271 70c multicolored 2.25 2.25
513 A271 70c multicolored 2.25 2.25
514 A271 70c multicolored 2.25 2.25
a. Block of 4, #511-514 9.00 9.00

Rio + 20 Type of 2012

2012, June 1 Litho. *Perf. 13x13¼*

515 A443 70c multicolored 2.10 2.10

Sport for Peace Type of 2012

Litho. With Foil Application

2012, Aug. 17 *Perf. 14½*

516 A444 62c multicolored 1.90 1.90
517 A444 70c multicolored 2.10 2.10
a. Souvenir sheet of 1 2.10 2.10

UNESCO World Heritage Sites in Africa Type of 2012

Designs: 62c, Kenya Lake System, Kenya. 70c, Medina of Marrakesh, Morocco.

2012, Sept. 5 Litho. *Perf. 13¼*

518 A445 62c multicolored 1.75 1.75
519 A445 70c multicolored 2.00 2.00

Miniature Sheet

Indigenous People — V114

No. 520 — Portrait of person from: a, Chile. b, Malaysia. c, China (woman with black hair). d, China (woman with flower in hair). e, Tanzania. f, Mongolia.

2012, Oct. 11 Litho. *Perf. 13¼x13*

520 V114 Sheet of 6 11.50 11.50
a.-f. 70c Any single 1.90 1.90

World Radio Day Type of 2013

Designs: 70c, Microphone and scripts. €1.70, Boy with radio.

2013, Feb. 13 Litho. *Perf. 13¼x13*

521 A448 70c multicolored 2.00 2.00
522 A448 €1.70 multicolored 5.00 5.00

People in Handprint — V115

People in Heart — V116

2013, Mar. 5 Litho. *Perf. 14x13½*

523 V115 62c multicolored 1.90 1.90

Perf. 13½x14

524 V116 €2.20 multicolored 6.50 6.50

World Heritage Sites, China, Type of 2013

Designs: Nos. 525, 527c, Great Wall of China. Nos. 526, 527f, Mausoleum of the First Qing Emperor. No. 527a, Mogao Caves. No. 527b, Potala Palace, Lhasa. No. 527d, Imperial Palace, Beijing. No. 527e, Mount Huangshan.

2013, Apr. 11 Litho. *Perf. 14x13½*

525 A452 70c multicolored 2.00 2.00
526 A452 €1.70 multicolored 5.00 5.00

Souvenir Booklet

527 Booklet, #527g-527l 25.00
a.-c. A452 30c any single .85 .85
d.-f. A452 40c any single 1.10 1.10
g. Booklet pane of 4 #527a 3.50 —
h. Booklet pane of 4 #527b 3.50 —
i. Booklet pane of 4 #527c 3.50 —
j. Booklet pane of 4 #527d 4.75 —
k. Booklet pane of 4 #527e 4.75 —
l. Booklet pane of 4 #527f 4.75 —

World Oceans Day V117

No. 528 — Fish from *One Fish, Two Fish, Red Fish, Blue Fish,* by Dr. Seuss: a, Green fish facing left, wave. b, Red fish facing right. c, Three green fish on plate. d, Red fish, back half of red fish, wave. e, Red fish facing left, front half of red fish facing right. f, Two red fish facing left. g, Two green fish facing right, wave. h, Red fish facing right, head of blue fish wearing hat. i, Yellow fish with green star, wave. j, Yellow fish, back of blue fish, wave. k, Two red fish, body of blue fish. l, Tail of yellow fish, two green fish facing left, wave.

2013, May 31 Litho. *Perf. 13*

528 V117 Sheet of 12 24.00 24.00
a.-l. 70c any single 2.00 2.00

Nebulae Type of 2013

Designs: No. 567, NGC 2346. No. 568, Sh 2-106.
1fr, Messier 16.

2013, Aug. 9 Litho. *Perf. 13¼*

529 A454 €1.70 multicolored 5.00 5.00
530 A454 €1.70 multicolored 5.00 5.00
a. Pair, #529-530 10.00 10.00

Souvenir Sheet

531 A454 62c multicolored 1.90 1.90

No. 531 contains one 44x44mm stamp.

Works of Disabled Artists Type of 2013

Designs: 70c, Electro Man, by Pete Eckert, U.S. €1.70, Dive Bomb, by Matt Sesow, U.S.

2013, Sept. 20 Litho. *Perf. 13¼x13*

532 A456 70c multicolored 2.00 2.00
533 A456 €1.70 multicolored 5.00 5.00

Endangered Species Type of 1993

Designs: No. 534, Hemigalus derbyanus. No. 535, Bubo ascalaphus. No. 536, Nycticebus coucang. No. 537, Zaglossus spp.

2013, Oct. 10 Litho. *Perf. 12¾x12½*

534 A271 70c multicolored 2.00 2.00
535 A271 70c multicolored 2.00 2.00
536 A271 70c multicolored 2.00 2.00
537 A271 70c multicolored 2.00 2.00
a. Block of 4, #534-537 8.00 8.00

UN Emblem V118

2013, Oct. 24 Litho. *Perf. 14½*

538 V118 70c gray blue & blue + label *4.00 4.00*

The full sheet sold for $14.20 or €9.90. The labels could be personalized.

Flags and Coins Type of 2006

No. 539 — Flag of: a, Malaysia, 50 sen coin. b, Nigeria, 1 naira coin. c, Zambia, 20 ngwee coin. d, Togo, 100 franc coin. e, Dominica, 5 cent coin. f, Chad, 100 franc coin. g, St. Vincent and the Grenadines, 5 cent coin. h, Syria, 25 pound coin.

2013, Nov. 6 Litho. *Perf. 13¼x13*

539 Sheet of 8 16.00 16.00
a.-h. A375 70c Any single 2.00 2.00

A column of rouletting in the middle of the sheet separates it into two parts.

International Day of Happiness Type of 2014

Designs: 90c, Happy Asian Boy at the Park, photograph by Alan Levenson, Russian word for "Happy." €1.70, Barbary Macacque with Baby, photograph by Gerhard Schulz, Arabic word for "Happy."

2014, Mar. 17 Litho. *Perf. 13¼x13*

540 A459 90c multicolored 2.75 2.75
541 A459 €1.70 multicolored 5.25 5.25

Miniature Sheet

International Year of Jazz — V119

No. 542: a, Silhouette of saxophonist in blue. b, Woman singing. c, Silhouette of man in red, neon lights. d, Bass player. e, Trombone in gold. f, Silhouette of saxophonist in black, silhouette of man holding trombone. g, "Cocktails" neon sign . h, Silhouette of bass player in orange. i, Stack of record albums. j, Cymbal. k, Trombone in silver. l, Silhouette of clarinetist in black.

2014, Apr. 30 Litho. *Perf. 13x13¼*

542 V119 Sheet of 12 24.00 24.00
a.-l. 70c Any single 2.00 2.00

Vienna International Center, 35th Anniv. — V120

No. 543: a, Vienna International Center under construction (towers and shadows), red panel. b, Vienna International Center, street light at left, green panel. c, Vienna International Center, curved building at left, green panel. d, Vienna International Center under construction (arch in foreground, cranes at right), red panel. e, Vienna International Center under construction (cranes at left, center and right), red panel. f, Doorway to Vienna International Center, green panel. g, View of curved buildings of Vienna International Center looking up from ground, green panel. h, Vienna International Center under construction (two cranes on central tower), red panel. i, Completed Vienna International Center, red panel. j, Flags in front of Vienna International Center.

2014, May 8 Litho. *Perf. 14¾*

543 V120 Sheet of 10 + 10 labels *30.00 30.00*
a.-j. 70c Any single + label *3.00 3.00*

The full sheet sold for $14.80 or €9.90. The generic labels are shown. Labels could be personalized.

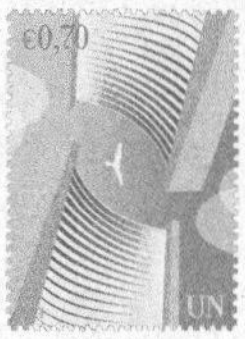

V121

V122

Printed by Lowe-Martin Group, Canada. Panes of 20. Designed by Sergio Baradat, U.S.

2014, June 6 Litho. *Perf. 13¼x13*

544 V121 70c multicolored 2.10 2.10
545 V122 €1.70 multicolored 5.25 5.25

Taj Mahal Types of 2014

2014, July 16 Engr. *Perf. 13¼x13*

546 A466 90c multicolored 2.75 2.75
547 A468 €1.70 multicolored 5.25 5.25

Souvenir Booklet

548 Booklet, #548g-548l 25.00
a. A463 30c multi .85 .85
b. A465 30c multi .85 .85
c. A466 30c multi .85 .85
d. A464 40c multi 1.20 1.20

e. A467 40c multi 1.20 1.20
f. A468 40c multi 1.20 1.20
g. Booklet pane of 4 #548a 3.40 —
h. Booklet pane of 4 #548b 3.40 —
i. Booklet pane of 4 #548c 3.40 —
j. Booklet pane of 4 #548d 4.80 —
k. Booklet pane of 4 #548e 4.80 —
l. Booklet pane of 4 #548f 4.80 —

International Year of Family Farming — V123

2014, Aug. 21 Litho. *Perf. 13x13¼*
549 V123 62c multi 1.90 1.90
550 V123 €1.70 multi 5.25 5.25

Global Education First Initiative Type of 2014

Designs: €1.70, Children boarding school bus. €2, Tree growing from book held by students.

2014, Sept. 18 Litho. *Perf. 13x13¼*
551 A470 €1.70 multicolored 5.25 5.25

Souvenir Sheet
Perf. 12½

552 A470 €2 multicolored 6.00 6.00

No. 552 contains one 32x32mm stamp.

Endangered Species Type of 2014

Maps and: No. 553, Cheilinus undulatus. No. 554, Carcharodon carcharias. No. 555, Manta birostris. No. 556, Polyodon spathula.

2014, Oct. 23 Litho. *Perf. 12¾x12½*
553 A471 70c multicolored 2.10 2.10
554 A471 70c multicolored 2.10 2.10
555 A471 70c multicolored 2.10 2.10
556 A471 70c multicolored 2.10 2.10
a. Block of 4, #553-556 8.50 8.50

Miniature Sheet

V124

No. 557: a, Flag on pole as seen from base of pole. b, Vienna International Center, structure in shadow at bottom. c, Persian Scholars Pavilion. d, Vienna International Center and fountain. e, Sailboat and Vienna International Center. f, Rowboat on water near Vienna International Center. g, Vienna International Center, flags and sculpture. h, Entrance to Vienna International Center. i, Woman Free sculpture near Vienna International Center. j, Aerial view of Vienna International Center.

2015, Jan. 23 Litho. *Perf. 14¾*
557 V124 Sheet of 10 *30.00 30.00*
a.-j. 80c Any single + label *3.00 3.00*

The full sheet sold for $15 or €10.90. The generic labels are shown. Labels could be personalized.

Flags and Coins Type of 2006

No. 558 — Flag of: a, Tuvalu, 10 cent coin. b, Malawi, 1 kwacha coin. c, Iraq, 50 dinar coin. d, St. Thomas and Prince Islands, 250 dobra coin. e, Botswana, 10 thebe coin. f, Uruguay, 5 peso coin. g, Bosnia and Herzegovina, 20 pfennig coin. h, Somalia, 25 shilling coin.

2015, Feb. 6 Litho. *Perf. 13¼x13*
558 Sheet of 8 18.00 18.00
a.-h. A375 80c Any single 2.25 2.25

A column of rouletting in the middle of the sheet separates it into two parts.

Miniature Sheets

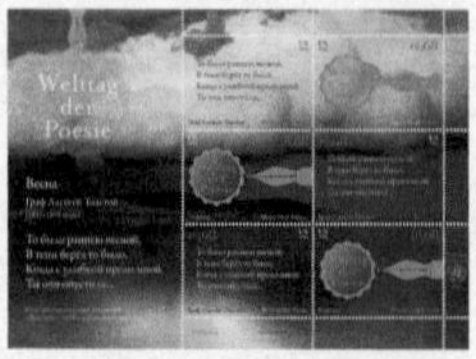

V125

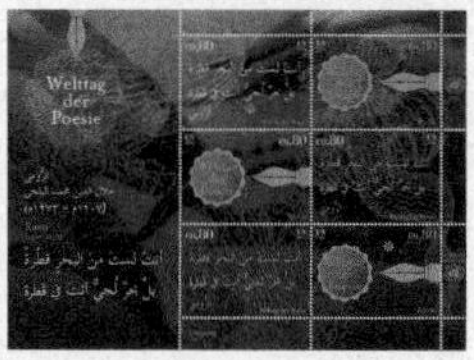

World Poetry Day V126

No. 559: a, Aleksey Tolstoy quotation in Russian in red brown, date in purple, "Welttag der Poesie" in red. b, Pen and circle, date in black, "Frühling" in purple. c, Pen and circle, date and "Frühling" in white, clouds above land in background. d, Tolstoy quotation in Russian in white, date in white, "Welttag der Poesie" in red. e, Tolstoy quotation in white, date and "Welttag der Poesie" in white. f, As "c," brown background.

No. 560: a, Rumi quotation in Arabic in light blue. b, Pen and red brown circle, denomination in red, purple jellyfish in background. c, Pen and red brown circle, denomination in white. d, Rumi quotation in orange, purple jellyfish in background. e, Rumi quotation in orange, red jellyfish tentacles in background. f, Pen and red brown circle, red denomination, red and purple jellyfish tentacles in background.

Perf. 14½x14¼

2015, Mar. 20 Litho.
559 V125 Sheet of 6 11.50 11.50
a.-f. 68c Any single 1.90 1.90
560 V126 Sheet of 6 13.50 13.50
a.-f. 80c Any single 2.25 2.25

Endangered Species Type of 2015

Designs: No. 561, Pteridophora alberti. No. 562, Astrapia splendidissima. No. 563, Paradisaea apoda. No. 564, Lophorina superba.

2015, Apr. 16 Litho. *Perf. 12½x12¾*
561 A476 80c multicolored 2.00 2.00
562 A476 80c multicolored 2.00 2.00
563 A476 80c multicolored 2.00 2.00
564 A476 80c multicolored 2.00 2.00
a. Block of 4, #561-564 8.00 8.00
Nos. 561-564 (4) 8.00 8.00

V127

V128

2015, May 7 Litho. *Perf. 13¼x13*
565 V127 68c multicolored 1.75 1.75
566 V128 80c multicolored 2.00 2.00

World Heritage Sites, Southeast Asia Type of 2015

Designs: Nos. 567, 569c, Ayutthaya, Thailand. Nos. 568, 569f, Hué Monuments, Viet Nam. No. 569a, Luang Prabang, Laos. No. 569b, Angkor Wat, Cambodia. No. 569d, Borobudur Temple, Indonesia. No. 569e, Cordillera, Philippines.

2015, June 5 Litho. *Perf. 14x13½*
567 A480 80c multicolored 2.00 2.00
568 A480 €1.70 multicolored 4.25 4.25

Souvenir Booklet

569 Booklet, #569g-569l 21.00
a.-c. A480 30c any single .75 .75
d.-f. A480 40c any single 1.00 1.00
g. Booklet pane of 4 #569a 3.00 —
h. Booklet pane of 4 #569b 3.00 —
i. Booklet pane of 4 #569c 3.00 —
j. Booklet pane of 4 #569d 4.00 —
k. Booklet pane of 4 #569e 4.00 —
l. Booklet pane of 4 #569f 4.00 —

End Violence Against Children Type of 2015

Designs: 68c, Gender-based violence. 80c, Child labor.

Perf. 14½x14¼

2015, Aug. 20 Litho.
570 A481 68c multicolored 1.75 1.75
571 A481 80c multicolored 2.00 2.00

ECOSOC Chamber V129

Trusteeship Council — V130

Visitors Lobby — V131

General Assembly Hall — V132

Trusteeship Council — V133

Printed by Cartor Security Printing, France. Panes of 6. Designed by Rorie Katz, U.S.

2015, Oct. 25 Litho. *Perf. 13¾*
572 V129 80c multicolored 2.00 2.00
573 V130 80c multicolored 2.00 2.00
a. Pair, #572-573 4.00 4.00
574 V131 €1.70 multicolored 4.25 4.25
575 V132 €1.70 multicolored 4.25 4.25
a. Pair, #574-575 8.50 8.50
Nos. 572-575 (4) 12.50 12.50

Souvenir Sheet
Perf. 13½

576 V133 €1.70 multicolored 4.25 4.25

United Nations, 70th anniv.

United Nations, 70th Anniv. Type of 2015

Designed by Sergio Baradat, U.S.

2015, Nov. 5 Litho. *Perf. 14¾*
577 A482 80c multi + label *4.00 4.00*
Sheet of 10 + 10 labels *40.00* —

The full sheet sold for $13.45 or €10.90. The sheet contains ten different generic labels. Labels could be personalized. The personalization of labels was available only at UN Headquarters, and not through mail order.

21st United Nations Climate Change Conference, Paris — V134

2015, Nov. 24 Litho. *Perf. 13¼*
578 V134 80c multicolored 3.00 3.00

Values are for stamps with surrounding selvage.

Free and Equal Type of 2016

Designs: 68c, Person coming out of closet. 80c, Gay men.

2016, Feb. 5 Litho. *Perf. 13½x13¼*
579 A491 68c multicolored 1.75 1.75
580 A491 80c multicolored 2.00 2.00

HeForShe Type of 2016

Designs: 1fr, Man, red background. 2fr, Woman, orange brown background.

2016, Mar. 8 Litho. *Perf. 12½x13*
581 A492 68c multicolored 1.75 1.75
582 A492 80c multicolored 2.00 2.00

Miniature Sheets

V135

International Dance Day — V136

No. 583 — Illustration of Spanish dancers by Allison Seiffer: a, Female dancer with fan. b, Male dancer with crossed arms. c, Red dress of dancer. d, Female dancer with male guitarist. e, Feet of dancer in ochre and green dress. f, Feet of male and female dancers, rose on floor.

No. 584 — Illustration of Middle Eastern dancers by Seiffer: a, Head of female dancer, "Welttanztag" in red, denomination in yellow. b, Head of female dancer, "Welttanztag" and denomination in red. c, Torso of dancer. d, Dancer, "Welttanztag" in black, denomination in yellow. e, Feet of dancer, "Welttanztag" in black. f, Feet of dancer and drum, "Welttanztag" in yellow.

2016, Apr. 29 Litho. *Perf. 13¼x13*
583 V135 Sheet of 6 10.00 10.00
a.-f. 68c Any single 1.60 1.60
584 V136 Sheet of 6 12.00 12.00
a.-f. 80c Any single 2.00 2.00

United Nations Industrial Development Organization, 50th Anniv. — V137

2016, May 12 Litho. *Perf. 14¾*
585 V137 80c multi + label *2.60 2.60*
Sheet of 10 + 10 labels *26.50* —

The full sheet sold for $13.12 and €10.90. One of the ten different generic labels is shown. Labels could be personalized. The personalization of labels was available only at UN Headquarters, and not through mail order.

International Day of United Nations Peacekeepers Type of 2016

Designs: 68c, Peacekeepers and African children. 80c, Peacekeepers in tank, Africans.

Litho. With Foil Application

2016, May 29 *Perf. 13¼x13*
586 A496 68c multicolored 1.75 1.75
587 A496 80c multicolored 2.00 2.00

Sport for Peace Type of 2016

Olympic rings and: No. 588, Weight lifting, denomination at LR. No. 589, Weight lifting, denomination at LL. No. 590, Fencing, denomination at UR. No. 591, Fencing, denonomiation at UL.

2016, July 22 Litho. *Perf. 14¼*

588 A498 68c multicolored 1.75 1.75
589 A498 68c multicolored 1.75 1.75
a. Pair, #588-589 3.50 3.50
590 A498 €1.70 multicolored 4.25 4.25
591 A498 €1.70 multicolored 4.25 4.25
a. Pair, #590-591 8.50 8.50
Nos. 588-591 (4) 12.00 12.00

Souvenir sheets of three bearing three stamps, one from each office are listed under United Nations, Offices in New York as Nos. 1141, 1161, 1177-1178, 1203, and 1208.

World Heritage Sites, Czech Republic Type of 2016

Designs: Nos. 592, 594c, Historic Town Center of Kutná Hora. Nos. 593, 594f, Historic Center of Cesky Krumlov. No. 594a, Historic Center of Prague. No. 594b, Gardens and Castle at Kroméríz. No. 594d, Holy Trinity Column, Olomouc. Nos. 594e, Lednice-Valtice Cultural Landscape.

2016, Sept. 8 Litho. *Perf. 14¼*

592 A500 68c multicolored 1.75 1.75
593 A500 €1.70 multicolored 4.25 4.25

Souvenir Booklet

594 Booklet, #594g-594l 20.50
a.-c. A500 30c any single .65 .65
d.-f. A500 40c any single 1.00 1.00
g. Booklet pane of 4 #594a 2.75 —
h. Booklet pane of 4 #594b 2.75 —
i. Booklet pane of 4 #594c 2.75 —
j. Booklet pane of 4 #594d 4.00 —
k. Booklet pane of 4 #594e 4.00 —
l. Booklet pane of 4 #594f 4.00 —

Comprehensive Nuclear Test-Ban Treaty Organization, 20th Anniv. — V138

2016, Sept. 23 Litho. *Perf. 14¾*

595 V138 80c multi + label *4.00 4.00*

The full sheet sold for $13.27 and €10.90. One of the ten different generic labels is shown. Labels could be personalized. The personalization of labels was available only at UN Headquarters, and not through mail order.

Miniature Sheet

World Wildlife Conference, Johannesburg — V139

No. 596 — Part of map of Africa and: a, Nilkrokodil (Nile crocodile). b, Kapgeier (Cape vulture). c, Steppenschuppentier (Cape pangolin). d, Mystacidium capense.

2016, Sept. 24 Litho. *Perf. 13x13½*

596 V139 Sheet of 4 17.00 17.00
a.-d. €1.70 Any single 4.25 4.25

Sustainable Development Goals Type of 2016

No. 597 — Inscription: a, 1 Keine armut. b, 2 Kein hunger. c, 3 Gesundheit und wohlergehen. d, 4 Hochwertige bildung. e, 5 Geschlechter-gleighheit. f, 6 Sauberes wasser und sanitär-einrichtungen. g, 7 Bezahlbare und saubere energie. h, 8 Menschenwürdige arbeit und wirtschafts-wachstum. i, 9 Industrie, innovation und infrastruktur. j, 10 Weniger ungleichheiten. k, 11 Nachhaltige städte und gemeinden. l, 12 Nachhaltige/r konsum und produktion. m, 13 Massnahmen zum klimaschutz. n, 14 Leben unter wasser. o, 15 Leben an land. p, 16 Frieden, gerechtigkeit und starke institutionen. q, 17 Partnerschaften zur erreichung der ziele.

2016, Oct. 24 Litho. *Perf. 13¼*

597 Sheet of 17 + label 28.50 28.50
a.-q. A503 68c Any single 1.60 1.60

Miniature Sheet

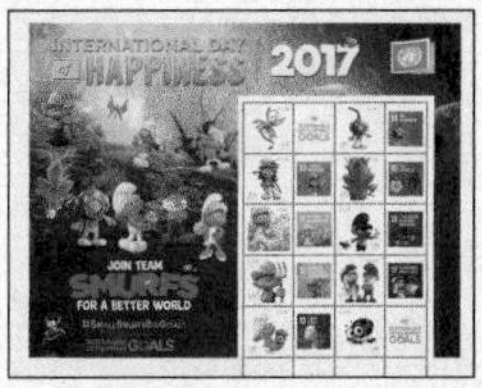

V140

No. 598: a, Insect. b, Smurf wearing diving helmet. c, Smurf holding archery bow. d, Flower with eyes. e, Smurf in park. f, Smurf with police hat, whistle and baton. g, Smurf holding pitchfork. h, Two Smurfs wearing red caps. i, Smurf holding garbage can. j, Ladybug.

2017, Mar. 20 Litho. *Perf. 14¾*

598 V140 Sheet of 10 + 10 labels *30.00 30.00*
a.-j. 80c Any single + label *3.00 3.00*

The full sheet sold for $14.95. The generic labels are shown. Labels could be personalized.

Miniature Sheets

V141

International Dance — V142

No. 599 — Illustration of Samba dancers by Victo Ngai: a, Lion's head. b, Black and tan female dancers. c, Dancers holding drums. d, Black female dancer. e, White female dancer. f, Brown female dancer.

No. 600 — Illustration of Ballet dancers by Ngai: a, Blue dancer with hand bent downward. b, Blue dancer with arm raised above head. c, Blue dancer with arms extended to side. d, Dancer with black dress. e, Head of dancer, tip of dress at bottom. f, Head of dancer facing right.

2017, Mar. 23 Litho. *Perf. 13¼x13*

599 V141 Sheet of 6 9.75 9.75
a.-f. 68c Any single 1.60 1.60
g. As #599, with Brasilia 2017 World Stamp Exhibition emblem overprinted in sheet margin 10.50 10.50
600 V142 Sheet of 6 11.50 11.50
a.-f. 80c Any single 1.90 1.90

Endangered Species Type of 2017

Designs: No. 601, Capra caucasica. No. 602, Nautilidae spp. No. 603, Siphonochilus aethiopicus. No. 604, Lygodactylus williamsi.

2017, May 11 Litho. *Perf. 12¾x12½*

601 A509 80c multicolored 1.90 1.90
602 A509 80c multicolored 1.90 1.90
603 A509 80c multicolored 1.90 1.90
604 A509 80c multicolored 1.90 1.90
a. Block of 4, #601-604 7.75 7.75
Nos. 601-604 (4) 7.60 7.60

World Environment Day Type of 2017

Designs: 68c, Supreme Court, Ottawa, Ontario, Canada. €1.70, Moraine Lake, Canada.

2017, June 5 Litho. *Perf. 13¼*

605 A510 68c multicolored 1.60 1.60
606 A510 €1.70 multicolored 4.00 4.00

World Heritage Sites Along the Silk Roads Type of 2017

Designs: Nos. 607, 609c, Tabriz Historic Bazaar Complex, Iran. Nos. 608, 609f, Safranbolu, Turkey. No. 609a, Longmen Grottoes, People's Republic of China. No. 609b, Historic Center of Bukhara, Uzbekistan. No. 609d, Sulaiman-Too Sacred Mountain, Kyrgyzstan. No. 609e, Kunya-Urgench, Turkmenistan.

2017, Aug. 3 Litho. *Perf. 14¼*

607 A512 80c multicolored 2.00 2.00
608 A512 €1.70 multicolored 4.25 4.25

Souvenir Booklet

609 Booklet, #609g-609l 23.50
a.-c. A512 30c any single .85 .85
d.-f. A512 40c any single 1.10 1.10
g. Booklet pane of 4 #609a 3.40 —
h. Booklet pane of 4 #609b 3.40 —
i. Booklet pane of 4 #609c 3.40 —
j. Booklet pane of 4 #609d 4.40 —
k. Booklet pane of 4 #609e 4.40 —
l. Booklet pane of 4 #609f 4.40 —

Miniature Sheet

V143

No. 610: a, Traunsee with ships and lakeshore buildings. b, Ort Castle and bridge at dusk. c, Aerial view of Cumberland Castle. d, Street in Gmunden, Austria. e, Gmunden City Hall. f, Ort Castle and bridge. g, Sailboat near Ort Castle. h, Villa Toscana. i, Aerial view of Traunsee. j, Ships on Traunsee.

2017, Aug. 24 Litho. *Perf. 14¾*

610 V143 Sheet of 10 + 10 labels *27.50 27.50*
a.-j. 68c Any single + label *2.75 2.75*

United Nations Postal Administration on the Traunsee, 35th anniv. The full sheet sold for $13.64. The generic labels are shown. Labels could be personalized.

Hands and Flower V144

Handshake and Flowers V145

Handshake and Flowers — V146

Printed by Johann Enschedé and Sons, the Netherlands. Panes of 20. Designed by Stranger and Stranger, U.S.

2017, Sept. 21 Litho. *Perf. 14x14¼*

611 V144 68c multicolored 1.75 1.75
612 V145 €1.70 multicolored 4.25 4.25

Souvenir Sheet

Perf. 14¼x13¾

613 V146 €1.70 multicolored 4.25 4.25

International Day of Peace.

World Food Day Type of 2017

Designs: 68c, Breads and grains. 80c, Steak, fish, chicken drumstick, shrimp, egg, beans, lemon slice.

2017, Oct. 16 Litho. *Perf. 13¼x14*

614 A516 68c multicolored 1.75 1.75
615 A516 80c multicolored 2.00 2.00

Endangered Species Type of 2018

Designs: No. 616, Hoodia pilifera. No. 617, Mantella madagascariensis. No. 618, Pangshua sylhetensis. No. 619, Hippocampus zebra.

2018, Mar. 2 Litho. *Perf. 12¾x12½*

616 A519 80c multicolored 2.00 2.00
617 A519 80c multicolored 2.00 2.00
618 A519 80c multicolored 2.00 2.00
619 A519 80c multicolored 2.00 2.00
a. Block of 4, #616-619 8.00 8.00
Nos. 616-619 (4) 8.00 8.00

World Health Day Type of 2018

Designs: 68c, Medical worker, people, globe, caduceus. €1.70, Coins entering piggy bank with white cross.

2018, Apr. 6 Litho. *Perf. 13x13¼*

620 A520 68c multicolored 1.90 1.90
621 A520 €1.70 multicolored 4.50 4.50

United Nations Emblem V147

2018 Litho. *Perf. 14¾*

622 V147 80c multi + label *2.75 2.75*
a. Less distinct year date and frame, lighter blue emblem *2.75 2.75*

Issued: No. 622, 5/26; No. 622a, 7/30. The full sheet sold for $14.32 and €10.90. One of the ten different generic labels is shown. Labels could be personalized. The personalization of labels was available only at UN Headquarters, and not through mail order.

UNISPACE + 50 Conferences Type of 2018

Designs: 68c, Great Red Spot of Jupiter. 80c, Aurora Australis from International Space Station.

€1.70, View of river delta from Copernicus Sentinel satellite.

2018, June 20 Litho. *Perf. 14x14¼*

623 A523 68c multicolored 1.90 1.90
624 A523 80c multicolored 2.25 2.25

Souvenir Sheet

Perf. 13¾

625 A523 €1.70 multicolored 4.50 4.50

No. 625 contains one 45x45mm stamp.

World Heritage Sites In the United Kingdom Type of 2018

Designs: Nos. 626, 628c, Conwy Castle. Nos. 627, 628f, Maritime Greenwich. No. 628a, Giant's Causeway. No. 628b, Stonehenge. No. 628d, Palace of Westminster. No. 628e, Edinburgh.

2018, Aug. 15 Litho. *Perf. 14¼*

626 A524 90c multicolored 2.40 2.40
627 A524 €1.80 multicolored 4.75 4.75

Souvenir Booklet

628 Booklet, #609g-609l 25.50
a.-c. A524 35c any single 1.00 1.00
d.-f. A524 40c any single 1.10 1.10
g. Booklet pane of 4 #628a 4.00 —
h. Booklet pane of 4 #628b 4.00 —
i. Booklet pane of 4 #628c 4.00 —
j. Booklet pane of 4 #628d 4.50 —
k. Booklet pane of 4 #628e 4.50 —
l. Booklet pane of 4 #628f 4.50 —

Miniature Sheet

International Music Day — V148

No. 629: a, Kalimba with three holes. b, Snare drum. c, Shekere. d, Castanets. e, Gong. f, Hourglass drum. g, Castanet with handles and tambourine stick. h, Cymbals. i, Djembe drum. j, Kalimba with one hole. k, Button accordion. l, Maracas and decorated stick.

2018, Oct. 1 Litho. *Perf. 14x13¼*

629 V148 Sheet of 12 24.50 24.50
a.-l. 80c Any single 2.00 2.00

V149

Non-Violence, Sculpture by Carl Fredrik Reuterswärd — V150

Printed by Johann Enschedé Stamps BV, the Netherlands. Panes of 20. Designed by Martin Mörck, Norway.

2018, Oct. 2 Litho. *Perf. 14x14¼*

630 V149 90c multicolored 2.40 2.40
631 V150 €2.30 multicolored 6.00 6.00

Miniature Sheet

World Languages — V151

No. 632 — Word bubbles with word for "Hello" in: a, Serbian or Croatian ("Sprachen der Welt" and denomination in red). b, Arabic ("Sprachen der Welt" and denomination in white). c, Korean ("Sprachen der Welt" in white, denomination in black), d, Dutch or German or Norwegian (Hallo). e, Greek and Turkish (Merhaba). f, Spanish (Hola).

2019, Feb. 21 Litho. *Perf. 13¼x13*

632 V151 Sheet of 6 12.50 12.50
a.-f. 80c Any single 2.00 2.00

Migration — V152

Printed by Lowe-Martin Group, Canada. Panes of 20. Designed by Chris Gash, U.S.

2019, Mar.15 Litho. *Perf. 13¼x13*

633 V152 €1.80 multicolored 4.75 4.75

Endangered Species Type of 2019

Designs: No. 634, Anguilla anguilla. No. 635, Dermochelys coriacea. No. 636, Acropora spp. No. 637, Huso huso.

2019, Apr. 26 Litho. *Perf. 12¾x12½*

634 A534 90c multicolored 2.25 2.25
635 A534 90c multicolored 2.25 2.25
636 A534 90c multicolored 2.25 2.25
637 A534 90c multicolored 2.25 2.25
a. Block of 4, #634-637 9.25 9.25
Nos. 634-637 (4) 9.00 9.00

Souvenir Sheet

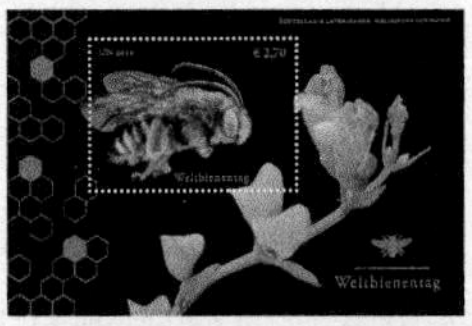

Long-horned Bee and Scutellaria Lateriflora — V153

Litho. With Foil Application

2019, May 20 *Perf. 13*

638 V153 €2.70 multicolored 7.00 7.00

World Bee Day.

V154

V155

V156

V157

International Labor Organization, Cent. — V158

2019, June 28 Litho. *Perf. 13½x14*

639 V154 80c multicolored 2.00 2.00
640 V155 80c multicolored 2.00 2.00
641 V156 80c multicolored 2.00 2.00
642 V157 80c multicolored 2.00 2.00
643 V158 80c multicolored 2.00 2.00
a. Horiz. strip of 5, #639-643 10.00 10.00
Nos. 639-643 (5) 10.00 10.00

V159

V160

V161

V162

United Nations Postal Administration in Vienna, 40th Anniv. — V163

2019, Aug. 23 Litho. *Perf. 14¾*

644 V159 90c multi + label *3.00 3.00*
645 V160 90c multi + label *3.00 3.00*
646 V161 90c multi + label *3.00 3.00*
647 V162 90c multi + label *3.00 3.00*
648 V163 90c multi + label *3.00 3.00*
a. Vert. strip of 5, #644-648, + 5 labels *15.00 15.00*
Nos. 644-648 (5) 15.00 15.00

The full sheets sold for $14.94 or €15.33. The generic labels are shown. Labels could be personalized. The personalization of labels was available only at UN Headquarters, and not through mail order.

Climate Change Type of 2019

Designs: 80c, Canyon and mining operation. 90c, Clouds and smokestack.
€1.80, Fish and corals.

2019, Sept. 23 Litho. *Perf. 14¼*

649 A543 80c multicolored 2.00 2.00
650 A543 90c multicolored 2.25 2.25

Souvenir Sheet

Perf.

651 A543 €1.80 multicolored 4.50 4.50

2019 United Nations Climate Change Conference, Madrid. No. 651 contains one 47mm diameter stamp.

World Heritage Sites in Cuba Type of 2019

Designs: Nos. 652, 654c, Camagüey. Nos. 653, 654f, San Pedro de la Rosa Castle. No. 654a, Morro Castle. No. 664b, Trinidad. No. 654d, Vinales Valley. No. 654e, Cienfuegos.

Litho. With Foil Application

2019, Oct. 24 *Perf. 14¼*

652 A545 90c multicolored 2.25 2.25
653 A545 €1.80 multicolored 4.50 4.50

Souvenir Booklet

654 Booklet, #1115g-1115l 25.00
a.-c. A545 35c Any single .95 .95
d.-f. A545 40c Any single 1.10 1.10
g. Booklet pane of 4 #654a 3.80 —
h. Booklet pane of 4 #654b 3.80 —
i. Booklet pane of 4 #654c 3.80 —
j. Booklet pane of 4 #654d 4.40 —
k. Booklet pane of 4 #654e 4.40 —
l. Booklet pane of 4 #654f 4.40 —

Complete booklet sold for $12.27.

Endangered Species Type of 2020

Designs: No. 655, Panthera leo. No. 656, Pelecanus crispus. No. 657, Phocoena phocoena. No. 658, Equus africanus.

Perf. 12¾x12½

2020, Feb. 17 Litho.

655 A546 90c multicolored 2.25 2.25
656 A546 90c multicolored 2.25 2.25
657 A546 90c multicolored 2.25 2.25
658 A546 90c multicolored 2.25 2.25
a. Block of 4, #655-658 9.00 9.00
Nos. 655-658 (4) 9.00 9.00

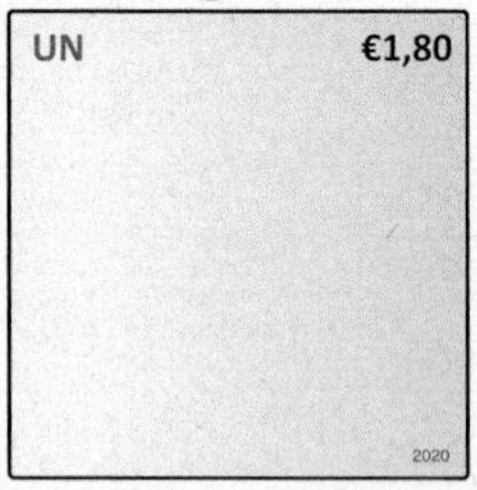

Blank Stamp On Which Stickers Can Be Applied V164

Designs: No. 1212, Hawksbill turtle. No. 1213, Queen conch. No. 1214, Mushroom coral. No. 1215, Humpback whale.

2020, Mar. 19 Litho. *Die Cut*

Self-Adhesive

659 V164 €1.80 multicolored with round-ed corners 4.50 4.50
a. With perpendicular corners and black frame line 4.50 4.50
b. Booklet pane of 6 #1236a 27.00

No. 659 was issued as a souvenir sheet having two different sheet margins, each with different stickers. No. 659a was issued in a booklet containing six panes of one stamp, with each pane having different margins and stickers. Each booklet pane contained one sticker depicting Hello Kitty, a color wheel with Hello Kitty at the center, one of six different Sustainable Development Goal emblems, along with a variety of other stickers. The two souvenir sheets had the same sheet margin and stickers found on two of the panes of No. 659b. No. 659b was sold folded, without any means of separation between the individual panes.

Lepidopterist, Artwork by Paul Villinski V165

Ruth, Costume by Nicole Dextras V166

2020, Apr. 22 Litho. *Perf. 13¼*

660 V165 85c multicolored 2.10 2.10
661 V166 €1.35 multicolored 3.50 3.50

Earth Day, 50th anniv. Because of the COVID-19 pandemic, Nos. 660-661 were not available for sale on day of issue stated on the first-day covers as they had not yet been printed and delivered.

Florence Nightingale (1820-1910), Nurse V167

2020, May 12 Litho. *Perf. 14*

662 V167 €1.35 multicolored 3.50 3.50

International Year of the Nurse and the Midwife.

World Heritage Sites in Russia Type of 2020

Designs: Nos. 663, 665c, Novodevichy Convent. Nos. 664, 665f, Kizhi Pogost. No. 665a, Lake Baikal. No. 665b, Kazan Kremlin. No. 665d, Kremlin and Red Square, Moscow. No. 665e, Saint Petersburg.

Perf. 14½x14¼

2020, Sept. 11 Litho.

663 A556 €1 multicolored 2.60 2.60
664 A556 €1.80 multicolored 4.75 4.75

Souvenir Booklet

665 Booklet, #1115g-1115l 27.00
a.-c. A556 35c any single 1.00 1.00
d.-f. A556 40c any single 1.25 1.25
g. Booklet pane of 4 #665a 4.00 —
h. Booklet pane of 4 #665b 4.00 —
i. Booklet pane of 4 #665c 4.00 —
j. Booklet pane of 4 #665d 5.00 —
k. Booklet pane of 4 #665e 5.00 —
l. Booklet pane of 4 #665f 5.00 —

Complete booklet sold for $12.94 or €10.

United Nations Emblem V168

2020, Oct. 2 Litho. *Perf. 14¾*

666 V168 €1 multi + label *3.25 3.25*
Sheet of 10 + 10 labels *33.50 —*

The full sheet sold for $16.70 or €12.90. One of the ten different generic labels is shown. Labels could be personalized. The personalization of labels was available only at UN Headquarters, and not through mail order.

Souvenir Sheet

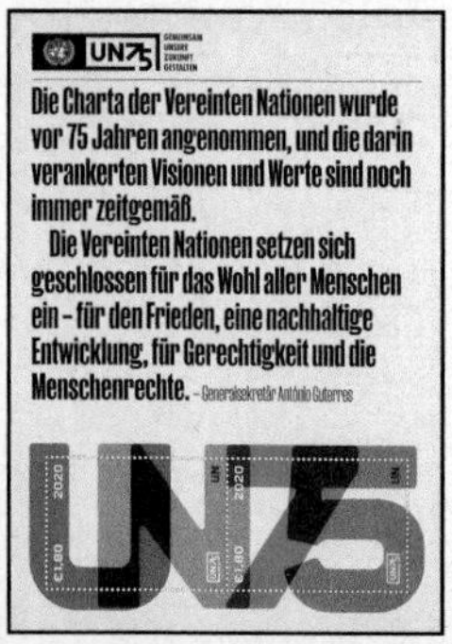
Die Charta der Vereinten Nationen wurde vor 75 Jahren angenommen, und die darin verankerten Visionen und Werte sind noch immer zeitgemäß.
Die Vereinten Nationen setzen sich geschlossen für das Wohl aller Menschen ein – für den Frieden, eine nachhaltige Entwicklung, für Gerechtigkeit und die Menschenrechte.
UN75

United Nations, 75th Anniv. V169

No. 667: a, Red "U," blue "N." b, Pink "7," green "5."

2020, Oct. 24 Litho. *Perf. 13¼*

667 V169 Sheet of 2 9.50 9.50
a.-b. €1.80 Either single 4.75 4.75

Souvenir Sheet

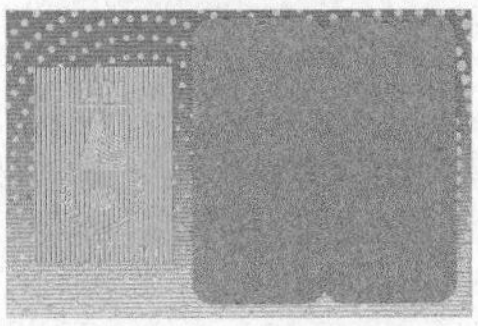

Vienna International Center and Emblem — V170

Litho. With Foil Application

2020, Nov. 24 *Die Cut Perf. 11½*

Self-Adhesive

668 V170 €7 multicolored 18.50 18.50

Crypto stamp. Unused value is for sheets with unscratched panels at right.

International Day for the Elimination of Racial Discrimination — V171

2021, Mar. 19 Litho. *Perf. 13¼x13*

669 V171 €1.80 multicolored 5.00 5.00

Endangered Species Type of 2021

Designs: No. 670, Neophema chrysogaster. No. 671, Babyrousa babyrussa. No. 672, Onychogalea fraenata. No. 673, Lepanthes telipogoniflora.

2021, Apr. 7 Litho. *Perf. 12¾x12½*

670 A565 90c multicolored 2.50 2.50
671 A565 90c multicolored 2.50 2.50
672 A565 90c multicolored 2.50 2.50
673 A565 90c multicolored 2.50 2.50
a. Block of 4, #670-673 10.00 10.00
Nos. 670-673 (4) 10.00 5.50

Rider on Orange Horse — V172

Rider on Brown Horse — V173

Rider on White Horse — V174

Golfer Contemplating Putt — V175

Golfer and Ball on Hill — V176

Female Golfer — V177

Doves and Olympic Flame V178

2021, July 23 Litho. *Perf. 13½*

674 V172 85c multicolored 2.25 2.25
675 V173 85c multicolored 2.25 2.25
676 V174 85c multicolored 2.25 2.25
a. Horiz. strip of 3, #674-676 6.75 6.75
677 V175 €1 multicolored 2.75 2.75
678 V176 €1 multicolored 2.75 2.75
679 V177 €1 multicolored 2.75 2.75
a. Horiz. strip of 3, #677-679 8.25 8.25
Nos. 674-679 (6) 15.00 15.00

Souvenir Sheet

680 V178 €1.80 multicolored 5.00 5.00

Sports for Peace, 2020 Summer Olympics, Tokyo. The 2020 Summer Olympics were postponed until 2021 because of the COVID-19 pandemic.

Waterways, Railways and Bridges World Heritage Sites Type of 2020

Designs: Nos. 681, 683c, Forth Bridge, Scotland. Nos. 682, 683f, Old Bridge, Mostar, Bosnia and Herzegovina. No. 683a, Rideau Canal, Canada. No. 683b, Rhaetian Railway, Switzerland and Italy. No. 683d, Grand Canal, People's Republic of China. No. 683e, Darjeeling Himalayan Railway, India.

2021, Aug. 25 Litho. *Perf. 14¼*

681 A575 €1 multicolored 2.75 2.75
682 A575 €1.80 multicolored 5.00 5.00

Souvenir Booklet

683 Booklet, #683g-683l 27.00
a.-c. A575 35c any single 1.00 1.00
d.-f. A575 40c any single 1.25 1.25
g. Booklet pane of 4 #683a 4.00 —
h. Booklet pane of 4 #683b 4.00 —
i. Booklet pane of 4 #683c 4.00 —
j. Booklet pane of 4 #683d 5.00 —
k. Booklet pane of 4 #683e 5.00 —
l. Booklet pane of 4 #683f 5.00 —

Complete booklet sold for $12.94 or €10.

Miniature Sheet

Comprehensive Nuclear Test Ban Treaty, 25th Anniv. — V179

No. 684: a, Hydroacoustic Station HA4, Crozet Islands, and penguins. b, Hydroacoustic Station HA3, Chile, with red sphere. c, Radionuclide Station RN68, Tristan da Cunha, in fenced enclosure. d, Radionuclide Station RN33, Germany, with green base. e, Large group of technicians at Infrasound Station IS33, Madagascar. f, Two technicians near antenna at Infrasound Station IS55, Antarctica. g, Two technicians at Auxiliary Seismic Station AS74, Oman. h, Vehicle and technician at Auxiliary Seismic Station AS69, New Zealand. i, Technician in protective clothing carrying equipment for field exercise, Kazakhstan. j, Technician for field exercise in aircraft above Jordan.

2021, Aug. 27 Litho. *Perf. 14½*

684 V179 Sheet of 10 + 10 labels *24.00 24.00*
a.-j. €1 Any single + label *2.40 2.40*

The full sheet sold for $12.00 or €12.90. The generic labels are shown. Labels could be personalized.

Miniature Sheet

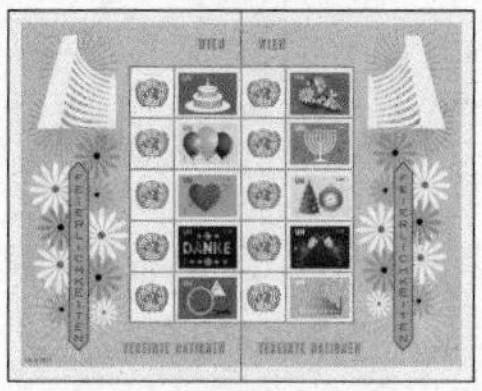

Celebrations — V180

No. 685: a, Birthday cake. b, Flower bouquet. c, Three balloons. d, Menorah. e, Heart and arrow. f, Christmas tree and ornament. g, "Danke." h, Champagne flutes. i, Diamond ring. j, Mosque.

2021, Nov. 4 Litho. *Perf. 14¼*

685 V180 Sheet of 10 *34.00 34.00*
a.-j. €1 Any single + label *3.25 3.25*

The full sheet sold for $16.93. The generic labels are shown. Labels could be personalized. The personalization of labels was available only at UN Headquarters, and not through mail order.

World Toilet Day — V181

2021, Nov. 19 Litho. *Perf. 14¼*

686 V181 €1 multicolored 2.75 2.75

Curler Delivering Stone V182

Curling Stones and Brooms V183

Skier in Air — V184

Skier On Snow V185

2022, Jan. 14 Litho. *Perf. 14¼*

687 V182 85c multicolored 2.10 2.10
688 V183 85c multicolored 2.10 2.10
a. Horiz. pair, #687-688 4.25 4.25
689 V184 €1.80 multicolored 4.50 4.50
690 V185 €1.80 multicolored 4.50 4.50
a. Horiz. pair, #689-690 9.00 9.00
Nos. 687-690 (4) 13.20 13.20

Sports for Peace, 2022 Winter Olympics, Beijing.

Endangered Species Type of 2022

Designs: No. 691, Dynastes satanas. No. 692, Hylocereus triangularis. No. 693, Cedrela odorata. No. 694, Acanthocereus tetragonus.

Perf. 12¾x12½

2022, Mar. 18 Litho.

691 A592 €1 multicolored 2.50 2.50
692 A592 €1 multicolored 2.50 2.50
693 A592 €1 multicolored 2.50 2.50
694 A592 €1 multicolored 2.50 2.50
a. Block of 4, #691-694 10.00 10.00
Nos. 691-694 (4) 10.00 10.00

Wangari Maathai (1940-2011), 2004 Nobel Peace Laureate V186

2022, Apr. 1 Litho. *Perf. 14¼*

695 V186 85c multicolored 2.25 2.25

Exploration of Mars Type of 2022

Designs: 85c, Landing area for People's Republic of China's Tianwen-1 Lander. €1, Zhurong Rover on Mars.
€1.80, Zhurong Rover Landing Platform.

2022, Apr. 24 Litho. *Perf. 13¼x13*

696 A593 85c multicolored 2.25 2.25
697 A593 €1 multicolored 2.50 2.50

Souvenir Sheet

Perf. 13½

698 A593 €1.80 multicolored 4.50 4.50

No. 698 contains one 44x44mm stamp.

Miniature Sheet

World Chess Day V187

No. 699: a, Chess board with black pieces, two pawns in forward positions. b, Player moving white king. c, Chairs and chess set on round table. d, Black pawn on chess board. e, Player toppling black king. f, Player moving black pawn. g, Table with chess boards and timers. h, Black and white knights. i, Chess board with black pieces, knight next to king. j, Chess board with black and white pieces, with toppled white king.

2022, July 20 Litho. *Perf. 14¼*

699 V187 Sheet of 10 + 10 labels *32.50 32.50*
a.-j. €1 Any single + label *3.25 3.25*

The full sheet sold for $16.10 or €12.90. The generic labels are shown. Labels could be personalized.

European Spa Towns World Heritage Sites Type of 2022

Designs: Nos. 700, 702c, Baden-Baden, Germany. Nos. 701, 702f, Baden bei Wien, Austria. No. 702a, Karlovy Vary, Czech Republic. No. 702b, Spa, Belgium. No. 702d, Montecatini Terme, Italy. No. 702e, Vichy, France.

2022, Sept. 9 Litho. *Perf. 14½x14¼*

700 A594 €1 multicolored 2.40 2.40
701 A594 €1.80 multicolored 4.25 4.25

Souvenir Booklet

702 Booklet, #1115g-1115l 23.50
a.-c. A594 35c any single .90 .90
d.-f. A594 40c any single 1.00 1.00
g. Booklet pane of 4 #702a 3.75 —
h. Booklet pane of 4 #702b 3.75 —
i. Booklet pane of 4 #702c 3.75 —
j. Booklet pane of 4 #702d 4.00 —
k. Booklet pane of 4 #702e 4.00 —
l. Booklet pane of 4 #702f 4.00 —

Complete booklet sold for $11.59 or €10.

Souvenir Sheet

Peace Dove V188

Litho. With Foil Application

2022, Nov. 18 *Die Cut Perf. 11½*

Self-Adhesive

703 V188 €3.65 multicolored 8.50 8.50

Crypto stamp. Unused value is for sheets with unscratched panels at right.

SEMI-POSTAL STAMPS

AIDS Awareness Semi-postal Type

Souvenir Sheet

2002, Oct. 24 Litho. *Perf. 14½*

B1 VSP1 51c + 25c multicolored 3.50 3.50

VSP2

Photograph of John Lennon (1940-80), by David Nutter — VSP3

2021, Sept. 21 Litho. ***Perf. 14¼***

B2 VSP2 €1 multicolored 4.00 4.00

Souvenir Sheet

Litho. With Foil Application

B3 VSP3 €2.85 multicolored 10.50 10.50

International Day of Peace. Surtax for United Nations peacekeeping efforts.

World Humanitarian Day — VSP4

2022, Aug. 19 Litho. ***Perf. 13¼x13***

B4 VSP4 €1.80 multicolored 5.75 5.75

Surtax for United Nations Central Emergency Response Fund.

U.N. TEMPORARY EXECUTIVE AUTHORITY, WEST NEW GUINEA

Temporary Executive Authority

LOCATION — Western half of New Guinea, southwest Pacific Ocean
GOVT. — Province of Indonesia
AREA — In 1958, the size was 151,789 sq. mi.
POP. — estimated at 730,000 in 1958
CAPITAL — Hollandia

The former Netherlands New Guinea became a territory under the administration of the United Nations Temporary Executive Authority on Oct. 1, 1962.

The territory came under Indonesian administration on May 1, 1963. For stamps issued by Indonesia see West Irian in Volume 3.

100 Cents = 1 Gulden
100 Cents = 1 Gulden

Catalogue values for all unused stamps in this country are for Never Hinged items.

First Printing (Hollandia)

Netherlands New Guinea Stamps of 1950-60 Overprinted

Overprint size: 17x3½mm. Top of "N" is slightly lower than the "U," and the base of the "T" is straight, or nearly so.

Photo.; Litho. (#4, 6, 8)

Perf. 12½x12, 12½x13½

1962, Oct. 1 Unwmk.

1	A4	1c	vermilion & yellow	.25	.25
2	A1	2c	deep orange	.25	.25
3	A4	5c	chocolate & yellow	.25	.25
4	A5	7c	org red, bl & brn vio	.25	*.35*
5	A4	10c	aqua & red brown	.25	*.35*
6	A5	12c	green, bl & brn vio	.25	*.35*
7	A4	15c	deep yel & red brn	.45	.45
8	A5	17c	brown violet & blue	.55	*.70*
9	A4	20c	lt bl grn & red brn	.60	*.75*
10	A6	25c	red	.40	*.55*
11	A6	30c	deep blue	.75	.75
12	A6	40c	deep orange	.75	.75
13	A6	45c	dark olive	1.25	*1.50*
14	A6	55c	slate blue	*29.00*	2.25
15	A6	80c	dull gray violet	6.00	6.00
16	A6	85c	dark violet brown	3.00	3.00
17	A6	1g	plum	9.25	3.00

Engr.

18	A3	2g	reddish brown	12.50	30.00
19	A3	5g	green	9.00	8.00
			Nos. 1-19 (19)	75.00	59.50

Overprinted locally and sold in West New Guinea. Stamps of the second printing were used to complete sets sold to collectors.

Second Printing (Haarlen, Netherlands)

Overprint size: 17x3½mm. Top of the "N" is slightly higher than the "U," and the base of the "T" is concave.

Photo.; Litho. (#4a, 6a, 8a)

Perf. 12½x12, 12½x13½

1962 Unwmk.

1a	A4	1c	vermilion & yellow	.25	.25
2a	A1	2c	deep orange	.25	.25
3a	A4	5c	chocolate & yellow	.25	.25
4a	A5	7c	org red, bl & brn vio	.25	.25
5a	A4	10c	aqua & red brown	.25	.25
6a	A5	12c	green, bl & brn vio	.25	.25
7a	A4	15c	deep yel & red brn	.50	.25
8a	A5	17c	brown violet & blue	.60	.40
9a	A4	20c	lt blue grn & red brn	.60	.40
10a	A6	25c	red	.35	.35
11a	A6	30c	deep blue	.90	.40
12a	A6	40c	deep orange	.90	.40
13a	A6	45c	dark olive	1.75	.75
14a	A6	55c	slate blue	5.00	1.00
15a	A6	80c	dull gray violet	7.00	*9.00*
16a	A6	85c	dark violet brown	3.75	*4.75*
17a	A6	1g	plum	4.25	2.00

Engr.

18a	A3	2g	reddish brown	16.00	*27.50*
19a	A3	5g	green	8.00	6.50
			Nos. 1a-19a (19)	51.10	55.20

Third Printing

Overprint 14mm long.

Photo.; Litho. (#4b, 6b, 8b)

Perf. 12½x12

1963, Mar. Photo. Unwmk.

1b	A4	1c	vermilion & yellow	*5.00*	*3.00*
3b	A4	5c	chocolate & yellow	*6.00*	*4.00*
4b	A5	7c	org red, bl & brn vio	*20.00*	*20.00*
5b	A4	10c	aqua & red brown	*6.00*	*4.00*
6b	A5	12c	green, bl & brn vio	*35.00*	*35.00*
7b	A4	15c	deep yel & red brn	*130.00*	*130.00*
8b	A5	17c	brown violet & blue	*15.00*	*12.00*
9b	A4	20c	lt blue grn & red brn	*7.50*	*5.00*
			Nos. 1b-9b (8)	*224.50*	*213.00*

The third printing was applied in West New Guinea and it is doubtful whether it was regularly issued. Used values are for canceled to order stamps.

Fourth Printing

Overprint 19mm long.

Photogravure

1963, Mar. Unwmk. ***Perf. 12½x12***

1c	A4	1c	vermilion & yellow	*50.00*	*50.00*
5c	A4	10c	aqua & red brown	*150.00*	*150.00*

The fourth printing was applied in West New Guinea and it is doubtful whether it was regularly issued. Used values are for canceled to order stamps.

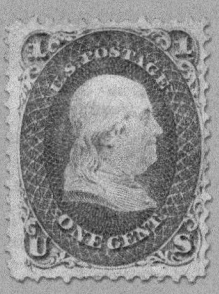

U.N. TRANSITIONAL AUTHORITY IN EAST TIMOR

A30

2000, Apr. 29 Litho. *Perf. 12x11¾*

350	A30	Dom. red & multi	*35.00*	*102.50*
351	A30	Int. blue & multi	*47.50*	*112.50*

No. 350 sold for 10c and No. 351 sold for 50c on day of issue.

U.N. INTERIM ADMINISTRATION, KOSOVO

These stamps were issued by the United Nations Interim Administration Mission in Kosovo and the Post & Telecommunications of Kosovo. Service was local for the first two months, with international use to start in mid-May.

100 pfennigs = 1 mark
100 cents = €1 (2002)

Catalogue values for all unused stamps in this country are for Never Hinged items.

Peace in Kosovo — A1

Designs: 20pf, Mosaic depicting Orpheus, c. 5th-6th cent., Podujeve. 30pf, Dardinian idol, Museum of Kosovo. 50pf, Silver coin of Damastion from 4th cent. B.C. 1m, Statue of Mother Teresa, Prizren. 2m, Map of Kosovo.

Perf. 13½x13, 13½x13¼ (30pf)

2000, Mar. 14 Litho. Unwmk.

1	A1	20pf multicolored	.65	.65
2	A1	30pf multicolored	1.25	1.25
3	A1	50pf multicolored	1.60	1.60
4	A1	1m multicolored	2.00	1.80
5	A1	2m multicolored	3.75	3.50
		Nos. 1-5 (5)	9.25	8.80

Nos. 1-5 were demonetized July 1, 2002.

Beginning with No. 6, Kosovan stamps were not available to collectors through the United Nations Postal Administration.

Peace in Kosovo — A2

Designs: 20pf, Bird. 30pf, Street musician. 50pf, Butterfly and pear. 1m, Children and stars. 2m, Globe and handprints.

2001, Nov. 12 Litho. *Perf. 14*

6	A2	20pf multicolored	1.00	1.00
7	A2	30pf multicolored	1.25	1.25
8	A2	50pf multicolored	2.00	2.00
9	A2	1m multicolored	4.00	4.00
10	A2	2m multicolored	7.50	7.50
		Nos. 6-10 (5)	15.75	15.75

Peace in Kosovo Type of 2001 With Denominations in Euros Only

2002, May 2 Litho. *Perf. 14*

11	A2	10c Like #6	.75	.75
12	A2	15c Like #7	1.00	1.00
13	A2	26c Like #8	1.50	1.50
14	A2	51c Like #9	4.50	4.50
15	A2	€1.02 Like #10	8.00	8.00
		Nos. 11-15 (5)	15.75	15.75

Christmas — A3

Designs: 50c, Candles and garland. €1, Stylized men.

2003, Dec. 20 Litho. *Perf. 14*

16	A3	50c multicolored	*7.50*	*7.50*
17	A3	€1 multicolored	*14.50*	*14.50*

Return of Refugees
A4

Five Years of Peace
A5

2004, June 29 Litho. *Perf. 13¼x13*

18	A4	€1 multicolored	*7.00*	*7.00*
19	A5	€2 multicolored	*16.00*	*16.00*

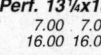

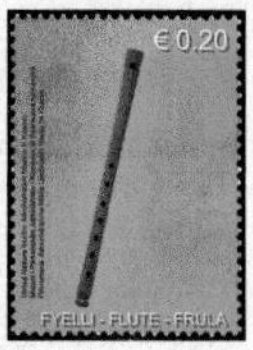
Musical Instruments — A6

2004, Aug. 31 Litho. *Perf. 13¼x13*

20	A6	20c Flute	*5.00*	*5.00*
21	A6	30c Ocarina	*10.00*	*10.00*

Aprons — A7

Vests — A8

Designs: 20c, Apron from Prizren. 30c, Apron from Rugova. 50c, Three vests. €1, Two vests.

2004, Oct. 28 Litho. *Perf. 13x13¼*

22	A7	20c multicolored	*5.50*	*5.50*
23	A7	30c multicolored	*8.50*	*8.50*
24	A8	50c multicolored	*12.00*	*12.00*
25	A8	€1 multicolored	*26.00*	*26.00*
		Nos. 22-25 (4)	*52.00*	*52.00*

Mirusha Waterfall — A9

2004, Nov. 26 Litho. *Perf. 13x13¼*

26	A9	€2 multicolored	*7.50*	*7.50*

House — A10

2004, Dec. 14 Litho. *Perf. 13x13¼*

27	A10	50c multicolored	*4.50*	*4.50*

Flowers — A11

2005, June 29 Litho. *Perf. 13½*

28	A11	15c Peony	*2.25*	*2.25*
29	A11	20c Poppies	*3.25*	*3.25*
30	A11	30c Gentian	*5.00*	*5.00*
		Nos. 28-30 (3)	*10.50*	*10.50*

A12

Handicrafts — A13

2005, July 20 *Perf. 13¼x13*

31	A12	20c shown	*2.50*	*2.50*
32	A12	30c Cradle	*3.00*	*3.00*
33	A13	50c shown	*3.25*	*3.25*
34	A12	€1 Necklace	*4.25*	*4.25*
		Nos. 31-34 (4)	*13.00*	*13.00*

Village — A14

Town — A15

City — A16

2005, Sept. 15 *Perf. 13x13½*

35	A14	20c multicolored	*2.00*	*2.00*
36	A15	50c multicolored	*3.00*	*3.00*
37	A16	€1 multicolored	*6.00*	*6.00*
		Nos. 35-37 (3)	*11.00*	*11.00*

Archaeological Artifacts — A17

2005, Nov. 2 *Perf. 13½x13*

38	A17	20c shown	*1.25*	*1.25*
39	A17	30c Statue	*1.75*	*1.75*
40	A17	50c Sculpture	*2.50*	*2.50*
41	A17	€1 Helmet	*7.50*	*7.50*
		Nos. 38-41 (4)	*13.00*	*13.00*

Minerals — A18

2005, Dec. 10 *Perf. 13x13½*

42	A18	€2 multicolored	*10.00*	*10.00*

A19

Europa — A20

2006, July 20 *Perf. 13¼x13*

43	A19	50c multicolored	*2.25*	*2.25*
44	A20	€1 multicolored	*4.25*	*4.25*

Exists Imperf. Value set of two, $75.

Fauna — A21

2006, May 23 Litho. *Perf. 13*

45	A21	15c Wolf	*1.00*	*1.00*
46	A21	20c Cow	*1.25*	*1.25*
47	A21	30c Pigeon	*1.40*	*1.40*
48	A21	50c Swan	*1.60*	*1.60*
49	A21	€1 Dog	*2.75*	*2.75*
a.		Souvenir sheet, #45-49, + label	*8.75*	*8.75*
		Nos. 45-49 (5)	*8.00*	*8.00*

Nos. 45-49 are inscribed CPU. Stamps with "Leoprint" imprint are from No. 63a.

No. 49a exists in two shades of green selvage.

Children — A22

Designs: 20c, Children in cradle. 30c, Children reading. 50c, Girls dancing. €1, Child in water.

2006, June 30 Litho. *Perf. 13*

50	A22	20c multicolored	*1.00*	*1.00*
51	A22	30c multicolored	*1.25*	*1.25*
52	A22	50c multicolored	*1.75*	*1.75*
53	A22	€1 multicolored	*3.50*	*3.50*
a.		Souvenir sheet, #50-53	*7.75*	*7.75*
		Nos. 50-53 (4)	*7.50*	*7.50*

Nos. 50-53 were printed by CPU & Moare. No. 53a was printed by two printers: 7,500 inscribed "CPU&Moare," and 5,000 inscribed "Leoprint."

Nos. 50-53 from CPO & Moare exists imperforate. Value, set, $75.

No. 53a by CPU & Moare exists imperforate. Value $75.

A23

A24

A25

Tourist Attractions
A26

2006, Sept. 1 Litho. *Perf. 13*

54	A23 20c multicolored	*1.00*	*1.00*
55	A24 30c multicolored	*1.25*	*1.25*
56	A25 50c multicolored	*1.75*	*1.75*
57	A26 €1 multicolored	*3.25*	*3.25*
a.	Souvenir sheet, #54-57	*9.50*	*9.50*
	Nos. 54-57 (4)	*7.25*	*7.25*

Nos. 54-57 were printed by CPU & Moare. No. 57a was printed by two printers: 7,500 inscribed "CPU&Moare," and 5,000 inscribed "Leoprint."

Intl. Peace Day — A27

2006, Sept. 21 Litho. *Perf. 13*

58	A27 €2 multicolored	*7.00*	*7.00*

Ancient Coins — A28

Various coins.

2006, Nov. 1 Litho. *Perf. 13*

59	A28 20c multicolored	*1.00*	*1.00*
60	A28 30c multicolored	*1.50*	*1.50*
61	A28 50c multicolored	*1.75*	*1.75*
62	A28 €1 multicolored	*3.25*	*3.25*
a.	Souvenir sheet, #59-62	*9.50*	*9.50*
	Nos. 59-62 (4)	*7.50*	*7.50*

Nos. 59-62 are inscribed CPU. Stamps with "Leoprint" imprint are from No. 63a.

No. 62a exists imperforate. Value, $75.

Sculpture — A29

2006, Dec. 1 Litho. *Perf. 13*

63	A29 €2 multicolored	*8.00*	*8.00*
a.	Miniature sheet, #45-57, 59-63, + 2 labels	*80.00*	*80.00*

Convention on the Rights of Persons With Disabilities — A30

Emblems of handicaps and: 20c, Children and butterfly. 50c, Handicapped women. 70c, Map of Kosovo. €1, Stylized flower.

2007, Apr. 23 Litho. *Perf. 14x14¼*

64	A30 20c multicolored	*1.25*	*1.25*
65	A30 50c multicolored	*2.50*	*2.50*
66	A30 70c multicolored	*3.00*	*3.00*
67	A30 €1 multicolored	*3.75*	*3.75*
a.	Souvenir sheet, #64-67	*12.50*	*12.50*
	Nos. 64-67 (4)	*10.50*	*10.50*

Color shades vary widely. Printer's waste of this issue exists in the marketplace, including partial prints, missing design elements, and missing colors.

Two varieties of No. 67a, exist differing in text surrounding the stamps. It has not been established if both varieties were officially issued.

Scouting, Cent. — A31

Europa — A32

2007, May 12 Litho. *Perf. 13¼*

68	A31 70c multicolored	*4.25*	*4.25*
69	A32 €1 multicolored	*6.25*	*6.25*
a.	Souvenir sheet, #68-69	*90.00*	*90.00*

A33

A34

A35

International Children's Day — A36

2007, June 1 Litho. *Perf. 13¼*

70	A33 20c multicolored	*1.25*	*1.25*
71	A34 30c multicolored	*1.50*	*1.50*
72	A35 70c multicolored	*2.50*	*2.50*
73	A36 €1 multicolored	*4.00*	*4.00*
	Nos. 70-73 (4)	*9.25*	*9.25*

Nos. 70-73 exist imperf. Value, set $45

Native Costumes — A37

Designs: 20c, Serbian woman. 30c, Prizren Region woman. 50c, Sword dancer. 70c, Drenica Region woman. €1, Shepherd, Rugova.

2007, July 6 Litho. *Perf. 13½x13¼*

74	A37 20c multicolored	*1.25*	*1.25*
75	A37 30c multicolored	*1.75*	*1.75*
76	A37 50c multicolored	*2.00*	*2.00*
77	A37 70c multicolored	*2.50*	*2.50*
78	A37 €1 multicolored	*3.25*	*3.25*
a.	Souvenir sheet, #74-78, + label	*12.50*	*12.50*
	Nos. 74-78 (5)	*10.75*	*10.75*

Masks — A38

Various masks.

Perf. 13½x13¼

2007, Sept. 11 Litho.

79	A38 15c multicolored	*.75*	*.75*
80	A38 30c multicolored	*1.00*	*1.00*
81	A38 50c multicolored	*2.00*	*2.00*
82	A38 €1 multicolored	*3.00*	*3.00*
	Nos. 79-82 (4)	*6.75*	*6.75*

Sports — A39

Designs: 20c, Soccer ball, basketball, two people standing, person in wheelchair. 50c, Wrestlers. €1, Symbols of 24 sports.

2007, Oct. 2 Litho. *Perf. 13¼x13½*

83	A39 20c multicolored	*1.00*	*1.00*
84	A39 50c multicolored	*2.25*	*2.25*
85	A39 €1 multicolored	*4.00*	*4.00*
	Nos. 83-85 (3)	*7.25*	*7.25*

Nos. 83-85 exist imperf. Value, set $65.

Architecture — A40

Designs: 30c, Stone bridge, Vushtrri. 50c, Hamam, Prizren. 70c, Tower. €1, Tower, diff.

2007, Nov. 6 Litho. *Perf. 13¼*

86	A40 30c multicolored	*1.50*	*1.50*
87	A40 50c multicolored	*2.00*	*2.00*
88	A40 70c multicolored	*2.50*	*2.50*
89	A40 €1 multicolored	*3.50*	*3.50*
	Nos. 86-89 (4)	*9.50*	*9.50*

Nos. 86-89 exist imperf. Value, set $85.

Locomotives — A41

Designs: €1, Diesel locomotive. €2, Steam locomotive

2007, Dec. 7 Litho. *Perf. 13¼*

90	A41 €1 multicolored	*4.00*	*4.00*
91	A41 €2 multicolored	*8.00*	*8.00*

Nos. 90-91 exist imperf. Value, set $125.

Skanderbeg (1405-68), Albanian National Hero — A42

2008, Jan. 17 Litho. *Perf. 13¼*

92	A42 €2 multicolored	*7.50*	*7.50*

No. 92 exists imperf. Value, $35.

Kosovo declared its independence from Serbia on Feb. 17, 2008, ending the United Nations Interim Administration. Stamps issued after Feb. 17, 2008, by the Republic of Kosovo will be listed under Kosovo in the *Scott Standard Postage Stamp Catalogue.*

ABU DHABI

ˌä-bü-ˈthä-bē

LOCATION — Arabia, on Persian Gulf
GOVT. — Sheikdom under British protection
POP. — 25,000 (estimated)
CAPITAL — Abu Dhabi

Abu Dhabi is one of six Persian Gulf sheikdoms to join the United Arab Emirates, which proclaimed its independence Dec. 2, 1971. See United Arab Emirates.

100 Naye Paise = 1 Rupee
1000 Fils = 1 Dinar (1966)

Catalogue values for all unused stamps in this country are for Never Hinged items.

Sheik Shakbut bin Sultan — A1

Gazelle — A1a

Palace — A2

Oil Rig and Camels — A2a

Perf. 14½

1964, Mar. 30 Photo. Unwmk.

1	A1 5np brt yellow green	4.00	*3.75*
2	A1 15np brown	3.00	2.00
3	A1 20np brt ultra	3.25	1.75
a.	Perf 13x13½	575.00	
4	A1 30np red orange	3.25	1.25
5	A1a 40np brt violet	6.00	1.00
6	A1a 50np brown olive	6.50	2.25
7	A1a 75np dk gray	9.00	6.75

Engr. *Perf. 13x13½*

8	A2 1r light green	5.00	2.50
9	A2 2r black	9.00	5.00
10	A2a 5r carmine rose	20.00	13.00
11	A2a 10r blue	26.00	15.00
	Nos. 1-11 (11)	95.00	54.25

For surcharges see Nos. 15-25.

Falcon Perched on Wrist — A3

40np, Falcon facing left. 2r, Falcon facing right.

1965, Mar. 30 Photo. *Perf. 14½*

12	A3 20np chlky blue & brn	13.50	2.75
13	A3 40np ultra & brown	17.00	3.50
14	A3 2r brt blue grn & gray brn	29.00	16.00
	Nos. 12-14 (3)	59.50	22.25

Nos. 1-11 Surcharged

a

b

c

1966, Oct. 1 Photo. *Perf. 14½*

15	A1 (a) 5f on 5np	10.00	5.00
16	A1 (a) 15f on 15np	12.00	9.00
17	A1 (a) 20f on 20np, perf 13x13½ (#3a)	14.00	7.00
a.	Perf 14½ (#3)	250.00	250.00
b.	As "a," inverted surcharge	700.00	*950.00*
18	A1 (a) 30f on 30np	14.00	*16.50*
a.	Double surcharge	400.00	
b.	Arabic surcharge "20f" instead of "30f"	*11,000.*	
19	A1a (b) 40f on 40np	13.00	1.50
20	A1a (b) 50f on 50np	35.00	*32.50*
21	A1a (b) 75f on 75np	35.00	*32.50*
a.	Double surcharge	400.00	

Engr.

Perf. 13x13½

22	A2 (c) 100f on 1r	17.00	4.00
23	A2 (c) 200f on 2r	17.50	13.00
24	A2a (c) 500f on 5r	42.50	*47.50*
25	A2a (c) 1d on 10r	62.50	*72.50*
	Nos. 15-25 (11)	272.50	*241.00*

Overprint on No. 25 has "1 Dinar" on 1 line and 3 bars through old denomination.

Crossed Flags of Abu Dhabi — A4

Sheik Zaid bin Sultan al Nahayan — A4a

Dorcas Gazelle — A5

200f, Falcon. 500f, 1d, Palace.

Engr.; Flags Litho.

1967, Apr. 1 *Perf. 13x13½*

26	A4 5f dpl grn & red	.40	.30
27	A4 15f dk brown & red	.60	.30
28	A4 20f Prus blue & red	1.00	.75
29	A4 35f purple & red	1.25	1.00

Engr.

30	A4a	40f blue green	1.50	1.20
31	A4a	50f lt brown	1.90	1.50
32	A4a	60f blue	2.10	1.60
33	A4a	100f car rose	3.50	2.75

Litho.

34	A5	125f brt yel grn & brn ol	7.50	6.50
35	A5	200f lt blue & lt brn	32.00	27.50
36	A5	500f dull org & brt redsh vio	22.50	17.50
37	A5	1d brt yel grn & bluish vio	60.00	50.00
		Nos. 26-37 (12)	134.25	110.90

For surcharge, see No. 55A.

Sheik Zaid bin Sultan al Nahayan — A6

1967, Aug. 6 Photo. *Perf. 14½x14*

38	A6	40f blue green	4.50	2.75
39	A6	50f org brown	5.50	2.25
40	A6	60f Prus blue	19.00	4.50
41	A6	100f carmine rose	28.00	11.00
		Nos. 38-41 (4)	57.00	20.50

Human Rights Flame and Sheik Zaid — A6a

Perf. 14½x14

1968, Apr. 1 Photo. Unwmk.

Emblem in Red and Green

42	A6a	35f peacock bl & gold	2.25	.90
43	A6a	60f dk blue & gold	3.50	1.25
44	A6a	150f dk brown & gold	9.00	3.00
		Nos. 42-44 (3)	14.75	5.15

International Human Rights Year.

Sheik Zaid and Coat of Arms — A7

Perf. 14x14½

1968, Aug. 6 Photo. Unwmk.

45	A7	5f multicolored	4.00	.60
46	A7	10f multicolored	4.00	.85
47	A7	100f multicolored	11.00	3.25
48	A7	125f multicolored	16.00	4.75
		Nos. 45-48 (4)	35.00	9.45

Accession of Sheik Zaid, 2nd anniversary.

Abu Dhabi Airport A8

5f, Buildings under construction and earth-moving equipment. 35f, New bridge and falcon. Each stamp shows different portrait of Sheik Zaid.

Perf. 12, 12½x13 (10f)

1969, Mar. 28 Litho.

Size: 5f, 35f, 59x34mm; 10f, 47x34mm

49	A8	5f multicolored	3.00	.55
50	A8	10f multicolored	7.50	1.00
51	A8	35f multicolored	32.50	8.00
		Nos. 49-51 (3)	43.00	9.55

Issued to publicize progress made in Abu Dhabi during preceding 2 years.

Sheik Zaid and Abu Dhabi Petroleum Co. — A9

Designs: 60f, Abu Dhabi Marine Areas drilling platform and helicopter. 125f, Zakum Field separator at night. 200f, Tank farm.

1969, Aug. 6 Litho. *Perf. 14x13½*

52	A9	35f olive grn & multi	2.00	.85
53	A9	60f yel brn & multi	9.50	2.25
54	A9	125f mag & multi	11.00	4.00
55	A9	200f org brn & multi	15.00	7.00
		Nos. 52-55 (4)	37.50	14.10

Accession of Sheik Zaid, 3rd anniversary.

No. 27 Surcharged "25" in Arabic

1969, Dec. 13

55A	A4	25f on 15f dk brn & red	*250.00*	*160.00*

Because of local demand for 25f stamps for mailing Christmas greeting cards abroad, the Director of Posts ordered that 20,000 examples of No. 27 be surcharged "25" in Arabic for emergency use. This surcharge was applied locally, using a hand numbering machine. All stamps were sold at post office counters between Dec. 13 and Dec. 24, and the majority were used on mail during this period. Stamps remained valid and exist on covers into 1970. Double overprints exist.

Sheik Zaid — A10

Sheik Zaid and Stallion — A11

5f, 25f, 60f, 90f, Oval frame around portrait. 150f, Gazelle and Sheik. 500f, Fort Jahili and Sheik. 1d, Grand Mosque and Sheik.

1970-71 Litho. *Perf. 14*

56	A10	5f lt green & multi	1.00	.25
57	A10	10f bister & multi	1.25	.25
58	A10	25f lilac & multi	2.00	.25
59	A10	35f dl blue vio & multi	2.25	.25
60	A10	50f sepia & multi	3.25	.40
61	A10	60f blue & multi	3.75	.50
62	A10	70f rose red & multi	6.00	.65
63	A10	90f magenta & multi	8.25	1.00
64	A11	125f multi ('71)	12.00	2.00
65	A11	150f multi ('71)	15.00	2.50
66	A11	500f multi ('71)	50.00	11.00
67	A11	1d multi ('71)	85.00	22.50
		Nos. 56-67 (12)	189.75	41.55

For surcharge see No. 80.

Sheik Zaid and Mt. Fuji A12

1970, Aug. Litho. *Perf. 13½x13*

68	A12	25f multicolored	4.25	1.25
69	A12	35f multicolored	6.00	2.00
70	A12	60f multicolored	11.00	4.00
		Nos. 68-70 (3)	21.25	7.25

Issued to publicize EXPO '70 International Exhibition, Osaka, Japan, Mar. 15-Sept. 13.

Abu Dhabi Airport — A13

Designs: 60f, Airport entrance. 150f, Aerial view of Abu Dhabi Town, vert.

Perf. 14x13½, 13½x14

1970, Sept. 22 Litho.

71	A13	25f multicolored	4.75	.85
72	A13	60f multicolored	9.00	2.00
73	A13	150f multicolored	20.00	5.25
		Nos. 71-73 (3)	33.75	8.10

Accession of Sheik Zaid, 4th anniversary.

Gamal Abdel Nasser — A14

1971, May 3 Litho. *Perf. 14*

74	A14	25f deep rose & blk	6.00	3.50
75	A14	35f rose violet & blk	8.00	5.25

In memory of Gamal Abdel Nasser (1918-1970), President of UAR.

Scout Cars — A15

Designs: 60f, Patrol boat. 125f, Armored car in desert. 150f, Meteor jet fighters.

1971, Aug. 6 Litho. *Perf. 13*

76	A15	35f multicolored	6.25	1.50
77	A15	60f multicolored	8.50	2.25
78	A15	125f multicolored	18.00	3.75
79	A15	150f multicolored	22.50	7.50
		Nos. 76-79 (4)	55.25	15.00

Accession of Sheik Zaid, 5th anniversary.

No. 60 Surcharged in Green

1971, Dec. 8 *Perf. 14*

80	A10	5f on 50f multi	*100.00*	*90.00*

Dome of the Rock, Jerusalem — A16

Different views of Dome of the Rock.

1972, June 3 *Perf. 13*

81	A16	35f lt violet & multi	30.00	5.75
82	A16	60f lt violet & multi	55.00	9.50
83	A16	125f lilac & multi	100.00	20.00
		Nos. 81-83 (3)	185.00	35.25

Nos. 80-83 were issued after Abu Dhabi joined the United Arab Emirates Dec. 2, 1971. Stamps of UAE replaced those of Abu Dhabi. UAE Nos. 1-12 were used only in Abu Dhabi except the 10f and 25f which were issued later in Dubai and Sharjah.

ADEN

'ä-dən

LOCATION — Southern Arabia
GOVT. — British colony and protectorate
AREA — 112,075 sq. mi.
POP. — 220,000 (est. 1964)
CAPITAL — Aden

Aden used India stamps before 1937.

In January, 1963, the colony of Aden (the port) and the sheikdoms and emirates of the Western Aden Protectorate formed the Federation of South Arabia. This did not include the Eastern Aden Protectorate with Kathiri and Qu'aiti States. Stamps of Aden, except those of Kathiri and Qu'aiti States, were replaced Apr. 1, 1965, by those of the Federation of South Arabia. See South Arabia and People's Democratic Republic of Yemen, Vol. 6.

12 Pies = 1 Anna
16 Annas = 1 Rupee
100 Cents = 1 Shilling (1951)

Catalogue values for unused stamps in this country are for Never Hinged items.

ISSUES UNDER BRITISH ADMINISTRATION

Dhow — A1

Perf. 13x11½

1937, Apr. 1 Engr. Wmk. 4

1	A1	½a lt green	4.50	3.00
2	A1	9p dark green	4.25	3.75
3	A1	1a black brown	4.00	2.25
4	A1	2a red	5.00	3.25
5	A1	2½a blue	7.25	2.50
6	A1	3a carmine rose	11.00	8.75
7	A1	3½a gray blue	9.50	6.00
8	A1	8a rose lilac	27.50	11.50
9	A1	1r brown	62.50	12.50
10	A1	2r orange yellow	125.00	40.00
11	A1	5r rose violet	300.00	*100.00*
12	A1	10r olive green	600.00	*400.00*
		Nos. 1-12 (12)	1,161.	*593.50*
		Set, hinged	775.00	

Common Design Types pictured following the introduction.

Coronation Issue

Common Design Type

1937, May 12 *Perf. 13½x14*

13	CD302	1a black brown	.75	*1.25*
14	CD302	2½a blue	.85	*1.40*
15	CD302	3½a gray blue	1.10	*3.00*
		Nos. 13-15 (3)	2.70	*5.65*
		Set, hinged	1.75	

Aidrus Mosque — A2

¾a, 5r, Camel Corpsman. 1a, 2r, Aden Harbor. 1½a, 1r, Adenese dhow. 2½a, 8a, Mukalla. 3a, 14a, 10r, Capture of Aden, 1839.

1939-48 Engr. Wmk. 4 *Perf. 12½*

16	A2	½a green (7/42)	1.75	.50
17	A2	¾a red brn	2.50	*1.10*
18	A2	1a brt lt blue	1.40	.40
19	A2	1½a red	2.50	.60
20	A2	2a dark brown	1.60	.25
21	A2	2½a brt ultra	1.60	.30
22	A2	3a rose car & dk brn	1.60	.25
23	A2	8a orange	2.00	.40
23A	A2	14a lt bl & brn blk ('45)	3.75	.90
24	A2	1r bright green	4.50	2.25
25	A2	2r dp mag & bl blk ('44)	10.00	3.00
26	A2	5r dp ol & lake brn (1/44)	30.00	20.00
27a	A2	10r dk pur & lake brn	40.00	35.00
		Nos. 16-27a (13)	103.20	64.95
		Set, hinged	42.50	

For shades, see the *Scott Classic Specialized Catalogue.*

Peace Issue

Common Design Type

Perf. 13½x14

1946, Oct. 15 Engr. Wmk. 4

28	CD303	1½a carmine	.25	*1.50*
29	CD303	2½a deep blue	.70	*1.00*

Return to peace at end of World War II.

Silver Wedding Issue

Common Design Types

1949, Jan. 17 Photo. *Perf. 14x14½*

30	CD304	1½a scarlet	.40	*1.50*

Engraved; Name Typographed

Perf. 11½x11

31	CD305	10r purple	40.00	*55.00*

25th anniv. of the marriage of King George VI and Queen Elizabeth.

UPU Issue

Common Design Types

Srchd. in Annas and Rupees

Engr.; Name typo. on Nos. 33-34

1949, Oct. 10 ***Perf. 13½, 11x11½***

32	CD306 2½a on 20c dp ultra		.55	*1.60*
33	CD307 3a on 30c dp car		1.90	1.60
34	CD308 8a on 50c org		1.90	*1.75*
35	CD309 1r on 1sh blue		1.50	*3.50*
	Nos. 32-35 (4)		5.85	*8.45*

75th anniv. of the formation of the UPU.

Nos. 18 and 20-27 Surcharged in Black or Carmine

1951, Oct. 1 **Wmk. 4** ***Perf. 12½***

36	A2	5c on 1a lt bl (#18a)	.30	*.40*
37	A2	10c on 2a sepia (#20a)	.25	*.45*
38	A2	15c on 2½a brt ultra (#21)	.50	*1.25*
a.		Double surcharge	*1,600.*	
		Hinged	*1,000.*	
39	A2	20c on 3a rose car & dk brn (#22)	.50	.50
40	A2	30c on 8a #23b (C)	.85	*.60*
41	A2	50c on 8a #23b	1.50	*.35*
42	A2	70c on 14a (#23A)	2.25	1.40
43	A2	1sh on 1r #24a	3.00	.30
44	A2	2sh on 2r #25	13.00	3.50
45	A2	5sh on 5r #26	25.00	15.00
46	A2	10sh on 10r #27	35.00	15.00
		Nos. 36-46 (11)	82.15	38.75
		Set, hinged	42.50	

Surcharge on No. 40 includes 2 bars.

Coronation Issue

Common Design Type

1953, June 2 **Engr.** ***Perf. 13½x13***

47	CD312	15c dk grn & blk	1.25	1.25

Minaret
A10

Camel Transport
A11

15c, Crater. 25c, Mosque. 35c, Dhow. 50c, Map. 70c, Salt works. 1sh, Dhow building. 1sh, 25c, Colony Badge. 2sh, Aden Protectorate levy. 5sh, Crater Pass. 10sh, Tribesman. 20sh, Aden in 1572.

Perf. 12, 12x13½ ('56)

1953-59 **Engr.** **Wmk. 4**

Size: 29x23, 23x29mm

48	A10	5c grn, perf 12x13½ ('56)	.25	.25
a.		Perf. 12 ('55)	2.25	*3.00*
b.		5c bluish grn, perf 12x13½ ('56)	.25	*1.00*
49	A11	10c orange	.35	.25
a.		10c vermilion ('55)	1.10	*.30*
50	A11	15c blue green	1.00	.55
a.		15c grayish grn ('59)	7.00	6.00
51	A11	25c carmine	.75	.50
a.		25c deep rose red ('56)	5.00	1.50
52	A10	35c ultra, perf. 12	2.00	1.00
a.		35c dp bl, perf 12x13½ ('58)	5.00	5.00
b.		35c vio bl, perf 12x13½ ('59)	12.50	4.00
53	A10	50c blue, perf 12	.35	.25
a.		As "b," perf 12x13½ ('56)	1.00	.25
b.		50c deep bl, perf 12 ('55)	3.00	2.00
54	A10	70c gray, perf 12	.50	.25
a.		As "b," perf 12x13½ ('56)	1.75	.25
b.		70c grayish blk, perf 12 ('54)	1.40	.90
55	A11	1sh pur & sepia	.50	.25
55A	A11	1sh vio & blk ('55)	1.40	.25
56	A10	1sh25c blk & lt blue ('56)	11.00	.45
57	A10	2sh car rose & sep	1.25	.50
57A	A10	2sh car & blk ('56)	11.50	.45
58	A10	5sh blue & sepia	2.00	1.00
58A	A10	5sh dk blue & blk ('56)	12.00	1.25
59	A10	10sh olive & sepia	2.00	*7.50*
60	A10	10sh ol gray & blk ('54)	12.50	1.50

Size: 36½x27mm

Perf. 13½x13

61	A11	20sh rose vio & dk brn	15.00	*20.00*
61A	A11	20sh lt vio & blk ('57)	45.00	18.00
		Nos. 48-61A (18)	119.35	54.20
		Set, hinged	70.00	

No. 60 has heavier shading on tribesman's lower garment than No. 59.

See Nos. 66-75. For overprints see Nos. 63-64.

Type of 1953

Inscribed: "Royal Visit 1954"

1954, Apr. 27 ***Perf. 12***

62	A11	1sh purple & sepia	.65	*4.00*

Nos. 50 & 56 Overprinted in Red

No. 63

No. 64

1959, Jan. 26 ***Perf. 12, 12x13½***

63	A11	15c dark blue green	.55	*2.00*
64	A10	1sh25c blk & light blue	1.00	*1.50*

Introduction of a revised constitution.

Freedom from Hunger Issue

Common Design Type

Perf. 14x14½

1963, June 4 **Photo.** **Wmk. 314**

65	CD314	1sh25c green	1.50	*1.75*

Types of 1953-57

Perf. 12x13½, 12 (#67-69, 73)

1964-65 **Engr.** **Wmk. 314**

66	A10	5c green ('65)	4.25	*9.50*
67	A11	10c orange	2.00	1.00
68	A11	15c Prus green	.90	*5.25*
69	A11	25c carmine	3.00	.40
70	A10	35c dk blue	7.25	*9.00*
71	A10	50c dull blue	1.25	1.10
72	A10	70c gray	2.75	*4.00*
73	A11	1sh vio & black	11.00	*15.00*
74	A10	1sh25c blk & lt blue	16.00	2.00
75	A10	2sh car & blk ('65)	6.75	*30.00*
		Nos. 66-75 (10)	55.15	*77.25*

KATHIRI STATE OF SEIYUN

LOCATION — In Eastern Aden Protectorate
GOVT. — Sultanate
CAPITAL — Seiyun

The stamps of the Kathiri State of Seiyun were valid for use throughout Aden. Used stamps generally bear Aden GPO or Aden Camp cancels. Examples with cancels from offices in the Eastern Protectorate command a premium.

Sultan Ja'far bin Mansur al Kathiri
A1

Seiyun
A2

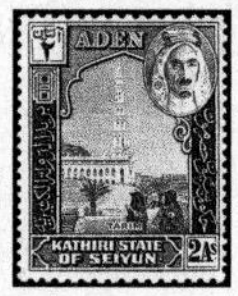

Minaret at Tarim — A3

Designs: 2½a, Mosque at Seiyun. 3a, Palace at Tarim. 8a, Mosque at Seiyun, horiz. 1r, South Gate, Tarim. 2r, Kathiri House. 5r, Mosque at Tarim.

1942 **Engr.** **Wmk. 4** ***Perf. 13¾x14***

1	A1	½a dark green	.25	*1.40*
2	A1	¾a copper brown	.50	*3.00*
3	A1	1a deep blue	.60	*1.50*

Perf. 13x11½, 11½x13

4	A2	1½a dark car rose	.65	*1.75*
5	A3	2a sepia brown	.40	*1.75*
6	A3	2½a deep blue	1.00	*2.00*
7	A2	3a dk car rose & dull brn	1.60	*3.00*
8	A2	8a orange red	3.00	1.25
9	A3	1r green	6.50	3.50
10	A2	2r rose vio & dk blue	13.50	*18.00*
11	A3	5r gray green & fawn	32.50	24.00
		Nos. 1-11 (11)	60.50	*61.15*
		Set, hinged	28.00	

For surcharges see Nos. 20-27.

Nos. 4, 6 Ovptd. in Black or Red

a

b

Perf. 13x11½, 11½x13

1946, Oct. 15 **Wmk. 4**

12	A2 (a)	1½a dark car rose	.25	*.65*
13	A3 (b)	2½a deep blue (R)	.25	.25
a.		Inverted overprint	1,300.	
		Hinged	775.00	
b.		Double overprint	1,800.	
		Hinged	1,050.	

Victory of the Allied Nations in WWII.

All examples of No. 13b have the 2nd overprint almost directly over the 1st.

Silver Wedding Issue

Common Design Types

1949, Jan. 17 **Photo.** ***Perf. 14x14½***

14	CD304	1½a scarlet	.35	*2.00*

Engraved; Name Typo.

Perf. 11½x11

15	CD305	5r green	17.50	*14.00*

25th anniv. of the marriage of King George VI and Queen Elizabeth.

UPU Issue

Common Design Types

Srchd. in Annas and Rupees

Engr.; Name Typo. on Nos. 17-18

1949, Oct. 10 ***Perf. 13½, 11x11½***

16	CD306 2½a on 20c dp ultra		.25	*4.00*
17	CD307 3a on 30c dp car		1.50	*4.00*
18	CD308 8a on 50c orange		.40	*4.00*
19	CD309 1r on 1sh blue		.60	*4.00*
	Nos. 16-19 (4)		2.75	*16.00*

75th anniv. of the formation of the UPU.

Nos. 3 and 5-11 Srchd. in Carmine or Black

Perf. 14, 13x11½, 11½x13

1951, Oct. 1 **Engr.** **Wmk. 4**

20	A1	5c on 1a (C)	.25	*2.00*
21	A3	10c on 2a #5a	.35	*1.75*
22	A3	15c on 2½a	.30	*2.25*
23	A2	20c on 3a #7	.35	*2.50*
24	A2	50c on 8a	.80	*1.60*
25	A3	1sh on 1r	2.50	*3.75*
26	A2	2sh on 2r #10	11.50	*30.00*
27	A3	5sh on 5r	34.00	*47.50*
		Nos. 20-27 (8)	50.05	91.35

Coronation Issue

Common Design Type

1953, June 2 ***Perf. 13½x13***

28	CD312	15c dk green & blk	.75	*1.50*

Sultan Hussein
A10

Seiyun Scene
A11

25c, Minaret at Tarim, vert. 35c, Mosque at Seiyun, vert. 50c, Palace at Tarim. 1sh, Mosque at Seiyun. 2sh, South Gate, Tarim, vert.. 5sh, Kathiri house. 10sh, Mosque entrance, Tarim, vert.

1954, Jan. 15 **Engr.** ***Perf. 12½***

29	A10	5c dark brown	.25	.25
30	A10	10c deep blue	.25	.25

Perf. 13x11½, 11½x13

31	A11	15c dk blue green	.25	.25
32	A11	25c dk car rose	.25	.25
33	A11	35c deep blue	.25	.25
34	A11	50c dk car rose & dk brn	.25	.25
35	A11	1sh deep orange	.25	.25
36	A11	2sh gray green	4.00	2.00
37	A11	5sh vio & dk blue	9.25	*8.00*
38	A11	10sh vio & yel brn	10.00	*8.50*
		Nos. 29-38 (10)	25.00	*20.25*

Perf. 11½x13, 13x11½

1964, July 1 **Wmk. 314**

Designs: 70c, Qarn Adh Dhabi. 1sh25c, Seiyun, horiz. 1sh50c, View of Gheil Omer, horiz.

39	A11	70c black	2.75	2.00
40	A11	1sh25c bright green	2.75	*7.50*
41	A11	1sh50c purple	2.75	*8.00*
		Nos. 39-41 (3)	8.25	*17.50*

QUAITI STATE OF SHIHR AND MUKALLA

LOCATION — In Eastern Aden Protectorate
GOVT. — Sultanate
CAPITAL — Mukalla

The stamps of the Quaiti State of Shihr and Mukalla were valid for use throughout Aden. Used stamps generally bear Aden GPO or Aden Camp cancels. Examples with cancels from offices in the Eastern Protectorate command a premium.

Sultan Sir Saleh bin Ghalib al Qu'aiti
A1

Mukalla Harbor
A2

Buildings at Shibam — A3

Designs: 2a, Gateway of Shihr. 3a, Outpost of Mukalla. 8a, View of 'Einat. 1r, Governor's Castle, Du'an. 2r, Mosque in Hureidha. 5r, Meshhed.

1942 **Engr.** **Wmk. 4** ***Perf. 13¾x14***

1	A1	½a dark green	1.40	.35
2	A1	¾a copper brown	2.00	.25
3	A1	1a deep blue	.80	.80

Perf. 13x11½, 11½x13

4	A2	1½a dk car rose	1.60	.35
5	A2	2a black brown	1.75	*1.25*
6	A3	2½a deep blue	.40	.25

7	A2	3a	dk car rose & dl brn	1.00	.75
8	A3	8a	orange red	1.10	.35
9	A2	1r	green	6.00	3.50
a.			Missing "A" in "CA" of watermark	1,300.	*1,200.*
10	A3	2r	rose vio & dk blue	16.00	12.00
11	A3	5r	gray grn & fawn	32.50	16.00
			Nos. 1-11 (11)	64.55	35.85

For surcharges see Nos. 20-27.

Nos. 4, 6 Ovptd. in Black or Carmine like Kathiri Nos. 12-13

1946, Oct. 15 ***Perf. 11½x13, 13x11½***

12	A2 (b)	1½a dk car rose	.25	*1.00*
13	A3 (a)	2½a deep blue (C)	.25	.25

Victory of the Allied Nations in WWII.

Silver Wedding Issue

Common Design Types

1949, Jan. 17 Photo. ***Perf. 14x14½***

14	CD304	1½a scarlet	.55	*2.50*

Engraved; Name Typo.

Perf. 11½x11

15	CD305	5r green	18.00	10.00

25th anniv. of the marriage of King George VI and Queen Elizabeth.

UPU Issue
Surcharged in Annas and Rupees

Common Design Types

No. 16

No. 17

Engr.; Name Typo. on Nos. 17 and 18

1949, Oct. 10 ***Perf. 13½, 11x11½***

16	CD306	2½a on 20c dp ultra	.25	*2.00*
17	CD307	3a on 30c dp car	1.50	*2.00*
18	CD308	8a on 50c org	.35	*2.00*
19	CD309	1r on 1sh blue	.50	*2.00*
a.		Surcharge omitted	*4,250.*	
		Hinged	*2,750.*	
		Nos. 16-19 (4)	2.60	8.00

Nos. 3, 5-11 & Types Surcharged in Carmine or Black

Nos. 20-21

Nos. 22-24

Nos. 25-27

Perf. 14, 13x11½, 11½x13

1951, Oct. 1 Engr. Wmk. 4

20	A1	5c on 1a (C)	.25	.25
21	A2	10c on 2a	.25	.25
22	A3	15c on 2½a	.25	.25
23	A2	20c on 3a #7	.30	*.75*
24	A3	50c on 8a org red	.45	*2.50*
25	A2	1sh on 1r	2.00	.55
26	A3	2sh on 2r	8.00	*24.00*
27	A3	5sh on 5r	17.00	*34.00*
		Nos. 20-27 (8)	28.50	*62.55*

Coronation Issue

Common Design Type

1953, June 2 Engr. ***Perf. 13½x13***

28	CD312	15c dk blue & black	1.10	.60

Qu'aiti State in Hadhramaut

Metal Work — A10

Fisheries — A11

Designs: 10c, Mat making. 15c, Weaving. 25c, Pottery. 35c, Building. 50c, Date cultivation. 90c, Agriculture. 1sh25c, 10sh, Lime burning. 2sh, Dhow building. 5sh, Agriculture.

Perf. 11½x13, 13½x14

1955, Sept. 1 Engr. Wmk. 4

29	A10	5c	greenish blue	.75	.25
30	A10	10c	black	1.00	.25
31	A10	15c	dk green	.75	.25
32	A10	25c	carmine	.40	.25
33	A10	35c	ultra	.75	.25
34	A10	50c	red orange	.75	.25
35	A10	90c	brown	.55	.25
36	A11	1sh	purple & blk	.75	.25
37	A11	1sh25c	red org & blk	.60	.55
38	A11	2sh	dk blue & blk	3.00	.60
39	A11	5sh	green & blk	4.00	2.25
40	A11	10sh	car & black	13.50	7.50
			Nos. 29-40 (12)	26.80	12.90

Types of 1955 with Portrait of Sultan Awadh Bin Saleh El-Qu'aiti

Design: 70c, Agriculture. Others as before.

1963, Oct. 20 Wmk. 314

41	A10	5c	greenish blue	.25	*1.40*
42	A10	10c	black	.25	*1.15*
43	A10	15c	dark green	.25	*1.40*
44	A10	25c	carmine	.25	*.60*
45	A10	35c	ultra	.25	*1.50*
46	A10	50c	red orange	.25	*.75*
47	A10	70c	brown	.25	.60
48	A11	1sh	purple & blk	.30	.30
49	A11	1sh25c	red org & blk	.50	*5.00*
50	A11	2sh	dk blue & blk	2.75	2.25
51	A11	5sh	green & blk	12.50	*25.00*
52	A11	10sh	car & black	27.00	*26.00*
			Nos. 41-52 (12)	44.80	*65.95*

AFARS & ISSAS

French Territory of the

'ä-ˌfär z̧ and ē-'sä z̧

LOCATION — East Africa
GOVT. — French Overseas Territory
AREA — 8,880 sq. mi.
POP. — 150,000 (est. 1974)
CAPITAL — Djibouti (Jibuti)

The French overseas territory of Somali Coast was renamed the French Territory of the Afars and Issas in 1967. It became the Djibouti Republic on June 27, 1977.

100 Centimes = 1 Franc

Catalogue values for all unused stamps in this country are for Never Hinged items.

Imperforates

Most stamps of Afars and Issas exist imperforate in issued and trial colors, and also in small presentation sheets in issued colors.

Grayheaded Kingfisher — A48

Xerus Rutilus — A48a

10fr, Halcyon leucocephala. 15fr, Haematopus ostralegus. 50fr, Tringa nebularia. 55fr, Coracias abyssinicus.

1967 Unwmk. Engr. ***Perf. 13***

310	A48	10fr multicolored	4.00	3.00
311	A48	15fr multicolored	5.25	4.00
312	A48	50fr multicolored	12.50	8.00
313	A48	55fr multicolored	17.50	11.00
314	A48a	60fr multicolored	24.00	17.50
		Nos. 310-314 (5)	63.25	43.50
		Nos. 310-314,C50 (6)	80.75	55.50

Issued: 10fr, 55fr, Aug. 21; 15fr, 50fr, 60fr, Sept. 25. See No. C50.

Soccer — A49

1967, Dec. 18 Engr. ***Perf. 13***

315	A49	25fr shown	3.50	2.75
316	A49	30fr Basketball	4.00	2.75

Common Design Types Pictured in section at front of book.

WHO Anniversary Issue

Common Design Type

1968, May 4 Engr. ***Perf. 13***

317	CD126	15fr multicolored	3.00	3.00

20th anniv. of WHO.

Damerdjog Fortress — A50

Administration Buildings: 25fr, Ali Adde. 30fr, Dorra. 40fr, Assamo.

1968, May 17 Engr. ***Perf. 13***

318	A50	20fr slate, brn & emer	1.25	1.00
319	A50	25fr brt grn, bl & brn	1.50	1.25
320	A50	30fr brn ol, brn org & sl	2.00	1.40
321	A50	40fr brn ol, sl & brt grn	3.25	2.75
		Nos. 318-321 (4)	8.00	6.40

Human Rights Year Issue

Common Design Type

1968, Aug. 10 Engr. ***Perf. 13***

322	CD127	10fr purple, ver & org	2.25	1.75
323	CD127	70fr green, pur & org	4.50	2.25

International Human Rights Year.

Radio-television Station, Djibouti — A52

High Commission Palace, Djibouti A53

Designs: 2fr, Justice Building. 5fr, Chamber of Deputies. 8fr, Great Mosque. 15fr, Monument of Free French Forces, vert. 40fr, Djibouti Post Office. 70fr, Residence of Gov. Léonce Lagarde at Obock. No. 332, Djibouti Harbormaster's Building. No. 333, Control tower, Djibouti Airport.

1968-70 Engr. ***Perf. 13***

324	A52	1fr multicolored	.50	.50
325	A52	2fr multicolored	.80	.75
326	A52	5fr multicolored	1.00	1.00
327	A52	8fr multicolored	1.25	1.25
328	A52	15fr multicolored	4.50	3.75
329	A52	40fr multicolored	3.75	2.75
330	A53	60fr multicolored	3.50	2.40
331	A52	70fr multicolored	4.25	3.00
332	A52	85fr multicolored	6.25	3.75
333	A52	85fr multicolored	6.50	4.25
		Nos. 324-333 (10)	32.30	23.40

Issued: No. 330, 1968; Nos. 324-328, 331-332, 1969; Nos. 329, 333, 1970.
See Nos. C54-C55.

Locust — A54

Designs: 50fr, Pest control by helicopter. 55fr, Pest control by plane.

1969, Oct. 6 Engr. ***Perf. 13***

334	A54	15fr brn, grn & slate	4.75	2.25
335	A54	50fr dk grn, bl & ol brn	3.00	2.25
336	A54	55fr red brn, bl & brn	3.50	2.25
		Nos. 334-336 (3)	11.25	6.75

Campaign against locusts.

ILO Issue

Common Design Type

1969, Nov. 24 Engr. ***Perf. 13***

337	CD131	30fr org, gray & lil	2.75	2.00

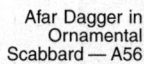

Afar Dagger in Ornamental Scabbard — A56

1970, Apr. 3 Engr. ***Perf. 13***

338	A56	10fr multicolored	1.40	.75
339	A56	15fr multicolored	1.75	.75
340	A56	20fr multicolored	2.00	1.00
341	A56	25fr multicolored	2.25	1.25
		Nos. 338-341 (4)	7.40	3.75

See No. 364.

UPU Headquarters Issue

Common Design Type

1970, May 20 Engr. ***Perf. 13***

342	CD133	25fr brn, brt grn & choc	2.50	1.40

Trapshooting A57

Motorboats A58

Designs: 50fr, Steeplechase. 55fr, Sailboat, vert. 60fr, Equestrians.

1970 Engr. ***Perf. 13***

343	A57	30fr dp brn, yel grn & brt bl	2.75	1.75
344	A58	48fr blue & multi	5.00	2.50
345	A58	50fr cop red, bl & pur	5.00	2.50
346	A58	55fr red brn, bl & ol	5.25	2.50
347	A58	60fr ol, blk & red brn	5.50	3.50
		Nos. 343-347 (5)	23.50	12.75

Issued: 30fr, 6/5; 48fr, 10/9; 50fr, 60fr, 11/6.

Automatic Ferry, Tadjourah — A59

1970, Nov. 25

348	A59	48fr blue, brn & grn	3.75	2.50

Volcanic Geode — A60

Diabase and Chrysolite — A61

10fr, Doleritic basalt. 15fr, Olivine basalt.

1971 Photo. ***Perf. 13***

349	A61	10fr black & multi	3.00	1.25
350	A61	15fr black & multi	3.50	1.75
351	A60	25fr black, crim & brn	7.00	3.25
352	A61	40fr black & multi	9.00	5.00
		Nos. 349-352 (4)	22.50	11.25

Issued: 10fr, 11/22; 15fr, 10/8; 25fr, 4/26; 40fr, 1/25.

A62

4fr, Manta birostris. 5fr, Coryphaena hippurus. 9fr, Pristis pectinatus.

1971, July 1 Photo. *Perf. 12x12½*

353	A62	4fr mulitcolored	2.25	1.25
354	A62	5fr multicolored	2.75	1.40
355	A62	9fr multicolored	4.75	2.25
		Nos. 353-355 (3)	9.75	4.90

See No. C60.

De Gaulle Issue

Common Design Type

Designs: 60fr, Gen. Charles de Gaulle, 1940. 85fr, Pres. de Gaulle, 1970.

1971, Nov. 9 Engr. *Perf. 13*

356	CD134	60fr ultra & blk	6.00	3.50
357	CD134	85fr dk vio bl & blk	6.50	4.00

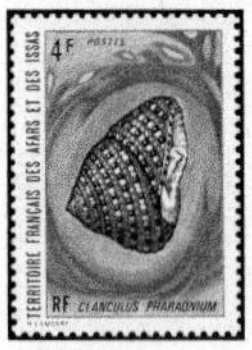

A63

Shells: 4fr, Strawberry Top. 9fr, Cypraea pantherina. 20fr, Bull-mouth helmet. 50fr, Ethiopian volute.

1972, Mar. 8 Photo. *Perf. 12½x13*

358	A63	4fr olive & multi	1.75	1.25
359	A63	9fr dk blue & multi	2.25	1.50
360	A63	20fr dp green & multi	4.25	2.25
361	A63	50fr dp claret & multi	7.00	3.00
		Nos. 358-361 (4)	15.25	8.00

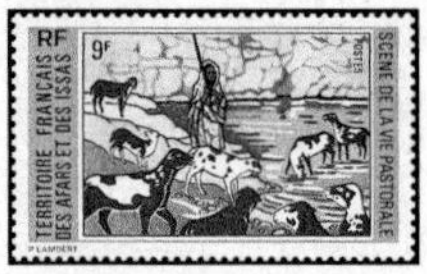

Shepherd A64

Design: 10fr, Dromedary breeding.

1973, Apr. 11 Photo. *Perf. 13*

362	A64	9fr blue & multi	1.50	.80
363	A64	10fr blue & multi	1.75	.85

Afar Dagger — A65

1974, Jan. 29 Engr. *Perf. 13*

364	A65	30fr slate grn & dk brn	1.50	.85

For surcharge see No. 379.

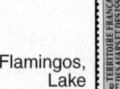

Flamingos, Lake Abbe — A66

Flamingos and different views of Lake Abbe.

1974, Feb. 22 Photo. *Perf. 13*

370	A66	5fr multicolored	1.75	1.00
371	A66	15fr multicolored	1.50	1.25
372	A66	50fr multicolored	3.00	2.00
		Nos. 370-372 (3)	6.25	4.25

Soccer Ball — A67

1974, May 24 Engr. *Perf. 13*

373	A67	25fr black & emerald	3.00	1.75

World Cup Soccer Championship, Munich, June 13-July 7.

Letters Around UPU Emblem — A68

1974, Oct. 9 Engr. *Perf. 13*

374	A68	20fr multicolored	1.25	.80
375	A68	100fr multicolored	2.75	2.25

Centenary of Universal Postal Union.

Oleo Chrysophylla — A69

Designs: 15fr, Ficus species. 20fr, Solanum adoense.

1974, Nov. 22 Photo.

376	A69	10fr shown	1.75	1.00
377	A69	15fr multicolored	2.00	1.10
378	A69	20fr multicolored	3.00	1.50
		Nos. 376-378 (3)	6.75	3.60

Day Primary Forest.

No. 364 Surcharged in Red

1975, Jan. 1 Engr. *Perf. 13*

379	A65	40fr on 30fr multi	2.00	1.25

Treasury A70

Design: 25fr, Government buildings.

1975, Jan. 7 Engr. *Perf. 13*

380	A70	8fr blue, gray & red	.65	.50
381	A70	25fr red, blue & indigo	1.50	.45

Darioconus Textile A71

Sea Shells: No. 383, Murex palmarosa. 10fr, Conus sumatrensis. 15fr, Cypraea pulchra. No. 386, 45fr, Murex scolopax. No. 387, Cypraea exhusta. 40fr, Ranella spinosa. 55fr, Cypraea erythraensis. 60fr, Conus taeniatus.

1975-76 Engr. *Perf. 13*

382	A71	5fr blue grn & brn	1.25	.85
383	A71	5fr blue & multi ('76)	1.25	1.00
384	A71	10fr lilac, blk & brn	2.50	.90
385	A71	15fr blue, ind & brn	3.25	1.40
386	A71	20fr purple & lt brn	5.00	3.00
387	A71	20fr brt grn & multi ('76)	2.75	1.25
388	A71	40fr green & brown	4.50	1.25
389	A71	45fr green, bl & bister	4.75	1.40
390	A71	55fr turq & multi ('76)	3.50	2.00
391	A71	60fr buff & sepia ('76)	6.50	2.75
		Nos. 382-391 (10)	35.25	15.80

Hypolimnas Misippus — A72

Butterflies: 40fr, Papilio nireus. 50fr, Acraea anemosa. 65fr, Holocerina smilax menieri. 70fr, Papilio demodocus. No. 397, Papilio dardanus. No. 398, Balachowsky gonimbrasca. 150fr, Vanessa cardui.

1975-76 Photo. *Perf. 13*

392	A72	25fr emerald & multi	3.75	1.60
393	A72	40fr yellow & multi	4.75	2.00
394	A72	50fr ultra & multi ('76)	5.50	1.75
395	A72	65fr ol & multi ('76)	5.50	2.50
396	A72	70fr violet & multi	6.75	3.00
397	A72	100fr blue & multi	8.50	3.75
398	A72	100fr Prus bl & multi ('76)	7.00	3.50
399	A72	150fr grn & multi ('76)	8.50	3.75
		Nos. 392-399 (8)	50.25	21.85

A73

Animals: No. 400, Hyaena hyaena. No. 401, Cercopithecus aethiops. No. 402, Equus asinus somalicus. No. 403, Dorcatragus megalotis. No. 404, Ichneumia albicauda. No. 405, Hystrix galeata. No. 406, Ictonyx striatus. No. 407, Orycteropus afer.

Perf. 13x12½, 12½x13

1975-76 Photo.

400	A73	10fr multicolored	1.25	1.00
401	A73	15fr multicolored	1.40	1.00
402	A73	15fr multicolored	1.60	1.25
403	A73	30fr multicolored	3.00	1.50
404	A73	50fr multicolored	2.75	1.75
405	A73	60fr multicolored	4.00	2.25
406	A73	70fr multicolored	5.50	2.75
407	A73	200fr multicolored	7.50	5.50
		Nos. 400-407 (8)	27.00	17.00

Nos. 401-402, 405 are vert.

Issued: 50fr, 60fr, 70fr, 2/21; No. 401, 200fr, 10/24; 10fr, No. 402, 30fr, 2/4/76.

Birds — A74

No. 413, Vidua macroura. No. 414, Psittacula krameri. No. 415, Cinnyris venustus. No. 416, Ardea goliath. No. 417, Scopus umbretta. No. 418, Oena capensis. No. 419, Platalea alba.

1975-76 Photo. *Perf. 12½x13*

413	A74	20fr multicolored	1.75	1.40
414	A74	25fr multicolored	2.50	.75
415	A74	50fr multicolored	3.25	1.80
416	A74	60fr multicolored	5.75	2.50
417	A74	100fr multicolored	9.25	3.00
418	A74	100fr multicolored	5.00	1.75
419	A74	300fr multicolored	12.00	4.50
		Nos. 413-419 (7)	39.50	15.70

Issued: 300fr, 6/15/76; 25fr, No. 418, 10/13/76; others 11/21 and 12/19/75.

Palms — A75

1975, Dec. 19 Engr. *Perf. 13*

421	A75	20fr multicolored	1.10	1.00

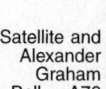

Satellite and Alexander Graham Bell — A76

1976, Mar. 10 Engr. *Perf. 13*

422	A76	200fr dp bl, org & sl grn	3.25	3.00

Centenary of the first telephone call by Alexander Graham Bell, Mar. 10, 1876.

Basketball — A77

1976, July 7 Litho. *Perf. 12½*

423	A77	10fr shown	.75	.40
424	A77	15fr Bicycling	1.00	.50
425	A77	40fr Soccer	1.75	1.00
426	A77	60fr Running	2.50	1.50
		Nos. 423-426 (4)	6.00	3.40

21st Olympic Games, Montreal, Canada, July 17-Aug. 1.

Pterois Radiata A78

1976, Aug. 10 Photo. *Perf. 13x13½*

428	A78	45fr blue & multi	3.75	1.50

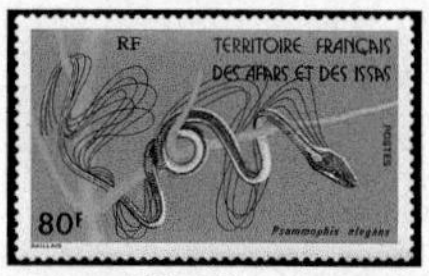

Psammophis Elegans — A79

Design: 70fr, Naja nigricollis, vert.

Perf. 13x13½, 13½x13

1976, Sept. 27 Photo.

430	A79	70fr ocher & multi	3.50	2.25
431	A79	80fr emerald & multi	6.00	2.75

Motorcyclist — A80

1977, Jan. 27 Litho. *Perf. 12x12½*

432	A80	200fr multicolored	6.00	3.00

Moto-Cross motorcycle race.

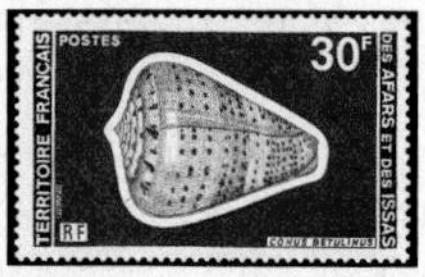

Conus Betulinus A81

Sea Shells: 5fr, Cyprea tigris. 70fr, Conus striatus. 85fr, Cyprea mauritiana.

1977 Engr. *Perf. 13*

433	A81	5fr multicolored	2.50	1.00
434	A81	30fr multicolored	2.75	1.00
435	A81	70fr multicolored	7.00	2.50
436	A81	85fr multicolored	6.00	3.75
		Nos. 433-436 (4)	18.25	8.25

Gaterin Gaterinus — A82

1977, Apr. 15 Photo. ***Perf. 13x12½***

437 A82 15fr shown 1.50 1.00
438 A82 65fr Barracudas 3.00 1.50

AIR POST STAMPS

AP16

200fr, Aquila rapax belisarius.

Unwmk.

1967, Aug. 21 Engr. ***Perf. 13***

C50 AP16 200fr multicolored 17.50 12.00

AP17

48fr, Parachutists. 85fr, Water skier & skin diver.

1968 Engr. ***Perf. 13***

C51 AP17 48fr multicolored 5.50 2.50
C52 AP17 85fr multicolored 7.00 4.50

Issue dates: 48fr, Jan. 5; 85fr, Mar. 15.

Aerial Map of the Territory AP18

1968, Nov. 15 Engr. ***Perf. 13***

C53 AP18 500fr bl, dk brn & ocher 23.00 13.00

Buildings Type of Regular Issue

100fr, Cathedral. 200fr, Sayed Hassan Mosque.

1969 Engr. ***Perf. 13***

C54 A53 100fr multi, vert. 5.50 2.50
C55 A53 200fr multi, vert. 8.50 5.50

Issue dates: 100fr, Apr. 4; 200fr, May 8.

Concorde Issue

Common Design Type

1969, Apr. 17

C56 CD129 100fr org red & ol 26.00 16.00

Arta Ionospheric Station — AP19

1970, May 8 Engr. ***Perf. 13***

C57 AP19 70fr multicolored 4.00 3.25

Japanese Sword Guard, Fish Design — AP20

200fr, Japanese sword guard, horse design.

Gold embossed

1970, Oct. 26 ***Perf. 12½***

C58 AP20 100fr multicolored 9.50 7.50
C59 AP20 200fr multicolored 12.50 9.00

EXPO '70 International Exposition, Osaka, Japan, Mar. 15-Sept. 13.

Scarus vetula AP21

1971, July 1 Photo. ***Perf. 12½***

C60 AP21 30fr black & multi 6.00 3.75

Djibouti Harbor AP22

1972, Feb. 3

C61 AP22 100fr blue & multi 4.50 3.00

New Djibouti harbor.

AP23

30fr, Pterocles lichtensteini. 49fr, Uppupa epops. 66fr, Capella media. 500fr, Francolinus ochroprectus.

1972 Photo. ***Perf. 12½x13***

C62 AP23 30fr multi 3.75 2.75
C63 AP23 49fr multi 6.25 3.75
C64 AP23 66fr multi 8.50 5.00
C65 AP23 500fr multi 30.00 17.50
Nos. C62-C65 (4) 48.50 29.00

Issue dates: No. C65, Nov. 3; others Apr. 21.

AP24

Olympic Rings and: 5fr, Running. 10fr, Basketball. 55fr, Swimming, horiz. 60fr, Olympic torch and Greek frieze, horiz.

1972, June 8 Engr. ***Perf. 13***

C66 AP24 5fr multicolored .90 .90
C67 AP24 10fr multicolored 1.00 .95
C68 AP24 55fr multicolored 2.25 1.75
C69 AP24 60fr multicolored 3.25 2.00
Nos. C66-C69 (4) 7.40 5.60

20th Olympic Games, Munich, 8/26-9/11.

Louis Pasteur AP25

100fr, Albert Calmette and C. Guérin.

1972, Oct. 5 Engr. ***Perf. 13***

C70 AP25 20fr multicolored 2.75 1.10
C71 AP25 100fr multicolored 5.50 4.00

Pasteur, Calmette, Guerin, chemists and bacteriologists, benefactors of mankind.

Map and Views of Territory AP26

200fr, Woman and Mosque of Djibouti, vert.

1973, Jan. 15 Photo. ***Perf. 13***

C72 AP26 30fr brown & multi 6.00 4.25
C73 AP26 200fr multicolored 11.00 8.50

Visit of Pres. Georges Pompidou of France, Jan. 15-17.

AP27

30fr, Oryx beisa. 50fr, Madoqua saltiana. 66fr, Felis caracal.

1973, Feb. 26 Photo. ***Perf. 13x12½***

C74 AP27 30fr multicolored 3.00 1.50
C75 AP27 50fr multicolored 4.25 2.75
C76 AP27 66fr multicolored 6.25 3.25
Nos. C74-C76 (3) 13.50 7.50

See Nos. C94-C96.

Celts — AP28

Various pre-historic flint tools. 40fr, 60fr, horiz.

1973 ***Perf. 13***

C77 AP28 20fr yel grn, blk & brn 4.50 2.50
C78 AP28 40fr yellow & multi 4.75 3.00
C79 AP28 49fr lilac & multi 8.75 3.75
C80 AP28 60fr blue & multi 6.25 5.00
Nos. C77-C80 (4) 24.25 14.25

Issued: 20fr, 49fr, 3/16; 40fr, 60fr, 9/7.

AP29

40fr, Octopus macropus. 60fr, Halicore dugong.

1973, Mar. 16

C81 AP29 40fr multicolored 3.75 2.25
C82 AP29 60fr multicolored 7.50 3.75

AP30

Copernicus: 8fr, Nicolaus Copernicus, Polish astronomer. 9fr, Wilhelm C. Roentgen, physicist, X-ray discoverer. No. C85, Edward Jenner, physician, discoverer of vaccination. No. C86, Marie Curie, discoverer of radium and polonium. 49fr, Robert Koch, physician and bacteriologist. 50fr, Clement Ader (1841-1925), French aviation pioneer. 55fr, Guglielmo Marconi, Italian electrical engineer, inventor. 85fr, Moliere, French playwright. 100fr, Henri Farman (1874-1937), French aviation pioneer. 150fr, Andre-Marie Ampere (1775-1836), French physicist. 250fr, Michelangelo Buonarroti (1475-1564), Italian sculptor, painter and architect.

1973-75 Engr. ***Perf. 13***

C83 AP30 8fr multicolored 1.00 1.00
C84 AP30 9fr multicolored 2.00 1.00
C85 AP30 10fr multicolored 2.25 1.00
C86 AP30 10fr multicolored 1.50 1.00
C87 AP30 49fr multicolored 4.00 2.50
C88 AP30 50fr multicolored 3.50 2.50
C89 AP30 55fr multicolored 2.25 2.00
C90 AP30 85fr multicolored 5.75 2.75
C91 AP30 100fr multicolored 3.75 3.00
C92 AP30 150fr multicolored 6.00 3.50
C93 AP30 250fr multicolored 9.00 6.00
Nos. C83-C93 (11) 41.00 26.25

Issued: 8fr, 85fr, 5/9/73; 9fr, No. C85, 49fr, 10/12/73; 100fr, 1/29/74; 55fr, 3/22/74; No. C86, 8/23/74; 150fr, 7/24/75; 250fr, 6/26/75; 50fr, 9/25/75.

AP31

20fr, Papio anubis. 50fr, Genetta tigrina, horiz. 66fr, Lapus habessinicus.

Perf. 12½x13, 13x12½

1973, Dec. 12 Photo.

C94 AP31 20fr multicolored 2.25 1.40
C95 AP31 50fr multicolored 3.75 2.00
C96 AP31 66fr multicolored 5.00 2.75
Nos. C94-C96 (3) 11.00 6.15

Spearfishing AP32

1974, Apr. 14 Engr. ***Perf. 13***

C97 AP32 200fr multicolored 8.00 7.00

No. C97 was prepared for release in Nov. 1972, for the 3rd Underwater Spearfishing Contest in the Red Sea. Dates were obliterated with a rectangle, and the stamp was not issued without this obliteration. Value without rectangle, $400.

Rock Carvings, Balho AP33

1974, Apr. 26

C98 AP33 200fr carmine & slate 9.00 7.00

Lake Assal AP34

Designs (Lake Assal): 50fr, Rock formations on shore. 85fr, Crystallized wood.

1974, Oct. 25 Photo. ***Perf. 13***

C99 AP34 49fr multicolored 2.25 1.75
C100 AP34 50fr multicolored 2.50 2.00
C101 AP34 85fr multicolored 5.00 3.75
Nos. C99-C101 (3) 9.75 7.50

Columba Guinea — AP35

1975, May 23 Photo. *Perf. 13*

C102	AP35	500fr multicolored	22.50	11.00

Djibouti Airport AP36

1977, Mar. 1 Litho. *Perf. 12*

C103	AP36	500fr multicolored	12.50	9.00

Opening of new Djibouti Airport.

Thomas A. Edison and Phonograph AP37

Design: 75fr, Alexander Volta, electric train, lines and light bulb.

1977, May 5 Engr. *Perf. 13*

C104	AP37	55fr multicolored	4.00	2.75
C105	AP37	75fr multicolored	6.25	4.75

Famous inventors: Thomas Alva Edison and Alexander Volta (1745-1827).

POSTAGE DUE STAMPS

Nomad's Milk Jug — D3

Perf. 14x13

1969, Dec. 15 Engr. Unwmk.

J49	D3	1fr red brn, red lil & sl	.50	*.65*
J50	D3	2fr red brn, emer & sl	.60	*.80*
J51	D3	5fr red brn, bl & slate	1.00	*1.20*
J52	D3	10fr red brn, brn & slate	1.75	*2.00*
		Nos. J49-J52 (4)	3.85	*4.65*

AFGHANISTAN

af-ˈga-nə-ˌstan

LOCATION — Central Asia, bounded by Iran, Turkmenistan, Uzbekistan, Tajikistan, Pakistan, and China
GOVT. — Republic
AREA — 251,773 sq. mi.
POP. — 23,500,000 (1995 est.)
CAPITAL — Kabul

Afghanistan changed from a constitutional monarchy to a republic in July 1973.

12 Shahi = 6 Sanar = 3 Abasi =
2 Krans = 1 Rupee Kabuli
60 Paisas = 1 Rupee (1921)
100 Pouls = 1 Rupee Afghani (1927)

Catalogue values for unused stamps in this country are for Never Hinged items, beginning with Scott 364 in the regular postage section, Scott B1 in the semi-postal section, Scott C7 in the airpost section, Scott O8 in officials section, and Scott RA6 in the postal tax section.

CHARACTERS OF VALUE.

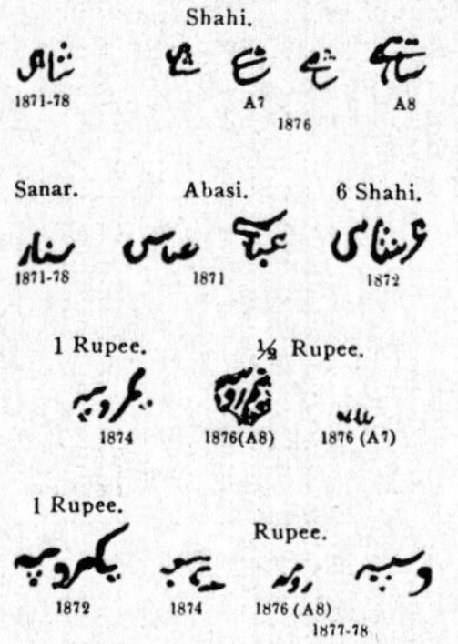

From 1871 to 1892 and 1898, the Moslem year date appears on the stamp. Numerals as follows:

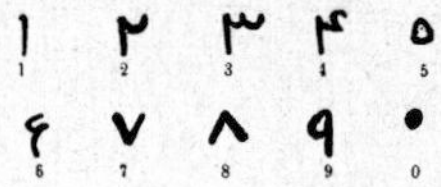

Until 1891, cancellation consisted of cutting or tearing a piece from the stamps. Such examples should not be considered as damaged.

Values are for cut square examples of good color. Cut to shape or faded examples sell for much less, particularly Nos. 1-10.

Nos. 1-108 are on laid paper of varying thickness except where wove is noted.

Until 1907, all stamps were issued ungummed.

The tiger's head on types A1 to A11 symbolizes the name of the contemporary amir, Sher (Tiger, or Lion) Ali.

Kingdom of Kabul

A1

Tiger's Head, Type I — A2

Tiger's Head, Type II — A2a

Both circles dotted. Thick outer circle usually measures 27.5mm-28mm in diameter.

Type I: well-defined inner and outer circles with evenly spaced dots.

Type II: less well-defined thin inner and outer circles, and dots are randomly spaced.

1871 Unwmk. Litho. *Imperf.*
Dated "1288"

1	A1	1sh black (30mm diameter)	1,350.	60.00
2	A2	1sh black	925.00	50.00
2A	A2a	1sh black	525.00	35.00
3	A2	1sa black	650.00	32.50
3A	A2a	1sa black	210.00	55.00
4	A2a	1ab black	150.00	60.00
		Nos. 1-4 (6)	3,810.	292.50

Nos. 1-4 are usually identified by plating. No. 1 was printed in a sheet of 15 (referred to as plate A). Nos. 2 and 3 were printing in sheets of 15 (10 of No. 2 and 5 of No. 3), referred to as plate B. Nos. 2A and 3A-4 were printed in sheets of 15 (5 of each denomination), referred to as plate C.

Similar designs without the tiger's head in the center are revenues.

A3

Outer circle dotted; inner circle plain.

Dated "1288"

5	A3	1sh black	525.00	35.00
6	A3	1sa black	300.00	50.00
7	A3	1ab black	200.00	32.50
		Nos. 5-7 (3)	1,025.	117.50

Nos. 5-7 were printed in sheets of 15 (5 of each denomination), referred to as plate D.

A4

Toned Wove Paper

1872 Dated "1289"

8	A4	6sh violet	*1,500.*	*900.*
9	A4	1rup violet	*1,750.*	*1,350.*

Two varieties of each. Date varies in location. Printed in sheets of 4 (2x2) containing two of each denomination.

Most used examples are smeared with a greasy ink cancel.

A4a

White Laid Paper

1873 Dated "1290"

10	A4a	1sh black	25.00	12.00
a.		Corner ornament missing	*750.00*	*750.00*
b.		Corner ornament retouched	*75.00*	*45.00*

15 varieties. Nos. 10a, 10b are the sixth stamp on the sheet.

A5

1873

11	A5	1sh black	22.50	11.00

Sixty varieties of each. No. 11 in violet is believed to be a proof.

1874 Dated "1291"

12	A5	1ab black	90.00	55.00
13	A5	½rup black	37.50	20.00
14	A5	1rup black	40.00	24.00
		Nos. 12-14 (3)	167.50	99.00

Five varieties of each.

Nos. 12-14 were printed on the same sheet. Se-tenant varieties exist.

A6

1875 Dated "1292"

15	A6	1sa black	*400.00*	*375.00*
a.		Wide outer circle	*1,250.*	*750.00*
16	A6	1ab black	425.00	400.00
17	A6	1sa brown violet	75.00	30.00
a.		Wide outer circle	300.00	*190.00*
18	A6	1ab brown violet	80.00	60.00

Ten varieties of the sanar, five of the abasi.

Nos. 15-16 and 17-18 were printed in the same sheets. Se-tenant pairs exist.

A7

1876 Dated "1293"

19	A7	1sh black	350.00	200.00
20	A7	1sa black	400.00	225.00
21	A7	1ab black	750.00	425.00
22	A7	½rup black	450.00	*275.00*
23	A7	1rup black	875.00	*275.00*
24	A7	1sh violet	*450.00*	275.00
25	A7	1sa violet	425.00	300.00
26	A7	1ab violet	525.00	275.00
27	A7	½rup violet	225.00	*60.00*
28	A7	1rup violet	225.00	*75.00*

12 varieties of the shahi and 3 each of the other values.

A8

1876 Dated "1293"

29	A8	1sh gray	16.00	10.00
29A	A8a	1sh gray	65.00	30.00
30	A8	1sa gray	20.00	8.00
31	A8	1ab gray	42.50	20.00
32	A8	½rup gray	50.00	25.00
33	A8	1rup gray	50.00	17.50
34	A8	1sh olive blk	140.00	80.00
35	A8	1sa olive blk	190.00	100.00
36	A8	1ab olive blk	400.00	250.00
37	A8	½rup olive blk	275.00	275.00
38	A8	1rup olive blk	375.00	400.00
39	A8	1sh green	30.00	8.00
40	A8	1sa green	40.00	25.00
41	A8	1ab green	85.00	60.00
42	A8	½rup green	125.00	80.00
43	A8	1rup green	110.00	125.00
44	A8	1sh ocher	32.50	15.00
45	A8	1sa ocher	40.00	24.00
46	A8	1ab ocher	80.00	50.00
47	A8	½rup ocher	100.00	65.00
48	A8	1rup ocher	140.00	125.00
49	A8	1sh violet	37.50	15.00
50	A8	1sa violet	37.50	15.00
51	A8	1ab violet	50.00	15.00
52	A8	½rup violet	70.00	27.50
53	A8	1rup violet	100.00	40.00

24 varieties of the shahi, 4 of which show denomination written:

A8a

12 varieties of the sanar, 6 of the abasi and 3 each of the ½ rupee and rupee.

A9

1877 Dated "1294"

54	A8a	1sh gray	10.00	*15.00*
55	A9	1sa gray	10.00	9.00
56	A9	1ab gray	11.00	9.00
57	A9	½rup gray	14.50	*20.00*
58	A9	1rup gray	16.00	*20.00*
59	A9	1sh black	14.50	*20.00*
60	A9	1sa black	25.00	*10.00*
61	A9	1ab black	42.50	*15.00*
62	A9	½rup black	45.00	*30.00*
63	A9	1rup black	45.00	*30.00*
64	A9	1sh green	32.50	32.50
65	A9	1sa green	15.00	*12.00*
66	A9	1ab green	17.50	*16.00*
67	A9	½rup green	30.00	*30.00*
68	A9	1rup green	27.50	*32.50*

69	A9	1sh	ocher	12.50	5.25
70	A9	1sa	ocher	12.50	7.25
71	A9	1ab	ocher	32.50	24.50
72	A9	½rup	ocher	40.00	35.00
73	A9	1rup	ocher	50.00	35.00
74	A9	1sh	violet	15.00	8.00
75	A9	1sa	violet	12.50	5.00
76	A9	1ab	violet	19.00	12.00
77	A9	½rup	violet	27.50	30.00
78	A9	1rup	violet	27.50	30.00

25 varieties of the shahi, 8 of the sanar, 3 of the abasi and 2 each of the ½ rupee and rupee.

Some examples of Nos. 54-78 show a "94" year date. These are valued less.

Nos. 64-68 in sage green on wove paper are proofs.

A10

A11

1878 **Dated "95"**

79	A10	1sh	gray	5.00	10.00
80	A10	1sa	gray	8.00	10.00
81	A10	1ab	gray	12.50	10.00
82	A10	½rup	gray	15.00	15.00
83	A10	1rup	gray	15.00	15.00
84	A10	1sh	black	10.00	
85	A10	1sa	black	10.00	
86	A10	1ab	black	37.50	
87	A10	½rup	black	35.00	
88	A10	1rup	black	35.00	
89	A10	1sh	green	32.50	*55.00*
90	A10	1sa	green	10.00	9.00
91	A10	1ab	green	35.00	30.00
92	A10	½rup	green	32.50	30.00
93	A10	1rup	green	60.00	40.00
94	A10	1sh	ocher	27.50	10.00
95	A10	1sa	ocher	12.00	*15.00*
96	A10	1ab	ocher	45.00	35.00
97	A10	½rup	ocher	65.00	45.00
98	A10	1rup	ocher	27.50	*30.00*
99	A10	1sh	violet	10.00	*15.00*
100	A10	1sa	violet	30.00	25.00
101	A10	1ab	violet	17.50	15.00
102	A10	½rup	violet	55.00	35.00
103	A10	1rup	violet	45.00	30.00
104	A11	1sh	gray	7.00	7.00
105	A11	1sh	black	*100.00*	50.00
106	A11	1sh	green	10.00	5.00
107	A11	1sh	ocher	10.00	9.00
108	A11	1sh	violet	8.00	8.00

40 varieties of the shahi, 30 of the sanar, 6 of the abasi and 2 each of the ½ rupee and 1 rupee.

The 1876, 1877 and 1878 issues were printed in separate colors for each main post office on the Peshawar-Kabul-Khulm (Tashkurghan) postal route. Some specialists consider the black printings to be proofs, trial colors or reprints from the original plates.

There are many shades of these colors.

1ab, Type I (26mm) A12

1ab, Type II (28mm) A13

A14

A15

Dated "1298", numerals scattered through design

Handstamped, in watercolor

1881-90

Thin White Laid Batonne Paper

109	A12	1ab	violet	5.00	3.00
109A	A13	1ab	violet	8.00	3.00
110	A12	1ab	black brn	8.00	3.00
a.			Ordinary thin wove paper	—	20.00
111	A12	1ab	rose	12.00	3.00
b.			Se-tenant with No. 111A	16.00	—
111A	A13	1ab	rose	9.00	3.00
112	A14	2ab	violet	10.00	3.00
113	A14	2ab	black brn	12.00	6.00
114	A14	2ab	rose	20.00	10.00
115	A15	1rup	violet	12.00	12.00
116	A15	1rup	black brn	14.00	10.00
117	A15	1rup	rose	12.50	7.50

Thin White Wove Batonne Paper

118	A12	1ab	violet	15.00	5.00
119	A12	1ab	vermilion	30.00	10.00
120	A12	1ab	rose	30.00	25.00
121	A14	2ab	violet	30.00	25.00
122	A14	2ab	vermilion	30.00	16.00
122A	A14	2ab	black brn		
123	A15	1rup	violet	15.00	8.00
124	A15	1rup	vermilion	14.00	7.50
125	A15	1rup	black brn	19.00	8.00

Thin White Laid Batonne Paper

126	A12	1ab	brown org	20.00	8.00
126A	A13	1ab	brn org (II)	22.50	9.00
127	A12	1ab	carmine lake	20.00	8.00
a.			Laid paper	22.50	10.00
128	A14	2ab	brown org	22.50	8.00
129	A14	2ab	carmine lake	20.00	8.00
130	A15	1rup	brown org	35.00	15.00
131	A15	1rup	car lake	37.50	15.00

Yellowish Laid Batonne Paper

132	A12	1ab	purple	10.00	10.00
133	A12	1ab	red	12.50	10.00

1884 **Colored Wove Paper**

133A	A13	1ab	purple, *yel* (II)	17.50	17.50
134	A12	1ab	purple, *grn*	20.00	
135	A12	1ab	purple, *blue*	32.50	21.00
136	A12	1ab	red, *grn*	37.50	
137	A12	1ab	red, *yel*	30.00	
139	A12	1ab	red, *rose*	50.00	
140	A14	2ab	red, *yel*	30.00	
142	A14	2ab	red, *rose*	30.00	
143	A15	1rup	red, *yel*	55.00	20.00
145	A15	1rup	red, *rose*	65.00	25.00

Thin Colored Ribbed Paper

146	A14	2ab	red, *yellow*	40.00
147	A15	1rup	red, *yellow*	80.00
148	A12	1ab	lake, *lilac*	40.00
149	A14	2ab	lake, *lilac*	40.00
150	A15	1rup	lake, *lilac*	40.00
151	A12	1ab	lake, *green*	40.00
152	A14	2ab	lake, *green*	40.00
153	A15	1rup	lake, *green*	40.00

1886-88 **Colored Wove Paper**

155	A12	1ab	black, *magenta*	60.00
156	A12	1ab	claret brn, *org*	50.00
156A	A12	1ab	red, *org*	40.00
156B	A14	2ab	red, *org*	40.00
156C	A15	1rup	red, *org*	40.00

Laid Batonné Paper

157	A12	1ab	black, *lavender*	40.00
158	A12	1ab	cl brn, *grn*	40.00
159	A12	1ab	black, *pink*	60.00
160	A14	2ab	black, *pink*	100.00
161	A15	1rup	black, *pink*	70.00

Laid Paper

162	A12	1ab	black, *pink*	80.00
163	A14	2ab	black, *pink*	80.00
164	A15	1rup	black, *pink*	80.00
165	A12	1ab	brown, *yel*	80.00
166	A14	2ab	brown, *yel*	80.00
167	A15	1rup	brown, *yel*	80.00
168	A12	1ab	blue, *grn*	80.00
169	A14	2ab	blue, *grn*	80.00
170	A15	1rup	blue, *grn*	80.00

1891 **Colored Wove Paper**

175	A12	1ab	green, *rose*	100.00
176	A15	1rup	pur, *grn batonne*	100.00

Nos. 109-176 fall into three categories:

1. Those regularly issued and in normal postal use from 1881 on, handstamped on thin white laid or wove paper in strip sheets containing 12 or more impressions of the same denomination arranged in two irregular rows, with the impressions often touching or overlappng.

2. The 1884 postal issues provisionally printed on smooth or ribbed colored wove paper as needed to supplement low stocks of the normal white paper stamps.

3. The "special" printings made in a range of colors on several types of laid or wove colored papers, most of which were never used for normal printings. These were produced periodically from 1886 to 1891 to meet philatelic demands. Although nominally valid for postage, most of the special printings were exported directly to fill dealers' orders, and few were ever postally used. Many of the sheets contained all three denominations with impressions separated by ruled lines. Sometimes different colors were used, so se-tenant multiples of denomination or color exist. Many combinations of stamp and paper colors exist besides those listed.

Various shades of each color exist.

Type A12 is known dated "1297."

Counterfeits, lithographed or typographed, are plentiful.

Kingdom of Afghanistan

A16

A17

A18

Dated "1309"

1891 **Pelure Paper** **Litho.**

177	A16	1ab	slate blue	2.00	2.00
a.			Tete beche pair	19.00	
178	A17	2ab	slate blue	12.00	12.00
179	A18	1rup	slate blue	27.50	—
			Nos. 177-179 (3)	41.50	14.00

Revenue stamps of similar design exist in various colors.

Nos. 177-179 were printed in panes on the same sheet, so se-tenant gutter pairs exist. Examples in black or red are proofs.

A Mosque Gate and Crossed Cannons (National Seal) — A19

Dated "1310" in Upper Right Corner

1892 **Flimsy Wove Paper**

180	A19	1ab	black, *green*	3.50	3.00
181	A19	1ab	black, *orange*	4.50	4.50
182	A19	1ab	black, *yellow*	3.50	3.00
183	A19	1ab	black, *pink*	4.00	3.25
184	A19	1ab	black, *lil rose*	4.00	4.00
185	A19	1ab	black, *blue*	6.00	5.50
186	A19	1ab	black, *salmon*	4.50	3.75
187	A19	1ab	black, *magenta*	4.00	4.00
188	A19	1ab	black, *violet*	4.00	4.00
188A	A19	1ab	black, *scarlet*	4.00	3.00

Many shades exist.

A20

A21

Undated

1894 **Flimsy Wove Paper**

189	A20	2ab	black, *green*	12.00	8.00
190	A21	1rup	black, *green*	14.50	13.00

24 varieties of the 2 abasi and 12 varieties of the rupee.

Nos. 189-190 and F3 were printed se-tenant in the same sheet. Pairs exist.

A21a

Dated "1316"

1898 **Flimsy Wove Paper**

191	A21a	2ab	black, *pink*	3.00
192	A21a	2ab	black, *magenta*	3.00
193	A21a	2ab	black, *yellow*	1.40
193A	A21a	2ab	black, *salmon*	3.50
194	A21a	2ab	black, *green*	1.75
195	A21a	2ab	black, *purple*	2.40
195A	A21a	2ab	black, *blue*	22.50
			Nos. 191-195A (7)	37.55

Nos. 191-195A were not regularly issued. Genuinely used examples are scarce. No. 195A was found in remainder stocks and probably was never released.

A22

A23

A24

1907 **Engr.** ***Imperf.***

Medium Wove Paper

196	A22	1ab	blue green	50.00	30.00
a.			1ab emerald	—	30.00
b.			Double impression	*500.00*	
c.			Printed on both sides		450.00
197	A22	1ab	brt blue	30.00	25.00
198	A23	2ab	deep blue	30.00	25.00
a.			Double impression	*550.00*	
199	A24	1rup	green	100.00	50.00
a.			1rup blue green	100.00	75.00

Zigzag Roulette 10

200	A22	1ab	green	*2,750.*	450.00
a.			Double impression		*1,500.*
b.			Printed on both sides		*1,750.*
c.			Double impression and printed on both sides		*2,500.*
d.			1ab blue green	*2,750.*	450.00
201	A23	2ab	blue	*2,500.*	—

1908 ***Serrate Roulette 13***

201A	A22	1ab	green	
b.			1ab emerald green	
201B	A23	2ab	blue	*3,500.*

Nos. 201A and 201Ab are only known used on cover.

No. 201B is known only unused.

Perf. 12 on 2, 3 or 4 Sides

202	A22	1ab	green	—	65.00
203	A23	2ab	deep blue	35.00	20.00
a.			Horiz. pair, imperf between	450.00	
204	A24	1rup	blue green	125.00	65.00
c.			Pair, imperf. between	400.00	
			Nos. 202-204 (3)	160.00	150.00

Twelve varieties of the 1 abasi, 6 of the 2 abasi, 4 of the 1 rupee.

Nos. 196-204 were issued in small sheets containing 3 or 4 panes. Gutter pairs, normal and tete beche, exist.

Two plates were used for the 1 abasi: plate I, inner vert. lines extend into lower left panel; plate II, inner vert. lines do not extend into lower left panel.

A25

A26

A27

1909-19 **Typo.** ***Perf. 12***

205	A25	1ab	ultra	5.00	2.00
a.			Imperf., pair	48.00	
206	A25	1ab	red ('16)	1.60	1.25
a.			Imperf.	30.00	
207	A25	1ab	rose ('18)	1.60	1.00
208	A26	2ab	green	2.75	2.25
a.			Imperf., pair	48.00	
b.			Horiz. pair, imperf. btwn.		
208C	A26	2ab	yellow ('16)	3.25	2.75
209	A26	2ab	bis ('18-'19)	3.25	*3.25*
210	A27	1rup	lilac brn	7.50	6.50
a.			1rup red brown	7.50	7.50
211	A27	1rup	ol bis ('16)	10.00	8.00
			Nos. 205-211 (8)	34.95	27.00

A28

1913

212	A28	2pa	drab brown	20.00	*12.00*
a.			2pa red brown	20.00	*12.00*

No. 212 is inscribed "Tiket waraq dak" (Postal card stamps). It was usable only on postcards and not accepted for postage on letters.

Nos. 196-212 sometimes show letters of a papermaker's watermark, "Howard & Jones, London."

Royal Star A29

1920, Aug. 24 ***Perf. 12***

Size: 39x46mm

214 A29 10pa rose 200.00 110.00
215 A29 20pa red brown 300.00 190.00
216 A29 30pa green 400.00 325.00
Nos. 214-216 (3) 900.00 625.00

Independence Day. Issued to commemorate the first and second anniversaries of the signing of the armistice (Aug. 24, 1919) that ended the war of independence (Third Afghan War).

Issued in sheets of two settings: wide gutter, with 19mm between stamps, narrow gutter, with 12mm to 13mm between stamps.

No. 214 exists in two sizes: 38.5mmx46mm, position 1 in the wide gutter sheet; 38.5mmx46mm, position 2, in the wide gutter and position 1 in the narrow gutter sheet.

1921, Mar. **Size: 22½x28¼mm**

217 A29 10pa rose 2.50 1.25
a. Perf. 11 ('27) 22.50 13.00
218 A29 20pa red brown 4.50 2.50
219 A29 30pa yel green 6.50 3.00
a. Tete beche pair 55.00 32.50
b. 30pa green 6.50 3.50
c. As "b," Tete beche pair 55.00 32.50
Nos. 217-219 (3) 13.50 6.75

3rd Independence Day.
Two types of the 10pa, three of the 20pa.

Hstmpd. in black on Nos. 217-219

1923, Feb. 26

219D A29a 10pa rose — 125.00
219E A29a 20pa red brown — 125.00
219F A29a 30pa yel green 400.00 —

5th Independence Day.
Two types of handstamp exist.
Forgeries exist.
See No. Q13B-Q13E.

These handstamps were used by the Kabul post office on incoming foreign mail from 1921 until Afghanistan joined the Universal Postal Union April 1, 1928. Afghan stamps were applied to foreign mail arriving in the country and were canceled with these postage-due handstamps to indicate that postage was to be collected from the addressee. The handstamps were applied primarily to Nos. 217-219, 227-235, 236, and 237-246. Values are the same as for stamps with postal cancellations. A third type of handstamp exists with no distinctive outer border.

A30

1924, Feb. 26 ***Perf. 12***

220 A30 10pa chocolate 45.00 30.00
a. Tete beche pair 150.00 100.00

6th Independence Day.
Printed in sheets of four consisting of two tete beche pairs, and in sheets of two. Two types exist.

Some authorities believe that Nos. Q15-Q16 were issued as regular postage stamps.

Crest of King Amanullah — A32

Size: 29x37mm

1925, Feb. 26 ***Perf. 12***

222 A32 10pa light brown 75.00 35.00

7th Independence Day.
Printed in sheets of 8 (two panes of 4).

Wove Paper

1926, Feb. 28 **Size: 26x33mm**

224 A32 10pa dark blue 8.00 8.00
a. Imperf., pair 32.50
b. Horiz. pair, imperf. btwn. 75.00
c. Vert. pair, imperf. btwn.
d. Laid paper 40.00 13.00

7th anniv. of Independence. Printed in sheets of 4, and in sheets of 8 (two panes of 4). Tete beche gutter pairs exist.

Tughra and Crest of Amanullah — A33

1927, Feb.

225 A33 10pa magenta 14.00 12.00
a. Vertical pair, imperf. between 75.00

Dotted Background

226 A33 10pa magenta 20.00 13.00
a. Horiz. pair, imperf. between 75.00

The surface of No. 226 is covered by a net of fine dots.
8th anniv. of Independence. Printed in sheets of 8 (two panes of 4).
Tete-beche gutter pairs exist. Value, pair $85.

National Seal — A34

A35

A36

1927, Oct. ***Imperf.***

227 A34 15p pink 1.40 1.40
228 A35 30p Prus green 2.75 1.25
229 A36 60p light blue 3.75 3.25
Nos. 227-229 (3) 7.90 5.90

1927, Nov. ***Perf. 11, 11¾***

230 A34 15p pink 1.75 1.40
231 A35 30p Prus green 3.25 1.40
232 A36 60p bright blue 3.50 2.00
a. Tete beche pair 17.50 17.50
Nos. 230-232 (3) 8.50 4.80

A37

A38

A39

A40

1928, Feb. ***Perf. 11, 11¾***

233 A37 10p gray green 1.25 .40
a. Tete beche pair 14.00 6.50
b. Vert. pair, imperf. horiz. 11.00 11.00
c. Vertical pair, imperf. between
234 A38 25p car rose 1.50 .40
235 A39 40p ultra 2.00 .75
a. Tete beche pair 15.00 *16.00*
236 A40 50p red 2.50 1.00
Nos. 233-236 (4) 7.25 2.55

Nos. 230-232 are usually imperforate on one or two sides. The sheets of these stamps are often imperforate at the outer margin. No. 233 was printed in sheets of nine and sheets of 20.

Tughra and Crest of Amanullah A41

1928, Feb. 27

236D A41 15p pink 5.00 5.00
a. Tete beche pair 12.00 10.00
b. Horiz. pair, imperf. vert. 22.50 19.00
c. As "a," imperf. vert., block of 4 75.00

9th anniv. of Independence. This stamp is always imperforate on one or two sides.

A 15p blue of somewhat similar design was prepared for the 10th anniv., but was not issued due to Amanullah's dethronement. Value, $15.

Types of 1927 in New Colors

A42

1929-30

236E A34 15p ultra 1.75 1.40
236F A42 30p dp green ('30) 1.75 1.25
236G A36 60p black ('29) 4.00 2.25
Nos. 236E-236G (3) 7.50 4.90

No. 236F has been redrawn. A narrow border of pearls has been added and "30," in European and Arabic numerals, inserted in the upper spandrels.

A43

1928-30 ***Perf. 11, 12***

237 A43 2p dull blue 7.75 4.50
a. Vertical pair, imperf. between 20.00
238 A43 2p lt rose ('30) .65 .55
240 A37 10p choc ('30) 3.00 1.25
a. 10p brown purple ('29) 8.50 8.50
242 A38 25p Prus green ('29) 4.00 1.25
244 A39 40p rose ('29) 3.50 1.25
a. Tete beche pair 14.50
b. Vert. pair, imperf. horiz. 11.00
246 A40 50p dk blue ('29) 5.00 1.50
Nos. 237-246 (6) 23.90 10.30

The sheets of these stamps are often imperforate at the outer margins.
Nos. 237-238 are newspaper stamps.

This handstamp was used for 10 months by the Revolutionary Gov't in Kabul as a control mark on outgoing mail. It occasionally fell on the stamps but there is no evidence that it was officially used as an overprint. Unused examples were privately made. Forgeries exist.

Independence Monument — A46

Laid Paper
Without Gum
Wmk. Large Seal in the Sheet

1931, Aug. **Litho.** ***Perf. 12***

262 A46 20p red 2.50 1.25

13th Independence Day.

National Assembly Chamber — A47

A48

National Assembly Building — A49

A50

National Assembly Chamber — A51

National Assembly Building — A52

Wove Paper

1932 **Unwmk.** **Typo.** ***Perf. 12***

263 A47 40p olive 1.15 .40
264 A48 60p violet 1.50 .80
265 A49 80p dark red 2.00 1.25
266 A50 1af black 16.00 7.50
267 A51 2af ultra 7.00 4.00
268 A52 3af gray green 7.50 3.50
Nos. 263-268 (6) 35.15 17.45

Formation of the Natl. Council. Imperforate or perforated examples on ungummed chalky paper are proofs. Covers of No. 263 imperf proofs are known used in May 1999.
See Nos. 304-305.

Mosque at Balkh — A53

Kabul Fortress — A54

Parliament House, Darul Funun — A55

Parliament House, Darul Funun — A56

Arch of Qalai Bist — A57

Memorial Pillar of Knowledge and Ignorance — A58

Independence Monument A59

Minaret at Herat A60

Arch of Paghman — A61

Ruins at Balkh — A62

Minarets of Herat A63

Great Buddha at Bamian A64

1932 **Typo.** ***Perf. 12***

269	A53	10p	brown	.80	.25
270	A54	15p	dk brown	.60	.30
271	A55	20p	red	.95	.25
272	A56	25p	dk green	1.35	.25
273	A57	30p	red	1.35	.25
274	A58	40p	orange	1.75	.50
275	A59	50p	blue	2.40	1.40
a.			Tete beche pair	12.00	
276	A60	60p	blue	2.25	.90
277	A61	80p	violet	4.00	2.00
278	A62	1af	dark blue	7.00	.80
279	A63	2af	dk red violet	7.75	3.00
280	A64	3af	claret	9.50	4.00
			Nos. 269-280 (12)	39.70	13.90

Counterfeits of types A53-A65 exist.
See Nos. 290-295, 298-299, 302-303.

Entwined 2's — A65

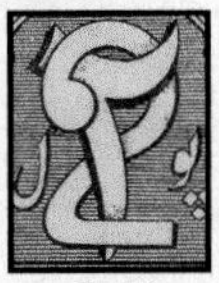

Type I

Type II

Two types:
Type I — Numerals shaded. Size about 21x29mm.
Type II — Numerals unshaded. Size about 21¾x30mm.

1931-38 ***Perf. 12, 11x12***

281	A65	2p	red brn (I)	.40	.50
282	A65	2p	olive blk (I) ('34)	.30	.80
283	A65	2p	grnsh gray (I) ('34)	.40	.75
283A	A65	2p	black (I) ('36)	.25	.75
284	A65	2p	salmon (II) ('38)	.50	.75
284A	A65	2p	rose (I) ('38)	.50	.90
b.			Imperf., pair	10.00	

Imperf

285	A65	2p	black (II) ('37)	.75	.75
286	A65	2p	salmon (II) ('38)	.75	.75
			Nos. 281-286 (8)	3.85	5.95

The newspaper rate was 2 pouls.

Independence Monument — A66

1932, Aug. ***Perf. 12***

287 A66 1af carmine 5.50 *15.00*

14th Independence Day.

A67

1929 Liberation Monument, Kabul.

1932, Oct. **Typo.**

288 A67 80p red brown 2.00 *7.50*

Arch of Paghman A68

1933, Aug.

289 A68 50p light ultra 3.00 *7.50*

15th Independence Day.
No. 289 exists imperf. Value, $5.

Types of 1932 and

Royal Palace, Kabul — A69

Darrah-Shikari Pass, Hindu Kush — A70

1934-38 **Typo.** ***Perf. 12***

290	A53	10p	deep violet	.30	.25
291	A54	15p	turq green	.50	.25
292	A55	20p	magenta	.50	.25
293	A56	25p	deep rose	.60	.25
294	A57	30p	orange	.65	.30
295	A58	40p	blue black	.75	.30
296	A69	45p	dark blue	2.75	1.50
297	A69	45p	red ('38)	.50	.25
298	A59	50p	orange	.80	.25
299	A60	60p	purple	1.00	.45
300	A70	75p	red	4.00	2.00
301	A70	75p	dk blue ('38)	1.00	.65
302	A61	80p	brown vio	1.60	.80
303	A62	1af	red violet	3.25	1.60
304	A51	2af	gray black	5.25	2.40
305	A52	3af	ultra	6.00	3.00
			Nos. 290-305 (16)	29.45	14.50

Nos. 290, 292, 300, 304, 305 exist imperf.

Independence Monument — A71

1934, Aug. **Litho.** **Without Gum**

306	A71	50p	pale green	3.25	2.75
a.			Tete beche pair	11.50	11.50

16th year of Independence. Each sheet of 40 (4x10) included 4 tete beche pairs as lower half of sheet was inverted.

Independence Monument — A74

1935, Aug. 15 **Laid Paper**

309 A74 50p dark blue 3.50 2.40

17th year of Independence.

Fireworks Display — A75

Wove Paper

1936, Aug. 15 ***Perf. 12***

310 A75 50p red violet 3.25 2.50

18th year of Independence.

Independence Monument and Nadir Shah — A76

1937

311	A76	50p	vio & bis brn	2.75	2.10
a.			Imperf., pair	9.50	9.50

19th year of Independence.

Mohammed Nadir Shah — A77

1938 **Without Gum** ***Perf. 11x12***

315	A77	50p	brt blue & sepia	2.75	2.40
a.			Imperf. pair	24.00	19.00

20th year of Independence.

Mohammed Nadir Shah — A78

1939 ***Perf. 11, 12x11***

317 A78 50p deep salmon 2.40 1.50

21st year of Independence.

National Arms — A79

Parliament House, Darul Funun — A80

Royal Palace, Kabul A81

Independence Monument A82

Independence Monument and Nadir Shah — A83

Mohammed Zahir Shah — A84

Mohammed Zahir Shah — A85

Perf. 11, 11x12, 12x11, 12

1939-61 **Typo.**

318	A79	2p	intense blk	.30	*.70*
318A	A79	2p	brt pink ('61)	.30	*.70*
			Size: 36.5x24mm		
319	A80	10p	brt purple	.30	.25
			Size: 31.5x21mm		
320	A80	15p	brt green	.35	.25
			Size: 34x22.5mm		
321	A80	20p	red lilac	.50	.25
322	A81	25p	rose red	.60	.30
322A	A81	25p	green ('41)	.35	.25
323	A81	30p	orange	.50	.25
a.			Vert. pair, imperf between		—
324	A81	40p	dk gray	1.00	.50
325	A82	45p	brt carmine	1.00	.40
326	A82	50p	dp orange	.80	.25
327	A82	60p	violet	1.00	.25
328	A83	75p	ultra	3.00	.80
328A	A83	75p	red vio ('41)	2.25	1.60
328C	A83	75p	brt red ('44)	4.00	3.00
328D	A83	75p	chnt brn ('49)	4.00	3.00
329	A83	80p	chocolate	2.00	1.00
a.			80p dull red violet (error)		
330	A84	1af	brt red violet	2.25	.80
330A	A85	1af	brt red vio ('44)	2.25	.90
331	A85	2af	copper red	3.00	.80
a.			2af deep rose red	4.25	1.75
332	A84	3af	deep blue	5.00	2.40
			Nos. 318-332 (21)	34.75	18.65

Many shades exist in this issue.
On No. 332, the King faces slightly left.
No. 318A issued with and without gum.
See Nos. 795A-795B. For similar design see No. 907A.

Mohammed Nadir Shah — A86

1940, Aug. 23 *Perf. 11*

333 A86 50p gray green 2.00 1.50

22nd year of Independence.

Independence Monument A87

Arch of Paghman A88

1941, Aug. 23 *Perf. 12*

334 A87 15p gray green 25.00 5.00
335 A88 50p red brown 2.50 2.10

23rd year of Independence.

Sugar Factory, Baghlan — A89

1942, Apr. *Perf. 12*

336 A89 1.25af blue (shades) 2.00 1.50
a. 1.25af ultra 2.50 1.75

In 1949, a 1.50af brown, type A89, was sold for 3af by the Philatelic Office, Kabul. It was not valid for postage. Value $6.

Independence Monument A90

Mohammed Nadir Shah and Arch of Paghman A91

1942, Aug. 23 *Perf. 12*

337 A90 35p bright green 3.75 3.50
338 A91 125p chalky blue 3.00 2.00

24th year of Independence.

Independence Monument and Nadir Shah — A92

Mohammed Nadir Shah — A93

Perf. 11x12, 12x11

1943, Aug. 25 Typo. Unwmk.

339 A92 35p carmine 17.50 15.00
340 A93 1.25af dark blue 3.50 2.50

25th year of Independence.

Tomb of Gohar Shad, Herat A94

Ruins of Qalai Bist A95

1944, May 1 *Perf. 12, 11x12*

341 A94 35p orange 1.50 .80
342 A95 70p violet 2.00 .80
a. 70p rose lilac 2.00 .80

A96

A97

1944, Aug. *Perf. 12*

343 A96 35p crimson 1.25 .65
344 A97 1.25af ultra 2.25 1.75

26th year of Independence.

Catalogue values for unused stamps in this section, from this point to the end of the section, are for Never Hinged items.

A98

A99

1945, July

345 A98 35p deep red lilac 2.50 .80
346 A99 1.25af blue 4.00 2.00

27th year of Independence.

Mohammed Zahir Shah A100

Independence Monument A101

Mohammed Nadir Shah — A102

1946, July

347 A100 15p emerald 1.25 .70
348 A101 20p dp red lilac 2.00 .85
349 A102 125p blue 3.75 2.00
Nos. 347-349 (3) 7.00 3.55

28th year of Independence.

Zahir Shah and Ruins of Qalai Bist — A103

A104

A105

1947, Aug.

350 A103 15p yellow green .80 .55
351 A104 35p plum 1.00 .65
352 A105 125p deep blue 2.75 1.60
Nos. 350-352 (3) 4.55 2.80

29th year of Independence.

Begging Child — A106

A107

1948, May Unwmk. Typo. *Perf. 12*

353 A106 35p yel green 4.75 4.00
354 A107 125p gray blue 4.75 4.00

Children's Day, May 29, 1948, and valid only on that day. Proceeds were used for Child Welfare.

A108

A109

A110

1948, Aug.

355 A108 15p green .65 .30
356 A109 20p magenta .80 .30
357 A110 125p dark blue 1.60 .80
Nos. 355-357 (3) 3.05 1.40

30th year of Independence.

United Nations Emblem A111

1948, Oct. 24

358 A111 125p dk violet blue 9.50 8.00

UN, 3rd anniv. Valid one day only. Sheets of 9.

Maiwand Victory Column, Kandahar A112

Zahir Shah and Ruins of Qalai Bist A113

Independence Monument and Nadir Shah — A114

1949, Aug. 24 Typo. *Perf. 12*

359 A112 25p green 1.25 .50
360 A113 35p magenta 1.50 .65
361 A114 1.25af blue 2.50 1.25
Nos. 359-361 (3) 5.25 2.40

31st year of Independence.

Nadir Shah — A117

1950, Aug.

364 A117 35p red brown .75 .30
365 A117 125p blue 2.00 .50

32nd year of Independence.

Medical School and Nadir Shah — A119

Size: 38x25mm

1950, Dec. 22 Typo. *Perf. 12*

367 A119 35p emerald 1.25 .65

Size: 46x30mm

368 A119 1.25af deep blue 4.00 2.00
a. 1.25af black (error) 7.00 2.50

19th anniv. of the founding of Afghanistan's Faculty of Medicine. On sale and valid for use on Dec. 22-28, 1950.

See Nos. RA9-RA10.

Minaret, Herat A120

Zahir Shah A121

Mosque of Khodja Abu Parsar, Balkh — A122

A123

A124

20p, Buddha at Bamian. 40p, Ruined arch. 45p, Maiwand Victory monument. 50p, View of Kandahar. 60p, Ancient tower. 70p, Afghanistan flag. 80p, 1af, Profile of Zahir Shah in uniform.

Imprint: "Waterlow & Sons Limited, London"

Photogravure, Engraved, Engraved and Lithographed

Perf. 12, 12½, 13x12½, 13½

1951, Mar. 21 Unwmk.

369 A120 10p yellow & brn .30 .25
370 A120 15p blue & brn .55 .25
371 A120 20p black 8.00 7.00
372 A121 25p green .50 .25
373 A122 30p cerise .65 .25
374 A121 35p violet .70 .25
375 A122 40p chestnut brn .70 .25
376 A120 45p deep blue .70 .25
377 A122 50p olive black 2.00 .25
378 A120 60p black 1.60 .30
379 A122 70p dk grn, blk, red & grn .90 .25
380 A123 75p cerise 1.25 .50
381 A123 80p carmine & blk 2.10 .90
382 A123 1af dp grn & vio 1.60 .65
383 A124 1.25af rose lil & blk 1.90 1.00
384 A124 2af ultra 2.75 .80
385 A124 3af ultra & blk 6.00 1.25
Nos. 369-385 (17) 32.20 14.65

Nos. 372, 374 and 381 to 385 are engraved, No. 379 is engraved and lithographed.

Imperfs. exist of the photogravure stamps.

See Nos. 445-451, 453, 552A-552D. For surcharges see Nos. B1-B2.

Arch of Paghman A125

Nadir Shah and Independence Monument A126

Overprint in Violet

Perf. 13½x13, 13

1951, Aug. 25 **Engr.**
386 A125 35p dk green & blk 1.10 .65
387 A126 1.25af deep blue 3.00 1.40

Overprint reads "Sol 33 Istiqlal" or "33rd Year of Independence." Overprint measures about 11mm wide.
See Nos. 398-399B, 441-442.

Proposed Flag of Pashtunistan A127

Design: 125p, Flag and Pashtunistan warrior.

1951, Sept. 2 **Litho.** ***Perf. 11½***
388 A127 35p dull chocolate 1.50 .75
389 A127 125p blue 3.00 2.00

Issued to publicize "Free Pashtunistan" Day. Exist Imperf.

Imperforates

From 1951 to 1958, quantities of nearly all locally-printed stamps were left imperforate and sold by the government at double face. From 1959 until March, 1964, many of the imperforates were sold for more than face value.

Avicenna — A128

1951, Nov. 4 **Typo.** ***Perf. 11½***
390 A128 35p deep claret 7.50 1.50
391 A128 125p blue 3.00 *4.00*

20th anniv. of the founding of the national Graduate School of Medicine.
Exist imperf. Value $27.50.

A129

Dove and UN Symbols — A130

1951, Oct. 24
392 A129 35p magenta .90 .40
393 A130 125p blue 2.25 1.75

7th anniv. of the UN. Exist imperf.

Amir Sher Ali Khan and Tiger Head Stamp — A131

Nos. 395, 397, Zahir Shah and stamp.

1951, Dec. 23 **Litho.**
394 A131 35p chocolate .85 .40
395 A131 35p rose lilac .85 .40
396 A131 125p ultra 1.25 .80
a. Cliche of 35p in plate of 125p 110.00 *200.00*
397 A131 125p aqua 1.25 .80
Nos. 394-397 (4) 4.20 2.40

76th anniv. of the UPU. Exist imperf. Values, set: unused $9; used $17.50.

Stamps of 1951 Without Overprint

Perf. 13½x13, 13

1952, Aug. 24 **Engr.**
398 A125 35p dk green & blk 1.50 .55
399 A126 1.25af deep blue 3.25 1.25

For overprints see Nos. 399A-399B, 441-442.

Same Overprinted in Violet

399A A125 35p dk grn & blk 4.00 2.25
399B A126 1.25af deep blue 4.00 2.25

Nos. 398-399B issued for 34th Independence Day.

Globe A132

Perf. 11½

1952, Oct. 25 **Unwmk.** **Litho.**
400 A132 35p rose .80 .65
401 A132 125p aqua 1.60 1.10

Issued to honor the United Nations. Exist Imperf. Values, set: unused $6; used $7.25.

Symbol of Medicine — A134

1952, Nov. ***Perf. 11½***
403 A134 35p chocolate .70 .50
404 A134 125p violet blue 2.00 1.40

21st anniv. of the natl. Graduate School of Medicine.
No. 404 is inscribed in French with white letters on a colored background.
Exist Imperf. Values, set: unused $3.50; used $4.50.

Tribal Warrior, Natl. Flag — A135

1952, Sept. 1 ***Perf. 11***
405 A135 35p red .80 .80
406 A135 125p dark blue 1.25 1.25

No. 406 is inscribed in French "Pashtunistan Day, 1952."
Exist imperf. Values, set, unused or used, $2.75.

Flags of Afghanistan & Pashtunistan A139

Badge of Pashtunistan A140

Perf. 10½x11, 11

1953, Sept. 1 **Unwmk.**
411 A139 35p vermilion .80 .80
412 A140 125p blue 1.25 1.25

Issued to publicize "Free Pashtunistan" Day."
Exist imperf. Values, set: unused, $3.50; used, $4.

Nadir Shah and Flag Bearer — A141

A142

1953, Aug. 24 ***Perf. 11***
413 A141 35p green .40 .25
414 A142 125p violet .80 .55

35th anniv. of Independence.
Exist imperf. Values, set: unused, $3.50; used, $4.

United Nations Emblem — A143

1953, Oct. 24
415 A143 35p lilac 1.00 .80
416 A143 125p violet blue 2.00 1.50

United Nations Day, 1953.
Exist imperf. Values, set, unused or used, $9.

A144

Nadir Shah — A145

1953, Nov. 29
417 A144 35p orange 1.50 1.50
418 A145 125p chalky blue 3.00 3.00

22nd anniv. of the founding of the Natl. Graduate School of Medicine.
Exist imperf. Values, set: unused, $9; used, $12.50.

35p. Original — Right character in second line of Persian inscription

Redrawn — Persian character

Original

Redrawn

1953
419 A144 35p deep orange 9.50 9.50
420 A145 125p chalky blue 9.50 9.50

Exist imperf.

Nadir Shah and Symbols of Independence A146

1954, Aug. **Typo.** ***Perf. 11***
421 A146 35p carmine rose .70 .40
422 A146 125p violet blue 2.00 .80

36th year of Independence.
Exist imperf. Values, set: unused, $6; used, $7.

Raising Flag of Pashtunistan A147

1954, Sept. ***Perf. 11½***
423 A147 35p chocolate .70 .40
424 A147 125p blue 2.00 .80

Issued to publicize "Free Pashtunistan" Day.
Exist imperf. Values, set: unused, $4.75; used, $6.50.

UN Flag and Map — A148

1954, Oct. 24 ***Perf. 11***
425 A148 35p carmine rose 1.25 1.25
426 A148 125p dk violet blue 3.25 2.25

9th anniv. of the United Nations.
Exist imperf. Values, set: unused, $9; used, $10.

UN Symbols — A149

Design: 125p, UN emblem & flags.

1955, June 26 **Litho.** ***Perf. 11***

Size: 26½x36mm

427 A149 35p dark green 1.10 .55

Size: 28½x36mm

428 A149 125p aqua 2.00 1.00

10th anniv. of the UN charter.
Exist imperf. Values, set: unused, $12; used, $12.50.

Nadir Shah (center) and Brothers — A150

1929 Civil War Scene and Zahir Shah — A151

1955, Aug. **Unwmk.** ***Perf. 11***
429 A150 35p brt pink .65 .40
430 A150 35p violet blue .65 .40
431 A151 125p rose lilac 1.40 .90
432 A151 125p light violet 1.40 .90
Nos. 429-432 (4) 4.10 2.60

37th anniv. of Independence.
Exist imperf. Values, set: unused, $12; used, $13.50.

Tribal Elders' Council and Pashtun Flag — A152

1955, Sept. 5
433 A152 35p orange brown .60 .25
434 A152 125p yellow green 2.00 .55

Issued for "Free Pashtunistan" Day.

Exist imperf. Values, set: unused, $7; used, $9.

UN Flag — A153

1955, Oct. 24 Unwmk. *Perf. 11*

435 A153 35p orange brown 1.10 .60
436 A153 125p brt ultra 2.00 1.10

10th anniv. of the United Nations.

Exist imperf. Value for set: unused, $15; used, $17.50.

A154

1956, Aug. Litho.

437 A154 35p lt green .55 .30
438 A154 140p lt violet blue 2.25 .90

38th year of Independence.

Exist imperf. Value for set: unused, $3; used, $4.

Jesh'n Exhibition Hall — A155

1956, Aug. 25

439 A155 50p chocolate .90 .40
440 A155 50p lt violet blue .90 .40

International Exposition at Kabul.

Of the 50p face value, only 35p paid postage. The remaining 15p went to the Exposition.

Exist imperf. Value for set: unused, $7; used, $8.

Nos. 398-399 Handstamped in Violet

a

b

1957, Aug. Engr. *Perf. 13½x13, 13*

441 A125 (a) 35p dk green & blk .65 .30
442 A126 (b) 1.25af deep blue 1.00 .70

Arabic overprint measures 19mm.

39th year of independence.

Pashtunistan Flag — A156

1957, Sept. 1 Litho. *Perf. 11*

443 A156 50p pale lilac rose 1.00 .55
444 A156 155p light violet 1.50 1.00

Issued for "Free Pashtunistan" Day. French inscription on No. 444. 15p of each stamp went to the Pashtunistan Fund.

Exist imperf. Values, set: unused, $4; used, $4.50.

Types of 1951 and

Game of Buzkashi — A157

Perf. 12, 12½, 12½x13, 13, 13x12, 13x12½, 13½x14

Photo., Engr., Engr.& Litho.

1957, Nov. 23 Unwmk.

Imprint: "Waterlow & Sons Limited, London"

445 A122 30p brown .40 .25
446 A122 40p rose red .55 .25
447 A122 50p yellow .65 .25
448 A120 60p ultra .80 .25
449 A123 75p brt violet 1.00 .25
450 A123 80p violet & brn 1.10 .25
451 A123 1af carmine & ultra 1.75 .25
452 A157 140p olive & dp claret 2.75 .65
453 A124 3af orange & blk 2.75 .90
Nos. 445-453 (9) 11.75 3.30

No. 452 lacks imprint.

Nadir Shah and Flag-bearer A158

1958, Aug. 25 *Perf. 13½x14*

454 A158 35p dp yellow green .50 .25
455 A158 140p brown 1.25 1.00

40th year of Independence.

Exposition Buildings — A159

1958, Aug. 23 Litho. *Perf. 11*

456 A159 35p brt blue green .50 .25
457 A159 140p vermilion 1.25 1.00

International Exposition at Kabul.

Exist imperf. Value set, unused or used, $4.

Pres. Celal Bayar of Turkey — A160

1958, Sept. 13 Unwmk.

458 A160 50p lt blue .30 .25
459 A160 100p brown .65 .30

Visit of President Celal Bayar of Turkey.

Exists Imperf. Values, set: unused, $2.25; used, $3.25.

Flags of UN and Afghanistan — A161

1958, Oct. 24 Photo. *Perf. 14x13½*

Flags in Original Colors

460 A161 50p dark gray .65 .65
461 A161 100p green 1.40 1.10

United Nations Day, Oct. 24.

Exist imperf. Value set, unused or used, $4.

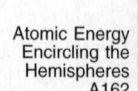

Atomic Energy Encircling the Hemispheres A162

1958, Oct. 20 *Perf. 13½x14*

462 A162 50p blue .55 .50
463 A162 100p dp red lilac .90 .65

Issued to promote Atoms for Peace.

Exist imperf. Value set, unused or used, $3.

UNESCO Building, Paris — A163

1958, Nov. 3

464 A163 50p dp yellow grn .70 .60
465 A163 100p brown olive .70 .70

UNESCO Headquarters in Paris opening, Nov. 3.

Exist imperf. Value set, unused or used, $5.

Globe and Torch — A164

Perf. 13½x14

1958, Dec. 10 Unwmk.

466 A164 50p lilac rose .40 .40
467 A164 100p maroon .90 *1.00*

10th anniv. of the signing of the Universal Declaration of Human Rights.

Exist imperf. Value set, unused or used, $3.50.

Nadir Shah and Flags — A165

1959, Aug. Litho. *Perf. 11 Rough*

468 A165 35p light vermilion .55 .50
469 A165 165p light violet 1.50 .65

41st year of Independence.

Exist imperf. Value set, unused or used, $2.50.

Uprooted Oak Emblem — A166

1960, Apr. 7 *Perf. 11*

470 A166 50p deep orange .25 .25
471 A166 165p blue .35 .25

World Refugee Year, 7/1/59-6/30/60.

Two imperf. souvenir sheets exist. Both contain a 50p and a 165p, type A166, with marginal inscriptions and WRY emblem in maroon. On one sheet the stamps are in the colors of Nos. 470-471 (size 108x81mm). Value $4.50. On the other, the 50p is blue and the 165p is deep orange (size 107x80mm). Value $6.

For surcharges see Nos. B35-B36.

Exist imperf. Value set, unused or used, $3.50.

Buzkashi — A167

1960, May 4 *Perf. 11, Imperf.*

472 A167 25p rose red .55 .25
473 A167 50p bluish green 1.40 .55
a. Cliche of 25p in plate of 50p 27.50 27.50

Exist imperf. Value set, unused or used, $2.50.

See Nos. 549-550A.

Independence Monument — A168

1960, Aug. *Perf. 11, 12*

474 A168 50p light blue .40 .25
475 A168 175p bright pink 1.00 .40

42nd Independence Day.

Exist imperf. Value set, unused or used, $1.75.

Globe and Flags — A169

1960, Oct. 24 Litho. *Perf. 11, 12*

476 A169 50p rose lilac .25 .25
477 A169 175p ultra 1.00 .65

UN Day.

Exist imperf. Value set, unused or used, $2.25.

An imperf. souvenir sheet contains one each of Nos. 476-477 with marginal inscriptions ("La Journée des Nations Unies 1960" in French and Persian) and UN emblem in light blue. Size: 127x85½mm. Value $5.50.

This sheet was surcharged "+20ps" in 1962. Value $5.50.

Teacher Pointing to Globe — A170

1960, Oct. 23 *Perf. 11*

478 A170 50p brt pink .40 .30
479 A170 100p brt green 1.00 .50

Issued to publicize Teacher's Day.

Exist imperf. Value set, unused or used, $2.50.

Mohammed Zahir Shah — A171

1960, Oct. 15

480 A171 50p red brown .65 .25
481 A171 150p dk car rose 1.60 .55

Honoring the King on his 46th birthday.

Exist imperf. Value set, unused or used, $2.50.

Buzkashi — A172

1960, Nov. 9 *Perf. 11*

482 A172 175p lt red brown 2.40 .50

Exists imperf. Value, unused or used, $3.

See Nos. 551-552.

No. 482 Overprinted in Bright Green

1960, Dec. 24

483 A172 175p red brown 2.00 2.00
a. Souv. sheet of 1, imperf. 6.00 *8.00*

17th Olympic Games, Rome, 8/25-9/11.

Exists imperf.

Value, unused or used, $4.

Mir Wais — A173

1961, Jan. 5 Unwmk. *Perf. 10½*

484 A173 50p brt rose lilac .65 .40
485 A173 175p ultra 1.10 .50
a. Souv. sheet, #484-485, imperf. 3.25 3.25

Mir Wais (1665-1708), national leader.
Exist imperf. Value set, unused or used, $2.25.

No Postal Need existed for the 1p-15p denominations issued with sets of 1961-63 (between Nos. 486 and 649, B37 and B65).
The lowest denomination actually used for non-philatelic postage in that period was 25p (except for the 2p newspaper rate for which separate stamps were provided).

Horse, Sheep and Camel — A174

Designs: No. 487, 175p, Rock partridge. 10p, 100p, Afghan hound. 15p, 150p, Grain & grasshopper, vert.

1961, Mar. 29 Photo. *Perf. 13½x14*

486 A174 2p maroon & buff .25 .25
487 A174 2p ultra & org .25 .25
488 A174 5p brown & yel .25 .25
489 A174 10p black & salmon .25 .25
490 A174 15p blue grn & yel .25 .25
491 A174 25p black & pink .25 .25
492 A174 50p black & citron .30 .30
493 A174 100p black & pink .45 .40
494 A174 150p green & yel .65 .65
495 A174 175p ultra & pink .80 .65
Nos. 486-495 (10) 3.70 3.50

Two souvenir sheets, perf. and imperf., contain 2 stamps, 1 each of No. 492-493. Value $3 each.

Afghan Fencing — A175

Designs: No. 497, 5p, 25p, 50p, Wrestlers. 10p, 100p, Man with Indian clubs. 15p, 150p, Afghan fencing. 175p, Children skating.

1961, July 6 *Perf. 13½x14*

496 A175 2p green & rose lil .25 .25
497 A175 2p brown & citron .25 .25
498 A175 5p gray & rose .25 .25
499 A175 10p blue & bister .25 .25
500 A175 15p sl bl & dl lil .25 .25
501 A175 25p black & dl bl .25 .25
502 A175 50p sl grn & bis brn .25 .25
503 A175 100p brown & bl grn .55 .55
504 A175 150p brown & org yel .90 .90
505 A175 175p black & blue .95 .95
Nos. 496-505 (10) 4.15 4.15

Issued for Children's Day.
A souvenir sheet exists, perf. and imperf., containing one each of Nos. 502-503. Values: perf $3.75; imperf $5.
For surcharges see Nos. B37-B41.

Bande Amir Lakes — A176

1961, Aug. 7 Photo. *Perf. 13½x14*

506 A176 3af brt blue .50 .25
507 A176 10af rose claret 1.25 1.25

Nadir Shah — A177

1961, Aug. 23 *Perf. 14x13½*

508 A177 50p rose red & blk .55 .50
509 A177 175p brt grn & org brn .90 .70

43rd Independence Day.
Exist imperf. Value set, unused or used, $2.50.

Two souvenir sheets, perf. and imperf., contain one each of Nos. 508-509. Value, each $2.50.

Girl Scout — A178

Perf. 14x13½

1961, July 23 Unwmk.

510 A178 50p dp car & dk gray .40 .25
511 A178 175p dp grn & rose brn 1.25 .50

Issued for Women's Day.
Exist imperf. Value set, unused or used, $4.50.
Two souvenir sheets exist, perf. and imperf., containing one each of Nos. 510-511. Value $5 each.

Exhibition Hall, Kabul — A179

1961, Aug. 23 *Perf. 13½x14*

512 A179 50p yel brn & yel grn .25 .25
513 A179 175p blue & brn .70 .50

International Exhibition at Kabul.

Pathan with Pashtunistan Flag — A180

1961, Aug. 31 Photo. *Perf. 14x13½*

514 A180 50p blk, lil & red .30 .25
515 A180 175p brn, grnsh bl & red .65 .55

Issued for "Free Pashtunistan Day."
Exist imperf. Value set, unused or used, $1.60.
Souvenir sheets exist perf. and imperf. containing one each of Nos. 514-515. Value $2.25 each.

Assembly Building — A181

1961, Sept. 10 *Perf. 12*

516 A181 50p dk gray & brt grn .25 .25
517 A181 175p ultra & brn .65 .50

Anniv. of the founding of the Natl. Assembly.
Exist imperf. Value set, unused or used, $1.25.
Souvenir sheets exist, perf. and imperf., containing one each of Nos. 516-517. Value $1.50 each.

Exterminating Anopheles Mosquito — A182

1961, Oct. 5 *Perf. 13½x14*

518 A182 50p blk & brn lil .60 .30
519 A182 175p maroon & brt grn 1.25 .90

Anti-Malaria campaign.
Exist imperf. Value set, unused or used, $4.
Souvenir sheets exist, perf. and imperf., containing one each of Nos. 518-519. Value $4.50 each.

Zahir Shah — A183

1961, Oct. 15 *Perf. 13½*

520 A183 50p rose lilac & grnish blue .30 .25
521 A183 175p emerald & red brn .90 .50

Issued to honor King Mohammed Zahir Shah on his 47th birthday.
See Nos. 609-612.

Pomegranates A184

Fruit: No. 523, 5p, 25p, 50p, Grapes. 10p, 150p, Apples. 15p, 175p, Pomegranates. 100p, Melons.

1961, Oct. 16 *Perf. 13½x14*
Fruit in Natural Colors

522 A184 2p black .25 .25
523 A184 2p green .25 .25
524 A184 5p lilac rose .25 .25
525 A184 10p lilac .25 .25
526 A184 15p dk blue .25 .25
527 A184 25p dull red .25 .25
528 A184 50p purple .25 .25
529 A184 100p brt blue .55 .55
530 A184 150p brown .90 .90
531 A184 175p olive gray .95 .95
Nos. 522-531 (10) 4.15 4.15

For Afghan Red Crescent Society.
Souvenir sheets exist, perf. and imperf., containing one each of Nos. 528-529. Value $2.25 each.
For surcharges see Nos. B42-B46.

UN Headquarters, NY — A185

1961, Oct. 24 *Perf. 13½x14*
Vertical Borders in Emerald, Red and Black

532 A185 1p rose lilac .25 .25
533 A185 2p slate .25 .25
534 A185 3p brown .25 .25
535 A185 4p ultra .25 .25
536 A185 50p rose red .25 .25
537 A185 75p gray .25 .25
538 A185 175p brt green .55 .55
Nos. 532-538 (7) 2.05 2.05

16th anniv. of the UN.
Nos. 536-538 exist imperf. Values, unused or used: 50p, 40c; 75p, 65c; 175p, $1.40.
Souvenir sheets exist, perf. and imperf., containing one each of Nos. 536-538. Value $3 each.

Children Giving Flowers to Teacher — A186

Designs: No. 540, 5p, 25p, 50p, Tulips. 10p, 100p, Narcissus. 15p, 150p, Children giving flowers to teacher. 175p, Teacher with children in front of school.

1961, Oct. 26 Photo. *Perf. 12*

539 A186 2p multicolored .25 .25
540 A186 2p multicolored .25 .25
541 A186 5p multicolored .25 .25
542 A186 10p multicolored .25 .25
543 A186 15p multicolored .25 .25
544 A186 25p multicolored .25 .25
545 A186 50p multicolored .25 .25
546 A186 100p multicolored .50 .50
547 A186 150p multicolored .80 .80
548 A186 175p multicolored .90 .90
Nos. 539-548 (10) 3.95 3.95

Issued for Teacher's Day.

Souvenir sheets exist, perf. and imperf. containing one each of Nos. 545-546. Value, 2 sheets, $4.50.
For surcharges see Nos. B47-B51.

Buzkashi Types of 1960

1961-72 Litho. *Perf. 10½, 11*

549 A167 25p violet 1.40 .25
b. 25p brt vio, typo. ('72) .25 .25
549A A167 25p citron ('63) 2.50 .25
550 A167 50p blue 2.00 .25
550A A167 50p yel org ('69) .50 .30
551 A172 100p citron .80 .25
551A A172 150p orange ('64) .65 .30
552 A172 2af lt green 1.50 1.00
Nos. 549-552 (7) 9.35 2.60

Zahir Shah Types of 1951
Imprint: "Thomas De La Rue & Co. Ltd."
Photo., Engr., Engr. & Litho.

1962 *Perf. 13x12, 13*

552A A123 75p brt purple 2.75 .25
552B A123 1af car & ultra 3.50 .30
552C A124 2af blue 7.25 .80
552D A124 3af orange & blk 10.00 1.00
Nos. 552A-552D (4) 23.50 2.35

People Raising UNESCO Symbol — A187

1962, July 2 Photo. *Perf. 14x13½*

553 A187 2p rose lil & brn .25 .25
554 A187 2p ol bis & brn .25 .25
555 A187 5p dp org & dk grn .25 .25
556 A187 10p gray & mag .25 .25
557 A187 15p blue & brn .25 .25
558 A187 25p org yel & pur .25 .25
559 A187 50p lt grn & pur .25 .25
560 A187 75p brt cit & brn .25 .25
561 A187 100p dp org & brn .30 .30
Nos. 553-561 (9) 2.30 2.30

15th anniv. of UNESCO. Souvenir sheets exist, perf. and imperf. One contains Nos. 558-559; the other contains Nos. 560-561. Value, $3.25 each perforated, $2.40 each imperf.
For surcharges see Nos. B52-B60.

Ahmad Shah — A188

1962, Feb. 24 Photo. *Perf. 13½*

562 A188 50p red brn & gray .25 .25
563 A188 75p green & salmon .30 .25
564 A188 100p claret & bister .40 .30
Nos. 562-564 (3) .95 .80

Ahmad Shah (1724-73), founded the Afghan kingdom in 1747 and ruled until 1773.

Afghan Hound — A189

Designs: 5p, 75p, Afghan cock. 10p, 100p, Kondjid plant. 15p, 125p, Astrakhan skins.

1962, Apr. 21 *Perf. 14x13½*

565 A189 2p rose & brn .25 .25
566 A189 2p lt green & brn .25 .25
567 A189 5p dp rose & claret .25 .25
568 A189 10p lt grn & sl grn .25 .25
569 A189 15p blue grn & blk .25 .25
570 A189 25p blue & brn .25 .25
571 A189 50p gray & brn .30 .25
572 A189 75p rose lil & lil .50 .30
573 A189 100p gray & dl grn .55 .40
574 A189 125p rose brn & blk .65 .50
Nos. 565-574 (10) 3.50 2.95

Agriculture Day.
Perf. and imperf. souvenir sheets exist. Set of 4 sheets, value $11.00.
Exist imperf. Value, set $5.50.

Athletes with Flag and Nadir Shah — A190

1962, Aug. 23 *Perf. 12*

575	A190	25p multicolored	.25	.25
576	A190	50p multicolored	.25	.25
577	A190	150p multicolored	.40	.30
		Nos. 575-577 (3)	.90	.80

44th Independence Day.

Woman in National Costume — A191

1962, Aug. 30 *Perf. 11½x12*

578	A191	25p lilac & brn	.25	.25
579	A191	50p green & brn	.25	.25
		Nos. 578-579,C15-C16 (4)	1.90	1.90

Issued for Women's Day. A souvenir sheet exists containing one each of Nos. 578-579, C15-C16. Value $4.50.

Man and Woman with Flag — A192

1962, Aug. 31 **Photo.**

580	A192	25p black, pale bl & red	.25	.25
581	A192	50p black, grn & red	.25	.25
582	A192	150p black, pink & red	.55	.40
		Nos. 580-582 (3)	1.05	.90

Issued for "Free Pashtunistan Day."

Malaria Eradication Emblem and Swamp — A193

1962, Sept. 5 *Perf. 14x13½*

583	A193	2p dk grn & ol gray	.25	.25
584	A193	2p dk green & sal	.25	.25
585	A193	5p red brn & ol	.25	.25
586	A193	10p red brn & brt grn	.25	.25
587	A193	15p red brn & gray	.25	.25
588	A193	25p brt bl & bluish grn	.25	.25
589	A193	50p brt bl & rose lil	.25	.25
590	A193	75p black & blue	.25	.25
591	A193	100p black & brt pink	.30	.25
592	A193	150p black & bis brn	.50	.40
593	A193	175p black & orange	.55	.50
		Nos. 583-593 (11)	3.35	3.15

WHO drive to eradicate malaria.
Perf. and imperf. souvenir sheets exist. Set of 4 sheets, value $14.
Exist imperf. Value, set $10.
For surcharges see Nos. B61-B71.

National Assembly Building A194

Perf. 10½, 11 (100p)

1962, Sept. 10 **Unwmk.** **Litho.**

594	A194	25p lt green	.25	.25
595	A194	50p blue	.45	.45
596	A194	75p rose	.60	.60
597	A194	100p violet	.75	.75
598	A194	125p ultra	1.00	1.00
		Nos. 594-598 (5)	3.05	3.05

Establishment of the National Assembly.

Horse Racing — A195

Designs: 2p, Horse racing. 3p, Wrestling. 4p, Weight lifting. 5p, Soccer.

1962, Sept. 22 **Photo.** *Perf. 12*

Black Inscriptions

599	A195	1p lt ol & red brn	.25	.25
600	A195	2p lt grn & red brn	.25	.25
601	A195	3p yellow & dk pur	.25	.25
602	A195	4p pale bl & grn	.25	.25
603	A195	5p bluish grn & dk brn	.25	.25
		Nos. 599-603,C17-C22 (11)	4.85	4.85

4th Asian Games, Djakarta, Indonesia.
Exist imperf. Value, set of 11, unused or used, $17.50.
Two souvenir sheets exist. A perforated one contains a 125p blue, dark blue and brown stamp in horse racing design. An imperf. one contains a 2af buff, purple and black stamp in soccer design. Value, $3.50 each.

Runners — A196

1p, 2p, Diver, vert. 4p, Peaches. 5p, Iris, vert.

Perf. 11½x12, 12x11½

1962, Oct. 2 **Unwmk.**

604	A196	1p rose lil & brn	.25	.25
605	A196	2p blue & brn	.25	.25
606	A196	3p brt blue & lil	.25	.25
607	A196	4p ol gray & multi	.25	.25
608	A196	5p gray & multi	.25	.25
		Nos. 604-608,C23-C25 (8)	4.45	4.45

Issued for Children's Day.
Exist imperf. Value, set of 8, unused or used, $27.50.

Zahir Shah Type of 1961, Dated "1962"

1962, Oct. 15 *Perf. 13½*

Various Frames

609	A183	25p lilac rose & brn	.25	.25
610	A183	50p orange brn & grn	.30	.25
611	A183	75p blue & lake	.50	.25
612	A183	100p green & red brn	.55	.25
		Nos. 609-612 (4)	1.60	1.00

Issued to honor King Mohammed Zahir Shah on his 48th birthday.

Grapes — A197

1962, Oct. 16 *Perf. 12*

613	A197	1p shown	.25	.25
614	A197	2p Grapes	.25	.25
615	A197	3p Pears	.25	.25
616	A197	4p Wistaria	.25	.25
617	A197	5p Blossoms	.25	.25
		Nos. 613-617,C26-C28 (8)	2.45	2.45

For the Afghan Red Crescent Society.
Exist imperf. Value, set of 8, unused or used, $20.

UN Headquarters, NY and Flags of UN and Afghanistan A198

1962, Oct. 24 **Unwmk.**

618	A198	1p multicolored	.25	.25
619	A198	2p multicolored	.25	.25
620	A198	3p multicolored	.25	.25
621	A198	4p multicolored	.25	.25
622	A198	5p multicolored	.25	.25
		Nos. 618-622,C29-C31 (8)	2.60	2.60

UN Day.
Exist imperf. Value, set of 8, unused or used, $9.50.

Souvenir sheets exist. One contains a single 4af ultramarine stamp, perforated; the other, a 4af ocher stamp, imperf. Value, 2 sheets, $9.25.

Boy Scout — A199

1962, Oct. 18 **Photo.** *Perf. 12*

623	A199	1p yel, dk grn & sal	.25	.25
624	A199	2p dl yel, slate & sal	.25	.25
625	A199	3p rose, blk & sal	.25	.25
626	A199	4p multicolored	.25	.25
		Nos. 623-626,C32-C35 (8)	3.65	3.65

Issued to honor the Boy Scouts.
Exist imperf. Value, set of 8, unused or used, $27.50.

Pole Vault — A200

2p, Pole Vault. 3p, High jump. 4p, 5p, Different blossoms.

1962, Oct. 25 **Unwmk.** *Perf. 12*

627	A200	1p lilac & dk grn	.25	.25
628	A200	2p yellow grn & brn	.25	.25
629	A200	3p bister & vio	.25	.25
630	A200	4p sal pink, grn & ultra	.25	.25
631	A200	5p yellow, grn & bl	.25	.25
		Nos. 627-631,C36-C37 (7)	2.75	2.75

Issued for Teacher's Day.
Exist imperf. Value, set of 7, unused or used, $12.

Rockets — A201

1962, Nov. 29

632	A201	50p pale lil & dk bl	.50	.50
633	A201	100p lt blue & red brn	1.25	1.25

UN World Meteorological Day.
Exist imperf. Value, set, unused or used, $25.
A souvenir sheet contains one 5af pink and green stamp. Value $6.

Ansari Mausoleum, Herat — A202

Perf. 13½

1963, Jan. 3 **Unwmk.** **Photo.**

634	A202	50p purple & green	.25	.25
635	A202	75p gray & magenta	.25	.25
636	A202	100p orange brn & brn	.35	.35
		Nos. 634-636 (3)	.85	.85

Khwaja Abdullah Ansari, Sufi, religious leader and poet, on the 900th anniv. of his death.

Sheep — A203

Silkworm, Cocoons, Moth and Mulberry Branch — A204

1963, Mar. 1 *Perf. 12*

637	A203	1p grnsh blue & blk	.25	.25
638	A203	2p yellow grn & blk	.25	.25
639	A203	3p lilac rose & blk	.25	.25
640	A204	4p gray, grn & brn	.25	.25
641	A204	5p red lil, grn & brn	.25	.25
		Nos. 637-641,C42-C44 (8)	3.10	3.10

Issued for the Day of Agriculture.
Exist imperf. Value, set of 8, unused or used, $12.

Rice — A205

Designs: 3p, Corn. 300p, Wheat emblem.

1963, Mar. 27 **Unwmk.** *Perf. 14*

642	A205	2p gray, claret & grn	.25	.25
643	A205	3p green, yel & ocher	.25	.25
644	A205	300p dk blue & yel	.60	.60
		Nos. 642-644,C45 (4)	2.20	2.20

FAO "Freedom from Hunger" campaign.

Meteorological Measuring Instrument A206

Designs: 3p, 10p, Weather station. 4p, 5p, Rockets in space.

1963, May 23 **Photo.** *Perf. 13½x14*

645	A206	1p dp magenta & brn	.25	.25
646	A206	2p brt blue & brn	.25	.25
647	A206	3p red & brown	.25	.25
648	A206	4p orange & lilac	.25	.25
649	A206	5p green & dl vio	.25	*.25*

Imperf

650	A206	10p red brn & grn	.45	.40
		Nos. 645-650,C46-C50 (11)	11.15	10.50

3rd UN World Meteorological Day, Mar. 23.

Independence Monument — A207

1963, Aug. 23 **Litho.** *Perf. 10½*

651	A207	25p lt green	.25	.25
652	A207	50p orange	.35	.25
653	A207	150p rose carmine	.50	.30
		Nos. 651-653 (3)	1.10	.80

45th Independence Day.

Pathans in Forest — A208

1963, Aug. 31 **Unwmk.** *Perf. 10½*

654	A208	25p pale violet	.25	.25
655	A208	50p sky blue	.25	.25
655A	A208	150p dull red brn	.60	.40
		Nos. 654-655A (3)	1.10	.90

Issued for "Free Pashtunistan Day."

4th Asian Games, Djakarta — A208a

2p, 250p, 300p, Wrestling. 3p, 10p, Tennis. 4p, 500p, Javelin. 5p, 9af, Shot put.

1963, Sept. 3 Litho. *Perf. 12*

656 A208a 2p rose vio & brn .25 .25
656A A208a 3p olive grn & brn .25 .25
656B A208a 4p blue & brn .25 .25
656C A208a 5p yel grn & brn .25 .25
656D A208a 10p lt bl grn & brn .25 .25
656E A208a 300p yellow & vio .45 .45
656F A208a 500p lt yel bis & brn .85 .85
656G A208a 9af pale grn & vio 1.40 1.40
Nos. 656-656G (8) 3.95 3.95

Souvenir Sheets

656H A208a 250p lilac & vio 2.00 2.00
656I A208a 300p blue & blk 2.00 2.00

Nos. 656E-656F are airmail. Nos. 656-656I exist imperf. Values, unused or used: set, $12; souvenir sheets, each $11.

National Assembly Building A209

1963, Sept. 10 *Perf. 11*

657 A209 25p gray .25 .25
658 A209 50p dull red .25 .25
659 A209 75p brown .25 .25
660 A209 100p olive .25 .25
661 A209 125p lilac .40 .25
Nos. 657-661 (5) 1.40 1.25

Issued to honor the National Assembly.

Balkh Gate — A210

1963, Oct. 8

662 A210 3af choc (screened margins) 1.00 .30
a. White margins 2.50 .55

In the original printing a halftone screen extended across the plate, covering the space between the stamps. A retouch removed the screen between the stamps (No. 662a).

Intl. Red Cross, Cent. — A210a

4p, 5p, 200p, 3af, Nurse holding patient, vert. 10p, 4af, 6af, Crown Prince Ahmed Shah.

1963, Oct. 9 *Perf. 13½*

662B A210a 2p olive, blk & red .25 .25
662C A210a 3p blue, blk & red .25 .25
662D A210a 4p lt grn, blk & red .25 .25
662E A210a 5p lt vio, blk & red .25 .25
662F A210a 10p gray grn, red & blk .25 .25
662G A210a 100p dull bl grn, red & blk .25 .25
662H A210a 200p lt brn, blk & red .25 .25
662I A210a 4af brt bl grn, red & blk .25 .25
m. Souvenir sheet of 1 1.75 1.60
662J A210a 6af lt brn, red & blk .25 .25
Nos. 662B-662J (9) 2.25 2.25

Souvenir Sheet

662K A210a 3af dl blue, blk & red 1.75

Nos. 662G-662K are airmail.
Nos. 662B-662K exist imperf. Values, unused or used: set, $12; souvenir sheets, each $11.

Zahir Shah — A211

1963, Oct. 15 *Perf. 10½*

663 A211 25p green .25 .25
663A A211 50p gray .25 .25
663B A211 75p carmine rose .30 .25
663C A211 100p dull redsh brn .50 .25
Nos. 663-663C (4) 1.30 1.00

King Mohammed Zahir Shah, 49th birthday.

Kemal Ataturk — A212

1963, Oct. 10 *Perf. 10½*

664 A212 1af blue .25 .25
665 A212 3af rose lilac .65 .50

25th anniv. of the death of Kemal Ataturk, president of Turkey.

Protection of Nubian Monuments A213

Designs: 5af, 7.50af, 10af, Ruins, vert.

Perf. 12, Imperf. (150p, 250p, 10af)

1963, Nov. 16 Photo.

666 A213 100p lil rose & blk .25 .25
666A A213 150p rose lil & blk .25 .30
666B A213 200p brown & blk .40 .40
666C A213 250p ultra & blk .50 .50
666D A213 500p green & blk 1.00 1.00
666E A213 5af greenish blue & gray bl 1.00 1.00
666F A213 7.50af red brn & gray bl 1.75 1.75
666G A213 10af ver & gray bl 1.90 1.90
Nos. 666-666G (8) 7.05 7.10

Nos. 666E-666G are airmail. No. 666D exists imperf. Value, unused or used, 95¢.

Women's Day — A213a

1964, Jan. 5 *Perf. 14x13½*

667 A213a 2p multicolored .25 .25
667A A213a 3p multicolored .25 .25
667B A213a 4p multicolored .25 .25
667C A213a 5p multicolored .25 .25
667D A213a 10p multicolored .25 .25
Nos. 667-667D (5) 1.25 1.25

Exist imperf. Value set, unused or used, $2.40.

A213b

Boy and Girl Scouts — A213c

Nos. 668F-668G, 668K-668M, Girl with flag.

1964, Jan. 5 *Perf. 13½x14, 14x13½*

668 A213b 2p multi .25 .25
668A A213b 3p multi .25 .25
668B A213b 4p multi .25 .25
668C A213b 5p multi .25 .25
668D A213b 10p multi .25 .25
668E A213c 2af multi .25 .25
668F A213c 2af multi .25 .25
668G A213c 2.50af multi .25 .25
668H A213c 3af multi .30 .30
668I A213c 4af multi .40 .40
668J A213c 5af multi .50 .50
668K A213c 12af multi 1.25 1.25
Nos. 668-668K (12) 4.45 4.45

Souvenir Sheets

668L A213c 5af multi 1.25 1.25
668M A213c 6af multi 1.25 2.00
668N A213c 6af multi 2.50 2.50
668O A213c 10af multi 2.50 2.50

Nos. 668E-668O are airmail.
Nos 668-668K, 668N-668O exist imperf. Values, unused or used: set, $15; souvenir sheets, each $7.

Children — A213d

2p, Playing ball. 4p, Swinging, jumping rope, vert. 5p, Skiing, vert.

1964, Jan. 22 *Perf. 12*

669 A213d 2p multi .25 .25
669A A213d 3p like #669 .25 .25
669B A213d 4p multi .25 .25
669C A213d 5p multi .25 .25
669D A213d 10p like #669 .25 .25
669E A213d 200p like #669C .75 .75
669F A213d 300p like #669B 1.10 1.10
Nos. 669-669F (7) 3.10 3.10

Nos. 669E-669F are airmail.
Nos. 669-669F exist imperf. Value set, unused or used, $27.50.

Red Crescent Society — A213e

Designs: 100p, 200p, Pierre and Marie Curie, physicists. 2.50af, 7.50af Nurse examining child. 3.50af, 5af, Nurse and patients.

Perf. 14, Imperf. (#670A, 670C-670D)

1964, Feb. 8

670 A213e 100p multi .50 .50
670A A213e 100p multi .50 .50
670B A213e 200p multi .80 .80
670C A213e 2.50af multi 1.25 1.25
670D A213e 3.50af multi 1.90 1.90
670E A213e 5af multi 2.10 2.10
670F A213e 7.50af multi 3.00 3.00
Nos. 670-670F (7) 10.05 10.05

Nos. 670A and 670E-F are airmail.

Teachers' Day — A213f

Flowers: 2p, 3p, 3af, 4af, Tulips. 4p, 5p, 3.50af, 6af, Flax. 10p, 1.50af, 2af, Iris.

Perf. 12, Imperf. (1.50af, 2af)

1964, Mar. 3

671 A213f 2p multicolored .25 .25
671A A213f 3p multicolored .25 .25
671B A213f 4p multicolored .25 .25
671C A213f 5p multicolored .25 .25
671D A213f 10p multicolored .25 .25
671E A213f 1.50af multicolored 2.25 2.25
671F A213f 2af multicolored 3.00 3.00
671G A213f 3af multicolored .90 .90
671H A213f 3.50af multicolored 1.10 1.10
Nos. 671-671H (9) 8.50 8.50

Souvenir Sheets

671I A213f 4af multi 2.40 2.40
671J A213f 6af multi, imperf 5.00 5.00

Nos. 671E-671J are airmail. Nos. 671-671D exist imperf. Value, each 20¢.

A213g

UN Day: 5p, 10p, 2af, 3af, 4af, Doctor and nurse, vert.

1964, Mar. 9 *Perf. 14*

672 A213g 2p multicolored .25 .25
672A A213g 3p multicolored .25 .25
672B A213g 4p multicolored .25 .25
672C A213g 5p multicolored .25 .25
672D A213g 10p multicolored .25 .25
672E A213g 100p multicolored .65 .65
672F A213g 2af multicolored 1.20 1.20
672G A213g 3af multicolored 1.75 1.75
Nos. 672-672G (8) 4.85 4.85

Souvenir Sheets

672H A213g 4af multi, imperf. 14.50 14.50
672I A213g 5af multi 3.25 3.25

Nos. 672E-672G are airmail.
Nos. 672-672G exist imperf. Value set, unused or used, $20.
For surcharges see Nos. B71A-B71J.

UNICEF — A213h

Design: 5af, 7.50af, 10af, Children eating.

Perf. 14x13½, Imperf. (150p, 250p, 10af)

1964, Mar. 15

673 A213h 100p multi .30 .30
673A A213h 150p multi 1.75 1.75
673B A213h 200p multi .65 .65
673C A213h 250p multi 3.00 3.00
673D A213h 5af multi 1.50 1.50
673E A213h 7.50af multi 2.40 2.40
673F A213h 10af multi 12.50 12.50
Nos. 673-673F (7) 22.10 22.10

Nos. 673D-673F are airmail.

Eradication of Malaria — A213i

4p, 5p, 5af, 10af Spraying mosquitoes.

1964, Mar. 15 *Perf. 13½*

674 A213i 2p lt red brn & yel grn .25 .25
674A A213i 3p olive grn & buff .25 .25
674B A213i 4p dk vio & bl grn .25 .25
674C A213i 5p brn & grn .25 .25
674D A213i 2af Prus bl & ver .65 .30
h. Souvenir sheet of 1 4.75 4.75
674E A213i 5af dk grn & lt red brn, imperf. 5.25 5.25
i. Souv. sheet of 1, imperf. 14.50 14.50
674F A213i 10af red brn & grnsh bl 2.75 1.75
Nos. 674-674F (7) 9.65 8.30

Stamp Like No. 674B Surcharged in Black

674G A213i 10p on 4p Prus bl & rose .90 .25

No. 674G not issued without surcharge.
Nos. 674D-674F are airmail.
Nos. 674-674C, 674G exist imperf. Values, each $2.75.

"Tiger's Head" of 1878 — A214

1964, Mar. 22 Photo. *Perf. 12*

675 A214 1.25af gold, grn & blk .25 .25
676 A214 5af gold, rose car & blk .55 .35

Issued to honor philately.

Unisphere and Flags — A215

1964, May 3 *Perf. 13½x14*

677 A215 6af crimson, gray & grn .25 .25

New York World's Fair, 1964-65.

Hand Holding Torch — A216

1964, May 12 Photo. *Perf. 14x13½*

678 A216 3.75af multicolored .25 .25

1st UN Seminar on Human Rights in Kabul, May 1964. The denomination in Persian at right erroneously reads "3.25" but the stamp was sold and used as 3.75af.

Kandahar Airport — A217

1964, Apr. Litho. *Perf. 10½, 11*

679 A217 7.75af dk red brown .65 .40
680 A217 9.25af lt blue .90 .80
681 A217 10.50af lt green 1.10 .95
682 A217 13.75af carmine rose 1.40 1.00
Nos. 679-682 (4) 4.05 3.15

Inauguration of Kandahar Airport.

Snow Leopard — A218

50p, Ibex, vert. 75p, Head of argali. 5af, Yak.

1964, June 25 Photo. *Perf. 12*

683 A218 25p yellow & blue 1.75 .25
684 A218 50p dl red & grn 2.00 .25
685 A218 75p Prus bl & lil 2.40 .25
686 A218 5af brt grn & dk brn 2.50 .90
Nos. 683-686 (4) 8.65 1.65

View of Herat A219

Flag and Map of Afghanistan A220

Tourist publicity: 75p, Tomb of Queen Gowhar Shad, vert.

1964, July 12 *Perf. 13½x14, 14x13½*

687 A219 25p sepia & bl .25 .25
688 A219 75p dp blue & buff .30 .25
689 A220 3af red, blk & grn .55 .25
Nos. 687-689 (3) 1.10 .75

Wrestling — A221

25p, Hurdling, vert. 1af, Diving, vert. 5af, Soccer.

1964, July 26 *Perf. 12*

690 A221 25p ol bis, blk & car .25 .25
691 A221 1af bl grn, blk & car .25 .25
692 A221 3.75af yel grn, blk & car .40 .25
693 A221 5af brn, blk & car .50 .30
a. Souv. sheet, #690-693, imperf. 1.25 1.25
Nos. 690-693 (4) 1.40 1.05

18th Olympic Games, Tokyo, Oct. 10-25, 1964. No. 693a sold for 15af. The additional 5af went to the Afghanistan Olympic Committee.

Flag and Outline of Nadir Shah's Tomb — A222

1964, Aug. 24 **Photo.**

695 A222 25p multicolored .25 .25
696 A222 75p multicolored .30 .25

Independence Day. The stamps were printed with an erroneous inscription in upper left corner: "33rd year of independence." This was locally obliterated on all stamps with a typographed gold bar. Value for set with gold bar omitted, $10.

Pashtunistan Flag — A223

1964, Sept. 1 **Unwmk.**

697 A223 100p gold, blk, red, bl & grn .55 .25

Issued for "Free Pashtunistan Day."

Zahir Shah — A225

1964, Oct. 17 *Perf. 14x13½*

699 A225 1.25af gold & yel grn .25 .25
700 A225 3.75af gold & rose .40 .40
701 A225 50af gold & gray 3.50 2.25
Nos. 699-701 (3) 4.15 2.90

King Mohammed Zahir Shah, 50th birthday.

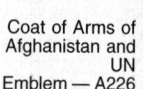

Coat of Arms of Afghanistan and UN Emblem — A226

1964, Oct. 24 *Perf. 13½x14*

702 A226 5af gold, blk & dl bl .25 .25

Issued for United Nations Day.

Emblem of Afghanistan Women's Association A227

1964, Nov. 9 Photo. Unwmk.

703 A227 25p pink, dk bl & emer .55 .30
704 A227 75p aqua, dk bl & emer .85 .40
705 A227 1af sil, dk bl & emer 1.10 .50
Nos. 703-705 (3) 2.50 1.20

Issued for Women's Day.

Poet Mowlana Nooruddin Abdul Rahman Jami (1414-1492) — A228

Perf. 11 Rough

1964, Nov. 23 **Litho.**

706 A228 1.50af blk, emer & yel .95 .95

No. 706 also exists clean-cut perf 10½.

Woodpecker A229

Birds: 3.75af, Black-throated jay, vert. 5af, Impeyan pheasant, vert.

Perf. 13½x14, 14x13½

1965, Apr. 20 Photo. Unwmk.

707 A229 1.25af multi 2.25 .40
708 A229 3.75af multi 4.90 .85
709 A229 5af multi 5.50 1.75
Nos. 707-709 (3) 12.65 3.00

ITU Emblem, Old and New Communication Equipment — A230

1965, May 17 *Perf. 13½x14*

710 A230 5af lt bl, blk & red .50 .35

Cent. of the ITU.

"Red City," Bamian — A231

Designs: 3.75af, Ruins of ancient Bamian city. 5af, Bande Amir, mountain lakes.

1965, May 30 *Perf. 13x13½*

711 A231 1.25af pink & multi .40 .25
712 A231 3.75af lt blue & multi .65 .25
713 A231 5af yellow & multi .95 .25
Nos. 711-713 (3) 2.00 .75

Issued for tourist publicity.

ICY Emblem — A232

1965, June 25 *Perf. 13½x13*

714 A232 5af multicolored .50 .30

International Cooperation Year, 1965.

ARIANA Air Lines Emblem and DC-3 — A233

5af, Airplane at right. 10af, Airplane on top.

Perf. 13½x14

1965, July 15 Photo. Unwmk.

715 A233 1.25af brt bl, gray & blk .30 .25
716 A233 5af red lil, blk & bl .90 .25
717 A233 10af bis, blk, bl gray & grn 1.50 .55
a. Souv. sheet, #715-717, imperf 3.00 3.00
Nos. 715-717 (3) 2.70 1.05

10th anniv. of Afghan Air Lines, ARIANA.

Nadir Shah — A234

1965, Aug. 23 *Perf. 14x13½*

718 A234 1af dl grn, blk & red brn .40 .25

For the 47th Independence Day.

Flag of Pashtunistan A235

Perf. 13½x14

1965, Aug. 31 Photo. Unwmk.

719 A235 1af multicolored .40 .25

Issued for "Free Pashtunistan Day."

Zahir Shah Signing Constitution A236

1965, Sept. 11 *Perf. 13x13½*

720 A236 1.50af brt grn & blk .40 .25

Promulgation of the new Constitution.

Zahir Shah and Oak Leaves — A237

1965, Oct. 14 *Perf. 14x13½*

721 A237 1.25af blk, ultra & salmon .25 .25
722 A237 6af blk, lt bl & rose lil .40 .35

King Mohammed Zahir Shah, 51st birthday.

Flags of UN and Afghanistan A238

1965, Oct. 24 *Perf. 13½x14*

723 A238 5af multicolored .25 .25

Issued for United Nations Day.

Dappled Ground Gecko — A239

Designs: 4af, Caucasian agamid (lizard). 8af, Horsfield's tortoise.

Perf. 13½x14

1966, May 10 Photo. Unwmk.

724 A239 3af tan & multi .90 .25
725 A239 4af brt grn & multi 1.10 .30
726 A239 8af violet & multi 1.75 .65
Nos. 724-726 (3) 3.75 1.20

Soccer Player and Globe — A240

1966, July 31 Litho. *Perf. 14x13½*

727 A240 2af rose red & blk .60 .25
728 A240 6af violet bl & blk 1.00 .30
729 A240 12af bister brn & blk 1.60 .60
Nos. 727-729 (3) 3.20 1.15

World Cup Soccer Championship, Wembley, England, July 11-30.

Cotton Flower and Boll — A241

5af, Silkworm. 7af, Farmer plowing with oxen.

1966, July 31 *Perf. 13½x14*

730 A241 1af multicolored .85 .25
731 A241 5af multicolored 1.60 .30
732 A241 7af multicolored 2.50 .50
Nos. 730-732 (3) 4.95 1.05

Issued for the Day of Agriculture.

Independence Monument — A242

1966, Aug. 23 Photo. ***Perf. 13½x14***
733 A242 1af multicolored .30 .25
734 A242 3af multicolored .85 .30

Issued to commemorate Independence Day.

Flag of Pashtunistan A243

Perf. 11 Rough

1966, Aug. 31 Litho.
735 A243 1af bright blue .50 .25

"Free Pashtunistan Day."

Bagh-i-Bala Park Casino — A244

Tourist publicity: 2af, Map of Afghanistan. 8af, Tomb of Abd-er-Rahman. The casino on 4af is the former summer palace of Abd-er-Rahman near Kabul.

1966, Oct. 3 Photo. ***Perf. 13½x14***
736 A244 2af red & multi .40 .25
737 A244 4af multicolored .80 .35
738 A244 8af multicolored 1.20 .80
a. Souvenir sheet of 3, #736-738, imperf. 3.50 3.50
Nos. 736-738 (3) 2.40 1.40

Zahir Shah — A245

1966, Oct. 14 ***Perf. 14x13½***
739 A245 1af dk slate grn .25 .25
740 A245 5af red brown .55 .30

King Mohammed Zahir Shah, 52nd birthday. See Nos. 760-761.

UNESCO Emblem — A246

1967, Mar. 6 Litho. ***Perf. 12***
741 A246 2af multicolored .30 .25
742 A246 6af multicolored .40 .25
743 A246 12af multicolored .90 .25
Nos. 741-743 (3) 1.60 .75

20th anniv. of UNESCO.

Zahir Shah and UN Emblem — A247

1967 Photo.
744 A247 5af multicolored .40 .25
745 A247 10af multicolored .80 .30

UN Intl. Org. for Refugees, 20th anniv.

New Power Station — A248

5af, Carpet, vert. 8af, Cement factory.

1967, Jan. 7 Photo. ***Perf. 13½x14***
746 A248 2af red lil & ol grn .30 .25
747 A248 5af multicolored .30 .25
748 A248 8af blk, dk bl & tan .60 .30
Nos. 746-748 (3) 1.20 .80

Issued to publicize industrial development.

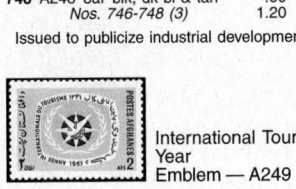

International Tourist Year Emblem — A249

Designs: 6af, International Tourist Year emblem and map of Afghanistan.

1967, May 11 Photo. ***Perf. 12***
749 A249 2af yel, blk & lt bl .40 .25
750 A249 6af bis brn, blk & lt bl .65 .25
a. Souv. sheet, #749-750, imperf 2.00 1.25

Intl. Tourist Year, 1967. No. 750a sold for 10af.

Power Dam, Dorunta — A250

6af, Sirobi Dam, vert. 8af, Reservoir at Jalalabad.

1967, July 2 Photo. ***Perf. 12***
751 A250 1af dk green & lil .40 .25
752 A250 6af red brn & grnsh bl .80 .25
753 A250 8af plum & dk bl 1.20 .40
Nos. 751-753 (3) 2.40 .90

Progress in agriculture through electricity.

Macaque — A251

Designs: 6af, Striped hyena, horiz. 12af, Persian gazelles, horiz.

1967, July 28 Photo. ***Perf. 12***
754 A251 2af dull yel & indigo .75 .25
755 A251 6af lt green & sepia 1.50 .30
756 A251 12af lt bl & red brn 2.25 .80
Nos. 754-756 (3) 4.50 1.35

Pashtun Dancers — A252

1967, Sept. 1 Photo. ***Perf. 12***
757 A252 2af magenta & violet .70 .25

Issued for "Free Pashtunistan Day."

Retreat of British at Maiwand — A253

1967, Aug. 24
758 A253 1af dk brn & org ver .40 .25
759 A253 2af dk brn & brt pink .80 .25

Issued to commemorate Independence Day.

King Type of 1966

1967, Oct. 15 Photo. ***Perf. 14x13½***
760 A245 2af brown red .25 .25
761 A245 8af dark blue .65 .30

Issued to honor King Mohammed Zahir Shah on his 53rd birthday.

Fireworks and UN Emblem — A254

1967, Oct. 24 Litho. ***Perf. 12***
762 A254 10af violet bl & multi .70 .40

Issued for United Nations Day.

Greco-Roman Wrestlers — A255

Design: 6af, Free style wrestlers.

1967, Nov. 20 Photo.
763 A255 4af ol grn & rose lil .40 .25
764 A255 6af dp carmine & brn .85 .25
a. Souv. sheet, #763-764, imperf 1.75 1.75

1968 Olympic Games.

Said Jamalluddin Afghan — A256

1967, Nov. 27
765 A256 1af magenta .25 .25
766 A256 5af brown .40 .25

Said Jamalluddin Afghan, politician (1839-97).

Bronze Vase, 11th-12th Centuries — A257

Design: 7af, Bronze vase, Ghasnavide era, 11th-12th centuries.

1967, Dec. 23 Photo. ***Perf. 12***
767 A257 3af lt green & brn .55 .25
768 A257 7af yel & slate grn 1.00 .25
a. Souv. sheet, #767-768, imperf 2.75 2.75

WHO Emblem — A258

1968, Apr. 7 Photo. ***Perf. 12***
769 A258 2af citron & brt bl .25 .25
770 A258 7af rose & brt bl .40 .30

20th anniv. of the WHO.

Karakul — A259

1968, May 20 Photo. ***Perf. 12***
771 A259 1af yellow & blk .25 .25
772 A259 6af lt blue & blk .85 .30
773 A259 12af ultra & dk brn 1.25 .50
Nos. 771-773 (3) 2.35 1.05

Issued for the Day of Agriculture.

Map of Afghanistan A260

Victory Tower, Ghazni A261

Design: 16af, Mausoleum, Ghazni.

1968, June 3 ***Perf. 13½x14, 12***
774 A260 2af red, blk, lt bl & grn .35 .25
775 A261 3af yel, dk brn & lt bl .45 .25
776 A261 16af pink & multi 1.50 .50
Nos. 774-776 (3) 2.30 1.00

Issued for tourist publicity.

Cinereous Vulture — A262

6af, Eagle owl. 7af, Greater flamingoes.

1968, July 3 ***Perf. 12***
777 A262 1af sky blue & multi 1.75 .65
778 A262 6af yellow & multi 4.00 2.00
779 A262 7af multicolored 6.00 2.25
Nos. 777-779 (3) 11.75 4.90

Game of "Pegsticking" A263

2af, Olympic flame & rings, vert. 12af, Buzkashi.

1968, July 20 Photo. ***Perf. 12***
780 A263 2af multicolored .35 .25
781 A263 8af orange & multi .50 .35
782 A263 12af multicolored 1.00 .60
Nos. 780-782 (3) 1.85 1.20

19th Olympic Games, Mexico City, 10/12-27.

Flower-decked Armored Car — A264

1968, Aug. 23
783 A264 6af multicolored .60 .25

Issued to commemorate Independence Day.

Flag of Pashtunistan A265

1968 Aug. 31 Photo. ***Perf. 12***
784 A265 3af multicolored .35 .25

Issued for "Free Pashtunistan Day."

Zahir Shah — A266

1968, Oct. 14 Photo. ***Perf. 12***
785 A266 2af ultra .25 .25
786 A266 8af brown .55 .30

King Mohammed Zahir Shah, 54th birthday.

Human Rights Flame — A267

1968, Oct. 24
787 A267 1af multicolored .25 .25
788 A267 2af violet, bis & blk .25 .25
789 A267 6af vio blk, bis & vio .60 .25
Nos. 787-789 (3) 1.10 .75

Souvenir Sheet
Imperf

790 A267 10af plum, bis & red org 1.75 1.75

International Human Rights Year.

Maolana Djalalodine Balkhi — A268

1968, Nov. 26 Photo. *Perf. 12*

791 A268 4af dk green & mag .35 .25

Balkhi (1207-73), historian.

Kushan Mural — A269

Design: 3af, Jug shaped like female torso.

1969, Jan. 2 *Perf. 12*

792 A269 1af dk grn, mar & yel .55 .25
793 A269 3af violet, gray & mar 1.20 .25
a. Souv. sheet, #792-793, imperf 2.40 1.75

Archaeological finds at Bagram, 1st cent. B.C. to 2nd cent. A.D.

ILO Emblem — A270

1969, Mar. 23 Photo. *Perf. 12*

794 A270 5af lt yel, lemon & blk .30 .25
795 A270 8af lt bl, grnsh bl & blk .55 .30

50th anniv. of the ILO.

National Arms — A270a

Rough Perf. 11

1969, May (?) Typo.

795A A270a 100p dark green *.40 .25*
795B A270a 150p deep brown *.55 .25*

Nos. 795A-795B were normally used as newspaper stamps. See Nos. 318-318A, 907A.

Badakhshan Scene — A271

Tourist Publicity: 2af, Map of Afghanistan. 7af, Three men on mules ascending the Pamir Mountains.

1969, July 6 Photo. *Perf. 13½x14*

796 A271 2af ocher & multi .70 .25
797 A271 4af multicolored .90 .30
798 A271 7af multicolored 1.40 .65
a. Souv. sheet, #796-798, imperf 3.00 2.40
Nos. 796-798 (3) 3.00 1.20

No. 798a sold for 15af.

Bust, from Hadda Treasure, 3rd-5th Centuries — A272

Designs: 5af, Vase and jug. 10af, Statue of crowned woman. 5af and 10af from Bagram treasure, 1st-2nd centuries.

1969, Aug. 3 Photo. *Perf. 14x13½*

799 A272 1af olive grn & gold .40 .25
800 A272 5af purple & gold .70 .25
801 A272 10af dp blue & gold 1.10 .30
Nos. 799-801 (3) 2.20 .80

Zahir Shah and Queen Humeira — A273

1969, Aug. 23 *Perf. 12*

802 A273 5af gold, dk bl & red brn .45 .25
803 A273 10af gold, dp lil & bl grn .80 .40

Issued to commemorate Independence Day.

Map of Pashtunistan and Rising Sun — A274

1969, Aug. 31 Typo. *Perf. 10½*

804 A274 2af lt blue & red .40 .25

Issued for "Free Pashtunistan Day."

Zahir Shah — A275

1969, Oct. 14 Photo. *Perf. 12*
Portrait in Natural Colors

805 A275 2af dk brown & gold .25 .25
806 A275 6af brown & gold .55 .25

King Mohammed Zahir Shah, 55th birthday.

UN Emblem and Flag of Afghanistan A276

1969, Oct. 24 Litho. *Perf. 13½*

807 A276 5af blue & multi .30 .25

Issued for United Nations Day.

ITU Emblem — A277

1969, Nov. 12

808 A277 6af ultra & multi .30 .25
809 A277 12af rose & multi .70 .40

Issued for World Telecommunications Day.

Crested Porcupine — A278

1af, Long-tailed porcupine. 8af, Red deer.

1969, Dec. 7 Photo. *Perf. 12*

810 A278 1af yellow & multi .50 .30
811 A278 3af blue & multi 1.10 .50
812 A278 8af pink & multi 2.00 1.00
Nos. 810-812 (3) 3.60 1.80

Man's First Footprints on Moon, and Earth — A279

1969, Dec. 28 *Perf. 13½x14*

813 A279 1af yel grn & multi .25 .25
814 A279 3af yellow & multi .30 .25
815 A279 6af blue & multi .45 .25
816 A279 10af rose & multi .60 .40
Nos. 813-816 (4) 1.60 1.15

Moon landing. See note after Algeria No. 427.

Anti-cancer Symbol — A280

1970, Apr. 7 Photo. *Perf. 14*

817 A280 2af dk grn & rose car .25 .25
818 A280 6af dk bl & rose claret .50 .25

Issued to publicize the fight against cancer.

Mirza Abdul Quader Bedel — A281

1970, May 6 *Perf. 14x13½*

819 A281 5af multicolored .40 .25

Mirza Abdul Quader Bedel (1643-1720), poet.

Education Year Emblem — A282

1970, June 7 Photo. *Perf. 12*

820 A282 1af black .25 .25
821 A282 6af deep rose .30 .25
822 A282 12af green .75 .40
Nos. 820-822 (3) 1.30 .90

International Education Year 1970.

Mother and Child — A283

1970, June 15 *Perf. 13½*

823 A283 6af yellow & multi .30 .25

Issued for Mother's Day.

UN Emblem, Scales of Justice, Spacecraft — A284

1970, June 26

824 A284 4af yel, dk bl & dp bl .25 .25
825 A284 6af pink, dk bl & brt bl .35 .25

25th anniversary of United Nations.

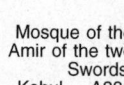

Mosque of the Amir of the two Swords, Kabul — A285

2af, Map of Afghanistan. 7af, Arch of Paghman.

1970, July 6 *Perf. 12*
Size: 30½x30½mm

826 A285 2af lt bl, blk & citron .30 .25

Size: 36x26mm

827 A285 3af pink & multi .50 .25
828 A285 7af yellow & multi .95 .25
Nos. 826-828 (3) 1.75 .75

Issued for tourist publicity.

Zahir Shah Reviewing Troops — A286

1970, Aug. 23 Photo. *Perf. 13½*

829 A286 8af multicolored .40 .25

Issued to commemorate Independence Day.

Pathans — A287

1970, Aug. 31 Typo. *Perf. 10½*

830 A287 2af ultra & red .40 .25

Issued for "Free Pashtunistan Day."

Quail — A288

4af, Golden eagle. 6af, Ringnecked pheasant.

1970, Sept. Photo. *Perf. 12*

831 A288 2af multicolored 2.10 .65
832 A288 4af multicolored 4.00 .95
833 A288 6af multicolored 5.25 1.60
Nos. 831-833 (3) 11.35 3.20

Zahir Shah — A289

1970, Oct. 14 Photo. *Perf. 14x13½*

834 A289 3af green & vio .25 .25
835 A289 7af dk bl & vio brn .70 .30

King Mohammed Zahir Shah, 56th birthday.

Red Crescents — A290

1970, Oct. 16 Typo. *Perf. 10½*

836 A290 2af black, gold & red .30 .25

Issued for the Red Crescent Society.

UN Emblem and Charter — A291

1970, Oct. 24 Photo. *Perf. 14*

837	A291	1af gold & multi	.25	.25
838	A291	5af gold & multi	.30	.25

United Nations Day.

Tiger Heads of 1871 — A292

1970, Nov. 10 *Perf. 12*

839	A292	1af sal, lt grnsh bl & blk	.30	.25
840	A292	4af lt ultra, yel & blk	.55	.25
841	A292	12af lilac, lt bl & blk	.95	.40
		Nos. 839-841 (3)	1.80	.90

Cent. of the 1st Afghan postage stamps. The postal service was established in 1870, but the 1st stamps were issued in May, 1871.

Globe and Waves — A293

1971, May 17 Photo. *Perf. 13½*

842	A293	12af green, blk & bl	.70	.40

3rd World Telecommunications Day.

Callimorpha Principalis — A294

Designs: 3af, Epizygaenella species. 5af, Parnassius autocrator.

1971, May 30 *Perf. 13½x14*

843	A294	1af vermilion & multi	1.25	.55
844	A294	3af yellow & multi	2.50	1.10
845	A294	5af ultra & multi	3.50	1.75
		Nos. 843-845 (3)	7.25	3.40

"UNESCO" and Half of Ancient Kushan Statue — A295

1971, June 26 Photo. *Perf. 13½*

846	A295	6af ocher & vio	.50	.25
847	A295	10af lt blue & mar	.80	.35

UNESCO-sponsored Intl. Kushani Seminar.

Tughra and Independence Monument A296

1971, Aug. 23

848	A296	7af rose red & multi	.55	.25
849	A296	9af red orange & multi	.90	.35

Independence Day.

Pashtunistan Square, Kabul — A297

1971, Aug. 31 Typo. *Perf. 10½*

850	A297	5af deep rose lilac	.50	.25

"Free Pashtunistan Day."

Zahir Shah — A298

1971, Oct. 14 Photo. *Perf. 12½x12*

851	A298	9af lt green & multi	.55	.30
852	A298	17af yellow & multi	1.10	.65

King Mohammed Zahir Shah, 57th birthday.

A299

Design: Map of Afghanistan, red crescent, various activities.

1971, Oct. 16 *Perf. 14x13½*

853	A299	8af lt bl, red, grn & blk	.50	.30

For Afghan Red Crescent Society.

Equality Year Emblem — A300

1971, Oct. 24 *Perf. 12*

854	A300	24af brt blue	1.50	.80

International Year Against Racial Discrimination and United Nations Day.

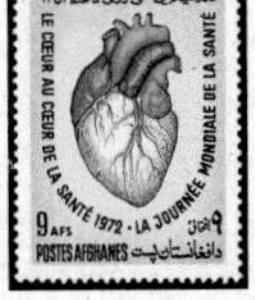

"Your Heart is your Health" — A301

1972, Apr. 7 Photo. *Perf. 14*

855	A301	9af pale yel & multi	.90	.30
856	A301	12af gray & multi	1.75	.40

World Health Day.

Tulip — A302

Designs: 10af, Rock partridge, horiz. 12af, Lynx, horiz. 18af, Allium stipitatum (flower).

1972, June 5 Photo. *Perf. 14*

857	A302	7af green & multi	1.25	.70
858	A302	10af blue & multi	7.50	1.60
859	A302	12af lt green & multi	2.40	1.25
860	A302	18af blue grn & multi	2.40	1.40
		Nos. 857-860 (4)	13.55	4.95

Buddhist Shrine, Hadda — A302a

Designs: 7af, Greco-Bactrian animal seal, 250 B.C. 9af, Greco-Oriental temple, Ai-Khanoum, 3rd-2nd centuries B.C.

1972, July 16 Photo. *Perf. 12*

861	A302a	3af brown & dl bl	.65	.25
862	A302a	7af rose claret & dl grn	.95	.30
863	A302a	9af green & lilac	1.40	.40
		Nos. 861-863 (3)	3.00	.95

Tourist publicity.

King and Queen Reviewing Parade A303

1972, Aug. 23 Photo. *Perf. 13½*

864	A303	25af gold & multi	4.50	1.25

Independence Day.

Used as a provisional in 1978 with king and queen portion removed.

Wrestling A304

10af, 19af, 21af, Wrestling, different hold.

1972, Aug. 26

865	A304	4af ol bis & multi	.25	.25
866	A304	8af lt blue & multi	.45	.25
867	A304	10af yel grn & multi	.60	.30
868	A304	19af multicolored	1.20	.45
869	A304	21af lilac & multi	1.25	.50
a.		Souv. sheet, #865-869, imperf	3.25	3.25
		Nos. 865-869 (5)	3.75	1.75

20th Olympic Games, Munich, Aug. 26-Sept. 11. No. 869a sold for 60af.

Pathan and View of Tribal Territory — A305

1972, Aug. 31 *Perf. 12½x12*

870	A305	5af ultra & multi	.50	.25

Pashtunistan day.

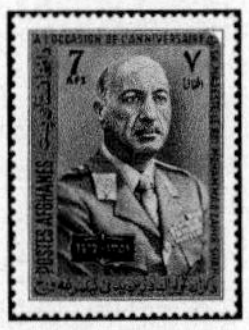

Zahir Shah — A306

1972, Oct. 14 Photo. *Perf. 14x13½*

871	A306	7af gold, blk & Prus bl	.65	.25
872	A306	14af gold, blk & lt brn	1.00	.40

58th birthday of King Mohammed Zahir Shah.

City Destroyed by Earthquake, Refugees A307

1972, Oct. 16 *Perf. 13½*

873	A307	7af lt bl, red & blk	.60	.25

For Afghan Red Crescent Society.

UN Emblem — A308

1972, Oct. 24

874	A308	12af lt ultra & blk	.60	.30

UN Economic Commission for Asia and the Far East (ECAFE), 25th anniv.

Ceramics — A309

Designs: 9af, Leather coat, vert. 12af, Metal ware, vert. 16af, Inlaid artifacts.

1972, Dec. 10 Photo. *Perf. 12*

875	A309	7af gold & multi	.40	.25
876	A309	9af gold & multi	.65	.30
877	A309	12af gold & multi	.70	.35
878	A309	16af gold & multi	1.00	.45
a.		Souv. sheet, #875-878, imperf	3.50	3.50
		Nos. 875-878 (4)	2.75	1.35

Handicraft industries. No. 878a sold for 45af.

WMO and National Emblems A310

1973, Apr. 3 Photo. *Perf. 14*

879	A310	7af lt lil & dk grn	.55	.25
880	A310	14af lt bl & dp claret	1.40	.40

Cent. of intl. meteorological cooperation.

Abu Rayhan al-Biruni — A311

1973, June 16 Photo. *Perf. 13½*

881	A311	10af multicolored	.50	.40

Millennium of birth (973-1048), philosopher and mathematician.

Family — A312

1973, June 30 Photo. *Perf. 13½*

882	A312	9af orange & red lil	.65	.25

Intl. Family Planning Fed., 21st anniv.

Republic

Impeyan Pheasant — A313

Birds: 9af, Great crested grebe. 12af, Himalayan snow cock.

1973, July 29 Photo. *Perf. 12x12½*

883	A313	8af yellow & multi	2.75	1.75
884	A313	9af blue & multi	3.25	2.25
885	A313	12af multicolored	4.00	3.00
		Nos. 883-885 (3)	10.00	7.00

Stylized Buzkashi Horseman A314

1973, Aug. *Perf. 13½*
886 A314 8af black .55 .30

Tourist publicity.

Fireworks A315

1973, Aug. 23 Photo. *Perf. 12*
887 A315 12af multicolored .60 .30

55th Independence Day.

Lake Abassine, Pashtunistan Flag — A316

1973, Aug. 31 *Perf. 14x13½*
888 A316 9af multicolored .55 .25

Pashtunistan Day.

Red Crescent — A317

1973, Oct. 16 *Perf. 13½*
889 A317 10af red, blk & gold .90 .25

Red Crescent Society.

Kemal Ataturk — A318

1973, Oct. 28 Litho. *Perf. 10½*
890 A318 1af blue .25 .25
891 A318 7af reddish brown 1.10 .25

50th anniversary of the Turkish Republic.

Human Rights Flame, Arms of Afghanistan A319

1973, Dec. 10 Photo. *Perf. 12*
892 A319 12af sil, blk & lt bl .45 .35

25th anniversary of the Universal Declaration of Human Rights.

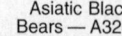

Asiatic Black Bears — A320

1974, Mar. 26 Litho. *Perf. 12*
893 A320 5af shown .65 .25
894 A320 7af Afghan hound 1.00 .40
895 A320 10af Persian goat 1.40 .50
896 A320 12af Leopard 1.75 .55
a. Souv. sheet, #893-896, imperf 10.00 10.00
Nos. 893-896 (4) 4.80 1.70

Worker and Farmer — A321

1974, May 1 Photo. *Perf. 13½x12½*
897 A321 9af rose red & multi .60 .30

International Labor Day, May 1.

Independence Monument and Arch — A322

1974, May 27 Photo. *Perf. 12*
898 A322 4af blue & multi .40 .25
899 A322 11af gold & multi .55 .25

56th Independence Day.

Arms of Afghanistan and Symbol of Cooperation A323

Pres. Mohammad Daoud Khan A324

5af, Flag of Republic of Afghanistan. 15af, Soldiers, coat of arms of the Republic.

Sizes: 4af, 15af, 36x22mm; 5af, 7af, 36x26, 26x36mm

1974, July 25 *Perf. 13½x12½, 14*
900 A323 4af multicolored .40 .25
901 A323 5af multicolored .55 .25
902 A324 7af green, brn & blk .65 .25
a. Souv. sheet, #901-902, imperf 1.75 1.75
903 A323 15af multicolored 1.25 .30
a. Souv. sheet, #900, 903, imperf 2.00 2.00
Nos. 900-903 (4) 2.85 1.05

1st anniv. of the Republic of Afghanistan.

Lesser Spotted Eagle — A325

Birds: 6af, White-fronted goose, ruddy shelduck and gray-lag goose. 11af, European coots and European crane.

1974, Aug. 6 Photo. *Perf. 13½x13*
904 A325 1af car rose & multi 2.00 .50
905 A325 6af blue & multi 4.50 .80
906 A325 11af yellow & multi 7.00 1.40
a. Strip of 3, #904-906 14.00 14.00

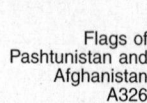

Flags of Pashtunistan and Afghanistan A326

1974, Aug. 31 Photo. *Perf. 14*
907 A326 5af multicolored .30 .25

Pashtunistan Day.

Coat of Arms — A326a

1974, Aug. Typo. *Rough Perf. 11*
907A A326a 100p green *4.00* .80

See Nos. 318-318A, 795A-795B.

Coat of Arms — A327

1974, Oct. 9
908 A327 7af gold, grn & blk .30 .25

Centenary of Universal Postal Union.

"un" and UN Emblem — A328

1974, Oct. 24 Photo. *Perf. 14*
909 A328 5af lt ultra & dk bl .40 .25

United Nations Day.

Minaret of Jam — A329

Buddha, Hadda — A330

14af, Lady riding griffin, 2nd century, Bagram.

1975, May 5 Photo. *Perf. 13½*
910 A329 7af multicolored .40 .25
911 A330 14af multicolored .75 .40
912 A330 15af multicolored .95 .40
a. Souv. sheet, #910-912, imperf. 3.50 3.50
Nos. 910-912 (3) 2.10 1.05

South Asia Tourism Year 1975.

New Flag of Afghanistan A331

1975, May 27 Photo. *Perf. 12*
913 A331 16af multicolored .80 .25

57th Independence Day.

Celebrating Crowd — A332

1975, July 17 Photo. *Perf. 13½*
914 A332 9af blue & multi .50 .25
915 A332 12af carmine & multi .65 .30

Second anniversary of the Republic.

Women's Year Emblems — A333

1975, Aug. 24 Photo. *Perf. 12*
916 A333 9af car, lt bl & blk .50 .25

International Women's Year 1975.

Pashtunistan Flag, Sun Rising Over Mountains — A334

1975, Aug. 31 *Perf. 13½*
917 A334 10af multicolored .40 .25

Pashtunistan Day.

Mohammed Akbar Khan — A335

1976, Feb. 4 Photo. *Perf. 14*
918 A335 15af lt brown & multi .55 .40

Mohammed Akbar Khan (1816-1846), warrior son of Amir Dost Mohammed Khan.

A336

Pres. Mohammad Daoud Khan — A337

1974-78 Photo. *Perf. 14*
919 A336 10af multi .65 .25
920 A336 16af multi ('78) 2.40 .90
921 A336 19af multi .90 .50
922 A336 21af multi 1.40 .55
923 A336 22af multi ('78) 3.50 1.90
924 A336 30af multi ('78) 4.75 2.75
925 A337 50af multi ('75) 2.75 1.40
926 A337 100af multi ('75) 5.50 2.40
Nos. 919-926 (8) 21.85 10.65

Arms of Republic, Independence Monument A338

1976, June 1 Photo. *Perf. 14*
927 A338 22af blue & multi .70 .50

58th Independence Day.

Flag Raising — A339

1976, July 17 Photo. *Perf. 14*
928 A339 30af multicolored .80 .55

Republic Day.

Mountain Peaks and Flag of Pashtunistan — A340

1976, Aug. 31 Photo. *Perf. 14*
929 A340 16af multicolored .65 .50

Pashtunistan Day.

Coat of Arms — A340a

1976, Sept. Litho. *Perf. 11 Rough*

930 A340a 25p salmon *25.00* —
931 A340a 50p lt green .55 .25
932 A340a 1af ultra .55 .25
Nos. 930-932 (3) 26.10 .50

Flag and Views on Open Book — A341

1977, May 27 Photo. *Perf. 14*

937 A341 20af green & multi .70 .60

59th Independence Day.

Pres. Daoud and National Assembly A342

President Taking Oath of Office — A343

Designs: 10af, Inaugural address. 18af, Promulgation of Constitution.

1977, June 22

938 A342 7af multicolored .80 .55
939 A343 8af multicolored .90 .70
940 A343 10af multicolored 1.10 .90
941 A342 18af multicolored 1.90 1.50
a. Souvenir sheet of 4 3.50 3.50
Nos. 938-941 (4) 4.70 3.65

Election of 1st Pres. and promulgation of Constitution. No. 941a contains 4 imperf. stamps similar to Nos. 938-941.

Jamalluddin Medal — A344

1977, July 6 Photo. *Perf. 14*

942 A344 12af blue, blk & gold .40 .30

Sajo Jamalluddin Afghani, reformer, 80th death anniversary.

Afghanistan Flag over Crowd — A345

1977, July 17

943 A345 22af multicolored .70 .55

Dancers, Fountain, Pashtunistan Flag — A346

1977, Aug. 31

944 A346 30af multicolored 1.10 .90

Pashtunistan Day.

Arms and Carrier Pigeon — A346a

1977, Oct. 30 Litho. *Perf. 11*

944A A346a 1af black & blue *5.00 2.50*

Members of Parliament Congratulating Pres. Daoud — A347

1978, Feb. 5 Litho. *Perf. 14*

945 A347 20af multicolored 2.00 1.10

Election of first president, first anniversary.

Map of Afghanistan, UPU Emblem — A348

1978, Apr. 1 Photo. *Perf. 14*

946 A348 10af green, blk & gold .40 .25

Afghanistan's UPU membership, 50th anniv.

Wall Telephone and Satellite Station — A349

1978, Apr. 12

947 A349 8af multicolored .40 .25

Afghanistan's ITU membership, 50th anniv.

Democratic Republic

Arrows Pointing to Crescent, Cross and Lion — A350

1978, July 6 Litho. *Perf. 11 Rough*

948 A350 3af black 1.25 .65

50th anniv. of Afghani Red Crescent Soc.

Khalq Party Emblem — A350a

1978, Aug. Litho. *Perf. 11*

948A A350a 1af rose red & gold 1.50 .65
948B A350a 4af rose red & gold 2.10 .90

Qalai Bist Arch — A351

Hazara Women — A351a

16af, Bamian Buddha.

1978, Aug. 19 *Perf. 14*

949 A351 16af multicolored 1.25 .50
949A A351 22af shown 1.50 .65
949B A351a 30af shown 2.10 1.10
Nos. 949-949B (3) 4.85 2.25

Men with Pashtunistan Flag — A352

1978, Aug. 31 *Perf. 11 Rough*

950 A352 7af ultra & red .50 .25

Pashtunistan Day.

Coat of Arms and Emblems — A353

1978, Sept. 8 *Perf. 11*

951 A353 20af rose red .90 .40

World Literacy Day.

A354

Perf. 11½ Rough

1978, Oct. 25 Litho.

952 A354 18af light green .95 .40

Hero of Afghanistan.

Khalq Party Flag — A355

1978, Oct. 19 Photo. *Perf. 11½*

953 A355 8af black, red & gold .65 .25
954 A355 9af black, red & gold .95 .25

"The mail serving the people."

Nour Mohammad Taraki — A356

1979, Jan. 1 Litho. *Perf. 12*

955 A356 12af multicolored .70 .25

Nour Mohammad Taraki, founder of People's Democratic Party of Afghanistan, installation as president.

Woman Breaking Chain — A357

1979, Mar. 8 Litho. *Perf. 11*

956 A357 14af red & ultra 1.25 .50

Women's Day. Inscribed "POSSTES."

Map of Afghanistan, Census Emblem — A358

1979, Mar. 25 Litho. *Perf. 12*

957 A358 3af multicolored .90 .70

First comprehensive population census.

Farmers — A359

1979, Mar. 21

958 A359 1af multicolored .65 .30

Agricultural advances.

Pres. Taraki Reading First Issue of Khalq A360

1979, Apr. 11 *Perf. 12½x12*

959 A360 2af multicolored .65 .25

Khalq, newspaper of People's Democratic Republic of Afghanistan.

Pres. Noor Mohammad Taraki — A361

Plaza with Tank Monument and Fountain A362

House where Revolution Started — A363

Designs: 50p, Taraki, tank. 12af, House where 1st Khalq Party Congress was held.

Perf. 12, 12½x12 (A362)

1979, Apr. 27 Litho.

959A A363 50p multicolored .65 .25
960 A361 4af multicolored .40 .25
961 A362 5af multicolored .55 .25
962 A363 6af multicolored .70 .25
963 A363 12af multicolored .80 .25
Nos. 959A-963 (5) 3.10 1.25

1st anniversary of revolution.

Carpenter and Blacksmith A364

1979, May 1 *Perf. 12*

964 A364 10af multicolored 1.10 .25

Int'l Labor Day.

Children, Flag and Map of Afghanistan A366

1979, June 1 Litho. *Perf. 12½x12*

966 A366 16af multicolored 2.00 .90

International Year of the Child.

Doves Circling Asia in Globe A366a

1979 Litho. *Perf. 11x10½*

966A A366a 2af red & blue 1.25 .25

Armed Afghans, Kabul Memorial and Arch — A367

1979, Aug. 19 Litho. *Perf. 12*

967 A367 30af multicolored 1.50 .90

60th independence day.

Pashtunistan Citizens, Flag — A368

1979, Aug. 31

968 A368 9af multicolored .70 .25

Pashtunistan Day.

UPU Day — A369

1979, Oct. 9 Litho. *Perf. 12*

969 A369 15af multicolored .65 .25

Tombstone — A369a

1979, Oct. 25 Litho. *Perf. 12½x12*

969A A369a 22af multicolored 2.40 1.25

International Women's Day — A370

1980, Mar. 8 Litho. *Perf. 12*

970 A370 8af multicolored 1.50 .50

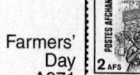

Farmers' Day A371

1980, Mar. 21 Litho. *Perf. 11½x12*

971 A371 2af multicolored 2.25 .70

Non-smoker and Smoker — A372

1980, Apr. 7 *Perf. 11½*

972 A372 5af multicolored 1.75 .70

Anti-smoking campaign; World Health Day.

Lenin, 110th Birth Anniversary A373

1980, Apr. 22 *Perf. 12x12½*

973 A373 12af multicolored 2.50 .85

People and Fist on Map of Afghanistan A374

1980, Apr. 27 Litho. *Perf. 12½x12*

974 A374 1af multicolored .70 .25

Saur Revolution, 2nd anniversary.

International Workers' Solidarity Day — A375

1980, May 1

975 A375 9af multicolored .50 .25

Wrestling, Moscow '80 Emblem — A376

1980, July 19 *Perf. 12x12½, 12½x12*

976 A376 3af Soccer, vert. .60 .25

977 A376 6af shown .70 .25

978 A376 9af Buzkashi .80 .25

979 A376 10af Pegsticking .95 .25

Nos. 976-979 (4) 3.05 1.00

22nd Summer Olympic Games, Moscow, July 19-Aug. 3.

61st Anniversary of Independence A377

1980, Aug. 19 Litho. *Perf. 12½x12*

980 A377 3af multicolored .85 .25

Pashtunistan Day — A378

1980, Aug. 30

981 A378 25af multicolored 1.00 .45

Intl. UPU Day — A379

1980, Oct. 9 Litho. *Perf. 12½x12*

982 A379 20af multicolored 1.00 .45

The resistance group headed by Amin Wardak released some stamps in 1980. Some of these are inscribed "WARDAK AFGHANISTAN," others "Solidarite Internationale Avec la Resistance Afghane." The status of these labels is questionable.

International Women's Day — A381

1981, Mar. 9 Litho. *Perf. 12½x12*

984 A381 15af multicolored 1.25 .35

Farmers' Day — A382

1981, Mar. 20 Litho. *Perf. 12½x12*

985 A382 1af multicolored 1.00 .25

Bighorn Mountain Sheep (Protected Species) — A383

1981, Apr. 4 *Perf. 12x12½*

986 A383 12af multicolored 2.40 .70

Saur Revolution, 3rd Anniversary — A384

1981, Apr. 27 *Perf. 11*

987 A384 50p brown .70 .25

Intl. Workers' Solidarity Day — A385

1981, May 1 *Perf. 12½x12*

988 A385 10af multicolored .95 .35

13th World Telecommunications Day — A387

1981, May 17 Litho. *Perf. 12½x12*

990 A387 9af multicolored .70 .25

Intl. Children's Day — A388

1981, June 1 *Perf. 12x12½*

991 A388 15af multicolored .95 .45

People's Independence Monument 62nd Anniv. of Independence A389

1981, Aug. 19

992 A389 4af multicolored 1.10 .30

Pashtunistan Day — A390

1981, Aug. 31 Litho. *Perf. 12*

992A A390 2af multicolored .70 .25

Intl. Tourism Day — A391

1981, Sept. 27 *Perf. 12½x12*

993 A391 5af multicolored .70 .25

World Food Day — A392

1981, Oct. 16

995 A392 7af multicolored .85 .25

Asia-Africa Solidarity Meeting A393

1981, Nov. 18 **Litho.** ***Perf. 11***
996 A393 8af blue .80 .25

Struggle Against Apartheid — A394

1981, Dec. 1 ***Perf. 12½x12***
997 A394 4af multicolored 1.00 .25

1300th Anniv. of Bulgaria — A395

1981, Dec. 9 ***Perf. 12x12½***
998 A395 20af multicolored 1.75 .50

Buzkashi Game — A395a

1980 **Photo.** ***Perf. 14***
998A A395a 50af multicolored 2.25 1.25
998B A395a 100af multicolored 4.50 1.75

Intl. Women's Day — A396

1982, Mar. 8 **Litho.** ***Perf. 12***
999 A396 6af multicolored .60 .25

Farmers' Day — A397

1982, Mar. 21
1000 A397 4af multicolored .70 .25

Judas Trees — A398

Designs: Various local plants.

1982, Apr. 9 **Litho.** ***Perf. 12***
1001 A398 3af shown .40 .25
1002 A398 4af Rose of Sharon .70 .25
1003 A398 16af Rhubarb plant 1.60 .35
Nos. 1001-1003 (3) 2.70 .85

Saur Revolution, 4th Anniv. — A399

1982, Apr. 27
1004 A399 1af multicolored 1.50 .25

George Dimitrov (1882-1947), First Prime Minister of Bulgaria — A400

1982, Apr. 30
1005 A400 30af multicolored 2.40 .85

Intl. Workers' Solidarity Day — A401

1982, May 1
1006 A401 10af multicolored .85 .25

Storks — A402

Nightingales — A402a

1982, May 31
1007 A402 6af multicolored 1.75 .50
1008 A402a 11af multicolored 2.75 .60

Hedgehogs A403

1982, July 6 **Litho.** ***Perf. 12***
1009 A403 3af shown .75 .25
1010 A403 14af Cobra 1.75 .25

See Nos. 1020-1022.

63rd Anniv. of Independence A404

1982, Aug. 19
1011 A404 20af multicolored 1.25 .50

Pashtunistan Day — A405

1982, Aug. 31
1012 A405 32af multicolored 2.50 .75

World Tourism Day — A406

1982, Sept. 27 **Litho.** ***Perf. 12***
1013 A406 9af multicolored .85 .35

UPU Day — A407

1982, Oct. 9
1014 A407 4af multicolored .95 .25

World Food Day — A408

1982, Oct. 16
1015 A408 9af multicolored 1.50 .35

37th Anniv. of UN — A409

1982, Oct. 24
1016 A409 15af multicolored 1.00 .45

ITU Plenipotentiaries Conference, Nairobi, Sept. — A410

1982, Oct. 26
1017 A410 8af multicolored .80 .25

TB Bacillus Centenary — A411

1982, Nov. 24 **Litho.** ***Perf. 12***
1018 A411 7af multicolored .50 .25

Human Rights Declaration, 34th Anniv. — A412

1982, Dec. 10
1019 A412 5af multicolored .45 .25

Animal Type of 1982

1982, Dec. 16
1020 A403 2af Lions .50 .25
1021 A403 7af Donkeys 1.00 .35
1022 A403 12af Marmots, vert. 2.25 .50
Nos. 1020-1022 (3) 3.75 1.10

Intl. Women's Day — A413

1983, Mar. 8
1023 A413 3af multicolored .25 .25

Mir Alicher Nawai Research Decade — A414

1983, Mar. 19
1024 A414 22af multicolored .95 .35

Farmers' Day — A415

1983, Mar. 21 **Litho.** ***Perf. 12***
1025 A415 10af multicolored .75 .25

5th Anniv. of Saur Revolution A416

1983, Apr. 27 **Litho.** ***Perf. 12***
1026 A416 15af multicolored .70 .35

Intl. Workers' Solidarity Day — A417

1983, May 1
1027 A417 2af multicolored .70 .25

World Communications Year — A418

4af, Modes of communication. 11af, Building.

1983, May 17
1028 A418 4af multicolored .45 .25
1029 A418 11af multicolored .75 .25

Intl. Children's Day — A419

1983, June 1 **Litho.** ***Perf. 12***
1030 A419 25af multicolored .80 .35

2nd Anniv. of National Front — A420

1983, June 15
1031 A420 1af multicolored .35 .25

Local Butterflies A421

Various butterflies. 9af, 13af vert.

1983, July 6
1032 A421 9af multicolored 1.10 .80
1033 A421 13af multicolored 2.50 1.40
1034 A421 21af multicolored 3.25 1.75
Nos. 1032-1034 (3) 6.85 3.95

Struggle Against Apartheid — A422

1983, Aug. 1 **Litho.** ***Perf. 12***
1035 A422 10af multicolored .55 .25

64th Anniv of Independence A423

1983, Aug. 19
1036 A423 6af multicolored .45 .25

Parliament House — A423a

100af, Afghan Woman, Camel.

1983, Sept. **Litho.** ***Perf. 12***
1036A A423a 50af shown 1.75 .35
1036B A423a 100af multi 4.25 .45

A424

World Tourism Day — A425

1983, Sept. 27 **Litho.** ***Perf. 12***
1037 A424 5af shown .45 .25
1038 A425 7af shown .60 .25
1039 A424 12af Golden statues .95 .25
1040 A425 16af Stone carving 1.25 .25
Nos. 1037-1040 (4) 3.25 1.00

World Communications Year — A426

14af, Dish antenna, dove. 15af, Building, flag.

1983, Oct. 9 **Litho.** ***Perf. 12***
1041 A426 14af multicolored .90 .25
1042 A426 15af multicolored .90 .25

World Food Day — A427

1983, Oct. 16 **Litho.** ***Perf. 12***
1043 A427 14af multicolored .90 .25

Sports — A428

1983, Nov. 1 **Litho.** ***Perf. 12***
1044 A428 1af Soccer .25 .25
1045 A428 18af Boxing 1.00 .35
1046 A428 21af Wrestling 1.25 .35
Nos. 1044-1046 (3) 2.50 .95

Pashtunistan Day — A428a

3af, Pathans Waving Flag.

1983, Nov. **Litho.** ***Perf. 12***
1046A A428a 3af multicolored .45 .25

Handicrafts A429

2af, Jewelry. 8af, Stone ashtrays, dishes. 19af, Furniture. 30af, Leather goods.

1983, Nov. 22
1047 A429 2af multicolored .25 .25
1048 A429 8af multicolored .35 .25
1049 A429 19af multicolored .60 .25
1050 A429 30af multicolored 1.50 .40
Nos. 1047-1050 (4) 2.70 1.15

UN Declaration of Human Rights, 35th Anniv. — A430

1983, Dec. 10 **Litho.** ***Perf. 12***
1051 A430 20af multicolored .95 .25

Kabul Polytechnical Institute, 20th Anniv. — A431

1983, Dec. 28 ***Perf. 12½x12***
1052 A431 30af multicolored 1.25 .35

1984 Winter Olympics — A432

1984, Jan. ***Perf. 12***
1053 A432 5af Figure skating .25 .25
1054 A432 9af Skiing .35 .25
1055 A432 11af Speed skating .50 .25
1056 A432 15af Hockey .60 .25
1057 A432 18af Biathlon .70 .25
1058 A432 20af Ski jumping .85 .25
1059 A432 22af Bobsledding 1.00 .25
Nos. 1053-1059 (7) 4.25 1.75

Intl. Women's Day — A433

1984, Mar. 8
1060 A433 4af multicolored .50 .25

Farmers' Day — A434

Various agricultural scenes.

1984, Mar. 21 **Litho.** ***Perf. 12***
1061 A434 2af multicolored .25 .25
1062 A434 4af multicolored .25 .25
1063 A434 7af multicolored .25 .25
1064 A434 9af multicolored .25 .25
1065 A434 15af multicolored .45 .25
1066 A434 18af multicolored .50 .25
1067 A434 20af multicolored .70 .25
Nos. 1061-1067 (7) 2.65 1.75

World Aviation Day — A435

1984, Apr. 12
1068 A435 5af Luna 1 .35 .25
1069 A435 8af Luna 2 .45 .25
1070 A435 11af Luna 3 .55 .25
1071 A435 17af Apollo 11 .70 .25
1072 A435 22af Soyuz 6 .90 .35
1073 A435 28af Soyuz 7 .90 .35
1074 A435 34af Soyuz 6, 7, 8 1.10 .45
Nos. 1068-1074 (7) 4.95 2.15

Souvenir Sheet

Perf. 12x12½
1075 A435 25af S. Koroliov 1.50 .90

No. 1075 contains one 30x41mm stamp.

Saur Revolution, 6th Anniv. — A436

1984, Apr. 27 ***Perf. 12***
1076 A436 3af multicolored .45 .25

65th Anniv. of Independence A437

1984, Aug. 19 **Litho.** ***Perf. 12***
1077 A437 6af multicolored .65 .25

Pashto's and Balutchi's Day — A438

3af, Symbolic sun, tribal terr.

1984, Aug. 31
1078 A438 3af multicolored .45 .25

Wildlife — A439

1af, Cape hunting dog, vert. 2af, Argali sheep, vert. 6af, Przewalski's horse. 8af, Wild boar, vert. 17af, Snow leopard. 19af, Tiger. 22af, Indian elephant, vert.

Perf. 12½x12, 12x12½

1984, May 5 **Litho.**
1079 A439 1af multicolored .25 .25
1080 A439 2af multicolored .25 .25
1081 A439 6af multicolored .60 .25
1082 A439 8af multicolored .90 .25
1083 A439 17af multicolored 1.75 .25
1084 A439 19af multicolored 3.00 .25
1085 A439 22af multicolored 3.25 .35
Nos. 1079-1085 (7) 10.00 1.85

19th UPU Congress, Hamburg — A440

25af, German postman, 17th cent. 35af, Postrider, 16th cent. 40af, Carrier pigeon, letter.

50af, Hamburg No. 3 in black.

1984, June 18 ***Perf. 12x12½***
1086 A440 25af multicolored .95 .30
1087 A440 35af multicolored 1.50 .45
1088 A440 40af multicolored 1.90 .55
Nos. 1086-1088 (3) 4.35 1.30

Souvenir Sheet

1089 A440 50af multicolored 2.75 1.75

No. 1089 contains one 30x40mm stamp.

Natl. Aviation, 40th Anniv. — A441

Soviet civil aircraft.

1984, June 29
1090 A441 1af Antonov AN-2 .25 .25
1091 A441 4af Ilyushin IL-12 .25 .25
1092 A441 9af Tupolev TU-104 .60 .25
1093 A441 10af Ilyushin IL-18 .90 .25
1094 A441 13af Tupolev TU-134 1.10 .25
1095 A441 17af Ilyushin IL-62 1.50 .30
1096 A441 21af Ilyushin IL-28 1.75 .40
Nos. 1090-1096 (7) 6.35 1.95

Ettore Bugatti (1881-1947), Type 43, Italy — A442

Classic automobiles and their designers: 5af, Henry Ford, 1903 Model A, US. 8af, Rene Panhard (1841-1908), 1899 Landau, France. 11af, Gottlieb Daimler (1834-1900), 1935 Daimler-Benz, Germany. 12af, Carl Benz (1844-1929), 1893 Victoris, Germany. 15af, Armand Peugeot (1848-1915), 1892 Vis-a-Vis, France. 22af, Louis Chevrolet (1879-1941), 1925 Sedan, US.

1984, June 30
1097 A442 2af multicolored .25 .25
1098 A442 5af multicolored .35 .25
1099 A442 8af multicolored .60 .25
1100 A442 11af multicolored .75 .25
1101 A442 12af multicolored 1.00 .25
1102 A442 15af multicolored 1.10 .25
1103 A442 22af multicolored 1.50 .35
Nos. 1097-1103 (7) 5.55 1.85

Qalai Bist Arch — A443

World Tourism Day: 2af, Ornamental buckled harness. 5af, Victory Monument and Memorial Arch, Kabul. 9af, Standing sculpture of Afghani ruler and attendants. 15af, Buffalo riders in snow. 19af, Camel driver, tent, camel in caparison. 21af, Horsemen playing buzkashi.

1984, Sept. 27
1104 A443 1af multicolored .25 .25
1105 A443 2af multicolored .25 .25
1106 A443 5af multicolored .25 .25
1107 A443 9af multicolored .25 .25
1108 A443 15af multicolored .45 .25
1109 A443 19af multicolored .90 .25
1110 A443 21af multicolored 1.00 .25
Nos. 1104-1110 (7) 3.35 1.75

UN World Food Day — A444

Fruit-bearing trees.

1984, Oct. 16
1111 A444 2af multicolored .25 .25
1112 A444 4af multicolored .25 .25
1113 A444 6af multicolored .35 .25
1114 A444 9af multicolored .50 .25
1115 A444 13af multicolored .60 .25
1116 A444 15af multicolored .75 .25
1117 A444 26af multicolored 1.25 .25
Nos. 1111-1117 (7) 3.95 1.75

People's Democratic Party, 20th Anniv. — A445

1985, Jan. 1

1118	A445	25af multicolored	1.25	.45

Farmer's Day — A446

1af, Oxen. 3af, Mare, foal. 7af, Brown horse. 8af, White horse, vert. 15af, Sheep, sheepskins. 16af, Shepherd, cattle, sheep. 25af, Family, camels.

1985, Mar. 2

1119	A446	1af multicolored	.35	.25
1120	A446	3af multicolored	.35	.25
1121	A446	7af multicolored	.35	.25
1122	A446	8af multicolored	.60	.25
1123	A446	15af multicolored	.95	.25
1124	A446	16af multicolored	1.10	.35
1125	A446	25af multicolored	1.60	.45
		Nos. 1119-1125 (7)	5.30	2.05

Geologist's Day — A447

1985, Apr. 5

1126	A447	4af multicolored	.35	.25

Lenin and Peasant Petitioners — A448

Lenin and: 10af, Lenin and Peasant Petitioners. 15af, Revolutionaries, 1917, Leningrad. 25af, Lenin leading Revolutionary Guards, 1917. 50af, Portrait.

1985, Apr. 21 ***Perf. 12x12½***

1127	A448	10af multicolored	.70	.25
1128	A448	15af multicolored	.85	.25
1129	A448	25af multicolored	1.50	.40
		Nos. 1127-1129 (3)	3.05	.90

Souvenir Sheet

1130	A448	50af multicolored	2.50	1.50

Saur Revolution, 7th Anniv. — A449

1985, Apr. 27

1131	A449	21af multicolored	1.00	.30

Berlin-Treptow Soviet War Memorial, Red Army at Siege of Berlin, 1945 — A450

9af, Victorious Motherland monument, fireworks over Kremlin. 10af, Caecilienhof, site of Potsdam Treaty signing, Great Britain, USSR & US flags.

1985, May 9 ***Perf. 12½x12***

1132	A450	6af multicolored	.60	.25
1133	A450	9af multicolored	.85	.25
1134	A450	10af multicolored	1.10	.25
		Nos. 1132-1134 (3)	2.55	.75

End of World War II, defeat of Nazi Germany, 40th anniv.

INTELSAT, 20th Anniv. — A451

Designs: 6af, INTELSAT I satellite orbiting Earth. 9af, INTELSAT VI. 10af, Delta D rocket launch, Cape Canaveral, vert.

Perf. 12x12½, 12½x12

1985, Apr. 6 **Litho.**

1135	A451	6af multicolored	.50	.25
1136	A451	9af multicolored	.70	.25
1137	A451	10af multicolored	.95	.25
		Nos. 1135-1137 (3)	2.15	.75

12th World Youth Festival, Moscow — A452

7af, Olympic stadium, Moscow. 12af, Festival emblem. 13af, Kremlin. 18af, Folk doll, emblem.

1985, May 5

1138	A452	7af multicolored	.25	.25
1139	A452	12af multicolored	.45	.25
1140	A452	13af multicolored	.55	.35
1141	A452	18af multicolored	.70	.60
		Nos. 1138-1141 (4)	1.95	1.45

Intl. Child Survival Campaign A453

1985, June 1

1142	A453	1af Weighing child	.25	.25
1143	A453	2af Immunization	.25	.25
1144	A453	4af Breastfeeding	.35	.25
1145	A453	5af Mother, child	.40	.25
		Nos. 1142-1145 (4)	1.25	1.00

Flowers — A454

2af, Oenothera affinis. 4af, Erythrina cristagalli. 8af, Tillandsia aeranthos. 13af, Vinca major. 18af, Mirabilis jalapa. 25af, Cypella herbertii. 30af, Clytostoma callistegioides.
75af, Sesbania punicea, horiz.

1985, July 5

1146	A454	2af multicolored	.25	.25
1147	A454	4af multicolored	.25	.25
1148	A454	8af multicolored	.45	.25
1149	A454	13af multicolored	.75	.25
1150	A454	18af multicolored	1.00	.30
1151	A454	25af multicolored	1.40	.30
1152	A454	30af multicolored	1.75	.30
		Nos. 1146-1152 (7)	5.85	1.90

Souvenir Sheet

Perf. 12½x11½

1153	A454	75af multicolored	4.50	.75

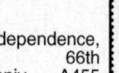

ARGENTINA '85.

Independence, 66th Anniv. — A455

1985, Aug. 19 ***Perf. 12x12½***

1154	A455	33af Mosque	1.50	.45

Pashto's and Balutchi's Day — A456

1985, Aug. 30

1155	A456	25af multicolored	1.50	.25

UN Decade for Women — A457

1985, Sept. 22

1156	A457	10af Emblems	*2.50*	.25

World Tourism Day, 10th Anniv. — A457a

1af, Guldara Stupa. 2af, Mirwais Tomb, vert. 10af, Statue of Bamyan, vert. 13af, No Gumbad Mosque, vert. 14af, Pule Kheshti Mosque. 15af, Bost Citadel. 20af, Ghazni Minaret, vert.

1985, Sept. 27 **Litho.** ***Perf. 12***

1156A	A457a	1af multi	.25	.25
1156B	A457a	2af multi	.25	.25
1156C	A457a	10af multi	.60	.25
1156D	A457a	13af multi	.85	.25
1156E	A457a	14af multi	.95	.25
1156F	A457a	15af multi	1.00	.25
1156G	A457a	20af multi	1.40	.25
		Nos. 1156A-1156G (7)	5.30	1.75

Sports — A457b

Perf. 12x12½, 12½x12

1985, Oct. 3 **Litho.**

1156H	A457b	1af Boxing	.25	.25
1156I	A457b	2af Volleyball	.25	.25
1156J	A457b	3af Soccer, vert.	.50	.25
1156K	A457b	12af Buzkashi	.75	.25
1156L	A457b	14af Weight lifting	.95	.25
1156M	A457b	18af Wrestling	1.00	.25
1156N	A457b	25af Peg sticking	1.25	.35
		Nos. 1156H-1156N (7)	4.95	1.85

World Food Day — A457c

1985, Oct. 16

1156O	A457c	25af multicolored	.95	.30

UN 40th Anniv. — A458

1985, Oct. 24 ***Perf. 12½x12***

1157	A458	22af multicolored	1.10	.30

A459

A459a

A459b

A459c

Birds — A459d

2af, Jay. 4af, Plover, hummingbird. 8af, Pheasant. 13af, Hoopoe. 18af, Falcon. 25af, Partridge. 30af, Pelicans, horiz.
75af, Parakeets.

1985, Oct. 25 ***Perf. 12½x12, 12x12½***

1158	A459	2af multicolored	.25	.25
1159	A459a	4af multicolored	.85	.45
1160	A459b	8af multicolored	.90	.45
1161	A459a	13af multicolored	1.40	.75
1162	A459	18af multicolored	1.60	.85
1163	A459b	25af multicolored	2.40	1.25
1164	A459c	30af multicolored	3.00	1.50
		Nos. 1158-1164 (7)	10.40	5.50

Souvenir Sheet

Perf. 12x12½

1165	A459d	75af multicolored	5.00	.75

Mushrooms — A460

3af, Tricholomopsis rutilans. 4af, Boletus miniatoporus. 7af, Amanita rubescens. 11af, Boletus scaber. 12af, Coprinus atramentarius. 18af, Hypholoma. 20af, Boletus aurantiacus.

1985, June 10 **Litho.** ***Perf. 12½x12***

1165A	A460	3af multicolored	.25	.25
1166	A460	4af multicolored	.40	.25
1167	A460	7af multicolored	.55	.30
1168	A460	11af multicolored	.80	.50
1169	A460	12af multicolored	1.00	.50
1170	A460	18af multicolored	1.40	.65
1171	A460	20af multicolored	1.60	.70
		Nos. 1165A-1171 (7)	6.00	3.15

World Wildlife Fund A461

1985, Nov. 25

1172	A461	2af Leopard, cubs	*.40*	*.25*
1173	A461	9af Adult's head	*1.25*	*.40*
1174	A461	11af Adult	*2.40*	*.75*
1175	A461	15af Cub	*3.75*	*1.10*
		Nos. 1172-1175 (4)	*7.80*	*2.50*

Motorcycle, Cent. A462

Designs: Different makes and landmarks.

1985, Dec. 16

1176	A462	2af multicolored	.25	.25
1177	A462	4af multicolored	.30	.25
1178	A462	8af multicolored	.50	.25
1179	A462	13af multicolored	.80	.25
1180	A462	18af multicolored	.90	.25
1181	A462	25af multicolored	1.25	.25
1182	A462	30af multicolored	1.25	.25
		Nos. 1176-1182 (7)	5.25	1.75

Souvenir Sheet

Perf. 11½x12½

1183 A462 75af multicolored 5.00 .75

People's Democratic Party, 21st Anniv. A463

1986, Jan. 1 ***Perf. 12½x12***

1184 A463 2af multicolored .35 .25

27th Soviet Communist Party Congress A464

1986, Mar. 31

1185 A464 25af Lenin .75 .40

First Man in Space, 25th Anniv. A465

Designs: 3af, Spacecraft. 7af, Soviet space achievement medal, vert. 9af, Rocket lift-off, vert. 11af, Yuri Gagarin, military decorations, vert. 13af, Gagarin, cosmonaut. 15af, Gagarin, politician. 17af, Gagarin wearing flight suit, vert.

Perf. 12½x12, 12x12½

1986, Apr. 12 **Litho.**

1186	A465	3af multicolored	.25	.25
1187	A465	7af multicolored	.25	.25
1188	A465	9af multicolored	.35	.25
1189	A465	11af multicolored	.45	.25
1190	A465	13af multicolored	.50	.25
1191	A465	15af multicolored	.50	.25
1192	A465	17af multicolored	.75	.25
		Nos. 1186-1192 (7)	3.05	1.75

A465a

Loya Jirgah (Grand Assembly) of the People's Democratic Republic, 1st anniv.

1986, Apr. 23 **Litho.** ***Perf. 12x12½***

1192A A465a 3af multicolored .25 .25

Intl. Day of Labor Solidarity — A465b

1986, May 1 ***Perf. 12½x12***

1192B A465b 5af multicolored .35 .25

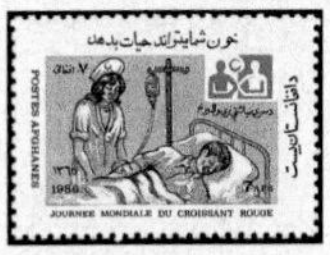

Intl. Red Crescent Day — A465c

1986, May 8 ***Perf. 12x12½***

1192C A465c 7af multicolored .45 .25

Intl. Children's Day — A466

1af, Mother, children, vert. 3af, Mother, child, vert. 9af, Children, map.

1986, June 1 ***Perf. 12***

1193	A466	1af multicolored	.25	.25
1194	A466	3af multicolored	.25	.25
1195	A466	9af multicolored	.40	.25
		Nos. 1193-1195 (3)	.90	.75

World Youth Day — A466a

1986, July 31 ***Perf. 12x12½***

1195A A466a 15af multicolored .70 .45

Pashtos' and Baluchis' Day — A467

1986, Aug. 31 ***Perf. 12x12½***

1196 A467 4af multicolored .25 .25

Intl. Peace Year — A468

1986, Sept. 30 **Photo.** ***Perf. 12½x12***

1197 A468 12af black & Prus blue .60 .25

A469

1986 World Cup Soccer Championships, Mexico — A470

Various soccer plays.

1986, Apr. 15 **Litho.** ***Perf. 12***

1198	A469	3af multi, vert.	.25	.25
1199	A469	4af multicolored	.35	.25
1200	A469	7af multicolored	.40	.25
1201	A469	11af multi, vert.	.70	.25
1202	A469	12af multicolored	.85	.25
1203	A469	18af multi, vert.	1.25	.25
1204	A469	20af multi, vert.	1.50	.25
		Nos. 1198-1204 (7)	5.30	1.75

Souvenir Sheet

Perf. 12½x12

1205 A470 75af multicolored 4.75 3.00

Lenin — A471

1986, Apr. 21 ***Perf. 12½x12***

1206 A471 16af multicolored .75 .45

A472

1986, Apr. 27 **Litho.** ***Perf. 12½x12***

1207 A472 8af multicolored .60 .25

Saur revolution, 8th anniv.

Natl. Independence, 67th Anniv. — A473

1986, Aug. 19 **Litho.** ***Perf. 12½x12***

1208 A473 10af multicolored .50 .25

Literacy Day — A474

1986, Sept. 18 ***Perf. 12x12½***

1209 A474 2af multicolored .25 .25

Dogs — A475

5af, St. Bernard. 7af, Collie. 8af, Pointer. 9af, Golden retriever. 11af, German shepherd. 15af, Bulldog. 20af, Afghan hound.

1986, May 19 **Litho.** ***Perf. 12x12½***

1210	A475	5af multicolored	.25	.25
1211	A475	7af multicolored	.40	.25
1212	A475	8af multicolored	.50	.25
1213	A475	9af multicolored	.60	.25
1214	A475	11af multicolored	.70	.25
1215	A475	15af multicolored	.95	.25
1216	A475	20af multicolored	1.25	.30
		Nos. 1210-1216 (7)	4.65	1.80

Lizards — A476

1986, July 7 ***Perf. 12x12½, 12½x12***

1217	A476	3af Cobra	.25	.25
1218	A476	4af shown	.25	.25
1219	A476	5af Praying mantis	.35	.25
1220	A476	8af Beetle	.50	.25
1221	A476	9af Tarantula	.60	.30
1222	A476	10af Python	.70	.35
1223	A476	11af Scorpions	.85	.35
		Nos. 1217-1223 (7)	3.50	2.00

Nos. 1217, 1219, 1221-1223 horiz.

STOCKHOLMIA '86 — A477

Ships.

1986, Aug. 28 ***Perf. 12½x12***

1224	A477	4af multicolored	.40	.25
1225	A477	5af multicolored	.60	.25
1226	A477	6af multicolored	.70	.25
1227	A477	7af multicolored	.85	.25
1228	A477	8af multicolored	1.00	.25
1229	A477	9af multicolored	1.10	.25
1230	A477	11af multicolored	1.40	.25
		Nos. 1224-1230 (7)	6.05	1.75

Souvenir Sheet

1231 A477 50af Galley 4.25 2.00

A479

1986, Sept. 14 ***Perf. 12***

1232 A479 3af lt blue, blk & olive gray .40 .25

Reunion of Afghan tribes under the Supreme Girgah.

A480

1986, Oct. 25 ***Perf. 12½x12***

1233 A480 3af black & brt ver .40 .25

Natl. youth solidarity.

Locomotives A481

1986, June 21 ***Perf. 12½x12***

1234	A481	4af multicolored	.25	.25
1235	A481	5af multicolored	.35	.25
1236	A481	6af multicolored	.45	.25
1237	A481	7af multicolored	.50	.25
1238	A481	8af multicolored	.65	.25
1239	A481	9af multicolored	.85	.25
1240	A481	11af multicolored	1.25	.25
		Nos. 1234-1240 (7)	4.30	1.75

Fish — A482

Various fish.

1986, May 25

1241	A482	5af multicolored	.25	.25
1242	A482	7af multicolored	.40	.25
1243	A482	8af multicolored	.50	.25
1244	A482	9af multicolored	.60	.25
1245	A482	11af multicolored	.85	.25
1246	A482	15af multicolored	1.10	.35
1247	A482	20af multicolored	1.50	.35
		Nos. 1241-1247 (7)	5.20	1.95

Saur Revolution, 9th Anniv. — A483

1987, Apr. 27 ***Perf. 12***

1248 A483 3af multicolored .25 .25

Natl. Reconciliation A484

1987, May 27 *Perf. 12x12½*

1249 A484 3af multicolored .25 .25

A485

A486

UN Child Survival Campaign — A487

1987, June 1 *Perf. 12*

1250 A485 1af multicolored .25 .25
1251 A486 5af multicolored .25 .25
1252 A487 9af multicolored .35 .25
Nos. 1250-1252 (3) .85 .75

Conference of Clergymen and Ulema, 1st Anniv. — A488

1987, June 30

1253 A488 5af multicolored .35 .25

Butterflies — A489

1987, July 3

1254 A489 7af multicolored .60 .35
1255 A489 9af multi, diff. .75 .35
1256 A489 10af multi, diff. 1.00 .50
1257 A489 12af multi, diff. 1.50 .50
1258 A489 15af multi, diff. 1.60 .70
1259 A489 22af multi, diff. 2.25 .95
1260 A489 25af multi, diff. 2.50 .95
Nos. 1254-1260 (7) 10.20 4.30

10af, 15af and 22af horiz.

A490

1987, Aug. 11

1261 A490 1af multicolored .25 .25

1st election of local representatives for State Power and Administration.

Natl. Independence, 68th Anniv. — A490a

1987, Aug. 19

1261A A490a 3af multicolored .25 .25

1st Artificial Satellite (Sputnik), 30th Anniv. — A491

1987, Oct. 4 **Litho.** *Perf. 12½x12*

1262 A491 10af Sputnik .40 .25
1263 A491 15af Rocket launch .60 .25
1264 A491 25af Soyuz .85 .25
Nos. 1262-1264 (3) 1.85 .75

World Post Day — A492

1987, Oct. 9 *Perf. 12x12½*

1265 A492 22af multicolored 1.10 .60

Intl. Communications and Transport Day — A493

1987, Oct. 24 *Perf. 12½x12*

1266 A493 42af multicolored 4.75 1.00

October Revolution in Russia, 70th Anniv. — A494

1987, Nov. 7

1267 A494 25af Lenin 1.25 .70

Mice — A495

Various mice. Nos. 1269-1272 horiz.

1987, Dec. 6 *Perf. 12½x12, 12x12½*

1268 A495 2af multicolored .40 .25
1269 A495 4af multi, diff. .50 .25
1270 A495 8af multi, diff. .60 .25
1271 A495 16af multi, diff. 1.00 .25
1272 A495 20af multi, diff. 1.25 .25
Nos. 1268-1272 (5) 3.75 1.25

Medicinal Plants — A496

1987, Nov. 11 **Litho.** *Perf. 12*

1273 A496 3af Castor bean .25 .25
1274 A496 6af Licorice .45 .25
1275 A496 9af Chamomile .75 .25
1276 A496 14af Datura 1.00 .25
1277 A496 18af Dandelion 1.25 .30
Nos. 1273-1277 (5) 3.70 1.30

Pashto's and Baluchis' Day — A497

1987, Aug. 30

1278 A497 4af multicolored .25 .25

Dinosaurs A498

3af, Mesosaurus. 5af, Styracosaurus. 10af, Uinatherium. 15af, Protoceratops. 20af, Stegosaurus. 25af, Ceratosaurus. 30af, Dinornis maximus.

Perf. 12½x12, 12x12½

1988, June 6 **Litho.**

1279 A498 3af multicolored .25 .25
1280 A498 5af multicolored .25 .25
1281 A498 10af multicolored .50 .25
1282 A498 15af multicolored .75 .25
1283 A498 20af multicolored 1.00 .30
1284 A498 25af multicolored 1.40 .35
1285 A498 30af multicolored 1.90 .60
Nos. 1279-1285 (7) 6.05 2.25

Nos. 1280-1283 horiz.

Pashtos' and Baluchis' Day — A499

1988, Aug. 30 *Perf. 12½x12*

1286 A499 23af multicolored .95 .60

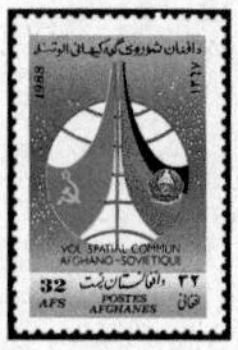

Afghan-Soviet Joint Space Flight — A500

1988, Aug. 30

1287 A500 32af multicolored 1.25 .50

Valentina Tereshkova, 1st Woman in Space, 25th Anniv. — A501

10af, Portrait, rocket, horiz. 15af, Lift-off, dove. 25af, Spacecraft, Earth, horiz.

1988, Oct. 16 *Perf. 12x12½, 12½x12*

1288 A501 10af multicolored .85 .35
1289 A501 15af multicolored .85 .30
1290 A501 25af multicolored 1.00 .45
Nos. 1288-1290 (3) 2.70 1.10

Traditional Crafts — A502

Perf. 12x12½, 12½x12

1988, Nov. 9 **Litho.**

1291 A502 2af Pitcher, bowls .25 .25
1292 A502 4af Vases .25 .25
1293 A502 5af Dress .25 .25
1294 A502 9af Mats, napkins .35 .25
1295 A502 15af Pocketbooks .60 .25
1296 A502 23af Jewelry .95 .25
1297 A502 50af Furniture 1.90 .25
Nos. 1291-1297 (7) 4.55 1.75

Nos. 1291-1292, 1294-1297 horiz.

Precious and Semiprecious Gems — A503

1988, Dec. 5 *Perf. 12½x12*

1298 A503 13af Emeralds 1.00 .25
1299 A503 37af Lapiz lazuli 2.25 .60
1300 A503 40af Rubies 2.50 .75
Nos. 1298-1300 (3) 5.75 1.60

1988 Winter Olympics, Calgary — A504

2af, Women's figure skating. 5af, Skiing. 9af, Bobsledding. 22af, Biathlon. 37af, Speed skating.

75af, Ice hockey.

1988, Dec. 25

1301 A504 2af multicolored .25 .25
1301A A504 5af multicolored .25 .25
1301B A504 9af multicolored .50 .25
1301C A504 22af multicolored 1.00 .35
1301D A504 37af multicolored 2.25 .65

Size: 80x60mm

1302 A504 75af multicolored 4.50 3.50
Nos. 1301-1302 (6) 8.75 5.25

A510

A511

A512

A513

A513a

Flowers A514

Various flowering plants.

Perf. 12x12½, 12½x12

1988, Jan. 27 **Litho.**

1303	A510	3af multicolored	.25	.25
1304	A511	5af multicolored	.35	.25
1305	A511	7af multi, vert.	.50	.25
1306	A512	9af multicolored	.70	.25
1307	A513	12af multicolored	1.25	.35
1308	A513a	15af multicolored	1.60	.35
1309	A514	24af multicolored	2.25	.35
		Nos. 1303-1309 (7)	6.90	2.05

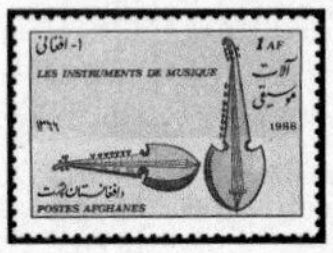

Traditional Musical Instruments A515

String and percussion instruments.

1988, Jan. 15 **Litho.** ***Perf. 12***

1310	A515	1af shown	.25	.25
1311	A515	3af drums	.25	.25
1312	A515	5af multi, diff.	.30	.25
1313	A515	15af multi, diff.	.70	.25
1314	A515	18af multi, diff.	1.00	.30
1315	A515	25af multi, diff.	1.40	.30
1316	A515	33af multi, diff.	1.90	.30
		Nos. 1310-1316 (7)	5.80	1.90

Admission of Afghanistan to the ITU and UPU, 60th Anniv. — A516

1988, Apr. 13 **Litho.** ***Perf. 12***

1317	A516	20af multicolored	.85	.50

Saur Revolution, 10th Anniv. — A517

1988, Apr. 23

1318	A517	10af multicolored	.50	.35

Fruit — A518

2af, Baskets, compote. 4af, Four baskets. 7af, Basket. 8af, Grapes, vert. 16af, Market. 22af, Market, diff. 25af, Vendor, vert.

1988, July 18 **Litho.** ***Perf. 12***

1319	A518	2af multicolored	.25	.25
1320	A518	4af multicolored	.35	.25
1321	A518	7af multicolored	.45	.25
1322	A518	8af multicolored	.50	.25
1323	A518	16af multicolored	.85	.35
1324	A518	22af multicolored	1.25	.35
1325	A518	25af multicolored	1.90	.35
		Nos. 1319-1325 (7)	5.55	2.05

Jawaharlal Nehru (1889-1964), 1st Prime Minister of Independent India — A519

1988, Nov. 14

1326	A519	40af multicolored	2.25	.85

Natl. Independence, 69th Anniv. — A520

1988, Aug. 1

1327	A520	24af multicolored	1.25	.70

Intl. Red Cross and Red Crescent Organizations, 125th Annivs. — A521

1988, Sept. 26

1328	A521	10af multicolored	.85	.50

Natl. Reconciliation Institute, 2nd Anniv. — A522

1989, Jan. 4

1329	A522	4af multicolored	.25	.25

Chess — A523

Boards, early matches and hand-made chessmen.

1989, Feb. 2 **Litho.** ***Perf. 12x12½***

1330	A523	2af Bishop	.25	.25
1331	A523	3af Queen	.35	.25
1332	A523	4af King (bust)	.45	.25
1333	A523	7af King, diff.	.70	.25
1334	A523	16af Knight	1.10	.25
1335	A523	24af Pawn	1.60	.35
1336	A523	45af Bishop, diff.	2.75	.45
		Nos. 1330-1336 (7)	7.20	2.05

Paintings by Picasso — A524

Designs: 4af, *The Old Jew.* 6af, *The Two Mountebanks. 8af, Portrait of Ambrouse Vollar. 22af, Woman of Majorca. 35af, Acrobat on the Ball. 75af, Usine a Horta de Ebro.*

1989, Feb. 13 **Litho.** ***Perf. 12½x12***

1341	A524	4af multicolored	.35	.25
1342	A524	6af multicolored	.45	.25
1343	A524	8af multicolored	.55	.25
1344	A524	22af multicolored	1.25	.25
1345	A524	35af multicolored	2.50	.25

Size: 71x90mm

Imperf

1346	A524	75af multicolored	4.75	1.25
		Nos. 1341-1346 (6)	9.85	2.50

Fauna — A525

3af, Allactaga euphratica. 4af, Equus hemionus. 14af, Felis lynx. 35af, Gypaetus barbatus. 44af, Capra falconeri.
100af, Naja oxiana.

1989, Feb. 20 **Litho.** ***Perf. 12½x12***

1347	A525	3af multicolored	.35	.25
1348	A525	4af multicolored	.35	.25
1349	A525	14af multicolored	1.00	.35
1350	A525	35af multicolored	3.75	1.60
1351	A525	44af multicolored	2.50	1.25

Size: 71x91mm

Imperf

1352	A525	100af multicolored	7.75	3.00
		Nos. 1347-1352 (6)	15.70	6.70

Intl. Women's Day — A526

1989, Mar. 8 ***Perf. 12½x12***

1353	A526	8af multicolored	.45	.25

Restoration and Development of San'a, Yemen — A527

1988, Dec. 27 **Litho.** ***Perf. 12***

1354	A527	32af multicolored	1.60	1.10

Agriculture Day — A528

1af, Cattle. 2af, Old and new plows. 3af, Field workers.

1989, Mar. 21

1355	A528	1af multicolored	.25	.25
1356	A528	2af multicolored	.25	.25
1357	A528	3af multicolored	.25	.25
		Nos. 1355-1357 (3)	.75	.75

World Meteorology Day — A529

32af, Emblems. 40af, Weather station, balloon, vert.

1989, Mar. 23

1358	A529	27af shown	1.25	.25
1359	A529	32af multicolored	1.75	.25
1360	A529	40af multicolored	2.25	.25
		Nos. 1358-1360 (3)	5.25	.75

Saur Revolution, 11th Anniv. — A530

1989, Apr. 27

1361	A530	20af multicolored	1.10	.25

Classic Automobiles A531

5af, 1910 Duchs, Germany. 10af, 1911 Ford, US. 20af, 1911 Renault, France. 25af, 1911, Russo-Balte, Russia. 30af, 1926 Fiat, Italy.

1989, Dec. 30 **Litho.** ***Perf. 12½x12***

1362	A531	5af multi	.45	.25
1363	A531	10af multi	.75	.25
1364	A531	20af multi	1.40	.25
1365	A531	25af multi	1.60	.35
1366	A531	30af multi	1.90	.35
		Nos. 1362-1366 (5)	6.10	1.45

Asia-Pacific Telecommunity, 10th Anniv. — A532

27af, Emblem, satellite dish.

1989, Aug. 3 ***Perf. 12***

1367	A532	3af shown	.25	.25
1368	A532	27af multicolored	1.10	.25

Teacher's Day — A533

1989, May 30 **Litho.** ***Perf. 12***

1369	A533	42af multicolored	2.25	.35

French Revolution, Bicent. — A534

1989, July **Litho.** ***Perf. 12***

1370	A534	25af multicolored	1.60	.95

Natl. Independence, 70th Anniv. — A535

1989, Aug. 18 **Litho.** ***Perf. 12***

1371	A535	25af multicolored	1.25	.35

A536

1989, Aug. 30

1372	A536	3af multicolored	.25	.25

Pashtos' and Baluchis' Day.

Birds — A537

3af, Platalea leucorodia. 5af, Porphyrio porhyrio. 10af, Botaurus stellaris, horiz. 15af, Pelecanus onocrotalus. 20af, Netta rufina. 25af, Cygnus olor. 30af, Phalacrocorax carbo, horiz.

1989, Dec. 5 **Litho.** ***Perf. 12***

1373	A537	3af multicolored	.25	.25
1374	A537	5af multicolored	.50	.25
1375	A537	10af multicolored	.95	.45
1376	A537	15af multicolored	1.25	.55
1377	A537	20af multicolored	1.60	.60
1378	A537	25af multicolored	2.25	.70
1379	A537	30af multicolored	2.50	.95
		Nos. 1373-1379 (7)	9.30	3.75

Tourism — A538

1af, Mosque. 2af, Minaret. 3af, Buzkashi, horiz. 4af, Jet over Hendo Kush, horiz.

1989, Dec.

1380	A538	1af multicolored	1.60	*3.25*
1381	A538	2af multicolored	3.25	*6.50*
1382	A538	3af multicolored	4.75	*9.50*
1383	A538	4af multicolored	6.50	*13.00*
		Nos. 1380-1383 (4)	16.10	*32.25*

Mavlavi Allahdad Balkhi, President of Post of the Afghanistan Postal Administration, has declared that "the stamps which have been printed after year 1989 are false stamps."

The following stamps have been condemned as unauthorized by the Afghan Ministry of Communications:

Dated 1996: *Mushrooms,* 6 stamps + souvenir sheet. *Bears,* 5 stamps + souvenir sheet. *1998 Word Soccer Cup Championships,* 6 stamps + souvenir sheet. *Silkworms,* 6 stamps + souvenir sheet. *Domestic Cats,* 6 stamps + souvenir sheet. *Horses,* 5 stamps + souvenir sheet. *Islamic Revolution,* 6 stamps. *Independence Anniv./Honoring Prophet Mohammed,* 2 stamps.

Dated 1997: *Tulips,* 6 stamps + souvenir sheet. *Llamas & Camels,* 6 stamps + souvenir sheet. *Domestic Cats,* 6 stamps + souvenir sheet. *Wildflowers,* 6 stamps + souvenir sheet. *Early Sailing Ships* (triangles), 6 stamps + souvenir sheet. *1998 Word Soccer Cup Championships,* 6 stamps + souvenir sheet. *Mushrooms,* 6 stamps + souvenir sheet.

Dated 1998: *Mushrooms,* 6 stamps + souvenir sheet. *Butterflies,* 6 stamps + souvenir sheet. *Princess Diana,* 9 stamps in a miniature sheet. *WWF (Wild Sheep),* strip of 4 stamps. *Wildlife,* 12 stamps. *Dogs,* 6 stamps + souvenir sheet. *Locomotives,* 6 stamps + souvenir sheet. *Prehistoric Animals,* 6 stamps + souvenir sheet. *Antique Cars,* 6 stamps + souvenir sheet. *Fish,* 6 stamps + souvenir sheet. *Birds,* 6 stamps + souvenir sheet.

Dated 1999: *Chess,* 6 stamps + souvenir sheet. *Mushrooms,* 6 stamps + souvenir sheet. *Locomotives,* 6 stamps + souvenir sheet. *Dogs,* 6 stamps + souvenir sheet. *Minerals,* 6 stamps + souvenir sheet. *Snails,* 6 stamps + souvenir sheet. *Vintage Race Cars,* 6 stamps + souvenir sheet. *China '99,* 12 stamps in a miniature sheet. *Cacti,* 6 stamps + souvenir sheet. *Horses,* 6 stamps + souvenir sheet. *Ferrari Automobiles,* 6 stamps + souvenir sheet. *Orchids,* 6 stamps + souvenir sheet. *Parrots,* 6 stamps + souvenir sheet. *Sailing Ships,* 6 stamps + souvenir sheet.

Dated 2000: *Cats,* 6 stamps + souvenir sheet. *WIPA 2000 (Birds),* 6 stamps + souvenir sheet.

Dated 2001: *Mushrooms,* 6 stamps + souvenir sheet. *Locomotives,* 6 stamps + souvenir sheet.

In addition to these sets, a number of bogus illegal issues have appeared. These issues include:

Beetles: miniature sheet of 9 different stamps.
Birds: 2 miniature sheets of 9 different stamps each.
Boats: 3 miniature sheets of 9 different stamps each.
Cars (Vintage): 3 miniature sheets of 9 different stamps each.
Cats: 3 miniature sheets of 9 different stamps each.
Chess: 3 miniature sheets of 9 different stamps each.
Dinosaurs: 3 miniature sheets of 9 different stamps each.
Dogs: 3 miniature sheets of 9 different stamps each.
Eagles & Owls: miniature sheet of 9 different stamps.
Eagles: miniature sheet of 9 different stamps.
Elvis Presley: 3 miniature sheets of 9 different stamps each.
Fauna of Afghanistan: miniature sheet of 9 different stamps.
Fish: miniature sheet of 9 different stamps.
Great People of the 20th Century: miniature sheet of 9 different stamps.
Horses: 2 miniature sheets of 9 different stamps each.
Korea/Japan World Soccer Cup: 2 souvenir sheets.
Locomotives: 2 souvenir sheets inscribed "Trains."
Locomotives: miniature sheet of 9 different stamps, inscribed "English Trains."
Marilyn Monroe: 3 miniature sheets of 9 different stamps each.
Marilyn Monroe: Block of 4 different stamps.
Mother Teresa & Pope John Paul II: 3 miniature sheets of 6 different stamps each + 3 souvenir sheets.
Osama Ben Laden Wanted Poster: 1 stamp in miniature sheet of 9.
Owls: 3 miniature sheets of 9 different stamps each + 2 souvenir sheets.
Paintings (Classic Posters): miniature sheet of 9 different stamps.
Paintings (Impressionists): 3 miniature sheets of 6 different stamps each + 3 souvenir sheets.
Plants: miniature sheet of 9 different stamps + souvenir sheet depicting orchid.
Princess Diana: miniature sheet of 9 different stamps.
Sports: 4 miniature sheets of 9 different stamps each, inscribed "Formula 2000."

Transitional Islamic State

Ahmed Shah Masood (1953?-2001), Military Leader — A539

2002 Litho. ***Perf. 13½x13***
1384 A539 14,000af multi *7.50 10.00*

National Understanding A540

2002, July 18 Litho. ***Perf. 13x13½***
1385 A540 11,000af multi *6.50 6.50*

Destruction of Bamyan Buddha Statue by Taliban Government — A541

2002, July 18 ***Perf. 13½x13***
1386 A541 25,000af multi *7.50 10.00*

On Oct. 8, 2002, a new currency was introduced. Old stamps not formerly authorized were issued and sold at face value without the zeros. The same was done with Nos. 1384-1386. Because there was no obliteration they can only be recognized with dated cancels.

Fourth Anniversary of the Islamic Revolution — A541a

2002 Litho. ***Perf. 12¾***
1386A A541a 800af multi *.75* —

No. 1386A was originally "issued" Dec. 20, 1996 but was not authorized for postal use until 2002. It was sold and valid for 8af.

Farmers' Day — A541b

2002 Litho. ***Perf. 12¾***
1386B A541b 1,500af multi *1.50* —

No. 1386B was originally "issued" Dec. 20, 1996 but was not authorized for postal use until 2002. It was sold and valid for 15af.

Mohammed's Birthday — A541c

2002 Litho. ***Perf. 12½x12¾***
1386C A541c 1,500af multi *1.50* —

No. 1386C was originally "issued" Dec. 26, 1996 but was not authorized for postal use until 2002. It was sold and valid for 15af.

77th Independence Day — A541d

2002 Litho. ***Perf. 12½x12¾***
1386D A541d 1,500af multi *.75* —

No. 1386D was originally "issued" Dec. 28, 1996 but was not authorized for postal use until 2002. It was sold and valid for 7af.

Universal Declaration of Human Rights, 55th Anniv. — A542

2002, Dec. 10 Litho. ***Perf. 13x12¾***
1387 A542 4af multi *3.50 3.50*

Farmer's Day — A543

Designs: 3af, Tractor. 6af, Oxen pulling plow.

2003, Mar. 21 Litho. ***Perf. 12¾x13***
1388 A543 3af shown *5.00* —
1389 A453 6af multi *10.00* —

Miniature Sheet

Orchids A544

No. 1390: a, 9af, Calanthe veitchii. b, 13af, Eulanthe sanderiana. c, 17af, Ordontioda vuylstekeae. d, 20af, Dendrobium infundibulum. e, 30af, Miltonsiopsis roezlii. f, 40af, Cattleya labiata. g, 100af, Vanda coerulea.

2003, Apr. 17 Litho. ***Perf. 13x12¾***
1390 A544 Sheet of 7, #a-g, + 2 labels *22.50 22.50*

No. 1390 exists in vertical (pictured) and horizontal formats. Value is the same.

Birthday of Mohammed A545

2003, May 14 Litho. ***Perf. 12¾x13***
1391 A545 10af multi *6.00 6.00*

World Tuberculosis Day — A546

Designs: 1af, Boy and girl holding sign. 4af, Caricatures of doctors and patients, horiz. 9af, Caricatures of patients, horiz.

Perf. 13x12¾, 12¾x13
2003, May 18 Litho.
1392-1394 A546 Set of 3 *6.00 6.00*

Loya Jurga — A547

2003, June 16 Litho. ***Perf. 12¾x13***
1395 A547 20af multi *4.00 4.00*

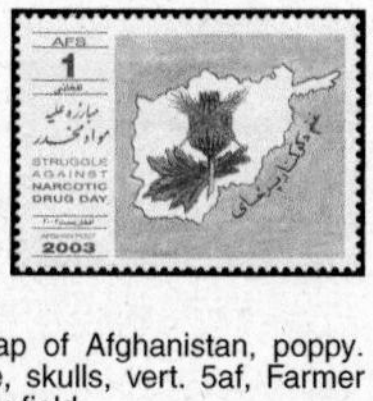

Day Against Narcotics A548

Designs: 1af, Map of Afghanistan, poppy. 2af, Poppy capsule, skulls, vert. 5af, Farmer and tractor in poppy field. 10af, Poppy capsule, skulls.

Perf. 12¾x13, 13x12¾

2003, June 25 **Litho.**
1396-1398 A548 Set of 3 *3.50 3.50*

Souvenir Sheet

1398A A548 10af multi 2.75 2.75

Dogs — A549

Designs: 10af, Rottweiler. 20af, Cocker spaniel. 30af, Doberman pinscher. 40af, Afghan hound. 50af, Giant schnauzer. 60af, Boxer.
150af, Afghan hound, diff.

2003, July 4 **Litho.** ***Perf. 13x12¾***
1399-1404 A549 Set of 6 *20.00* —

Souvenir Sheet

1405 A549 150af multi *14.50* —

Lighthouses — A550

Designs: 10af, Bird Island, South Africa. 20af, Cordouan, France. 30af, Mahota Pagoda, China. 50af, Bay Canh, Viet Nam. 60af, Cap Roman Rock, South Africa. 100af, Mikomoto Shima, Japan.
150af, Bell Rock, Great Britain.

2003, Aug. 5
1406-1411 A550 Set of 6 *22.50* —

Souvenir Sheet

1412 A550 150af multi *14.50* —

Independence, 84th Anniv. — A551

2003, Aug. 19 **Litho.** ***Perf. 12¾x13***
1413 A551 15af multi *3.50 3.50*

Intl. Literacy Day — A552

2003, Sept. 8 **Litho.** ***Perf. 12¾x13***
1414 A552 2af multi *1.00 1.00*

Miniature Sheet

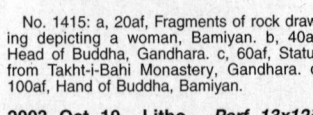

Heritage of Afghanistan — A553

No. 1415: a, 20af, Fragments of rock drawing depicting a woman, Bamiyan. b, 40af, Head of Buddha, Gandhara. c, 60af, Statue from Takht-i-Bahi Monastery, Gandhara. d, 100af, Hand of Buddha, Bamiyan.

2003, Oct. 10 **Litho.** ***Perf. 13x12¾***
1415 A553 Sheet of 4, #a-d *22.50* —

Revelation of the Koran to Mohammed A554

2003, Nov. 23 **Litho.** ***Perf. 12¾x13***
1416 A554 9af multi *6.50 6.50*

A555

Afghanistan Tourism Day—A555a

Designs: 8af, 25af, Fort. 12af, Bust, jar, historical artifacts.

2003, Dec. 16 **Litho.** ***Perf. 12¾x13***
1417 A555 4af shown *.75 .75*
1418 A555a 8af ol grn & multi *1.00 1.00*
1418A A555 12af multi *1.25 1.25*
Nos. 1417-1418A (3) *3.00 3.00*

Souvenir Sheet

1418B A555a 25af lil & multi *3.00 3.00*

Animals A556

Designs: 6af, Leopard. 11af, Jackal. 15af, Wild goat.
40af, Leopard facing left.

2003 **Litho.** ***Perf. 12¾***
1419-1421 A556 Set of 3 *5.00 5.00*

Souvenir Sheet

1422 A556 40af multi *8.25 8.25*

World Post Day — A557

2003, Oct. 9 **Litho.** ***Perf. 12¾x13***
1423 A557 8af multi *2.50 2.50*

Int'l. Women's Day — A558

2004 **Litho.** ***Perf. 12¾x13***
1424 A558 6af multi *1.50 1.50*

World Tuberculosis Day — A559

Designs: 1af, Woman, hands holding medicine and bloody tissue. 4af, Woman wearing mask, child. 9af, Eight men. 12af, Man, map of Afghanistan, vert. 15af, Doctor touching patient, people in white in background, vert.

Perf. 12¾x13, 13x12¾

2004, Mar. 23 **Litho.**
1425 A559 1af multi *.35 .35*
1426 A559 4af multi *.75 .75*
1427 A559 9af multi *1.50 1.50*
1428 A559 12af multi *2.00 2.00*
1429 A559 15af multi *2.50 2.50*
Nos. 1425-1429 (5) *7.10 7.10*

Pres. Hamid Karzai A560

Karzai and Map of Afghanistan A561

2004, Oct. 7 ***Perf. 13x12¾***
1430 A560 12af multi *3.00 3.00*
1431 A561 12af multi *5.00 5.00*

Oath of Pres. Karzai.

First Direct Presidential Election A562

Denominations: 15af, 25af.

2004, Oct. 9 **Litho.** ***Perf. 12¾x13***
1432-1433 A562 Set of 2 *7.00 7.00*

Two types of Arabic inscriptions exist on each stamp. Values the same.

Afghanistan postal officials declared a set of eight stamps depicting soccer players and a set of eight stamps depicting FIFA Presidents as "not authorized."

The editors are seeking more information about the status of a set of four Worldwide Fund for Nature stamps depicting the Himalayan musk deer.

Souvenir Sheet

Inauguration of Pres. Karzai — A563

2004, Dec. 7 **Litho.** ***Perf. 13½***
1434 A563 100af multi *18.00 18.00*

Diplomatic Relations Between Afghanistan and People's Republic of China, 50th Anniv. A564

2005, Jan. 20 **Litho.** ***Perf. 12***
1435 A564 25af multi *3.00 3.00*

Souvenir Sheet
Printed On Cloth
Without Gum
Perf. 13¼x13

1436 A564 150af multi *24.00 24.00*

No. 1436 contains one 60x40mm stamp.

Mine Clearance Campaign A565

Designs: 1af, Mine danger warning sign. 2af, Mine clearer with dog, vert. 3af, Mine clearer with metal detector, vert.

2006, Apr. 4 ***Perf. 13¼x13, 13x13¼***
1437-1439 A565 Set of 3 *2.00 2.00*

Independence, 87th Anniv. — A566

2006, Aug. 19 ***Perf. 13x13¼***
1440 A566 45af multi *8.00 8.00*

World Literacy Day — A567

2006, Sept. 8
1441 A567 12af multi *2.00 2.00*

World Post Day — A568

Color of "2006": No. 1442, 15af, Light green. No. 1443, 15af, Black.

2006, Sept. 9 ***Perf. 13¼x13***
1442-1443 A568 Set of 2 *4.50 4.50*

The length of the Arabic inscription on the top of the stamp is longer on No. 1442 than on No. 1443.

World Tourism Day — A569

Designs: 15af, Lamp, pitchers, bowl, building. 30af, Pitchers, cup, mountain.

2006, Sept. 27 **Litho.** ***Perf. 13¼x13***
1444 A569 15af multi *2.50 2.50*
1445 A569 30af multi *4.50 4.50*

Campaign for Elimination of Violence Against Women — A570

Designs: 12af, Woman behind barbed wire, chain, hands unlocking lock. 14af, Woman, roots. 19af, Eyes of woman, needle and thread closing eye hole of burqa, horiz.

Perf. 13x13¼, 13¼x13

2006, Nov. 25 **Litho.**
1446-1448 A570 Set of 3 *6.75 6.75*

Mevlana Jalal ad-Din ar-Rumi (1207-73), Islamic Philosopher A571

Designs: 65af, Birthplace at Balkh. 85af, Mevlana and whirling dervishes, vert.
150af, Mevlana, whirling dervishes, birthplace at Balkh, horiz.

Perf. 13¼x13, 13x13¼

2006, Nov. 26
1449-1450 A571 Set of 2 *15.00* —

Size: 106x78mm

Imperf

1451 A571 150af multi *30.00 30.00*

No. 1451 contains two perforated labels lacking country name or value. See Iran No. 2911, Syria No. 1574, Turkey No. 2971.

Successful Completion of Bonn Process — A572

2007, Apr. 19 *Perf. 13¼x13*
1452 A572 25af multi *4.00 4.00*

Dated 2006.

Mevlana Jalal ad-Din ar-Rumi (1207-73), Islamic Philosopher A573

2007, May 24
1453 A573 40af multi *6.00 6.00*

Milli Attan Dance — A574

2007, Aug. 19
1454 A574 38af multi *6.00 6.00*

Natl. Day of Fine Arts — A575

Singers: 20af, Ustad Awal Mir. 22af, Mirmun Parwin.

2007, Sept. 25 *Perf. 13x13¼*
1455-1456 A575 Set of 2 *7.50 7.50*

Third Meeting of Economic Cooperation Organization Postal Authorities, Tehran — A576

2007, Dec. 22 *Perf. 13¼x13*
1457 A576 8af multi *2.00 2.00*

National Unity — A577

Emperors: 25af, Ahmad Shah Baba (c. 1723-73). 30af, Mirwais Nika. 34af, Sultan Mahmood Ghaznawi (979-1030).

2007, Dec. 22 *Perf. 13x13¼*
1458-1460 A577 Set of 3 *12.00 12.00*

Red Crescent Society — A578

2009, Jan. 21 Litho. *Perf. 13x13¼*
1461 A578 17af multi *2.40 2.40*

Rudaki (c. 859-c.940), Poet — A579

2009, Jan. 21
1462 A579 55af multi *6.50 6.50*

World Enviornmental Protection Day — A580

2010, Jan. 1 Litho. *Perf. 13½x12¾*
1463 A580 5af multi 1.25 1.25

World Literacy Day — A581

2011, Jan. 1 Litho. *Perf. 14*
1464 A581 22af multi 4.00 4.00

Khwaja Abdullah Ansari (1006-88), Religious Commentator — A582

2012, Jan. 1 Litho. *Perf. 14*
1465 A582 50af multi — —

Dated 2009. See Iran No. 3016, Tajikistan No. 366.

Emblem and Flags of Members of South Asian Association for Regional Cooperation A583

2012, Feb. 1 Litho. *Perf. 13½x12¾*
1466 A583 40af multi 6.50 6.50

World Peace Day — A584

2012, Feb. 1 Litho. *Perf. 13½x12¾*
1467 A584 50af multi 6.50 6.50

Dated 2011.

SEMI-POSTAL STAMPS

Catalogue values for unused stamps in this section are for Never Hinged items.

No. 373 Surcharged in Violet

1952, July 12 Unwmk. *Perf. 12½*
B1 A122 40p + 30p cerise 5.25 3.00
B2 A122 125p + 30p cerise 7.75 3.50

1000th anniv. of the birth of Avicenna.

Children at Play — SP1

1955, July 3 Typo. *Perf. 11*
B3 SP1 35p + 15p dk green 1.25 .70
B4 SP1 125p + 25p purple 2.50 1.25

The surtax was for child welfare.
Exist imperf. Values, set: unused $6.50; used $7.

Amir Sher Ali Khan, Tiger Head Stamp and Zahir Shah — SP2

1955, July 2 Litho.
B5 SP2 35p + 15p carmine 1.00 .55
B6 SP2 125p + 25p pale vio bl 1.90 1.00

85th anniv. of the Afghan post.
Exist imperf. Values, set: unused $5; used $6.

Children at Play — SP3

1956, June 20 Typo.
B7 SP3 35p + 15p brt vio bl .90 .40
B8 SP3 140p + 15p dk org brn 2.25 .85

Issued for Children's Day. The surtax was for child welfare. No. B8 inscribed in French.
Exist imperf. Values, set: unused $8; used $8.75.

Pashtunistan Monument, Kabul — SP4

1956, Sept. 1 Litho.
B9 SP4 35p + 15p dp violet .40 .25
B10 SP4 140p + 15p dk brown 1.10 .75

"Free Pashtunistan" Day. The surtax aided the "Free Pashtunistan" movement.
No. B9 measures 30½x19½mm; No. B10, 29x19mm. On sale and valid for use only on Sept. 1-2.
Exist imperf. Values, set: unused $6; used $7.50.

Globe and Sun — SP5

1956, Oct. 24 *Perf. 11*
B11 SP5 35p + 15p ultra 1.00 .90
B12 SP5 140p + 15p red brown 1.90 1.60

Afghanistan's UN admission, 10th anniv.
Exist imperf. Values, set: unused $14; used $17.50.

Children on Seesaw — SP6

1957, June 20 Unwmk.
B13 SP6 35p + 15p brt rose .85 .55
B14 SP6 140p + 15p ultra 1.60 1.40

Children's Day. Surtax for child welfare.
Exist imperf. Values, set: unused $3.25; used $4.

UN Headquarters and Emblems — SP7

1957, Oct. 24 *Perf. 11 Rough*
B15 SP7 35p + 15p red brown .60 .40
B16 SP7 140p + 15p lt ultra 1.10 1.10

United Nations Day.
Exist imperf. Values, set: unused $6; used $7.50.

Swimming Pool and Children — SP8

1958, June 22 *Perf. 11*
B17 SP8 35p + 15p rose .65 .40
B18 SP8 140p + 15p dl red brn .80 .65

Children's Day. Surtax for child welfare.
Exist imperf. Values, set: unused $5; used $6.

Pashtunistan Flag — SP9

1958, Aug. 31
B19 SP9 35p + 15p lt blue .40 .25
B20 SP9 140p + 15p red brown 1.00 .65

Issued for "Free Pashtunistan Day."
Exist imperf. Values, set: unused $4; used $5.

Children Playing Tug of War — SP10

1959, June 23 Litho. *Perf. 11*
B21 SP10 35p + 15p brown vio .60 .35
B22 SP10 165p + 15p brt pink 1.25 .50

Children's Day. Surtax for child welfare.
Exist imperf. Value set, unused or used, $5.

Pathans in Tribal Dance — SP11

Perf. 11 Rough

1959, Sept. Unwmk.
B23 SP11 35p + 15p green .60 .35
B24 SP11 165p + 15p orange 1.25 .75

Issued for "Free Pashtunistan Day."
Exist imperf. Value set, unused or used, $2.50.

Afghan Cavalryman with UN Flag — SP12

1959, Oct. 24 *Perf. 11 Rough*
B25 SP12 35p + 15p orange .35 .25
B26 SP12 165p + 15p lt bl grn .75 .45

Issued for United Nations Day.
Exist imperf. Value set, unused or used, $2.50.

Children — SP13

1960, Oct. 23 **Litho.**

B27 SP13 75p + 25p lt ultra .90 .35
B28 SP13 175p + 25p lt green 1.75 .50

Children's Day. Surtax for child welfare.
Exist imperf. Value set, unused or used, $2.75.

Man with Spray Gun — SP14

1960, Sept. 6 ***Perf. 11 Rough***

B29 SP14 50p + 50p orange 1.40 1.25
B30 SP14 175p + 50p red brown 3.50 2.75

11th anniversary of the WHO malaria control program in Afghanistan.
Exist imperf. Value set, unused or used, $7.50.

SP15

1960, Sept. 1 **Unwmk.**

B31 SP15 50p + 50p rose .60 .30
B32 SP15 175p + 50p dk blue 1.40 1.10

Issued for "Free Pashtunistan Day."
Exist imperf. Value set, unused or used, $3.25.

Ambulance SP16

1960, Oct. 16 ***Perf. 11***

Crescent in Red

B33 SP16 50p + 50p violet .65 .50
B34 SP16 175p + 50p blue 1.75 1.00

Issued for the Red Crescent Society.
Exist imperf. Value set, unused or used, $3.25.

Nos. 470-471 Surcharged in Blue or Orange

1960, Dec. 31 **Litho.** ***Perf. 11***

B35 A166 50p + 25p dp org (Bl) 1.75 1.75
B36 A166 165p + 25p blue (O) 1.75 1.75

Exist imperf. Value set, unused or used, $11.
The souvenir sheets described after No. 471 were surcharged in carmine "+25 Ps" on each stamp. Values: normal colors, unused $6, used $6.50; reversed colors, unused $7.50, used $9.50.
See general note after No. 485.

Nos. 496-500 Surcharged

Perf. 13½x14

1961, July 6 **Unwmk.** **Photo.**

B37 A175 2p + 25p green & rose lil .50 .50
B38 A175 2p + 25p brown & cit .50 .50
B39 A175 5p + 25p gray & rose .50 .50
B40 A175 10p + 25p blue & bis .50 .50
B41 A175 15p + 25p sl bl & dl lil .50 .50
Nos. B37-B41 (5) 2.50 2.50

UNICEF. The same surcharge was applied to an imperf. souvenir sheet like that noted after No. 505. Value $5.

Nos. 522-526 Surcharged "+25PS" and Crescent in Red

1961, Oct. 16 ***Perf. 13½x14***

B42 A184 2p + 25p black .50 .50
B43 A184 2p + 25p green .50 .50
B44 A184 5p + 25p lilac rose .50 .50
B45 A184 10p + 25p lilac .50 .50
B46 A184 15p + 25p dk blue .50 .50
Nos. B42-B46 (5) 2.50 2.50

Issued for the Red Crescent Society.

Nos. 539-543 Surcharged in Red: "UNESCO + 25PS"

1962 ***Perf. 12***

B47 A186 2p + 25p multi .40 .40
B48 A186 2p + 25p multi .40 .40
B49 A186 5p + 25p multi .40 .40
B50 A186 10p + 25p multi .40 .40
B51 A186 15p + 25p multi .40 .40
Nos. B47-B51 (5) 2.00 2.00

UNESCO. The same surcharge was applied to the souvenir sheets mentioned after No. 548. Value, 2 sheets, $10.

Nos. 553-561 Surcharged: "Dag Hammarskjöld +20PS"

1962, Sept. 17 ***Perf. 14x13½***

B52 A187 2p + 20p .25 .25
B53 A187 2p + 20p .25 .25
B54 A187 5p + 20p .25 .25
B55 A187 10p + 20p .25 .25
B56 A187 15p + 20p .25 .25
B57 A187 25p + 20p .25 .25
B58 A187 50p + 20p .30 .30
B59 A187 75p + 20p .50 .50
B60 A187 100p + 20p .80 .80
Nos. B52-B60 (9) 3.10 3.10

In memory of Dag Hammarskjold, Sec. Gen. of the UN, 1953-61. Perf. and imperf. souvenir sheets exist. Value, 2 sheets, $6.50.

Nos. 583-593 Surcharged "+15PS"

1963, Mar. 15 ***Perf. 14x13½***

B61 A193 2p + 15p 1.00 1.00
B62 A193 2p + 15p 1.00 1.00
B63 A193 5p + 15p 1.00 1.00
B64 A193 10p + 15p 1.00 1.00
B65 A193 15p + 15p 1.00 1.00
B66 A193 25p + 15p 1.00 1.00
B67 A193 50p + 15p 1.00 1.00
B68 A193 75p + 15p 1.00 1.00
B69 A193 100p + 15p 1.00 1.00
B70 A193 150p + 15p 1.00 1.00
B71 A193 175p + 15p 1.00 1.00
Nos. B61-B71 (11) 11.00 11.00

WHO drive to eradicate malaria.

Nos. 672-672G, 672I Surcharged in Various Positions

1964, Mar. 9

B71A A213g 2p + 50p .25 .25
B71B A213g 3p + 50p .25 .25
B71C A213g 4p + 50p .25 .25
B71D A213g 5p + 50p .25 .25
B71E A213g 10p + 50p .25 .25
B71F A213g 100p + 50p .70 .70
B71G A213g 2af + 50p 1.50 1.50
B71H A213g 3af + 50p 2.10 2.10
Nos. B71A-B71H (8) 5.55 5.55

Souvenir Sheet

B71J A213g 5af + 50p 4.50 4.50

Nos. B71E-B71G are airmail semi-postals.

Blood Transfusion Kit — SP17

1964, Oct. 18 **Litho.** ***Perf. 10½***

B72 SP17 1af + 50p black & rose .40 .30

Issued for the Red Crescent Society and Red Crescent Week, Oct. 18-24.

First Aid Station — SP18

1965, Oct. 16 **Photo.** ***Perf. 13½x14***

B73 SP18 1.50af + 50p multi .35 .25

Issued for the Red Crescent Society.

Children Playing — SP19

1966, Nov. 28 **Photo.** ***Perf. 13½x14***

B74 SP19 1af + 1af yel grn & cl .30 .25
B75 SP19 3af + 2af yel & brn .65 .25
B76 SP19 7af + 3af rose lil & grn .95 .50
Nos. B74-B76 (3) 1.90 1.00

Children's Day.

Nadir Shah Presenting Society Charter — SP20

1967, Feb. 15 **Photo.** ***Perf. 13x14***

B77 SP20 2af + 1af red & dk grn .35 .25
B78 SP20 5af + 1af lil rose & brn .75 .35

Issued for the Red Crescent Society.

Vaccination — SP21

1967, June 6 **Photo.** ***Perf. 12***

B79 SP21 2af + 1af yellow & blk .25 .25
B80 SP21 5af + 2af pink & brn .65 .35

The surtax was for anti-tuberculosis work.

Red Crescent — SP22

1967, Oct. 18 **Photo.** ***Perf. 12***

Crescent in Red

B81 SP22 3af + 1af gray ol & blk .25 .25
B82 SP22 5af + 1af dl bl & blk .40 .25

Issued for the Red Crescent Society.

Queen Humeira — SP23

1968, June 14 **Photo.** ***Perf. 12***

B83 SP23 2af + 2af red brown .35 .25
B84 SP23 7af + 2af dull green .90 .60

Issued for Mother's Day.

Red Crescent — SP24

1968, Oct. 16 **Photo.** ***Perf. 12***

B85 SP24 4af + 1af yel, blk & red .60 .25

Issued for the Red Crescent Society.

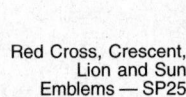

Red Cross, Crescent, Lion and Sun Emblems — SP25

1969, May 5 **Litho.** ***Perf. 14x13½***

B86 SP25 3af + 1af multicolored .65 .35
B87 SP25 5af + 1af multicolored .80 .35

League of Red Cross Societies, 50th anniv.

Mother and Child — SP26

1969, June 14 **Photo.** ***Perf. 12***

B88 SP26 1af + 1af yel org & brn .30 .25
B89 SP26 4af + 1af rose lil & pur .50 .35
a. Souvenir sheet of 2 2.50 2.50

Mother's Day. No. B89a contains 2 imperf. stamps similar to Nos. B88-B89. Sold for 10af.

Red Crescent — SP27

1969, Oct. 16 **Photo.** ***Perf. 12***

B90 SP27 6af + 1af multi .80 .30

Issued for the Red Crescent Society.

UN and FAO Emblems, Farmer — SP28

1973, May 24 **Photo.** ***Perf. 13½***

B91 SP28 14af + 7af grnsh bl & lil 1.40 .90

World Food Program, 10th anniversary.

Dome of the Rock, Jerusalem — SP29

1977, Sept. 11 **Photo.** ***Perf. 14***

B92 SP29 12af + 3af multi 2.10 .60

Surtax for Palestinian families and soldiers.

15 Cent. (lunar) of Islamic Pilgrimage (Hegira) SP30

1981, Jan. 17 **Litho.** ***Perf. 12½x12***

B93 SP30 13af + 2af multi 1.75 .30

Red Crescent Aid Programs — SP31

1981, May 8 ***Perf. 12x12½***

B94 SP31 1af + 4af multi .65 .80

Intl. Year of the Disabled — SP32

1981, Oct. 12 *Perf. 12x12½*

B95 SP32 6af + 1af multi .90 .50

AIR POST STAMPS

Plane over Kabul — AP1

Perf. 12, 12x11, 11

1939, Oct. 1 Typo. Unwmk.

C1 AP1 5af orange 5.00 4.00
a. Imperf., pair ('47) 29.00 29.00
b. Horiz. pair, imperf. vert. 32.50 32.50
C2 AP1 10af blue 5.00 4.00
a. 10af lt bl 8.00 6.00
b. Imperf., pair ('47) 29.00
c. Horiz. pair, imperf. vert. 32.50
C3 AP1 20af emerald 10.00 6.00
a. Imperf., pair ('47) 29.00
b. Horiz. pair, imperf. vert. 32.50
c. Vert. pair, imperf. horiz. 35.00
Nos. C1-C3 (3) 20.00 14.00

These stamps come with clean-cut or rough perforations.

Exist imperf. Value, set $30.

Counterfeits exist.

Catalogue values for unused stamps in this section, from this point to the end of the section, are for Never Hinged items.

1948, June 14 *Perf. 12x11½*

C4 AP1 5af emerald 20.00 20.00
C5 AP1 10af red orange 20.00 20.00
C6 AP1 20af blue 20.00 20.00
Nos. C4-C6 (3) 60.00 60.00

Imperforates exist.

Forgeries exist.

Plane over Palace Grounds, Kabul — AP2

Imprint: "Waterlow & Sons, Limited, London"

1951-54 Engr. *Perf. 13½*

C7 AP2 5af henna brn 3.00 .60
C8 AP2 5af dp grn ('54) 1.60 .40
C9 AP2 10af gray 6.50 1.60
C10 AP2 20af dark blue 9.00 2.50

1957

C11 AP2 5af ultra 1.75 .50
C12 AP2 10af dark vio 2.50 .90
Nos. C7-C12 (6) 24.35 6.50

See No. C38.

Ariana Plane over Hindu Kush — AP3

Perf. 11, Imperf.

1960-63 Litho. Unwmk.

C13 AP3 75p light vio .55 .25
C14 AP3 125p blue .75 .35

Perf. 10½, 11

C14A AP3 5af citron ('63) 1.25 .80
Nos. C13-C14A (3) 2.55 1.40

Imperf examples of Nos. C13-C14 are valued at approx. 50 percent more than the values shown.

Girl Scout — AP4

1962, Aug. 30 Photo. *Perf. 11½x12*

C15 AP4 100p ocher & brn .50 .50
C16 AP4 175p brt yel grn & brn .90 .90

Women's Day. See Nos. 578-579 and note on souvenir sheet.

Sports Type of Regular Issue, 1962

25p, 50p, Horse racing. 75p, 100p, Wrestling. 150p, Weight lifting. 175p, Soccer.

1962, Sept. 25 Unwmk. *Perf. 12*
Black Inscriptions

C17 A195 25p rose & red brn .25 .25
C18 A195 50p gray & red brn .30 .30
C19 A195 75p pale vio & dk grn .50 .50
C20 A195 100p gray ol & dk pur .65 .65
C21 A195 150p rose lil & grn .90 .90
C22 A195 175p sal & brn 1.00 1.00
Nos. C17-C22 (6) 3.60 3.60

Children's Day Type of Regular Issue

Perf. 11½x12, 12x11½

1962, Oct. 14 Unwmk.

C23 A196 75p Runners .60 .60
C24 A196 150p Peaches 1.10 1.10
C25 A196 200p Iris, vert. 1.50 1.50
Nos. C23-C25 (3) 3.20 3.20

A souvenir sheet contains one each of Nos. C23-C25. Value $4.00.

Red Crescent Type of Regular Issue

1962, Oct. 16 *Perf. 12*
Fruit and Flowers in Natural Colors; Carmine Crescent

C26 A197 25p Grapes .25 .25
C27 A197 50p Pears .30 .30
C28 A197 100p Wistaria .65 .65
Nos. C26-C28 (3) 1.20 1.20

Two souvenir sheets exist. One contains a 150p gray brown stamp in blossom design, the other a 200p gray stamp in wistaria design, imperf. Value, each $5.00.

UN Type of Regular Issue

1962, Oct. 24 Photo.
Flags in Original Colors, Black Inscriptions

C29 A198 75p blue .30 .30
C30 A198 100p lt brn .45 .45
C31 A198 125p brt grn .60 .60
Nos. C29-C31 (3) 1.35 1.35

Boy Scout Type of Regular Issue

1962, Oct. 25 Unwmk. *Perf. 12*

C32 A199 25p gray, blk, dl grn & sal .30 .30
C33 A199 50p grn, brn & sal .55 .55
C34 A199 75p bl grn, red brn & sal .80 .80
C35 A199 100p bl, slate & sal 1.00 1.00
Nos. C32-C35 (4) 2.65 2.65

Teacher's Day Type of Regular Issue

1962, Oct. 25

C36 A200 100p Pole vault .60 .60
C37 A200 150p High jump .90 .90

A souvenir sheet contains one 250p pink and slate green stamp in design of 150p. Values: perf $2.50; imperf $21.

Type of 1951-54
Imprint: "Thomas De La Rue & Co. Ltd."

1962 Engr. *Perf. 13½*

C38 AP2 5af ultra 12.00 .90

Agriculture Types of Regular Issue
Unwmk.

1963, Mar. 1 Photo. *Perf. 12*

C42 A204 100p dk car, grn & brn .35 .35
C43 A203 150p ocher & blk .60 .60
C44 A204 200p ultra, grn & brn .90 .90
Nos. C42-C44 (3) 1.85 1.85

Hands Holding Wheat Emblem — AP5

1963, Mar. 27 Photo. *Perf. 14*

C45 AP5 500p lil, lt brn & brn 1.10 1.10

FAO "Freedom from Hunger" campaign.

Two souvenir sheets exist. One contains a 1000p blue green, light brown and brown, type AP5, imperf. The other contains a 200p brown and green and 300p ultramarine, yellow and ocher in rice and corn designs, type A205. Values $5.50 and $4.

Meteorological Day Type of Regular Issue

Designs: 100p, 500p, Meteorological measuring instrument. 200p, 400p, Weather station. 300p, Rockets in space.

1963, May 23 *Imperf.*

C46 A206 100p brn & bl 3.00 3.00

Perf. 13½x14

C47 A206 200p brt grn & lil .90 .90
C48 A206 300p dk bl & rose 1.40 1.20
C49 A206 400p bl & dl red brn 1.90 1.75
C50 A206 500p car rose & gray grn 2.25 2.00
Nos. C47-C50 (4) 6.45 5.85

Nos. C47 and C50 printed se-tenant.

Nos. C47 and C50 exist imperf. Values, unused or used: 200p, $6; 500p, $16.

Two souvenir sheets exist. One contains a 125p red and brown stamp in rocket design. The other contains a 100p blue and dull red brown in "rockets in space" design. Values $4.50 and $11.

Kabul International Airport — AP8

Perf. 12x11½

1964, Apr. Unwmk. Photo.

C57 AP8 10af red lil & grn .75 .25
C58 AP8 20af dk grn & red lil .90 .35
a. Perf. 12 ('68) 5.00 3.00
C59 AP8 50af dk bl & grnsh bl 2.50 1.00
a. Perf. 12 ('68) 8.00 5.00
Nos. C57-C59 (3) 4.15 1.60

Inauguration of Kabul Airport Terminal.

Nos. C58a-C59a are 36mm wide. Nos. C58-C59 are 35½mm wide.

Zahir Shah and Kabul Airport AP9

100af, Zahir Shah and Ariana Plane.

1971 Photo. *Perf. 12½x13½*

C60 AP9 50af multi 4.00 4.00
C61 AP9 100af blk, red & grn 5.00 3.00

Remainders of No. C60 were used, summer in 1978, with king's portrait torn or cut off.

REGISTRATION STAMPS

R1

Dated "1309"
Pelure Paper

1891 Unwmk. Litho. *Imperf.*

F1 R1 1r slate blue 2.40
a. Tete beche pair 13.50

Genuinely used examples of No. F1 are rare. Counterfeit cancellations exist.

R2

Dated "1311"

1893 Thin Wove Paper

F2 R2 1r black, *green* 2.00

Genuinely used examples of No. F2 are rare. Counterfeit cancellations exist.

R3

1894 Undated

F3 R3 2ab black, *green* 9.50 *11.00*

12 varieties. See note below Nos. 189-190.

R4

1898-1900 Undated

F4 R4 2ab black, *deep rose* 4.50 4.50
F5 R4 2ab black, *lilac rose* 6.50 5.00
F6 R4 2ab black, *magenta* 8.00 5.00
F7 R4 2ab black, *salmon* 4.50 4.50
F8 R4 2ab black, *orange* 4.50 4.50
F9 R4 2ab black, *yellow* 4.50 3.50
F10 R4 2ab black, *green* 4.50 3.50
Nos. F4-F10 (7) 37.00 30.50

Many shades of paper.

Nos. F4-F10 come in two sizes, measured between outer frame lines: 52x36mm, 1st printing; 46x33mm, 2nd printing. The outer frame line (not pictured) is 3-6mm from inner frame line.

Used on P.O. receipts.

OFFICIAL STAMPS

Coat of Arms — O1

1909 Unwmk. Typo. *Perf. 12*
Wove Paper

O1 O1 red 1.25 1.25
a. Carmine ('19?) 2.50 6.50

Later printings of No. O1 in scarlet, vermilion, claret, etc., on various types of paper, were issued until 1927.

Coat of Arms — O2

1939-68? Typo. *Perf. 11, 12*

O3 O2 15p emerald 1.10 .80
O4 O2 30p ocher ('40) 1.50 1.50
O5 O2 45p dark carmine 1.25 1.25

O6	O2 50p brt car ('68)	.70	.70
a.	50p carmine rose ('55)	1.25	.70
O7	O2 1af brt red violet	2.00	1.75
	Nos. O3-O7 (5)	6.55	6.00

Size of 50p, 24x31mm, others 22½x28mm.

Catalogue values for unused stamps in this section, from this point to the end of the section, are for Never Hinged items.

1964-65 Litho. *Perf. 11*

O8	O2 50p rose	.90	.90
a.	50p salmon ('65)	2.00	2.00

Stamps of this type are revenues.

PARCEL POST STAMPS

Coat of Arms — PP1

PP2

PP3

PP4

1909 Unwmk. Typo. *Perf. 12*

Q1	PP1 3sh bister	1.25	*2.25*
a.	Imperf., pair	—	
Q2	PP2 1kr olive gray	3.50	*3.50*
a.	Imperf., pair	—	
Q3	PP3 1r orange	3.25	3.25
Q4	PP3 1r olive green	24.00	4.50
Q5	PP4 2r red	4.00	4.00
	Nos. Q1-Q5 (5)	36.00	17.50

Type I

Type II

A 1909 undenominated dull olive green Official parcel post stamp exists with two types. Type I has thinner and more rays below the crest; Type II has fewer and wider rays. Values: *$450* each. A pair, imperf between, exists. Value, $1,500. A complete sheet of two is known perforated on all sides.

1916-18

Q6	PP1 3sh green	1.75	*3.50*
Q7	PP2 1kr pale red	3.00	1.50
a.	1kr rose red ('18)	4.00	4.00
Q8	PP3 1r brown org	3.50	1.75
a.	1r deep brown ('18)	12.00	3.00
Q9	PP4 2r blue	6.25	*6.50*
	Nos. Q6-Q9 (4)	14.50	*13.25*

Nos. Q1-Q9 sometimes show letters of the papermaker's watermark "HOWARD & JONES LONDON."

Ungummed stamps are remainders. They sell for one-third the price of mint stamps.

Old Habibia College, Near Kabul PP5

1921 Wove Paper

Q10	PP5 10pa chocolate	5.00	5.75
a.	Tete beche pair	22.50	22.50
Q11	PP5 15pa light brn	7.00	7.50
a.	Tete beche pair	27.50	27.50
Q12	PP5 30pa red violet	12.50	7.50
a.	Tete beche pair	40.00	40.00
b.	Laid paper	*15.00*	*15.00*
Q13	PP5 1r brt blue	14.00	14.00
a.	Tete beche pair	65.00	65.00
	Nos. Q10-Q13 (4)	38.50	34.75

Stamps of this issue are usually perforated on one or two sides only.

The laid paper of No. Q12b has a papermaker's watermark in the sheet.

Handstamped in black on Nos. Q10-Q13

PP5a

1923, Feb. 26

Q13B	PP5a 10pa chocolate	—	—
Q13C	PP5a 15pa light brn	—	—
Q13D	PP5a 30pa red violet	—	—
Q13E	PP5a 1r brt blue		

5th Independence Day.

Two types of handstamp exist.

Forgeries exist.

The existence of No. Q13E has been questioned. The editors are seeking information on this stamp.

PP6

1924-26 Wove Paper

Q15	PP6 5kr ultra ('26)	*400.00*	*400.00*
Q16	PP6 5r lilac	20.00	25.00

A 15r rose exists, but is not known to have been placed in use. Value, unused $400.

PP7

PP8

1928-29 *Perf. 11, 11 Horizontally*

Q17	PP7 2r yellow orange	8.00	7.00
Q18	PP7 2r green ('29)	7.50	7.50
Q19	PP8 3r deep green	10.50	10.50
Q20	PP8 3r brown ('29)	9.50	10.50
	Nos. Q17-Q20 (4)	35.50	35.50

A 3r violet imperforate stamp in design No. PP8 exists and is likely a proof. Value, *$250.*

POSTAL TAX STAMPS

Aliabad Hospital near Kabul — PT1

Pierre and Marie Curie — PT2

Perf. 12x11½, 12

1938, Dec. 22 Typo. Unwmk.

RA1	PT1 10p peacock grn	3.25	*5.00*
RA2	PT2 15p dull blue	3.25	*5.00*

Obligatory on all mail Dec. 22-28, 1938. The money was used for the Aliabad Hospital. See note with CD80.

Catalogue values for unused stamps in this section, from this point to the end of the section, are for Never Hinged items.

PT3

Begging Child — PT4

1949, May 28 Typo. *Perf. 12*

RA3	PT3 35p red orange	3.25	2.10
RA4	PT4 125p ultra	4.00	2.10

United Nations Children's Day, May 28.

Obligatory on all foreign mail on that date. Proceeds were used for child welfare.

Paghman Arch and UN Emblem — PT5

1949, Oct. 24

RA5	PT5 125p dk blue green	15.00	9.00

4th anniv. of the UN. Valid one day only. Issued in sheets of 9 (3x3).

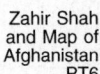

Zahir Shah and Map of Afghanistan PT6

1950, Mar. 30 Typo.

RA6	PT6 125p blue green	4.50	1.50

Return of Zahir Shah from a trip to Europe for his health. Valid for two weeks. The tax was used for public health purposes.

Hazara Youth — PT7

1950, May 28 Typo. *Perf. 11½*

RA7	PT7 125p dk blue green	4.50	2.50

Tax for Child Welfare. Obligatory and valid only on May 28, 1950, on foreign mail.

Ruins of Qalai Bist and Globe PT8

1950, Oct. 24

RA8	PT8 1.25af ultramarine	9.00	5.25

5th anniv. of the UN. Proceeds went to Afghanistan's UN Projects Committee.

Zahir Shah and Medical Center — PT9

1950, Dec. 22 Typo. *Perf. 11½*

Size: 38x25mm

RA9	PT9 35p carmine	1.25	.60

Size: 46x30mm

RA10	PT9 1.25af black	7.50	2.50

The tax was for the national Graduate School of Medicine.

Koochi Girl with Lamb — PT10

Kohistani Boy and Sheep — PT11

1951, May 28

RA11 PT10 35p emerald 1.50 .90
RA12 PT11 1.25af ultramarine 1.50 .90

The tax was for Child Welfare.

Distributing Gifts to Children PT12

Qandahari Boys Dancing the "Attan" PT13

1952, May 28 **Litho.**

RA13 PT12 35p chocolate .80 .65
RA14 PT13 125p violet 1.60 .95

The tax was for Child Welfare.
Exist imperf. Values, set: unused $6; used $9.50.

Soldier Receiving First Aid — PT14

1952, Oct. 19

RA15 PT14 10p light green .80 .65

Exist imperf. Value: unused $2.50; used $4.

Stretcher-bearers and Wounded — PT15

Soldier Assisting Wounded PT16

1953, Oct.

RA16 PT15 10p yel grn & org red .80 .80
RA17 PT16 10p vio brn & org red .80 .80

Exist imperf. Values, set: unused $4; used $5.

Prince Mohammed Nadir — PT17

1953, May 28

RA18 PT17 35p orange yellow .50 .25
RA19 PT17 125p chalky blue .90 .55

No. RA19 is inscribed in French "Children's Day." The tax was for child welfare.
Exist imperf. Values, set: unused $4; used $5.

Map and Young Musicians PT18

1954, May 28 **Unwmk.** ***Perf. 11***

RA20 PT18 35p purple .65 .40
RA21 PT18 125p ultra 1.90 1.25

No. RA21 is inscribed in French. The tax was for child welfare.
Exist imperf. Values, set: unused $4.50; used $6.50.

PT19

1954, Oct. 17 ***Perf. 11½***

RA22 PT19 20p blue & red .75 .35

Exists imperf. Values: unused $2; used $2.50.

Red Crescent — PT20

1955, Oct. 18 ***Perf. 11***

RA23 PT20 20p dull grn & car .70 .35

Exists imperf. Values: unused $1.50; used $2.

Zahir Shah and Red Crescent — PT21

1956, Oct. 18

RA24 PT21 20p lt grn & rose car .40 .25

Exists imperf. Value, unused or used, $1.25.

Red Crescent Headquarters, Kabul — PT22

1957, Oct. 17

RA25 PT22 20p lt ultra & car .90 .60

Exists imperf. Values: unused $2; used $2.50.

Map and Crescent — PT23

1958, Oct. **Unwmk.** ***Perf. 11***

RA26 PT23 25p yel grn & red .40 .30

Exists imperf. Values: unused 50¢; used 80¢.

PT24

1959, Oct. 17 **Litho.** ***Perf. 11***

RA27 PT24 25p lt violet & red .40 .25

The tax on Nos. RA15-RA17, RA22-RA27 was for the Red Crescent Society. Use of these stamps was required for one week.
Exists imperf. Values: unused 50¢; used 80¢.

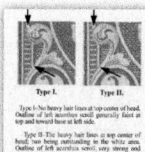

AGÜERA, LA

ä-gwä'rä

LOCATION — An administrative district in southern Rio de Oro on the northwest coast of Africa.

GOVT. — Spanish possession

AREA — Because of indefinite political boundaries, figures for area and population are not available.

100 Centimos = 1 Peseta

Type of 1920 Issue of Rio de Oro Overprinted

1920, June Typo. Unwmk. *Perf. 13*

1	A8	1c blue green	2.75	*3.25*
2	A8	2c olive brown	2.75	*3.25*
3	A8	5c deep green	2.75	*3.25*
4	A8	10c light red	2.75	*3.25*
5	A8	15c yellow	2.75	*3.25*
6	A8	20c lilac	2.75	*3.25*
7	A8	25c deep blue	2.75	*3.25*
8	A8	30c dark brown	2.75	*3.25*
9	A8	40c pink	2.75	*3.25*
10	A8	50c bright blue	9.00	*10.00*
11	A8	1p red brown	15.00	*20.00*
12	A8	4p dark violet	42.50	*50.00*
13	A8	10p orange	90.00	*115.00*
		Nos. 1-13 (13)	181.25	224.25
		Set, never hinged	400.00	

Very fine examples of Nos. 1-13 will be somewhat off center. Well-centered examples are uncommon and will sell for more.

King Alfonso XIII — A2

1922, June

14	A2	1c turquoise bl (I)	1.00	*1.50*
15	A2	2c dark green	1.50	*1.50*
16	A2	5c blue green	1.50	*1.50*
17	A2	10c red	1.50	*1.50*
18	A2	15c red brown	1.50	*1.50*
19	A2	20c yellow	1.50	*1.50*
20	A2	25c deep blue	1.50	*1.50*
21	A2	30c dark brown	1.50	*1.50*
22	A2	40c rose red	1.75	*2.00*
23	A2	50c red violet	6.25	*5.75*
24	A2	1p rose	14.50	*15.00*
25	A2	4p violet	37.50	*40.00*
26	A2	10p orange	55.00	*60.00*
		Nos. 14-26 (13)	126.50	134.75
		Set, never hinged	200.00	

Nos. 1-26 with A.000.000 on reverse are specimens. For detailed listings, see the Scott Classic Specialized catalog.

For later issues, see Spanish Sahara.

AITUTAKI

ˌīt-ə-'täk-ē

LOCATION — One of the larger Cook Islands, in the South Pacific Ocean northeast of New Zealand

GOVT. — A dependency of New Zealand

AREA — 7 sq. mi.

POP. — 2,335 (1981)

The Cook Islands were attached to New Zealand in 1901. Stamps of Cook Islands were used in 1892-1903 and 1932-72.

Aitutaki acquired its own postal service in August 1972, though remaining part of Cook Islands.

12 Pence = 1 Shilling

100 Cents = 1 Dollar (1972)

Catalogue values for unused stamps in this country are for Never Hinged items, beginning with Scott 37.

Watermark

Wmk. 61- Single-lined NZ and Star Close Together

Stamps of New Zealand Surcharged in Red or Blue

a

b

c

d

e

f

1903 Engr. Wmk. 61 *Perf. 14*

1	A18(a)	½p green (R)	5.00	*7.00*
2	A35(b)	1p rose (Bl)	5.50	*6.25*

Perf. 11

3	A22(c)	2½p blue (R)	20.00	14.00
4	A23(d)	3p yel brn (Bl)	18.00	*18.00*
5	A26(e)	6p red (Bl)	32.50	26.00
6	A29(f)	1sh scar (Bl)	55.00	*90.00*
a.		1sh orange red (Bl)	72.50	*110.00*

1911, Sept. Typo. *Perf. 14x15*

7	A41(a)	½p yel grn (R)	1.25	*9.00*

Engr.

Perf. 14

9	A22(c)	2½p dp blue (R)	8.25	*19.00*

g

h

1913-16 Typo.

10	A42(b)	1p rose (Bl)	3.25	*14.00*

Engr.

12	A41(g)	6p car rose (Bl) ('16)	55.00	*140.00*
13	A41(h)	1sh ver (Bl) ('14)	62.50	*160.00*

1916-17 *Perf. 14x13½, 14x14½*

17	A45(g)	6p car rose (Bl)	2.00	*18.00*
18	A45(h)	1sh ver (Bl) ('17)	15.00	*100.00*
		Nos. 1-18 (13)	283.25	*621.25*

New Zealand Stamps of 1909-19 Overprinted in Red or Dark Blue

1917-20 Typo. *Perf. 14x15*

19	A43	½p yellow grn ('20)	1.00	*6.50*
20	A42	1p car (Bl) ('20)	6.50	*37.50*
21	A47	1½p gray black	5.00	*35.00*
22	A47	1½p brown org ('19)	.90	*7.50*
23	A43	3p choc (Bl) ('19)	4.00	*22.50*

Perf. 14x13½, 14x14½

Engr.

24	A44	2½p dull blue ('18)	1.75	*18.00*
25	A45	3p vio brn (Bl) ('18)	1.00	*32.50*
26	A45	6p car rose (Bl)	5.00	*25.00*
27	A45	1sh vermilion (Bl)	10.00	*35.00*
		Nos. 19-27 (9)	35.15	219.50

Landing of Capt. Cook A15

Avarua Waterfront A16

Capt. James Cook A17

Palm A18

Houses at Arorangi A19

Avarua Harbor A20

1920 Engr. Unwmk. *Perf. 14*

28	A15	½p green & black	3.50	26.00
29	A16	1p car & blk	3.50	18.00
30	A17	1½p brown & blk	7.00	*14.00*
31	A18	3p dp blue & blk	2.75	*16.00*
32	A19	6p slate & red brn	6.25	16.00
33	A20	1sh claret & blk	10.00	*16.00*
		Nos. 28-33 (6)	33.00	*106.00*

Inverted centers, double frames, etc. are from printers waste.

Rarotongan Chief (Te Po) — A21

1924-27 Wmk. 61 *Perf. 14*

34	A15	½p green & blk ('27)	3.00	*25.00*
35	A16	1p carmine & blk	7.00	*14.00*
36	A21	2½p blue & blk ('27)	10.00	*85.00*
		Nos. 34-36 (3)	20.00	*124.00*

Catalogue values for unused stamps in this section, from this point to the end of the section, are for Never Hinged items.

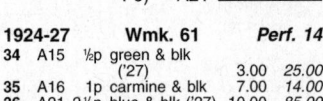

Cook Islands Nos. 199-200, 202, 205-206, 210, 212-213, 215-217 Ovptd.

1972 Photo. Unwmk. *Perf. 14x13½*

37	A34	½c gold & multi	.40	*.90*
38	A34	1c gold & multi	.85	*1.25*
39	A34	2½c gold & multi	2.50	*7.50*
40	A34	4c gold & multi	.85	*1.00*
41	A34	5c gold & multi	3.00	*8.50*
42	A34	10c gold & multi	3.00	*6.25*
43	A34	20c gold & multi	3.75	*1.10*
44	A34	25c gold & multi	.90	*1.25*
45	A34	50c gold & multi	2.75	*3.25*
46	A35	$1 gold & multi	4.50	*6.00*
47	A35	$2 gold & multi	1.00	*1.10*
		Nos. 37-47 (11)	23.50	*38.10*

Overprint horizontal on Nos. 46-47. On $2, overprint is in capitals of different font; size: 21x3mm.

Issued: Nos. 37-46, Aug. 9; No. 47, Nov. 24.

Same Overprint Horizontal in Silver On Cook Islands Nos. 330-332

1972, Oct. 27 *Perf. 13½*

48	A53	1c gold & multi	.25	.25
49	A53	5c gold & multi	.25	.25
50	A53	10c gold & multi	.30	.30
		Nos. 48-50 (3)	.80	.80

Fluorescence

Starting in 1972, stamps carry a "fluorescent security underprinting" in a multiple pattern of New Zealand's coat of arms with "Aitutaki" above, "Cook Islands" below and two stars at each side.

Silver Wedding Type of Cook Islands

1972, Nov. 20 Photo. *Perf. 13½*

Size: 29x40mm

51	A54	5c silver & multi	3.25	2.50

Size: 66x40mm

52	A54	15c silver & multi	1.25	1.25

25th anniversary of the marriage of Queen Elizabeth II and Prince Philip. Nos. 51-52 printed in sheets of 5 stamps and one label.

Flower Issue of Cook Islands Overprinted

1972, Dec. 11 Photo. *Perf. 14x13½*

53	A34	½c on #199	.25	.25
54	A34	1c on #200	.25	.25
55	A34	2½c on #202	.25	.25
56	A34	4c on #205	.30	.25
57	A34	5c on #206	.30	.25
58	A34	10c on #210	.40	.35
59	A34	20c on #212	1.25	.45
60	A34	25c on #213	.55	*.60*
61	A34	50c on #215	.85	*.90*
62	A35	$1 on #216	1.25	*1.75*
		Nos. 53-62 (10)	5.65	*5.30*

See Nos. 73-76.

The Passion of Christ, by Mathias Grunewald — A22

Paintings: No. 63b, St. Veronica, by Rogier van der Weyden. No. 63c, Crucifixion, by Raphael. No. 63d, Resurrection, by della Francesca. No. 64a, Last Supper, by Master of Amiens. No. 64b, Condemnation of Christ, by Hans Holbein, the Elder. No. 64c, Crucifixion, by Rubens. No. 64d, Resurrection, by El Greco. No. 65a, Passion of Christ, by El Greco. No. 65b, St. Veronica, by Jakob Cornelisz. No. 65c, Crucifixion, by Rubens. No. 65d, Resurrection, by Dierik Bouts.

Perf. 13½

1973, Apr. 6 Photo. Unwmk.

63		Block of 4	1.00	.40
a.-d.		A22 1c any single	.25	.25
64		Block of 4	1.25	1.00
a.-d.		A22 5c any single	.30	.25
65		Block of 4	1.40	*1.75*
a.-d.		A22 10c any single	.35	.25
		Nos. 63-65 (3)	3.65	3.15

Easter. Printed in blocks of 4 in sheets of 40. Design descriptions in top and bottom margins.

Coin Type of Cook Islands

Queen Elizabeth II Coins: 1c, Taro leaf. 2c, Pineapples. 5c, Hibiscus. 10c, Oranges. 20c, Fairy terns. 50c, Bonito. $1, Tangaroa, Polynesian god of creation, vert.

1973, May 14 *Perf. 13x13½*

Size: 37x24mm

66	A55	1c dp car & multi	.25	.25
67	A55	2c blue & multi	.25	.25
68	A55	5c green & multi	.25	.25

Size: 46x30mm

69	A55	10c vio blue & multi	.25	.25
70	A55	20c green & multi	.30	.30
71	A55	50c dp car & multi	.60	.40

Size: 32x54½mm

72	A55	$1 blue, blk & sil	.80	.50
		Nos. 66-72 (7)	2.70	2.20

Cook Islands coinage commemorating silver wedding anniv. of Queen Elizabeth II.

Printed in sheets of 20 stamps and label showing Westminster Abbey.

Cook Islands Nos. 208, 210, 212 and 215 Overprinted Like Nos. 53-62 and: "TENTH ANNIVERSARY/ CESSATION/ OF/ NUCLEAR TESTING/ TREATY"

1973, July Photo. *Perf. 14x13½*

73	A34	8c gold & multi	.25	.25
74	A34	10c gold & multi	.25	.25
75	A34	20c gold & multi	.35	.35
76	A34	50c gold & multi	.75	.75
		Nos. 73-76 (4)	1.60	1.60

Nuclear Test Ban Treaty, 10th anniv., protest against French nuclear testing on Mururoa Atoll.

Princess Anne, Hibiscus — A23

Design: 30c, Mark Phillips and hibiscus.

1973, Nov. 14 Photo. *Perf. 13½x14*

77	A23	25c gold & multi	.25	.25
78	A23	30c gold & multi	.30	.30
a.		Souvenir sheet of 2, #77-78	.65	.65

Wedding of Princess Anne and Capt. Mark Phillips.

Virgin and Child, by Il Perugino A24

Paintings of the Virgin and Child by various masters — No. 79: a, Van Dyck. b, Bartolommeo Montagna. c, Carlo Crivelli. d, Il Perugino. No. 80: a, Cima da Conegliano. b, Memling. c, Veronese. d, Veronese. No. 81: a, Raphael. b, Lorenzo Lotto. c, Del Colle. d, Memling.

1973, Dec. Photo. *Perf. 13*

79	A24	1c Block of 4, #a.-d.	.50	.50
80	A24	5c Block of 4, #a.-d.	1.00	1.00
81	A24	10c Block of 4, #a.-d.	1.25	1.25
		Nos. 79-81 (3)	2.75	2.75

Christmas. Printed in blocks of 4 in sheets of 48. Design descriptions in margins.

Murex Ramosus — A25

Terebra Maculata A26

Pacific Shells: 1c, Nautilus macromphalus. 2c, Harpa major. 3c, Phalium strigatum. 4c, Cypraea talpa. 5c, Mitra stictica. 8c, Charonia tritonis. 10c, Murex triremis. 20c, Oliva sericea. 25c, Tritonalia rubeta. 60c, Strombus latissimus. $1, Biplex perca. $5, Cypraea hesitata.

1974-75 Photo. *Perf. 13*

82	A25	½c silver & multi	.95	.95
83	A25	1c silver & multi	.95	.95
84	A25	2c silver & multi	.95	.95
85	A25	3c silver & multi	.95	.95
86	A25	4c silver & multi	.95	.95
87	A25	5c silver & multi	.95	.95
88	A25	8c silver & multi	.95	.95
89	A25	10c silver & multi	.95	.85
90	A25	20c silver & multi	1.25	.85
91	A25	25c silver & multi	1.25	.85
92	A25	60c silver & multi	3.75	1.10
93	A25	$1 silver & multi	2.50	1.25

Perf. 14

94	A26	$2 silver & multi	6.00	6.00
95	A26	$5 silver & multi	27.50	9.50
		Nos. 82-95 (14)	49.85	27.05

Issued: Nos. 82-93, 1/31/74; $2, 1/20/75; $5, 2/28/75.

For overprints see Nos. O1-O16.

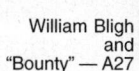

William Bligh and "Bounty" — A27

No. 96, shown. No. 97, "Bounty" at sea. No. 98, Bligh and "Bounty" off Aitutaki. No. 99, Chart of Aitutaki, 1856. No. 100, James Cook and "Resolution". No. 101, Maps of Aitutaki and Pacific Ocean.

Size: 38x22mm

1974, Apr. 11 Photo. *Perf. 13*

96	A27	1c multicolored	.45	.45
97	A27	1c multicolored	.45	.45
a.		Pair, #96-97	1.00	1.00
98	A27	5c multicolored	1.00	1.00
99	A27	5c multicolored	1.00	1.00
a.		Pair, #98-99	2.25	2.25
100	A27	8c multicolored	1.25	1.25
101	A27	8c multicolored	1.25	1.25
a.		Pair, #100-101	2.75	2.75
		Nos. 96-101,C1-C6 (12)	10.60	10.10

Capt. William Bligh (1754-1817), European discoverer of Aitutaki, Apr. 11, 1789.

Aitutaki Nos. 1 & 2 Map and UPU Emblem — A28

Design: 50c, Aitutaki Nos. 4 and 28, map of Aitutaki and UPU emblem.

1974, July 15 Photo. *Perf. 13½*

102	A28	25c blue & multi	.75	.75
103	A28	50c blue & multi	1.00	1.00
a.		Souvenir sheet of 2, #102-103	2.00	2.00

UPU, cent. Printed in sheets of 5 plus label showing UPU emblem.

A29

Designs: Paintings of the Virgin and Child by: 1c, Van der Goes. 5c, Giovanni Bellini. 8c, Gerard David. 10c, Antonello da Messina. 25c, Joos van Cleve. 30c, Maitre de St. Catherine.

1974, Oct. 11 Photo. *Perf. 13½*

104	A29	1c multicolored	.25	.25
105	A29	5c multicolored	.25	.25
106	A29	8c multicolored	.25	.25
107	A29	10c multicolored	.25	.25
108	A29	25c multicolored	.35	.35
109	A29	30c multicolored	.75	.75
a.		Souvenir sheet of 6, #104-109	2.00	2.00
		Nos. 104-109 (6)	2.10	2.10

Christmas. Nos. 104-109 printed in sheets of 15 stamps and corner label. See Nos. B1-B6.

A30

Designs: Churchill portraits — 10c, Dublin, Age 5. 25c, As young man. 30c, Inspecting troops, WWII. 50c, Painting. $1, Giving V sign.

1974, Nov. 29 Photo. *Perf. 14*

110	A30	10c multicolored	.25	.25
111	A30	25c multicolored	.25	.25
112	A30	30c multicolored	.30	.25
113	A30	50c multicolored	.50	.50
114	A30	$1 multicolored	.85	.85
a.		Souvenir sheet of 5, #110-114 + label, perf. 13½	4.50	4.50
		Nos. 110-114 (5)	2.15	2.10

Sir Winston Churchill (1874-1965). Nos. 110-114 printed in sheets of 5 stamps and corner label.

Emblem US & USSR Flags — A31

50c, Icarus and Apollo Soyuz spacecraft.

1975, July 24 Photo. *Perf. 13x14½*

115	A31	25c multicolored	.30	.30
116	A31	50c multicolored	.65	.65
a.		Souvenir sheet of 2	1.40	1.40

Apollo Soyuz space test project (Russo-American cooperation), launching July 15; link-up July 17. Nos. 115 and 116 each printed in sheets of 5 stamps and one label showing area of Apollo splash-downs. No. 116a contains one each of Nos. 115-116 with gold and black border and inscription.

Madonna and Child, by Pietro Lorenzetti — A32

Paintings: 7c, Adoration of the Kings, by Rogier van der Weyden. 15c, Madonna and Child, by Bartolommeo Montagna. 20c, Adoration of the Shepherds.

1975, Nov. 24 Photo. *Perf. 14x13½*

117	A32	Strip of 3	.35	.35
a.		6c St. Francis	.25	.25
b.		6c Madonna and Child	.25	.25
c.		6c St. John the Evangelist	.25	.25
118	A32	Strip of 3	.40	.40
a.		7c One King	.25	.25
b.		7c Madonna and Child	.25	.25
c.		7c Two Kings	.25	.25
119	A32	Strip of 3	.75	.75
a.		15c St. Joseph	.25	.25
b.		15c Madonna and Child	.25	.25
c.		15c St. John the Baptist	.25	.25
120	A32	Strip of 3	1.10	1.10
a.		20c One Shepherd	.25	.25
b.		20c Madonna and Child	.25	.25
c.		20c Two Shepherds	.25	.25
d.		Souv. sheet of 12, #117-120, perf. 13½	2.75	2.75
		Nos. 117-120 (4)	2.60	2.60

Christmas. Nos. 117-120 printed in sheets of 30 (10 strips of 3).

For surcharges see Nos. B7-B10.

Descent from the Cross, detail — A33

Designs (Painting, Flemish School, 16th Century): 30c, Virgin Mary, disciple and body of Jesus. 35c, Mary Magdalene and disciple.

1976, Apr. 5 Photo. *Perf. 13½*

121	A33	15c gold & multi	.25	.25
122	A33	30c gold & multi	.30	.30
123	A33	35c gold & multi	.45	.45
a.		Souvenir sheet of 3	1.25	1.25
		Nos. 121-123 (3)	1.00	1.00

Easter. No. 123a contains 3 stamps similar to Nos. 121-123, perf. 13, in continuous design without gold frames and white margins.

Declaration of Independence — A34

Paintings by John Trumbull: 35c, Surrender of Cornwallis at Yorktown. 50c, Washington's Farewell Address. a, "1976 BICENTENARY." b, "UNITED STATES." c, "INDEPENDENCE 1776."

1976, June 1 Photo. *Perf. 13½*

124	A34	Strip of 3	1.25	1.25
a.-c.		30c any single	.30	.30
125	A34	Strip of 3	1.50	1.50
a.-c.		35c any single	.40	.40
126	A34	Strip of 3	2.00	2.00
a.-c.		50c any single	.55	.55
d.		Souvenir sheet of 9 (3x3)	5.00	5.00
		Nos. 124-126 (3)	4.75	4.75

American Bicentennial. Nos. 124-126 printed in sheets of 5 strips of 3 and 3-part corner label showing portrait of John Trumbull, commemorative inscription and portraits of Washington (30c), John Adams (35c) and Jefferson (50c). No. 126d contains 3 strips similar to Nos. 124-126.

Bicycling — A35

Montreal Olympic Games Emblem and: 35c, Sailing. 60c, Field hockey. 70c, Running.

1976, July 15 Photo. *Perf. 13x14*

127	A35	15c multicolored	.30	.25
128	A35	35c multicolored	.50	.45
129	A35	60c multicolored	.75	.70
130	A35	70c multicolored	1.00	.90
a.		Souvenir sheet of 4	3.00	3.00
		Nos. 127-130 (4)	2.55	2.30

21st Olympic Games, Montreal, Canada, July 17-Aug. 1. Nos. 127-130 printed in sheets of 5 stamps and label showing coat of Arms and Montreal Olympic Games emblem. No. 130a contains 4 stamps similar to Nos. 127-130 with gold margin around each stamp.

Nos. 127-130a Overprinted

1976, July 30

131	A35	15c multicolored	.25	.25
132	A35	35c multicolored	.40	.40
133	A35	60c multicolored	.80	.80
134	A35	70c multicolored	.80	.80
a.		Souvenir sheet of 4	2.50	2.50
		Nos. 131-134 (4)	2.25	2.25

Visit of Queen Elizabeth II to Montreal and official opening of the Games. Each stamp of No. 134a has diagonal overprint. Sheet margin has additional overprint: "ROYAL VISIT OF H.M. QUEEN ELIZABETH II/OFFICIALLY OPENED 17 JULY 1976."

Annunciation A36

Designs: Nos. 137-138, Angel appearing to the shepherds. Nos. 139-140, Nativity. Nos. 141-142, Three Kings.

1976, Oct. 18 *Perf. 13½x13*

135		6c dk green & gold	.25	.25
136		6c dk green & gold	.25	.25
a.	A36	Pair, #135-136	.25	.25
137		7c dk brown & gold	.25	.25
138		7c dk brown & gold	.25	.25
a.	A36	Pair, #137-138	.25	.25
139		15c dk blue & gold	.25	.25
140		15c dk blue & gold	.25	.25
a.	A36	Pair, #139-140	.30	.30
141		20c purple & gold	.25	.25
142		20c purple & gold	.25	.25
a.	A36	Pair, #141-142	.40	.40
b.		Souvenir sheet of 8	1.50	1.50
		Nos. 135-142 (8)	2.00	2.00

Christmas. No. 142b contains 8 stamps similar to Nos. 135-142 with white margin around each pair of stamps.

For overprints see Nos. B11-B18.

A. G. Bell and 1876 Telephone A38

Design: 70c, Satellite and radar.

1977, Mar. 3 Photo. *Perf. 13½x13*

143	A38 25c rose & multi	.25	.25
144	A38 70c violet & multi	.40	.40
a.	Souvenir sheet of 2	1.50	1.50

Centenary of first telephone call by Alexander Graham Bell, Mar. 10, 1876. No. 144a contains a 25c in colors of 70c and 70c in colors of 25c.

Calvary (detail), by Rubens — A39

Paintings by Rubens: 20c, Lamentation. 35c, Descent from the Cross.

1977, Mar. 31 Photo. *Perf. 13½x14*

145	A39 15c gold & multi	.50	.50
146	A39 20c gold & multi	.65	.65
147	A39 35c gold & multi	.85	.85
a.	Souv. sheet, #145-147, perf. 13	2.25	2.25
	Nos. 145-147 (3)	2.00	2.00

Easter, and 400th birth anniv. of Peter Paul Rubens (1577-1640), Flemish painter.

Capt. Bligh, "Bounty" and George III — A40

Designs: 35c, Rev. John Williams, George IV, First Christian Church. 50c, British flag, map of Aitutaki, Queen Victoria. $1, Elizabeth II and family on balcony after coronation.

1977, Apr. 21 *Perf. 13½*

148	A40 25c gold & multi	.25	.25
149	A40 35c gold & multi	.30	.30
150	A40 50c gold & multi	.50	.50
151	A40 $1 gold & multi	1.25	1.25
a.	Souvenir sheet of 4, #148-151	2.25	2.25
	Nos. 148-151 (4)	2.30	2.30

Reign of Queen Elizabeth II, 25th anniv.
For overprint & surcharge see Nos. O11, O15.

Annunciation A41

Designs: No. 154, Virgin, Child and ox. No. 155, Joseph and donkey (Nativity). No. 156, Three Kings. No. 157, Virgin and Child. No. 158, Joseph. No. 159, Virgin, Child and donkey (Flight into Egypt).

1977, Oct. 14 Photo. *Perf. 13½x14*

152	6c multicolored	.25	.25
153	6c multicolored	.25	.25
a.	A41 Pair, #152-153	.25	.25
154	7c multicolored	.25	.25
155	7c multicolored	.25	.25
a.	A41 Pair, #154-155	.25	.25
156	15c multicolored	.25	.25
157	15c multicolored	.25	.25
a.	A41 Pair, #156-157	.30	.30
158	20c multicolored	.25	.25
159	20c multicolored	.25	.25
a.	A41 Pair, #158-159	.40	.40
b.	Souvenir sheet of 8, #152-159	1.75	1.75
	Nos. 152-159 (8)	2.00	2.00

Christmas.
For surcharges see Nos. B19-B26a.

Hawaiian Wood Figurine — A43

Designs: 50c, Talbot hunting dog, figurehead of "Resolution", horiz. $1, Temple figure.

1978, Jan. 19 Litho. *Perf. 13½*

160	A43 35c multicolored	.45	.45
161	A43 50c multicolored	.70	.70
162	A43 $1 multicolored	1.00	1.00
a.	Souvenir sheet of 3, #160-162	2.75	2.75
	Nos. 160-162 (3)	2.15	2.15

Bicentenary of Capt. Cook's arrival in Hawaii. Nos. 160-162 issued in sheets of 6.

Jesus Carrying Cross, by Simone di Martini — A44

Paintings: 20c, Avignon Pietà, 15th Century. 35c, Christ at Emmaus, by Rembrandt.

1978, Mar. 17 Photo. *Perf. 13½x14*

163	A44 15c gold & multi	.25	.25
164	A44 20c gold & multi	.25	.25
165	A44 35c gold & multi	.30	.30
a.	Souvenir sheet of 3	1.00	1.00
	Nos. 163-165 (3)	.80	.80

Easter. No. 165a contains one each of Nos. 163-165, perf. 13½, and label showing Louvre, Paris. See Nos. B27-B29.

Souvenir Sheet

25th Anniv. of Coronation of Queen Elizabeth II. — A45

1978, June 15 Photo. *Perf. 13½x13*

166	A45 Sheet of 6	2.50	2.50
a.	$1 Yale of Beaufort	.35	.35
b.	$1 Elizabeth II	.35	.35
c.	$1 Ancestral statue	.35	.35
d.	Souvenir sheet of 6	2.25	2.25

No. 166d contains 2 strips of Nos. 166a-166c separated by horizontal slate green gutter showing Royal family on balcony, silver marginal inscription.

Virgin and Child, by Dürer — A46

Designs: Various paintings of the Virgin and Child by Albrecht Dürer.

1978, Dec. 4 Photo. *Perf. 14½x13*

167	A46 15c multicolored	.35	.35
168	A46 17c multicolored	.40	.40
169	A46 30c multicolored	.55	.55
170	A46 35c multicolored	.65	.65
	Nos. 167-170 (4)	1.95	1.95

Christmas; 450th death anniv. of Albrecht Dürer (1471-1528), German painter. Nos. 167-170 issued in sheets of 5 stamps and corner label. See No. B30.

Capt. Cook, by Nathaniel Dance — A47

Design: 75c, "Resolution" and "Adventure," by William Hodges.

1979, July 20 Photo. *Perf. 14x13½*

171	A47 50c multicolored	1.50	1.00
172	A47 75c multicolored	2.00	1.50
a.	Souvenir sheet of 2, #171-172	2.75	2.75

Capt. James Cook (1728-1779), explorer, death bicentenary.

Boy Holding Hibiscus, IYC Emblem — A48

IYC Emblem and: 35c, Boy playing guitar. 65c, Boys in outrigger canoe.

1979, Oct. 1 Photo. *Perf. 14x13½*

173	A48 30c multicolored	.25	.25
174	A48 35c multicolored	.35	.35
175	A48 65c multicolored	.45	.45
	Nos. 173-175 (3)	1.05	1.05

See No. B31.

Aitutaki No. 102, Hill, Penny Black — A49

Designs: Nos. 176, 178-179, 181, paintings of letter writers, Flemish School, 17th century.

1979, Nov. 14 Photo. *Perf. 13*

176	A49 50c Gabriel Metsu	.50	.50
177	A49 50c shown	.50	.50
178	A49 50c Jan Vermeer	.50	.50
a.	Strip of 3, #176-178	1.50	1.50
179	A49 65c Gerard Terborch	.60	.60
180	A49 65c No. 103 (like No. 177)	.60	.60
181	A49 65c Jan Vermeer	.60	.60
a.	Strip of 3, #179-181	2.00	2.00
	Nos. 176-181 (6)	3.30	3.30

Souvenir Sheet

182	Sheet of 6	2.75	2.75
a.	A49 30c like No. 176	.40	.40
b.	A49 30c like No. 177	.40	.40
c.	A49 30c like No. 178	.40	.40
d.	A49 30c like No. 179	.40	.40
e.	A49 30c like No. 180	.40	.40
f.	A49 30c like No. 181	.40	.40

Sir Rowland Hill (1795-1879), originator of penny postage. Nos. 176-178 and 179-181 printed in sheets of 9.

Descent from the Cross, Detail — A50

Easter: 30c, 35c, Descent from the Cross, by Quentin Metsys (details).

1980, Apr. 3 Photo. *Perf. 13x13½*

183	A50 20c multicolored	.50	.40
184	A50 30c multicolored	.60	.50
185	A50 35c multicolored	.70	.60
	Nos. 183-185 (3)	1.80	1.50

See No. B32.

Albert Einstein — A51

No. 187, Formula, atom structure. No. 188, Portrait, diff. No. 189, Atomic blast. No. 190, Portrait, diff. No. 191, Atomic blast, trees.

1980, July 21 Photo. *Perf. 14*

186	A51 12c shown	.65	.65
187	A51 12c multicolored	.65	.65
a.	Pair, #186-187	1.50	1.50
188	A51 15c multicolored	.70	.70
189	A51 15c multicolored	.70	.70
a.	Pair, #188-189	1.60	1.60
190	A51 20c multicolored	.80	.80
191	A51 20c multicolored	.80	.80
a.	Pair, #190-191	2.00	2.00
b.	Souv. sheet of 6, #186-191, perf. 13	5.00	5.00
	Nos. 186-191 (6)	4.30	4.30

Albert Einstein (1879-1955), theoretical physicist.

A52

No. 192, Ancestral Figure, Aitutaki. No. 193, God image staff, Rarotonga. No. 194, Trade adze, Mangaia. No. 195, Tangaroa carving, Rarotonga. No. 196, Wooden image, Aitutaki. No. 197, Hand club, Rarotonga. No. 198, Carved mace, Mangaia. No. 199, Fisherman's god, Rarotonga. No. 200, Ti'i image, Aitutaki. No. 201, Fisherman's god, diff. No. 202, Carved mace, Cook Islands. No. 203, Tangaroa, diff. No. 204, Chief's headdress, Aitutaki. No. 205, Carved mace, diff. No. 206, God image staff, diff.

1980, Sept. 26 Photo. *Perf. 14*

192	A52 6c multicolored	.25	.25
193	A52 6c multicolored	.25	.25
194	A52 6c multicolored	.25	.25
195	A52 6c multicolored	.25	.25
a.	Block of 4, #192-195	.60	.60
196	A52 12c multicolored	.25	.25
197	A52 12c multicolored	.25	.25
198	A52 12c multicolored	.25	.25
199	A52 12c multicolored	.25	.25
a.	Block of 4, #196-199	.85	.85
200	A52 15c multicolored	.25	.25
201	A52 15c multicolored	.25	.25
202	A52 15c multicolored	.25	.25
203	A52 15c multicolored	.25	.25
a.	Block of 4, #200-203	1.00	1.00
204	A52 20c multicolored	.40	.40
205	A52 20c multicolored	.40	.40
206	A52 20c multicolored	.40	.40
207	A52 20c like #195	.40	.40
a.	Block of 4, #204-207	1.50	1.50
b.	Souvenir sheet of 16, #192-207	4.00	4.00

Third South Pacific Arts Festival, Port Moresby, Papua New Guinea.

A53

Virgin and Child, Sculptures.

1980, Nov. 21 Photo. *Perf. 13x13½*

208	A53 15c 13th cent.	.25	.25
209	A53 20c 14th cent.	.25	.25
210	A53 25c 15th cent.	.30	.30
211	A53 35c 15th cent., diff.	.40	.40
	Nos. 208-211 (4)	1.20	1.20

Christmas. See No. B33.

Mourning Virgin, by Pedro Roldan — A54

Easter (Roldan Sculptures): 40c, Christ. 50c, Mourning St. John.

1981, Mar. 31 Photo. *Perf. 14*

212 A54 30c green & gold .35 .35
213 A54 40c brt purple & gold .40 .40
214 A54 50c dk blue & gold .45 .45
Nos. 212-214 (3) 1.20 1.20

See No. B34.

Sturnus Vulgaris — A55

No. 216, Poephila gouldiae. No. 217, Petroica multicolor. No. 218, Pachycephala pectoralis. No. 219, Falco peregrinus. No. 220, Rhipidura rufifrons. No. 221, Tyto alba. No. 222, Padda oryzivora. No. 223, Artamus leucorhynchus. No. 224, Vini peruviana. No. 225, Columba livia. No. 226, Porphyrio porphyria. No. 227, Geopelia striata. No. 228, Lonchura castaneothorax. No. 229, Acridotheres tristis. No. 230, Egretta sacra. No. 231, Diomeda melanophris. No. 232, Numenius phaeopus. No. 233, Gygis alba. No. 234, Pluvialis dominica. No. 235, Sula leucogaster. No. 236, Anas superciliosa. No. 237, Anas acuta. No. 238, Fregata minor. No. 239, Stercorarius pomarinus. No. 240, Conopoderas caffra. No. 241, Lalage maculosa. No. 242, Gallirallus philippensis. No. 243, Vini stepheni. No. 244, Diomedea epomophora. No. 245, Ptilinopus victor. No. 246, Erythrura cyaneovirens. $1, Myiagra azureocapilla. $2, Myiagra vanikorensis. $4, Amandava amandava. $5, Halcyon recurvirostris.

1981-82 *Perf. 14x13½, 13½x14*

215 A55 1c shown .40 .25
216 A55 1c multicolored .40 .25
a. Pair, #215-216 1.00 .30
217 A55 2c multicolored .45 .25
218 A55 2c multicolored .45 .25
a. Pair, #217-218 1.10 .30
219 A55 3c multicolored .55 .25
220 A55 3c multicolored .55 .25
a. Pair, #219-220 1.25 .30
221 A55 4c multicolored .65 .25
222 A55 4c multicolored .65 .25
a. Pair, #221-222 1.50 .35
223 A55 5c multicolored .70 .25
224 A55 5c multicolored .70 .25
a. Pair, #223-224 1.60 .40
225 A55 6c multicolored .75 .25
226 A55 6c multicolored .75 .25
a. Pair, #225-226 1.75 .40
227 A55 10c multicolored .85 .25
228 A55 10c multicolored .85 .25
a. Pair, #227-228 2.00 .75
229 A55 12c multicolored .90 .30
230 A55 12c multicolored .90 .30
a. Pair, #229-230 2.10 .85
231 A55 15c multicolored 1.00 .40
232 A55 15c multicolored 1.00 .40
a. Pair, #231-232 2.75 *1.25*
233 A55 20c multicolored 1.25 .50
234 A55 20c multicolored 1.25 .50
a. Pair, #233-234 3.25 *1.50*
235 A55 25c multicolored 1.40 .60
236 A55 25c multicolored 1.40 .60
a. Pair, #235-236 3.75 *1.60*
237 A55 30c multicolored 1.50 .65
238 A55 30c multicolored 1.50 .65
a. Pair, #237-238 4.00 *2.00*
239 A55 35c multicolored 1.60 .75
240 A55 35c multicolored 1.60 .75
a. Pair, #239-240 4.25 *3.00*
241 A55 40c multicolored 1.75 .90
242 A55 40c multicolored 1.75 .90
a. Pair, #241-242 4.50 *3.25*
243 A55 50c multicolored 2.00 1.00
244 A55 50c multicolored 2.00 1.00
a. Pair, #243-244 5.00 *3.50*
245 A55 70c multicolored 4.25 2.00
246 A55 70c multicolored 4.25 2.00
e. Pair, #245-246 11.00 *7.50*

Size: 35x47mm

Photo. *Perf. 13½*

246A A55 $1 multicolored 5.00 3.75
246B A55 $2 multicolored 5.50 *7.50*
246C A55 $4 multicolored 9.00 *13.50*
246D A55 $5 multicolored 11.00 *17.50*
Nos. 215-246D (36) 70.50 59.95

Issued: Nos. 215-230, 4/6; Nos. 231-238, 5/8; Nos. 239-246, 1/14/82; Nos. 246A-246B, 2/15/82.

Nos. 231-246 horiz.

For surcharges and overprint see Nos. 293-306, 452-454, O40-O41.

Prince Charles and Lady Diana — A56

Perf. 13x13½, 13½x13

1981, June 10 Photo.

247 A56 60c Charles, vert. .40 .40
248 A56 80c Lady Diana, vert. .50 .50
Complete booklet, one sheet of 4 each #247-248 6.00
249 A56 $1.40 Shown .60 .60
Nos. 247-249 (3) 1.50 1.50

Royal Wedding. Issued in sheets of 4.

For overprints and surcharges see Nos. 265-267, 307, 309, 355, 405-407, B35-B37.

1982 World Cup Soccer A57

Designs: Various soccer players.

1981, Nov. 30 Photo. *Perf. 14*

250 A57 12c Pair, #250a-250b 1.10 1.00
251 A57 15c Pair, #251a-251b 1.25 1.10
252 A57 20c Pair, #252a-252b 1.50 1.25
253 A57 25c Pair, #253a-253b 1.75 1.40
Nos. 250-253 (4) 5.60 4.75

See No. B38.

Christmas — A58

Rembrandt Etchings: 15c, Holy Family, 1632, vert. 30c, Virgin with Child, 1634, vert. 40c, Adoration of the Shepherds, 1654. 50c, Holy Family with Cat, 1644.

1981, Dec. 10 *Perf. 14*

254 A58 15c gold & dk brown .50 .50
255 A58 30c gold & dk brown .65 .60
256 A58 40c gold & dk brown .75 .75
257 A58 50c gold & dk brown 1.00 1.00
Nos. 254-257 (4) 2.90 2.85

Souvenir Sheets

258 A58 80c + 5c like #254 .80 .75
259 A58 80c + 5c like #255 .80 .75
260 A58 80c + 5c like #256 .80 .75
261 A58 80c + 5c like #257 .80 .75

Nos. 258-261 have multicolored margins showing entire etching. Surtax on Nos. 258-261 was for local charities.

21st Birthday of Princess Diana — A59

1982, June 24 Photo. *Perf. 14*

262 A59 70c shown 1.75 .75
263 A59 $1 Wedding portrait 1.75 .90
264 A59 $2 Diana, diff. 2.75 1.50
a. Souvenir sheet of 3, #262-264 6.00 6.00
Nos. 262-264 (3) 6.25 3.15

See Nos. 268-270a. For surcharges see Nos. 308, 310.

Nos. 247-249 Overprinted

a

b

1982, July 13 *Perf. 13x13½,13½x13*

265 A56 60c Pair, #a.-b. 1.50 1.25
266 A56 80c Pair, #a.-b. 2.25 2.00
267 A56 $1.40 Pair, #a.-b. 3.75 3.25
Nos. 265-267 (3) 7.50 6.50

Nos. 265-267 were overprinted with alternating inscriptions within the sheet.

Nos. 262-264a Inscribed: "Royal Birth 21 June 1982 Prince William Of Wales"

1982, Aug. 5 *Perf. 14*

268 A59 70c multicolored .70 .70
269 A59 $1 multicolored 1.50 1.50
270 A59 $2 multicolored 2.00 2.00
a. Souvenir sheet of 3 5.00 5.00
Nos. 268-270 (3) 4.20 4.20

Christmas — A60

Madonna and Child Sculptures, 12th-15th Cent.

1982, Dec. 10 Photo. *Perf. 13*

271 A60 18c multicolored .65 .65
272 A60 36c multicolored .75 .75
273 A60 48c multicolored .90 .90
274 A60 60c multicolored 1.25 1.25
Nos. 271-274 (4) 3.55 3.55

Souvenir Sheet

275 Sheet of 4 4.50 4.50
a. A60 18c + 2c like 18c .70 .70
b. A60 36c + 2c like 36c .80 .80
c. A60 48c + 2c like 48c 1.00 1.00
d. A60 60c + 2c like 60c 1.25 1.25

Surtax was for children's charities.

Commonwealth Day — A61

1983, Mar. 14 Photo. *Perf. 13x13½*

276 A61 48c Bananas .95 .95
277 A61 48c Ti'i statuette .95 .95
278 A61 48c Boys canoeing .95 .95
279 A61 48c Capt. Bligh, Bounty .95 .95
a. Block of 4, #276-279 4.75 4.75

Scouting Year — A62

1983, Apr. 18 Photo. *Perf. 14*

280 A62 36c Campfire .50 .50
281 A62 48c Salute .60 .60
282 A62 60c Hiking .70 .70
Nos. 280-282 (3) 1.80 1.80

Souvenir Sheet

Perf. 13½

283 Sheet of 3 2.50 2.50
a. A62 36c + 3c like #280 .60 .60
b. A62 48c + 3c like #281 .70 .70
c. A62 60c + 3c like #282 .90 .90

Surtax was for benefit of Scouting.

Nos. 280-283 Overprinted

1983, July 11 Photo. *Perf. 14*

284 A62 36c multicolored .85 .85
285 A62 48c multicolored 1.00 1.00
286 A62 60c multicolored 1.25 1.25
Nos. 284-286 (3) 3.10 3.10

Souvenir Sheet

287 Sheet of 3 3.00 3.00
a. A62 36c + 3c like #284 .65 .65
b. A62 48c + 3c like #285 .80 .80
c. A62 60c + 3c like #286 1.00 1.00

A63

Manned Flight Bicentenary: Modern sport balloons.

1983, July 22 Photo. *Perf. 14x13*

288 A63 18c multicolored .60 .60
289 A63 36c multicolored .75 .75
290 A63 48c multicolored 1.00 1.00
291 A63 60c multicolored 1.25 1.25
Nos. 288-291 (4) 3.60 3.60

Souvenir Sheet

292 A63 $2.50 multicolored 3.25 3.25

Nos. 233-246, 246D, 248-249 Surcharged in Black

Nos. 263-264 Surcharged in Black and Gold

1983, Sept. 22

293 A55 18c on 20c, #233 2.75 1.00
294 A55 18c on 20c, #234 2.75 1.00
a. Pair, #293-294 6.00 2.25
295 A55 36c on 25c, #235 3.25 1.25
296 A55 36c on 25c, #236 3.25 1.25
a. Pair, #295-296 7.25 3.00
297 A55 36c on 30c, #237 3.25 1.25
298 A55 36c on 30c, #238 3.25 1.25
a. Pair, #297-298 7.25 3.00
299 A55 36c on 35c, #239 3.50 1.40
300 A55 36c on 35c, #240 3.50 1.40
a. Pair, #299-300 7.50 3.25
301 A55 48c on 40c, #241 4.50 1.40
302 A55 48c on 40c, #242 4.50 1.40
a. Pair, #301-302 10.00 3.25
303 A55 48c on 50c, #243 4.50 1.40
304 A55 48c on 50c, #244 4.50 1.40
a. Pair, #303-304 10.00 3.25
305 A55 72c on 70c, #245 7.50 2.50
306 A55 72c on 70c, #246 7.50 2.50
a. Pair, #305-306 16.50 7.50
307 A56 96c on 80c, #248 3.00 2.25
308 A59 96c on $1, #263 2.75 2.00
309 A56 $1.20 on $1.40, #249 3.00 2.25
310 A59 $1.20 on $2, #264 2.75 2.00

Size: 35x47mm

311 A55 $5.60 on $5, #246D 20.00 10.00
Nos. 293-311 (19) 90.00 38.90

Nos. 307-308, 310-311 vert.

A64

60, Global coverage. 96c, Communications satellite.

1983, Sept. 29 Photo. *Perf. 14*

312 A64 48c shown .80 .55
313 A64 60c multicolored 1.25 .70
314 A64 96c multicolored 1.50 1.25
a. Souvenir sheet of 3, #312-314 3.25 3.25
Nos. 312-314 (3) 3.55 2.50

World Communications Year.

Christmas — A65

Raphael Paintings — 36c, Madonna of the Chair. 48c, Alba Madonna. 60c, Connestabile Madonna.

1983, Nov. 21 Photo. *Perf. 13½x14*

315 A65 36c multicolored .75 .40
316 A65 48c multicolored 1.00 .80
317 A65 60c multicolored 1.50 1.00
Nos. 315-317 (3) 3.25 2.20

Souvenir Sheet

318	Sheet of 3	3.50	3.50
a.	A65 36c + 3c like #315	1.00	1.00
b.	A65 48c + 3c like #316	1.10	1.10
c.	A65 60c + 3c like #317	1.25	1.25

1983, Dec. 15 ***Imperf.***

Size: 46x46mm

319	A65 85c + 5c like #315	1.50	1.50
320	A65 85c + 5c like #316	1.50	1.50
321	A65 85c + 5c like #317	1.50	1.50
	Nos. 319-321 (3)	4.50	4.50

Surtax was for children's charities.

Local Birds — A66

1984 **Photo.** ***Perf. 14***

322	A66	2c as No. 216	1.75	.90
323	A66	3c as No. 215	1.75	.90
324	A66	5c as No. 217	1.75	1.00
325	A66	10c as No. 218	2.50	1.00
326	A66	12c as No. 220	2.50	1.00
327	A66	18c as No. 219	2.50	1.25
328	A66	24c as No. 221	2.50	1.25
329	A66	30c as No. 222	2.50	1.25
330	A66	36c as No. 223	2.50	1.25
331	A66	48c as No. 224	2.50	1.25
332	A66	50c as No. 225	2.75	1.75
333	A66	60c as No. 226	2.75	1.75
334	A66	72c as No. 227	3.25	1.75
335	A66	96c as No. 228	3.25	1.75
336	A66	$1.20 as No. 229	3.25	2.50
337	A66	$2.10 as No. 230	3.75	3.50
338	A66	$3 as No. 246A	5.25	4.50
339	A66	$4.20 as No. 246B	4.00	*5.75*
340	A66	$5.60 as No. 246C	5.25	*7.00*
341	A66	$9.60 as No. 246D	8.00	*10.00*
		Nos. 322-341 (20)	64.25	51.30

For overprints and surcharges see Nos. O17-O39.

1984 Summer Olympics — A67

1984, July 24 **Photo.** ***Perf. 13x13½***

342	A67	36c Javelin	.50	.50
343	A67	48c Shot put	.60	.60
344	A67	60c Hurdles	.70	.70
345	A67	$2 Handball	2.00	2.00
		Nos. 342-345 (4)	3.80	3.80

Souvenir Sheet

346	Sheet of 4	3.50	3.50
a.	A67 36c + 5c like #342	.40	.40
b.	A67 48c + 5c like #343	.55	.55
c.	A67 60c + 5c like #344	.65	.65
d.	A67 $2 + 5c like #345	1.50	1.50

Surtax was for benefit of local sports.

Nos. 342-345 Overprinted in Gold and Black

1984, Aug. 21 **Photo.** ***Perf. 13x13½***

347	A67	36c multicolored	.40	.40
348	A67	48c multicolored	.50	.50
349	A67	60c multicolored	.60	.60
350	A67	$2 multicolored	1.75	1.75
		Nos. 347-350 (4)	3.25	3.25

Ausipex '84 — A68

60c, William Bligh, map. 96c, Bounty, map. $1.40, Stamps, map.

1984, Sept. 14 **Photo.** ***Perf. 14***

351	A68	60c multicolored	3.75	3.75
352	A68	96c multicolored	3.75	3.75
353	A68	$1.40 multicolored	3.75	3.75
		Nos. 351-353 (3)	11.25	11.25

Souvenir Sheet

354	Sheet of 3	8.00	8.00
a.	A68 60c + 5c like #351	1.75	1.75
b.	A68 96c + 5c like #352	2.25	2.25
c.	A68 $1.40 + 5c like #353	3.50	3.50

For overprint see No. 399.

No. 247 Surcharged

1984, Oct. 10 **Photo.** ***Perf. 13x13½***

355	A56 $3 on 60c multi	2.75	3.00

Issued in sheets of 4.

A69

1984, Nov. 16 **Photo.** ***Perf. 13***

356	A69	36c Annunciation	.45	.45
357	A69	48c Nativity	.55	.55
358	A69	60c Epiphany	.65	.65
359	A69	96c Flight into Egypt	.85	.85
		Nos. 356-359 (4)	2.50	2.50

Souvenir Sheets

Size: 45x53mm

Imperf

360	A69	90c + 7c like #356	1.10	1.10
361	A69	90c + 7c like #357	1.10	1.10
362	A69	90c + 7c like #358	1.10	1.10
363	A69	90c + 7c like #359	1.10	1.10

Christmas.

A70

1984, Dec. 10 **Photo.** ***Perf. 13½x14***

364	A70	48c Diana, Henry	2.25	2.25
365	A70	60c William, Henry	2.25	2.25
366	A70	$2.10 Family	3.00	3.00
		Nos. 364-366 (3)	7.50	7.50

Souvenir Sheet

367	Sheet of 3	6.00	6.00
a.	A70 96c + 7c like #364	2.00	2.00
b.	A70 96c + 7c like #365	2.00	2.00
c.	A70 96c + 7c like #366	2.00	2.00

Christmas, Birth of Prince Henry, Sept. 15.
Surtax was for benefit of local children's charities.

Audubon Birth Bicentenary — A71

Illustrations of bird species by John J. Audubon — 55c, Gray kingbird. 65c, Bohemian waxwing. 75c, Summer tanager. 95c, Cardinal. $1.15, White-winged crossbill.

1985, Mar. 22 **Litho.** ***Perf. 13***

368	A71	55c multicolored	1.10	1.10
369	A71	65c multicolored	1.25	1.25
370	A71	75c multicolored	1.50	1.50
371	A71	95c multicolored	1.75	1.75
372	A71	$1.15 multicolored	2.25	2.25
		Nos. 368-372 (5)	7.85	7.85

Queen Mother, 85th Birthday — A72

Photographs: 55c, Lady Elizabeth Bowes-Lyon, age 7. 65c, Engaged to the Duke of York, 75c, Duchess of York with daughter, Elizabeth. $1.30, Holding the infant Prince Charles. $3, Portrait taken on 63rd birthday.

1985-86 ***Perf. 13½x13***

373	A72	55c multicolored	.55	.55
374	A72	65c multicolored	.65	.65
375	A72	75c multicolored	.75	.75
376	A72	$1.30 multicolored	1.25	1.25
a.		Souvenir sheet of 4, #373-376	8.25	8.25
		Nos. 373-376 (4)	3.20	3.20

Souvenir Sheet

377	A72	$3 multicolored	3.50	3.50

Nos. 373-376 printed in sheets of 4.
Issued: No. 376a, 8/4/86; others, 6/14/85.
For overprint see No. 446.

Intl. Youth Year — A73

Designs: 75c, The Calmady Children, by Thomas Lawrence (1769-1830). 90c, Madame Charpentier's Children, by Renoir (1841-1919). $1.40, Young Girls at Piano, by Renoir.

1985, Sept. 16 **Photo.** ***Perf. 13***

378	A73	75c multicolored	2.50	2.50
379	A73	90c multicolored	2.50	2.50
380	A73	$1.40 multicolored	3.00	3.00
		Nos. 378-380 (3)	8.00	8.00

Souvenir Sheet

381	Sheet of 3	6.50	6.50
a.	A73 75c + 10c like #378	1.50	1.50
b.	A73 90c + 10c like #379	1.75	1.75
c.	A73 $1.40 + 10c like #380	2.50	2.50

Surcharged for children's activities.

Adoration of the Magi, by Giotto di Bondone (1276-1337) A74

Nos. 382, 384, Giotto probe. Nos. 383, 385, Planet A probe.

1985, Nov. 15 **Photo.** ***Perf. 13½x13***

382	A74	95c multicolored	1.50	1.50
383	A74	95c multicolored	1.50	1.50
a.		Pair, #382-383	3.50	3.50
384	A74	$1.15 multicolored	1.50	1.50
385	A74	$1.15 multicolored	1.50	1.50
a.		Pair, #384-385	3.50	3.50
		Nos. 382-385 (4)	6.00	6.00

Souvenir Sheet

Imperf

386	A74	$6.40 multicolored	13.50	13.50

Christmas, return of Halley's Comet, 1985-86.

Halley's Comet — A75

Designs: 90c, Halley's Comet, A.D. 684, wood engraving, Nuremberg Chronicles. $1.25, Sighting of 1066, Bayeux Tapestry, detail, c. 1092, France. $1.75, The Comet Inflicting Untold Disasters, 1456, Lucerne Chronicles, by Diebolt Schilling. $4.20, Melancolia I, engraving by Durer.

1986, Feb. 25 **Photo.** ***Perf. 13½x13***

387	A75	90c multicolored	1.25	1.25
388	A75	$1.25 multicolored	1.50	1.50
389	A75	$1.75 multicolored	2.25	2.25
		Nos. 387-389 (3)	5.00	5.00

Souvenir Sheets

390	Sheet of 3 + label	6.50	6.50
a.	A75 95c, like #387	2.00	2.00
b.	A75 95c, like #388	2.00	2.00
c.	A75 95c, like #389	2.00	2.00

Imperf

391	A75	$4.20 multicolored	5.75	5.75

Elizabeth II, 60th Birthday — A76

1986, Apr. 21 ***Perf. 14***

392	A76	95c Coronation portrait	1.10	1.10

Souvenir Sheet

Perf. 13½

393	A76	$4.20 Portrait, diff.	5.25	5.25

No. 392 printed in sheets of 5 with label picturing U.K. flag and Queen's flag for New Zealand.

Statue of Liberty, Cent. — A77

1986, June 27 **Photo.** ***Perf. 14***

394	A77	$1 Liberty head	1.50	1.50
395	A77	$2.75 Statue	3.00	3.00

Souvenir Sheet

Perf. 13½

396	Sheet of 2	3.25	3.25
a.	A77 $1.25 like $1	1.50	1.50
b.	A77 $1.25 like $2.75	1.50	1.50

For surcharges see Nos B45, B49.

Wedding of Prince Andrew and Sarah Ferguson — A78

1986, July 23 ***Perf. 14***

397	A78	$2 multicolored	2.60	2.60

Souvenir Sheet

Perf. 13½

398	A78	$5 multicolored	6.00	6.00

No. 397 printed in sheets of 5 plus label picturing Westminster Abbey.
For surcharge see No. B48.

No. 354 Overprinted

1986, Aug. 4 **Photo.** ***Perf. 14***

399	Sheet of 3	13.00	13.00
a.	A68 60c + 5c like #351	3.00	3.00
b.	A68 96c + 5c like #352	3.50	3.50
c.	A68 $1.40 + 5c like #353	6.00	6.00

STAMPEX '86, Adelaide, Aug. 4-10.

Christmas — A79

Paintings by Albrecht Durer: 75c, No. 404a, St. Anne with Virgin and Child. $1.35, No. 404b, Virgin and Child. $1.95, No. 404c, Adoration of the Magi. $2.75, No. 404d, Rosary Festivity.

1986, Nov. 21 Litho. *Perf. 13½*

400	A79	75c multicolored	1.25	1.25
401	A79	$1.35 multicolored	2.00	2.00
402	A79	$1.95 multicolored	3.00	3.00
403	A79	$2.75 multicolored	4.25	4.25
		Nos. 400-403 (4)	10.50	10.50

Souvenir Sheet

404	Sheet of 4	14.00	14.00
a.-d.	A79 $1.65 any single	3.25	3.25

For surcharges see Nos. B39-B44, B46-B47, B50-B54.

Nos. 247-249 Srchd. in Gold and Black

1987, Nov. 20 Photo. *Perf. 13x12½*

405	A56	$2.50 on 60c No. 247	2.40	2.40
406	A56	$2.50 on 80c No. 248	2.40	2.40
407	A56	$2.50 on $1.40 No. 249	2.40	2.40
		Nos. 405-407 (3)	7.20	7.20

Issued in sheets of 4 with margin inscriptions overprinted with gold bar and "40th Anniversary of the Royal Wedding / 1947-1987" in black; "OVERPRINTED BY NEW ZEALAND GOVERNMENT PRINTER, / WELLINGTON, NOVEMBER 1987" at left.

A80

The Virgin with Garland, by Rubens A81

Painting details.

1987, Dec. 10 Photo. *Perf. 13x13½*

408	A80	70c UL	2.00	2.00
409	A80	85c UR	2.10	2.10
410	A80	$1.50 LL	2.25	2.25
411	A80	$1.85 LR	3.00	3.00
		Nos. 408-411 (4)	9.35	9.35

Souvenir Sheets

412	Sheet of 4	13.00	13.00
a.	A80 95c like No. 408	3.00	3.00
b.	A80 95c like No. 409	3.00	3.00
c.	A80 95c like No. 410	3.00	3.00
d.	A80 95c like No. 411	3.00	3.00

Perf. 13

413	A81	$6 multicolored	14.00	14.00

Christmas.

1988 Summer Olympics, Seoul A82

Flags of Korea, Aitutaki, ancient and modern events, and Seoul Games emblem or $50 silver coin issued to commemorate the participation of Aitutaki athletes in the Olympics for the 1st time: 70c, No. 418a, Obverse of silver coin, chariot race, running. 85c, Emblem, running, soccer. 95c, Emblem, boxing, handball. $1.40, No. 418b, Reverse of coin, spearmen, women's tennis.

1988, Aug. 22 Photo. *Perf. 14½x15*

414	A82	70c multicolored	2.00	2.00
415	A82	85c multicolored	2.25	2.25
416	A82	95c multicolored	2.50	2.50
417	A82	$1.40 multicolored	3.00	3.00
		Nos. 414-417 (4)	9.75	9.75

Souvenir Sheet

418	Sheet of 2	7.50	7.50
a.-b.	A82 $2 any single	3.25	3.25

Nos. 414-417 Ovptd. with Names of 1988 Olympic Gold Medalists

a

b

c

d

1988, Oct. 10 Litho. *Perf. 14½x15*

419	A82 (a)	70c on No. 414	1.75	1.75
420	A82 (b)	85c on No. 415	1.75	1.75
421	A82 (c)	95c on No. 416	2.75	2.75
422	A82 (d)	$1.40 on No. 417	2.75	2.75
		Nos. 419-422 (4)	9.00	9.00

Griffith is spelled incorrectly on No. 419.

Christmas — A83

Paintings by Rembrandt: 55c, Adoration of the Shepherds (detail), National Gallery, London. 70c, Holy Family, Alte Pinakothek, Munich. 85c, Presentation in the Temple, Kunsthalle, Hamburg. 95c, The Holy Family, Louvre, Paris. $1.15, Presentation in the Temple, diff., Mauritshuis, The Hague. $4.50, Adoration of the Shepherds (entire painting).

1988, Nov. 2 Photo. *Perf. 13½*

423	A83	55c multicolored	1.75	1.75
424	A83	70c multicolored	1.90	1.90
425	A83	85c multicolored	2.00	2.00
426	A83	95c multicolored	2.25	2.25
427	A83	$1.15 multicolored	2.50	2.50
		Nos. 423-427 (5)	10.40	10.40

Souvenir Sheet

Perf. 14

428	A83	$4.50 multicolored	8.00	8.00

No. 428 contains one 52x34mm stamp.

A84

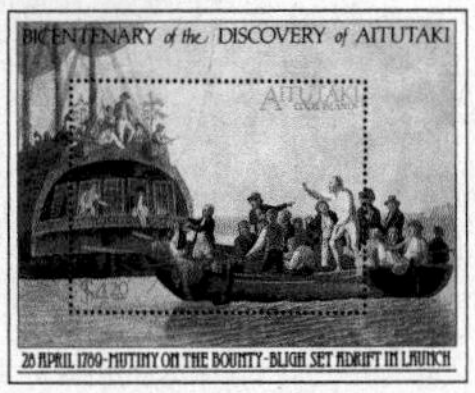

Mutiny on the *Bounty*, 200th Anniv. A85

55c, Ship, Capt. Bligh. 65c, Breadfruit. 75c, Bligh, chart. 95c, Bounty off Aitutaki. $1.65, Christian, Bligh.
$4.20, Castaways.

1989, July 3 Photo. *Perf. 13½*

429	A84	55c multicolored	2.00	2.00
430	A84	65c multicolored	2.25	2.25
431	A84	75c multicolored	2.50	2.50
432	A84	95c multicolored	2.75	2.75
433	A84	$1.65 multicolored	3.75	3.75
		Nos. 429-433 (5)	13.25	13.25

Souvenir Sheet

434	A85	$4.20 multicolored	11.00	11.00

Discovery of Aitutaki by William Bligh, bicent.

1st Moon Landing, 20th Anniv. — A86

Apollo 11 mission emblem, American flag, eagle, "The Eagle has landed" and: 75c, Astronaut standing on the lunar surface. $1.15, Conducting an experiment in front of the lunar module. $1.80, Carrying equipment. $6.40, Raising the flag.

1989, July 28 Photo. *Perf. 13½x13*

435	A86	75c multicolored	2.50	2.50
436	A86	$1.15 multicolored	3.25	3.25
437	A86	$1.80 multicolored	3.75	3.75
		Nos. 435-437 (3)	9.50	9.50

Souvenir Sheet

Perf. 13½

438	A86	$6.40 multicolored	9.50	9.50

No. 438 contains one 42x31mm stamp.

Christmas — A87

Details from *Virgin in Glory*, by Titian: 70c, Virgin. 85c, Christ child. 95c, Angel. $1.25, Cherubs. $6, Entire painting.

1989, Nov. 20 Photo. *Perf. 13½x13*

439	A87	70c multicolored	2.10	2.10
440	A87	85c multicolored	2.25	2.25
441	A87	95c multicolored	2.40	2.40
442	A87	$1.25 multicolored	3.50	3.50
		Nos. 439-442 (4)	10.25	10.25

Souvenir Sheet

Perf. 13½

443	A87	$6 multicolored	11.00	11.00

No. 443 contains one 45x60mm stamp.

World Environmental Protection — A88

Designs: a, Human comet, World Philatelic Programs emblem. b, Comet tail and "Protect The Endangered Earth!" $3, Human comet, emblem and inscription.

1990, Feb. 16 Photo. *Perf. 13½x13*

444	A88	Pair	5.75	5.75
a.-b.		$1.75 any single	2.50	2.50

Souvenir Sheet

445	A88	$3 multicolored	7.00	7.00

No. 376a Overprinted

Designs: 55c, Lady Elizabeth Bowes-Lyon, 1907. 65c, Lady Elizabeth engaged to Duke of York. 75c, As Duchess of York with daughter Elizabeth. $1.30, As Queen Mother with grandson.

1990, July 16 Litho. *Perf. 13½x13*

446	Sheet of 4	13.00	13.00
a.	A72 55c multicolored	2.75	2.75
b.	A72 65c multicolored	3.00	3.00
c.	A72 75c multicolored	3.25	3.25
d.	A72 $1.30 multicolored	3.50	3.50

Christmas — A89

Paintings: 70c, Madonna of the Basket by Correggio. 85c, Virgin and Child by Morando. 95c, Adoration of the Child by Tiepolo. $1.75, Mystic Marriage of St. Catherine by Memling. $6, Donne Triptych by Memling.

1990, Nov. 28 Litho. *Perf. 14*

447	A89	70c multicolored	1.50	1.50
448	A89	85c multicolored	1.60	1.60
449	A89	95c multicolored	1.75	1.75
450	A89	$1.75 multicolored	2.50	2.50
		Nos. 447-450 (4)	7.35	7.35

Souvenir Sheet

451	A89	$6 multicolored	13.00	13.00

Nos. 246A-246B Overprinted

1990, Dec. 5 Photo. *Perf. 13½*

452	A55	$1 multicolored	4.75	4.75
453	A55	$2 multicolored	5.75	5.75

Birdpex '90, 20 Intl. Ornithological Congress, New Zealand.

No. 246D Overprinted

1991, Apr. 22 Photo. *Perf. 13*

454	A55	$5 multicolored	11.00	11.00

Christmas — A90

Paintings: 80c, The Holy Family, by Mengs. 90c, Virgin and Child, by Fra Filippo Lippi. $1.05, Virgin and Child, by Durer. $1.75, Adoration of the Shepherds, by De La Tour. $6, The Holy Family, by Michelangelo.

1991, Nov. 13 Litho. *Perf. 14*

455 A90 80c multicolored 1.75 1.75
456 A90 90c multicolored 1.90 1.90
457 A90 $1.05 multicolored 2.00 2.00
458 A90 $1.75 multicolored 2.50 2.50
Nos. 455-458 (4) 8.15 8.15

Souvenir Sheet

459 A90 $6 multicolored 13.00 13.00

1992 Summer Olympics, Barcelona A91

1992, July 29 Litho. *Perf. 14*

460 A91 95c Hurdles 2.00 2.00
461 A91 $1.25 Weight lifting 2.25 2.25
462 A91 $1.50 Judo 2.75 2.75
463 A91 $1.95 Soccer 3.25 3.25
Nos. 460-463 (4) 10.25 10.25

6th Festival of Pacific Arts, Rarotonga A92

Canoes: 30c, Vaka Motu. 50c, Hamatafua. 95c, Alia Kalia Ndrua. $1.75, Hokule'a Hawaiian. $1.95, Tuamotu Pahi.

1992, Oct. 16 Litho. *Perf. 14x15*

464 A92 30c multicolored .85 .85
465 A92 50c multicolored 1.00 1.00
466 A92 95c multicolored 2.00 2.00
467 A92 $1.75 multicolored 3.00 3.00
468 A92 $1.95 multicolored 3.50 3.50
Nos. 464-468 (5) 10.35 10.35

For overprints see Nos. 524-528.

Nos. 464-468 Overprinted

1992, Oct. 16

469 A92 30c on #464 1.00 1.00
470 A92 50c on #465 1.75 1.75
471 A92 95c on #466 2.75 2.75
472 A92 $1.75 on #467 3.75 3.75
473 A92 $1.95 on #468 4.50 4.50
Nos. 469-473 (5) 13.75 13.75

Christmas — A93

Designs: Different details from Virgin's Nativity, by Guido Reni.

1992, Nov. 19 Litho. *Perf. 13½*

474 A93 80c multicolored 1.90 1.90
475 A93 90c multicolored 2.00 2.00
476 A93 $1.05 multicolored 2.10 2.10
477 A93 $1.75 multicolored 2.50 2.50
Nos. 474-477 (4) 8.50 8.50

Souvenir Sheet

478 A93 $6 like #476 8.00 8.00

No. 478 contains one 39x50mm stamp.

Discovery of America, 500th Anniv. — A94

Designs: $1.25, Columbus being blessed as he departs from Spain. $1.75, Map of Columbus' four voyages. $1.95, Columbus landing in New World.

1992, Dec. 11 *Perf. 14x15*

479 A94 $1.25 multicolored 2.75 2.75
480 A94 $1.75 multicolored 3.50 3.50
481 A94 $1.95 multicolored 3.75 3.75
Nos. 479-481 (3) 10.00 10.00

Coronation of Queen Elizabeth II, 40th Anniv. — A95

Designs: a, Victoria, Edward VII. b, George V, George VI. c, Elizabeth II.

1993, June 4 Litho. *Perf. 14*

482 A97 $1.75 Strip of 3, #a.-c. 10.00 10.00

Christmas — A96

Religious sculpture: 80c, Madonna and Child, by Nino Pisano. 90c, Virgin on Rosebush, by Luca Della Robbia. $1.15, Virgin with Child and St. John, by Juan Francisco Rusticí. $1.95, Virgin with Child, by Michelangelo. $3, Madonna and Child, by Jacopo Della Quercia.

1993, Oct. 29 Litho. *Perf. 14*

483 A96 80c multicolored 1.00 1.00
484 A96 90c multicolored 1.25 1.25
485 A96 $1.15 multicolored 1.75 1.75
486 A96 $1.95 multicolored 2.50 2.50

Size: 32x47mm

Perf. 13½

487 A96 $3 multicolored 3.50 3.50
Nos. 483-487 (5) 10.00 10.00

1994 Winter Olympics, Lillehammer — A97

Designs: a, Ice hockey. b, Ski jumping. c, Cross-country skiing.

1994, Feb. 11 Litho. *Perf. 14*

488 A97 $1.15 Strip of 3, #a.-c. 12.00 12.00

Flowers — A98

Hibiscus A98a

1994-97 Litho. *Perf. 13½*

489 A98 5c Prostrate morning glory .50 .50
490 A98 10c White frangipani .60 .60
491 A98 15c Red hibiscus .75 .75
492 A98 20c Yellow allamanda .85 .85
493 A98 25c Royal poinciana .85 .85
494 A98 30c White gardenia .85 .85
495 A98 50c Pink frangipani 1.00 1.00
496 A98 80c Morning glory 1.25 1.25
497 A98 85c Yellow mallow 1.50 1.50
498 A98 90c Red coral tree 1.50 1.50
499 A98 $1 Cup of gold 1.60 1.60
500 A98 $2 Red cordia 2.00 2.00
501 A98a $3 multicolored 4.25 4.25
502 A98a $5 multicolored 5.00 5.00
503 A98a $8 multicolored 8.00 8.00
Nos. 489-503 (15) 30.50 30.50

Issued: 5c-90c, 2/17; $1, $2, 4/29; $3, $5, 11/18; $8, 11/21/97.

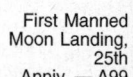

First Manned Moon Landing, 25th Anniv. — A99

Designs: No. 506, Astronauts Collins, Armstrong, Aldrin. No. 507, Splash down in South Pacific.

1994, July 20 Litho. *Perf. 14*

506 A99 $2 multicolored 6.50 6.50
507 A99 $2 multicolored 6.50 6.50

Christmas A100

Paintings: No. 508a, The Madonna of the Basket, by Corregio. b, Virgin & Child with Saints, by Hans Memling. c, The Virgin & Child with Flowers, by Dolci. d, Virgin & Child with Angels, by Bergognone.

No. 509a, The Adoration of the Kings, by Dosso. b, The Virgin & Child, by Bellini. c, The Virgin & Child, by Schiavone. d, Adoration of the Kings, by Dolci.

1994, Nov. 30 Litho. *Perf. 14*

508 A100 85c Block of 4, #a.-d. 4.75 4.75
509 A100 90c Block of 4, #a.-d. 5.50 5.50

End of World War II, 50th Anniv. A101

Designs: a, Battle of Britain, 1940. b, Battle of Midway, June 1942.

1995, Sept. 4 Litho. *Perf. 13½x13*

510 A101 $4 Pair, #a.-b. 20.00 20.00

No. 510 issued in sheets of 4 stamps.

Queen Mother, 95th Birthday — A102

1995, Sept. 14 Litho. *Perf. 13x13½*

511 A102 $4 multicolored 9.50 9.50

UN, 50th Anniv. A103

1995, Oct. 18 Litho. *Perf. 13½*

512 A103 $4.25 multicolored 7.50 7.50

Year of the Sea Turtle — A104

1995, Dec. 1 Litho. *Perf. 14x13½*

513 A104 95c Green 2.25 2.25
514 A104 $1.15 Leatherback 2.75 2.75
515 A104 $1.50 Olive Ridley 3.00 3.00
516 A104 $1.75 Loggerhead 3.25 3.25
Nos. 513-516 (4) 11.25 11.25

Queen Elizabeth II, 70th Birthday — A105

1996, June 24 Litho. *Perf. 14*

517 A105 $4.50 multicolored 8.25 8.25

No. 517 was issued in sheets of 4.

Modern Olympic Games, Cent. — A106

Designs: No. 518, Pierre de Coubertin, Olympic torch, parading athletes, 1896. No. 519, Modern sprinters, US flag, Atlanta, 1996.

1996, July 11 Litho. *Perf. 14*

518 A106 $2 multicolored 4.50 4.50
519 A106 $2 multicolored 4.50 4.50
a. Pair, #518-519 10.00 10.00

Queen Elizabeth II and Prince Philip, 50th Wedding Anniv. — A107

Designs: $2.50, Queen Elizabeth II, Prince Philip, Queen Mother, and King George VI. $6, like No. 520, close-up.

1997, Nov. 20 Litho. *Perf. 14*

520 A107 $2.50 multicolored 3.75 3.75

Souvenir Sheet

521 A107 $6 multicolored 8.00 8.00

No. 520 was issued in sheets of 4.

Diana, Princess of Wales (1961-97) — A108

1998, Apr. 15 Litho. *Perf. 14*

522 A108 $1 multicolored 1.00 1.00

Souvenir Sheet

523 A108 $4 like #522 5.00 5.00

No. 522 was issued in sheets of 5 + label. No. 523 is a continuous design.

For surcharge see No. B55.

Nos. 464-468 Overprinted

1999, Dec. 31 Litho. *Perf. 14x15*

524 A92 30c on #464 .55 .55
525 A92 50c on #465 .70 .70
526 A92 95c on #466 1.00 1.00
527 A92 $1.75 on #467 1.50 1.50
528 A92 $1.95 on #468 1.75 1.75
Nos. 524-528 (5) 5.50 5.50

Queen Mother, 100th Birthday A109

No. 529: a, Wearing crown, blue-toned photograph. b, Wearing crown, color photograph. c, Wearing hat. d, With King George VI.

2000, Oct. 20 Litho. *Perf. 14*

529 A109 $3 Sheet of 4, #a-d 11.00 11.00

Souvenir Sheet

530 A109 $7.50 With flowers 7.00 7.00

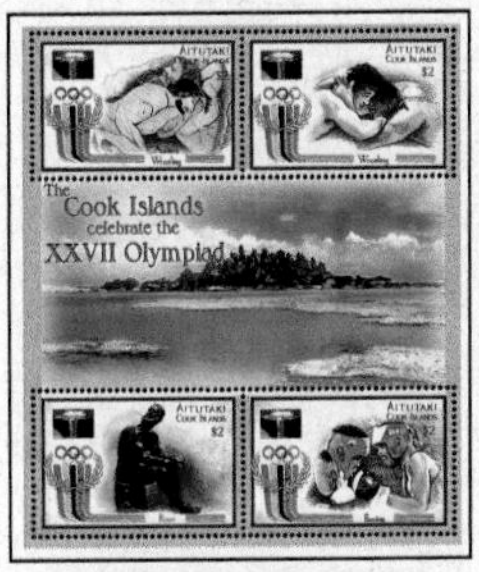

2000 Summer Olympics, Sydney — A110

No. 531: a, Ancient wrestling. b, Wrestling. c, Ancient boxer. d, Boxing.

2000, Dec. 14 Litho. *Perf. 14*

531 A110 $2 Sheet of 4, #a-d 7.25 7.25

Souvenir Sheet

532 A110 $2.75 Torch relay 3.00 3.00

Worldwide Fund for Nature (WWF) — A111

Various views of two blue lorikeets: 80c, 90c, $1.15, $1.95.

2002, Sept. 3 Litho. *Perf. 14*

533-536 A111 Set of 4 5.75 5.75

Nos. 533-536 were each issued in sheets of four with a label featuring an enlarged design of the stamp. Value, set of four sheets $24.

United We Stand — A112

2003, Sept. 30 Litho. *Perf. 14*

537 A112 $1.15 multi 1.50 1.50

Printed in sheets of 4.

Pope John Paul II (1920-2005) — A113

2005, Nov. 11 Litho. *Perf. 14*

538 A113 $1.95 multi 3.75 3.75

Printed in sheets of 5 + label.

Worldwide Fund for Nature (WWF) — A114

Blue moon butterfly: 80c, Caterpillar and chrysalis. 90c, Female. $1.15, Male. $1.95. Male, diff.

2008, Nov. 18 Litho. *Perf. 13½*

539-542 A114 Set of 4 6.00 6.00

Nos. 539-542 were each issued in sheets of four with a label featuring an enlarged design of the stamp. Value, set of four sheets $25.

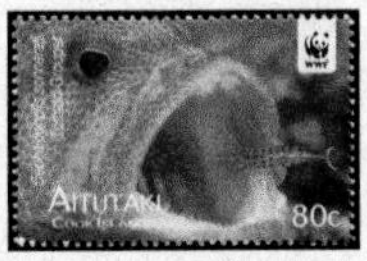

Worldwide Fund for Nature (WWF) — A115

Designs: 80c, Tomato grouper. 90c, Peacock grouper. $1.10, Pair of Tomato groupers. $1.20, Head of Peacock grouper.

2010, Dec. 9 *Perf. 14*

543-546 A115 Set of 4 5.00 5.00

Tourism — A116

Designs: 10c, Airplane, island. 20c, Bent palm tree, sun on horizon. 30c, Beach. 40c, Ship, islands. 50c, Road in forest. 60c, Islands and beach (at right) under dark skies. 70c, People fishing. 80c, Bent palm tree. 90c, Huts. $1, Islands and beach (at left). $1.10, Fence near beach. $1.20, Sun at horizon. $1.50, Moon above island. $2, Mountain on island. $3, Building and courtyard.

2010, Dec. 10

547	A116	10c multi	.30	.30
548	A116	20c multi	.35	.35
549	A116	30c multi	.40	.40
550	A116	40c multi	.90	.90
551	A116	50c multi	.70	.70
552	A116	60c multi	.85	.85
553	A116	70c multi	1.00	1.00
554	A116	80c multi	1.10	1.10
555	A116	90c multi	1.15	1.15
556	A116	$1 multi	1.25	1.25
557	A116	$1.10 multi	1.40	1.40
558	A116	$1.20 multi	1.50	1.50
559	A116	$1.50 multi	1.75	1.75
560	A116	$2 multi	2.25	2.25
561	A116	$3 multi	3.75	3.75
a.		Sheet of 15, #547-561	19.50	19.50
		Nos. 547-561 (15)	18.65	18.65

A117

Engagement of Prince William and Catherine Middleton — A118

Designs: Nos. 562, 565a, 567, 50c, Middleton. Nos. 563, 565b, 568, $5, Prince playing polo.

No. 564: a, Prince in military uniform. b, Prince playing polo. c, Middleton, fence. d, Prince, man and woman in background. e, Middleton, woman in background. f, Couple, Prince at left. g, Middleton with black hat. h, Prince. i, Couple, Middleton at left. j, Hands of couple, engagement ring.

$8.10, Couple, Prince in uniform at left.

2011, Jan. 14 *Perf. 14*

562 A117 50c multi .75 .75

563 A117 $5 multi 7.00 7.00

Miniature Sheets

564 A118 $1 Sheet of 10, #a-j 12.50 12.50

Perf. 13¾x13½

565 A117 Sheet of 2, #a-b + label 8.00 8.00

Souvenir Sheets

Perf. 14¼

566	A117	$8.10 multi	11.00	11.00
567	A117	$11 multi	16.00	16.00
568	A117	$11 multi	16.00	16.00
		Nos. 566-568 (3)	43.00	43.00

No. 565 contains two 28x44mm stamps. Nos. 566-568 each contain one 38x50mm stamp.

Peonies — A119

2011, Apr. 8 Litho. *Perf. 13¼*

569 A119 90c multi 1.25 1.25

Souvenir Sheet

Perf. 14¾x14

570 A119 $6.60 Peonies in vase, horiz. 10.50 10.50

No. 569 was printed in sheets of 6. No. 570 contains one 48x42mm stamp.

Souvenir Sheet

Wedding of Prince William and Catherine Middleton — A120

No. 571 — Bride and groom: a, $1.10, Walking down aisle. b, $1.20, Kneeling.

2011, July 15 *Perf. 15x14¼*

571 A120 Sheet of 2, #a-b 4.00 4.00

Aitutaki Marine Research Center — A121

Designs: 10c, Suspended cages underwater. 20c, Station manager Richard Story. 80c, Tridacna maxima. 90c, Tridacna maxima, diff. $1.10, Tridacna derasa. $1.20, Tridacna derasa, diff.

No. 578, vert.: a, $2, Researcher underwater. b, $3, Researcher lifting cage on boat.

2011, July 25 *Perf. 14¼x14*

572-577 A121 Set of 6 7.25 7.25

Souvenir Sheet

Perf. 13¾

578 A121 Sheet of 2, #a-b 8.50 8.50

Nos. 572-577 each were printed in sheets of 4. No. 578 contains two 30x38mm stamps.

Christmas — A122

No. 579 — Items from Christmas song "The Twelve Days of Christmas": a, Nine ladies dancing. b, Ten lords a leaping. c, Eleven pipers piping. d, Twelve drummers drumming.

2011, Dec. 24 Litho. *Perf. 13¼*

579		Horiz. strip of 4	8.25	8.25
a.	A122	90c multi	1.50	1.50
b.	A122	$1 multi	1.60	1.60
c.	A122	$1.20 multi	1.90	1.90
d.	A122	$2 multi	3.25	3.25
e.		Souvenir sheet of 4, #579a-579d	8.25	8.25

No. 579 was printed in sheets containing three strips.

Beatification of Pope John Paul II — A123

No. 580: a, $1.10, Pope Benedict XVI. b, $5.10, Pope John Paul II.

2012, Jan. 10 *Perf. 13¾*

580 A123 Horiz. pair, #a-b 10.50 10.50

No. 580 was printed in sheets containing two pairs.

Cetaceans A124

Designs: Nos. 581, 593a, 20c, Humpback whale. Nos. 582, 593b, 30c, Humpback whale tail. Nos. 583, 593c, 50c, Humpback whale, diff. Nos. 584, 593d, 80c, Striped dolphins. Nos. 585, 593e, 90c, Striped dolphins, diff. Nos. 586, 593f, $1, Striped dolphins, diff. Nos. 587, 593g, $1.10, Striped dolphin. Nos. 588, 593h, $1.20, Striped dolphins, diff. Nos. 589, 593i, $5, Striped dolphins, diff. Nos. 590, 593j, $6, Humpback whale tail, diff. Nos. 591, 593k, $7.50, Humpback whale, diff. Nos. 592, 593l, $10, Humpback whale, diff.

2012, June 22 *Perf. 14*

Stamps Without Dark Blue Frame Near Denomination

581-592 A124 Set of 12 55.00 55.00

Stamps With Dark Blue Frame All Around

593 A124 Sheet of 12, #a-l 55.00 55.00

Entombment of Christ, by Pietro Lorenzetti A125

The Last Supper, by Lorenzetti — A126

Madonna with St. Francis and St. John the Evangelist, by Lorenzetti — A127

Deposition of Christ from the Cross, by Lorenzetti — A128

The Flagellation of Christ, by Lorenzetti — A129

Entry of Christ Into Jerusalem, by Lorenzetti — A130

Perf. 14¾x14¼

2012, Nov. 16 **Litho.**

Stamps With White Frames

594	Horiz. pair	2.80	2.80
a.	A125 80c multi	1.40	1.40
b.	A126 80c multi	1.40	1.40
595	Horiz. pair	3.00	3.00
a.	A127 90c multi	1.50	1.50
b.	A128 90c multi	1.50	1.50
596	Horiz. pair	10.00	10.00
a.	A129 $3 multi	5.00	5.00
b.	A130 $3 multi	5.00	5.00
	Nos. 594-596 (3)	15.80	15.80

Miniature Sheet

Stamps Without White Frame

597	Sheet of 6	16.00	16.00
a.	A125 80c multi	1.40	1.40
b.	A126 80c multi	1.40	1.40
c.	A127 90c multi	1.50	1.50
d.	A128 90c multi	1.50	1.50
e.	A129 $3 multi	5.00	5.00
f.	A130 $3 multi	5.00	5.00

Christmas.

Personalizable Stamp — A131

A131a

A131b

2012, Dec. 21 **Litho.** ***Perf. 14x14¾***

598	A131 $4 multi	6.75	6.75
a.	A131a 50c multi	.70	.70
b.	A131b $1 multi	1.40	1.40

Christmas (#598a, 598b). Issued: Nos. 598a, 598b, 12/16/19. Nos. 598a-598b have the same frame as the personalizable stamp No. 598, but have different denominations. The editors do not know if 50c and $1 stamps having these frames were made available to the public that may have different personalized images other than the images shown above placed in the vignette area. The editors also do not know if there are stamps of type A131 that are available in denominations other than 50c, $1, or $4.

Miniature Sheet

New Year 2013 (Year of the Snake) A132

No. 599 — Snake with background color of: a, Green. b, Yellow, c, Pink. d, Violet.

2013, Feb. 21 **Litho.** ***Perf. 14¾x14***

599	A132 $1.20 Sheet of 4, #a-d	8.00	8.00

Cetaceans A133

Various boats and: Nos. 600, 612a, 10c, Humpback whale. Nos. 601, 612b, 40c, Humpback whale, diff. Nos. 602, 612c, 60c, Humpback whale, diff. Nos. 603, 612d, 70c, Striped dolphin. Nos. 604, 612e, $1.50, Striped dolphin, diff. Nos. 605, 612f, $1.80, Striped dolphin, diff. Nos. 606, 612g, $2, Striped dolphin, diff. Nos. 607, 612h, $2.25, Striped dolphin, diff. Nos. 608, 612i, $2.50, Striped dolphin, diff. Nos. 609, 612j, Humpback whale, diff. Nos. 610, 612k, $4, Humpback whale, diff. Nos. 611, 612l, $20, Humpback whale, diff.

2013, June 5 **Litho.** ***Perf. 14***

Stamps With White Frames

600-611	A133 Set of 12	62.50	62.50

Miniature Sheet

Stamps Without White Frames

612	A133 Sheet of 12, #a-l	62.50	62.50

Souvenir Sheet

Birth of Prince George of Cambridge — A134

No. 613: a, $1.30, Duchess of Cambridge. b, $1.50, Duchess of Cambridge reviewing Scouts, Duchess and Duke of Cambridge kissing. c, $1.70, Duchess of Cambridge, diff.

2013, Aug. 1 **Litho.** ***Perf. 13½***

613	A134 Sheet of 3, #a-c	7.25	7.25

Souvenir Sheet

China International Collection Expo — A135

No. 614: a, $1.50, Painting by Paul Gauguin. b, $1.70, Beijing Exhibition Center.

2013, Sept. 26 **Litho.** ***Perf. 12***

614	A135 Sheet of 2, #a-b	5.50	5.50

Pres. John F. Kennedy (1917-63) — A136

Designs: $2.50, Kennedy and quotation. $2.90, Kennedy.

2013, Nov. 8 **Litho.** ***Perf. 14¼***

615-616	A136 Set of 2	9.00	9.00

Christmas — A137

Religious paintings by: $1, William Brassey Hole. $1.30, Bernardino Luini.

No. 619 — Religious paintings by: a, $2, Gentile da Fabriano. b, $2.40, Marten de Vos. c, $2.60, Pietro Perugino.

2013, Nov. 18 **Litho.** ***Perf. 13¼***

617-618	A137 Set of 2	4.00	4.00

Souvenir Sheet

619	A137 Sheet of 3, #a-c	11.50	11.50

Miniature Sheet

New Year 2014 (Year of the Horse) A138

No. 620 — Color of horse: a, $1, Purple. b, $1.30, White, horiz. c, $1.50, Dark blue. d, $1.70, Yellow, horiz.

2014, Jan. 10 **Litho.** ***Perf. 13¾***

620	A138 Sheet of 4, #a-d	9.00	9.00

Miniature Sheet

Easter A139

No. 621 — Religious paintings by: a, 50c, Benvenuto Garofalo. b, $1, Tiziano Vecelli (Titian). c, $1.30, Piero della Francesca. d, $1.50, Peter Paul Rubens. e, $1.70, Ambrogio Borgognone.

$9.50, Painting by Paolo Veronese.

2014, Apr. 9 **Litho.** ***Perf. 13¼***

621	A139 Sheet of 5, #a-e, + label	10.50	10.50

Souvenir Sheet

622	A139 $9.50 multi	16.50	16.50

Worldwide Fund for Nature (WWF) — A140

Various depictions of spotted reef crab: $1, $1.30, $1.70, $2.10.

2014, Nov. 28 **Litho.** ***Perf. 14***

623-626	A140 Set of 4	9.75	9.75
626a	Souvenir sheet of 4, #623-626	9.75	9.75

Nos. 623-626 were each printed in sheets of 4.

Souvenir Sheet

Christmas — A141

No. 627 — Religious paintings by: a, Fra Angelico. b, Pieter Breugel, the Elder. c, Paolo Schiavo.

Perf. 14¾x14¼

2014, Dec. 12 **Litho.**

627	A141 $1.50 Sheet of 3, #a-c	7.00	7.00

Souvenir Sheet

New Year 2015 (Year of the Sheep) A142

No. 628 — Sheep with background color of: a, $3.80, Green. b, $4.10, Orange.

2015, Jan. 5 **Litho.** ***Perf. 13¼***

628	A142 Sheet of 2, #a-b	11.50	11.50

Miniature Sheet

Easter A143

No. 629 — Paintings depicting Jesus Christ by: a, Bartolomé Esteban Murillo. b, Albrecht Altdorfer. c, John Singleton Copley. d, William Blake.

2015, Mar. 31 **Litho.** ***Perf. 14x14¼***

629	A143 $2 Sheet of 4, #a-d	12.50	12.50

Souvenir Sheet

Birth of Princess Charlotte of Cambridge — A144

No. 630: a, Duchess of Cambridge holding Princess Charlotte. b, Duke of Cambridge and Prince George.

Perf. 14¾x14¼

2015, June 23 **Litho.**

630	A144 $4.50 Sheet of 2, #a-b	12.00	12.00

New Year 2016 (Year of the Monkey) — A145

Designs: $2.60, Monkey and red chop mark. $3, Monkey, diff.

No. 633: a, $3.80, Monkey and red chop mark. b, $4.10, Monkey, diff.

2015, Sept. 25 **Litho.** ***Perf. 13¼***

631-632	A145 Set of 2	7.25	7.25

Souvenir Sheet

633	A145 Sheet of 2, #a-b	10.50	10.50

No. 633 contains two 50x50mm diamond-shaped stamps.

Miniature Sheet

Queen Elizabeth II, Longest-Reigning British Monarch — A146

No. 634 — Various photographs of Queen Elizabeth II: a, $1.30. b, $1.50. c, $1.70. d, $2.

2015, Nov. 20 Litho. *Perf. 14x14¼*
634 A146 Sheet of 4, #a-d 8.75 8.75

Souvenir Sheet

Christmas — A147

No. 635 — Details from *The Nativity,* by Lorenzo Monaco: a, Virgin Mary. b, Infant Jesus and farm animals, c, St. Joseph.

2015, Dec. 9 Litho. *Perf. 13¼*
635 A147 $1 Sheet of 3, #a-c 4.00 4.00

Souvenir Sheet

Queen Elizabeth II, 90th Birthday A148

No. 636 — Queen Elizabeth II: a, Without hat. b, With hat.

2016, May 10 Litho. *Perf. 13¼*
636 A148 $3 Sheet of 2, #a-b 8.25 8.25

Marae Moana Marine Park — A149

Designs: 30c, Short-finned pilot whales. 50c, Whitetip reef shark. 80c, Common dolphins. $1, Emblem of Marae Moana Marine Park. $1.10, Humpback whales. $1.30, Blue shark. $1.50, Tiger shark. $1.70, Spinner dolphin. $2, Killer whale.

2016, May 27 Litho. *Perf. 14¼x14¾*

637	A149	30c	multi	.40	.40
638	A149	50c	multi	.70	.70
639	A149	80c	multi	1.10	1.10
640	A149	$1	multi	1.40	1.40
641	A149	$1.10	multi	1.75	1.75
642	A149	$1.30	multi	1.90	1.90
643	A149	$1.50	multi	2.10	2.10
644	A149	$1.70	multi	2.40	2.40
645	A149	$2	multi	2.75	2.75
	Nos. 637-645 (9)			14.50	14.50

New Year 2017 (Year of the Rooster) — A150

Designs: $2.30, Rooster, green & orange tail feathers. $4.50, Rooster, green tail feathers.

2016, Aug. 10 Litho. *Perf. 13½*
646-647 A150 Set of 2 10.00 10.00
647a Souvenir sheet of 2, #646-647 10.00 10.00

Worldwide Fund for Nature (WWF) — A151

Chatham albatrosses: Nos. 648, 652a, $1, Two on cliff, one in flight. Nos. 649, 652b, $1.70, Adult and juvenile. Nos. 650, 652c, $2, Bird in flight. Nos. 651, 652d, $2.40, Two adults and nest.

2016, Dec. 6 Litho. *Perf. 14¾x14¼*
Stamps With White Frames
648-651 A151 Set of 4 10.00 10.00
Stamps Without White Frames
652 A151 Block or horiz. strip of 4, #a-d 10.00 10.00

For surcharges, see Nos. 682-687.

A152

Christmas A153

No. 653 — Stained-glass window depicting: a, Adoration of the Shepherds. b, Holy Family.
No. 654 — Stained-glass window depicting: a, Holy Family and cows. b, Holy Family, diff.

2016, Dec. 19 Litho. *Perf. 13¼*
653 A152 50c Horiz. pair, #a-b 1.40 1.40
654 A153 $1 Horiz. pair, #a-b 2.75 2.75

Miniature Sheet

Easter A154

No. 655 — Paintings of the Resurrection of Christ by: a, Gustave Doré. b, Gebhard Fugel. c, James Jacques Tissot. d, Master of Wittingau.

2017, Apr. 12 Litho. *Perf. 13*
655 A154 $1 Sheet of 4, #a-d 5.50 5.50

Miniature Sheet

Pres. John F. Kennedy (1917-63) — A155

No. 656 — Pres. Kennedy: a, $1, With Wernher von Braun. b, $1, With others watching television coverage of first U.S. manned space flight. c, $2.50, With W. Averill Harriman and Dean Rusk. d, $2.50, Delivering speech on Nuclear Test Ban Treaty.

2017, July 3 Litho. *Perf. 13*
656 A155 Sheet of 4, #a-d 10.50 10.50

Miniature Sheet

Reign of Queen Elizabeth II, 65th Anniv. A156

No. 657 — Queen Elizabeth II: a, Holding handbag. b, Standing near railing. c, Holding paper. d, Wearing turquoise green hat and jacket.

2017, July 17 Litho. *Perf. 13*
657 A156 $2.50 Sheet of 4, #a-d 15.00 15.00

New Year 2018 (Year of the Dog) — A157

Designs: $3, Dog. $3.80, Figurine of dog.

2017, Nov. 1 Litho. *Perf. 13¼*
658-659 A157 Set of 2 9.50 9.50
659a Souvenir sheet of 2, #658-659 9.50 9.50

Christmas — A158

No. 660, $1: a, Moon and palm trees. b, Sailboat.
No. 661, $2.40: a, Scallop shell. b, Holly and sea turtle.

2017, Dec. 5 Litho. *Perf. 12½*
Horiz. pairs, #a-b
660-661 A158 Set of 2 9.75 9.75

Butterflies — A159

No. 662: a, Great eggfly butterfly. b, Blue-spotted Charaxes butterfly. c, Karner blue butterfly. d, Monarch butterfly.

2017, Dec. 8 Litho. *Perf. 12½*
662 A159 $2.50 Block of 4, #a-d 14.50 14.50

Miniature Sheet

Easter A160

No. 663: a, $1, Tulip. b, $1, Church, chalice and bread. c, $2.40, Sun, cross and dove. d, $2.40, Easter eggs, shells and butterflies.

2018, Mar. 19 Litho. *Perf. 13*
663 A160 Sheet of 4, #a-d 10.00 10.00

Birdpex Philatelic Exhibition, Mondorf-les-Bains, Luxembourg — A161

No. 664: a, $1, Hawaiian petrel. b, $4.80, Juan Fernandez petrels.

2018, May 4 Litho. *Perf. 13*
664 A161 Horiz. pair, #a-b 8.25 8.25

Wedding of Prince Harry and Meghan Markle A162

No. 665: a, Prince Charles bringing bride to groom. b, Couple kissing.
$8, Bride and groom on church steps.

2018, Aug. 2 Litho. *Perf. 13*
665 A162 $4.80 Sheet of 2, #a-b 13.00 13.00

Souvenir Sheet

666 A162 $8 multi 11.00 11.00

New Year 2019 (Year of the Pig) — A163

Pig facing: $3, Right. $3.80, Left.

2018, Dec. 10 Litho. *Perf. 13¼*
667-668 A163 Set of 2 9.00 9.00

Birds of Prey — A164

Designs: Nos. 669, 681a, 20c, Bonelli's eagle. Nos. 670, 681b, 30c, Pearl kite. Nos. 671, 681c, 40c, Black-breasted buzzard kite. Nos. 672, 681d, 50c, Brahminy kite. Nos. 673, 681e, $1, Oriental honey buzzard. Nos. 674, 681f, $2, Henst's goshawk. Nos. 675, 681g, $2.40, Cuban black hawk. Nos. 676, 681h, $2.60, Double-toothed kite. Nos. 677, 681i, $4.50, Crowned eagle. Nos. 678, 681j, $5, African marsh harrier. Nos. 679, 681k, $7.50, White-bellied sea eagle. Nos. 680, 681l, $10, Pacific baza.

2018, Dec. 27 Litho. *Perf. 13*
Stamps With White Frames

669	A164	20c	multi	.25	.25
670	A164	30c	multi	.40	.40
671	A164	40c	multi	.55	.55

672 A164	50c	multi	.65	.65
673 A164	$1	multi	1.40	1.40
674 A164	$2	multi	2.75	2.75
a.	Souvenir sheet of 6, #669-674		6.00	6.00
675 A164	$2.40	multi	3.25	3.25
676 A164	$2.60	multi	3.50	3.50
677 A164	$4.50	multi	6.00	6.00
678 A164	$5	multi	6.75	6.75
679 A164	$7.50	multi	10.00	10.00
680 A164	$10	multi	13.50	13.50
a.	Souvenir sheet of 6, #675-680		43.00	43.00
	Nos. 669-680 (12)		49.00	49.00

Miniature Sheet
Stamps Without White Frames

681 A164 Sheet of 12, #a-l 49.00 49.00

Stamps on Nos. 674a and 680a have white frames on one or two sides. See Nos. 690-695.

Nos. 649-651 Surcharged

Methods and Perfs. As Before

2019, Aug. 5

682 A151	50c on $1.70 #649	.65	.65
683 A151	50c on $2 #650	.65	.65
684 A151	50c on $2.40 #651	.65	.65
685 A151	$1 on $1.70 #649	1.25	1.25
686 A151	$1 on $2 #650	1.25	1.25
687 A151	$1 on $2.40 #651	1.25	1.25
	Nos. 682-687 (6)	5.70	5.70

New Year 2020 (Year of the Rat) — A165

Rat facing: $3, Right. $3.80, Left.

2019, Oct. 11 Litho. *Perf. 13¼*

688-689 A165 Set of 2 8.75 8.75

Birds of Prey Type of 2018

Designs: Nos. 690, 694a, $2.50, Long-crested eagle. Nos. 691, 694b, $3, Spanish imperial eagle. Nos. 692, 694c, $4, Tawny eagle. Nos. 693, 694d, $6, Verreaux's eagle.

2019, Nov. 15 Litho. *Perf. 13*

690 A164	$2.50	multi	3.25	3.25
691 A164	$3	multi	4.00	4.00
692 A164	$4	multi	5.25	5.25
693 A164	$6	multi	8.00	8.00
	Nos. 690-693 (4)		20.50	20.50

Stamps Without White Frames
Stamp Size: 48x40mm
Perf. 13¼x13

694 A164 Block or vert. strip of 4, #a-d 20.50 20.50
e. Souvenir sheet of 4, #694a-694d 20.50 20.50

Nos. 694a-694d were printed in sheets of 8 containing two of each stamp. Stamps on No. 694e have white frames on two adjacent sides.

Owls — A166

Designs: Nos. 695, 699a, $5.50, Barred owl. Nos. 696, 699b, $6.70, Little owl. Nos. 697, 699c, $22.40, Whiskered screech owl. Nos. 698, 699d, $29.90, Verreaux's eagle owl.

2019, Nov. 20 Litho. *Perf. 13*

695 A166	$5.50	multi	7.25	7.25
696 A166	$6.70	multi	8.75	8.75
697 A166	$22.40	multi	29.00	29.00
698 A166	$29.90	multi	39.00	39.00
	Nos. 695-698 (4)		84.00	84.00

Stamps Without White Frames
Stamp Size: 48x40mm
Perf. 13¼x13

699 A166 Block or vert. strip of 4, #a-d 84.00 84.00
e. Souvenir sheet of 4, #699a-699d 84.00 84.00

Nos. 699a-699d were printed in sheets of 8 containing two of each stamp. Stamps on No. 699e have white frames on two adjacent sides.

Turtles — A167

Designs: Nos. 700, 708a, 50c, Olive ridley sea turtle in water. Nos. 701, 708b, $1, Olive ridley sea turtle exiting water. Nos. 702, 708c, $5, Olive ridley sea turtle hatchling on beach. Nos. 703, 708d, $7, Olive ridley sea turtle in water, diff. Nos. 704, 709a, $10, Loggerhead sea turtle in water. Nos. 705, 709b, $20, Loggerhead sea turtle hatchling on beach. Nos 706, 709c, $30, Loggerhead sea turtle in water, diff. Nos. 707, 709d, $34.70, Head of Loggerhead sea turtle.

2020, Jan. 15 Litho. *Perf. 13*
Stamps With White Frames

700 A167	50c	multi	.65	.65
701 A167	$1	multi	1.30	1.30
702 A167	$5	multi	6.50	6.50
703 A167	$7	multi	9.00	9.00
704 A167	$10	multi	13.00	13.00
705 A167	$20	multi	26.00	26.00
706 A167	$30	multi	39.00	39.00
707 A167	$34.70	multi	45.00	45.00
	Nos. 700-707 (8)		140.45	140.45

Stamps Without White Frames
Stamp Size: 48x40mm
Perf. 13¼x13

708 A167 Block or vert. strip of 4, #a-d 17.50 17.50
e. Souvenir sheet of 4, #708a-708d 17.50 17.50
709 A167 Block or vert. strip of 4, #a-d 125.00 125.00
e. Souvenir sheet of 4, #709a-709d 125.00 125.00

Nos. 708a-708d and 709a-709d were printed in sheets of 8 containing two of each stamp. Stamps on Nos. 708e and 709e have white frames on two adjacent sides.

Birds of Paradise — A168

Designs: Nos. 710, 714a, $2.50, Greater bird-of-paradise. Nos. 711, 714b, $3, Standardwing bird-of-paradise. Nos. 712, 714c, $4, Red bird-of-paradise. Nos. 713, 714d, $6, King of Saxony bird-of-paradise.

2020, May 8 Litho. *Perf. 13*
Stamps With White Frames

710 A168	$2.50	multi	3.25	3.25
711 A168	$3	multi	3.75	3.75
712 A168	$4	multi	5.00	5.00
713 A168	$6	multi	7.50	7.50
	Nos. 710-713 (4)		19.50	19.50

Stamps Without White Frames
Stamp Size: 48x40mm
Perf. 13¼x13

714 A168 Block or vert. strip of 4, #a-d 19.50 19.50
e. Souvenir sheet of 4, #714a-714d 19.50 19.50

Nos. 714a-714d were printed in sheets of 8 containing two of each stamp. Stamps on No. 714e have white frames on two adjacent sides.

Geese — A169

Designs: Nos. 715, 719a, $5.50, Nene geese. Nos. 716, 719b, $6.70, Red-breasted geese. Nos. 717, 719c, $22.40, Bar-headed geese. Nos. 718, 719d, $29.90, Kelp geese.

2020, May 20 Litho. *Perf. 13*
Stamps With White Frames

715 A169	$5.50	multi	7.00	7.00
716 A169	$6.70	multi	8.50	8.50
717 A169	$22.40	multi	28.00	28.00
718 A169	$29.90	multi	37.50	37.50
	Nos. 715-718 (4)		81.00	81.00

Stamps Without White Frames
Stamp Size: 48x40mm
Perf. 13¼x13

719 A169 Block or vert. strip of 4, #a-d 81.00 81.00
e. Souvenir sheet of 4, #719a-719d 81.00 81.00

Nos. 719a-719d were printed in sheets of 8 containing two of each stamp. Stamps on No. 719e have white frames on two adjacent sides.

Butterflies A170

Designs: Nos. 720, 728a, 50c, Great purple hairstreak butterfly. Nos. 721, 728b, $1, Red admiral butterfly. Nos. 722, 728c, $5, Holly blue butterfly. Nos. 723, 728d, $7, Cryptic wood white butterfly. Nos. 724, 729a, $10, Silver-washed frittilary butterfly. Nos. 725, 729b, $20, Painted lady butterfly. Nos. 726, 729c, $30, Checkered skipper butterfly. Nos. 727, 729d, $34.70, Large white butterfly.

2020, June 15 Litho. *Perf. 13*
Stamps With White Frames

720 A170	50c	multi	.65	.65
721 A170	$1	multi	1.30	1.30
722 A170	$5	multi	6.50	6.50
723 A170	$7	multi	9.00	9.00
724 A170	$10	multi	13.00	13.00
725 A170	$20	multi	26.00	26.00
726 A170	$30	multi	39.00	39.00
727 A170	$34.70	multi	45.00	45.00
	Nos. 720-727 (8)		140.45	140.45

Stamps Without White Frames
Stamp Size: 48x40mm
Perf. 13¼x13

728 A170 Block or vert. strip of 4, #a-d 17.50 17.50
e. Souvenir sheet of 4, #728a-728d 17.50 17.50
729 A170 Block or vert. strip of 4, #a-d 125.00 125.00
e. Souvenir sheet of 4, #729a-729d 125.00 125.00

Nos. 728a-728d and 729a-729d were printed in sheets of 8 containing two of each stamp. Stamps on Nos. 728e and 729e have white frames on two adjacent sides.

Souvenir Sheet

New Year 2021 (Year of he Ox) A171

2021, Apr. 7 Litho. *Perf. 13¼x13*

730 A171 $5.30 multi 7.75 7.75

Elephants A172

Various photographs of elephants at the Smithsonian Institution National Zoological Park Conservation Biology Institute: 50c, Two elephants. $1, One elephant. $2, Elephant spraying itself with water. $4.50, Elephant with trunk raised.

$10, Elephant spraying itself with dirt.

2021, May 5 Litho. *Perf. 13*

731-734 A172 Set of 4 12.00 12.00

Souvenir Sheet
Perf. 13¼x13

735 A172 $10 multi 14.50 14.50

No. 735 contains one 48x40mm stamp.

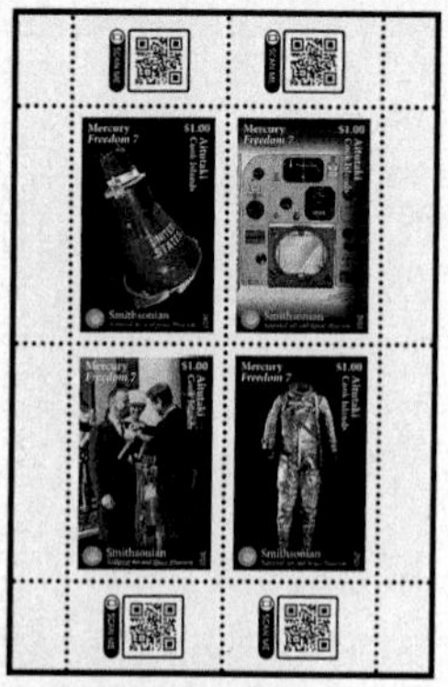

A173

A174

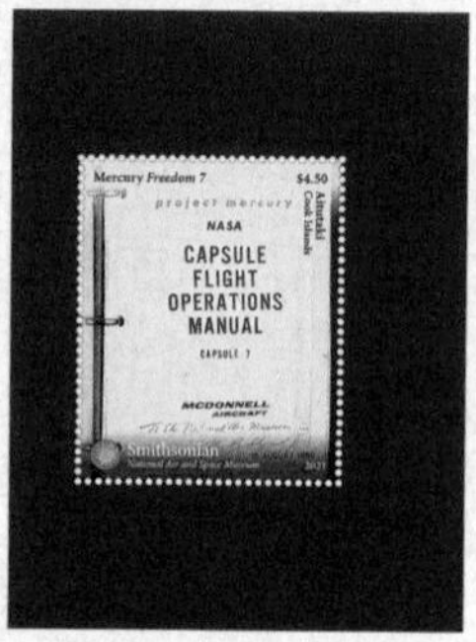

Project Mercury A175

No. 736: a, Freedom 7 capsule. b, Drawing of instrument panel of Freedom 7. c. Pres. John F. Kennedy awarding Distinguished Service Medal to Freedom 7 astronaut Alan B. Shepard, Jr. d, Shepard's spacesuit.

$2.50, Launch of Freedom 7. $4.50, Front page of Freedom 7's Capsule Flight Operations Manual.

2021, May 5 Litho. *Perf. 13*

736 A173 $1 Sheet of 4, #a-d 6.00 6.00

Souvenir Sheets
Perf. 13x13¼

737 A174 $2.50 multi 3.75 3.75
738 A175 $4.50 multi 6.50 6.50

Souvenir Sheets

Observation Tower of Steven F. Udvar-Hazy Center of Smithsonian Institution's National Air and Space Museum — A176

Owlets From Smithsonian Institution's National Zoo Named "Increase" and "Diffusion" — A177

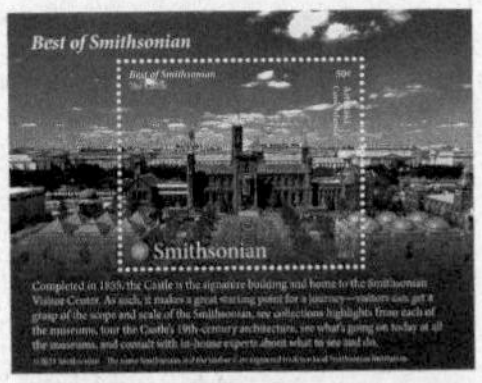

The Castle, Visitor's Center of the Smithsonian Institution — A178

Katherine Dulin Folger Rose Garden of the Smithsonian Institution — A179

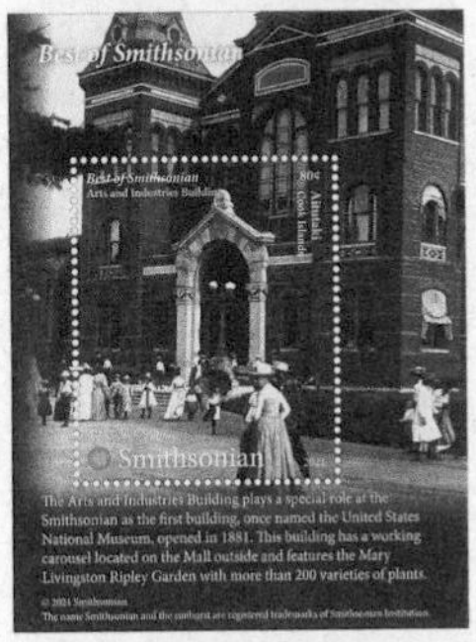

Arts and Industries Building of the Smithsonian Institution — A180

Sculpture at the Smithsonian Institution's National Museum of the American Indian — A181

2021, May 5 Litho. *Perf. 13¼x13*

739	A176	30c multi	.45	.45
740	A177	40c multi	.60	.60
741	A178	50c multi	.75	.75
742	A179	70c multi	1.00	1.00

Perf. 13x13¼

743	A180	80c multi	1.25	1.25
744	A181	90c multi	1.30	1.30
		Nos. 739-744 (6)	5.35	5.35

SEMI-POSTAL STAMPS

Christmas Type of 1974

Designs: 1c+1c, like No. 104. 5c+1c, like No. 105. 8c+1c, like No. 106. 10c+1c, like No. 107. 25c+1c, like No. 108. 30c+1c, like No. 109.

1974, Dec. 2 Photo. *Perf. 13½*

B1	A29	1c + 1c multicolored	.25	.25
B2	A29	5c + 1c multicolored	.25	.25
B3	A29	8c + 1c multicolored	.25	.25
B4	A29	10c + 1c multicolored	.25	.25
B5	A29	25c + 1c multicolored	.30	.30
B6	A29	30c + 1c multicolored	.30	.30
		Nos. B1-B6 (6)	1.60	1.60

Surtax was for child welfare.

Nos. 117-120 Surcharged in Silver

1975, Dec. 19 Photo. *Perf. 14x13½*

B7	A32	Strip of 3	.45	.45
a.-c.		6c+1c any single	.25	.25
B8	A32	Strip of 3	.50	.50
a.-c.		7c+1c any single	.25	.25
B9	A32	Strip of 3	1.00	1.00
a.-c.		15c+1c any single	.30	.30
B10	A32	Strip of 3	1.50	1.50
a.-c.		20c+1c any single	.45	.45
		Nos. B7-B10 (4)	3.45	3.45

Christmas. The surtax was for children's activities during holiday season.

Nos. 135-142a Surcharged in Silver

1976, Nov. 19 Photo. *Perf. 13½x13*

B11		6c + 1c multicolored	.25	.25
B12		6c + 1c multicolored	.25	.25
a.	A36	Pair, #B11-B12	.25	.25
B13		7c + 1c multicolored	.25	.25
B14		7c + 1c multicolored	.25	.25
a.	A36	Pair, #B13-B14	.25	.25
B15		15c + 1c multicolored	.25	.25
B16		15c + 1c multicolored	.25	.25
a.	A36	Pair, #B15-B16	.45	.45
B17		20c + 1c multicolored	.30	.30
B18		20c + 1c multicolored	.50	.50
a.	A36	Pair, #B17-B18	1.00	1.00
b.		Souvenir sheet of 8	2.00	2.00

Surtax was for child welfare. Stamps of No. B18b each surcharged 2c.

Nos. 152-159a Surcharged in Black

1977, Nov. 15 *Perf. 13½x14*

B19		6c + 1c multicolored	.25	.25
B20		6c + 1c multicolored	.25	.25
a.	A41	Pair, #B19-B20	.25	.25
B21		7c + 1c multicolored	.25	.25
B22		7c + 1c multicolored	.25	.25
a.	A41	Pair, #B21-B22	.25	.25
B23		15c + 1c multicolored	.25	.25
B24		15c + 1c multicolored	.25	.25
a.	A41	Pair, #B23-B24	.50	.50
B25		20c + 1c multicolored	.30	.30
B26		20c + 1c multicolored	.30	.30
a.	A41	Pair, #B25-B26	.65	.65
b.		Souvenir sheet of 8	2.50	2.50
		Nos. B19-B26 (8)	2.10	2.10

Surtax was for child welfare. Stamps of No. B26b each surcharged 2c.

Easter Type of 1978

Souvenir Sheets

Paintings: No. B27, like No. 163. No. B28, like No. 164. No. B29, like No. 165.

1978, Mar. 17 Photo. *Perf. 14*

B27	A44	50c + 5c multicolored	.55	.55
B28	A44	50c + 5c multicolored	.55	.55
B29	A44	50c + 5c multicolored	.55	.55

Nos. B27-B29 contain one stamp 33x25mm.

Christmas Type of 1978

Souvenir Sheet

1978, Dec. 4 Photo. *Perf. 14½x13*

B30		Sheet of 4	2.25	2.25
a.	A46	15c + 2c like #167	.25	.25
b.	A46	17c + 2c like #168	.30	.30
c.	A46	30c + 2c like #169	.45	.45
d.	A46	35c + 2c like #170	.60	.60

Year of the Child Type

Souvenir Sheet

1979, Oct. 1 Photo. *Perf. 14x13½*

B31		Sheet of 3	1.25	1.25
a.	A48	30c + 3c like #173	.30	.30
b.	A48	35c + 3c like #174	.35	.35
c.	A48	65c + 3c like #175	.45	.45

Easter Type of 1980

Souvenir Sheet

No. B32 shows entire painting in continuous design. Nos. B32a-B32c similar to Nos. 183-185. Size of Nos. B32a-B32c: 25x50mm.

1980, Apr. 3 Photo. *Perf. 13x13½*

B32		Sheet of 3	1.90	1.90
a.	A50	20c + 2c multicolored	.45	.45
b.	A50	30c + 2c multicolored	.60	.60
c.	A50	35c + 2c multicolored	.75	.75

Christmas Type of 1980

Souvenir Sheet

1980, Nov. 21 Photo. *Perf. 13x13½*

B33		Sheet of 4	1.50	1.50
a.	A53	15c + 2c like #208	.25	.25
b.	A53	20c + 2c like #209	.30	.30
c.	A53	25c + 2c like #210	.35	.35
d.	A53	35c + 2c like #211	.45	.45

Easter Type of 1981

Souvenir Sheet

1981, Mar. 31 Photo. *Perf. 13½*

B34		Sheet of 3	1.65	1.65
a.	A54	30c + 2c like #212	.35	.35
b.	A54	40c + 2c like #213	.50	.50
c.	A54	50c + 2c like #214	.65	.65

Nos. 247-249 Surcharged

1981, Nov. 23 Photo. *Perf. 13x13½*

B35	A56	60 + 5c multi	.65	.65
B36	A56	80 + 5c multi	.70	.70
B37	A56	$1.40 + 5c multi	.90	.90
		Nos. B35-B37 (3)	2.25	2.25

Intl. Year of the Disabled. Surtax was for the handicapped.

Soccer Type of 1981

Souvenir Sheet

a-b, 12c+2c. c-d, 15c+2c. e-f, 20c+2c. g-h, 25c+2c.

1981, Nov. 30 *Perf. 14*

B38	A57	Sheet of 8, multi	6.00	6.00

No. B38 contains stamps with 2c surtax similar to Nos. 250-253. Surtax was for local sports.

Nos. 400-404 Surcharged

1986, Nov. 25 Litho. *Perf. 13½*

B39	A79	75c + 10c multi	3.00	3.00
B40	A79	$1.35 + 10c multi	3.50	3.50
B41	A79	$1.95 + 10c multi	4.25	4.25
B42	A79	$2.75 + 10c multi	5.25	5.25
		Nos. B39-B42 (4)	16.00	16.00

Souvenir Sheet

B43		Sheet of 4	16.50	16.50
a.-d.		A79 $1.65 +10c on #404a-404d, each	4.00	4.00

State visit of Pope John Paul II. For surcharges see Nos. B51-B54.

Nos. 394-395, 397 and 400-403 Surcharged in Silver or Black

1987, Apr. 29 Litho. *Perf. 13½, 14*

B44	A79	75c + 50c #400	3.50	2.50
B45	A77	$1 + 50c #394 (B)	4.25	3.50
B46	A79	$1.35 + 50c #401	5.75	5.00
B47	A79	$1.95 + 50c #402	6.25	5.00
B48	A78	$2 + 50c #397	6.50	5.00
B49	A77	$2.75 + 50c #395 (B)	8.00	6.25
B50	A79	$2.75 + 50c #403	8.50	7.25
		Nos. B44-B50 (7)	42.75	34.50

Nos. B39-B42 Surcharged in Silver

1987, Apr. 29 Litho. *Perf. 13½*

B51	A79	75c + 50c No. B39	4.00	4.00
B52	A79	$1.35 + 50c No. B40	4.50	4.50
B53	A79	$1.95 + 50c No. B41	4.75	4.75
B54	A79	$2.75 + 50c No. B42	6.00	6.00
		Nos. B51-B54 (4)	19.25	19.25

No. 523 Surcharged in Silver

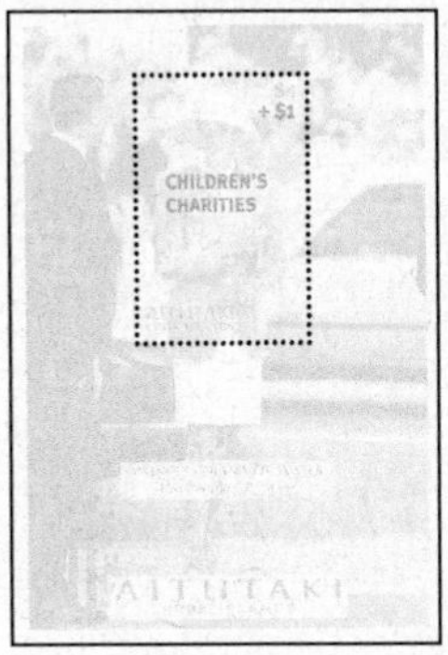

Souvenir Sheet

1998, Nov. 19 Litho. *Perf. 14*

B55	A108	$4 + $1 multicolored	6.25	6.25

AIR POST STAMPS

Capt. Bligh Type of 1974

1974, Sept. 9 Litho. *Perf. 13*

Size: 46x26mm

C1	A27	10c Bligh and "Bounty"	.75	.60
C2	A27	10c "Bounty" at sea	.75	.60
a.		Pair, #C1-C2	1.75	1.75
C3	A27	25c Bligh and "Bounty"	.85	.75
C4	A27	25c Chart, 1856	.85	.75
a.		Pair, #C3-C4	2.00	2.00
C5	A27	30c Cook and "Resolution"	1.00	1.00
C6	A27	30c Maps	1.00	1.00
a.		Pair, #C5-C6	2.75	2.75
		Nos. C1-C6 (6)	5.20	4.70

See note after No. 101.

OFFICIAL STAMPS

Nos. 83-90, 92-95, 150-151 Ovptd. or Srchd. in Black, Silver or Gold

1978-79 Photo. *Perf. 13x13½*

O1	A25	1c multi	1.10	.25
O2	A25	2c multi	1.75	.25
O3	A25	3c multi	1.75	.25
O4	A25	4c multi (G)	1.75	.25
O5	A25	5c multi	1.75	.25
O6	A25	8c multi	1.75	.25
O7	A25	10c multi	2.00	.25
O8	A25	15c on 60c multi	3.50	.25
O9	A25	18c on 60c multi	3.50	.25
O10	A25	20c multi (G)	3.50	.25
O11	A40	50c multi	1.50	.70
O12	A25	60c multi	12.00	.80
O13	A25	$1 multi	12.00	1.00
O14	A26	$2 multi	11.00	.80
O15	A40	$4 on $1 multi (S)	2.50	.80
O16	A26	$5 multi	13.00	1.50
		Nos. O1-O16 (16)	74.35	8.10

Overprint on 4c, 20c, $1 diagonal.

Issued: Nos. O14-O16, 2/20/79; others, 11/3/78.

Stamps of 1983-84 Ovptd. or Surcharged in Green

or Gold (#O29-O32)

1985, Aug. 9 ***Perf. 14, 13x13½***

O17	A66	2c No. 322	2.10	2.10
O18	A66	5c No. 324	2.50	2.50
O19	A66	10c No. 325	3.00	3.00
O20	A66	12c No. 326	3.25	3.00
O21	A66	18c No. 327	4.00	3.50
O22	A66	20c on 24c No. 328	4.50	3.75
O23	A66	30c No. 329	3.50	2.50
O24	A66	40c on 36c No. 330	3.50	2.50
O25	A66	50c No. 332	3.50	2.50
O26	A66	55c on 48c No. 331	3.50	2.50
O27	A66	60c No. 333	4.00	2.75
O28	A66	65c on 72c No. 334	4.00	2.75
O29	A61	75c on 48c No. 276	2.50	2.10
O30	A61	75c on 48c No. 277	2.50	2.10
O31	A61	75c on 48c No. 278	2.50	2.10
O32	A61	75c on 48c No. 279	2.50	2.10
a.		Block of 4, Nos. O29-O32	11.00	11.00
O33	A66	80c on 96c No. 335	4.00	3.75
		Nos. O17-O33 (17)	55.35	45.50

Nos. 336-341 Overprinted Like Nos. O17-O21, O23, O25, O27 in Metallic Green

1986, Oct. 1 ***Perf. 14***

O34	A66	$3 multi	8.50	6.50
O35	A66	$4.20 multi	11.00	8.50
O36	A66	$5.60 multi	12.00	10.00
O37	A66	$9.60 multi	15.00	12.00

1988-91 ***Perf. 14***

O38	A66	$1.20 multi	5.00	2.50
O39	A66	$2.10 multi	7.50	4.00

Nos. 246C-246D Surcharged in Metallic Blue

O40	A55	$14 on $4 (B)	17.50	14.00
O41	A55	$18 on $5 (B)	22.50	19.00
		Nos. O34-O41 (8)	99.00	76.50

Issue dates: July 2, 1991; others, June 15.

AJMAN

äj-'man

LOCATION — Oman Peninsula, Arabia, on Persian Gulf
GOVT. — Sheikdom under British Protection
AREA — 100 sq. mi.
POP. — 4,400
CAPITAL — Ajman

Ajman is one of six Persian Gulf sheikdoms to join the United Arab Emirates, which proclaimed its independence Dec. 2, 1971. See United Arab Emirates.

100 Naye Paise = 1 Rupee

Catalogue values for all unused stamps in this country are for Never Hinged items.

Sheik Rashid bin Humaid al Naimi & Arab Stallion — A1

Designs: 2np, 50np, Regal angelfish. 3np, 70np, Camel. 4np, 1r, Angelfish. 5np, 1.50r, Green turtle. 10np, 2r, Jewelfish. 15np, 3r, White storks. 20np, 5r, White-eyed gulls. 30np, 10r, Lanner falcon. 40np as 1np.

Photo. & Litho.
1964 **Unwmk.** ***Perf. 14***
Size: 35x22mm

1	A1	1np gold & multi	.25	.25
2	A1	2np gold & multi	.25	.25
3	A1	3np gold & multi	.25	.25
4	A1	4np gold & multi	.25	.25
5	A1	5np gold & multi	.25	.25
6	A1	10np gold & multi	.25	.25
7	A1	15np gold & multi	.25	.25
8	A1	20np gold & multi	.25	.25
9	A1	30np gold & multi	.25	.25

Size: 42x27mm

10	A1	40np gold & multi	.25	.25
11	A1	50np gold & multi	.25	.25
12	A1	70np gold & multi	.25	.25
13	A1	1r gold & multi	.40	.25
14	A1	1.50r gold & multi	.80	.35
15	A1	2r gold & multi	1.00	.50

Size: 53x33½mm

16	A1	3r gold & multi	1.50	1.00
17	A1	5r gold & multi	4.00	2.40
18	A1	10r gold & multi	7.50	3.75
		Nos. 1-18 (18)	18.20	11.25

Issued: Nos. 1-9, 6/20; Nos. 10-15, 9/7; Nos. 16-18, 11/4. Exist imperf. Value, set $30.

Pres. and Mrs. John F. Kennedy with Caroline — A2

Pres. Kennedy: 10np, As a boy in football uniform. 15np, Diving. 50np, As navy lieutenant, receiving Navy and Marine Corps Medal from Capt. Frederic L. Conklin. 1r, Sailing with Jacqueline Kennedy. 2r, With Eleanor Roosevelt. 5r, With Lyndon B. Johnson and Hubert H. Humphrey. 10r, Portrait.

1964, Dec. 15 **Photo.** ***Perf. 13½x14***

19	A2	10np grn & red lil	.25	.25
20	A2	15np Prus bl & vio	.25	.25
21	A2	50np org brn & dk bl	.25	.25
22	A2	1r brn & Prus grn	.50	.30
23	A2	2r red lil & dp ol	.75	.50
24	A2	3r grn & red brn	1.50	.75
25	A2	5r vio & brn	2.75	2.00
26	A2	10r dk bl & red brn	5.50	3.50
		Nos. 19-26 (8)	11.75	7.80

John F. Kennedy (1917-63). Exist imperf. Value, set $17.50. A souvenir sheet contains one each of Nos. 23-26. Value, perf or imperf, $25.

Runners at Start — A3

10np, 1.50r, Boxing. 25np, 2r, Judo. 50np, 5r, Gymnast on vaulting horse. 1r, 3r, Sailing yacht.

1965, Jan. 12 **Photo.** ***Perf. 13½x14***

27	A3	5np red brn, brt pink & Prus grn	.25	.25
28	A3	10np dk ol grn, bl gray & red brn	.25	.25
29	A3	15np dk vio, grn & sep	.25	.25
30	A3	25np bl sal pink & blk	.25	.25
31	A3	50np mar, bl & ind	.25	.25
32	A3	1r dk grn, lil & ultra	.50	.25
33	A3	1.50r lil, grn & brn	.75	.50
34	A3	2r red org, bis & dk bl	1.25	.70
35	A3	3r dk brn, grnsh bl & lil	2.00	1.25
36	A3	5r grn, yel & red brn	3.25	1.75
		Nos. 27-36 (10)	9.00	5.70

18th Olympic Games, Tokyo, Oct. 10-25, 1964. Exist imperf. Value, set $12. A souvenir sheet contains four stamps similar to Nos. 33-36 in changed colors. Values: perf $10; imperf $14.

Stanley Gibbons Catalogue, 1865, U.S. No. 1X2 — A4

Designs: 10np, Austria, Scarlet Mercury 1856. 15np, British Guiana 1c, 1856. 25np, Canada 12p, 1851. 50np, Hawaii 2c, 1851. 1r, Mauritius 2p, 1847. 3r, Switzerland, Geneva 10c, 1843. 5r, Tuscany 31, 1860. 5np, 15np, 50np and 3r show first edition of Stanley Gibbons Catalogue; 10np, 25np, 1r and 5r show 1965 Elizabethan Catalogue.

1965, May 6 **Unwmk.** ***Perf. 13***

37	A4	5np multi	.25	.25
38	A4	10np multi	.25	.25
39	A4	15np multi	.25	.25
40	A4	25np multi	.25	.25
41	A4	50np multi	.25	.25
42	A4	1r multi	.50	.25
43	A4	3r multi	1.50	.50
a.		Souv. sheet of 4, #38-39, 42-43	4.50	
44	A4	5r multi	3.00	1.10
a.		Souv. sheet of 4, #37, 40-41, 44	4.00	
		Nos. 37-44 (8)	6.25	3.10

Gibbons Catalogue Cent. Exhib., London, Feb. 17-20. Nos. 43a and 44a for 125th anniv. of 1st postage stamp. Exist imperf. Value, set $9. Sheets exist imperf. Value for both sheets, $7.

Stamps of Ajman were replaced in 1972 by those of United Arab Emirates.

AIR POST STAMPS

Type of Regular Issue, 1964

Designs: 15np, Arab stallion. 25np, Regal angelfish. 35np, Camel. 50np, Angelfish. 75np, Green turtle. 1r, Jewelfish. 2r, White storks. 3r, White-eyed gulls. 5r, Lanner falcon.

Photo. & Litho.
1965 **Unwmk.** ***Perf. 14***
Size: 42x25½mm

C1	A1	15np silver & multi	.25	.25
C2	A1	25np silver & multi	.25	.25
C3	A1	35np silver & multi	.25	.25
C4	Al	50np silver & multi	.50	.25
C5	A1	75np silver & multi	.75	.25
C6	A1	1r silver & multi	1.00	.25

Size: 53x33½mm

C7	A1	2r silver & multi	1.50	.75
C8	A1	3r silver & multi	3.00	1.00
C9	A1	5r silver & multi	4.50	1.75
		Nos. C1-C9 (9)	12.00	5.00

Issued: Nos. C1-C6, 11/15; Nos. C7-C9, 12/18. Exist imperf. Value, set $25.

AIR POST OFFICIAL STAMPS

Type of Regular Issue, 1964

Designs: 75np, Jewelfish. 2r, White storks. 3r, White-eyed gulls. 5r, Lanner falcon.

Photo. & Litho.
1965, Dec. 18 **Unwmk.** ***Perf. 14***
Size: 42x25½mm

CO1	A1	75np gold & multi	.75	.35

Size: 53x33½mm

CO2	A1	2r gold & multi	2.25	.50
CO3	A1	3r gold & multi	3.00	1.00
CO4	A1	5r gold & multi	5.00	1.40
		Nos. CO1-CO4 (4)	11.00	3.25

OFFICIAL STAMPS

Type of Regular Issue, 1964

25np, Arab stallion. 40np, Regal angelfish. 50np, Camel. 75np, Angelfish. 1r, Green turtle.

Photo. & Litho.
1965, Dec. 1 **Unwmk.** ***Perf. 14***
Size: 42x25½mm

O1	A1	25np gold & multi	.30	.25
O2	A1	40np gold & multi	.40	.25
O3	A1	50np gold & multi	.50	.30
O4	A1	75np gold & multi	.60	.35
O5	A1	1r gold & multi	.90	.40
		Nos. O1-O5 (5)	2.70	1.55

ALAOUITES

'al-au-‚wītz

LOCATION — A division of Syria, in Western Asia
GOVT. — Under French Mandate
AREA — 2,500 sq. mi.
POP. — 278,000 (approx. 1930)
CAPITAL — Latakia

This territory became an independent state in 1924, although still administered under the French Mandate. In 1930, it was renamed Latakia, and Syrian stamps overprinted "Lattaquie" superseded the stamps of Alaouites. For these and subsequent issues, see Latakia and Syria.

100 Centimes = 1 Piaster

Issued under French Mandate

Stamps of France Surcharged

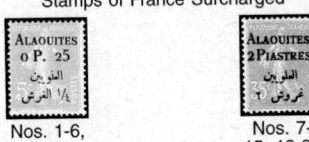

Nos. 1-6, 16-18

Nos. 7-15, 19-21

1925 Unwmk. *Perf. 14x13½*

1	A16	0.10p on 2c vio brn	4.00	4.00
2	A22	0.25p on 5c orange	4.00	4.00
3	A20	0.75p on 15c gray grn	7.25	7.25
4	A22	1p on 20c red brn	4.00	4.00
5	A22	1.25p on 25c blue	4.50	4.50
6	A22	1.50p on 30c red	14.50	14.50
7	A22	2p on 35c violet	4.75	*4.75*
8	A18	2p on 40c red & pale bl	5.50	5.50
9	A18	2p on 45c grn & bl	19.00	19.00
10	A18	3p on 60c vio & ultra	8.75	8.75
11	A20	3p on 60c lt vio	14.00	14.00
b.		Double surcharge	165.00	165.00
12b	A20	4p on 85c vermilion	4.00	*4.00*
c.		As "b," inverted surcharge	60.00	60.00
13	A18	5p on 1fr cl & ol grn	8.50	8.50
14	A18	10p on 2fr org & pale bl	13.00	13.00
15	A18	25p on 5fr bl & buff	16.00	16.00
		Nos. 1-15 (15)	131.75	131.75

Two types of surcharge exist on the 4p and on the 5p-25p. For detailed listings, see the *Scott Classic Specialized Catalogue of Stamps and Covers 1840-1940.*

For overprints, see Nos. C1-C4.

Same Surcharges on Pasteur Stamps of France

16	A23	0.50p on 10c green	3.00	3.00
17	A23	0.75p on 15c green	3.75	3.75
18	A23	1.50p on 30c red	3.00	3.00
19	A23	2p on 45c red	3.75	3.75
20	A23	2.50p on 50c blue	5.25	5.25
21	A23	4p on 75c blue	9.00	9.00
		Nos. 16-21 (6)	27.75	*27.75*

Two types of overprints exist on No. 21. For detailed listings, see *Scott Classic Specialized Catalogue of Stamps and Covers 1840-1940.*

Inverted Surcharges

1a	A16	0.10p on 2c vio brn	50.00
2a	A22	0.25p on 5c orange	50.00
3a	A20	0.75p on 15c gray grn	50.00
4a	A22	1p on 20c red brn	50.00
5a	A22	1.25p on 25c blue	50.00
6a	A22	1.50p on 30c red	60.00
7a	A22	2p on 35c violet	50.00
8a	A18	2p on 40c red & pale bl	50.00
9a	A18	2p on 45c grn & bl	60.00
10a	A18	3p on 60c vio & ultra	50.00
11a	A20	3p on 60c lt vio	60.00
12a	A20	4p on 85c vermilion	50.00
13a	A18	5p on 1fr cl & ol grn	60.00
14a	A18	10p on 2fr org & pale bl	70.00
15a	A18	25p on 5fr bl & buff	70.00
16a	A23	0.50p on 10c green	40.00
17a	A23	0.75p on 15c green	40.00
18a	A23	1.50p on 30c red	45.00
19a	A23	2p on 45c red	40.00
20a	A23	2.50p on 50c blue	40.00
21a	A23	4p on 75c blue	40.00

Stamps of Syria, 1925, Overprinted in Red, Black or Blue

On A3, A5

On A4

1925, Mar. 1 *Perf. 12½, 13½*

25	A3	0.10p dk violet (R)	1.50	*2.25*
a.		Double overprint	42.50	42.50
b.		Inverted overprint	45.00	
c.		Black overprint	37.50	37.50
e.		"ALAOUITE," instead of "ALAOUITES"	30.00	*30.00*
26	A4	0.25p olive black (R)	2.25	*3.00*
a.		Inverted overprint	40.00	
b.		Blue overprint	50.00	50.00
27	A4	0.50p yellow green	1.75	1.75
a.		Inverted overprint	40.00	40.00
b.		Blue overprint	50.00	50.00
c.		Red overprint	50.00	50.00
d.		"ALAOUITE," instead of "ALAOUITES"	50.00	50.00
e.		Double overprint	50.00	50.00
28	A4	0.75p brown orange	2.00	*2.25*
a.		Inverted overprint	45.00	*60.00*
b.		Double overprint	47.50	*65.00*
29	A5	1p magenta	2.75	2.75
a.		Inverted overprint	40.00	*47.50*
30	A4	1.25p deep green	3.25	*3.50*
a.		Red overprint	50.00	50.00
b.		Double overprint		75.00
31	A4	1.50p rose red (Bl)	2.75	*3.00*
a.		Inverted overprint	45.00	45.00
b.		Black overprint	40.00	40.00
c.		As "b", inverted	80.00	
32	A4	2p dk brown (R)	2.75	*3.50*
a.		Blue overprint	65.00	65.00
b.		Inverted overprint	40.00	40.00
33	A4	2.50p pck blue (R)	4.25	*4.50*
a.		Black overprint	65.00	65.00
34	A4	3p orange brown	2.50	*2.75*
a.		Inverted overprint	40.00	40.00
b.		Blue overprint	70.00	70.00
c.		Double overprint		90.00
35	A4	5p violet	3.75	*4.00*
a.		Red overprint	70.00	70.00
b.		Inverted overprint	42.50	
36	A4	10p violet brown	5.50	*6.00*
37	A4	25p ultra (R)	9.00	*10.00*
		Nos. 25-37 (13)	44.00	*49.25*

For overprints see Nos. C5-C19.

Stamps of Syria, 1925, Surcharged in Black or Red

Nos. 38-42

Nos. 43-45

1926

38	A4	3.50p on 0.75p brn org	2.50	*2.75*
a.		Surcharged on face and back	25.00	25.00
39	A4	4p on 0.25p ol blk	2.50	*2.50*
40	A4	6p on 2.50p pck bl (R)	3.00	*3.25*
41	A4	12p on 1.25p dp grn	3.25	*3.50*
a.		Inverted surcharge	35.00	35.00
42	A4	20p on 1.25p dp grn	5.25	5.25
43	A4	4.50p on 0.75p brn org	5.25	3.25
a.		Inverted surcharge	60.00	60.00
b.		Double surcharge	55.00	55.00
44	A4	7.50p on 2.50p pck bl	4.75	3.25
45	A4	15p on 25p ultra	8.75	5.50
a.		Inverted surcharge	50.00	
		Nos. 38-45 (8)	35.25	*29.25*

Two types of overprints exist on No. 39. For detailed listings, see *Scott Classic Specialized Catalogue of Stamps and Covers 1840-1940.*

For overprint, see No. C21.

Syria No. 199 Ovptd. in Red like No. 25

1928

46	A3	5c on 0.10p dk violet	2.00	1.75
a.		Double surcharge	50.00	

Syria Nos. 178 and 174 Surcharged like Nos. 43-45 in Red

47	A4	2p on 1.25p dp green	16.00	8.00
a.		Double surcharge	60.00	
b.		Inverted surcharge	50.00	50.00
48	A4	4p on 0.25p olive black	11.00	6.50
a.		Double surcharge	50.00	50.00
b.		Inverted surcharge	50.00	50.00

For overprint see No. C20.

49	A4	4p on 0.25p olive black	82.50	50.00
a.		Double impression	150.00	
		Nos. 46-49 (4)	111.50	66.25

AIR POST STAMPS

Nos. 8, 10, 13 & 14 with Additional Ovpt. in Black

1925, Jan. 1 Unwmk. *Perf. 14x13½*

C1b	A18	2p on 40c	17.00	15.00
C2	A18	3p on 60c	22.50	*20.00*
a.		Inverted overprint	125.00	125.00
C3	A18	5p on 1fr	17.00	14.00
a.		Inverted overprint	37.50	*37.50*
C4	A18	10p on 2fr	22.00	15.00
a.		Inverted overprint	35.00	*35.00*
		Nos. C1-C4 (4)	78.50	*64.00*

Two types of overprints exist on Nos. C1-C4. For detailed listings, see *Scott Classic Specialized Catalogue of Stamps and Covers 1840-1940.*

Nos. 32, 34, 35 & 36 With Additional Ovpt. in Green

1925, Mar. 1 *Perf. 13½*

C5	A4	2p dark brown	7.50	6.00
a.		Inverted overprint	75.00	75.00
b.		Red overprint	125.00	
C6	A4	3p orange brown	7.50	6.00
a.		Inverted overprint	75.00	75.00
b.		Red overprint	100.00	
C7	A4	5p violet	7.50	6.00
a.		Inverted overprint	75.00	75.00
b.		Red overprint	100.00	
C8	A4	10p violet brown	7.50	6.00
a.		Inverted overprint	75.00	75.00
b.		Red overprint	100.00	
		Nos. C5-C8 (4)	30.00	24.00

Nos. 32, 34, 35 & 36 With Additional Ovpt. in Red

1926, May 1

C9	A4	2p dark brown	7.50	6.50
a.		Red overprint double	175.00	175.00
b.		Black overprint double	175.00	175.00
c.		Black overprint inverted	70.00	70.00
C10	A4	3p orange brown	7.50	6.50
a.		Black overprint inverted	70.00	70.00
C11	A4	5p violet	8.50	7.50
a.		Black overprint inverted	70.00	70.00
C12	A4	10p violet brown	8.50	7.50
a.		Black overprint inverted	70.00	70.00
		Nos. C9-C12 (4)	32.00	28.00

No. C9 has the original overprint in black.

Double or inverted overprints, original or plane, are known on most of Nos. C9-C12. Value, each $75. Value for example with both original and plane overprint inverted, each $150.

The red plane overprint was also applied to Nos. C5-C8. These are believed to have been essays, and were not regularly issued. Value, each $100.

Nos. 27c, 37 and Syria No. 177 With Addtl. Ovpt. of Airplane in Red or Black

1929, June-July

C17	A4	0.50p yel grn (R)	5.00	5.00
a.		Plane overprint double	250.00	
b.		Plane ovpt. on face and back	60.00	
c.		Pair with plane overprint Tête-bêche	325.00	
d.		Double overprint	225.00	225.00
e.		Overprint inverted	125.00	
f.		Plane only inverted	250.00	
C18	A5	1p magenta (Bk)	9.00	9.00
a.		Red overprint	50.00	
C19	A4	25p ultra (R)	52.50	40.00
a.		Plane overprint inverted	125.00	125.00
b.		Surcharge double	150.00	150.00
		Nos. C17-C19 (3)	66.50	54.00

Nos. 28 and 30 exist with additional overprint of airplane in red. These stamps were never issued. Value, each $100.

Nos. 47 and 45 With Additional Ovpt. of Airplane in Red

1929-30

C20	A4	2p on 1.25p ('30)	7.25	7.25
a.		Surcharge inverted	60.00	60.00
b.		Double surcharge	85.00	85.00
c.		Triple surcharge	200.00	
C21	A4	15p on 25p (Bk + R)	57.50	50.00
a.		Plane overprint inverted	225.00	225.00

POSTAGE DUE STAMPS

Postage Due Stamps of France, 1893-1920, Surcharged Like No. 1 (Nos. J1-J2) or No. 7 (Nos. J3-J5)

1925 Unwmk. *Perf. 14x13½*

J1	D2	0.50p on 10c choc	9.00	9.00
J2	D2	1p on 20c ol grn	9.00	9.00
J3	D2	2p on 30c red	9.50	9.50
J4	D2	3p on 50c vio brn	9.50	9.50
J5	D2	5p on 1fr red brn, *straw*	10.00	10.00
		Nos. J1-J5 (5)	47.00	*47.00*

Two types of overprints exist on No. J5. For detailed listings, see *Scott Classic Specialized Catalogue of Stamps and Covers 1840-1940.*

1925 Syria Postage Due Stamps Overprinted in Black, Blue or Red

1925 *Perf. 13½*

J6	D5	0.50p brown, *yel*	5.50	*5.50*
a.		Blue overprint	45.00	
b.		Red overprint	45.00	
c.		Overprint inverted	37.50	37.50
J7	D6	1p vio, *rose* (Bl)	5.00	*5.00*
a.		Black overprint	155.00	155.00
b.		Double overprint (Bk + Bl)	175.00	175.00
c.		Overprint inverted	40.00	40.00
J8	D5	2p blk, *blue* (R)	6.75	6.75
a.		Blue overprint	45.00	
J9	D5	3p blk, *red org* (Bl)	9.00	9.00
a.		Overprint inverted	35.00	
J10	D5	5p blk, *bl grn* (R)	11.00	11.00
a.		Overprint inverted	30.00	30.00
b.		Black overprint	45.00	
		Nos. J6-J10 (5)	37.25	37.25

The stamps of Alaouites were superseded in 1930 by those of Latakia.

ALBANIA

al-'bā-nē-ə

LOCATION — Southeastern Europe
GOVT. — Republic
AREA — 11,101 sq. mi.
POP. — 3,364,571 (1999 est.)
CAPITAL — Tirana

After the outbreak of World War I, the country fell into a state of anarchy when the Prince and all members of the International Commission left Albania. Subsequently General Ferrero in command of Italian troops declared Albania an independent country. A constitution was adopted and a republican form of government was instituted which continued until 1928 when, by constitutional amendment, Albania was declared to be a monarchy. The President of the republic, Ahmed Zogu, became king of the new state. Many unlisted varieties or surcharges and lithographed labels are said to have done postal duty in Albania and Epirus during this unsettled period.

On April 7, 1939, Italy invaded Albania. King Zog fled but did not abdicate. The King of Italy acquired the crown.

Germany occupied Albania from September, 1943, until late 1944 when it became an independent state. The People's Republic began in January, 1946.

40 Paras = 1 Piaster = 1 Grossion
100 Centimes = 1 Franc (1917)
100 Qintar = 1 Franc
100 Qintar (Qindarka) = 1 Lek (1947)

Catalogue values for unused stamps in this country are for Never Hinged items, beginning with Scott 458 in the regular postage section, Scott B34 in the semi-postal section, and Scott C67 in the airpost section.

Watermarks

Wmk. 125 — Lozenges

Wmk. 220 — Double Headed Eagle

Issues of 1908 Turkey Stamps Handstamped

Perf. 12, 13½ and Compound

1913, June **Unwmk.**

1	A19	2½pi violet brown	750.00	900.00

With Additional Overprint in Carmine

2	A19	10pa blue green	675.00	650.00

Handstamped on Issue of 1909

4	A21	5pa ocher	450.00	450.00
5	A21	10pa blue green	350.00	225.00
6	A21	20pa car rose	350.00	250.00
7	A21	1pi ultra	325.00	250.00
8	A21	2pi blue black	500.00	450.00
10	A21	5pi dark violet	1,400.	1,500.
11	A21	10pi dull red	*5,000.*	*4,750.*

For surcharge see No. 19.

Additional values of 25pi dark green and 50pi red brown were overprinted and sold only to dealers. Values, 25pi $8,000, 50pi $16,000.

With Additional Overprint in Blue or Carmine

13A	A21	10pa blue green	900.00	850.00
14	A21	20pa car rose (Bl)	800.00	850.00
15	A21	1pi brt blue (C)	1,900.	1,750.
15A	A21	2pi brt blue (C)	3,750.	3,500.

Handstamped on Newspaper Stamp of 1911

17	A21	2pa olive green	425.00	425.00

Handstamped on Postage Due Stamp of 1908

18	A19	1pi black, *dp rose*	3,000.	2,500.
a.		Inverted overprint	—	—

No. 18 was used for regular postage.

No. 6 Surcharged With New Value

19	A21	10pa on 20pa car rose	1,250.	1,250.
a.		"11" instead of "10"	—	—
b.		Inverted surcharge	3,250.	—
c.		Double surcharge	—	—

A1

Handstamped on White Laid Paper Without Eagle and Value Issued Without Gum

1913, July ***Imperf.***

20	A1	(1pi) black	325.00	*525.00*
		Cut to shape	190.00	*275.00*
a.		Sewing machine perf.	575.00	*725.00*

Value Typewritten in Violet Issued Without Gum

1913, Aug. **With Eagle**

21	A1	10pa violet	12.00	12.00
a.		Double impression	—	—
22	A1	20pa red & black	16.00	13.50
a.		"2p para"	—	—
23	A1	1gr black	16.00	16.00
24	A1	2gr blue & violet	20.00	16.00
25	A1	5gr violet & blue	24.00	21.00
26	A1	10gr blue	24.00	21.00
		Nos. 21-26 (6)	112.00	99.50

Nos. 21-26 exist with the eagle inverted or omitted and with numerous errors in the figures of value and the spelling of the word "grosh."

A2

Handstamped on White Laid Paper Eagle and Value in Black Issued Without Gum

1913, Nov. ***Perf. 11½***

27	A2	10pa green	4.00	3.25
b.		Eagle and value in green	1,750.	1,750.
c.		10pa red (error)	32.50	32.50
d.		10pa violet (error)	32.50	32.50
29	A2	20pa red	6.00	4.75
b.		20pa green (error)	42.50	32.50
30	A2	30pa violet	6.00	4.75
a.		30pa ultramarine (error)	32.50	32.50
b.		30pa red (error)	32.50	32.50
31	A2	1gr ultramarine	8.00	7.25
a.		1gr green (error)	32.50	32.50
b.		1gr black (error)	32.50	32.50
c.		1gr violet (error)	32.50	32.50
33	A2	2gr black	12.00	8.00
a.		2gr violet (error)	40.00	40.00
b.		2gr blue (error)	40.00	40.00
		Nos. 27-33 (5)	36.00	28.00

The stamps of this issue are known with eagle or value inverted or omitted.

1st anniv. of Albanian independence.

Counterfeits exist.

Skanderbeg (George Castriota) — A3

1913, Dec. **Typo.** ***Perf. 14***

35	A3	2q orange brn & buff	3.50	1.75
36	A3	5q green & blue grn	3.50	1.75
37	A3	10q rose red	3.50	1.75
38	A3	25q dark blue	3.50	1.75
39	A3	50q violet & red	8.50	3.50
40	A3	1fr deep brown	20.00	10.50
		Nos. 35-40 (6)	42.50	*21.00*

For overprints and surcharges see Nos. 41-52, 105, J1-J9.

Nos. 35-40 Handstamped in Black or Violet

1914, Mar. 7

41	A3	2q orange brn & buff	50.00	*65.00*
42	A3	5q grn & bl grn (V)	50.00	*65.00*
43	A3	10q rose red	50.00	*65.00*
44	A3	25q dark blue (V)	50.00	*65.00*
45	A3	50q violet & red	50.00	*65.00*
46	A3	1fr deep brown	50.00	*65.00*
		Nos. 41-46 (6)	300.00	390.00

Issued to celebrate the arrival of Prince Wilhelm zu Wied on Mar. 7, 1914.

Nos. 35-40 Surcharged in Black

a

b

1914, Apr. 2

47	A3 (a)	5pa on 2q	2.10	2.10
48	A3 (a)	10pa on 5q	2.10	2.10
49	A3 (a)	20pa on 10q	3.50	2.75
50	A3 (b)	1gr on 25q	3.50	3.50
51	A3 (b)	2gr on 50q	3.50	3.50
52	A3 (b)	5gr on 1fr	14.00	10.50
		Nos. 47-52 (6)	28.70	24.45

For overprints see Nos. 105, J6-J9.

Inverted Surcharge

47a	A3 (a)	5pa on 2q	24.00	24.00
48a	A3 (a)	10pa on 5q	22.50	22.50
49a	A3 (a)	20pa on 10q	24.00	24.00
50a	A3 (b)	1gr on 25q	24.00	24.00
51a	A3 (b)	2gr on 50q	28.00	28.00
52b	A3 (b)	5gr on 1fr	90.00	90.00
		Nos. 47a-52b (6)	212.50	212.50

Korce (Korytsa) Issues

A4

1914 **Handstamped** ***Imperf.***

52A	A4	10pa violet & red	200.00	200.00
c.		10pa black & red	325.00	325.00
53	A4	25pa violet & red	200.00	200.00
a.		25pa black & red	425.00	425.00

Nos. 52A-53a were handstamped directly on the cover, so the paper varies. They were also produced in sheets; these are rarely found. Nos. 52A-53a were issued by Albanian military authorities.

Counterfeits exists of Nos. 52A and 53.

A5

1917 **Typo. & Litho.** ***Perf. 11½***

54	A5	1c dk brown & grn	17.50	12.00
55	A5	2c red & green	17.50	12.00
56	A5	3c gray grn & grn	17.50	12.00
57	A5	5c green & black	16.00	8.00
58	A5	10c rose red & black	16.00	8.00
59	A5	25c blue & black	16.00	8.00
60	A5	50c violet & black	16.00	10.00
61	A5	1fr brown & black	16.00	10.00
		Nos. 54-61 (8)	132.50	80.00

A6

1917-18

62	A6	1c dk brown & grn	2.75	2.40
63	A6	2c red brown & grn	2.75	2.40
a.		"CTM" for "CTS"	72.50	120.00
64	A6	3c black & green	2.75	2.40
a.		"CTM" for "CTS"	80.00	135.00
65	A6	5c green & black	4.00	4.00
66	A6	10c dull red & black	4.00	4.00
67	A6	50c violet & black	7.25	6.50
68	A6	1fr red brn & black	20.00	17.50
		Nos. 62-68 (7)	43.50	39.20

Counterfeits abound of Nos. 54-68, 80-81.

No. 65 Surcharged in Red

1918

80	A6	25c on 5c green & blk	275.00	*325.00*

A7

1918

81	A7	25c blue & black	72.50	95.00

General Issue

A8

A9

Handstamped in Rose or Blue — XVI MCMXIX

1919 ***Perf. 12½***

84	A8	(2)q on 2h brown	7.50	7.50
85	A8	5q on 16h green	7.50	7.50
86	A8	10q on 8h rose (Bl)	7.50	7.50
87	A8	25q on 64h blue	8.50	8.50
88	A9	25q on 64h blue	*300.00*	*300.00*
89	A8	50q on 32h violet	7.50	7.50
90	A8	1fr on 1.28k org, *bl*	9.00	9.00
		Nos. 84-90 (7)	*347.50*	*347.50*

See Nos. J10-J13. Compare with types A10-A14. For overprints see Nos 91-104.

Handstamped in Rose or Blue

1919, Jan. 16

91	A8	(2)q on 2h brown	14.00	14.00
92	A8	5q on 16h green	10.50	10.50
93	A8	10q on 8h rose (Bl)	10.50	10.50
94	A8	25q on 64h blue	140.00	140.00
95	A9	25q on 64h blue	45.00	60.00
96	A8	50q on 32h violet	14.00	14.00
97	A8	1fr on 1.28k org, *bl*	14.00	14.00
		Nos. 91-97 (7)	248.00	263.00

Handstamped in Violet

1919

No.	Type	Description	Unused	Used
98	A8	(2)q on 2h brown	17.50	17.50
99	A8	5q on 16h green	17.50	17.50
100	A8	10q on 8h rose	17.50	17.50
101	A8	25q on 64h blue	17.50	17.50
102	A9	25q on 64h blue	140.00	140.00
103	A8	50q on 32h violet	17.50	17.50
104	A8	1fr on 1.28k org, *bl*	17.50	17.50
		Nos. 98-104 (7)	245.00	245.00

No. 50 Overprinted in Violet

1919 ***Perf. 14***

No.	Type	Description	Unused	Used
105	A3	1gr on 25q blue	32.50	25.00

A10

A11

1919, June 5 ***Perf. 11½, 12½***

No.	Type	Description	Unused	Used
106	A10	10q on 2h brown	7.00	7.00
107	A11	15q on 8h rose	7.00	7.00
108	A11	20q on 16h green	7.00	7.00
109	A10	25q on 64h blue	7.00	7.00
110	A11	50q on 32h violet	7.00	7.00
111	A11	1fr on 96h orange	7.00	7.00
112	A10	2fr on 1.60k vio, *buff*	25.00	21.00
		Nos. 106-112 (7)	67.00	63.00

Nos. 106-108, 110 exist with inverted surcharge.

A12

A13

Surcharged in Black or Violet

1919

No.	Type	Description	Unused	Used
113	A12	10q on 8h car	7.00	7.00
114	A12	15q on 8h car (V)	7.00	7.00
115	A13	20q on 16h green	7.00	7.00
116	A13	25q on 32h violet	7.00	7.00
117	A13	50q on 64h blue	20.00	14.00
118	A13	1fr on 96h orange	8.50	7.00
119	A12	2fr on 1.60k vio, *buff*	14.00	10.50
		Nos. 113-119 (7)	70.50	59.50

A14

Overprinted in Blue or Black Without New Value

1920 ***Perf. 12½***

No.	Type	Description	Unused	Used
120	A14	1q gray (Bl)	100.00	95.00
121	A14	10q rose (Bk)	14.00	*32.50*
a.		Double overprint	150.00	*150.00*
122	A14	20q brown (Bl)	45.00	40.00
123	A14	25q blue (Bk)	525.00	*600.00*
124	A14	50q brown vio (Bk)	60.00	*80.00*
		Nos. 120-124 (5)	744.00	*847.50*

Counterfeit overprints exist of Nos. 120-128.

Surcharged in Color Noted with New Value

No.	Type	Description	Unused	Used
125	A14	2q on 10q rose (R)	14.00	*21.00*
126	A14	5q on 10q rose (G)	14.00	*17.50*
127	A14	25q on 10q rose (Bl)	14.00	*21.00*
128	A14	50q on 10q rose (Br)	14.00	*35.00*
		Nos. 125-128 (4)	56.00	94.50

Stamps of type A14 (Portrait of the Prince zu Wied) were not placed in use without overprint or surcharge.

A15

Post Horn Overprinted in Black

1920 ***Perf. 14x13***

No.	Type	Description	Unused	Used
129	A15	2q orange	10.50	8.50
130	A15	5q deep green	17.50	15.00
131	A15	10q red	32.50	32.50
132	A15	25q light blue	55.00	30.00
133	A15	50q gray green	12.50	10.50
134	A15	1fr claret	12.50	10.50
		Nos. 129-134 (6)	140.50	107.00

Type A15 was never placed in use without post horn or "Besa" overprint.

Stamps of Type A15 (No Post Horn) Overprinted

1921

No.	Type	Description	Unused	Used
135	A15	2q orange	7.00	7.00
136	A15	5q deep green	7.00	7.00
137	A15	10q red	14.00	12.00
138	A15	25q light blue	25.00	21.00
139	A15	50q gray green	14.00	12.00
140	A15	1fr claret	14.00	12.00
		Nos. 135-140 (6)	81.00	71.00

For surcharge & overprints see Nos. 154, 156-157.

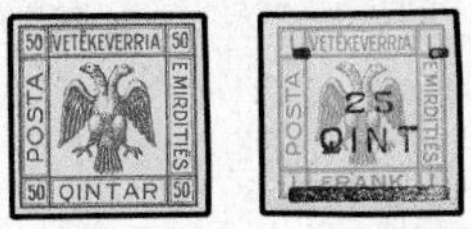

Stamps of these types, and with "TAKSE" overprint, were unauthorized and never placed in use. They are common.

Gjirokaster — A18

Korcha — A19

Designs: 5q, Kanina. 10q, Berati. 25q, Bridge at Vezirit. 50q, Rozafat. 2fr, Dursit.

1923 **Typo.** ***Perf. 12½, 11½***

No.	Type	Description	Unused	Used
147	A18	2q orange	.70	*1.40*
148	A18	5q yellow green	.70	*1.10*
149	A18	10q carmine	.70	*1.10*
150	A18	25q dark blue	.70	*1.10*
151	A18	50q dark green	.70	*1.10*
152	A19	1fr dark violet	.70	*2.75*
153	A19	2fr olive green	4.25	*8.00*
		Nos. 147-153 (7)	8.45	*16.55*

For overprints & surcharges see Nos. 158-185, B1-B8.

No. 135 Surcharged

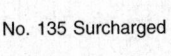

1922 ***Perf. 14x13***

No.	Type	Description	Unused	Used
154	A15	1q on 2q orange	3.25	*8.50*

Stamps of Type A15 (No Post Horn) Overprinted

1922

No.	Type	Description	Unused	Used
156	A15	5q deep green	5.00	*8.00*
157	A15	10q red	5.00	*8.00*

Nos. 147-151 Ovptd. in Black and Violet

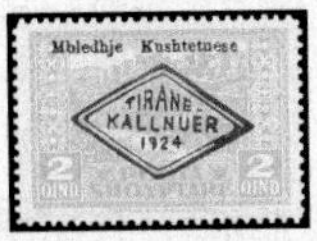

1924, Jan. ***Perf. 12½***

No.	Type	Description	Unused	Used
158	A18	2q red orange	12.50	*20.00*
159	A18	5q yellow green	12.50	*20.00*
160	A18	10q carmine	9.00	*14.50*
161	A18	25q dark blue	9.00	*14.50*
162	A18	50q dark green	15.00	*20.00*
		Nos. 158-162 (5)	58.00	89.00

The words "Mbledhje Kushtetuese" are in taller letters on the 25q than on the other values. Opening of the Constituent Assembly.

Counterfeits of Nos. 158 and 161 are plentiful.

No. 147 Surcharged

1924

No.	Type	Description	Unused	Used
163	A18	1q on 2q red orange	3.00	*8.00*

Nos. 163, 147-152 Overprinted

1924

No.	Type	Description	Unused	Used
164	A18	1q on 2q orange	2.75	*7.25*
165	A18	2q orange	2.75	*7.25*
166	A18	5q yellow green	2.75	*7.25*
167	A18	10q carmine	2.75	*7.25*
168	A18	25q dark blue	2.75	*7.25*
169	A18	50q dark green	6.25	*14.00*
170	A19	1fr dark violet	6.25	*17.50*
		Nos. 164-170 (7)	26.25	*67.75*

Issued to celebrate the return of the Government to the Capital after a revolution.

Nos. 163, 147-152 Overprinted

1925

No.	Type	Description	Unused	Used
171	A18	1q on 2q orange	3.25	*8.00*
172	A18	2q orange	3.25	*8.00*
173	A18	5q yellow green	3.25	*8.00*
174	A18	10q carmine	3.25	*8.00*
175	A18	25q dark blue	3.25	*8.00*
176	A18	50q dark green	3.25	*12.00*
177	A19	1fr dark violet	6.25	*16.00*
		Nos. 171-177 (7)	25.75	*68.00*

Proclamation of the Republic, Jan. 21, 1925. The date "1921" instead of "1925" occurs once in each sheet of 50.

Counterfeits exist.

Nos. 163, 147-153 Overprinted

1925

No.	Type	Description	Unused	Used
178	A18	1q on 2q orange	1.10	*1.60*
a.		Inverted overprint	12.50	12.50
179	A18	2q orange	1.10	*1.60*
180	A18	5q yellow green	1.10	*1.60*
a.		Inverted overprint	12.50	12.50
181	A18	10q carmine	1.10	*1.60*
182	A18	25q dark blue	1.10	*1.60*
183	A18	50q dark green	1.10	*1.60*
184	A19	1fr dark violet	5.00	*4.00*
185	A19	2fr olive green	7.50	*4.00*
		Nos. 178-185 (8)	19.10	17.60

Counterfeits exist.

President Ahmed Zogu

A25 A26

1925 ***Perf. 13½, 13½x13***

No.	Type	Description	Unused	Used
186	A25	1q orange	.25	.25
187	A25	2q red brown	.25	2.00
188	A25	5q green	.25	.25
189	A25	10q rose red	.25	.25
a.		Perf 11½	20.00	10.00
190	A25	15q gray brown	.75	*2.00*
191	A25	25q dark blue	.25	.25
192	A25	50q blue green	.85	*1.50*
193	A26	1fr red & ultra	1.75	2.00
194	A26	2fr green & orange	1.90	*2.00*
195	A26	3fr brown & violet	4.00	*5.00*
196	A26	5fr violet & black	5.00	6.75
		Nos. 186-196 (11)	15.50	22.25

No. 193 in ultramarine and brown, and No. 194 in green and brown were not regularly issued. Value, set $15.

For overprints & surcharges see Nos. 197-209, 238-248.

Nos. 186-196 Overprinted in Various Colors

1927

No.	Type	Description	Unused	Used
197	A25	1q orange (V)	.60	1.00
198	A25	2q red brn (G)	.25	.30
199	A25	5q green (R)	1.25	.50
200	A25	10q rose red (Bl)	.25	.30
a.		Perf 11½	25.00	20.00
201	A25	15q gray brn (G)	7.00	*12.50*
202	A25	25q dk blue (R)	.50	1.00
203	A25	50q blue grn (Bl)	.50	.40
204	A26	1fr red & ultra (Bk)	1.40	*.55*
205	A26	2fr green & org (Bk)	1.50	*.80*
206	A26	3fr brown & vio (Bk)	3.50	*1.60*
207	A26	5fr violet & blk (Bk)	3.50	*2.75*
		Nos. 197-207 (11)	20.25	21.70

No. 200 exists perf. 11.

For surcharges see Nos. 208-209, 238-240.

Nos. 200, 202 Surcharged in Black or Red

1928

No.	Type	Description	Unused	Used
208	A25	1q on 10q rose red	.50	.55
a.		Inverted surcharge	4.00	4.00
209	A25	5q on 25q dk blue (R)	.50	.55
a.		Inverted surcharge	4.00	4.00

A27

King Zog I — A28

Black Overprint

1928 ***Perf. 14x13½***

No.	Type	Description	Unused	Used
210	A27	1q orange brown	5.00	*9.50*
211	A27	2q slate	5.00	*9.50*
212	A27	5q blue green	5.00	*12.00*
213	A27	10q rose red	4.00	*12.00*
214	A27	15q bister	15.00	*47.50*
215	A27	25q deep blue	6.00	*12.00*
216	A27	50q lilac rose	10.00	*15.00*

Red Overprint

Perf. 13½x14

No.	Type	Description	Unused	Used
217	A28	1fr blue & slate	10.00	12.00
		Nos. 210-217 (8)	60.00	*129.50*

Compare with types A29-A32.

A29

A30

Black or Red Overprint

1928 ***Perf. 14x13½***

No.	Type	Description	Unused	Used
218	A29	1q orange brown	12.50	*25.00*
219	A29	2q slate (R)	12.50	*25.00*
220	A29	5q blue green	10.00	*20.00*
221	A29	10q rose red	10.00	*16.00*
222	A29	15q bister	15.00	*27.50*
223	A29	25q deep blue (R)	10.00	*16.00*
224	A29	50q lilac rose	10.00	*16.00*

Perf. 13½x14

No.	Type	Description	Unused	Used
225	A30	1fr blue & slate (R)	12.50	*20.00*
226	A30	2fr green & slate (R)	12.50	*20.00*
		Nos. 218-226 (9)	105.00	185.50

Proclamation of Ahmed Zogu as King of Albania.

A31

A32

Black Overprint

1928 *Perf. 14x13½*

No.	Type	Description	Unused	Used
227	A31	1q orange brown	.40	*1.25*
228	A31	2q slate	.40	*1.25*
229	A31	5q blue green	2.75	*3.50*
230	A31	10q rose red	.40	*1.25*
231	A31	15q bister	15.00	*24.00*
232	A31	25q deep blue	.40	*1.25*
233	A31	50q lilac rose	.75	*2.00*

Perf. 13½x14

No.	Type	Description	Unused	Used
234	A32	1fr blue & slate	1.50	*2.50*
235	A32	2fr green & slate	1.50	*4.00*
236	A32	3fr dk red & ol bis	7.50	*12.00*
237	A32	5fr dull vio & gray	7.50	*16.00*
		Nos. 227-237 (11)	38.10	69.00

The overprint reads "Kingdom of Albania."

Nos. 203, 202, 200 Surcharged in Black

1929 *Perf. 13½x13, 11½*

No.	Type	Description	Unused	Used
238	A25	1q on 50q blue green	.40	*.55*
239	A25	5q on 25q dark blue	.40	*.55*
240	A25	15q on 10q rose red	.60	*1.00*
		Nos. 238-240 (3)	1.40	2.10

Nos. 186-189, 191-194 Overprinted in Black or Red

1929 *Perf. 11½, 13½*

No.	Type	Description	Unused	Used
241	A25	1q orange	8.00	*20.00*
242	A25	2q red brown	8.00	*20.00*
243	A25	5q green	8.00	*20.00*
244	A25	10q rose red	8.00	*20.00*
245	A25	25q dark blue	8.00	*20.00*
246	A25	50q blue green (R)	11.00	*24.00*
247	A26	1fr red & ultra	15.00	*35.00*
248	A26	2fr green & orange	15.00	*35.00*
		Nos. 241-248 (8)	81.00	194.00

34th birthday of King Zog. The overprint reads "Long live the King."

Lake Butrinto A33

King Zog I A34

Zog Bridge A35

Ruin at Zog Manor A36

Perf. 14, 14½

1930, Sept. 1 Photo. Wmk. 220

No.	Type	Description	Unused	Used
250	A33	1q slate	.25	.25
251	A33	2q orange red	.25	.25
252	A34	5q yellow green	.25	.25
253	A34	10q carmine	.25	.25
254	A34	15q dark brown	.25	.25
255	A34	25q dark ultra	.25	.25
256	A33	50q slate green	.70	.55
257	A35	1fr violet	1.10	1.00
258	A35	2fr indigo	1.50	1.10
259	A36	3fr gray green	3.50	2.25
260	A36	5fr orange brown	4.50	3.50
		Nos. 250-260 (11)	12.80	9.90

2nd anniversary of accession of King Zog I.

For overprints see Nos. 261-270, 299-309, J39. For surcharges see Nos. 354-360.

Nos. 250-259 Overprinted in Black

1934, Dec. 24

No.	Type	Description	Unused	Used
261	A33	1q slate	7.00	*12.00*
262	A33	2q orange red	7.00	*12.00*
263	A34	5q yellow green	7.00	9.50
264	A34	10q carmine	9.25	*12.00*
265	A34	15q dark brown	9.25	*12.00*
266	A34	25q dark ultra	9.25	*12.00*
267	A33	50q slate green	10.00	*16.00*
268	A35	1fr violet	11.00	*20.00*
269	A35	2fr indigo	12.00	*25.00*
270	A36	3fr gray green	15.00	*35.00*
		Nos. 261-270 (10)	96.75	165.50

Tenth anniversary of the Constitution.

Allegory of Death of Skanderbeg A37

Albanian Eagle in Turkish Shackles A38

5q, 25q, 40q, 2fr, Eagle with wings spread.

1937 Unwmk. Perf. 14

No.	Type	Description	Unused	Used
271	A37	1q brown violet	.25	.25
272	A38	2q brown	.50	.35
273	A38	5q lt green	.50	.50
274	A37	10q olive brown	.50	*.80*
275	A38	15q rose red	.80	*1.00*
276	A38	25q blue	1.50	*2.00*
277	A37	50q deep green	3.75	3.25
278	A38	1fr violet	9.00	6.00
279	A38	2fr orange brown	12.00	9.00
		Nos. 271-279 (9)	28.80	23.15

Souvenir Sheet

No.	Type	Description	Unused	Used
280		Sheet of 3	17.50	*125.00*
a.	A37	20q red violet	3.50	*6.25*
b.	A38	30q olive brown	3.50	*6.25*
c.	A38	40q red	3.50	*6.25*

25th anniv. of independence from Turkey, proclaimed Nov. 28, 1912.

Queen Geraldine and King Zog — A40

1938 *Perf. 14*

No.	Type	Description	Unused	Used
281	A40	1q slate violet	.30	.40
282	A40	2q red brown	.30	.40
283	A40	5q green	.30	.40
284	A40	10q olive brown	1.10	.80
285	A40	15q rose red	1.10	.80
286	A40	25q blue	2.75	2.00
287	A40	50q Prus green	5.75	4.00
288	A40	1fr purple	11.50	8.00
		Nos. 281-288 (8)	23.10	16.80

Souvenir Sheet

No.	Type	Description	Unused	Used
289		Sheet of 4	32.50	*125.00*
a.	A40	20q dark red violet	7.75	*9.75*
b.	A40	30q brown olive	7.75	*9.75*

Wedding of King Zog and Countess Geraldine Apponyi, Apr. 27, 1938.

No. 289 contains 2 each of Nos. 289a, 289b.

Queen Geraldine A42

National Emblems A43

Designs: 10q, 25q, 30q, 1fr, King Zog.

1938

No.	Type	Description	Unused	Used
290	A42	1q dp red violet	.25	*.55*
291	A43	2q red orange	.25	*.55*
292	A42	5q deep green	.50	.50
293	A42	10q red brown	.50	*1.00*
294	A42	15q deep rose	1.00	*1.25*
295	A42	25q deep blue	1.40	1.40
296	A43	50q gray black	8.50	6.00
297	A42	1fr slate green	12.50	9.00
		Nos. 290-297 (8)	24.90	20.25

Souvenir Sheet

No.	Type	Description	Unused	Used
298		Sheet of 3	22.50	*75.00*
b.	A43	20q Prussian green	7.00	*12.00*
c.	A42	30q deep violet	7.00	*12.00*

10th anniv. of royal rule. They were on sale for 3 days (Aug. 30-31, Sept. 1) only, during which their use was required on all mail.

No. 298 contains Nos. 294, 298b, 298c.

Issued under Italian Dominion

Nos. 250-260 Overprinted in Black

1939 Wmk. 220 Perf. 14

No.	Type	Description	Unused	Used
299	A33	1q slate	1.25	*1.25*
300	A33	2q orange red	1.25	*1.25*
301	A34	5q yellow green	1.25	*1.25*
302	A34	10q carmine	1.25	*1.25*
303	A34	15q dark brown	2.00	*3.75*
304	A34	25q dark ultra	2.00	*3.75*
305	A33	50q slate green	2.50	*5.00*
306	A35	1fr violet	2.50	*5.00*
307	A35	2fr indigo	3.25	*9.50*
308	A36	3fr gray green	7.75	*22.50*
309	A36	5fr orange brown	10.00	*25.00*
		Nos. 299-309 (11)	35.00	79.50

Resolution adopted by the Natl. Assembly, Apr. 12, 1939, offering the Albanian Crown to Italy.

A46

A47

Native Costumes — A48

King Victor Emmanuel III

A49 A50

Native Costume A51

Monastery A52

Designs: 2fr, Bridge at Vezirit. 3fr, Ancient Columns. 5fr, Amphitheater.

1939 Unwmk. Photo. Perf. 14

No.	Type	Description	Unused	Used
310	A46	1q blue gray	1.25	.50
311	A47	2q olive green	1.25	.50
312	A48	3q golden brown	1.25	.50
313	A49	5q green	1.25	.25
314	A50	10q brown	1.25	.25
315	A50	15q crimson	1.25	.25
316	A50	25q sapphire	2.00	.80
317	A50	30q brt violet	2.50	1.40
318	A51	50q dull purple	3.25	3.25
319	A49	65q red brown	5.00	11.50
320	A52	1fr myrtle green	7.50	9.50
321	A52	2fr brown lake	11.50	19.00
322	A52	3fr brown black	19.00	35.00
323	A52	5fr gray violet	25.00	*50.00*
		Nos. 310-323 (14)	83.25	132.70

For overprints and surcharges see Nos. 331-353.

King Victor Emmanuel III — A56

1942 Photo.

No.	Type	Description	Unused	Used
324	A56	5q green	1.25	*2.00*
325	A56	10q brown	1.25	*2.00*
326	A56	15q rose red	1.25	*2.00*
327	A56	25q blue	1.25	*2.00*
328	A56	65q red brown	3.50	*4.00*
329	A56	1fr myrtle green	3.50	*4.00*
330	A56	2fr gray violet	3.50	*4.00*
		Nos. 324-330 (7)	15.50	20.00

Conquest of Albania by Italy, 3rd anniv.

No. 311 Surcharged in Black

No.	Type	Description	Unused	Used
331	A47	1q on 2q olive green	1.60	*4.00*

Issued under German Administration

Stamps of 1939 Overprinted in Carmine or Brown

1943

No.	Type	Description	Unused	Used
332	A47	2q olive green	1.00	*4.00*
333	A48	3q golden brown	1.00	*4.00*
334	A49	5q green	1.00	*4.00*
335	A50	10q brown	1.00	*4.00*
336	A50	15q crimson (Br)	1.00	*4.00*
337	A50	25q sapphire	1.00	*4.00*
338	A50	30q brt violet	1.00	*4.00*
339	A49	65q red brown	1.50	*8.00*
340	A52	1fr myrtle green	6.25	*24.00*
341	A52	2fr brown lake	7.75	*80.00*
342	A52	3fr brown black	60.00	*200.00*

Surcharged with New Values

No.	Type	Description	Unused	Used
343	A48	1q on 3q gldn brn	1.00	*8.00*
344	A49	50q on 65q red brn	1.50	*12.00*
		Nos. 332-344 (13)	85.00	*360.00*

Proclamation of Albanian independence.

The overprint "14 Shtator 1943" on Nos. 324 to 328 is private and fraudulent.

Independent State

Nos. 312 to 317 and 319 to 321 Surcharged with New Value and Bars in Black or Carmine, and:

1945

No.	Type	Description	Unused	Used
345	A48	30q on 3q gldn brn	3.00	*12.00*
346	A49	40q on 5q green	3.00	*12.00*
347	A50	50q on 10q brown	3.00	*12.00*
348	A50	60q on 15q crimson	3.00	*12.00*
349	A50	80q on 25q saph (C)	3.00	*12.00*
350	A50	1fr on 30q brt violet	3.00	*12.00*
351	A49	2fr on 65q red brn	3.00	*12.00*
352	A52	3fr on 1fr myr green	3.00	*12.00*
353	A52	5fr on 2fr brown lake	3.00	*12.00*
		Nos. 345-353 (9)	27.00	*108.00*

"DEMOKRATIKE" is not abbreviated on Nos. 352 and 353.

Nos. 250, 251, 256 and 258 Surcharged in Black or Carmine, and

1945 Wmk. 220

No.	Type	Description	Unused	Used
354	A33	30q on 1q slate	2.00	*6.00*
355	A33	60q on 1q slate	2.00	*6.00*
356	A33	80q on 1q slate	2.00	*6.00*
357	A33	1fr on 1q slate	4.00	*12.00*
358	A33	2fr on 2q org red	5.00	*13.50*
359	A33	3fr on 50q sl grn	10.00	*25.00*
360	A35	5fr on 2fr indigo	12.50	*40.00*
		Nos. 354-360 (7)	37.50	*108.50*

Albanian Natl. Army of Liberation, 2nd anniv.

The surcharge on No. 360 is condensed to fit the size of the stamp.

Country House, Labinot — A57

40q, 60q, Bridge at Berat. 1fr, 3fr, Permet.

Perf. 11½

1945, Nov. 28 Unwmk. Typo.

No.	Type	Description	Unused	Used
361	A57	20q bluish green	.30	*1.20*
362	A57	30q deep orange	.40	*1.75*
363	A57	40q brown	.40	*1.75*
364	A57	60q red violet	.60	*2.50*
365	A57	1fr rose red	1.50	*5.00*
366	A57	3fr dark blue	10.00	*21.00*
		Nos. 361-366 (6)	13.20	*33.20*

Counterfeits: lithographed; genuine: typographed.

For overprints and surcharges see Nos. 367-378, 418-423, B28-B33.

Nos. 361 to 366 Overprinted in Black

1946

367	A57	20q	bluish green	.60	*1.40*
368	A57	30q	deep orange	.80	*1.75*
369	A57	40q	brown	1.00	*2.10*
370	A57	60q	red violet	1.60	*3.50*
371	A57	1fr	rose red	6.00	*12.50*
372	A57	3fr	dark blue	10.00	*21.00*
			Nos. 367-372 (6)	20.00	*42.25*

Convocation of the Constitutional Assembly, Jan. 10, 1946.

People's Republic

#361-366 Overprinted in Black

1946 *Perf. 11*

373	A57	20q	bluish green	.40	*1.10*
374	A57	30q	deep orange	.60	*1.40*
375	A57	40q	brown	1.00	*2.75*
376	A57	60q	red violet	2.00	*5.25*
377	A57	1fr	rose red	6.00	*14.00*
378	A57	3fr	dark blue	10.00	*21.00*
			Nos. 373-378 (6)	20.00	*45.50*

Proclamation of the Albanian People's Republic.
Some values exist perf 11½.
For surcharges see Nos. 418-423.

Globe, Dove and Olive Branch — A60

Perf. 11½, Imperf.

1946, Mar. 8 **Typo.**

Denomination in Black

379	A60	20q	lilac & dull red	.25	*1.25*
380	A60	40q	dp lilac & dull red	.45	*1.75*
381	A60	50q	violet & dull red	.90	*2.50*
382	A60	1fr	lt blue & red	1.60	*5.00*
383	A60	2fr	dk blue & red	2.00	*8.00*
			Nos. 379-383 (5)	5.20	*18.50*

International Women's Congress.
Counterfeits exist.

Athletes with Shot and Indian Club — A61

Perf. 11½

1946, Oct. 6 **Litho.** **Unwmk.**

384	A61	1q	grnsh black	5.00	*8.50*
385	A61	2q	green	5.00	*8.50*
386	A61	5q	brown	5.00	*8.50*
387	A61	10q	crimson	5.00	*8.50*
388	A61	20q	ultra	5.00	*8.50*
389	A61	40q	rose violet	5.00	*8.50*
390	A61	1fr	deep orange	12.50	*25.00*
			Nos. 384-390 (7)	42.50	*76.00*

Balkan Games, Tirana, Oct. 6-13.

Qemal Stafa — A62

1947, May 5 *Perf. 12½x11½*

391	A62	20q	brn & yel brn	5.00	*11.00*
392	A62	28q	dk blue & blue	5.00	*11.00*
393	A62	40q	brn blk & gray brn	5.00	*11.00*
a.			Souvenir sheet, #391-393	90.00	*110.00*
			Nos. 391-393 (3)	15.00	*33.00*

5th anniv. of the death of Qemal Stafa.

Young Railway Laborers — A64

1947, May 16 *Perf. 11½*

395	A64	1q	brn blk & gray brn	2.00	1.40
396	A64	4q	dk green & green	2.00	1.40
397	A64	10q	blk brn & bis brn	2.00	1.60
398	A64	15q	dk red & red	2.00	1.60
399	A64	20q	indigo & bl gray	4.00	3.00
400	A64	28q	dk blue & blue	6.00	2.50
401	A64	40q	brn vio & rose vio	12.50	14.50

Perf. 13x12½

402	A64	68q	dk brn & org brn	15.00	*25.00*
			Nos. 395-402 (8)	45.50	51.00

Issued to publicize the construction of the Durres Elbasan Railway by Albanian youths.
The 4q, 20q, 28q and 40q exist perf 13x12½.

Citizens Led by Hasim Zeneli A65

Enver Hoxha and Vasil Shanto A66

Inauguration of Vithkuq Brigade — A67

Vojo Kushi — A68

1947, July 10 **Litho.**

403	A65	16q	brn org & red brn	4.00	*7.00*
404	A66	20q	org brn & dk brn	4.00	*7.00*
405	A67	28q	blue & dk blue	4.00	*7.00*
406	A68	40q	lilac & dk brn	4.00	*7.00*
			Nos. 403-406 (4)	16.00	*28.00*

4th anniv. of the formation of Albania's army, July 10, 1943.

Conference Building Ruins, Peza — A69

1947, Sept. 16

407	A69	2 l	red violet	2.50	*5.25*
408	A69	2.50 l	deep blue	2.50	*5.25*

Peza Conf., Sept. 16, 1942, 5th anniv.

Disabled Soldiers — A70

1947, Nov. 17 *Perf. 12½x11½*

408A	A70	1 l	red	7.00	*11.00*

Disabled War Veterans Cong., 11/14-20/47.

A71

A73

2 l, Banquet. 2.50 l, Peasants rejoicing.

Perf. 11½x12½, 12½x11½

1947, Nov. 17 **Unwmk.**

409	A71	1.50 l	dull violet	3.50	*7.00*
410	A71	2 l	brown	3.50	*7.00*
411	A71	2.50 l	blue	3.50	*7.00*
412	A73	3 l	rose red	3.50	*7.00*
			Nos. 409-412 (4)	14.00	*28.00*

Agrarian reform law of 11/17/46, 1st anniv.

Burning Farm Buildings — A74

Designs: 2.50 l, Trench scene. 5 l, Firing line. 8 l, Winter advance. 12 l, Infantry column.

1947, Nov. 29 *Perf. 11½x12½*

413	A74	1.50 l	red	2.00	*3.00*
414	A74	2.50 l	rose brown	2.00	*3.00*
415	A74	5 l	blue	4.00	*6.00*
416	A74	8 l	purple	6.00	*9.00*
417	A74	12 l	brown	10.00	*14.00*
			Nos. 413-417 (5)	24.00	*35.00*

3rd anniv. of Albania's liberation.

Nos. 373 to 378 Surcharged with New Value and Bars in Black

1948, Feb. 22 *Perf. 11*

418	A57	50q	on 30q dp org	.25	*.50*
419	A57	1 l	on 20q bluish grn	.40	.85
420	A57	2.50 l	on 60q red vio	1.00	*2.50*
421	A57	3 l	on 1fr rose red	1.40	*3.25*
422	A57	5 l	on 3fr dk bl	3.00	*5.25*
423	A57	12 l	on 40q brown	8.00	*14.00*
			Nos. 418-423 (6)	14.05	*26.35*

The two bars consist of four type squares each set close together.
Some values exist perf 11½.

Map, Train and Construction Workers — A75

1948, June 1 **Litho.** *Perf. 11½*

424	A75	50q	dk car rose	1.00	1.10
425	A75	1 l	lt green & blk	1.00	1.10
426	A75	1.50 l	deep rose	1.60	1.75
427	A75	2.50 l	org brn & dk brn	2.50	2.25
428	A75	5 l	dull blue	4.00	4.25
429	A75	8 l	sal & dk brn	7.00	7.00
430	A75	12 l	red vio & dk vio	12.00	8.50
431	A75	20 l	olive gray	16.00	17.50
			Nos. 424-431 (8)	45.10	43.45

Issued to publicize the construction of the Durres-Tirana Railway.

Marching Soldiers — A76

Design: 8 l, Battle scene.

1948, July 10

432	A76	2.50 l	yellow brown	2.00	3.50
433	A76	5 l	dark blue	2.75	5.00
434	A76	8 l	violet gray	5.25	7.00
			Nos. 432-434 (3)	10.00	15.50

5th anniv. of the formation of Albania's army.

Bricklayer, Flag, Globe and "Industry" — A77

1949, May 1 **Photo.** *Perf. 12½x12*

435	A77	2.50 l	olive brown	.60	*1.75*
436	A77	5 l	blue	1.20	*1.75*
437	A77	8 l	violet brown	2.25	*4.50*
			Nos. 435-437 (3)	4.05	*8.00*

Issued to publicize Labor Day, May 1, 1949.

Map and Soldier — A78

1949, July 10 **Unwmk.**

438	A78	2.50 l	brown	.60	*1.75*
439	A78	5 l	light ultra	1.20	*2.75*
440	A78	8 l	brown orange	2.25	*5.25*
			Nos. 438-440 (3)	4.05	9.75

6th anniv. of the formation of Albania's army.

Enver Hoxha — A79

1949, Oct. 16 **Engr.** *Perf. 12½*

441	A79	50q	purple	.25	.25
442	A79	1 l	dull green	.25	.25
443	A79	1.50 l	car lake	.25	.25
444	A79	2.50 l	brown	.35	.25
445	A79	5 l	violet blue	.80	.70
446	A79	8 l	sepia	1.50	2.10
447	A79	12 l	rose lilac	4.00	3.50
448	A79	20 l	gray blue	4.75	5.25
			Nos. 441-448 (8)	12.15	12.55

Albanian Citizen and Spasski Tower, Kremlin — A80

1949, Sept. 10 **Photo.** *Perf. 12½x12*

449	A80	2.50 l	orange brown	.60	*1.50*
450	A80	5 l	deep ultra	1.50	*3.50*

Albanian-Soviet friendship.

Albanian Soldier and Flag — A81

Battle Scene — A82

1949, Nov. 29 **Unwmk.** *Perf. 12*

451	A81	2.50 l	brown	.40	*1.10*
452	A82	3 l	dark red	.40	*2.10*
453	A81	5 l	violet	1.25	*2.75*
454	A82	8 l	black	2.50	*5.25*
			Nos. 451-454 (4)	4.55	*11.20*

Fifth anniversary of Albania's liberation.

Joseph V. Stalin — A83

1949, Dec. 21

455	A83	2.50 l	dark brown	.40	*1.40*
456	A83	5 l	violet blue	1.00	*2.50*
457	A83	8 l	rose brown	2.75	*6.00*
			Nos. 455-457 (3)	4.15	*9.90*

70th anniv. of the birth of Joseph V. Stalin.

Canceled to Order

Beginning in 1950, Albania sold some issues in sheets canceled to order. Values in second column, when much less than unused, are for "CTO" examples. Postally used stamps are valued at slightly less than, or the same as, unused.

Catalogue values for unused stamps in this section, from this point to the end of the section, are for Never Hinged items.

Symbols of UPU and Postal Transport — A84

1950, July 1 Photo. *Perf. 12x12½*

458	A84	5 l blue	2.00	1.40
459	A84	8 l rose brown	4.00	1.90
460	A84	12 l sepia	8.00	2.40
		Nos. 458-460 (3)	14.00	5.70

75th anniv. (in 1949) of the UPU.

Sami Frasheri — A85

Authors: 2.50 l, Andon Zako. 3 l, Naim Frasheri. 5 l, Kostandin Kristoforidhi.

1950, Nov. 5 *Perf. 14*

461	A85	2 l dark green	1.00	.40
462	A85	2.50 l red brown	1.40	.45
463	A85	3 l brown carmine	3.00	.65
464	A85	5 l deep blue	3.50	.80
		Nos. 461-464 (4)	8.90	2.30

"Jubilee of the Writers of the Renaissance."

Arms and Albanian Flags — A86

1951, Jan. 11 Engr. *Perf. 14x13½*

465	A86	2.50 l brown carmine	1.60	.30
466	A86	5 l deep blue	3.25	.65
467	A86	8 l sepia	5.25	1.25
		Nos. 465-467 (3)	10.10	2.20

5th anniv. of the formation of the Albanian People's Republic.

Skanderbeg — A87

1951, Mar. 1

468	A87	2.50 l brown	1.75	.30
469	A87	5 l violet	3.25	.55
470	A87	8 l olive bister	5.25	1.10
		Nos. 468-470 (3)	10.25	1.95

483rd anniv. of the death of George Castriota (Skanderbeg).

Enver Hoxha and Congress of Permet — A88

1951, May 24 Photo. *Perf. 12*

471	A88	2.50 l dark brown	.70	.25
472	A88	3 l rose brown	.70	.35
473	A88	5 l violet blue	1.75	.55
474	A88	8 l rose lilac	3.25	.85
		Nos. 471-474 (4)	6.40	2.00

Congress of Permet, 7th anniversary.

Child and Globe A89

Weighing Baby A90

1951, July 16

475	A89	2 l green	1.75	.80
476	A90	2.50 l brown	2.50	.95
477	A90	3 l red	3.25	1.25
478	A89	5 l blue	5.00	1.40
		Nos. 475-478 (4)	12.50	4.40

Intl. Children's Day, June 1, 1951.

Enver Hoxha and Birthplace of Albanian Communist Party — A91

1951, Nov. 8 Photo. *Perf. 14*

479	A91	2.50 l olive brown	.50	.25
480	A91	3 l rose brown	.50	.40
481	A91	5 l dark slate blue	1.10	.65
482	A91	8 l black	2.10	.90
		Nos. 479-482 (4)	4.20	2.20

Albanian Communist Party, 10th anniv.

Battle Scene — A92

Designs: 5 l, Schoolgirl, "Agriculture and Industry." 8 l, Four portraits.

1951, Nov. 28 *Perf. 12x12½*

483	A92	2.50 l brown	.70	.25
484	A92	5 l blue	1.40	.50
485	A92	8 l brown carmine	3.25	.85
		Nos. 483-485 (3)	5.35	1.60

Albanian Communist Youth Org., 10th anniv.

Albanian Heroes (Haxhija, Lezha, Giylbegaj, Mazi and Deda) — A93

Designs: Nos. 486-489 each show 5 "Heroes of the People"; No. 490 shows 2 (Stafa and Shanto).

1950, Dec. 25 Unwmk. *Perf. 14*

486	A93	2 l dark green	.75	.25
487	A93	2.50 l purple	1.10	.25
488	A93	3 l scarlet	2.25	.35
489	A93	5 l brt blue	3.75	.45
490	A93	8 l olive brown	7.50	1.25
		Nos. 486-490 (5)	15.35	2.55

6th anniv. of Albania's liberation.

Tobacco Factory, Shkoder — A94

Composite, Lenin Hydroelectric Plant — A95

Designs: 1 l, Canal. 2.50 l, Textile factory. 3 l, "8 November" Cannery. 5 l, Motion Picture Studio, Tirana. 8 l, Stalin Textile Mill, Tirana. 20 l, Central Hydroelectric Dam.

1953, Aug. 1 *Perf. 12x12½, 12½x12*

491	A94	50q red brown	.45	.25
492	A94	1 l dull green	.85	.25
493	A94	2.50 l brown	.85	.25
494	A94	3 l rose brown	1.25	.50
495	A94	5 l blue	2.10	.75
496	A94	8 l brown olive	2.50	1.00
497	A95	12 l deep plum	4.25	1.50
498	A94	20 l slate blue	6.00	3.25
		Nos. 491-498 (8)	18.25	7.75

Liberation Scene — A96

1954, Nov. 29 *Perf. 12x12½*

499	A96	50q brown violet	.25	.25
500	A96	1 l olive green	.55	.25
501	A96	2.50 l yellow brown	.80	.25
502	A96	3 l carmine rose	1.60	.35
503	A96	5 l gray blue	2.40	.50
504	A96	8 l rose brown	4.00	1.00
		Nos. 499-504 (6)	9.60	2.60

10th anniversary of Albania's liberation.

School — A97

Pandeli Sotiri, Petro Nini Luarasi, Nuci Naci — A98

1956, Feb. 23 Unwmk.

505	A97	2 l rose violet	.40	.25
506	A98	2.50 l lt green	.55	.35
507	A98	5 l ultra	1.40	.60
508	A97	10 l brt grnsh blue	4.75	1.00
		Nos. 505-508 (4)	7.10	2.20

Opening of the 1st Albanian school, 70th anniv.

Flags — A99

Designs: 5 l, Labor Party headquarters, Tirana. 8 l, Marx and Lenin.

1957, June 1 Engr. *Perf. 11½x11*

509	A99	2.50 l brown	.35	.25
510	A99	5 l lt violet blue	1.00	.25
511	A99	8 l rose lilac	1.40	1.00
		Nos. 509-511 (3)	2.75	1.50

Albania's Labor Party, 15th anniv.

Congress Emblem — A100

1957, Oct. 4 Unwmk. *Perf. 11½*

512	A100	2.50 l gray brown	.50	.25
513	A100	3 l rose red	.50	.25
514	A100	5 l dark blue	.50	.25
515	A100	8 l green	2.50	.65
		Nos. 512-515 (4)	4.00	1.40

4th Intl. Trade Union Cong., Leipzig, 10/4-15.

Lenin and Cruiser "Aurora" — A101

1957, Nov. 7 Litho. *Perf. 10½*

516	A101	2.50 l violet brown	.50	.25
517	A101	5 l violet blue	1.50	.25
518	A101	8 l gray	1.50	.35
		Nos. 516-518 (3)	3.50	.85

40th anniv. of the Russian Revolution.

Albanian Fighter Holding Flag — A102

1957, Nov. 28 *Perf. 10½*

519	A102	1.50 l magenta	.45	.30
520	A102	2.50 l brown	.85	.30
521	A102	5 l blue	1.25	.90
522	A102	8 l green	3.50	1.25
		Nos. 519-522 (4)	6.05	2.75

Proclamation of independence, 45th anniv.

Naum Veqilharxhi — A103

1958, Feb. 1 Unwmk.

523	A103	2.50 l dark brown	.45	.25
524	A103	5 l violet blue	.90	.25
525	A103	8 l rose lilac	2.75	.60
		Nos. 523-525 (3)	4.10	1.10

160th anniv. of the birth of Naum Veqilharxhi, patriot and writer.

Luigj Gurakuqi (1879-1925), Writer & Politician — A104

1958, Apr. 15 Photo. *Perf. 10½*

526	A104	1.50 l dark green	.40	.25
527	A104	2.50 l brown	.40	.25
528	A104	5 l blue	.40	.25
529	A104	8 l sepia	3.50	.75
		Nos. 526-529 (4)	4.70	1.50

Transfer of the ashes of Luigj Gurakuqi.

Soldiers — A105

2.50 l, 11 l, Airman, sailor, soldier and tank.

1958, July 10 Litho.

530	A105	1.50 l blue green	.25	.25
531	A105	2.50 l dark red brown	.25	.25
532	A105	8 l rose red	.90	.35
533	A105	11 l bright blue	2.00	.60
		Nos. 530-533 (4)	3.40	1.45

15th anniversary of Albanian army.

Cerciz Topulli and Mihal Grameno A106

Buildings and Tree A107

1958, July 1

534	A106	2.50 l dk olive bister	.35	.25
535	A107	3 l green	.35	.25
536	A106	5 l blue	1.25	.60
537	A107	8 l red brown	2.00	.70
		Nos. 534-537 (4)	3.95	1.80

50th anniversary, Battle of Mashkullore.

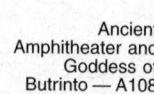

Ancient Amphitheater and Goddess of Butrinto — A108

1959, Jan. 25 Litho. *Perf. 10½*

538	A108	2.50 l redsh brown	.45	.25
539	A108	6.50 l lt blue green	1.40	.30
540	A108	11 l dark blue	2.75	.75
		Nos. 538-540 (3)	4.60	1.30

Cultural Monuments Week.

Frederic Joliot-Curie and World Peace Congress Emblem — A109

1959, July 1 Unwmk.

541	A109	1.50 l carmine rose	1.75	.25
542	A109	2.50 l rose violet	3.50	.30
543	A109	11 l blue	9.00	1.50
		Nos. 541-543 (3)	14.25	2.05

10th anniv. of the World Peace Movement.

Basketball — A110

Sports: 2.50 l, Soccer, 5 l, Runner. 11 l, Man and woman runners with torch and flags.

1959, Nov. 20 *Perf. 10½*

544 A110 1.50 l bright violet .90 .25
545 A110 2.50 l emerald .90 .25
546 A110 5 l carmine rose 1.75 .25
547 A110 11 l ultra 5.50 1.75
Nos. 544-547 (4) 9.05 2.50

1st Albanian Spartacist Games.

Fighter and Flags — A111

Designs: 2.50 l, Miner with drill standing guard. 3 l, Farm woman with sheaf of grain. 6.50 l, Man and woman in laboratory.

1959, Nov. 29

548 A111 1.50 l brt carmine .90 .25
549 A111 2.50 l red brown 1.20 .25
550 A111 3 l brt blue green 1.75 .30
551 A111 6.50 l bright red 3.50 .50
a. Souvenir sheet 8.00 11.00
Nos. 548-551 (4) 7.35 1.30

15th anniversary of Albania's liberation.

No. 551a contains one each of Nos. 548-551, imperf. and all in bright carmine. Inscribed ribbon frame of sheet and frame lines for each stamp are blue green.

Mother and Child, UN Emblem — A112

1959, Dec. 5 **Unwmk.**

552 A112 5 l lt grnsh blue 4.00 1.00
a. Miniature sheet 6.50 9.50

10th anniv. (in 1958) of the signing of the Universal Declaration of Human Rights.

No. 552a contains one imperf. stamp similar to No. 552; ornamental border.

Woman with Olive Branch — A113

1960, Mar. 8 **Litho.** *Perf. 10½*

553 A113 2.50 l chocolate .75 .25
554 A113 11 l rose carmine 3.00 .50

50th anniv. of Intl. Women's Day, Mar. 8.

Alexander Moissi — A114

1960, Apr. 20

555 A114 3 l deep brown .35 .25
556 A114 11 l Prus green 1.40 .35

80th anniversary of the birth of Alexander Moissi (Moisiu) (1880-1935), German actor.

Lenin — A115

1960, Apr. 22

557 A115 4 l Prus blue 1.40 .25
558 A115 11 l lake 3.50 .40

90th anniversary of birth of Lenin.

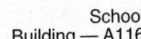

School Building — A116

1960, May 30 **Litho.** *Perf. 10½*

559 A116 5 l green 1.50 .50
560 A116 6.50 l plum 1.50 .50

1st Albanian secondary school, 50th anniv.

Soldier on Guard Duty — A117

1960, May 12 **Unwmk.** *Perf. 10½*

561 A117 1.50 l carmine rose .35 .25
562 A117 11 l Prus blue 2.00 .40

15th anniversary of the Frontier Guards.

Liberation Monument, Tirana, Family and Policeman — A118

1960, May 14

563 A118 1.50 l green .35 .25
564 A118 8.50 l brown 2.50 .40

15th anniversary of the People's Police.

Congress Site — A119

1960, Mar. 25

565 A119 2.50 l sepia .45 .25
566 A119 7.50 l dull blue 1.10 .25

40th anniversary, Congress of Louchnia.

Pashko Vasa — A120

Designs: 1.50 l, Jani Vreto. 6.50 l, Sami Frasheri. 11 l, Page of statutes of association.

1960, May 5

567 A120 1 l gray olive .35 .25
568 A120 1.50 l brown .35 .25
569 A120 6.50 l blue 1.10 .25
570 A120 11 l rose red 3.50 .35
Nos. 567-570 (4) 5.30 1.10

80th anniv. (in 1959) of the Association of Albanian Authors.

Albanian Fighter and Cannon — A121

1960, Aug. 2 **Litho.** *Perf. 10½*

571 A121 1.50 l olive brown .35 .25
572 A121 2.50 l maroon .75 .35
573 A121 5 l dark blue 1.50 .45
Nos. 571-573 (3) 2.60 1.05

Battle of Viona (against Italian troops), 40th anniv.

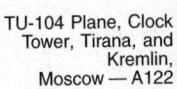

TU-104 Plane, Clock Tower, Tirana, and Kremlin, Moscow — A122

1960, Aug. 18

574 A122 1 l redsh brown .75 .25
575 A122 7.50 l brt grnsh blue 2.50 .35
576 A122 11.50 l gray 4.50 .60
Nos. 574-576 (3) 7.75 1.20

TU-104 flights, Moscow-Tirana, 2nd anniv.

Rising Sun and Federation Emblem — A123

1960, Nov. 10 **Unwmk.** *Perf. 10½*

577 A123 1.50 l ultra .35 .25
578 A123 8.50 l red 1.50 .35

Intl. Youth Federation, 15th anniv.

Ali Kelmendi — A124

1960, Dec. 5 **Litho.** *Perf. 10½*

579 A124 1.50 l pale gray grn .35 .25
580 A124 11 l dull rose lake 1.50 .30

Ali Kelmendi, communist leader, 60th birthday.

Flags of Russia and Albania and Clasped Hands — A125

1961, Jan. 10 **Unwmk.** *Perf. 10½*

581 A125 2 l violet .35 .25
582 A125 8 l dull red brown 1.50 .35

15th anniv. of the Albanian-Soviet Friendship Society.

Marx and Lenin — A126

1961, Feb. 13 **Litho.**

583 A126 2 l rose red .35 .25
584 A126 8 l violet blue 1.50 .25

Fourth Communist Party Congress.

Man from Shkoder — A127

Costumes: 1.50 l, Woman from Shkoder. 6.50 l, Man from Lume. 11 l, Woman from Mirdite.

1961, Apr. 28 *Perf. 10½*

585 A127 1 l slate .75 .30
586 A127 1.50 l dull claret .75 .40
587 A127 6.50 l ultra 3.00 1.00
588 A127 11 l red 5.00 2.50
Nos. 585-588 (4) 9.50 4.20

Otter — A128

Designs: 6.50 l, Badger. 11 l, Brown bear.

1961, June 25 **Unwmk.** *Perf. 10½*

589 A128 2.50 l grayish blue 3.00 .35
590 A128 6.50 l blue green 6.00 1.00
591 A128 11 l dark red brown 13.50 5.00
Nos. 589-591 (3) 22.50 6.35

Dalmatian Pelicans — A129

1961, Sept. 30 *Perf. 14*

592 A129 1.50 l shown 3.50 .50
593 A129 7.50 l Gray herons 5.00 1.50
594 A129 11 l Little egret 9.00 2.00
Nos. 592-594 (3) 17.50 4.00

Cyclamen — A130

1961, Oct. 27 **Litho.**

595 A130 1.50 l shown 1.50 .30
596 A130 8 l Forsythia 5.00 1.50
597 A130 11 l Lily 6.50 2.00
Nos. 595-597 (3) 13.00 3.80

Milosh G. Nikolla — A131

1961, Oct. 30 *Perf. 14*

598 A131 50q violet brown .35 .30
599 A131 8.50 l Prus green 1.40 .80

50th anniv. of the birth of Milosh Gjergi Nikolla, poet.

Flag with Marx and Lenin — A132

1961, Nov. 8

600 A132 2.50 l vermilion .65 .30
601 A132 7.50 l dull red brown 2.50 .85

20th anniv. of the founding of Albania's Communist Party.

Worker, Farm Woman and Emblem — A133

1961, Nov. 23 **Unwmk.** *Perf. 14*

602 A133 2.50 l violet blue .45 .30
603 A133 7.50 l rose claret 1.75 1.25

20th anniv. of the Albanian Workers' Party.

Yuri Gagarin and Vostok 1 — A134

1962, Feb. 15 **Unwmk.** *Perf. 14*

604 A134 50q blue .90 *1.40*
605 A134 4 l red lilac 3.50 *3.50*
606 A134 11 l dk slate grn 9.00 *10.00*
Nos. 604-606 (3) 13.40 *14.90*

1st manned space flight, made by Yuri A. Gagarin, Soviet astronaut, Apr. 12, 1961.

Nos. 604-606 were overprinted with an overall yellow tint and with "POSTA AJRORE" (Air Mail) in maroon or black in 1962. Value: set, maroon ovpt., $90 mint, $130 used; set, black ovpt., $300 mint, $400 used.

Petro Nini Luarasi — A135

1962, Feb. 28 **Litho.**
607 A135 50q Prus blue .40 .30
608 A135 8.50 l olive gray 3.00 1.00

50th anniv. (in 1961) of the death of Petro Nini Luarasi, Albanian patriot.

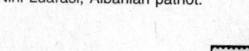

Malaria Eradication Emblem — A136

1962, Apr. 30 **Unwmk.** ***Perf. 14***
609 A136 1.50 l brt green .45 .25
610 A136 2.50 l brown red .45 .25
611 A136 10 l red lilac .90 .25
612 A136 11 l blue .90 .35
Nos. 609-612 (4) 2.70 1.10

WHO drive to eradicate malaria.
Souvenir sheets, perf. and imperf., contain one each of Nos. 609-612. Value $30 each.
Nos. 609-612 imperf., value, set $25.

Camomile — A137

Medicinal plants.

1962, May 10
613 A137 50q shown .30 .30
614 A137 8 l Linden 1.25 .60
615 A137 11.50 l Garden sage 2.00 .90
Nos. 613-615 (3) 3.55 1.80

Value, imperf. set $30 mint, $40 used.

Woman Diver — A138

2.50 l, Pole vault. 3 l, Mt. Fuji & torch, horiz. 9 l, Woman javelin thrower. 10 l, Shot putting.

1962, May 31 ***Perf. 14***
616 A138 50q brt grnsh bl & blk .25 .25
617 A138 2.50 l gldn brn & sepia .25 .25
618 A138 3 l blue & gray .35 .25
619 A138 9 l rose car & dk brn 1.75 .25
620 A138 10 l olive & blk 1.75 .30
Nos. 616-620 (5) 4.35 1.30

1964 Olympic Games, Tokyo. Value, imperf set, $50 mint, $70 used. A 15 l (like 3 l) exists in souv. sheet, perf. and imperf. Value, each $35 mint, $50 used.

Globe and Orbits A139

Dog Laika and Sputnik 2 A140

Designs: 1.50 l, Rocket to the sun. 20 l, Lunik 3 photographing far side of the moon.

1962, June **Unwmk.** ***Perf. 14***
621 A139 50q violet & org .40 .25
622 A140 1 l blue grn & brn .75 .30
623 A140 1.50 l yellow & ver 1.25 .40
624 A139 20 l magenta & bl 8.00 5.50
Nos. 621-624 (4) 10.40 6.45

Russian space explorations.

Nos. 621-624 exist imperf in changed colors. Value, mint $65, used $75.
Two miniature sheets exist, containing one 14-lek picturing Sputnik 1. The perforated 14-lek is yellow and brown; the imperf. red and brown. Value, each mint $65, used $75.

Soccer Game, Map of South America — A141

2.50 l, 15 l, Soccer game and globe as ball.

1962, July **Litho.**
625 A141 1 l org & dk pur .35 .25
626 A141 2.50 l emer & bluish grn .70 .25
627 A141 6.50 l lt brn & pink .70 .25
628 A141 15 l bluish grn & mar 1.75 .40
Nos. 625-628 (4) 3.50 1.15

World Soccer Championships, Chile, 5/30-6/17.
Exist imperforate in changed colors. Value, mint $40, used $75.
Two miniature sheets exist, each containing a single 20-lek in design similar to A141. The perf. sheet is brown and green; the imperf., brown and orange. Value, mint $40, used $75.

Map of Europe and Albania — A142

Designs: 1 l, 2.50 l, Map of Adriatic Sea and Albania and Roman statue.

1962, Aug.
630 A142 50q multicolored .40 *.75*
631 A142 1 l ultra & red .80 *2.00*
632 A142 2.50 l blue & red 6.50 *8.50*
633 A142 11 l multicolored 9.00 *17.50*
Nos. 630-633 (4) 16.70 *28.75*

Tourist propaganda. Imperforates in changed colors exist. Value, mint $35, used $70.
Miniature sheets containing a 7 l and 8 l stamp, perf. and imperf., exist. Value, mint $40, used $75.

Woman of Dardhe — A143

Regional Costumes: 1 l, Man from Devoll. 2.50 l, Woman from Lunxheri. 14 l, Man from Gjirokaster.

1962, Sept.
635 A143 50q car, bl & pur .35 .25
636 A143 1 l red brn & ocher .35 .25
637 A143 2.50 l vio, yel grn & blk 1.10 .60
638 A143 14 l red brn & pale grn 5.25 1.60
Nos. 635-638 (4) 7.05 2.70

Exist imperf. Value, set, mint $40, used $60.

Chamois — A144

Animals: 1 l, Lynx, horiz. 1.50 l, Wild boar, horiz. 15 l, 20 l, Roe deer.

1962, Oct. 24 **Unwmk.** ***Perf. 14***
639 A144 50q sl grn & dk pur .35 .25
640 A144 1 l orange & blk 1.40 .25
641 A144 1.50 l red brn & blk 1.75 .25
642 A144 15 l yel ol & red brn 15.00 1.00
Nos. 639-642 (4) 18.50 1.75

Miniature Sheet

643 A144 20 l yel ol & red brn 135.00 145.00

Imperfs. in changed colors, value Nos. 639-642 $60, No. 643 $125.

Ismail Qemali — A145

Designs: 1 l, Albania eagle. 16 l, Eagle over fortress formed by "RPSH."

1962, Dec. 28 **Litho.**
644 A145 1 l red & red brn .45 .25
645 A145 3 l org brn & blk 2.50 .25
646 A145 16 l dk car rose & blk 4.00 .50
Nos. 644-646 (3) 6.95 1.00

50th anniv. of independence. Imperfs. in changed colors, value, set $40 mint, $60 used.

Monument of October Revolution — A146

1963, Jan. 5 **Unwmk.** ***Perf. 14***
647 A146 5 l shown .85 .25
648 A146 10 l Lenin statue 2.00 .35

October Revolution (Russia, 1917), 45th anniv.

Henri Dunant, Cross, Globe and Nurse — A147

1963, Jan 25 **Unwmk.** ***Perf. 14***
649 A147 1.50 l rose lake, red & blk .35 .25
650 A147 2.50 l lt bl, red & blk .70 .25
651 A147 6 l emerald, red & blk 1.75 .25
652 A147 10 l dull yel, red & blk 2.75 .60
Nos. 649-652 (4) 5.55 1.35

Cent. of the Geneva Conf., which led to the establishment of the Intl. Red Cross in 1864.
Imperfs. in changed colors, value, set $60.

Stalin and Battle of Stalingrad — A148

1963, Feb. 2
653 A148 8 l dk green & slate 7.00 1.00

Battle of Stalingrad, 20th anniv. See No. C67.

Andrian G. Nikolayev — A149

Designs: 7.50 l, Vostoks 3 and 4 and globe, horiz. 20 l, Pavel R. Popovich. 25 l, Nikolayev, Popovich and globe with trajectories.

1963, Feb. 28 **Litho.**
654 A149 2.50 l vio bl & sepia .35 .35
655 A149 7.50 l lt blue & blk 1.10 .70
656 A149 20 l violet & sepia 2.75 2.25
Nos. 654-656 (3) 4.20 3.30

Miniature Sheet

657 A149 25 l vio bl & sepia 35.00 35.00

1st group space flight of Vostoks 3 and 4, Aug. 11-15, 1962. Imperfs in changed colors, value: Nos. 654-656 $45 mint or used; No. 657 perf, $45 mint or used; No. 657 imperf, $50 mint or used.

"Albania" Decorating Police Officer — A150

1963, Mar. 20 **Unwmk.** ***Perf. 14***
658 A150 2.50 l crim, mag & blk .70 .25
659 A150 7.50 l org ver, dk red & blk 2.50 .25

20th anniversary of the security police.

Polyphylla Fullo — A151

Beetles: 1.50 l, Lucanus cervus. 8 l, Procerus gigas. 10 l, Cicindela albanica.

1963, Mar. 20
660 A151 50q ol grn & brn .85 .35
661 A151 1.50 l blue & brn 1.40 .35
662 A151 8 l dl rose & blk vio 6.00 1.25
663 A151 10 l brt citron & blk 8.00 1.40
Nos. 660-663 (4) 16.25 3.35

1913 Stamp and Postmark — A152

10 l, Stamps of 1913, 1937 and 1962.

1963, May 5
664 A152 5 l yel, buff, bl & blk 1.40 .25
665 A152 10 l car rose, grn & blk 2.50 .45

50th anniversary of Albanian stamps.

Boxer — A153

Designs: 3 l, Basketball baskets. 5 l, Volleyball. 6 l, Bicyclists. 9 l, Gymnast. 15 l, Hands holding torch, and map of Japan.

1963, May 25 ***Perf. 13½***
666 A153 2 l yel, blk & red brn .40 *.70*
667 A153 3 l ocher, brn & bl .50 *1.40*
668 A153 5 l gray bl, red brn & brn .85 *1.40*
669 A153 6 l gray, dk gray & grn 1.10 *3.50*
670 A153 9 l rose, red brn & bl 1.75 *6.50*
Nos. 666-670 (5) 4.60 *13.50*

Miniature Sheet

671 A153 15 l lt bl, car, blk & brn 13.50 13.50

1964 Olympic Games in Tokyo. Value, imperfs. Nos. 666-670 $15, No. 671 $20.

Crested Grebe — A154

Birds: 3 l, Golden eagle. 6.50 l, Gray partridges. 11 l, Capercaillie.

1963, Apr. 20 **Litho.** ***Perf. 14***
672 A154 50q multicolored 1.10 .25
673 A154 3 l multicolored 2.00 .50
674 A154 6.50 l multicolored 5.25 1.25
675 A154 11 l multicolored 7.00 2.00
Nos. 672-675 (4) 15.35 4.00

Soldier and Building — A155

2.50 l, Soldier with pack, ship, plane. 5 l, Soldier in battle. 6 l, Soldier, bulldozer.

1963, July 10 Unwmk. *Perf. 12*

676	A155 1.50 l brick red, yel & blk	.45	.25
677	A155 2.50 l bl, ocher & brn	.90	.25
678	A155 5 l bluish grn, gray & blk	1.25	.25
679	A155 6 l red brn, buff & bl	1.75	.25
	Nos. 676-679 (4)	4.35	1.00

Albanian army, 20th anniversary.

Maj. Yuri A. Gagarin — A156

Designs: 5 l, Maj. Gherman Titov. 7 l, Maj. Andrian G. Nikolayev. 11 l, Lt. Col. Pavel R. Popovich. 14 l, Lt. Col. Valeri Bykovski. 20 l, Lt. Valentina Tereshkova.

1963, July 30

Portraits in Yellow and Black

680	A156 3 l brt purple	.70	.25
681	A156 5 l dull blue	.70	.25
682	A156 7 l gray	.95	.25
683	A156 11 l deep claret	2.10	.35
684	A156 14 l blue green	3.00	.60
685	A156 20 l ultra	4.75	1.10
	Nos. 680-685 (6)	12.20	2.80

Man's conquest of space. Value, imperf. set $40.

Volleyball — A157

1963, Aug. 31 *Perf. 12x12½*

686	A157 2 l shown	—	—
687	A157 3 l Weight lifting	—	—
688	A157 5 l Soccer	—	—
689	A157 7 l Boxing	—	—
690	A157 8 l Rowing	—	—

European championships. Imperfs. in changed colors, value set $35.

Papilio Podalirius — A158

1963, Sept. 29 Litho.

Various Butterflies and Moths in Natural Colors

691	A158 1 l red	.35	.25
692	A158 2 l blue	.70	.25
693	A158 4 l dull lilac	1.40	.60
694	A158 5 l pale green	1.60	.60
695	A158 8 l bister	3.25	1.25
696	A158 10 l light blue	4.00	1.75
	Nos. 691-696 (6)	11.30	4.70

Oil Refinery, Cerrik — A159

2.50 l, Food processing plant, Tirana, horiz. 30 l, Fruit canning plant. 50 l, Tannery, horiz.

1963, Nov. 15 Unwmk. *Perf. 14*

697	A159 2.50 l rose red, *pnksh*	.75	.25
698	A159 20 l slate grn, *grnsh*	3.00	.25
699	A159 30 l dull pur, *grysh*	7.50	.55
700	A159 50 l ocher, *yel*	7.50	.85
	Nos. 697-700 (4)	18.75	1.90

Industrial development in Albania.
For surcharges see Nos. 841-846.

Flag and Shield — A160

1963, Nov. 24 *Perf. 12½x12*

701	A160 2 l grnsh bl, blk, ocher & red	.45	.25
702	A160 8 l blue, blk, ocher & red	1.75	.50

1st Congress of Army Aid Assn.

Chinese, Caucasian and Negro Men — A161

1963, Dec. 10 *Perf. 12x11½*

703	A161 3 l bister & blk	.40	.25
704	A161 5 l bister & ultra	.75	.25
705	A161 7 l bister & vio	1.90	.30
	Nos. 703-705 (3)	3.05	.80

15th anniv. of the Universal Declaration of Human Rights.

Slalom Ascent — A162

Designs: 50q, Bobsled, horiz. 6.50 l, Ice hockey, horiz. 12.50 l, Women's figure skating. No. 709A, Ski jumper.

1963, Dec. 25 *Perf. 14*

706	A162 50q grnsh bl & blk	.35	.25
707	A162 2.50 l red, gray & blk	.45	.25
708	A162 6.50 l yel, blk & gray	.90	.25
709	A162 12.50 l red, blk & yel grn	1.75	.55
	Nos. 706-709 (4)	3.45	1.30

Miniature Sheet

709A	A162 12.50 l multi	20.00	20.00

9th Winter Olympic Games, Innsbruck, Jan. 29-Feb. 9, 1964. Imperfs. in changed colors, value Nos. 706-709 $75, No. 709A $50.

Lenin — A163

1964, Jan. 21 *Perf. 12½x12*

710	A163 5 l gray & bister	.90	.25
711	A163 10 l gray & ocher	2.00	.30

40th anniversary, death of Lenin.

Hurdling — A164

Designs: 3 l, Track, horiz. 6.50 l, Rifle shooting, horiz. 8 l, Basketball.

Perf. 12½x12, 12x12½

1964, Jan. 30 Litho.

712	A164 2.50 l pale vio & ultra	.40	.25
713	A164 3 l lt grn & red brn	.75	.35
714	A164 6.50 l blue & claret	1.10	1.00
715	A164 8 l lt blue & ocher	2.25	1.60
	Nos. 712-715 (4)	4.50	3.20

1st Games of the New Emerging Forces, GANEFO, Jakarta, Indonesia, Nov. 10-22, 1963.

Fish — A165

1964, Feb. 26 Unwmk. *Perf. 14*

716	A165 50q Sturgeon	.40	.25
717	A165 1 l Gilthead	.75	.25
718	A165 1.50 l Striped mullet	1.10	.25
719	A165 2.50 l Carp	1.50	.25
720	A165 6.50 l Mackerel	2.25	.40
721	A165 10 l Lake Ohrid trout	3.75	.50
	Nos. 716-721 (6)	9.75	1.90

Wild Animals A166

1964, Mar. 28 *Perf. 12½x12*

722	A166 1 l Red Squirrel	.45	.25
723	A166 1.50 l Beech marten	.85	.25
724	A166 2 l Red fox	.85	.40
725	A166 2.50 l Hedgehog	1.25	.40
726	A166 3 l Hare	1.75	.60
727	A166 5 l Jackal	1.75	.60
728	A166 7 l Wildcat	3.50	.60
729	A166 8 l Wolf	4.50	.95
	Nos. 722-729 (8)	14.90	4.05

Lighting Olympic Torch — A167

5 l, Torch, globes. 7 l, 15 l, Olympic flag, Mt. Fuji. 10 l, National Stadium, Tokyo.

1964, May 18 *Perf. 12x12½*

730	A167 3 l lt yel grn, yel & buff	.45	*.70*
731	A167 5 l red & vio blue	.65	*1.00*
732	A167 7 l lt bl, ultra & yel	.90	*1.50*
733	A167 10 l orange, bl & vio	1.25	*2.50*
	Nos. 730-733 (4)	3.25	*5.70*

Miniature Sheet

734	A167 15 l lt bl, ultra & org	20.00	20.00

18th Olympic Games, Tokyo, Oct. 10-25, 1964. No. 734 contains one 49x62mm stamp. Imperfs. in changed colors, value Nos. 730-733 $17.50, No. 734 $22.50.

See No. 745.

Partisans A168

5 l, Arms of Albania. 8 l, Enver Hoxha.

Perf. 12½x12

1964, May 24 Litho. Unwmk.

735	A168 2 l orange, red & blk	1.10	.25
736	A168 5 l multicolored	2.75	.30
737	A168 8 l red brn, blk & red	5.50	.90
	Nos. 735-737 (3)	9.35	1.45

20th anniv. of the Natl. Anti-Fascist Cong. of Liberation, Permet, May 24, 1944. The label attached to each stamp, without perforations between, carries a quotation from the 1944 Congress.

Albanian Flag and Revolutionists — A169

Perf. 12½x12

1964, June 10 Litho. Unwmk.

738	A169 2.50 l red & gray	.40	.25
739	A169 7.50 l lilac rose & gray	1.10	.25

Albanian revolution of 1924, 40th anniv.

Full Moon — A170

Designs: 5 l, New moon. 8 l, Half moon. 11 l, Waning moon. 15 l, Far side of moon.

1964, June 27 *Perf. 12x12½*

740	A170 1 l purple & yel	.25	.25
741	A170 5 l violet & yel	.50	.25
742	A170 8 l blue & yel	.75	.30
743	A170 11 l green & yel	3.00	.45
	Nos. 740-743 (4)	4.50	1.25

Miniature Sheet

Perf. 12 on 2 sides

744	A170 15 l ultra & yel	12.50	12.50

No. 744 contains one stamp, size: 35x36mm, perforated at top and bottom. Imperfs. in changed colors, value Nos. 740-743 $16, No. 744 $15.

No. 733 with Added Inscription "Rimini 25-VI-64"

1964 *Perf. 12x12½*

745	A167 10 l orange, bl & vio	7.00	7.00

"Toward Tokyo 1964" Phil. Exhib. at Rimini, Italy, June 25-July 6.

Wren — A171

Birds: 1 l, Penduline titmouse. 2.50 l, Green woodpecker. 3 l, Tree creeper.4 l, Nuthatch. 5 l, Great titmouse. 6 l, Goldfinch. 18 l, Oriole.

1964, July 31 *Perf. 12x12½*

746	A171 50q multi	.45	.25
747	A171 1 l orange & multi	.90	.25
748	A171 2.50 l multi	1.25	.40
749	A171 3 l blue & multi	1.75	.40
750	A171 4 l yellow & multi	2.25	.80
751	A171 5 l blue & multi	2.75	.80
752	A171 6 l lt vio & multi	3.00	1.25
753	A171 18 l pink & multi	5.50	2.75
	Nos. 746-753 (8)	17.85	6.90

Running and Gymnastics — A172

Sport: 2 l, Weight lifting, judo. 3 l, Equestrian, bicycling. 4 l, Soccer, water polo. 5 l, Wrestling, boxing. 6 l, Pentathlon, hockey. 7 l, Swimming, sailing. 8 l, Basketball, volleyball. 9 l, Rowing, canoeing. 10 l, Fencing, pistol shooting. 20 l, Three winners.

Perf. 12x12½

1964, Sept. 25 Litho. Unwmk.

754	A172 1 l lt bl, rose & emer	.25	.25
755	A172 2 l bis brn, bluish grn & vio	.25	.25
756	A172 3 l vio, red org & ol bis	.25	.25
757	A172 4 l grnsh bl, ol & ultra	.45	.35
758	A172 5 l grnsh bl, car & pale lil	.45	.35
759	A172 6 l dk bl, org & lt bl	.70	.75
760	A172 7 l dk bl, lt ol & org	.70	.75
761	A172 8 l emer, gray & yel	.90	.75
762	A172 9 l bl, yel & lil rose	.90	.75
763	A172 10 l brt grn, org brn & yel grn	1.25	1.00
	Nos. 754-763 (10)	6.10	5.45

Miniature Sheet

Perf. 12

764	A172 20 l violet & lemon	15.00	15.00

18th Olympic Games, Tokyo, Oct. 10-25. No. 764 contains one stamp, size: 41x68mm. Imperfs in changed colors, value: Nos. 754-763, $17.50 mint, $25 used; No. 764, $20 mint, $25 used.

Arms of People's Republic of China A173

Mao Tse-tung and Flag A174

1964, Oct. 1 ***Perf. 11½x12, 12x11½***

765 A173 7 l black, red & yellow *10.00* *4.50*
766 A174 8 l black, red & yellow *10.00* *6.00*

People's Republic of China, 15th anniv.

Karl Marx — A175

Designs: 5 l, St. Martin's Hall, London. 8 l, Friedrich Engels.

1964, Nov. 5 ***Perf. 12x11½***

767 A175 2 l red, lt vio & blk .90 .45
768 A175 5 l gray blue 2.25 1.40
769 A175 8 l ocher, blk & red 4.00 1.75
Nos. 767-769 (3) 7.15 3.60

Centenary of First Socialist International.

Jeronim de Rada — A176

1964, Nov. 15 ***Perf. 12½x11½***

770 A176 7 l slate green 1.10 .35
771 A176 8 l dull violet 1.90 .60

Birth of Jeronim de Rada, poet, 150th anniv.

Arms of Albania A177

Factories A178

Designs: 3 l, Combine harvester. 4 l, Woman chemist. 10 l, Hands holding Communist Party book, hammer and sickle.

Perf. 11½x12, 12x11½

1964, Nov. 29

772 A177 1 l multicolored .45 .40
773 A178 2 l red, yel & vio bl .80 .80
774 A178 3 l red, yel & brn 1.20 1.25
775 A178 4 l red, yel & gray grn 1.50 1.60
776 A177 10 l red, bl & blk 3.50 4.00
Nos. 772-776 (5) 7.45 8.05

20th anniversary of liberation.

Planet Mercury — A179

Planets: 2 l, Venus and rocket. 3 l, Earth, moon and rocket. 4 l, Mars and rocket. 5 l, Jupiter. 6 l, Saturn. 7 l, Uranus. 8 l, Neptune. 9 l, Pluto. 15 l, Solar system and rocket.

1964, Dec. 15 ***Perf. 12x12½***

777 A179 1 l yellow & pur .25 .25
778 A179 2 l multicolored .25 .25
779 A179 3 l multicolored .40 .40
780 A179 4 l multicolored .40 .40
781 A179 5 l yel, dk pur & brn .80 .60
782 A179 6 l lt grn, vio brn & yel 1.20 .60
783 A179 7 l yellow & grn 1.40 .90
784 A179 8 l yellow & vio 1.60 1.00
785 A179 9 l lt grn, yel & blk 1.75 1.25
Nos. 777-785 (9) 8.05 5.65

Miniature Sheet

Perf. 12 on 2 sides

786 A179 15 l car, bl, yel & grn 25.00 35.00

No. 786 contains one stamp, size: 62x51mm, perforated at top and bottom. Imperfs. in changed colors. Value Nos. 777-785, $30; No. 786, $25.

European Chestnut — A180

1965, Jan. 25 ***Perf. 11½x12***

787 A180 1 l shown .25 .25
788 A180 2 l Medlars .35 .25
789 A180 3 l Persimmon .55 .25
790 A180 4 l Pomegranate .75 .40
791 A180 5 l Quince 1.50 .50
792 A180 10 l Orange 3.00 1.00
Nos. 787-792 (6) 6.40 2.65

Symbols of Industry — A181

Designs: 5 l, Books, triangle and compass. 8 l, Beach, trees and hotel.

1965, Feb. 20

793 A181 2 l blk, car rose & pink *7.50* 7.00
794 A181 5 l yel, gray & blk *12.00* 10.50
795 A181 8 l blk, vio bl & lt bl *15.00* 13.00
Nos. 793-795 (3) *34.50* 30.50

Professional trade associations, 20th anniv.

Water Buffalo — A182

Various designs: Water buffalo.

1965, Mar. ***Perf. 12x11½***

796 A182 1 l lt yel grn, yel & brn blk .75 .35
797 A182 2 l lt bl, dk gray & blk 1.50 .65
798 A182 3 l yellow, brn & grn 2.25 1.10
799 A182 7 l brt grn, yel & brn blk 5.25 1.50
800 A182 12 l pale lil, dk brn & ind 9.00 1.75
Nos. 796-800 (5) 18.75 5.35

Mountain View, Valbona A183

1.50 l, Seashore. 3 l, Glacier and peak. 4 l, Gorge. 5 l, Mountain peaks. 9 l, Lake and hills.

1965, Mar. **Litho.** ***Perf. 12***

801 A183 1.50 l multi 1.10 .35
802 A183 2.50 l multi 2.75 .70
803 A183 3 l multi, vert. 2.75 .70
804 A183 4 l multi, vert. 3.50 1.25
805 A183 5 l multi 4.00 1.50
806 A183 9 l multi 11.00 3.00
Nos. 801-806 (6) 25.10 7.50

Frontier Guard — A184

1965, Apr. 25 **Unwmk.**

807 A184 2.50 l lt blue & multi 1.25 .25
808 A184 12.50 l lt ultra & multi 7.25 .90

20th anniversary of the Frontier Guards.

Small-bore Rifle Shooting, Prone — A185

Designs: 2 l, Rifle shooting, standing. 3 l, Target over map of Europe, showing Bucharest. 4 l, Pistol shooting. 15 l, Rifle shooting, kneeling.

1965, May 10

809 A185 1 l lil, car rose, blk & brn .35 .25
810 A185 2 l bl, blk, brn & vio bl .35 .25
811 A185 3 l pink & car rose .70 .25
812 A185 4 l bis, blk & vio brn 1.40 .25
813 A185 15 l brt grn, brn & vio brn 4.25 .50
Nos. 809-813 (5) 7.05 1.50

European Shooting Championships, Bucharest.

ITU Emblem, Old and New Communications Equipment — A186

1965, May 17 ***Perf. 12½x12***

814 A186 2.50 l brt grn, blk & lil rose .75 .25
815 A186 12.50 l vio, blk & brt bl 4.25 .30

Centenary of the ITU.

Col. Pavel Belyayev — A187

Designs: 2 l, Voskhod II. 6.50 l, Lt. Col. Alexei Leonov. 20 l, Leonov floating in space.

1965, June 15 ***Perf. 12***

816 A187 1.50 l lt blue & brn .25 .25
817 A187 2 l dk bl, lt vio & lt ultra .25 .25
818 A187 6.50 l lilac & brn .30 .25
819 A187 20 l chlky bl, yel & blk 3.00 .40
Nos. 816-819 (4) 3.80 1.15

Miniature Sheet

Perf. 12 on 2 sides

820 A187 20 l brt bl, org & blk 11.00 11.00

Space flight of Voskhod II and 1st man walking in space, Lt. Col. Alexei Leonov. No. 820 contains one stamp, size: 51x59½mm, perforated at top and bottom. Imperf., brt grn background, value $12.

Marx and Lenin — A188

1965, June 21 ***Perf. 12***

821 A188 2.50 l dk brn, red & yel .60 .25
822 A188 7.50 l sl grn, org ver & buff 2.40 .25

6th Conf. of Postal Ministers of Communist Countries, Peking, June 21-July 15.

Mother and Child — A189

2 l, Pioneers. 3 l, Boy and girl at play, horiz. 4 l, Child on beach. 15 l, Girl with book.

Perf. 12½x12, 12x12½

1965, June 29 **Litho.** **Unwmk.**

823 A189 1 l brt bl, rose lil & blk .25 .25
824 A189 2 l salmon, vio & blk .25 .25
825 A189 3 l green, org & vio .30 .25
826 A189 4 l multicolored .70 .25
827 A189 15 l lil rose, brn & ocher 3.25 .50
Nos. 823-827 (5) 4.75 1.50

Issued for International Children's Day.

Statue of Magistrate — A190

Designs: 1 l, Amphora. 2 l, Illyrian armor. 3 l, Mosaic, horiz. 15 l, Torso, Apollo statue.

1965, July 20 ***Perf. 12***

828 A190 1 l lt ol, org & brn .25 .25
829 A190 2 l gray grn, grn & brn .25 .25
830 A190 3 l tan, brn, car & lil .30 .25
831 A190 4 l green, bis & brn 1.10 .25
832 A190 15 l gray & pale claret 2.75 .65
Nos. 828-832 (5) 4.65 1.65

Flowers — A191

1965, Aug. 11 ***Perf. 12½x12***

833 A191 1 l Fuchsia .25 .25
834 A191 2 l Cyclamen .50 .25
835 A191 3 l Tiger lily .75 .25
836 A191 3.50 l Iris 1.10 .25
837 A191 4 l Dahlia 1.10 .25
838 A191 4.50 l Hydrangea 1.50 .25
839 A191 5 l Rose 1.50 .30
840 A191 7 l Tulips 2.25 .35
Nos. 833-840 (8) 8.95 2.15

Nos. 698-700 Surcharged New Value and Two Bars

1965, Aug. 16 ***Perf. 14***

841 A159 5q on 30 l .60 .60
842 A159 15q on 30 l .60 .60
843 A159 25q on 50 l 1.00 1.00
844 A159 80q on 50 l 2.00 2.00
845 A159 1.10 l on 20 l 3.00 3.00
846 A159 2 l on 20 l 5.00 5.00
Nos. 841-846 (6) 12.20 12.20

White Stork — A192

Migratory Birds: 20q, Cuckoo. 30q, Hoopoe. 40q, European bee-eater. 50q, European nightjar. 1.50 l, Quail.

1965, Aug. 31 ***Perf. 12***

847 A192 10q yel, blk & gray .35 .35
848 A192 20q brt pink, blk & dk bl .75 .35
849 A192 30q violet, blk & bis 1.10 .50
850 A192 40q emer, blk yel & org 1.50 .70
851 A192 50q ultra, brn & red brn 1.90 .95
852 A192 1.50 l bis, red brn & dp org 5.50 2.75
Nos. 847-852 (6) 11.10 5.60

"Homecoming," by Bukurosh Sejdini — A193

1965, Sept. 26 Litho. *Perf. 12x12½*

853	A193	25q olive black	1.75	.40
854	A193	65q blue black	5.25	1.60
855	A193	1.10 l black	7.50	3.25
		Nos. 853-855 (3)	14.50	5.25

Second war veterans' meeting.

Hunting — A194

1965, Oct. 6 Litho. Unwmk.

856	A194	10q Capercaillie	.35	.25
857	A194	20q Deer	.65	.25
858	A194	30q Pheasant	.75	.25
859	A194	40q Mallards	1.25	.25
860	A194	50q Boar	1.40	.25
861	A194	1 l Rabbit	3.25	.55
		Nos. 856-861 (6)	7.65	1.80

Oleander — A195

Flowers: 20q, Forget-me-nots. 30q, Pink. 40q, White water lily. 50q, Bird's foot. 1 l, Corn poppy.

1965, Oct. 26 *Perf. 12½x12*

862	A195	10q brt bl, grn & car rose	.25	.25
863	A195	20q org red, bl, brn & grn	.35	.25
864	A195	30q vio, car rose & grn	.45	.25
865	A195	40q emerald, yel & blk	.65	.30
866	A195	50q org brn, yel & grn	1.10	.40
867	A195	1 l yel grn, blk & rose red	2.50	1.60
		Nos. 862-867 (6)	5.30	3.05

Hotel Turizmi, Fier — A196

Buildings: 10q, Hotel, Peshkopi. 15q, Sanatorium, Tirana. 25q, Rest home, Pogradec. 65q, Partisan Sports Arena, Tirana. 80q, Rest home, Mali Dajt. 1.10 l, Culture House, Tirana. 1.60 l, Hotel Adriatik, Durres. 2 l, Migjeni Theater, Shkoder. 3 l, Alexander Moissi House of Culture, Durres.

1965, Oct. 27 *Perf. 12x12½*

868	A196	5q blue & blk	.25	.25
869	A196	10q ocher & blk	.25	.25
870	A196	15q dull grn & blk	.25	.25
871	A196	25q violet & blk	.25	.25
872	A196	65q lt brn & blk	.70	.50
873	A196	80q yel grn & blk	1.40	.50
874	A196	1.10 l lilac & blk	2.00	.50
875	A196	1.60 l lt vio bl & blk	2.75	1.40
876	A196	2 l dull rose & blk	3.50	1.40
877	A196	3 l gray & blk	6.25	2.50
		Nos. 868-877 (10)	17.60	7.80

Freighter "Teuta" — A197

Ships: 20q, Raft. 30q, Sailing ship, 19th cent. 40q, Sailing ship, 18th cent. 50q, Freighter "Vlora." 1 l, Illyric galleys.

1965, Nov. 16

878	A197	10q brt grn & dk grn	.30	.25
879	A197	20q ol bis & dk grn	.30	.25
880	A197	30q lt & dp ultra	.35	.25
881	A197	40q vio & dp vio	.45	.25
882	A197	50q pink & dk red	1.25	.25
883	A197	1 l bister & brn	3.25	.45
		Nos. 878-883 (6)	5.90	1.70

Brown Bear — A198

Various Albanian bears. 50q, 55q, 60q, horiz.

1965, Dec. 7 *Perf. 11½x12*

884	A198	10q bister & dk brn	.35	.25
885	A198	20q pale brn & dk brn	.35	.25
886	A198	30q bis, dk brn & car	.70	.25
887	A198	35q pale brn & dk brn	.85	.25
888	A198	40q bister & dk brn	1.00	.25
889	A198	50q bister & dk brn	1.75	.25
890	A198	55q bister & dk brn	2.25	.30
891	A198	60q pale brn, dk brn & car	3.75	.50
		Nos. 884-891 (8)	11.00	2.30

Basketball and Players — A199

10q, Games' emblem (map of Albania and basket). 30q, 50q, Players with ball (diff. designs). 1.40 l, Basketball medal on ribbon.

1965, Dec. 15 Litho. *Perf. 12½x12*

892	A199	10q blue, yel & car	.25	.25
893	A199	20q rose lil, lt brn & blk	.25	.25
894	A199	30q bis, lt brn, red & blk	.30	.25
895	A199	50q lt grn, lt brn & blk	1.00	.25
896	A199	1.40 l rose, blk, brn & yel	2.25	.50
		Nos. 892-896 (5)	4.05	1.50

7th Balkan Basketball Championships, Tirana, Dec. 15-19.

Arms of Republic and Smokestacks — A200

Arms and: 10q, Book. 30q, Wheat. 60q, Book, hammer & sickle. 80q, Factories.

1966, Jan. 11 Litho. *Perf. 11½x12*

Coat of Arms in Gold

897	A200	10q crimson & brn	.25	.25
898	A200	20q blue & vio bl	.25	.25
899	A200	30q org yel & brn	.50	.25
900	A200	60q yel grn & brt grn	1.20	.25
901	A200	80q crimson & brn	1.40	.25
		Nos. 897-901 (5)	3.60	1.25

Albanian People's Republic, 20th anniv.

Cow — A201

1966, Feb. 25 *Perf. 12½x12, 12x12½*

902	A201	10q shown	.25	.25
903	A201	20q Pig	.40	.25
904	A201	30q Ewe & lamb	.75	.30
905	A201	35q Ram	1.20	.30
906	A201	40q Dog	1.50	.30
907	A201	50q Cat, vert.	1.75	.30
908	A201	55q Horse, vert.	2.00	.40
909	A201	60q Ass, vert.	4.00	.60
		Nos. 902-909 (8)	11.85	2.70

Soccer Player and Map of Uruguay — A202

5q, Globe in form of soccer ball. 15q, Player, map of Italy. 20q, Goalkeeper, map of France. 25q, Player, map of Brazil. 30q, Player, map of Switzerland. 35q, Player, map of Sweden. 40q, Player, map of Chile. 50q, Player, map of Great Britain. 70q, World Championship cup & ball.

1966, Mar. 20 Litho. *Perf. 12*

910	A202	5q gray & dp org	.25	.25
911	A202	10q lt brn, bl & vio	.25	.25
912	A202	15q cit, dk bl & brt bl	.25	.25
913	A202	20q org, vio bl & brt bl	.25	.25
914	A202	25q salmon & sepia	.25	.25
915	A202	30q lt yel grn & brn	.35	.25
916	A202	35q lt ultra & emer	.50	.25
917	A202	40q pink & brown	.55	.25
918	A202	50q pale grn, mag & rose red	.75	.25
919	A202	70q gray, brn, yel & blk	1.25	.30
		Nos. 910-919 (10)	4.65	2.55

World Cup Soccer Championship, Wembley, England, July 11-30.

Andon Zako Cajupi — A203

1966, Mar. 27 Unwmk.

920	A203	40q bluish blk	.65	.25
921	A203	1.10 l dark green	2.00	.40

Andon Zako Cajupi, poet, birth centenary.

Painted Lady — A204

Designs: 20q, Blue dragonfly. 30q, Cloudless sulphur butterfly. 35q, 40q, Splendid dragonfly. 50q, Machaon swallow-tail. 55q, Sulphur butterfly. 60q, Whitemarbled butterfly.

1966, Apr. 21 Litho. *Perf. 11½x12*

922	A204	10q multicolored	.45	.25
923	A204	20q yellow & multi	.55	.25
924	A204	30q yellow & multi	.75	.25
925	A204	35q sky blue & multi	1.10	.25
926	A204	40q multicolored	1.60	.25
927	A204	50q rose & multi	2.25	.25
928	A204	55q multicolored	2.75	.25
929	A204	60q multicolored	7.00	.35
		Nos. 922-929 (8)	16.45	2.10

WHO Headquarters, Geneva, and Emblem — A205

Designs (WHO Emblem and): 35q, Ambulance and stretcher bearers, vert. 60q, Albanian mother and nurse weighing infant, vert. 80q, X-ray machine and hospital.

Perf. 12x12½, 12½x12

1966, May 3 Litho.

930	A205	25q lt blue & blk	.40	.25
931	A205	35q salmon & ultra	.75	.25
932	A205	60q lt grn, bl & red	1.20	.25
933	A205	80q yel, bl, grn & lt brn	1.50	.25
		Nos. 930-933 (4)	3.85	1.00

Inauguration of the WHO Headquarters, Geneva.

Bird's Foot Starfish — A206

Designs: 25q, Starfish. 35q, Brittle star. 45q, But-thorn starfish. 50q, Starfish. 60q, Sea cucumber. 70q, Sea urchin.

1966, May 10 *Perf. 12x12½*

934	A206	15q multicolored	.25	.25
935	A206	25q multicolored	.45	.30
936	A206	35q multicolored	.75	.40
937	A206	45q multicolored	1.00	.45
938	A206	50q multicolored	1.10	.55
939	A206	60q multicolored	1.60	.75
940	A206	70q multicolored	2.00	1.90
		Nos. 934-940 (7)	7.15	4.60

Luna 10 — A207

30q, 80q, Trajectory of Luna 10, earth & moon.

1966, June 10 *Perf. 12x12½*

941	A207	20q blue, yel & blk	.35	.25
942	A207	30q yel grn, blk & bl	.70	.25
943	A207	70q vio, yel & blk	1.40	.25
944	A207	80q yel, vio, grn & blk	2.50	.50
		Nos. 941-944 (4)	4.95	1.25

Launching of the 1st artificial moon satellite, Luna 10, Apr. 3, 1966.

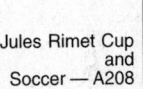

Jules Rimet Cup and Soccer — A208

Designs: Various scenes of soccer play.

1966, July 12 Litho. *Perf. 12x12½*

Black Inscriptions

945	A208	10q ocher & lilac	.30	.25
946	A208	20q lt blue & cit	.35	.25
947	A208	30q brick red & Prus bl	.50	.25
948	A208	35q lt ultra & rose	.70	.25
949	A208	40q yel grn & lt red brn	.70	.25
950	A208	50q lt red brn & yel grn	.85	.25
951	A208	55q rose lil & yel grn	.85	.25
952	A208	60q dp rose & ocher	1.75	.25
		Nos. 945-952 (8)	6.00	2.00

World Cup Soccer Championship, Wembley, England, July 11-30.

Water Level Map of Albania — A209

30q, Water measure & fields. 70q, Turbine & pylon. 80q, Hydrological decade emblem.

1966, July *Perf. 12½x12*

953	A209	20q brick red, blk & org	.50	.25
954	A209	30q emer, blk & lt brn	.50	.25
955	A209	70q brt violet & blk	1.50	.25
956	A209	80q brt bl, org, yel & blk	2.50	.45
		Nos. 953-956 (4)	5.00	1.20

Hydrological Decade (UNESCO), 1965-74.

Greek Turtle A210

Designs: 15q, Grass snake. 25q, European pond turtle. 30q, Wall lizard. 35q, Wall gecko. 45q, Emerald lizard. 50q, Slowworm. 90q, Horned viper (or sand viper).

1966, Aug. 10 Litho. *Perf. 12½x12*

957	A210	10q gray & multi	.25	.25
958	A210	15q yellow & multi	.30	.25
959	A210	25q ultra & multi	.35	.25
960	A210	30q multicolored	.45	.25
961	A210	35q multicolored	.70	.25
962	A210	45q multicolored	.85	.25
963	A210	50q orange & multi	1.00	.30
964	A210	90q lilac & multi	1.75	.55
		Nos. 957-964 (8)	5.65	2.35

Persian Cat — A211

Cats: 10q, Siamese, vert. 15q, European tabby, vert. 25q, Black kitten. 60q, 65q, 80q, Various Persians.

Perf. 12x12½, 12½x12

1966, Sept. 20 Litho.

965	A211	10q multicolored	.35	.25
966	A211	15q blk, sepia & car	.35	.25
967	A211	25q blk, dk & lt brn	.70	.25
968	A211	45q blk, org & yel	1.00	.25
969	A211	60q blk, brn & yel	1.75	.30
970	A211	65q multicolored	1.75	.40
971	A211	80q blk, gray & yel	2.50	.50
		Nos. 965-971 (7)	8.40	2.20

Pjeter Budi, Writer — A212

1966, Oct. 5 *Perf. 12x12½*

972	A212	25q buff & slate grn	.75	.25
973	A212	1.75 l gray & dull claret	2.25	.45

UNESCO Emblem — A213

Designs (UNESCO Emblem and): 15q, Open book, rose and school. 25q, Male folk dancers. 1.55 l, Jug, column and old building.

1966, Oct. 20 Litho. *Perf. 12*

974	A213	5q lt gray & multi	.25	.25
975	A213	15q dp blue & multi	.25	.25
976	A213	25q gray & multi	.30	.25
977	A213	1.55 l multi	2.25	.50
		Nos. 974-977 (4)	3.05	1.25

20th anniv. of UNESCO.

A214

Designs: 15q, Hand holding book with pictures of Marx, Engels, Lenin and Stalin. 25q, Map of Albania, hammer and sickle, symbols of agriculture and industry. 65q, Symbolic grain and factories. 95q, Fists holding rifle, spade, axe, sickle and book.

1966, Nov. 1 Litho. *Perf. 11½x12*

978	A214	15q vermilion & gold	.25	.25
979	A214	25q multicolored	.25	.25
980	A214	65q brn, brn org & gold	1.20	.25
981	A214	95q yellow & multi	1.50	.40
		Nos. 978-981 (4)	3.20	1.15

Albanian Communist Party, 5th Cong.

A215

Designs: 15q, Hammer and sickle, Party emblem in sunburst. 25q, Partisan and sunburst. 65q, Steel worker and blast furnace. 95q, Combine harvester, factories, and pylon.

1966, Nov. 8

982	A215	15q orange & multi	.40	.25
983	A215	25q red & multi	.40	.25
984	A215	65q multicolored	1.20	.25
985	A215	95q blue & multi	1.20	.40
		Nos. 982-985 (4)	3.20	1.15

25th anniv. of the founding of the Albanian Workers Party.

Russian Wolfhound A216

Dogs: 15q, Sheep dog. 25q, English setter. 45q, English springer spaniel. 60q, Bulldog. 65q, Saint Bernard. 80q, Dachshund.

1966, Oct. 30 Litho. *Perf. 12½x12*

986	A216	10q green & multi	.40	.25
987	A216	15q multicolored	.65	.25
988	A216	25q lilac & multi	.80	.25
989	A216	45q rose & multi	1.20	.35
990	A216	60q brown & multi	1.60	.40
991	A216	65q ultra & multi	1.75	.45
992	A216	80q blue grn & multi	3.25	.50
		Nos. 986-992 (7)	9.65	2.45

Ndre Mjeda — A217

1966 *Perf. 12½x12*

993	A217	25q brt bl & dk brn	.35	.25
994	A217	1.75 l brt grn & dk brn	2.40	.65

Birth Centenary of the priest Ndre Mjeda.

Proclamation — A218

Designs: 10q, Banner, man and woman holding gun and axe, horiz. 1.85 l, man with axe and banner and partisan with gun.

1966, Dec. 25 *Perf. 11½x12, 12x11½*

995	A218	5q lt brn, red & blk	.25	.25
996	A218	10q red, blk, gray & bl	.40	.25
997	A218	1.85 l red, blk & salmon	2.40	.30
		Nos. 995-997 (3)	3.05	.80

Albanian Communist Party, 25th anniv.

Golden Eagle — A219

Birds of Prey: 15q, European sea eagle. 25q, Griffon vulture. 40q, Common sparrowhawk. 50q, Osprey. 70q, Egyptian vulture. 90q, Kestrel.

1966, Dec. 20 Litho. *Perf. 11½x12*

998	A219	10q gray & multi	.35	.25
999	A219	15q multicolored	.35	.25
1000	A219	25q citron & multi	.70	.25
1001	A219	40q multicolored	1.00	.25
1002	A219	50q multicolored	1.40	.30
1003	A219	70q yellow & multi	2.00	.40
1004	A219	90q multicolored	3.00	.50
		Nos. 998-1004 (7)	8.80	2.20

Hake — A220

Fish: 15q, Red mullet. 25q, Opah. 40q, Atlantic wolf fish. 65q, Lumpfish. 80q, Swordfish. 1.15 l, Shorthorn sculpin.

1967, Jan. 20 Photo. *Perf. 12x11½*

Fish in Natural Colors

1005	A220	10q blue	.35	.25
1006	A220	15q lt yellow grn	.35	.25
1007	A220	25q Prus blue	.65	.25
1008	A220	40q emerald	.65	.25
1009	A220	65q brt blue grn	1.00	.30
1010	A220	80q blue	1.60	.40
1011	A220	1.15 l brt green	2.50	.65
		Nos. 1005-1011 (7)	7.10	2.35

White Pelican — A221

Designs: Various groups of pelicans.

1967, Feb. 22 Litho. *Perf. 12*

1012	A221	10q pink & multi	.25	.25
1013	A221	15q pink & multi	.25	.25
1014	A221	25q pink & multi	1.00	.25
1015	A221	50q pink & multi	2.00	.25
1016	A221	2 l pink & multi	5.00	.75
		Nos. 1012-1016 (5)	8.50	1.75

Camellia — A222

Flowers: 10q, Chrysanthemum. 15q, Hollyhock. 25q, Flowering Maple. 35q, Peony. 65q, Gladiolus. 80q, Freesia. 1.15 l, Carnation.

Unwmk.

1967, Apr. 12 Litho. *Perf. 12*

Flowers in Natural Colors

1017	A222	5q pale brown	.25	.25
1018	A222	10q lt lilac	.25	.25
1019	A222	15q gray	.25	.25
1020	A222	25q ultra	.45	.25
1021	A222	35q lt blue	.70	.25
1022	A222	65q lt blue grn	1.40	.25
1023	A222	80q lt bluish gray	1.75	.30
1024	A222	1.15 l dull yellow	2.10	.45
		Nos. 1017-1024 (8)	7.15	2.25

Congress Emblem and Power Station — A223

1967, Apr. 24 Litho. *Perf. 12*

1025	A223	25q multi	.75	.25
1026	A223	1.75 l multi	2.25	.55

Cong. of the Union of Professional Workers, Tirana, Apr. 24.

Rose — A224

Various Roses in Natural Colors.

1967, May 15 *Perf. 12x12½*

1027	A224	5q blue gray	.35	.25
1028	A224	10q brt blue	.35	.25
1029	A224	15q rose violet	.35	.25
1030	A224	25q lemon	.35	.25
1031	A224	35q brt grnsh blue	.70	.25
1032	A224	65q gray	1.00	.25
1033	A224	80q brown	1.00	.30
1034	A224	1.65 l gray green	2.75	.50
		Nos. 1027-1034 (8)	6.85	2.30

Seashore, Bregdet Borsh A225

Views: 15q, Buthrotum, vert. 25q, Shore, Fshati Piqeras. 45q, Shore, Bregdet. 50q, Shore, Bregdet Himare. 65q, Ship, Sarande (Santi Quaranta). 80q, Shore, Dhermi. 1 l, Sunset, Bregdet, vert.

Perf. 12x12½, 12½x12

1967, June 10

1035	A225	15q multicolored	.40	.25
1036	A225	20q multicolored	.40	.25
1037	A225	25q multicolored	.80	.35
1038	A225	45q multicolored	.80	.35
1039	A225	50q multicolored	.80	.35
1040	A225	65q multicolored	1.50	.50
1041	A225	80q multicolored	1.50	.70
1042	A225	1 l multicolored	2.40	1.00
		Nos. 1035-1042 (8)	8.60	3.75

Fawn — A226

Roe Deer: 20q, Stag, vert. 25q, Doe, vert. 30q, Young stag and doe. 35q, Doe and fawn. 40q, Young stag, vert. 65q, Stag and doe, vert. 70q, Running stag and does.

Perf. 12½x12, 12x12½

1967, July 20 Litho.

1043	A226	15q multicolored	.35	.25
1044	A226	20q multicolored	.35	.25
1045	A226	25q multicolored	.70	.25
1046	A226	30q multicolored	.70	.25
1047	A226	35q multicolored	1.00	.25
1048	A226	40q multicolored	1.00	.25
1049	A226	65q multicolored	2.10	.35
1050	A226	70q multicolored	2.75	.55
		Nos. 1043-1050 (8)	8.95	2.40

Man and Woman from Madhe — A227

Regional Costumes: 20q, Woman from Zadrimes. 25q, Dancer and drummer, Kukesit. 45q, Woman spinner, Dardhes. 50q, Farm couple, Myseqese. 65q, Dancer with tambourine, Tirana. 80q, Man and woman, Dropullit. 1 l, Piper, Laberise.

1967, Aug. 25 *Perf. 12*

1051	A227	15q tan & multi	.40	.25
1052	A227	20q lt yellow grn	.40	.25
1053	A227	25q multicolored	.40	.25
1054	A227	45q sky blue & multi	.80	.25
1055	A227	50q lemon & multi	.80	.30
1056	A227	65q pink & multi	.80	.40
1057	A227	80q multicolored	1.60	.45
1058	A227	1 l gray & multi	1.60	.60
		Nos. 1051-1058 (8)	6.80	2.75

Fighters and Newspaper — A228

75q, Printing plant, newspapers, microphone. 2 l, People holding newspaper.

1967, Aug. 25 *Perf. 12½x12*

1059	A228	25q multicolored	.35	.25
1060	A228	75q pink & multi	1.00	.50
1061	A228	2 l multicolored	2.75	1.25
		Nos. 1059-1061 (3)	4.10	2.00

Issued for the Day of the Press.

Street Scene, by Kole Idromeno A229

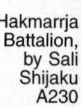

Hakmarrja Battalion, by Sali Shijaku A230

Designs: 20q, David, fresco by Onufri, 16th century, vert. 45q, Woman's head, ancient mosaic, vert. 50q, Men on horseback from 16th century icon, vert. 65q, Farm Women, by Zef Shoshi. 80q, Street Scene, by Vangjush Mio. 1 l, Bride, by Kolé Idromeno, vert.

Perf. 12, 12x12½, (A230)

1967, Oct. 25 **Litho.**

1062	A229	15q multicolored	.45	.25
1063	A229	20q multicolored	.45	.25
1064	A230	25q multicolored	1.00	.25
1065	A229	45q multicolored	1.00	.25
1066	A229	50q multicolored	1.00	.25
1067	A230	65q multicolored	1.75	.25
1068	A230	80q multicolored	1.75	.30
1069	A230	1 l multicolored	4.00	.35
		Nos. 1062-1069 (8)	11.40	2.15

Lenin at Storming of Winter Palace — A231

Designs: 15q, Lenin and Stalin, horiz. 50q, Lenin and Stalin addressing meeting. 1.10 l, Storming of the Winter Palace, horiz.

1967, Nov. 7 ***Perf. 12***

1070	A231	15q red & multi	.30	.25
1071	A231	25q slate grn & blk	.55	.25
1072	A231	50q brn, blk & brn vio	.75	.25
1073	A231	1.10 l lilac, gray & blk	1.50	.30
		Nos. 1070-1073 (4)	3.10	1.05

50th anniv. of the Russian October Revolution.

Rabbit — A232

Designs: Various hares and rabbits. The 15q, 25q, 35q, 40q and 1 l are horizontal.

1967, Sept. 30

1074	A232	15q orange & multi	.25	.25
1075	A232	20q brt yel & multi	.35	.25
1076	A232	25q lt brn & multi	.35	.25
1077	A232	35q multicolored	.75	.25
1078	A232	40q yellow & multi	.75	.25
1079	A232	50q pink & multi	2.25	.25
1080	A232	65q multicolored	2.25	.35
1081	A232	1 l lilac & multi	3.00	.55
		Nos. 1074-1081 (8)	9.95	2.40

University, Torch and Book — A233

1967, Sept. 15 **Litho.** ***Perf. 12***

1082	A233	25q multi	.35	.25
1083	A233	1.75 l multi	2.25	.35

10th anniv. of the founding of the State University, Tirana.

Coat of Arms and Soldiers — A234

65q, Arms, Factory, grain, flag, gun, radio tower. 1.20 l, Arms, hand holding torch.

1967, Sept. 16 ***Perf. 12x11½***

1084	A234	15q multi	.30	.25
1085	A234	65q multi	.75	.25
1086	A234	1.20 l multi	1.50	.25
		Nos. 1084-1086 (3)	2.55	.75

25th anniversary of the Democratic Front.

Turkey — A235

Designs: 20q, Duck. 25q, Hen. 45q, Rooster. 50q, Guinea fowl. 65q, Goose, horiz. 80q, Mallard, horiz. 1 l, Chicks, horiz.

Perf. 12x12½, 12½x12

1967, Nov. 25 **Photo.**

1087	A235	15q gold & multi	.25	.25
1088	A235	20q gold & multi	.25	.25
1089	A235	25q gold & multi	.30	.25
1090	A235	45q gold & multi	1.00	.25
1091	A235	50q gold & multi	1.00	.25
1092	A235	65q gold & multi	1.00	.25
1093	A235	80q gold & multi	1.75	.35
1094	A235	1 l gold & multi	3.25	.45
		Nos. 1087-1094 (8)	8.80	2.30

Skanderbeg A236

Designs: 10q, Arms of Skanderbeg. 25q, Helmet and sword. 30q, Kruje Castle. 35q, Petreles Castle. 65q, Berati Castle. 80q, Skanderbeg addressing national chiefs. 90q, Battle of Albulenes.

1967, Dec. 10 **Litho.** ***Perf. 12x12½***

Medallion in Bister and Dark Brown

1095	A236	10q gold & violet	.25	.25
1096	A236	15q gold & rose car	.25	.25
1097	A236	25q gold & vio bl	.30	.25
1098	A236	30q gold & dk blue	.40	.25
1099	A236	35q gold & maroon	.50	.25
1100	A236	65q gold & green	.80	.25
1101	A236	80q gold & gray brn	1.60	.30
1102	A236	90q gold & ultra	1.60	.35
		Nos. 1095-1102 (8)	5.70	2.15

500th anniv. of the death of Skanderbeg (George Castriota), national hero.

10th Winter Olympic Games, Grenoble, France, Feb. 6-18 — A237

Designs: 15q, 2 l, Winter Olympics emblem. 25q, Ice hockey. 30q, Women's figure skating. 50q, Slalom. 80q, Downhill skiing. 1 l, Ski jump.

1967-68

1103	A237	15q multicolored	.25	.25
1104	A237	25q multicolored	.25	.25
1105	A237	30q multicolored	.25	.25
1106	A237	50q multicolored	.30	.25
1107	A237	80q multicolored	.75	.25
1108	A237	1 l multicolored	1.60	.25
		Nos. 1103-1108 (6)	3.40	1.50

Miniature Sheet

Imperf

1109	A237	2 l red, gray & brt bl ('68)	6.50	4.50

Nos. 1103-1108 issued Dec. 29, 1967.

Skanderbeg Monument, Kruje — A238

Designs: 10q, Skanderbeg monument, Tirana. 15q, Skanderbeg portrait, Uffizi Galleries, Florence. 25q, engraved portrait of Gen. Tanush Topia. 35q, Portrait of Gen. Gjergj Arianti, horiz. 65q, Portrait bust of Skanderbeg by O. Paskali. 80q, Title page of "The Life of Skanderbeg." 90q, Skanderbeg battling the Turks, painting by S. Rrota, horiz.

Perf. 12x12½, 12½x12

1968, Jan. 17 **Litho.**

1110	A238	10q multicolored	.35	.25
1111	A238	15q multicolored	.35	.25
1112	A238	25q blk, yel & lt bl	.75	.25
1113	A238	30q multicolored	.75	.25
1114	A238	35q lt vio, pink & blk	.75	.25
1115	A238	65q multicolored	1.50	.30
1116	A238	80q pink, blk & yel	2.25	.50
1117	A238	90q beige & multi	2.25	.65
		Nos. 1110-1117 (8)	8.95	2.70

500th anniv. of the death of Skanderbeg (George Castriota), national hero.

Carnation — A239

1968, Feb. 15 ***Perf. 12***

Various Carnations in Natural Colors

1118	A239	15q green	.25	.25
1119	A239	20q dk brown	.25	.25
1120	A239	25q brt blue	.25	.25
1121	A239	50q gray olice	.70	.25
1122	A239	80q bluish gray	.90	.25
1123	A239	1.10 l violet gray	1.50	.40
		Nos. 1118-1123 (6)	3.85	1.65

"Electrification" — A240

65q, Farm tractor, horiz. 1.10 l, Cow & herd.

1968, Mar. 5 **Litho.** ***Perf. 12***

1124	A240	25q multi	.35	.25
1125	A240	65q multi	1.10	.30
1126	A240	1.10 l multi	1.40	.40
		Nos. 1124-1126 (3)	2.85	.95

Fifth Farm Cooperatives Congress.

Goat — A241

Various goats. 15q, 20q, 25q are vertical.

1968, Mar. 25 ***Perf. 12x12½, 12½x12***

1127	A241	15q multi	.25	.25
1128	A241	20q multi	.25	.25
1129	A241	25q multi	.35	.25
1130	A241	30q multi	.35	.25
1131	A241	40q multi	.50	.25
1132	A241	50q multi	.50	.25
1133	A241	80q multi	1.50	.25
1134	A241	1.40 l multi	2.25	.40
		Nos. 1127-1134 (8)	5.95	2.15

Zef N. Jubani — A242

1968, Mar. 30 ***Perf. 12***

1135	A242	25q yellow & choc	.35	.25
1136	A242	1.75 l lt violet & blk	1.90	.50

Sesquicentennial of the birth of Zef N. Jubani, writer and scholar.

Physician and Hospital — A243

Designs (World Health Organization Emblem and): 65q, Hospital and microscope, horiz. 1.10 l, Mother feeding child.

Perf. 12½x12, 12x12½

1968, Apr. 7 **Litho.**

1137	A243	25q green & claret	.25	.25
1138	A243	65q black, yel & bl	.90	.30
1139	A243	1.10 l black & dp org	1.10	.40
		Nos. 1137-1139 (3)	2.25	.95

20th anniv. of WHO.

Scientist — A244

Women: 15q, Militia member. 60q, Farm worker. 1 l, Factory worker.

1968, Apr. 14 ***Perf. 12***

1140	A244	15q ver & dk red	.35	.25
1141	A244	25q blue grn & grn	.35	.25
1142	A244	60q dull yel & brn	1.10	.25
1143	A244	1 l lt vio & vio	1.90	.40
		Nos. 1140-1143 (4)	3.70	1.15

Albanian Women's Organization, 25th anniv.

Karl Marx — A245

Designs: 25q, Marx lecturing to students. 65q, "Das Kapital," "Communist Manifesto" and marching crowd. 95q, Full-face portrait.

1968, May 5 **Litho.** ***Perf. 12***

1144	A245	15q gray, dk bl & bis	.45	.25
1145	A245	25q brn vio, dk brn & dl yel	.60	.25
1146	A245	65q gray, blk, brn & car	1.25	.25
1147	A245	95q gray, ocher & blk	3.00	.50
		Nos. 1144-1147 (4)	5.30	1.25

Karl Marx, 150th birth anniversary.

Heliopsis — A246

Flowers: 20q, Red flax. 25q, Orchid. 30q, Gloxinia. 40q, Turk's-cap lily. 80q, Amaryllis. 1.40 l, Red magnolia.

1968, May 10 ***Perf. 12x12½***

1148	A246	15q gold & multi	.25	.25
1149	A246	20q gold & multi	.25	.25
1150	A246	25q gold & multi	.30	.25
1151	A246	30q gold & multi	.35	.25
1152	A246	40q gold & multi	.35	.25
1153	A246	80q gold & multi	1.10	.40
1154	A246	1.40 l gold & multi	1.90	.60
		Nos. 1148-1154 (7)	4.50	2.25

Proclamation of Prizren — A247

25q, Abdyl Frasheri. 40q, House in Prizren.

1968, June 10 Litho. *Perf. 12*

1155	A247	25q emerald & blk	.40	.25
1156	A247	40q multicolored	.75	.25
1157	A247	85q yellow & multi	1.10	.30
		Nos. 1155-1157 (3)	2.25	.80

League of Prizren against the Turks, 90th anniv.

Shepherd, by A. Kushi — A248

Paintings from Tirana Art Gallery: 20q, View of Tirana, by V. Mio, horiz. 25q, Mountaineer, by G. Madhi. 40q, Refugees, by A. Buza. 80q, Guerrillas of Shahin Matrakut, by S. Xega. 1.50 l, Portrait of an Old Man, by S. Papadhimitri. 1.70 l, View of Scutari, by S. Rrota. 2.50 l, Woman in Scutari Costume, by Z. Colombi.

1968, June 20 *Perf. 12x12½*

1158	A248	15q gold & multi	.25	.25
1159	A248	20q gold & multi	.25	.25
1160	A248	25q gold & multi	.25	.25
1161	A248	40q gold & multi	.25	.25
1162	A248	80q gold & multi	.55	.25
1163	A248	1.50 l gold & multi	1.40	.30
1164	A248	1.70 l gold & multi	2.25	.55
		Nos. 1158-1164 (7)	5.20	2.10

Miniature Sheet

Perf. 12½xImperf.

1165	A248	2.50 l multi	2.75	2.50

No. 1165 contains one stamp, size: 50x71mm.

Soldier and Guns A249

25q, Sailor, warships. 65q, Aviator, planes, vert. 95q, Militiamen, woman.

1968, July 10 Litho. *Perf. 12*

1166	A249	15q multicolored	.35	.25
1167	A249	25q multicolored	.35	.25
1168	A249	65q multicolored	1.50	.25
1169	A249	95q multicolored	2.25	.25
		Nos. 1166-1169 (4)	4.45	1.00

25th anniversary of the People's Army.

Squid — A250

Designs: 20q, Crayfish. 25q, Whelk. 50q, Crab. 70q, Spiny lobster. 80q, Shore crab. 90q, Norway lobster.

1968, Aug. 20

1170	A250	15q multicolored	.35	.25
1171	A250	20q multicolored	.35	.25
1172	A250	25q multicolored	.35	.25
1173	A250	50q multicolored	.35	.25
1174	A250	70q multicolored	.75	.30
1175	A250	80q multicolored	1.90	.35
1176	A250	90q multicolored	1.90	.40
		Nos. 1170-1176 (7)	5.95	2.05

Women's Relay Race A251

Sport: 20q, Running. 25q, Women's discus. 30q, Equestrian. 40q, High jump. 50q, Women's hurdling. 80q, Soccer. 1.40 l, Woman diver. 2 l, Olympic stadium.

1968, Sept. 23 Photo. *Perf. 12*

1177	A251	15q multicolored	.25	.25
1178	A251	20q multicolored	.25	.25
1179	A251	25q multicolored	.25	.25
1180	A251	30q multicolored	.25	.25
1181	A251	40q multicolored	.30	.25
1182	A251	50q multicolored	.30	.25
1183	A251	80q multicolored	.75	.25
1184	A251	1.40 l multicolored	1.50	.35
		Nos. 1177-1184 (8)	3.85	2.10

Souvenir Sheet

Perf. 12½ Horizontally

1185	A251	2 l multicolored	3.00	2.50

19th Olympic Games, Mexico City, Oct. 12-27. No. 1185 contains one rectangular stamp, size: 64x54mm. Value of imperfs., Nos. 1177-1184 $10.50, No. 1185 $7.50.

Enver Hoxha — A252

1968, Oct. 16 Litho. *Perf. 12*

1186	A252	25q blue gray	.40	.25
1187	A252	35q rose brown	.40	.25
1188	A252	80q violet	.80	.35
1189	A252	1.10 l brown	1.20	.50
		Nos. 1186-1189 (4)	2.80	1.35

Souvenir Sheet

Imperf

1190	A252	1.50 l rose red, bl vio & gold	*75.00*	*75.00*

60th birthday of Enver Hoxha, First Secretary of the Central Committee of the Communist Party of Albania.

Book and Pupils — A253

1968, Nov. 14 Photo.

1191	A253	15q mar & slate grn	.40	.25
1192	A253	85q gray olive & sepia	2.50	.25

60th anniv. of the Congress of Monastir, Nov. 14-22, 1908, which adopted a unified Albanian alphabet.

Waxwing A254

Birds: 20q, Rose-colored starling. 25q, Kingfishers. 50q, Long-tailed tits. 80q, Wallcreeper. 1.10 l, Bearded tit.

1968, Nov. 15 Litho.

Birds in Natural Colors

1193	A254	15q lt blue & blk	.25	.25
1194	A254	20q bister & blk	.25	.25
1195	A254	25q pink & blk	.40	.25
1196	A254	50q lt yel grn & blk	1.00	.25
1197	A254	80q bis brn & blk	2.00	.35
1198	A254	1.10 l pale grn & blk	3.00	.55
		Nos. 1193-1198 (6)	6.90	1.90

Mao Tse-tung A255

1968, Dec. 26 Litho. *Perf. 12½x12*

1199	A255	25q gold, red & blk	1.00	.40
1200	A255	1.75 l gold, red & blk	6.50	3.50

75th birthday of Mao Tse-tung.

Adem Reka and Crane — A256

Portraits: 10q, Pjeter Lleshi and power lines. 15q, Mohammed Shehu and Myrteza Kepi. 25q, Shkurte Vata and women railroad workers. 65q, Agron Elezi, frontier guard. 80q, Ismet Bruçaj and mountain road. 1.30 l, Fuat Cela, blind revolutionary.

1969, Feb. 10 Litho. *Perf. 12x12½*

1201	A256	5q multicolored	.35	.25
1202	A256	10q multicolored	.35	.25
1203	A256	15q multicolored	.70	.25
1204	A256	25q multicolored	1.00	.25
1205	A256	65q multicolored	1.40	.25
1206	A256	80q multicolored	1.40	.25
1207	A256	1.30 l multicolored	2.10	.25
		Nos. 1201-1207 (7)	7.30	1.75

Contemporary heroine and heroes.

Meteorological Instruments A257

Designs: 25q, Water gauge. 1.60 l, Radar, balloon and isobars.

1969, Feb. 25 *Perf. 12*

1208	A257	15q multicolored	.50	.25
1209	A257	25q ultra, org & blk	.50	.25
1210	A257	1.60 l rose vio, yel & blk	2.75	.60
		Nos. 1208-1210 (3)	3.75	1.10

20th anniv. of Albanian hydrometeorology.

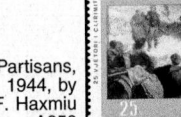

Partisans, 1944, by F. Haxmiu A258

Paintings: 5q, Student Revolutionists, by P. Mele, vert. 65q, Steel Mill, by C. Ceka. 80q, Reconstruction, by V. Kilica. 1.10 l, Harvest, by N. Jonuzi. 1.15 l, Terraced Landscape, by S. Kaceli. 2 l, Partisans' Meeting.

Perf. 12x12½, 12½x12

1969, Apr. 25 Litho.

Size: 31½x41½mm

1211	A258	5q buff & multi	.25	.25

Size: 51½x30½mm

1212	A258	25q buff & multi	.25	.25

Size: 40½x32mm

1213	A258	65q buff & multi	.30	.25

Size: 51½x30½mm

1214	A258	80q buff & multi	.35	.25
1215	A258	1.10 l buff & multi	.75	.25
1216	A258	1.15 l buff & multi	.75	.25
		Nos. 1211-1216 (6)	2.65	1.50

Miniature Sheet

Imperf

Size: 111x90mm

1217	A258	2 l ocher & multi	2.00	1.50

Leonardo da Vinci, Self-portrait — A259

Designs (after Leonardo da Vinci): 35q, Lilies. 40q, Design for a flying machine, horiz. 1 l, Portrait of Beatrice. No. 1222, Portrait of a Noblewoman. No. 1223, Mona Lisa.

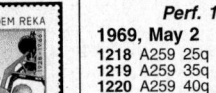

Perf. 12x12½, 12½x12

1969, May 2 Litho.

1218	A259	25q gold & sepia	.25	.25
1219	A259	35q gold & sepia	.35	.25
1220	A259	40q gold & sepia	.50	.25
1221	A259	1 l gold & multi	1.40	.25
1222	A259	2 l gold & sepia	2.75	.55
		Nos. 1218-1222 (5)	5.25	1.55

Miniature Sheet

Imperf

1223	A259	2 l gold & multi	5.50	2.50

Leonardo da Vinci (1452-1519), painter, sculptor, architect and engineer.

First Congress Meeting Place — A260

Designs: 1 l, Albanian coat of arms. 2.25 l, Two partisans with guns and flag.

1969, May 24 *Perf. 12*

1224	A260	25q lt grn, blk & red	.35	.25
1225	A260	2.25 l multi	2.75	1.00

Souvenir Sheet

1226	A260	1 l gold, bl, blk & red	*35.00*	*35.00*

25th anniversary of the First Anti-Fascist Congress of Permet, May 24, 1944.

Albanian Violet — A261

Designs: Violets and Pansies.

1969, June 30 Litho. *Perf. 12x12½*

1227	A261	5q gold & multi	.25	.25
1228	A261	10q gold & multi	.25	.25
1229	A261	15q gold & multi	.30	.25
1230	A261	20q gold & multi	.35	.25
1231	A261	25q gold & multi	.35	.25
1232	A261	80q gold & multi	1.10	.35
1233	A261	1.95 l gold & multi	1.90	.65
		Nos. 1227-1233 (7)	4.50	2.25

Plum, Fruit and Blossoms — A262

Designs: Blossoms and Fruits.

1969, Aug. 10 Litho. *Perf. 12*

1234	A262	10q shown	.25	.25
1235	A262	15q Lemon	.25	.25
1236	A262	25q Pomegranate	.30	.25
1237	A262	50q Cherry	.75	.25
1238	A262	80q Peach	1.10	.25
1239	A262	1.20 l Apple	1.90	.40
		Nos. 1234-1239 (6)	4.55	1.65

Basketball — A263

Designs: 10q, 80q, 2.20 l, Various views of basketball game. 25q, Hand aiming ball at basket and map of Europe, horiz.

1969, Sept. 15 Litho. *Perf. 12*

1240	A263	10q multi	.35	.25
1241	A263	15q buff & multi	.35	.25
1242	A263	25q blue & multi	.35	.25

1243	A263	80q	multi	1.00	.25
1244	A263	2.20 l	multi	2.00	.50
			Nos. 1240-1244 (5)	4.05	1.50

16th European Basketball Championships, Naples, Italy, Sept. 27-Oct. 5.

Runner — A264

Designs: 5q, Games' emblem. 10q, Woman gymnast. 20q, Pistol shooting. 25q, Swimmer at start. 80q, Bicyclist. 95q, Soccer.

1969, Sept. 30

1245	A264	5q	multicolored	.25	.25
1246	A264	10q	multicolored	.25	.25
1247	A264	15q	multicolored	.30	.25
1248	A264	20q	multicolored	.35	.25
1249	A264	25q	multicolored	.35	.25
1250	A264	80q	multicolored	1.00	.25
1251	A264	95q	multicolored	1.40	.25
			Nos. 1245-1251 (7)	3.90	1.75

Second National Spartakiad.

Electronic Technicians, Steel Ladle — A265

25q, Mao Tse-tung with microphones. 1.40 l, Children holding Mao's red book.

1969, Oct. 1 Litho. *Perf. 12*

1252	A265	25q	multi, vert.	*2.50*	*.60*
1253	A265	85q	multi	*7.50*	*2.25*
1254	A265	1.40 l	multi, vert.	*12.00*	*4.00*
			Nos. 1252-1254 (3)	*22.00*	*6.85*

People's Republic of China, 20th anniv.

Enver Hoxha — A266

Designs: 80q, Pages from Berat resolution. 1.45 l, Partisans with flag.

1969, Oct. 20 Litho. *Perf. 12*

1255	A266	25q	multicolored	.25	.25
1256	A266	80q	gray & multi	.55	.25
1257	A266	1.45 l	ocher & multi	1.60	.45
			Nos. 1255-1257 (3)	2.40	.95

25th anniv. of the 2nd reunion of the Natl. Antifascist Liberation Council, Berat.

Soldiers A267

Designs: 30q, Oil refinery. 35q, Combine harvester. 45q, Hydroelectric station and dam. 55q, Militia woman, man and soldier. 1.10 l, Dancers and musicians.

1969, Nov. 29

1258	A267	25q	multi	.30	.25
1259	A267	30q	multi	.35	.25
1260	A267	35q	multi	.50	.25
1261	A267	45q	multi	.85	.25
1262	A267	55q	multi	1.20	.30
1263	A267	1.10 l	multi	2.00	.45
			Nos. 1258-1263 (6)	5.20	1.75

25th anniv. of the socialist republic.

Joseph V. Stalin, (1879-1953), Russian Political Leader — A268

1969, Dec. 21 Litho. *Perf. 12*

1264	A268	15q	lilac	.25	.25
1265	A268	25q	slate blue	.40	.25
1266	A268	1 l	brown	1.40	.25
1267	A268	1.10 l	violet blue	1.60	.25
			Nos. 1264-1267 (4)	3.65	1.00

Head of Woman — A269

Greco-Roman Mosaics: 25q, Geometrical floor design, horiz. 80q, Bird and tree, horiz. 1.10 l, Floor with birds and grapes, horiz. 1.20 l, Fragment with corn within oval design.

1969, Dec. 25 *Perf. 12½x12*

1268	A269	15q	gold & multi	.25	.25
1269	A269	25q	gold & multi	.25	.25
1270	A269	80q	gold & multi	.75	.25
1271	A269	1.10 l	gold & multi	1.00	.25
1272	A269	1.20 l	gold & multi	1.50	.35
			Nos. 1268-1272 (5)	3.75	1.35

Cancellation of 1920 — A270

25q, Proclamation and congress site.

1970, Jan. 21 Litho. *Perf. 12*

1273	A270	25q	red, gray & blk	.35	.25
1274	A270	1.25 l	dk grn, yel & blk	2.25	.25

Congress of Louchnia, 50th anniversary.

Worker, Student and Flag — A271

1970, Feb. 11 *Perf. 12½x12*

1275	A271	25q	red & multi	.35	.25
1276	A271	1.75 l	red & multi	2.25	.50

Vocational organizations in Albania, 25th anniv.

Turk's-cap Lily — A272

Lilies: 5q, Cernum, vert. 15q, Madonna, vert. 25q, Royal, vert. 1.10 l, Tiger. 1.15 l, Albanian.

Perf. 11½x12, 12x11½

1970, Mar. 10 Litho.

1277	A272	5q	multi	.25	.25
1278	A272	15q	multi	.25	.25
1279	A272	25q	multi	.75	.25
1280	A272	80q	multi	1.50	.25
1281	A272	1.10 l	multi	2.25	.25
1282	A272	1.15 l	multi	2.60	.30
			Nos. 1277-1282 (6)	7.60	1.55

Lenin — A273

Designs (Lenin): 5q, Portrait, vert. 25q, As volunteer construction worker. 95q, Addressing crowd. 1.10 l, Saluting, vert.

1970, Apr. 22 Litho. *Perf. 12*

1283	A273	5q	multi	.25	.25
1284	A273	15q	multi	.25	.25
1285	A273	25q	multi	.35	.25
1286	A273	95q	multi	.90	.25
1287	A273	1.10 l	multi	1.60	.25
			Nos. 1283-1287 (5)	3.35	1.25

Centenary of birth of Lenin (1870-1924).

Frontier Guard — A274

1970, Apr. 25

1288	A274	25q	multi	.40	.25
1289	A274	1.25 l	multi	2.00	.50

25th anniversary of Frontier Guards.

Soccer Players A275

Designs: 5q, Jules Rimet Cup and globes. 10q, Aztec Stadium, Mexico City. 25q, Defending goal. 65q, 80q, No. 1296, Two soccer players in various plays. No. 1297, Mexican horseman and volcano Popocatepetl.

1970, May 15 Litho. *Perf. 12½x12*

1290	A275	5q	multicolored	.25	.25
1291	A275	10q	multicolored	.25	.25
1292	A275	15q	multicolored	.25	.25
1293	A275	25q	lt green & multi	.25	.25
1294	A275	65q	pink & multi	.55	.25
1295	A275	80q	lt blue & multi	.75	.40
1296	A275	2 l	yellow & multi	1.50	.45
			Nos. 1290-1296 (7)	3.80	2.10

Souvenir Sheet

Perf 12 x Imperf

1297	A275	2 l	multicolored	2.75	2.75

World Soccer Championships for the Jules Rimet Cup, Mexico City, May 31-June 21, 1970. No. 1297 contains one large horizontal stamp. Nos. 1290-1297 exist imperf. Value: Nos. 1290-1296, mint or used, $12; No. 1297, mint $10, used $5.

UPU Headquarters and Monument, Bern — A276

1970, May 30 Litho. *Perf. 12½x12*

1298	A276	25q	ultra, gray & blk	.25	.25
1299	A276	1.10 l	org, buff & blk	1.00	.25
1300	A276	1.15 l	grn, gray & blk	1.25	.30
			Nos. 1298-1300 (3)	2.50	.80

Inauguration of the new UPU Headquarters in Bern.

Bird and Grapes Mosaic — A277

Mosaics, 5th-6th centuries, excavated near Pogradec: 10q, Waterfowl and grapes. 20q, Bird and tree stump. 25q, Bird and leaves. 65q, Fish. 2.25 l, Peacock, vert.

1970, July 10 *Perf. 12½x12, 12x12½*

1301	A277	5q	multi	.25	.25
1302	A277	10q	multi	.25	.25
1303	A277	20q	multi	.30	.25
1304	A277	25q	multi	.35	.25
1305	A277	65q	multi	.75	.25
1306	A277	2.25 l	multi	2.60	.35
			Nos. 1301-1306 (6)	4.50	1.60

Fruit Harvest and Dancers — A278

Designs: 25q, Contour-plowed fields and conference table. 80q, Cattle and newspapers. 1.30 l, Wheat harvest.

1970, Aug. 28 Litho. *Perf. 12x11½*

1307	A278	15q	brt violet & blk	.35	.25
1308	A278	25q	dp blue & blk	.35	.25
1309	A278	80q	dp brown & blk	1.00	.25
1310	A278	1.30 l	org brn & blk	1.40	.25
			Nos. 1307-1310 (4)	3.10	1.00

25th anniv. of the agrarian reform law.

Attacking Partisans — A279

Designs: 25q, Partisans with horses and flag. 1.60 l, Partisans.

1970, Sept. 3 *Perf. 12*

1311	A279	15q	org brn & blk	.25	.25
1312	A279	25q	brn, yel & blk	.50	.25
1313	A279	1.60 l	dp grn & blk	1.50	.35
			Nos. 1311-1313 (3)	2.25	.85

50th anniversary of liberation of Vlona.

Miners, by Nexhmedin Zajmi A280

Paintings from the National Gallery, Tirana: 5q, Bringing in the Harvest, by Isuf Sulovari, vert. 15q, The Activists, by Dhimitraq Trebicka, vert. 65q, Instruction of Partisans, by Hasan Nallbani. 95q, Architectural Planning, by Vilson Kilica. No. 1319, Woman Machinist, by Zef Shoshi, vert. No. 1320, Partisan Destroying Tank, by Sali Shijaku, vert.

Perf. 12½x12, 12x12½

1970, Sept. 25 Litho.

1314	A280	5q	multicolored	.25	.25
1315	A280	15q	multicolored	.25	.25
1316	A280	25q	multicolored	.25	.25
1317	A280	65q	multicolored	.25	.25
1318	A280	95q	multicolored	.95	.25
1319	A280	2 l	multicolored	1.75	.35
			Nos. 1314-1319 (6)	3.70	1.60

Miniature Sheet

Imperf

1320	A280	2 l	multicolored	2.50	1.50

Electrification Map of Albania — A281

Designs: 25q, Light bulb, hammer and sickle emblem, map of Albania and power graph. 80q, Linemen at work. 1.10 l, Use of electricity on the farm, in home and business.

1970, Oct. 25 Litho. *Perf. 12*

1321	A281	15q	multi	.25	.25
1322	A281	25q	multi	.35	.25
1323	A281	80q	multi	1.00	.25
1324	A281	1.10 l	multi	1.20	.25
			Nos. 1321-1324 (4)	2.80	1.00

Albanian village electrification completion.

Friedrich Engels — A282

Designs: 1.10 l, Engels as young man. 1.15 l, Engels addressing crowd.

1970, Nov. 28 Litho. *Perf. 12x12½*

1325	A282	25q bister & dk bl	.35	.25
1326	A282	1.10 l bis & dp claret	.95	.25
1327	A282	1.15 l bis & dk ol grn	1.20	.30
		Nos. 1325-1327 (3)	2.50	.80

150th anniv. of the birth of Friedrich Engels (1820-95), German socialist, collaborator with Karl Marx.

Factories — A282a

Designs: 10q, Tractor factory, Tirana, horiz. 15q, Fertilizer factory, Fier, horiz. 20q, Superphosphate factory, Lac. 25q, Cement factory, Elbasan, horiz. 80q, Coking plant, Qyteti Stalin, horiz.

1970-71 Litho. *Perf. 12*

1327A	A282a	10q multi	250.00	160.00
1327B	A282a	15q multi	250.00	160.00
1327C	A282a	20q multi	250.00	160.00
1327D	A282a	25q multi	250.00	160.00
1327E	A282a	80q multi	250.00	160.00
		Nos. 1327A-1327E (5)	1,250.	800.00

Issue dates: 15q, 12/4/70. 10q, 20q, 25q, 80q, 1/20/71.

Ludwig van Beethoven — A283

Designs: 5q, Birthplace, Bonn. 25q, 65q, 1.10 l, various portraits. 1.80 l, Scene from Fidelio, horiz.

1970, Dec. 16 Litho. *Perf. 12*

1328	A283	5q dp plum & gold	.25	.25
1329	A283	15q brt rose lil & sil	.25	.25
1330	A283	25q green & gold	.35	.25
1331	A283	65q magenta & sil	.85	.25
1332	A283	1.10 l dk blue & gold	1.75	.30
1333	A283	1.80 l black & sil	2.75	.50
		Nos. 1328-1333 (6)	6.20	1.80

Ludwig van Beethoven (1770-1827), composer.

Coat of Arms — A284

Designs: 25q, Proclamation. 80q, Enver Hoxha reading proclamation. 1.30 l, Young people and proclamation.

1971, Jan. 11 Litho. *Perf. 12*

1334	A284	15q lt bl, gold, blk & red	.25	.25
1335	A284	25q rose lil, blk, gold & gray	.25	.25
1336	A284	80q emerald, blk & gold	.85	.25
1337	A284	1.30 l yel org, blk & gold	1.20	.30
		Nos. 1334-1337 (4)	2.55	1.05

Declaration of the Republic, 25th anniv.

"Liberty" — A285

Designs: 50q, Women's brigade. 65q, Street battle, horiz. 1.10 l, Execution, horiz.

Perf. 12x11½, 11½x12

1971, Mar. 18 Litho.

1338	A285	25q dk bl & bl	.35	.25
1339	A285	50q slate green	.50	.25
1340	A285	65q dk brn & chest	.75	.25
1341	A285	1.10 l purple	1.25	.25
		Nos. 1338-1341 (4)	2.85	1.00

Centenary of the Paris Commune.

Black Men — A286

1.10 l, Men of 3 races. 1.15 l, Black protest.

1971, Mar. 21 *Perf. 12x12½*

1342	A286	25q blk & bis brn	.25	.25
1343	A286	1.10 l blk & rose car	.75	.25
1344	A286	1.15 l blk & ver	.90	.25
		Nos. 1342-1344 (3)	1.90	.75

Intl. year against racial discrimination.

Tulip — A287

Designs: Various tulips.

1971, Mar. 25

1345	A287	5q multi	.25	.25
1346	A287	10q yellow & multi	.25	.25
1347	A287	15q pink & multi	.30	.25
1348	A287	20q lt blue & multi	.35	.25
1349	A287	25q multi	.35	.25
1350	A287	80q multi	1.00	.25
1351	A287	1 l multi	1.75	.25
1352	A287	1.45 l citron & multi	2.10	.30
		Nos. 1345-1352 (8)	6.35	2.05

Horseman, by Dürer — A288

Art Works by Dürer: 15q, Three peasants. 25q, Dancing peasant couple. 45q, The bagpiper. 65q, View of Kalkrebut, horiz. 2.40 l, View of Trent, horiz. 2.50 l, Self-portrait.

Perf. 11½x12, 12x11½

1971, May 15 Litho.

1353	A288	10q blk & pale grn	.30	.25
1354	A288	15q black & pale lil	.30	.25
1355	A288	25q blk & pale bl	.35	.25
1356	A288	45q blk & pale rose	.90	.25
1357	A288	65q black & multi	1.75	.25
1358	A288	2.40 l black & multi	5.50	.40
		Nos. 1353-1358 (6)	9.10	1.65

Miniature Sheet

Imperf

1359	A288	2.50 l multi	3.50	2.50

Albrecht Dürer (1471-1528), German painter and engraver.

Satellite Orbiting Globe — A289

Designs: 1.20 l, Government Building, Tirana, and Red Star emblem. 2.20 l, like 60q, 2.50 l, Flag of People's Republic of China forming trajectory around globe.

1971, June 10 Litho. *Perf. 12x12½*

1360	A289	60q purple & multi	.60	.25
1361	A289	1.20 l ver & multi	1.40	.30
1362	A289	2.20 l green & multi	2.50	.50

Imperf

1363	A289	2.50 l vio blk & multi	5.00	2.75
		Nos. 1360-1363 (4)	9.50	3.80

Space developments of People's Republic of China.

Mao Tse-tung — A290

Designs: 1.05 l, House where Communist Party was founded, horiz. 1.20 l, Peking crowd with placards, horiz.

1971, July 1 *Perf. 12x12½, 12½x12*

1364	A290	25q silver & multi	*.85*	*.25*
1365	A290	1.05 l silver & multi	*2.25*	*2.00*
1366	A290	1.20 l silver & multi	*3.25*	*2.25*
		Nos. 1364-1366 (3)	*6.35*	*4.50*

50th anniv. of Chinese Communist Party.

Crested Titmouse A291

1971, Aug. 15 Litho. *Perf. 12½x12*

1367	A291	5q shown	.25	.25
1368	A291	10q European serin	.30	.25
1369	A291	15q Linnet	.45	.25
1370	A291	25q Firecrest	.70	.25
1371	A291	45q Rock thrush	1.00	.25
1372	A291	60q Blue tit	1.75	.50
1373	A291	2.40 l Chaffinch	6.25	2.75
a.		Block of 7, #1367-1373 + label	17.50	15.00
		Nos. 1367-1373 (7)	10.70	4.50

Continuous design with bird's nest label at upper left.

Nos. 1367-1372 exist in blocks of 8, with two labels. Value: unused $55; used $25.

Olympic Rings and Running A292

Designs (Olympic Rings and): 10q, Hurdles. 15q, Canoeing. 25q, Gymnastics. 80q, Fencing. 1.05 l, Soccer. 2 l, Runner at finish line. 3.60 l, Diving, women's.

1971, Sept. 15

1374	A292	5q green & multi	.25	.25
1375	A292	10q multicolored	.25	.25
1376	A292	15q blue & multi	.25	.25
1377	A292	25q violet & multi	.25	.25
1378	A292	80q lilac & multi	.75	.25
1379	A292	1.05 l multicolored	.95	.25
1380	A292	3.60 l multicolored	3.00	.50
		Nos. 1374-1380 (7)	5.70	2.00

Souvenir Sheet

Imperf

1381	A292	2 l brt blue & multi	3.25	1.50

20th Olympic Games, Munich, Aug. 26-Sept. 10, 1972.

Workers with Flags — A293

Designs: 1.05 l, Party Headquarters, Tirana, and Red Star. 1.20 l, Rifle, star, flag and "VI."

1971, Nov. 1 *Perf. 12*

1382	A293	25q multi	.35	.25
1383	A293	1.05 l multi	1.00	.25
1384	A293	1.20 l multi, vert.	1.40	.30
		Nos. 1382-1384 (3)	2.75	.80

6th Congress of Workers' Party.

Factories and Workers — A294

Designs: 80q, "XXX" and flag, vert. 1.55 l, Enver Hoxha and flags.

1971, Nov. 8

1385	A294	15q gold, sil, lil & yel	.25	.25
1386	A294	80q gold, sil & red	.90	.25
1387	A294	1.55 l gold, sil, red & brn	1.90	.30
		Nos. 1385-1387 (3)	3.05	.80

30th anniversary of Workers' Party.

Construction Work, by M. Fushekati — A295

Contemporary Albanian Paintings: 5q, Young Man, by R. Kuci, vert. 25q, Partisan, by D. Jukniu, vert. 80q, Fliers, by S. Kristo. 1.20 l, Girl in Forest, by A. Sadikaj. 1.55 l, Warriors with Spears and Shields, by S. Kamberi. 2 l, Freedom Fighter, by I. Lulani.

Perf. 12x12½, 12½x12

1971, Nov. 20

1388	A295	5q gold & multi	.25	.25
1389	A295	15q gold & multi	.25	.25
1390	A295	25q gold & multi	.25	.25
1391	A295	80q gold & multi	.75	.25
1392	A295	1.20 l gold & multi	.85	.25
1393	A295	1.55 l gold & multi	1.00	.30
		Nos. 1388-1393 (6)	3.35	1.55

Miniature Sheet

Imperf

1394	A295	2 l gold & multi	2.75	1.75

Young Workers' Emblem — A296

1971, Nov. 23 *Perf. 12x12½*

1395	A296	15q lt blue & multi	.25	.25
1396	A296	1.35 l grnsh gray & multi	1.25	.30

Albanian Young Workers' Union, 30th anniv.

"Halili and Hajria" Ballet A297

Scenes from "Halili and Hajria" Ballet: 10q, Brother and sister. 15q, Hajria before Sultan

Suleiman. 50q, Hajria and husband. 80q, Execution of Halili. 1.40 l, Hajria killing her husband.

1971, Dec. 27 *Perf. 12½x12*

1397	A297	5q silver & multi	.25	.25
1398	A297	10q silver & multi	.25	.25
1399	A297	15q silver & multi	.25	.25
1400	A297	50q silver & multi	.60	.25
1401	A297	80q silver & multi	1.00	.50
1402	A297	1.40 l silver & multi	2.00	.90
		Nos. 1397-1402 (6)	4.35	2.40

Albanian ballet Halili and Hajria after drama by Kol Jakova.

Biathlon and Olympic Rings A298

Designs (Olympic Rings and): 10q, Sledding. 15q, Ice hockey. 20q, Bobsledding. 50q, Speed skating. 1 l, Slalom. 2 l, Ski jump. 2.50 l, Figure skating, pairs.

1972, Feb. 10

1403	A298	5q lt olive & multi	.25	.25
1404	A298	10q lt violet & multi	.25	.25
1405	A298	15q multicolored	.25	.25
1406	A298	20q pink & multi	.25	.25
1407	A298	50q lt blue & multi	.50	.25
1408	A298	1 l ocher & multi	.80	.25
1409	A298	2 l lilac & multi	1.75	.40
		Nos. 1403-1409 (7)	4.05	1.90

Souvenir Sheet

Imperf

1410	A298	2.50 l blue & multi	3.00	1.75

11th Winter Olympic Games, Sapporo, Japan, Feb. 3-13.

Wild Strawberries A299

Wild Fruits and Nuts: 10q, Blackberries. 15q, Hazelnuts. 20q, Walnuts. 25q, Strawberry-tree fruit. 30q, Dogwood berries. 2.40 l, Rowan berries.

1972, Mar. 20 **Litho.** *Perf. 12*

1411	A299	5q lt grn & multi	.25	.25
1412	A299	10q yellow & multi	.25	.25
1413	A299	15q lt vio & multi	.25	.25
1414	A299	20q pink & multi	.25	.25
1415	A299	25q multi	.25	.25
1416	A299	30q multi	.35	.25
1417	A299	2.40 l multi	3.00	.50
		Nos. 1411-1417 (7)	4.60	2.00

"Your Heart is Your Health" — A300

World Health Day: 1.20 l, Cardiac patient and electrocardiogram.

1972, Apr. 7 *Perf. 12x12½*

1418	A300	1.10 l multicolored	1.25	.40
1419	A300	1.20 l rose & multi	1.40	.85

Worker and Student — A301

7th Trade Union Cong., May 8: 2.05 l, Assembly Hall, dancers and emblem.

1972, Apr. 24 **Litho.** *Perf. 11½x12½*

1420	A301	25q multi	.50	.25
1421	A301	2.05 l blue & multi	2.00	.40

Qemal Stafa — A302

Designs: 15q, Memorial flame. 25q, Monument "Spirit of Defiance," vert.

1972, May 5 *Perf. 12½x12, 12x12½*

1422	A302	15q gray & multi	.25	.25
1423	A302	25q sal rose, blk & gray	.30	.25
1424	A302	1.90 l dull yel & blk	1.75	.35
		Nos. 1422-1424 (3)	2.30	.85

30th anniversary of the murder of Qemal Stafa and of Martyrs' Day.

Camellia — A303

Designs: Various camellias.

1972, May 10 *Perf. 12x12½*

Flowers in Natural Colors

1425	A303	5q lt blue & blk	.25	.25
1426	A303	10q citron & blk	.25	.25
1427	A303	15q grnsh gray & blk	.25	.25
1428	A303	25q pale sal & blk	.25	.25
1429	A303	45q gray & blk	.45	.25
1430	A303	50q sal pink & blk	.85	.25
1431	A303	2.50 l bluish gray & blk	3.25	.90
		Nos. 1425-1431 (7)	5.55	2.40

High Jump A304

Designs (Olympic and Motion Emblems and): 10q, Running. 15q, Shot put. 20q, Bicycling. 25q, Pole vault. 50q, Hurdles, women's. 75q, Hockey. 2 l, Swimming. 2.50 l, Diving, women's.

1972, June 30 **Litho.** *Perf. 12½x12*

1432	A304	5q multicolored	.25	.25
1433	A304	10q lt brn & multi	.25	.25
1434	A304	15q lt lil & multi	.25	.25
1435	A304	20q multicolored	.30	.25
1436	A304	25q lt vio & multi	.30	.25
1437	A304	50q lt grn & multi	.50	.25
1438	A304	75q multicolored	1.00	.25
1439	A304	2 l multicolored	3.00	.35
		Nos. 1432-1439 (8)	5.85	2.10

Miniature Sheet

Imperf

1440	A304	2.50 l multi	3.50	2.50

20th Olympic Games, Munich, Aug. 26-Sept. 11. Nos. 1432-1439 each issued in sheets of 8 stamps and one label (3x3) showing Olympic rings in gold.

Autobus — A305

25q, Electric train. 80q, Ocean liner Tirana. 1.05 l, Automobile. 1.20 l, Trailer truck.

1972, July 25 **Litho.** *Perf. 12*

1441	A305	15q org brn & multi	.25	.25
1442	A305	25q gray & multi	.35	.25
1443	A305	80q dp grn & multi	.50	.25
1444	A305	1.05 l multi	.70	.25
1445	A305	1.20 l multi	1.40	.25
		Nos. 1441-1445 (5)	3.20	1.25

Arm Wrestling — A306

Folk Games: 10q, Piggyback ball game. 15q, Women's jumping. 25q, Rope game (srum). 90q, Leapfrog. 2 l, Women throwing pitchers.

1972, Aug. 18

1446	A306	5q multi	.25	.25
1447	A306	10q lt bl & multi	.25	.25
1448	A306	15q rose & multi	.25	.25
1449	A306	25q lt bl & multi	.25	.25
1450	A306	90q ocher & multi	.85	.25
1451	A306	2 l lt grn & multi	1.60	.30
		Nos. 1446-1451 (6)	3.45	1.55

1st National Festival of People's Games.

Mastheads A307

30th Press Day: 25q, Printing press. 1.90 l, Workers reading paper.

1972, Aug. 25

1452	A307	15q lt bl & blk	.25	.25
1453	A307	25q red, grn & blk	.25	.25
1454	A307	1.90 l lt vio & blk	1.40	.40
		Nos. 1452-1454 (3)	1.90	.90

Map of Peza Area, Memorial Tablet — A308

25q, Guerrillas with flag. 1.90 l, Peza Conference memorial.

1972, Sept. 16

1455	A308	15q shown	.25	.25
1456	A308	25q multicolored	.35	.25
1457	A308	1.90 l multicolored	1.90	.40
		Nos. 1455-1457 (3)	2.50	.90

30th anniversary, Conference of Peza.

Partisans, by Sotir Capo A309

Paintings: 10q, Woman, by Ismail Lulani, vert. 15q, "Communists," by Lec Shkreli, vert. 20q, View of Nendorit, 1941, by Sali Shijaku, vert. 50q, Woman with Sheaf, by Zef Shoshi, vert. 1 l, Landscape with Children, by Dhimitraq Trebicka. 2 l, Women on Bicycles, by Vilson Kilica. 2.30 l, Folk Dance, by Abdurrahim Buza.

Perf. 12½x12, 12x12½

1972, Sept. 25 **Litho.**

1458	A309	5q gold & multi	.25	.25
1459	A309	10q gold & multi	.25	.25
1460	A309	15q gold & multi	.25	.25
1461	A309	20q gold & multi	.25	.25
1462	A309	50q gold & multi	.25	.25
1463	A309	1 l gold & multi	.70	.25
1464	A309	2 l gold & multi	1.75	.40
		Nos. 1458-1464 (7)	3.70	1.90

Miniature Sheet

Imperf

1465	A309	2.30 l gold & multi	2.75	1.75

No. 1465 contains one 41x68mm stamp.

Congress Emblem — A310

Design: 2.05 l, Young worker with banner.

1972, Oct. 23 **Litho.** *Perf. 12*

1466	A310	25q silver, red & gold	.50	.25
1467	A310	2.05 l silver & multi	1.90	.50

Union of Working Youth, 6th Congress.

Hammer and Sickle — A311

Design: 1.20 l, Lenin as orator.

1972, Nov. 7 **Litho.** *Perf. 11½x12*

1468	A311	1.10 l multi	1.10	.25
1469	A311	1.20 l multi	2.25	.30

Russian October Revolution, 55th anniv.

Ismail Qemali — A312

Designs: 15q, Albanian fighters, horiz. 65q, Rally, horiz. 1.25 l, Coat of arms.

Perf. 12x11½, 11½x12

1972, Nov. 29

1470	A312	15q red, brt bl & blk	.25	.25
1471	A312	25q yel, blk & red	.25	.25
1472	A312	65q red, sal & blk	.50	.25
1473	A312	1.25 l dl red & blk	1.60	.25
		Nos. 1470-1473 (4)	2.60	1.00

60th anniv. of independence.

Cock, Mosaic — A313

Mosaics, 2nd-5th centuries, excavated near Buthrotium and Apollonia: 10q, Bird, vert. 15q, Partridges, vert. 25q, Warrior's legs. 45q, Nymph riding dolphin, vert. 50q, Fish, vert. 2.50 l, Warrior with helmet.

1972, Dec. 10 *Perf. 12½x12, 12x12½*

1474	A313	5q silver & multi	.25	.25
1475	A313	10q silver & multi	.25	.25
1476	A313	15q silver & multi	.25	.25
1477	A313	25q silver & multi	.25	.25
1478	A313	45q silver & multi	.40	.25
1479	A313	50q silver & multi	.55	.25
1480	A313	2.50 l silver & multi	2.10	.80
		Nos. 1474-1480 (7)	4.05	2.30

Nicolaus Copernicus — A314

Designs: 10q, 25q, 80q, 1.20 l, Various portraits of Copernicus. 1.60 l, Heliocentric solar system.

1973, Feb. 19 **Litho.** *Perf. 12x12½*

1481	A314	5q lil rose & multi	.25	.25
1482	A314	10q dull ol & multi	.25	.25
1483	A314	25q multicolored	.25	.25
1484	A314	80q lt violet & multi	.25	.25
1485	A314	1.20 l blue & multi	1.40	.30
1486	A314	1.60 l gray & multi	2.25	.40
		Nos. 1481-1486 (6)	4.65	1.70

500th anniversary of the birth of Nicolaus Copernicus (1473-1543), Polish astronomer.

Flowering Cactus A315

Designs: Various flowering cacti.

1973, Mar. 25 **Litho.** ***Perf. 12***

1487	A315	10q multicolored	.30	.25
1488	A315	15q multicolored	.30	.25
1489	A315	20q beige & multi	.30	.25
1490	A315	25q gray & multi	.30	.25
1491	A315	30q beige & multi	4.25	1.50
1492	A315	65q gray & multi	1.40	.25
1493	A315	80q multicolored	1.40	.25
1494	A315	2 l multicolored	1.75	.60
a.		Block of 8, #1487-1494	16.00	8.00
		Nos. 1487-1494 (8)	10.00	3.60

A block containing Nos. 1487-1490, 1492-1494 and a label exists.

Guard and Factories A316

1.80 l, Guard and guards with prisoner.

1973, Mar. 20 **Litho.** ***Perf. 12½x12***

1495	A316	25q ultra & blk	.35	.25
1496	A316	1.80 l dk red & multi	2.00	.40

30th anniv. of the State Security Branch.

Common Tern — A317

Sea Birds: 15q, White-winged black terns, vert. 25q, Black-headed gull, vert. 45q, Great black-headed gull. 80q, Slender-billed gull, vert. 2.40 l, Sandwich terns.

1973, Apr. 30 ***Perf. 12½x12, 12x12½***

1497	A317	5q gold & multi	.25	.25
1498	A317	15q gold & multi	.25	.25
1499	A317	25q gold & multi	.30	.25
1500	A317	45q gold & multi	.75	.25
1501	A317	80q gold & multi	1.90	.25
1502	A317	2.40 l gold & multi	3.75	.55
		Nos. 1497-1502 (6)	7.20	1.80

Letters, 1913 Cancellation and Post Horn — A318

Design: 1.80 l, Mailman, 1913 cancel.

1973, May, 5 **Litho.** ***Perf. 12x11½***

1503	A318	25q red & multi	.70	.25
1504	A318	1.80 l red & multi	2.75	.55

60th anniversary of Albanian stamps.

Farmer, Worker, Soldier — A319

Design: 25q, Woman and factory, vert.

1973, June 4 ***Perf. 12***

1505	A319	25q carmine rose	.35	.25
1506	A319	1.80 l yel, dp org & blk	2.00	.50

7th Congress of Albanian Women's Union.

Creation of General Staff, by G. Madhi A320

Designs: 40q, "August 1949," sculpture by Sh. Haderi, vert. 60q, "Generation after Generation," sculpture by H. Dule, vert. 80q, "Defend Revolutionary Victories," by M. Fushekati.

1973, July 10 **Litho.** ***Perf. 12½x12***

1507	A320	25q gold & multi	*8.00*	*10.00*
1508	A320	40q gold & multi	*8.00*	*10.00*
1509	A320	60q gold & multi	*8.00*	*10.00*
1510	A320	80q gold & multi	*8.00*	*10.00*
		Nos. 1507-1510 (4)	*32.00*	*40.00*

30th anniversary of the People's Army.

"Electrification," by S. Hysa — A321

Albanian Paintings: 10q, Woman Textile Worker, by N. Nallbani. 15q, Gymnasts, by M. Fushekati. 50q, Aviator, by F. Stamo. 80q, Fascist Prisoner, by A. Lakuriqi. 1.20 l, Workers with Banner, by P. Mele. 1.30 l, Farm Woman, by Zef Shoshi. 2.05 l, Battle of Tenda, by F. Haxhiu. 10q, 50q, 80q, 1.20 l, 1.30 l, vertical.

Perf. 12½x12, 12x12½

1973, Aug. 10

1511	A321	5q gold & multi	.25	.25
1512	A321	10q gold & multi	.25	.25
1513	A321	15q gold & multi	.25	.25
1514	A321	50q gold & multi	.25	.25
1515	A321	80q gold & multi	.25	.25
1516	A321	1.20 l gold & multi	1.00	.25
1517	A321	1.30 l gold & multi	2.00	.25
		Nos. 1511-1517 (7)	4.25	1.75

Souvenir Sheet

Imperf

1518	A321	2.05 l multi	2.75	1.75

Mary Magdalene, by Caravaggio — A322

Paintings by Michelangelo da Caravaggio: 10q, The Lute Player, horiz. 15q, Self-portrait. 50q, Boy Carrying Fruit and Flowers. 80q, Still Life, horiz. 1.20 l, Narcissus. 1.30 l, Boy Peeling Apple. 2.05 l, Man with Feathered Hat.

Perf. 12x12½, 12½x12

1973, Sept. 28

1519	A322	5q gold & multi	.25	.25
1520	A322	10q gold & multi	.25	.25
1521	A322	15q gold, blk & gray	.25	.25
1522	A322	50q gold & multi	.25	.25
1523	A322	80q gold & multi	.55	.25
1524	A322	1.20 l gold & multi	.70	.30
1525	A322	1.30 l gold & multi	1.40	.30
		Nos. 1519-1525 (7)	3.65	1.85

Souvenir Sheet

Imperf

1526	A322	2.05 l multi	5.00	3.50

Michelangelo da Caravaggio (Merisi; 1573?-1609), Italian painter. No. 1526 contains one stamp, size: 63x73mm.

Soccer A323

Designs: 5q-1.25 l, Various soccer scenes. 2.05 l, Ball in goal and list of cities where championships were held.

1973, Oct. 30 **Litho.** ***Perf. 12½x12***

1527	A323	5q multi	.25	.25
1528	A323	10q multi	.25	.25
1529	A323	15q multi	.25	.25
1530	A323	20q multi	.25	.25
1531	A323	25q multi	.25	.25
1532	A323	90q multi	.40	.25
1533	A323	1.20 l multi	.80	.25
1534	A323	1.25 l multi	1.25	.25
		Nos. 1527-1534 (8)	3.70	2.00

Minature Sheet

Imperf

1535	A323	2.05 l multi	3.00	2.00

World Soccer Cup, Munich 1974.

Weight Lifter — A324

Designs: Various stages of weight lifting. 1.20 l, 1.60 l, horiz.

1973, Oct. 30 **Litho.** ***Perf. 12***

1536	A324	5q multi	.25	.25
1537	A324	10q multi	.25	.25
1538	A324	25q multi	.25	.25
1539	A324	90q multi	.25	.25
1540	A324	1.20 l multi	.65	.25
1541	A324	1.60 l multi	1.60	.25
		Nos. 1536-1541 (6)	3.25	1.50

Weight Lifting Championships, Havana, Cuba.

Cement Factory, Kavaje A325

Harvester Combine A326

Skiers and Hotel — A326a

Mountain Lake — A326b

Designs: 10q, Ali Kelmendi truck factory and tank cars, horiz. 15q, Ballet. 25q, "Communication." 60q, Resort, horiz. 1 l, Mao Tse-tung textile mill. 1.20 l, Steel workers. 2.40 l, Welder and pipe. 3 l, Skanderbeg Monument, Tirana. 5 l, Roman arches, Durres.

Perf. 12½x12, 12x12½

1973-74 **Litho.**

1543	A325	5q gold & multi	.25	.25
1544	A325	10q gold & multi	.25	.25
1545	A325	15q gold & multi	.40	.25
1545A	A326	20q gold & multi	.25	.25
1546	A325	25q gold & multi	.25	.25
1547	A326a	35q gold & multi	.30	.25
1548	A325	60q gold & multi	.80	.25
1549	A326b	80q gold & multi	1.40	.25
1549A	A325	1 l gold & multi	.25	.25
1549B	A325	1.20 l gold & multi	.95	.25
1549C	A326b	2.40 l gold & multi	1.90	.35
1550	A326b	3 l gold & multi	3.50	.35
1551	A325	5 l gold & multi	3.50	.60
		Nos. 1543-1551 (13)	14.00	3.80

Issue dates: Nos. 1545-1546, 1549-1550, Dec. 5, 1973; others, 1974.

Mao Tse-tung — A327

80th birthday of Mao Tse-tung: 1.20 l, Mao Tse-tung addressing crowd.

1973, Dec. 26 ***Perf. 12***

1552	A327	85q multicolored	*11.00*	*1.25*
1553	A327	1.20 l multicolored	*17.00*	*2.25*

Old Man and Dog, by Gericault — A328

Paintings by Jean Louis André Theodore Gericault: 10q, Horse's Head. 15q, Male Model. 25q, Head of Black Man. 1.20 l, Self-portrait. 2.05 l, Raft of the Medusa, horiz. 2.20 l, Battle of the Giants.

Perf. 12x12½, 12½x12

1974, Jan. 18 **Litho.**

1554	A328	10q gold & multi	.25	.25
1555	A328	15q gold & multi	.25	.25
1556	A328	20q gold & multi	.25	.25
1557	A328	25q gold & blk	.25	.25
1558	A328	1.20 l gold & multi	1.40	.25
1559	A328	2.20 l gold & multi	2.60	.40
		Nos. 1554-1559 (6)	5.00	1.65

Souvenir Sheet

Imperf

1560	A328	2.05 l gold & multi	3.00	1.90

No. 1560 contains one 87x78mm stamp.

Lenin, by Pandi Mele — A329

Designs: 25q, Lenin with Sailors on Cruiser Aurora, by Dhimitraq Trebicka, horiz. 1.20 l, Lenin, by Vilson Kilica.

1974, Jan. 21 ***Perf. 12½x12, 12x12½***

1561	A329	25q gold & multi	*.90*	*.25*
1562	A329	60q gold & multi	*2.10*	*.25*
1563	A329	1.20 l gold & multi	*6.00*	*.55*
		Nos. 1561-1563 (3)	*9.00*	*1.05*

50th anniv. of the death of Lenin.

Swimming Duck, Mosaic A330

Designs: Mosaics from the 5th-6th Centuries A.D., excavated near Buthrotium, Pogradec and Apollonia.

1974, Feb. 20 **Litho.** ***Perf. 12½x12***

1564	A330	5q shown	.25	.25
1565	A330	10q Bird, flower	.25	.25
1566	A330	15q Vase, grapes	.25	.25
1567	A330	25q Duck	.25	.25
1568	A330	40q Donkey, bird	.25	.25
1569	A330	2.50 l Sea horse	1.25	.40
		Nos. 1564-1569 (6)	2.50	1.65

Soccer A331

Various scenes from soccer. 2.05 l, World Soccer Cup & names of participating countries.

1974, Apr. 25 **Litho.** ***Perf. 12½x12***

1570	A331	10q gold & multi	.25	.25
1571	A331	15q gold & multi	.25	.25
1572	A331	20q gold & multi	.25	.25
1573	A331	25q gold & multi	.25	.25
1574	A331	40q gold & multi	.25	.25
1575	A331	80q gold & multi	.55	.25
1576	A331	1 l gold & multi	.70	.30
1577	A331	1.20 l gold & multi	1.20	.40
		Nos. 1570-1577 (8)	3.70	2.20

Souvenir Sheet
Imperf

1578 A331 2.05 l gold & multi 4.00 1.75

World Cup Soccer Championship, Munich, June 13-July 7. No. 1578 contains one stamp (60x60mm) with simulated perforations. Nos. 1570-1577 exist imperf, No. 1578 with simulated perfs omitted. Values $10 and $20, respectively.

Arms of Albania, Soldier — A332

Design: 1.80 l, Soldier and front page of 1944 Congress Book.

1974, May 24 Litho. *Perf. 12*

1579 A332 25q multicolored .35 .25
1580 A332 1.80 l multicolored 1.40 .30

30th anniversary of the First Anti-Fascist Liberation Congress of Permet.

Medicinal Plants — A333

10q, Bittersweet. 15q, Arbutus. 20q, Lilies of the valley. 25q, Autumn crocus. 40q, Borage, horiz. 80q, Soapwort, horiz. 2.20 l, Gentian, horiz.

1974, May 5 *Perf. 12x12½*

1581 A333 10q multicolored .25 .25
1582 A333 15q multicolored .25 .25
1583 A333 20q multicolored .25 .25
1584 A333 25q multicolored .25 .25
1585 A333 40q multicolored .45 .25
1586 A333 80q multicolored .85 .25
1587 A333 2.20 l multicolored 2.50 .45
Nos. 1581-1587 (7) 4.80 1.95

Revolutionaries with Albanian Flag — A334

1.80 l, Portraits of 5 revolutionaries, vert.

Perf. 12½x12, 12x12½

1974, June 10

1588 A334 25q red, blk & lil .35 .25
1589 A334 1.80 l yel, red & blk 1.40 .45

50th anniversary Albanian Bourgeois Democratic Revolution.

European Redwing A335

Designs: Songbirds; Nos. 1597-1600 vert.

Perf. 12½x12, 12x12½

1974, July 15 Litho.

1594 A335 10q shown .25 .25
1595 A335 15q European robin .25 .25
1596 A335 20q Greenfinch .25 .25
1597 A335 25q Bullfinch .25 .25
1598 A335 40q Hawfinch .35 .25
1599 A335 80q Blackcap 1.40 .25
1600 A335 2.20 l Nightingale 2.75 .50
Nos. 1594-1600 (7) 5.50 2.00

Globe — A336

Cent. of UPU: 1.20 l, UPU emblem. 2.05 l, Jet over globe.

1974, Aug. 25 Litho. *Perf. 12x12½*

1601 A336 85q grn & multi 1.20 .25
1602 A336 1.20 l vio & ol grn 1.75 .25

Miniature Sheet
Imperf

1603 A336 2.05 l blue & multi 15.00 25.00

Widows, by Sali Shijaku A337

Albanian Paintings: 15q, Drillers, by Danish Jukniu, vert. 20q, Workers with Blueprints, by Clirim Ceka. 25q, Call to Action, by Spiro Kristo, vert. 40q, Winter Battle, by Sabaudin Xhaferi. 80q, Comrades, by Clirim Ceka, vert. 1 l, Aiding the Partisans, by Guri Madhi. 1.20 l, Teacher with Pupils, by Kleo Nini Brezat. 2.05 l, Comrades in Arms, by Guri Madhi.

Perf. 12½x12, 12x12½

1974, Sept. 25

1604 A337 10q silver & multi .25 .25
1605 A337 15q silver & multi .25 .25
1606 A337 20q silver & multi .25 .25
1607 A337 25q silver & multi .25 .25
1608 A337 40q silver & multi .30 .25
1609 A337 80q silver & multi .70 .25
1610 A337 1 l silver & multi 1.00 .25
1611 A337 1.20 l silver & multi 1.40 .25
Nos. 1604-1611 (8) 4.40 2.00

Miniature Sheet
Imperf

1612 A337 2.05 l silver & multi 2.75 1.75

Crowd on Tien An Men Square — A338

Design: 1.20 l, Mao Tse-tung, vert.

1974, Oct. 1 *Perf. 12*

1613 A338 85q gold & multi *6.00* 1.50
1614 A338 1.20 l gold & multi *9.50* 2.50

25th anniversary of the proclamation of the People's Republic of China.

Women's Volleyball — A339

Spartakiad Medal and: 15q, Women hurdlers. 20q, Women gymnasts. 25q, Mass exercises in Stadium. 40q, Weight lifter. 80q, Wrestlers. 1 l, Military rifle drill. 1.20 l, Soccer.

1974, Oct. 9 *Perf. 12x12½*

1615 A339 10q multi .25 .25
1616 A339 15q multi .25 .25
1617 A339 20q multi .25 .25
1618 A339 25q gray & multi .25 .25
1619 A339 40q multi .25 .25
1620 A339 80q multi .35 .25
1621 A339 1 l multi .70 .25
1622 A339 1.20 l tan & multi 1.00 .25
Nos. 1615-1622 (8) 3.30 2.00

National Spartakiad, Oct. 9-17.

View of Berat — A340

Designs: 80q, Enver Hoxha addressing Congress, bas-relief, horiz. 1 l, Hoxha and leaders leaving Congress Hall.

Perf. 12x12½, 12½x12

1974, Oct. 20 Litho.

1623 A340 25q rose car & blk .35 .25
1624 A340 80q yel, brn & blk 1.00 .25
1625 A340 1 l dp lilac & blk 2.00 .30
Nos. 1623-1625 (3) 3.35 .80

30th anniversary of 2nd Congress of Berat.

Anniversary Emblem, Factory Guards A341

35q, Chemical industry. 50q, Agriculture. 80q, Arts. 1 l, Atomic diagram & computer. 1.20 l, Youth education. 2.05 l, Crowd & History Book.

1974, Nov. 29 Litho. *Perf. 12½x12*

1626 A341 25q green & multi .25 .25
1627 A341 35q ultra & multi .25 .25
1628 A341 50q brown & multi .25 .25
1629 A341 80q multicolored .35 .25
1630 A341 1 l violet & multi .85 .25
1631 A341 1.20 l multicolored 1.00 .30
Nos. 1626-1631 (6) 2.95 1.55

Miniature Sheet
Imperf

1632 A341 2.05 l gold & multi 2.75 1.50

30th anniv. of liberation from Fascism.

Artemis, from Apolloni — A342

1974, Dec. 25 Photo. *Perf. 12x12½*

1633 A342 10q shown .25 .25
1634 A342 15q Zeus statue .25 .25
1635 A342 20q Poseidon statue .30 .25
1636 A342 25q Illyrian helmet .35 .25
1637 A342 40q Amphora .70 .25
1638 A342 80q Agrippa 1.00 .25
1639 A342 1 l Demosthenes 1.40 .30
1640 A342 1.20 l Head of Bilia 2.00 .35
Nos. 1633-1640 (8) 6.25 2.15

Miniature Sheet
Imperf

1641 A342 2.05 l Artemis & amphora 3.50 2.10

Archaeological discoveries in Albania.

Workers and Factories — A343

25q, Handshake, tools and book, vert.

1975, Feb. 11 Litho. *Perf. 12*

1642 A343 25q brown & multi .35 .25
1643 A343 1.80 l yellow & multi 1.40 .35

Albanian Trade Unions, 30th anniversary.

Chicory — A344

1975, Feb. 15

1644 A344 5q shown .25 .25
1645 A344 10q Houseleek .25 .25
1646 A344 15q Columbine .25 .25
1647 A344 20q Anemone .25 .25
1648 A344 25q Hibiscus .25 .25
1649 A344 30q Gentian .35 .25
1650 A344 35q Hollyhock .35 .25
1651 A344 2.70 l Iris 1.10 .45
Nos. 1644-1651 (8) 3.05 2.20

Protected flowers.

Jesus, from Doni Madonna — A345

Works by Michelangelo: 10q, Slave, sculpture. 15q, Head of Dawn, sculpture. 20q, Awakening Giant, sculpture. 25q, Cumaenian Sybil, Sistine Chapel. 30q, Lorenzo di Medici, sculpture. 1.20 l, David, sculpture. 2.05 l, Self-portrait. 3.90 l, Delphic Sybil, Sistine Chapel.

1975, Mar. 20 Litho. *Perf. 12x12½*

1652 A345 5q gold & multi .25 .25
1653 A345 10q gold & multi .25 .25
1654 A345 15q gold & multi .25 .25
1655 A345 20q gold & multi .25 .25
1656 A345 25q gold & multi .25 .25
1657 A345 30q gold & multi .25 .25
1658 A345 1.20 l gold & multi .55 .25
1659 A345 3.90 l gold & multi 1.60 .50
Nos. 1652-1659 (8) 3.65 2.25

Miniature Sheet
Imperf

1660 A345 2.05 l gold & multi 3.50 2.00

Michelangelo Buonarroti (1475-1564), Italian sculptor, painter and architect.

Two-wheeled Cart — A346

Albanian Transportation of the Past: 5q, Horseback rider. 15q, Lake ferry. 20q, Coastal three-master. 25q, Phaeton. 3.35 l, Early automobile on bridge.

1975, Apr. 15 Litho. *Perf. 12½x12*

1661 A346 5q bl grn & multi .25 .25
1662 A346 10q ol & multi .25 .25
1663 A346 15q lil & multi .25 .25
1664 A346 20q multi .25 .25
1665 A346 25q multi .25 .25
1666 A346 3.35 l ocher & multi 1.90 .50
Nos. 1661-1666 (6) 3.15 1.75

Guard at Frontier Stone — A347

Guardsman and Militia — A348

1975, Apr. 25 *Perf. 12*

1667 A347 25q multi .30 .25
1668 A348 1.80 l multi 1.25 .35

30th anniversary of Frontier Guards.

Posting Illegal Poster A349

Designs: 60q, Partisans in battle. 1.20 l, Partisan killing German soldier, and Albanian coat of arms.

1975, May 9 *Perf. 12½x12*

1669	A349	25q	multi	.25	.25
1670	A349	60q	multi	.50	.25
1671	A349	1.20 l	red & multi	1.00	.30
			Nos. 1669-1671 (3)	1.75	.80

30th anniversary of victory over Fascism.

European Widgeons A350

Waterfowl: 5q, Anas penelope. 10q, Netta rufina. 15q, Anser albifrons. 20q, Anas acuta. 25q, Mergus serrator. 30q, Pata somateria. 35q, Cignus cignus. 2.70 l, Spatula clypeata.

1975, June 15 **Litho.** *Perf. 12*

1672	A350	5q	brt blue & multi	.25	.25
1673	A350	10q	yel grn & multi	.25	.25
1674	A350	15q	brt rose lil & multi	.25	.25
1675	A350	20q	bl grn & multi	.25	.25
1676	A350	25q	multicolored	.25	.25
1677	A350	30q	multicolored	.30	.25
1678	A350	35q	orange & multi	.45	.25
1679	A350	2.70 l	multi	2.75	.90
			Nos. 1672-1679 (8)	4.75	2.65

Shyqyri Kanapari, by Musa Qarri — A351

Albanian Paintings: 10q, Woman Saving Children in Sea, by Agim Faja. 15q, "November 28, 1912" (revolution), by Petrit Ceno, horiz. 20q, "Workers Unite," by Sali Shijaku. 25q, The Partisan Shota Galica, by Ismail Lulani. 30q, Victorious Resistance Fighters, 1943, by Nestor Jonuzi. 80q, Partisan Couple in Front of Red Flag, by Vilson Halimi. 2.05 l, Dancing Procession, by Abdurahim Buza. 2.25 l, Republic Day Celebration, by Fatmir Haxhiu, horiz.

Perf. 12x12½, 12½x12

1975, July 15 **Litho.**

1680	A351	5q	gold & multi	.25	.25
1681	A351	10q	gold & multi	.25	.25
1682	A351	15q	gold & multi	.25	.25
1683	A351	20q	gold & multi	.25	.25
1684	A351	25q	gold & multi	.25	.25
1685	A351	30q	gold & multi	.25	.25
1686	A351	80q	gold & multi	.30	.25
1687	A351	2.25 l	gold & multi	1.40	.45
			Nos. 1680-1687 (8)	3.20	2.20

Miniature Sheet

Imperf

1688	A351	2.05 l	gold & multi	2.50	1.75

Nos. 1680-1687 issued in sheets of 8 stamps and gold center label showing palette and easel.

Farmer Holding Reform Law — A352

Design: 2 l, Produce and farm machinery.

1975, Aug. 28 *Perf. 12*

1689	A352	15q	multicolored	.40	.25
1690	A352	2 l	multicolored	2.00	.50

Agrarian reform, 30th anniversary.

Alcynonium Palmatum — A353

Corals: 10q, Paramuricea chamaeleon. 20q, Coralium rubrum. 25q, Eunicella covalini. 3.70 l, Cladocora cespitosa.

1975, Sept. 25 **Litho.** *Perf. 12*

1691	A353	5q	blue, ol & blk	.30	.25
1692	A353	10q	blue & multi	.30	.25
1693	A353	20q	blue & multi	.30	.25
1694	A353	25q	blue & blk	.30	.25
1695	A353	3.70 l	blue & blk	3.00	.80
			Nos. 1691-1695 (5)	4.20	1.80

Bicycling — A354

Designs (Montreal Olympic Games Emblem and): 10q, Canoeing. 15q, Fieldball. 20q, Basketball. 25q, Water polo. 30q, Hockey. 1.20 l, Pole vault. 2.05 l, Fencing. 2.15 l, Montreal Olympic Games emblem and various sports.

1975, Oct. 20 **Litho.** *Perf. 12½*

1696	A354	5q	multi	.25	.25
1697	A354	10q	multi	.25	.25
1698	A354	15q	multi	.25	.25
1699	A354	20q	multi	.40	.25
1700	A354	25q	multi	.45	.25
1701	A354	30q	multi	.55	.25
1702	A354	1.20 l	multi	1.50	.30
1703	A354	2.05 l	multi	2.75	.45
			Nos. 1696-1703 (8)	6.40	2.25

Miniature Sheet

Imperf

1704	A354	2.15 l	org & multi	4.00	4.00

21st Olympic Games, Montreal, July 18-Aug. 8, 1976. Nos. 1696-1703 exist imperf. Value $10.

Power Lines Leading to Village — A355

Designs: 25q, Transformers and insulators. 80q, Dam and power station. 85q, Television set, power lines, grain and cogwheel.

1975, Oct. 25 *Perf. 12x12½*

1705	A355	15q	ultra & yel	.25	.25
1706	A355	25q	brt vio & pink	.25	.25
1707	A355	80q	lt grn & gray	.60	.25
1708	A355	85q	ocher & brn	1.40	.45
			Nos. 1705-1708 (4)	2.50	1.20

General electrification, 5th anniversary.

Child, Rabbit and Teddy Bear Planting Tree A356

Fairy Tales: 10q, Mother fox. 15q, Ducks in school. 20q, Little pigs building house. 25q, Animals watching television. 30q, Rabbit and bear at work. 35q, Working and playing ants. 2.70 l, Wolf in sheep's clothes.

1975, Dec. 25 **Litho.** *Perf. 12½x12*

1709	A356	5q	black & multi	.25	.25
1710	A356	10q	black & multi	.25	.25
1711	A356	15q	black & multi	.25	.25
1712	A356	20q	black & multi	.30	.25
1713	A356	25q	black & multi	.40	.25
1714	A356	30q	black & multi	.50	.25
1715	A356	35q	black & multi	.55	.25
1716	A356	2.70 l	black & multi	3.00	.75
			Nos. 1709-1716 (8)	5.50	2.50

Arms, People, Factories — A357

Design: 1.90 l, Arms, government building, celebrating crowd.

1976, Jan. 11 **Litho.** *Perf. 12*

1717	A357	25q	gold & multi	.35	.25
1718	A357	1.90 l	gold & multi	2.25	.35

30th anniversary of proclamation of Albanian People's Republic.

Ice Hockey, Olympic Games' Emblem — A358

Designs: 10q, Speed skating. 15q, Biathlon. 50q, Ski jump. 1.20 l, Slalom. 2.15 l, Figure skating, pairs. 2.30 l, One-man bobsled.

1976, Feb. 4

1719	A358	5q	silver & multi	.25	.25
1720	A358	10q	silver & multi	.25	.25
1721	A358	15q	silver & multi	.25	.25
1722	A358	50q	silver & multi	.25	.25
1723	A358	1.20 l	silver & multi	.75	.25
1724	A358	2.30 l	silver & multi	1.00	.40
			Nos. 1719-1724 (6)	2.75	1.65

Miniature Sheet

Perf. 12 on 2 sides x Imperf.

1725	A358	2.15 l	silver & multi	2.50	2.00

12th Winter Olympic Games, Innsbruck, Austria, Feb. 4-15.

Meadow Saffron — A359

Medicinal Plants: 10q, Deadly night-shade. 15q, Yellow gentian. 20q, Horse chestnut. 70q, Shield fern. 80q, Marshmallow. 2.30 l, Thorn apple.

1976, Apr. 10 **Litho.** *Perf. 12x12½*

1726	A359	5q	black & multi	.25	.25
1727	A359	10q	black & multi	.25	.25
1728	A359	15q	black & multi	.25	.25
1729	A359	20q	black & multi	.25	.25
1730	A359	70q	black & multi	.35	.25
1731	A359	80q	black & multi	.60	.25
1732	A359	2.30 l	black & multi	1.75	.35
			Nos. 1726-1732 (7)	3.70	1.85

Bowl and Spoon A360

15q, Flask, vert. 20q, Carved handles, vert. 25q, Pistol and dagger. 80q, Wall hanging, vert. 1.20 l, Earrings and belt buckle. 1.40 l, Jugs, vert.

1976 **Litho.** *Perf. 12½x12, 12x12½*

1733	A360	10q	lilac & multi	.25	.25
1734	A360	15q	gray & multi	.25	.25
1735	A360	20q	multi	.25	.25
1736	A360	25q	car & multi	.25	.25
1737	A360	80q	yellow & multi	.25	.25
1738	A360	1.20 l	multi	.75	.30
1739	A360	1.40 l	tan & multi	1.50	.40
			Nos. 1733-1739 (7)	3.50	1.95

Natl. Ethnographic Conf., Tirana, June 28.
For surcharge see No. 1873.

Founding of Cooperatives, by Zef Shoshi — A361

Paintings: 10q, Going to Work, by Agim Zajmi, vert. 25q, Crowd Listening to Loudspeaker, by Vilson Kilica. 40q, Woman Welder, by Sabaudin Xhaferi, vert. 50q, Factory, by Isuf Sulovari, vert. 1.20 l, 1942 Revolt, by Lec Shkreli, vert. 1.60 l, Coming Home from Work, by Agron Dine. 2.05 l, Honoring a Young Pioneer, by Andon Lakuriqi.

Perf. 12½x12, 12x12½

1976, Aug. 8 **Litho.**

1740	A361	5q	gold & multi	.25	.25
1741	A361	10q	gold & multi	.25	.25
1742	A361	25q	gold & multi	.25	.25
1743	A361	40q	gold & multi	.25	.25
1744	A361	50q	gold & multi	.25	.25
1745	A361	1.20 l	gold & multi	.75	.55
1746	A361	1.60 l	gold & multi	1.00	.85
			Nos. 1740-1746 (7)	3.00	2.65

Miniature Sheet

Perf. 12 on 2 sides x Imperf.

1747	A361	2.05 l	gold & multi	2.50	1.50

Red Flag, Agricultural Symbols — A362

Design: 1.20 l, Red flag and raised pickax.

1976, Nov. 1

1748	A362	25q	multi	.30	.25
1749	A362	1.20 l	multi	1.75	.50

7th Workers Party Congress.

Enver Hoxha, Partisans and Albanian Flag — A363

1.90 l, Demonstrators with Albanian flag.

1976, Oct. 28 *Perf. 12x12½*

1750	A363	25q	multi	.40	.25
1751	A363	1.90 l	multi	1.60	.65

Anti-Fascist demonstrations, 35th anniv.

Attacking Partisans, Meeting House — A364

Designs (Red Flag and): 25q, Partisans, pickax and gun. 80q, Workers, soldiers, pickax and gun. 1.20 l, Agriculture and industry. 1.70 l, Dancers, symbols of science and art.

1976, Nov. 8 **Litho.** *Perf. 12x12½*

1752	A364	15q	gold & multi	.25	.25
1753	A364	25q	gold & multi	.25	.25
1754	A364	80q	gold & multi	.70	.25

1755 A364 1.20 l gold & multi 1.00 .25
1756 A364 1.70 l gold & multi 1.40 .25
Nos. 1752-1756 (5) 3.60 1.25

35th anniv. of 1st Workers Party Congress.

Young Workers and Track — A365

1.25 l, Young soldiers and Albanian flag.

1976, Nov. 23 ***Perf. 12***
1757 A365 80q yellow & multi *1.25 .35*
1758 A365 1.25 l carmine & multi *2.25 .50*

Union of Young Communists, 35th anniv.

"Cuca e Maleve" Ballet — A366

Scenes from ballet "Mountain Girl."

1976, Dec. 14 ***Perf. 12***
1759 A366 10q gold & multi .25 *.50*
1760 A366 15q gold & multi .25 *.50*
1761 A366 20q gold & multi .25 *1.00*
1762 A366 25q gold & multi .30 *2.00*
1763 A366 80q gold & multi .85 *3.00*
1764 A366 1.20 l gold & multi 1.00 *4.00*
1765 A366 1.40 l gold & multi 1.40 *4.00*
Nos. 1759-1765 (7) 4.30 *15.00*

Miniature Sheet

Perf. 12 on 2 sides x Imperf.

1766 A366 2.05 l gold & multi 3.25 2.75

Bashtove Castle — A367

Albanian Castles: 15q, Gjirokaster. 20q, Ali Pash Tepelene. 25q, Petrele. 80q, Berat. 1.20 l, Durres. 1.40 l, Kruje.

1976, Dec. 30 **Litho.** ***Perf. 12***
1767 A367 10q black & dull bl .25 .25
1768 A367 15q black & grn .25 .25
1769 A367 20q black & gray .25 .25
1770 A367 25q black & brn .25 .25
1771 A367 80q black & rose .80 .35
1772 A367 1.20 l black & vio 1.00 .50
1773 A367 1.40 l black & brn red 1.50 .55
Nos. 1767-1773 (7) 4.30 2.40

Skanderbeg's Shield and Spear — A368

Skanderbeg's Weapons: 80q, Helmet, sword and scabbard. 1 l, Halberd, quiver with arrows, crossbow and spear.

1977, Jan. 28 **Litho.** ***Perf. 12***
1774 A368 15q silver & multi 1.25 .40
1775 A368 80q silver & multi 4.25 2.50
1776 A368 1 l silver & multi 6.50 5.00
Nos. 1774-1776 (3) 12.00 7.90

Skanderbeg (1403-1468), national hero.

Ilia Qiqi, Messenger in Storm — A369

Modern Heroes: 10q, Ilia Dashi, sailor in battle. 25q, Fran Ndue Ivanaj, fisherman in storm. 80q, Zeliha Allmetaj, woman rescuing child. 1 l, Ylli Zaimi, rescuing goats from flood. 1.90 l, Isuf Plloci, fighting forest fire.

1977, Feb. 28 **Litho.** ***Perf. 12x12½***
1777 A369 5q brown & multi .25 .25
1778 A369 10q ultra & multi .25 .25
1779 A369 25q blue & multi .40 .25
1780 A369 80q ocher & multi .90 .35
1781 A369 1 l brown & multi 1.25 .45
1782 A369 1.90 l brown & multi 2.60 1.40
Nos. 1777-1782 (6) 5.65 2.95

Polyvinylchloride Plant, Vlore — A370

6th Five-year plan: 25q, Naphtha fractioning plant, Ballsh. 65q, Hydroelectric station and dam, Fjerzes. 1 l, Metallurgical plant and blast furance, Elbasan.

1977, Mar. 29 **Litho.** ***Perf. 12½x12***
1783 A370 15q silver & multi .35 .25
1784 A370 25q silver & multi .40 .25
1785 A370 65q silver & multi 1.10 .35
1786 A370 1 l silver & multi 1.60 .65
Nos. 1783-1786 (4) 3.45 1.50

Qerime Halil Galica — A371

Design: 1.25 l, Qerime Halil Galica "Shota" and father Azem Galica.

1977, Apr. 20 **Litho.** ***Perf. 12***
1787 A371 80q dark red 1.10 .30
1788 A371 1.25 l gray blue 1.60 .70

"Shota" Galica, communist fighter.

Victory Monument, Tirana — A372

Red Star and: 80q, Clenched fist, Albanian flag. 1.20 l, Bust of Qemal Stafa, poppies.

1977, May 5 **Litho.** ***Perf. 12***
1789 A372 25q multi .35 .25
1790 A372 80q multi 1.25 .45
1791 A372 1.20 l multi 2.00 .85
Nos. 1789-1791 (3) 3.60 1.55

35th anniversary of Martyrs' Day.

Physician Visiting Farm, Mobile Clinic — A373

10q, Cowherd, cattle ranch. 20q, Militia woman helping with harvest, rifle, combine. 80q, Modern village, highway, power lines. 2.95 l, Tractor, greenhouses.

1977, June 18
1792 A373 5q multi .25 .25
1793 A373 10q multi .25 .25
1794 A373 20q multi .30 .25
1795 A373 80q multi 1.00 .25
1796 A373 2.95 l multi 3.50 .75
Nos. 1792-1796 (5) 5.30 1.75

"Socialist transformation of the villages."

Armed Workers, Flag and Factory — A374

1.80 l, Workers with proclamation and flags.

1977, June 20
1797 A374 25q multi 1.00 .25
1798 A374 1.80 l multi 1.50 .80

9th Labor Unions Congress.

Kerchief Dance — A375

Designs: Various folk dances.

1977, Aug. 20 **Litho.** ***Perf. 12***
1799 A375 5q multi .25 .25
1800 A375 10q multi .25 .25
1801 A375 15q multi .25 .25
1802 A375 25q multi .25 .25
1803 A375 80q multi .25 .25
1804 A375 1.20 l multi .70 .35
1805 A375 1.55 l multi 1.00 .45
Nos. 1799-1805 (7) 2.95 2.05

Miniature Sheet

Perf. 12 on 2 sides x Imperf.

1806 A375 2.05 l multi 3.50 2.00

See Nos. 1836-1840, 1884-1888.

Attack — A376

Designs: 25q, Enver Hoxha addressing Army. 80q, Volunteers and riflemen. 1 l, Volunteers, hydrofoil patrolboat and MiG planes. 1.90 l, Volunteers and Albanian flag.

1977, July 10 **Litho.** ***Perf. 12***
1807 A376 15q gold & multi .30 .25
1808 A376 25q gold & multi .30 .25
1809 A376 80q gold & multi .90 .35
1810 A376 1 l gold & multi 1.50 .50
1811 A376 1.90 l gold & multi 2.50 .90
Nos. 1807-1811 (5) 5.50 2.25

"One People-One Army."

Armed Workers, Article 3 of Constitution A377

Design: 1.20 l, Symbols of farming and fertilizer industry, Article 25 of Constitution.

1977, Oct.
1812 A377 25q red, gold & blk .40 .25
1813 A377 1.20 l red, gold & blk 1.50 .50

New Constitution.

Picnic — A378

Film Frames: 15q, Telephone lineman in winter. 25q, Two men and a woman. 80q, Workers. 1.20 l, Boys playing in street. 1.60 l, Harvest.

1977, Oct. 25 **Litho.** ***Perf. 12½x12***
1814 A378 10q blue green .35 .35
1815 A378 15q multi .35 .35
1816 A378 25q black .35 .35
1817 A378 80q multi 1.40 1.40
1818 A378 1.20 l deep claret 2.00 2.00
1819 A378 1.60 l multi 2.25 2.25
Nos. 1814-1819 (6) 6.70 6.70

Albanian films.

Farm Workers in Field, by V. Mio — A379

Paintings by V. Mio: 10q, Landscape in Snow. 15q, Grazing Sheep under Walnut Tree in Spring. 25q, Street in Korce. 80q, Horseback Riders on Mountain Pass. 1 l, Boats on Shore. 1.75 l, Tractors Plowing Fields. 2.05 l, Self-portrait.

1977, Dec. 25 **Litho.** ***Perf. 12½x12***
1820 A379 5q gold & multi .25 .25
1821 A379 10q gold & multi .25 .25
1822 A379 15q gold & multi .25 .25
1823 A379 25q gold & multi .25 .25
1824 A379 80q gold & multi .35 .25
1825 A379 1 l gold & multi .60 .25
1826 A379 1.75 l gold & multi 1.00 .25
Nos. 1820-1826 (7) 2.95 1.75

Miniature Sheet

Imperf.; Perf. 12 Horiz. between Vignette and Value Panel

1827 A379 2.05 l gold & multi 3.50 2.25

Pan Flute — A380

Folk Musical Instruments: 25q, Single-string goat's-head fiddle. 80q, Woodwind. 1.20 l, Drum. 1.70 l, Bagpipe. Background shows various woven folk patterns.

1978, Jan. 20 ***Perf. 12x12½***
1828 A380 15q multi .40 .25
1829 A380 25q multi .75 .25
1830 A380 80q multi 2.00 1.00
1831 A380 1.20 l multi 3.50 2.00
1832 A380 1.70 l multi 9.00 3.50
Nos. 1828-1832 (5) 15.65 7.00

Albanian Flag, Monument and People — A381

25q, Ismail Qemali, fighters, horiz. 1.65 l, People dancing around Albanian flag, horiz.

Perf. 12½x12, 12x12½

1977, Nov. 28
1833 A381 15q multi .25 .25
1834 A381 25q multi .30 .25
1835 A381 1.65 l multi 1.50 1.25
Nos. 1833-1835 (3) 2.05 1.75

65th anniversary of independence.

Folk Dancing Type of 1977

Designs: Various dances.

1978, Feb. 15 **Litho.** ***Perf. 12***
1836 A375 5q multi .25 .25
1837 A375 25q multi .25 .25
1838 A375 80q multi .75 .30
1839 A375 1 l multi .75 .40
1840 A375 2.30 l multi 1.75 1.40
Nos. 1836-1840 (5) 3.75 2.60

Nos. 1836-1840 have white background around dancers, Nos. 1799-1805 have pinkish shadows.

Tractor Drivers, by Dhimitraq Trebicka — A382

Working Class Paintings: 80q, Steeplejack, by Spiro Kristo. 85q, "A Point in the Discussion," by Skender Milori. 90q, Oil rig crew, by Anesti Cini, vert. 1.60 l, Metal workers, by Ramadan Karanxha. 2.20 l, Political discussion, by Sotiraq Sholla.

1978, Mar. 25 **Litho.** ***Perf. 12***
1841 A382 25q multi .25 .25
1842 A382 80q multi .35 .25
1843 A382 85q multi .45 .25
1844 A382 90q multi .50 .30
1845 A382 1.60 l multi 1.40 .90
Nos. 1841-1845 (5) 2.95 1.95

Miniature Sheet

Perf. 12 on 2 sides x Imperf.

1846 A382 2.20 l multi 7.00 2.75

Woman with Rifle and Pickax — A383

1.95 l, Farm & Militia women, industrial plant.

1978, June 1 Litho. *Perf. 12*

1847	A383	25q gold & red	.35	.25
1848	A383	1.95 l gold & red	5.25	1.50

8th Congress of Women's Union.

Children and Flowers — A384

Designs: 10q, Children with rifle, ax, book and flags. 25q, Dancing children in folk costume. 1.80 l, Children in school.

1978, June 1 Litho.

1849	A384	5q multi	.25	.25
1850	A384	10q multi	.25	.25
1851	A384	25q multi	.45	.25
1852	A384	1.80 l multi	3.00	.90
		Nos. 1849-1852 (4)	3.95	1.65

International Children's Day.

Spirit of Skanderbeg as Conqueror — A385

10q, Battle at Mostar Bridge. 80q, Marchers, Albanian flag. 1.20 l, Riflemen in winter battle. 1.65 l, Abdyl Frasheri (1839-92). 2.20 l, Rifles, scroll, pen, League building. 2.60 l, League headquarters, Prizren.

1978, June 10 Litho. *Perf. 12*

1853	A385	10q multi	.25	.25
1854	A385	25q multi	.25	.30
1855	A385	80q multi	.90	.30
1856	A385	1.20 l multi	1.25	.65
1857	A385	1.65 l multi	2.00	1.00
1858	A385	2.60 l multi	3.25	1.50
		Nos. 1853-1858 (6)	7.90	4.00

Miniature Sheet

Perf. 12 on 2 sides x Imperf.

1859	A385	2.20 l multi	3.25	2.25

Centenary of League of Prizren.

Guerrillas and Flag, 1943 — A386

Designs: 25q, Soldier, sailor, airman, militiaman, horiz. 1.90 l, Members of armed forces, civil guards, and Young Pioneers.

1978, July 10 *Perf. 11½x12½*

1860	A386	5q multi	.35	.25
1861	A386	25q multi	.70	.25
1862	A386	1.90 l multi	4.50	1.50
		Nos. 1860-1862 (3)	5.55	2.00

35th anniversary of People's Army.

Woman with Machine Carbine — A387

25q, Man with target rifle, horiz. 95q, Man shooting with telescopic sights, horiz. 2.40 l, Woman target shooting with pistol.

Perf. 12½x12, 12x12½

1978, Sept. 20 Litho.

1863	A387	25q black & yel	.25	.25
1864	A387	80q orange & blk	.50	.35
1865	A387	95q red & blk	.75	.50
1866	A387	2.40 l carmine & blk	1.90	1.50
		Nos. 1863-1866 (4)	3.40	2.60

32nd National Rifle-shooting Championships, Sept. 20.

Kerchief Dance — A388

15q, Musicians. 25q, Fiddler with single-stringed instrument. 80q, Dancers, men. 1.20 l, Saber dance. 1.90 l, Singers, women.

1978, Oct. 6 *Perf. 12*

1867	A388	10q multi	.25	.25
1868	A388	15q multi	.25	.25
1869	A388	25q multi	.25	.25
1870	A388	80q multi	.25	.25
1871	A388	1.20 l multi	.65	.25
1872	A388	1.90 l multi	1.60	1.25
		Nos. 1867-1872 (6)	3.25	2.50

National Folklore Festival.

See Nos. 2082-2085, 2289-2290.

No. 1736 Surcharged with New Value, 2 Bars and "RICCIONE 78"

1978 Litho. *Perf. 12½x12*

1873	A360	3.30 l on 25q multi	10.00	10.00

Riccione 78 Philatelic Exhibition.

Enver Hoxha — A389

1978, Oct. 16 Litho. *Perf. 12x12½*

1874	A389	80q red & multi	.40	.35
1875	A389	1.20 l red & multi	.75	.35
1876	A389	2.40 l red & multi	1.50	1.00
		Nos. 1874-1876 (3)	2.65	1.70

Miniature Sheet

Perf. 12½ on 2 sides x Imperf.

1877	A389	2.20 l red & multi	3.50	2.00

70th birthday of Enver Hoxha, First Secretary of Central Committee of the Communist Party of Albania.

Woman and Wheat — A390

25q, Woman with egg crates. 80q, Shepherd, sheep. 2.60 l, Milkmaid, cows.

1978, Dec. 15 *Perf. 12x12½*

1878	A390	15q multicolored	.40	.40
1879	A390	25q multicolored	.55	.40
1880	A390	80q multicolored	2.00	1.50
1881	A390	2.60 l multicolored	7.50	5.00
		Nos. 1878-1881 (4)	10.45	7.30

Dora d'Istria — A391

Design: 1.10 l, Full portrait of Dora d'Istria, author; birth sesquicentennial.

1979, Jan. 22 Litho. *Perf. 12*

1882	A391	80q lt grn & blk	1.10	.75
1883	A391	1.10 l vio brn & blk	1.90	1.50

Folk Dancing Type of 1977

Designs: Various folk dances.

1979, Feb. 25

1884	A375	15q multi	.35	.25
1885	A375	25q multi	.35	.25
1886	A375	80q multi	1.50	.75
1887	A375	1.20 l multi	1.75	1.00
1888	A375	1.40 l multi	2.00	1.40
		Nos. 1884-1888 (5)	5.95	3.65

Nos. 1884-1888 have white background. Denomination in UL on No. 1885, in UR on No. 1802; LL on No.1886, UL on No. 1803.

Tower House — A392

Traditional Houses: 15q, Stone gallery house, horiz. 80q, House with wooden galleries, horiz. 1.20 l, Galleried tower house. 1.40 l, 1.90 l, Tower houses, diff.

1979, Mar. 20

1889	A392	15q multi	.25	.25
1890	A392	25q multi	.25	.25
1891	A392	80q multi	.75	.25
1892	A392	1.20 l multi	1.00	.45
1893	A392	1.40 l multi	1.50	.65
		Nos. 1889-1893 (5)	3.75	1.85

Miniature Sheet

Perf. 12 on 2 sides x Imperf.

1894	A392	1.90 l multi	6.00	3.75

See Nos. 2015-2018.

Soldier, Factories, Wheat — A393

1.65 l, Soldiers, workers and coat of arms.

1979, May 14 Litho. *Perf. 12*

1895	A393	25q multi	.75	.35
1896	A393	1.65 l multi	3.50	2.00

Congress of Permet, 35th anniversary.

Albanian Flag — A394

1979, June 4

1897	A394	25q multi	.75	.35
1898	A394	1.65 l multi	3.50	2.25

5th Congress of Albanian Democratic Front.

Alexander Moissi, (1880-1935), Actor — A395

1979, Apr 2

1899	A395	80q multi	1.00	.35
1900	A395	1.10 l multi, diff.	1.50	1.00

Vasil Shanto, (1913-44) — A396

Design: 25q, 90q, Qemal Stafa (1921-42).

1979, May 5

1901	A396	15q multi	.25	.25
1902	A396	25q multi	.35	.25
1903	A396	60q multi	1.20	.60
1904	A396	90q multi	2.10	1.25
		Nos. 1901-1904 (4)	3.90	2.35

Shanto and Stafa, anti-Fascist fighters. For similar design see A410.

Winter Campaign, by Arben Basha A397

Paintings of Military Scenes by: 25q, Ismail Lulani. 80q, Myrteza Fushekati. 1.20 l, Muhamet Deliu. 1.40 l, Jorgji Gjikopulli. 1.90 l, Fatmir Haxhiu.

1979, July 15 Litho. *Perf. 12½x12*

1905	A397	15q multi	.25	.25
1906	A397	25q multi	.25	.25
1907	A397	80q multi	.75	.25
1908	A397	1.20 l multi	1.00	.45
1909	A397	1.40 l multi	1.50	.75
		Nos. 1905-1909 (5)	3.75	1.95

Miniature Sheet

Perf. 12 on 2 sides x Imperf.

1910	A397	1.90 l multi	3.00	2.00

Athletes Surrounding Flag — A398

1979, Oct. 1 Litho. *Perf. 12*

1911	A398	15q shown	.25	.25
1912	A398	25q Shooting	.25	.25
1913	A398	80q Dancing	.70	.25
1914	A398	1.20 l Soccer	.85	.60
1915	A398	1.40 l High jump	1.20	.85
		Nos. 1911-1915 (5)	3.25	2.20

Liberation Spartakiad, 35th anniversary.

Literary Society Headquarters — A399

Albanian Literary Society Centenary: 25q, Seal and charter. 80q, Founder. 1.55 l, 1879 Headquarters.
1.90 l, Founders.

1979, Oct. 12

1916	A399	25q multi	.25	.25
1917	A399	80q multi	.75	.35
1918	A399	1.20 l multi	1.00	.60
1919	A399	1.55 l multi	1.25	.75
		Nos. 1916-1919 (4)	3.25	1.95

Miniature Sheet

Perf. 12½ on 2 sides x Imperf.

1920	A399	1.90 l multi	2.75	2.00

Congress Statute, Coat of Arms — A400

1979, Oct. 20 Photo. *Perf. 12x12½*

1921	A400	25q multi	1.00	.75
1922	A400	1.65 l multi	4.00	2.50

2nd Congress of Berat, 35th anniversary.

Industry and Culture — A401

5q, Children Entering School, Books. 10q, Communications. 15q, Steel workers. 20q, Dancers, instruments. 25q, Newspapers, radio, television. 60q, Textile worker. 80q, Armed forces. 1.20 l, Industry. 1.60 l, Transportation. 2.40 l, Agriculture. 3 l, Medicine.

1979 Litho. *Perf. 12½x12*

1923	A401	5q shown	.25	.25
1924	A401	10q multi	.25	.25
1925	A401	15q multi	.25	.25
1926	A401	20q multi	.25	.25
1927	A401	25q multi	.25	.25
1928	A401	60q multi	1.00	.25
1929	A401	80q multi	1.40	.25
1930	A401	1.20 l multi	2.40	.25
1931	A401	1.60 l multi	3.25	.40
1932	A401	2.40 l multi	5.00	.45
1932A	A401	3 l multi	6.75	.60
		Nos. 1923-1932A (11)	21.05	3.45

Workers and Factory — A402

Worker, Red Flag and: 80q, Hand holding sickle and rifle. 1.20 l, Red star and open book. 1.55 l, Open book and cogwheel.

1979, Nov. 29

1933	A402	25q	multi	.25	.25
1934	A402	80q	multi	.75	.35
1935	A402	1.20 l	multi	.90	.75
1936	A402	1.55 l	multi	1.50	.90
			Nos. 1933-1936 (4)	3.40	2.25

35th anniversary of independence.

Joseph Stalin — A403

Design: 1.10 l, Stalin on dais, horiz.

1979, Dec. 21 **Litho.** ***Perf. 12***

1937	A403	80q	red & dk bl	1.10	.75
1938	A403	1.10 l	red & dk bl	1.50	1.50

Joseph Stalin (1879-1953), birth centenary.

Fireplace and Pottery, Korcar — A404

Home Furnishings: 80q, Cupboard bed, dagger, pistol, ammunition pouch, Shkodar. 1.20 l, Stool, pot, chair, Mirdit. 1.35 l, Chimney, dagger, jacket, Gjirokaster.

1980, Feb. 27 **Litho.** ***Perf. 12***

1939	A404	25q	multi	.25	.25
1940	A404	80q	multi	.50	.50
1941	A404	1.20 l	multi	1.10	.75
1942	A404	1.35 l	multi	1.50	1.50
			Nos. 1939-1942 (4)	3.35	3.00

See Nos. 1985-1988.

Pipe, Painted Flask — A405

80q, Leather handbags. 1.20 l, Carved eagle, embroidered rug. 1.35 l, Lace.

1980, Mar. 4

1943	A405	25q	shown	.25	.25
1944	A405	80q	multi	.50	.50
1945	A405	1.20 l	multi	1.10	.75
1946	A405	1.35 l	multi	1.50	1.50
			Nos. 1943-1946 (4)	3.35	3.00

Prof. Aleksander Xhuvanit Birth Centenary — A406

1980, Mar. 14

1947	A406	80q	multi	1.40	1.00
1948	A406	1 l	multi	1.75	1.75

Revolutionaries on Horseback A407

Insurrection at Kosove, 70th Anniversary: 1 l, Battle scene.

1980, Apr. 4

1949	A407	80q	red & black	1.50	1.10
1950	A407	1 l	red & black	2.25	1.90

Soldiers and Workers Laboring to Aid the Stricken Populations, by D. Jukniu and I. Lulani — A408

1980, Apr. 15 **Litho.** ***Perf. 12½***

1951	A408	80q	lt blue & multi	1.50	1.10
1952	A408	1 l	lt blue grn & multi	2.25	1.90

Lenin, 110th Birth Anniversary — A409

1980, Apr. 22

1953	A409	80q	multi	1.50	1.10
1954	A409	1 l	multi	2.25	1.90

Misto Mame and Ali Demi, War Martyrs — A410

War Martyrs: 80q, Sadik Staveleci, Vojo Kusji, Hoxhi Martini. 1.20 l, Bule Naipi, Persefoni Kokedhima. 1.35 l, Ndoc Deda, Hydajet Lezha, Naim Gyylbegu, Ndoc Mazi, Ahmed Haxha.

1980, May 5

1955	A410	25q	multi	.25	.25
1956	A410	80q	multi	.70	.50
1957	A410	1.20 l	multi	1.20	.70
1958	A410	1.35 l	multi	1.40	1.40
			Nos. 1955-1958 (4)	3.55	2.85

See Nos. 2012A-2012D, 2025-2028, 2064-2067, 2122-2125, 2171-2174, 2207-2209.

Scene from "Mirela" — A411

1980, June 7

1959	A411	15q	shown	.25	.25
1960	A411	25q	The Scribbler	.25	.25
1961	A411	80q	Circus Bears	.80	.80
1962	A411	2.40 l	Waterdrops	2.75	2.75
			Nos. 1959-1962 (4)	4.05	4.05

Carrying Iron Castings in the Enver Hoxha Tractor Combine, by S. Shijaku and M. Fushekati A412

Paintings (Gallery of Figurative Paintings, Tirana): 80q, The Welder, by Harilla Dhima. 1.20 l, Steel Erectors, by Petro Kokushta. 1.35 l, Pandeli Lena, 1.80 l Communists, by Vilson Kilica.

1980, July 22

1963	A412	25q	multi	.25	.25
1964	A412	80q	multi	.70	.70
1965	A412	1.20 l	multi	1.20	1.20
1966	A412	1.35 l	multi	1.40	1.40
			Nos. 1963-1966 (4)	3.55	3.55

Imperf

1967	A412	1.80 l	multi	3.00	2.50

No. 1967 measures 66x82mm and has a row of perforations above and below the vignette.

Gate, Parchment Miniature, 11th Cent. — A413

Bas reliefs of the Middle Ages: 80q, Eagle, 13th cent. 1.20 l, Heraldic lion, 14th cent. 1.35 l, Pheasant, 14th cent.

1980, Sept. 27 **Litho.** ***Perf. 12***

1968	A413	25q	gold & blk	.25	.25
1969	A413	80q	gold & blk	.55	.55
1970	A413	1.20 l	gold & blk	1.20	1.20
1971	A413	1.35 l	gold & blk	1.20	1.20
			Nos. 1968-1971 (4)	3.20	3.20

Divjaka National Park — A414

1980, Nov. 6 **Photo.**

1972	A414	80q	shown	.75	.60
1973	A414	1.20 l	Lura	1.10	1.10
1974	A414	1.60 l	Thethi	1.90	1.60
			Nos. 1972-1974 (3)	3.75	3.30

Souvenir Sheet

Perf. 12½ Horiz.

1975	A414	1.80 l	Llogara Park	3.50	3.50

Citizens, Flag and Arms of Albania — A415

1 l, People's Party Headquarters, Tirana.

1981, Jan. 11 **Litho.** ***Perf. 12***

1976	A415	80q	multicolored	1.00	.70
1977	A415	1 l	multicolored	1.40	.70

35th anniversary of the Republic.

Child's Bed — A416

80q, Wooden bucket, brass bottle. 1.20 l, Shoes. 1.35 l, Jugs.

1981, Mar. 20 **Litho.** ***Perf. 12***

1978	A416	25q	multicolored	.25	.25
1979	A416	80q	multicolored	.50	.40
1980	A416	1.20 l	multicolored	.80	.70
1981	A416	1.35 l	multicolored	1.00	.90
			Nos. 1978-1981 (4)	2.55	2.25

A417

80q, Soldiers. 1 l, Sword combat. 1.80 l, Soldier with pistol.

1981, Apr. 20

1982	A417	80q	multicolored	.70	.70
1983	A417	1 l	multicolored	.85	.70

Souvenir Sheet

Perf. 12½ Vert.

1984	A417	1.80 l	multicolored	2.75	2.00

Battle of Shtimje centenary.

Home Furnishings Type of 1980

25q, House interior, Labara. 80q, Labara, diff. 1.20 l, Mat. 1.35 l, Dibres.

1981, Feb. 25 **Litho.** ***Perf. 12***

1985	A404	25q	multicolored	.25	.25
1986	A404	80q	multicolored	.35	.25
1987	A404	1.20 l	multicolored	.85	.40
1988	A404	1.35 l	multicolored	1.00	.90
			Nos. 1985-1988 (4)	2.45	1.80

A419

Designs: Children's circus.

1981, June ***Perf. 12***

1989	A419	15q	multi	.25	.25
1990	A419	25q	multi	.50	.40
1991	A419	80q	multi	.80	.65
1992	A419	2.40 l	multi	1.00	.90
			Nos. 1989-1992 (4)	2.55	2.20

Soccer Players — A420

1982 World Cup Soccer Elimination Games: Various soccer players.

1981, Mar. 31 **Litho.** ***Perf. 12***

1993	A420	25q	multi	.70	.35
1994	A420	80q	multi	2.50	1.50
1995	A420	1.20 l	multi	3.50	2.60
1996	A420	1.35 l	multi	4.25	3.00
			Nos. 1993-1996 (4)	10.95	7.45

Allies, by S. Hysa — A421

Paintings: 80q, Warriors, by A. Buza. 1.20 l, Rallying to the Flag, Dec. 1911, by A. Zajmi, vert. 1.35 l, My Flag is My Heart, by L. Cefa, vert. 1.80 l, Circling the Flag in a Common Cause, by N. Vasia.

1981, July 10 ***Perf. 12½x12***

1997	A421	25q	multi	.25	.25
1998	A421	80q	multi	.75	.35
1999	A421	1.20 l	multi	.85	.75
2000	A421	1.35 l	multi	1.50	.85
			Nos. 1997-2000 (4)	3.35	2.20

Souvenir Sheet

Perf. 12½ Horiz.

2001	A421	1.80 l	multi	2.75	2.50

No. 2001 contains one 55x55mm stamp.

Rifleman — A422

1981, Aug. 30 ***Perf. 12***

2002	A422	25q	shown	.25	.25
2003	A422	80q	Weight lifting	.50	.35
2004	A422	1.20 l	Volleyball	.75	.65
2005	A422	1.35 l	Soccer	1.00	.75
			Nos. 2002-2005 (4)	2.50	2.00

Albanian Workers' Party, 8th Congress — A423

80q, Flag, star. 1 l, Flag, hammer & sickle.

1981, Nov. 1

2006	A423	80q	multicolored	.60	.45
2007	A423	1 l	multicolored	.85	.75

Albanian Workers' Party, 40th Anniv. — A424

80q, Symbols of industrialization. 2.80 l, Fist, emblem.
1.80 l, Enver Hoxha, Memoirs.

1981, Nov. 8

2008 A424 80q multicolored .35 .35
2009 A424 2.80 l multicolored 1.75 1.40

Souvenir Sheet

Perf. 12 Horiz.

2010 A424 1.80 l multicolored 3.75 3.75

Communist Youth Org., 40th Anniv. — A425

1981, Nov. 23

2011 A425 80q Star, ax, map .75 .75
2012 A425 1 l Flags, star 1.50 1.40

War Martyrs Type of 1980

25q, Perlat Rexhepi (1919-42) and Branko Kadia (1921-42). 80q, Xheladin Beqiri (1908-44) and Hajdar Dushi (1916-44). 1.20 l, Koci Bako (1905-41), Vasil Laci (1923-41) and Mujo Ulqinaku (1898-1939). 1.35 l, Mine Peza (1875-1942) and Zoja Cure (1920-44).

1981, May 5 Litho. *Perf. 12*

2012A A410 25q silver & multi .25 .25
2012B A410 80q gold & multi .65 .35
2012C A410 1.20 l silver & multi .80 .75
2012D A410 1.35 l gold & multi 1.40 .85
Nos. 2012A-2012D (4) 3.10 2.20

Fan S. Noli, Writer, Birth Centenary — A426

1982, Jan. 6 Litho. *Perf. 12*

2013 A426 80q lt ol grn & gold 1.00 .50
2014 A426 1.10 l lt red brn & gold 1.25 .75

Traditional Houses Type of 1979

1982, Feb. *Perf. 12½x12*

2015 A392 25q Bulqize .25 .25
2016 A392 80q Lebush .90 .65
2017 A392 1.20 l Bicaj 1.30 .90
2018 A392 1.55 l Klos 1.75 1.10
Nos. 2015-2018 (4) 4.20 2.90

TB Bacillus Centenary A428

1982, Mar. 24 *Perf. 12*

2019 A428 80q Globe 3.75 1.50
2020 A428 1.10 l Koch 5.25 2.50

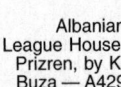

Albanian League House, Prizren, by K. Buza — A429

Kosova Landscapes: 25q, Castle at Prizrenit, by G. Madhi. 1.20 l, Mountain Gorge at Rogove, by K. Buza. 1.55 l, Street of the Hadhji at Zekes, by G. Madhi. 25q, 1.20 l, 1.55 l vert.

Perf. 12x12½, 12½x12

1982, Apr. 15 Litho.

2021 A429 25q multi .35 .25
2022 A429 80q multi 1.10 .90
2023 A429 1.20 l multi 1.90 1.10
2024 A429 1.55 l multi 2.75 1.25
Nos. 2021-2024 (4) 6.10 3.50

War Martyrs Type of 1980

Designs: 25q, Hibe Palikuqi, Liri Gero. 80q, Mihal Duri, Kajo Karafili. 1.20 l, Fato Dudumi, Margarita Tutulani, Shejnaze Juka. 1.55 l, Memo Meto, Gjok Doci.

1982, May *Perf. 12*

2025 A410 25q multi .35 .25
2026 A410 80q multi .85 .60
2027 A410 1.20 l multi 1.25 .75
2028 A410 1.55 l multi 1.75 1.00
Nos. 2025-2028 (4) 4.20 2.60

Loading Freighter A430

Children's Paintings.

1982, June 15 *Perf. 12½x12*

2029 A430 15q shown .40 .25
2030 A430 80q Forest .85 .45
2031 A430 1.20 l City 1.25 .90
2032 A430 1.65 l Park 2.50 1.25
Nos. 2029-2032 (4) 5.00 2.85

9th Congress of Trade Unions — A431

80q, Workers, factories. 1.10 l, Emblem, flag.

1982, June 6 Litho. *Perf. 12*

2033 A431 80q multicolored 2.00 1.25
2034 A431 1.10 l multicolored 2.75 1.50

Alpine Village Festival, by Danish Jukniu — A432

Industrial Development Paintings: 80q, Hydroelectric Station Builders, by Ali Miruku. 1.20 l, Steel Workers, by Clirim Ceka. 1.55 l, Oil drillers, by Pandeli Lena. 1.90 l, Trapping the Furnace, by Jorgji Gjikopulli.

1982, July *Perf. 12½*

2035 A432 25q multi .30 .25
2036 A432 80q multi 1.00 1.00
2037 A432 1.20 l multi 1.50 1.20
2038 A432 1.55 l multi 2.25 1.50
Nos. 2035-2038 (4) 5.05 3.95

Souvenir Sheet

Perf. 12 Horiz.

2039 A432 1.90 l multi 3.50 2.50

No. 2039 contains one 54x48mm stamp.

Communist Party Newspaper "Voice of the People," 40th Anniv. — A432a

80q, Newspapers. 1.10 l, Paper, press.

1982, Aug. 25 Litho. *Perf. 12*

2039A A432a 80q multi *75.00 70.00*
2039B A432a 1.10 l multi *75.00 70.00*

40th Anniv. of Democratic Front — A433

80q, Glory to the Heroes of Peza Monument. 1.10 l, Marchers.

1982, Sept. 16 *Perf. 12*

2040 A433 80q multi *6.00* 2.50
2041 A433 1.10 l multi *8.50* 3.50

8th Youth Congress — A434

1982, Oct. 4

2042 A434 80q multi *2.50* 2.00
2043 A434 1.10 l multi *4.00* 3.00

Handmade Shoulder Bags — A435

25q, Rug, horiz. 1.20 l, Wooden pots, bowls, horiz. 1.55 l, Jug.

1982, Nov.

2044 A435 25q multi .40 .25
2045 A435 80q multi .90 .50
2046 A435 1.20 l multi 1.25 .75
2047 A435 1.55 l multi 2.00 1.10
Nos. 2044-2047 (4) 4.55 2.60

70th Anniv. of Independence A436

20q, Ishamil Qemali. 1.20 l, Partisans. 2.40 l, Partisans, diff.
1.90 l, Independence Monument, Tirana.

1982, Nov. 28

2048 A436 20q multicolored .30 .25
2049 A436 1.20 l multicolored 1.40 .85
2050 A436 2.40 l multicolored 7.50 1.50
Nos. 2048-2050 (3) 9.20 2.60

Souvenir Sheet

Perf. 12 Horiz.

2051 A436 1.90 l multicolored 3.75 3.00

Dhermi Beach — A437

1982, Dec. 20

2052 A437 25q shown .25 .25
2053 A437 80q Sarande .75 .45
2054 A437 1.20 l Ksamil 1.00 .90
2055 A437 1.55 l Lukove 1.50 1.00
Nos. 2052-2055 (4) 3.50 2.60

Handkerchief Dancers — A438

Folkdancers — 80q, With kerchief, drum. 1.20 l, With guitar, flute, tambourine. 1.55 l, Women.

1983, Feb. 20 Litho. *Perf. 12*

2056 A438 25q multi .25 .25
2057 A438 80q multi .50 .25
2058 A438 1.20 l multi .90 .75
2059 A438 1.55 l multi 1.20 1.00
Nos. 2056-2059 (4) 2.85 2.25

A439

1983, Mar. 14 Litho. *Perf. 12*

2060 A439 80q multi 1.50 .75
2061 A439 1.10 l multi 1.90 1.00

Karl Marx (1818-83).

A440

80q, Electricity generation. 1.10 l, Gas & oil production.

1983, Apr. 20

2062 A440 80q multi 1.00 .60
2063 A440 1.10 l multi 1.25 .90

Energy development.

War Martyrs Type of 1980

Designs: 25q, Asim Zeneli (1916-43), Nazmi Rushiti (1919-42). 80q, Shyqyri Ishmi (1922-42), Shyqyri Alimerko (1923-43), Myzafer Asqeriu (1918-42). 1.20 l, Qybra Sokoli (1924-44), Qeriba Derri (1905-44), Ylbere Bilibashi (1928-44). 1.55 l, Themo Vasi (1915-43), Abaz Shehu (1905-42).

1983, May 5 Litho. *Perf. 12*

2064 A410 25q multi .25 .25
2065 A410 80q multi .75 .30
2066 A410 1.20 l multi 1.25 .75
2067 A410 1.55 l multi 1.90 1.00
Nos. 2064-2067 (4) 4.15 2.30

Women's Union, 9th Congress — A441

1983, June 1 Litho. *Perf. 12x12½*

2068 A441 80q red & gold 1.25 .75
2069 A441 1.10 l blue & gold 1.50 1.00

Bicycling — A442

1983, June 20 *Perf. 12*

2070 A442 25q shown .25 .25
2071 A442 80q Chess .75 .25
2072 A442 1.20 l Gymnastics 1.25 .75
2073 A442 1.55 l Wrestling 1.50 1.00
Nos. 2070-2073 (4) 3.75 2.25

40th Anniv. of People's Army — A443

20q, Armed services. 1.20 l, Soldier, gun barrels. 2.40 l, Factory guard, crowd.

1983, July 10

2074 A443 20q multicolored .25 .25
2075 A443 1.20 l multicolored 1.25 .75
2076 A443 2.40 l multicolored 2.25 1.25
Nos. 2074-2076 (3) 3.75 2.25

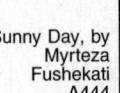

Sunny Day, by Myrteza Fushekati A444

Paintings: 80q, Messenger of the Grasp, by Niko Progi. 1.20 l, 29 November 1944, by Harilla Dhimo. 1.55 l, Fireworks, by Pandi Mele. 1.90 l, Partisan Assault, by Sali Shijaku and M. Fushekati.

1983, Aug. 28 Litho. *Perf. 12½x12*

2077 A444 25q multi .25 .25
2078 A444 80q multi .85 .40
2079 A444 1.20 l multi 1.00 .75
2080 A444 1.55 l multi 1.50 .85
Nos. 2077-2080 (4) 3.60 2.25

Souvenir Sheet

Perf. 12

2081	A444	1.90 l	multi	8.50	6.00

Folklore Festival Type of 1978

Gjirokaster Folklore Festival: folkdances: 25q, Sword dance. 80q, Kerchief dance. 1.20 l, Shepherd flautists. 1.55 l, Garland dance.

1983, Oct. 6 Litho. *Perf. 12*

2082	A388	25q	multicolored	.25	.25
2083	A388	80q	multicolored	1.50	.75
2084	A388	1.20 l	multicolored	1.50	.90
2085	A388	1.55 l	multicolored	3.00	2.00
			Nos. 2082-2085 (4)	6.25	3.90

World Communications Year — A446

1983, Nov. 10

2086	A446	60q	multicolored	.45	.35
2087	A446	1.20 l	multicolored	1.30	1.00

75th Birthday of Enver Hoxha — A447

1983, Oct. 16 Litho. *Perf. 12½*

2088	A447	80q	multi	.90	.75
2089	A447	1.20 l	multi	1.50	1.25
2090	A447	1.80 l	multi	2.00	1.75
			Nos. 2088-2090 (3)	4.40	3.75

Souvenir Sheet

Perf. 12 Horiz.

2091	A447	1.90 l	multi	3.50	3.00

The Right to a Joint Triumph, by J. Keraj — A448

Era of Skanderbeg in Figurative Art: 80q, The Heroic Center of the Battle of Krujes, by N. Bakalli. 1.20 l, The Rights of the Enemy after our Triumph, by N. Progri. 1.55 l, The Discussion at Lezhes, by B. Ahmeti. 1.90 l, Victory over the Turks, by G. Madhi.

1983, Dec. 10 *Perf. 12½x12*

2092	A448	25q	multi	.35	.25
2093	A448	80q	multi	1.10	.75
2094	A448	1.20 l	multi	1.50	.90
2095	A448	1.55 l	multi	2.25	1.10
			Nos. 2092-2095 (4)	5.20	3.00

Souvenir Sheet

Perf. 12 Horiz.

2096	A448	1.90 l	multi	6.00	6.00

Greco-Roman Ruins of Illyria — A449

80q, Amphitheater, Buthroxtum. 1.20 l, Colonnade, Apollonium. 1.80 l, Vaulted gallery, amphitheater at Epidamnus.

1983, Dec. 28 *Perf. 12*

2097	A449	80q	multicolored	1.50	1.10
2098	A449	1.20 l	multicolored	2.25	1.50
2099	A449	1.80 l	multicolored	2.25	1.75
			Nos. 2097-2099 (3)	6.00	4.35

Archeological Discoveries — A450

Designs: Apollo, 3rd cent. 25q, Tombstone, Korce, 3rd cent. 80q, Apollo, diff. 1st cent. 1.10 l, Earthenware pot (child's head), Tren, 1st cent. 1.20 l, Man's head, Dyrrah, 2.20 l, Eros with Dolphin, statue Bronze Dyrrah, 3rd cent.

1984, Feb. 25 *Perf. 12x12½*

2100	A450	15q	multi	.25	.25
2101	A450	25q	multi	.25	.25
2102	A450	80q	multi	.80	.50
2103	A450	1.10 l	multi	1.20	.75
2104	A450	1.20 l	multi	1.60	.85
2105	A450	2.20 l	multi	2.50	1.00
			Nos. 2100-2105 (6)	6.60	3.60

Clock Towers — A451

1984, Mar. 30 Litho. *Perf. 12*

2106	A451	15q	Gjirokaster	.25	.25
2107	A451	25q	Kavaje	.25	.25
2108	A451	80q	Elbasan	.80	.50
2109	A451	1.10 l	Tirana	1.00	.75
2110	A451	1.20 l	Peqin	1.25	.90
2111	A451	2.20 l	Kruje	2.25	1.50
			Nos. 2106-2111 (6)	5.80	4.15

40th Anniv. of Liberation — A452

15q, Student & microscope. 25q, Guerrilla with flag. 80q, Children with flag. 1.10 l, Soldier. 1.20 l, Workers with flag. 2.20 l, Militia at dam.

1984, Apr. 20 Litho. *Perf. 12*

2112	A452	15q	multi	.25	.25
2113	A452	25q	multi	.25	.25
2114	A452	80q	multi	.90	.45
2115	A452	1.10 l	multi	1.20	.75
2116	A452	1.20 l	multi	1.50	.90
2117	A452	2.20 l	multi	2.25	1.10
			Nos. 2112-2117 (6)	6.35	3.70

Children — A453

15q, Children reading. 25q, Young pioneers. 60q, Gardening. 2.80 l, Kite flying.

1984, May Litho. *Perf. 12*

2118	A453	15q	multicolored	.45	.25
2119	A453	25q	multicolored	1.00	.25
2120	A453	60q	multicolored	1.75	.90
2121	A453	2.80 l	multicolored	3.25	1.60
			Nos. 2118-2121 (4)	6.45	3.00

War Martyrs Type of 1980

Designs: 15q, Manush Almani, Mustafa Matohiti, Kastriot Muco. 25q, Zaho Koka, Reshit Collaku, Maliq Muco. 1.20 l, Lefter Talo, Tom Kola, Fuat Babani. 2.20 l, Myslysm Shyri, Dervish Hexali, Skender Caci.

1984, May 5 Litho. *Perf. 12*

2122	A410	15q	multi	.45	.25
2123	A410	25q	multi	.90	.25
2124	A410	1.20 l	multi	1.60	.90
2125	A410	2.20 l	multi	3.00	2.00
			Nos. 2122-2125 (4)	5.95	3.40

A454

80q, Enver Hoxha. 1.10 l, Resistance fighter.

1984, May 24 Litho. *Perf. 12*

2126	A454	80q	multicolored	2.25	1.50
2127	A454	1.10 l	multicolored	2.75	1.75

40th anniv. of Permet Congress.

A455

15q, Goalkeeper. 25q, Referee. 1.20 l, Map of Europe. 2.20 l, Field diagram.

1984, June 12 Litho. *Perf. 12*

2128	A455	15q	multicolored	1.00	.25
2129	A455	25q	multicolored	1.00	.25
2130	A455	1.20 l	multicolored	3.00	.75
2131	A455	2.20 l	multicolored	3.50	1.50
			Nos. 2128-2131 (4)	8.50	2.75

European soccer championships.

Freedom Came, by Myrteza Fushekati A456

Paintings, Tirana Gallery of Figurative Art: 25q, Morning, by Zamir Mati, vert. 80q, My Darling, by Agim Zajmi, vert. 2.60 l, For the Partisans, by Arben Basha. 1.90 l, Eagle, by Zamir Mati, vert.

1984, June 12 *Perf. 12½*

2132	A456	15q	multi	.40	.25
2133	A456	25q	multi	.80	.35
2134	A456	80q	multi	2.00	1.10
2135	A456	2.60 l	multi	3.25	1.75
			Nos. 2132-2135 (4)	6.45	3.45

Souvenir Sheet

Perf. 12 Horiz.

2136	A456	1.90 l	multi	7.00	3.50

Flora — A457

15q, Moraceae L. 25q, Plantaginaceae L. 1.20 l, Hypericaceae L. 2.20 l, Leontopodium alpinum.

1984, Aug. 20 Litho. *Perf. 12*

2137	A457	15q	multicolored	2.25	.60
2138	A457	25q	multicolored	3.00	1.10
2139	A457	1.20 l	multicolored	8.25	3.50
2140	A457	2.20 l	multicolored	17.00	6.50
			Nos. 2137-2140 (4)	30.50	11.70

AUSIPEX '84, Melbourne, Sept. 21-30 — A458

Perf. 12 Horiz.

1984, Sept. 21 Litho.

2141	A458	1.90 l	Sword dancers, emblem	3.50	3.50

A459

Forestry, logging, UNFAO emblem — 15q, Beech trees, transport. 25q, Pine forest, logging cable. 1.20 l, Firs, sawmill. 2.20 l, Forester clearing woods.

1984, Sept. 25 *Perf. 12*

2142	A459	15q	multi	.80	.45
2143	A459	25q	multi	1.25	.75
2144	A459	1.20 l	multi	4.00	2.50
2145	A459	2.20 l	multi	6.00	3.25
			Nos. 2142-2145 (4)	12.05	6.95

View of Gjirokaster — A460

1984, Oct. 13 *Perf. 12½*

2146	A460	1.20 l	multicolored	2.00	2.00

EURPHILA '84, Rome.

5th National Spartakiad — A461

15q, Soccer. 25q, Women's track & field. 80q, Weight lifting. 2.20 l, Pistol shooting. 1.90 l, Opening ceremony, red flags.

1984, Oct. 19 *Perf. 12*

2147	A461	15q	multicolored	.25	.25
2148	A461	25q	multicolored	.30	.25
2149	A461	80q	multicolored	.75	.30
2150	A461	2.20 l	multicolored	2.10	1.50
			Nos. 2147-2150 (4)	3.40	2.30

Souvenir Sheet

Perf. 12 Horiz.

2151	A461	1.90 l	multicolored	3.50	2.25

November 29 Revolution, 40th Anniv. — A462

80q, Industrial reconstruction. 1.10 l, Natl. flag, partisans.
1.90 l, Gen. Enver Hoxha reading 1944 declaration.

1984, Nov. 29 *Perf. 12*

2152	A462	80q	multicolored	2.00	.75

2153 A462 1.10 l multicolored 2.50 1.00

Souvenir Sheet

Perf. 12 Horiz.

2154 A462 1.90 l multicolored 3.50 3.50

Archaeological Discoveries from Illyria — A463

Designs: 15q, Iron Age water container. 80q, Terra-cotta woman's head, 6th-7th cent. B.C. 1.20 l, Aphrodite, bust, 3rd cent. B.C. 1.70 l, Nike, A.D. 1st-2nd cent. bronze statue.

1985, Feb. 25 ***Perf. 12x12½***

2155	A463	15q multi		.40	.25
2156	A463	80q multi		1.50	.75
2157	A463	1.20 l multi		2.00	.90
2158	A463	1.70 l multi		3.00	1.50
		Nos. 2155-2158 (4)		6.90	3.40

Hysni Kapo (1915-1980), Natl. Labor Party Leader — A464

1985, Mar. 4 ***Perf. 12***

2159	A464	90q red & blk	1.40	1.00
2160	A464	1.10 l chlky bl & blk	1.75	1.50

OLYMPHILEX '85, Lausanne A465

25q, Women's track & field. 60q, Weight lifting. 1.20 l, Soccer. 1.50 l, Women's pistol shooting.

1985, Mar. 18

2161	A465	25q multicolored	.25	.25
2162	A465	60q multicolored	.65	.35
2163	A465	1.20 l multicolored	1.10	.90
2164	A465	1.50 l multicolored	2.00	1.00
		Nos. 2161-2164 (4)	4.00	2.50

Johann Sebastian Bach — A466

80q, Portrait, manuscript. 1.20 l, Eisenach, birthplace.

1985, Mar. 31

2165	A466	80q multicolored	16.00	8.00
2166	A466	1.20 l multicolored	20.00	10.00

Gen. Enver Hoxha (1908-1985) A467

1985, Apr. 11 ***Perf. 12½***

2167 A467 80q multicolored 2.25 1.90

Souvenir Sheet

Imperf

2168 A467 1.90 l multicolored 3.25 3.25

Natl. Frontier Guards, 40th Anniv. — A468

25q, Guardsman, family. 80q, At frontier post.

1985, Apr. 25 ***Perf. 12***

2169	A468	25q multicolored	1.00	.75
2170	A468	80q multicolored	2.75	2.00

War Martyrs Type of 1980

25q, Mitro Xhani (1916-44), Nimete Progonati (1929-44), Kozma Nushi (1909-44). 40q, Ajet Xhindoli (1922-43), Mustafa Kacaci (1903-44), Estref Caka Osaja (1919-44). 60q, Celo Sinani (1929-44), Lt. Ambro Andoni (1920-44), Meleq Gosnishti (1913-44). 1.20 l, Thodhori Mastora (1920-44), Fejzi Micoli (1919-45), Hysen Cino (1920-44).

1985, May 5

2171	A410	25q multi	.55	.35
2172	A410	40q multi	.85	.70
2173	A410	60q multi	1.40	.85
2174	A410	1.20 l multi	2.50	2.00
		Nos. 2171-2174 (4)	5.30	3.90

Victory over Fascism — A469

25q, Rifle, red flag, inscribed May 9. 80q, Hand holding rifle, globe, broken swastika.

1985, May 9

2175	A469	25q multi	*22.50*	*35.00*
2176	A469	80q multi	*60.00*	*90.00*

End of World War II, 40th anniv.

Primary School, by Thoma Malo — A470

Paintings, Tirana Gallery of Figurative Art: 80q, The Heroes, by Hysen Devolli, vert. 90q, In Our Days, by Angjelin Dodmasej, vert. 1.20 l, Going Off to Sow, by Ksenofon Dilo. 1.90 l, Foundry Workers, by Mikel Gurashi.

1985, June 25 ***Perf. 12½***

2177	A470	25q multi	.25	.25
2178	A470	80q multi	1.00	.75
2179	A470	90q multi	1.25	1.00
2180	A470	1.20 l multi	1.60	1.25
		Nos. 2177-2180 (4)	4.10	3.25

Souvenir Sheet

Perf. 12 Horiz.

2181 A470 1.90 l multi 3.25 2.75

Basketball Championships, Spain — A471

Various plays.

1985, July 20 **Litho.** ***Perf. 12***

2182	A471	25q dull bl & blk	.30	.25
2183	A471	80q dull grn & blk	1.10	.35
2184	A471	1.20 l dl vio & blk	1.40	.90
2185	A471	1.60 l dl rose & blk	2.25	1.50
		Nos. 2182-2185 (4)	5.05	3.00

Fruits — A472

1985, Aug. 20

2186	A472	25q Oranges	.40	.25
2187	A472	80q Plums	2.00	1.10
2188	A472	1.20 l Apples	3.25	1.50
2189	A472	1.60 l Cherries	4.00	2.25
		Nos. 2186-2189 (4)	9.65	5.10

Architecture A473

1985, Sept. 20

2190	A473	25q Kruja	.40	.40
2191	A473	80q Gjirokastra	1.90	1.10
2192	A473	1.20 l Berati	2.25	1.50
2193	A473	1.60 l Shkodera	3.00	1.75
		Nos. 2190-2193 (4)	7.55	4.75

Natl. Folk Theater Festival — A474

Various scenes from folk plays.

1985, Oct. 6

2194	A474	25q multi	.40	.25
2195	A474	80q multi	1.10	.75
2196	A474	1.20 l multi	1.50	.90
2197	A474	1.60 l multi	2.00	1.40

Size: 56x82mm

Imperf

2198	A474	1.90 l multi	3.00	2.25
		Nos. 2194-2198 (5)	8.00	5.55

Socialist People's Republic, 40th Anniv. — A475

25q, Natl. crest, vert. 80q, Proclamation, 1946.

1986, Jan. 11 **Litho.** ***Perf. 12½***

2199	A475	25q multicolored	1.50	.75
2200	A475	80q multicolored	3.00	1.50

A476

Designs: 25q, Dam, River Drin, Melgun. 80q, Bust of Enver Hoxha, dam power house.

1986, Feb. 20 ***Perf. 12***

2201	A476	25q multi	*5.50*	2.00
2202	A476	80q multi	*12.00*	7.00

Enver Hoxha hydro-electric power station, Koman.

A477

Flowers: 25q, Gymnospermium shqipetarum. 1.20 l, Leucojum valentinum.

1986, Mar. 20 **Litho.** ***Perf. 12***

2203	A477	25q multi	2.00	1.00
2204	A477	1.20 l multi	8.00	4.00
a.		Pair, #2203-2204	12.00	12.00

Nos. 2203-2204 exist imperf. Value, pair: mint $40, used $35.

A478

Famous Men A479

Designs: 25q, Maxim Gorky, Russian author. 80q, Andre Marie Ampere, French physicist. 1.20 l, James Watt, English inventor of modern steam engine. 2.40 l, Franz Liszt, Hungarian composer.

1986, Apr. 20

2205		Strip of 4	*10.00*	6.50
a.	A478	25q dull red brown	.40	.40
b.	A478	80q dull violet	1.60	1.00
c.	A478	1.20 l blue green	3.00	1.60
d.	A478	2.40 l dull lilac rose	5.75	3.75

Size: 88x72mm

Imperf

2206 A479 1.90 l multi *5.00* 3.00

No. 2206 has central area picturing Gorky, Ampere, Watt and Liszt, perf. 12½.

War Martyrs Type of 1980

25q, Ramiz Aranitasi (1923-43), Inajete Dumi (1924-44) and Laze Nuro Ferraj (1897-1944). 80q, Dine Kalenja (1919-44), Kozma Naska (1921-44), Met Hasa (1929-44) and Fahri Ramadani (1920-44). 1.20 l, Hiqmet Buzi (1927-44), Bajram Tusha (1922-42), Mumin Selami (1923-42) and Hajrfdin Bylyshi (1923-42).

1986, May 5 ***Perf. 12***

2207	A410	25q multi	1.25	1.00
2208	A410	80q multi	3.25	1.60
2209	A410	1.20 l multi	5.25	3.25
		Nos. 2207-2209 (3)	9.75	5.85

A480

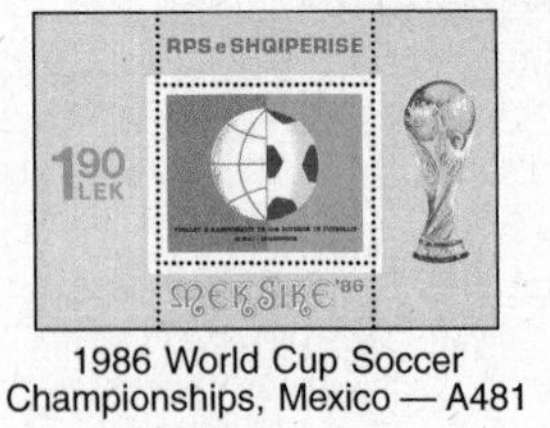

1986 World Cup Soccer Championships, Mexico — A481

25q, Globe, world cup. 1.20 l, Player, soccer ball.

1986, May 31 **Litho.** ***Perf. 12***

2210	A480	25q multicolored	.40	.30
2211	A480	1.20 l multicolored	2.00	1.50

Size: 97x64mm

Imperf

2212	A481	1.90 l multicolored	3.00	2.25
		Nos. 2210-2212 (3)	5.40	4.05

No. 2212 has central label, perf. 12½.

Transportation Workers' Day, 40th Anniv. — A482

1986, Aug. 10 **Litho.** ***Perf. 12***

2213 A482 1.20 l multi 11.00 6.50

Prominent Albanians A483

Designs: 30q, Naim Frasheri (1846-1900), poet. 60q, Ndre Mjeda (1866-1937), poet. 90q, Petro Nini Luarasi (1865-1911), poet, journalist. 1 l, Andon Zako Cajupi (1866-1930), poet. 1.20 l, Millosh Gjergj Nikolla Migjeni (1911-1938), novelist. 2.60 l, Urani Rumbo (1884-1936), educator.

1986, Sept. 20 Litho. *Perf. 12*

2214	A483	30q multi	.55	.30
2215	A483	60q multi	.90	.75
2216	A483	90q multi	1.50	1.00
2217	A483	1 l multi	1.90	1.25
2218	A483	1.20 l multi	2.25	1.50
2219	A483	2.60 l multi	6.00	2.50
		Nos. 2214-2219 (6)	13.10	7.30

Albanian Workers' Party, 9th Congress, Tirana — A484

1986, Nov. 3 Litho. *Perf. 12*

2220	A484	30q multi	*7.50*	5.50

No. 2220 exists with country name misspelled "SHQIPERSIE." Value, mint, $150.

A485

Albanian Workers' Party, 45th Anniv.: 30q, Handstamp, signature of Hoxha. 1.20 l, Marx, Engels, Lenin and Stalin, party building.

1986, Nov. 8

2221	A485	30q multi	*4.00*	1.00
2222	A485	1.20 l multi	*11.00*	3.00

A486

Statue of Mother Albania.

1986, Nov. 29 *Perf. 12x12½*

2223	A486	10q peacock blue	.25	.25
2224	A486	20q henna brn	.25	.25
2225	A486	30q vermilion	.25	.25
2226	A486	50q dk olive bis	.25	.25
2227	A486	60q lt olive grn	.35	.25
2228	A486	80q rose	.25	.25
2229	A486	90q ultra	.50	.25
2230	A486	1.20 l green	1.00	.50
2231	A486	1.60 l red vio	1.25	.60
2232	A486	2.20 l myrtle grn	2.00	1.25
2233	A486	3 l brn org	2.50	1.75
2234	A486	6 l yel bister	5.00	3.25
		Nos. 2223-2234 (12)	13.85	9.10

For surcharges see Nos. 2435-2439.

Artifacts — A487

Designs: 30q, Head of Aesoulapius, 5th cent. B.C. Byllis, marble. 80q, Aphrodite, 3rd cent. B.C., Fier, terracotta. 1 l, Pan, 3rd-2nd cent, B.C., Byllis, bronze. 1.20 l, Jupiter, A.D. 2nd cent., Tirana, limestone.

1987, Feb. 20

2235	A487	30q multi	1.00	.60
2236	A487	80q multi	2.00	1.00
2237	A487	1 l multi	3.00	1.40
2238	A487	1.20 l multi	4.00	2.50
		Nos. 2235-2238 (4)	10.00	5.50

A488

Gun, quill pen, book of the alphabet and: 30q, Monument, vert. 80q, School, Korca. 1.20 l, Students.

1987, Mar. 7 *Perf. 12*

2239	A488	30q multi	.40	.25
2240	A488	80q multi	1.25	.50
2241	A488	1.20 l multi	1.75	1.25
		Nos. 2239-2241 (3)	3.40	2.00

First Albanian school, cent.

A489

Famous Men: 30q, Victor Hugo, French author. 80q, Galileo Galilei, Italian mathematician, philosopher. 90q, Charles Darwin, British biologist. 1.30 l, Miguel Cervantes, Spanish novelist.

1987, Apr. 20

2242	A489	30q multi	.45	.25
2243	A489	80q multi	1.10	.50
2244	A489	90q multi	1.60	1.10
2245	A489	1.30 l multi	2.25	1.75
		Nos. 2242-2245 (4)	5.40	3.60

World Food Day — A490

30q, Forsythia europaea. 90q, Moltkia doerfleri. 2.10 l, Wulfenia baldacii.

1987, May 20

2246	A490	30q multicolored	.55	.30
2247	A490	90q multicolored	1.10	.75
2248	A490	2.10 l multicolored	2.40	2.10
		Nos. 2246-2248 (3)	4.05	3.15

10th Trade Unions Cong. — A491

1987, June 25

2249	A491	1.20 l multi	4.00	3.00

Sowing, by Bujar Asllani A492

Paintings in the Eponymous Museum, Tirana: 30q, The Sustenance of Industry, by Myrteza Fushekati, vert. 80q, The Gifted Partisan, by Skender Kokobobo, vert. 1.20 l, At the Forging Block, by Clirim Ceka.

Perf. 12x12½, 12½x12

1987, July 20 Litho.

2250	A492	30q multi	.50	.40
2251	A492	80q multi	.80	.80
2252	A492	1 l shown	1.20	1.00
2253	A492	1.20 l multi	1.60	1.40
		Nos. 2250-2253 (4)	4.10	3.60

A493

OLYMPHILEX '87, Rome, Aug. 29-Sept. 6 — A494

1987, Aug. 29 Litho. *Perf. 12½*

2254	A493	30q Hammer throw	.40	.40
2255	A493	90q Running	1.25	.80
2256	A493	1.10 l Shot put	1.25	1.00

Size: 85x60mm

2257	A494	1.90 l Runner, globe	2.50	2.00
		Nos. 2254-2257 (4)	5.40	4.20

Famous Men — A495

Designs: 30q, Themistokli Germenji (1871-1917), author, politician. 80q, Bajram Curri (1862-1925), founder of the Albanian League. 90q, Aleks Stavre Drenova (1872-1947), poet. 1.30 l, Gjerasim D. Qiriazi (1861-1894), teacher, journalist.

1987, Sept. 30 *Perf. 12*

2258	A495	30q multi	.25	.25
2259	A495	80q multi	.90	.30
2260	A495	90q multi	1.10	.75
2261	A495	1.30 l multi	1.90	1.50
		Nos. 2258-2261 (4)	4.15	2.80

Albanian Labor Party Congress, Tirana — A496

1987, Oct. 22 Litho. *Perf. 12*

2262	A496	1.20 l multi	5.00	3.50

Natl. Independence, 75th Anniv. — A497

1987, Nov. 27

2263	A497	1.20 l State flag	5.50	4.00

Postal Administration, 75th Anniv. — A498

1987, Dec. 5

2264	A498	90q P.O. emblem	5.00	3.50
2265	A498	1.20 l State seal	7.00	7.00

Art & Literature — A499

Portraits: 30q, Lord Byron (1788-1824), English Poet. 1.20 l, Eugene Delacroix (1798-1863), French painter.

1988, Mar. 10

2266	A499	30q org brn & blk	*4.00*	3.25
2267	A499	1.20 l pale vio & blk	*16.00*	12.50

WHO, 40th Anniv. — A500

1988, Apr. 7

2268	A500	90q multi	*22.50*	20.00
2269	A500	1.20 l multi	*30.00*	25.00

Flowers — A501

Designs: 30q, Sideritis raeseri. 90q, Lunaria telekiana. 2.10 l, Sanguisorba albanica.

1988, May 20 Booklet Stamps

2270	A501	30q multicolored	8.00	5.00
2271	A501	90q multicolored	16.00	11.00
2272	A501	2.10 l multicolored	24.00	16.00
a.		Bklt. pane of 3, plus label	50.00	50.00
		Nos. 2270-2272 (3)	48.00	32.00

10th Women's Federation Congress — A502

1988, June 6

2273	A502	90q blk, red & dark org	21.00	19.00

European Soccer Championships A503

Various athletes.

1.90 l, Goalie designs of Nos. 2274-2276.

1988, June 10

2274	A503	30q multicolored	2.00	2.00
2275	A503	80q multicolored	3.00	3.00
2276	A503	1.20 l multicolored	5.00	5.00

Size: 79x68mm

Imperf

2277	A503	1.90 l multicolored	12.00	12.00
		Nos. 2274-2277 (4)	22.00	22.00

League of Prizren, 110th Anniv. — A504

1988, June 10 Litho. *Perf. 12*

2278	A504	30q Hands	*40.00*	*40.00*
2279	A504	1.20 l House	*70.00*	*70.00*

People's Army, 45th Anniv. — A505

1988, July 10
2280 A505 60q shown *40.00 40.00*
2281 A505 90q Soldier statue *70.00 70.00*

Famous Albanians — A506

Designs: 30q, Mihal Grameno (1871-1931), author. 90q, Bajo Topulli (1868-1930), freedom fighter. 1 l, Murat Toptani (1868-1917), poet. 1.20 l, Jul Variboba, poet.

1988, Aug. 15
2282 A506 30q multi *15.00 15.00*
2283 A506 90q multi *25.00 25.00*
2284 A506 1 l multi *30.00 30.00*
2284A A506 1.20 l multi *40.00 40.00*
Nos. 2282-2284A (4) *110.00 110.00*

Migjeni (1911-1938), Poet — A507

1988, Aug. 26 Litho. *Perf. 12*
2285 A507 90q silver & brown *12.00 12.00*

Ballads — A508

1988, Sept. 5
2286 A508 30q Dede Skurra 10.00 8.00
2287 A508 90q Omeri Iri 25.00 21.00
2288 A508 1.20 l Gjergj Elez Alia 30.00 25.00
Nos. 2286-2288 (3) 65.00 54.00

Folklore Festival Type of 1978

30q, Kerchief Dance. 1.20 l, Dancers with raised arm.

1988, Oct. 6
2289 A388 30q multi *30.00 30.00*
2290 A388 1.20 l multi *110.00 90.00*

Enver Hoxha Museum A510

Perf. 12x12½, 12½x12
1988, Oct. 16 Litho.
2291 A510 90q Portrait, vert. 4.00 4.00
2292 A510 1.20 l shown 6.00 6.00

Hoxha (1908-85), Communist leader.

Monastir Congress, 80th Anniv. — A511

1988, Nov. 14 Litho. *Perf. 12*
2293 A511 60q Scroll *22.50* 20.00
2294 A511 90q Book, building *35.00* 30.00

Locomotives, Map Showing Rail Network — A512

1989, Feb. 28 Litho. *Perf. 12½x12*
2295 A512 30q 1947 .25 .25
2296 A512 90q 1949 .75 .35
2297 A512 1.20 l 1978 1.00 .60
2298 A512 1.80 l 1985 1.60 .75
2299 A512 2.40 l 1988 3.75 1.50
Nos. 2295-2299 (5) 7.35 3.45

Archaeological Treasures — A513

30q, Illyrian grave. 90q, Warrior on horseback.

1989, Mar. 10 Litho. *Perf. 12*
2300 A513 30q blk & tan .25 .25
2301 A513 90q blk & dl grn .90 .75
2302 A513 2.10 l shown 1.50 1.25
Nos. 2300-2302 (3) 2.65 2.25

Folklore — A514

1989, Apr. 5 Litho. *Perf. 12x12½*
2303 A514 30q multicolored .45 .25
2304 A514 80q multi, diff. .90 .50
2305 A514 1 l multi, diff. .90 .75
2306 A514 1.20 l multi, diff. 1.25 1.10
Nos. 2303-2306 (4) 3.50 2.60

Flowers — A515

Designs: 30q, Aster albanicus. 90q, Orchis x paparisti. 2.10 l, Orchis albanica.

1989, May 10 *Perf. 12*
2307 A515 30q multicolored .75 .30
2308 A515 90q multicolored 3.25 1.10
2309 A515 2.10 l multicolored 5.25 1.75
Nos. 2307-2309 (3) 9.25 3.15

Famous People — A516

Designs: 30q, Johann Strauss the Younger (1825-1899), composer. 80q, Marie Curie (1867-1834), chemist. 1 l, Federico Garcia Lorca (1898-1936), poet. 1.20 l, Albert Einstein (1879-1955), physicist.

1989, June 3
2310 A516 30q gold & blk brn .35 .25
2311 A516 80q gold & blk brn .75 .45
2312 A516 1 l gold & blk brn 1.10 .90
2313 A516 1.20 l gold & blk brn 1.50 1.25
a. Block of 4, #2310-2313 5.50 4.75
Nos. 2310-2313 (4) 3.70 2.85

6th Congress of Albanian Democratic Front — A517

1989, June 26
2314 A517 1.20 l multicolored 7.25 4.00

French Revolution, Bicent. — A518

90q, Storming of the Bastille. 1.20 l, Statue.

1989, July 7 Litho. *Perf. 12½*
2315 A518 90q multicolored .65 .45
2316 A518 1.20 l shown 1.20 .75

Illyrian Ship — A519

80q, Caravel. 90q, 3-masted schooner. 1.30 l, Modern cargo ship.

1989, July 25 *Perf. 12*
2317 A519 30q shown .35 .25
2318 A519 80q multicolored .70 .50
2319 A519 90q multicolored .70 .70
2320 A519 1.30 l multicolored 1.00 1.00
Nos. 2317-2320 (4) 2.75 2.45

A520

Famous Men: 30q, Pjeter Bogdani (1625-1689), writer. 80q, Gavril Dara (1826-1889), poet. 90q, Thimi Mitko (1820-1890), writer. 1.30 l, Kole Idromeno (1860-1939), painter.

1989, Aug. 30 Litho. *Perf. 12*
2321 A520 30q multicolored .25 .25
2322 A520 80q multicolored .55 .30
2323 A520 90q multicolored .95 .60
2324 A520 1.30 l multicolored 1.60 .75
Nos. 2321-2324 (4) 3.35 1.90

A521

1989, Sept. 29
2325 A521 90q shown .70 .60
2326 A521 1.20 l Workers 1.00 .50

First Communist International, 125th anniv.

Spartakiad Games — A522

1989, Oct. 27 *Perf. 12x12½*
2327 A522 30q Gymnastics .25 .25
2328 A522 80q Soccer .50 .25
2329 A522 1 l Cycling .55 .45
2330 A522 1.20 l Running .85 .75
Nos. 2327-2330 (4) 2.15 1.70

Miniature Sheet

45th Anniv. of Liberation — A523

1989, Nov. 29 *Perf. 12x12½*
2331 A523 Sheet of 4 4.25 4.25
a. 30q Revolutionary .50 .25
b. 80q "45" 1.00 .30
c. 1 l Coat of arms 1.00 .50
d. 1.20 l Workers 1.00 .85

Rupicapra Rupicapra — A524

1990, Mar. 15 *Perf. 12*
2332 A524 10q Two adults .25 .25
2333 A524 30q Adult, kid .55 .25
2334 A524 80q Adult 1.60 .75
2335 A524 90q Adult head 1.60 1.00
a. Block of 4, #2332-2335 6.00 6.00

World Wildlife Fund.

Tribal Masks — A525

1990, Apr. 4 *Perf. 12x12½*
2336 A525 30q shown .30 .30
2337 A525 90q multi, diff. .65 .40
2338 A525 1.20 l multi, diff. .90 .55
2339 A525 1.80 l multi, diff. 1.40 .80
Nos. 2336-2339 (4) 3.25 2.05

Mushrooms A526

30q, Amanita caesarea. 90q, Lepiota procera. 1.20 l, Boletus edulis. 1.80 l, Clathrus cancelatus.

1990, Apr. 28 Litho. *Perf. 12*
2340 A526 30q multicolored .25 .25
2341 A526 90q multicolored .50 .40
2342 A526 1.20 l multicolored .85 .80
2343 A526 1.80 l multicolored 1.20 1.00
Nos. 2340-2343 (4) 2.80 2.45

First Postage Stamp, 150th Anniv. — A527

1990, May 6 *Perf. 12*
2344 A527 90q shown .45 .45
2345 A527 1.20 l Post rider .90 .90
2346 A527 1.80 l Carriage 1.75 1.25
a. Bklt. pane of 3, #2344-2346 + label 3.50
Nos. 2344-2346 (3) 3.10 2.60

World Cup Soccer, Italy — A528

1990, June Litho. *Perf. 12*
2347 A528 30q multicolored .30 .30
2348 A528 90q multi, diff. .65 .65
2349 A528 1.20 l multi, diff. 1.10 .90

Size: 80x63mm

Imperf

2350 A528 3.30 l multi, diff. 3.25 3.25
Nos. 2347-2350 (4) 5.30 5.10

Vincent Van Gogh, Death Cent. — A529

Self portraits and: 30q, Details from various paintings. 90q, Woman in field. 2.10 l, Asylum. 2.40 l, Self-portrait.

1990, July 27

2351 A529 30q multicolored .40 .40
2352 A529 90q multicolored .80 .80
2353 A529 2.10 l multicolored 1.75 1.75

Size: 87x73mm

Imperf

2354 A529 2.40 l multicolored 4.00 4.00
Nos. 2351-2354 (4) 6.95 6.95

Albanian Folklore A530

Scenes from medieval folktale of "Gjergj Elez Alia": 30q, Alia lying wounded. 90q, Alia being helped onto horse. 1.20 l, Alia fighting Bajloz. 1.80 l, Alia on horseback over severed head of Bajloz.

1990, Aug. 30 ***Perf. 12½x12***

2355 A530 30q multicolored .30 .30
2356 A530 90q multicolored .70 .40
2357 A530 1.20 l multicolored 1.00 .80
2358 A530 1.80 l multicolored 1.50 1.00
Nos. 2355-2358 (4) 3.50 2.50

Founding of Berat, 2400th Anniv. — A531

Designs: 30q, Xhamia E Plumbit. 90q, Kisha E Shen Triadhes. 1.20 l, Ura E Beratit. 1.80 l, Onufri-Piktor Mesjetar. 2.40 l, Nikolla-Piktor Mesjetar.

1990, Sept. 20 ***Perf. 12½***

2359 Block of 5 + 4 labels 5.00 5.00
a. A531 30q multi .25 .25
b. A531 90q multi .25 .25
c. A531 1.20 l multi .60 .60
d. A531 1.80 l multi 1.00 1.00
e. A531 2.40 l multi 1.25 1.25

No. 2359 was sold in souvenir folders for 9.90 l.

Illyrian Heroes — A532

1990, Oct. 20 ***Perf. 12***

2360 A532 30q Pirroja .25 .25
2361 A532 90q Teuta .50 .50
2362 A532 1.20 l Bato .75 .75
2363 A532 1.80 l Bardhyli 1.00 1.00
Nos. 2360-2363 (4) 2.50 2.50

Intl. Literacy Year — A533

1990, Oct. 30

2364 A533 90q lt bl & multi .65 .60
2365 A533 1.20 l pink & multi .90 .90

Albanian Horseman by Eugene Delacroix — A534

Designs: 1.20 l, Albanian Woman by Camille Corot. 1.80 l, Skanderbeg by unknown artist.

1990, Nov. 30 ***Perf. 12x12½***

2366 A534 30q multicolored .30 .30
2367 A534 1.20 l multicolored .90 .70
2368 A534 1.80 l multicolored 1.25 1.00
Nos. 2366-2368 (3) 2.45 2.00

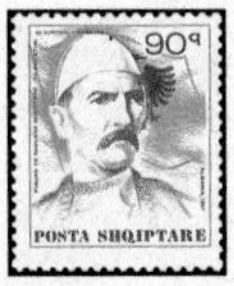

A535

1.20 l, Boletini standing.

1991, Jan. 23 Litho. ***Perf. 12x12½***

2369 A535 90q shown .60 .50
2370 A535 1.20 l multicolored .90 .70

Isa Boletini (1864-1916), freedom fighter.

A536

1991, Jan. 30 Litho. ***Perf. 12***

Background Color

2371 A536 90q pale yellow .60 .50
2372 A536 1.20 l pale gray .90 .70

Arberi State, 800th anniv.

Pierre Auguste Renoir (1841-1919), Painter — A537

Paintings: 30q, Girl Reading, 1876, vert. 90q, The Swing, 1876, vert. 1.20 l, Boating Party, 1868-1869. 1.80 l, Flowers and grapes, 1878. 3 l, Self-portrait.

1991, Feb. 25 ***Perf. 12½x12***

2373 A537 30q multicolored .50 .25
2374 A537 90q multicolored .75 .50
2375 A537 1.20 l multicolored 1.10 .90
2376 A537 1.80 l multicolored 1.75 1.40

Size: 95x75mm

Imperf

2377 A537 3 l multicolored 4.00 4.00
Nos. 2373-2377 (5) 8.10 7.05

Flowers — A538

30q, Cistus albanicus. 90q, Trifolium pilczii. 1.80 l, Lilium albanicum.

1991, Mar. 30 ***Perf. 12***

2378 A538 30q multicolored .30 .30
2379 A538 90q multicolored .70 .70
2380 A538 1.80 l multicolored 1.40 1.00
Nos. 2378-2380 (3) 2.40 2.00

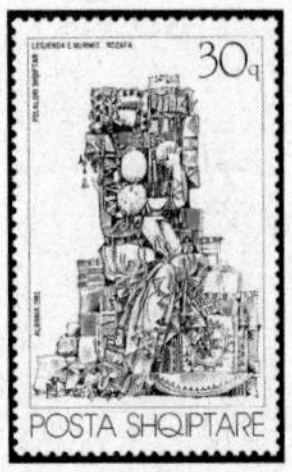

Legend of Rozafa — A539

Various scenes from legend.

1991, Sept. 30 Litho. ***Perf. 12x12½***

2381 A539 30q multicolored .30 .30
2382 A539 90q multicolored .50 .30
2383 A539 1.20 l multicolored 1.00 .70
2384 A539 1.80 l multicolored 1.40 1.20
Nos. 2381-2384 (4) 3.20 2.50

For surcharges see Nos. 2586, 2604.

Wolfgang Amadeus Mozart, Death Bicent. — A540

1991, Oct. 5 Litho. ***Perf. 12***

2385 A540 90q Conducting .75 .45
2386 A540 1.20 l Portrait 1.00 .70
2387 A540 1.80 l Playing piano 1.60 1.20

Size: 89x70mm

Imperf

2388 A540 3 l Medal, score 4.00 4.00
Nos. 2385-2388 (4) 7.35 6.35

Airplanes A541

Designs: 30q, Glider, Otto Lilienthal, 1896. 80q, Avion III, Clement Ader, 1897. 90q, Flyer, Wright Brothers, 1903. 1.20 l, Concorde. 1.80 l, Tupolev 114. 2.40 l, Dornier 31 E.

1992, Jan. 27 Litho. ***Perf. 12½x12***

2389 A541 30q multicolored .30 .30
2390 A541 80q multicolored .45 .35
2391 A541 90q multicolored .65 .55
2392 A541 1.20 l multicolored .90 .65
2393 A541 1.80 l multicolored .90 .65
2394 A541 2.40 l multicolored 1.40 1.20
Nos. 2389-2394 (6) 4.60 3.70

No. 2393 misidentifies a Tupolev 144.

Explorers A542

1992, Jan. 10

2395 A542 30q Bering .30 .30
2396 A542 90q Columbus .70 .30
2397 A542 1.80 l Magellan 1.50 .90
Nos. 2395-2397 (3) 2.50 1.50

1992 Winter Olympics, Albertville — A543

30q, Ski jumping. 90q, Cross country skiing. 1.20 l, Pairs figure skating. 1.80 l, Luge.

1992, Feb. 15 Litho. ***Perf. 12½***

2398 A543 30q multicolored .30 .30
2399 A543 90q multicolored .60 .45
2400 A543 1.20 l multicolored .90 .60
2401 A543 1.80 l multicolored 1.40 1.00
Nos. 2398-2401 (4) 3.20 2.35

For surcharge see No. 2598.

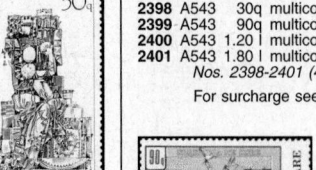

Participation of Albania in Conference on Security and Cooperation in Europe, Berlin (1991) — A544

1992, Mar. 31 Litho. ***Perf. 12½x12***

2402 A544 90q shown .85 .85
2403 A544 1.20 l Flags, map 1.10 1.10
a. Pair, #2402-2403 3.50 3.50

Dated 1991. Issued in sheets containing 2 No. 2403a, 3 each Nos. 2402-2403 + 2 labels. No. 2402 was also issued in sheets of 16.

Albanian Admission to CEPT — A545

90q, Envelopes, CEPT emblem.

1992, Apr. 25 Litho. ***Perf. 12½***

2404 A545 90q blk, blue & red lil .90 .90
2405 A545 1.20 l blk, pur & red lil 1.20 1.20
a. Pair, #2404-2405 2.25 2.25

Issued in sheets containing 2 No. 2405a, 3 each Nos. 2404-2405 and 2 labels.

Martyrs' Day A546

90q, Freedom flame, vert. 4.10 l, Flowers.

1992, May 5 ***Perf. 12x12½***

2406 A546 90q multicolored .50 .50

Perf. 12½x12

2407 A546 4.10 l multicolored 2.50 2.00

European Soccer Championships, Sweden'92 A547

Various stylized designs of soccer plays.

1992, June 10 Litho. ***Perf. 12***

2408 A547 30q green & lt grn .50 .25
2409 A547 90q blue & pink 1.00 .50
2410 A547 10.80 l henna & tan 6.00 3.75

Size: 90x70mm

Imperf

2411 A547 5 l tan, lt green & pink 4.00 4.00
Nos. 2408-2411 (4) 11.50 8.50

1992 Summer Olympics, Barcelona A548

1992, June 14 Litho. ***Perf. 12***

2412 A548 30q Tennis .35 .35
2413 A548 90q Baseball 1.00 .55
2414 A548 1.80 l Table tennis 2.00 1.50

Size: 90x70mm

Imperf

2415 A548 5 l Torch bearer 4.00 4.00
Nos. 2412-2415 (4) 7.35 6.40

United Europe — A549

1992, July 10 Litho. *Perf. 12*

2416	A549	1.20 l	multicolored	1.10	.75

Horses — A550

30q, Native. 90q, Nonius. 1.20 l, Arabian, vert. 10.60 l, Haflinger, vert.

1992, Aug. 10 Litho. *Perf. 12*

2417	A550	30q	multicolored	.25	.25
2418	A550	90q	multicolored	.40	.40
2419	A550	1.20 l	multicolored	.55	.55
2420	A550	10.60 l	multicolored	5.25	4.25
			Nos. 2417-2420 (4)	6.45	5.45

For surcharge, see No. 2781.

Discovery of America, 500th Anniv. — A551

Map of North and South America and: 60q, Columbus, sailing ships. 3.20 l, Columbus meeting natives. 5 l, Map, Columbus.

1992, Aug. 20

2421	A551	60q	blk, bl & gray	*.45*	*.45*
2422	A551	3.20 l	blk, brn & gray	*3.25*	*3.25*

Size: 90x70mm

Imperf

2423	A551	5 l	multi	*70.00*	*70.00*

Mother Theresa, Infant — A552

1992, Oct. 4 Litho. *Perf. 12x12½*

2424	A552	40q	fawn	.30	.30
2425	A552	60q	brown	.30	.30
2426	A552	1 l	violet	.30	.30
2427	A552	1.80 l	gray	.30	.30
2428	A552	2 l	red	.30	.30
2429	A552	2.40 l	green	.30	.30
2430	A552	3.20 l	blue	.40	.40
2431	A552	5.60 l	rose violet	.60	.60
2432	A552	7.20 l	olive	1.00	1.00
2433	A552	10 l	org brn	1.25	1.25
			Nos. 2424-2433 (10)	5.05	5.05

See Nos. 2472-2476.
For surcharge, see No. 2786.

A553

1993, Apr. 25 Litho. *Perf. 12*

2434	A553	16 l	multicolored	2.50	2.50

Visit of Pope John Paul II.

Nos. 2223-2226, 2229 Surcharged

1993, May 2 Litho. *Perf. 12x12½*

2435	A486	3 l	on 10q	.25	.25
2436	A486	6.50 l	on 20q	.55	.55
2437	A486	13 l	on 30q	1.60	1.60
2438	A486	20 l	on 90q	2.40	2.40
2439	A486	30 l	on 50q	3.25	3.25
			Nos. 2435-2439 (5)	8.05	8.05

Lef Nosi (1873-1945), Minister of Posts — A554

1993, May 5 Litho. *Perf. 12*

2440	A554	6.50 l	ol brn & bister	.90	.90

First Albanian postage stamps, 80th anniv.

Europa — A555

Contemporary paintings by: 3 l, A. Zajmi, vert. 7 l, E. Hila. 20 l, B. Ahmeti-Peizazh.

1993, May 28 Litho. *Perf. 12*

2441	A555	3 l	multicolored	.90	.90
2442	A555	7 l	multicolored	3.50	3.50

Size: 116x122mm

2443	A555	20 l	multicolored	6.50	6.50
			Nos. 2441-2443 (3)	10.90	10.90

1993 Mediterranean Games, France — A556

3 l, Running. 16 l, Kayaking. 21 l, Cycling. 20 l, Mediterranean map.

1993, June 20 Litho. *Perf. 12*

2444	A556	3 l	multicolored	.30	.30
2445	A556	16 l	multicolored	1.75	1.75
2446	A556	21 l	multicolored	2.40	2.40

Size: 111x78mm

Imperf

2447	A556	20 l	multicolored	3.25	3.25
			Nos. 2444-2447 (4)	7.70	7.70

For surcharge, see No. 2789.

Frang Bardhi, Author, 350th Death Anniv. — A557

1993, Aug. 20 Litho. *Perf. 12x12½*

2448	A557	6.50 l	shown	1.10	1.10

Size: 89x101mm

Imperf

2449	A557	20 l	Writing at desk	3.50	3.50

A558

68 l, Mascot, ball, US map.

1994, July 17 Litho. *Perf. 12*

2450	A558	42 l	shown	1.10	1.10
2451	A558	68 l	multicolored	1.60	1.60

1994 World Cup Soccer Championships, US.

A559

European Inventors, Discoveries: 50 l, Gjovalin Gjadri, engineer. 100 l, Karl von Ghega, Austrian engineer. 150 l, Sketch of road project.

1994, Dec. 31 Litho. *Perf. 14*

2452	A559	50 l	multicolored	1.50	1.50
2453	A559	100 l	multicolored	2.25	2.25

Size: 50x70mm

Imperf

2454	A559	150 l	multicolored	3.75	3.75
			Nos. 2452-2454 (3)	7.50	7.50

Europa (No. 2454).

Ali Pasa of Tepelene (Lion of Janina) (1744-1822) A560

1995, Jan. 28 *Perf. 14*

2455	A560	60 l	shown	1.40	1.40

Size: 70x50mm

Imperf

2456	A560	100 l	Tepelene Palace	2.50	2.50

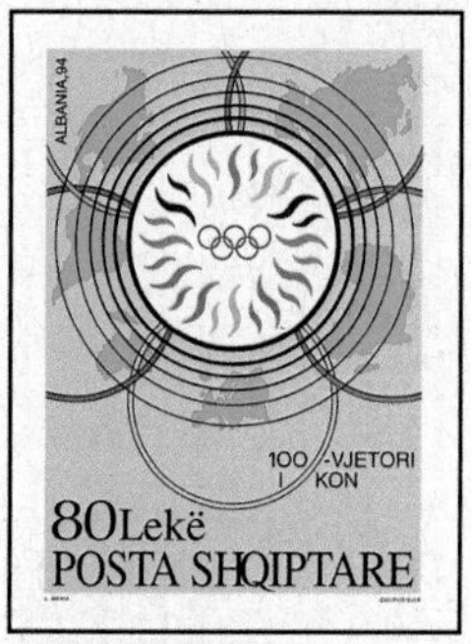

Intl. Olympic Committee, Cent. — A561

1995, Feb. 2 *Imperf.*

2457	A561	80 l	multicolored	2.25	2.25

Karl Benz (1844-1929), Automobile Pioneer — A562

Designs: 5 l, Automobile company emblem, Benz. 10 l, Modern Mercedes Benz automobile. 60 l, First four-wheel Benz 1886 motor car. 125 l, Pre-war Mercedes touring car.

1995, Jan. 21 Litho. *Perf. 14*

2458	A562	5 l	multicolored	.30	.30
2459	A562	10 l	multicolored	.30	.30
2460	A562	60 l	multicolored	.90	.90
2461	A562	125 l	multicolored	3.00	3.00
			Nos. 2458-2461 (4)	4.50	4.50

Liberation, 50th Anniv. (in 1994) — A563

1995, Jan. 28 Litho. *Perf. 14*

2462	A563	50 l	black, gray & red	1.25	1.25

Dated 1994.

Miniature Sheet

Albania '93 A564

Composers: a, 3 l, Wagner. b, 6.50 l, Grieg. c, 11 l, Gounod. d, 20 l, Tchaikovsky.

1995, Jan. 26 *Perf. 12*

2463	A564	Sheet of 4, #a.-d.		2.50	2.50

Voskopoja Academy, 250th Anniv. — A565

Buildings of Voskopoja.

1995, Feb. 2

2464		42 l	multicolored	.90	.90
2465		68 l	multicolored	2.25	2.25
a.	A565		Pair, #2464-2465	3.50	3.50

Bleta Apricula — A566

5 l, On flower. 10 l, Honeycomb, bee. 25 l, Emerging from cell of honeycomb.

1995, Aug. 20 Litho. *Perf. 12*

2466	A566	5 l	multicolored	.30	.30
2467	A566	10 l	multicolored	.30	.30
2468	A566	25 l	multicolored	1.25	1.25
			Nos. 2466-2468 (3)	1.85	1.85

Peace & Freedom — A567

Stylized hands reaching for: 50 l, Olive branch. 100 l, Peace dove.
150 l, Stylized person.

1995, Aug. 10 *Perf. 13½x14*

2469	A567	50 l	multicolored	1.75	1.75
2470	A567	100 l	multicolored	3.50	3.50

Size: 80x60mm

Imperf

2471	A567	150 l	multicolored	5.00	5.00
			Nos. 2469-2471 (3)	10.25	10.25

Europa.
For surcharges, see Nos. B39-B40.

Mother Teresa Type of 1992

1994-95 Litho. *Perf. 12x12½*

2472	A552	5 l	violet	.30	.30
2473	A552	18 l	orange	1.10	1.10
2474	A552	20 l	rose lilac	.45	.45
2475	A552	25 l	green	1.75	1.75
2476	A552	60 l	olive	1.75	1.75
			Nos. 2472-2476 (5)	5.35	5.35

Issued: 20 l, 1994; 60 l, 1995; others, 7/94.

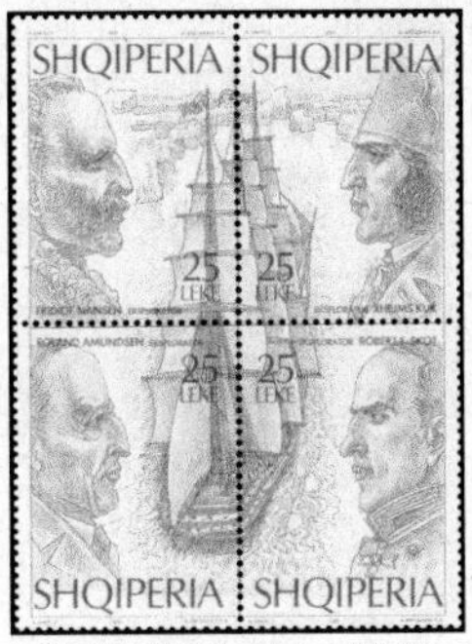

Arctic Explorers — A568

Designs: a, Fridtjof Nansen (1861-1930), Norway. b, James Cook (1728-79), England. c, Roald Amundsen (1872-1928), Norway. d, Robert F. Scott (1872-1928), Great Britain.

1995, Sept. 14 Litho. ***Perf. 13½x14***

2477 A568 25 l Block of 4, #a.-d. 3.50 3.50

For surcharges, see No. 2790.

UN, 50th Anniv. — A569

100 l, Like #2478, flags streaming to right.

1995, Sept. 14 Litho. ***Perf. 14x13½***

2478 A569 2 l shown .25 .25
2479 A569 100 l multicolored 2.40 1.90

For surcharge, see No. 2782.

Poets — A570

1995 ***Perf. 13½x14***

2480 A570 25 l Paul Éluard .65 .65
2481 A570 50 l Sergei Yesenin 1.25 1.25
a. Pair, #2480-2481 2.00 2.00

Entry into Council of Europe — A571

Designs: 25 l, Doves flying from headquarters, Strasbourg. 85 l, Albanian eagle over map of Europe.

1995 ***Perf. 14x13½***

2482 A571 25 l multicolored .90 .90
2483 A571 85 l multicolored 3.25 3.25

For surcharge see No. 2583

Jan Kukuzeli, Composer — A572

Stylized figure: 18 l, Writing. 20 l, Holding hand to head. 100 l, Holding up scroll of paper.

1995, Oct. 17 ***Perf. 13½x14***

2484 A572 18 l multicolored .50 .50
2485 A572 20 l multicolored .50 .50

Size: 74x74mm

2486 A572 100 l multicolored 2.75 2.75
Nos. 2484-2486 (3) 3.75 3.75

For surcharge, see No. 2787.

World Tourism Organization, 20th Anniv. — A573

Stylized designs: 18 l, Church, saint holding scroll. 20 l, City, older buildings. 42 l, City, modern buildings.

1995, Oct. 17

2487 A573 18 l multicolored .50 .50
2488 A573 20 l multicolored .70 .65
2489 A573 42 l multicolored 1.50 1.40
Nos. 2487-2489 (3) 2.70 2.55

For surcharge, see No. 2788.

Fables of Jean de la Fontaine (1621-95) — A574

Designs: 2 l, Raptor, turtle, wolf, goose, mouse, lion, rats. 3 l, Crow, goose, dog, foxes. 25 l, Insect, doves, frogs. 60 l, Drawings of Da la Fontaine, animals, birds.

1995, Aug. 20 Litho. ***Perf. 14x13½***

2490 A574 2 l multicolored .25 .25
2491 A574 3 l multicolored .25 .25
2492 A574 25 l multicolored .50 .50

Imperf

Size: 73x56mm

2493 A574 60 l multicolored 2.00 2.00
Nos. 2490-2493 (4) 3.00 3.00

For surcharges, see Nos. 2783, 2784, 2791.

Folklore Festival, Berat — A575

Stylized designs: 5 l, Men's choir. 50 l, Costumed woman seated in chair.

1995, Oct. 17 Litho. ***Perf. 13½x14***

2494 A575 5 l multicolored .25 .25
2495 A575 50 l multicolored 1.20 1.20

Motion Pictures, Cent. — A576

1995, Nov. 17

2496 A576 10 l Louis Lumiere .25 .25
2497 A576 85 l Auguste Lumiere 1.50 1.50
a. Pair, #2496-2497 2.00 2.00

Elvis Presley (1935-77) — A577

1995, Nov. 20 Litho. ***Perf. 14x13½***

2498 A577 3 l orange & multi .30 .30
2499 A577 60 l green & multi 1.75 1.75

For surcharge, see No. 2785.

A578

1995, Nov. 25 ***Perf. 13½x14***

2500 A578 10 l 1925 Bank notes .30 .30
2501 A578 25 l 1995 Bank notes .80 .80

National Bank, 70th anniv.

A579

50 l, Maiden planting tree.

1995, Nov. 27 Litho. ***Perf. 13½x14***

2502 A579 5 l shown .25 .25
2503 A579 50 l multicolored 1.50 1.50

Democracy, 5th anniv.

A580

Designs: 25 l, Soccer ball, British flag, map of Europe, stadium. 100 l, Soccer ball, player.

1996, June 4 ***Perf. 14***

2504 A580 25 l multicolored .50 .50
2505 A580 100 l multicolored 2.25 2.25

Euro '96, European Soccer Championships, Great Britain.

For surcharge, see No. 2792.

Mother Teresa — A581

150 l, Mother Teresa, diff.

1996, May 5 ***Perf. 13½x14***

2506 A581 25 l blue & multi 1.00 1.00
2507 A581 100 l red & multi 2.50 2.50

Size: 52x74mm

Imperf

2508 A581 150 l multi 6.25 6.25
Nos. 2506-2508 (3) 9.75 9.75

Europa. For overprints see Nos. 2551, 2582.

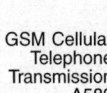

GSM Cellular Telephone Transmission A582

Designs: 10 l, Satellite transmitting signals. 60 l, Uses for cellular telephone, vert.

Perf. 13x13½, 13½x13

1996, Aug. 1 Litho.

2509 A582 10 l multicolored .25 .25
2510 A582 60 l multicolored 1.50 1.50

1996 Summer Olympic Games, Atlanta — A583

Stylized designs: 5 l, Runners. 25 l, Throwers. 60 l, Jumpers. 100 l, Emblem, US flag.

1996, Aug. 3 Litho. ***Perf. 13x14***

2511 A583 5 l multicolored .25 .25
2512 A583 25 l multicolored .55 .55
2513 A583 60 l multicolored 1.50 1.50

Size: 52x37mm

Imperf

2514 A583 100 l multicolored 2.25 2.25
Nos. 2511-2514 (4) 4.55 4.55

Gottfried Wilhelm Leibniz (1646-1716), Mathematician A584

85 l, René Descartes (1596-1650), mathematician.

1996, Sept. 20 Litho. ***Perf. 14***

2515 A584 10 l multicolored .40 .40
2516 A584 85 l multicolored 2.00 2.00

Paintings by Francisco Goya (1746-1828) A585

Designs: 10 l, The Naked Maja. 60 l, Dona Isabel Cobos de Porcel. 100 l, Self portrait.

1996, Sept. 25 ***Perf. 14x13½***

2517 A585 10 l multicolored .30 .30
2518 A585 60 l multicolored 1.40 1.40

Souvenir Sheet

2519 A585 100 l multicolored 2.50 2.50

Religious Engravings — A586

Designs: a, 5 l, Book cover showing crucifixion, angels. b, 25 l, Medallion of crucifixion. c, 85 l, Book cover depicting life of Christ.

1996, Nov. 5 ***Perf. 13x13½***

2520 A586 Block of 3, #a.-c. + label 2.75 2.75

UNICEF, 50th Anniv. — A587

Children's paintings: 5 l, Fairy princess. 10 l, Doll, sun. 25 l, Sea life. 50 l, House, people.

1996, Nov. 11 ***Perf. 13½***

2521 A587 5 l multicolored .25 .25
2522 A587 10 l multicolored .25 .25
2523 A587 25 l multicolored .80 .80
2524 A587 50 l multicolored 1.20 1.20
Nos. 2521-2524 (4) 2.50 2.50

Gjergj Fishta (1871-1940), Writer, Priest — A588

60 l, Battle scene, portrait.

1996, Dec. 20 ***Perf. 13½x14***

2525 A588 10 l shown .25 .25
2526 A588 60 l multicolored 1.40 1.40

Omar Khayyam — A589

1997, Mar. 6 *Perf. 14*

2527 A589 20 l shown .50 .50
2528 A589 50 l Portrait, diff. 1.10 1.10

A590

1997, Mar. 20 *Perf. 14x14½*

2529 A590 20 l Portrait .40 .40
2530 A590 60 l Printing press 1.20 1.20
a. Pair, #2529-2530 1.75 1.75

Johannes Gutenberg (1397?-1468).

A591

The Azure Eye (Stories and Legends): 30 l, Dragon on rock looking at warrior, donkey. 100 l, Dragon drinking water from pond, warrior.

1997, May 5 Litho. *Perf. 13x14*

2531 A591 30 l multicolored .70 .70
2532 A591 100 l multicolored 2.25 2.25

Europa.

A592

1997, Apr. 10 *Perf. 14*

2533 10 l Pelicanus crispus .25 .25
2534 80 l Pelicans, diff. 1.40 1.40
a. A592 Pair, #2533-2534 2.50 2.50

No. 2534a is a continuous design.

A593

1997, June 25 Litho. *Perf. 14*

2535 A593 10 l blk & dark brn .25 .25
2536 A593 25 l blk & blue blk .75 .75

Souvenir Sheet

2537 A593 80 l gray brown 2.00 2.00

Faik Konica (1875-1942), writer and politician.

No. 2537 contains one 22x26mm stamp.

A594

1997 Mediterranean Games, Bari: 20 l, Man running. 30 l, Woman running, 3-man canoe. 100 l, Man breaking finish line, silhouettes of man and woman.

1997, June 13

2538 A594 20 l multicolored .40 .40
2539 A594 30 l multicolored .80 .80

Size: 52x74mm

Imperf

2540 A594 100 l multicolored 2.00 2.00

Skanderbeg — A595

1997, Aug. 25 Litho. *Perf. 13*

2541 A595 5 l red brn & red .25 .25
2542 A595 10 l dp ol & ol .25 .25
2543 A595 20 l dp grn & grn .40 .40
2544 A595 25 l dp mag & red lil .50 .50
2545 A595 30 l dk vio & vio .60 .60
2546 A595 50 l black .85 .85
2547 A595 60 l brn & lt brn 1.00 1.00
2548 A595 80 l dk brown & brn 1.60 1.60
2549 A595 100 l dk red brown & red brn 1.90 1.90
2550 A595 110 l dark blue 2.10 2.10
Nos. 2541-2550 (10) 9.45 9.45

No. 2507 Ovptd. in Silver "HOMAZH / 1910-1997"

1997 *Perf. 13½x14*

2551 A581 100 l red & multi 2.50 2.50

Religious Manuscripts — A596

Albanian Codex: a, 10 l, 11th cent. b, 25 l, 6th cent. c, 60 l, 6th cent., diff.

1997, Nov. 15 Litho. *Perf. 13x14*

2552 A596 Block of 3, #a.-c. + label 2.25 2.25

See No. 2575.

Post and Telecommunications Administration, 85th Anniv. — A597

1997, Dec. 4 *Perf. 13½*

2553 A597 10 l multi .25 .25
2554 A597 30 l multi, diff. .75 .75

A598

1998, Mar. 25 Litho. *Perf. 14*

2555 A598 30 l red brn & multi .60 .60
2556 A598 100 l tan & multi 1.90 1.90
a. Pair, #2555-2556 2.50 2.50

Nikete Dardani, musician.

A599

Legends of Pogradec Ohrid Lake: a, 30 l, Old man seated at table. b, 50 l, Three Graces. c, 60 l, Two women, fountain. d, 80 l, Iceman.

1998, Apr. 15

2557 A599 Block of 4, #a.-d. 3.50 3.50

A600

1998, May 5 Litho. *Perf. 13x14*

2558 A600 60 l shown 1.50 1.50
2559 A600 100 l multi, diff. 2.25 2.25

Size: 50x72mm

Imperf

2560 A600 150 l multi, diff. 3.50 3.50

Europa (folk festivals).

A601

Albanian League of Prizren, 120th anniv.: a, 30 l, Abdyl Frasheri. b, 50 l, Sulejman Vokshi. c, 60 l, Iljaz Pashe Dibra. d, 80 l, Ymer Prizreni.

1998, June 10 Litho. *Perf. 13½x13*

2561 A601 Block of 4, #a.-d. 2.75 2.75

1998 World Cup Soccer Championships, France — A602

Stylized soccer players.

1998, June 10 *Perf. 13½*

2562 A602 60 l multicolored 1.00 1.00
2563 A602 100 l multicolored 2.00 2.00

Size: 50x73mm

Imperf

2564 A602 120 l Mascot 2.25 2.25

European Youth Greco-Roman Wrestling Championships, Albania — A603

1998, July 5 *Perf. 13½*

2565 A603 30 l shown .50 .50
2566 A603 60 l Wrestlers, diff. 1.00 1.00
a. Pair, #2565-2566 1.60 1.60

Eqerem Cabej (1908-1980), Albanian Etymologist — A604

1998, Aug. 7 *Perf. 14*

2567 A604 60 l yel brn & multi .80 .80
2568 A604 80 l brn red & multi 1.20 1.20
a. Pair, #2567-2568 2.25 2.25

Paul Gauguin (1848-1903) A605

Paintings (details): 60 l, The Vision after the Sermon. 80 l, Ea Haere la Oe.

120 l, Stylized design to resemble self-portrait.

1998, Sept. 10 *Perf. 13½*

2569 A605 60 l multicolored 1.00 1.00
2570 A605 80 l multicolored 1.40 1.40
a. Pair, #2569-2570 2.25 2.25

Size: 50x73mm

Imperf

2571 A605 120 l multicolored 2.25 2.25

Epitaph of Gllavenica, 14th Cent. Depiction of Christ — A606

Designs: 30 l, Entire cloth showing artwork. 80 l, Closer view.

100 l, Upper portion of cloth, vert.

1998, Oct. 5 *Perf. 14½x14*

2572 A606 30 l multicolored .50 .50
2573 A606 80 l multicolored 1.50 1.50

Souvenir Sheet

Perf. 13

2574 A606 100 l multicolored 1.75 1.75

No. 2574 contains one 25x29mm stamp.

Religious Manuscripts Type of 1997

Illustrations from Purple Codex, Gold Codex: a, 30 l, Manuscript, columns on sides, arched top. b, 50 l, Manuscript cover with embossed pictures of icons. c, 80 l, Manuscript picturing cathedral, birds.

1998, Oct. 15 *Perf. 13x14*

2575 A596 Block of 3, #a.-c. + label 3.00 3.00

Mikel Koliqi (1902-97), First Albanian Cardinal — A607

1998, Nov. 28 *Perf. 14*

2576 A607 30 l shown .50 .50
2577 A607 100 l Portrait, facing 1.75 1.75
a. Pair, #2576-2577 2.50 2.50

Mother Teresa (1910-97) — A608

60 l, With child, horiz.

Perf. 14x13½, 13½x14

1998, Sept. 5 **Photo.**

2578 A608 60 l multicolored 1.50 1.50
2579 A608 100 l shown 2.50 2.50

See Italy Nos. 2254-2255.

Diana, Princess of Wales (1961-97) — A609

100 l, With Mother Teresa.

1998, Aug. 31 Litho. *Perf. 13½*

2580 A609 60 l shown *2.00 2.00*
2581 A609 100 l multicolored *3.00 3.00*

No. 2508 Overprinted in Blue

1998, Oct. 23 Litho. *Imperf.*

2582 A581 150 l multicolored 8.00 8.00

No. 2482 Surcharged

1999, Apr. 20 Litho. *Perf. 14x13½*

2583 A571 150 l on 25 l multi 3.25 3.25

Famous Americans — A610

a, Washington. b, Lincoln. c. Martin Luther King, Jr.

1999, Mar. 15 *Perf. 14*

2584 A610 150 l Block of 3, #a.-c. + label 9.00 9.00

Monachus Albiventer — A611

Seals: a, 110 l, One looking left, one looking right. b, 150 l, Both looking right. c, 110 l, Mirror image of No. 2585b. d, 150 l, Mirror image of No. 2585a.

1999, Apr. 10

2585 A611 Sheet of 4, #a.-d. 10.00 10.00

No. 2382 Surcharged

1999, Apr. 24 Litho. *Perf. 12x12¼*

2586 A539 150 l on 90 l multi 3.25 3.25

IBRA '99, Nuremburg.

A612

1999, Apr. 25 Litho. *Perf. 13½x13¾*

2587 A612 10 l blue & multi .75 .75
2588 A612 100 l green & multi 4.00 4.00

Souvenir Sheet

Perf. 13

2589 A612 250 l green & multi 5.00 5.00

NATO, 50th anniv. No. 2589 contains one 30x50mm stamp.

A613

Cartoon mouse: a, 80 l, Writing. b, 110 l, Holding chin. c, 150 l, Wearing bow tie. d, 60 l, Pointing.

1999, Apr. 30 Litho. *Perf. 13x13¾*

2590 A613 Strip of 4, #a.-d. 8.50 8.50

Animated films.

Europa — A614

1999, May 1 Litho. *Perf. 13¾x13*

2591 A614 90 l Thethi Park 2.00 2.00
2592 A614 310 l Lura Park 4.50 4.50

Imperf

Size: 80x60mm

2592A A614 350 l Kombetare Park 6.50 6.50
Nos. 2591-2592A (3) 13.00 13.00

Illyrian Coins — A615

Designs: a, 200 l, Kings of Illyria — Monumiou c. 300-280 BC cow suckling calf, square containing double stellate pattern, and Epidamos-Dyrrachium c. 623 BC, square with double stellate. b, 20 l, Damastion c. 395-380 BC siver drachm portable ingot, Byllis c. 238-168 BC AE13 serpent entwined around cornucopia, Skodra after 168 BC, AE17 war galley, and other war galley coin. c, 10l, Epirote Republic before 238 BC silver tetraobol with jugate busts of Zeus and Dione on obverse and thunderbolt within oak wreath reverse. 310 l, Kings of Illyria — Genthos c. 197-168 BC head wearing kausia.

1999, June 1 Litho. *Perf. 13¾x13¼*

2593 A615 Strip of 3, #a.-c. 5.00 5.00

Souvenir Sheet

Perf. 13

2594 A615 310 l multicolored 6.50 6.50

Charlie Chaplin — A616

Designs: 30 l, Holding cigarette. 50 l, Tipping hat. 250 l, Dancing.

1999, June 20 Litho. *Perf. 14x14¼*

2595 A616 30 l multicolored .75 .75
2596 A616 50 l multicolored 1.50 1.50
2597 A616 250 l multicolored 6.00 6.00
a. Booklet pane, 2 each #2595-2597, perf. 14¼ vert. 70.00
Complete booklet 70.00
Nos. 2595-2597 (3) 8.25 8.25

In No. 2597a, the 30 l stamps are at the ends of the pane and the 250 l stamps are in the middle.

No. 2398 Surcharged

1999, July 2 Litho. *Perf. 12½*

2598 A543 150 l on 30q multi 3.00 3.00

PhilexFrance 99.

Holocaust — A617

1999, July 6 Litho. *Perf. 14x14¼*

2599 A617 30 l brown & multi .60 .60
2600 A617 150 l gray & multi 3.25 3.25

First Manned Moon Landing, 30th Anniv. A618

No. 2601: a, 30 l, Astronaut, earth. b, 150 l, Lunar Module. c, 300 l, Astronaut, flag. 280 l, Lift-off.

1999, July 25 Litho. *Perf. 13¼x14*

2601 A618 Strip of 3, #a.-c 10.00 10.00

Souvenir Sheet

Perf. 13

2602 A618 280 l multicolored 6.00 6.00

No. 2602 contains one 25x29mm stamp.

UPU, 125th Anniv. A619

Background colors: a, 20 l, aquamarine and brown. b, 60 l, bister and dark blue.

1999, Aug. 1 Litho. *Perf. 14x14¼*

2603 A619 Pair, #a.-b. 2.00 2.00

No. 2383 Surcharged in Brown, Symbol in Red and Green

1999 Method & Perf. as Before

2604 A539 150 l on 1.20 l multi 3.00 3.00

China 1999 World Philatelic Exhibition.

A620

Background colors: a, 10 l, Yellow. b, 20 l, Orange. c, 200 l, Green.

1999, Sept. 2 Litho. *Perf. 14x14¼*

2605 A620 Strip of 3, #a.-c. 5.00 5.00

First Natl. Track & Field Championships, 70th anniv.

A621

30 l, Madonna and Child.

1999, Oct. 30 *Perf. 14*

2606 A621 30 l multicolored .50 .50
2607 A621 300 l shown 6.00 6.00
a. Souv. sheet, 2 ea #2606-2607 12.00 12.00

Art by Onufri of Elbasan.

Famous Albanians — A622

Designs: a, 10 l, Bilal Golemi (1899-1955), veterinarian. b, 20 l, Azem Galica (1889-1924), freedom fighter. c, 50 l, Viktor Eftimiu (1889-1972), writer. d, 300 l, Lasgush Poradeci (1900-87), poet.

1999, Nov. 28 Litho. *Perf. 14¼x14*

2608 A622 Block of 4, #a.-d. 8.00 8.00

Carnival Masks — A623

1999, Dec. 1 *Perf. 13¾*

2609 A623 30 l shown .50 .50
2610 A623 300 l Turkey head 6.50 6.50

Millennium — A624

2000, Mar. 27 Litho. ***Perf. 13½x14***
2611 A624 40 l red & multi .75 .75
2612 A624 90 l blue & multi 2.00 2.00

Native Costumes — A625

a, 5 l, Librazhdi. b, 10 l, Malesia e Madhe woman. c, 15 l, Malesia e Madhe man. d, 20 l, Tropoje. e, 30 l, Dumrea. f, 35 l, Tirana man. g, 40 l, Tirana woman. h, 45 l, Arbereshe. i, 50 l, Gjirokaster. j, 55 l, Lunxheri. k, 70 l, Cameria. l, 90 l, Laberia.

2000, Mar. 28 ***Perf. 13x13¾***
2613 A625 Booklet pane of 12 9.00 9.00
Booklet, #2613 12.00

Gustave Mayer (1850-1900), Student of Albanian Culture — A626

Colors: a, 50 l, olive green. b, 130 l, carmine lake.

2000, Mar. 30 ***Perf. 13½x14***
2614 A626 Pair, #a-b 3.50 3.50

Cartoon Duck — A627

Duck with: a, 250 l, Top hat. b, 10 l, Ten-gallon hat. c, 30 l, Cap. d, 90 l, Bow.

2000, Apr. 6 Litho. ***Perf. 13x13¾***
2615 A627 Strip of 4, #a-d 7.50 7.50

Grand Prix Race Cars — A628

Various cars.

2000, Apr. 10 Litho. ***Perf. 14¼x14***
2616 Bklt. pane of 10 + 2 labels 12.50 12.50
a.-j. A628 30 l any single 1.25 1.25
Booklet, #2616 15.00

Holy Year 2000 — A629

Designs: 15 l, Church with bell tower. 40 l, Church with conical roof. 90 l, Ruins.
250 l, Aerial view of ruins.

2000, Apr. 22 Litho. ***Perf. 13¾x14***
2617-2619 A629 Set of 3 4.00 4.00

Souvenir Sheet

Perf. 13¾

2620 A629 250 l multi 4.50 4.50

No. 2620 contains one 38x38mm stamp.

Europa, 2000

Common Design Type

2000, May 9 ***Perf. 13x13¾***
2621 CD17 130 l multi 3.00 3.00

Souvenir Sheet

Perf. 13

2622 CD17 300 l Detail of #2621 6.50 6.50

No. 2622 contains one 25x29mm stamp.

Miniature Sheet

Wild Animals A630

No. 2623: a, 10 l, Canis lupus. b, 40 l, Ursus arctos. c, 90 l, Sus scrofa. d, 220 l, Vulpes vulpes.

2000, May 17 ***Perf. 14¼x13¾***
2623 A630 Sheet of 4, #a-d 7.50 7.50

Gustav Mahler (1860-1911), Composer — A631

2000, May 30 ***Perf. 13½x14***
2624 A631 130 l multi 2.50 2.50

WIPA 2000 Stamp Exhibition, Vienna.

European Soccer Championships A632

10 l, Goalie. 120 l, Player heading ball. 260 l, Player kicking ball.

2000, June 1 ***Perf. 13¾x13¼***
2625-2626 A632 Set of 2 2.50 2.50

Imperf

Size: 81x60mm

2627 A632 260 l multi 5.00 5.00

Paintings by Pablo Picasso A633

Various unnamed paintings or self-portraits: 30 l, Brown panel. 40 l, Green panel. 130 l, Self-portrait, with Espana 2000 philatelic exhibition emblem, vert. 250 l, Blue panel.

2000 Litho. ***Perf. 13¾***
2628-2631 A633 Set of 4 6.50 6.50

Souvenir Sheet

Perf. 13

2632 A633 400 l Self-portrait 8.00 8.00

No. 2632 contains one 25x29mm stamp.
Issued: 130 l, 10/6; others 6/7.

2000 Summer Olympics, Sydney — A634

No. 2633: a, 10 l, Basketball. b, 40 l, Soccer. c, 90 l, Runner. d, 250 l, Cycling.

2000, July 1 ***Perf. 14x14¼***
2633 A634 Block of 4, #a-d 8.00 8.00

First Zeppelin Flight, Cent. A635

No. 2634: a, 15 l, LZ-1 over Friedrichshafen. b, 30 l, Airship over Paris. c, 300 l, R34 over New York.
No. 2635, Ferdinand von Zeppelin.

2000, July 2 ***Perf. 13¾x13***
2634 A635 Sheet of 3, #a-c 7.50 7.50

Souvenir Sheet

Perf. 13

2635 A635 300 l multi 6.50 6.50

No. 2634 contains three 40x28mm stamps.

Flowers A636

No. 2636: a, 50 l, Gentiana lutea. b, 70 l, Gentiana cruciata.

2000, Oct. 10 ***Perf. 13¼x14***
2636 A636 Pair, #a-b 2.75 2.75

Famous Albanians — A637

a, 30 l, Naim Frasheri, writer (1845-1900). b, 50 l, Bajram Curri, politician (1862-1925).

2000, Nov. 28 ***Perf. 14¼x13¾***
2637 A637 Pair, #a-b 2.00 2.00

UN High Commissioner on Refugees, 50th Anniv. — A638

50 l, Mother & child. 90 l, Mother & child, diff.

2000, Dec. 14 ***Perf. 13¾x14¼***
2638-2639 A638 Set of 2 3.00 3.00

Famous Albanians — A639

No. 2640: a, Ahmed Myftar Dede. b, Sali Njazi Dede.

2001, Feb. 22 Litho. ***Perf. 14¼x14***
2640 A639 90 l Horiz. pair, #a-b 4.50 4.50

Native Costumes — A640

No. 2641: a, Man from Tropoje. b, Woman from Lume. c, Woman from Mirdite. d, Man from Lume. e, Woman from Zadrime. f, Woman from Shpati. g, Man from Kruje. h, Woman from Macukulli. i, Woman from Dardhe. j, Man from Lushnje. k, Woman from Dropulli. l, Woman from Shmili.

2001, Mar. 15 ***Perf. 13x13¾***
2641 A640 20 l Sheet of 12, #a-l 9.00 9.00
Booklet, #2641 11.00 11.00

See Nos. 2669, 2701, 2760, 2770.

Flowers A641

No. 2642: a, 10 l, Magnolia grandiflora. b, 20 l, Rosa virginiana. c, 90 l, Dianthus barbatus. d, 140 l, Syringa vulgaris.

2001, Mar. 30 ***Perf. 14x14¼***
2642 A641 Block of 4, #a-d 5.00 5.00

Cartoon Dog A642

Denominations: a, 50 l. b, 90 l. c, 140 l, d, 20 l.

2001, Apr. 6 ***Perf. 13x13¾***
2643 A642 Strip of 4, #a-d 5.00 5.00

Opera Composers A643

Designs: No. 2644, 90 l, Vincenzo Bellini (1801-35). No. 2645, 90 l, Giuseppe Verdi (1813-1901).
300 l, Bellini and Verdi.

2001, Apr. 20 ***Perf. 13¾x13***
2644-2645 A643 Set of 2 3.50 3.50

Souvenir Sheet

Perf. 13¾

2646 A643 300 l multi 5.00 5.00

Europa — A644

Designs: 40 l, Waterfall, cliffs. 110 l, Waterfall, boulders. 200 l, Water, shoreline.
350 l, Ripples in water, vert.

2001, Apr. 29 ***Perf. 13¾x14***
2647-2649 A644 Set of 3 6.50 6.50

Souvenir Sheet

Perf. 12¾x13

2650 A644 350 l multi 7.00 7.00

No. 2650 contains one 25x29mm stamp.

Domestic Animals A645

No. 2651: a, 10 l, Horse. b, 15 l, Donkey. c, 80 l, Cat. d, 90 l, Dog.
300 l, Cat.

2001, May 17 ***Perf. 14¼x14***
2651 A645 Sheet of 4, #a-d 4.00 4.00

Souvenir Sheet
Perf. 12¾x13
2652 A645 300 l shown 5.00 5.00

No. 2651 contains four 42x26mm stamps.

2001 Mediterranean Games, Tunis, Tunisia — A646

No. 2653: a, 10 l, Swimmer. b, 90 l, Runners. c, 140 l, Cyclists.
260 l, Discus thrower.

2001, June 1 ***Perf. 14¼x14***
2653 A646 Vert. strip of 3, #a-c 5.00 5.00

Souvenir Sheet
Perf. 13x12¾
2654 A646 260 l multi 9.00 9.00

No. 2654 contains one 29x25mm stamp.

History of Aviation A647

No. 2655: a, Clement Ader's flight of Eole, Oct. 9, 1890. b, Louis Blériot's flight of Blériot IX over English Channel, July 25, 1909. c, Charles Lindbergh's solo transatlantic flight of Spirit of St. Louis, May, 1927. d, Flight over Tirana, May 30, 1925. e, Antonov AN-10, 1956. f, First Concorde flight, Feb. 9, 1969. g, First Boeing 747 flight, Jan. 22, 1970. h, First flight of Space Shuttle Columbia, Apr. 12, 1981.

2001, June 20 ***Perf. 13¾x13***
2655 A647 40 l Sheet of 8, #a-h 8.00 8.00

Bridges A648

No. 2656: a, 10 l, Tabakeve. b, 20 l, Kamares. c, 40 l, Golikut. d, 90 l, Mesit.
250 l, Tabakeve.

2001, July 20 ***Perf. 13¾x13¼***
2656 A648 Sheet of 4, #a-d 3.25 3.25

Souvenir Sheet
Perf. 12¾x13
2657 A648 250 l shown 5.00 5.00

No. 2656 contains four 38x30mm stamps.

Coats of Arms — A649

Arms of: 20 l, Dimitri of Arber. 45 l, Balsha. 50 l, Muzaka. 90 l, George Castrioti (Skanderbeg).

2001, Sept. 12 ***Perf. 12¾x13***

2658 A649 20 l multi	.50	.50
a. Booklet pane of 4	2.00	
2659 A649 45 l multi	1.00	1.00
a. Booklet pane of 4	9.00	
2660 A649 50 l multi	1.10	1.10
a. Booklet pane of 4	4.50	
2661 A649 90 l multi	2.00	2.00
a. Booklet pane of 4	8.00	
Booklet, #2658a-2661a	24.00	
Nos. 2658-2661 (4)	4.60	4.60

See Nos. 2681-2684, 2709-2712, 2775, 2797-2800, 2801-2804.

Year of Dialogue Among Civilizations — A650

Colors of denomination: 45 l, Green. 50 l, Black. 120 l, White.

2001, Oct. 6 ***Perf. 13½x14***
2662-2664 A650 Set of 3 5.00 5.00

Nobel Prizes, Cent. — A651

Laureates: 10 l, Doctors Without Borders, Peace, 1999. 20 l, Wilhelm C. Roentgen, Physics, 1901. 90 l, Ferid Murad, Physiology or Medicine, 1988. 200 l, Mother Teresa, Peace, 1979.

2001, Dec. 1 ***Perf. 13¾x13¼***
2665-2668 A651 Set of 4 7.50 7.50

Costumes Type of 2001

No. 2669: a, Man from Gjakova. b, Woman from Prizren. c, Man from Shkoder. d, Woman from Shkoder. e, Man from Berat. f, Woman from Berat. g, Woman from Elbasan. h, Man from Elbasan. i, Woman from Vlore. j, Man from Vlore. k, Woman from Gjirokaster. l, Woman from Delvina.

2002, Mar. 20 **Litho.** ***Perf. 13x13¾***
2669 A640 30 l Sheet of 12, #a-l 8.75 8.75
Complete booklet, #2669 9.75

Cartoon Deer A652

No. 2670: a, 50 l, Deer. b, 90 l, Deer and rabbit. c, 140 l, Deer, diff. d, 20 l, Deer and rabbit, diff.

2002, Apr. 8 ***Perf. 13x13¾***
2670 A652 Horiz. strip of 4, #a-d 5.50 5.50

Fireplaces — A653

Fireplace color: a, 30 l, Deep brown. b, 40 l, Henna brown. 50 l, Orange brown. 90 l, Chestnut.

2002, Apr. 15 **Litho.** ***Perf. 14***
2671 A653 Sheet of 4, #a-d 4.00 4.00

Europa — A654

Designs: 40 l, High wire act. 90 l, Acrobats. 220 l, Contortionist.
350 l, Trained horse act.

2002, May 1 **Litho.** ***Perf. 13x13¾***
2672-2674 A654 Set of 3 6.50 6.50

Souvenir Sheet
Perf. 13¾
2675 A654 350 l multi 7.50 7.50

No. 2675 contains one 37x37mm stamp.

2002 World Cup Soccer Championships, Japan and Korea — A655

Emblem, soccer ball and stylized players: 20 l, 30 l, 90 l, 120 l
360 l, Stylized player and emblem.

2002, May 6 **Litho.** ***Perf. 13¾x13¼***
2676-2679 A655 Set of 4 5.00 5.00

Souvenir Sheet
Perf. 13
2680 A655 360 l multi 7.00 7.00

No. 2680 contains one 50x29mm stamp.

Arms Type of 2001

2002, May 12 ***Perf. 13***

2681 A649 20 l Gropa	.40	.40
a. Booklet pane of 4	1.75	—
2682 A649 45 l Skurra	.90	.40
a. Booklet pane of 4	4.00	—
2683 A649 50 l Bua	1.00	1.00
a. Booklet pane of 4	4.50	—
2684 A649 90 l Topia	2.00	2.00
a. Booklet pane of 4	9.00	—
Complete booklet, #2681a-2684a	20.00	
Nos. 2681-2684 (4)	4.30	3.80

Cacti A656

No. 2685: a, Opuntia catingola. b, Neoporteria pseudoreicheana. c, Lobivia shaferi. d, Hylocereus undatus. e, Borzicactus madisoniorum.

2002, May 17 ***Perf. 14***
2685 A656 50 l Sheet of 5, #a-e 5.00 5.00

Blood Donation — A657

Letters "A," "B," and "O" with: No. 2686, 90 l, Stylized people. No. 2687, 90 l, Wings.

2002, June 16 ***Perf. 13¾x14¼***
2686-2687 A657 Set of 2 4.00 4.00

Sportsmen A658

No. 2688: a, Naim Kryeziu, soccer player. b, Riza Lushta, soccer player. c, Ymer Pampuri, weight lifter.
300 l, Loro Borici, soccer player, vert.

2002, July 3 ***Perf. 14¼x14***
2688 Horiz. strip of 3 3.50 3.50
a.-c. A658 50 l Any single 1.10 1.10

Size: 60x80mm
Imperf
2689 A658 300 l multi 6.00 6.00

Intl. Federation of Stamp Dealers Associations, 50th Anniv. — A659

Designs: 50 l, Man, #2471. 100 l, Map of Albania, Europe, cube of blue spheres.

2002, Sept. 1 **Litho.** ***Perf. 13¾x13¼***
2690-2691 A659 Set of 2 3.00 3.00

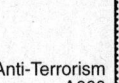

Anti-Terrorism A660

Designs: 100 l, Statue of Liberty. 150 l, World Trade Center on fire.
350 l, Statue of Liberty and World Trade Center, vert.

2002, Sept. 11 ***Perf. 13¾x13***
2692-2693 A660 Set of 2 5.00 5.00

Souvenir Sheet
Perf. 13
2694 A660 350 l multi 7.00 7.00

No. 2694 contains one 29x50mm stamp.

Mediterranean Sealife — A661

No. 2695: a, Caretta caretta. b, Delphinus delphis. c, Prionace glauca. d, Balaenoptera physalus. e, Torpedo torpedo. f, Octopus vulgaris.

Perf. 14¼x14¾
2002, Sept. 12 **Litho.**
2695 A661 50 l Sheet of 6, #a-f 6.00 6.00

Famous Albanians — A662

No. 2696: a, Tefta Tashko Koço (1910-47), singer. b, Naim Frasheri (1923-75), actor. c,

Kristaq Antoniu (1909-79), singer. d, Panajot Kanaçi (1923-96), choreographer.

2002, Oct. 6 *Perf. 13¾*
2696 A662 50 l Block of 4, #a-d 4.00 4.00

Independence, 90th Anniv. — A663

Designs: 20 l, Flags of Albania and other nations. 90 l, People, Albanian flag.

2002, Nov. 28 Litho. *Perf. 13½x14*
2697-2698 A663 Set of 2 2.00 2.00

Post and Telecommunications Administration, 90th Anniv. — A664

Designs: 20 l, Satellite dish. 90 l, Telegraph, air mail envelope.

2002, Dec. 4
2699-2700 A664 Set of 2 2.00 2.00

Costumes Type of 2001

No. 2701: a, Woman from Kelmendi. b, Man from Zadrime. c, Woman from Zerqani. d, Man from Peshkopi. e, Man from Malesia e Tiranes. f, Woman from Malesia e Tiranes. g, Woman from Fushe Kruje. h, Man from Shpati. i, Woman from Myzeqe. j, Woman from Labinoti. k, Man from Korce. l, Woman from Laberi.

2003, Apr. 1 Litho. *Perf. 13¼*
2701 A640 30 l Sheet of 12, #a-l 8.00 8.00
Booklet, #2701 10.00 10.00

Characterizations of Popeye — A665

No. 2702: a, 80 l, Popeye and Olive Oyl. b, 150 l, Popeye smoking pipe. c, 40 l, Popeye and Brutus. d, 50 l, Popeye walking.

2003, Apr. 6
2702 A665 Strip of 4, #a-d 7.00 7.00

Castles A666

No. 2703: a, 10 l, Porto Palermo. b, 20 l, Petrela. c, 50 l, Kruja. d, 120 l, Preza.

2003, Apr. 15 Litho. *Perf. 13¼*
2703 A666 Sheet of 4, #a-d 6.00 6.00

Europa — A667

Poster art: 150 l, Onufri. 200 l, Various posters.
350 l, Face from Onufri poster.

2003, Apr. 30 *Perf. 14*
2704-2705 A667 Set of 2 *6.00 6.00*

Souvenir Sheet

2706 A667 350 l multi *8.00 8.00*

First Albanian Stamps, 90th Anniv. — A668

Designs: 50 l, Stamped envelopes, sheets of stamps. 1000 l, Seal of Post, Telegraph and Telephone Ministry.

2003, May 12 *Perf. 13¼*
2707-2708 A668 Set of 2 *22.50 22.50*

Arms Type of 2001

Family arms: 10 l, Arianiti. 20 l, Jonima. 70 l, Dukagjini. 120 l, Kopili.

2003, May 12
2709 A649 10 l multi .30 .30
a. Booklet pane of 4 1.25 —
2710 A649 20 l multi .50 .50
a. Booklet pane of 4 2.25 —
2711 A649 70 l multi 1.50 1.50
a. Booklet pane of 4 7.00 —
2712 A649 120 l multi 2.50 2.50
a. Booklet pane of 4 11.00 —
Complete booklet, #2709a, 2710a, 27111a, 2712a 24.00
Nos. 2709-2712 (4) 4.80 4.80

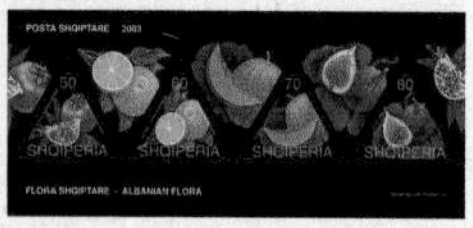

Fruit A669

No. 2713: a, 50 l, Punica gramatunil. b, 60 l, Citrus medica. c, 70 l, Cucumis melo. d, 80 l, Ficus.

Serpentine Die Cut 6¼

2003, May 17 Self-Adhesive
2713 A669 Sheet of 4, #a-d 5.50 5.50

Roman Emperors from Illyria and Coins Depicting Them — A670

No. 2714: a, Diocletian (c. 245-c. 313). b, Justinian I (483-565). c, Claudius II (214-70). d, Constantine I (the Great) (d. 337).

2003, June 20 Litho. *Perf. 13¼*
2714 A670 70 l Block of 4, #a-d 6.00 6.00

Birds A671

No. 2715: a, Ciconia ciconia. b, Aquilia chrysaetos. c, Bubo bubo. d, Tetrao urogallos.

2003, Aug. 20 *Perf. 14½x14¼*
2715 A671 70 l Sheet of 4, #a-d 6.00 6.00

First International Soccer Match in Albania, 90th Anniv. — A672

No. 2716: a, Denomination at right. b, Denomination at left.

2003, Sept. 2
2716 A672 80 l Horiz. pair, #a-b 3.50 3.50

Paintings by Edouard Manet — A673

Designs: 40 l, Lunch in the Workshop (detail). 100 l, The Fifer.
250 l, Manet, horiz.

2003, Sept. 20 *Perf. 14½x14¼*
2717-2718 A673 Set of 2 3.00 3.00

Souvenir Sheet

Perf. 14¼x14½

2719 A673 250 l multi 4.50 4.50

Sculptors A674

No. 2720: a, Odhise Paskali. b, Janaq Paco. c, Llazar Nikolla. d, Murat Toptani.

2003, Oct. 6 *Perf. 13¼*
2720 A674 50 l Block of 4, #a-d 4.00 4.00

Beatification of Mother Teresa — A675

Sculptures of Mother Teresa: 40 l, Profile. 250 l, Front view.
350 l, Mother Teresa praying.

2003, Oct. 19 *Perf. 13¼*
2721-2722 A675 Set of 2 6.00 6.00

Souvenir Sheet

Perf.

2723 A675 350 l multi 7.00 7.00

No. 2723 contains one 40mm diameter stamp.

Natural Monuments A676

Designs: 20 l, Divjaka Forest Park. 30 l, Fir trees, Hotova. 200 l, Fir tree, Drenova.

2003, Oct. 20 *Perf. 13¼*
2724-2726 A676 Set of 3 5.00 5.00

Tour de France Bicycle Race, Cent. — A677

Designs: 50 l, Cyclist, "100," map of France. 100 l, Cyclists, French flag.

2003, Nov. 1 *Perf. 14¼x14½*
2727-2728 A677 Set of 2 3.00 3.00

Europa — A678

Various vacation spots with country name in: No. 2729, 200 l, White. No. 2730, 200 l, Light blue.
350 l, Orange.

2004, June 23 Litho. *Perf. 13½*
2729-2730 A678 Set of 2 9.00 9.00
a. Booklet pane, 4 each #2729-2730, perf. 13½ on 3 sides 46.00 —
Complete booklet, #2730a 46.00

Souvenir Sheet

Perf. 14¼x13½

2731 A678 350 l multi 9.00 9.00

No. 2731 contains one 29x37mm stamp.
In No. 2730a, the two columns in the middle are tete-beche pairs of Nos. 2729-2730.

European Soccer Championships, Portugal — A679

Various players: 20 l, 40 l, 50 l, 200 l.
350 l, Player (37mm diameter stamp).

2004, June 24 *Perf. 14*
2732-2735 A679 Set of 4 7.00 7.00

Souvenir Sheet

Perf.

2736 A679 350 l multi 8.00 8.00

2004 Summer Olympics, Athens — A680

Designs: 10 l, Statue of discus thrower. 200 l, Bust.
350 l, Torch bearer.

2004, Aug. 12 *Perf. 13½*
2737-2738 A680 Set of 2 4.50 4.50

Souvenir Sheet

Perf. 13½x13¾

2739 A680 350 l multi 8.00 8.00

No. 2739 contains one 38x54mm stamp.

Prince Wilhelm zu Wied (1876-1945), Appointed Ruler of Albania — A681

Designs: 40 l, With hat. 150 l, Without hat.

2004, Aug. 30 Litho. *Perf. 13½*
2740-2741 A681 Set of 2 4.00 4.00

Characterizations of Bugs Bunny — A682

No. 2742 — Background color: a, 40 l, Orange. b, 50 l, Light blue. c, 80 l, Purple. d, 150 l, Green.

2004, Sept. 15
2742 A682 Horiz. strip of 4, #a-d 7.00 7.00

Icons Painted by Nikolla Onufri — A683

Various saints: 10 l, 20 l, 1000 l.

2004, Oct. 3 *Perf. 14*
2743-2745 A683 Set of 3 22.50 22.50

Souvenir Sheet

Perf. 13½x14¼

2746 A683 400 l Saint, diff. 9.00 9.00

Souvenir Sheet

Ladybugs — A684

No. 2747: a, With 12 spots, on flower. b, With 5 spots, on flower. c, With wings extended. d, On leaves.

2004, Oct. 10 *Perf. 14*
2747 A684 80 l Sheet of 4, #a-d 7.00 7.00

Entertainment Personalities — A685

No. 2748: a, Ndrek Luca (1924-93), actor. b, Jorgjia Truja (1909-94), singer, film director. c, Maria Kraja (1911-99), opera singer. d, Zina Andri (1924-80), actress, theater director.

2004, Oct. 12 *Perf. 13¾x13½*
2748 A685 50 l Block of 4, #a-d 4.50 4.50

Coats of Arms — A686

Designs: 20 l, Spani. 40 l, Gjuraj. 80 l, Zahariaj. 150 l, Dushmani.

2004, Oct. 25 *Perf. 13¾x14*
2749 A686 20 l multi .50 .50
a. Booklet pane of 4 2.00 —
2750 A686 40 l multi .80 .80
a. Booklet pane of 4 3.50 —
2751 A686 80 l multi 2.00 2.00
a. Booklet pane of 4 8.00 —
2752 A686 150 l multi 3.25 3.25
a. Booklet pane of 4 14.00 —
Complete booklet, #2749a-2752a 29.00
Nos. 2749-2752 (4) 6.55 6.55

Souvenir Sheet

Dahlias A687

No. 2753: a, Pink flower with small petals, large bud in front. b, Bud in back. c, Small flower at right. d, Red flower with large petals, small bud in front.

2004, Nov. 1 *Perf. 14*
2753 A687 80 l Sheet of 4, #a-d 7.00 7.00

Art in National Gallery — A688

No. 2745 — Art by: a, Unknown artist (Madonna and Child). b, Mihal Anagnosti. c, Onufer Qiprioti. d, Cetiret. e, Onuferi. f, Kel Kodheli. g, Vangjush Mio. h, Abdurahim Buza. i, Mustafa Arapi. j, Guri Madhi. k, Janaq Paço. l, Zef Kolombi. m, Hasan Reçi. n, Vladimir Jani. o, Halim Beqiri. p, Edison Gjergo. q, Naxhi Bakalli. r, Agron Bregu. s, Edi Hila. t, Artur Muharremi. u, Rembrandt. v, Gazmend Leka. w, Damien Hirst. x, Edvin Rama. y, Ibrahim Kodra.

2004, Nov. 20 *Perf. 14*
2754 Sheet of 25 12.50 12.50
a.-y. A688 20 l Any single .50 .50

NATO in Kosovo, 5th Anniv. — A689

NATO emblem and: 100 l, Pennants and stars. 200 l, Doves, UN flag.
350 l, Buildings, Albanian flag.

2004, Nov. 28 *Perf. 14¼x13½*
2755-2756 A689 Set of 2 7.00 7.00

Souvenir Sheet

2757 A689 350 l multi 8.00 8.00

Liberation From Nazi Occupation, 60th Anniv. — A690

Designs: 50 l, Two doves. 200 l, One dove.

2004, Nov. 29 *Perf. 13¾x13½*
2758-2759 A690 Set of 2 6.00 6.00

Native Costumes Type of 2001

No. 2760: a, Woman from Gramshi (showing back). b, Woman from Gramshi (showing front). c, Woman from Korça with blue skirt. d, Man from Kolonja. e, Woman from Korça with red dress. f, Woman from Librazhdi. g, Woman from Permeti. h, Woman from Pogradeci. i, Man from Skrapari. j, Woman from Skrapari. k, Woman from Tepelena. l, Woman from Vlora.

2004, Dec. 4 *Perf. 13½*
2760 A640 30 l Sheet of 12, #a-l 10.00 10.00
Complete booklet, #2760 11.50

Europa Stamps, 50th Anniv. (in 2006) — A691

Vignettes similar to: 200 l, #2558. 250 l, #2471, horiz.
500 l, #2675.

2005, Oct. 1 **Litho.** *Perf. 13¾*
2761-2762 A691 Set of 2 10.00 10.00

Souvenir Sheet

2763 A691 500 l multi 10.00 10.00

No. 2763 contains one 38x38mm stamp.

A692

Europa — A693

2005, Oct. 5 *Perf. 14x13¾*
2764 A692 200 l multi 5.00 5.00
a. Perf. 13¼x13¾ on 2 or 3 sides 5.00 5.00
2765 A693 200 l multi 5.00 5.00
a. Perf. 13¼x13¾ on 2 or 3 sides 5.00 5.00

Souvenir Sheet

Perf. 12¾x13

2766 A633 350 l Stuffed cabbage 9.00 9.00
a. Booklet pane, #2766, 3 each #2764a, 2765a 40.00 —
Complete booklet, #2766a 55.00

No. 2766 contains one 25x30mm stamp. Serial number is at top right of sheet margin on No. 2766, and on binding stub on No. 2766a. No. 2766a sold for 1650 l.

Admission to the United Nations, 50th Anniv. — A694

2005, Oct. 19 *Perf. 12¾*
2767 A694 40 l multi .80 .80

Cartoon Characters: — A695

No. 2768 — Tom & Jerry: a, 150 l, Tom. b, 40 l, Tom & Jerry. c, 50 l, Tom & Jerry, diff. d, 80 l, Jerry.

2005, Oct. 20 *Perf. 14*
2768 A695 Horiz. strip of 4, #a-d 6.00 6.00

Paintings — A696

Various unattributed paintings: a, Mountain, town and river. b, Castle and aqueduct. c, Crowd, minaret. d, Castle on mountain, people near river.

2005, Oct. 21
2769 Horiz. strip of 4 20.00 20.00
a. A696 10 l multi .30 .30
b. A696 20 l multi .30 .30
c. A696 30 l multi .60 .60
d. A696 1000 l multi 17.50 17.50

Costumes Type of 2001

No. 2770: a, Man, Tirana. b, Woman, Bende Tirana. c, Woman, Zall Dajt. d, Man, Kavaje-Durres. e, Woman, Has. f, Man, Mat. g, Woman, Liqenas. h, Woman, Klenje. i, Woman, Maleshove. j, Woman, German. k, Woman, Kruje. l, Man, Reç.

2005, Oct. 24 *Perf. 14x13¾*
2770 A640 30 l Sheet of 12, #a-l 8.00 8.00
Complete booklet, #2770 13.00

Complete booklet sold for 460 l.

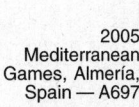

2005 Mediterranean Games, Almería, Spain — A697

2005, Oct. 25 *Perf. 14¼x13¾*
2771 Horiz. strip of 3 5.00 5.00
a. A697 20 l Runner in blocks .40 .40
b. A697 60 l Gymnastics 1.00 1.00
c. A697 120 l Relay race 2.00 2.00

Souvenir Sheet

Perf. 12¾x13

2772 A697 300 l Diver 7.50 7.50

No. 2772 contains one 50x30mm stamp.

Rotary International, Cent. — A698

Rotary International emblem and: 30 l, Map of North America. 150 l, Rays and "100 Vjet," vert.

2005, Nov. 11 *Perf. 13¾*
2773-2774 A698 Set of 2 4.00 4.00

Arms Type of 2001

No. 2775 — Arms of: a, Bua Despots. b, Karl Topia. c, Dukagjini II. d, Engjej.

2005, Nov. 14 *Perf. 12¾*
2775 Horiz. strip of 4 5.00 5.00
a. A649 10 l multi .30 .30
b. A649 30 l multi .50 .50
c. A649 100 l multi 1.50 1.50
d. A649 150 l multi 2.50 2.50
e. Booklet pane, 4 #2775a 1.30 —
f. Booklet pane, 4 #2775b 2.50 —
g. Booklet pane, 4 #2775c 7.00 —
h. Booklet pane, 4 #2775d 11.00 —
Complete booklet, #2775e-2775h 25.00

Souvenir Sheet

Portulaca Flowers A699

No. 2776: a, Yellow flowers. b, Three white flowers. c, Red and bright yellow flowers. d, Pink flower. e, Red flower.

2005, Nov. 17 *Perf. 14*
2776 A699 70 l Sheet of 5, #a-e 10.50 10.50

Cycling in Albania, 80th Anniv. — A700

2005, Nov. 20 *Perf. 13¼x13¾*
2777 Strip of 3 6.50 6.50
a. A700 50 l blue & multi 1.25 1.25
b. A700 60 l red & multi 1.75 1.75
c. A700 120 l bright red & multi 3.25 3.25

Souvenir Sheet

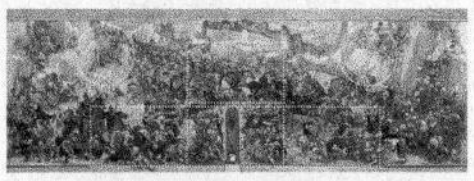

Skanderbeg (1405-68), National Hero — A701

No. 2778 — Various scenes of warriors in battle: a, 40 l (50x30mm). b, 50 l (50x30mm). c, 60 l (50x30mm). d, 70 l (50x30mm). e, 80 l (30mm diameter). f, 90 l (30mm diameter).

2005, Nov. 28 *Perf. 13*
2778 A701 Sheet of 6, #a-f 12.00 12.00

End of World War II, 60th Anniv. A702

No. 2779: a, 50 l, Doves, roses, army helmet. b, 200 l, Statues, flags, dove.

2005, Nov. 29 *Perf. 14x13¾*
2779 A702 Horiz. pair, #a-b 5.25 5.25

Marubi Family Artists — A703

No. 2780: a, Matia Kodheli-Marubi. b, Gege Marubi. c, Pjeter Marubi. d, Kel Marubi.

2005, Dec. 4
2780 Horiz. strip of 4 7.50 7.50
a. A703 10 l multi .30 .30
b. A703 20 l multi .50 .50
c. A703 70 l multi 1.75 1.75
d. A703 200 l multi 5.00 5.00

Nos. 2417, 2433, 2446, 2477, 2478, 2484, 2487, 2490-2492, 2498 and 2504 Surcharged

Methods and Perfs as Before

2006

2781	A550	on 30q #2417	*25.00*	*25.00*
2782	A569	on 2 l #2478	*15.00*	*15.00*
2783	A574	on 2 l #2490	*15.00*	*15.00*
2784	A574	on 3 l #2491	*15.00*	*15.00*
2785	A577	on 3 l #2498	*15.00*	*15.00*
2786	A552	on 10 l #2433	*30.00*	*30.00*
2787	A572	on 18 l #2484	*20.00*	*20.00*
2788	A573	on 18 l #2487	*20.00*	*20.00*
2789	A556	on 21 l #2446	*20.00*	*20.00*
2790	A568	on 25 l #2477 (block of 4, #a-d)	*150.00*	*150.00*
2791	A574	on 25 l #2492	*30.00*	*30.00*
2792	A580	on 25 l #2504	*30.00*	*30.00*
		Nos. 2781-2789,2791-2792 (11)	235.00	235.00

Location of surcharge varies.

Visit of Pres. George W. Bush to Albania
A704

No. 2793 — Photograph of Bush in: a, 20 l, Blue. b, 40 l, Green. c, 80 l, Full color.

200 l, Statue of Liberty, flags of US and Albania, horiz.

Perf. 13¼x13½

2007, June 10 **Litho.**

2793	A704	Horiz. strip of 3, #a-c	3.50	3.50

Souvenir Sheet

Perf. 13½x13¼

2794	A704	200 l multi	4.50	4.50

Italian Delegation of Experts in Albania, 10th Anniv. — A705

Perf. 13¼x13½

2007, Sept. 15 **Litho.**

Granite Paper

2795	A705	40 l multi	1.25	1.25

Miniature Sheet

Albanian Flag A706

No. 2796 — Various depictions of Albanian flag blowing in wind: a, 5 l. b, 10 l. c, 20 l. d, 30 l. e, 40 l. f, 50 l. g, 60 l. h, 70 l. i, 80 l. j, 100 l. k, 1000 l. l, 2000 l.

2007, Oct. 5 **Litho.** ***Perf. 13¼x13***

2796	A706	Sheet of 12, #a-l	90.00	90.00

Arms Type of 2001

Arms of: 20 l, Despot Andrea II Muzaka. 40 l, Matrenga family. 80 l, Leke Dukagjini. 150 l, Konstantin Kastrioti.

2007, Oct. 15 **Litho.** ***Perf. 12¾x13¼***

2797	A649	20 l multi	1.75	1.75
2798	A649	40 l multi	3.50	3.50
2799	A649	80 l multi	6.50	6.50
2800	A649	150 l multi	12.00	12.00
a.		Vert. strip of 4, #2797-2800	*150.00*	—
		Nos. 2797-2800 (4)	23.75	23.75

Nos. 2797-2800 are dated 2006.

Arms Type of 2001

Arms of: 10 l, Lança family. 20 l, Riki family. 60 l, Kokini family. 100 l, Zako family.

2007, Oct. 17 **Litho.** ***Perf. 12¾x13¼***

2801	A649	10 l multi	.50	.50
2802	A649	20 l multi	1.00	1.00
2803	A649	60 l multi	3.00	3.00
2804	A649	100 l multi	5.50	5.50
a.		Vert. strip of 4, #2801-2804	150.00	150.00
		Nos. 2801-2804 (4)	10.00	10.00

Europa — A707

Men and women and: No. 2805, 200 l, Flag of European Union, map of Europe. No. 2806, 200 l, Flag and map of Albania.

350 l, Men, women, flags of Albania and European Union, horiz.

2007, Oct. 23 **Litho.** ***Perf. 13x13¼***

2805-2806	A707	Set of 2	10.00	10.00

Souvenir Sheet

Perf. 13¼x13

2807	A707	350 l multi	9.00	9.00

No. 2807 contains one 30x25mm stamp. Dated 2006.

Europa — A708

Designs: 100 l, Scouts, flags, mountain. 150 l, Scouts, flags, mountain, diff.

250 l, Knot, horiz.

2007, Oct. 24 ***Perf. 13¼x13***

2808-2809	A708	Set of 2	5.00	5.00

Souvenir Sheet

2810	A708	250 l multi	5.75	5.75

Scouting, cent. No. 2810 contains one 30x25mm stamp.

Pink Panther A709

No. 2811 — Pink Panther: a, 150 l, Wearing uniform. b, 40 l, Wearing bowtie. c, 50 l, With inspector. d, 80 l, With elbow resting on orange panel.

2007, Oct. 25 ***Perf. 13***

2811	A709	Horiz. strip of 4, #a-d	7.00	7.00

Children's Art — A710

No. 2812 — Art by: a, 10 l, Arkida Lema. b, 40 l, Amarilda Prifti. c, 50 l, Iliaz Kasa. d, 80 l, Klaudia Mezini, horiz.

2007, Oct. 29 ***Perf. 13***

2812	A710	Horiz. strip of 4, #a-d	7.00	7.00

Frescoes — A712

Designs: 70 l, sower, by David Selenices. 110 l, Floral mural, Et'hem Bey Mosque, Tirana.

2007, Oct. 31 **Litho.** ***Perf. 13***

2814-2815	A712	Set of 2	6.00	6.00

Miniature Sheet

Native Costumes — A713

No. 2816: a, German woman. b, Kurbin man. c, Golloborde woman. d, Kerrabe Malesi man. e, Gur i Bardhe woman. f, Martanesh woman. g, Puke woman. h, Serice Labinot woman. i, Shen Gjergj woman. j, Tirane Qytet woman. k, Zalle Dajt man. l, Zaranike Godolesh woman.

2008, Nov. 1 **Litho.** ***Perf. 13***

2816	A713	40 l Sheet of 12, #a-l	12.00	12.00

Dated 2006. A sheet of 20 l stamps depicting native costumes with country name at left was issued on Nov. 2 in limited quantities to those with reservations to purchase the sheet, and later was sold at an inflated price. Value, $100.

Tourism — A714

No. 2817: a, Thethi National Park (Parku Kombetar Thethit). b, Lures Lake (Liqenet e Lures). c, Kanina Castle (Kalaja e Kanines). d, Karavasta Lagoon (Laguna e Karavastase).

2007, Nov. 5

2817		Horiz. strip of 4	7.00	7.00
a.	A714	40 l green & multi	1.00	1.00
b.	A714	50 l red violet & multi	1.25	1.25
c.	A714	60 l red & multi	1.50	1.50
d.	A714	70 l blue violet & multi	2.25	2.25

Trees of Elbasan — A715

Designs: 70 l, Tree and pond. 90 l, Hollowed-out tree.

2007, Nov. 8 ***Perf. 13x13¼***

2818-2819	A715	Set of 2	4.50	4.50

Dated 2006.

Pope Clement XI (1649-1721) — A716

No. 2820: a, 30 l, Red background. b, 120 l, Blue background.

2007, Nov. 9 ***Perf. 13¼x13***

2820	A716	Vert. pair, #a-b	4.50	4.50

Dated 2006.

Léopold Sédar Senghor (1906-2001), First President of Senegal — A717

Color of photograph: 40 l, Sepia. 80 l, Black.

2007, Nov. 10

2821-2822	A717	Set of 2	4.00	4.00

Dated 2006.

Albania as Balkan Soccer Champions, 60th Anniv. (in 2006) — A718

Background colors: 10 l, Buff and red. 80 l, Light and dark blue.

2007, Nov. 11 ***Perf. 13x13¼***

2823-2824	A718	Set of 2	10.00	10.00

Dated 2006.

Miniature Sheet

Gjirokaster UNESCO World Heritage Site — A719

No. 2825: a, 10 l, Cannons. b, 20 l, Wall decoration. c, 30 l, Building. d, 60 l, Bridge. e, 80 l, Aerial view of town. f, 90 l, Castle atop cliff.

2007, Nov. 12 ***Perf. 13¼x13***

2825	A719	Sheet of 6, #a-f	9.00	9.00

Dated 2006.

Participation of Albanian Military in International Missions, 10th Anniv. (in 2006) — A720

Designs: 10 l, Soldier in gas mask. 100 l, Soldiers in raft.

2008, Nov. 13

2826-2827	A720	Set of 2	3.00	3.00

Dated 2006.

Mother Teresa (1910-97), 1978 Nobel Peace Laureate — A721

Background color: 60 l, Orange yellow. 130 l, Brown. 200 l, Red.

2007, Nov. 15 ***Perf. 13¼x13***

2828-2829	A721	Set of 2	7.50	7.50

Souvenir Sheet

2830	A721	200 l multi		—

Statue of Gaia Found Near Durres — A722

No. 2831: a, 30 l, Small image of statue. b, 120 l, Large image of statue.

2007, Nov. 16 Litho. *Perf. 13¼x13*
2831 A722 Vert. pair, #a-b 10.00 10.00

A 200 l souvenir sheet issued with this set was sold in limited quantities to those with reservations to purchase the sheet, and later was sold at an inflated price. Value, $250.

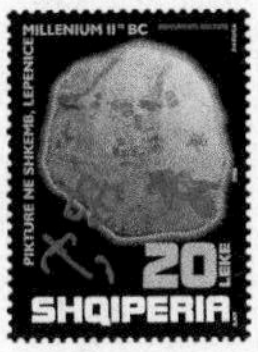

Prehistoric Cave and Rock Drawings — A723

Designs: 20 l, Rock drawings, Lepenice. 100 l, Rock drawing, Tren.
300 l, Cave drawing, Tren.

2007, Nov. 19 *Perf. 13¼x13*
2832-2833 A723 Set of 2 3.00 3.00

Souvenir Sheet

Perf. 13x13¼

2834 A723 300 l multi 6.00 6.00

Dated 2006.

Famous Men — A724

No. 2835: a, Osman Kazazi (1917-99), resistance leader. b, Pjeter Arbnori (1935-2006), politician. c, Lasgush Poradeci (1899-1987), writer. d, Cesk Zadeja (1927-97), musician.

2007, Nov. 22 *Perf. 13¼x13*
2835 Horiz. strip of 4 5.00 5.00
a. A724 10 l multi 1.25 1.25
b. A724 20 l multi 1.25 1.25
c. A724 60 l multi 1.25 1.25
d. A724 100 l multi 1.25 1.25

Famous Men — A725

No. 2836: a, Abdurrahim Buza (1905-87), painter. b, Aleks Buda (1911-93), historian. c, Thimi Mitko (1820-90), writer. d, Martin Camaj (1925-94), writer.

2007, Nov. 22 *Perf. 13x13¼*
2836 Horiz. strip of 4 5.75 5.75
a.-d. A725 50 l Any single 1.25 1.25

Dated 2006.

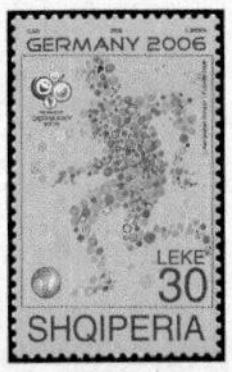

2006 World Cup Soccer Championships, Germany — A726

Stylized soccer players with background colors of: 30 l, Yellow. 60 l, Red. 120 l, Black.
350 l, Emblem of 2006 World Cup.

2007, Nov. 26
2837-2839 A726 Set of 3 10.00 10.00

Souvenir Sheet

2840 A726 350 l multi 15.00 15.00

Dated 2006.

Independence, 95th Anniv. — A727

Ismail Qemali (1844-1919), first Albanian Prime Minister and: 50 l, Heraldic eagle and years. 110 l, Text.

2007, Nov. 28 *Perf. 13x13¼*
2841-2842 A727 Set of 2 3.50 3.50

Vegetables A728

No. 2843: a, Garlic. b, Onions. c, Peppers. d, Tomatoes.

2007, Dec. 3 Litho. *Perf. 12¾*
2843 Horiz. strip of 4 + 3 labels 12.50 12.50
a.-d. A728 80 l Any single 3.00 3.00

Wulfenia Baldacci — A729

2007, Dec. 4 Litho. *Perf. 13*
2844 Horiz. pair + central label 10.00 10.00
a. A729 70 l lilac & multi 3.75 3.75
b. A729 100 l buff & multi 5.25 5.25

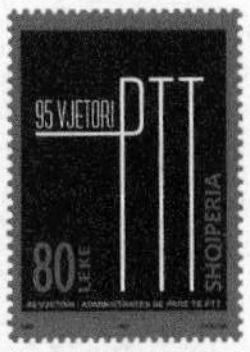

Albanian Post and Telecommunications Department, 95th Anniv. — A730

Denomination in: 80 l, Red. 90 l, Black.

2007, Dec. 5 *Perf. 13¼x13*
2845-2846 A730 Set of 2 3.50 3.50

Miniature Sheet

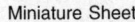

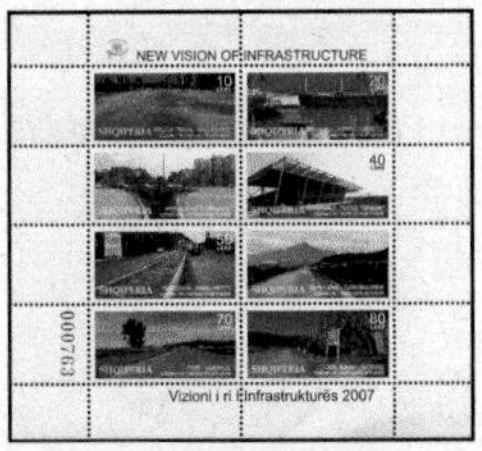

Infrastructure Development — A731

No. 2847: a, 10 l, Trans-Balkan Road. b, 20 l, Port of Durres. c, 30 l, Road, Tirana. d, 40 l, Mother Teresa Terminal. e, 50 l, Road, Shkoder. f, 60 l, Tepelene-Gjirokaster Road. g, 70 l, Fier-Lushnje Road. h, 80 l, Kalimash-Morine Road.
150 l, Mother Teresa Air Terminal, Tirana.

2007, Dec. 7 *Perf. 13¼x12¾*
2847 A731 Sheet of 8, #a-h 9.50 9.50

Souvenir Sheet

2848 A731 150 l multi 4.50 4.50

Invitation to Join NATO A732

No. 2849 — NATO emblem and: a, 40 l, Flags of member nations. b, 60 l, Heraldic eagles.

2008, Apr. 12 Litho. *Perf. 13x13¼*
2849 A732 Horiz. pair, #a-b 2.00 2.00

Children's Drawings — A733

No. 2850 — Dove and: a, 40 l, Black doves and flowers. b, 70 l, Boat on water.

2008, June 1 Litho. *Perf. 13x13¼*
2850 A733 Horiz. pair, #a-b 3.00 3.00

UEFA Euro 2008 Soccer Championships, Austria and Switzerland — A734

No. 2851: a, 50 l, Map of Switzerland. b, 250 l, Map of Austria
200 l, Mascots, vert.

2008, June 16 *Perf. 13x13¼*
2851 A734 Horiz. pair, #a-b 8.00 8.00

Souvenir Sheet

Perf. 13¼x13

2852 A734 200 l multi 5.00 5.00

Prizren League, 130th Anniv. — A735

No. 2853: a, 100 l, Handwritten document. b, 150 l, Building, Albanian flag.

2008, June 27 *Perf. 13¼x13*

Granite Paper

2853 A735 Vert. pair, #a-b 7.50 7.50

First Albanian Postage Stamps, 95th Anniv. — A736

2008, June 30 Litho.
2854 A736 40 l multi 1.00 1.00

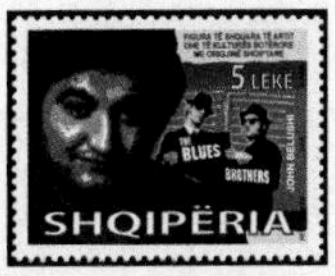

Famous People of Albanian Heritage — A737

No. 2855: a, John Belushi (1949-82), actor. b, Gjon Mili (1904-84), photographer. c, Mimar Sinan (1489-1588), architect. d, Ibrahim Kodra (1918-2006), artist.

2008, July 9 *Perf. 13x13¼*
2855 Horiz. strip of 4 5.50 5.50
a. A737 5 l multi .30 .30
b. A737 10 l multi .30 .30
c. A737 20 l multi .30 .30
d. A737 200 l multi 4.00 4.00

A738

Europa A739

Hand holding quill pen and: 100 l, Map of Europe. 150 l, Map of Albania and Adriatic region.

2008, July 15 *Perf. 13¼x13*

Granite Paper (#2856-2857)

2856-2857 A738 Set of 2 6.50 6.50

Souvenir Sheet

Perf. 13x13¼

2858 A739 250 l multi 6.50 6.50

Poppies — A740

No. 2859: a, 50 l, Two poppies. b, 150 l, One poppy.

2008, July 30 *Perf. 13¼x13*

Granite Paper

2859 A740 Vert. pair, #a-b 5.00 5.00

2008 Summer Olympics, Beijing — A741

No. 2860: a, Soccer. b, Water polo. c, Running. d, Cycling.

2008, Aug. 8 *Perf. 13x13¼*
2860 Horiz. strip of 4 4.00 4.00
a. A741 20 l multi .60 .60
b. A741 30 l multi .80 .80
c. A741 40 l multi 1.00 1.00
d. A741 50 l multi 1.40 1.40

Landscapes — A742

No. 2861: a, 60 l, Osumit Canyon. b, 250 l, Komanit Lake.

2008, Aug. 25 *Perf. 13*
2861 A742 Horiz. pair, #a-b 9.00 9.00

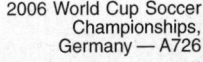

King Zog (1895-1961) — A743

No. 2862 — Denomination color: a, 40 l, Black. b, 100 l, Red.

2008, Sept. 1 ***Perf. 13x13¼***
2862 A743 Horiz. pair, #a-b 4.25 4.25

Freedom Fighters A744

No. 2863: a, 40 l, Azem Hajdari (1963-98), assassinated politician. b, 200 l, Adem Jashari (1955-98), Kosovar independence leader.

2008, Sept. 12
2863 A744 Horiz. pair, #a-b 7.00 7.00

Independence of Kosovo — A745

No. 2864: a, 20 l, Ymer Prizreni (1820-87), political leader. b, 30 l, Isa Boletini (1864-1916), military leader. c, 40 l, Ibrahim Rugova (1944-2006), President of Kosovo. d, 50 l, Azem Galica (1889-1924), military leader. e, 70 l, Adem Jashari (1955-98), independence leader.

2008, Sept. 20 ***Perf. 13¼x13***
2864 A745 Block of 5, #a-e, + 4 labels 6.00 6.00

Roman Emperors of Illyrian Origin — A746

No. 2865: a, 30 l, Decius (201-51). b, 200 l, Maximinus Thrax (173-238).

2008, Oct. 3 ***Perf. 13***
2865 A746 Vert. pair, #a-b 6.50 6.50

Harry Potter A747

No. 2866 — Harry Potter and: a, 20 l, Professor Dumbledore. b, 30 l, Kreacher. c, 50 l, Hermione Granger and friends. d, 100 l, Kreacher.

2008, Oct. 15 ***Perf. 13x13¼***
2866 A747 Block of 4, #a-d 7.50 7.50

A booklet containing a pane of Nos. 2866a-2866d sold for 550 l.

Monastir Congress, Cent. — A748

No. 2867: a, 40 l, Building. b, 100 l, Pages with handwritten Albanian alphabet.

2008, Nov. 14 ***Perf. 13***
2867 A748 Horiz. pair, #a-b 4.50 4.50

Archaeology A749

No. 2868: a, Ruins of synagogue, Sarande. b, Site at Orikumit. c, Site at Antigonese.

2008, Dec. 5 ***Perf. 13***

2868	Horiz. strip of 3	4.50	4.50
a.	A749 10 l multi	.30	.30
b.	A749 50 l multi	1.75	1.75
c.	A749 80 l multi	2.25	2.25

Universal Postal Union, 135th Anniv. A750

No. 2869 — Emblems of Albania Post and UPU, world map and background color of: a, 100 l, Yellow bister. b, 200 l, Light blue, vert.

Perf. 13x13¼ (#2869a), 13¼x13 (#2869b)

2009, Oct. 9 **Litho.**
2869 A750 Pair, #a-b 6.50 6.50

Stan Laurel (1890-1965) and Oliver Hardy (1892-1957), Comedians — A751

No. 2870 — Laurel and Hardy: a, 150 l, Holdings hats. b, 200 l, Wearing hats.
300 l, Laurel and Hardy wearing mortarboards, horiz.

2009, Oct. 16 **Litho.** ***Perf. 13¼x13***
2870 A751 Vert. pair, #a-b 10.00 10.00

Souvenir Sheet

Perf. 13x13¼

2871 A751 300 l multi 8.00 8.00

Weight Lifting A752

No. 2872 — Various weight lifters and: a, 10 l, Oval with latitudinal and longitudinal lines. b, 60 l, Olympic rings. c, 120 l, Circles and stars. d, 150 l, Double-headed eagle of Albanian arms.

2009, Oct. 21 ***Perf. 13¼x13***
2872 A752 Block of 4, #a-d 9.00 9.00

European Court of Human Rights, 50th Anniv. — A753

2009, Oct. 30 ***Perf. 13***
2873 A753 200 l multi 5.50 5.50

Council of Europe, 60th Anniv. — A754

2009, Nov. 2
2874 A754 150 l multi 4.00 4.00

Albanian Painters A755

No. 2875: a, 40 l, Abidin Dino (1913-93). b, 50 l, Lin Delija (1926-94). c, 60 l, Lika Janko (1928-2001). d, 150 l, Artur Tashko (1901-94).

2009, Nov. 11
2875 A755 Block of 4, #a-d 7.00 7.00

Traffic Safety A756

No. 2876 — Traffic officer: a, 5 l, Holding matador's red cape. 1000 l, Stopping traffic.

2009, Nov. 16 ***Perf. 13¼x13***
2876 A756 Horiz. pair, #a-b *25.00 25.00*

Diplomatic Relations Between Albania and People's Republic of China, 60th Anniv. — A757

2009, Nov. 23 ***Perf. 13***
2877 A757 20 l multi .50 .50

Albanian Iso-polyphonic Singers, UNESCO Intangible Cultural Heritage — A758

No. 2878: a, 40 l, Singers. b, 250 l, Musicians.

2009, Nov. 25 ***Perf. 13¼x13***
2878 A758 Horiz. pair, #a-b 6.00 6.00

End of World War II, 65th Anniv. A759

No. 2879 — Double-headed eagle and: a, 70 l, Soldier. b, 200 l, Bombers.

2009, Nov. 29 ***Perf. 13x13¼***
2879 A759 Horiz. pair, #a-b 6.00 6.00

Legend of Mujit and Halitit A760

No. 2880: a, 30 l, Man being held against giant's breasts. b, 200 l, Man and woman on horse.

2009, Dec. 5
2880 A760 Horiz. pair, #a-b 6.00 6.00

Religious Art and Buildings A761

No. 2881: a, Mosque, Berat. b, Church, Korçe. c, Church, Lezhe.

2009, Dec. 9 ***Perf. 13¼x13***

2881	Horiz. strip of 3	7.00	7.00
a.	A761 90 l multi	1.75	1.75
b.	A761 100 l multi	2.00	2.00
c.	A761 120 l multi	2.50	2.50

Europa — A762

Designs: 200 l, Planets, dish antenna. 250 l, Spacecraft and exploration vehicle on Mars.
350 l, Satellite above planet.

2009, Dec. 11 ***Perf. 13x13¼***
2882 A762 200 l multi 4.00 4.00
2883 A762 250 l multi 5.00 5.00

Souvenir Sheet

Perf. 13¼x13

2884	A762 350 l multi	8.00	8.00
a.	Booklet pane, #2882-2884	22.50	—
	Complete booklet, #2884a	22.50	

Intl. Year of Astronomy. No. 2884 contains one 30x25mm stamp.

Archaeological Sites — A763

No. 2885: a, 30 l, Fort, Tirana. b, 250 l, Tomb, Kamenica.

2009, Dec. 16 ***Perf. 13***
2885 A763 Horiz. pair, #a-b 6.00 6.00

National Theater — A764

No. 2886 — Scenes from plays: a, Shi ne Plazh. b, Pallati 176. c, Apologjia e Vertete e Sokratit.

2009, Dec. 21

2886	Horiz. strip of 3	7.00	7.00
a.	A764 20 l multi	.40	.40
b.	A764 80 l multi	1.60	1.60
c.	A764 200 l multi	4.00	4.00

Central State Archives, 60th Anniv.
A765

No. 2887: a, 40 l, Book, handwritten manuscript. b, 60 l, Scroll.

2009, Dec. 28

2887 A765 Horiz. pair, #a-b 2.25 2.25

Albanian-Italian Friendship
A766

2010, Apr. 12 **Litho.** ***Perf. 13***

2888 A766 40 l multi 1.75 1.75

Mother Teresa (1910-97), Humanitarian — A767

2010, Aug. 26

2889 A767 100 l multi 2.50 2.50

See Kosovo No. 154, Macedonia No. 529.

Visaless Entry Into Europe for Albanians
A768

2010, Nov. 8 ***Perf. 13x13¼***

2890 A768 40 l multi .80 .80

National Library. 50th Anniv.
A769

No. 2891: a, 10 l, Man reading book. b, 1000 l, Man at computer.

2011, Feb. 18

2891 A769 Horiz. pair, #a-b 20.00 20.00

Dated 2010.

Student's Protest Movement, 20th Anniv. — A770

No. 2892: a, 40 l, Protestors, man at microphone. b, 60 l, Toppling of Enver Hoxha statue.
200 l, Students giving "V" for victory hand sign, vert.

2011, Feb. 20 ***Perf. 13***

2892 A770 Horiz. pair, #a-b 2.50 2.50

Souvenir Sheet

2893 A770 200 l multi 4.00 4.00

Dated 2010.

Europa — A771

No. 2894 — Characters from children's stories: a, 100 l, Sun, donkey and rooster. b, 150 l, Bird and cat in balloons, girl.
250 l, Girl, stack of books, horiz.

2011, Feb. 25 ***Perf. 13¼x13***

2894 A771 Vert. pair, #a-b 5.50 5.50

Souvenir Sheet

Perf. 13x13¼

2895 A771 250 l multi 5.50 5.50

Dated 2010.

Underwater Archaeology — A772

No. 2896: a, 50 l, Close-up of underwater artifact. b, 250 l, Items on seabed.

2011, Mar. 2 ***Perf. 13¼x13***

2896 A772 Horiz. pair, #a-b 6.00 6.00

Dated 2010.

2010 World Cup Soccer Championships, South Africa — A773

No. 2897 — Emblem, ball and players: a, 80 l. b, 120 l.
200 l, Two players.

2011, Mar. 10 ***Perf. 13¼x13***

2897 A773 Horiz. pair, #a-b 4.00 4.00

Souvenir Sheet

2898 A773 200 l multi 4.00 4.00

Dated 2010.

Albanian Peacekeeping Force — A774

No. 2899: a, 50 l, Helicopter, soldiers. b, 200 l, Soldier, tank.

2011, Mar. 21

2899 A774 Horiz. pair, #a-b 5.25 5.25

Dated 2010.

Lushnja Congress, 90th Anniv. — A775

No. 2900: a, 70 l, Document and seal. b, 150 l, Building.

2011, Mar. 23

2900 A775 Horiz. pair, #a-b 4.50 4.50

Dated 2010.

National Cultural Heritage Day — A776

No. 2901: a, House, Gjirokaster. b, Apron, Dumre. c, Fortress, Tirana. d, Lute, Shkoder.
200 l, Woman, Zadrime.

2011, Mar. 31 ***Perf. 13x13¼***

2901	Horiz. strip of 4	6.50	6.50
a.	A776 10 l multi	.25	.25
b.	A776 70 l multi	1.40	1.40
c.	A776 80 l multi	1.60	1.60
d.	A776 120 l multi	2.50	2.50

Souvenir Sheet

2902 A776 200 l multi 4.25 4.25

Dated 2010.

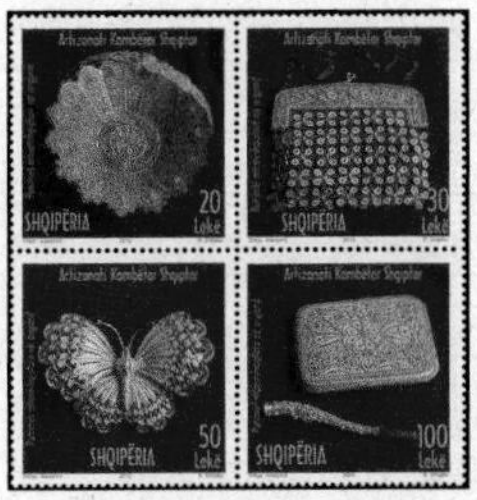

Items Made of Silver
A777

No. 2903: a, Pendant. b, Purse. c, Butterfly. d, Decorated case and cylinder with tip.
200 l, Open case and cylinder.

2011, Apr. 6 ***Perf. 13***

2903 A777 Block of 4, #a-d 4.25 4.25

Souvenir Sheet

2904 A777 200 l multi 4.25 4.25

Dated 2010.

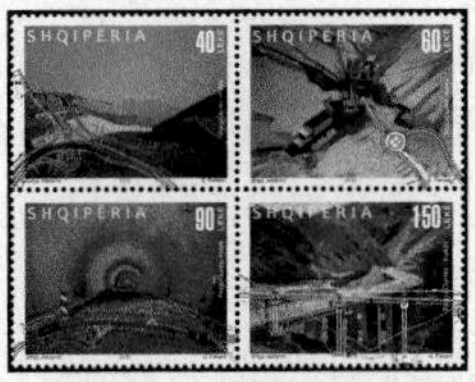

Durres-Kukes Road — A778

No. 2905 — Road design and: a, 40 l, Hills. b, 60 l, Construction equipment. c, 90 l, Tunnel. d, 150 l, Bridge.

2011, Apr. 11 ***Perf. 13x13¼***

2905 A778 Block of 4, #a-d 7.00 7.00

Dated 2010.

Miniature Sheet

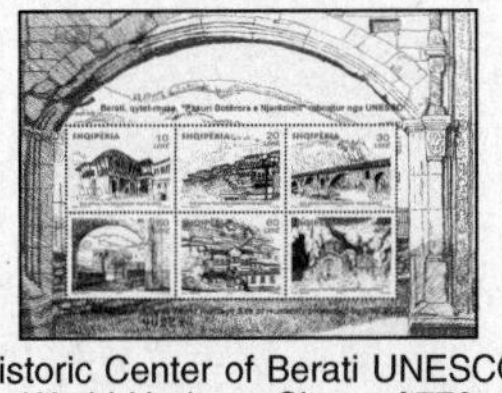

Historic Center of Berati UNESCO World Heritage Site — A779

No. 2906: a, 10 l, Building. b, 20 l, Buildings on hillside, street light. c, 30 l, Bridge. d, 50 l, Archway, fence on wall, buildings. e, 60 l, Buildings on hillside. 80 l, Church.

2011, Apr. 11 ***Perf. 13x13¼***

2906 A779 Sheet of 6, #a-f 7.00 7.00

Europa — A780

Map of Europe with tree trunks and hills in: 200 l, Brown. 250 l, Green.

2011, July 30 ***Perf. 13¼x13***

2907 A780 200 l multi 4.25 4.25

Souvenir Sheet

2908 A780 250 l multi 5.25 5.25

Intl. Year of Forests.

Boxing
A781

No. 2909: a, 50 l, Boxers, boxer with red shirt at left. b, 100 l, Boxers, boxer with red shirt at right.
250 l, Boxer throwing punch.

2011, Aug. 26

2909 A781 Horiz. pair, #a-b 3.00 3.00

Souvenir Sheet

2910 A781 250 l multi 5.00 5.00

Multi-party Elections, 20h Anniv. — A782

2011, Sept. 1 ***Perf. 13x13¼***

2911 A782 150 l multi 3.00 3.00

Ismail Kadare, Writer — A783

2011, Sept. 12 ***Perf. 13***

2912 A783 40 l multi 1.00 1.00

Tourism
A784

No. 2913: a, 80 l, Valbona River and mountains. b, 120 l, Rocks in Valbona River.

2011, Sept. 27

2913 A784 Horiz. pair, #a-b 4.00 4.00

Albanian Red Cross, 90th Anniv.
A785

No. 2914 — Emblem and: a, 70 l + 10 l, Aid to pregnant woman, first aid. b, 120 l, Woman receiving two bags.

2011, Oct. 4

2914 A785 Horiz. pair, #a-b 4.00 4.00

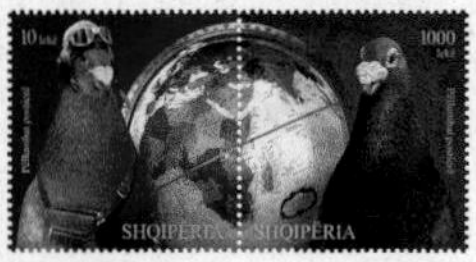
Carrier Pigeons A786

No. 2915 — Globe and: a, 10 l, Pigeon with mail bag. b, 1000 l, Pigeon without mail bag.

2011, Oct. 9

2915 A786 Horiz. pair, #a-b 22.50 22.50

Mosaics A787

No. 2916 — Mosaic from: a, 20 l, St. Michael's Basilica, Arapaj. b, 60 l, Church, Antigone. c, 120 l, Mesaplikut Basilica.

2011, Oct. 14 **Litho.**

2916 A787 Horiz. strip of 3, #a-c 4.00 4.00

Forum of States on Adriatic and Ionian Seas — A788

2011, Nov. 18 ***Perf. 13x13¼***

2917 A788 90 l multi 1.75 1.75

Flowers A789

No. 2918: a, 30 l, Gymnospermium shqipetarum. b, 70 l, Viola kosaninii.c, 100 l, Aster albanicus subsp. paparisoi.

2011, Dec. 5 ***Perf. 13¼x13***

2918 A789 Horiz. strip of 3, #a-c 4.00 4.00

Academy of Arts, 45th Anniv. — A790

2011, Dec. 15 ***Perf. 13***

2919 A790 250 l multi 5.50 5.50

Nudes A791

No. 2920 — Nude: a, 10 l, Painting by Vangjush Mio. b, 90 l, Painting by Abdurrahim Buza. c, 100 l, Scuplture by Janaq Paço.
250 l, Nude sculpture by Paço, diff.

2011, Dec. 22 ***Perf. 13x13¼***

2920 A791 Horiz. strip of 3, #a-c 4.00 4.00

Souvenir Sheet

2921 A791 250 l multi 5.50 5.50

Democracy in Albania, 20th Anniv. — A792

2012, Mar. 22 ***Perf. 13***

2922 A792 100 l multi 1.90 1.90

Europa A793

No. 2923 — Various tourist attractions: a, 30 l. b, 250 l.

2012, Sept. 21 ***Perf. 13x13¼***

2923 A793 Horiz. pair, #a-b 5.25 5.25

2012 European Soccer Championships, Poland and Ukraine — A794

No. 2924 — Emblem, soccer ball, flags of European nations and large flag of: a, 100 l, Poland. b, 200 l, Ukraine.

2012, Sept. 28 ***Perf. 13***

2924 A794 Horiz. pair, #a-b 6.00 6.00

Kin Dushi (1922-94), Writer — A795

2012, Oct. 3 ***Perf. 13x13¼***

2925 A795 150 l multi 2.75 2.75

Albanian Membership in Universal Postal Union, 90th Anniv. — A796

2012, Oct. 9 ***Perf. 13¼x12¾***

2926 A796 250 l multi 4.75 4.75

Revolts Against Ottoman Rule, Cent. A797

No. 2927: a, 10 l, Rebel leader, row of rebels. b, 1000 l, Rebels.

2012, Oct. 19 ***Perf. 13***

2927 A797 Horiz. pair, #a-b 18.50 18.50

Souvenir Sheet

Rock Art A798

No. 2928 — Rock art at: a, 20 l, Rubik. b, 60 l, Boville. c, 150 l, Lepenice.

2012, Oct. 29 ***Perf. 13¼x13***

2928 A798 Sheet of 3, #a-c 4.25 4.25

Linguists Who Have Studied Albanian Language A799

No. 2929: a, Eric Hamp. b, Norbert Jokl (1877-1942). c, Holger Pedersen (1867-1953).

2012, Nov. 16 ***Perf. 13***

2929 Horiz. strip of 3 3.50 3.50
a. A799 50 l multi .95 .95
b. A799 60 l multi 1.10 1.10
c. A799 70 l multi 1.40 1.40

See No. 2947.

Dancers — A800

No. 2930 — Dancers from: a, Tropoje. b, Tirana. c, Cameri. d, Lushnje.

2012, Nov. 23 ***Perf. 13x13¼***

2930 Horiz. strip of 4 6.25 6.25
a. A800 20 l multi .40 .40
b. A800 40 l multi .75 .75
c. A800 120 l multi 2.25 2.25
d. A800 150 l multi 2.75 2.75

Independence, Cent. — A801

2012, Nov. 23 ***Perf. 13¼x13***

2931 A801 40 l black & red .75 .75

Declaration of Independence, Cent. — A802

No. 2932: a, People, Albanian flag. b, People, Albanian flag, diff. c, Flags, United Nations Headquarters. d, Flags, NATO emblem.

2012, Nov. 28 ***Perf. 13x13¼***

2932 Horiz. strip of 4 5.50 5.50
a. A802 50 l multi .95 .95
b. A802 60 l multi 1.10 1.10
c. A802 70 l multi 1.40 1.40
d. A802 100 l multi 1.90 1.90
e. Booklet pane of 4, #2932a-2932d 5.50 —
Complete booklet, #2932e 5.50

Albanian Army, Cent. A803

No. 2933: a, 90 l, Soldiers in traditional costumes. b, 150 l, Soldiers wearing helmets.

2012, Dec. 4 **Litho.**

2933 A803 Horiz. pair, #a-b 4.50 4.50

Albanian Post, Telegraph and Telephone Administration, Cent. — A804

No. 2934 — Telephone, poles, wires, and: a, 80 l, Envelopes, mailbox. b, 200 l, Letter in open envelope.

2012, Dec. 5 ***Perf. 13***

2934 A804 Horiz. pair, #a-b 5.25 5.25
c. Booklet pane of 2, #2934a-2934b, + 2 labels 5.25 —
Complete booklet, #2934c 5.25

Marine Life and Plants A805

No. 2935: a, 10 l, Fish, sea grasses, diver. b, 250 l, Fish, sea grasses, coral.

2012, Dec. 14 ***Perf. 13x12¾***

2935 A805 Horiz. pair, #a-b 5.00 5.00
c. Booklet pane of 2, #2935a-2935b 5.00 —
Complete booklet, #2935c 5.00

First Handstamped Envelope of Albania, Cent. — A806

No. 2936: a, 120 l, Front of addressed handstamped envelope. b, 150 l, Back of envelope, handstamp.

2013, May 5 ***Perf. 13***

2936 A806 Horiz. pair, #a-b 5.25 5.25
c. Booklet pane of 2, #2936a-2936b 5.25 —
Complete booklet, #2936c 5.25

World Track and Field Championships, Moscow — A807

No. 2937: a, 30 l, Runner. b, 200 l, High jumper.
250 l, Pole vaulter.

2013, Aug. 27 **Litho.** ***Perf. 13***

2937 A807 Horiz. pair, #a-b 4.50 4.50

Souvenir Sheet

2938 A807 250 l multi 4.75 4.75

Vedat Kokona (1913-98), Lexicographer A808

2013, Aug. 30 **Litho.** ***Perf. 13***

2939 A808 150 l multi 3.00 3.00

Europa A809

No. 2940 — Globe, parcels, envelopes and: a, 80 l, Postal van and truck. b, 200 l, Airplane, train and ship.

2013, Oct. 4 **Litho.** ***Perf. 13¼x13***

2940 A809 Horiz. pair, #a-b 5.50 5.50
c. Booklet pane of 2, #2940a-2940b 5.50 —
Complete booklet, #2940c 5.50

Albanian Police, Cent. A810

No. 2941 — Flag and: a, 10 l, Policewoman. b, 250 l, Policeman.

2013, Oct. 18 **Litho.** ***Perf. 13¼x13***

2941 A810 Horiz. pair, #a-b 5.00 5.00

Flowers — A811

No. 2942: a, Scilla albanica. b, Gymnospermium maloi. c, Tulipa albanica.

2013, Oct. 30 Litho. *Perf. 13x13¼*

2942	Horiz. strip of 3	5.00	5.00
a.	A811 20 l multi	.40	.40
b.	A811 90 l multi	1.75	1.75
c.	A811 175 l multi	2.75	2.75

17th Mediterranean Games, Mersin, Turkey — A812

No. 2943: a, 40 l, Diving, swimming, synchronized swimming. b, 150 l, Volleyball, weight lifting, cycling.
200 l, Rowing, horiz.

2013, Nov. 6 Litho. *Perf. 13¼x13*

2943	A812 Horiz. pair, #a-b	4.75	4.75

Souvenir Sheet

Perf. 13x13¼

2944	A812 200 l multi	4.00	4.00

International Red Cross, 150th Anniv. — A813

No. 2945 — Red cross and: a, 40 l, Aid workers helping injured man, feeding woman. b, 150 l, Worker giving bags of goods to man.
250 l, Aid workers assisting injured man.

2013, Nov. 15 Litho. *Perf. 13*

2945	A813 Horiz. pair, #a-b	3.75	3.75

Souvenir Sheet

2946	A813 250 l multi	5.00	5.00

Linguists Type of 2012

No. 2947 — Historians: a, Milan Sufflay (1879-1931). b, Konstantin Jiracek (1854-1918). c, Ludwig von Thallóczy (1854-1916).

2013, Nov. 25 Litho. *Perf. 13*

2947	Horiz. strip of 3	5.25	5.25
a.	A799 10 l multi	.25	.25
b.	A799 100 l multi	2.00	2.00
c.	A799 150 l multi	3.00	3.00

Recent Archaeological Finds — A814

No. 2948: a, Bronze foot, 2nd-3rd cent. b, Bronze fibula with horse design, 7th-8th cent. c, Marble statue of an aristocrat, 2nd cent. d, Relief of Heraclius and Apollo, 2nd cent.

2013, Dec. 3 Litho. *Perf. 13*

2948	Horiz. strip of 4	6.50	6.50
a.	A814 20 l multi	.35	.35
b.	A814 90 l multi	1.75	1.75
c.	A814 100 l multi	2.00	2.00
d.	A814 120 l multi	2.40	2.40

Nikolla Naço (1843-1913), Newspaper Editor — A815

2013, Dec. 18 Litho. *Perf. 13¼x13*

2949	A815 200 l multi	4.00	4.00

2014 World Cup Soccer Championships, Brazil — A816

No. 2950: a, Mascot. b, Mascot holding soccer ball. c, Mascot dribbling soccer ball.
140 l, Emblem, vert.

2014, July 9 Litho. *Perf. 13*

2950	Horiz. strip of 3	3.25	3.25
a.	A816 10 l multi	.25	.25
b.	A816 50 l multi	1.00	1.00
c.	A816 100 l multi	2.00	2.00

Souvenir Sheet

2951	A816 140 l multi	2.75	2.75

Visit to Albania of Pope Francis — A817

2014, Sept. 21 Litho. *Perf. 13*

2952	A817 100 l multi	1.90	1.90

Europa A818

No. 2953: a, 100 l, Gajdja (bagpipes). b, 150 l, Lodra (drum).

2014, Oct. 9 Litho. *Perf. 13¼x13*

2953	A818 Horiz. pair, #a-b	4.50	4.50
c.	Souvenir sheet of 2, #2953a-2953b + central label	4.50	4.50
	Complete booklet, #2953c	4.50	

Kuçi Assembly, 400th Anniv. — A819

No. 2954: a, 80 l, Participants examining document. b, 150 l, Participants.
200 l, Participants, diff.

2014, Oct. 14 Litho. *Perf. 13x13¼*

2954	A819 Horiz. pair, #a-b	4.25	4.25

Souvenir Sheet

2955	A819 200 l multi	3.75	3.75

Souvenir Sheet

Relations Between Albania and Kuwait A820

No. 2956: a, 100 l, Shiekh Sabah, emir of Kuwait. b, Handshake, flags of Albania and Kuwait.

2014, Nov. 11 Litho. *Perf. 13¼x13*

2956	A820 100 l Sheet of 2, #a-b	3.50	3.50

Sulejman Pashe Delvina (1884-1933), Prime Minister — A821

2014, Nov. 18 Litho. *Perf. 13¼x13*

2957	A821 150 l multi	2.75	2.75

Reptiles and Amphibians — A822

No. 2958: a, 80 l, Caretta caretta. b, 170 l, Hyla arborea.

2014, Nov. 22 Litho. *Perf. 13*

2958	A822 Horiz. pair, #a-b	4.50	4.50

Miniature Sheet

Coronation of Prince William of Wied, Cent. — A823

No. 2959: a, 60 l, Princess Sophie (1885-1936), wife of Prince William. b, 70 l, Crown, arms of Albania. c, 80 l, Star with eagle in circle. d, 90 l, Prince William of Wied (1876-1945).

2014, Nov. 26 Litho. *Perf. 13¼x13*

2959	A823 Sheet of 4, #a-d	5.50	5.50

World War II Liberation of Albania, 70th Anniv. — A824

2014, Nov. 29 Litho. *Perf. 13*

2960	A824 40 l multi	.70	.70

Archaeological Items From Dyrrachium (Dürres) — A825

No. 2961 — Depictions of Artemis: a, 50 l, Statue, 4th cent. B.C. b, 60 l, Bust, 4th cent. B.C. c, 70 l, Marble bust, 4th cent. B.C. d, 90 l, Bronze statue, 3rd cent. B.C.

2014, Dec. 5 Litho. *Perf. 13*

2961	Horiz. strip of 4	4.75	4.75
a.	A825 50 l multi	.90	.90
b.	A825 60 l multi	1.00	1.00
c.	A825 70 l multi	1.25	1.25
d.	A825 90 l multi	1.60	1.60

Albanian Candidacy for European Union Membership A826

2014, Dec. 8 Litho. *Perf. 13x13¼*

2962	A826 40 l multi	.70	.70

William Shakespeare (1564-1616), Writer — A827

2014, Dec. 12 Litho. *Perf. 13*

2963	A827 150 l multi	2.60	2.60

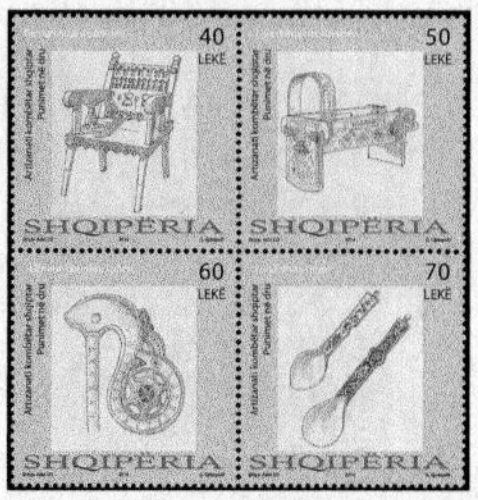

Wooden Handicrafts — A828

No. 2964: a, 40 l, Chair, Mirdite. b, 50 l, Cradle, Rreshen. c, 60 l, Shepherd's crook, Laberi. d, 70 l, Spoons, Tirana.
180 l, Ceiling decorations, Leuse.

2014, Dec. 19 Litho. *Perf. 13*

2964	A828 Block of 4, #a-d	4.00	4.00

Souvenir Sheet

2965	A828 180 l multi	3.25	3.25

Icons in Museums — A829

No. 2966 — Icon from: a, 10 l, Himare. b, 30 l. Dhermi. c, 40 l, Dhermi, diff. d, 70 l, Vuno. e, 90 l, Deme. f, 100 l, Vuno, diff.

2014, Dec. 24 Litho. *Perf. 13¼x13*

2966	A829 Sheet of 6, #a-f	6.00	6.00
g.	Booklet pane of 6, #2966a-2966f	6.00	—
	Complete booklet, #2966g	6.00	

No. 2966g has a decorative, curved pane margin.

Elez Isufi (1861-1924), Guerrilla Leader — A830

2014, Dec. 29 Litho. *Perf. 13¼x13*

2967	A830 1000 l multi	17.50	17.50

Europa — A831

2015, Sept. 2 Litho. *Perf. 13¼x13*

2968	A831 130 l multi	2.10	2.10

Souvenir Sheet

2969	A831 250 l multi	4.00	4.00
a.	Booklet pane of 2, #2968-2969	6.25	—
	Complete booklet, #2969a	6.25	

National Parks — A832

No. 2970: a, Shebenik-Jabllanice National Park. b, Bredhi i Hotoves National Park. c, Dajti National Park.

2015, Sept. 16 Litho. *Perf. 13¼x13*

2970	Horiz. strip of 3	5.00	5.00
a.	A832 50 l multi	.80	.80
b.	A832 100 l multi	1.60	1.60
c.	A832 150 l multi	2.50	2.50

Early Locomotives and Their Inventors — A833

No. 2971: a, 50 l, New Castle, Richard Trevithick (1771-1833). b, 60 l, Salamanca, Matthew Murray (1765-1826). c, 90 l, Rocket, Robert Stephenson (1803-59). d, 100 l, Locomotion, George Stephenson (1781-1848).

Perf. 13¼x12¾

2015, Sept. 27 Litho.
2971 A833 Block of 4, #a-d 5.00 5.00

Locomotives, 190th anniv.

Famous Men A834

No. 2972: a, 40 l, Dhimiter Shuteriqi (1915-2003), writer. b, 50 l, Zef Skiroi (1865-1927), poet. c, 60 l, Mahir Domi (1915-2000), linguist. d, 100 l, Gaqo Avrazi (1915-85), composer.

2015, Sept. 28 Litho. *Perf. 13¼x13*
2972 A834 Block of 4, #a-d 4.00 4.00

Albanian Soccer Federation, 85th Anniv. — A835

No. 2973 — Federation emblem and: a, 5 l, Soccer ball, goaltender and net. b, 10 l, Grass. c, 1000 l, Soccer ball and player making scissor kick.

2015, Oct. 8 Litho. *Perf. 13¼x13*
2973 A835 Horiz. strip of 3, #a-c 16.00 16.00

Famous Men — A836

No. 2974: a, Nicéphore Niépce (1765-1833), inventor of photography, b, Carl Patsch (1865-1945), historian. c, Boris Pasternak (1890-1960), 1958 Nobel laureate in Literature. d, Norman Wisdom (1915-2010), comedian and actor.

2015, Oct. 9 Litho. *Perf. 13*
2974 Horiz. strip of 4 4.25 4.25
a. A836 10 l multi .25 .25
b. A836 60 l multi .95 .95
c. A836 80 l multi 1.25 1.25
d. A836 100 l multi 1.60 1.60

United Nations, 70th Anniv. — A837

2015, Oct. 24 Litho. *Perf. 13¼x13*
2975 A837 180 l multi 3.00 3.00

Ceramic Vessels A838

No. 2976 — Various vessels: a, 50 l. b, 60 l. c, 70 l. d, 120 l
200 l, Various ceramic vessels, diff.

2015, Nov. 6 Litho. *Perf. 13*
2976 A838 Block of 4, #a-d 4.75 4.75

Souvenir Sheet

2977 A838 200 l multi 3.25 3.25

Recent Archaeological Discoveries — A839

No. 2978: a, 10 l, Ivory mirror handle, 4th-5th cent. B.C. b, 30 l, Marble statue of officer, 1st cent. B.C. c, 60 l, Bronze utensil handle, 6th-7th cent. B.C. d, 150 l, Bronze statue of Hermes, 1st cent. B.C.

2015, Nov. 16 Litho. *Perf. 13*
2978 A839 Block of 4, #a-d 4.00 4.00

International Telecommunication Union, 150th Anniv. — A840

2015, Dec. 5 Litho. *Perf. 13*
2979 A840 2500 l multi 40.00 40.00

Marine Life A841

No. 2980: a, 5 l, Sabella spallanzanii. b, 150 l, Antedon mediterranea.
250 l, Cotylorhiza tuberculata.

2015, Dec. 23 Litho. *Perf. 13¼x13*
2980 A841 Horiz. pair, #a-b 2.50 2.50

Souvenir Sheet

2981 A841 250 l multi 4.00 4.00

2016 European Soccer Championships, France — A842

No. 2982 — Emblem and player with denomination at: a, 70 l, UL. b, 100 l, UR.

2016, June 10 Litho. *Perf. 13x13¼*
2982 A842 Horiz. pair, #a-b 2.75 2.75

Europa — A843

2016, July 9 Litho. *Perf. 13x13¼*
2983 A843 200 l multi 3.25 3.25

Think Green Issue.

Flowers — A844

No. 2984: a, Tulipa kosovarica. b, Campanula comosiformis. c, Solenanthus albanicus.

2016, July 27 Litho. *Perf. 13¼x13*
2984 Horiz. strip of 3 4.00 4.00
a. A844 20 l multi .35 .35
b. A844 30 l multi .50 .50
c. A844 190 l multi 3.00 3..00

Balkanfila 2016 Intl. Stamp Exhibition, Tirana — A845

2016, Aug. 9 Litho. *Perf. 13x13¼*
2985 A845 250 l multi 4.25 4.25

Famous Men — A846

No. 2986: a, Ndre Mjeda (1866-1937), poet. b, Kole Jakova (1916-2002), writer. c, Jusuf Vrioni (1916-2001), diplomat and translator.

2016, Aug. 17 Litho. *Perf. 13x13¼*
2986 Horiz. strip of 3 3.50 3.50
a. A846 10 l multi .25 .25
b. A846 50 l multi .80 .80
c. A846 150 l multi 2.40 2.40

Albania, 2015-17 Member of United Nations Human Rights Council — A847

2016, Aug. 29 Litho. *Perf. 13x13¼*
2987 A847 1000 l multi 16.50 16.50

Albanian Literary Commission, Cent. — A848

2016, Sept. 1 Litho. *Perf. 13*
2988 A848 60 l multi 1.00 1.00

Canonization of St. Teresa of Calcutta (Mother Teresa) — A849

2016, Sept. 4 Litho. *Perf. 13x13¼*
2989 A849 120 l multi 2.00 2.00
a. Booklet pane of 1 2.00 —
Complete booklet, #2989a 2.00

Carved Stone Containers — A850

No. 2990 — Various containers: a, 10 l. b, 80 l. c, 130 l. d, 180 l.
250 l, Bowl with lid.

2016, Sept. 27 Litho. *Perf. 13*
2990 A850 Block of 4, #a-d 6.50 6.50

Souvenir Sheet

2991 A850 250 l multi 4.25 4.25

Miguel de Cervantes (1547-1616), Writer — A851

Designs: 140 l, Cervantes, Don Quixote on horse, windmill.
200 l, Don Quixote and Sancho Panza, vert.

2016, Oct. 9 Litho. *Perf. 13x13¼*
2992 A851 140 l multi 2.25 2.25

Souvenir Sheet

2993 A851 200 l multi 3.25 3.25

Dritero Agolli (1931-2017), Writer — A852

2016, Oct. 13 Litho. *Perf. 13*
2994 A852 120 l multi 2.00 2.00

Autonomous Republic of Korçe, Cent. — A853

No. 2995: a, 5 l, Themistokli Germenji (1871-1917), prefect, flag and building. b, 2500 l, Soldiers and civilians.

2016, Dec. 10 Litho. *Perf. 13*
2995 A853 Horiz. pair, #a-b 39.00 39.00

Flora A854

No. 2996: a, 150 l, Ajuga reptans. b, 250 l, Vaccinium myrtillus.

2017, Nov. 1 Litho. *Perf. 13¼x13*
2996 A854 Horiz. pair, #a-b 7.00 7.00

Berat Castle Ruins — A855

2017, Nov. 18 Litho. ***Perf. 13x13¼***

2997 A855 200 l multi 3.75 3.75

Souvenir Sheet

2998 A855 250 l multi 4.50 4.50

Europa.

Divjake-Karavasta National Park — A856

No. 2999: a, 40 l, Various birds. b, 1000 l, Flamingo and water buffalos.

2017, Nov. 24 Litho. ***Perf. 13¼x13***

2999 A856 Horiz. pair, #a-b 18.50 18.50

Famous Albanians — A857

No. 3000: a, Musine Kokalari (1917-83), writer. b, Zef Kolombi (1907-49), painter. c, Prenke Jakova (1917-69), composer. d, Dom Nikolle Kaçorri (1862-1917), politician.

2017, Dec. 5 Litho. ***Perf. 13x13¼***

3000 Horiz. strip of 4 4.00 4.00
- ***a.*** A857 10 l multi .25 .25
- ***b.*** A857 40 l multi .75 .75
- ***c.*** A857 70 l multi 1.25 1.25
- ***d.*** A857 90 l multi 1.75 1.75

Famous Men — A858

No. 3001: a, Ferdinand von Zeppelin (1838-1917), manufacturer of Zeppelin airships. b, Edgar Degas (1834-1917), painter. c, Stefan Zweig (1881-1942), writer.

2017, Dec. 12 Litho. ***Perf. 13***

3001 Horiz. strip of 3 4.75 4.75
- ***a.*** A858 20 l multi .40 .40
- ***b.*** A858 90 l multi 1.75 1.75
- ***c.*** A858 140 l multi 2.60 2.60

2017 World Aquatics Championships, Budapest, Hungary — A859

No. 3002: a, 60 l, Swimming, water polo, synchronized swimming. b, 90 l, Synchronized swimming and various swimming strokes.

2017, Dec. 15 Litho. ***Perf. 13¼x13***

3002 A859 Horiz. pair, #a-b 2.75 2.75

International Immigration Day — A860

No. 3003 — Emigrants, ship, emblem of Pan-Albanian Federation of America and: a, 60 l, Statue of Liberty. b, 250 l, Map of Europe.

2017, Dec. 18 Litho. ***Perf. 13x13¼***

3003 A860 Horiz. pair, #a-b 5.75 5.75

Lynx — A861

Lynx facing: 120 l, Right. 1.90 l, Left.

2017, Dec. 21 Litho. ***Perf. 13x13¼***

3004 A861 120 l multi 2.25 2.25

Souvenir Sheet

3005 A861 190 l multi 3.50 3.50

Glassware — A862

No. 3006: a, 5 l, Three bottles with caps. b, 40 l, Vase and three small glasses. c, 90 l Pitcher with lid and two bowls. d, 130 l, Two pitchers.

200 l, Five glasses and two vases.

2017, Dec. 23 Litho. ***Perf. 13***

3006 A862 Block of 4, #a-d 4.75 4.75

Souvenir Sheet

3007 A862 200 l multi 3.75 3.75

Albanian Art — A863

Inscriptions: 30 l, Portreti i Skenderbeut (Portrait of Skanderbeg). 40 l, Skice, studim (Study sketch), horiz. 50 l, Kaloresi (Cavalry), horiz. 80 l, Leningradi ne shi (Leningrad in the Rain), horiz. 90 l, Skice, studim (Study sketch of girl). 100 l, Ne gjume (Asleep). 180 l, Rrobaqepesja (Seamstress). 190 l, Varrimi i shokut (Burial of a Friend).

2017, Dec. 27 Litho. ***Perf. 13***

3008-3015 A863 Set of 8 14.00 14.00

European Day of Personal Data Protection — A864

2017, Dec. 28 Litho. ***Perf. 13x13¼***

3016 A864 2500 l multi 45.00 45.00

Year of Skanderbeg A865

2018, May 5 Litho. ***Perf. 13***

3017 A865 250 l multi 4.75 4.75

Skanderbeg (1405-68), Albanian national hero.

Europa — A866

Designs: 200 l, Gorica Bridge, Berat. 250 l, Mesi Bridge, Shkoder.

2018, Oct. 25 Litho. ***Perf. 13x13¼***

3018 A866 200 l multi 3.75 3.75

Souvenir Sheet

3019 A866 250 l multi 4.50 4.50
- ***a.*** Booklet pane of 2, #3018-3019 8.25 —
- Complete booklet, #3019a 8.25

Souvenir Sheet

Skanderbeg (1405-68), Albanian National Hero — A867

No. 3020: a, 150 l, 16th cent. engraving of Skanderbeg by Dominicus Custos. b, 250 l, Skanderbeg with sword.

2018, Nov. 6 Litho. ***Perf. 13x13¼***

3020 A867 Sheet of 2, #a-b 7.50 7.50

Famous Men A868

No. 3021: a, 90 l, Claude Debussy (1862-1918), composer. b, 180 l, Gustav Klimt (1862-1918), painter.

2018, Nov. 16 Litho. ***Perf. 13***

3021 A868 Horiz. pair, #a-b 5.00 5.00

Flowers A869

No. 3022: a, 40 l, Abelmoschus esculentus. b, 1000 l, Hypericum perforatum.

2018, Dec. 7 Litho. ***Perf. 13¼x13***

3022 A869 Horiz. pair, #a-b 19.50 19.50

Fish A870

No. 3023: a, 5 l, Acipenser sturio. b, 190 l, Salmo trutta.

2018, Dec. 14 Litho. ***Perf. 13¼x13***

3023 A870 Horiz. pair, #a-b 3.75 3.75

Historical Anniversaries A871

No. 3024: a, Publication of *Dottrina Christiana,* 400th anniv. b, Fourteen Points of Pres. Woodrow Wilson, cent. c, Committee for the National Defense of Kosovo, cent.

2018, Dec. 14 Litho. ***Perf. 13¼x13***

3024 Horiz. strip of 3 5.75 5.75
- ***a.*** A871 50 l multi .90 .90
- ***b.*** A871 120 l multi 2.25 2.25
- ***c.*** A871 140 l multi 2.60 2.60

Tourism A872

No. 3025: a, 40 l, Hills and waterfall near Permet. b, 2500 l, Katiu Bridge near Permet.

2018, Dec. 22 Litho. ***Perf. 13***

3025 A872 Horiz. pair, #a-b 47.50 47.50

Embrodery Patterns — A873

No. 3026 — Various embroidery patterns: a, 40 l. b, 80 l. c, 90 l. d, 130 l.

200 l, Embroidery pattern, diff.

2018, Dec. 27 Litho. ***Perf. 13***

3026 A873 Block of 4, #a-d 6.25 6.25

Souvenir Sheet

3027 A873 200 l multi 3.75 3.75

Albanian Art — A874

Designs: 10 l, Erdhi Liria (Freedom came). 20 l, Fshatarja (Rustic scene of farmwoman drinking) (43x31mm). 30 l, Portret Punetoreje (Work portrait) (31x43mm). 40 l, Toke e Begate (Prosperous Land). 60 l, Vagonisti (Miner pushing rail car) (31x43mm). 70 l, Te Korrurat (Harvested), horiz. 90 l, Vjitja (Woman and plants) (31x43mm). 100 l, Mikpritja (Woman holding dish) (40x40mm).

2018, Dec. 29 Litho. ***Perf. 13***

3028-3035 A874 Set of 8 7.75 7.75

Albanian Parliamentarism, Cent. — A875

Designs: 200 l, Republic of Albania Assembly Building.

No. 3037: a, Congress of Lushnja Building, 1920. b, National Council Building, 1920-25. c, Albanian parliamentarism centenary emblem. d, Chamber of Deputies Building, 1925-44.

2020, Jan. 21 Litho. ***Perf. 13¼x13***

3036 A875 200 l multi 3.75 3.75

Miniature Sheet

3037 Sheet of 5, #3036, 3037a-3037d, + 4 labels 6.50 6.50
- ***a.*** A875 20 l multi .35 .35
- ***b.*** A875 30 l multi .55 .55
- ***c.*** A875 40 l multi .75 .75
- ***d.*** A875 60 l multi 1.10 1.10

Souvenir Sheet

Liberation of Albania, 75th Anniv. — A876

No. 3038: a, 50 l, Mother Albania statue, Tirana. b, 250 l, Poppies.

2020, Feb. 10 Litho. ***Perf. 13x13¼***

3038 A876 Sheet of 2, #a-b 5.50 5.50

Messenger on Via Egnatia and Ship — A877

Post Rider on Via Egnatia A878

2021, Feb. 22 Litho. *Perf. 13x13¼*
3039 A877 150 l multi 3.00 3.00

Souvenir Sheet

3040 A878 250 l multi 5.00 5.00
a. Booklet pane of 2, #3039-3040 8.00 —
Complete booklet, #3040a 8.00

Europa. Ancient Postal Routes.

Ludwig van Beethoven (1770-1827), Composer — A879

Designs: 180 l, Face of Beethoven. 200 l, Half of Beethoven's face.

2021, Mar. 5 Litho. *Perf. 13½x13*
3041 A879 180 l multi 3.50 3.50

Souvenir Sheet

3042 A879 200 l multi 4.00 4.00

Trees and Their Blossoms — A880

No. 3043: a, 60 l, Laurus nobilis. b, 130 l, Aesculus hippocastanum.

2021, Mar. 15 Litho. *Perf. 13½x13*
3043 A880 Horiz. pair, #a-b 3.75 3.75

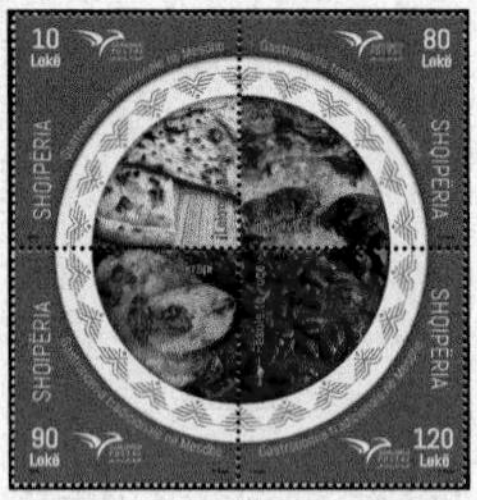

Traditional Cuisine — A881

No. 3044: a, 10 l, Lekror ne saç (vegetable pie). b, 80 l, Tave kosi (baked lamb and yogurt). c, 90 l, Tave krapi (carp casserole). d, 120 l, Fasule te kuqe (red beans).

2021, Mar. 30 Litho. *Perf. 13*
3044 A881 Block of 4, #a-d 5.75 5.75

Bazaars A882

No. 3045 — Craftsman and bazaar site in: a, 10 l, Korçe. b, 40 l, Kruje. c, 50 l, Shkoder. d, 200 l, Tirana.

2021, Apr. 11 Litho. *Perf. 13¼x13*
3045 A882 Block of 4, #a-d 6.00 6.00

Robotics A883

No. 3046 — Craftsman and bazaar site in: a, 140 l, Robot. b, 190 l, Robotic hand.

2021, Apr. 19 Litho. *Perf. 13x13¼*
3046 A883 Horiz. pair, #a-b 6.50 6.50

Bank Buildings A884

No. 3047 — Various banks with background color of: a, 20 l, Lilac. b, 30 l, Yellow. c, 80 l, Green. d, 120 l, Salmon.

2021, Apr. 28 Litho. *Perf. 13¼x13*
3047 A884 Block of 4, #a-d 5.00 5.00

Miniature Sheet

Famous Men A885

No. 3048: a, 10 l, Vexhi Buharaja (1920-87), writer and translator. b, 20 l, Ramadan Sokoli (1920-2008), composer. c, 40 l, Kristo Frasheri (1920-2016), historian. d, 90 l, Shaban Demiraj (1920-2014), linguist. e, 100 l, Sander Prosi (1920-85), actor.

2021, May 10 Litho. *Perf. 13*
3048 A885 Sheet of 5, #a-e, + 4 labels 5.25 5.25

Souvenir Sheet

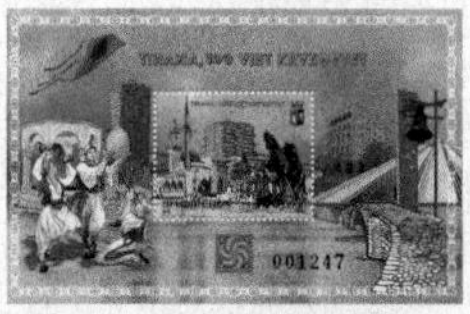

Tirana as Capital of Albania, Cent. A886

2021, May 24 Litho. *Perf. 13x13¼*
3049 A886 100 l multi 2.00 2.00

Ancient Coins A887

No. 3050: a, 30 l, Epirus silver coin, 234-168 B.C. b, 70 l, Apollonia silver coin, 44-27 B.C. c, 90 l, Shkoder bronze coin, 168 B.C. d, 250 l, Dürres silver coin, 350-250 B.C.

2021, June 2 Litho. *Perf. 13*
3050 A887 Block of 4, #a-d 8.75 8.75

Dated 2020.

2020 European Soccer Championships — A888

No. 3051 — Map of Europe, 2020 European Soccer Championships emblem, soccer player and denomination: a, 20 l. b, 200 l.

2021, June 11 Litho. *Perf. 13*
3051 A888 Horiz. pair, #a-b 4.25 4.25

The 2020 European Soccer Championships were postponed until 2021 because of the COVID-19 pandemic.

Souvenir Sheet

Ecotourism — A889

No. 3052: a, 80 l, Otok and Lake Cerknica, Slovenia. b, 100 l, Zvernec Island and Narta Lagoon, Albania.

2021, Dec. 22 Litho. *Perf. 14¼*
3052 A889 Sheet of 2, #a-b 4.00 4.00

Joint issue between Albania and Slovenia. See Slovenia No. 1474.

Endangered Animals — A890

2022, Mar. 30 Litho. *Perf. 13¼x13*
3053 A890 150 l multi 2.75 2.75

Souvenir Sheet

3054 A890 250 l multi 4.50 4.50
a. Booklet pane fo 2, #3053-3054 7.25 —
Complete booklet, #3054a 7.25

Europa. Dated 2021.

Flora A891

No. 3055: a, 5 l, Rosmarinus officinalis. b, 30 l, Origanum heracleoticum. c, 200 l, Lilium albanicum.

2022, Apr. 4 Litho. *Perf. 13¼x13*
3055 A891 Horiz. strip of 3, #a-c 4.25 4.25

Dated 2021.

Souvenir Sheets

Famous Men A892

Designs: 10 l, Ali Pasha of Gusinje (1828-88), military commander. 20 l, Naum Naçi, (1871-1927), teacher and writer. 50 l, Mustafa Krantja (1921-2002), composer and conductor. 100 l, Guri Madhi (1921-88), painter. 140 l, Andrea Mano (1919-2000), sculptor. 180 l, Pandi Raidhi (1931-99), actor.

2022, Apr. 11 Litho. *Perf. 13¼x13*
3056-3061 A892 Set of 6 8.75 8.75

Dated 2021.

Egyptian Vulture A893

No. 3062: a, 50 l, Two vultures. b, 250 l, Two vultures, diff.

2022, Apr. 14 Litho. *Perf. 13¼x13*
3062 A893 Horiz. pair, #a-b 5.25 5.25

Dated 2021.

Vehicles of Rally Albania A894

No. 3063: a, 20 l, Motorcycle. b, 40 l, Truck. c, 80 l, Off-road vehicle. d, 130 l, All-terrain vehicle.

2022, Apr. 18 Litho. *Perf. 13¼x13*
3063 A894 Block of 4, #a-d 4.75 4.75

Dated 2021.

Souvenir Sheet

Houses of Worship A895

2022, Apr. 25 Litho. *Perf. 13*
3064 A895 190 l multi 3.50 3.50

Dated 2021.

Rights of Children A896

No. 3065: a, 40 l, Six children. b, 120 l, Five children.

2022, Apr. 28 Litho. *Perf. 13*
3065 A896 Horiz. pair, #a-b 3.00 3.00

Dated 2021.

Gjipe Canyon A897

No. 3066 — Various views of canyon: a, 100 l. b, 150 l.

2022, May 2 Litho. *Perf. 13*
3066 A897 Horiz. pair, #a-b 4.50 4.50

Tourism. Dated 2021.

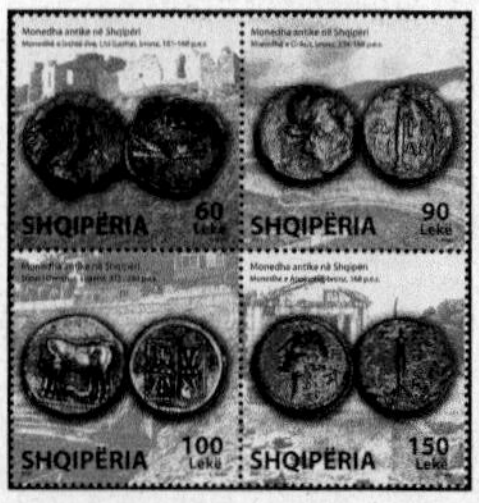

Ancient Coins A898

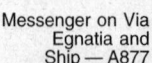

No. 3067: a, 60 l, Bronze Illyrian coin, 181-168 B.C. b, 90 l, Bronze coin of Oricum, 234-168 B.C. c, 100 l, Silver stater from mint at Dyrrachium (Durres), 375-280 B.C. d, 150 l, Bronze coin of Apollonia, 168 B.C.

2022, May 6 **Litho.** ***Perf. 13***
3067 A898 Block of 4, #a-d 7.25 7.25

Dated 2021.

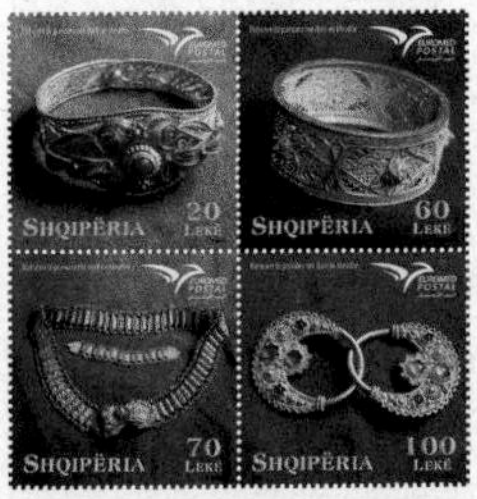

Handmade Jewelry — A899

No. 3068 — Various pieces of jewelry with denomination of: a, 20 l. b, 60 l. c, 70 l. d, 100 l.

2022, May 11 **Litho.** ***Perf. 13***
3068 A899 Block of 4, #a-d 4.50 4.50

Dated 2021.

SEMI-POSTAL STAMPS

Nos. 148-151 Surcharged in Red and Black

1924, Nov. 1

B1 A18 5q + 5q yel grn 11.00 *30.00*
B2 A18 10q + 5q carmine 11.00 *30.00*
B3 A18 25q + 5q dark blue 11.00 *30.00*
B4 A18 50q + 5q dark grn 11.00 *30.00*
Nos. B1-B4 (4) 44.00 *120.00*

Nos. B1 to B4 with Additional Surcharge in Red and Black

1924

B5 A18 5q + 5q + 5q yel grn 11.00 26.00
B6 A18 10q + 5q + 5q car 11.00 26.00
B7 A18 25q + 5q + 5q dk bl 11.00 26.00
B8 A18 50q + 5q + 5q dk grn 11.00 26.00
Nos. B5-B8 (4) 44.00 *104.00*

Issued under Italian Dominion

Nurse and Child — SP1

Unwmk.

1943, Apr. 1 **Photo.** ***Perf. 14***

B9 SP1 5q + 5q dark grn 1.00 *1.50*
B10 SP1 10q + 10q olive brn 1.00 *1.50*
B11 SP1 15q + 10q rose red 1.00 *1.50*
B12 SP1 25q + 15q saphire 1.00 *2.75*
B13 SP1 30q + 20q violet 1.00 *2.75*
B14 SP1 50q + 25q dk org 1.00 *2.75*
B15 SP1 65q + 30q grnsh blk 1.40 *4.00*
B16 SP1 1fr + 40q chestnut 3.00 *5.25*
Nos. B9-B16 (8) 10.40 *22.00*

The surtax was for the control of tuberculosis.

For surcharges see Nos. B24-B27.

Issued under German Administration

War Victims — SP2

1944, Sept. 22

B17 SP2 5g + 5(q) dp grn 2.50 *17.00*
B18 SP2 10g + 5(q) dp brn 2.50 *17.00*
B19 SP2 15g + 5(q) car lake 2.50 *17.00*
B20 SP2 25g + 10(q) dp blue 2.50 *17.00*
B21 SP2 1fr + 50q dk olive 2.50 *17.00*
B22 SP2 2fr + 1(fr) purple 2.50 *17.00*
B23 SP2 3fr + 1.50(fr) dk org 2.50 *17.00*
Nos. B17-B23 (7) 17.50 *119.00*

Surtax for victims of World War II.

Independent State

Nos. B9 to B12 Surcharged in Carmine

1945, May 4 **Unwmk.** ***Perf. 14***

B24 SP1 30q +15q on 5q+5q 5.00 *13.00*
B25 SP1 50q +25q on 10q+10q 7.50 *13.00*
B26 SP1 1fr +50q on 15q+10q 12.50 *27.50*
B27 SP1 2fr +1fr on 25q+15q 17.50 *37.50*
Nos. B24-B27 (4) 42.50 91.00

The surtax was for the Albanian Red Cross.

People's Republic

Nos. 361 to 366 Overprinted in Red (cross) and Surcharged in Black

1946, July 16 ***Perf. 11***

B28 A57 20q + 10q bluish grn 11.00 *30.00*
B29 A57 30q + 15q dp org 11.00 *30.00*
B30 A57 40q + 20q brown 11.00 *30.00*
B31 A57 60q + 30q red vio 11.00 *30.00*
B32 A57 1fr + 50q rose red 11.00 *30.00*
B33 A57 3fr + 1.50fr dk bl 11.00 *30.00*
Nos. B28-B33 (6) 66.00 *180.00*

To honor and benefit the Congress of the Albanian Red Cross.

Counterfeits: lithographed; genuine: typographed.

Catalogue values for unused stamps in this section, from this point to the end of the section, are for Never Hinged items.

SP3

First Aid and Red Cross: 25q+5q, Nurse carrying child on stretcher. 65q+25q, Symbolic blood transfusion. 80q+40q, Mother and child.

1967, Dec. 1 **Litho.** ***Perf. 11½x12***

B34 SP3 15q + 5q blk, red & brn .75 .35
B35 SP3 25q + 5q multi 1.50 .80
B36 SP3 65q + 25q multi 5.00 2.75
B37 SP3 80q + 40q multi 7.00 4.00
Nos. B34-B37 (4) 14.25 7.90

6th congress of the Albanian Red Cross.

SP4

1996, Aug. 5 **Litho.** ***Perf. 13½x13***
B38 SP4 50 l +10 l multi 1.60 1.60

Albanian Red Cross, 75th anniv.

Nos. 2469-2470 Surcharged

Methods and Perfs as Before

2001, Mar. 12

B39 A567 80 l +10 l on 50 l multi 4.50 4.50
B40 A567 130 l +20 l on 100 l multi 7.50 7.50

AIR POST STAMPS

Airplane Crossing Mountains — AP1

Wmk. 125

1925, May 30 **Typo.** ***Perf. 14***

C1 AP1 5q green 2.25 *3.50*
C2 AP1 10q rose red 2.25 *3.50*
C3 AP1 25q deep blue 2.25 *3.50*
C4 AP1 50q dark green 3.50 *6.00*
C5 AP1 1fr dk vio & blk 6.25 *10.50*
C6 AP1 2fr ol grn & vio 10.50 *17.50*
C7 AP1 3fr brn org & dk grn 12.50 *17.50*
Nos. C1-C7 (7) 39.50 *62.00*

Nos. C1-C7 exist imperf. Value $3,000.

For overprint see Nos. C8-C28.

Nos. C1-C7 Overprinted

1927, Jan. 18

C8 AP1 5q green 5.25 *10.50*
a. Dbl. overprint, one invtd. 50.00
C9 AP1 10q rose red 5.25 *10.50*
a. Inverted overprint 45.00
b. Dbl. overprint, one invtd. 50.00
C10 AP1 25q deep blue 4.75 *9.50*
C11 AP1 50q dark grn 3.25 *6.50*
a. Inverted overprint 45.00
C12 AP1 1fr dk vio & blk 3.25 *6.50*
a. Inverted overprint 45.00
b. Double overprint 45.00
C13 AP1 2fr ol grn & vio 7.50 *10.50*
C14 AP1 3fr brn org & dk grn 10.50 *15.00*
Nos. C8-C14 (7) 39.75 *69.00*

Nos. C1-C7 Overprinted

1928, Apr. 21

C15 AP1 5q green 5.25 *10.50*
a. Inverted overprint 70.00
C16 AP1 10q rose red 5.25 *10.50*
C17 AP1 25q deep blue 5.25 *10.50*
C18 AP1 50q dark green 10.00 *21.00*
C19 AP1 1fr dk vio & blk 55.00 *110.00*
C20 AP1 2fr ol grn & vio 55.00 *110.00*
C21 AP1 3fr brn org & dk grn 55.00 *110.00*
Nos. C15-C21 (7) 190.75 *382.50*

First flight across the Adriatic, Valona to Brindisi, Apr. 21, 1928.

The variety "SHQYRTARE" occurs once in the sheet for each value. Value 3 times normal.

Nos. C1-C7 Overprinted in Red Brown

1929, Dec. 1

C22 AP1 5q green 6.00 *8.75*
C23 AP1 10q rose red 6.00 *8.75*
C24 AP1 25q deep blue 6.00 *8.75*
C25 AP1 50q dk grn 125.00 *175.00*
C26 AP1 1fr dk vio & blk 250.00 *200.00*
C27 AP1 2fr ol grn 250.00 *375.00*
C28 AP1 3fr brn org & dk grn 250.00 *375.00*
Nos. C22-C28 (7) 893.00 *1,151.*

Excellent counterfeits exist.

King Zog and Airplane over Tirana — AP2

AP3

1930, Oct. 8 **Photo.** **Unwmk.**

C29 AP2 5q yellow green 1.00 *1.75*
C30 AP2 15q rose red 1.00 *1.75*
C31 AP2 20q slate blue 1.00 *1.75*
C32 AP2 50q olive green 2.00 *2.75*
C33 AP3 1fr dark blue 3.00 *5.25*
C34 AP3 2fr olive brown 10.00 *17.50*
C35 AP3 3fr purple 22.50 17.50
Nos. C29-C35 (7) 40.50 *48.25*

For overprints and surcharges see Nos. C36-C45.

Nos. C29-C35 Overprinted

1931, July 6

C36 AP2 5q yellow grn 5.25 *10.50*
a. Double overprint *140.00*
C37 AP2 15q rose red 5.25 *10.50*
C38 AP2 20q slate blue 5.25 *10.50*
C39 AP2 50q olive grn 5.25 *10.50*
C40 AP3 1fr dark blue 30.00 *60.00*
C41 AP3 2fr olive brn 30.00 *60.00*
C42 AP3 3fr purple 30.00 *60.00*
a. Inverted overprint *275.00*
Nos. C36-C42 (7) 111.00 *222.00*

1st air post flight from Tirana to Rome.

Only a very small part of this issue was sold to the public. Most of the stamps were given to the Aviation Company to help provide funds for conducting the service.

Issued under Italian Dominion

Nos. C29-C30 Overprinted in Black

1939, Apr. 19 **Unwmk.** ***Perf. 14***

C43 AP2 5q yel green 3.00 *7.00*
C44 AP2 15q rose red 3.00 *7.00*

No. C32 With Additional Surcharge

C45 AP2 20q on 50q ol grn 5.00 *11.50*
a. Inverted overprint — —
Nos. C43-C45 (3) 11.00 *25.50*

See note after No. 309.

King Victor Emmanuel III and Plane over Mountains — AP4

1939, Aug. 4 **Photo.**

C46 AP4 20q brown 35.00 15.00

Shepherds
AP5

Map of Albania Showing Air Routes
AP6

Designs: 20q, Victor Emmanuel III and harbor view. 50q, Woman and river valley. 1fr, Bridge at Vezirit. 2fr, Ruins. 3fr, Women waving to plane.

1940, Mar. 20 **Unwmk.**

C47	AP5	5q green	1.25	*1.25*
C48	AP6	15q rose red	1.25	*1.90*
C49	AP5	20q deep blue	2.50	*3.25*
C50	AP6	50q brown	3.25	*9.50*
C51	AP5	1fr myrtle green	6.50	*12.50*
C52	AP6	2fr brown black	9.50	*19.00*
C53	AP6	3fr rose violet	16.00	*25.00*
		Nos. C47-C53 (7)	40.25	*72.40*

People's Republic

Vuno-Himare — AP12

Albanian Towns: 1 l, 10 l, Rozafat-Shkoder. 2 l, 20 l, Keshtjelle-Butrinto.

1950, Dec. 15 **Engr.** ***Perf. 12½x12***

C54	AP12	50q gray black	.25	*1.00*
C55	AP12	1 l red brown	1.00	*.80*
C56	AP12	2 l ultra	.50	*1.60*
C57	AP12	5 l deep green	2.00	*3.00*
C58	AP12	10 l deep blue	4.50	*5.50*
C59	AP12	20 l purple	10.00	11.00
		Nos. C54-C59 (6)	18.25	*22.90*

Nos. C56-C58 Surcharged with New Value and Bars in Red or Black

1952-53

C60	AP12	50q on 2 l (R)	90.00	*150.00*
C61	AP12	50q on 5 l	22.50	*30.00*
C62	AP12	2.50 l on 5 l (R)	150.00	*175.00*
C63	AP12	2.50 l on 10 l	25.00	*45.00*
		Nos. C60-C63 (4)	287.50	*400.00*

Issued: Nos. C60, C62, 12/26/52; Nos. C61, C63, 3/14/53.

Catalogue values for unused stamps in this section, from this point to the end of the section, are for Never Hinged items.

Banner with Lenin, Map of Stalingrad and Tanks — AP13

1963, Feb. 2 **Litho.** ***Perf. 14***

C67	AP13	7 l grn & dp car	8.00	3.00

20th anniversary, Battle of Stalingrad.

Sputnik and Sun — AP14

Designs: 3 l, Lunik 4. 5 l, Lunik 3 photographing far side of the Moon. 8 l, Venus space probe. 12 l, Mars 1.

1963, Oct. 31 **Unwmk.** ***Perf. 12***

C68	AP14	2 l org, yel & blk	.35	.35
C69	AP14	3 l multi	.70	.35
C70	AP14	5 l rose lil, yel & blk	1.00	.35
C71	AP14	8 l multi	1.75	.70
C72	AP14	12 l blue & org	3.50	2.75
		Nos. C68-C72 (5)	7.30	4.50

Russian interplanetary explorations.

Nos. C68 and C71 Overprinted "Riccione 23-8-1964"

1964, Aug. 23

C73	AP14	2 l org, yel & blk	7.00	*14.00*
C74	AP14	8 l multicolored	14.00	*21.00*

Intl. Space Exhib. in Riccione, Italy.

Plane over Berat — AP15

1975, Nov. 25 **Litho.** ***Perf. 12***

C75	AP15	20q multi	.25	.25
C76	AP15	40q Gjirokaster	.30	.25
C77	AP15	60q Sarande	.55	.30
C78	AP15	90q Durres	1.10	.35
C79	AP15	1.20 l Kruje	1.40	.70
C80	AP15	2.40 l Boga	2.75	1.40
C81	AP15	4.05 l Tirana	4.25	2.10
		Nos. C75-C81 (7)	10.60	5.35

SPECIAL DELIVERY STAMPS

Issued under Italian Dominion

King Victor Emmanuel III — SD1

1940 **Unwmk.** **Photo.** ***Perf. 14***

E1	SD1	25q bright violet	4.50	*7.50*
E2	SD1	50q red orange	11.50	*18.00*

Issued under German Administration

No. E1 Overprinted in Carmine

1943

E3	SD1	25q bright violet	12.50	*24.00*

Proclamation of Albanian independence.

POSTAGE DUE STAMPS

Nos. 35-39 Handstamped in Various Colors

1914, Feb. 23 **Unwmk.** ***Perf. 14***

J1	A3	2q org brn & buff (Bl)	10.50	4.50
a.		Violet ovpt.	30.00	26.00
b.		Black ovpt.	30.00	30.00
J2	A3	5q green (R)	10.50	4.50
a.		Violet ovpt.	37.50	37.50
b.		Blue ovpt.	30.00	30.00
J3	A3	10q rose red (Bl)	15.00	4.50
a.		Violet ovpt.	30.00	26.00
J4	A3	25q dark blue (R)	17.50	4.50
J5	A3	50q vio & red (Bk)	26.00	14.00
		Nos. J1-J5 (5)	79.50	32.00

The two parts of the overprint are handstamped separately. Stamps exist with one or both handstamps inverted, double or omitted.

Nos. 48-51 Overprinted in Black

1914, Apr. 16

J6	A3 (a)	10pa on 5q green	5.25	4.50
J7	A3 (a)	20pa on 10q rose red	5.25	4.50
J8	A3 (b)	1gr on 25q blue	5.25	4.50
J9	A3 (b)	2gr on 50q vio & red	5.25	4.50
		Nos. J6-J9 (4)	21.00	18.00

Same Design as Regular Issue of 1919, Overprinted

1919, Feb. 10 ***Perf. 11½, 12½***

J10	A8	(4)q on 4h rose	13.00	10.50
J11	A8	(10)q on 10k red, *grn*	13.00	10.50
J12	A8	20q on 2k org, *gray*	13.00	10.50
J13	A8	50q on 5k brn, *yel*	13.00	10.50
		Nos. J10-J13 (4)	52.00	42.00

Nos. J10-J12 exist with overprint in red. Value, each $50.

Fortress at Scutari — D3

Post Horn Overprinted in Black

1920, Apr. 1 ***Perf. 14x13***

J14	D3	4q olive green	.75	*4.50*
J15	D3	10q rose red	1.50	*6.50*
J16	D3	20q bister brn	1.50	*6.50*
J17	D3	50q black	4.00	*17.50*
		Nos. J14-J17 (4)	7.75	*35.00*

D5

Background of Red Wavy Lines

1922 ***Perf. 12½, 11½***

J23	D5	4q black, *red*	1.10	*4.50*
J24	D5	10q black, *red*	1.10	*4.50*
J25	D5	20q black, *red*	1.10	*4.50*
J26	D5	50q black, *red*	1.10	*4.50*
		Nos. J23-J26 (4)	4.40	*18.00*

Nos. J23-J26 Overprinted in White

1925

J27	D5	4q black, *red*	1.90	*4.50*
J28	D5	10q black, *red*	1.90	*4.50*
J29	D5	20q black, *red*	1.90	*4.50*
J30	D5	50q black, *red*	1.90	*4.50*
		Nos. J27-J30 (4)	7.60	*18.00*

The 10q with overprint in gold was a trial printing. It was not put in use.

D7

Overprinted "QIND. AR" in Red

1926, Dec. 24 ***Perf. 13½x13***

J31	D7	10q dark blue	.75	3.50
J32	D7	20q green	.75	3.50
J33	D7	30q red brown	1.50	*7.00*
J34	D7	50q dark brown	2.75	*13.00*
		Nos. J31-J34 (4)	5.75	*27.00*

Coat of Arms — D8

Wmk. Double Headed Eagle (220)

1930, Sept. 1 **Photo.** ***Perf. 14, 14½***

J35	D8	10q dark blue	6.75	*21.00*
J36	D8	20q rose red	2.75	*13.00*
J37	D8	30q violet	2.75	*13.00*
J38	D8	50q dark green	2.75	*13.00*
		Nos. J35-J38 (4)	15.00	*60.00*

Nos. J36-J38 exist with overprint "14 Shtator 1943" (see Nos. 332-344) which is private and fraudulent on these stamps.

No. 253 Overprinted

1936 ***Perf. 14***

J39	A34	10q carmine	10.00	*45.00*
a.		Hyphens on each side of "Takse" ('39)	100.00	*200.00*

Issued under Italian Dominion

Coat of Arms — D9

1940 **Unwmk.** **Photo.** ***Perf. 14***

J40	D9	4q red orange	*20.00*	*45.00*
J41	D9	10q bright violet	*20.00*	*45.00*
J42	D9	20q brown	*20.00*	*45.00*
J43	D9	30q dark blue	*20.00*	*45.00*
J44	D9	50q carmine rose	*20.00*	*45.00*
		Nos. J40-J44 (5)	*100.00*	*225.00*

CENTRAL ALBANIA

After the departure of Prince Wilhelm of Wied Oct. 2, 1914, Essad Pasha established a regime in Durres, which, with Serbian support, soon included much of central Albania. The regime issued stamps, overprinted on previously issued Albanian regular postage, postage due, and revenue stamps, and on unissued stamps commissioned in 1913 by an earlier government, which were in use during 1915/1916. Essad's Central Albania collapsed with the Austro-Hungarian invasion of the area in the spring of 1916.

Albania Nos. 35-37, 47-52 Handstamped in Black, Blue, Red or Violet

1915 ***Perf. 14***

1	A3	2q orange brn & buff	28.00	27.00
2	A3	5q green & bl grn	60.00	60.00
3	A3	10q rose red	40.00	37.50
4	A3	25q dark blue	55.00	65.00
5	A3	50q violet & red	55.00	65.00
6	A3(a)	5pa on 2q org brn & buff	40.00	37.50
7	A3(a)	10pa on 5q grn & bl grn	17.00	17.00
8	A3(a)	20pa on 10q rose red	17.00	17.00
9	A3(b)	1gr on 25q dk bl	17.00	17.00
10	A3(b)	2gr on 50q vio & red	17.00	17.00
11	A3(b)	5gr on 1r dp brown	37.50	50.00
		Nos. 1-11 (11)	383.50	410.00

Crescent Handstamp in Black or Violet on Unissued Stamps of Albania

12	A1	2pa orange	9.25	6.25
13	A1	5pa violet	9.25	8.75
14	A1	10pa green	9.25	9.25
15	A1	20pa red	9.25	6.25
16	A1	40pa blue	12.00	6.25
17	A1	100pa pink	28.00	11.50
18	A1	5pi black	80.00	32.00
		Nos. 12-18 (7)	157.00	80.25

Handstamp on Albania Fiscal Stamps

19	A2	10pa green	11.00	*11.50*
20	A2	20pa red	11.00	8.75
21	A2	50pa blue	7.50	6.25
22	A2	3pi rose	7.50	6.25
23	A2	6pi chocolate	17.00	13.50
		Nos. 19-23 (5)	54.00	46.25

POSTAGE DUE STAMPS

Large "T" Handstamp on Albania Nos. 47-52

J1	A3	2q orange brn & buff	45.00	42.50
J2	A3(a)	10pa on 5q grn & bl grn	28.00	27.00
J3	A3(a)	20pa on 10q rose red	28.00	27.00
J4	A3(b)	1gr on 25q dk bl	28.00	27.00
J5	A3(b)	2gr on 50q vio & red	28.00	27.00
		Nos. J1-J5 (5)	157.00	150.50

ALEXANDRETTA

ˌa-lig-ˌzan-ˈdre-tə

LOCATION — A political territory in northern Syria, bordering on Turkey
GOVT. — French mandate
AREA — 10,000 sq. mi. (approx.)
POP. — 270,000 (approx.)

Included in the Syrian territory mandated to France under the Versailles Treaty, the name was changed to Hatay in 1938. The following year France returned the territory to Turkey in exchange for certain concessions. See Hatay.

100 Centimes = 1 Piaster

Stamps of Syria, 1930-36, Overprinted or Surcharged in Black or Red

a

b

c

d

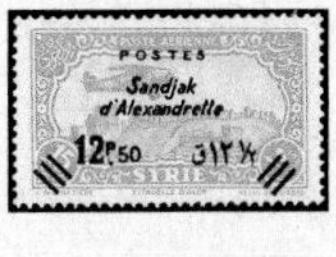

e

1938 Unwmk. *Perf. 12x12½*

1	A6 (a)	0.10p vio brn	3.50	3.50
2	A6 (a)	0.20p brn org	3.50	3.00

Perf. 13½

3	A9 (b)	0.50p vio (R)	4.50	3.50
4	A10 (b)	1p bis brn	4.50	3.00
5	A9 (b)	2p dk vio (R)	5.75	3.50
6	A13 (b)	3p yel grn (R)	9.00	7.00
7	A10 (b)	4p yel org	10.00	7.00
8	A16 (b)	6p grnsh blk (R)	12.00	8.00
9	A18 (b)	25p vio brn	25.00	25.00
10	A15 (c)	0.75p org red	9.00	9.00
11	A10 (d)	2.50p on 4p yel org	7.50	4.00
12	AP2 (e)	12.50p on 15p org red	20.00	15.00
		Nos. 1-12 (12)	114.25	91.50
		Set, never hinged	275.00	

Issue dates: Nos. 1-9, Apr. 14, Nos. 10-12, Sept. 2.

Nos. 4, 7, 10-12 Ovptd. in Black

1938, Nov. 10

13	A15	75c	60.00	60.00
a.		Overprint inverted	500.00	
14	A10	1p	37.50	37.50
a.		"Sandjah d'Alexandrette" omitted	325.00	
15	A10	2.50p on 4p	32.50	32.50
16	A10	4p	37.50	37.50
a.		"Sandjah d'Alexandrette" omitted	325.00	
17	AP2	12.50p on 15p	80.00	80.00
a.		"Sandjah d'Alexandrette" omitted	1,500.	
		Nos. 13-17 (5)	247.50	247.50
		Set, never hinged	500.00	

Death of Kemal Ataturk, pres. of Turkey.

AIR POST STAMPS

Air Post Stamps of Syria, 1937, Overprinted Type "b" in Red or Black

1938, Apr. 14 Unwmk. *Perf. 13*

C1	AP14	½p dark vio (R)	4.50	*5.00*
C2	AP15	1p black (R)	4.50	*5.50*
C3	AP14	2p blue grn (R)	5.50	*7.50*
C4	AP15	3p deep ultra	6.00	*8.00*
C5	AP14	5p rose lake	11.00	*18.00*
C6	AP15	10p red brown	11.50	*20.00*
C7	AP14	15p lake brown	14.50	*23.50*
C8	AP15	25p dk blue (R)	20.00	*31.00*
		Nos. C1-C8 (8)	77.50	*118.50*
		Set, never hinged	225.00	

POSTAGE DUE STAMPS

Postage Due Stamps of Syria, 1925-31, Ovptd. Type "b" in Black or Red

1938, Apr. 14 Unwmk. *Perf. 13½*

J1	D5	0.50p brown, *yel*	6.50	5.75
J2	D6	1p violet, *rose*	7.50	6.50
J3	D5	2p blk, *blue* (R)	8.50	8.00
J4	D5	3p blk, *red org*	10.00	9.00
J5	D5	5p blk, *bl grn* (R)	16.00	14.50
J6	D7	8p blk, *gray bl* (R)	22.50	20.00
		Nos. J1-J6 (6)	71.00	63.75
		Set, never hinged	225.00	

On No. J2, the overprint is vertical, reading up, other denominations, horizontal.

Stamps of Alexandretta were discontinued in 1938 and replaced by those of Hatay.

ALGERIA

al-ˈjir-ē-ə

LOCATION — North Africa
GOVT. — Republic
AREA — 919,595 sq. mi.
POP. — 29,300,000 (1998 est.)
CAPITAL — Algiers

The former French colony of Algeria became an integral part of France on Sept. 1, 1958, when French stamps replaced Algerian stamps. Algeria became an independent country July 3, 1962.

100 Centimes = 1 Franc
100 Centimes = 1 Dinar (1964)

Catalogue values for unused stamps in this country are for Never Hinged items, beginning with Scott 109 in the regular postage section, Scott B27 in the semi-postal section, Scott C1 in the airpost section, Scott CB1 in the airpost semi-postal section, Scott J25 in the postage due section, and Scott Q73 in the parcel post section.

Stamps of France Overprinted in Red, Blue or Black

a

b

c

d

1924-26 Unwmk. *Perf. 14x13½*

1	A16(a)	1c dk gray (R)	.40	.40
2	A16(a)	2c vio brn	.40	.40
3	A16(a)	3c orange	.40	.40
4	A16(a)	4c yel brn (Bl)	.40	.40
5	A22(a)	5c org (Bl)	.40	.40
6	A16(a)	5c grn ('25)	.80	.80
7	A23(a)	10c green	.80	.40
b.		Booklet pane of 10	—	
		Complete booklet, 2 #7b	300.00	
8	A22(a)	10c grn ('25)	.80	.40
a.		Pair, one without overprint	1,500.	
9	A20(a)	15c slate grn	.40	.40
10	A23(a)	15c grn ('25)	1.20	.40
11	A22(a)	15c red brn (Bl) ('26)	.40	.40
12	A22(a)	20c red brn (Bl)	.40	.40
a.		Pair, one without overprint	1,500.	
13	A22(a)	25c blue (R)	.80	.40
a.		Booklet pane of 10	—	
		Complete booklet, 2 #13a	1,450.	
b.		Pair, one without overprint	1,750.	
14	A23(a)	30c red (Bl)	2.40	.80
15	A22(a)	30c cerise ('25)	.80	.80
a.		"ALGERIE" double	225.00	150.00
16	A22(a)	30c lt bl (R) ('25)	.80	.80
a.		Booklet pane of 10	—	
		Complete booklet, 2 #16a	550.00	
17	A22(a)	35c violet	.80	.80
18	A18(b)	40c red & pale bl	1.20	.80
19	A22(a)	40c ol brn (R) ('25)	1.20	.80
20	A18(b)	45c grn & bl (R)	1.20	.80
a.		Double overprint	350.00	
21	A23(a)	45c red (Bl) ('25)	1.25	.80
22	A23(a)	50c blue (R)	1.20	.80
23	A20(a)	60c lt violet	1.20	.80
a.		Inverted overprint		*2,900.*
24	A20(a)	65c rose (Bl)	1.20	.80
25	A23(a)	75c blue (R)	1.25	.75
a.		Double overprint	300.00	300.00
26	A20(a)	80c ver ('26)	2.00	1.20
27	A20(a)	85c ver (Bl)	1.20	1.20
28	A18(b)	1fr cl & ol grn	2.00	1.20
a.		Olive green omitted	325.00	325.00
29	A22(a)	1.05fr ver ('26)	1.60	1.60
30	A18(c)	2fr org & pale bl	2.40	1.60
31	A18(b)	3fr vio & bl ('26)	5.50	2.40
a.		Blue omitted	325.00	
32	A18(d)	5fr bl & buff (R)	16.00	12.00
		Nos. 1-32 (32)	52.80	36.35

No. 15 was issued precanceled only. Values for precanceled stamps in first column are for those which have not been through the post and have original gum. Values in second column are for postally used, gumless stamps.

For surcharges see Nos. 75, P1.

Street in Kasbah, Algiers
A1

Mosque of Sidi Abd-er-Rahman
A2

La Pêcherie Mosque
A3

Marabout of Sidi Yacoub
A4

1926-39 Typo. *Perf. 14x13½*

33	A1	1c olive	.25	.25
a.		Imperforate	110.00	
34	A1	2c red brown	.25	.25
35	A1	3c orange	.25	.25
36	A1	5c blue green	.25	.25
37	A1	10c brt violet	.40	.25
a.		Booklet pane of 10	—	
		Complete booklet, 2 #37a	400.00	
38	A2	15c orange brn	.40	.25
a.		Imperforate	110.00	
b.		Booklet pane of 10	—	
		Complete booklet, 2 #38b	350.00	
39	A2	20c green	.40	.25
40	A2	20c deep rose	.25	.25
a.		Imperforate	120.00	
41	A2	25c blue grn	.40	.25
42	A2	25c blue ('27)	.80	.40
a.		Imperforate	120.00	
43	A2	25c vio bl ('39)	.25	.25
44	A2	30c blue	.40	.40
a.		Imperforate	120.00	
45	A2	30c bl grn ('27)	1.25	.80
46	A2	35c dp violet	1.60	1.20
47	A2	40c olive green	.40	.25
a.		Booklet pane of 10	—	
		Complete booklet, 2 #47a	325.00	
b.		Imperforate	120.00	
48	A3	45c violet brn	.80	.40
49	A3	50c blue	.40	.40
a.		Booklet pane of 10	—	
		Complete booklet, 2 #49a	400.00	
b.		Imperforate	125.00	
c.		Vert. pair, #49 and 49b	225.00	
50	A3	50c dk red ('30)	.40	.25
a.		Booklet pane of 10	—	
		Complete booklet, 2 #50a	450.00	
b.		Imperforate	120.00	
51	A3	60c yellow grn	.40	.40
52	A3	65c blk brn ('27)	3.25	2.40
53	A1	65c ultra ('38)	.40	.40
a.		Booklet pane of 10	—	
		Complete booklet, 2 #53a	160.00	
54	A3	75c carmine	1.20	.80
a.		Imperforate	125.00	
b.		Vert. pair, #54 and 54a	225.00	
55	A3	75c blue ('29)	4.75	.80
56	A3	80c orange red	1.20	.80
57	A3	90c red ('27)	8.00	4.00
a.		Imperforate	120.00	
58	A4	1fr gray grn & red brn	1.20	.80
a.		Imperforate	175.00	
59	A3	1.05fr lt brown	1.20	.80
60	A3	1.10fr mag ('27)	8.00	4.00
61	A4	1.25fr dk bl & ultra	1.60	1.20
62	A4	1.50fr dk bl & ultra ('27)	5.50	.80
a.		Imperforate	400.00	
63	A4	2fr prus bl & blk brn	4.75	1.20
a.		Imperforate	125.00	
64	A4	3fr violet & org	8.00	1.60
65	A4	5fr red & violet	16.00	4.75
66	A4	10fr ol brn & rose ('27)	80.00	47.50
a.		Imperforate	725.00	
67	A4	20fr vio & grn ('27)	8.00	8.00
		Nos. 33-67 (35)	162.60	86.85

A 90c red, design A1, was prepared but not issued. Values: unused $950, never hinged $1,350.

Type A4, 50c blue and rose red, inscribed "CENTENAIRE-ALGERIE" is France No. 255.

See design A24. For stamps and types surcharged see Nos. 68-74, 131, 136, 187, B1-B13, J27, P2.

Stamps of 1926 Surcharged

1927

68	A2	10c on 35c dp violet	.25	.25
69	A2	25c on 30c blue	.25	.25
70	A2	30c on 25c blue grn	.40	.25
71	A3	65c on 80c yel grn	1.60	1.20
72	A3	90c on 80c org red	1.40	.95
73	A3	1.10fr on 1.05fr lt brn	1.00	.50
74	A4	1.50fr on 1.25fr dk bl & ultra	3.25	1.50
		Nos. 68-74 (7)	8.15	4.90

Bars cancel the old value on Nos. 68, 69, 73, 74.

No. 4 Surcharged

1927

75	A16	5c on 4c yellow brown	.40	.40
a.		Blue surcharge	1,250.	*1,400.*

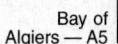

Bay of Algiers — A5

1930, May 4 **Engr.** ***Perf. 12½***

78 A5 10fr red brown 21.00 21.00
a. Imperf., pair 150.00

Cent. of Algeria and for Intl. Phil. Exhib. of North Africa, May, 1930.

One example of No. 78 was sold with each 10fr admission.

Travel across the Sahara — A6

Arch of Triumph, Lambese — A7

Admiralty Building, Algiers — A8

Kings' Tombs near Touggourt — A9

El-Kebir Mosque, Algiers A10

Oued River at Colomb-Bechar A11

Sidi Bon Medine— Cemetery at Tlemcen A13

View of Ghardaia A12

1936-41 **Engr.** ***Perf. 13***

79 A6 1c ultra .25 .40
80 A11 2c dk violet .25 .40
81 A7 3c dk blue grn .25 .40
82 A12 5c red violet .40 .25
83 A8 10c emerald .25 .40
84 A9 15c red .25 .40
85 A13 20c dk blue grn .40 .40
86 A10 25c rose vio 1.20 .80
87 A12 30c yellow grn .80 .40
88 A9 40c brown vio .40 .40
89 A13 45c deep ultra 2.00 1.20
On cover 4.50
90 A8 50c red 1.20 .40
91 A6 65c red brn 8.00 4.00
92 A6 65c rose car ('37) .80 .80
93 A6 70c red brn ('39) .40 .40
94 A11 75c slate bl .80 .40
95 A7 90c henna brn 2.40 1.60
96 A10 1fr brown .80 .40
97 A8 1.25fr lt violet 1.20 .80
98 A8 1.25fr car rose ('39) .80 .40
99 A11 1.50fr turq blue 2.40 .80
99A A11 1.50fr rose ('40) .80 .80
100 A12 1.75fr henna brn .40 .40
101 A7 2fr dk brown .80 .40
102 A6 2.25fr yellow grn 20.00 13.50
103 A12 2.50fr dk ultra ('41) .80 .80
104 A13 3fr magenta 1.20 .80
105 A10 3.50fr pck blue 6.50 4.00
106 A8 5fr slate blue 1.60 .80
107 A11 10fr henna brn 1.20 .80
108 A9 20fr turq blue 1.60 1.20
Nos. 79-108 (31) 60.15 38.95

See Nos. 124-125, 162.

Nos. 82 and 100 with surcharge "E. F. M. 30frs" (Emergency Field Message) were used in 1943 to pay cable tolls for US and Canadian servicemen.

For other surcharges see Nos. 122, B27.

Catalogue values for unused stamps in this section, from this point to the end of the section, are for Never Hinged items.

Algerian Pavilion — A14

1937 ***Perf. 13***

109 A14 40c brt green 2.00 1.20
110 A14 50c rose carmine 2.00 .80
111 A14 1.50fr blue 2.75 1.20
112 A14 1.75fr brown black 2.75 1.60
Nos. 109-112 (4) 9.50 4.80

Paris International Exposition.

Constantine in 1837 — A15

1937

113 A15 65c deep rose 1.20 .80
114 A15 1fr brown 12.00 1.60
115 A15 1.75fr blue green 1.60 .80
116 A15 2.15fr red violet 1.60 .80
Nos. 113-116 (4) 16.40 4.00

Taking of Constantine by the French, cent.

Ruins of a Roman Villa — A16

1938

117 A16 30c green 2.00 .80
118 A16 65c ultra .80 .80
119 A16 75c rose violet 2.00 .80
120 A16 3fr carmine rose 5.50 4.00
121 A16 5fr yellow brown 8.00 5.50
Nos. 117-121 (5) 18.30 11.90

Centenary of Philippeville.

No. 90 Surcharged in Black

1938

122 A8 25c on 50c red .80 .40
a. Double surcharge 100.00 60.00
b. Inverted surcharge 72.50 47.50
c. Pair, one without surcharge 400.00

Types of 1936 Numerals of Value on Colorless Background

1939

124 A7 90c henna brown 1.20 .40
125 A10 2.25fr blue green 1.20 .80

For surcharge see No. B38.

American Export Liner Unloading Cargo — A17

1939

126 A17 20c green 4.00 1.60
127 A17 40c red violet 4.00 1.60
128 A17 90c brown black 2.40 .80
129 A17 1.25fr rose 9.50 4.00
130 A17 2.25fr ultra 4.00 2.40
Nos. 126-130 (5) 23.90 10.40

New York World's Fair.

Type of 1926, Surcharged in Black

Two types of surcharge:
I — Bars 6mm
II — Bars 7mm

1939-40 ***Perf. 14x13½***

131 A1 1fr on 90c crimson (I) .80 .40
a. Booklet pane of 10 —
Complete booklet, 2 #131a 625.00
b. Double surcharge (I) 175.00
c. Inverted surcharge (I) 87.50
d. Pair, one without surch. (I) *1,800.*
e. Type II ('40) 8.00 1.60
f. Inverted surcharge (II) 95.00
g. Pair, one without surch. (II) *1,800.*

View of Algiers — A18

1941 **Typo.**

132 A18 30c ultra .50 .30
133 A18 70c sepia .50 .30
134 A18 1fr carmine rose .50 .30
Nos. 132-134 (3) 1.50 .90

See No. 163.

Marshal Pétain — A19

1941 **Engr.** ***Perf. 13***

135 A19 1fr dark blue .50 .30

For stamp and type surcharged see Nos. B36-B37.

No. 53 Surcharged in Black

1941 ***Perf. 14x13½***

136 A1 50c on 65c ultra .70 .25
a. Booklet pane of 10 —
Complete booklet, 2 #136a 120.00
b. Inverted surcharge 95.00
c. Pair, one without surch. 225.00

Marshal Pétain — A20

1942 ***Perf. 14x13***

137 A20 1.50fr orange red .30 .25

Four other denominations of type A20 exist but were not placed in use. Values: 4fr, $1,300; 5fr, $1,100; 10fr, 20fr, each $600.

Constantine A21

Oran A22

Arms of Algiers — A23

Engraver's Name at Lower Left

1942-43 **Photo.** ***Perf. 12***

138 A21 40c dark vio ('43) .70 .40
139 A22 60c rose ('43) .55 .25
140 A21 1.20fr yel grn ('43) .30 .25
141 A23 1.50fr car rose .30 .25
142 A22 2fr sapphire .80 .25
143 A21 2.40fr rose ('43) .55 .25
144 A23 3fr sapphire .95 .25
145 A21 4fr blue ('43) .70 .25
146 A22 5fr yel grn ('43) .65 .30
Nos. 138-146 (9) 5.50 2.45

For type surcharged see No. 166.

No. 142 exists in green and violet. Value, each $60.

Imperforates

Nearly all of Algeria Nos. 138-285, B39-B96, C1-C12 and CB1-CB3 exist imperforate. See note after France No. 395.

Without Engraver's Name

1942-45 **Typo.** ***Perf. 14x13½***

147 A23 10c dull brn vio ('45) .30 .25
148 A22 30c dp bl grn ('45) .30 .25
149 A21 40c dull brn vio ('45) .30 .25
150 A22 60c rose ('45) .30 .25
151 A21 70c deep bl ('45) .30 .25
152 A23 80c dk bl grn ('43) 1.25 .90
153 A21 1.20fr dp bl grn ('45) .50 .30
154 A23 1.50fr brt rose ('43) .30 .25
155 A22 2fr dp blue ('45) .30 .25
156 A21 2.40fr rose ('45) .80 .65
157 A23 3fr dp blue ('45) .55 .40
158 A22 4.50fr brown vio .30 .25
Nos. 147-158 (12) 5.50 4.25

For surcharge see No. 190.

La Pêcherie Mosque — A24

1942 **Typo.**

159 A24 50c dull red .55 .25
a. Booklet pane of 10 —
Complete booklet, 2 #159a 325.00

1942 **Photo.** ***Perf. 12***

160 A24 40c gray green .55 .25
161 A24 50c red .55 .25

Types of 1936-41, Without "RF"

1942 **Engr.** ***Perf. 13***

162 A11 1.50fr rose .55 .25

Typo. ***Perf. 14x13½***

163 A18 30c ultra .55 .25

"One Aim Alone" A25

"Victory" A26

1943 **Litho.** ***Perf. 12***

164 A25 1.50fr deep rose .55 .25
165 A26 1.50fr dark blue .55 .25

Type of 1942-3 Surcharged with New Value in Black

1943 **Photo.**

166 A22 2fr on 5fr red orange .30 .25
a. Surcharge omitted 325.00

Summer Palace, Algiers — A27

1944, Dec. 1 **Litho.**

167 A27 15fr slate 2.00 1.75
168 A27 20fr lt blue grn 2.00 .80
169 A27 50fr dk carmine 1.60 .80
170 A27 100fr deep blue 4.00 2.50
171 A27 200fr dull bis brn 5.50 2.75
Nos. 167-171 (5) 15.10 8.60

Marianne A28

Gallic Cock A29

1944-45

172 A28 10c gray .55 .30
173 A28 30c red violet .30 .25
174 A29 40c rose car ('45) .50 .30

175 A28 50c red .50 .30
176 A28 80c emerald .30 .25
177 A29 1fr green ('45) .30 .25
178 A28 1.20fr rose lilac .30 .25
179 A28 1.50fr dark blue .30 .25
a. Double impression 70.00
180 A29 2fr red .30 .25
a. Double impression 85.00
181 A29 2fr dk brown ('45) .30 .25
182 A28 2.40fr rose red .55 .25
183 A28 3fr purple .55 .40
184 A29 4fr ultra ('45) .30 .25
185 A28 4.50fr olive blk .95 .70
186 A29 10fr grnsh blk ('45) 1.90 .95
Nos. 172-186 (15) 7.90 5.20

No. 38 Surcharged in Black

1944 ***Perf. 14x13½***
187 A2 30c on 15c orange brn 1.20 .50
a. Inverted surcharge 70.00

This stamp exists precanceled only. See note below No. 32.

No. 154 Surcharged

1945
190 A23 50c on 1.50fr brt rose .55 .40
a. Inverted surcharge 72.50

Stamps of France, 1944, Overprinted Type "a" of 1924 in Black

1945-46
191 A99 80c yellow grn .65 .25
192 A99 1fr grnsh blue .50 .25
193 A99 1.20fr violet .70 .25
194 A99 2fr violet brown .90 .25
195 A99 2.40fr carmine rose 1.20 .40
196 A99 3fr orange 1.00 .30
Nos. 191-196 (6) 4.95 1.70

Stamps of France, 1945-47, Overprinted in Black, Red or Carmine

1945-47
197 A145 40c lilac rose .30 .25
198 A145 50c violet bl (R) .30 .25
199 A146 60c brt ultra (R) .95 .25
200 A146 1fr rose red ('47) .50 .25
201 A146 1.50fr rose lilac ('47) .50 .25
202 A147 2fr myr grn (R) ('46) .30 .25
203 A147 3fr deep rose .70 .25
204 A147 4.50fr ultra (C) ('47) 2.00 .25
205 A147 5fr lt green ('46) .50 .25
206 A147 10fr ultra 1.75 .50
Nos. 197-206 (10) 7.80 2.75

France No. 383 Surcharged and Overprinted in Black

1946
207 A99 2fr on 1.50fr henna brn .50 .25
a. Without "2F" 525.00

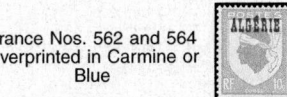

France Nos. 562 and 564 Overprinted in Carmine or Blue

1947
208 A153 10c dp ultra & blk (C) .30 .25
209 A155 50c brown, yel & red (Bl) .80 .30

Constantine A30

Algiers A31

Arms of Oran — A32

Perf. 14x13½
1947-49 **Unwmk.** **Typo.**
210 A30 10c dk grn & brt red .30 .25
211 A31 50c black & orange .30 .25
212 A32 1fr ultra & yellow .30 .25
213 A30 1.30fr blk & grnsh bl 1.90 1.25
214 A31 1.50fr pur & org yel .50 .25
215 A32 2fr blk & brt grn .30 .25
216 A30 2.50fr blk & brt red 1.20 .80
217 A31 3fr vio brn & grn .55 .25
218 A32 3.50fr lt grn & rose lil .55 .25
219 A30 4fr dk brn & brt grn .45 .25
220 A31 4.50fr ultra & scar .55 .25
221 A31 5fr blk & grnsh bl .30 .25
222 A32 6fr brown & scarlet 1.00 .30
223 A32 8fr choc & ultra ('48) .65 .25
224 A30 10fr car & choc ('48) 1.00 .40
225 A31 15fr black & red ('49) 1.10 .25
Nos. 210-225 (16) 10.95 5.75

See Nos. 274-280, 285.

Peoples of the World — A33

1949, Oct. 24 **Engr.** ***Perf. 13***
226 A33 5fr green 2.75 2.00
227 A33 15fr scarlet 3.50 2.00
228 A33 25fr ultra 6.00 5.25
Nos. 226-228 (3) 12.25 9.25

75th anniv. of the UPU.

Grapes — A34

25fr, Dates. 40fr, Oranges and lemons.

1950, Feb. 25
229 A34 20fr multicolored 2.75 .80
230 A34 25fr multicolored 3.25 1.25
231 A34 40fr multicolored 7.25 1.60
Nos. 229-231 (3) 13.25 3.65

Apollo of Cherchell — A35

Designs: 12fr, 18fr, Isis statue, Cherchell. 15fr, 20fr, Child with eagle.

1952 **Unwmk.** ***Perf. 13***
240 A35 10fr gray black .65 .25
241 A35 12fr orange brn 1.25 .40
242 A35 15fr deep blue 1.10 .25
243 A35 18fr rose red 1.10 .40
244 A35 20fr deep green 1.60 .25
245 A35 30fr deep blue 1.90 .95
Nos. 240-245 (6) 7.60 2.50

War Memorial, Algiers — A38

1952, Apr. 11
246 A38 12fr dark green 2.00 .80

Issued to honor the French Africa Army.

Fossilized Nautilus A39

Phonolite Dike A40

1952, Aug. 11
247 A39 15fr brt crimson 6.50 2.75
248 A40 30fr deep ultra 3.50 1.60

19th Intl. Geological Cong., Algiers, 9/8-15.

French and Algerian Soldiers and Camel — A41

1952, Nov. 30
249 A41 12fr chestnut brown 2.50 1.75

50th anniv. of the establishment of the Sahara Companies.

Eugène Millon A42

François C. Maillot A43

Portrait: 50fr, Alphonse Laveran.

Unwmk.
1954, Jan. 4 **Engr.** ***Perf. 13***
250 A42 25fr dk grn & choc 2.00 .80
251 A43 40fr org brn & brn car 3.00 1.20
252 A42 50fr ultra & indigo 3.00 .80
Nos. 250-252 (3) 8.00 2.80

Military Health Service.

Oranges — A44

1954, May 8
253 A44 15fr indigo & blue 2.00 1.20

3rd Intl. Cong. on Agronomy, Algiers, 1954.

Type of France, 1954 Overprinted type "a" in Black

Unwmk.
1954, June 6 **Engr.** ***Perf. 13***
254 A240 15fr rose carmine 2.00 1.20

Liberation of France, 10th anniversary.

Darguinah Hydroelectric Works — A45

1954, June 19
255 A45 15fr lilac rose 1.60 1.20

Opening of Darguinah hydroelectric works.

Patio of Bardo Museum — A46

1954 **Typo.** ***Perf. 14x13½***
257 A46 12fr red brn & brn org .80 .30
258 A46 15fr dk blue & blue .70 .25

See Nos. 267-271.

Type of France, 1954, Overprinted type "a" in Carmine

1954 **Engr.** ***Perf. 13***
260 A247 12fr dark green 2.00 1.00

150th anniv. of the 1st Legion of Honor awards at Camp de Boulogne.

St. Augustine — A47

1954, Nov. 11
261 A47 15fr chocolate 1.60 1.25

1600th anniv. of the birth of St. Augustine.

Aesculapius Statue and Ei Kattar Hospital, Algiers — A48

1955, Apr. 3 **Unwmk.** ***Perf. 13***
262 A48 15fr red 1.60 .80

Issued to publicize the 30th French Congress of Medicine, Algiers, April 3-6, 1955.

Chenua Mountain and View of Tipasa — A49

1955, May 31
263 A49 50fr brown carmine 1.50 .95

2000th anniv. of the founding of Tipasa.

Type of France, 1955 Overprinted type "a" in Red

1955, June 13
264 A251 30fr deep ultra 2.00 1.20

Rotary Intl., 50th anniv.

Marianne — A50

Perf. 14x13½
1955, Oct. 3 **Typo.** **Unwmk.**
265 A50 15fr carmine .80 .25

See No. 284.

Great Kabylia Mountains — A51

1955, Dec. 17 **Engr.** ***Perf. 13***
266 A51 100fr indigo & ultra 6.50 .80

Bardo Type of 1954, "Postes" and "Algerie" in White

Perf. 14x13½
1955-57 **Unwmk.** **Typo.**
267 A46 10fr dk brn & lt brn .80 .25
268 A46 12fr red brn & brn org ('56) .40 .25
269 A46 18fr crimson & ver ('57) 1.00 .30
270 A46 20fr grn & yel grn ('57) .90 .50
271 A46 25fr purple & brt purple 1.00 .25
Nos. 267-271 (5) 4.10 1.55

Marshal Franchet d'Esperey — A52

1956, May 25 Engr. *Perf. 13*

272 A52 15fr sapphire & indigo 2.00 1.20

Birth cent. of Marshal Franchet d'Esperey.

Marshal Jacques Leclerc — A53

1956, Nov. 29

273 A53 15fr red brown & sepia 2.00 1.60

Death of Marshal Leclerc.
For design surcharged see No. B90.

Type of 1947-49 and

Arms of Bône — A54

Arms: 2fr, Tizi-Quzou. 3fr, Mostaganem. 5fr, Tlemcen. 10fr, Setif. 12fr, Orleansville.

1956-58 Typo. *Perf. 14x13½*

274 A54 1fr green & ver .30 .25
275 A54 2fr ver & ultra ('58) 1.00 .55
276 A54 3fr ultra & emer ('58) 1.40 .30
277 A54 5fr ultra & yellow .80 .25
278 A31 6fr red & grn ('57) 1.40 .80
279 A54 10fr dp cl & emer ('58) 1.50 .90
280 A54 12fr ultra & red ('58) 1.75 .90
Nos. 274-280 (7) 8.15 3.95

Nos. 275 and 279 are inscribed "Republique Francaise." See No. 285.

View of Oran — A55

1956-58 Engr. *Perf. 13*

281 A55 30fr dull purple 1.20 .40
282 A55 35fr car rose ('58) 2.40 .80

Electric Train Crossing Bridge — A56

1957, Mar. 25

283 A56 40fr dk blue grn & emer 2.40 .55

Marianne Type of 1955 Inscribed "Algerie" Vertically
Perf. 14x13½

1957, Dec. 2 Typo. Unwmk.

284 A50 20fr ultra .95 .25

Arms Type of 1947-49 Inscribed "Republique Francaise"

1958, July

285 A31 6fr red & green 37.50 28.00

Independent State

France Nos. 939, 968, 945-946 & 1013 Ovptd. in Black or Red

No. 286

No. 287

No. 288

No. 289

No. 290

1962, July 2

Typographed Overprint

286 A336 10c brt green .80 .45
287 A349 25c lake & gray .80 .45
288 A339 45c brt vio & ol gray 7.50 3.75
289 A339 50c sl grn & lt claret 7.50 3.75
290 A372 1fr dk bl, sl & bis 4.75 1.75
Nos. 286-290 (5) 21.35 10.15

Handstamped Overprint

286a A336 10c bright green 1.00 .45
287a A349 25c lake & gray 1.00 .45
288a A339 45c brt vio & ol gray 30.00 22.50
289a A339 50c sl grn & lt claret 30.00 22.50
290a A372 1fr dk bl, sl & bis 7.00 3.00
Nos. 286a-290a (5) 69.00 48.90

Post offices were authorized to overprint their stock of these 5 French stamps. The size of the letters was specified as 3x6mm each, but various sizes were used. The post offices had permission to make their own rubber stamps. Typography, pen or pencil were also used. Many types exist. Colors of handstamped overprints include black, red, blue, violet. "EA" stands for Etat Algérien.

Mosque, Tlemcen A57

Roman Gates of Lodi, Médéa A58

5c, Kerrata Gorge. 10c, Dam at Foum el Gherza. 95c, Oil field, Hassi Messaoud.

1962, Nov. 1 Engr. *Perf. 13*

291 A57 5c Prus grn, grn & choc .25 .25
292 A58 10c ol blk & dk bl .25 .25
293 A57 25c sl grn, brn & ver .50 .25
294 A57 95c dk bl, blk & bis 2.75 .95
295 A58 1fr green & blk 2.40 1.50
Nos. 291-295 (5) 6.15 3.20

The designs of Nos. 291-295 are similar to French issues of 1959-61 with "Republique Algerienne" replacing "Republique Francaise."

Flag, Rifle, Olive Branch — A59

Design: Nos. 300-303, Broken chain, dove, and rifle added to design A59.

1963, Jan. 6 Litho. *Perf. 12½*
Flag in Green and Red

296 A59 5c bister brown .25 .25
297 A59 10c blue .25 .25
298 A59 25c vermilion 1.75 .25
299 A59 95c violet 1.35 .75
300 A59 1fr green 1.20 .35
301 A59 2fr brown 3.00 .75
302 A59 5fr lilac 5.25 3.00
303 A59 10fr gray 20.00 14.00
Nos. 296-303 (8) 33.05 19.60

Nos. 296-299 for the successful revolution and Nos. 300-303 the return of peace.

Men of Various Races, Wheat Emblem and Globe — A60

1963, Mar. 21 Engr. *Perf. 13*

304 A60 25c maroon, dl grn & yel .65 .25

FAO "Freedom from Hunger" campaign.

Map of Algeria and Emblems — A61

1963, July 5 Unwmk. *Perf. 13*

305 A61 25c bl, dk brn, grn & red .65 .25

1st anniv. of Algeria's independence.

Physicians from 13th Century Manuscript — A62

1963, July 29 Engr.

306 A62 25c brn red, grn & bis 2.00 .55

2nd Congress of the Union of Arab physicians.

Orange and Blossom — A63

1963 *Perf. 14x13*

307 A63 8c gray grn & org .25 .25
308 A63 20c slate & org red .25 .25
309 A63 40c grnsh bl & org .70 .30
310 A63 55c ol grn & org red 1.00 .55
Nos. 307-310 (4) 2.20 1.35

Nos. 307-310 issued precanceled only. See note below No. 32.

Scales and Scroll — A64

1963, Oct. 13 Unwmk. *Perf. 13*

311 A64 25c blk, grn & rose red .65 .35

Issued to honor the new constitution.

Guerrillas — A65

1963, Nov. 1

312 A65 25c dk brn, yel grn & car .65 .35

9th anniversary of Algerian revolution.

Centenary Emblem — A66

1963, Dec. 8 Photo. *Perf. 12*

313 A66 25c lt vio bl, yel & dk red .90 .60

Centenary of International Red Cross.

UNESCO Emblem, Scales and Globe — A67

1963, Dec. 16 Unwmk. *Perf. 12*

314 A67 25c lt blue & blk .65 .25

15th anniv. of the Universal Declaration of Human Rights.

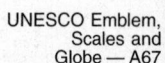

Workers — A68

1964, May 1 Engr. *Perf. 13*

315 A68 50c dull red, red org & bl 1.25 .40

Issued for the Labor Festival.

Map of Africa and Flags — A69

1964, May 25 Unwmk. *Perf. 13*

316 A69 45c blue, orange & car 1.00 .35

Africa Day on the 1st anniv. of the Addis Ababa charter on African unity.

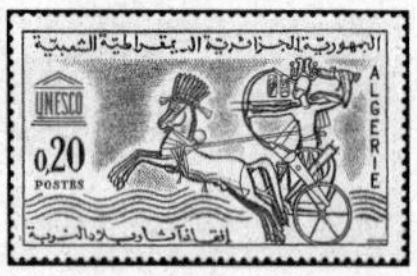

Ramses II Battling the Hittites (from Abu Simbel) A70

Design: 30c, Two statues of Ramses II.

1964, June 28 Engr. *Perf. 13*

317 A70 20c choc, red & vio bl .90 .40
318 A70 30c brn, red & grnsh bl 1.05 .55

UNESCO world campaign to save historic monuments in Nubia.

A71

5c, 25c, 85c, Tractors. 10c, 30c, 65c, Men working with lathe. 12c, 15c, 45c, Electronics center & atom symbol. 20c, 50c, 95c, Draftsman & bricklayer.

1964-65 Typo. *Perf. 14x13½*

319 A71 5c red lilac .25 .25
320 A71 10c brown .25 .25
321 A71 12c emerald ('65) .45 .25
322 A71 15c dk blue ('65) .30 .25
323 A71 20c yellow .45 .25
324 A71 25c red .45 .25
325 A71 30c purple ('65) .35 .25
326 A71 45c rose car .65 .25
327 A71 50c ultra .65 .25
328 A71 65c orange .70 .25
329 A71 85c green 1.40 .25
330 A71 95c car rose 1.75 .35
Nos. 319-330 (12) 7.65 3.10

For surcharges see Nos. 389, 424.

A72

1964, Aug. 30 Engr. *Perf. 13*

331 A72 85c Communications tower 1.90 .75

Inauguration of the Hertzian cable telephone line Algiers-Annaba.

Industrial & Agricultural Symbols — A73

1964, Sept. 26 Typo. *Perf. 13½x14*

332 A73 25c lt ultra, yel & red .60 1.25

1st Intl. Fair at Algiers, Sept. 26-Oct. 11.

Gas Flames and Pipes — A74

1964, Sept. 27

333 A74 30c violet, blue & yel .85 .50

Arzew natural gas liquification plant opening.

Planting Trees — A75

1964, Nov. 29 **Unwmk.**

334 A75 25c slate grn, yel & car .50 .25

National reforestation campaign.

Children and UNICEF Emblem — A76

1964, Dec. 13 ***Perf. 13½x14***

335 A76 15c pink, vio bl & lt grn .50 .25

Issued for Children's Day.

Decorated Camel Saddle — A77

1965, May 29 **Typo.** ***Perf. 13½x14***

336 A77 20c blk, red, emer & brn .70 .25

Handicrafts of Sahara.

ICY Emblem — A78

1965, Aug. 29 **Engr.** ***Perf. 13***

337 A78 30c blk, mar & bl grn .90 .40
338 A78 60c blk, brt bl & bl grn 1.25 .50

International Cooperation Year, 1965.

ITU Emblem — A79

1965, Sept. 19

339 A79 60c purple, emer & buff .90 .50
340 A79 95c dk brn, mar & buff 1.25 .55

Cent. of the ITU.

Musicians — A80

Miniatures by Mohammed Racim: 60c, Two female musicians. 5d, Algerian princess and antelope.

1965, Dec. 27 **Photo.** ***Perf. 11½***

341 A80 30c multicolored 1.75 .65
342 A80 60c multicolored 2.50 1.25
343 A80 5d multicolored 14.00 7.50
Nos. 341-343 (3) 18.25 9.40

Bulls, Painted in 6000 B.C. — A81

Wall Paintings from Tassili-N-Ajjer, c. 6000 B.C.: No. 345, Shepherd, vert. 2d, Fleeing ostriches. 3d, Two girls, vert.

1966, Jan. 29 **Photo.** ***Perf. 11½***

344 A81 1d brn, bis & red brn 4.50 2.75
345 A81 1d gray, blk, ocher & dk brn 4.50 2.75
346 A81 2d brn, ocher & red brn 10.00 4.75
347 A81 3d buff, blk, ocher & brn red 10.00 4.75
Nos. 344-347 (4) 29.00 15.00

See Nos. 365-368.

Pottery — A82

Handicrafts from Great Kabylia: 50c, Weaving, woman at loom, horiz. 70c, Jewelry.

1966, Feb. 26 **Engr.** ***Perf. 13***

348 A82 40c Prus bl, brn red & blk .50 .35
349 A82 50c dk red, ol & ocher .75 .40
350 A82 70c vio bl, blk & red 1.25 .55
Nos. 348-350 (3) 2.50 1.30

Weather Balloon, Compass Rose and Anemometer A83

1966, Mar. 23 **Engr.** **Unwmk.**

351 A83 1d claret, brt bl & grn 1.25 .50

World Meteorological Day.

Book, Grain, Cogwheel and UNESCO Emblem — A84

Design: 60c, Grain, cogwheel, book and UNESCO emblem.

1966, May 2 **Typo.** ***Perf. 13x14***

352 A84 30c yellow bis & blk .45 .25
353 A84 60c dk red, gray & blk .70 .40

Literacy as basis for development.

WHO Headquarters, Geneva — A85

1966, May 30 **Engr.** ***Perf. 13***

354 A85 30c multicolored .45 .35
355 A85 60c multicolored .85 .40

Inauguration of the WHO Headquarters, Geneva.

Algerian Scout Emblem A86

Arab Jamboree Emblem A87

1966, July 23 **Photo.** ***Perf. 12x12½***

356 A86 30c multicolored 1.25 .60
357 A87 1d multicolored 1.75 .65

No. 356 commemorates the 30th anniv. of the Algerian Mohammedan Boy Scouts. No. 357, the 7th Arab Boy Scout Jamboree, held at Good Daim, Libya, Aug. 12.

Map of Palestine and Victims — A88

1966, Sept. 26 **Typo.** ***Perf. 10½***

358 A88 30c red & black .60 .25

Deir Yassin Massacre, Apr. 9, 1948.

Abd-el-Kader — A89

1966, Nov. 2 **Photo.** ***Perf. 11½***

359 A89 30c multicolored .25 .25
360 A89 95c multicolored 1.05 .40

Transfer from Damascus to Algiers of the ashes of Abd-el-Kader (1807?-1883), Emir of Mascara. See Nos. 382-387.

UNESCO Emblem — A90

1966, Nov. 19 **Typo.** ***Perf. 10½***

361 A90 1d multicolored 1.05 .40

20th anniv. of UNESCO.

Horseman — A91

Miniatures by Mohammed Racim: 1.50d, Woman at her toilette. 2d, The pirate Barbarossa in front of the Admiralty.

1966, Dec. 17 **Photo.** ***Perf. 11½***

Granite Paper

362 A91 1d multicolored 3.25 1.50
363 A91 1.50d multicolored 5.25 1.75
364 A91 2d multicolored 6.50 3.50
Nos. 362-364 (3) 15.00 6.75

Wall Paintings Type of 1966

Wall Paintings from Tassili-N-Ajjer, c. 6000 B.C.: 1d, Cow. No. 366, Antelope. No. 367, Archers. 3d, Warrior, vert.

1967, Jan. 28 **Photo.** ***Perf. 11½***

365 A81 1d brn, bis & dl vio 3.25 1.90
366 A81 2d brn, ocher & red brn 5.00 3.75
367 A81 2d brn, yel & red brn 5.00 3.75
368 A81 3d blk, gray, yel & red brn 7.00 5.25
Nos. 365-368 (4) 20.25 14.65

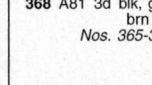

Bardo Museum A92

La Kalaa Minaret A93

Design: 1.30d, Ruins at Sedrata.

1967, Feb. 27 **Photo.** ***Perf. 13***

369 A92 35c multicolored .40 .25
370 A93 95c multicolored .90 .50
371 A92 1.30d multicolored 1.50 .65
Nos. 369-371 (3) 2.80 1.40

Moretti and International Tourist Year Emblem — A94

Design: 70c, Tuareg riding camel, Tassili, and Tourist Year Emblem, vert.

1967, Apr. 29 **Litho.** ***Perf. 14***

372 A94 40c multi .70 .40
373 A94 70c multi 1.40 .60

International Tourist Year, 1967.

Spiny-tailed Agamid — A95

Designs: 20c, Ostrich, vert. 40c, Slender-horned gazelle, vert. 70c, Fennec.

1967, June 24 **Photo.** ***Perf. 11½***

374 A95 5c bister & blk .70 .70
375 A95 20c ocher, blk & pink 1.40 .70
376 A95 40c ol bis, blk & red brn 2.10 1.00
377 A95 70c gray, blk & dp org 2.75 1.75
Nos. 374-377 (4) 6.95 4.15

Dancers — A96

Typographed and Engraved

1967, July 4 ***Perf. 10½***

378 A96 50c gray vio, yel & blk .90 .40

National Youth Festival.

Map of the Mediterranean and Sport Scenes — A97

1967, Sept. 2 **Typo.** ***Perf. 10½***

379 A97 30c black, red & blue .65 .40

Issued to publicize the 5th Mediterranean Games, Tunis, Sept. 8-17.

Skiers A98

Olympic Emblem and Sports A99

1967, Oct. 21 Engr. *Perf. 13*

380 A98 30c brt blue & ultra .90 .40
381 A99 95c brn org, pur & brt grn 1.65 .75

Issued to publicize the 10th Winter Olympic Games, Grenoble, Feb. 6-18, 1968.

Abd-el-Kader Type of 1966

Lithographed, Photogravure

1967-71 *Perf. 13½, 11½*

382 A89 5c dull pur ('68) .25 .25
383 A89 10c green .25 .25
383A A89 10c sl grn (litho., '69) .25 .25
383B A89 25c orange ('71) .30 .25
384 A89 30c black ('68) .35 .25
385 A89 30c lt violet ('68) .45 .25
386 A89 50c rose claret .75 .25
387 A89 70c violet blue .85 .30
Nos. 382-387 (8) 3.45 2.05

No. 383, 50c and 70c, issued Nov. 13, 1967, are on granite paper, photo. The 5c, No.383A, 25c and 30c are litho., perf. 13½; others, perf. 11½.

The three 1967 stamps (No. 383, 50c, 70c) have numerals thin, narrow and close together; the Arabic inscription at lower right is 2mm high. The 5 litho. stamps are redrawn, with numerals thicker and spaced more widely; Arabic at lower right 3mm high.

Boy Scouts Holding Jamboree Emblem — A100

1967, Dec. 23 Engr. *Perf. 13*

388 A100 1d multicolored 1.90 .70

12th Boy Scout World Jamboree, Farragut State Park, Idaho, Aug. 1-9.

No. 324 Surcharged

1967 Typo. *Perf. 14x13½*

389 A71 30c on 25c red .65 .25

Mandolin — A101

1968, Feb. 17 Photo. *Perf. 12½x13*

390 A101 30c shown .55 .25
391 A101 40c Lute .75 .40
392 A101 1.30d Rebec 2.75 1.10
Nos. 390-392 (3) 4.05 1.75

Nememcha Rug — A102

Algerian Rugs: 70c, Guergour. 95c, Djebel-Amour. 1.30d, Kalaa.

1968, Apr. 13 Photo. *Perf. 11½*

393 A102 30c multi .95 .60
394 A102 70c multi 1.75 .95
395 A102 95c multi 3.00 2.00
396 A102 1.30d multi 3.50 1.50
Nos. 393-396 (4) 9.20 5.05

Human Rights Flame — A103

1968, May 18 Typo. *Perf. 10½*

397 A103 40c blue, red & yel .65 .80

International Human Rights Year, 1968.

WHO Emblem — A104

1968, May 18

398 A104 70c blk, lt bl & yel .80 .40

20th anniv. of the WHO.

Welder — A105

1968, June 15 Engr. *Perf. 13*

399 A105 30c gray, brn & ultra .45 .25

Algerian emigration to Europe.

Athletes, Olympic Flame and Rings — A106

50c, Soccer player. 1d, Mexican pyramid, emblem, Olympic flame, rings & athletes, horiz.

Perf. 12½x13, 13x12½

1968, July 4 Photo.

400 A106 30c green, red & yel .65 .50
401 A106 50c rose car & multi .95 .60
402 A106 1d dk grn, org, brn & red 1.60 .95
Nos. 400-402 (3) 3.20 2.05

19th Olympic Games, Mexico City, 10/12-27.

Scouts and Emblem — A107

1968, July 4 *Perf. 13*

403 A107 30c multicolored .65 .25

8th Arab Boy Scout Jamboree, Algiers, 1968.

Barbary Sheep — A108

1968, Oct. 19 Photo. *Perf. 11½*

404 A108 40c shown .90 .40
405 A108 1d Red deer 2.10 .65

Hunting Scenes, Djemila — A109

Design: 95c, Neptune's chariot, Timgad, horiz. Both designs are from Roman mosaics.

Perf. 12½x13, 13x12½

1968, Nov. 23 Photo.

406 A109 40c gray & multi .60 .25
407 A109 95c gray & multi 1.35 .55

"Industry" — A110

Designs: No. 409, Miner with drill. 95c, "Energy" (circle and rays).

1968, Dec. 14 *Perf. 11½*

408 A110 30c dp orange & sil .45 .25
409 A110 30c brown & multi .45 .25
410 A110 95c silver, red & blk 1.25 .40
Nos. 408-410 (3) 2.15 .90

Issued to publicize industrial development.

Opuntia Ficus Indica — A111

Flowers: 40c, Carnations. 70c, Roses. 95c, Bird-of-paradise flower.

1969, Jan. Photo. *Perf. 11½*

Flowers in Natural Colors

411 A111 25c pink & blk .65 .45
412 A111 40c yellow & blk 1.10 .60
413 A111 70c gray & blk 1.65 .75
414 A111 95c brt blue & blk 2.90 1.10
Nos. 411-414 (4) 6.30 2.90

See Nos. 496-499.

Irrigation Dam at Djorf Torba-Oued Guir — A112

Design: 1.50d, Truck on Highway No. 51 and camel caravan.

1969, Feb. 22 Photo. *Perf. 11½*

415 A112 30c multi .55 .25
416 A112 1.50d multi 1.90 .75

Public works in the Sahara.

Mail Coach — A113

1969, Mar. 22 Photo. *Perf. 11½*

417 A113 1d multicolored 2.60 .75

Issued for Stamp Day, 1969.

Capitol, Timgad — A114

1d, Septimius Temple, Djemila, horiz.

1969, Apr. 5 Photo. *Perf. 13x12½*

418 A114 30c gray & multi .55 .25
419 A114 1d gray & multi 1.35 .50

Second Timgad Festival, Apr. 4-8.

ILO Emblem — A115

1969, May 24 Photo. *Perf. 11½*

420 A115 95c dp car, yel & blk 1.15 .45

50th anniv. of the ILO.

Arabian Saddle — A116

Algerian Handicrafts: 30c, Bookcase. 60c, Decorated copper plate.

1969, June 28 Photo. *Perf. 12x12½*

Granite Paper

421 A116 30c multicolored .45 .25
422 A116 60c multicolored .85 .35
423 A116 1d multicolored 1.50 .65
Nos. 421-423 (3) 2.80 1.25

No. 321 Surcharged

1969 Typo. *Perf. 14x13½*

424 A71 20c on 12c emerald .50 .25

Pan-African Culture Festival Emblem — A117

1969, July 19 Photo. *Perf. 12½*

425 A117 30c multicolored .60 .25

1st Pan-African Culture Festival, Algiers, 7/21-8/1.

African Development Bank Emblem — A118

1969, Aug. 23 Typo. *Perf. 10½*

426 A118 30c dull blue, yel & blk .60 .25

5th anniv. of the African Development Bank.

Astronauts and Landing Module on Moon — A119

Perf. 12½x11½

1969, Aug. 23 Photo.

427 A119 50c gold & multi 1.10 .50

Man's 1st landing on the moon, July 20, 1969. US astronauts Neil A. Armstrong and Col. Edwin E. Aldrin, Jr., with Lieut. Col. Michael Collins piloting Apollo 11.

Algerian Women, by Dinet — A120

1.50d, The Watchmen, by Etienne Dinet.

1969, Nov. 29 Photo. *Perf. 14½*

428 A120 1d multi 2.00 .80
429 A120 1.50d multi 2.50 1.25

Mother and Child — A121

1969, Dec. 27 Photo. *Perf. 11½*
430 A121 30c multicolored .65 .40

Issued to promote mother and child protection.

Agricultural Growth Chart, Tractor and Dam — A122

30c, Transportation and development. 50c, Abstract symbols of industrialization.

1970, Jan. 31 Photo. *Perf. 12½*
Size: 37x23mm
431 A122 25c dk brn, yel & org .30 .25

Litho. *Perf. 14*
Size: 49x23mm
432 A122 30c blue & multi 1.00 .25

Photo. *Perf. 12½*
Size: 37x23mm
433 A122 50c rose lilac & blk .60 .25
Nos. 431-433 (3) 1.90 .75

Four-Year Development Plan.

Old and New Mail Delivery — A123

1970, Feb. 28 Photo. *Perf. 11½*
Granite Paper
434 A123 30c multicolored .70 .25

Issued for Stamp Day.

Spiny Lobster — A124

Designs: 40c, Mollusks. 75c, Retepora cellulosa. 1d, Red coral.

1970, Mar. 28
435 A124 30c ocher & multi .55 .25
436 A124 40c multicolored .80 .40
437 A124 75c ultra & multi 1.35 .55
438 A124 1d lt blue & multi 2.10 .80
Nos. 435-438 (4) 4.80 2.00

Oranges, EXPO '70 Emblem — A125

Designs (EXPO '70 Emblem and): 60c, Algerian pavilion. 70c, Grapes.

1970, Apr. 25 Photo. *Perf. 12½x12*
439 A125 30c lt blue, grn & org .65 .25
440 A125 60c multicolored .65 .40
441 A125 70c multicolored 1.30 .60
Nos. 439-441 (3) 2.60 1.25

EXPO '70 International Exhibition, Osaka, Japan, Mar. 15-Sept. 13, 1970.

Olives, Oil Bottle — A126

1970, May 16 Photo. *Perf. 12½x12*
442 A126 1d yellow & multi 2.00 .80

Olive Year, 1969-1970.

Common Design Types pictured following the introduction.

UPU Headquarters Issue
Common Design Type

1970, May 30 *Perf. 13*
Size: 36x26mm
443 CD133 75c multicolored 1.10 .40

Saber — A127

Designs: 40c, Guns, 18th century, horiz. 1d, Pistol, 18th century, horiz.

1970, June 27 Photo. *Perf. 12½*
444 A127 40c yellow & multi 1.10 .60
445 A127 75c red & multi 1.50 .80
446 A127 1d multicolored 2.10 1.10
Nos. 444-446 (3) 4.70 2.50

Map of Arab Countries and Arab League Flag — A128

Typographed and Engraved
1970, July 25 *Perf. 10½*
447 A128 30c grn, ocher & lt bl .55 .25

25th anniversary of the Arab League.

Vladimir Lenin — A129

1970, Aug. 29 Litho. *Perf. 11½x12*
448 A129 30c brown & buff 2.50 .40

Lenin (1870-1924), Russian communist leader.

Exhibition Hall and Algiers Fair Emblem A130

1970, Sept. 11 Engr. *Perf. 14x13½*
449 A130 60c lt olive green .65 .30

New Exhibition Hall for Algiers Intl. Fair.

Education Year Emblem, Blackboard, Atom Symbol — A131

Koran Page — A132

1970, Oct. 24 Photo. *Perf. 14*
450 A131 30c pink, blk, gold & lt bl .50 .25
451 A132 3d multicolored 4.00 1.75

Issued for International Education Year.

Great Mosque, Tlemcen — A133

Design: 40c, Ketchaoua Mosque, Algiers, vert. 1d, Mosque, Sidi-Okba, vert.

1970-71 Litho. *Perf. 14*
456 A133 30c multicolored .40 .25
457 A133 40c sepia & lemon ('71) .50 .25
458 A133 1d multicolored 1.00 .40
Nos. 456-458 (3) 1.90 .90

Symbols of the Arts — A134

1970, Dec. 26 Photo. *Perf. 13x12½*
459 A134 1d grn, lt grn & org 1.00 .50

Main Post Office, Algiers — A135

1971, Jan. 23 *Perf. 11½*
460 A135 30c multicolored 1.00 .40

Stamp Day, 1971.

Hurdling — A136

40c, Vaulting, vert. 75c, Basketball, vert.

1971, Mar. 7 Photo. *Perf. 11½*
461 A136 20c lt blue & slate .45 .25
462 A136 40c lt ol grn & slate .55 .40
463 A136 75c salmon pink & slate .95 .60
Nos. 461-463 (3) 1.95 1.25

Mediterranean Games, Izmir, Turkey, Oct. 1971.

Symbolic Head — A137

1971, Mar. 27 *Perf. 12½*
464 A137 60c car rose, blk & sil .65 .30

Intl. year against racial discrimination.

Emblem and Technicians A138

1971, Apr. 24 Photo. *Perf. 12½x12*
465 A138 70c cl, org & bluish blk .75 .30

Founding of the Institute of Technology.

Woman from Aurès — A139

Regional Costumes: 70c, Man from Oran. 80c, Man from Algiers. 90c, Woman from Amour Mountains.

1971, Oct. 16 *Perf. 11½*
466 A139 50c gold & multi 1.10 .50
467 A139 70c gold & multi 1.40 .80
468 A139 80c gold & multi 1.75 .95
469 A139 90c gold & multi 2.10 1.00
Nos. 466-469 (4) 6.35 3.25

See Nos. 485-488, 534-537.

UNICEF Emblem, Birds and Plants — A140

1971, Dec. 6 *Perf. 11½*
470 A140 60c multicolored .75 .50

25th anniv. of UNICEF.

Lion of St. Mark — A141

1.15d, Bridge of Sighs, Venice, vert.

1972, Jan. 24 Litho. *Perf. 12*
471 A141 80c multi 1.10 .55
472 A141 1.15d multi 2.25 .95

UNESCO campaign to save Venice.

Javelin — A142

Designs: 25c, Bicycling, horiz. 60c, Wrestling. 1d, Gymnast on rings.

1972, Mar. 25 Photo. *Perf. 11½*
473 A142 25c maroon & multi .40 .25
474 A142 40c ocher & multi .50 .25
475 A142 60c ultra & multi 1.10 .50
476 A142 1d rose & multi 1.50 .55
Nos. 473-476 (4) 3.50 1.55

20th Olympic Games, Munich, 8/26-9/11.

Book and Book Year Emblem — A143

1972, Apr. 15
477 A143 1.15d bister, brn & red .80 .50

International Book Year 1972.

Mailmen — A144

1972, Apr. 22
478 A144 40c gray & multi .70 .25

Stamp Day 1972.

Flowers — A145

1972, May 27

479 A145	50c Jasmine		.65	.40
480 A145	60c Violets		.65	.50
481 A145	1.15d Tuberose		1.75	.65
	Nos. 479-481 (3)		3.05	1.55

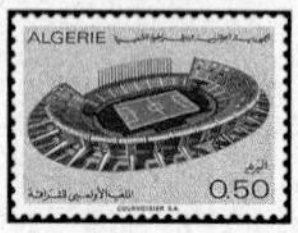

Olympic Stadium, Chéraga — A146

1972, June 10

482 A146 50c gray, choc & grn .70 .40

New Day, Algerian Flag — A147

1972, July 5

483 A147 1d green & multi 1.15 .60

10th anniversary of independence.

Festival Emblem — A148

1972, July 5 Litho. *Perf. 10½*

484 A148 40c grn, dk brn & org .60 .25

1st Arab Youth Festival, Algiers, July 5-11.

Costume Type of 1971

Regional Costumes: 50c, Woman from Hoggar. 60c, Kabyle woman. 70c, Man from Mzab. 90c, Woman from Tlemcen.

1972, Nov. 18 Photo. *Perf. 11½*

485 A139	50c gold & multi	1.40	.65
486 A139	60c gold & multi	1.75	.65
487 A139	70c gold & multi	1.90	.95
488 A139	90c gold & multi	2.25	1.10
	Nos. 485-488 (4)	7.30	3.35

Mailing a Letter — A149

1973, Jan. 20 Photo. *Perf. 11*

489 A149 40c orange & multi .60 .25

Stamp Day.

Ho Chi Minh, Map of Viet Nam — A150

1973, Feb. 17 Photo. *Perf. 11½*

490 A150 40c multicolored .90 .35

To honor the people of Viet Nam.

Embroidery from Annaba — A151

Designs: 60c, Tree of Life pattern from Algiers. 80c, Constantine embroidery.

1973, Feb. 24

491 A151	40c gray & multi	.55	.30
492 A151	60c blue and multi	.80	.50
493 A151	80c dk red, gold & blk	1.25	.65
	Nos. 491-493 (3)	2.60	1.45

Stylized Globe and Wheat — A152

1973, Mar. 26 Photo. *Perf. 11½*

494 A152 1.15d brt rose lil, org & grn .80 .35

World Food Program, 10th anniversary.

Soldier and Flag — A153

1973, Apr. 23 Photo. *Perf. 14x13½*

495 A153 40c multicolored .60 .25

Honoring the National Service.

Flower Type of 1969

30c, Opuntia ficus indica. 40c, Roses. 1d, Carnations. 1.15d, Bird-of-paradise flower.

1973, May 21 Photo. *Perf. 11½*

Flowers in Natural Colors

496 A111	30c pink & blk	.75	.25
497 A111	40c gray & blk	.90	.40
498 A111	1d yellow & multi	2.00	.65
499 A111	1.15d multi	3.25	.95
	Nos. 496-499 (4)	6.90	2.25

For overprints and surcharges see Nos. 518-519, 531.

OAU Emblem — A154

1973, May 28 Photo. *Perf. 12½x13*

500 A154 40c multicolored .60 .25

Org. for African Unity, 10th anniv.

Desert and Fruitful Land, Farmer and Family A155

1973, June 18 *Perf. 11½*

501 A155 40c gold & multi .70 .25

Agricultural revolution.

Map of Africa, Scout Emblem — A156

1973, July 16 Litho. *Perf. 10½*

502 A156 80c purple .80 .40

24th Boy Scout World Conference (1st in Africa), Nairobi, Kenya, July 16-21.

Algerian PTT Emblem — A157

1973, Aug. 6 *Perf. 14*

503 A157 40c blue & orange .60 .25

Adoption of new emblem for Post, Telegraph and Telephone System.

Conference Emblem — A158

Perf. 13½x12½

1973, Sept. 5 Photo.

504 A158	40c dp rose & multi	.40	.30
505 A158	80c blue grn & multi	.75	.40

4th Summit Conference of Non-aligned Nations, Algiers, Sept. 5-9.

Port of Skikda — A159

1973, Sept. 29 Photo. *Perf. 11½*

506 A159 80c ocher, blk & ultra .70 .40

New port of Skikda.

Young Workers — A160

1973, Oct. 22 Photo. *Perf. 13*

507 A160 40c multicolored .60 .25

Voluntary work service.

Arms of Algiers — A161

1973, Dec. 22 Photo. *Perf. 13*

508 A161 2d gold & multi 2.75 1.40

Millennium of Algiers.

Infant — A162

1974, Jan. 7 Litho. *Perf. 10½x11*

509 A162 80c orange & multi .70 .50

Fight against tuberculosis.

No. 509 exists with 1973 year date. Value $60.

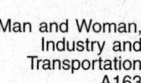

Man and Woman, Industry and Transportation A163

1974, Feb. 18 Photo. *Perf. 11½*

510 A163 80c multicolored .85 .40

Four-year plan.

A164

1974, Feb. 25 Photo. *Perf. 11½*

511 A164 1.50d multi 2.75 1.40

Millennium of the birth of abu-al-Rayhan al-Biruni (973-1048), philosopher and mathematician.

Map and Colors of Algeria, Tunisia, Morocco — A165

1974, Mar. 4 Photo. *Perf. 13*

512 A165 40c gold & multi .60 .25

Maghreb Committee for Coordination of Posts and Telecommunications.

Hand Holding Rifle — A166

1974, Mar. 25 *Perf. 11½*

513 A166 80c red & black .70 .25

Solidarity with the struggle of the people of South Africa.

Mother and Children — A167

1974, Apr. 8 *Perf. 13½*

514 A167 85c multicolored .70 .25

Honoring Algerian mothers.

Village A168

Designs: 80c, Harvest. 90c, Tractor and sun. Designs after children's drawings.

1974, June 15 **Size: 45x26mm**
515 A168 70c multicolored .65 .25

Size: 48x33mm

516 A168 80c multicolored .85 .40
517 A168 90c multicolored 1.05 .60
Nos. 515-517 (3) 2.55 1.25

Nos. 498-499 Overprinted

1974, June 22 **Photo.** ***Perf. 11½***
518 A111 1d multi 1.65 .80
519 A111 1.15d multi 2.25 1.25

1974 Flower Show.

Stamp Vending Machine — A169

1974, Oct. 7 **Photo.** ***Perf. 13***
520 A169 80c multicolored .85 .25

Stamp Day 1974.

UPU Emblem and Globe — A170

1974, Oct. 14 ***Perf. 14***
521 A170 80c multicolored 1.00 .40

Centenary of Universal Postal Union.

"Revolution" A171

Soldiers and Mountains A172

Raising New Flag — A173

Design: 1d, Algerian struggle for independence (people, sun and fields).

1974, Nov. 4 **Photo.** ***Perf. 14***
522 A171 40c multicolored .50 .25
523 A172 70c multicolored .70 .25
524 A173 95c multicolored .90 .35
525 A171 1d multicolored 1.15 .40
Nos. 522-525 (4) 3.25 1.25

20th anniv. of the start of the revolution.

"Horizon 1980" — A174

1974, Nov. 23 **Photo.** ***Perf. 13***
526 A174 95c ocher, dk red & blk .70 .40

10-year development plan, 1971-1980.

Ewer and Basin — A175

1974, Dec. 21 ***Perf. 11½***
527 A175 50c shown .55 .30
528 A175 60c Coffee pot .75 .40
529 A175 95c Sugar bowl 1.00 .55
530 A175 1d Bath tub 1.40 .65
Nos. 527-530 (4) 3.70 1.90

17th century Algerian copperware.

No. 497 Surcharged in Black

1975, Jan. 4
531 A111 50c on 40c multi 2.50 .55

Mediterranean Games' Emblem — A176

1975, Jan. 27 ***Perf. 13½***
532 A176 50c purple, yel & grn .45 .25
533 A176 1d orange, bl & mar .80 .35

Mediterranean Games, Algiers, 1975.

Costume Type of 1971

Regional Costumes: No. 534, Woman from Hoggar. No. 535, Woman from Algiers. No. 536, Woman from Oran. No. 537, Man from Tlemcen.

1975, Feb. 22 **Photo.** ***Perf. 11½***
534 A139 1d gold & multi 1.50 .75
535 A139 1d gold & multi 1.50 .75
536 A139 1d gold & multi 1.50 .75
537 A139 1d gold & multi 1.50 .75
Nos. 534-537 (4) 6.00 3.00

Map of Arab Countries, ALO Emblem — A177

1975, Mar. 10 **Litho.** ***Perf. 10½x11***
538 A177 50c red brown .60 .30

Arab Labor Organization, 10th anniversary.

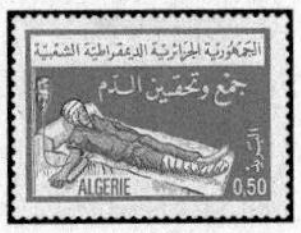

Blood Transfusion — A178

1975, Mar. 15 ***Perf. 14***
539 A178 50c car rose & multi .75 .40

Blood donation and transfusions.

Post Office, Al-Kantara — A179

1975, May 10 **Photo.** ***Perf. 11½***
Granite Paper
540 A179 50c multicolored .65 .25

Stamp Day 1975.

Policeman and Map of Algeria — A180

1975, June 1 **Photo.** ***Perf. 13***
541 A180 50c multicolored 1.00 .40

Natl. Security and 10th Natl. Police Day.

Ground Receiving Station — A181

Designs: 1d, Map of Algeria with locations of radar sites, transmission mast and satellite. 1.20d, Main and subsidiary stations.

1975, June 28 **Photo.** ***Perf. 13***
542 A181 50c blue & multi .50 .25
543 A181 1d blue & multi .85 .25
544 A181 1.20d blue & multi 1.10 .40
Nos. 542-544 (3) 2.45 .90

National satellite telecommunications network.

Revolutionary with Flag — A182

1975, Aug. 20 **Photo.** ***Perf. 11½***
545 A182 1d multicolored .65 .35

August 20th Revolutionary Movement (Skikda), 20th anniversary.

Swimming and Games' Emblem — A183

Perf. 13x13½, 13½x13
1975, Aug. 23 **Photo.**
546 A183 25c shown .25 .25
547 A183 50c Judo, map .40 .25
548 A183 70c Soccer, vert. .60 .30
549 A183 1d Running, vert. .80 .40
550 A183 1.20d Handball, vert. 1.00 .60
a. Souv. sheet, #546-550, perf 13 6.75 6.75
Nos. 546-550 (5) 3.05 1.80

7th Mediterranean Games, Algiers, 8/23-9/46.

No. 550a sold for 4.50d. Exists imperf., same value.

Setif, Guelma, Kherrata — A184

1975 **Litho.** ***Perf. 13½x14***
551 A184 5c orange & blk .25 .25
552 A184 10c emerald & brn .25 .25
553 A184 25c dl blue & blk .25 .25
554 A184 30c lemon & blk .40 .25
555 A184 50c brt grn & blk .40 .25
556 A184 70c fawn & blk .45 .25
557 A184 1d vermilion & blk .75 .35
Nos. 551-557 (7) 2.75 1.85

30th anniv. of victory in World War II.
Issued: 50c, 1d, Nov. 3; others, Dec. 17.
For surcharge see No. 611.

Map of Maghreb and APU Emblem — A185

1975, Nov. 20 **Photo.** ***Perf. 11½***
558 A185 1d multicolored .70 .40

10th Cong. of Arab Postal Union, Algiers.

Mosaic, Bey Constantine's Palace — A186

Dey-Alger Palace A187

Famous buildings: 2d, Prayer niche, Medersa Sidi-Boumediene, Tlemcen.

1975, Dec. 22
559 A186 1d lt blue & multi 1.05 .40
560 A186 2d buff & multi 2.10 .95
561 A187 2.50d buff & blk 2.75 1.40
Nos. 559-561 (3) 5.90 2.75

Al-Azhar University — A188

Perf. 11½x12½
1975, Dec. 29 **Litho.**
562 A188 2d multicolored 2.10 .80

Millennium of Al-Azhar University.

Red-billed Firefinch — A189

Birds: 1.40d, Black-headed bush shrike, horiz. 2d, Blue tit. 2.50d, Blackbellied sand-grouse, horiz.

1976, Jan. 24 **Photo.** ***Perf. 11½***
563 A189 50c multi 1.75 .70
564 A189 1.40d multi 3.00 1.25
565 A189 2d multi 3.50 1.40
566 A189 2.50d multi 4.00 2.00
Nos. 563-566 (4) 12.25 5.35

See Nos. 595-598.

Telephones 1876 and 1976 — A190

1976, Feb. 23 Photo. *Perf. 13½x13*

567 A190 1.40d rose, dk & lt bl 1.00 .55

Centenary of first telephone call by Alexander Graham Bell, Mar. 10, 1876.

Map of Africa with Angola and its Flag — A191

1976, Feb. 23 *Perf. 11½*

568 A191 50c brown & multi .60 .25

Algeria's solidarity with the People's Republic of Angola.

A192

Sahraoui flag and child, map of former Spanish Sahara.

1976, Mar. 15 Photo. *Perf. 11½*

569 A192 50c multicolored .55 .25

Algeria's solidarity with Sahraoui Arab Democratic Republic, former Spanish Sahara.

Stamp Day — A193

1976, Mar. 22

570 A193 1.40d Mailman 1.25 .40

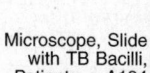

Microscope, Slide with TB Bacilli, Patients — A194

1976, Apr. 26 *Perf. 13x13½*

571 A194 50c multicolored 1.05 .30

Fight against tuberculosis.

"Setif, Guelma, Kherrata" — A195

1976, May 24 Photo. *Perf. 13½x13*

572 A195 50c blue & yellow .60 .25

a. Booklet pane of 6 8.00

b. Booklet pane of 10 12.00

No. 572 was issued in booklets only.

Ram's Head over Landscape — A196

1976, June 17 Photo. *Perf. 11½*

573 A196 50c multicolored .70 .25

Livestock breeding.

People Holding Torch, Map of Algeria — A197

1976, June 29 Photo. *Perf. 14x13½*

574 A197 50c multicolored .60 .25

National Charter.

Palestine Map and Flag — A198

1976, July 12 *Perf. 11½*

Granite Paper

575 A198 50c multicolored .65 .25

Solidarity with the Palestinians.

Map of Africa — A199

1976, Oct. 3 Litho. *Perf. 10½x11*

576 A199 2d dk blue & multi 1.50 .65

2nd Pan-African Commercial Fair, Algiers.

Blind Brushmaker A200

The Blind, by Dinet — A201

1976, Oct. 23 Photo. *Perf. 14½*

577 A200 1.20d blue & multi .95 .50

578 A201 1.40d gold & multi .95 .65

Rehabilitation of the blind.

"Constitution 1976" A202

1976, Nov. 19 Photo. *Perf. 11½*

579 A202 2d multicolored 1.50 .65

New Constitution.

Soldiers Planting Seedlings — A203

1976, Nov. 25 Litho. *Perf. 12*

580 A203 1.40d multicolored 1.50 .55

Green barrier against the Sahara.

Ornamental Border and Inscription A204

1976, Dec. 18 Photo. *Perf. 11½*

Granite Paper

581 A204 2d multicolored 1.50 .65

Re-election of Pres. Houari Boumediene. See No. 627.

Map with Charge Zones and Dials — A205

1977, Jan. 22 *Perf. 13*

582 A205 40c silver & multi .50 .25

Inauguration of automatic national and international telephone service.

People and Buildings — A206

1977, Jan. 29 Photo. *Perf. 11½*

583 A206 60c on 50c multi .60 .25

2nd General Population and Buildings Census. No. 583 was not issued without the typographed red brown surcharge, date, and bars.

Sahara Museum, Uargla — A207

1977, Feb. 12 Litho. *Perf. 14*

584 A207 60c multicolored .60 .40

El-Kantara Gorge — A208

Perf. 12½x13½

1977, Feb. 19 Photo.

585 A208 20c green & yellow .25 .25

a. Bklt. pane, 3 #585, 4 #586 + label 6.00

b. Bklt. pane, 5 #585, 2 #587 + label 7.00

586 A208 60c brt lilac & yel .25 .25

587 A208 1d brown & yellow .65 .25

Nos. 585-587 (3) 1.15 .75

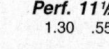

National Assembly A209

1977, Feb. 27 *Perf. 11½*

588 A209 2d multicolored 1.30 .55

People and Flag A210

Soldier and Flag A211

Perf. 13½, 11½ (3d)

1977, Mar. 12 Photo.

589 A210 2d multicolored 1.30 .55

590 A211 3d multicolored 2.10 .80

Solidarity with the peoples of Zimbabwe (Rhodesia), 2d; Namibia, 3d.

Winter, Roman Mosaic — A212

The Seasons from Roman Villa, 2nd century A.D.: 1.40d, Fall. 2d, Summer. 3d, Spring.

1977, Apr. 21 Photo. *Perf. 11½*

Granite Paper

591 A212 1.20d multi 1.50 .75

592 A212 1.40d multi 1.50 .75

593 A212 2d multi 2.40 1.15

594 A212 3d multi 3.25 1.50

a. Souv. sheet, #591-594 12.00 12.00

Nos. 591-594 (4) 8.65 4.15

No. 594a sold for 8d and exists imperf.

Bird Type of 1976

Birds: 60c, Tristram's warbler. 1.40d, Moussier's redstart, horiz. 2d, Temminck's horned lark, horiz. 3d, Eurasian hoopoe.

1977, May 21 Photo. *Perf. 11½*

595 A189 60c multi 1.30 .65

596 A189 1.40d multi 1.90 .90

597 A189 2d multi 3.00 1.30

598 A189 3d multi 4.25 1.90

Nos. 595-598 (4) 10.45 4.75

Horseman — A213

Design: 5d, Attacking horsemen, horiz.

1977, June 25 Photo. *Perf. 11½*

599 A213 2d multicolored 2.00 .80

600 A213 5d multicolored 5.00 2.00

Flag Colors, Games Emblem A214

Wall Painting, Games Emblem A215

1977, Sept. 24 Photo. *Perf. 11½*

601 A214 60c multi	.55	.25
602 A215 1.40d multi	1.30	.60

3rd African Games, Algiers 1978.

Village and Tractor — A216

1977, Nov. 12 *Perf. 14x13*

603 A216 1.40d multi 1.00 .40

Socialist agricultural village.

Almohades Dirham, 12th Century A217

Ancient Coins: 1.40d, Almohades coin, 12th century. 2d, Almoravides dinar, 11th century.

1977, Dec. 17 Photo. *Perf. 11½*

604 A217 60c ultra, sil & blk	.55	.40
605 A217 1.40d grn, gold & brn	1.30	.60
606 A217 2d red brn, gold & brn	1.75	.90
Nos. 604-606 (3)	3.60	1.90

Flowering Trees — A218

1978, Feb. 11 Photo. *Perf. 11½*

607 A218 60c Cherry	.55	.25
608 A218 1.20d Peach	1.05	.70
609 A218 1.30d Almond	1.20	.75
610 A218 1.40d Apple	1.45	.80
Nos. 607-610 (4)	4.25	2.50

No. 555 Surcharged in Black

1978, Feb. 11 Litho. *Perf. 13½x14*

611 A184 60c on 50c .80 .25

Children with Traffic Signs and Car — A219

1978, Apr. 29 Photo. *Perf. 11½*

612 A219 60c multicolored .80 .25

Road safety and protection of children.

Sports and Games Emblems — A220

Designs (Games Emblem and): 40c, Volleyball. 60c, Rowing, vert. 1.20d, Basketball. 1.30d, Hammer throwing, vert. 1.40d, Map of Africa and boxers, vert.

1978, July 13 Photo. *Perf. 11½*

613 A220 40c multi	.25	.25
614 A220 60c multi	.45	.25
615 A220 1.20d multi	1.00	.40
616 A220 1.30d multi	1.00	.50
617 A220 1.40d multi	1.40	.60
Nos. 613-617 (5)	4.10	2.00

3rd African Games, Algiers, July 13-28.

TB Patient Returning to Family — A221

1978, Oct. 5 Photo. *Perf. 13½x14*

618 A221 60c multicolored .70 .25

Anti-tuberculosis campaign.

Holy Kaaba — A222

1978, Oct. 28 Photo. *Perf. 11½*

619 A222 60c multicolored .80 .25

Pilgrimage to Mecca.

National Servicemen Building Road — A223

1978, Nov. 4

620 A223 60c multicolored .80 .25

African Unity Road from El Goleah to In Salah, inauguration.

Fibula — A224

Jewelry: 1.35d, Pendant. 1.40d, Ankle ring.

1978, Dec. 21 Photo. *Perf. 12x11½*

621 A224 1.20d multi	1.20	.50
622 A224 1.35d multi	1.45	.60
623 A224 1.40d multi	1.75	.75
Nos. 621-623 (3)	4.40	1.85

Pres. Boumediene — A225

1979, Jan. 7 Photo. *Perf. 12x11½*

624 A225 60c green, red & brown .55 .25

Houari Boumediene, pres. of Algeria 1965-1978.

Torch and Books — A226

1979, Jan. 27 Photo. *Perf. 11½*

625 A226 60c multicolored .55 .25

Natl. Front of Liberation Party Cong.

Pres. Boumediene A227

1979, Feb. 4 Photo. *Perf. 11½*

626 A227 1.40d multi 1.25 .55

40 days after death of Pres. Houari Boumediène.

Ornamental Type of 1976

Proclamation of new President.

1979, Feb. 10

627 A204 2d multicolored 1.50 .40

Election of Pres. Chadli Bendjedid.

A229

1979, Apr. 18 Photo. *Perf. 11½*

628 A229 60c multicolored .50 .25

Sheik Abdul-Hamid Ben Badis (1889-1940).

A230

Designs: 1.20d, Telephone dial, map of Africa. 1.40d, Symbolic Morse key and waves.

1979, May 19 Photo. *Perf. 13½x14*

629 A230 1.20d multi	.85	.30
630 A230 1.40d multi	1.05	.50

Telecom '79 Exhib., Geneva, Sept. 20-26.

Harvest, IYC Emblem — A231

1.40d, Dancers and IYC emblem, vert.

Perf. 11½x11, 11x11½

1979, June 21

631 A231 60c multi	.55	.25
632 A231 1.40d multi	1.10	.50

International Year of the Child.

Nuthatch — A232

1979, Oct. 20 Photo. *Perf. 11½*

633 A232 1.40d multicolored 2.40 1.25

A233

Designs: 1.40d, Flag, soldiers and workers. 3d, Revolutionaries and emblem.

1979, Nov. 1 Photo. *Perf. 12½*

634 A233 1.40d multi 1.00 .30

Size: 37x48mm

Perf. 11½

635 A233 3d multi 1.90 .85

November 1 revolution, 25th anniversary.

Hegira, 1500 Anniv. — A234

1979, Dec. 2 Photo. *Perf. 11½*

636 A234 3d multicolored 2.00 .75

Camels, Lion, Men and Slave — A235

Dionysian Procession (Setif Mosaic): 1.35d, Elephants, tigers and women. 1.40d, Men in tiger-drawn cart. No. 639a has continuous design.

Granite Paper

1980, Feb. 16 Photo. *Perf. 11½*

637 A235 1.20d multi	1.50	.40
638 A235 1.35d multi	1.50	.55
639 A235 1.40d multi	1.75	.80
a. Strip of 3, #637-639	5.75	5.75

Science Day — A236

1980, Apr. 19 Photo. *Perf. 12*

640 A236 60c multicolored .65 .25

Dam and Workers — A237

1980, June 17 Photo. *Perf. 11½*

641 A237 60c multicolored .60 .25

Extraordinary Congress of the National Liberation Front Party.

Olympic Sports, Moscow '80 Emblem — A238

50c, Flame, rings, vert.

1980, June 28

642 A238 50c multicolored .45 .25
643 A238 1.40d shown .90 .50

22nd Summer Olympic Games, Moscow, July 19-Aug. 3.

20th Anniversary of OPEC A239

60c, Men holding OPEC emblem, vert.

Perf. 11x10½, 10½x11

1980, Sept. 15 Engr.

644 A239 60c multicolored .60 .25
645 A239 1.40d shown 1.40 .50

Aures Valley — A240

1980, Sept. 25 Litho. *Perf. 13½x14*

646 A240 50c shown .45 .25
647 A240 1d El Oued Oasis .85 .25
648 A240 1.40d Tassili Rocks 1.25 .40
649 A240 2d View of Algiers 2.10 .70
Nos. 646-649 (4) 4.65 1.60

World Tourism Conf., Manila, Sept. 27.

Avicenna (980-1037), Philosopher and Physician — A241

1980, Oct. 25 Photo. *Perf. 12*

650 A241 2d multicolored 2.25 .80

Ruins of El Asnam A242

1980, Nov. 13 Photo. *Perf. 12*

651 A242 3d multicolored 2.10 .55

Earthquake relief.

Crown — A243

No. 652, Necklace, vert. No. 653, Earrings, bracelet, vert. No. 654, Crown.

Granite Paper

1980, Dec. 20 Photo. *Perf. 12*

652 A243 60c multi .60 .25
653 A243 1.40d multi 1.00 .50
654 A243 2d multi 1.50 .65
Nos. 652-654 (3) 3.10 1.40

See Nos. 705-707.

1980-1984 Five-Year Plan — A244

1981, Jan. 29 Litho. *Perf. 14*

655 A244 60c multicolored .60 .25

Basket Weaving A245

Granite Paper

1981, Feb. 19 Photo. *Perf. 12½*

656 A245 40c shown .40 .25
657 A245 60c Rug weaving .50 .25
658 A245 1d Coppersmith .80 .25
659 A245 1.40d Jeweler 1.10 .45
Nos. 656-659 (4) 2.80 1.20

Cedar Tree — A246

Arbor Day: 1.40d, Cypress tree, vert.

Granite Paper

1981, Mar. 19 Photo. *Perf. 12*

660 A246 60c multi .40 .25
661 A246 1.40d multi 1.10 .60

Mohamed Bachir el Ibrahimi (1869-1965) A247

Children Going to School A248

1981, Apr. 16 Granite Paper

662 A247 60c multicolored .60 .25
663 A248 60c multicolored .60 .25

Science Day.

12th International Hydatidological Congress, Algiers — A249

1981, Apr. 23 *Perf. 14x13½*

664 A249 2d multicolored 2.00 .50

13th World Telecommunications Day — A250

1981, May 14 Photo. *Perf. 14x13½*

665 A250 1.40d multi 1.25 .25

Disabled People and Hand Offering Flower A251

1.20d, Symbolic globe, vert.

Perf. 12½x13, 13x12½

1981, June 20 Litho.

666 A251 1.20d multicolored .95 .25
667 A251 1.40d shown 1.10 .30

Intl. Year of the Disabled.

Papilio Machaon — A252

1.20d, Rhodocera rhamni. 1.40d, Charaxes jasius. 2d, Papilio podalirius.

1981, Aug. 20 Photo. *Perf. 11½*

Granite Paper

668 A252 60c shown .90 .35
669 A252 1.20d multicolored 1.60 .50
670 A252 1.40d multicolored 2.00 .90
671 A252 2d multicolored 2.50 .90
Nos. 668-671 (4) 7.00 2.65

Monk Seal — A253

1981, Sept. 17 *Perf. 14x13½*

672 A253 60c shown .90 .40
673 A253 1.40d Macaque 1.90 .80

World Food Day — A254

1981, Oct. 16 Photo. *Perf. 14x14½*

674 A254 2d multicolored 1.25 .50

Cave Drawings of Tassili — A255

Various cave drawings. 1.60d, 2d horiz.

1981, Nov. 21 *Perf. 11½*

675 A255 60c multi .60 .25
676 A255 1d multi 1.20 .40
677 A255 1.60d multi 1.65 .55
678 A255 2d multi 2.25 .80
Nos. 675-678 (4) 5.70 2.00

Galley, 17-18th Cent. — A256

1981, Dec. 17 Photo. *Perf. 11½*

679 A256 60c shown .70 .50
680 A256 1.60d Ship, diff. 1.90 .95

1982 World Cup Soccer — A257

Designs: Various soccer players.

Perf. 13x12½x 12½x13

1982, Feb. 25 Litho.

681 A257 80c multi, vert. .65 .25
682 A257 2.80d multi 2.00 .80

TB Bacillus Centenary — A258

1982, Mar. 20 Photo. *Perf. 14½x14*

683 A258 80c multi .60 .25

Painted Stand — A259

1982, Apr. 24 Photo. *Perf. 11½*

Granite Paper

684 A259 80c Mirror, vert. .50 .25
685 A259 2d shown 1.25 .45

Size: 48x33mm

686 A259 2.40d Chest 1.75 .60
Nos. 684-686 (3) 3.50 1.30

Djamaael Djadid Mosque, Algiers — A260

No. 688, Sidi Boumediene Mosque, Tlemcen. No. 689, Garden of Dey, Algiers.

1982, May 15 Litho. *Perf. 14*

Size: 32x22mm

687 A260 80c brown .50 .25
a. Size: 30½x21mm 3.50 .75
688 A260 2.40d purple 1.50 .50
689 A260 3d slate 2.00 .60
a. Size: 30½x21mm 5.00 1.25
Nos. 687-689 (3) 4.00 1.35

See Nos. 731-734, 745-747, 774, 778-783.

A261

Medicinal plants: No. 690, Callitris articulata. No 691, Artemisia herba-alba. No. 692, Ricinus communis. No. 693, Thymus fontanesii.

1982, May 27 Photo. *Perf. 11½*

Granite Paper

690 A261 50c multi .40 .25
691 A261 80c multi .60 .25
692 A261 1d multi .90 .40
693 A261 2.40d multi 1.75 .75
Nos. 690-693 (4) 3.65 1.65

A262

No. 694, Riflemen. No. 695, Soldiers, horiz. No. 696, Symbols, citizens, horiz. No. 697, Emblem.

1982, July 5 **Granite Paper**

694 A262 50c multi .45 .25
695 A262 80c multi .55 .25
696 A262 2d multi 1.40 .75
Nos. 694-696 (3) 2.40 1.25

Souvenir Sheet

697 A262 5d multi 5.50 5.50

Independence, 20th anniv.
No. 697 contains one 32x39mm stamp.

Soummam Congress — A263

1982, Aug. 20 **Litho.**

698 A263 80c Congress building .60 .25

Scouting Year — A264

1982, Oct. 21 **Photo.**
Granite Paper

699 A264 2.80d multi 2.00 .60

Palestinian Child — A265

1982, Nov. 25 **Litho.** ***Perf. 10½***

700 A265 1.60d multi .95 .30

Chlamydotis Undulata — A266

Protected birds: No. 701, Geronticus eremita, horiz. No. 702, Chlamydotis Undulata. No. 703, Aguila rapax, horiz. No. 704, Gypaetus barbatus.

Perf. 15x14, 14x15

1982, Dec. 23 **Photo.**

701 A266 50c mutli .75 .55
702 A266 80c multi 1.15 .75
703 A266 2d multi 2.10 1.50
704 A266 2.40d multi 2.75 1.90
Nos. 701-704 (4) 6.75 4.70

Jewelry Type of 1980

1983, Feb. 10 ***Perf. 11½***
Granite Paper

705 A243 50c Picture frame .35 .25
706 A243 1d Flaska .60 .40
707 A243 2d Brooch, horiz. 1.25 .65
Nos. 705-707 (3) 2.20 1.30

A267

80c, Abies numidica, vert. 2.80d, Acacia raddiana.

1983, Mar. 17 **Photo.**
Granite Paper

708 A267 80c multicolored .70 .25
709 A267 2.80d multicolored 2.25 .80

Intl. Arbor Day.

Various Minerals — A268

1.20d, 2.40d horiz.

Granite Paper

Perf. 12x12½, 12½x12

1983, Apr. 21 **Photo.**

710 A268 70c multi 1.25 .35
711 A268 80c multi 1.40 .50
712 A268 1.20d multi 1.60 .65
713 A268 2.40d multi 2.50 1.25
Nos. 710-713 (4) 6.75 2.75

30th Anniv. of Intl. Customs Cooperation Council — A269

1983, May 14 **Photo.** ***Perf. 11½***
Granite Paper

714 A269 80c multi .70 .25

Emir Abdelkader Death Centenary A270

1983, May 22 **Photo.** ***Perf. 12***
Granite Paper

715 A270 4d multi 2.40 .90

Local Mushrooms — A271

No. 716, Amanita muscaria. No. 717, Amanita phalloides. No. 718, Pleurotus eryngii. No. 719, Tefezia leonis.

1983, July 21 ***Perf. 14x15***

716 A271 50c multi 1.00 .35
717 A271 80c multi 1.45 .75
718 A271 1.40d multi 3.00 1.10
719 A271 2.80d multi 4.50 2.10
Nos. 716-719 (4) 9.95 4.30

A272

1983, Sept. 1 **Photo.** ***Perf. 11½***

720 A272 80c multi .70 .25

ibn-Khaldun, historian, philosopher.

World Communications Year — A273

80c, Post Office, Algiers. 2.40d, Telephone, circuit box.

Perf. 11½x12½

1983, Sept. 22 **Litho.**

721 A273 80c multicolored .55 .25
722 A273 2.40d multicolored 1.40 .60

Goat and Tassili Mountains A274

80c, Tuaregs in native costume. 2.40d, Animals, rock painting. 2.80d, Rock formation.

1983, Oct. 20 **Litho.** ***Perf. 12½x13***

723 A274 50c shown .40 .25
724 A274 80c multicolored .50 .25
725 A274 2.40d multicolored 1.40 .55
726 A274 2.80d multicolored 1.75 .75
Nos. 723-726 (4) 4.05 1.80

Sloughi Dog — A275

Perf. 14x14½, 14½x14

1983, Nov. 24 **Photo.**

727 A275 80c shown 1.10 .35
728 A275 2.40d Sloughi, horiz. 2.75 .95

Natl. Liberation Party, 5th Congress A276

80c, Symbols of development. 5d, Emblem.

1983, Dec. 19 **Photo.** ***Perf. 11½***

729 A276 80c multicolored .80 .40

Souvenir Sheet

730 A276 5d multicolored 5.00 5.00

No. 730 contains one 32x38mm stamp.

View Type of 1982

10c, View of Oran, 1830. 1d, Sidi Abderahman and Taalibi Mosques. 2d, Bejaia, 1830. 4d, Constantine, 1830.

1984, Jan. 26 **Litho.** ***Perf. 14***
Size: 32x22mm

731 A260 10c multicolored .25 .25
a. Size: 30½x21mm .80 .40
732 A260 1d multicolored .50 .25
a. Size: 30½x21mm 1.50 .80
733 A260 2d multicolored 1.00 .50
a. Size: 30½x21mm 3.00 1.50
734 A260 4d multicolored 2.50 .65
a. Size: 30½x21mm 6.00 1.50
Nos. 731-734 (4) 4.25 1.65

Pottery — A278

Perf. 11½x12, 12x11½

1984, Feb. 23 **Photo.**
Granite Paper

735 A278 80c Jug, vert. .50 .25
736 A278 1d Platter .65 .40
737 A278 2d Oil lamp, vert. 1.40 .60
738 A278 2.40d Pitcher 1.75 .75
Nos. 735-738 (4) 4.30 2.00

Fountains of Old Algiers — A279

Various fountains.

1984, Mar. 22 **Photo.** ***Perf. 11½***
Granite Paper

739 A279 50c multi .25 .25
740 A279 80c multi .55 .40
741 A279 2.40d multi 1.40 .65
Nos. 739-741 (3) 2.20 1.30

1984 Summer Olympics — A280

1984, May 19 **Photo.** ***Perf. 11½***
Granite Paper

742 A280 1d multi 1.25 .40

Brown Stallion — A281

1984, June 14 **Photo.** ***Perf. 11½***
Granite Paper

743 A281 80c shown .80 .40
744 A281 2.40d White mare 2.10 .95

View Type of 1982

1984 **Litho.** ***Perf. 14***
Size: 32x22mm

745 A260 5c Mustapha Pacha .50 .25
a. Size: 30½x21mm .80 .40
746 A260 20c Bab Azzoun .50 .25
d. Size: 30½x21mm 1.00 .60
746A A260 30c Algiers .50 .25
d. Size: 30½x21mm 1.50 .50
746B A260 40c Kolea .50 .25
746C A260 50c Algiers .50 .25
e. Size: 30½x21mm 1.50 .50
747 A260 70c Mostaganem .60 .25
a. Size: 30½x21mm 2.00 1.00
Nos. 745-747 (6) 3.10 1.50

Issued: Nos. 745, 746, 747, 7/19; Nos. 746A-746C, 10/20.

Lute — A282

Native musical instruments.

1984, Sept. 22 **Litho.** ***Perf. 15x14***

748 A282 80c shown .60 .25
749 A282 1d Drum .90 .40
750 A282 2.40d Fiddle 1.75 .75
751 A282 2.80d Bagpipe 2.00 .95
Nos. 748-751 (4) 5.25 2.35

30th Anniv. of Algerian Revolution A284

80c, Partisans. 5d, Algerian flags, vert.

1984, Nov. 3 **Photo.** ***Perf. 11½x12***

757 A284 80c multicolored .85 .25

Souvenir Sheet

758 A284 5d multicolored 5.50 5.50

M'Zab Valley — A285

80c, Map of valley. 2.40d, Town of M'Zab, vert.

1984, Dec. 15 ***Perf. 15x14, 14x15***

759 A285 80c multicolored .75 .25
760 A285 2.40d multicolored 1.75 .60

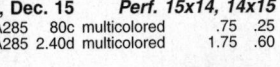

18th and 19th Century Metalware — A286

1985, Jan. 26 Photo. *Perf. 11½*

761 A286 80c Coffee pot .60 .25
762 A286 2d Bowl, horiz. 1.25 .65
763 A286 2.40d Covered bowl 1.75 .85
Nos. 761-763 (3) 3.60 1.75

Fish — A287

50c, Thunnus thynnus. 80c, Sparus aurata. 2.40d, Epinephelus guaza. 2.80d, Mustelus mustelus.

1985, Feb. 23 Photo. *Perf. 15x14*

764 A287 50c multicolored .50 .25
765 A287 80c multicolored .90 .40
766 A287 2.40d multicolored 2.25 1.10
767 A287 2.80d multicolored 2.75 1.25
Nos. 764-767 (4) 6.40 3.00

National Games — A288

1985, Mar. 28 *Perf. 11½x12*
Granite Paper

768 A288 80c Doves, emblem .80 .25

Environmental Conservation A289

1985, Apr. 25 *Perf. 13½*

769 A289 80c Stylized trees .70 .25
770 A289 1.40d Stylized waves 1.00 .40

View Type of 1982 and

The Casbah — A290

View of Constantine A290a

Street Scene in Algiers A290b

Designs: 2.50d, Djamaael Djadid Mosque, Algiers. 2.90d, like No. 746. 5d, like No. 746A. 1.50d, like No. 746B. 4.20d, like No. 764.

Perf. 13½x12½, 13 (#774, 4.20d),
Perf. 13½x14 (#775)
Perf. 14½x14 (2d)

Photo., Litho. (2d, 6,20d, 7.50d, #775)

1985-94

771 A290 20c dk blue & buff .25 .25
772 A290 80c sage grn & buff .60 .25
773 A290a 1d dk olive grn .50 .25
a. Bklt. pane of 5 + label 4.00
774 A260 1.50d dull red .55 .25
775 A290b 1.50d red brn & brn .40 .25
a. Booklet pane of 6 2.75
776 A290b 2d dk bl & lt bl .40 .25
a. Booklet pane of 5 + label 3.00
777 A290 2.40d chestnut & buff 1.75 .25
a. Bklt. pane of 5 (20c, 3 80c, 2.40d) + label 5.75
778 A260 2.50d bluish green 1.00 .25
779 A260 2.90d slate 1.25 .25
780 A260 4.20d gray green 1.40 .35
781 A260 5d dp bis & blk 2.10 .40

Perf. 14

782 A260 6.20d like #731 1.10 .30
783 A260 7.50d like #745 1.75 .30
Nos. 771-783 (13) 13.05 3.60

Nos. 771-772, 777 issued only in booklet panes.

Issued: 20c, 80c, 2.40d, 6/1/85; 1d, 1/26/89; 2.50d, 2.90d, 5d, 2/23/89; No. 774, 4.20d, 3/21/91; No. 775, 5/20/92; 6.20d, 7.50d, 4/22/92; 2d, 10/21/93; No. 776a, 10/21/94.

See No. 1010.

UN, 40th Anniv. — A291

1985, June 26 Photo. *Perf. 14*

784 A291 1d Dove, emblem, 40 .90 .25

Natl. Youth Festival — A292

1985, July 5 Litho. *Perf. 13½*

785 A292 80c multicolored .70 .25

Intl. Youth Year — A293

80c, Silhouette, globe, emblem, vert. 1.40d, Doves, globe.

1985, July 5

786 A293 80c multicolored .60 .25
787 A293 1.40d multicolored .90 .40

World Map, OPEC — A294

1985, Sept. 14 Photo. *Perf. 12½x13*

788 A294 80c multicolored .80 .25

Organization of Petroleum Exporting Countries, 25th anniv.

Family Planning — A295

1985, Oct. 3 Litho. *Perf. 14*

789 A295 80c Mother and sons .60 .25
790 A295 1.40d Weighing infant .90 .40
791 A295 1.70d Breast-feeding 1.30 .50
Nos. 789-791 (3) 2.80 1.15

El-Meniaa Township — A296

80c, Chetaibi Bay, horiz. 2.40d, Bou Noura Town, horiz.

1985, Oct. 24 Engr. *Perf. 13*

792 A296 80c multicolored .50 .25
793 A296 2d shown 1.40 .40
794 A296 2.40d multicolored 1.60 .60
Nos. 792-794 (3) 3.50 1.25

The Palm Grove, by N. Dinet — A297

1985, Nov. 21 Photo. *Perf. 11½x12*
Granite Paper

795 A297 2d multicolored 1.50 .75
796 A297 3d multi, diff. 2.10 1.10

Tapestries — A298

Various designs.

1985, Dec. 19 Granite Paper

797 A298 80c multi .70 .50
798 A298 1.40d multi 1.40 .75
799 A298 2.40d multi 2.00 1.25
800 A298 2.80d multi 2.50 1.75
Nos. 797-800 (4) 6.60 4.25

Wildcats — A299

80c, Felis margarita. 1d, Felis caracal. 2d, Felis sylvestris. 2.40d, Felis serval, vert.

1986, Jan. 23 *Perf. 12x11½, 11½x12*
Granite Paper

801 A299 80c multicolored 1.40 .60
802 A299 1d multicolored 1.75 .70
803 A299 2d multicolored 2.50 .90
804 A299 2.40d multicolored 3.50 1.60
Nos. 801-804 (4) 9.15 3.80

UN Child Survival Campaign — A300

80c, Oral vaccine. 1.40d, Mother, child, sun. 1.70d, Three children.

1986, Feb. 13 Litho. *Perf. 13½*

805 A300 80c multicolored .55 .25
806 A300 1.40d multicolored 1.10 .65
807 A300 1.70d multicolored 1.60 .85
Nos. 805-807 (3) 3.25 1.75

Algerian General Worker's Union, 30th Anniv. — A301

1986, Feb. 24 *Perf. 12½*
Granite Paper

808 A301 2d multicolored 1.50 .60

National Charter — A302

Granite Paper

1986, Mar. 6 Photo. *Perf. 11½*

809 A302 4d multicolored 3.00 1.25

Natl. Day of the Disabled — A303

1986, Mar. 15 *Perf. 12½x13*

810 A303 80c multicolored .70 .30

A304

1986, Apr. 17 Litho. *Perf. 14x15*

811 A304 80c multicolored .75 .40

Anti-Tuberculosis campaign.

A305

2d, Soccer ball, sombrero. 2.40d, Soccer players.

1986, Apr. 24 *Perf. 14*

812 A305 2d multicolored 1.50 .55
813 A305 2.40d multicolored 1.75 .65

1986 World Cup Soccer Championships, Mexico.

Inner Courtyards — A306

Granite Paper

1986, May 15 Photo. *Perf. 11½*

814 A306 80c multicolored .70 .30
815 A306 2.40d multi, diff. 1.90 .95
816 A306 3d multi, diff. 2.40 1.25
Nos. 814-816 (3) 5.00 2.50

Blood Donation Campaign — A307

1986, June 26 Litho. *Perf. 13½*

817 A307 80c multicolored 1.40 .40

Southern District Radio Communication Inauguration — A308

1986, July *Perf. 13*

818 A308 60c multicolored .50 .25

Mosque Gateways — A309

2d, Door. 2.40d, Ornamental arch.

Granite Paper

1986, Sept. 27 Photo. ***Perf. 12x11½***

819 A309	2d multicolored		1.40	.60
820 A309	2.40d multicolored		1.60	.85

Intl. Peace Year — A310

Perf. 13½x14½

1986, Oct. 16 **Photo.**

821 A310	2.40d multi	1.60	.60

Folk Dancing — A311

1986, Nov. 22 Litho. ***Perf. 14x13½***

822 A311	80c Woman, scarf	.70	.25
823 A311	2.40d Woman, diff.	1.75	.70
824 A311	2.80d Man, sword	1.90	.80
	Nos. 822-824 (3)	4.35	1.75

Flowers — A312

80c, Narcissus tazetta. 1.40d, Iris unguicularis. 2.40d, Capparis spinosa. 2.80d, Gladiolus segetum.

1986, Dec. 18 Photo. ***Perf. 14***

825 A312	80c multicolored	.70	.30
826 A312	1.40d multicolored	1.25	.60
827 A312	2.40d multicolored	1.75	1.00
828 A312	2.80d multicolored	2.10	1.25
	Nos. 825-828 (4)	5.80	3.15

See Nos. 936-938.

Abstract Paintings by Mohammed Issia Khem — A313

2d, Man and woman, vert. 5d, Man and books.

Perf. 11½x12, 12x11½

1987, Jan. 29 **Litho.**

829 A313	2d multicolored	1.50	.85
830 A313	5d multicolored	3.25	2.00

Jewelry from Aures — A314

Granite Paper

1987, Feb. 27 Photo. ***Perf. 12***

831 A314	1d Earrings	.75	.45
832 A314	1.80d Bracelets	1.20	.70
833 A314	2.90d Nose rings	1.75	1.10
834 A314	3.30d Necklace	2.10	1.25
	Nos. 831-834 (4)	5.80	3.50

Nos. 831-833 vert.

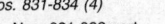

Petroglyphs, Atlas — A315

1987, Mar. 26 Litho. ***Perf. 12x11½***

Granite Paper

835 A315	1d Man and woman	1.10	.70
836 A315	2.90d Goat	2.50	1.40
837 A315	3.30d Horse, bull	2.75	1.40
	Nos. 835-837 (3)	6.35	3.50

Syringe as an Umbrella — A316

Granite Paper

1987, Apr. 7 ***Perf. 11½***

838 A316	1d multicolored	.80	.25

Child Immunization Campaign, World Health Day.

Volunteers — A317

1987, Apr. 23 ***Perf. 10½***

839 A317	1d multicolored	.55	.30

Third General Census — A318

1987, May 21 ***Perf. 13½***

840 A318	1d multicolored	.70	.30

Algerian Postage, 25th Anniv. A319

War Orphans' Fund label (1fr + 9fr) of 1962.

Granite Paper

1987, July 5 Photo. ***Perf. 11½x12***

841 A319	1.80d multicolored	2.75	.70

A320

A321

1987, July 5 **Granite Paper**

842 A320	1d multicolored	.60	.25

Souvenir Sheet

843 A321	5d multicolored	5.50	5.50

Natl. independence, 25th anniv.

Amateur Theater Festival, Mostaganem A322

Granite Paper

1987, July 20 ***Perf. 12x11½***

844 A322	1d Actors on stage	.55	.25
845 A322	1.80d Theater	.95	.60
a.	Pair, #844-845	1.50	1.50

No. 845a has continuous design.

Mediterranean Games, Latakia — A323

1987, Aug. 6 ***Perf. 13x12½, 12½x13***

846 A323	1d Discus	.60	.30
847 A323	2.90d Tennis, vert.	1.50	.85
848 A323	3.30d Team handball	1.75	1.00
	Nos. 846-848 (3)	3.85	2.15

Birds — A324

1d, Phoenicopterus ruber roseus. 1.80d, Porphyrio porphyrio. 2.50d, Elanus caeruleus. 2.90d, Milvus milvus.

1987 Litho. ***Perf. 13½***

849 A324	1d multicolored	.85	.50
850 A324	1.80d multicolored	1.40	1.00
851 A324	2.50d multicolored	2.25	1.25
852 A324	2.90d multicolored	2.50	1.50
	Nos. 849-852 (4)	7.00	4.25

Agriculture A325

No. 853, Planting. No. 854, Reservoir. No. 855, Harvesting crop, vert. No. 856, Produce, vert.

Perf. 10½x11, 11x10½

1987, Nov. 26 **Litho.**

853 A325	1d multicolored	.65	.25
854 A325	1d multicolored	.65	.25
855 A325	1d multicolored	.65	.25
856 A325	1d multicolored	.65	.25
	Nos. 853-856 (4)	2.60	1.00

African Telecommunications Day — A326

1987, Dec. 7 ***Perf. 10½***

857 A326	1d multicolored	.90	.25

Transportation A327

1987, Dec. 18 Litho. ***Perf. 10½x11***

858 A327	2.90d shown	1.50	.70
859 A327	3.30d Diesel train	3.00	1.50

Algerian Universities A328

Various campuses.

1987, Dec. 26 ***Perf. 10½x11, 11x10½***

860 A328	1d shown	.50	.25
861 A328	2.50d multi, diff.	1.30	.50
862 A328	2.90d multi, diff.	1.50	.60
863 A328	3.30d multi, diff., vert.	1.75	.70
	Nos. 860-863 (4)	5.05	2.05

Intl. Rural Development Fund, 10th Anniv. — A329

1988, Jan. 27 ***Perf. 10½x11***

864 A329	1d multicolored	.80	.25

Autonomy of State-owned Utilities — A330

1988, Feb. 27 Litho. ***Perf. 11x10½***

865 A330	1d multicolored	.60	.25

Intl. Women's Day — A331

1988, Mar. 10 Litho. ***Perf. 11x10½***

866 A331	1d multicolored	.70	.25

Arab Scouts, 75th Anniv. — A332

1988, Apr. 7 Litho. ***Perf. 10½***

867 A332	2d multicolored	1.20	.50

1988 Summer Olympics, Seoul — A333

1988, July 23 Litho. ***Perf. 10½***

868 A333	2.90d multicolored	1.60	.85

Hot Springs — A334

2.90d, Caverns, horiz. 3.30d, Gazebo, fountain, horiz.

1988, July 16

869 A334	1d shown	.45	.25
870 A334	2.90d multicolored	1.50	.60
871 A334	3.30d multicolored	1.75	.70
	Nos. 869-871 (3)	3.70	1.55

World Wildlife Fund — A335

Barbary apes, Macaca sylvanus: 50c, Adult. 90c, Family. 1d, Close-up, vert. 1.80d, Seated on branch, vert.

1988, Sept. 17 Litho. *Perf. 10½*

872 A335 50c multicolored 1.00 .45
873 A335 90c multicolored 1.25 .65
874 A335 1d multicolored 1.75 .90
875 A335 1.80d multicolored 3.00 1.60
Nos. 872-875 (4) 7.00 3.60

Intl. Literacy Day — A336

1988, Sept. 10 Photo. *Perf. 10½*

876 A336 2.90d multicolored 1.50 .85

WHO, 40th Anniv. — A337

1988, Oct. 15

877 A337 2.90d multicolored 1.50 .70

Fight Apartheid — A338

1988, Nov. 19 Litho. *Perf. 10½x11*

878 A338 2.50d multicolored 1.25 .50

Natl. Front Congress — A339

1988, Nov. 29 *Perf. 11x10½*

879 A339 1d multicolored .60 .25

Agriculture A340

No. 880, Irrigation. No. 881, Orchard, fields, livestock.

1988, Dec. 24 *Perf. 10½*

880 A340 1d multicolored .55 .25
881 A340 1d multicolored .55 .25

Natl. Goals — A342

No. 887, Ancient fort. No. 888, Telecommunications. No. 889, Modern buildings.

1989, Mar. 9 Litho. *Perf. 11½*
Granite Paper

886 A342 1d shown .50 .25
887 A342 1d multicolored .50 .25
888 A342 1d multicolored .50 .25
889 A342 1d multicolored .50 .25
Nos. 886-889 (4) 2.00 1.00

Nos. 887-889 horiz.

Airports — A343

2.90d, Oran Es Senia, horiz. 3.30d, Tebessa, horiz.

1989, Mar. 23 *Perf. 10½x11, 11x10½*

890 A343 2.90d multicolored 1.20 .55
891 A343 3.30d multicolored 1.40 .70
892 A343 5d shown 2.10 1.25
Nos. 890-892 (3) 4.70 2.50

Development of the South — A344

1d, Irrigation. 1.80d, Building. 2.50d, Fossil fuel extraction, vert.

1989, Apr. 24 Litho. *Perf. 13½*

893 A344 1d multicolored .50 .25
894 A344 1.80d multicolored .70 .40
895 A344 2.50d multicolored 1.05 .55
Nos. 893-895 (3) 2.25 1.20

Eradicate Locusts — A345

1989, May 25 *Perf. 10½*

896 A345 1d multicolored .50 .25

National Service — A346

1989, May 11 Litho. *Perf. 13½*

897 A346 2d multicolored 1.40 .70

1st Moon Landing, 20th Anniv. — A347

4d, Astronaut, lunar module, Moon's surface.

1989, July 23 Litho. *Perf. 13½*

898 A347 2.90d shown 1.25 .60
899 A347 4d multi, vert. 1.60 .90

Interparliamentary Union, Cent. — A348

1989, Sept. 4 *Perf. 10½*

900 A348 2.90d gold, brt rose lil & blk 1.20 .40

Produce — A349

1989, Sept. 23 Litho. *Perf. 11½*
Granite Paper

901 Strip of 3 4.00 4.00
a. A349 2d multi, diff. .75 .50
b. A349 3d multi, diff. 1.20 .65
c. A349 5d shown 1.90 1.20

Fish — A350

1d, Sarda sarda. 1.80d, Zeus faber. 2.90d, Pagellus bogaraveo. 3.30d, Xiphias gladius.

1989, Oct. 27 Litho. *Perf. 13½*

902 A350 1d multicolored .70 .30
903 A350 1.80d multicolored 1.25 .50
904 A350 2.90d multicolored 1.90 .70
905 A350 3.30d multicolored 2.25 .90
Nos. 902-905 (4) 6.10 2.40

Algerian Revolution, 35th Anniv. — A351

1989, Nov. 4 Litho. *Perf. 13½*

906 A351 1d multicolored .50 .25

African Development Bank, 25th Anniv. — A352

1989, Nov. 18 *Perf. 10½*

907 A352 1d multicolored .50 .25

Mushrooms — A353

No. 908, Boletus satanas. No. 909, Psalliota xanthoderma. No. 910, Lepiota procera. No. 911, Lactarius deliciosus.

1989, Dec. 16 *Perf. 13½*

908 A353 1d mutli 1.00 .30
909 A353 1.80d multi 1.50 .75
910 A353 2.90d multi 2.40 1.00
911 A353 3.30d multi 3.25 1.25
Nos. 908-911 (4) 8.15 3.30

A354

1990, Jan. 18 Litho. *Perf. 10½*

912 A354 1d multicolored .50 .25

Pan-African Postal Union, 10th anniv.

Energy Conservation — A355

1990, Feb. 22 Litho. *Perf. 14*

913 A355 1d multicolored .60 .25

A356

1990, Mar. 2 Photo. *Perf. 11½*

914 A356 3d multicolored 1.30 .60

African Soccer Championships.

A357

1990, May 17 Litho. *Perf. 13½*

917 A357 2.90d shown 1.10 .60
918 A357 5d Trophy 2.00 1.10

World Cup Soccer Championships, Italy.

Rural Electrification A358

1990, June 21

919 A358 2d multicolored .90 .30

Youth A359

Youth Holding Rainbow A360

1990, July 6 *Perf. 13½*

920 A359 2d multicolored .85 .30
921 A360 3d multicolored 1.25 .50

Maghreb Arab Union — A361

1990 *Perf. 14x13½*

922 A361 1d multicolored .50 .25

Vocations — A362

1990, Apr. 26 Litho. *Perf. 12½*

923 A362 2d Craftsmen .75 .40
924 A362 2.90d Auto mechanics 1.00 .60
925 A362 3.30d Deep sea fishing 1.75 .75
Nos. 923-925 (3) 3.50 1.75

Organization of Petroleum Exporting Countries (OPEC), 30th Anniv. — A363

1990 *Perf. 13½*
926 A363 2d multicolored 1.50 .30

Savings Promotion — A364

1990, Oct. 31 **Litho.** *Perf. 14*
927 A364 1d multicolored .50 .25

Namibian Independence A365

1990, Nov. 8
928 A365 3d multicolored 1.00 .30

Farm Animals — A366

1990, Nov. 29 *Perf. 13½*

929	A366	1d Duck	.50	.25
930	A366	2d Rabbit, horiz.	1.00	.40
931	A366	2.90d Turkey	1.30	.65
932	A366	3.30d Rooster, horiz.	1.60	.85
		Nos. 929-932 (4)	4.40	2.15

Anti-French Riots, 30th Anniv. — A367

1990, Dec. 11
933 A367 1d multicolored .65 .25

A368

1990, Dec. 20 *Perf. 14*
934 A368 1d multicolored .40 .25

Fight against respiratory diseases.

Constitution, 2nd Anniv. — A369

1991, Feb. 24 **Litho.** *Perf. 13½*
935 A369 1d multicolored .55 .25

Flower Type of 1986

2d, Jasminum fruticans. 4d, Dianthus crinitus. 5d, Cyclamen africanum.

1991, May 23 **Litho.** *Perf. 13½*
Size: 26x36mm

936	A312	2d multicolored	.80	.30
937	A312	4d multicolored	1.90	.70
938	A312	5d multicolored	2.25	1.00
		Nos. 936-938 (3)	4.95	2.00

Children's Drawings — A370

1991, June 3 **Litho.** *Perf. 13½*
939 A370 3d shown 1.20 .50
940 A370 4d Children playing 1.20 .50

Maghreb Arab Union Summit — A371

1991, June 10
941 A371 1d multicolored .45 .25

Geneva Convention on Refugees, 40th Anniv. — A372

1991, July 28 **Litho.** *Perf. 14½x13½*
942 A372 3d multicolored 1.00 .35

Postal Service — A373

4.20d, Expo emblem, vert.

1991, Oct. 12 *Perf. 14*
943 A373 1.50d shown .60 .25
944 A373 4.20d multicolored 1.25 .50

Telecom '91, 6th World Forum and Exposition on Telecommunications, Geneva, Switzerland (No. 944).

Butterflies A374

2d, Zerynthia rumina. 4d, Melitaea didyma. 6d, Vanessa atalanta. 7d, Nymphalis polychloros.

Granite Paper

1991, Nov. 21 **Litho.** *Perf. 11½*

945	A374	2d multicolored	.85	.35
946	A374	4d multicolored	1.20	.50
947	A374	6d multicolored	1.65	.75
948	A374	7d multicolored	2.00	1.10
		Nos. 945-948 (4)	5.70	2.70

A375

3d, Necklace. 4d, Jewelry of Southern Tuaregs. 5d, Brooch. 7d, Rings, horiz.

Granite Paper

1991, Dec. 21 *Perf. 12*

949	A375	3d multicolored	.75	.30
950	A375	4d multicolored	.85	.45
951	A375	5d multicolored	1.00	.70
952	A375	7d multicolored	1.75	1.10
		Nos. 949-952 (4)	4.35	2.55

Algerian Women — A376

1992, Mar. 8 **Litho.** *Perf. 14*
953 A376 1.50d multicolored .50 .25

Gazelles — A377

Designs: 1.50d, Gazella dorcas. 6.20d, Gazella cuvieri. 8.60d, Gazella dama.

1992, May 13 *Perf. 14½x13*

954	A377	1.50d multicolored	.50	.35
955	A377	6.20d multicolored	1.10	.75
956	A377	8.60d multicolored	1.75	1.10
		Nos. 954-956 (3)	3.35	2.20

1992 Summer Olympics, Barcelona — A379

1992, June 24 **Litho.** *Perf. 14*
958 A379 6.20d Runners 1.25 .50

Independence, 30th Anniv. — A381

1992, July 7 **Litho.** *Perf. 14*
960 A381 5d multicolored 1.00 .30

Medicinal Plants — A382

No. 961, Ajuga iva. No. 962, Rhamnus alaternus. No. 963, Silybum marianum. No. 964, Lavandula stoechas.

1992, Sept. 23 **Litho.** *Perf. 14*

961	A382	1.50d multi	.50	.25
962	A382	5.10d multi	1.20	.50
963	A382	6.20d multi	1.30	.60
964	A382	8.60d multi	1.60	.85
		Nos. 961-964 (4)	4.60	2.20

Post Office Modernization — A383

1992, Oct. 10 **Litho.** *Perf. 14*
965 A383 1.50d multicolored .40 .25

Marine Life — A384

Designs: 1.50d, Hippocampus hippocampus. 2.70d, Caretta caretta. 6.20d, Muraena helena. 7.50d, Palinurus elephas.

1992, Dec. 23

966	A384	1.50d multicolored	.60	.25
967	A384	2.70d multicolored	.90	.25
968	A384	6.20d multicolored	1.90	.65
969	A384	7.50d multicolored	2.10	.85
		Nos. 966-969 (4)	5.50	2.00

Pres. Mohammad Boudiaf (1919-92) — A385

Granite Paper

1992, Nov. 3 **Litho.** *Perf. 11½*
970 A385 2d green & multi .35 .25
971 A385 8.60d blue & multi 1.60 .85

Coins — A386

1.50d, Numidia, 2nd cent. BC. 2d, Dinar, 14th cent. 5.10d, Dinar, 11th cent. 6.20d, Abdelkader, 19th cent.

Granite Paper

1992, Dec. 16 **Litho.** *Perf. 11½*

972	A386	1.50d multicolored	.30	.25
973	A386	2d multicolored	.40	.25
974	A386	5.10d multicolored	.90	.35
975	A386	6.20d multicolored	1.15	.50
		Nos. 972-975 (4)	2.75	1.35

Door Knockers — A387

1993, Feb. 17 **Litho.** *Perf. 14*

976	A387	2d Algiers	.30	.25
977	A387	5.60d Constantine	.80	.40
978	A387	8.60d Tlemcen	1.50	.65
		Nos. 976-978 (3)	2.60	1.30

Flowering Trees — A388

4.50d, Neflier (medlar), horiz. 8.60d, Cognassier (quince). 11d, Abricotier (apricot).

Granite Paper

1993, Mar. 17 *Perf. 12x11½, 11½x12*

979	A388	4.50d multicolored	.85	.40
980	A388	8.60d multicolored	1.75	.75
981	A388	11d multicolored	2.25	1.00
		Nos. 979-981 (3)	4.85	2.15

Natl. Coast Guard Service, 20th Anniv. — A389

1993, Apr. 3 **Litho.** *Perf. 14*
982 A389 2d multicolored 1.10 .30

Traditional Grain Processing — A390

1993, May 19 Litho. *Perf. 14*

983 A390 2d Container .45 .25
984 A390 5.60d Millstone .90 .50
985 A390 8.60d Press 1.40 .65
Nos. 983-985 (3) 2.75 1.40

Royal Mausoleums A391

1993, June 16 Litho. *Perf. 14*

986 A391 8.60d Mauretania 1.25 .60
987 A391 12d El Khroub 2.00 .85

Ports — A392

1993, Oct. 20 Litho. *Perf. 14x13½*

988 A392 2d Annaba .35 .25
989 A392 8.60d Arzew 1.50 .55

Varanus Griseus — A393

Design: 2d, Chamaeleo vulgaris, vert.

Perf. 13½x14, 14x13½

1993, Nov. 20

990 A393 2d multicolored .50 .25
991 A393 8.60d multicolored 1.75 .80

Tourism — A394

1993, Dec. 18 Litho. *Perf. 14x13½*

992 A394 2d Tipaza .35 .25
993 A394 8.60d Kerzaz 1.10 .50

A395

1994, Jan. 2 *Perf. 13½x14*

994 A395 2d multicolored .60 .25

SONATRACH (Natl. Society for Research, Transformation, and Commercialization of Hydrocarbons), 30th anniv.

Chahid Day — A396

1994, Feb. 18 Litho. *Perf. 13½x14*

995 A396 2d multicolored .60 .25

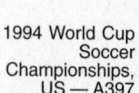

1994 World Cup Soccer Championships, US — A397

1994, Mar. 16 *Perf. 14x13½*

996 A397 8.60d multicolored 2.25 .85

Orchids — A398

5.60d, Orchis simia lam. 8.60d, Ophrys lutea cavan. 11d, Ophrys apifera huds.

1994, Apr. 20 Litho. *Perf. 11½*
Granite Paper

997 A398 5.60d multicolored 1.50 .60
998 A398 8.60d multicolored 1.75 .85
999 A398 11d multicolored 2.75 1.25
Nos. 997-999 (3) 6.00 2.70

Ancient Petroglyphs — A399

3d, Inscriptions. 10d, Man on horse.

1994, May 21 Litho. *Perf. 13x14*

1000 A399 3d multicolored .95 .25
1001 A399 10d multicolored 2.10 .75

A400

1994, June 25

1002 A400 12d multicolored 1.90 .65

Intl. Olympic Committee, cent.

World Population Day — A401

1994, July 13

1003 A401 3d multicolored .50 .25

Views of Algiers Type of 1992

Design: 3d, like No. 775.

1994, July 13 Litho. *Perf. 14*

1010 A290b 3d dk blue & lt blue .75 .25

Jewelry from Saharan Atlas Region — A402

Perf. 13½x14, 14x13½
1994, Oct. 18 Litho.

1019 A402 3d Fibules, vert. .60 .25
1020 A402 5d Belt .90 .30
1021 A402 12d Bracelets 2.40 .85
Nos. 1019-1021 (3) 3.90 1.40

Algerian Revolution, 40th Anniv. — A403

1994, Nov. 3 Litho. *Perf. 13½x14*

1022 A403 3d multicolored .40 .25

A404

1994, Nov. 16 Litho. *Perf. 13½x14*

1023 A404 3d Ladybugs .50 .25
1024 A404 12d Beetles 2.00 .75

Fight Against AIDS — A405

1994, Dec. 1 Litho. *Perf. 14x13½*

1025 A405 3d multicolored 1.00 .25

Folk Dances — A406

1994, Dec. 17 Litho. *Perf. 13½x14*

1026 A406 3d Algeroise .40 .30
1027 A406 10d Constantinoise 1.20 .75
1028 A406 12d Alaoui 1.40 .90
Nos. 1026-1028 (3) 3.00 1.95

See Nos. 1170-1172.

Minerals — A407

1994, Sept. 21

1029 A407 3d Gres lite-erode .60 .25
1030 A407 5d Cipolin 1.00 .50
1031 A407 10d Marne a turitella 2.40 .95
Nos. 1029-1031 (3) 4.00 1.70

World Tourism Organization, 20th Anniv. — A408

1995, Jan. 28 Litho. *Perf. 14x13½*

1032 A408 3d multicolored .40 .25

Honey Bees — A409

1995, Feb. 22 *Perf. 13½x14, 14x13½*

1033 A409 3d shown .40 .30
1034 A409 13d On flower, horiz. 1.60 .90

Flowers — A410

Granite Paper

1995, Mar. 29 Photo. *Perf. 11½*

1035 A410 3d Dahlias .50 .30
1036 A410 10d Zinnias 1.50 .80
1037 A410 13d Lilacs 1.75 .90
Nos. 1035-1037 (3) 3.75 2.00

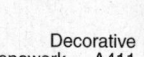

Decorative Stonework — A411

Various patterns.

1995, Apr. 19 *Perf. 14*

1039 A411 3d brown .60 .30
1040 A411 4d green .75 .30
1041 A411 5d deep claret .90 .30
Nos. 1039-1041 (3) 2.25 .90

End of World War II, 50th Anniv. — A413

1995, May 3 *Perf. 14x13½*

1048 A413 3d multicolored .70 .30

Souvenir Sheet

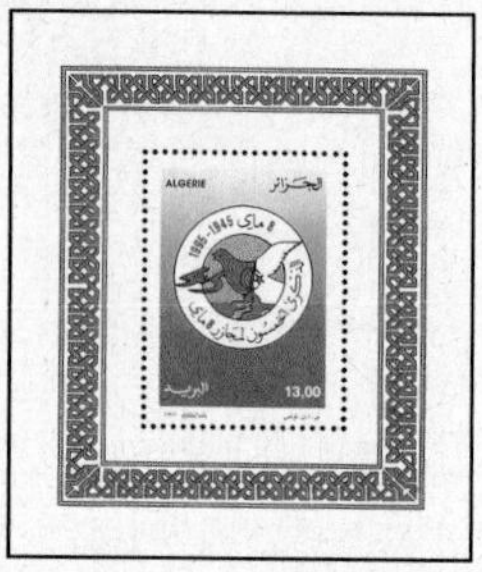

VE Day, 50th Anniv. A414

1995, May 10 Litho. *Perf. 13½x14*

1049 A414 13d multicolored 7.00 7.00

Volleyball, Cent. — A415

1995, June 14

1050 A415 3d multicolored .65 .30

Environmental Protection — A416

3d, Air, water pollution. 13d, Air pollution.

1995, June 5

1051 A416 3d multicolored .40 .30
1052 A416 13d multicolored 1.60 .85

General Electrification — A417

1995, July 5 Litho. *Perf. 13½x14*

1053 A417 3d multicolored .65 .30

UN, 50th Anniv. — A418

1995, Oct. 24 *Perf. 14x13½*

1054 A418 13d multicolored 2.50 1.00

Pottery — A419

10d, Pot, Lakhdaria. 20d, Pitcher, Aokas. 21d, Jar, Larbaa Nath Iraten. 30d, Vase, Ouadhia.

1995, Nov. 14 Litho. *Perf. 14*

1055	A419	10d dark brown	1.00	.50
1056	A419	20d dull maroon	2.10	1.00
1057	A419	21d golden brown	2.10	1.00
1058	A419	30d dark rose brown	3.25	1.25
		Nos. 1055-1058 (4)	8.45	3.75

Aquatic Birds — A420

1995, Dec. 20 Litho. *Perf. 14x13½*

1059	A420	3d Tadorna tadorna	.70	.25
1060	A420	5d Gallinago gallinago	1.20	.40

1996 Summer Olympics, Atlanta — A421

1996, Jan. 24 Litho. *Perf. 14x13½*

1061	A421	20d multicolored	2.10	1.00

Touareg Leather Crafts — A422

Perf. 14x13½, 13½x14

1996, Feb. 14 Litho.

1062	A422	5d shown	1.00	.30
1063	A422	16d Saddle bag, vert.	1.50	1.00

Pasteur Institute of Algeria — A423

1996, Mar. 20 Litho. *Perf. 13½x14*

1064	A423	5d multicolored	.75	.25

Youm El Ilm — A424

Designs: 16d, Dove, stylus, vert. 23d, Open book showing pencil, stylus, compass, satellite in earth orbit, vert.

Perf. 14x13½,13½x14

1996, Apr. 16 Litho.

1065	A424	5d multicolored	.55	.30
1066	A424	16d multicolored	1.40	.80
1067	A424	23d multicolored	2.50	1.25
		Nos. 1065-1067 (3)	4.45	2.35

Minerals — A425

Mineral, region: 10d, Iron, Djebel-Ouenza. 20d, Gold, Tirek-Amesmessa.

1996, May 6 Litho. *Perf. 14x13½*

1068	A425	10d multicolored	1.15	.55
1069	A425	20d multicolored	2.10	1.00

Butterflies A426

Designs: 5d, Pandoriana pandora. 10d, Coenonympha pamphilus. 20d, Cynthia cardui. 23d, Melanargia galathea.

1996, June 12 Litho. *Perf. 11½*

Granite Paper

1070	A426	5d multicolored	.75	.30
1071	A426	10d multicolored	1.25	.60
1072	A426	20d multicolored	2.75	1.00
1073	A426	23d multicolored	3.00	1.50
		Nos. 1070-1073 (4)	7.75	3.40

Civil Protection — A427

5d, Giving medical aid, ambulance. 23d, Prevention of natural disasters, vert.

Perf. 14x13½, 13½x14

1996, Oct. 9 Litho.

1074	A427	5d multicolored	.60	.30
1075	A427	23d multicolored	2.75	1.25

World Day Against Use of Illegal Drugs — A428

1996, June 26 Litho. *Perf. 14x13½*

1076	A428	5d multicolored	.70	.30

UNICEF, 50th Anniv. — A429

Stylized designs: 5d, Two children, wreath, pencils, flowers. 10d, Five children, pencil, key, flower, flag, hypodermic.

1996, Nov. 20 Litho. *Perf. 13½x14*

1077	A429	5d multicolored	.40	.30
1078	A429	10d multicolored	.80	.45

4th General Census — A430

1997, Feb. 12 Litho. *Perf. 14x13½*

1079	A430	5d multicolored	.50	.30

Protest at Ouargla, 35th Anniv. — A431

1997, Feb. 27 *Perf. 13½x14*

1080	A431	5d multicolored	.50	.30

Interior Courts of Algerian Dwellings — A432

Designs: 5d, Palace of Hassan Pasha. 10d, Khedaouj El-Amia, Algiers. 20d, Palace of Light. 30d, Abdellatif Villa.

1996, Dec. 18 Litho. *Perf. 13½x14*

1081	A432	5d multicolored	.40	.25
1082	A432	10d multicolored	.80	.45
1083	A432	20d multicolored	1.75	1.00
1084	A432	30d multicolored	2.50	1.40
		Nos. 1081-1084 (4)	5.45	3.10

Paintings by Ismail Samsom (1934-88) — A433

20d, Woman with Pigeons. 30d, Interrogation.

1996, Dec. 25 *Perf. 14*

1085	A433	20d multicolored	1.25	1.00
1086	A433	30d multicolored	1.75	1.50

Victory Day, 35th Anniv. — A434

1997, Mar. 19 *Perf. 14x13½*

1087	A434	5d multicolored	.50	.25

Flowers — A435

Designs: 5d, Ficaria verna. 16d, Lonicera arborea. 23d, Papaver rhoeas.

1997, Apr. 23 Litho. *Perf. 13½x14*

1088	A435	5d multicolored	.50	.30
1089	A435	16d multicolored	1.40	.90
1090	A435	23d multicolored	2.00	1.50
		Nos. 1088-1090 (3)	3.90	2.70

World Day to Stop Smoking — A436

1997, May 31 Litho. *Perf. 13½x14*

1091	A436	5d multicolored	.65	.25

Legislative Elections — A437

1997, June 4

1092	A437	5d multicolored	.45	.25

Scorpions — A438

Designs: 5d, Buthus occitanus tunetanus. 10d, Androctonus australis hector.

1997, June 18 *Perf. 14x13½*

1093	A438	5d multicolored	.55	.30
1094	A438	10d multicolored	.95	.60

Natl. Independence, 35th Anniv. — A439

Designs: 5d, Crowd celebrating, flags. 10d, Doves, broken chain, "35," flag.

1997, July 5 Litho. *Perf. 14x13½*

1095	A439	5d multicolored	.50	.25

Souvenir Sheet

Perf. 14

1096	A439	10d multicolored	2.75	2.75

No. 1096 contains one 30x40mm stamp.

Wood Carvings — A440

Designs: 5d, Inscription, Nedroma Mosque. 23d, Door, Ketchaoua Mosque.

1997, Jan. 15 Litho. *Perf. 13½x14*

1097	A440	5d multicolored	.50	.30
1098	A440	23d multicolored	1.75	1.10

Moufdi Zakaria (1908-77), poet. — A441

1997, Aug. 17 Litho. *Perf. 13½x14*

1099	A441	5d multicolored	.50	.25

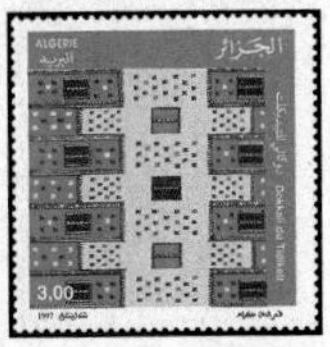

Textile Patterns — A442

1997, Sept. 17 Litho. *Perf. 14*

1100	A442	3d Dokkali	.40	.30
1101	A442	5d Tellis	.50	.30
1102	A442	10d Bou-Taleb	.90	.60
1103	A442	20d Ddil	1.75	1.25
		Nos. 1100-1103 (4)	3.55	2.45

Natl. Police Force, 25th Anniv. — A443

1997, Oct. 6 *Perf. 14x13½*

1104	A443	5d multicolored	.60	.25

Express Mail Service — A444

1997, Oct. 9

1105	A444	5d multicolored	.60	.25

Local Elections — A445

1997, Oct. 23 ***Perf. 13½x14***

1106 A445 5d multicolored .50 .25

Lighthouses A446

5d, Tenes. 10d, Cape Caxine, vert.

Perf. 14x13½, 13½x14

1997, Nov. 5 **Litho.**

1107 A446 5d multicolored .65 .25
1108 A446 10d multicolored 1.50 .70

New Airpost Service, 1st Anniv. — A447

1997, Nov. 17 ***Perf. 14x13½***

1109 A447 5d multicolored .60 .25

Shells — A448

Designs: 5d, Chlamys varia. 10d, Bolinus brandaris. 20d, Hinia reticulata, vert.

Perf. 14x13½, 13½x14

1997, Dec. 17 **Litho.**

1110 A448 5d multicolored .90 .25
1111 A448 10d multicolored 1.50 .60
1112 A448 20d multicolored 3.00 1.20
Nos. 1110-1112 (3) 5.40 2.05

A449

1997, Dec. 25 ***Perf. 13½x14***

1113 A449 5d multicolored .60 .25

Election of the Natl. Council.

A450

Completion of Government Reforms: a, Natl. flag, people, book, ballot box. b, People, open book, torch. c, Ballot box. d, Flag, rising sun, flower. e, Ballots, building, flag.

1997, Dec. 30 **Litho.** ***Perf. 13½x14***

1114 A450 5d Strip of 5, #a.-e. 2.50 2.50

Bombing of Sakiet Sidi Youcef, 40th Anniv. — A451

1998, Feb. 8 **Litho.** ***Perf. 14x13½***

1115 A451 5d multicolored .70 .25

National Archives — A452

1998, Feb. 16

1116 A452 5d multicolored .50 .25

Intl. Women's Day — A453

1998, Mar. 8 **Litho.** ***Perf. 14x13½***

1117 A453 5d multicolored .50 .25

Expo '98, Lisbon — A454

1998, Jan. 21 **Litho.** ***Perf. 14x13½***

1118 A454 5d shown .50 .25

Size: 80x75mm

Imperf

1119 A454 24d Mosaic 3.25 3.25

1998 World Cup Soccer Championships, Paris — A455

1998, Apr. 15 **Litho.** ***Perf. 13½x14***

1120 A455 24d multi 2.40 1.25

Algiers Casbah — A456

Designs: 5d, Aerial view, vert. 10d, Buildings, vert. 24d, Aerial view, diff.

1998, Apr. 22 ***Perf. 13½x14, 14x13½***

1121 A456 5d multi .40 .25
1122 A456 10d multi .75 .60
1123 A456 24d multi 1.75 1.25
Nos. 1121-1123 (3) 2.90 2.10

Zaatcha Resistance A457

1998, May 20 ***Perf. 13¼x13***

1124 A457 5d multi .50 .25

Tourism — A458

5d, Mountains, farm, desert, vert. 10d, Youths, modes of transportation. 24d, Taghit.

Perf. 13½x14, 14x13½

1998, June 4 **Litho.**

1125 A458 5d multi .40 .25
1126 A458 10d multi .80 .50
1127 A458 24d multi 1.75 1.25
Nos. 1125-1127 (3) 2.95 2.00

Arab Post Day — A459

1998, Aug. 3 **Litho.** ***Perf. 14x13½***

1128 A459 5d multi .75 .25

Interpol, 75th Anniv. — A460

1998, Sept. 7 **Litho.** ***Perf. 14x13½***

1129 A460 5d multi .60 .25

Creation of Provisional Government, 40th Anniv. A461

1998, Sept. 19 ***Perf. 13¼x13***

1130 A461 5d multi .50 .25

Natl. Diplomacy Day — A462

1998, Oct. 8 ***Perf. 14***

1131 A462 5d multi .50 .25

Algerian Olympic Committee, 35th Anniv. — A463

1998, Oct. 18 ***Perf. 14x13½***

1132 A463 5d multi .60 .25

Birds — A464

Designs: 5d, Pandion haliaetus. 10d, Larus audouinii. 24d, Phalacrocorax aristotelis, vert. 30d, Phalacrocorax carbo, vert.

Perf. 14x13½, 13½x14

1998, Nov. 11

1133 A464 5d multi .70 .25
1134 A464 10d multi 1.40 .60
1135 A464 24d multi 2.75 1.25
1136 A464 30d multi 3.50 1.75
Nos. 1133-1136 (4) 8.35 3.85

See Nos. 1204-1207, 1325-1326.

Universal Declaration of Human Rights, 50th Anniv. — A465

1998, Dec. 10 **Litho.** ***Perf. 14x13½***

1137 A465 5d Profiles, emblem .60 .25
1138 A465 24d shown 2.25 1.00

Spinning and Weaving Tools — A466

Designs: 5d, Comb, vert. 10d, Cards. 20d, Spindle, vert. 24d, Loom, vert.

1999, Jan. 20 ***Perf. 13½x14, 14x13½***

1139 A466 5d multi .55 .25
1140 A466 10d multi 1.00 .50
1141 A466 20d multi 2.10 1.00
1142 A466 24d multi 2.50 1.25
Nos. 1139-1142 (4) 6.15 3.00

Natl. Chahid Day — A467

1999, Feb. 18 ***Perf. 13x13¼***

1143 A467 5d multi .50 .25

Flowering Trees — A468

1999, Mar. 17 ***Perf. 14x13½, 13½x14***

1144 A468 5d Pear .50 .25
1145 A468 10d Plum .90 .50
1146 A468 24d Orange, vert. 2.10 1.25
Nos. 1144-1146 (3) 3.50 2.00

Presidential Elections — A469

1999, Apr. 15 ***Perf. 13x13¼***

1147 A469 5d multi .50 .25

Handicrafts A470

Designs: 5d, Tlemcen mosaic, 14th cent., vert. 10d, Mosaic, Al Qal'a of Beni Hammad, 11th cent, vert. 20d, Cradle. 24d, Table.

1999, Apr. 18 ***Perf. 13¼x14, 14x13¼***

1148 A470 5d multi .55 .25
1149 A470 10d multi .90 .60
1150 A470 20d multi 1.75 1.00
1151 A470 24d multi 2.10 1.25
Nos. 1148-1151 (4) 5.30 3.10

7th African Games, Johannesburg A471

Stylized athletes and: 5d, Map of Africa, vert. 10d, South African flag.

1999, May 12 ***Perf. 13¼x14, 14x13¼***

1152 A471 5d multi .45 .25
1153 A471 10d multi .80 .50

Rocks — A472

1999, June 6 ***Perf. 13¼x14***

1154 A472 5d Gneiss .45 .25
1155 A472 20d Granite 1.60 1.00
1156 A472 24d Schist 2.00 1.25
Nos. 1154-1156 (3) 4.05 2.50

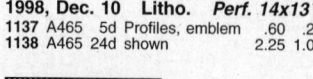

A473

1999, July 12 *Perf. 13x13¼*
1157 A473 5d multi .50 .25

Organization of African Unity, 35th summit.

A474

1999, July 12 *Perf. 13¼x14*
1158 A474 5d multi .50 .25

Organization of African Unity Convention on Refugees.

Police Day — A475

1999, July 22 *Perf. 13x13¼*
1159 A475 5d multicolored 1.00 .25

Intl. Year of Culture and Peace (in 2000) — A476

1999, Sept. 14 **Litho.** *Perf. 14*
1160 A476 5d multi .50 .25

Fish — A477

Designs: 5d, Dentex dentex. 10d, Mullus surmuletus. 20d, Dentex gibbosus. 24d, Diplodus sargus.

1999, Sept. 15 *Perf. 14x13¼*
1161 A477 5d multi .65 .25
1162 A477 10d multi 1.25 .50
1163 A477 20d multi 2.25 1.00
1164 A477 24d multi 3.25 1.25
Nos. 1161-1164 (4) 7.40 3.00

Civil Peace Referendum — A478

1999, Sept. 16 *Perf. 13¼x14*
1165 A478 5d multi .50 .25

UPU, 125th Anniv. — A479

1999, Oct. 9 *Perf. 14x13¼*
1166 A479 5d multi .55 .25

World Post Day — A480

1999, Oct. 9 **Litho.** *Perf. 14x13½*
1167 A480 5d multi .55 .25

Intl. Rural Women's Day — A481

1999, Oct. 14 **Litho.** *Perf. 14x13¼*
1168 A481 5d multi .55 .25

Algerian Revolution, 45th Anniv. — A482

Soldiers and: a, Helicopters, burning flag. b, Burning flag.

1999, Nov. 1 *Perf. 13x13¼*
1169 A482 5d Pair, #a.-b. 1.25 1.25

Folk Dances Type of 1994

1999, Dec. 15 *Perf. 13¼x14*
1170 A406 5d Chaoui .60 .25
1171 A406 10d Targuie 1.10 .50
1172 A406 24d Mzab 2.25 1.25
Nos. 1170-1172 (3) 3.95 2.00

Millennium — A483

No. 1173: a, Doves, UN emblem. b, Sun, plant, trees. c, Umbrella over wheat and corn plants. d, Microscope and flasks. e, Crane, ship, truck. f, Train, Concorde, satellite dish, satellite, Moon. g, Windmills. h, Globe, ballot box. i, Apollo 15 astronauts on Moon. j, Film, inkwell, musical instrument and notes.

No. 1174: a, Dove with olive branch. b, Hand, flora, fauna. c, Satellites, computer, map of Africa and Europe. d, Heart, staff of Aesculapius, Red Cross, Red Crescent. e, Stylized globe and arrows. f, Animals, film, violin, painting, book. g, Flame, sun, water. h, Hand holding plant. i, symbols of democracy. j, Satellite, planets, space shuttle, astronaut.

Sawtooth Die Cut 6¼ Vert.

2000, Jan. 19 **Self-Adhesive**

Booklet Stamps

1173 Bklt. pane of 10 + 2 labels 10.00
a.-j. A483 5d any single .50 .50
1174 Bklt. pane of 10 + 2 labels 10.00
a.-j. A483 5d any single .50 .50

Birds — A484

Designs: No. 1175, 5d, Canary (serin cini). No. 1176, 5d, Finch (pinson), vert. 10d, Bullfinch (bouvreuil). 24d, Goldfinch (chardonneret), vert.

Perf. 14x13¼, 13¼x14

2000, Jan. 19 **Litho.**
1175-1178 A484 Set of 4 5.50 5.50

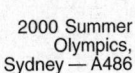

Expo 2000, Hanover — A485

2000, Feb. 16 **Litho.** *Perf. 14x13¼*
1179 A485 5d multi .60 .30

2000 Summer Olympics, Sydney — A486

2000, Mar. 22
1180 A486 24d multi 2.50 1.25

Telethon 2000 — A487

2000, Apr. 8 *Perf. 13¼x14*
1181 A487 5d multi .75 .25

Civil Concord — A488

Designs: 5d, Dove, handshake, crowd, vert. 10d, Handshake, hands releasing dove. 20d, Handshake, doves, flowers. 24d, Doves, flowers, handshake, vert.

Perf. 11½x11¾, 11¾x11½

2000, Apr. 15
1182-1185 A488 Set of 4 6.50 3.25

National Library A489

2000, Apr. 16 *Perf. 13½x13*
1186 A489 5d multi .60 .25

Blood Donation — A490

2000, May 2 *Perf. 13¼x14*
1187 A490 5d multi .60 .25

Tuareg Handicrafts A491

Background colors: 5d, Rose. 10d, Buff, vert.

2000, May 17 *Perf. 14*
1188-1189 A491 Set of 2 1.60 .75

Famous Men — A492

No. 1190, Mohammed Dib (b. 1920), writer. No. 1191, Mustapha Kateb (1920-89), actor. No. 1192, Ali Maachi (1927-58), musician. No. 1193, Mohamed Racim (1896-1975), artist.

2000, June 8 *Perf. 13¼x13*
1190-1193 A492 10d Set of 4 4.25 2.00

Insects — A493

No. 1194, 5d, Hanneton. No. 1195, 5d, Anthrene. 10d, Vrillete du pain. 24d, Carabe.

2000, Sept. 20 *Perf. 13¼x14*
1194-1197 A493 Set of 4 5.25 2.50

Roman Cinerary Urns Found at Tipasa — A494

2000, Oct. 18 **Litho.** *Perf. 14*
1198-1200 A494 Set of 3, 5d, 10d, 24d 4.25 2.25

Orchids — A495

Designs: 5d, Limodorum abortivum. 10d, Orchis papilionacea. 24d, Orchis provincialis.

2000, Dec. 13 **Litho.** *Perf. 14*
1201-1203 A495 Set of 3 4.50 2.50

Bird Type of 1998

Designs: No. 1204, 5d, Anser anser. No. 1205, 5d, Recurvirostra avosetta, vert. 10d, Botaurus stellaris, vert. 24d, Numenius arquata.

2001, Jan. 24
1204-1207 A464 Set of 4 5.00 2.75

Handicrafts A496

Designs: 5d, Skampla, vert. 10d, Etagere. 24d, Mirror, vert.

2001, Feb. 21
1208-1210 A496 Set of 3 4.50 2.50

National Parks — A497

Designs: 5d, Belezma, vert. 10d, Gouraya. 20d, Théniet el Had. 24d, El Kala, vert.

2001, Mar. 21 *Perf. 13¼x14, 14x13¼*
1211-1214 A497 Set of 4 7.00 3.25

1st Intl. Colloquium on St. Augustine of Hippo A498

Designs: 5d, Statue of St. Augustine (25x37mm). 24d, Mosaic.

Perf. 13¼x14, 13¼x13 (24d)

2001, Mar. 31

1215-1216 A498 Set of 2 3.50 1.60

Silver Coins A499

Designs: 5d, 1830 Ryal boudjou. 10d, 1826 Double boudjou. 24d, 1771 Ryal drahem.

2001, Apr. 25 Litho. ***Perf. 13½x13***

1217-1219 A499 Set of 3 4.50 2.25

Natl. Scouting Day — A500

2001, May 27 Litho. ***Perf. 14***

1220 A500 5d multi .60 .25

Palestinian Intifada — A501

2001, June 2

1221 A501 5d multi .60 .25

Children's Games — A502

Designs: No. 1222, 5d, Jacks. No. 1223, 5d, Hopscotch. No. 1224, 5d, Top spinning. No. 1225, 5d, Marbles.

2001, June 2

1222-1225 A502 Set of 4 2.50 .90

Natl. Asthma Day — A503

2001, June 9

1226 A503 5d multi .50 .25

14th Mediterranean Games, Tunis, Tunisia — A504

Designs: No. 1227, 5d, Map, "50." No. 1228, 5d, Runners, emblem.

2001, July 25 Litho. ***Perf. 14***

1227-1228 A504 Set of 2 1.00 .50

15th World Festival of Youth and Students — A505

2001, Aug. 8

1229 A505 5d multi .50 .25

Natl. Mujahedeen Day — A506

2001, Aug. 20 ***Perf. 13¼x14***

1230 A506 5d multi .50 .25

Intl. Teachers' Day — A507

2001, Oct. 6 Litho. ***Perf. 13¼x14***

1231 A507 5d multi .50 .25

Year of Dialogue Among Civilizations — A508

2001, Oct. 9

1232 A508 5d multi .75 .30

Natl. Emigration Day — A509

2001, Oct. 17 ***Perf. 14x13¼***

1233 A509 5d multi .50 .25

19th Cent. Revolt Leaders — A510

Designs: No. 1234, 5d, Sheik El-Mokrani, 1871-73. No. 1235, 5d, Sheik Bouamama, 1881-1908.

2001, Nov. 1 ***Perf. 13¼x14***

1234-1235 A510 Set of 2 1.10 .50

Jewelry From Aurès Region — A511

Designs: No. 1236, 5d, Fibula. No. 1237, 5d, Earring. 24d, Pendant.

2002, Jan. 23

1236-1238 A511 Set of 3 3.00 3.00

2002 World Cup Soccer Championships, Japan and Korea — A512

Designs: 5d, Goalie, ball, net, pagoda. 24d, Oriental man, ball, vert.

2002, Feb. 27 ***Perf. 14x13¼, 13¼x14***

1239-1240 A512 Set of 2 2.75 2.00

Ceasefire With French Forces, 40th Anniv. — A513

2002, Mar. 19 ***Perf. 13x13½***

1241 A513 5d multi .70 .40

Villages — A514

Designs: No. 1242, 5d, Sidi-Ouali. No. 1243, 5d, Casbah of Ighzar.

2002, Apr. 17 Litho. ***Perf. 14x13¼***

1242-1243 A514 Set of 2 1.00 .80

World Basketball Championships, Indianapolis — A515

2002, May 15 ***Perf. 13¼x14***

1244 A515 5d multi .75 .45

Children's Day — A516

Children's art: No. 1245, 5d, Shown. No. 1246, 5d, Two girls, one waving.

2002, June 1 ***Perf. 14x13¼***

1245-1246 A516 Set of 2 1.00 .80

Mohamed Temmam (1915-88), Artist — A517

Designs: No. 1247, 10d, Self-portrait. No. 1248, 10d, Tailor.

2002, June 8 ***Perf. 13x13¼***

1247-1248 A517 Set of 2 2.00 1.50

Independence, 40th Anniv. — A518

Designs: 5d, Emblem. 24d, People with flag.

2002, July 5 Litho. ***Perf. 14***

1249-1250 A518 Set of 2 2.50 2.00

Rocks and Minerals — A519

Designs: No. 1251, 5d, Conglomerate rock. No. 1252, 5d, Galena. No. 1253, 5d, Calcite, vert. No. 1254, 5d, Feldspar, vert.

2002, July 24

1251-1254 A519 Set of 4 2.00 2.00

Lighthouses A520

Designs: 5d, Cherchell. 10d, Cap de Fer. 24d, Ile de Rachgoun.

2002, Sept. 11

1255-1257 A520 Set of 3 3.25 3.25

Reorganization of Postal Service — A521

2002, Oct. 9

1258 A521 5d multi .50 .50

Pottery — A522

Designs: No. 1259, 5d, Oil lamp. No. 1260, 5d, Jar with handles, Iraten. No. 1261, 5d, Jar, Miliana. No. 1262, 5d, Cooking pot and couscousier, Lakhdaria.

2002, Oct. 23

1259-1262 A522 Set of 4 2.00 2.00

Intl. Day for Tolerance — A523

2002, Nov. 16 Litho. ***Perf. 14***

1263 A523 24d multi 2.00 2.00

Shells — A524

Designs: No. 1264, 5d, Acanthocardia aculeata. No. 1265, 5d, Venus verrucosa. No. 1266, 5d, Epitonium commune. No. 1267, 5d, Xenophora crispa.

2002, Dec. 4 Litho. ***Perf. 14***

1264-1267 A524 Set of 4 2.50 2.50

Medicinal Plants — A525

Designs: 5d, Eucalyptus globulus. 10d, Malva sylvestris. 24d, Laurus nobilis.

2002, Dec. 21

1268-1270 A525 Set of 3 3.25 3.25

Algeria — France Year — A526

Designs: 5d, Eiffel Tower, Paris and Martyr's Monument, Algiers, vert. 24d, Flags of Algeria and France.

2003, Feb. 19

1271-1272 A526	Set of 2	2.50	2.50

10th Arab Games — A527

2003, Feb. 26

1273 A527	5d multi	.40	.40

Intl. Year of Water — A528

Designs: 5d, El Maadjen, Relizane. 10d, Well, M'zab Valley. 24d, Kesria, Timimoun.

2003, Mar. 22 Litho. *Perf. 14*

1274-1276 A528	Set of 3	3.50	3.50

Vandal Tablets — A529

Designs: 10d, Slave sale document, 494. 24d, Tablet for calculations, 493, vert.

Perf. 13x13¼, 13¼x13

2003, Apr. 23 Litho.

1277-1278 A529	Set of 2	3.00	3.00

Portions of the designs were applied by a thermographic process producing a shiny, raised effect.

Natl. Students Day — A530

2003, May 19 Litho. *Perf. 14*

1279 A530	5d multi	.40	.40

Snails — A531

Designs: 5d, Rumina decollata. 24d, Heix aspersa.

2003, May 21 Litho. *Perf. 14*

1280-1281 A531	Set of 2	2.50	2.50

African Union, 1st Anniv. — A532

2003, July 9 *Perf. 13¼x14*

1282 A532	5d multi	.50	.50

Seaweeds — A533

Designs: 5d, Ulva lactuca. 24d, Gymnogongrus crenulatus.

2003, July 30 Litho. *Perf. 14*

1283-1284 A533	Set of 2	2.50	2.50

Roman Mosaics — A534

Designs: 5d, Farm Work. 10d, Ulysses and the Sirens. 24d, Hunting Scene.

2003, Sept. 17 *Perf. 13½x14*

1285-1287 A534	Set of 3	3.00	3.00

Algerian Olympic Committee, 40th Anniv. — A535

2003, Oct. 18 Litho. *Perf. 14x13½*

1288 A535	5d multi	.50	.50

World Diabetes Prevention Day — A536

2003, Nov. 14 *Perf. 13½x14*

1289 A536	5d multi	.50	.50

Architectural Decorations — A537

Designs: 5d, Door, Hassan Pacha Palace, Algiers. 10d, Window, Hassan Pacha Palace. 24d, Ceiling, Djamaa Edjedid, Algiers.

2003, Dec. 17 Litho. *Perf. 13x13¼*

1290-1292 A537	Set of 3	3.00	3.00

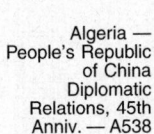

Algeria — People's Republic of China Diplomatic Relations, 45th Anniv. — A538

2003, Dec. 22 *Perf. 12*

1293 A538	5d multi	.50	.50

2004 Summer Olympics, Athens — A539

Olympic rings, Parthenon and: 5d, Hurdler. 10d, Torch bearer.

2004, Feb. 29 *Perf. 13¼x14*

1294-1295 A539	Set of 2	1.25	1.25

Intl. Women's Day — A540

2004, Mar. 8

1296 A540	5d multi	.50	.50

Arbor Day — A541

Trees: 5d, Olive. 10d, Date palm, vert.

Perf. 14x13¼, 13¼x14

2004, Mar. 21 Litho.

1297-1298 A541	Set of 2	1.25	1.25

Numidian Kings — A542

Designs: No. 1299, 5d, Massinissa (r. 203 BC-148 BC). No. 1300, 5d, Micipsa (r. 148 BC-118 BC). No. 1301, 5d, Jugurtha (r. 118 BC-105 BC). No. 1302, 5d, Juba I (r. 63 BC-50 to 46 BC). No. 1303, 5d, Juba II (r. 29 BC- 25 BC).

2004, Mar. 31 Litho. *Perf. 13¼x14*

1299-1303 A542	Set of 5	2.25	2.25

2004 Presidential Elections — A543

Litho. & Embossed

2004, Apr. 8 *Perf. 13¼x13*

1304 A543	24d multi	2.25	2.25

FIFA (Fédération Internationale de Football Association), Cent. — A544

"100" and: 5d, Goalie. 24d, Soccer balls, world map.

Perf. 14, 14x13¼ (24d)

2004, May 21 Litho.

1305-1306 A544	Set of 2	2.50	2.50

Dromedary A545

2004, June 9 Litho. *Perf. 14x13¼*

1307 A545	24d multi	2.25	2.25

Blood Donation Day — A546

2004, June 14 *Perf. 14*

1308 A546	5d multi	.50	.50

Professional Training — A547

2004, June 23

1309 A547	5d multi	.50	.50

Intl. Chess Federation (FIDE), 80th Anniv. — A548

2004, July 21 Litho. *Perf. 14*

1310 A548	5d multi	1.20	.50

CNEP Bank, 40th Anniv. — A549

Bank emblems and: 5d, Bank notes. 24d, Algiers.

2004, Aug. 10 Litho. *Perf. 14*

1311-1312 A549	Set of 2	2.50	2.50

Roses — A550

2004, Oct. 20 Litho. *Perf. 14*

Color of Rose

1313 A550	15d yellow	1.00	1.00
1314 A550	20d yellow, diff.	2.00	2.00
1315 A550	30d red	3.00	3.00
1316 A550	50d pink	4.00	4.00
	Nos. 1313-1316 (4)	10.00	10.00

Sixth Pan-African Conference of Red Cross and Red Crescent, Algiers — A551

2004, Sept. 8 Litho. *Perf. 14*

1317 A551	24d multi	2.25	2.25

Sahara Desert Landmarks A552

Designs: 5d, In Téhaq. 24d, Ekanassay, vert.

Perf. 14, 14¼x14 (24d)

2004, Sept. 15

1318-1319 A552	Set of 2	2.50	2.50

Revolutionary Committee of Unity and Action, 50th Anniv. A553

2004, Nov. 1 Litho. *Perf. 13¼x13*

1320 A553	15d multi	1.75	1.75

Souvenir Sheet

Start of Algerian Revolution, 50th Anniv. — A554

2004, Nov. 1 Litho. ***Perf. 13½x13***
1321 A554 30d multi 2.50 2.50

Launch of ALSAT 1 Satellite, 2nd Anniv. — A555

2004, Nov. 28 Litho. ***Perf. 14x13½***
1322 A555 30d multi 2.50 2.50

Environmental Protection A556

2004, Dec. 22
1323 A556 15d multi 1.25 1.25

Rabah Bitat (1925-2000), Politician — A557

2004, Dec. 29 Litho. ***Perf. 14x13½***
1324 A557 15d multi 1.25 1.25

Bird Type of 1998

Designs: 10d, Columba palumbus. 15d, Columba livia.

2005, Jan. 26 Litho. ***Perf. 14x13½***
1325-1326 A464 Set of 2 2.25 2.25

Flowers — A559

Designs: 15d, Echium australis. 30d, Borago officinalis.

2005, Feb. 23 Litho. ***Perf. 13½x14***
1327-1328 A559 Set of 2 3.50 3.50

Day of the Handicapped A560

2005, Mar. 14 ***Perf. 14x13½***
1329 A560 15d multi 1.10 1.10

Arab League Emblem and Algerian Flag — A561

Inscription commemorating: 15d, 17th Arab Summit, Algiers. 30d, Arab League, 60th anniv., vert.

2005, Mar. 22 ***Perf. 14x13½, 13½x14***
1330-1331 A561 Set of 2 3.50 3.50

National Reconciliation A562

2005, Apr. 8 ***Perf. 14x13½***
1332 A562 15d multi 1.25 1.25

Madrases A563

Madras in: 10d, Algiers. 15d, Constantine. 30d, Tlemcen.

2005, Apr. 16
1333-1335 A563 Set of 3 4.50 4.50

Science Day.

Intl. Day of Intellectual Property — A564

2005, Apr. 26
1336 A564 15d multi 1.25 1.25

Intl. Day of Work Safety and Health — A565

2005, Apr. 28 ***Perf. 13½x14***
1337 A565 15d multi 1.25 1.25

Massacres of May 8, 1945, 60th Anniv. — A566

2005, May 8 Litho. ***Perf. 14x13¼***
1338 A566 15d multi 1.25 1.25

15th Mediterranean Games, Almeria, Spain — A567

Games emblem and: 15d, Medal, stylized athletes. 30d, Mediterranean Sea and "2005," horiz.

2005, May 28 ***Perf. 13¼x14, 14x13¼***
1339-1340 A567 Set of 2 3.50 3.50

Poets — A568

Designs: 10d, Lakhdar Ben Khlouf. 15d, Mohamed Ben M'sayeb. 20d, Si Mohand-Ou-M'hand. 30d, Aissa El-Djermouni.

2005, June 8 Litho. ***Perf. 13x13½***
1341-1344 A568 Set of 4 6.50 6.50

World Day Against Drug Abuse — A569

2005, June 26 ***Perf. 14x13½***
1345 A569 15d multi 1.50 1.50

General Algerian Muslim Student's Union, 50th Anniv. — A570

2005, July 9 Litho. ***Perf. 13½x14***
1346 A570 15d multi 1.25 1.25

Leopards — A571

Leopard: 15d, Sitting. 30d, Standing.

2005, July 21 ***Perf. 14x13½***
1347-1348 A571 Set of 2 3.50 3.50

World Summit on the Information Society, Tunis — A572

2005, July 27 ***Perf. 13½x14***
1349 A572 15d multi 1.75 1.75

Moudjahid Day — A573

2005, Aug. 20
1350 A573 15d multi 1.25 1.25

Uprising at Constantine and Philippeville, 50th anniv.

Intl. Year of Sports and Physical Education — A574

2005, Sept. 7 Litho. ***Perf. 13¼x14***
1351 A574 30d multi 2.40 2.40

Forts — A575

Designs: 10d, Lighthouse Fort, Algiers. 15d, Cap Matifou Fort, Algiers. 30d, Santa Cruz Fort, Oran.

2005, Sept. 15 ***Perf. 14x13¼***
1352-1354 A575 Set of 3 4.50 4.50

September 29, 2005 Referendum A576

2005 Litho. ***Perf. 14x13½***
1355 A576 15d multi 1.15 1.15

Acquisition of Control of Broadcasting, 43rd Anniv. — A577

2005, Oct. 28
1356 A577 30d multi 2.25 2.25

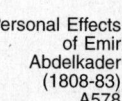

Personal Effects of Emir Abdelkader (1808-83) A578

Designs: 15d, Saddle. 30d, Boots. 40d, Vest, vert. 50d, Signet, vert.

2005, Nov. 1 ***Perf. 14x13½, 13½x14***
1357-1360 A578 Set of 4 10.50 10.50

Miguel de Cervantes (1547-1616), Writer — A579

2005, Nov. 16 Litho. ***Perf. 13½x14***
1361 A579 30d multi 2.25 2.25

Public Destruction of Mines — A580

2005, Nov. Litho. ***Perf. 13½x14***
1362 A580 30d multi 2.25 2.25

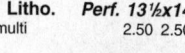

World AIDS Day — A581

2005, Dec. 1 Litho. ***Perf. 13½x14***
1363 A581 30d multi 2.50 2.50

Numidian Kings — A582

Designs: 15d, Ptolemy of Mauretania, ruler from 23-40 A.D. 30d, Syphax, ruler from 220-203 B.C.

2005, Dec. 14 Litho. ***Perf. 13¼x14***
1364-1365 A582 Set of 2 3.25 3.25

Emblem and Headquarters of Algeria Post — A583

2006, Jan. 14 *Perf. 14x13¼*
1366 A583 30d multi 2.25 2.25

Birds — A584

Designs: 10d, Ciconia ciconia. 15d, Ciconia nigra. 20d, Platalea leucorodia. 30d, Grus grus.

2006, Jan. 25 *Perf. 13x13½*
1367-1370 A584 Set of 4 5.50 5.50

2006 Winter Olympics, Turin — A585

2006, Feb. 1 *Perf. 14x13¼*
1371 A585 15d multi 1.10 1.10

General Union of Algerian Workers, 50th Anniv. — A586

2006, Feb. 24 *Perf. 13¼x14*
1372 A586 15d multi 1.10 1.10

2006 World Cup Soccer Championships, Germany — A587

2006, Mar. 22
1373 A587 30d multi 2.25 2.25

Opening of New Algiers Airport — A588

2006, Apr. 8 *Perf. 14x13¼*
1374 A588 30d multi 2.25 2.25

Student's Day, 50th Anniv. — A589

2006, May 19 *Perf. 13x13½*
1375 A589 20d multi 1.40 1.40

World Environment Day — A590

2006, June 5 *Perf. 14*
1376 A590 30d multi 2.25 2.25

Soummam Congress, 50th Anniv. — A591

2006, Aug. 20 *Perf. 13x13½*
1377 A591 20d multi 1.50 1.50

16th Arab Scholars' Games — A592

2006, Sept. 2 *Perf. 13¼x14*
1378 A592 30d multi 2.25 2.25

Intl. Year of Deserts and Desertifcation A593

Designs: No. 1379, 15d, Oasis. No. 1380, 15d, Oasis, sand dunes and water.

2006, Sept. 20 **Litho.** *Perf. 14*
1379-1380 A593 Set of 2 2.25 2.25

World Teachers Day — A594

2006, Oct. 5
1381 A594 20d multi 1.40 1.40

Arbor Day — A595

Trees: 20d, Atlas pistachio. 30d, Pomagranate.

2006, Oct. 25
1382-1383 A595 Set of 2 3.75 3.75

Sino-African Cooperation Summit, Beijing — A596

2006, Nov. 4 *Perf. 12*
1384 A596 30d multi 2.25 2.25

19th Century Powder Flasks — A597

Background color: 15d, Pink. 20d, Pale green.

2006, Nov. 22 **Litho.** *Perf. 13½x14*
1385-1386 A597 Set of 2 3.00 3.00

Transitory Arab Parliament, 1st Anniv. A598

2006, Dec. 17 *Perf. 13½x13*
1387 A598 15d multi 1.10 1.10

El Moudjahid Newspaper, 50th Anniv. — A599

2006, Dec. 18 *Perf. 14*
1388 A599 30d multi 2.25 2.25

Desalinization of Sea Water — A600

2006, Dec. 20
1389 A600 20d multi 1.50 1.50

A601

Algiers, 2007 Arab Cultural Capital A602

2007, Jan. 12 **Litho.** *Perf. 13½x13*
1390 A601 15d multi 1.25 1.25
1391 A602 30d multi 2.25 2.25

Lighthouses A603

Lighthouse at: 15d, Ilot d'Arzew. 20d, Cap Sigli. 38d, Ras-afia.

2007, Feb. 14 **Litho.** *Perf. 14*
1392-1394 A603 Set of 3 5.25 5.25

Employment of Women — A604

2007, Mar. 8 **Litho.** *Perf. 14*
1395 A604 15d multi 1.25 1.25

Sheikh Mohamed Ameziane Belhaddad (1790-1873), Leader of 1871 Rebellion — A605

2007, Apr. 8 *Perf. 13x13¼*
1396 A605 15d multi 1.25 1.25

Ksars A606

Village scenes: No. 1397, 15d, Kenadsa. No. 1398, 15d, Temacine, vert.

2007, Apr. 21 *Perf. 13¼x13, 13x13¼*
1397-1398 A606 Set of 2 2.25 2.25

2nd Afro-Asiatic Games, Algiers — A607

2007, May 18 **Litho.** *Perf. 14*
1399 A607 15d multi 1.10 1.10

9th All-African Games, Algiers — A608

2007, May 18
1400 A608 15d multi 1.10 1.10

Gardens A609

Designs: 15d, Landon Gardens, Biskra. 20d, Ibn Badis Gardens, Oran. 38d, Essai du Hamma Gardens, Algiers.

2007, June 5 *Perf. 13½x13*
1401-1403 A609 Set of 3 5.50 5.50

National Gendarmerie, 45th Anniv. — A610

Designs: 15d, Gendarmerie emblem. 38d, Gendarmerie emblem, gendarme and automobile.

2007, June 25 **Litho.** *Perf. 14*
1404-1405 A610 Set of 2 4.00 4.00

Independence, 45th Anniv. — A611

Designs: 15d, People, flags and dove. 20d, Anniversary emblem, vert.

2007, July 5 *Perf. 13¼x13*
1406 A611 15d multi 1.25 1.25

Imperf
Size: 60x77mm

1407 A611 20d multi 3.00 3.00

Ceramics — A612

Designs: No. 1408, 15d, Jar with handles. No. 1409, 15d, Glazed jar without handles. 20d, Censer. 38d, Lamp, horiz.

2007, Aug. 5 Litho. *Perf. 14*
1408-1411 A612 Set of 4 6.00 6.00

Endangered Animals A613

Designs: 15d, Striped hyena. 38d, White-tailed fox.

2007, Sept. 12 *Perf. 13¼x13*
1412-1413 A613 Set of 2 3.25 3.25

Theaters — A614

Theater in: No. 1414, 15d, Setif. No. 1415, 15d, Oran. 20d, Annaba, horiz. 38d, Algiers.

Perf. 13x13¼, 13¼x13
2007, Oct. 24 Litho.
1414-1417 A614 Set of 4 5.75 5.75

Encyclopedia of Algerian Postage Stamps — A615

2007, Nov. 1 *Perf. 13x13¼*
1418 A615 15d multi 1.40 1.40

Bey Ahmed of Constantine (1784-1850), Leader of 1836-48 Resistance Against French — A616

2007, Nov. 7
1419 A616 15d multi 1.25 1.25

National Artisan's Day — A617

2007, Nov. 9 *Perf. 13¼x14*
1420 A617 15d multi 1.40 1.40

Tilapia — A618

2007, Dec. 12 Litho. *Perf. 14*
1421 A618 15d multi 1.50 1.50

Miniature Sheet

Emir Abdelkader (1808-83) — A619

No. 1422: a, Abdelkader seated. b, Abdelkader standing. c, Abdelkader, diff.

2007, Dec. 15

1422	A619 Sheet of 3	5.00	5.00
a.-b.	15d Either single	1.10	1.10
c.	38d multi	2.75	2.75

Fifth General Census — A620

2008, Jan. 16 *Perf. 14x13¼*
1423 A620 15d multi 1.25 1.25

French Air Raid on Sakiet Sidi Youssef, Tunisia, 50th Anniv. — A621

2008, Feb. 8 Litho. *Perf. 13x13¼*
1424 A621 15d multi 1.25 1.25

Miniature Sheet

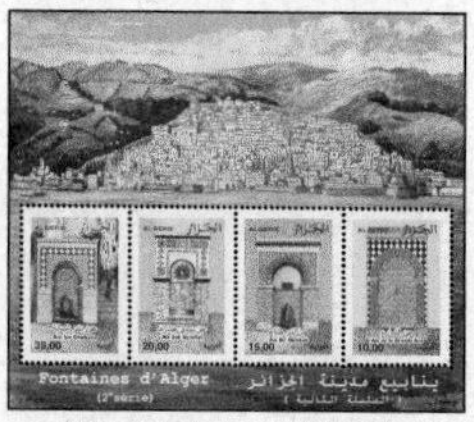
Fountains — A621a

2008, Feb. 23 *Perf. 14*

1425	A621a Sheet of 4	5.50	5.50
a.	10d Ain de la Grande Rue	.65	.65
b.	15d Ain Bir Djebbah	1.00	1.00
c.	20d Ain Sidi Abdellah	1.35	1.35
d.	38d Ain Bir Chebana	2.60	2.60

Miniature Sheet

Water and Sustainable Development — A622

No. 1428: a, Issakarssen Wetlands. b, Reghaia Wetlands. c, Guerbes Wetlands. d, Emblem of Expo Zaragoza 2008.

2008, Mar. 22 Litho. *Perf. 14*

1428	A622 Sheet of 4, #a-d	5.50	5.50
a.	10d multi	.65	.65
b.	15d multi	1.00	1.00
c.	20d multi	1.35	1.35
d.	38d multi	2.60	2.60

Souvenir Sheet

National Liberation Front Soccer Team, 50th Anniv. — A623

2008, Apr. 12 Litho. *Perf.*
1429 A623 38d multi 2.75 2.75

No. 1429 contains one 36mm diameter stamp.

Writers — A624

No. 1430: a, Redha Houhou (1911-56). b, Abdelhamid Benhadouga (1925-96). c, Malek Bennabi (1905-73). d, Kateb Yacine (1929-89).

2008, Apr. 16 Litho. *Perf. 14x13½*

1430	Horiz. strip of 4	4.25	4.25
a.-d.	A624 15d Any single	1.00	1.00

Children and New Technologies — A625

2008, June 1 *Perf. 13½x14*
1431 A625 15d multi 1.05 1.05

Souvenir Sheet

Baya Mahieddine (1931-98), Artist — A626

No. 1432: a, 15d, Mahieddine. b, 38d, Painting by Mahieddine.

2008, June 8 *Perf. 14*
1432 A626 Sheet of 2, #a-b 4.00 4.00

Kassamen, Algerian National Anthem, by Moufdi Zakaria — A627

2008, July 3 *Perf. 13x13¼*
1433 A627 15d multi 1.05 1.05

Railway Stations — A628

Station in: 10d, Algiers. 15d, Constantine. 20d, Oran. 38d, Skikda.

2008, July 9 *Perf. 14x13½*
1434-1437 A628 Set of 4 5.00 5.00

Ferhat Abbas (1899-1985), President of First Algerian Temporary Government — A629

2008, Sept. 19 *Perf. 13x13¼*
1438 A629 15d multi 1.10 1.10

2008 Summer Olympics, Beijing — A630

Designs: No. 1439, 15d, Fencing. No. 1440, 15d, Wrestling.

2008, July 23 Litho. *Perf. 14x13½*
1439-1440 A630 Set of 2 2.10 2.10

National Popular Army — A631

2008, Nov. 1
1441 A631 15d multi 1.05 1.05

12th Session of Government Postage Stamp Printers Assoc., Algiers — A632

2008, Nov. 5 *Perf. 13x13¼*
1442 A632 15d multi 1.05 1.05

Miniature Sheet

Bridges in Constantine — A633

No. 1443: a, 10d, Sidi M'Cid Bridge. b, 15d, Sidi Rached Bridge. c, 20d, El Kantara Bridge. d, 38d, La Medersa Bridge.

2008, Nov. 26 *Perf. 14*
1443 A633 Sheet of 4, #a-d 5.00 5.00

Universal Declaration of Human Rights, 60th Anniv. — A634

2008, Dec. 10 *Perf. 14x13½*
1444 A634 15d multi 1.05 1.05

Cities — A635

Designs: 10d, Tebessa. 15d, Saida. 20d, Miliana. 38d, Biskra.

2008, Dec. 18 *Perf. 13¼x13*
1445-1448 A635 Set of 4 5.00 5.00

Diplomatic Relations Between Algeria and People's Republic of China, 50th Anniv. — A636

2008, Dec. 20 *Perf. 12*
1449 A636 15d multi 1.10 1.10

Louis Braille (1809-52), Educator of the Blind — A637

2009, Jan. 4 *Perf. 13½x14*
1450 A637 15d multi 1.10 1.10

Mausoleums — A638

Mausoleum of: 15d, Sidi Abderrahmane, Algiers. 20d, Sidi Ibrahim El Atteuf, Ghardaia, horiz.

2009, Feb. 25 *Perf. 13½x14, 14x13½*
1451-1452 A638 Set of 2 2.25 2.25

Natl. Day of the Handicapped — A639

Designs: 15d, Silhouettes of man with raised arm and man in wheelchair. 20d, Athlete in wheelchair, hand prints.

2009, Mar. 14 *Perf. 13½x14*
1453-1454 A639 Set of 2 2.25 2.25

Protection of Polar Regions and Glaciers — A640

2009, Mar. 28 **Litho.**
1455 A640 38d multi 2.75 2.75

Presidential Elections — A641

2009, Apr. 9 *Perf. 13x13¼*
1456 A641 15d multi 1.00 1.00

Items in National Museum — A642

Designs: 15d, Wooden sandals. 20d, Fragment of silver brooch. 30d, Vest.

2009, Apr. 18 *Perf. 14x13½*
1457-1459 A642 Set of 3 4.50 4.50

University of Algiers, Cent. — A643

2009, May 11
1460 A643 15d multi 1.00 1.00

Jewelry of Southern Algeria — A644

Designs: 1d, Silver fibulas. 5d, Amulet necklace. 9d, Pectoral jewelry and chain. 10d, Circular fibula.

2009, May 13 *Perf. 13¾*
1461-1464 A644 Set of 4 1.75 1.75

Protection of Children From Cyberspace Dangers — A645

2009, May 17 *Perf. 14x13½*
1465 A645 15d multi 1.10 1.10

16th Mediterranean Games, Pescara, Italy — A646

Designs: 15d, Sailboarding. 20d, Equestrian, horiz.

Perf. 13½x14, 14x13½
2009, June 3 **Litho.**
1466-1467 A646 Set of 2 2.40 2.40

Roman Era Archaeological Sites — A647

Designs: 15d, Madaure archaeological site. 20d, Khemissa archaeological site. 30d, Old Theater, Guelma.

2009, June 14 *Perf. 13½x14*
1468-1470 A647 Set of 3 4.25 4.25

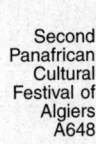

Second Panafrican Cultural Festival of Algiers A648

Designs: 15d, Shown. 20d, Map of Africa, antelope, geometric designs.

2009, July 4 *Perf. 13¼x13*
1471-1472 A648 Set of 2 2.25 2.25

"The Child of Today, the Man of Tomorrow" A649

"I Love My Country" A650

2009, June 26 *Perf. 13½x14*
1473 A649 15d multi 1.00 1.00
1474 A650 20d multi 1.25 1.25

Algerian Electricity and Gas Company, 40th Anniv. — A651

2009, July 28
1475 A651 15d multi 1.00 1.00

Traffic Safety — A652

2009, Aug. 6
1476 A652 15d multi 1.00 1.00

Fishing Ports — A653

Designs: 15d, Bouharoun. 20d, Béni Saf. 30d, Stora.

2009, Sept. 2 **Litho.** *Perf. 13½x13*
1477-1479 A653 Set of 3 4.25 4.25

Protection of the Aged — A654

2009, Oct. 10 *Perf. 13½x14*
1480 A654 15d multi 1.00 1.00

National Armed Forces — A655

2009, Nov. 1 **Litho.** *Perf. 13x13¼*
1481 A655 15d multi 1.00 1.00

Olive Oil Production A656

Designs: 15d, Picking olives. 20d, Pressing olives, vert.

Perf. 13¼x13, 13x13¼
2009, Nov. 25
1482-1483 A656 Set of 2 2.40 2.40

Folktales — A657

No. 1484: a, Loundja, la Fille de l'Ogre. b, Badra. c, La Fée Colombe. d, La Rose Rouge.

2009, Dec. 7 **Litho.** *Perf. 13x13¼*
1484 Block or strip of 4 4.25 4.25
a.-d. A657 15d Any single .95 .95

Birds of Prey — A658

Designs: 15d, Aquila chrysaetos. 20d, Falco biarmicus, vert. 30d, Falco peregrinus, vert.

2010, Jan. 27 *Perf. 13¼x13, 13x13¼*
1485-1487 A658 Set of 3 4.50 4.50

Victims of French Nuclear Testing in Algeria A659

2010, Feb. 10 *Perf. 13¼x13*
1488 A659 15d multi 1.60 1.60

Forts — A660

Designs: 15d, Fort de l'Empereur, Bordj Moulay Hassan, Algiers. 20d, Gouraya Fort, Béjaia.

2010, Feb. 15
1489-1490 A660 Set of 2 2.50 2.50

Expo 2010, Shanghai A661

Designs: 15d, Stylized people, flowers, buildings. 38d, Algeria Pavilion.

2010, Mar. 24 **Litho.** *Perf. 13¼x13*
1491-1492 A661 Set of 2 3.75 3.75

16th Intl. Conference on Liquified Gas, Oran — A662

Conference emblem, world map and: 15d, Gas plant. 20d, Port, horiz.

2010, Apr. 18 *Perf. 13x13½, 13½x13*
1493-1494 A662 Set of 2 2.50 2.50

May 8, 1945 Massacres, 65th Anniv. — A663

2010, May 8 ***Perf. 13¼***
1495 A663 15d multi 1.00 1.00

2010 World Cup Soccer Championships, South Africa — A664

Designs: No. 1496, 15d, World Cup trophy, flags of participating countries. No. 1497, 15d, Player, crowd holding Algerian flags.
No. 1498: a, Fox playing soccer. b, Player, soccer ball.

2010, May 8 ***Perf. 13x13¼***
1496-1497 A664 Set of 2 2.00 2.00

Souvenir Sheet

Imperf

1498 A664 15d Sheet of 2, #a-b 2.00 2.00

Ahellil of Gourara UNESCO World Intangible Cultural Heritage A665

2010, June 2 ***Perf. 13¼x13***
1499 A665 15d multi 1.15 1.15

Martyr's Sanctuary, Algiers — A666

2010, June 20
1500 A666 (15d) multi 1.10 1.10

African Year of Peace and Security — A667

2010, July 19 ***Perf. 13x13¼***
1501 A667 15d multi 1.10 1.10

Caves A668

Designs: No. 1502, 15d, Béni Add Cave, Ain Fezza. No. 1503, 15d, Ziama Cave, Mansouriah.

2010, July 25 ***Perf. 13¼x13***
1502-1503 A668 Set of 2 2.10 2.10

Organization of the Petroleum Exporting Countries, 50th Anniv. A669

Designs: 15d, Emblem. 38d, Emblem, world map, oil tanker.

2010, Sept. 14 **Litho.** ***Perf. 13¼x13***
1504-1505 A669 Set of 2 3.75 3.75

Mosques — A670

Designs: 15d, El Hanafi Mosque, Blida. 20d, Sidi Ali Dib Mosque, Skikda. 30d, Grand Mosque, Nedroma.

2010, Sept. 15 ***Perf. 13x13¼***
1506-1508 A670 Set of 3 4.50 4.50

Dates — A671

Date varieties: No. 1509, 15d, Degla Beida. No. 1510, 15d, Akerbuch. No. 1511, 15d, Ghars, vert. No. 1512, 15d, Deglet Nour, vert.

2010, Oct. 6 ***Perf. 13¼x13, 13x13¼***
1509-1512 A671 Set of 4 4.50 4.50

Handcrafted Items — A672

Designs: 15d, Candlestick holder. 20d, Quanoun (musical instrument). 30d, Leather-covered chest with handles, horiz.

Perf. 13¼x14, 14x13¼

2010, Nov. 30 **Litho.**
1513-1515 A672 Set of 3 4.50 4.50

Trees — A673

Designs: 15d, Cork oak. 20d, Carob tree. 30d, Soapberry tree. 38d, Argan tree.

2011, Jan. 29 ***Perf. 13¼x13***
1516-1519 A673 Set of 4 6.25 6.25

Tlemcen, 2011 Capital of Islamic Culture — A674

Designs: 15d, Minaret of Mansoura. 20d, Door knocker, Side Boumedienne Mosque.

2011, Feb. 15 **Litho.** ***Perf. 13x13¼***
1520-1521 A674 Set of 2 2.10 2.10

Snakes — A675

Designs: No. 1522, 15d, Couleuvre a diademe (diadem snake). No. 1523, 15d, Vipere a cornes (Saharan horned viper).

2011, Mar. 13
1522-1523 A675 Set of 2 2.00 2.00

First Economic Census — A676

2011, Apr. 12 ***Perf. 13½x14***
1524 A676 15d multi .90 .90

18th Cent. Tableware From Algiers A677

Designs: 15d, Couscous dish. 30d, Butter dish.

2011, Apr. 19 ***Perf. 13¼x13***
1525-1526 A677 Set of 2 2.75 2.75

Telecenters A678

2011, May 17 ***Perf. 14x13½***
1527 A678 15d multi 1.10 1.10

Campaign Against Human Immunodeficiency Virus — A679

2011, June 30 ***Perf. 13½x14***
1528 A679 15d multi 1.10 1.10

Benyoucef Benkhedda (1920-2003), Politician — A680

2011, Sept. 19 ***Perf. 13x13¼***
1529 A680 15d multi .90 .90

A681

Comic Strips — A682

2011, Sept. 25 ***Perf. 13¼x14***
1530 A681 15d multi .90 .90
1531 A682 15d multi .90 .90

World Post Day — A683

Main post office in: No. 1532, 15d, Constantine. No. 1533, 15d, Oran.

2011, Oct. 9 ***Perf. 14x13¼***
1532-1533 A683 Set of 2 1.90 1.90

Paris Massacre of Algerian Protestors, 50th Anniv. — A684

2011, Oct. 17 ***Perf. 13x13¼***
1534 A684 15d multi .90 .90

Algerian Press Service, 50th Anniv. — A685

2011, Oct. 25 ***Perf. 14x13¼***
1535 A685 15d multi .90 .90

Army Museum A686

2011, Nov. 1 ***Perf. 13¼x13***
1536 A686 15d multi .90 .90

Souvenir Sheet

Algiers Metro A687

No. 1537: a, Train at station, people on platform. b, Train in tunnel.

2011, Nov. 14 ***Perf. 14***
1537 A687 15d Sheet of 2, #a-b 2.00 2.00

Sheep A688

Sheep breeds: No. 1538, 15d, Ouled Djallal. No. 1539, 15d, El Hamra.

2011, Nov. 16 ***Perf. 13¼x13***
1538-1539 A688 Set of 2 2.00 2.00

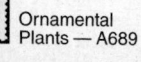

Ornamental Plants — A689

Designs: 15d, Bougainvillea. 20d, Glycine (wisteria). 30d, Mimosa, horiz. 38d, Galant de nuit (night-blooming cestrum), horiz.

2011, Dec. 26 ***Perf. 13x13¼, 13¼x13***
1540-1543 A689 Set of 4 6.25 6.25

Ceasefire Between Algeria and France, 50th Anniv. — A690

2012, Mar. 19 Litho. ***Perf. 13x13¼***
1544 A690 15d multi .90 .90

Expo 2012, Yeosu, South Korea A691

2012, Mar. 21 ***Perf. 13¼x13***
1545 A691 15d multi .90 .90

Wainscoting — A692

Designs: 15d, Door, Dar Aziza, Algiers. 20d, Ceiling, Dar Aziza. 30d, Window, Hassen Pacha Palace, Algiers.

2012, Mar. 26 ***Perf. 13x13¼***
1546-1548 A692 Set of 3 3.75 3.75

Snails — A693

Designs: 15d, Theba pisana. 20d, Eobania vermiculata.

2012, Mar. 28
1549-1550 A693 Set of 2 2.10 2.10

Ulemas — A694

Designs: 15d, Sheikh Larbi Djedri Tebessi (1895-1957). 20d, Sheikh Embarek El-Mili (1898-1945). 30d, Sheikh Ahmed Hamani (1915-98).

2012, Apr. 16 Litho. ***Perf. 13x13¼***
1551-1553 A694 Set of 3 3.75 3.75

City Scenes — A695

Designs: 15d, Casbah of Dellys. 20d, Saracen Gate, Bejaia. 30d, Casbah of Constantine.

2012, June 26
1554-1556 A695 Set of 3 3.75 3.75

2012 Summer Olympics, London — A696

Designs: 15d, Judo, London Eye. 38d, Rowing, Tower Bridge, vert.

Perf. 14x13¼, 13¼x14

2012, June 27
1557-1558 A696 Set of 2 1.40 1.40

Algerian Armed Forces, 50th Anniv. — A697

Designs: No. 1559, 15d, Gendarme on motorcycle. No. 1560, 15d, Tank. No. 1561, 15d, Missiles. No. 1562, 15d, Airplane in flight. No. 1563, 15d, Member of Republican Guard on horse. No. 1564, 15d, Naval vessel.

2012, July 5 ***Perf. 14***

Stamps With Year and Inscriptions At Bottom

1559-1564 A697 Set of 6 2.25 2.25
1561a Souvenir sheet of 3, #1559-1561, with year and inscriptions at bottom of stamp removed 1.10 1.10
1564a Souvenir sheet of 3, #1562-1564, with year and inscriptions at bottom of stamp removed 1.10 1.10

Souvenir Sheet

Algerian Independence, 50th Anniv. — A698

2012, July 5 ***Imperf.***
1565 A698 15d multi .40 .40

Wheat Varieties — A699

Designs: 15d, Bousselam. 20d, Mohamed Ben Bachir. 30d, Hedba 03.

2012, Sept. 29 ***Perf. 13x13¼***
1566-1568 A699 Set of 3 1.75 1.75

Algerian Radio and Television, 50th Anniv. A700

2012, Oct. 28 ***Perf. 13¼x13***
1569 A700 15d multi .40 .40

Postage Stamps of Independent Algeria, 50th Anniv. A701

2012, Nov. 1
1570 A701 15d multi .40 .40

Medicinal Plants — A702

Designs: 15d, Globularia vulgaris. 20d, Glycyrrhiza glabra. 30d, Menyanthes trifoliata.

2012, Dec. 11 Litho. ***Perf. 13x13¼***
1571-1573 A702 Set of 3 1.75 1.75

Diplomatic Relations Between Algeria and Russia, 50th Anniv. A703

2012, Dec. 18 Litho. ***Perf. 13¼x13***
1574 A703 15d multi .40 .40

Roman Mosaics — A704

Mosaic depicting: 15d, Muse. 20d, Hunting scene.

2012, Dec. 18 Litho. ***Perf. 13x13¼***
1575-1576 A704 Set of 2 .90 .90

Yennayer Festival (Berber New Year) — A705

2013, Jan. 12 Litho. ***Perf. 13x13¼***
1577 A705 15d multi .40 .40

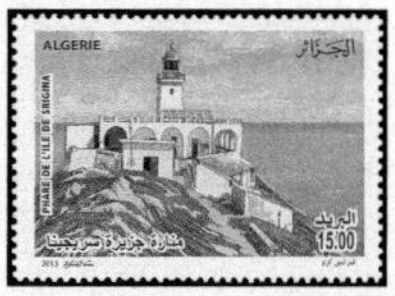

Lighthouses A706

Designs: 15d, Srigina Island Lighthouse. 20d, Cap Bougaroun Lighthouse. 30d, Cap Ivi Lighthouse.

2013, Feb. 27 Litho. ***Perf. 13¼x13***
1578-1580 A706 Set of 3 3.75 3.75

Fruit and Blossoms A707

Designs: 15d, Apricots. 20d, Cherries.

2013, Mar. 3 Litho. ***Perf. 13¼x13***
1581-1582 A707 Set of 2 1.90 1.90

First Chinese Medical Team in Algeria, 50th Anniv. — A708

2013, Apr. 16 Litho. ***Perf. 12***
1583 A708 15d multi .40 .40

Souvenir Sheet

1584 A708 50d multi 1.25 1.25

National Copyright Office, 40th Anniv. — A709

2013, Apr. 26 Litho. ***Perf. 13x13¼***
1585 A709 15d multi .40 .40

National Administration School A710

2013, Apr. 29 Litho. ***Perf. 13¼x13***
1586 A710 15d multi .40 .40

Roman Pottery — A711

Designs: No. 1587, 15d, Two-handled urn with lid, denomination at LL (shown). No. 1588, 15d, Two-handled urn without lid, denomination at LL. No. 1589, 15d, Single-handled urn without lid, denomination at LR.

2013, May 5 Litho. ***Perf. 13x13¼***
1587-1589 A711 Set of 3 1.25 1.25

Improvements in Road Safety With Global Positioning Satellite Technology — A712

2013, May 17 Litho. ***Perf. 13x13¼***
1590 A712 15d multi .40 .40

Algerian Insurance and Re-insurance Company, 50th Anniv. — A713

2013, June 8 Litho. ***Perf. 13x13¼***
1591 A713 15d multi .40 .40

Police Day — A714

2013, July 22 Litho. *Perf. 13x13¼*
1592 A714 15d multi .40 .40

Marine Life — A715

Designs: No. 1593, 15d, Paracentrotus lividus. No. 1594, 15d, Bathynectes maravigna. No. 1595, 15d, Haliotis tuberculata.

2013, Aug. 3 Litho. *Perf. 13¼x13*
1593-1595 A715 Set of 3 1.25 1.25

Flowers — A716

Designs: No. 1596, 15d, Carnations. No. 1597, 15d, Petunias.

2013, Aug. 5 Litho. *Perf. 13x13¼*
1596-1597 A716 Set of 2 .75 .75

22nd African Regional Conference of Interpol, Oran — A717

2013, Sept. 10 Litho. *Perf. 13¼x13*
1598 A717 38d multi .95 .95

Algerian Olympic Committee, 50th Anniv. — A718

Olympic rings, "50," and: 15d, Stylized bird. 30d, Stylized bird and torch, vert.

2013, Oct. 28 Litho. *Perf. 14*
1599-1600 A718 Set of 2 1.10 1.10

Transportation A719

Designs: 15d, Cable cars, Constantine. 20d, Tram, Oran.

2013, Oct. 30 Litho. *Perf. 13¼x13*
1601-1602 A719 Set of 2 .90 .90

Diplomatic Relations Between Algeria and People's Republic of China, 55th Anniv. — A720

2013, Dec. 20 Litho. *Perf. 12*
1603 A720 15d multi .40 .40

Fish Farming — A721

Designs: 15d, Floating cages. 20d, Cleno-pharyngodon idella.

2013, Dec. 24 Litho. *Perf. 14*
1604-1605 A721 Set of 2 .90 .90

Sonatrach (State-owned Oil and Gas Corporation), 50th Anniv. — A722

2013, Dec. 31 Litho. *Perf. 13x13¼*
1606 A722 15d multi .40 .40

Souvenir Sheet

1607 A722 50d multi 1.40 1.40

No. 1607 contains one 35x48mm stamp.

Flowers — A723

Designs: 15d, Ornithogalum arabicum. 20d, Bellis sylvestris. 30d, Calendula arvensis.

2014, Jan. 29 Litho. *Perf. 14*
1608-1610 A723 Set of 3 1.75 1.75

Constitutional Council Building, Algiers, 25th Anniv. A724

2014, Feb. 23 Litho. *Perf. 13¼x13*
1611 A724 15d multi .40 .40

Coins — A725

Obverse and reverse of Almohad dinar from: 15d, 524-58. 20d, 580-95.

2014, Feb. 26 Litho. *Perf. 13¼x13*
1612-1613 A725 Set of 2 .90 .90

Supreme Court, 50th Anniv. — A726

2014, Mar. 2 Litho. *Perf. 14*
1614 A726 15d multi .40 .40

National Day of Handicapped Persons — A727

2014, Mar. 14 Litho. *Perf. 13x13¼*
1615 A727 15d multi .40 .40

Intl. Day of Anti-Personnel Mine Victims — A728

2014, Apr. 4 Litho. *Perf. 13x13¼*
1616 A728 15d multi .40 .40

2014 Presidential Election A729

2014, Apr. 16 Litho. *Perf. 13¼x13*
1617 A729 15d multi .40 .40

19th Century Kitchen Tools — A730

Designs: 15d, Coffee mill, Algiers. 20d, Tuareg sugar hammer, horiz. 30d, Tuareg sugar shears, horiz.

Perf. 13x13¼, 13¼x13
2014, Apr. 28 Litho.
1618-1620 A730 Set of 3 1.75 1.75

Amazigh High Commission, 19th Anniv. — A731

2014, May 27 Litho. *Perf. 13¼x14*
1621 A731 15d multi .40 .40

17th Ministerial Conference of the Non-Aligned Movement, Algiers — A732

Designs: No. 1622, 15d, Stylized dove with olive branch, globe with Algeria highlighted. No. 1623, 15d, Conference emblem.

2014, May 28 Litho. *Perf. 13x13¼*
1622-1623 A732 Set of 2 .75 .75
1623a Souvenir sheet of 2, #1622-1623 .75 .75

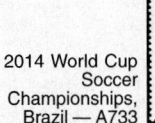

2014 World Cup Soccer Championships, Brazil — A733

Algerian soccer player dribbling ball with country name in: 15d, White. 38d, Green.

2014, June 26 Litho. *Perf. 13x13¼*
1624-1625 A733 Set of 2 1.40 1.40

Olympic Complex, Oran — A734

2014, July 5 Litho. *Perf. 13¼x13*
1626 A734 15d multi .40 .40

Traditional Women's Veils — A735

Designs: 15d, Haik. 30d, M'laya.

2014, Aug. 27 Litho. *Perf. 13x13¼*
1627-1628 A735 Set of 2 1.10 1.10

Prehistoric Art — A736

Designs: 15d, Painting on rock of horse-drawn chariot. 20d, Head of ram. 30d, Baetulus, vert.

2014, Sept. 1 Litho. *Perf. 14*
1629-1631 A736 Set of 3 1.60 1.60

Souvenir Sheet

Rugs A737

No. 1632: a, Rug from Serbia ("Radomir Bojanic" inscribed at LR). b, Rug from Algeria (Arabic script at LR)

2014, Oct. 7 Litho. *Perf. 13¼x14*
1632 A737 15d Sheet of 2, #a-b .75 .75

See Serbia No. 647.

World Post Day — A738

2014, Oct. 9 Litho. *Perf. 13¼x14*
1633 A738 15d multi .35 .35

Algerian War of Independence, 60th Anniv. — A739

2014, Nov. 1 Litho. ***Perf. 13x13¼***
1634 A739 15d multi .35 .35

Sheikh Abdelkrim Dali (1914-78), Musician — A740

2014, Nov. 16 Litho. ***Perf. 13x13¼***
1635 A740 15d multi .35 .35

Bridges A741

Designs: No. 1636, 15d, Saleh Bey Viaduct, Constantine. No. 1637, 15d, Highway bridge and Algerian flag, vert.

Perf. 13¼x13, 13x13¼
2014, Nov. 19 Litho.
1636-1637 A741 Set of 2 .70 .70

Intl. Year of Solidarity With the Palestinian People A742

2014, Dec. 13 Litho. ***Perf. 13¼x13***
1638 A742 15d multi .35 .35

Expo 2015, Milan — A743

Designs: 15d, Globe, hand holding wheat stalks, silhouettes of people. 38d, Stylized fish and fruit, horiz.

2014, Dec. 22 Litho. ***Perf. 14***
1639-1640 A743 Set of 2 1.25 1.25

Bordj el Kifan, Algiers — A744

2015 Litho. ***Perf. 14x13¾***
1641 A744 4d pale orange .25 .25
1642 A744 10d lt blue .25 .25
1643 A744 25d green .55 .55

Issued: 4d, 10d, 8/5; 25d, 1/4.

Algerian Customs A745

2015, Jan. 26 Litho. ***Perf. 13¼x13***
1644 A745 25d multi .55 .55

Intl. Day of the Fight Against Cancer — A746

2015, Feb. 4 Litho. ***Perf. 14***
1645 A746 25d multi .55 .55

World Consumer Rights Day — A747

World map, bar code and: 25d, Shopping cart. 30d, Umbrella.

2015, Mar. 15 Litho. ***Perf. 13½x14***
1646-1647 A747 Set of 2 1.25 1.25

A748

A749

Constantine, 2015 Capital of Arab Culture — A750

Perf. 13x13¼, 13¼x13
2015, Apr. 16 Litho.
1648 A748 10d multi .25 .25
1649 A749 25d multi .55 .55

Souvenir Sheet

1650 A750 60d purple & blk 1.25 1.25

Diplomatic Relations Between Algeria and Mexico, 50th Anniv. — A751

2015, Apr. 23 Litho. ***Perf. 13x13¼***
1651 A751 25d multi .55 .55

Mosques — A752

El Aatiq Mosque in: No. 1652, 25d, Ghardaia. No. 1653, 25d, Metlili, vert.

Perf. 14x13½, 13½x14
2015, May 28 Litho.
1652-1653 A752 Set of 2 1.00 1.00

World Refugee Day — A753

2015, June 20 Litho. ***Perf. 13½x14***
1654 A753 25d multi .50 .50

Traditional Costumes — A754

Man and woman from: 25d, Algiers. 30d, Kabylie.

2015, July 15 Litho. ***Perf. 13x13¼***
1655-1656 A754 Set of 2 1.10 1.10

Famous Men — A755

Designs: No. 1657, 25d, Abdelhamid Benhadouga (1925-96), writer. No. 1658, 25d, M'hamed Issiakhem (1928-85), painter. No. 1659, 25d, Ismail Samsom (1934-88), painter, vert. No. 1660, 25d, Mouloud Feraoun (1913-62), writer, vert.

Perf. 14x13½, 13½x14
2015, Sept. 21 Litho.
1657-1660 A755 Set of 4 1.90 1.90

Day of Algerian Diplomacy A756

2015, Oct. 8 Litho. ***Perf. 13¼x13***
1661 A756 25d multi .50 .50

United Nations, 70th Anniv. — A757

2015, Oct. 24 Litho. ***Perf. 14x13½***
1662 A757 25d multi .50 .50

Algerian Revolution, 61st Anniv. — A758

2015, Nov. 1 Litho. ***Perf. 13½x14***
1663 A758 25d multi .50 .50

A759

Energy — A760

2015, Nov. 11 Litho. ***Perf. 14x13½***
1664 A759 10d multi .25 .25
1665 A760 25d multi .50 .50

A761

Arab Family Day — A762

2015, Dec. 7 Litho. ***Perf. 13½x14***
1666 A761 25d multi .50 .50

Perf. 14x13½

1667 A762 30d multi .60 .60

International Year of Light — A763

2015, Dec. 20 Litho. ***Perf. 13½x14***
1668 A763 25d multi .50 .50

International Telecommunication Union, 150th Anniv. — A764

2015, Dec. 22 Litho. ***Perf. 14x13½***
1669 A764 25d multi .50 .50

Fish — A765

Designs: 25d, Scorpaena scrofa. 50d, Mugil cephalus.

2016, Jan. 20 Litho. ***Perf. 14x13½***
1670-1671 A765 Set of 2 1.40 1.40

Medicinal Plants — A766

Designs: 10d, Persicaria hydropiper. 25d, Eupatorium cannabinum.

2016, Feb. 10 Litho. ***Perf. 13½x14***
1672-1673 A766 Set of 2 .65 .65

Campaign Against Domestic Violence — A767

2016, Feb. 24 Litho. ***Perf. 14x13½***
1674 A767 25d multi .45 .45

Southern Algeria Development — A768

2016, Mar. 16 Litho. ***Perf. 13½x14***
1675 A768 25d multi .50 .50

Beni Haroun Dam — A769

2016, Mar. 22 Litho. *Perf. 13¼x13*
1676 A769 25d multi .50 .50

World Autism Day — A770

Children's art: 25d, City. 50d, Flowers.

2016, Apr. 2 Litho. *Perf. 13¼x13*
1677-1678 A770 Set of 2 1.40 1.40

Museums A771

Designs: No. 1679, 25d, Ahmed Zabana National Public Museum, Oran. No. 1680, 25d, Cirta National Public Museum, Constantine. No. 1681, 25d, Nasreddine Dinet National Public Museum, Boussaada.

2016, Apr. 18 Litho. *Perf. 13¼x13*
1679-1681 A771 Set of 3 1.40 1.40

Gun — A772

Gorgon's Mask — A773

2016, May 18 Litho. *Perf. 13¼x13*
1682 A772 25d multi .45 .45

Perf. 13x13¼
1683 A773 50d multi .90 .90

2016 Summer Olympics, Rio de Janeiro — A774

Statue of Christ the Redeemer, Rio de Janeiro, and: 10d, Weight lifting. 25d, Boxing. 50d, Statue of Christ the Redeemer, soccer.

2016, June 1 Litho. *Perf. 13x13¼*
1684-1685 A774 Set of 2 .65 .65

Souvenir Sheet
1686 A774 50d multi .90 .90

Harbors — A775

Harbor of: 10d, El Djamila. 25d, Sidi Fredj. 50d, Tigzirt.

2016, June 22 Litho. *Perf. 14x13½*
1687-1689 A775 Set of 3 1.60 1.60

Dances — A776

Designs: 10d, Baba Merzoug-Karkabo. 25d, El Baroude. 50d, El Hadra.

2016, July 20 Litho. *Perf. 14x13½*
1690-1692 A776 Set of 3 1.60 1.60

Cities — A777

Designs: No. 1693, 25d, Mostaganem. No. 1694, 25d, Djelfa.

2016, Aug. 3 Litho. *Perf. 13¼x13*
1693-1694 A777 Set of 2 .95 .95

Soummam Conference, 60th Anniv. — A778

2016, Aug. 20 Litho. *Perf. 13x13¼*
1695 A778 25d multi .45 .45

Architecture A779

Designs: 25d, Faculty of Medicine Building, Laghouat. 50d, Faculty of Law Building, Algiers.

2016, Sept. 7 Litho. *Perf. 13¼x13*
1696-1697 A779 Set of 2 1.40 1.40

Emblem of Professional Education and Job Training — A780

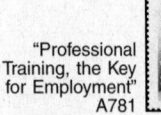

"Professional Training, the Key for Employment" A781

2016, Oct. 5 Litho. *Perf. 14*
1698 A780 10d multi .25 .25
1699 A781 25d multi .45 .45

Institute of Diplomacy and International Relations — A782

2016, Oct. 24 Litho. *Perf. 14x13½*
1700 A782 25d multi .45 .45

Mohammed Aissa Messaoudi (1931-94), Journalist — A783

2016, Oct. 28 Litho. *Perf. 13x13¼*
1701 A783 25d multi .45 .45

"Taxation To Build the Algeria of Tomorrow" A784

Land Registry A785

2016, Nov. 9 Litho. *Perf. 13½x14*
1702 A784 10d multi .25 .25

Perf. 14x13½
1703 A785 25d multi .45 .45

Atlas Lion — A786

2016, Dec. 14 Litho. *Perf. 13¼x13*
1704 A786 50d multi .90 .90

Modernization of Justice System A787

2017, Jan. 15 Litho. *Perf. 13¼x13*
1705 A787 25d multi .45 .45

Spas — A788

Designs: 5d, Hammam Essalihine. 20d, Hammam Bouhadjar. 25d, Hammam Zelfana.

2017, Jan. 29 Litho. *Perf. 14x13¼*
1706-1708 A788 Set of 3 .95 .95

Berber as an Official Language in Algeria, 1st Anniv. — A789

2017, Feb. 7 Litho. *Perf. 13x13¼*
1709 A789 25d multi .45 .45

Campaign Against Food Wastage A790

Prevention of Food Poisoning A791

2017, Mar. 15 Litho. *Perf. 14x13¼*
1710 A790 25d multi .45 .45

Perf. 13¼x14
1711 A791 25d multi .45 .45

International Trisomy 21 (Down Syndrome) Day — A792

2017, Mar. 21 Litho. *Perf. 13¼x13*
1712 A792 25d multi .45 .45

Souvenir Sheet

Tinhinan Jewelry A793

No. 1713: a, 10d, Necklace. b, 20d, Gold bracelets. c, 20d, Gold pendant.

2017, Apr. 18 Litho. *Perf. 14*
1713 A793 Sheet of 3, #a-c .95 .95

Second Session of the Specialized Technical Committee on Social Development, Labor and Employment of the African Union — A794

2017, Apr. 26 Litho. *Perf. 13¼x14*
1714 A794 25d multi .45 .45

Theaters — A795

Theater in: No. 1715, 25d, Sidi Bel Abbes. No. 1716, 25d, Tizi Ouzou. No. 1717, 25d, Bejaia.

2017, May 18 Litho. *Perf. 13¼x14*
1715-1717 A795 Set of 3 .95 .95

Warda Al-Jazairia (1939-2012), Singer — A796

Fadila Dziria (1917-70), Singer — A797

2017, June 8 Litho. *Perf. 13x13¼*
1718 A796 50d multi .95 .95
1719 A797 50d multi .95 .95

Miniature Sheet

Waterfalls — A798

No. 1720: a, Oued El Bared Waterfall, Setif. b, Tifrit Waterfall, Saida. c, Sidi Ouadah Waterfall, Tiaret. d, Lakhdaria Waterfall, Bouira.

2017, June 24 Litho. ***Perf. 14x13¼***
1720 A798 25d Sheet of 4, #a-d 1.90 1.90

Miniature Sheet

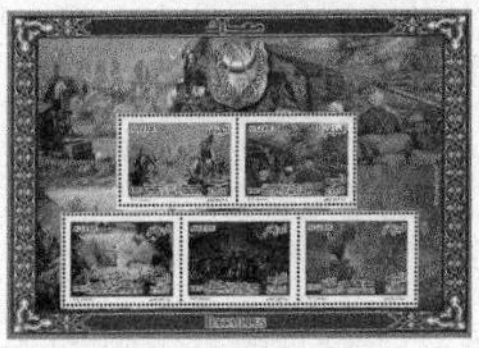

Battles A799

No. 1721: a, Battle of Bir El Gharama, 1881. b, Battle of Bir Teskift, 1957. c, Battle of Djbel Bouk'hil, 1961. d, Battle of Kheng Ennetah, 1832. e, Battle of Ain Zana, 1959.

2017, July 5 Litho. ***Perf. 14x13¼***
1721 A799 25d Sheet of 5, #a-e 2.40 2.40

Souvenir Sheet

Algerian Police Force, 55th Anniv. A800

2017, July 23 Litho. ***Perf. 14***
1722 A800 25d multi .50 .50

Road Safety — A801

2017, Aug. 6 Litho. ***Perf. 14x13¼***
1723 A801 25d multi .45 .45

Dangers of the Internet — A802

2017, Aug. 6 Litho. ***Perf. 13¼x14***
1724 A802 25d multi .45 .45

Algiers Architecture A803

Designs: No. 1725, 25d, International Conference Center. No. 1726, 25d, Opera House.

2017, Sept. 10 Litho. ***Perf. 13¼x13***
1725-1726 A803 Set of 2 .90 .90

National Office of Weights and Measures, 31st Anniv. — A804

2017, Sept. 29 Litho. ***Perf. 13¼x14***
1727 A804 25d multi .45 .45

Fruits and Vegetables A805

Designs: No. 1728, 25d, Citrouilles (squashes). No. 1729, 25d, Aubergines (eggplants). No. 1730, 25d, Clementines. No. 1731, 25d, Pêches (peaches).

2017, Oct. 16 Litho. ***Perf. 14***
1728-1731 A805 Set of 4 1.75 1.75

Blood Donation A806

2017, Oct. 25 Litho. ***Perf. 13¼x13***
1732 A806 25d multi .45 .45

Diplomatic Relations Between Algeria and Viet Nam, 55th Anniv. — A807

2017, Oct. 28 Litho. ***Perf. 14x13¼***
1733 A807 25d multi .45 .45

Souvenir Sheet

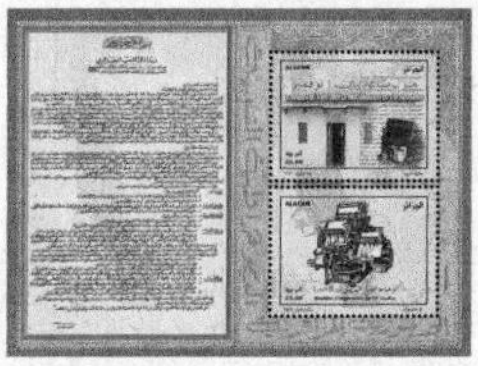

National Liberation Front Proclamation of November 1, 1954 — A808

No. 1734: a, House from which proclamation was made, and printing press. b, Printing press.

2017, Nov. 1 Litho. ***Perf. 14x13¼***
1734 A808 25d Sheet of 2, #a-b .90 .90

Fidel Castro (1926-2016), President of Cuba — A809

2017, Nov. 26 Litho. ***Perf. 13x13¼***
1735 A809 25d multi .45 .45

Mouloud Mammeri (1917-89), Writer — A810

Litho. & Engr.
2017, Dec. 28 ***Perf. 13x13¼***
1736 A810 50d black .90 .90

Campaign Against Violence — A811

2018, Jan. 2 Litho. ***Perf. 14¼***
1737 A811 25d multi + label .45 .45

National Day of Municipalities A812

2018, Jan. 18 Litho. ***Perf. 13¼x13***
1738 A812 25d multi .45 .45

New Cities — A813

Designs: No. 1739, 25d, Ali Mendjeli. No. 1740, 25d, Sidi Abdellah.

2018, Jan. 28 Litho. ***Perf. 14x13¼***
1739-1740 A813 Set of 2 .90 .90

International Mother Language Day — A814

2018, Feb. 21 Litho. ***Perf. 13x13¼***
1741 A814 25d multi .45 .45

International Decade of Water for Sustainable Development A815

Foggaras (water systems) in Adrar Province: No. 1742, 25d, Foggara El Beidha, Tidikelt Region. No. 1743, 25d, Foggara El Kbira, Gourara Region. No. 1744, 25d, Foggara Armoul, Touât Region.

2018, Mar. 22 Litho. ***Perf. 14x13¼***
1742-1744 A815 Set of 3 1.40 1.40

National Service, 50th Anniv. — A816

2018, Apr. 8 Litho. ***Perf. 13x13¼***
1745 A816 25d multi .45 .45

2018 World Cup Soccer Championships, Russia — A817

2018, Apr. 21 Litho. ***Perf. 14x13¼***
1746 A817 25d multi .45 .45

Historical Sites — A818

Designs: 5d, Jedar near Tiaret. 10d, Ruins of Tiddis, vert. 20d, Cedias Mausoleum, Khenchela, vert. 25d, El Mokrani Castle, Bordj Bou Arreridj.

Perf. 14x13¼, 13¼x14
2018, May 12 Litho.
1747-1750 A818 Set of 4 1.10 1.10

International Day of Living Together in Peace — A819

2018, May 16 Litho. ***Perf. 13x13¼***
1751 A819 25d multi .45 .45

International Day of Biological Diversity — A820

2018, May 22 Litho. ***Perf. 14***
1752 A820 25d multi .45 .45

Couscous A821

2018, June 12 Litho. ***Perf. 13¼x13***
1753 A821 25d multi .45 .45

United Nations Day for Public Service — A822

2018, June 23 Litho. ***Perf. 13x13¼***
1754 A822 25d multi .45 .45

Freedom Fighters A823

Designs: 10d, Cherif Boubaghla (?-1854). 20d, Sheikh Amoud (1859-1929), vert. 25d, Bennacer Ben Chohra (1804-84), vert.

Perf. 13¼x13, 13x13¼
2018, July 5 Litho.
1755-1757 A823 Set of 3 .95 .95

Blaoui el Houari (1926-2017), Singer — A824

2018, July 19 Litho. ***Perf. 13x13¼***
1758 A824 50d multi .85 .85

Souvenir Sheet

Nelson Mandela (1918-2013), President of South Africa — A825

2018, July 18 Litho. ***Perf. 13¼***
1759 A825 100d multi 1.75 1.75

A826

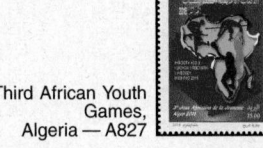

Third African Youth Games, Algeria — A827

2018, July 19 Litho. ***Perf. 13¼x14***
1760 A826 25d multi .45 .45
1761 A827 25d multi .45 .45

Zaouia (Islamic School) A828

Dome of Zaouia, Map of Algeria, Muslim Man and Calligrapher A829

2018, Sept. 1 Litho. ***Perf. 14***
1762 A828 25d multi — —
Perf. 13¼
1763 A829 25d multi — —

Sbiba Festival A830

No. 1764: a, Four Tuareg dancers. b, Tuareg dancers and festival attendees.

2018, Sept. 27 Litho. ***Perf. 14x13½***
1764 A830 25d Horiz. pair, #a-b — —

Honeycomb, Bees and Eucalyptus Blossoms A831

Honeycomb, Bees and Jujube Blossoms A832

2018, Oct. 16 Litho. ***Perf. 14¼***
1765 A831 25d multi — —
1766 A832 25d multi — —

National Press Day — A833

2018, Oct. 22 Litho. ***Perf. 13x13½***
1767 A833 25d multi — —

Green City — A834

2018, Oct. 25 Litho. ***Perf. 13x13½***
1768 A834 25d multi — —

Mostefa Ben Boulaid (1917-56), Revolution Leader A835

Mourad Didouche (1927-55), Revolution Leader A836

Larbi Ben M'hidi (1923-57), Revolution Leader A837

Colonel Amirouchené Ait Hamouda (1926-59), Revolution Leader A838

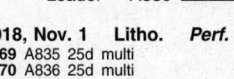

Colonel Youcef Zighoud (1921-56), Revolution Leader — A839

2018, Nov. 1 Litho. ***Perf. 13½x14***
1769 A835 25d multi — —
1770 A836 25d multi — —
1771 A837 25d multi — —
1772 A838 25d multi — —
1773 A839 25d multi — —

Martyrs of the Algerian Revolution.

Souvenir Sheet

Proclamation Declaring the Formation of the State of Palestine, 30th Anniv. — A840

2018, Nov. 15 Litho. ***Perf. 13½x13***
1774 A840 70d multi — —

Women's Entrepreneurship Day — A841

2018, Nov. 21 Litho. ***Perf. 14x13¼***
1775 A841 25d multi .45 .45

Launch of Alcomsat-1, 1st Anniv. — A842

2018, Dec. 11 Litho. ***Perf. 13½x14***
1776 A842 25d multi — —

World Arabic Language Day — A843

2018, Dec. 18 Litho. ***Perf. 13x13½***
1777 A843 50d multi — —

Diplomatic Relations Between Algeria and People's Republic of China, 60th Anniv. A844

2018, Dec. 20 Litho. ***Perf. 13½x13***
1778 A844 25d multi — —

Pres. Houari Boumédiène (1932-78) — A845

2018, Dec. 27 Litho. ***Perf. 13x13½***
1779 A845 50d multi — —

International Year of the Periodic Table of Elements A846

2019, Jan. 2 Litho. ***Perf. 13¼x13***
1780 A846 25d multi .45 .45

Women in Health Services in the Algerian Revolution — A847

No. 1781: a, Female health care worker treating standing soldier in forest. b, Male and female health care workers treating soldiers sitting against rock face.

2019, Feb. 18 Litho. ***Perf. 14x13½***
1781 A847 25d Horiz. pair, #a-b — —

Mar. 8, 1974, Crash of Airplane Carrying Algerian Journalists in Hanoi, Viet Nam — A848

2019, Mar. 8 Litho. ***Perf. 13½x13***
1782 A848 25d multi — —

International Labor Organization, Cent. — A849

2019, Mar. 9 Litho. ***Perf. 13½x13***
1783 A849 25d multi — —

Emiliano Zapata (1879-1919), Leader of Mexican Revolution A850

2019, Apr. 10 Litho. ***Perf. 13½x13***
1784 A850 25d multi — —

Souvenir Sheet

Science Day A851

2019, Apr. 16 Litho. ***Imperf.***
1785 A851 50d multi — —

Souvenir Sheet

Protected Species — A852

No. 1786: a, Oryx dammah. b, Cobra from North Africa.

2019, May 11 Litho. *Perf. 14x13½*
1786 A852 25d Sheet of 2, #a-b — —

2019 Africa Cup of Nations Soccer Tournament, Egypt — A853

2019, May 15 Litho. *Perf.*
1787 A853 25d multi — —

Traditional Costumes — A854

Designs: No. 1788, 25d, Woman wearing Tlemcenian scarf. No. 1789, 25d, Man wearing burnous of Southern Algeria. No. 1790, 25d, Woman wearing Kabyle dress. No. 1791, 25d, Man wearing clothing of Aurès.

2019, July 8 Litho. *Perf. 13x13½*
1788-1791 A854 Set of 4 — —

National Society for Electricity and Gas (Sonelgaz), 50th Anniv. — A855

2019, July 28 Litho. *Perf. 13x13½*
1792 A855 25d multi — —

Ahmed Zabana (1926-56), Revolution Leader A856

Ali Ammar (1930-57), Revolution Leader A857

Malika Gaid (1933-58), Revolutionary Hero and Nurse — A858

Hassiba Ben Bouali (1938-57), Revolutionary Hero — A859

Ourida Meddad (1938-57), Revolutionary Hero — A860

2019, Oct. 3 Litho. *Perf. 13½x14*

1793	Vert. strip of 5	—	—
a.	A856 25d multi	—	—
b.	A857 25d multi	—	—
c.	A858 25d multi	—	—
d.	A859 25d multi	—	—
e.	A860 25d multi	—	—

Martyrs of the Algerian Revolution.

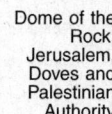

Mohamed Seddik Ben Yahia (1932-82), Politician — A861

2019, Oct. 8 Litho. *Perf. 13x13½*
1794 A861 50d multi — —

Dome of the Rock, Jerusalem, Doves and Palestinian Authority Flag — A862

2019, Oct. 9 Litho. *Perf. 13½x13*
1795 A862 100d multi — —

Jerusalem, capital of the Palestinian Authority.

World Organ Donation and Transplantation Day — A863

2019, Oct. 20 Litho. *Perf. 14x13½*
1796 A863 25d multi — —

24th Algiers International Book Fair — A864

2019, Nov. 2 Litho. *Perf. 13x13½*
1797 A864 25d multi — —

Souvenir Sheet

National Handicrafts Day — A865

No. 1798: a, Southern milk churn. b, Central milk churn.

2019, Nov. 11 Litho. *Perf. 14x13½*
1798 A865 50d Sheet of 2, #a-b — —

Algerian Sign Language Dictionary — A866

2019, Dec. 5 Litho. *Perf. 13x13½*
1799 A866 25d multi — —

Stone Engravings, Sfissifa Station A867

Ain El Haneche Archaeological Site — A868

Abou Al Mouhajir Dinar Mosque, Mila — A869

2020, Jan. 25 Litho. *Perf. 13½x13*

1800	A867 25d multi	—	—
1801	A868 25d multi	—	—
1802	A869 25d multi	—	—

Archaeological sites and treasures.

Myotis Nattereri — A870

Hirundo Rustica — A871

Bubo Ascalaphus — A872

2020, Feb. 22 Litho. *Perf. 13¼*

1803	A870 20d multi	—	—
1804	A871 25d multi	—	—

Perf. 13¼x14

1805	A872 30d multi	—	—

Repatriation From France of Skulls of 24 Zaatcha Resistance Fighters A873

2020, Aug. 20 Litho. *Perf. 13¼x13*
1806 A873 25d multi — —

People Playing Khargba A877

People Playing Sig — A878

2021, Apr. 18 Litho. *Perf. 13¼x13*
1810 A877 25d multi — —

Perf. 14

1811 A878 50d multi — —

Fruits — A879

Designs: 25d, Blackberries. 50d, Strawberry.

2021, May 16 Litho. *Perf. 14*
1812-1813 A879 Set of 2 — —

Algerian Cuisine A880

Designs: 25d, Rechta (noodles). 50d, Harira (soup).

2021, May 18 Litho. *Perf. 13¼x13*
1814-1815 A880 Set of 2 — —

Recycling Economy — A881

2021, June 6 Litho. *Perf. 13¼x14*
1816 A881 25d multi — —

People Celebrating Independence Day — A882

2021, July 5 Litho. *Perf. 13¼x13*
1817 A882 25d multi — —

2020 Summer Olympics, Tokyo — A885

Designs: 25d, Kayaker and Mount Fuji. 50d, Karatekas and torii.

2021, July 15 Litho. *Perf. 14*
1820-1821 A885 Set of 2 — —

The 2020 Summer Olympics were postponed until 2021 because of the COVID-19 pandemic.

Tambourine A886

Goblet Drum — A887

2021, Oct. 1 Litho. *Perf. 14*
1822 A886 25d multi — —
Perf. 14x13½
1823 A887 50d multi — —

World Teacher's Day — A888

2021, Oct. 5 Litho. *Perf. 13½x13*
1824 A888 50d multi — —

Djamaa El Djazair Mosque, Muhammadia A889

2021, Oct. 19 Litho. *Perf. 13½x13*
1825 A889 50d multi — —

Medjerda River — A890

2021, Oct. 24 Litho. *Perf. 13½x13*
1826 A890 50d multi — —

Joint issue between Algeria and Tunisia. See Tunisia No. 1769.

Group of 22, House of Lyes Deriche and Algerian Flags A891

2021, Nov. 1 Litho. *Imperf.*
1827 A891 100d multi — —

Start of Algerian War of Independence and Declaration of November 1, 1954, 67th anniv.

Saddlemaking — A892

No. 1828: a, Decorated saddle. b, Saddle and saddlemaking tools.

2021, Nov. 9 Litho. *Perf. 14x13½*
1828 A892 25d Horiz. pair, #a-b — —

2021 Africa Cup of Nations Soccer Tournament, Cameroun — A893

2022, Jan. 9 Litho. *Perf. 13x13½*
1829 A893 25d multi — —

The 2021 Africa Cup of Nations Soccer Tournament was postponed until 2022 because of the COVID-19 pandemic.

Mohamed Balouizdad (1924-52), President of Special Organization — A894

2022, Feb. 15 Litho. *Perf. 13x13½*
1830 A894 25d multi — —

Special Organization, 75th anniv.

Cohesion Between the Algerian People and Their Army — A895

2022, Feb. 23 Litho. *Perf. 13½x13*
1831 A895 25d multi — —

National Remembrance Day — A897

2022, May 8 Litho. *Perf. 13¼x13*
1834 A897 25d multi — —

Traditional Costumes from Oran — A899

Gallal — A900

2022, May 18 Litho. *Perf. 13¼x14*
1836 A899 25d multi — —
Perf. 14x13¼
1837 A900 25d multi — —

SEMI-POSTAL STAMPS

Regular Issue of 1926 Surcharged in Black or Red

1927 Unwmk. *Perf. 14x13½*

B1	A1	5c +5c bl grn	1.60	1.60
B2	A1	10c +10c lilac	1.60	1.60
B3	A2	15c +15c org brn	1.60	1.60
B4	A2	20c +20c car rose	1.60	1.60
B5	A2	25c +25c bl grn	1.60	1.60
B6	A2	30c +30c lt bl	1.60	1.60
B7	A2	35c +35c dp vio	1.60	1.60
B8	A2	40c +40c ol grn	1.60	1.60
B9	A3	50c +50c dp bl (R)	1.60	1.60
a.		Double surcharge	425.00	*425.00*
B10	A3	80c +80c red org	1.60	1.60
B11	A4	1fr +1fr gray grn & red brn	1.60	1.60
B12	A4	2fr +2fr Prus bl & blk brn	32.50	32.50
B13	A4	5fr +5fr red & vio	42.50	42.50
		Nos. B1-B13 (13)	92.60	92.60

The surtax was for the benefit of wounded soldiers. Government officials speculated in this issue.

Railroad Terminal, Oran SP1

Ruins at Djemila SP2

Mosque of Sidi Abd-er-Rahman — SP3

Designs: 10c+10c, Rummel Gorge, Constantine. 15c+15c, Admiralty Buildings, Algiers. 25c+25c, View of Algiers. 30c+30c, Trajan's Arch, Timgad. 40c+40c, Temple of the North, Djemila. 75c+75c Mansourah Minaret, Tlemcen. 1f+1f, View of Ghardaia. 1.50f+1.50f, View of Tolga. 2f+2f, Tuareg warriors. 3f+3f, Kasbah, Algiers.

1930 Engr. *Perf. 12½*

B14	SP1	5c +5c orange	12.00	12.00
B15	SP1	10c +10c ol grn	12.00	12.00
B16	SP1	15c +15c dk brn	12.00	12.00
B17	SP1	25c +25c black	12.00	12.00
B18	SP1	30c +30c dk red	12.00	12.00
B19	SP1	40c +40c ap grn	12.00	12.00
B20	SP2	50c +50c ultra	9.50	9.50
B21	SP2	75c +75c red pur	9.50	9.50
B22	SP2	1fr +1fr org red	9.50	9.50
B23	SP2	1.50fr +1.50fr deep ultra	9.50	9.50
B24	SP2	2fr +2fr dk car	9.50	9.50
B25	SP2	3fr +3fr dk grn	9.50	9.50
B26	SP3	5fr +5fr grn & car	24.00	24.00
a.		Center inverted	750.00	
		Nos. B14-B26 (13)	153.00	153.00

Centenary of the French occupation of Algeria. The surtax on the stamps was given to the funds for the celebration.

Nos. B14-B26 exist imperf. Value, set in pairs, $800.

Catalogue values for unused stamps in this section, from this point to the end of the section, are for Never Hinged items.

No. 102 Surcharged in Red

1938 *Perf. 13*

B27	A6	65c +35c on 2.25fr yel grn	1.60	1.20
a.		Inverted surcharge	350.00	
b.		Pair, one without surcharge	1,875.	

20th anniversary of Armistice.

No. 79 with surcharge is considered an essay. Values: unused $260, never hinged $350.

René Caillié, Charles Lavigerie and Henri Duveyrier SP14

1939 Engr.

B28	SP14	30c +20c dk bl grn	2.40	2.40
B29	SP14	90c +60c car rose	2.40	2.40
B30	SP14	2.25fr +75c ultra	20.00	16.00
B31	SP14	5fr +5fr brn blk	40.00	32.50
		Nos. B28-B31 (4)	64.80	53.30

Pioneers of the Sahara.

French and Algerian Soldiers — SP15

1940 Photo. *Perf. 12*

B32	SP15	1fr +1fr bl & car	1.60	1.20
a.		Double surcharge	260.00	
B33	SP15	1fr +2fr brn rose & blk	1.60	1.20
B34	SP15	1fr +4fr dp grn & red	2.40	2.00
B35	SP15	1fr +9fr brn & car	4.00	2.75
		Nos. B32-B35 (4)	9.60	7.15

The surtax was used to assist the families of mobilized men.

Nos. B32-B35 exist without surcharge. Value set, $325.

Type of Regular Issue, 1941 Surcharged in Carmine

1941 Engr. *Perf. 13*
B36 A19 1fr +4fr black .70 .30

No. 135 Surcharged in Carmine

B37 A19 1fr +4fr dark blue .70 .30

The surtax was for National Relief.

No. 124 Surcharged in Black

1942

B38	A7	90c +60c henna brn	.60	.25
a.		Double surcharge	175.00	

The surtax was used for National Relief. The stamp could also be used as 1.50 francs for postage.

Mother and Child — SP16

1943, Dec. 1 Litho. *Perf. 12*

B39	SP16	50c +4.50fr brt pink	1.00	*1.30*
B40	SP16	1.50fr +8.50fr lt grn	1.00	*1.30*
B41	SP16	3fr +12fr dp bl	1.00	*1.30*
B42	SP16	5fr +15fr vio brn	1.00	*1.40*
		Nos. B39-B42 (4)	4.00	*5.30*

The surtax was for the benefit of soldiers and prisoners of war.

Planes over Fields — SP17

Unwmk.
1945, July 2 Engr. *Perf. 13*
B43 SP17 1.50fr +3.50fr lt ultra, red org & blk 1.15 .85

The surtax was for the benefit of Algerian airmen and their families.

France No. B192 Overprinted Type "a" of 1924 in Black

1945
B44 SP146 4fr +6fr dk vio brn 1.15 .85

The surtax was for war victims of the P.T.T.

Overprinted in Blue on Type of France, 1945

1945, Oct. 15

B45 SP150 2fr +3fr dk brn 1.15 .85

For Stamp Day.

Overprinted in Blue on Type of France, 1946

1946, June 29

B46 SP160 3fr +2fr red 1.70 1.25

For Stamp Day.

Children Playing by Stream — SP18

Girl — SP19

Athlete SP20

Repatriated Prisoner and Bay of Algiers SP21

1946, Oct. 2 Engr. *Perf. 13*

B47 SP18 3fr +17fr dark grn 2.75 2.25
B48 SP19 4fr +21fr red 2.75 2.25
B49 SP20 8fr +27fr rose lilac 7.25 6.25
B50 SP21 10fr +35fr dark blue 3.25 2.50
Nos. B47-B50 (4) 16.00 13.25

Type of France, 1947, Overprinted type "a" of 1924 in Carmine

1947, Mar. 15

B51 SP172 4.50fr +5.50fr dp ultra 1.75 1.25

For Stamp Day.

Same on Type of France, 1947, Surcharged Like No. B36 in Carmine

1947, Nov. 13

B52 A173 5fr +10fr dk Prus grn 1.60 1.25

Type of France, 1948, Overprinted in Dark Green — f

1948, Mar. 6

B53 SP176 6fr +4fr dk grn 1.75 1.25

For Stamp Day.

Type of France, 1948, Overprinted in Blue

1948, May

B54 A176 6fr +4fr red 1.70 1.25

Battleship Richelieu and the Admiralty, Algiers — SP22

Aircraft Carrier Arromanches SP23

Unwmk.

1949, Jan. 15 Engr. *Perf. 13*

B55 SP22 10fr +15fr dp blue 10.00 8.00
B56 SP23 18fr +22fr red 10.00 8.00

The surtax was for naval charities.

Type of France, 1949, Overprinted in Blue — g

1949, Mar. 26

B57 SP180 15fr +5fr lilac rose 3.25 2.25

For Stamp Day, Mar. 26-27.

Type of France, 1950, Overprinted type "f" in Green

1950, Mar. 11

B58 SP183 12fr +3fr blk brn 3.25 2.75

For Stamp Day, Mar. 11-12.

Foreign Legionary — SP24

1950, Apr. 30

B59 SP24 15fr +5fr dk grn 3.00 2.40

Charles de Foucauld and Gen. J. F. H. Laperrine — SP25

1950, Aug. 21 Unwmk. *Perf. 13*

B60 SP25 25fr +5fr brn ol & brn blk 8.00 6.25

50th anniversary of the presence of the French in the Sahara.

Emir Abd-el-Kader and Marshal T. R. Bugeaud — SP26

1950, Aug. 21

B61 SP26 40fr +10fr org brn & blk brn 8.00 6.25

Unveiling of a monument to Emir Abd-el-Kader at Cacheron.

Col. Colonna d'Ornano and Fine Arts Museum, Algiers — SP27

1951, Jan. 11

B62 SP27 15fr +5fr blk brn, vio brn & red brn 1.40 1.25

Death of Col. Colonna d'Ornano, 10th anniv.

Type of France, 1951, Overprinted type "a" of 1924 in Black

1951, Mar. 10

B63 SP186 12fr +3fr brown 2.75 2.50

For Stamp Day.

Type of France, 1952, Overprinted type "g" in Dark Blue

1952, Mar. 8 Unwmk. *Perf. 13*

B64 SP190 12fr +3fr dk bl 2.75 2.50

For Stamp Day.

French Military Medal — SP28

Unwmk.

1952, July 5 Engr. *Perf. 13*

B65 SP28 15fr +5fr grn, yel & brn 3.50 2.75

Centenary of the creation of the French Military Medal.

Type of France 1952, Surcharged type "g" and Surtax in Black

1952, Sept. 15

B66 A222 30fr +5fr dp ultra 4.00 3.25

10th anniv. of the defense of Bir-Hakeim.

View of El Oued — SP29

Design: 12fr+3fr, View of Bou-Noura.

1952, Nov. 15 Engr.

B67 SP29 8fr +2fr ultra & red 3.25 3.00
B68 SP29 12fr +3fr red 6.50 4.75

The surtax was for the Red Cross.

Type of France, 1953, Overprinted type "a" of 1924 in Black

1953, Mar. 14 Engr.

B69 SP193 12fr +3fr purple 2.50 2.40

For Stamp Day. Surtax for Red Cross.

Victory of Cythera — SP30

Unwmk.

1953, Dec. 18 Engr. *Perf. 13*

B70 SP30 15fr +5fr blk brn & brn 1.60 1.25

The surtax was for army welfare work.

Type of France, 1954, Overprinted type "a" of 1924 in Black

1954, Mar. 20 Unwmk. *Perf. 13*

B71 SP196 12fr +3fr scarlet 2.25 2.00

For Stamp Day.

Soldiers and Flags — SP31

1954, Mar. 27

B72 SP31 15fr +5fr dk brn 2.00 1.25

The surtax was for old soldiers.

Foreign Legionary — SP32

1954, Apr. 30

B73 SP32 15fr +5fr dk grn 3.00 2.50

The surtax was for the welfare fund of the Foreign Legion.

Nurses and Verdun Hospital, Algiers — SP33

15fr+5fr, J. H. Dunant & ruins at Djemila.

1954, Oct. 30

B74 SP33 12fr +3fr indigo & red 6.50 5.50
B75 SP33 15fr +5fr pur & red 7.50 6.25

The surtax was for the Red Cross.

Earthquake Victims and Ruins SP34

First Aid SP35

Design: Nos. B80-B81, Removing wounded.

1954, Dec. 5

B76 SP34 12fr +4fr dk vio brn 3.50 2.75
B77 SP34 15fr +5fr dp bl 3.50 2.75
B78 SP35 18fr +6fr lil rose 4.50 3.50
B79 SP35 20fr +7fr violet 4.50 3.50
B80 SP35 25fr +8fr rose brn 4.50 3.50
B81 SP35 30fr +10fr brt bl grn 4.50 3.50
Nos. B76-B81 (6) 25.00 19.50

The surtax was for victims of the Orleansville earthquake disaster of September 1954.

Type of France, 1955, Overprinted type "a" of 1924 in Black

1955, Mar. 19

B82 SP199 12fr +3fr dp ultra 2.75 2.25

For Stamp Day, Mar. 19-20.

Women and Children — SP36

1955, Nov. 5

B83 SP36 15fr +5fr blue & indigo 1.40 1.25

The tax was for war victims.

Cancer Victim — SP37

1956, Mar. 3 Unwmk. *Perf. 13*

B84 SP37 15fr +5fr dk brn 2.00 1.60

The surtax was for the Algerian Cancer Society. The male figure in the design is Rodin's "Age of Bronze."

Type of France, 1956, Overprinted type "a" of 1924 in Black

1956, Mar.

B85 SP202 12fr +3fr red 2.50 2.00

For Stamp Day, Mar. 17-18.

Foreign Legion Rest Home — SP38

1956, Apr. 29

B86 SP38 15fr +5fr dk bl grn 2.50 2.00

Honoring the French Foreign Legion.

Type of France, 1957, Overprinted type "f" in Black

1957, Mar. 16 Engr. *Perf. 13*
B87 SP204 12fr +3fr dull purple 2.00 1.60

For Stamp Day and to honor the Maritime Postal Service.

Fennec — SP39

Design: 15fr+5fr, Stork flying over roofs.

1957, Apr. 6
B88 SP39 12fr +3fr red brn & red 9.00 7.25
B89 SP39 15fr +5fr sepia & red 9.00 7.25

The surtax was for the Red Cross.

Regular Issue of 1956 Srchd. in Dark Blue

1957, June 18
B90 A53 15fr +5fr scar & rose red 2.50 1.60

17th anniv. of General de Gaulle's appeal for a Free France.

The Giaour, by Delacroix SP40

On the Banks of the Oued, by Fromentin SP41

Design: 35fr+10fr, Dancer, by Chasseriau.

Unwmk.
1957, Nov. 30 Engr. *Perf. 13*
B91 SP40 15fr +5fr dk car 8.00 7.00
B92 SP41 20fr +5fr grn 8.00 7.00
B93 SP40 35fr +10fr dk bl 9.00 7.25
Nos. B91-B93 (3) 25.00 21.25

Surtax for army welfare organizations.

Type of France Overprinted type "f" in Blue

1958, Mar. 15 Unwmk. *Perf. 13*
B94 SP206 15fr +5fr org brn 2.00 1.60

For Stamp Day.

Bird-of-Paradise Flower — SP42

1958, June 14 Engr. *Perf. 13*
B95 SP42 20fr +5fr grn, org & vio 5.50 4.00

The surtax was for Child Welfare.

Arms & Marshal's Baton — SP43

1958, July 20
B96 SP43 20fr +5fr ultra, car & grn 2.50 2.00

Marshal de Lattre Foundation.

Independent State

Clasped Hands, Wheat, Olive Branch — SP44

1963, May 27 Unwmk. *Perf. 13*
B97 SP44 50c +20c sl grn, brt grn & car 1.10 .65

Surtax for the Natl. Solidarity Fund.

Burning Books — SP45

1965, June 7 Engr. *Perf. 13*
B98 SP45 20c +5c ol grn, red & blk .50 .40

Burning of the Library of Algiers, 6/7/62.

Soldiers and Woman Comforting Wounded Soldier — SP46

1966, Aug. 20 Photo. *Perf. 11½*
B99 SP46 30c +10c multi 1.25 .70
B100 SP46 95c +10c multi 1.75 1.25

Day of the Moudjahid (Moslem volunteers).

Red Crescent, Boy and Girl — SP47

1967, May 27 Litho. *Perf. 14*
B101 SP47 30c +10c brt grn, brn & car .85 .50

Algerian Red Crescent Society.

SP48

Flood Victims — SP48a

1969, Nov. 15 Typo. *Perf. 10½*
B102 SP48 30c +10c multi .70 .50

Litho.
B103 SP48a 95c +25c multi 1.60 .95

Red Crescent Flag — SP49

1971, May 17 Engr. *Perf. 10½*
B104 SP49 30c +10c slate grn & car .70 .40

Algerian Red Crescent Society.

Intl. Children's Day — SP50

1989, June 1 Litho. *Perf. 10½x11*
B105 SP50 1d +30c multi .70 .55

Surtax for child welfare.

Solidarity with Palestinians — SP51

1990, Dec. 9 Litho. *Perf. 10½x11*
B106 SP51 1d +30c multi .70 .45

Natl. Solidarity with Education — SP52

1995, Sept. 20 Litho. *Perf. 13x14*
B107 SP52 3d +50c multi .60 .30

Red Crescent Society — SP53

1998, May 2 Litho. *Perf. 13x13¼*
B108 SP53 5d +1d multi .50 .30

World Children's Day — SP54

No. B110, Flower, child, adult, vert.

1998, June 1 *Perf. 14x13½, 13½x14*
B109 SP54 5d +1d shown .50 .25
B110 SP54 5d +1d multi .50 .25

Flood Victim Relief — SP55

2001, Dec. 24 Litho. *Perf. 13¼x14*
B111 SP55 5d +5d multi 1.00 .75

Earthquake Relief — SP56

2003, Dec. 3 Litho. *Perf. 13¼x14*
B112 SP56 5d +5d multi .90 .90

TeleFood — SP57

Children's drawings with: No. B113, 5d+1d, Blue frame. No. B114, 5d+1d, Pink frame.

Perf. 14, 14x13½ (#B114)
2004, Oct. 16 Litho.
B113-B114 SP57 Set of 2 1.00 1.00

AIR POST STAMPS

Catalogue values for unused stamps in this section are for Never Hinged items.

Plane over Algiers Harbor — AP1

Two types of 20fr:
Type I — Monogram "F" without serifs. "POSTE" indented 3mm.
Type II — Monogram "F" with serifs. "POSTE" indented 4½mm.

Unwmk.
1946, June 20 Engr. *Perf. 13*

C1	AP1	5fr red	.30	.25
C2	AP1	10fr deep blue	.30	.25
C3	AP1	15fr deep green	1.20	.40
C4	AP1	20fr brown (II)	1.10	.25
C4A	AP1	20fr brown (I)	225.00	140.00
C5	AP1	25fr violet	1.40	.25
C6	AP1	40fr gray black	1.60	.65
		Nos. C1-C4,C5-C6 (6)	5.90	2.05

For surcharges see Nos. C7, CB1-CB2.

No. C1 Surcharged in Black

1947, Jan. 18

C7	AP1 (4.50fr) on 5fr red	.35	.25
a.	Inverted surcharge	800.00	600.00
b.	Double surcharge	1,000.	700.00
c.	Pair, one without surcharge	1,200.	

Storks over Mosque AP2

Plane over Village AP3

1949-53

C8	AP2	50fr green	4.50	.90
C9	AP3	100fr brown	3.50	.65
C10	AP2	200fr bright red	10.50	5.25
C11	AP3	500fr ultra ('53)	32.50	20.00
		Nos. C8-C11 (4)	51.00	26.80

Beni Bahdel Dam — AP4

1957, July 1 Unwmk. *Perf. 13*
C12 AP4 200fr dark red 9.50 2.00

Independent State

Caravelle over Ghardaia AP5

Designs: 2d, Caravelle over El Oued. 5d, Caravelle over Tipasa.

1967-68 Engr. *Perf. 13*

C13	AP5	1d lil, org brn & emer	1.40	.60
C14	AP5	2d brt bl, org brn & emer	3.25	1.40
C15	AP5	5d brt bl, grn & org brn ('68)	8.50	3.25
		Nos. C13-C15 (3)	13.15	5.25

Plane over Casbah, Algiers — AP6

Designs: 3d, Plane over Oran. 4d, Plane over Rhumel Gorge.

1971-72 Photo. *Perf. 12½*

C16	AP6	2d grysh blk & multi	2.50	1.00
C17	AP6	3d violet & blk	3.75	1.60
C18	AP6	4d blk & multi	4.25	2.00
		Nos. C16-C18 (3)	10.50	4.60

Issued: 2d, 6/12/71; 3d, 4d, 2/28/72.

Storks and Plane — AP7

1979, Mar. 24 Photo. *Perf. 11½*

C19	AP7	10d multi	6.50	2.50

Plane Approaching Coastal City — AP8

1991, Apr. 26 Litho. *Perf. 13½*

C20	AP8	10d shown	3.00	1.50
C21	AP8	20d Plane over city	6.00	3.00

Plane Over Djidjelli Corniche — AP9

1993, Sept. 25 Engr. *Perf. 13½x14*

C22	AP9	50d blue, grn & brn	6.75	3.25

AIR POST SEMI-POSTAL STAMPS

Catalogue values for unused stamps in this section are for Never Hinged items.

No. C2 Surcharged in Carmine

1947, June 18 *Perf. 13*

CB1	AP1	10fr +10fr deep blue	2.50	1.75

7th anniv. of Gen. Charles de Gaulle's speech in London, June 18, 1940.

No. C1 Surcharged in Blue

1948, June 18

CB2	AP1	5fr +10fr red	2.50	1.75

8th anniv. of Gen. Charles de Gaulle's speech in London, June 18, 1940.

Monument, Clock Tower and Plane — SPAP1

1949, Nov. 10 Engr. Unwmk.

CB3	SPAP1	15fr +20fr dk brn	7.00	5.25

25th anniv. of Algeria's 1st postage stamps.

POSTAGE DUE STAMPS

D1

Perf. 14x13½

1926-27 Typo. Unwmk.

J1	D1	5c light blue	.40	.30
J2	D1	10c dk brn	.40	.30
J3	D1	20c olive grn	.80	.30
J4	D1	25c car rose	.80	.65
J5	D1	30c rose red	1.20	.50
J6	D1	45c blue grn	1.60	.65
J7	D1	50c brn vio	.80	.25
J8	D1	60c green ('27)	3.25	.90
J9	D1	1fr red brn, *straw*	.40	.30
J10	D1	2fr lil rose ('27)	.80	.30
J11	D1	3fr deep blue ('27)	.80	.30
		Nos. J1-J11 (11)	11.25	4.75

See Nos. J25-J26, J28-J32. For surcharges, see Nos. J18-J20.

D2

1926-27

J12	D2	1c olive grn	.40	.40
J13	D2	10c violet	1.60	.80
J14	D2	30c bister	1.60	.80
J15	D2	60c dull red	1.20	.80
J16	D2	1fr brt vio ('27)	20.00	4.00
J17	D2	2fr lt bl ('27)	16.00	1.60
		Nos. J12-J17 (6)	40.80	8.40

See note below France No. J51. For surcharges, see Nos. J21-J24.

Stamps of 1926 Surcharged

1927

J18	D1	60c on 20c olive grn	2.00	.80
J19	D1	2fr on 45c blue grn	2.75	1.60
J20	D1	3fr on 25c car rose	1.60	.80
		Nos. J18-J20 (3)	6.35	3.20

Recouvrement Stamps of 1926 Surcharged

1927-32

J21	D2	10c on 30c bis ('32)	5.50	4.00
J22	D2	1fr on 1c olive grn	4.00	1.60
J23	D2	1fr on 60c dl red ('32)	24.00	.80
J24	D2	2fr on 10c violet	16.00	12.00
		Nos. J21-J24 (4)	49.50	18.40

Catalogue values for unused stamps in this section, from this point to the end of the section, are for Never Hinged items.

Type of 1926, Without "R F"

1942 Typo. *Perf. 14x13½*

J25	D1	30c dark red	1.25	1.25
J26	D1	2fr magenta	1.75	*2.75*

Type of 1926 Surcharged in Red

1944 *Perf. 14x13½*

J27	A2	50c on 20c yel grn	1.00	.70
a.		Inverted surcharge	27.50	
b.		Double surcharge	70.00	

No. J27 was issued precanceled only. See note after No. 32.

Type of 1926

1944 Litho. *Perf. 12*

J28	D1	1.50fr brt rose lilac	1.00	.50
J29	D1	2fr greenish blue	1.25	.90
J30	D1	5fr rose carmine	1.25	1.10
		Nos. J28-J30 (3)	3.50	2.50

Type of 1926

1947 Typo. *Perf. 14x13½*

J32	D1	5fr green	2.50	1.25

France Nos. J80-J81 Overprinted in Carmine or Black

1947

J33	D5	10c sepia (C)	.50	.25
J34	D5	30c bright red violet	.65	.25

D3

Perf. 14x13

1947-55 Unwmk. Engr.

J35	D3	20c red	.70	.35
J36	D3	60c ultra	1.00	.45
J37	D3	1fr dk org brn	.50	.35
J38	D3	1.50fr dull green	1.50	1.10
J39	D3	2fr red	.70	.35
J40	D3	3fr violet	.75	.45
J41	D3	5fr ultra ('49)	1.10	.35
J42	D3	6fr black	.85	.45
J43	D3	10fr lil rose	1.40	.45
J44	D3	15fr ol grn ('55)	1.40	1.25
J45	D3	20fr brt grn	1.10	.85
J46	D3	30fr red org ('55)	2.50	1.50
J47	D3	50fr indigo ('51)	4.75	2.75
J48	D3	100fr brt bl ('53)	17.50	8.50
		Nos. J35-J48 (14)	35.75	19.15

Independent State

France Nos. J93-J97 Overprinted in Black

Perf. 14x13½

1962, July 2 Typo. Unwmk.

Handstamped Overprint

J49	D6	5c bright pink	7.00	7.00
J50	D6	10c red orange	7.00	7.00
J51	D6	20c olive bister	7.00	7.00
J52	D6	50c dark green	10.00	10.00
J53	D6	1fr deep green	14.00	14.00
		Nos. J49-J53 (5)	45.00	45.00

Typographed Overprint

J49a	D6	5c bright pink	23.00	17.00
J50a	D6	10c red orange	23.00	17.00
J51a	D6	20c olive bister	23.00	17.00
J52a	D6	50c dark green	50.00	35.00
J53a	D6	1fr deep green	70.00	55.00
		Nos. J49a-J53a (5)	189.00	141.00

See note after No. 290.

Scales — D4

1963, June 25 *Perf. 14x13½*

J54	D4	5c car rose & blk	.25	.25
J55	D4	10c olive & car	.25	.25
J56	D4	20c ultra & blk	.55	.30
J57	D4	50c bister brn & grn	1.25	.80
J58	D4	1fr lilac & org	2.25	2.00
		Nos. J54-J58 (5)	4.55	3.60

No. J58 Surcharged with New Value & 3 Bars

1968, Mar. 28 Typo. *Perf. 14x13½*

J59	D4	60c on 1fr lilac & org	1.25	1.00

Grain — D5

1972-93 Litho. *Perf. 13½x14*

J60	D5	10c bister	.25	.25
J61	D5	20c deep brown	.25	.25
J62	D5	40c orange	.25	.25
J63	D5	50c dk vio blue	.30	.25
J64	D5	80c dk olive gray	.75	.30
J65	D5	1d green	.90	.55
a.		yel green, perf. 14¼x14	.25	.25
J66	D5	2d blue	1.75	1.00
a.		Prus bl, perf. 14¼x14	.25	.25
J67	D5	3d violet	.50	.25
J68	D5	4d lilac rose	.65	.35
		Nos. J60-J68 (9)	5.60	3.45

Issued: 3d, 4d, 1/21/93; others, 10/21/72.

Nos. J65a is inscribed "B ALGERIE" at bottom right. No. J66a is inscribed "B ALGERIE" or "BC ALGERIE."

Main Post Office, Algiers — D6

2006, Mar. 28 Litho. *Perf. 13¾x14*

J69	D6	5d green	.90	.90
J70	D6	10d blue	1.60	1.60

NEWSPAPER STAMPS

Nos. 1 and 33 Surcharged in Red

1924-26 Unwmk. *Perf. 14x13½*

P1	A16	½c on 1c dk gray	.40	.40
a.		Triple surcharge	300.00	
P2	A1	½c on 1c olive ('26)	.40	.40

PARCEL POST STAMPS

Inscribed "I APPORT A LA GARE" — PP1

1899 Typo. *Perf. 11½x11*

Q1	PP1	25c blue, *bl*	28.00	22.50
		Never hinged	67.50	

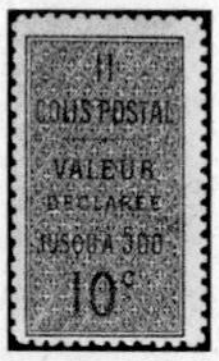

Inscribed "II VALEUR DECLAREE" — PP2

1899 Typo. *Perf. 11½x11*

Q2	PP2	10c black, *yelsh*	125.00	75.00
		Never hinged	275.00	

Inscribed "III LIVRAISON PAR EXPRESS" — PP3

1899 Typo. *Perf. 11½x11*

Q3 PP3 25c lilac		16.00	10.00
Never hinged		35.00	
	Nos. Q1-Q3 (3)	169.00	107.50

Nos. Q1-Q3 were reprinted with minor design and color variations in 1912, 1916 (just the 10c), 1918-20 (25c blue and 10c black), and 1921-23.

Types of 1899 Overprinted in Blue or Black

1924

Q4 PP1 25c blue, *bl* (Blk)	3.75	3.75
Q5 PP2 15c black (Bl)	2.75	2.75
Q6 PP3 60c brown (Blk)	3.75	3.75
Nos. Q4-Q6 (3)	10.25	10.25

Nos. Q4, Q5 and Q6 were not issued without overprint. Nos. Q4 and Q5 were reprinted with minor design and color variations in 1926.

Type of 1899

1924

Q7 PP1 60c blue	350.00
Never hinged	*550.00*
a. Tete beche pair	*3,000.*

Overprinted "CONTROLE REPARTITEUR" in Blue or Black

PP4

1924-27

Q8 PP4 5c green (Blk)	1.80	1.80
Q9 PP4 15c yellow (Bl)	1.80	1.80
Q10 PP4 35c vermilion (Blk)	1.80	1.80
Q11 PP4 60c violet (Bl)	2.25	1.80
Q12 PP4 1fr black (Bl)	2.25	1.80
Nos. Q8-Q12 (5)	9.90	9.00

Nos. Q8-Q12 were not issued without overprint.

"Majoration" indicates an increase in the postal rate.

No. Q6 Surcharged in Black

No. Q13

No. Q14

No. Q13 — Two wide-spaced bars over value, in black.

No. Q14 — Two narrow-spaced bars over value, in black.

1927

Q13 PP3 65c on 60c brown	20.00	20.00
Q14 PP3 65c on 60c brown	7.00	7.00

New Designs With "CONTROLE REPARTITEUR" Overprint in Blue or Black

PP5

No. Q15 Surcharged in Black

PP6

PP7

No. Q22 Surcharged in Black

1927

Q15 PP5 50c black (Bl)	5.00	5.00
Q16 PP5 1.50fr on 50c black	5.00	5.00
Q17 PP5 2fr on 50c black	5.00	5.00
Q18 PP5 2.50fr on 50c black	5.00	5.00
Q19 PP6 95c green (Blk)	7.00	6.00
Q20 PP6 1.40fr green (Blk)	7.00	6.00
Q21 PP6 1.55fr green (Blk)	7.00	6.00
Q22 PP7 50c rose (Blk)	8.00	8.00
Q23 PP7 1.50fr on 50c rose (Blk)	5.00	5,00
Q24 PP7 2fr on 50c rose (Blk)	8.00	8.00
Q25 PP7 2.50fr on 50c rose (Blk)	8.00	8.00
Nos. Q15-Q25 (11)	70.00	62.50

Nos. Q15-Q25 were not issued without overprint.

Nos. Q19-Q21 Surcharged in Black

1929, Jan.

Q26 PP6 1fr on 95c grn (Blk)	4.50	3.50
Q27 PP6 1.50fr on 1.40fr grn (Blk)	4.50	3.50
Q28 PP6 1.65fr on 1.55fr grn (Blk)	4.50	4.50
Nos. Q26-Q28 (3)	13.50	11.50

1929, July

Q29 PP6 1.05fr on 95c grn (Blk)	6.00	6.00
Q30 PP6 1.60fr on 1.40fr grn (Blk)	6.00	6.00
Q31 PP6 1.75fr on 1.55fr grn (Blk)	6.00	6.00
Nos. Q29-Q31 (3)	18.00	18.00

1930

Three types of the 1.15fr surcharge and two types of the 1.85fr surcharge exist.

1.15fr SURCHARGE:
Type I — slanted serif on "1" of "15".
Type II — straight serif on "1" of "15".
Type III — heavily curved serif on "5" of "15".
1.85fr SURCHARGE:
Type I — narrow curved top on "5" of "85".
Type II — heavily curved top on "5" of "85".

Q32 PP6 1.15fr on 95c grn (Blk) (I)	3.50	3.50
a. Type II	13.00	13.00
b. Type III	45.00	45.00
Q33 PP6 1.70fr on 1.40fr grn (Blk)	6.00	6.00
Q34 PP6 1.85fr on 1.55fr grn (Blk) (I)	4.50	4.50
b. Type III	45.00	45.00
Nos. Q32-Q34 (3)	14.00	14.00

Nos. Q19-Q20 Surcharged in Black

Two types of the 2fr surcharge exist.
Type I — narrow "2".
Type II — thick "2".
Three types of the 2.25fr surcharge exist.
Type I — narrow "2.25".
Type II — raised "25".
Type III — thick "2.25".

1932

Q35 PP6 1.50fr on 95c grn (Blk)	35.00	35.00
Q36 PP6 2fr on 1.40fr grn (Blk) (I)	32.50	32.50
a. Type II	72.50	72.50
Q37 PP6 2.25fr on 1.55fr grn (Blk)	35.00	35.00
a. Type II	72.50	72.50
b. Type III	82.50	82.50
Nos. Q35-Q37 (3)	102.50	102.50

PP8

1935

Q38 PP8 2c blue	22.50	22.50
Q39 PP8 3.50fr blue	22.50	22.50

Nos. Q38-Q39 were not issued without overprint.

No. Q15 Surcharged

1937

Q40 PP5 60c on 50c black	14.00	14.00
Q41 PP5 1.80fr on 50c black	20.00	20.00
Q42 PP5 2.40fr on 50c black	20.00	20.00
Q43 PP5 3fr on 50c black	20.00	20.00
Nos. Q40-Q43 (4)	74.00	74.00

Type of 1927 Overprinted "CONTROLE REPARTITEUR" in Black

Q44 PP6 1.50fr green	35.00	35.00
Q45 PP6 2fr green	35.00	35.00
Q46 PP6 2.25fr green	35.00	35.00
Nos. Q44-Q46 (3)	105.00	105.00

Nos. Q44-Q46 were not issued without overprint.

Nos. Q38-Q39 Surcharged

Q47 PP8 2.25fr on 2fr blue	14.50	14.50
a. 2.25fr on 3.50fr blue (error)	1,450.	1,200.
Q48 PP8 4.25fr on 3.50fr blue	14.50	14.50
a. 4.25fr on 2fr blue (error)	1,450.	1,200.

Stamps Inscribed "VALEUR DECLAREE" Overprinted "CONTROLE REPARTITEUR" in Blue

PP9

1938

Q49 PP9 60c black	25.00	25.00
Q50 PP9 1.80fr black	25.00	25.00
Q51 PP9 2.40fr black	25.00	25.00
Q52 PP9 3fr black	25.00	25.00
Nos. Q49-Q52 (4)	100.00	100.00

Nos. Q49-Q52 were not issued without overprint.

Nos. Q44-Q46 Surcharged in Black and Overprinted "CONTROLE REPARTITEUR" in Blue or Black

1938

Q53 PP6 2fr on 1.50fr grn	10.00	10.00
Q54 PP6 2.50fr on 2fr grn	9.00	9.00
Q55 PP6 3fr on 2.25fr grn	9.00	9.00
Nos. Q53-Q55 (3)	28.00	28.00

Overprinted "CONTROLE REPARTITEUR" in Blue

1938

Q56 PP8 2.25fr dk blue	26.00	26.00
Q57 PP8 4.25fr dk blue	26.00	26.00

Nos. Q56-Q57 were not issued without overprint.

Type of 1938 Overprinted "CONTROLE" in Violet

1939

Q58 PP9 60c black	18.00	18.00
Q59 PP9 1.80fr black	26.00	26.00
Q60 PP9 2.40fr black	26.00	26.00
Q61 PP9 3fr black	26.00	26.00
Nos. Q58-Q61 (4)	96.00	96.00

Nos. Q58-Q61 were not issued without overprint.

Type of 1938 Surcharged in Black and Overprinted "CONTROLE" in Violet

1939

Q62 PP6 2fr on 1.50fr grn	22.50	22.50
Q63 PP6 2.50fr on 2fr grn	22.50	22.50
Q64 PP6 3fr on 2.25fr grn	22.50	22.50
Nos. Q62-Q64 (3)	67.50	67.50

Nos. Q62-Q64 were not issued without overprint.

Overprinted "CONTROLE" in Violet

Inscribed "C.F.A. COLIS POSTAL REMBOURSEMENT DOMICILE" — PP10

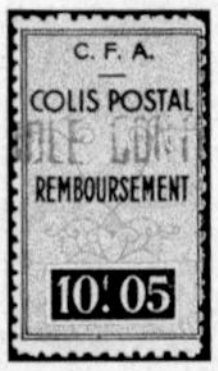

Inscribed "C.F.A. COLIS POSTAL REMBOURSEMENT" PP11

1939

Q65 PP10 2fr yel & org	18.00	18.00
Q66 PP11 3.80fr vio & blk	18.00	18.00
Q67 PP11 5.05fr vio & blk	18.00	18.00
Q68 PP11 7.55fr vio & blk	18.00	18.00
Q69 PP11 10.05fr vio & blk	18.00	18.00
Q70 PP11 15.05fr vio & blk	18.00	18.00
Nos. Q65-Q70 (6)	108.00	108.00

Nos. Q65-Q70 were not issued without overprint.

Type of 1935 Overprinted "CONTROLE" in Violet

1939

Q71 PP8 2.25fr dk blue 26.00 26.00
Q72 PP8 4.25fr dk blue 26.00 26.00
Nos. Q65-Q70 (6) 108.00 108.00

Nos. Q71-Q72 were not issued without overprint.

Catalogue values for unused stamps in this section, from this point to the end of the section, are for Never Hinged items.

No. Q58 Surcharged in Black or Red

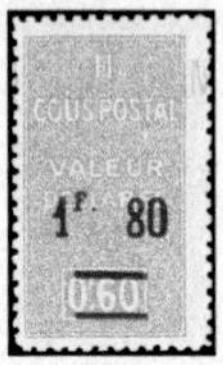

1941

Q73 PP9 1.80fr on 60c blk (Blk) 10.00 5.00
a. Tete beche pair 140.00
Q74 PP9 1.80fr on 60c blk (R) 10.00 5.00

No. Q45-Q46 Surcharged in Violet

1941

Q75 PP6 2.20fr on 2fr grn 35.00 20.00
Q76 PP6 2.80fr on 2fr grn 28.00 17.50
a. Imperf. 100.00
Q77 PP6 3.30fr on 2fr grn — 325.00
Q78 PP6 2.20fr on 2.25fr grn 210.00 130.00
Q79 PP6 2.80fr on 2.25fr grn 425.00 280.00
a. Imperf. 500.00
Q80 PP6 3.30fr on 2.25fr grn 42.50 25.00
a. Imperf. 105.00
Nos. Q75-Q80 (6) 740.50 797.50

Nos. Q65-Q70 Surcharged in Black or Red

1941

Q81 PP10 2.20fr on 2fr yel & org 11.00 6.00
Q82 PP11 4.15fr on 3.80fr vio & blk (Blk) 7.00 3.50
Q83 PP11 4.15fr on 3.80fr vio & blk (R) 10.00 6.00
Q84 PP11 5.55fr on 5.05fr vio & blk 21.00 14.00
Q85 PP11 8.25fr on 7.55fr vio & blk 22.00 14.00
Q86 PP11 11.05fr on 10.05fr vio & blk 70.00 42.50
Q87 PP11 16.55fr on 15.05fr vio & blk 70.00 42.50
Nos. Q81-Q87 (7) 211.00 128.50

Nos. Q71, Q72 Surcharged in Black

1941

Q88 PP8 2.40fr on 2.25fr dk bl 15.00 10.00
Q89 PP8 7.20fr on 4.25fr dk bl 15.00 10.00

Nos. Q88 and Q89 were intended for use on bulky packages.

Overprinted "Controle des Recettes" in Violet

Philippeville Railway Station — PP12

1941-42

Q90 PP12 60c black 10.00 7.00
a. Imperf. 32.50
Q91 PP12 1.80fr black 5.00 3.00
a. Imperf. 32.50
Q92 PP12 2.40fr black 22.00 15.00
a. Imperf. 60.00
Q93 PP12 3fr black 17.50 10.00
a. Imperf. 42.50
Nos. Q90-Q93 (4) 54.50 35.00

Overprinted "Controle des Recettes" in Violet

Locomotive and Mountains PP13

1941-42

Q94 PP13 2.20fr yel grn 15.00 10.00
a. Imperf. 42.50
Q95 PP13 2.80fr yel grn 7.00 4.00
Q96 PP13 3.30fr yel grn 7.00 4.00
a. Double impression 75.00
Nos. Q94-Q96 (3) 29.00 18.00

Nos. Q94-Q96 were intended for use on parcels delivered by autorail.

Overprinted "Controle des Recettes" in Violet

Viaduct over Chiffa Gorge — PP14

Locomotive and passenger cars crossing M'raier Oasis — PP15

1941-42

Q97 PP14 2.20fr orange 25.00 17.50
a. Imperf. 75.00
b. Double impression 75.00
Q98 PP15 4.15fr lilac 9.00 6.00
a. Double impression 75.00
Q99 PP15 5.55fr lilac 7.00 4.00
a. Imperf. 37.50
Q100 PP15 8.25fr lilac 14.00 10.00
a. Imperf. 42.50
Q101 PP15 11.05fr lilac 22.00 14.00
a. Double impression 42.50
Q102 PP15 16.55fr lilac 7.00 5.00
a. Imperf. 37.50
b. Double impression 65.00
c. 16.55fr black (error) 950.00
Nos. Q97-Q102 (6) 84.00 56.50

No. Q102c is an error of color; 100 examples were printed.

Type of 1935 Overprinted "Controle des Recettes" in Black

1941-42

Q103 PP8 2.40fr dk bl 5.00 3.00
a. Imperf. 32.50
Q104 PP8 7.20fr dk bl 5.00 3.00
a. Imperf. 32.50

Nos. Q103-Q104 were intended for bulky packages.

No. Q90, Q92, Q93 With Manuscript Surcharge in Red

1943

Q105 PP12 90c on 60c blk 90.00 55.00
Q106 PP12 2.70fr on 2.40fr blk 90.00 55.00
Q107 PP12 6.30fr on 2.40fr blk 90.00 55.00
Q108 PP12 9.90fr on 2.40fr blk 90.00 55.00
Q109 PP12 13.50fr on 3fr blk 90.00 55.00
Q110 PP12 17.10fr on 3fr blk 105.00 55.00
Q111 PP12 20.70fr on 3fr blk 105.00 55.00
a. Imperf. 950.00
Nos. Q105-Q111 (7) 660.00 385.00

Two horizontal bars in red obliterate original denominations.

Q97-Q101 Surcharged With Manuscript Numerals in Red

1943

Q112 PP14 2.70fr on 2.20fr yel brn 90.00 55.00
Q113 PP13 5.80fr on 4.15fr lil 105.00 55.00
Q114 PP13 8fr on 5.55fr lil 105.00 55.00
Q115 PP13 10.30fr on 8.25fr lil 105.00 55.00
Q116 PP13 12.50fr on11.05fr lil 105.00 55.00
Nos. Q112-Q116 (5) 510.00 275.00

Two horizontal bars in red obliterate original denominations.

Type of 1924 Overprinted "Controle Des Recettes" in Black

1943

Q117 PP4 45c lilac 15.00 10.00
a. Imperf. 45.00

"Majoration" indicates an increase in the postal rate.

Type of 1941-42 Overprinted "Controle des Recettes" in Violet

1943

Q118 PP12 90c orange 4.00 2.50
a. Imperf. 18.00
Q119 PP12 1.80fr orange 4.00 2.50
a. Imperf. 18.00
Q120 PP12 2.70fr orange 4.00 2.50
a. Imperf. 18.00
Q121 PP12 6.30fr orange 4.00 2.50
a. Imperf. 18.00
Q122 PP12 9.90fr orange 4.00 2.50
a. Imperf. 18.00
Q123 PP12 13.50fr orange 4.00 2.50
a. Imperf. 18.00
Q124 PP12 17.10fr orange 4.00 2.50
a. Imperf. 18.00
Q125 PP12 20.70fr orange 4.00 3.00
a. Imperf. 18.00
Nos. Q118-Q125 (8) 32.00 20.50

Types of 1941-42 Overprinted "Controle des Recettes" in Violet

1943

Q126 PP13 2.70fr green 15.00 10.00
a. Imperf. 28.00
Q127 PP13 3.90fr green 11.00 7.00
a. Imperf. 30.00
Q128 PP13 4.20fr green 15.00 10.00
a. Imperf. 30.00
Q129 PP15 5.80fr lilac 15.00 10.00
a. Imperf. 30.00
Q130 PP15 8fr lilac 15.00 10.00
a. Imperf. 30.00
Q131 PP15 10.30fr lilac 15.00 10.00
a. Imperf. 30.00
Q132 PP15 12.50fr lilac 15.00 10.00
a. Imperf. 30.00
Q133 PP15 17.40fr lilac 15.00 10.00
a. Imperf. 30.00
Nos. Q126-Q133 (8) 116.00 77.00

Nos. Q126-Q128 were for delivery by autorail. Nos. Q129-Q133 were for delivery by Michelin train.

Type of 1935 Overprinted "Controle des Recettes" in Violet

1943

Q134 PP8 6.50fr dk bl 15.00 10.00
a. Imperf. 30.00
Q135 PP8 9.70fr dk bl 15.00 10.00
a. Imperf. 30.00
Q136 PP8 12.20fr dk bl 18.00 14.00
a. Imperf. 30.00
Nos. Q134-Q136 (3) 48.00 34.00

Nos. Q134-Q136 were intended for use on bulky parcels.

Nos. Q126-Q133 Surcharged in Black

1944

Q137 PP13 3.20fr on 2.70fr grn 11.00 7.00
a. Imperf. 30.00
Q138 PP13 4.60fr on 3.90fr grn 21.00 15.00
Q139 PP13 4.90fr on 4.20fr grn 15.00 10.00
Q140 PP15 6.20fr on 5.80fr lil 25.00 15.00
Q141 PP15 8.40fr on 8fr lil 25.00 15.00
a. Surcharge inverted 60.00
b. Dbl. surch., one invtd. 70.00
Q142 PP15 10.70fr on 10.30fr lil 25.00 15.00
Q143 PP15 12.90fr on 12.50fr lil 15.00 10.00
Q144 PP15 18.60fr on 17.40fr lil 4.00 2.50
Nos. Q137-Q144 (8) 141.00 89.50

Four vertical bars obliterate the original denominations of Nos. Q137-Q144.

Nos. Q137-Q139 were for delivery by autorail. Nos. Q140-Q144 were for delivery by Michelin train.

Nos. Q134-Q136 Surcharged in Black

1944

Q145 PP8 7.60fr on 6.50fr dk bl 15.00 10.00
a. Imperf. 30.00
Q146 PP8 11.30fr on 9.70fr dk bl 11.00 7.00
a. Imperf. 30.00
Q147 PP8 14.20fr on 12.20fr dk bl 11.00 7.00
a. Imperf. 30.00
Nos. Q145-Q147 (3) 37.00 24.00

Nos. Q145-Q147 were intended for use on bulky parcels. Four vertical bars obliterate the original denominations.

Nos. Q126-Q133 Surcharged in Black

No. Q148

No. Q151

1945

Q148 PP13 4.10fr on 2.70fr grn 3.00 2.00
Q149 PP13 5.20fr on 3.90fr grn 3.00 2.00
Q150 PP13 6.20fr on 4.20fr grn 3.00 2.00
a. Imperf. 18.00
Q151 PP14 7.40fr on 5.80fr lil 3.00 2.00
a. Imperf. 22.00
Q152 PP14 9.60fr on 8fr lil 3.00 2.00
a. Imperf. 22.00
Q153 PP14 11.90fr on 10.30fr lil 3.00 2.00
a. Imperf. 22.00
b. Dbl.surch., one invtd. 75.00
Q154 PP14 14.10fr on 12.50fr lil 3.00 2.00
a. Imperf. 22.00
Nos. Q148-Q154 (7) 21.00 14.00

Four vertical bars obliterate the orginal denominations of Nos. Q148-Q154.

Nos. Q148-Q150 were for delivery by autorail. Nos. Q151-Q154 were for delivery by Michelin train.

Nos. Q134-Q136 Surcharged in Black

No. Q155

1944

Q155 PP8 8.80fr on 6.50fr dk bl 3.00 2.00
a. Imperf. 22.00
Q156 PP8 13.40fr on 9.70fr dk bl 3.00 2.00
a. Imperf. 22.00
Q157 PP8 18fr on 12.20fr dk bl 3.00 2.00
a. Imperf. 22.00
Nos. Q155-Q157 (3) 9.00 6.00

Nos. Q155-Q157 were for use on bulky packages. Four vertical bars obliterate the original denominations.

Type of 1941-42 Overprinted "Controle des Recettes" in Violet

No. Q158

No. Q160

1945-46

Q158 PP13 5.20fr green 3.00 2.00
a. Imperf. 18.00
Q159 PP13 9fr green 3.00 2.00
a. Imperf. 18.00
Q160 PP15 7.30fr lilac 3.00 2.00
a. Imperf. 18.00
Q161 PP15 9.50fr lilac 3.00 2.00
a. Imperf. 18.00
Q162 PP15 11.80fr lilac 3.00 2.00
a. Imperf. 18.00
Q163 PP15 11.80fr lilac 3.00 2.00
a. Imperf. 18.00

Q164 PP15 18.60fr lilac 3.50 2.00
a. Imperf. 18.00
Q165 PP15 25fr lilac 3.50 2.00
a. Imperf. 18.00
Nos. Q160-Q165 (6) 19.00 12.00

Nos. Q158-Q159 were for delivery by autorail. Nos. Q160-Q165 were for delivery by Michelin train.

Overprinted "Controle des Recettes" in Violet

Bon Train Station PP16

1945-46

Q166 PP16 12.40fr pale bl, rough impression 3.50 2.00
a. Imperf. 18.00
Q167 PP16 12.40fr pale bl, fine impression 18.00 12.00
a. Imperf. 32.00
Q168 PP16 18.80fr pale bl, rough impression 4.00 3.00
a. Imperf. 18.00
Q169 PP16 18.80fr pale bl, fine impression 15.00 10.00
a. Imperf. 32.00
Q170 PP16 25.20fr pale bl, rough impression 4.00 3.00
a. Imperf. 18.00
Q171 PP16 25.20fr bl, fine impression 17.00 10.00
a. Imperf. 32.00
Nos. Q166-Q171 (6) 61.50 40.00

Nos. Q166-Q171 were intended for use on bulky parcels.

Nos. Q158, Q164, Q166-Q171 Surcharged in Black

No. Q178

1946

Q172 PP13 7fr on 5.20fr grn 3.00 2.00
a. Imperf. 18.00
Q173 PP15 18.50fr on 18.60fr lil 3.00 2.00
a. Imperf. 18.00
b. Double surcharge 60.00
c. Doule surch., one invtd. 70.00
Q174 PP15 20fr on 18.60fr lil 210.00
Q175 PP16 15fr on 12.40fr pale bl 3.00 2.00
a. Imperf. 18.00
Q176 PP16 15fr on 12.40fr bl 16.00 10.00
a. Imperf. 32.00
Q177 PP16 20fr on 18.80fr pale bl 3.00 2.00
a. Imperf. 18.00
Q178 PP16 20fr on 18.80fr bl 16.00 10.00
a. Imperf. 32.00
Q179 PP16 30fr on 25.20fr pale bl 3.00 2.00
a. Imperf. 18.00
Q180 PP16 30fr on 25.20fr bl 16.00 10.00
a. Imperf. 32.00
Nos. Q172-Q180 (9) 273.00 40.00

Four vertical bars obliterate the original denominations of Nos. Q172-Q180.

No. Q172 was for delivery by autorail. Nos. Q173-Q174 were for delivery by Michelin train. Nos. Q175-Q180 were intended for use on bulky packages.

Nos. Q158, Q164, Q166-Q171 Surcharged in Black

No. Q181

No. Q183

No. Q189

1947

Q181 PP13 8fr on 7fr on 5.20fr grn 3.00 2.00
a. Imperf. 25.00
Q182 PP13 10fr on 9fr grn 3.00 2.00
a. Imperf. 25.00
Q183 PP15 8.30fr on 7.30fr lil 3.00 2.00
a. Imperf. 25.00
Q184 PP15 10.50fr on 9.50fr lil 4.00 2.00
a. Imperf. 25.00
Q185 PP15 12.80fr on 11.80fr lil 3.00 2.00
a. Imperf. 25.00
Q186 PP15 15fr on 14fr lil 4.00 2.00
a. Imperf. 25.00
Q187 PP15 19.50fr on 18.50fr on 18.60fr lil 3.00 2.00
a. Imperf. 25.00
Q188 PP15 26fr on 25fr lil 4.00 2.00
a. Imperf. 25.00
Q189 PP16 17fr on 15fr on 12.40fr pale bl 3.00 2.00
a. Imperf. 25.00
Q190 PP16 17fr on 15fr on 12.40fr bl 16.00 11.00
a. Imperf. 39.00
Q191 PP16 23fr on 20fr on 18.80fr pale bl 3.00 2.00
Q192 PP16 23fr on 20fr on 18.80fr bl 16.00 11.00
Q193 PP16 35fr on 30fr on 25.20fr pale bl 3.00 2.00
Q194 PP16 35fr on 30fr on 25.20fr bl 16.00 11.00
Nos. Q181-Q194 (14) 84.00 55.00

Four vertical bars obliterate the original denominations of Nos. Q181-Q194.

Nos. Q181-Q182 were for delivery by autorail. Nos. Q183-Q188 were for delivery by Michelin train. Nos. Q189-Q194 were intended for use on bulky packages.

Nos. Q158, Q164, Q166-Q171 Surcharged in Black

No. Q195

No. Q197

No. Q203

1947

Q195 PP13 10fr on 7fr on 5.20fr grn 3.00 2.00
a. Imperf. 25.00
Q196 PP13 13fr on 9fr grn 3.00 2.00
a. Imperf. 25.00
Q197 PP15 10.30fr on 7.30fr lil 3.00 2.00
a. Imperf. 32.50
Q198 PP15 12.50fr on 9.50fr lil 3.00 2.00
a. Imperf. 32.50
Q199 PP15 14.80fr on 11.80fr lil 3.00 2.00
Q200 PP15 17fr on 14fr lil 3.00 2.00
a. Double surcharge 42.00
Q201 PP15 21.50fr on 18.50fr on 18.60fr lil 3.00 2.00
a. Inverted surcharge 60.00
Q202 PP15 28fr on 25fr lil 4.00 2.00
Q203 PP16 22fr on 15fr on 12.40fr pale bl 3.00 2.00
Q204 PP16 22fr on 15fr on 12.40fr bl 16.00 11.00
Q205 PP16 30fr on 20fr on 18.80fr pale bl 3.00 2.00
Q206 PP16 30fr on 20fr on 18.80fr bl 16.00 11.00
Q207 PP16 46fr on 30fr on 25.20fr pale bl 3.00 2.00
a. Double surcharge 32.50
Q208 PP16 46fr on 30fr on 25.20fr bl 16.00 11.00
Nos. Q195-Q208 (14) 82.00 55.00

Four vertical bars obliterate the original denominations of Nos. Q181-Q194.

Nos. Q195-Q196 were for delivery by autorail. Nos. Q197-Q202 were for delivery by Michelin train. Nos. Q203-Q208 were intended for use on bulky packages.

Nos. Q158, Q164, Q166-Q171 Surcharged in Black

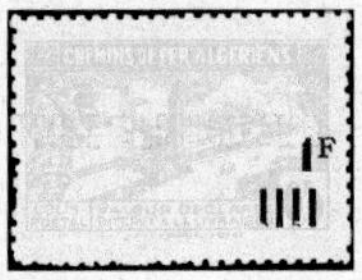

No. Q209

No. Q218

No. Q223

1948-49

Q209 PP12 1fr on 90c yel 3.00 2.00
a. Imperf. 14.00
Q210 PP12 1fr on 13.50fr org 4.00 2.00
a. Imperf. 14.00
Q211 PP12 2fr on 1.80fr org 3.00 2.00
Q212 PP12 3fr on 2.70fr org 3.00 2.00
Q213 PP12 7fr on 6.30fr org 3.00 2.00
Q214 PP12 11fr on 9.90fr org 3.00 2.00
Q215 PP12 15fr on 13.50fr org 3.00 2.00
a. Imperf. 14.00
b. Inverted surcharge 27.50
Q216 PP12 19fr on 17.10fr org 3.00 2.00
a. Imperf. 14.00
Q217 PP12 23fr on 20.70fr org 3.00 2.00
a. Imperf. 14.00
b. Double surcharge 39.00
c. Double surch., one inverted 30.00
Q218 PP15 13fr on 10.30fr on 7.30fr lil 3.00 2.00
Q219 PP15 15fr on 12.50fr on 9.50fr lil 3.00 2.00
Q220 PP15 19fr on 14.80fr on 11.80fr lil 3.00 2.00
a. Imperf. 15.00
Q221 PP15 24fr on 14fr lil 3.00 2.00
a. Imperf. 15.00
Q222 PP15 30fr on 28fr on 25fr lil 3.00 2.00
a. Imperf. 15.00
Q223 PP13 14fr on 4.10fr on 2.70fr grn 3.00 2.00
a. Imperf. 25.00
b. Double surcharge 42.00
Q224 PP13 17fr on 10fr on 9fr grn 3.00 2.00
a. Imperf. 25.00
Q225 PP13 19fr on 9fr grn 3.00 2.00
a. Imperf. 25.00
Nos. Q209-Q225 (17) 52.00 34.00

Four vertical bars obliterate the original denominations of Nos. Q209-Q225.

Nos. Q218-Q222 were for delivery by Michelin train. Nos. Q223-Q225 were for delivery by autorail.

ALLENSTEIN

ˈa-lən-ˌshtin

LOCATION — In East Prussia
AREA — 4,457 sq. mi.
POP. — 540,000 (estimated 1920)
CAPITAL — Allenstein

Allenstein, a district of East Prussia, held a plebiscite in 1920 under the Versailles Treaty, voting to join Germany rather than Poland. Later that year, Allenstein became part of the German Republic.

100 Pfennig = 1 Mark

Stamps of Germany, 1906-20, Overprinted

Perf. 14, 14½, 14x14½, 14½x14

1920 **Wmk. 125**

1 A16 5pf green .45 *1.20*
2 A16 10pf carmine .45 *1.20*
3 A22 15pf dk vio .45 *1.20*
4 A22 15pf vio brn 5.50 *12.00*
5 A16 20pf bl vio .45 *1.75*
6 A16 30pf org & blk, *buff* .45 *1.75*
7 A16 40pf lake & blk .45 *1.20*
8 A16 50pf pur & blk, *buff* .45 *1.20*
9 A16 75pf grn & blk .45 *1.20*
10 A17 1m car rose 1.60 *5.00*
a. Double overprint 250.00 *1,000.*
11 A17 1.25m green 1.60 5.25
a. Double overprint — —
12 A17 1.50m yel brn 1.00 *4.00*
13 A21 2.50m lilac rose 2.50 *10.50*
14 A19 3m blk vio 2.50 *5.25*
a. Double overprint 300.00 *1,050.*
Never hinged 575.00
b. Inverted overprint — —
Nos. 1-14 (14) 18.30 *52.70*
Set, never hinged 52.00

Overprinted

15 A16 5pf green .40 *1.00*
16 A16 10pf carmine .40 *1.00*
17 A22 15pf dark vio .40 *1.00*
18 A22 15pf vio brn 20.00 *40.00*
19 A16 20pf blue vio .65 *1.50*
20 A16 30pf org & blk, *buff* .40 *1.00*
21 A16 40pf lake & blk .40 *1.00*
22 A16 50pf pur & blk, *buff* .40 *1.00*
23 A16 75pf grn & blk .65 *1.50*
24 A17 1m car rose 1.60 3.00
a. Inverted overprint 600.00 *800.00*
Never hinged 800.00
25 A17 1.25m green 1.60 *3.00*
26 A17 1.50m yel brn 1.25 *3.00*
27 A21 2.50m lilac rose 2.75 *7.50*
28 A19 3m blk vio 1.75 3.00
a. Inverted overprint 400.00 *975.00*
Never hinged 725.00
b. Double overprint 200.00 *600.00*
Never hinged 600.00
Nos. 15-28 (14) 32.65 *68.50*
Set, never hinged 80.00

The 40pf carmine rose (Germany No. 124) exists with this oval overprint, but it is doubtful whether it was regularly issued. Value $110 hinged, $210 never hinged.

ANDORRA, SPANISH ADMINISTRATION

an-'dor-ə

LOCATION — On the southern slope of the Pyrenees Mountains between France and Spain.
GOVT. — Co-principality
AREA — 179 sq. mi.
POP. — 72,766 (July 1, 1996)
CAPITAL — Andorra la Vella

Andorra was subject to the joint control of France and the Spanish Bishop of Urgel and paid annual tribute to both. In 1993, Andorra became a constitutional coprincipality, governed by its own parliament.

100 Centimos = 1 Peseta
100 Centimes = 1 Franc
100 Cents = 1 Euro (2002)

Catalogue values for unused stamps in the Spanish Administration for this country are for Never Hinged items, beginning with Scott 50 in the regular postage section and Scott C2 in the airpost section; for the French Administration of this country, Never Hinged items begin at Scott 78 for regular postage, Scott B1 for the semi-postal section, Scott C1 for the airpost section, and Scott J21 for the postage due section.

A majority of the Spanish Andorra stamps issued to about 1950 are poorly centered. The fine examples that are valued will be somewhat off center. Very poorly centered examples (perfs cutting design) sell for less. Well centered very fine stamps are scarce and sell for approximately twice the values shown (Nos. 1-24, E1-E3), or 50% more (Nos. 25-49, E4-E5).

Stamps of Spain, 1922-26, Overprinted in Red or Black

Perf. 13½x12½, 12½x11½, 14

1928 **Unwmk.**

1	A49	2c olive green	.55	.55

Control Numbers on Back

2	A49	5c car rose (Bk)	.80	.80
3	A49	10c green	.80	.80
4	A49	15c slate blue	3.25	3.25
5	A49	20c violet	3.25	3.50
6	A49	25c rose red (Bk)	3.25	3.50
b.		Inverted ovpt., perf 14	130.00	—
7	A49	30c black brown	18.00	16.50
b.		Inverted ovpt., perf 12½x11½	130.00	50.00
8	A49	40c deep blue	18.00	11.00
9	A49	50c orange (Bk)	18.00	14.50
c.		Inverted ovpt., perf 14	130.00	—
10	A49a	1p blue blk	23.00	*23.50*
11	A49a	4p lake (Bk)	150.00	*175.00*
12	A49a	10p brown (Bk)	275.00	275.00
a.		Double overprint	*700.00*	
		Nos. 1-12 (12)	513.90	527.90
		Set, never hinged	1,200.	

Counterfeit overprints exist.

Nos. 1-12 perf 14 are worth much more. See the *Scott Classic Specialized Catalogue.*

La Vall
A1

St. Juan de Caselles
A2

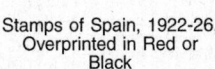

St. Julia de Loria
A3

St. Coloma
A4

General Council — A5

1929, Nov. 25 **Engr.** ***Perf. 14***

13	A1	2c olive green	1.10	.60

Control Numbers on Back

14	A2	5c carmine lake	3.50	1.25
15	A3	10c yellow green	3.50	*4.50*
16	A4	15c slate green	3.50	*4.50*
17	A3	20c violet	3.50	*4.50*
18	A4	25c carmine rose	7.75	6.25
19	A1	30c olive brown	115.00	*175.00*
20	A2	40c dark blue	4.50	3.00
21	A3	50c deep orange	5.50	4.50
22	A5	1p slate	12.50	14.50
23	A5	4p deep rose	90.00	*110.00*
24	A5	10p bister brown	100.00	*140.00*
		Nos. 13-24 (12)	350.35	*468.60*
		Set, never hinged	800.00	

Nos. 13-24 exist imperforate with control numbers on the back. Value, $2,200 unused; $3,150 never hinged.

1931-38 ***Perf. 11½***

13a	A1	2c	6.25	.80

Control Numbers on Back

14a	A2	5c	10.00	2.25
15a	A3	10c	10.00	2.00
16a	A4	15c	30.00	25.00
17a	A3	20c	10.00	6.00
18a	A4	25c	10.00	6.00
19a	A1	30c ('33)	175.00	65.00
20a	A2	40c ('35)	17.00	13.00
22a	A5	1p ('38)	40.00	25.00
		Nos. 13a-22a (9)	308.25	145.05
		Set, never hinged	500.00	

Without Control Numbers

1936-43 ***Perf. 11½x11***

25	A1	2c red brown ('37)	2.00	1.60
26	A2	5c dark brown	2.00	1.60
27	A3	10c blue green	13.00	3.25
a.		10c yellow green	150.00	80.00
		Never hinged	200.00	
28	A4	15c blue green ('37)	7.50	3.50
a.		15c yellow green	8.00	5.75
29	A3	20c violet	7.00	3.50
30	A4	25c deep rose ('37)	3.25	*3.25*
31	A1	30c carmine	5.50	3.25
31A	A2	40c dark blue	*750.00*	—
		Never hinged	1,250.	
32	A1	45c rose red ('37)	2.00	1.60
33	A3	50c deep orange	10.00	5.75
34	A1	60c deep blue ('37)	7.00	3.50
34A	A5	1p slate	*1,000.*	—
		Never hinged	*2,000.*	
35	A5	4p deep rose ('43)	40.00	*47.50*
36	A5	10p bister brn ('43)	52.50	*57.50*
		Nos. 25-31,32-34,35-36 (12)	151.75	135.80
		Set, never hinged	325.00	

Exist imperforate. Value hinged, $275.

Beware of counterfeits of Nos. 31A and 34A. Purchase of stamps with certificates is strongly advised.

Edelweiss
A6

Provost
A7

Coat of Arms
A8

Plaza of Ordino
A9

Chapel of Meritxell
A10

Map
A11

1948-53 **Unwmk.** **Photo.** ***Perf. 12½***

37	A6	2c brn olive ('51)	.35	.35
38	A6	5c orange ('53)	.35	.35
39	A6	10c blue ('53)	.35	.35

Engr. ***Perf. 9½x10***

40	A7	20c brown vio	4.25	2.75
41	A7	25c org, perf. 12½ ('53)	3.00	2.10
42	A8	30c dk slate grn	4.25	3.25
43	A9	50c deep green	5.00	4.75
44	A10	75c dark blue	6.50	4.75
45	A9	90c dp car rose	3.50	3.50
46	A10	1p brt orange ver	5.00	4.25
47	A8	1.35p dk blue vio	3.50	3.50

Perf. 10

48	A11	4p ultra ('53)	4.75	*8.50*
49	A11	10p dk vio brn ('51)	11.00	11.00
		Nos. 37-49 (13)	51.80	49.40
		Set, never hinged	120.00	

Catalogue values for unused stamps in this section, from this point to the end of the section, are for Never Hinged items.

Bridge of St. Anthony
A12

Madonna of Meritxell, 8th Century
A13

Designs: 70c, Aynos pasture. 1p, View of Canillo. 2p, St. Coloma. 2.50p, Arms of Andorra. 3p, Old Andorra, horiz. 5p, View of Ordino, horiz.

1963-64 **Unwmk.** **Engr.** ***Perf. 13***

50	A12	25c dk gray & sepia	.30	.25
51	A12	70c dk sl grn & brn blk	.40	.35
52	A12	1p slate & dull pur	.85	.45
53	A12	2p violet & dull pur	.85	.50
54	A12	2.50p rose claret	.85	.70
55	A12	3p blk & grnsh gray	1.60	.80
56	A12	5p dk brn & choc	2.50	1.25
57	A13	6p sepia & car	3.50	2.75
		Nos. 50-57 (8)	10.85	7.05

Issued: 25c-2p, 7/20/63; 2.50p-6p, 2/29/64.

Narcissus — A14

1966, June 10 **Engr.** ***Perf. 13***

58	A14	50c shown	.85	.50
59	A14	1p Pinks	.85	.50
60	A14	5p Jonquils	2.50	1.50
61	A14	10p Hellebore	1.75	1.00
		Nos. 58-61 (4)	5.95	3.50

Common Design Types pictured following the introduction.

Europa Issue 1972

Common Design Type

1972, May 2 **Photo.** ***Perf. 13***

Size: 25½x38mm

62	CD15	8p multicolored	*60.00*	*60.00*

Encamp Valley — A15

Tourist publicity: 1.50p, Massana (village). 2p, Skiing on De La Casa Pass. 5p, Pessons Lake, horiz.

1972, July 4 **Photo.** ***Perf. 13***

63	A15	1p multicolored	.50	.40
64	A15	1.50p multicolored	.75	.40
65	A15	2p multicolored	2.25	1.00
66	A15	5p multicolored	3.00	1.10
		Nos. 63-66 (4)	6.50	2.90

Butterfly Stroke — A16

Design: 2p, Volleyball, vert.

1972, Oct. **Photo.** ***Perf. 13***

67	A16	2p lt blue & multi	.35	.35
68	A16	5p multicolored	.55	.55

20th Olympic Games, Munich, 8/26-9/11.

St. Anthony Singers — A17

1.50p, Les Caramelles (boys' choir). 2p, Nativity scene. 5p, Man holding giant cigar, vert. 8p, Hermit of Meritxell, vert. 15p, Marratxa dancers.

1972, Dec. 5 **Photo.** ***Perf. 13***

69	A17	1p multicolored	.35	.25
70	A17	1.50p multicolored	.35	.25
71	A17	2p multicolored	.45	.35
72	A17	5p multicolored	.60	.45
73	A17	8p multicolored	.90	.50
74	A17	15p multicolored	1.75	1.10
		Nos. 69-74 (6)	4.40	2.90

Andorran customs. No. 71 is for Christmas.

Europa Issue 1973

Common Design Type and

Symbol of Unity — A18

1973, Apr. 30 **Photo.** ***Perf. 13***

75	A18	2p ultra, red & blk	*.40*	*.25*

Size: 37x25mm

76	CD16	8p tan, red & blk	*1.25*	*.85*

Nativity — A19

Christmas: 5p, Adoration of the Kings. Designs are from altar panels of Meritxell Parish Church.

1973, Dec. 14 **Photo.** ***Perf. 13***

77	A19	2p multicolored	.40	.30
78	A19	5p multicolored	1.25	1.00

Virgin of Ordino — A20

Europa: 8p, Les Banyes Cross.

1974, Apr. 29 Photo. *Perf. 13*

79	A20	2p multicolored	*.90*	*.70*
80	A20	8p slate & brt blue	*2.75*	*1.75*

Cupboard
A21

Crowns of Virgin and Child of Roser
A22

1974, July 30 Photo. *Perf. 13*

81	A21	10p multicolored	2.00	1.60
82	A22	25p dark red & multi	3.75	3.25

UPU Monument, Bern — A23

1974, Oct. 9 Photo. *Perf. 13*

83	A23	15p multicolored	1.75	1.75

Centenary of Universal Postal Union.

Nativity — A24

Christmas: 5p, Adoration of the Kings.

1974, Dec. 4 Photo. *Perf. 13*

84	A24	2p multicolored	.80	.70
85	A24	5p multicolored	1.90	1.60

Mail Delivery, Andorra, 19th Century — A25

1975, Apr. 4 Photo. *Perf. 13*

86	A25	3p multicolored	.45	.45

Espana 75 Intl. Philatelic Exhibition, Madrid, 4/4-13.

12th Century Painting, Ordino Church — A26

Design: 12p, Christ in Glory, 12th century Romanesque painting, Ordino church.

1975, Apr. 28 Photo. *Perf. 13*

87	A26	3p multicolored	*1.25*	*.70*
88	A26	12p multicolored	*2.25*	*1.40*

Urgel Cathedral and Document — A27

1975, Oct. 4 Photo. *Perf. 13*

89	A27	7p multicolored	1.75	1.25

Millennium of consecration of Urgel Cathedral, and Literary Festival 1975.

Nativity, Ordino — A28

Christmas: 7p, Adoration of the Kings, Ordino.

1975, Dec. 3 Photo. *Perf. 13*

90	A28	3p multicolored	.40	.40
91	A28	7p multicolored	.85	.85

Caldron and CEPT Emblem — A29

Europa: 12p, Chest and CEPT emblem.

1976, May 3 Photo. *Perf. 13*

92	A29	3p bister & multi	*.40*	.25
93	A29	12p yel & multi, horiz.	*1.00*	.50

Slalom and Montreal Olympic Emblem — A30

Design: 15p, One-man canoe and Montreal Olympic emblem, horiz.

1976, July 9 Photo. *Perf. 13*

94	A30	7p multicolored	.45	.25
95	A30	15p multicolored	.90	.40

21st Olympic Games, Montreal, Canada, July 17-Aug. 1.

Nativity — A31

Christmas: 25p, Adoration of the Kings. Wall paintings in La Massana Church.

1976, Dec. 7 Photo. *Perf. 13*

96	A31	3p multicolored	.50	.25
97	A31	25p multicolored	1.00	.35

View of Ansalonge
A32

Europa: 12p, Xuclar, valley, mountains.

1977, May 2 Litho. *Perf. 13*

98	A32	3p multicolored	*.35*	.25
99	A32	12p multicolored	*.90*	.40

Cross of Terme — A33

Christmas: 12p, Church of St. Miguel d'Engolasters.

1977, Dec. 2 Photo. *Perf. 13x12½*

100	A33	5p multicolored	.45	.35
101	A33	12p multicolored	1.10	.65

Souvenir Sheet

A34

Designs: 5p, Map of Post Offices. 10p, Mail delivery. 20p, Post Office, 1928. 25p, Andorran coat of arms.

1978, Mar. 31 Photo. *Perf. 13x13½*

102	A34	Sheet of 4	1.60	1.60
a.		5p multicolored	.35	.35
b.		10p multicolored	.35	.35
c.		20p multicolored	.35	.35
d.		25p multicolored	.35	.35

Spanish postal service in Andorra, 50th anniv.

La Vall — A35

Europa: 12p, St. Juan de Caselles.

1978, May 2 *Perf. 13*

103	A35	5p multicolored	*.40*	.25
104	A35	12p multicolored	*.90*	.40

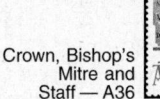

Crown, Bishop's Mitre and Staff — A36

1978, Sept. 24 Photo. *Perf. 13*

105	A36	5p brown, car & yel	.85	.40

700th anniversary of the signing of treaty establishing Co-Principality of Andorra.

Holy Family — A37

Christmas: 25p, Adoration of the Kings. Both designs after frescoes in the Church of St. Mary d'Encamp.

1978, Dec. 5 Photo. *Perf. 13*

106	A37	5p multicolored	.25	.25
107	A37	25p multicolored	.65	.35

Young Woman — A38

Designs: 5p, Young man. 12p, Bridegroom and bride riding mule.

1979, Feb. 14 Photo. *Perf. 13*

108	A38	3p multicolored	.25	.25
109	A38	5p multicolored	.25	.25
110	A38	12p multicolored	.40	.30
		Nos. 108-110 (3)	.90	.80

Old Mail Truck — A39

Europa: 12p, Stampless covers of 1846 & 1854.

1979, Apr. 30 Engr. *Perf. 13*

111	A39	5p yel grn & dk blue	*.40*	.25
112	A39	12p dk red & violet	*.85*	.40

Children Holding Hands — A40

1979, Oct. 18 Photo. *Perf. 13*

113	A40	19p multicolored	.90	.35

International Year of the Child.

St. Coloma's Church — A41

Christmas: 25p, Agnus Dei roundel, St. Coloma's Church.

1979, Nov. 28 Photo. *Perf. 13½*

114	A41	8p multicolored	.25	.25
115	A41	25p multicolored	.70	.40

Bishop Pere d'Arg — A42

Bishops of Urgel: 5p, Josep Caixal. 13p, Joan Benlloch.

1979, Dec. 27 Engr.

116	A42	1p dk blue & brown	.30	.25
117	A42	5p rose lake & purple	.30	.25
118	A42	13p brown & dk green	.30	.30
		Nos. 116-118 (3)	.90	.80

See Nos. 132-133, 159, 175, C4.

Antoni Fiter, Magistrate — A43

Europa: 19p, Francesc Cairat, magistrate.

1980, Apr. 28 Photo. *Perf. 13x13½*

119	A43	8p bister, blk & brn	*.35*	.25
120	A43	19p lt green & blk	*.85*	.40

Boxing, Moscow '80 Emblem — A44

1980, July 23 Photo. *Perf. 13½x13*

121	A44	5p Downhill skiing	.25	.25
122	A44	8p shown	.25	.25
123	A44	50p Target shooting	.80	.40
		Nos. 121-123 (3)	1.30	.90

12th Winter Olympic Games, Lake Placid, NY, Feb. 12-24 (5p); 22nd Summer Olympic Games, Moscow, July 19-Aug. 3.

Nativity — A45

1980, Dec. 12 Litho. *Perf. 13*

124	A45	10p Nativity, vert.	.25	.25
125	A45	22p shown	.65	.30

Christmas 1980.

Children Dancing at Santa Anna Feast — A46

Europa: 30p, Going to church on Aplec de la Verge de Canolich Day.

1981, May 7 Photo. *Perf. 13*

126	A46	12p multicolored	*.40*	.25
127	A46	30p multicolored	*.85*	.40

50th Anniv. of Police Force — A47

1981, July 2 Photo. *Perf. 13½x13*

128	A47	30p multicolored	.85	.35

Intl. Year of the Disabled — A48

1981, Oct. 8 Photo. *Perf. 13½*

129	A48	50p multicolored	1.25	.40

Christmas 1981 — A49

Designs: Encamp Church retable.

1981, Dec. 3 Photo. *Perf. 13½*

130	A49	12p Nativity	.40	.25
131	A49	30p Adoration	.80	.45

Bishops of Urgel Type of 1979

1981, Dec. 12 Engr. *Perf. 13½*

132	A42	7p Salvador Casanas	.30	.25
133	A42	20p Josep de Boltas	.55	.25

Natl. Arms — A51

1982, Feb. 17 Photo. *Perf. 13x13½*

134	A51	1p bright pink	.25	.25
135	A51	3p bister brown	.25	.25
136	A51	7p red orange	.25	.25
137	A51	12p lake	.25	.25
138	A51	15p ultra	.30	.25
139	A51	20p blue green	.40	.40
140	A51	30p crimson rose	.80	.40

Perf. 13½x12½

1982, Sept. 30 Engr.

Size: 25½x30½mm

141	A51	50p dark green	1.00	.40
142	A51	100p dark blue	1.75	.80
		Nos. 134-142 (9)	5.25	3.25

For type A51 without "PTA" see Nos. 192-198.

Europa 1982 — A52

14p, New Reforms, 1866, vert. 33p, Reform of Institutions, 1981.

1982, May 12 Photo. *Perf. 13*

143	A52	14p multicolored	*.35*	.25
144	A52	33p multicolored	*1.00*	.40

1982 World Cup — A53

Designs: Various soccer players.

1982, June 13 Photo. *Perf. 13x13½*

145	A53	14p multicolored	1.05	1.05
146	A53	33p multicolored	1.90	1.90
a.		Pair, #145-146 + label	3.25	3.25

A54

Anniversaries: 9p, Permanent Spanish and French delegations, cent. 14p, 50th anniv. of Andorran stamps, horiz. 23p, St. Francis of Assisi (1182-1226). 33p, Anyos Pro-Vicarial District membership centenary (Relacio sobre la Vall de Andorra titlepage).

1982, Sept. 7 Engr. *Perf. 13*

147	A54	9p dk blue & brown	.30	.25
148	A54	14p black & green	.80	.40
149	A54	23p dk blue & brown	.60	.25
150	A54	33p black & olive grn	.60	.40
		Nos. 147-150 (4)	2.30	1.30

A55 A55a

Christmas: 14p, Madonna and Child, Andorra la Vieille Church, vert. 33p, El Tio de Nadal (children in traditional costumes striking hollow tree).

Perf. 13x13½, 13½x13

1982, Dec. 9 Photo.

151	A55	14p multicolored	.40	.25
152	A55a	33p multicolored	.85	.40

Europa 1983 — A56

16, La Cortinada Church, architect, 12th cent. 38p, Water mill, 16th cent.

1983, June 7 Photo. *Perf. 13*

153	A56	16p multicolored	*.40*	.25
154	A56	38p multicolored	*.85*	.40

Local Mushrooms — A57

16p, Lactarius sanguifluus.

1983, July 20 Photo. *Perf. 13x12½*

155	A57	16p multicolored	.80	.60

See Nos. 165, 169, 172.

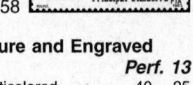

Universal Suffrage, 50th Anniv. — A58

Photogravure and Engraved

1983, Sept. 6 *Perf. 13*

156	A58	10p multicolored	.40	.25

Visit of Monsignor Jacinto Verdaguer Bishop and Co-Prince — A59

1983, Sept. 6

157	A59	50p multicolored	1.00	.55

Christmas 1983 — A60

Saint Cerni de Nagol, Romanesque fresco, Church of San Cerni de Nagol.

1983, Nov. 24 Photo. *Perf. 13½*

158	A60	16p multicolored	.45	.25

Bishops of Urgel Type of 1979

26p, Joan J. Laguarda Fenollera.

1983, Dec. 7 Engr. *Perf. 13*

159	A42	26p multicolored	.80	.40

1984 Winter Olympics — A62

1984, Feb. 17 Litho. *Perf. 13½x14*

160	A62	16p Ski jumping	.80	.25

ESPANA '84 — A63

1984, Apr. 27 Photo. *Perf. 13*

161	A63	26p Emblems	.80	.40

Europa (1959-84) — A64

1984, May 5 Engr.

162	A64	16p brown	*.60*	.25
163	A64	38p blue	*.90*	*.40*

1984 Summer Olympics — A65

1984, Aug. 9 Litho. *Perf. 13½x14*

164	A65	40p Running	1.25	.60

Mushroom Type of 1983

11p, Morchella esculenta.

1984, Sept. 27 Photo. *Perf. 13x12½*

165	A57	11p multicolored	*7.25*	2.00

Christmas 1984 — A66

1984, Dec. 6 Photo. *Perf. 13½*

166	A66	17p Nativity carving	.50	.25

Europa 1985 — A67

18p, Mossen Enric Arfany, composer, natl. hymn score. 45p, Musician Playing Viol, Romanesque fresco detail, La Cortinada Church, vert.

1985, May 3 Engr. *Perf. 13½*

167	A67	18p dk vio, grn & chocolate	*.45*	.25
168	A67	45p green & chocolate	*1.40*	*.40*

Mushroom Type of 1983

Perf. 13½x12½

1985, Sept. 19 Photo.

169	A57	30p Gyromitra esculenta	1.10	.40

Pal Village — A68

1985, Nov. 7 Engr. *Perf. 13½*

170	A68	17p brt ultra & dk blue	.50	.25

Christmas 1985 — A69

Fresco: Angels Playing Trumpet and Psaltery, St. Bartholomew Chapel.

1985, Dec. 11 Photo. *Perf. 13½x13*

171	A69	17p multicolored	.50	.25

Mushroom Type of 1983

Perf. 13½x12½

1986, Apr. 10 Photo.

172	A57	30p Marasmius oreades	.90	.40

Europa 1986 — A70

1986, May 5 Engr. *Perf. 13*

173	A70	17p Water	*.40*	.30
174	A70	45p Soil and air	*1.60*	*.60*

Bishops of Urgel Type of 1979

1986, Sept. 11 Engr. *Perf. 13½*

175	A42	35p Justi Guitart	.80	.40

Christmas — A72

Santa Roma de Les Bons Church bell.

1986, Dec. 11 Litho. *Perf. 14*

176	A72	19p multicolored	.50	.25

A73

Contemporary Natl. Coat of Arms.

1987, Mar. 27 Photo. *Perf. 14*

177	A73	48p multicolored	.90	.40

Visit of the co-princes: the Bishop of Urgel and president of France, September 26, 1986.

Europa 1987 — A74

Modern architecture: 19p, Meritxell Sanctuary interior. 48p, Sanctuary exterior, vert.

1987, May 15 Engr. *Perf. 14x13½*
178 A74 19p dark blue & brown *.40* .40
179 A74 48p dark blue & brown *1.60* .40

Souvenir Sheet

1992 Summer Olympics, Barcelona — A75

20p, House of the Valleys. 50p, Bell tower, Chapel of the Archangel Michael, and torch-bearer.

1987, July 20 Photo. *Perf. 14*
180 A75 Sheet of 2 4.00 4.00
a. 20p multicolored 1.20 1.20
b. 50p multicolored 2.25 2.25

Local Mushrooms — A76

1987, Sept. 11 *Perf. 13½x12½*
181 A76 100p Boletus edulis 2.25 1.25

Christmas — A77

Design: Detail from a Catalan manuscript, De Nativitat, by R. Llull.

1987, Nov. 18 Litho. *Perf. 14*
182 A77 20p multicolored .50 .25

Lance and Arrowhead (Bronze Age) — A78

1988, Mar. 25 Photo. *Perf. 14*
183 A78 50p multicolored .90 .40

Europa 1988 — A79

Transport and communications: 20p, Les Bons, a medieval road. 45p, Trader and pack mules, early 20th cent.

1988, May 5 Engr. *Perf. 14x13½*
184 A79 20p dark bl & dark red *.45* .25
185 A79 45p dark bl & dark red *1.50* .40

Pyrenean Mastiff — A80

1988, July 26 Litho. *Perf. 14x13½*
186 A80 20p multicolored 1.50 .60

Bishop of Urgel and Seigneur of Caboet Confirming Co-Principality, 700th Anniv. — A81

1988, Oct. 24 Litho. *Perf. 14x13½*
187 A81 20p gold, blk & int blue .60 .30

Christmas 1988 — A82

1988, Nov. 30 Litho. *Perf. 14x13½*
188 A82 20p multicolored .50 .25

Arms Type of 1982 Without "PTA"

1988, Dec. 2 Photo. *Perf. 13x13½*
192 A51 20p brt blue green .50 .25

Size: 25x30½mm

Perf. 13½x12½

Engr.

194 A51 50p grnsh black 1.00 .40
196 A51 100p dark blue 2.25 .80
198 A51 500p dark brown 8.25 3.00
Nos. 192-198 (4) 12.00 4.45

Europa 1989 — A83

Perf. 14x13½, 13½x14

1989, May 8 Litho. & Engr.
200 A83 20p Leapfrog, vert. *.55* *.40*
201 A83 45p Tug of war *1.50* *.80*

Santa Roma Church, Les Bons — A84

Litho. & Engr.

1989, June 20 *Perf. 13½x14*
202 A84 50p blk, dp bl & grn bl 1.25 .40

Anniv. Emblem — A85

1989, Oct. 26 Litho. *Perf. 14x13½*
203 A85 20p multicolored .80 .40

Intl. Red Cross and Red Crescent societies, 125th annivs.; Year for the Protection of Human Life.

Christmas — A86

The Immaculate Conception.

1989, Dec. 1
204 A86 20p multicolored .50 .25

Europa 1990 — A87

Post offices.

Perf. 13½x14, 14x13½

1990, May 17 Photo.
205 A87 20p shown *.55* .25
206 A87 50p Post office, vert. *1.40* *.40*

Gomphidius Rutilus — A88

1990, June 21 Litho. *Perf. 13x13½*
207 A88 45p multicolored 1.50 .60

Plandolit House — A89

Litho. & Engr.

1990, Oct. 17 *Perf. 13x12½*
208 A89 20p brown & org yel .50 .25

Christmas — A90

1990, Nov. 26 Litho. *Perf. 14x13½*
209 A90 25p lake, brn & bister .60 .30

4th Games of the Small European States — A91

1991, Apr. 29 Photo. *Perf. 13½x14*
210 A91 25p Discus *.60* .30
211 A91 45p High jump, runner *1.00* *.40*

Europa — A92

Perf. 14x13½, 13½x14

1991, May 10 Litho.
212 A92 25p Olympus-1 satellite *.70* .40
213 A92 55p Olympus-1, horiz. *2.50* .80

Macrolepiota Procera — A93

1991, Sept. 20 Litho. *Perf. 13x12½*
214 A93 45p multicolored 1.40 .40

Christmas — A94

1991, Nov. 29 Photo. *Perf. 14x13½*
215 A94 25p multicolored 1.00 .40

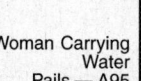

Woman Carrying Water Pails — A95

1992, Feb. 14 Photo. *Perf. 13½x14*
216 A95 25p multicolored .80 .40

European Discovery of America, 500th Anniv. — A96

Perf. 14x13½, 13½x14

1992, May 8 Photo.
217 A96 27p Santa Maria, vert. *.65* .40
218 A96 45p King Ferdinand *2.25* .40

Europa.

1992 Summer Olympics, Barcelona — A97

1992, July 22 Photo. *Perf. 13½x14*
219 A97 27p Kayak .80 .40

Nativity Scene, by Fra Angelico — A98

1992, Nov. 18 Photo. *Perf. 14*
220 A98 27p multicolored .80 .40

Natl. Automobile Museum — A99

Litho. & Engr.

1992, Sept. 10 *Perf. 13½x14*
221 A99 27p 1894 Benz 1.00 .40

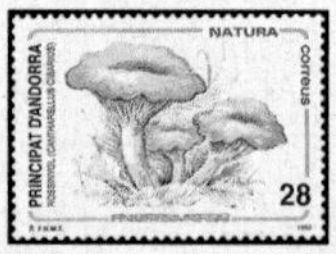

Cantharellus Cibarius — A100

1993, Mar. 25 Photo. *Perf. 13½x14*
222 A100 28p multicolored 1.00 .40

Contemporary Paintings — A101

Europa: 28p, Upstream, by John Alan Morrison. 45p, Rhythm, by Angel Calvente, vert.

Perf. 13½x14, 14x13½

1993, May 20 Litho.
223 A101 28p multicolored *.75* .40
224 A101 45p multicolored *1.50* *.80*

Art and Literature Society, 25th Anniv. — A102

1993, Sept. 23 Litho. *Perf. 14*
225 A102 28p multicolored .80 .40

Christmas — A103

Litho. & Engr.

1993, Nov. 25 ***Perf. 14x13½***
226 A103 28p multicolored .80 .40

Souvenir Sheet

Constitution, 1st Anniv. — A104

1994, Mar. 14 **Photo.** ***Perf. 14***
227 A104 29p multicolored 1.00 .75

Sir Alexander Fleming (1881-1955), Co-discoverer of Penicillin — A105

1994, May 6 **Photo.** ***Perf. 13½x14***
228 A105 29p Portrait *.60 .40*
229 A105 55p AIDS virus *1.50 .80*

Europa.

Hygrophorus Gliocyclus A106

1994, Sept. 27 **Photo.** ***Perf. 14***
230 A106 29p multicolored 1.00 .50

Christmas — A107

1994, Nov. 29 **Photo.** ***Perf. 14x13½***
231 A107 29p multicolored 1.00 .50

Nature Conservation in Europe — A108

1995, Mar. 23 **Photo.** ***Perf. 14***
232 A108 30p Farm in valley .70 .45
233 A108 60p Stone fence, valley 1.35 .75

Europa — A109

1995, May 8 **Photo.** ***Perf. 14***
234 A109 60p multicolored *1.60 .80*

Christmas — A110

1995, Nov. 8 **Photo.** ***Perf. 14***
235 A110 30p Flight to Egypt 1.00 .40

Entrance Into Council of Europe — A111

1995, Nov. 10
236 A111 30p multicolored *1.10* .40

Mushrooms A112

30p, Ramaria aurea. 60p, Tuber melanosporum.

1996, Apr. 30 **Photo.** ***Perf. 14***
237 A112 30p multicolored .90 .35
238 A112 60p multicolored 1.60 .80

Isabelle Sandy (1884-1975), Writer — A113

1996, May 7
239 A113 60p brown & violet *1.75 .80*

Europa.

Intl. Museum Day — A114

Design: Antique coal-heated iron.

1996, Sept. 12 **Photo.** ***Perf. 14***
240 A114 60p multicolored 1.10 .55

Christmas A115

The Annunciation, by Andrew Martin, 1753, St. Eulalia d'Encamp Church.

1996, Nov. 26 **Photo.** ***Perf. 14***
241 A115 30p multicolored .90 .40

Museums of Andorra — A116

Early bicycles designed by: 32p, Karl Drais, 1818. 65p, Pierre Michaux, 1861.

1997, Apr. 28 **Photo.** ***Perf. 14***
242 A116 32p multicolored .70 .35
243 A116 65p multicolored 1.40 .70

See Nos. 248-249.

A117

Europa (Stories and Legends): Hikers watching family of bears crossing over river on fallen tree.

1997, May 6 **Photo.** ***Perf. 14***
244 A117 65p multicolored *1.75 .80*

UNESCO — A118

1997, Sept. 30 **Photo.** ***Perf. 14***
245 A118 32p multicolored .80 .35

Christmas — A119

1997, Nov. 25 **Photo.** ***Perf. 14***
246 A119 32p multicolored .75 .35

1998 Winter Olympic Games, Nagano — A120

1998, Feb. 23 **Photo.** ***Perf. 14***
247 A120 35p Slalom skier .80 .35

Museums of Andorra Type of 1997

Early bicycles: 35p, Kangaroo, 1878. 70p, Hirondelle, 1889.

1998, Apr. 24 **Photo.** ***Perf. 13½x14***
248 A116 35p multicolored .60 .35
249 A116 70p multicolored 1.25 .70

Harlequins, Canillas Carnival — A121

1998, May 22 **Photo.** ***Perf. 14***
250 A121 70p multicolored *1.50 .70*

Europa.

Manual Digest, 250th Anniv. — A122

1998, Sept. 30 **Photo.** ***Perf. 14***
251 A122 35p multicolored .70 .40

Inauguration of the Postal Museum of Andorra — A123

1998, Nov. 19 **Photo.** ***Perf. 14***
252 A123 70p multicolored 1.25 .75

Christmas A124

1998, Nov. 26
253 A124 35p multicolored .80 .40

Museums of Andorra — A125

Early bicycles designed by: 35p, Salvo, 1878, vert. 70p, Rudge, 1883.

1999, Jan. 29 **Photo.** ***Perf. 14***
254 A125 35p multicolored .70 .40
255 A125 70p multicolored 1.10 .75

Council of Europe, 50th Anniv. — A126

1999, Apr. 29 **Photo.** ***Perf. 14***
256 A126 35p multicolored .80 .40

Incles Valley — A127

1999, May 6
257 A127 70p multicolored 1.60 .80

Europa.

Transporting Mail on Horseback A128

1999, Feb. 18 **Photo.** ***Perf. 14***
258 A128 35p black & sepia 1.00 .50

Restoration of Casa Rull, Sispony, La Massana — A129

1999, Sept. 22 **Photo.** ***Perf. 13½x14***
259 A129 35p multicolored .90 .45

Christmas — A130

1999, Nov. 10 **Engr.** ***Perf. 14x13½***
260 A130 35p orange brn & brn .90 .45

St. Coloma's Church — A131

1999, Nov. 12 **Photo.**
261 A131 35p multicolored .80 .40

European heritage.

Europa, 2000
Common Design Type

2000, May 11 Photo. ***Perf. 13¾***
262 CD17 70p multicolored *1.75* *.80*

Angonella Lakes — A132

2000, June 29 Photo. ***Perf. 13¾x14***
263 A132 35p multicolored .90 .45

Casa Lacruz — A133

2000, July 20 Photo. ***Perf. 13¾x14***
264 A133 35p multicolored .90 .45

China, Areny-Plandolit Museum — A134

2000, July 27 ***Perf. 14x13¾***
265 A134 70p multicolored 1.50 .75

2000 Summer Olympics, Sydney — A135

2000, Sept. 29 Photo. ***Perf. 14x13½***
266 A135 70p multicolored 1.50 .75

European Convention on Human Rights, 50th Anniv. — A136

2000, Nov. 3 ***Perf. 13½x14***
267 A136 70p multicolored 1.60 .75

Natl. Archives, 25th Anniv. — A137

2000, Nov. 14 ***Perf. 14x13½***
268 A137 35p multicolored .80 .40

Christmas — A138

2000, Nov. 22
269 A138 35p multicolored 1.00 .40

Rec de Solà — A139

2001, Mar. 30 Photo. ***Perf. 14x13¾***
270 A139 40p multicolored .80 .60

Europa — A140

2001, May 16 ***Perf. 13¾x14***
271 A140 75p multicolored *1.50* *.85*

Casa Palau, Sant Julià de Lòria — A141

2001, June 20 Photo. ***Perf. 14x13¾***
272 A141 75p multi 1.25 .75

Chapel of the Virgin of Meritxell, 25th Anniv. of Rebuilding — A142

2001, Sept. 7 Photo. ***Perf. 14x13¾***
273 A142 40p multi .90 .60

Natl. Auditorium, 10th Anniv. — A143

2001, Sept. 20 ***Perf. 13¾x14***
274 A143 75p multi 1.50 1.00

Christmas A144

2001, Nov. 20 Photo. ***Perf. 13¾x14***
275 A144 40p multi 1.00 .55

100 Cents = 1 Euro (€)

Coat of Arms — A145

2002, Jan. 2 Photo. ***Perf. 12¾x13¼***
276 A145 25c brown orange .85 .60
277 A145 50c claret 1.40 1.10

Birds — A146

Designs: 25c, Prunella collaris. 50c, Montifringilla nivalis.

2002, Mar. 27 ***Perf. 13¾x14***
278-279 A146 Set of 2 2.50 2.00

Intl. Year of Mountains — A147

2002, Apr. 5
280 A147 50c multi 1.75 1.10

Europa — A148

2002, May 9
281 A148 50c multi *14.00* *3.50*

Architectural Heritage — A149

Designs: €1.80, Casa Fusilé, Escaldes-Engordany. €2.10, Farga Rossell Centre, La Massana.

2002, June 14 Photo. ***Perf. 14x13¾***
282-283 A149 Set of 2 11.00 9.00

Historic Automobiles — A150

Designs: 25c, Pinette. 50c, Rolls-Royce, horiz.

2002, Oct. 8 ***Perf. 14x13¾, 13¾x14***
284-285 A150 Set of 2 2.25 2.00

Christmas — A151

2002, Nov. 26 ***Perf. 13¾x14***
286 A151 25c multi .90 .70

Artistic Heritage A152

Various religious murals from Santa Coloma Church: a, 25c. b, 75c. c, 50c.

2002, Nov. 28 ***Perf. 14x13¾***
287 A152 Horiz. strip of 3, #a-c 4.25 3.50

Sassanat Bridge — A153

Perf. 13½x13¾
2003, Feb. 27 **Photo.**
288 A153 26c multi 1.40 .60

Constitution, 10th Anniv. — A154

2003, Mar. 14 Photo. ***Perf. 13¾x14***
289 A154 76c multi 2.50 1.75

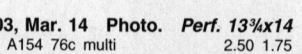

Europa — A155

2003, Apr. 24 ***Perf. 14x13¾***
290 A155 76c multi *2.25* *1.10*

Oenanthe Oenanthe — A156

2003, June 11 Photo. ***Perf. 14x13¾***
291 A156 26c multi 1.25 .90

Admission to United Nations, 10th Anniv. — A157

2003, July 28 Photo. ***Perf. 13¾x14***
292 A157 76c multi 2.50 1.75

Automobiles A158

Designs: 51c, 1908 Carter, vert. 76c, 1928 Peugeot.

2003, Oct. 15 ***Perf. 14x13¾, 13¾x14***
293-294 A158 Set of 2 7.00 7.00

Christmas A159

2003, Nov. 20 ***Perf. 13¾x14***
295 A159 26c multi .90 .60

Coat of Arms — A160

2004, Jan. 2 ***Perf. 12¾x13¼***
296 A160 27c bright blue .70 .60
297 A160 52c olive green 1.40 1.25
298 A160 77c red orange 2.00 1.75
Nos. 296-298 (3) 4.10 3.60

See Nos. 308-310, 319-320, 327-328.

Art by Joaquim Mir — A161

Designs: 27c, Fira del Bestiar. 52c, L'Escorxador, vert.

2004 ***Perf. 13¾x14, 14x13¾***
299-300 A161 Set of 2 2.25 1.75

Issued: 27c, 2/20; 52c, 3/18.

Europa — A162

2004, Apr. 29 Photo. ***Perf. 14x13¾***
301 A162 77c black *2.00 1.60*

Fringilla Coelebs — A163

2004, June 15 Photo. ***Perf. 13¾x14***
302 A163 27c multi 1.00 .60

Automobiles A164

Designs: €1.90, 1939 Simca 508-C. €2.19, 1955 Messerschmitt KR-1.

2004, Oct. 15 Photo. ***Perf. 13¾x14***
303-304 A164 Set of 2 11.00 9.50

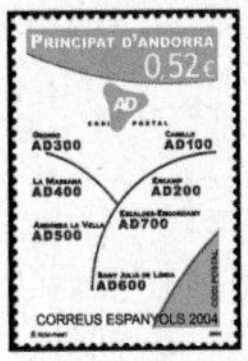

Postal Code — A165

2004, Oct. 25 ***Perf. 14x13¾***
305 A165 52c multi 1.60 1.25

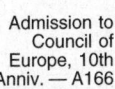

Admission to Council of Europe, 10th Anniv. — A166

2004, Nov. 10 ***Perf. 13¾x14***
306 A166 52c multi 1.50 1.25

Christmas A167

2004, Nov. 22
307 A167 27c multi 1.00 .75

Arms Type of 2004

2005, Jan. 28 Litho. ***Perf. 12¾x13¼***
308 A160 28c blue .70 .65
309 A160 53c yel green 1.35 1.25
310 A160 78c brt pink 2.00 1.75
Nos. 308-310 (3) 4.05 3.65

Selection of Madriu-Peralita-Claror Valley as UNESCO World Heritage Site — A168

2005, Mar. 7 Photo. ***Perf. 14x13¾***
311 A168 28c multi .90 .90

Endless, Sculpture by Mark Brusse — A169

2005, Mar. 14 ***Perf. 13¾x14***
312 A169 53c multi 1.50 1.10

Europa — A170

2005, Apr. 15 Photo. ***Perf. 13¾x14***
313 A170 78c multi *2.50 1.60*

9th Games of Small European States — A171

2005, May 20 Photo. ***Perf. 14x13¾***
314 A171 €1.95 multi 5.50 4.25

Caritas Andorra, 25th Anniv. — A172

2005, June 15
315 A172 28c multi .70 .70

Cinclus Cinclus — A173

2005, July 11 Photo. ***Perf. 13¾x14***
316 A173 €2.21 multi 6.25 6.25

Christmas A174

2005, Nov. 2 Photo. ***Perf. 13¾x14***
317 A174 28c blk & org 1.00 .65

2006 Winter Olympics, Turin — A175

2006, Feb. 6
318 A175 29c multi 1.00 .70

Arms Type of 2004

2006, Mar. 1 Litho. ***Perf. 12¾x13¼***
319 A160 29c yel brown .75 .65
320 A160 57c blue 1.50 1.25

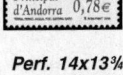

Earth, Fire, Water and Wind, Sculpture by Satoru Sato — A176

2006, Apr. 10 Photo. ***Perf. 14x13¾***
321 A176 78c multi 2.50 1.75

Europa — A177

2006, May 16 ***Perf. 13¾x14***
322 A177 57c multi 1.75 1.75

Perdix Perdix — A178

2006, June 6
323 A178 €2.39 multi 6.75 6.75

Fulbright Scholarships A179

2006, Aug. 8 Photo. ***Perf. 13¾x14***
324 A179 57c multi 1.75 1.45

UNESCO, 60th Anniv., Andorran National UNESCO Committee, 10th Anniv. — A180

2006, Oct. 2 ***Perf. 14x13¾***
325 A180 €2.33 multi 6.50 6.50

Christmas A181

2006, Nov. 2 Photo. ***Perf. 13¾x14***
326 A181 29c multi 1.00 .80

Arms Type of 2004

2007, Jan. 19 Litho. ***Perf. 12¾x13¼***
327 A160 30c red .75 .75
328 A160 58c gray 1.50 1.50

Santa Eulalia d'Encamp Church, by Francesc Galobardes — A182

2007, Feb. 12 Photo. ***Perf. 14x13¾***
329 A182 30c multi .80 .80

Europa — A183

2007, Apr. 23 Photo. ***Perf. 14x13¾***
330 A183 58c multi 1.60 1.60

Scouting, cent.

Jordino Family, Sculptures by Rachid Khimoune — A184

2007, May 21
331 A184 €2.43 multi 6.75 6.75

Tetrao Urogallus A185

2007, July 4 Photo. ***Perf. 13¾x14***
332 A185 €2.49 multi 7.00 7.00

Casa de la Vall, by Francesc Galobardes A186

2007, Sept. 10
333 A186 78c multi 2.25 2.25

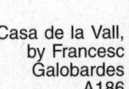

Andorran Red Cross, 25th Anniv. — A187

2007, Oct. 15 Photo. ***Perf. 13¾x14***
334 A187 30c black & red .90 .90

Christmas A188

2007, Nov. 2
335 A188 30c multi .90 .90

Gypaetus Barbatus — A189

2008, Jan. 24 Photo. ***Perf. 13¾***
336 A189 31c multi .90 .90

Carro Votiu, Sculpture by Jordi Casamajor — A190

2008, Jan. 24 ***Perf. 12¾x13***
337 A190 60c multi 1.60 1.60

Constitution, 15th Anniv. — A191

2008, Mar. 12 Photo. ***Perf. 14x13¾***
338 A191 31c multi .90 .90

Europa — A192

2008, Apr. 23
339 A192 60c black & deep blue 1.90 1.90

Andorran Science Society, 25th Anniv. — A193

2008, May 14
340 A193 78c blue & black 2.25 2.25

Souvenir Sheet

Expo Zaragoza 2008 A194

2008, June 13 Photo. *Perf. 13¾*
341 A194 €2.60 multi 7.50 7.50

2008 Summer Olympics, Beijing — A195

2008, July 8 Litho. *Perf. 14x13¾*
342 A195 60c multi 1.90 1.90

Vall del Comapedrosa — A196

2008, Sept. 15
343 A196 €2.44 multi 6.25 6.25

Sispony, by Carme Massana A197

2008, Oct. 13 Photo. *Perf. 12¾*
344 A197 31c multi .90 .90

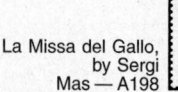

La Missa del Gallo, by Sergi Mas — A198

2008, Nov. 11
345 A198 31c multi .90 .90

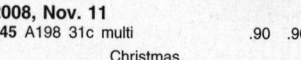

Christmas.

Narcissus — A199

Die Cut Perf. 13
2009, Jan. 17 Litho.
Self-Adhesive
346 A199 32c multi .85 .85

Andorran School, 25th Anniv. — A200

2009, Feb. 9 *Perf. 14x13¾*
347 A200 62c multi 1.60 1.60

Mercè Rodoreda (1908-83), Writer — A201

2009, Mar. 6
348 A201 78c black 2.00 2.00

Council of Europe, 60th Anniv. — A202

2009, Apr. 6 Litho. *Perf. 14x13¾*
349 A202 32c multi 1.00 1.00

Europa — A203

2009, Apr. 23
350 A203 62c multi 1.75 1.75

Intl. Year of Astronomy.

Souvenir Sheet

Madrid Bridge A204

2009, May 18 Photo.
351 A204 €2.70 multi 6.50 6.50

Eurasian Sparrowhawk — A205

2009, Sept. 10 Photo. *Perf. 14x13¾*
352 A205 €2.47 multi 6.75 6.75

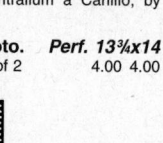

Paintings — A206

Designs: 62c, El Tarter, by Francesc Galobardes. 78c, Contrallum a Canillo, by Carme Massana.

2009, Oct. 8 Photo. *Perf. 13¾x14*
353-354 A206 Set of 2 4.00 4.00

Christmas A207

2009, Nov. 2 Litho.
355 A207 32c multi .95 .95

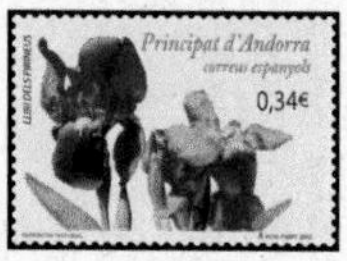

Pyrenees Iris — A208

Die Cut Perf. 13
2010, Jan. 12 Litho.
Self-Adhesive
356 A208 34c multi .90 .90

Jacint Verdaguer (1845-1902), Poet — A209

Litho. & Engr.
2010, Feb. 8 *Perf. 14x13¾*
357 A209 64c black & red 1.75 1.75

Paris Bridge, Andorra la Vella — A210

2010, Mar. 5 Litho.
358 A210 €2.75 multi 7.00 7.00

Europa — A211

2010, May 6 Photo. *Perf. 13¼x13¾*
359 A211 64c multi 1.75 1.75

Bonfire — A212

2010, June 1 *Perf. 13¾x13¼*
360 A212 64c multi 1.60 1.60

2010 World Cup Soccer Championships, South Africa — A213

2010, June 1
361 A213 78c multi 1.90 1.90

Recycling A214

Perf. 13¾x13¼
2010, Sept. 6 Photo.
362 A214 €2.49 multi 7.00 7.00

Churches — A215

Nos. 363: a, Sant Joan de Caselles Church. b, Sant Romà de Les Bons Church, horiz.

Perf. 13¼x13, 13x13¼
2010, Oct. 6 Engr.
363 A215 78c Sheet of 2, #a-b 4.50 4.50

See Andorra, French Administration No. 679.

Christmas A216

2010, Nov. 2 Photo. *Perf. 13¾x13¼*
364 A216 34c multi .95 .95

Escaldes-Engordany Parish, 2011 Capital of Catalan Culture — A217

Die Cut Perf. 13
2011, Jan. 12 Litho.
Self-Adhesive
365 A217 35c multi .95 .95

Miquel Marti i Pol (1929-2003), Writer — A218

2011, Feb. 7 *Perf. 14x13¾*
366 A218 65c black & gray 1.75 1.75

Europa — A219

2011, Apr. 4
367 A219 65c multi 1.75 1.75

Intl. Year of Forests.

Casa Farràs — A220

2011, May 3 *Perf. 13¾x14*
368 A220 80c multi 2.40 2.40

Painted Keystone, Sant Esteve Church — A221

2011, June 1
369 A221 €2.55 multi 7.00 7.00

Venice Biennale — A222

Artwork by: 80c, Helena Guàrdia. €2.55, Francisco Sánchez.

2011, July 1
370-371 A222 Set of 2 9.25 9.25

Equality of the Sexes — A223

2011, Sept. 8 ***Perf. 14x13¾***
372 A223 80c multi 2.25 2.25

America Issue, Mailbox — A224

2011, Oct. 11 ***Perf. 13¾x14***
373 A224 80c multi 2.25 2.25

Christmas A225

2011, Nov. 3
374 A225 35c multi 1.10 1.10
a. Tete-beche pair 2.50 2.50

Rossell Forge Interpretive Center, La Massana, 10th Anniv, — A226

2012, Jan. 9 Litho. *Die Cut Perf. 13*
Self-Adhesive
375 A226 36c multi 1.10 1.10

Agustí Bartra (1908-82), Poet — A227

2012, Feb. 27 ***Perf. 14x13¾***
376 A227 51c black 1.40 1.40

Europa — A228

2012, Apr. 4 ***Perf. 13¾x14***
377 A228 70c multi 1.90 1.90

CIAM Building, Escaldes-Engordany — A229

2012, May 3
378 A229 85c multi 2.25 2.25

Wood Carving, Sant Marti de la Cortinada Church, Ordino — A230

2012, June 1 ***Perf. 14x13¾***
379 A230 85c multi 2.25 2.25

A231

Art — A232

2012, July 2 ***Perf. 13¾x14***
380 A231 €2.90 multi 7.50 7.50
Perf. 14x13¾
381 A232 €2.90 multi 7.50 7.50

Civic Values — A233

2012, Sept. 10 ***Perf. 14x13¾***
382 A233 85c multi 2.25 2.25

America Issue, Cosmological Legend — A234

2012, Oct. 11
383 A234 85c multi 1.75 1.75

Christmas — A235

2012, Nov. 5
384 A235 36c multi .95 .95

Salvador Espriu (1913-85), Poet — A236

2013, Jan. 10 ***Die Cut Perf. 13***
Self-Adhesive
385 A236 37c multi 1.00 1.00

A237

2013, Feb. 21 ***Perf. 13¾x14***
386 A237 75c multi 2.00 2.00

Road between Andorra and La Seu d'Urgell, Spain, cent.

Areny-Plandolit Museum, Ordino — A238

2013, Mar. 4 ***Perf. 14x13¾***
387 A238 52c multi 1.40 1.40

Souvenir Sheet

Winter Jazz Festival A239

2013, Apr. 1 ***Perf. 13¼x13¾***
388 A239 €2.72 multi 7.00 7.00

Europa — A240

2013, Apr. 23 ***Perf. 13¾x13¼***
389 A240 75c multi 2.00 2.00

Women in Portuguese Costumes A241

2013, May 6 ***Perf. 13½x13¼***
390 A241 90c multi 2.40 2.40

Casa dels Russos — A242

2013, June 3
391 A242 75c multi 2.00 2.00

Souvenir Sheet

School Correspondence — A243

Perf. 13¼x13¾
2013, Sept. 16 Litho.
392 A243 €2.72 multi 7.50 7.50

Diversity and Anti-Discrimination — A244

2013, Oct. 3 Litho. *Perf. 13¾x13¼*
393 A244 90c multi 2.50 2.50

A245

Christmas — A246

2013, Nov. 4 Litho. *Perf. 13¼x13¾*
394 A245 37c multi 1.00 1.00
395 A246 75c multi 2.00 2.00

14th Intl. Winter Road Conference, Andorra — A247

2014, Jan. 13 Litho. *Perf. 13¼x13¾*
396 A247 38c multi 1.10 1.10

Coat of Arms — A248

2014, Feb. 3 Litho. *Perf. 13¼x13¾*
397 Vert. strip of 5 4.50 4.50
a. A248 1c gray .25 .25
b. A248 2c brown .25 .25
c. A248 5c blue .25 .25
d. A248 50c dull green 1.40 1.40
e. A248 €1 red 2.75 2.75

Sculpture by Samantha Bosque — A249

2014, Mar. 3 Litho. *Perf. 13¼x13¾*
398 A249 54c multi 1.50 1.50

Closure of Radio Andorra, 30th Anniv. — A250

2014, Apr. 7 Litho. *Perf. 13¾x13¼*
399 A250 92c multi 2.60 2.60

Accordion — A251

2014, Apr. 23 Litho. ***Perf. 13¼x13¾***
400 A251 76c multi 2.10 2.10

Europa.

Andorra Ultra Trail, Vallnord — A252

2014, June 9 Litho. ***Perf. 13¾x13¼***
401 A252 76c red & black 2.10 2.10

Filipinos in Andorra — A253

2014, July 7 Litho. ***Perf. 13¾x13¼***
402 A253 92c multi 2.50 2.50

Intl. Year of Family Farming — A254

Perf. 13¾x13¼
2014, Sept. 15 Litho.
403 A254 76c multi 2.00 2.00

Souvenir Sheet

Mural in Sant Martí de la Cortinada Church — A255

2014, Oct. 6 Litho. ***Perf. 13¼x13¾***
404 A255 €2.72 multi 6.75 6.75

Christmas A256

2014, Nov. 5 Litho. ***Perf. 13¾x13¼***
405 A256 38c multi .95 .95

Casa Felipó — A257

Perf. 13¼x13¾
2014, Nov. 10 Litho.
406 A257 €2.72 multi 6.75 6.75

Virgin of Meritxell — A258

2015, Jan. 13 Litho. ***Perf. 14x13¾***
407 A258 A multi .95 .95

No. 407 sold for 42c on day of issue.

Chamois — A259

2015, Feb. 9 Litho. ***Perf. 13¾x14***
408 A259 €1 multi 2.25 2.25

Higher Education in Andorra, 25th Anniv. — A260

2015, Mar. 2 Litho. ***Perf. 13¾x13¼***
409 A260 55c multi 1.25 1.25

Europa — A261

2015, Apr. 23 Litho. ***Perf. 13¾x13¼***
410 A261 90c multi 2.10 2.10

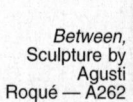

Between, Sculpture by Agusti Roqué — A262

2015, May 1 Litho. ***Perf. 13¾x13¼***
411 A262 €2.84 multi 6.50 6.50

Venice Biennale.

2015 World Motorcycling Trial Grand Prix, Andorra — A263

Perf. 13¾x13¼
2015, June 10 Litho.
412 A263 €1 multi 2.25 2.25

English Community in Andorra — A264

2015, July 8 Litho. ***Perf. 13¼x13¾***
413 A264 90c multi 2.00 2.00

Joan Martí Alanis (1929-2009), Bishop of Urgel and Co-Prince — A265

2015, Sept. 8 Litho. ***Perf. 13¼x13¾***
414 A265 42c multi .95 .95

Age of Majority at 18, 30th Anniv. — A266

2015, Sept. 8 Litho. ***Perf. 13¾***
415 A266 €1 multi 2.25 2.25

Souvenir Sheet

Hotel Rosaleda, Encamp — A267

2015, Oct. 15 Litho. ***Perf. 13¼x13¾***
416 A267 €2.84 multi 6.25 6.25

Christmas A268

2015, Nov. 2 Litho. ***Perf. 13¾x13¼***
417 A268 42c multi .95 .95

Dolors Parella i Fivaller (d. 1855), Murdered Baroness — A269

2015, Nov. 4 Litho. ***Perf. 13¼x13¾***
418 A269 90c multi 1.90 1.90

Coat of Arms — A270

2016, Jan. 13 Litho. ***Perf. 14x13½***
419 A270 A magenta & black 1.00 1.00

No. 419 sold for 45c on day of issue. See No. 431.

Dog from Retable in Church of Sant Cristòfol, d'Anyós — A271

2016, Feb. 9 Litho. ***Perf. 14x13½***
420 A271 €1.30 multi 3.00 3.00

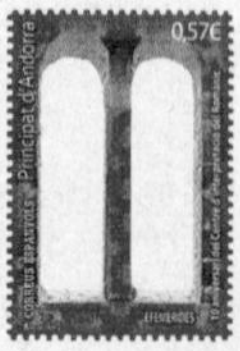

Interpretive Center for Romanesque Art, Pal, 10th Anniv. — A272

2016, Mar. 2 Litho. ***Perf. 13¼x13¾***
421 A272 57c multi 1.25 1.25

No. 421 has two die cut openings in the interior of the arches.

Europa — A273

2016, Apr. 22 Litho. ***Perf. 13¾x13¼***
422 A273 €1.15 multi 2.75 2.75

Think Green Issue.

Anima Compartida, by Joan Xandri — A274

2016, May 11 Litho. ***Perf. 13¾x13¼***
423 A274 €2.95 multi 6.75 6.75

2015 Venice Biennale.

Andorra la Vella, 2016 Ibero-American Capital of Culture — A275

Perf. 13¾x13¼
2016, June 10 Litho.
424 A275 €1.30 multi 3.00 3.00

French Community in Andorra — A276

2016, July 8 Litho. ***Perf. 13¼x13¾***
425 A276 €1.15 multi 2.60 2.60

Tree of Science — A277

2016, Sept. 8 Litho. ***Perf. 13¾x13¼***
426 A277 45c blk & brn 1.00 1.00

Ramon Llull (c. 1232-c. 1315), philosopher.

Reforms of 1866, 150th Anniv. — A278

2016, Sept. 8 Litho. ***Perf. 13¼x13¾***
427 A278 €1.30 multi 3.00 3.00

Souvenir Sheet

Vilanova Clinic A279

2016, Oct. 14 Litho. ***Perf. 13¼x13¾***
428 A279 €2.95 multi 6.50 6.50

Christmas — A280

2016, Nov. 4 Litho. *Perf. 13¼x13¾*
429 A280 45c Pastorets .95 .95

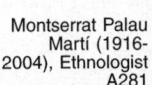

Montserrat Palau Martí (1916-2004), Ethnologist A281

2016, Nov. 8 Litho. *Perf. 13¾x13¼*
430 A281 €1.15 multi 2.50 2.50

Coat of Arms Type of 2016

2017, Jan. 13 Litho. *Perf. 14x13½*
431 A270 A blue & black 1.10 1.10

No. 431 sold for 50c on day of issue.

Argentine Community in Andorra — A282

Perf. 13¼x13¾
2017, Feb. 24 Litho.
432 A282 €1.25 multi 2.75 2.75

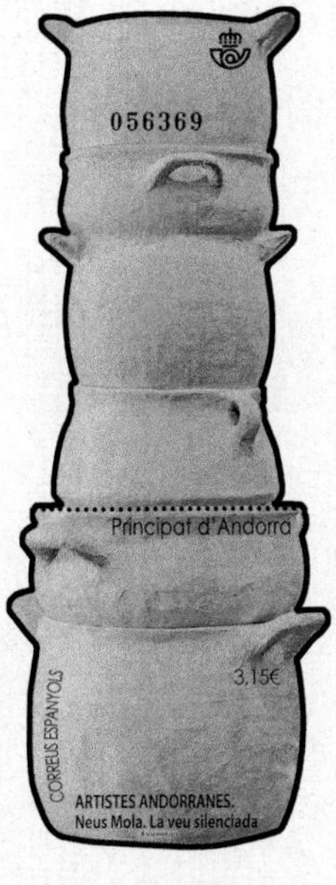
La Veu Silenciada (The Silenced Voice), by Neus Mola A283

Perf. 13¼ Horiz. at Top
2017, Mar. 9 Litho.
433 A283 €3.15 multi + label 6.75 6.75

No. 433 was sold folded.

Castell de les Bons — A284

2017, Apr. 21 Litho. *Perf. 13¼x13¾*
434 A284 €1.25 multi 2.75 2.75

Europa.

Pere Canturri (1935-2015), Historian and Governmental Minister — A285

2017, Apr. 28 Litho. *Perf. 13¼x13¾*
435 A285 60c multi 1.40 1.40

Souvenir Sheet

Sculptures — A286

No. 436: a, Lost Origin, by Zoe. b, Omphalos, by Jordi Casamajor.

2017, May 11 Litho. *Perf. 13¼x13¾*
436 A286 Sheet of 2 2.50 2.50
a. 50c multi 1.10 1.10
b. 60c multi 1.40 1.40

Birch Tree and Leaf — A287

2017, June 5 Litho. *Perf. 13¾x13¼*
437 A287 €1.35 multi 3.25 3.25

Estany d'Encamp A288

2017, July 8 Litho. *Perf. 13¾x13¼*
438 A288 €1.25 multi 3.00 3.00

Julià Reig i Ribó (1911-96), Politician — A289

2017, Sept. 8 Litho. *Perf. 13¾x13¼*
439 A289 €1.35 multi 3,25 3.25

Pilar Riberaygua (1953-2002), Artist and Gallery Owner — A290

Perf. 13¾x13¼
2017, Sept. 22 Litho.
440 A290 €1.25 multi 3.00 3.00

Souvenir Sheet

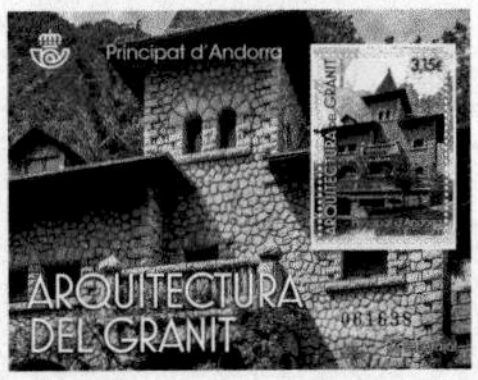
Arajol Chalet A291

2017, Oct. 14 Litho. *Perf. 13¼x13¾*
441 A291 €3.15 multi 7.50 7.50

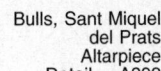

Bulls, Sant Miquel del Prats Altarpiece Detail — A292

2017, Nov. 3 Litho. *Perf. 13¾x13¼*
442 A292 €1.35 multi 3.25 3.25

Christmas — A293

Die Cut Perf. 13
2017, Nov. 8 Litho.
On Wood Veneer
Self-Adhesive
443 A293 50c multi 1.25 1.25

Coat of Arms — A294

2018, Jan. 2 Litho. *Perf. 14x13¾*
444 A294 A multi 1.40 1.40

No. 444 sold for 55c on day of issue.

Dante Alighieri (c. 1265-1321), Writer — A295

2018, Feb. 24 Litho. *Perf. 13¾*
445 A295 €1.35 multi 3.25 3.25

Italian Community in Andorra.

Souvenir Sheet

Andorran Constitution, 25th Anniv. — A296

2018, Mar. 14 Litho. *Perf. 13x13½*
446 A296 €3.30 multi 8.25 8.25

Escaldes-Engordany Parish, 40th Anniv. — A297

2018, Apr. 6 Litho. *Perf. 13x13½*
447 A297 55c multi 1.40 1.40

Engordany Bridge — A298

2018, Apr. 23 Litho. *Perf. 14¼x14*
448 A298 €1.35 multi 3.25 3.25

Europa. Stone grit is affixed to portions of the design.

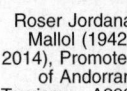

Roser Jordana Mallol (1942-2014), Promoter of Andorran Tourism — A299

2018, May 16 Litho. *Perf. 13½x13*
449 A299 €1.35 multi 3.25 3.25

Walnuts and Leaf of Walnut Tree — A300

2018, May 25 Litho. *Perf. 13½x13*
450 A300 €1.45 multi 3.50 3.50

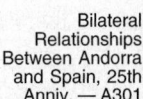

Bilateral Relationships Between Andorra and Spain, 25th Anniv. — A301

2018, June 5 Litho. *Perf. 13½x13*
451 A301 €1.35 multi 3.25 3.25

Summer Solstice Festival, UNESCO Intangible Cultural Heritage — A302

2018, June 22 Litho. *Perf. 13½x13*
452 A302 €1.45 multi 3.50 3.50

European Year of Cultural Heritage — A303

2018, July 5 Litho. *Perf. 13¼x13¾*
453 A303 €1.45 multi 3.50 3.50

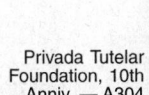

Privada Tutelar Foundation, 10th Anniv. — A304

2018, Aug. 9 Litho. *Perf. 13¼x13¾*
454 A304 65c multi 1.50 1.50

View of Escaldes From Els Vilars — A305

2018, Sept. 17 Litho. *Perf. 13½x13*
455 A305 €1.45 multi 3.50 3.50

Cultural Guide Courses, 25th Anniv. — A306

2018, Oct. 10 Litho. *Perf. 13¾x13¼*
456 A306 €1.45 multi 3.50 3.50

Souvenir Sheet

Christmas Diorama (unfolded) — A307

2018, Nov. 8 Litho. *Perf. 13¾*
457 A307 €3.30 multi 7.50 7.50

No. 457 was sold with a fold in the sheet margin so the stamp would appear through the holes in the illustration printed on the back of the sheet margin.

Flag of Andorra — A308

2019, Jan. 4 Litho. *Perf. 13½x13*
458 A308 A multi 1.40 1.40

No. 458 sold for 60c on day of issue. Compare with No. 472.

Tradition of Burning of Christmas Trees — A309

2019, Jan. 24 Litho. *Perf. 13½x13*
459 A309 €1.40 multi 3.25 3.25

General Council of the Valleys, 600th Anniv. — A310

2019, Feb. 11 Litho. *Perf. 13½x13*
460 A310 €3.50 multi 8.00 8.00

A311

Design: Maria Lluisa de Riba (1908-93), last heir of Rossell family, and Rossell house, Ordino.

2019, Mar. 8 Litho. *Perf. 13½x13*
461 A311 €1.50 multi 3.50 3.50

European Robin A312

2019, Apr. 26 Litho. *Perf. 13¼x13½*
462 A312 €1.40 multi 3.25 3.25

Europa.

Souvenir Sheet

Andorran Foods A313

No. 463: a, Chickory. b, Escudella.

2019, May 11 Litho. *Perf. 13x13¾*
463 A313 Sheet of 2 6.75 6.75
a. €1.40 multi 3.25 3.25
b. €1.50 multi 3.50 3.50

Souvenir Sheet

Hydroelectric Power in Andorra, 90th Anniv. — A314

Litho. With Lenticular Lens Affixed
2019, May 31 *Perf. 14½x14¾*
464 A314 €4 multi 9.00 9.00

Holly Leaves and Berries — A315

Litho. With Foil Application
2019, July 8 *Perf. 13¾x13¼*
465 A315 70c multi 1.60 1.60

La Purito Cycling Tour, 5th Anniv. — A316

2019, Aug. 4 Litho. *Perf. 13¾x13¼*
466 A316 70c multi 1.60 1.60

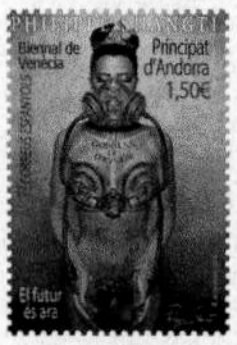

Goddess of Oxygen, by Philippe Shangti — A317

2019, Sept. 8 Litho. *Perf. 13x13½*
467 A317 €1.50 multi 3.25 3.25

Venice Art Biennale.

Molleres de Meritxell, by Francesc Galobardes A318

2019, Sept. 22 Litho. *Perf. 13½x13*
468 A318 €1.40 multi 3.25 3.25

The Firebird — A319

2019, Oct. 14 Litho. *Perf. 13x13½*
469 A319 70c multi 1.60 1.60

Russian community in Andorra.

Admission of Andorra to Council of Europe, 25th Anniv. — A320

2019, Nov. 8 Litho. *Perf. 13*
470 A320 €1.40 multi + label 3.25 3.25

See Andorra (French Administration) No. 815.

Christmas — A321

2019, Nov. 8 Engr. *Perf. 13x13½*
471 A321 60c black 1.40 1.40

Flag of Andorra — A322

2020, Jan. 3 Litho. *Perf. 13½x13*
472 A322 A multi 1.50 1.50

No. 472 sold for 65c on day of issue. Compare with No. 458.

27th Ibero-American Summit of Heads of State and Government, Andorra — A323

Perf. 13¼x13½
2020, Feb. 11 Litho.
473 A323 75c multi 1.75 1.75

Carolina Plandolit i Pelati (?-1902), Wife of Guillem d'Areny i Plandolit, First Syndic of the General Council — A324

2020, Mar. 6 Litho. *Perf. 13x13½*
474 A324 €1.55 multi 3.50 3.50

Wolf and Protective Collar for Sheepdogs — A325

2020, Mar. 19 Litho. *Perf. 13x13½*
475 A325 €1.45 multi 3.25 3.25

Cal Pal Manor House, La Cortinada — A326

2020, May 14 Litho. *Perf. 13¾x13¼*
476 A326 75c multi 1.75 1.75

Postal Carriers and Map of Andorra-La Seu d'Urgell, Spain Postal Route — A327

2020, May 14 Litho. *Perf. 13¼x13¾*
477 A327 €1.45 multi 3.25 3.25

Europa.

Souvenir Sheet

Andorran Woman Suffrage Decree, 50th Anniv. A328

2020, May 29 Litho. *Perf. 13¼*
478 A328 €3.80 multi 8.50 8.50

Beyondwalls, Painting on Land by Saype — A329

Perf. 13¾x13¼
2020, June 30 Litho.
479 A329 €1.45 multi 3.25 3.25

2019 L'Andart Biennale.

Linden Leaf and Blossom — A330

2020, July 8 Litho. *Perf. 13½x13¼*
480 A330 €1.45 multi 3.50 3.50

Collada dels Meners A331

2020, Aug. 4 Litho. *Perf. 13x13½*
481 A331 €1.40 multi 3.50 3.50

Diplomatic Relations Between Andorra and Liechtenstein, 25th Anniv. — A332

2020, Sept. 8 Litho. *Perf. 13¾x13¼*
482 A332 €1.55 multi 3.75 3.75

Pep Aguareles (1965-2019), Photographer A333

2020, Oct. 9 Litho. *Perf. 13¾x13¼*
483 A333 €1.45 multi 3.50 3.50

Souvenir Sheet

Chinese Community in Andorra — A334

2020, Oct. 21 Litho. *Perf. 13¼*
484 A334 €3.80 multi 9.00 9.00

Casa de la Vall A335

Litho. & Engr.
2020, Nov. 5 *Perf. 13x12½*
485 A335 €2.40 multi + 2 flanking labels 5.75 5.75

Candidacy of Casa de la Vall, Castell de Foix and Cathedral of the See of Urgell (shown on flanking labels) for UNESCO World Heritage Site status. See French Andorra No. 828.

Canopy of the Chapel of St. Bartholomew A336

2020, Nov. 5 Litho. *Perf. 13½*
486 A336 65c multi 1.60 1.60

Christmas.

Flag of Andorra — A337

2021, Jan. 18 Litho. *Perf. 13¾x13¼*
487 A337 A multi 1.75 1.75

No. 487 sold for 70c on day of issue.

Souvenir Sheet

Tribute to Workers During the COVID-19 Pandemic — A338

2021, Jan. 19 Litho. *Perf. 13½x13¼*
488 A338 €4.15 multi 10.00 10.00

Harlequins of Canillo — A339

Perf. 13½x13¼
2021, Feb. 12 Litho.
489 A339 €1.50 multi 3.75 3.75

Marcella Pelegrí, Primary School Teacher — A340

2021, Mar. 8 Litho. *Perf. 13½x13¼*
490 A340 €1.60 multi 3.75 3.75

Antoni Morell (1941-2020), Writer — A341

2021, Apr. 23 Litho. *Perf. 13½x13¼*
491 A341 70c multi 1.75 1.75

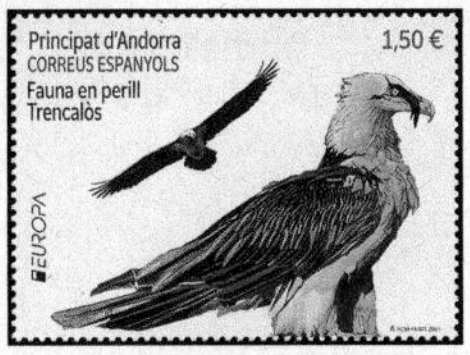

Bearded Vulture A342

2021, Apr. 30 Litho. *Perf. 13¼x13½*
492 A342 €1.50 multi 3.75 3.75

Europa.

Borda de l'Any de la Part Winery A343

2021, May 3 Litho. *Perf. 13¼x13½*
493 A343 €2.50 multi 6.00 6.00

Hiker — A344

2021, June 2 Litho. *Perf. 13¾x13¼*
494 A344 80c multi 1.90 1.90

Elder Blossoms A345

2021, July 8 Litho. *Perf. 13¾x13¼*
495 A345 €1.50 multi 3.75 3.75

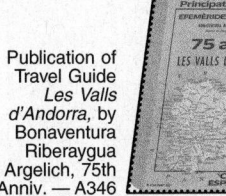

Publication of Travel Guide *Les Valls d'Andorra,* by Bonaventura Riberaygua Argelich, 75th Anniv. — A346

2021, Aug. 4 Litho. *Perf. 13x13¼*
496 A346 €1.60 multi 3.75 3.75

Coronation of Our Lady of Meritxell, Cent. — A347

2021, Sept. 7 Litho. *Perf. 13¼x13¾*
497 A347 €2 multi 4.75 4.75

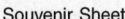

Souvenir Sheet

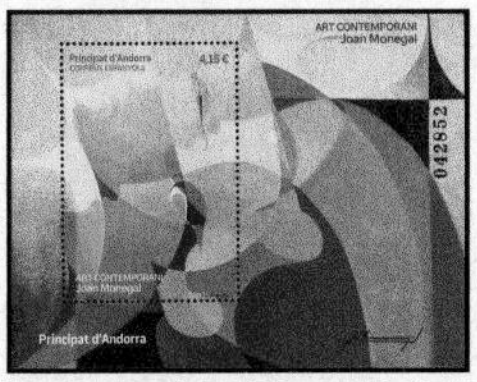

Painting by Joan Monegal (1933-81) — A348

2021, Oct. 9 Litho. *Perf. 13¾x13¼*
498 A348 €4.15 multi 9.75 9.75

Peruvian Community in Andorra — A349

2021, Oct. 21 Litho. *Perf. 13¼x13¾*
499 A349 €1.60 multi 3.75 3.75

Rotonda Restaurant, c. 1960 — A350

2021, Nov. 5 Litho. *Perf. 13¼x13½*
500 A350 €2.50 multi 5.75 5.75

St. Sylvester's Day Race, Sant Julia de Loria — A351

2021, Nov. 5 Litho. *Perf. 13x13¼*
501 A351 70c multi 1.60 1.60

Christmas.

Flag of Andorra — A352

Litho. With Foil Application
2022, Jan. 3 *Perf. 13½x13*
502 A352 A sil & multi 1.75 1.75

No. 502 sold for 75c on day of issue.

Dance of the Bear — A353

2022, Feb. 11 Litho. *Perf. 13x13½*
503 A353 €1.65 multi 3.75 3.75

Europa Cup 2022-23 Season Skiing Finals, Soldeu — A354

2022, Mar. 14 Litho. *Perf. 13½x13*
504 A354 €1.75 multi 4.00 4.00

Eurasian Eagle-Owl — A355

2022, Mar. 25 Litho. *Perf. 13½x13*
505 A355 €4.60 multi 10.50 10.50

Barri, Art Installation by Miquel Mercè — A356

2022, Apr. 22 Litho. *Perf. 13x13½*
506 A356 €1.75 multi 4.00 4.00

Andorra L'Andart International Biennial.

Legend of Meritxell — A357

2022, May 19 Litho. *Perf. 13¾x13¼*
507 A357 €1.65 multi 3.50 3.50

Europa.

Estany de les Salamandres A358

2022, June 2 Litho. *Perf. 13¾x13¼*
508 A358 €1.75 multi 3.75 3.75

Hazelnut Tree — A359

2022, July 8 Litho. *Perf. 13¾x13¼*
509 A359 €1.65 multi 3.50 3.50

Dancers at Monumental Bull Ring, Escaldes — A360

2022, July 22 Litho. *Perf. 13½*
510 A360 €1.75 multi 3.75 3.75

AIR POST STAMPS

A set of 12 stamps, inscribed "CORREU AER / SOBRETAXA" was authorized in 1932 for a proposed private air service between Andorra and Barcelona. These stamps were prepared but not issued. Value, set unused $32, never hinged. $42.50. The stamps were also overprinted "FRANQUICIA DEL CONSELL" for official use. Value, set $140.

Catalogue values for unused stamps in this section are for Never Hinged items.

AP1

Unwmk.

1951, June 27 Engr. *Perf. 11*

C1	AP1	1p dark violet brown	25.00	4.25

AP2

Litho. & Engr.

1983, Oct. 20 *Perf. 13*

C2	AP2	20p brown & bis brn	.40	.25

Jaime Sansa Nequi, Episcopal Church official.

AP3

1984, Oct. 25 Photo. *Perf. 13*

C3	AP3	20p multicolored	.40	.25

Pyrenees Art Center.

Bishops of Urgel Type of 1979

1985, June 13 Engr. *Perf. 13½*

C4	A42	20p Ramon Iglesias	.40	.25

SPECIAL DELIVERY STAMPS

Special Delivery Stamp of Spain, 1905 Overprinted

1928 Unwmk. *Perf. 14*

Without Control Number on Back

E1	SD1	20c red	80.00	95.00
		Never hinged	150.00	

With Control Number on Back

E2	SD1	20c pale red	55.00	55.00
		Never hinged	95.00	

Eagle over Mountain Pass — SD2

1929 *Perf. 14*

With Control Number on Back

E3	SD2	20c scarlet	25.00	20.00
		Never hinged	35.00	

Perf 11½ examples are numbered A000.000 and are specimens. Value, $400.

No. E3 exists imperforate with control numbers on the back. Value, $110 unused, $155 never hinged.

1937 *Perf. 11½x11*

Without Control Number on Back

E4	SD2	20c red	7.75	9.50
		Never hinged	8.75	

Arms and Squirrel — SD3

1949 Unwmk. Engr. *Perf. 10x9½*

E5	SD3	25c red	5.75	4.50
		Never hinged	8.25	

ANDORRA, FRENCH ADMINISTRATION

Stamps and Types of France, 1900-1929, Overprinted

Perf. 14x13½

1931, June 16 Unwmk.

1	A16	1c gray	1.00	1.00
a.		Double overprint	1,800.	2,500.
b.		Double overprint	1,800.	
2	A16	2c red brown	1.40	1.40
3	A16	3c orange	1.40	1.40
4	A16	5c green	2.10	2.40
5	A16	10c lilac	3.50	3.75
6	A22	15c red brown	5.50	5.50
7	A22	20c red violet	7.75	8.25
8	A22	25c yellow brn	9.50	10.00
9	A22	30c green	9.00	9.50
10	A22	40c ultra	10.00	12.00
11	A20	45c lt violet	40.00	40.00
12	A20	50c vermilion	45.00	45.00
a.		Pair, one without overprint	475.00	
13	A20	65c gray green	20.00	20.00
14	A20	75c rose lilac	14.00	14.00
15	A22	90c red	26.00	30.00
16	A20	1fr dull blue	30.00	34.00
17	A22	1.50fr light blue	40.00	42.50

Overprinted

18	A18	2fr org & pale bl	24.00	30.00
19	A18	3fr brt vio & rose	100.00	120.00
20	A18	5fr dk bl & buff	130.00	135.00
21	A18	10fr grn & red	275.00	275.00
22	A18	20fr mag & grn	375.00	450.00
		Nos. 1-22 (22)	1,170.	1,291.

See No. P1 for ½c on 1c gray.

Nos. 9, 15 and 17 were not issued in France without overprint.

Chapel of Meritxell — A50

Bridge of St. Anthony A51

St. Miguel d'Engolasters A52

Gorge of St. Julia — A53

Old Andorra — A54

1932-43 Engr. *Perf. 13*

23	A50	1c gray blk	.55	.55
24	A50	2c violet	.95	.80
25	A50	3c brown	.80	.65
26	A50	5c blue green	.95	.90
27	A51	10c dull lilac	1.30	1.30
28	A50	15c deep red	1.90	1.75
29	A51	20c lt rose	12.00	9.75
30	A52	25c brown	5.75	5.25
31	A51	25c brn car ('37)	11.00	14.00
32	A51	30c emerald	4.25	3.75
33	A51	40c ultra	12.00	9.75
34	A51	40c brn blk ('39)	1.45	1.40
35	A51	45c lt red	12.00	9.75
36	A51	45c bl grn ('39)	6.75	5.50
37	A52	50c lilac rose	13.50	13.00
38	A51	50c lt vio ('39)	6.50	5.75
38A	A51	50c grn ('40)	2.00	1.90
39	A51	55c lt vio ('38)	23.00	16.50
40	A51	60c yel brn ('38)	1.50	1.25
41	A52	65c yel grn	55.00	55.00
42	A51	65c blue ('38)	17.00	13.50
43	A51	70c red ('39)	2.75	2.10
44	A52	75c violet	11.50	7.75
45	A51	75c ultra ('39)	5.00	4.75
46	A51	80c green ('38)	29.00	21.00
46A	A53	80c bl grn ('40)	.50	.60
47	A53	90c deep rose	6.25	5.25
48	A53	90c dk grn ('39)	4.25	4.25
49	A53	1fr blue grn	20.00	13.50
50	A53	1fr scarlet ('38)	31.00	22.00
51	A53	1fr dp ultra ('39)	.50	.50
51A	A53	1.20fr brt vio ('42)	.50	.50
52	A50	1.25fr rose car ('33)	55.00	42.50
52A	A50	1.25fr rose ('38)	6.00	3.50
52B	A53	1.30fr sepia ('40)	.50	.50
53	A54	1.50fr ultra	25.00	16.00
53A	A53	1.50fr crim ('40)	.50	.50
54	A53	1.75fr violet ('33)	105.00	120.00
55	A53	1.75fr dk bl ('38)	50.00	47.50
56	A53	2fr red violet	11.50	9.50
56A	A50	2fr rose red ('40)	1.60	1.60
56B	A50	2fr dk bl grn ('42)	.50	.50
57	A50	2.15fr dk vio ('38)	60.00	55.00
58	A50	2.25fr ultra ('39)	9.00	8.00
58A	A50	2.40fr red ('42)	.65	.50
59	A50	2.50fr gray blk ('39)	9.75	7.75
59A	A50	2.50fr dp ultra ('40)	2.40	2.10
60	A53	3fr orange brn	14.00	9.00
60A	A50	3fr red brn ('40)	.50	.50
60B	A50	4fr sl bl ('42)	.50	.50
60C	A50	4.50fr dp vio ('42)	1.75	1.60
61	A54	5fr brown	.95	.70
62	A54	10fr violet	.95	.70
62B	A54	15fr dp ultra ('42)	1.20	1.00
63	A54	20fr rose lake	1.25	.85
63A	A51	50fr turq bl ('43)	1.75	1.50
		Nos. 23-63A (56)	661.65	586.00

A 20c ultra exists but was not issued. Value: unused, $20,000; never hinged $30,000.

No. 37 Surcharged in Black

1935, Sept. 18

64	A52	20c on 50c lil rose	18.50	17.00
a.		Double surcharge	6,500.	

Coat of Arms — A55

1936-42 *Perf. 14x13*

65	A55	1c black ('37)	.25	.25
66	A55	2c blue	.25	.25
67	A55	3c brown	.25	.25
68	A55	5c rose lilac	.25	.25
69	A55	10c ultra ('37)	.25	.25
70	A55	15c red violet	2.75	2.25
71	A55	20c emerald ('37)	.25	.25
72	A55	30c cop red ('38)	.60	.70
72A	A55	30c blk brn ('42)	.25	.40
73	A55	35c Prus grn ('38)	70.00	70.00
74	A55	40c cop red ('42)	.60	.60
75	A55	50c Prus grn ('42)	.60	.60
76	A55	60c turq bl ('42)	.60	.60
77	A55	70c vio ('42)	.60	.60
		Nos. 65-77 (14)	77.50	77.25
		Set, never hinged	135.00	

Catalogue values for unused stamps in this section, from this point to the end of the section, are for Never Hinged items.

Coat of Arms — A56

1944

78	A56	10c violet	.30	.30
79	A56	30c deep magenta	.30	.30
80	A56	40c dull blue	.30	.30
81	A56	50c orange red	.30	.30
82	A56	60c black	.30	.30
83	A56	70c brt red violet	.30	.30
84	A56	80c blue green	.30	.30
		Nos. 78-84 (7)	2.10	2.10

See No. 114.

St. Jean de Caselles — A57

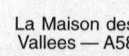

La Maison des Vallees — A58

Old Andorra — A59

Provost — A60

1944-47 *Perf. 13*

85	A57	1fr brown violet	.25	.25
86	A57	1.20fr blue	.25	.25
87	A57	1.50fr red	.25	.25
88	A57	2fr dk blue grn	.25	.25
89	A58	2.40fr rose red	.25	.25
90	A58	2.50fr rose red ('46)	7.25	.80
91	A58	3fr sepia	.25	.25
92	A58	4fr ultra	.40	.25
93	A59	4.50fr brown blk	.40	.25
94	A58	4.50fr dk bl grn ('47)	9.50	5.50
95	A59	5fr ultra	.35	.25
96	A59	5fr Prus grn ('46)	1.40	.50
97	A59	6fr rose car ('45)	.35	.25
98	A59	10fr Prus green	.35	.25
99	A59	10fr ultra ('46)	2.40	.40

100 A60 15fr rose lilac .95 .40
101 A60 20fr deep blue .95 .40
102 A60 25fr lt rose red ('46) 5.50 1.90
103 A60 40fr dk green ('46) 5.50 2.00
104 A60 50fr sepia 1.75 1.40
Nos. 85-104 (20) 38.55 16.05

1948-49

105 A58 4fr lt blue grn 1.60 .80
106 A59 6fr violet brn .80 .40
107 A59 8fr indigo 1.25 1.20
108 A59 12fr bright red 1.25 1.20
109 A59 12fr blue grn ('49) 1.50 .75
110 A59 15fr crimson ('49) 1.00 .55
111 A60 18fr deep blue 5.00 2.40
112 A60 20fr dark violet 3.50 2.00
113 A60 25fr ultra ('49) 2.50 1.20
Nos. 105-113 (9) 18.40 10.50

1949-51 ***Perf. 14x13, 13***

114 A56 1fr deep blue .95 .65
115 A57 3fr red ('51) 7.25 4.75
116 A57 4fr sepia 2.50 2.25
117 A58 5fr emerald 3.75 2.75
118 A58 5fr purple ('51) 13.50 4.75
119 A58 6fr blue grn ('51) 7.25 3.25
120 A58 8fr brown .95 .75
121 A59 15fr blk brn ('51) 16.00 3.00
122 A59 18fr rose red ('51) 30.00 15.00
123 A60 30fr ultra ('51) 40.00 22.50
Nos. 114-123 (10) 122.15 59.65

Les Escaldres Spa — A61

St. Coloma Belfry — A62

Designs: 15fr-25fr, Gothic cross. 30fr-75fr, Village of Les Bons.

1955-58 **Unwmk.** **Engr.** ***Perf. 13***

124 A61 1fr dk gray bl .25 .25
125 A61 2fr dp green .35 .25
126 A61 3fr red .35 .25
127 A61 5fr chocolate .35 .25
128 A62 6fr dk bl grn .80 .80
129 A62 8fr rose brown .80 .80
130 A62 10fr brt violet 1.25 .80
131 A62 12fr indigo 1.60 .80
132 A61 15fr red 1.60 .85
133 A61 18fr blue grn 2.00 .85
134 A61 20fr dp purple 3.50 2.00
135 A61 25fr sepia 3.50 2.00
136 A62 30fr deep blue 40.00 19.50
137 A62 35fr Prus bl ('57) 12.00 7.25
138 A62 40fr dk green 47.50 28.00
139 A62 50fr cerise 4.50 3.25
140 A62 65fr purple ('58) 12.00 6.50
141 A62 70fr chestnut ('57) 7.25 6.50
142 A62 75fr violet blue 65.00 45.00
Nos. 124-142 (19) 204.60 125.90

Issued: 35fr, 70fr, 8/19; 65fr, 2/10; others, 2/15.

Coat of Arms A63

Gothic Cross, Meritxell A64

65c, 85c, 1fr, Engolasters Lake.

1961, June 19 **Typo.** ***Perf. 14x13***

143 A63 5c brt green & blk .25 .25
144 A63 10c red, pink & blk .25 .25
145 A63 15c blue & black .25 .25
146 A63 20c yellow & brown .40 .30

Engr. ***Perf. 13***

147 A64 25c violet, bl & grn .60 .30
148 A64 30c mar, ol grn & brn .70 .50
149 A64 45c indigo, bl & grn 17.50 16.00
150 A64 50c pur, lt brn & ol grn 1.50 1.25
151 A64 65c bl, ol & brn 22.00 18.50
152 A64 85c rose lil, vio bl & brn 22.00 18.50
153 A64 1fr grnsh bl, ind & brn 1.50 1.25
Nos. 143-153 (11) 66.95 57.35

See Nos. 161-166A.

Imperforates

Most stamps of Andorra, French Administration, from 1961 onward exist imperforate in issued and trial colors, and also in small presentation sheets in issued colors.

Common Design Types pictured following the introduction.

Telstar Issue

Common Design Type

1962, Sept. 29 **Engr.**

154 CD111 50c ultra & purple 2.00 1.60

1st television connection of the US and Europe through the Telstar satellite, 7/11-12.

"La Sardane" — A66

Charlemagne Crossing Andorra — A67

1fr, Louis le Debonnaire giving founding charter.

1963, June 22 **Unwmk.** ***Perf. 13***

155 A66 20c lil rose, cl & ol grn 5.00 5.00
156 A67 50c sl grn & dk car rose 8.50 8.50
157 A67 1fr red brn, ultra & dk grn 14.00 14.00
Nos. 155-157 (3) 27.50 27.50

Old Andorra Church and Champs-Elysées Palace — A68

1964, Jan. 20 **Engr.**

158 A68 25c vio brn, grn & blk 2.00 1.60

"PHILATEC," Intl. Philatelic and Postal Techniques Exhib., Paris, June 5-21, 1964.

Bishop of Urgel and Seigneur of Caboet Confirming Co-Principality, 1288 — A69

Design: 60c, Napoleon re-establishing Co-principality, 1806.

1964, Apr. 25 **Engr.** ***Perf. 13***

159 A69 60c dk brn, red brn & sl grn 22.50 22.50
160 A69 1fr brt bl, org brn & blk 22.50 22.50

Arms Type of 1961

1964, May 16 **Typo.** ***Perf. 14x13***

161 A63 1c dk blue & gray .25 .25
162 A63 2c black & orange .25 .25
163 A63 12c purple, emer & yel .90 .90
164 A63 18c black, lil & pink 1.00 1.00
Nos. 161-164 (4) 2.40 2.40

Scenic Type of 1961

Designs: 40c, 45c, Gothic Cross, Meritxell. 60c, 90c, Pond of Engolasters.

1965-71 **Engr.** ***Perf. 13***

165 A64 40c dk brn, org brn & sl grn 1.00 .80
165A A64 45c vio bl, ol bis & slate 1.10 .80
166 A64 60c org brn & dk brn 1.60 1.25
166A A64 90c ultra, bl grn & bister 2.00 1.00
Nos. 165-166A (4) 5.70 3.85

Issued: 40c, 60c, Apr. 24, 1965. 45c, June 13, 1970. 90c, Aug. 28, 1971.

Syncom Satellite over Pleumeur-Bodou Station — A70

1965, May 17 **Unwmk.**

167 A70 60c dp car, lil & bl 6.50 4.75

Cent. of the ITU.

Andorra House, Paris — A71

1965, June 5

168 A71 25c dk bl, org brn & ol gray 1.25 .80

Ski Lift — A72

Design: 25c, Chair lift, vert.

1966, Apr. 2 **Engr.** ***Perf. 13***

169 A72 25c brt bl, grn & dk brn 1.60 1.25
170 A72 40c mag, brt ultra & sep 2.40 1.60

Winter sports in Andorra.

FR-1 Satellite A73

1966, May 7 ***Perf. 13***

171 A73 60c brt bl, grn & dk grn 2.10 1.60

Issued to commemorate the launching of the scientific satellite FR-1, Dec. 6, 1965.

Europa Issue, 1966

Common Design Type

1966, Sept. 24 **Engr.** ***Perf. 13***

Size: 21½x35½mm

172 CD9 60c brown *3.00 3.00*

Folk Dancers, Sculpture by Josep Viladomat — A74

1967, Apr. 29 **Engr.** ***Perf. 13***

173 A74 30c ol grn, dp grn & slate 1.25 .80

Cent. (in 1966) of the New Reform, which reaffirmed and strengthened political freedom in Andorra.

Europa Issue, 1967

Common Design Type

1967, Apr. 29

Size: 22x36mm

174 CD10 30c bluish blk & lt bl *4.25 1.75*
175 CD10 60c dk red & brt pink *6.50 4.50*

Telephone Encircling the Globe — A75

1967, Apr. 29

176 A75 60c dk car, vio & blk 2.00 1.25

Automatic telephone service.

Injured Father at Home — A76

1967, Sept. 23 **Engr.** ***Perf. 13***

177 A76 2.30fr ocher, dk red brn & brn red 9.75 7.50

Introduction of Social Security System.

Jesus in Garden of Gethsemane A77

Designs (from 16th century frescoes in La Maison des Vallees): 30c, The Kiss of Judas. 60c, The Descent from the Cross (Pieta).

1967, Sept. 23

178 A77 25c black & red brn .80 .80
179 A77 30c purple & red lilac .80 .80
180 A77 60c indigo & Prus blue 1.60 1.25
Nos. 178-180 (3) 3.20 2.85

See Nos. 185-187.

Downhill Skier — A78

1968, Jan. 27 **Engr.** ***Perf. 13***

181 A78 40c org, ver & red lil 1.60 1.25

10th Winter Olympic Games, Grenoble, France, Feb. 6-18.

Europa Issue, 1968

Common Design Type

1968, Apr. 27 **Engr.** ***Perf. 13***

Size: 36x22mm

182 CD11 30c gray & brt bl *6.50 3.00*
183 CD11 60c brown & lilac *10.00 7.00*

High Jump — A79

1968, Oct. 12 **Engr.** ***Perf. 13***

184 A79 40c brt blue & brn 1.50 1.25

19th Olympic Games, Mexico City, Oct. 12-27.

Fresco Type of 1967

Designs (from 16th century frescoes in La Maison des Vallees): 25c, The Scourging of Christ. 30c, Christ Carrying the Cross. 60c, The Crucifixion. (All horiz.)

1968, Oct. 12

185 A77 25c dk grn & gray grn .85 .80
186 A77 30c dk brown & lilac .85 .80
187 A77 60c dk car & vio brn 1.75 1.25
Nos. 185-187 (3) 3.45 2.85

Europa Issue, 1969
Common Design Type

1969, Apr. 26 Engr. *Perf. 13*
188 CD12 40c rose car, gray & dl bl *7.50 3.50*
189 CD12 70c indigo, dl red & ol *11.00 8.50*

10th anniv. of the Conf. of European Postal and Telecommunications Administrations.

Kayak on Isere River — A80

1969, Aug. 2 Engr. *Perf. 13*
190 A80 70c dk sl grn, ultra & ind 2.50 2.75

Intl. Canoe & Kayak Championships, Bourg-Saint-Maurice, Savoy, July 31-Aug. 6.

Drops of Water & Diamond — A80a

1969, Sept. 27 Engr. *Perf. 13*
191 A80a 70c blk, dp ultra & grnsh bl 3.25 4.00

European Water Charter.

St. John, the Woman and the Dragon — A81

The Revelation (From the Altar of St. John, Caselles): 40c, St. John Hearing Voice from Heaven on Patmos. 70c, St. John and the Seven Candlesticks.

1969, Oct. 18
192 A81 30c brn, dp pur & brn red .75 .75
193 A81 40c gray, dk brn & brn ol 1.10 1.10
194 A81 70c dk red, maroon & brt rose lilac 1.40 1.40
Nos. 192-194 (3) 3.25 3.25

See Nos. 199-201, 207-209, 214-216.

Field Ball — A82

1970, Feb. 21 Engr. *Perf. 13*
195 A82 80c multi 2.00 2.00

Issued to publicize the 7th International Field Ball Games, France, Feb. 26-Mar. 8.

Europa Issue, 1970
Common Design Type

1970, May 2 Engr. *Perf. 13*
Size: 36x22mm
196 CD13 40c orange *6.00 2.50*
197 CD13 80c violet blue *14.00 6.00*

Shot Put — A83

1970, Sept. 11 Engr. *Perf. 13*
198 A83 80c bl & dk brn 2.00 2.00

1st European Junior Athletic Championships, Colombes, France, Sept. 11-13.

Altar Type of 1969

The Revelation (from the Altar of St. John, Caselles): 30c, St. John recording angel's message. 40c, Angel erecting column symbolizing faithful in heaven. 80c, St. John's trial in kettle of boiling oil.

1970, Oct. 24
199 A81 30c dp car, dk brn & brt pur .90 .90
200 A81 40c violet & slate grn 1.10 1.10
201 A81 80c ol, dk bl & car rose 1.90 1.90
Nos. 199-201 (3) 3.90 3.90

Ice Skating — A84

1971, Feb. 20 Engr. *Perf. 13*
202 A84 80c dk red, red lil & pur 2.00 2.00

World Figure Skating Championships, Lyons, France, Feb. 23-28.

Capercaillie — A85

Nature protection: No. 204, Brown bear.

1971, Apr. 24 Photo. *Perf. 13*
203 A85 80c multicolored 3.25 3.25
Engr.
204 A85 80c blue, grn & brn 2.40 2.40

Europa Issue, 1971
Common Design Type

1971, May 8 Engr. *Perf. 13*
Size: 35½x22mm
205 CD14 50c rose red *8.00 2.25*
206 CD14 80c lt blue green *12.00 5.50*

Altar Type of 1969

The Revelation (from the Altar of St. John, Caselles): 30c, St. John preaching, Rev. 1:3. 50c, "The Sign of the Beast . . ." Rev. 16:1-2. 90c, The Woman, Rev. 17:1.

1971, Sept. 18
207 A81 30c dl grn, ol & brt grn 1.25 1.00
208 A81 50c rose car, org & ol brn 1.60 1.25
209 A81 90c blk, dk pur & bl 2.40 2.00
Nos. 207-209 (3) 5.25 4.25

Europa Issue 1972
Common Design Type

1972, Apr. 29 Photo. *Perf. 13*
Size: 21½x37mm
210 CD15 50c brt mag & multi *7.50 2.50*
211 CD15 90c multicolored *13.50 4.50*

Golden Eagle — A86

1972, May 27 Engr.
212 A86 60c dk grn, olive & plum 5.00 3.25

Nature protection.

Shooting — A87

1972, July 8
213 A87 1fr dk purple 3.75 2.00

20th Olympic Games, Munich, 8/26-9/11.

Altar Type of 1969

The Revelation (from the Altar of St. John, Caselles): 30c, St. John, bishop and servant. 50c, Resurrection of Lazarus. 90c, Angel with lance and nails.

1972, Sept. 16 Engr. *Perf. 13*
214 A81 30c dk ol, gray & red lil 1.25 .85
215 A81 50c vio blue & slate 1.50 1.25
216 A81 90c dk Prus bl & sl grn 2.40 2.40
Nos. 214-216 (3) 5.15 4.50

De Gaulle as Coprince of Andorra — A88

90c, De Gaulle in front of Maison des Vallées.

1972, Oct. 23 Engr. *Perf. 13*
217 A88 50c violet blue 2.00 2.00
218 A88 90c dk carmine 3.00 3.00
a. Pair, #217-218 + label 6.00 6.00

Visit of Charles de Gaulle to Andorra, 5th anniv.
See Nos. 399-400.

Europa Issue 1973
Common Design Type

1973, Apr. 28 Photo. *Perf. 13*
Size: 36x22mm
219 CD16 50c violet & multi *9.00 3.00*
220 CD16 90c dk red & multi *11.00 8.00*

Virgin of Canolich — A89

1973, June 16 Engr. *Perf. 13*
221 A89 1fr ol, Prus bl & vio 2.25 1.60

Lily — A90

45c, Iris. 50c, Columbine. 65c, Tobacco. No. 226, Pinks. No. 227, Narcissuses.

1973-74 Photo. *Perf. 13*
222 A90 30c car rose & multi .80 .80
223 A90 45c yel grn & multi .40 .40
224 A90 50c buff & multi 1.75 1.75
225 A90 65c gray & multi .40 .40
226 A90 90c ultra & multi 1.50 1.50
227 A90 90c grnsh bl & multi 1.25 1.25
Nos. 222-227 (6) 6.10 6.10

Issued: 30c, 50c, No. 226, 7/7/73. 45c, 65c, No. 227, 4/6/74.
See Nos. 238-240.

Blue Titmouse — A91

Nature protection: 60c, Citril finch and mistletoe. 80c, Eurasian bullfinch. 1fr, Lesser spotted woodpecker.

1973-74 Photo. *Perf. 13*
228 A91 60c buff & multi 4.00 1.75
229 A91 80c gray & multi 4.00 2.25
230 A91 90c gray & multi 2.75 1.25
231 A91 1fr yel grn & multi 2.75 1.60
Nos. 228-231 (4) 13.50 6.85

Issued: 90c, 1fr, 10/27/73. 60c, 80c, 9/21/74.

Europa Issue

Virgin of Pal — A92

90c, Virgin of Santa Coloma. Statues are polychrome 12th cent. carvings by rural artists.

1974, Apr. 27 Engr. *Perf. 13*
232 A92 50c multicolored *9.00 3.00*
233 A92 90c multicolored *12.50 7.00*

Arms of Andorra and Cahors Bridge — A93

1974, Aug. 24 Engr. *Perf. 13*
234 A93 1fr blue, vio & org 1.00 .80

First anniv. of meeting of the co-princes of Andorra: Pres. Georges Pompidou of France and Msgr. Juan Marti Alanis, Bishop of Urgel.

Mail Box, Chutes and Globe — A94

1974, Oct. 5 Engr. *Perf. 13*
235 A94 1.20fr multi 1.25 1.25

Centenary of Universal Postal Union.

Coronation of St. Marti, 16th Century — A95

Europa: 80c, Crucifixion, 16th cent., vert.

Perf. 11½x13, 13x11½
1975, Apr. 26 Photo.
236 A95 80c gold & multi *4.50 3.00*
237 A95 1.20fr gold & multi *6.50 4.00*

Flower Type of 1973

Designs: 60c, Gentian. 80c, Anemone. 1.20fr, Autumn crocus.

1975, May 10 Photo. *Perf. 13*
238 A90 60c olive & multi .50 .40
239 A90 80c brt rose & multi 1.25 .80
240 A90 1.20fr green & multi 1.25 .80
Nos. 238-240 (3) 3.00 2.00

Abstract Design A96

1975, June 7 **Engr.** ***Perf. 13***
241 A96 2fr bl, magenta & emer 1.75 1.50

ARPHILA 75 International Philatelic Exhibition, Paris, June 6-16.

A97

1975, Aug. 23 **Engr.** ***Perf. 13***
242 A97 80c violet bl & blk 1.00 1.00

Georges Pompidou (1911-74), pres. of France and co-prince of Andorra (1969-74).

A98

1975, Nov. 8 **Engr.** ***Perf. 13***
243 A98 1.20fr Costume, IWY Emblem 1.25 1.00

International Women's Year.

Skier and Snowflake — A99

1976, Jan. 31 **Engr.** ***Perf. 13***
244 A99 1.20fr multicolored 1.50 1.10

12th Winter Olympic Games, Innsbruck, Austria, Feb. 4-15.

Telephone and Satellite — A100

1976, Mar. 20 **Engr.** ***Perf. 13***
245 A100 1fr multicolored 1.00 1.00

Centenary of first telephone call by Alexander Graham Bell, Mar. 10, 1976.

Catalan Forge — A101

Europa: 1.20fr, Woolen worker.

1976, May 8 **Engr.** ***Perf. 13***
246 A101 80c multi *3.25 1.00*
247 A101 1.20fr multi *4.75 1.75*

Thomas Jefferson — A102

1976, July 3 **Engr.** ***Perf. 13***
248 A102 1.20fr multi 1.25 1.00

American Bicentennial.

Trapshooting — A103

1976, July 17 **Engr.** ***Perf. 13***
249 A103 2fr multi 1.75 1.40

21st Olympic Games, Montreal, Canada, July 17-Aug. 1.

Meritxell Sanctuary and Old Chapel A104

1976, Sept. 4 **Engr.** ***Perf. 13***
250 A104 1fr multi 1.00 1.00

Dedication of rebuilt Meritxell Church, Sept. 8, 1976.

Apollo — A105

Design: 1.40fr, Morio butterfly.

1976, Oct. 16 **Photo.** ***Perf. 13***
251 A105 80c black & multi 1.90 1.25
252 A105 1.40fr salmon & multi 3.25 2.00

Nature protection.

Ermine — A106

1977, Apr. 2 **Photo.** ***Perf. 13***
253 A106 1fr vio bl, gray & blk 1.60 1.25

Nature protection.

St. Jean de Caselles — A107

Europa: 1.40fr, Sant Vicens Castle.

1977, Apr. 30 **Engr.** ***Perf. 13***
254 A107 1fr multi *3.00 1.25*
255 A107 1.40fr multi *4.75 2.00*

Manual Digest, 1748, Arms of Andorra — A108

1977, June 11 **Engr.** ***Perf. 13***
256 A108 80c grn, bl & brn .90 .90

Establishment of Institute of Andorran Studies.

St. Romanus of Caesarea — A109

1977, July 23 **Engr.** ***Perf. 12½x13***
257 A109 2fr multi 1.75 1.50

Design from altarpiece in Church of St. Roma de les Bons.

General Council Chamber A110

Guillem d'Arény Plandolit A111

1977, Sept. 24 **Engr.** ***Perf. 13***
258 A110 1.10fr multi 1.40 1.00
259 A111 2fr car & dk brn 1.40 1.00

Andorran heritage. Guillem d'Arény Plandolit started Andorran reform movement in 1866.

Squirrel — A112

1978, Mar. 18 **Engr.** ***Perf. 13***
260 A112 1fr multi .90 .75

Flag and Valira River Bridge — A113

1978, Apr. 8
261 A113 80c multi .65 .65

Signing of the treaty establishing the Co-Principality of Andorra, 700th anniv.

Pal Church — A114

Europa: 1.40fr, Charlemagne's Castle, Charlemagne on horseback, vert.

1978, Apr. 29 **Engr.** ***Perf. 13***
262 A114 1fr multi *3.00 1.50*
263 A114 1.40fr multi *5.50 2.75*

Virgin of Sispony — A115

1978, May 20 **Engr.** ***Perf. 12x13***
264 A115 2fr multi 1.50 1.25

Visura Tribunal — A116

1978, June 24 **Engr.** ***Perf. 13***
265 A116 1.20fr multi 1.00 .50

Preamble of 1278 Treaty A117

1978, Sept. 2 **Engr.** ***Perf. 13x12½***
266 A117 1.70fr multi 1.00 .75

700th anniversary of the signing of treaty establishing Co-Principality of Andorra.

Pyrenean Chamois — A118

1979, Mar. 26 **Engr.** ***Perf. 13***
267 A118 1fr multi .65 .65

White Partridges — A119

1979, Apr. 7 **Photo.** ***Perf. 13***
268 A119 1.20fr multi 1.50 .75

Nature protection. See Nos. 288-289.

French Mailman, 1900 — A120

Europa: 1.70fr, 1st French p.o. in Andorra.

1979, Apr. 28 **Engr.** ***Perf. 13***
269 A120 1.20fr multi *2.00 .75*
270 A120 1.70fr multi *4.00 1.25*

Falcon, Pre-Roman Painting — A121

1979, June 2 **Engr.** ***Perf. 12½x13***
271 A121 2fr multi 1.10 .90

Child with Lambs, Church, IYC Emblem. — A122

1979, July 7 **Photo.** ***Perf. 13***
272 A122 1.70fr multi 1.20 .85

International Year of the Child.

Trobada Monument — A123

1979, Sept. 29 **Engr.** ***Perf. 13***
273 A123 2fr multi 1.25 1.00

Co-Principality of Andorra, 700th anniv

Judo Hold — A124

1979, Nov. 24 **Engr.** ***Perf. 13***
274 A124 1.30fr multi .90 .75

World Judo Championships, Paris, Dec. 1979.

Farm House, Cortinada — A125

1980, Jan. 26 **Engr.** ***Perf. 13***
275 A125 1.10fr multi .75 .60

Cross-Country Skiing — A126

1980, Feb. 9
276 A126 1.80fr ultra & lil rose 1.50 1.10

13th Winter Olympic Games, Lake Placid, NY, Feb. 12-24.

A128

1980, Aug. 30 **Engr.** ***Perf. 13***
278 A128 1.20fr multi .75 .75

World Bicycling championships.

A129

Europa: 1.30fr, Charlemagne (742-814). 1.80fr, Napoleon I (1769-1821).

1980, Apr. 26 **Engr.** ***Perf. 13***
279 A129 1.30fr multi *1.75 .60*
280 A129 1.80fr gray grn & brn *2.00 1.00*

Pyrenees Lily — A130

1.10fr, Dog-toothed violet.

1980 **Photo.**
281 A130 1.10fr multicolored .75 .55
282 A130 1.30fr shown .75 .65

Nature protection. Issue dates: 1.10fr, June 21; 1.30fr, May 17.

De La Vall House, 400th Anniversary of Restoration A131

1980, Sept. 6 **Engr.**
283 A131 1.40fr multi .75 .65

Angel, Church of St. Cerni de Nagol, Pre-Romanesque Fresco — A132

1980, Oct. 25 ***Perf. 13x12½***
284 A132 2fr multi 1.25 1.25

Bordes de Mereig Mountain Village — A133

1981, Mar. 21 **Engr.** ***Perf. 13***
285 A133 1.40fr bl gray & dk brn .80 .80

Europa Issue

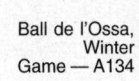

Ball de l'Ossa, Winter Game — A134

2fr, El Contrapas dance.

1981, May 16 **Engr.**
286 A134 1.40fr shown *1.50 .50*
287 A134 2fr multicolored *1.75 1.00*

Bird Type of 1979

1.20fr, Phylloscopus bonelli. 1.40fr, Tichodroma muraria.

1981, June 20 **Photo.**
288 A119 1.20fr multicolored .65 .65
289 A119 1.40fr multicolored 1.00 .65

World Fencing Championship, Clermont-Ferrand, July 2-13 — A135

1981, July 4 **Engr.**
290 A135 2fr bl & blk .90 .80

St. Martin, 12th Cent. Tapestry — A136

1981, Sept. 5 **Engr.** ***Perf. 12x13***
291 A136 3fr multi 1.25 1.00

Intl. Drinking Water Decade — A137

1981, Oct. 17 ***Perf. 13***
292 A137 1.60fr multi .75 .50

Intl. Year of the Disabled — A138

1981, Nov. 7
293 A138 2.30fr multi 1.00 .65

Europa 1982 — A139

1.60fr, Creation of Andorran govt., 1982. 2.30fr, Land Council, 1419.

1982, May 8 **Engr.** ***Perf. 13***
294 A139 1.60fr multi *1.50 .70*
295 A139 2.30fr multi *2.00 .70*

1982 World Cup A140

Various soccer players.

1982, June 12 **Engr.** ***Perf. 13***
296 1.60fr red & dk brn .80 .65
297 2.60fr red & dk brn 1.10 .95
a. A140 Pair, #296-297 + label 2.25 2.25

Souvenir Sheet

No. 52 A141

1982, Aug. 21 **Engr.**
298 A141 5fr blk & rose car 2.40 2.40

1st Andorran Stamp Exhib., 8/21-9/19.

Horse, Roman Wall Painting A142

1982, Sept. 4 **Photo.** ***Perf. 13x12½***
299 A142 3fr multi 1.25 1.00

Wild Cat — A143

1982, Oct. 9 **Engr.** ***Perf. 13***
300 A143 1.80fr shown 1.10 .85
301 A143 2.60fr Pine trees .90 .75

TB Bacillus Centenary — A144

1982, Nov. 13
302 A144 2.10fr Koch, lungs .85 .65

St. Thomas Aquinas (1225-74) — A145

1982, Dec. 4
303 A145 2fr multi .85 .65

Manned Flight Bicentenary A146

1983, Feb. 26 **Engr.**
304 A146 2fr multi .90 .75

Nature Protection — A147

1983, Apr. 16 **Engr.** ***Perf. 13***
305 A147 1fr Birch trees .40 .30
306 A147 1.50fr Trout .75 .55

See Nos. 325-326.

Catalane Gold Works — A148

1983, May 7 **Engr.** ***Perf. 13***
307 A148 1.80fr Exterior *1.00 .50*
308 A148 2.60fr Interior *1.60 .80*

Europa.

30th Anniv. of Customs Cooperation Council — A149

3fr, Letter of King Louis XIII.

1983, May 14
309 A149 3fr multicolored 1.25 1.00

First Arms of Valleys of Andorra — A150

1983, Sept. 3 **Engr.** ***Perf. 13***
310 A150 5c olive grn & red .25 .25
311 A150 10c grn & olive grn .25 .25
312 A150 20c brt pur & red .25 .25
313 A150 30c brn vio & red .35 .35
314 A150 40c dk bl & vio .35 .35
315 A150 50c gray & red .25 .25
316 A150 1fr deep magenta .25 .25
317 A150 2fr org red & red brn .90 .40
318 A150 5fr dk brn & red 1.25 .80
Nos. 310-318 (9) 4.10 3.15

See Nos. 329-335, 380-385, 464-465.

Painting, Cortinada Church — A151

1983, Sept. 24 ***Perf. 12x13***
319 A151 4fr multi 1.75 1.00

Plandolit House — A152

1983, Oct. 15 **Photo.** ***Perf. 13***
320 A152 1.60fr dp ultra & brn .75 .55

1984 Winter Olympics — A153

1984, Feb. 18 **Engr.**
321 A153 2.80fr multicolored 1.25 .90

Pyrenees Region Work Community (Labor Org.) — A154

1984, Apr. 28 **Engr.** ***Perf. 13***
322 A154 3fr brt blue & sepia 1.20 .90

Europa (1959-84) — A155

1984, May 5 **Engr.**
323 A155 2fr brt grn *1.60 .80*
324 A155 2.80fr rose car *2.75 1.40*

Nature Protection Type of 1983

1984, July 7 **Engr.** ***Perf. 13***
325 A147 1.70fr Chestnut tree .80 .40
326 A147 2.10fr Walnut tree 1.20 .65

Pyrenees Art Center — A155a

1984, Sept. 7 **Engr.**
327 A155a 3fr multi 1.40 1.00

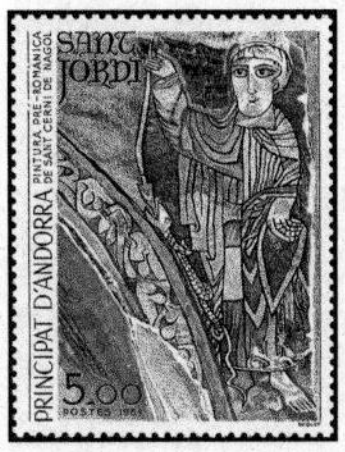

Romanesque Fresco, Church of St. Cerni de Nagol — A156

1984, Nov. 17 ***Perf. 12x13***
328 A156 5fr multi 2.25 1.90

First Arms Type of 1983

1984-87 **Engr.** ***Perf. 13***
329 A150 1.90fr emerald 3.25 .80
330 A150 2.20fr red orange 1.25 .40
a. Bklt. pane, 2 #329, 6 #330 15.00
331 A150 3fr bl grn & red brn 1.50 1.00
332 A150 4fr brt org & brn 3.50 1.25
333 A150 10fr brn org & blk 3.50 1.60
334 A150 15fr grn & dk grn 5.00 2.40
335 A150 20fr brt bl & red brn 7.00 2.75
Nos. 329-335 (7) 25.00 10.20

Nos. 329-330 issued in booklets only.
Issued: 3fr, 20fr, 12/1/84; 10fr, 2/9/85; 4fr, 15fr, 4/19/86; 1.90fr, 2.20fr, 3/28/87.

Saint Julia Valley — A157

1985, Apr. 13 **Engr.**
336 A157 2fr multi 1.00 .60

Europa 1985 — A158

2.10fr, Le Val D'Andorre. 3fr, Instruments.

1985, May 4 **Engr.**
337 A158 2.10fr multicolored *1.75 .75*
338 A158 3fr multicolored *4.00 1.25*

Intl. Youth Year — A159

1985, June 8 **Engr.**
339 A159 3fr multicolored 1.25 .90

Wildlife Conservation A160

1.80fr, Anas platyrhynchos. 2.20fr, Carduelis carduelis.

1985, Aug. 3 **Photo.**
340 A160 1.80fr multicolored 1.00 .65
341 A160 2.20fr multicolored 1.40 .85

Two Saints, Medieval Fresco in St. Cerni de Nagol Church — A161

1985, Sept. 14 **Engr.** ***Perf. 12½x13***
342 A161 5fr multicolored 2.00 1.75

Postal Museum Inauguration — A162

1986, Mar. 22 **Engr.** ***Perf. 13***
343 A162 2.20fr like No. 269 1.00 .65

Europa 1986 — A163

1986, May 3 **Engr.** ***Perf. 13***
344 A163 2.20fr Ansalonga *2.50 .90*
345 A163 3.20fr Isard *5.00 1.60*

1986 World Cup Soccer Championships, Mexico — A164

1986, June 14
346 A164 3fr multi 1.50 1.00

Angonella Lake — A165

1986, June 28
347 A165 2.20fr multi 1.00 .70

Manual Digest Frontispiece, 1748 — A166

1986, Sept. 6 **Engr.**
348 A166 5fr chnt brn, gray ol & blk 2.25 1.40

Intl. Peace Year — A167

1986, Sept. 27
349 A167 1.90fr bl gray & grnsh bl 1.00 .65

St. Vincenc d'Enclar — A168

1986, Oct. 18 **Engr.** ***Perf. 13½x13***
350 A168 1.90fr multicolored .95 .65

Contemporary Natl. Coat of Arms — A169

1987, Mar. 27 **Litho.** ***Perf. 12½x13***
351 A169 2.20fr multi 1.60 1.60

Visit of the French co-prince.

Europa 1987 — A170

2.20fr, Meritxell Sanctuary. 3.40fr, Pleta D'Ordino.

1987, May 2 **Engr.** ***Perf. 13***
352 A170 2.20fr multicolored *2.00 .80*
353 A170 3.40fr multicolored *4.50 2.00*

Ransol Village — A171

1987, June 13 **Photo.**
354 A171 1.90fr multicolored 1.25 1.00

Nature — A172

1.90fr, Cavall rogenc. 2.20fr, Graellsia isabellae.

1987, July 4
355 A172 1.90fr multicolored 1.25 .80
356 A172 2.20fr multicolored 1.60 1.25

Aryalsu, Romanesque Painting, La Cortinada Church — A173

Litho. & Engr.

1987, Sept. 5 ***Perf. 12½x13***
357 A173 5fr multi 2.50 1.60

Hiker Looking at Map — A174

1987, Sept. 19 **Engr.** ***Perf. 13***
358 A174 2fr olive, grn & dark brn vio 1.00 .60

Medieval Iron Key, La Cortinada — A175

1987, Oct. 17 **Litho.**
359 A175 3fr multi 1.25 1.00

Andorran Coat of Arms — A176

Booklet Stamp

1988, Feb. 6 **Engr.** ***Perf. 13***
360 A176 2.20fr red 1.00 .50
a. Bklt. pane of 5 5.00
Complete bklt., 2 #360a 10.00

See Nos. 386-388.

Shoemaker's Last from Roc de l'Oral — A177

1988, Feb. 13 **Photo.**
361 A177 3fr multi 1.50 1.10

Rugby — A178

1988, Mar. 19 **Engr.** ***Perf. 13½x13***
362 A178 2.20fr blk, org, turq grn 1.20 .95

Europa 1988 — A179

Transport and communication: 2.20fr, Broadcast tower. 3.60fr, Computer graphics.

1988, Apr. 30 Engr. *Perf. 13*
363 A179 2.20fr multicolored *1.75 .90*
364 A179 3.60fr multicolored *3.75 1.10*

Hot Springs, Escaldes — A180

1988, May 14 Engr.
365 A180 2.20fr Prus blue, org brn & emer 1.25 .80

Tor D'Ansalonga Farmhouse, Ansalonga Pass — A181

1988, June 11 Engr.
366 A181 2fr multi 1.10 .65

Sheepdog — A182

1988, July 2 Photo.
367 A182 2fr shown 1.50 .60
368 A182 2.20fr Hare 1.50 .60

Roman Fresco, 8th Cent., St. Steven's Church, Andorre-La-Vieille — A183

1988, Sept. 3 Engr. *Perf. 13x12½*
369 A183 5fr multicolored 2.25 1.50

French Revolution, Bicent. — A184

1989, Jan. 1 Litho. *Perf. 13*
370 A184 2.20fr red & vio bl 1.00 1.00

Poble de Pal Village — A185

1989, Mar. 4 Engr. *Perf. 13*
371 A185 2.20fr indigo & lilac 1.00 .65

Europa 1989 — A186

Children's games: 2.20fr, Human tower. 3.60fr, The handkerchief.

1989, Apr. 29 Engr. *Perf. 13*
372 A186 2.20fr multi *2.00 .80*
373 A186 3.60fr multi *2.50 1.75*

Red Cross — A187

1989, May 6
374 A187 3.60fr multi 1.75 1.25

Visigothic — Merovingian Age Cincture from a Column, St. Vicenc D'Anclar — A188

1989, June 3 Photo.
375 A188 3fr multi 1.40 1.10

Wildlife — A189

1989, Sept. 16 Engr. *Perf. 13*
376 A189 2.20fr Wild boar 1.25 .90
377 A189 3.60fr Newt 2.00 1.25

Scene of Salome from the Retable of St. Michael of Mosquera, Encamp A190

1989, Oct. 14 *Perf. 13x13½*
378 A190 5fr multi 2.50 1.25

La Margineda Bridge — A191

1990, Feb. 26 Engr. *Perf. 13*
379 A191 2.30fr multi 1.25 .60

Tourism.

Arms Types of 1983 and 1988

1990-93 Engr. *Perf. 13*
380 A150 2.10fr green 1.00 .40
381 A150 2.20fr green 1.25 .40
382 A150 2.30fr vermilion 1.00 .40
383 A150 2.40fr green 1.40 .80
384 A150 2.50fr vermilion 1.25 .40
385 A150 2.80fr vermilion 1.60 .40
Nos. 380-385 (6) 7.50 2.80

Booklet Stamps

Perf. 13

386 A176 2.30fr red 1.00 .40
a. Booklet pane of 5 5.00
387 A176 2.50fr vermilion 1.25 .40
a. Booklet pane of 5 6.25
388 A176 2.80fr red 1.25 .40
c. Booklet pane of 5 6.25
Nos. 386-388 (3) 3.50 1.20

Issued: 2.20fr, #384, 10/26/91; #387, 10/21/91; 2.40fr, 2.80fr, 8/9/93; 2.10fr, 2.30fr, 1990.

Llorts Mines — A193

1990, Apr. 21 Engr. *Perf. 12½x13*
390 A193 3.20fr multicolored 1.75 1.00

Europa — A194

Designs: 2.30fr, Early post office. 3.20fr, Modern post office.

1990, May 5 *Perf. 13*
391 A194 2.30fr blk & scar *2.00 .75*
392 A194 3.20fr scar & vio *3.00 1.50*

Otter — A195

1990, May 25 *Perf. 12x13*
393 A195 2.30fr Roses, vert. 1.10 .55
394 A195 3.20fr shown 1.75 1.00

Censer of St. Roma of Les Bons — A196

1990, June 25 *Perf. 12½x13*
395 A196 3fr multicolored 1.25 .65

Tobacco Drying Sheds, Les Bons — A197

1990, Sept. 15 Engr. *Perf. 12½x13*
396 A197 2.30fr multi 1.00 .65

St. Coloma (Detail) — A198

1990, Oct. 8 *Perf. 12½x13*
397 A198 5fr multi 2.50 1.50

Coin from Church of St. Eulalia d'Encamp — A199

1990, Oct. 27 Litho. *Perf. 13*
398 A199 3.20fr multi 1.40 .75

De Gaulle Type of 1972 Dated 1990

1990, Oct. 23 Engr. *Perf. 13*
399 A88 2.30fr vio bl 1.00 .65
400 A88 3.20fr dk car 1.25 1.10
a. Pair, #399-400 + label 2.50 2.50

Birth centenary of De Gaulle.

4th Games of the Small European States — A200

1991, Apr. 8 Photo. *Perf. 13*
401 A200 2.50fr multicolored 1.00 .60

Chapel of St. Roma Dels Vilars — A201

1991, Mar. 9 Engr. *Perf. 13*
402 A201 2.50fr multicolored 1.10 .65

Europa — A202

2.50fr, TV satellite. 3.50fr, Telescope, horiz.

1991, Apr. 27 *Perf. 13x12½, 12½x13*
403 A202 2.50fr multicolored *2.75 1.75*
404 A202 3.50fr multicolored *4.50 2.25*

Bottles from Tombs of St. Vincenc d'Enclar — A203

1991, May 11 Photo. *Perf. 13*
405 A203 3.20fr multicolored 1.50 1.00

Farm Animals — A204

1991, June 22 Engr. *Perf. 13*
406 A204 2.50fr Sheep 1.25 .80
407 A204 3.50fr Cow 2.00 1.25

Petanque World Championships A205

1991, Sept. 14 Engr. *Perf. 13*
408 A205 2.50fr multicolored 1.25 .95

Wolfgang Amadeus Mozart, Death Bicent. — A206

1991, Oct. 5
409 A206 3.40fr multicolored 1.75 1.10

Virgin and Child of St. Julia and St. Germa — A207

1991, Nov. 16 Engr. *Perf. 12½x13*
410 A207 5fr multicolored 2.00 1.00

1992 Winter Olympics, Albertville — A208

1992, Feb. 10 Litho. *Perf. 13*
411 A208 2.50fr Slalom skiing 1.25 1.00
412 A208 3.40fr Figure skating 1.25 1.00
a. Pair, #411-412 + label 2.75 2.75

Church of St. Andrew of Arinsal — A209

1992, Mar. 21 Engr. *Perf. 12x13*
413 A209 2.50fr black & tan .75 .50

Discovery of America, 500th Anniv. — A210

2.50fr, Columbus' fleet. 3.40fr, Landing in New World.

1992, Apr. 25 ***Perf. 13***

414	A210 2.50fr multicolored	*2.50*	*1.00*
415	A210 3.40fr multicolored	*5.00*	*2.00*

Europa.

1992 Summer Olympics, Barcelona — A211

1992, June 8 **Litho.** ***Perf. 13***

416	A211 2.50fr Kayaking	1.25	1.00
417	A211 3.40fr Shooting	1.25	1.00
a.	Pair, #416-417 + label	2.75	2.75

European Globeflower — A212

Design: 3.40fr, Vulture, horiz.

1992, July 6

418	A212 2.50fr multicolored	1.25	.65
419	A212 3.40fr multicolored	1.75	1.00

Martyrdom of St. Eulalia — A213

1992, Sept. 14 **Photo.** ***Perf. 13***

420	A213 4fr multicolored	1.50	.95

Sculpture by Mauro Staccioli — A214

1992, Oct. 5 **Engr.** ***Perf. 12½x13***

421	A214 5fr multicolored	2.00	1.00

Ordino Arcalis '91.

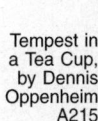

Tempest in a Tea Cup, by Dennis Oppenheim A215

1992, Nov. 14 **Engr.** ***Perf. 13x12½***

422	A215 5fr multicolored	2.00	1.00

Skiing in Andorra — A216

Ski resorts: No. 423: a, 2.50fr, Soldeu El Tarter. b, 3.40fr, Arinsal.

No. 424: a, 2.50fr, Pas de la Casa-Grau Roig. b, 2.50fr, Ordino Arcalis. c, 3.40fr, Pal.

1993, Mar. 13 **Litho.** ***Perf. 13***

423	A216 Pair, #a.-b. + label	2.60	2.60
424	A216 Strip of 3, #a.-c.	3.75	3.75

Sculptures A217

Europa: 2.50fr, "Estructures Autogeneradores," by Jorge du Bon, vert. 3.40fr, Sculpture, "Fisicromia per Andorra," by Carlos Cruz-Diez.

1993, May 15 **Engr.** ***Perf. 12½x13***

425	A217 2.50fr multicolored	*1.60*	*1.25*

Litho.

Perf. 14x13½

426	A217 3.40fr multicolored	*2.00*	*1.50*

Butterflies — A218

2.50fr, Polymmatus icarus. 4.20fr, Nymphalidae.

1993, June 28 **Litho.** ***Perf. 13***

427	A218 2.50fr multicolored	1.20	.65
428	A218 4.20fr multicolored	1.90	1.40

Tour de France Bicycle Race — A219

1993, July 20 **Litho.** ***Perf. 13***

429	A219 2.50fr multicolored	1.25	.65

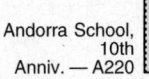

Andorra School, 10th Anniv. — A220

1993, Sept. 20 **Litho.** ***Perf. 13***

430	A220 2.80fr multicolored	1.25	1.00

Un Lloc Paga, by Michael Warren — A221

1993, Oct. 18 **Engr.** ***Perf. 12½x13***

431	A221 5fr blue & black	2.00	1.50

Sculpture, by Erik Dietman — A222

1993, Nov. 8 **Engr.** ***Perf. 12½x13***

432	A222 5fr multicolored	2.00	1.50

1994 Winter Olympics, Lillehammer A223

1994, Feb. 21 **Litho.** ***Perf. 13***

433	A223 3.70fr multicolored	2.25	1.50

1st Anniversary of the Constitution — A224

Designs: 2.80fr, Monument, by Emili Armengol. 3.70fr, Stone tablet with inscription.

1994, Mar. 15 **Litho.** ***Perf. 13***

434	A224 2.80fr multicolored	1.25	1.00
435	A224 3.70fr multicolored	1.25	1.00
a.	Pair, #434-435 + label	2.75	2.75

European Discoveries A225

Europa: 2.80fr, Discovery of AIDS virus. 3.70fr, Radio diffusion.

1994, May 7 **Litho.** ***Perf. 13***

436	A225 2.80fr multicolored	*1.75*	*.90*
437	A225 3.70fr multicolored	*2.75*	*1.25*

1994 World Cup Soccer Championships, US — A226

1994, June 20

438	A226 3.70fr multicolored	2.00	1.25

Tourist Sports — A227

Designs: No. 439, Mountain climbing. No. 440, Fishing. No. 441, Horseback riding. No. 442, Mountain biking.

1994, July 11

439	A227 2.80fr multicolored	1.20	1.00
440	A227 2.80fr multicolored	1.20	1.00
a.	Pair, #439-440 + label	2.50	2.50
441	A227 2.80fr multicolored	1.20	1.00
442	A227 2.80fr multicolored	1.20	1.00
a.	Pair, #441-442 + label	2.50	2.50
	Nos. 439-442 (4)	4.80	4.00

Butterflies — A228

2.80fr, Iphiclides podalirus. 4.40fr, Aglais urticae.

1994, Sept. 5 **Litho.** ***Perf. 13***

443	A228 2.80fr multicolored	1.60	.65
444	A228 4.40fr multicolored	2.25	.95

A229

1994, Oct. 22 **Litho.** ***Perf. 13***

445	A229 2.80fr multicolored	1.10	.65

Meeting of the Co-Princes, 1st anniv.

A230

1995, Feb. 27 **Litho.** ***Perf. 13***

446	A230 2.80fr multicolored	1.50	.50

European Nature Conservation Year

1995 World Cup Rugby Championships A231

1995, Apr. 24 **Litho.** ***Perf. 13***

447	A231 2.80fr multicolored	1.50	.75

Peace & Freedom — A232

Europa: 2.80fr, Dove with olive branch. 3.70fr, Flock of doves.

1995, Apr. 29

448	A232 2.80fr multicolored	*1.90*	*.75*
449	A232 3.70fr multicolored	*3.00*	*1.00*

Caritas in Andorra, 15th Anniv. — A233

1995, May 15 **Litho.** ***Perf. 13***

450	A233 2.80fr multicolored	1.40	.65

Caldea Health Spa — A234

1995, June 26 **Litho.** ***Perf. 13***

451	A234 2.80fr multicolored	1.20	.65

Ordino Natl. Auditorium A235

1995, July 10 **Litho. & Engr.**

452	A235 3.70fr black & buff	1.50	1.00

Virgin of Meritxell A236

1995, Sept. 11 **Litho.** ***Perf. 14***

453	A236 4.40fr multicolored	1.75	.95

Protection of Nature — A237

Butterflies: 2.80fr, Papallona llimonera, vert. 3.70fr, Papallona melanargia galathea.

1995, Sept. 25 ***Perf. 13***

454	A237 2.80fr multicolored	1.50	1.00
455	A237 3.70fr multicolored	1.75	1.25

UN, 50th Anniv. — A238

2.80fr, Flag, emblem. 3.70fr, Emblem, "50," flag.

1995, Oct. 21 Litho. *Perf. 13*

456 A238 2.80fr multicolored 1.25 1.00
457 A238 3.70fr multicolored 1.25 1.00
a. Pair, #456-457 + label 2.75 2.75

Andorra's Entrance into Council of Europe — A239

1995, Nov. 4

458 A239 2.80fr multicolored 1.40 .65

World Skiing Championships, Ordino Arcalis — A240

1996, Jan. 29 Litho. *Perf. 13*

459 A240 2.80fr multicolored 1.10 .65

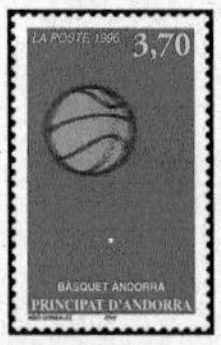

Basketball in Andorra — A241

1996, Jan. 29 Litho. *Perf. 13*

460 A241 3.70fr multicolored 1.50 .95

Our Lady of Meritxell Special School, 25th Anniv. — A242

1996, Feb. 17 Litho. *Perf. 13*

461 A242 2.80fr multicolored 1.10 .65

Songbirds — A243

3fr, Pit riog. 3.80fr, Mallarenga carbonera.

1996, Mar. 25

462 A243 3fr multicolored 1.25 .65
463 A243 3.80fr multicolored 1.75 1.40

First Arms Type of 1983

1996, Apr. 17 Engr. *Perf. 13*

464 A150 2.70fr green .95 .65
465 A150 3fr red 1.20 .35

Cross of St. James d'Engordany — A244

1996, Apr. 20 Litho.

466 A244 3fr multicolored 1.25 .65

Censer of St. Eulalia d'Encamp A245

1996, Apr. 20

467 A245 3.80fr multicolored 1.50 1.20

Europa — A246

3fr, Ermessenda de Castellbo.

1996, May 6

468 A246 3fr multicolored *1.90 1.00*

Chess — A247

1996, June 8 Litho. *Perf. 13*

469 A247 4.50fr multicolored 1.90 1.00

1996 Summer Olympic Games, Atlanta — A248

1996, June 29 Litho. *Perf. 13*

470 A248 3fr multicolored 1.50 .70

Arms of the Community of Canillo — A249

Serpentine Die Cut 7 Vert.

1996, June 10 Litho.

Self-Adhesive

471 A249 (3fr) multicolored 1.20 .45
a. Booklet of 10 12.00

Natl. Children's Choir, 5th Anniv. — A250

1996, Sept. 14 *Perf. 13*

472 A250 3fr multicolored 1.20 .60

Livestock Fair — A251

1996, Oct. 26 Engr. *Perf. 12x13*

473 A251 3fr multicolored 1.20 .60

Churches — A252

Designs: No. 474, St. Romá de Les Bons. No. 475, St. Coloma.

1996, Nov. 16 Litho. *Perf. 13*

474 A252 6.70fr multicolored 2.75 1.40
475 A252 6.70fr multicolored 2.75 1.40

A253

1997, Jan. 7 Litho. *Perf. 13*

476 A253 3fr multicolored 1.20 .60

Pres. Francois Mitterrand (1916-96).

A254

Sawtooth Die Cut 7 Vert. x Straight Die Cut

1997, Feb. 24 Litho.

Self-Adhesive

477 A254 (3fr) Arms of Encamp 1.50 .45
a. Booklet pane of 10 15.00

By its nature, No. 477a is a complete booklet. The peelable paper backing serves as a booklet cover.

A255

1997, Mar. 22 *Perf. 13*

478 A255 3fr Volleyball 1.25 .60

"The White Lady" — A256

1997, June 10 Litho. *Perf. 13*

479 A256 3fr multicolored *1.75 .90*

Europa (Stories and Legends).

Oreneta Cuablanca A257

1997, May 31 Litho. *Perf. 13*

480 A257 3.80fr multicolored 2.40 1.25

Paintings of Mills — A258

1997, Sept. 15 Litho. *Perf. 13*

481 A258 3fr Cal Pal, vert. 1.25 .60
482 A258 4.50fr Mas d'en Sole 2.00 1.00

Religious Artifacts — A259

Designs: 3fr, Monstrance of St. Iscle and St. Victoria. 15.50fr, Altar piece of St. Pierre d'Alxirivall.

1997, Oct. 27

483 A259 3fr multicolored 1.40 .60
484 A259 15.50fr multicolored 5.50 2.75
a. Pair, #483-484 + label 7.50 7.50

Legends — A260

Designs: No. 485, Legend of Meritxell. No. 486, The cross of seven arms. 3.80fr, The fountain of Esmelicat.

1997, Nov. 22 Litho. *Perf. 13*

485 A260 3fr multicolored 1.40 .60
486 A260 3fr multicolored 1.40 .60
487 A260 3.80fr multicolored 2.00 1.00
a. Strip of 3, #485-487 5.00 5.00

Chapel of St. Miguel d'Engolasters — A261

1997, Nov. 28 Litho. *Perf. 13*

488 A261 3fr multicolored 1.20 .60

Monaco Intl. Philatelic Exhibition.

Happy Anniversary — A262

1998, Jan. 3 Litho. *Perf. 13*

489 A262 3fr Juggling candles 1.20 .60

1998 Winter Olympic Games, Nagano — A263

1998, Feb. 14

490 A263 4.40fr multicolored 2.00 1.00

Arms of Ordino — A264

Serpentine Die Cut Vert.

1998, Mar. 7 Self-Adhesive Litho.

Booklet Stamp

491 A264 (3fr) multicolored 1.25 .30
a. Booklet pane of 10 12.50
Complete booklet, #491a 12.50

See Nos. 504, 518, 531.

Mesa de Vila Church A265

1998, Mar. 28 *Perf. 13*

492 A265 4.50fr multicolored 2.25 2.00

Rotary Club of Andorra, 20th Anniv. — A265a

1998, Apr. 11

493 A265a 3fr multicolored 1.20 .60

Finch — A266

1998 Litho. *Perf. 13*
494 A266 3.80fr multicolored 2.00 1.00

1998 World Cup Soccer Championships, France — A267

1998, June 6 Litho. *Perf. 13*
495 A267 3fr multicolored 1.60 1.25

For overprint see No. 499.

Music Festival — A268

1998, June 20 Litho. *Perf. 13*
496 A268 3fr multicolored *1.50 .90*

Europa.

Expo '98, Lisbon — A269

1998, July 6
497 A269 5fr multicolored 2.25 1.40

Chalice, House of the Valleys — A270

1998, Sept. 19 Litho. *Perf. 13*
498 A270 4.50fr multicolored 2.25 1.00

No. 495 Overprinted

1998, Nov. 16
499 A267 3fr multicolored 2.75 1.50

Early Maps of Andorra — A271

1998, Nov. 16
500 A271 3fr 1717, vert. 2.00 1.25
501 A271 15.50fr 1777 8.00 3.50

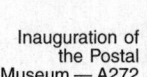

Inauguration of the Postal Museum — A272

1998, Nov. 19 Litho. *Perf. 13*
502 A272 3fr multicolored 1.20 .60

Manual Digest, 250th Anniv. — A273

1998, Dec. 7
503 A273 3.80fr multicolored 1.50 1.00

Arms Type of 1998
Self-Adhesive
Serpentine Die Cut Vert.

1999, Jan. 18 Booklet Stamp
504 A264 (3fr) La Massana 1.25 .55
a. Booklet pane of 10 12.50

No. 504a is a complete booklet.

Recycling — A274

1999, Mar. 13 Litho. *Perf. 13*
505 A274 5fr multicolored 2.25 1.40

Sorteny Valley A275

1999, Apr. 10
506 A275 3fr multicolored *2.00 1.25*

Europa.

Council of Europe, 50th Anniv. — A276

1999, May 5 Litho. *Perf. 13*
507 A276 3.80fr multicolored 1.60 1.00

First Stage Coach — A277

1999, May 15
508 A277 2.70fr multi 1.60 1.25

1999 European National Soccer Championships A278

1999, June 10 Photo. *Perf. 13*
509 A278 4.50fr multicolored 2.25 1.50

PhilexFrance 99 — A279

1999, July 2 Litho. *Perf. 13x13¼*
510 A279 3fr multicolored 1.20 .60

Historic View of Pal — A280

Perf. 13x13¼, 13¼x13
1999, July 10 Litho.
511 A280 3fr shown 1.20 .60
512 A280 3fr Different view, vert. 1.40 .60

International Federation of Photographic Art, 50th Anniv. — A281

1999, July 24 Litho. *Perf. 13*
513 A281 4.40fr multicolored 2.25 1.00

Casa Rull, Sispony — A282

1999, Sept. 6 Litho. *Perf. 13x13¼*
514 A282 15.50fr multicolored 6.00 3.50

Chest With Six Locks A283

1999, Oct. 9 Litho. *Perf. 13x13¼*
515 A283 6.70fr multicolored 2.75 1.50

Christmas A284

1999, Nov. 27 Litho. *Perf. 13*
516 A284 3fr multicolored 1.20 .60

Year 2000 — A285

2000, Jan. 5 Litho. *Perf. 13x13¼*
517 A285 3fr multicolored 1.20 .60

Arms Type of 1998
Self-Adhesive
Serpentine Die Cut 6½ Vert.

2000, Feb. 26 Booklet Stamp
518 A264 (3fr) Andorra-la-Vielle 1.25 .40
a. Booklet pane of 10 12.50

No. 518a is a complete booklet.

Snowboarding — A286

2000, Mar. 17 Litho. *Perf. 13*
519 A286 4.50fr multi 2.00 1.00

Montserrat Caballé Chant Competition A287

2000, Apr. 3 Booklet Stamp *Perf. 13x13¼*
520 A287 3.80fr multi 2.00 1.00

Campanula Cochlearifolia — A288

2000, Apr. 17 Litho. *Perf. 13*
521 A288 2.70fr multi 1.20 .60

Europa, 2000
Common Design Type

2000, May 9 *Perf. 13½x13*
522 CD17 3fr multi *2.00 1.00*

Festivals — A289

No. 523: a, Canòlic. b, Meritxell.

2000, May 27 Litho. *Perf. 13*
523 Pair + central label 3.00 3.00
a.-b. A289 3fr Any single 1.25 .60

Pardal Comú — A290

2000, July 7 Litho. *Perf. 13*
524 A290 4.40fr multi 2.00 1.00

A291

2000, Sept. 11 Litho. *Perf. 13*
525 A291 5fr multi 2.00 1.00

2000 Summer Olympics, Sydney.

World Tourism Day — A292

2000, Sept. 28
526 A292 3fr multi 1.20 .60

Expo 2000, Hanover — A293

2000, Oct. 6 Litho. *Perf. 13*
527 A293 3fr multi 1.20 .60

"Europe, A Common Heritage" — A294

2000, Nov. 4 Litho. *Perf. 13½x13*
528 A294 3.80fr multi 1.60 1.00

Prehistoric Pottery of Prats A295

2000, Dec. 16 *Perf. 13x13¼*
529 A295 6.70fr multi 3.00 1.50

National Archives, 25th Anniv. — A296

2000, Dec. 22 ***Perf. 13***

530 A296 15.50fr multi 7.50 4.50

Arms Type of 1998

Serpentine Die Cut 6½ Vert.

2001, Feb. 19 **Litho.**

Booklet Stamp

Self-Adhesive

531 A264 (3fr) Sant Julià de Lòria 1.25 .40

a. Booklet, 10 #531 12.50

Canillo Aliga Mountain Station — A297

2001, Feb. 10 **Litho.** ***Perf. 13***

532 A297 4.50fr multi 2.00 1.00

Casa Cristo Museum — A298

2001, Feb. 17 ***Perf. 13¼x13***

533 A298 6.70fr multi 2.75 1.50

Andorran Heritage A299

No. 534: a, Legend of Engolasters Lake. b, Foundation of Andorra.

2001, Mar. 23 ***Perf. 13***

534 A299 3fr Pair, #a-b, with central label 3.00 3.00

Intl. Book Day — A300

2001, Apr. 23 **Litho.** ***Perf. 13***

535 A300 3.80fr multi 1.75 1.00

Europa — A301

2001, Apr. 28

536 A301 3fr multi *2.00 1.00*

A302

3fr, Raspberries, vert.

2001, May 12

537 A302 3fr multicolored 1.20 .60
538 A302 4.40fr shown 2.00 1.00

European Language Year — A303

2001, June 16 **Litho.** ***Perf. 13***

539 A303 3.80fr multi 1.75 1.00

Escaldes-Engordany Jazz Festival — A304

2001, July 7

540 A304 3fr multi 1.60 .70

General Council's Kitchen — A305

2001, Aug. 10

541 A305 5fr multi 2.50 1.50

Chapel of the Virgin of Meritxell, 25th Anniv. of Rebuilding A306

2001, Sept. 7 **Litho.** ***Perf. 13***

542 A306 3fr multi 1.60 .80

Hotel Pla — A307

2001, Oct. 12

543 A307 15.50fr multi 6.50 3.00

Cross of Terme — A308

2001, Nov. 17 **Litho.** ***Perf. 13½x13***

544 A308 2.70fr multi 1.25 .75

100 Cents = 1 Euro (€)

National Arms — A309

Legends

A310 A311

Designs: 10c, Legend of Meritxell. 20c, Fountain of Esmelicat. 50c, The Cross with Seven Arms. €1, The Founding of Andorra. €2, Legend of Engolasters Lake. €5, The White Lady.

Perf. 13¼ (A309), 13¼x13

2002, Jan. 2 **Photo. (A309), Litho.**

545 A309 1c yel & multi .25 .25
546 A309 2c tan & multi .25 .25
547 A309 5c bl & multi .25 .25
548 A310 10c multi .25 .25
549 A310 20c multi .50 .40
550 A309 (46c) red & multi 1.00 .40
551 A310 50c multi 2.25 .80
552 A311 €1 multi 2.50 1.00
553 A311 €2 multi 4.50 1.50
554 A311 €5 multi 12.00 5.00
Nos. 545-554 (10) 23.75 10.10

See Nos. 577, 618, 635, 661-666, 680.

Traffic Safety Education in Schools — A312

2002, Jan. 25 **Litho.** ***Perf. 13½x13***

555 A312 69c multi 2.25 1.00

2002 Winter Olympics, Salt Lake City — A313

2002, Feb. 2 **Litho.** ***Perf. 13***

556 A313 58c multi 1.50 .75

Hotel Rosaleda — A314

2002, Mar. 16 **Litho.** ***Perf. 13***

557 A314 46c multi 2.25 1.00

World Day for Water — A315

2002, Mar. 22 **Litho.** ***Perf. 13***

558 A315 67c multi 1.60 1.00

Europa — A316

2002, May 10 **Litho.** ***Perf. 13***

559 A316 46c multi *2.00 .40*

Bilberries — A317

2002, July 6 **Litho.** ***Perf. 13***

560 A317 46c multi 1.60 .80

Seated Nude, Sculpture by Josep Viladomat — A318

2002, Aug. 24 **Litho.** ***Perf. 13¼x13***

561 A318 €2.36 multi 6.50 3.25

Envalira Tunnel — A319

2002, Sept. 2 ***Perf. 13***

562 A319 46c multi 1.75 .80

Piper of Ordino — A320

2002, Sept. 27

563 A320 41c multi 1.75 .80

See No. 578.

Detail of Santa Coloma Wall Painting A321

2002, Nov. 16 **Litho.** ***Perf. 13***

564 A321 €1.02 multi 3.00 1.75

Comú d'Escaldes — Engordany Coat of Arms — A322

Serpentine Die Cut 6¾ Vert.

2003, Jan. 20 **Photo.**

Booklet Stamp

Self-Adhesive

565 A322 (46c) multi 1.40 .50

a. Booklet pane of 10 14.00

Legend of the Margineda Pine — A323

2003, Feb. 10 **Litho.** ***Perf. 13***

566 A323 69c multi 2.00 1.00

See No. 579.

Constitution, 10th Anniv. — A324

2003, Mar. 14 Litho. *Perf. 13x13½*
567 A324 €2.36 multi 6.50 3.50

Buildings, Les Bons — A325

2003, Mar. 31 *Perf. 13*
568 A325 67c multi 2.25 1.25

Hotel Mirador — A326

2003, Apr. 12 Litho. *Perf. 13*
569 A326 €1.02 multi 3.00 2.00

Europa — A327

2003, May 17
570 A327 46c multi *1.75 .80*

Falles de San Joan — A328

2003, June 23 Litho. *Perf. 13*
571 A328 50c multi 1.60 .80

A329

2003, July 5
572 A329 50c multi 1.75 .80

Tour de France bicycle race, cent.

A330

2003, Aug. 8
573 A330 90c multi 2.50 1.50

World Track and Field Championships, Paris.

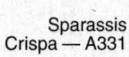

Sparassis Crispa — A331

Currants — A332

2003, Sept. 15 Litho. *Perf. 13*
574 A331 45c multi 1.50 1.00
575 A332 75c multi 2.25 1.00

Telephones in Andorra, Cent. — A333

2003, Oct. 30 Litho. *Perf. 13*
576 A333 50c multi 1.75 .65

Types of 2002-03 Inscribed "Postes"

2003, Nov. 29 Photo. *Perf. 13x13¼*
577 A309 (45c) green & multi 1.30 .80

Litho.
Perf. 13

578 A320 75c multi 3.25 2.00
579 A323 90c multi 3.25 2.25
Nos. 577-579 (3) 7.80 5.05

Maternity, by Paul Gauguin — A334

2003, Nov. 29 Litho. *Perf. 13¼x13*
580 A334 75c multi 3.00 1.75

St. Anthony's Auction — A335

2004, Jan. 17 Litho. *Perf. 13*
581 A335 50c multi 1.25 .60

Children of the World — A336

2004, Mar. 20 Litho. *Perf. 13*
582 A336 50c multi 1.25 .60

Hotel Valira — A337

2004, Apr. 17 Litho. *Perf. 13*
583 A337 €1.11 multi 3.00 2.50

Europa — A338

2004, May 7 Litho. *Perf. 13*
584 A338 50c multi *1.40 .60*

A339

2004, May 15
585 A339 45c multi 1.25 .65

Legend of the Castle of St. Vincent.

A340

2004, June 26
586 A340 75c multi 1.75 .90

Madriu-Peralita-Claror Valley, UNESCO World Heritage Site candidate.

Poblet de Fontenada A341

2004, July 3
587 A341 50c multi 1.40 .60

2004 Summer Olympics, Athens — A342

2004, Aug. 7 Litho. *Perf. 13*
588 A342 90c multi 2.50 1.75

Margineda Bridge — A343

No. 589: a, €1, Black and white sketch. b, €2, Full color painting.

2004, Oct. 2
589 A343 Horiz. pair, #a-b, + central label 8.00 8.00

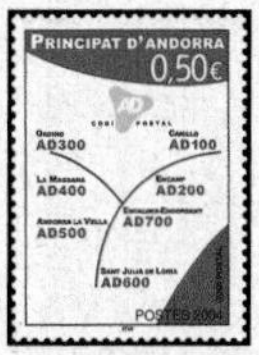
Postal Code — A344

2004, Oct. 23 *Perf. 13¼x13*
590 A344 50c multi 1.40 .60

Admission to Council of Europe, 10th Anniv. — A345

2004, Nov. 6
591 A345 €2.50 multi 6.50 4.00

Christmas — A346

2004, Dec. 4 *Perf. 13*
592 A346 50c multi 1.40 .60

The Magi — A347

2005, Jan. 5
593 A347 50c multi 1.50 .65

Selection of Madriu-Peralita-Claror Valley as UNESCO World Heritage Site — A348

2005, Jan. 22
594 A348 50c multi 1.40 .60

Legend of Rat Pass — A349

2005, Feb. 12
595 A349 48c multi 1.50 .65

Aegolius Funereus — A350

2005, Apr. 6 Litho. *Perf. 13*
596 A350 90c multi 2.50 2.25

Europa — A351

2005, May 7 Litho. *Perf. 13x13¼*
597 A351 55c multi *1.60 1.40*

Souvenir Sheet

9th Games of Small European States — A352

No. 598: a, 53c, Shooting. b, 55c, Track and field. c, 82c, Swimming. d, €1, Basketball.

2005, May 28 *Perf. 13¼x13*
598 A352 Sheet of 4, #a-d 8.00 8.00

Bordes d'Ensegur — A353

2005, June 11 Litho. *Perf. 13*
599 A353 €2.50 multi 6.50 5.00

Police Motorcycle — A354

2005, July 2

600 A354 53c multi 1.50 1.20

Prats de Santa Coloma, by J. Mir — A355

2005, Aug. 10 ***Perf. 13x13¼***

601 A355 82c multi 2.25 1.75

Calones Hostel — A356

2005, Sept. 10 Litho. *Perf. 13*

602 A356 €1.98 multi 6.00 4.50

Josep Alsina Photography Business — A357

2005, Oct. 8 Litho. *Perf. 13¼x13*

603 A357 53c multi 1.40 .65

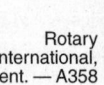

Rotary International, Cent. — A358

2005, Nov. 5 ***Perf. 13***

604 A358 55c multi 1.40 .65

Adoration of the Shepherds, by Antoni Viladomat A359

2005, Dec. 7 Litho. *Perf. 13*

605 A359 €1.22 multi 3.50 3.00

Animals — A360

Designs: No. 606, 53c, Ursus arctos. No. 607, 53c, Rupicapra pyrenaica, vert.

2006, Jan. 16

606-607 A360 Set of 2 3.00 2.50

See Nos. 619-620, 633-634, 648-649, 670-671.

2006 Winter Olympics, Turin — A361

No. 608: a, 55c, Alpine skiing. b, 75c, Cross-country skiing.

2006, Feb. 4

608 A361 Horiz. pair, #a-b, + central label 3.50 3.50

Tobacco Museum — A362

2006, Mar. 4 Litho. *Perf. 13*

609 A362 82c multi 2.00 1.50

Decree of Napoleon I, Bicent. — A363

2006, Mar. 27

610 A363 53c multi 1.40 .65

Legend of the Bear Cave — A364

2006, Apr. 10 Litho. *Perf. 13*

611 A364 48c multi 2.00 1.00

Europa — A365

2006, May 9 Litho. *Perf. 13x13¼*

612 A365 53c multi 1.40 .65

Sorteny Valley Nature Park — A366

2006, June 10 ***Perf. 13***

613 A366 55c multi 1.40 .65

Pablo Casals (1876-1973), Cellist — A367

2006, July 31 Litho. *Perf. 13*

614 A367 90c multi 2.25 2.10

Ford Model T — A368

2006, Sept. 2 Litho. *Perf. 13*

615 A368 85c multi 2.25 2.10

Montserrat Procession, by Josp Borrell — A369

2006, Nov. 4 Litho. *Perf. 13¼x13*

616 A369 €1.30 multi 3.25 3.00

Retable, St. Martin's Church, Cortinada A370

2006, Dec. 2 ***Perf. 13***

617 A370 54c multi 1.40 .65

Arms Type of 2002 Inscribed "Postes"

2007, Jan. 13 ***Perf. 13x13¼***

618 A309 60c multi 1.50 .75

Animals Type of 2006

Designs: 54c, Marmota marmota, vert. 60c, Sciurus vulgaris.

2007, Jan. 20 ***Perf. 13***

619-620 A360 Set of 2 3.00 2.50

Legend of the Wolf's Testament — A371

2007, Feb. 24

621 A371 49c multi 1.40 .65

Predelle, Prats — A372

2007, Mar. 17 Litho. *Perf. 13¼x13*

622 A372 €1.30 multi 3.50 3.25

Compare with types A383, A396, A414 and A420.

National Arms — A373

Serpentine Die Cut 11

2007, Apr. 2 Litho.

Booklet Stamp

Self-Adhesive

623 A373 (54c) multi 1.60 1.60

a. Booklet pane of 10 16.00

b. Booklet pane of 12 21.00

Issued: No. 623b, 3/1/16. Stamps in No. 623b sold for 80c on day of issue.

Rose — A374

2007, Apr. 23 Photo. *Perf. 13¼*

624 A374 86c multi 2.25 2.00

Values are for stamps with surrounding selvage.

Europa — A375

2007, May 5 Litho. *Perf. 13¼x13*

625 A375 54c multi 1.75 1.60

Scouting, cent.

Joining of Meritxell and Sabart A376

No. 626: a, Madonna and Child. b, Priest.

2007, June 2 Litho. *Perf. 13*

626 A376 54c Horiz. pair, #a-b, + central label 3.00 3.00

Engine — A377

2007, July 10

627 A377 60c multi 1.50 1.25

2007 Rugby World Cup, France — A378

2007, Sept. 1 Litho. *Perf. 13¼*

628 A378 85c multi 2.00 1.50

Values are for stamps with surrounding selvage.

Comapedrosa Valley — A379

2007, Oct. 6 Litho. *Perf. 13¼x13*

629 A379 €3.04 multi 7.50 6.50

Prehistoric People — A380

Prehistoric people at: 60c, Margineda Grotto. 85c, Cedre.

2007, Nov. 10

630-631 A380 Set of 2 4.00 3.50

Retable, St. Martin's Church, Cortinada A381

2007, Dec. 3 Litho. ***Perf. 13***
632 A381 54c multi 1.40 .65

Animals Type of 2006

Designs: 54c, Vulpes vulpes. 60c, Sus scrofa, vert.

2008, Jan. 28
633-634 A360 Set of 2 3.50 3.00

Arms Type of 2002 Inscribed "Postes"

2008, Mar. 1 Photo. ***Perf. 13x13¼***
635 A309 65c blue & multi 1.50 1.00

Legend of the Treasure of the Fountain of Manegó — A382

2008, Mar. 8 Litho. ***Perf. 13***
636 A382 50c multi 1.25 .75

Predelle, Prats — A383

2008, Apr. 12 ***Perf. 13¼x13***
637 A383 €1.33 multi 3.50 3.50

Compare with Types A372, A396, A414 and A420.

Cartercar Automobile A384

2008, May 3 Litho. ***Perf. 13***
638 A384 65c multi 1.75 1.50

Europa — A385

2008, May 17
639 A385 55c multi 1.50 .75

Miniature Sheet

2008 Summer Olympics, Beijing — A386

No. 640: a, Kayaking. b, Running. c, Swimming. d, Judo.

2008, June 16 Litho. ***Perf. 13x13½***
640 A386 55c Sheet of 4, #a-d 6.00 6.00

Olympex 2008 Philatelic Exhibition, Beijing (#640d).

Narcissus Poeticus — A387

2008, June 18 ***Perf. 13¼x13***
641 A387 55c multi 1.50 .75

No. 641 is impregnated with a narcissus scent.

Vall d'Incles — A388

2008, July 5 ***Perf. 13***
642 A388 €2.80 multi 7.50 7.50

Universal Male Suffrage, 75th Anniv. — A389

2008, Aug. 30 Litho. ***Perf. 13***
643 A389 55c multi 1.40 .75

Sustainable Development A390

2008, Oct. 4 Litho. ***Perf. 13***
644 A390 88c multi 2.00 1.25

Roc d'Enclar — A391

2008, Nov. 8 ***Perf. 13¼***
645 A391 85c multi 2.00 1.25

Retable of St. Mark and St. Mary — A392

2008, Dec. 13 ***Perf. 13***
646 A392 55c multi 1.40 .75

Louis Braille (1809-52), Educator of the Blind — A393

2009, Jan. 24 **Engr.**
647 A393 88c multi 2.00 1.25

Animals Type of 2006

Designs: 55c, Equus mulus, vert. 65c, Bos taurus.

2009, Feb. 14 Litho. ***Perf. 13***
648-649 A360 Set of 2 2.75 2.00

Legend of the Devils of Aixirvall — A394

2009, Mar. 7
650 A394 51c multi 1.40 .75

Souvenir Sheet

Protection of Polar Regions and Glaciers — A395

No. 651: a, 56c, Emperor penguins. b, 85c, Boat off shore in polar regions, vert.

Perf. 13x13¼, 13¼x13 (85c)

2009, Mar. 27 Litho. & Engr.
651 A395 Sheet of 2, #a-b, + label 3.50 3.50

Predelle, Prats — A396

2009, Apr. 18 Litho. ***Perf. 13¼x13***
652 A396 €1.35 multi 3.50 3.50

Compare with types A372, A383, A414 and A420.

Europa — A397

2009, May 2 ***Perf. 13***
653 A397 56c multi 1.40 .75

Intl. Year of Astronomy.

Early Renault Automobile A398

2009, May 16
654 A398 70c multi 1.75 1.00

St. Joan de Caselles, by Maurice Utrillo A399

2009, May 23 ***Perf. 13x13¼***
655 A399 90c multi 2.25 1.50

Cercle des Pessons — A400

2009, June 13 Litho. ***Perf. 13***
656 A400 €2.80 multi 7.50 6.00

Tour de France Bicycle Race — A401

2009, July 11
657 A401 56c multi 1.40 .75

Arts and Letters Circle, 40th Anniv. — A402

2009, Oct. 3 Litho. ***Perf. 13***
658 A402 51c multi 1.40 .75

Romanesque Art — A403

2009, Nov. 7 ***Perf. 13¼x13***
659 A403 85c multi 2.00 1.50

Epiphany — A404

2009, Dec. 12 ***Perf. 13***
660 A404 56c multi 1.40 .75

Arms Type of 2002 Inscribed "POSTES"

2010, Jan. 4 Photo. ***Perf. 13x13¼***

661	A309	1c	yel & multi	.25	.25
662	A309	5c	lt bl & multi	.25	.25
663	A309	10c	org & multi	.25	.25
664	A309	20c	lilac & multi	.45	.45
665	A309	50c	ol grn & multi	1.25	1.25
666	A309	(70c)	dk bl & multi	1.60	1.60
			Nos. 661-666 (6)	4.05	4.05

2010 Winter Olympics, Vancouver A405

2010, Jan. 23 Photo. ***Perf. 13x13¼***
667 A405 85c multi 2.00 1.50

Casamanya Peak — A406

2010, Feb. 15 Litho. ***Perf. 13***
668 A406 €2.80 multi 6.50 5.00

Rights of the Child Convention, 20th Anniv. — A407

2010, Mar. 2 **Photo.**
669 A407 56c multi 1.40 .75

Animals Type of 2006

Designs: 56c, Gyps fulvus, vert. 90c, Ovis aries.

2010, Mar. 8 **Litho.** ***Perf. 13***
670-671 A360 Set of 2 3.00 2.25

Andorran Embassy, Brussels A408

2010, Apr. 12 **Engr.** ***Perf. 13***
672 A408 70c multi + label 1.75 1.75

Legend of Charlemagne's Chair — A409

2010, Apr. 26 **Litho.** ***Perf. 13***
673 A409 51c multi 1.25 .65

Europa — A410

Litho. & Embossed with Foil Application

2010, May 10 ***Perf. 13¼***
674 A410 56c multi 1.40 1.00

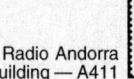

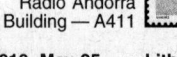

Radio Andorra Building — A411

2010, May 25 **Litho.** ***Perf. 13***
675 A411 56c multi 1.40 1.00

1985 Ferrari 328 GTS — A412

2010, June 21 **Litho.** ***Perf. 13***
676 A412 70c multi 1.75 1.75

Still Life, by Carme Massana — A413

2010, July 12 ***Perf. 13¼x13***
677 A413 95c multi 2.50 2.50

Predelle, Prats — A414

2010, Sept. 6 **Litho.** ***Perf. 13¼x13***
678 A414 €1.40 multi 3.75 3.75

Compare with types A372, A383, A396 and A420.

Souvenir Sheet

Churches — A415

No. 679: a, Sant Joan de Caselles Church. b, Sant Romà de Les Bons Church, horiz.

Perf. 13¼x13, 13x13¼

2010, Oct. 4 **Engr.**
679 A415 58c Sheet of 2, #a-b 3.25 3.25

See Andorra, Spanish Administration No. 363.

Arms Type of 2002 Inscribed "POSTES"

2010, Oct. 18 **Photo.** ***Perf. 13x13¼***
680 A309 (58c) red & multi 1.75 1.75

Feudal Andorra — A416

681 A416 87c multi 2.40 2.40

Christmas — A417

2010, Nov. 29 ***Perf. 13***
682 A417 58c multi 1.60 1.60

Legend of St. Joan de Caselles — A418

2011, Feb. 12 **Litho.** ***Perf. 13***
683 A418 €2.80 multi 8.00 8.00

Francophonia A419

2011, Mar. 19 ***Perf. 13x13¼***
684 A419 87c multi 2.50 2.50

Predelle, Prats — A420

2011, Apr. 9 ***Perf. 13¼x13***
685 A420 €1.40 multi 4.00 4.00

Compare with types A372, A383, A386 and A414.

Europa — A421

Silk-Screened on Wood Veneer

2011, May 7 ***Serpentine Die Cut 11***

Self-Adhesive

686 A421 58c black & white 1.75 1.75

Intl. Year of Forests.

Councilor, by Francesc Borràs (1891-1968) A422

2011, May 21 **Litho.** ***Perf. 13***
687 A422 95c multi 2.75 2.75

Placeta de Sant Esteve A423

2011, June 4 **Engr.**
688 A423 58c multi 1.75 1.75

Soriano-Pedroso Automobile A424

2011, June 18 **Litho.**
689 A424 75c multi 2.10 2.10

Rugby — A425

2011, July 9 **Photo.** ***Perf. 13***
690 A425 89c multi 2.40 2.40

Values are for stamps with surrounding selvage.

Souvenir Sheet

Dance of the Seven Parishes, Plaza Benlloch A426

2011, July 16 **Litho. & Engr.**
691 A426 €1.45 multi 4.25 4.25

Flora — A427

Designs: 60c, Rhododendron ferrugineum. €1, Rosa sempervirens, horiz.

2011, Sept. 4 **Litho.** ***Perf. 13***
692-693 A427 Set of 2 4.50 4.50

See Nos. 706-707, 720-721, 751, 782.

Council of the Land — A428

2011, Sept. 24 ***Perf. 13x13¼***
694 A428 89c multi 2.50 2.50

Leaf and Coat of Arms — A429

2011, Oct. 1 **Photo.** ***Perf. 13x13¼***
695 A429 (57c) multi 1.60 1.60

Angel From Santa Eulalia d'Encamp Retable — A430

2011, Nov. 26 **Litho.** ***Perf. 13***
696 A430 60c multi 1.60 1.60

Legend of the Shop of the Sorceresses — A431

2012, Jan. 14
697 A431 €2.78 multi 7.50 7.50

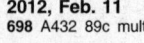

Women's World Cup Alpine Skiing Races, Soldeu — A432

2012, Feb. 11 ***Perf. 13x13¼***
698 A432 89c multi 2.40 2.40

Massana Valley, by Joaquim Mir (1873-1940) A433

2012, Mar. 3
699 A433 €1 multi 2.60 2.60

Souvenir Sheet

Restoration of Casa de la Vall, 50th Anniv. — A434

No. 700 — Casa de la Vall in: a, 1962. b, 2012.

2012, Mar. 10 **Litho. & Engr.**
700 A434 60c Sheet of 2, #a-b 3.25 3.25

Bugatti 37 Race Car — A435

2012, Apr. 14 **Litho.** ***Perf. 13***
701 A435 77c multi 2.10 2.10

Souvenir Sheet

Europa A436

2012, May 5 **Litho.** ***Perf. 13¼x13***
702 A436 77c multi 2.00 2.00

Noi. 702 has die cut opening in center of stamp.

Placeta de la Consòrcia, Andorra la Vella — A437

2012, June 8 **Engr.** ***Perf. 13x12¾***
703 A437 60c multi 1.50 1.50

Judo — A438

2012, July 6 **Litho.** ***Perf. 13***
704 A438 77c multi 1.90 1.90

Souvenir Sheet

Marratxa Dance — A439

Litho. & Engr.

2012, July 20 ***Perf. 13x13¼***
705 A439 €1.45 multi 3.75 3.75

Flora Type of 2011

Designs: 60c, Sempervivum montanum. €1, Eryngium bourgatii.

2012, Sept. 14 **Litho.** ***Perf. 13***
706-707 A427 Set of 2 4.25 4.25

Woman Suffrage, 42nd Anniv. — A440

2012, Oct. 5 ***Perf. 13¼x13***
708 A440 89c multi 2.25 2.25

Andorran Presidency of the Council of Europe — A441

2012, Oct. 26
709 A441 €1 multi 2.60 2.60

King Henri IV of France (1553-1610), Co-Prince of Andorra — A442

2012, Nov. 8 **Engr.** ***Perf. 13x13¼***
710 A442 60c multi 1.60 1.60
a. Sheet of 10, 5 each #710, France #4297 16.00 16.00

See France No. 4297.

Angel From Roser d'Ordino Retable — A443

2012, Nov. 23 **Litho.** ***Perf. 13***
711 A443 57c multi 1.50 1.50

Legend of Moixella — A444

2013, Jan. 12
712 A444 €2.78 multi 7.50 7.50

Souvenir Sheet

Bear Ball, Encamp A445

Litho. & Engr.

2013, Feb. 23 ***Perf. 13x13¼***
713 A445 €1.55 multi 4.00 4.00

Constitution, 20th Anniv. — A446

2013, Mar. 16 **Litho.** ***Perf. 13***
714 A446 63c multi 1.60 1.60

Cord 810 Phaeton — A447

2013, Apr. 13
715 A447 95c multi 2.50 2.50

Plaça Rebés, Andorra la Vella A448

2013, May 11 **Engr.** ***Perf. 12¾***
716 A448 63c multi 1.75 1.75

Europa — A449

2013, May 18 **Litho.** ***Perf. 13¼***
717 A449 80c multi 2.25 2.25

Retable, Church of Sant Miquel, Prats — A450

2013, July 6 **Litho.** ***Perf. 13¼x13***
718 A450 €1.05 multi 2.75 2.75

Andorran School, 30th Anniv. — A451

2013, July 27 **Litho.** ***Perf. 13***
719 A451 63c multi 1.75 1.75

Flora Type of 2011

Designs: 58c, Papaver rhoeas. €1.05, Paeonia mascula, horiz.

2013, Sept. 7 **Litho.** ***Perf. 13***
720-721 A427 Set of 2 4.50 4.50

First French School in Canillo, Cent. — A452

2013, Oct. 2 **Litho.** ***Perf. 13¼***
722 A452 63c multi 1.75 1.75

Andorran Presidency of the Working Community of the Pyrenees A453

2013, Oct. 5 **Litho.** ***Perf. 13¼***
723 A453 95c multi 2.60 2.60

El Pas de la Casa, Painting by Véronique Bandry — A454

2013, Oct. 26 **Litho.** ***Perf. 13¼x13***
724 A454 €1.55 multi 4.25 4.25

Angel, Saint Joan de Sispony Church — A455

2013, Nov. 12 **Litho.** ***Perf. 13***
725 A455 58c multi 1.60 1.60

Christmas.

Legend of the Canòlich Sanctuary — A456

2014, Jan. 11 **Litho.** ***Perf. 13***
726 A456 €3.50 multi 9.50 9.50

Schools in Partnership With UNESCO — A457

2014, Feb. 15 **Litho.** ***Perf. 13¼***
727 A457 66c multi 1.90 1.90

1917 Hispano Guadalajara Automobile A458

2014, Mar. 29 **Litho.** ***Perf. 13***
728 A458 98c multi 2.75 2.75

Cyanistes Caeruleus A459

2014, May 3 **Engr.** ***Perf. 13¼***
729 A459 66c multi 1.90 1.90

Bagpipes — A460

2014, May 24 **Litho.** ***Perf. 13¼***
730 A460 83c multi 2.25 2.25

Europa.

Madriu-Perafita-Claror Valley — A461

2014, June 16 **Litho.** ***Perf. 13***
731 A461 98c multi 2.75 2.75

Buildings in Engordany — A462

2014, June 16 **Engr.** ***Perf. 13x12¾***
732 A462 66c multi 1.90 1.90

Fixats en la Contemporaneitat, by Javier Balmaseda — A463

2014, July 11 **Litho.** ***Perf. 13x13¼***
733 A463 €1.65 multi 4.50 4.50

Souvenir Sheet

Santa Anna Ball A464

Litho. & Engr.
2014, July 25 ***Perf. 13x13¼***
734 A464 €1.65 multi 4.50 4.50

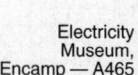

Electricity Museum, Encamp — A465

2014, July 25 **Litho.** ***Perf. 13x13¼***
735 A465 €1.10 multi 3.00 3.00

Pitavola Butterfly — A466

2014, Sept. 6 **Litho.** ***Perf. 13***
736 A466 83c multi 2.10 2.10

Detail From Sant Miquel de Prats Retable — A467

2014, Sept. 27 **Litho.** ***Perf. 13¼x13***
737 A467 €1.10 multi 2.75 2.75

Skis and Ski Poles — A468

2014, Oct. 18 **Litho.** ***Perf. 13¼***
738 A468 83c multi 2.10 2.10

Esteve Albert (1914-95), Writer — A469

2014, Nov. 9 **Engr.** ***Perf. 13¼***
739 A469 66c ochre & blk 1.75 1.75

Christmas A470

2014, Nov. 29 **Litho.** ***Perf. 13***
740 A470 66c multi 1.75 1.75

Instinct of Conservation, by Javier Balmaseda — A471

2015, Jan. 3 **Litho.** ***Perf. 13x13¼***
741 A471 €1.90 multi 4.50 4.50

Legend of the First Snow — A472

2015, Feb. 7 **Litho.** ***Perf. 13***
742 A472 €3.67 multi 8.25 8.25

Citroen DS 21 — A473

2015, Mar. 20 **Litho.** ***Perf. 13***
743 A473 €1.20 multi 2.75 2.75

Departure of French Gendarmes Led by Col. René Baulard, 75th Anniv. — A474

2015, Apr. 11 **Litho.** ***Perf. 13***
744 A474 76c multi 1.75 1.75

Europa — A475

2015, May 9 **Litho.** ***Perf. 13¼***
745 A475 95c multi 2.10 2.10

Trobada Monument — A476

2015, June 13 **Engr.** ***Perf. 13¼***
746 A476 €1.25 multi 2.75 2.75

Comapedrosa, Highest Peak in Andorra — A477

2015, June 20 **Litho.** ***Perf. 13¼***
747 A477 76c multi 1.75 1.75

Inside, by Agustí Roqué A478

2015, July 4 **Litho.** ***Perf. 13x13¼***
748 A478 €3.05 multi 6.75 6.75

Venice Biennale.

Souvenir Sheet

Contrapas Dance — A479

Litho. & Engr.
2015, July 18 ***Perf. 13x13¼***
749 A479 €1.90 multi 4.25 4.25

UCI Mountain Bike and Trials World Championships, Vallnord — A480

2015, Aug. 29 **Litho.** ***Perf. 13¼x13***
750 A480 €1.20 multi 2.75 2.75

Flora Type of 2011 and

Parnassius Apollo — A481

Design: 76c, Thymus vulgaris, vert.

2015, Oct. 2 **Engr.** ***Perf. 13***
751 A427 76c multi 1.60 1.60
752 A481 95c multi 2.25 2.25

Ramon d'Areny-Plandolit, Philatelist, and Maximum Cards — A482

2015, Nov. 7 **Engr.** ***Perf. 13x12½***
753 A482 €1.25 multi 2.75 2.75

Live Nativity Scene, Engordany A483

2015, Nov. 27 **Litho.** ***Perf. 13***
754 A483 76c multi 1.60 1.60

Christmas.

2014 Andorran Coinage A484

No. 755: a, 1-cent, 2-cent, 5-cent and 2-euro coins. b, 10-cent, 20-cent, 50-cent and 1-euro coins.

2016, Jan. 8 **Litho.** ***Perf. 13***
755 A484 80c Horiz. pair, #a-b 3.50 3.50

Women's Alpine Skiing World Cup Race at Soldeu-El Tarter — A485

2016, Feb. 27 **Litho.** ***Perf. 13¼***
756 A485 €1.25 multi 2.75 2.75

Donzella Cremada Rock Carving — A486

2016, Mar. 19 **Litho.** ***Perf. 13***
757 A486 €3.77 multi 8.75 8.75

Reforms of 1866, 150th Anniv. — A487

2016, Apr. 23 **Litho.** ***Perf. 13¼***
758 A487 €1 multi 2.40 2.40

The Republic, Statue by Josep Viladomat (1899-1989) and Escaldes-Engordany Art Center — A488

2016, Apr. 6 **Engr.** ***Perf. 13¼***
759 A488 80c multi 1.90 1.90

Europa — A489

2016, May 8 **Litho.** ***Perf. 13¼***
760 A489 €1 multi 2.25 2.25

Think Green Issue.

Dancing Giants of Andorra Festival — A490

2016, June 10 **Litho.** ***Perf. 13¼***
761 A490 80c multi 1.90 1.90

Souvenir Sheet

Sardana Dance A491

Litho. & Engr.

2016, July 15 ***Perf. 13x13¼***
762 A491 €1.60 multi 3.75 3.75

Intimitat Compartida, by Joan Xandri A492

2016, July 29 **Litho.** ***Perf. 13x13¼***
763 A492 €3.20 multi 7.25 7.25

2015 Venice Biennale.

Clipol Bus — A493

2016, Sept. 2 **Litho.** ***Perf. 13***
764 A493 €1.25 multi 2.75 2.75

Isabelle Sandy (1884-1975), Writer — A494

2016, Oct. 7 **Engr.** ***Perf. 13¼***
765 A494 €1.60 multi 3.50 3.50

Lavender A495

Catalan Sheepdog A496

Litho. & Engr.

2016, Nov. 5 ***Perf. 13***
766 A495 80c multi 1.75 1.75
767 A496 €1 multi 2.25 2.25

Angels Painted by Antoni Viladomat i Manalt (1678-1755) A497

2016, Nov. 25 **Litho.** ***Perf. 13***
768 A497 80c multi 1.75 1.75

Legend of the Cave of Arans — A498

2017, Jan. 13 **Litho.** ***Perf. 13***
769 A498 €3.95 multi 8.50 8.50

Opening of Carmen Thyssen Museum, Escaldes-Engordany — A499

2017, Feb. 3 **Litho.** ***Perf. 13¼x13***
770 A499 €1.30 multi 2.75 2.75

Philandorre Philatelic Association, 40th Anniv. — A500

2017, Mar. 9 **Engr.** ***Perf. 13***
771 A500 85c multi + label 1.90 1.90

Comic Festival, La Massana — A501

2017, Apr. 7 **Litho.** ***Perf. 13¼***
772 A501 €1.70 multi 3.75 3.75

Sant Vincenç d'Enclar Castle — A502

2017, May 6 **Litho.** ***Perf. 13¼***
773 A502 €1.10 multi 2.50 2.50

Europa.

Castellars Making Human Tower — A503

2017, May 26 **Litho.** ***Perf. 13¼***
774 A503 85c multi 1.90 1.90

Maria Assumpta D'Areny Plandolit (1860-92), Daughter of Andorran Reformer Guillem d'Areny Plandolit — A504

2017, June 21 **Engr.** ***Perf. 13¼***
775 A504 €1.10 multi 2.50 2.50

Souvenir Sheet

Stick Dancing — A505

Litho. & Engr.

2017, July 8 ***Perf. 13x13¼***
776 A505 €1.70 multi 4.00 4.00

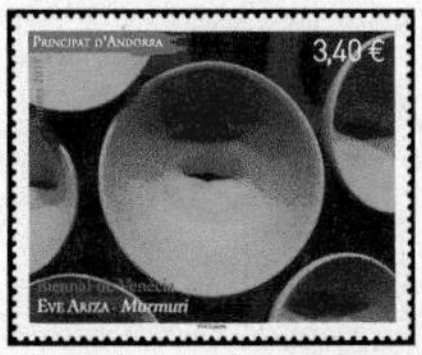

Murmuri, by Eve Ariza A506

2017, July 22 **Litho.** ***Perf. 13***
777 A506 €3.40 multi 8.00 8.00

2017 Venice Art Biennale.

Roc del Quer, Canillo A507

2017, Sept. 2 **Photo.** ***Perf. 13x12¾***
778 A507 €1.30 multi 3.00 3.00

Photograph of 1967 Visit of French President Charles de Gaulle to Andorra, by Fèlix Peig Ballart (1917-2007) A508

2017, Sept. 15 **Litho.** ***Perf. 13¼***
779 A508 85c multi 2.00 2.00

Pere Canturri (1935-2015), Historian and Governmental Minister — A509

2017, Oct. 7 **Litho.** ***Perf. 13¼***
780 A509 €1.10 multi 2.60 2.60

Peugeot 172 M — A510

2017, Nov. 10 **Litho.** ***Perf. 13***
781 A510 85c multi 2.10 2.10

Flora Type of 2011 and

Salamandra Salamandra A511

Design: 85c, Cerastium pyrenaicum, horiz.

2017, Nov. 13 **Engr.** ***Perf. 13***
782 A427 85c multi 2.10 2.10
783 A511 €1.10 multi 2.60 2.60

Christmas A512

2017, Nov. 24 **Litho.** ***Perf. 13***
784 A512 85c multi 2.10 2.10

Legend of the Snow Maiden — A513

2018, Jan. 12 **Litho.** ***Perf. 13***
785 A513 €4.05 multi 10.00 10.00

Tenth Conference on Snow and Mountain Tourism, Escaldes-Engordany — A514

2018, Feb. 2 **Litho.** ***Perf. 13¼***
786 A514 €1.30 multi 3.25 3.25

Andorran Constitution, 25th Anniv. — A515

2018, Mar. 9 **Engr.** ***Perf. 13¼***
787 A515 95c multi 2.40 2.40

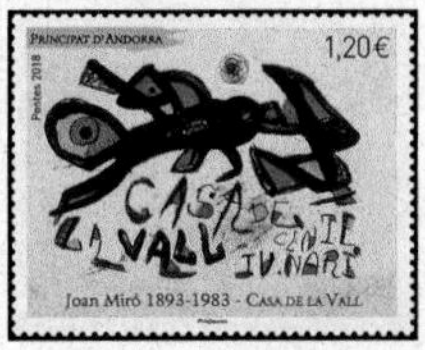

Casa de la Vall, by Joan Miró (1893-1983) A516

2018, Apr. 6 **Litho.** ***Perf. 13x13¼***
788 A516 €1.20 multi 3.00 3.00

Caramelles (Singers) — A517

2018, Apr. 20 **Litho.** ***Perf. 13¼***
789 A517 95c multi 2.25 2.25

Tosca Bridge — A518

2018, May 4 Engr. *Perf. 13¼*
790 A518 €1.20 multi 3.00 3.00

Europa.

Souvenir Sheet

Summer Solstice Festival, UNESCO Intangible Cultural Heritage — A519

2018, June 8 Litho. *Perf. 13x13¼*
791 A519 €1.90 multi 4.50 4.50

Escaldes-Engordany Parish, 40th Anniv. — A520

2018, June 14 Litho. *Perf. 13¼*
792 A520 80c multi 1.90 1.90

Pompeu Fabra (1868-1948), Linguist — A521

2018, July 20 Engr. *Perf. 13*
793 A521 €1.30 multi 3.00 3.00

Church of Santa Coloma and Icon — A522

2018, Aug. 10 Engr. *Perf. 13*
794 A522 €1.20 multi 2.75 2.75

European Year of Cultural Heritage.

Sweet Candies Caramels, Sculpture by Laurence Jenkell A523

2018, Sept. 14 Litho. *Perf. 13x13¼*
795 A523 €1.20 multi 2.75 2.75

Otter — A524

2018, Sept. 28 Litho. *Perf. 13*
796 A524 95c multi 2.25 2.25

Lídia Armengol i Vila (1948-91), Politician — A525

2018, Oct. 5 Engr. *Perf. 13¼*
797 A525 €1.20 choc & org red 2.75 2.75

Citroen CX — A526

2018, Nov. 9 Litho. *Perf. 13*
798 A526 €1.90 multi 4.50 4.50

Detail From Retable of Santa Creu de Canillo Church — A527

2018, Nov. 17 Litho. *Perf. 13*
799 A527 95c multi 2.25 2.25

Andorra Coat of Arms — A528

2019, Jan. 2 Photo. *Perf. 13x13¼*
800 A528 (€1.30) multi 3.00 3.00

Legend of the White Horse of Solana — A529

2019, Jan. 4 Litho. *Perf. 13*
801 A529 €4.18 multi 9.75 9.75

Escudelle of St. Anthony Festival, 50th Anniv. — A530

2019, Jan. 17 Litho. *Perf. 13x13¼*
802 A530 88c multi 2.10 2.10

General Council of Andorra, 600th Anniv. — A531

2019, Feb. 11 Litho. *Perf. 13x13¼*
803 A531 €1.05 multi 2.40 2.40

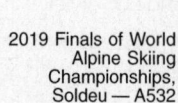

2019 Finals of World Alpine Skiing Championships, Soldeu — A532

2019, Mar. 9 Litho. *Perf. 13¼*
804 A532 €1.30 multi 3.00 3.00

Estanyó del Querol Lake A533

2019, Apr. 13 Litho. *Perf. 13*
805 A533 €1.05 multi 2.40 2.40

Lagopus Muta — A534

2019, May 10 Engr. *Perf. 13x13¼*
806 A534 €1.30 multi 3.00 3.00

Europa.

Andorra Hydroelectric Forces (Electric Company), 90th Anniv. — A535

2019, May 31 Litho. *Perf. 13x13¼*
807 A535 €1.05 multi 2.40 2.40

Andorra, by Eduard Arranz Bravo — A536

2019, July 5 Litho. *Perf. 13¼x13*
808 A536 €1.05 black & red 2.40 2.40

Julia Bonet Fité (1922-2011), Businesswoman, and Her Perfume Shop — A537

2019, July 19 Engr. *Perf. 13x13¼*
809 A537 €1.30 multi 3.00 3.00

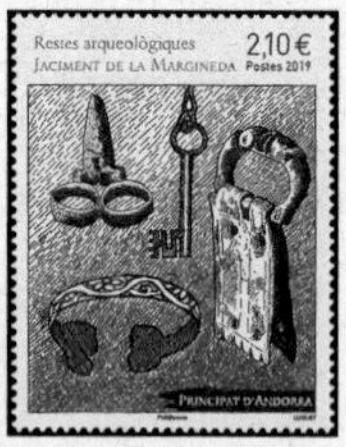

Artifacts From La Margineda Archaeological Site — A538

2019, Aug. 9 Engr. *Perf. 13x13¼*
810 A538 €2.10 multi 4.75 4.75

Renault 4CV — A539

2019, Sept. 6 Litho. *Perf. 13¼*
811 A539 €1.05 multi 2.40 2.40

Argynnis Pandora — A540

Ursus Arctos — A541

2019, Oct. 4 Litho. *Perf. 13*
812 A540 €1.05 multi 2.40 2.40

Engr.
813 A541 €1.30 dark brown 3.00 3.00

Detail From Retable of Santa Creu de Canillo Church — A542

2019, Nov. 2 Litho. *Perf. 13*
814 A542 €1.05 multi 2.40 2.40

Admission of Andorra to Council of Europe, 25th Anniv. — A543

2019, Nov. 8 Litho. *Perf. 13*
815 A543 €1.30 multi + label 3.00 3.00

See Andorra (Spanish Administration) No. 470.

Envalira Pass — A544

2020, Jan. 4 Litho. *Perf. 13*
816 A544 €4.30 multi 9.50 9.50

Victoria Zorzano (1908-98), Radio Announcer — A545

2020, Feb. 8 Engr. *Perf. 13¼*
817 A545 €1.40 multi 3.25 3.25

International Francophone Organization, 50th Anniv. — A546

2020, Mar. 20 Litho. *Perf. 13¼x13*
818 A546 €1.16 multi 2.50 2.50

Hiking Boots — A547

2020, Apr. 4 Litho. *Perf. 13¼x13*
819 A547 €1.16 multi 2.60 2.60

Andorra GR7 long-distance hiking trail.

Map of 19th Century Andorra la Vella-L'Ospitalet, France Postal Route — A548

2020, May 11 Litho. ***Perf. 13x13¼***
820 A548 €1.40 multi 3.25 3.25

Europa.

Espai Columba Museum, 1st Anniv. — A549

2020, June 12 Litho. ***Perf. 13x13¼***
821 A549 €1.16 multi 2.60 2.60

Oncorhynchus Mykiss — A550

2020, June 19 Litho. ***Perf. 13***
822 A550 €1.16 multi 2.60 2.60

L'Orri del Cubil Archaeological Site — A551

2020, July 3 Engr. ***Perf. 13***
823 A551 €2.32 multi 5.50 5.50

Esbalçat Pond A552

2020, Aug. 21 Litho. ***Perf. 13***
824 A552 €1.16 multi 2.75 2.75

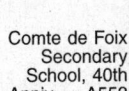

Comte de Foix Secondary School, 40th Anniv. — A553

2020, Sept. 11 Engr. ***Perf. 13¼***
825 A553 €1.96 black & red 4.50 4.50

Jacques Chirac (1932-2019), President of France and Co-Prince of Andorra — A554

2020, Sept. 26 Litho. ***Perf. 13¼***
826 A554 €1.16 multi 2.75 2.75

Abies Alba — A555

2020, Oct. 2 Litho. ***Perf. 13***
827 A555 €1.40 multi 3.25 3.25

Casa de la Vall A556

2020, Nov. 5 Engr. ***Perf. 13¼***
828 A556 €2.32 multi + 2 flanking labels 5.75 5.75

Candidacy of Casa de la Vall, Castell de Foix and Cathedral of the See of Urgell (shown on flanking labels) for UNESCO World Heritage Site status. See Spanish Andorra No. 485.

Hartung Sparta Nature, Automobile Manufactured in Andorra — A557

2020, Nov. 6 Litho. ***Perf. 13¼***
829 A557 €1.40 multi 3.50 3.50

Tradition of Eating Grapes As Bells Ring in New Year's Day — A558

2020, Nov. 6 Litho. ***Perf. 13¼x13***
830 A558 €1.16 multi 2.75 2.75

Col de Beixalis — A559

2021, Jan. 2 Litho. ***Perf. 13***
831 A559 €4.40 multi 11.00 11.00

Tribute to Workers During the COVID-19 Pandemic — A560

2021, Feb. 27 Litho. ***Perf. 13¼***
832 A560 €1.28 multi 3.25 3.25

Opening of Prisunic Shopping Center — A561

2021, Mar. 19 Litho. ***Perf. 13¼***
833 A561 €1.28 multi 3.00 3.00

Bailen Guai Motorbike — A562

2021, Apr. 23 Engr. ***Perf. 13¼x13***
834 A562 €1.50 multi 3.75 3.75

Galemys Pyrenaicus — A563

2021, May 14 Litho. ***Perf. 13¼***
835 A563 €1.50 multi 3.75 3.75

Europa.

Pilar Maestre and Huguet Mir (1880-1957), Primary School Teachers — A564

2021, June 4 Litho. ***Perf. 13¼***
836 A564 €1.28 multi 3.00 3.00

Nsapoleon Bonaparte (1769-1821), Emperor of France — A565

2021, June 17 Engr. ***Perf. 13***
837 A565 €2.56 gold & blk 6.00 6.00

Stages 15 and 16 of the 2021 Tour de France in Andorra — A566

Digital Printing

2021, July 13 ***Perf. 13¼***
838 A566 €1.50 multi 3.75 3.75

Cabana Sorda Lake A567

2021, July 23 Litho. ***Perf. 13***
839 A567 €1.28 multi 3.00 3.00

Oil Lamp From Church of Santa Eulalia d'Encamp A568

2021, Aug. 6 Engr. ***Perf. 13¼x13***
840 A568 €2.56 multi 6.00 6.00

Adoption of "El Gran Carlemany" as National Anthem, Cent. — A569

2021, Sept. 6 Litho. ***Perf. 13x13¼***
841 A569 €1.28 multi 3.00 3.00

Manuel Mas (1946-2001), Foreign Minister — A570

2021, Sept. 24 Litho. ***Perf. 13¼x13***
842 A570 €1.50 multi 3.50 3.50

The Time Game, Sculpture by Judit Gaste Flinch — A571

2021, Oct. 15 Litho. ***Perf. 13***
843 A571 €2.56 multi 6.00 6.00

Alnus Glutinosa — A572

2021, Nov. 5 Engr. ***Perf. 13***
844 A572 €1.50 multi 3.50 3.50

Angel in St. Bartomeu Chapel, Sant Julià de Lòria — A573

Digital Printing

2021, Nov. 5 ***Perf. 13***
845 A573 €1.28 multi 3.00 3.00

Pic de Carroi — A574

2022, Jan. 3 Litho. ***Perf. 13***
846 A574 €4.55 multi 10.50 10.50

Valéry Giscard d'Estaing (1926-2020), Co-Prince of Andorra and President of France — A575

2022, Feb. 2 Litho. ***Perf. 13¼***
847 A575 €1.43 multi 3.25 3.25

Rosa Ferrer (1960-2018), Minister of Health, Welfare and Employment — A576

2022, Mar. 8 Litho. ***Perf. 13¼***
848 A576 €2.32 multi 5.25 5.25

Catalan Studies Program at Charles University, Prague, 30th Anniv. — A577

2022, Apr. 8 Litho. *Perf. 13¼*

849	A577	€1.65 multi	3.50	3.50

Legends of Charlemagne (747-814) — A578

2022, May 13 Litho. *Perf. 13¼*

850	A578	€1.65 multi	3.50	3.50

Europa.

Brown Cow — A579

2022, May 27 Litho. *Perf. 13¼*

851	A579	€1.16 multi	2.50	2.50

Volkswagen 1303S — A580

2022, June 23 Engr. *Perf. 13¼*

852	A580	€1.65 multi	3.50	3.50

Estany de l'Isla A581

2022, July 9 Litho. *Perf. 13*

853	A581	€1.65 multi	3.50	3.50

Luna Park — A582

2022, July 22 Litho. *Perf. 13¼*

854	A582	€1.43 multi	3.00	3.00

Execution of Joana Call for Witchcraft, 550th Anniv. — A583

2022, Aug. 5 Engr. *Perf. 13*

855	A583	€2.32 multi	4.75	4.75

Destruction of Our Lady of Meritxell Icon in Meritxell Sanctuary Fire, 50th Anniv. — A584

2022, Sept. 9 Litho. *Perf. 13¼*

856	A584	€1.43 multi	3.00	3.00

SEMI-POSTAL STAMP

Catalogue values for unused stamps in this section are for Never Hinged items.

Virgin of St. Coloma — SP1

Unwmk.

1964, July 25 Engr. *Perf. 13*

B1	SP1	25c + 10c multi	24.00	24.00

The surtax was for the Red Cross.

AIR POST STAMPS

Catalogue values for unused stamps in this section are for Never Hinged items.

Chamois — AP1

Unwmk.

1950, Feb. 20 Engr. *Perf. 13*

C1	AP1	100fr indigo	87.50	60.00

East Branch of Valira River — AP2

1955-57

C2	AP2	100fr dark green	16.00	10.50
C3	AP2	200fr cerise	32.50	16.00
C4	AP2	500fr dp bl ('57)	120.00	65.00
		Nos. C2-C4 (3)	168.50	91.50

No. C3 in dark green was not regularly issued. Value, $3,500.

D'Inclès Valley — AP3

1961-64 Unwmk. *Perf. 13*

C5	AP3	2fr red, ol gray & cl	1.25	1.25
C6	AP3	3fr bl, mar & slate grn	1.60	1.60
C7	AP3	5fr rose lil & red org	3.25	2.40
C8	AP3	10fr bl grn & slate grn	4.75	4.50
		Nos. C5-C8 (4)	10.85	9.75

Issued: 10fr, 4/25/64; others, 6/19/61.

POSTAGE DUE STAMPS

Postage Due Stamps of France, 1893-1931, Overprinted

On Stamps of 1893-1926

1931-33 Unwmk. *Perf. 14x13½*

J1	D2	5c blue	2.40	2.40
J2	D2	10c brown	2.40	2.40
J3	D2	30c rose red	1.60	1.60
J4	D2	50c violet brn	2.40	2.40
J5	D2	60c green	34.00	34.00
J6	D2	1fr red brn, *straw*	2.40	2.40
J7	D2	2fr brt violet	16.00	16.00
J8	D2	3fr magenta	3.25	3.25
		Nos. J1-J8 (8)	64.45	64.45

On Stamps of 1927-31

J9	D4	1c olive grn	3.25	3.25
J10	D4	10c rose	5.50	*6.50*
J11	D4	60c red	27.50	26.50
J12	D4	1fr Prus grn ('32)	110.00	*120.00*
J13	D4	1.20fr on 2fr bl	80.00	80.00
J14	D4	2fr ol brn ('33)	200.00	*225.00*
J15	D4	5fr on 1fr vio	120.00	120.00
		Nos. J9-J15 (7)	546.25	581.25

D5

D6

1935-41 Typo.

J16	D5	1c gray green	3.25	3.25
J17	D6	5c light blue ('37)	6.75	6.75
J18	D6	10c brown ('41)	4.00	*5.50*
J19	D6	2fr violet ('41)	11.00	8.75
J20	D6	5fr red orange ('41)	19.00	11.00
		Nos. J16-J20 (5)	44.00	35.25

Catalogue values for unused stamps in this section, from this point to the end of the section, are for Never Hinged items.

Wheat Sheaves — D7

1943-46 *Perf. 14x13½*

J21	D7	10c sepia	.80	.70
J22	D7	30c brt red vio	.90	.70
J23	D7	50c blue grn	1.25	1.10
J24	D7	1fr brt ultra	1.10	.90
J25	D7	1.50fr rose red	6.75	5.50
J26	D7	2fr turq blue	1.75	1.60
J27	D7	3fr brown org	2.00	1.90
J28	D7	4fr dp vio ('45)	6.25	5.50
J29	D7	5fr brt pink	4.25	3.75
J30	D7	10fr red org ('45)	6.50	5.50
J31	D7	20fr olive brn ('46)	7.75	6.50
		Nos. J21-J31 (11)	39.30	33.65

Inscribed: "Timbre Taxe"

1946-53

J32	D7	10c sepia ('46)	1.60	1.60
J33	D7	1fr ultra	.80	.80
J34	D7	2fr turq blue	1.25	1.25
J35	D7	3fr orange brn	2.75	2.75
J36	D7	4fr violet	3.50	3.50
J37	D7	5fr brt pink	2.75	2.75
J38	D7	10fr red orange	4.75	4.75
J39	D7	20fr olive brn	8.00	8.00
J40	D7	50fr dk green ('50)	47.50	47.50
J41	D7	100fr dp green ('53)	120.00	120.00
		Nos. J32-J41 (10)	192.90	192.90

Inscribed: "Timbre Taxe"

1961, June 19 *Perf. 14x13½*

J42	D7	5c rose pink	4.00	4.00
J43	D7	10c red orange	8.00	8.00
J44	D7	20c olive	12.00	12.00
J45	D7	50c dark slate green	24.00	24.00
		Nos. J42-J45 (4)	48.00	48.00

D8

1964-71 Typo. *Perf. 14x13½*

J46	D8	5c Centaury ('65)	.25	.25
J47	D8	10c Gentian ('65)	.25	.25
J48	D8	15c Corn poppy	.25	.25
J49	D8	20c Violets ('71)	.30	.25
J50	D8	30c Forget-me-not	.40	.30
J51	D8	40c Columbine ('71)	.55	.40
J52	D8	50c Clover ('65)	.65	.55
		Nos. J46-J52 (7)	2.65	2.25

D9

1985, Oct. 21 Engr. *Perf. 13*

J53	D9	10c Holly	.25	.25
J54	D9	20c Blueberries	.25	.25
J55	D9	30c Raspberries	.25	.25
J56	D9	40c Bilberries	.25	.25
J57	D9	50c Blackberries	.25	.25
J58	D9	1fr Broom	.40	.40
J59	D9	2fr Rosehips	.95	.65
J60	D9	3fr Nightshade	1.25	.95
J61	D9	4fr Nabiu	1.50	1.25
J62	D9	5fr Strawberries	1.90	1.50
		Nos. J53-J62 (10)	7.25	6.00

NEWSPAPER STAMP

France No. P7 Overprinted

1931 Unwmk. *Perf. 14x13½*

P1	A16	½c on 1c gray	1.25	1.25
a.		Double overprint	*2,750.*	
		Never Hinged	*3,600.*	

ANGOLA

aŋ'gō-lə

LOCATION — S.W. Africa between Zaire and Namibia.
GOVT. — Republic
AREA — 481,351 sq. mi.
POP. — 11,177,537 (1999 est.)
CAPITAL — Luanda

Angola was a Portuguese overseas territory until it became independent November 11, 1975, as the People's Republic of Angola.

1000 Reis = 1 Milreis
100 Centavos = 1 Escudo (1913, 1954)
100 Centavos = 1 Angolar (1932)
10 Lweys = 1 Kwanza (1977)

Catalogue values for unused stamps in this country are for Never Hinged items, beginning with Scott 328 in the regular postage section, Scott C26 in the air-post section, Scott J31 in the postage due section, and Scott RA7 in the postal tax section.

Watermark

Wmk. 232 — Maltese Cross

Portuguese Crown — A1

Perf. 12½, 13½

1870-77 Typo. Unwmk.

Thin to Medium Paper

1	A1	5r gray black	3.25	2.00
2	A1	10r yellow	30.00	20.00
3	A1	20r bister	3.00	2.25
4	A1	25r red	15.00	10.00
5	A1	40r blue ('77)	275.00	175.00
6	A1	50r green	70.00	15.00
7	A1	100r lilac	6.50	3.50
8	A1	200r orange ('77)	4.50	2.00
9	A1	300r choc ('77)	6.00	3.50

1881-85 *Perf. 12½, 13½*

10	A1	10r green ('83)	8.50	4.75
11	A1	20r carmine rose ('85)	21.00	14.00
12	A1	25r violet ('85)	12.50	5.00
13	A1	40r buff ('82)	13.00	4.75
15	A1	50r blue	45.00	10.00
		Nos. 10-15 (5)	100.00	38.50

Two types of numerals are found on #2, 11, 13, 15.

The cliche of 40r in plate of 20r error, was discovered before the stamps were issued. All examples were defaced by a blue pencil mark. Values, $2,100 unused; in pair with 20r, $2,400.

In perf. 12½, Nos. 1-4, 4a and 6, as well as 7a, were printed in 1870 on thicker paper and 1875 on normal paper. Stamps of the earlier printing sell for 2 to 5 times more than those of the 1875 printing.

Some reprints of the 1870-85 issues are on a smooth white chalky paper, ungummed and perf. 13½. Value, each $17.50.

Other reprints of these issues are on thin ivory paper with shiny white gum and clear-cut perf. 13½. Value, each $24.

King Luiz — A2

1886 Embossed *Perf. 12½*

16	A2	5r black	14.00	6.50
17	A2	10r green	14.00	6.50
18	A2	20r rose	19.00	12.50
19	A2	25r red violet	15.00	4.00
20	A2	40r chocolate	17.50	7.50
21	A2	50r blue	21.00	4.00
22	A2	100r yellow brn	30.00	10.00
23	A2	200r gray violet	40.00	13.00
24	A2	300r orange	40.00	14.00
		Nos. 16-24 (9)	210.50	78.00

For surcharges see Nos. 61-69, 172-174, 208-210.

Reprints of 5r, 20r & 100r have cleancut perf. 13½.

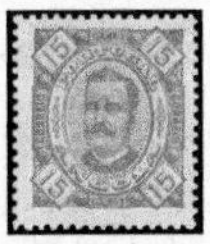

King Carlos — A3

1893-94 Typo. *Perf. 11½, 12½, 13½*

25	A3	5r yellow	3.75	1.50
26	A3	10r redsh violet	5.00	3.00
27a	A3	15r chocolate	7.00	3.00
28	A3	20r lavender	7.00	3.00
29c	A3	25r green	7.00	3.75
30b	A3	50r light blue	10.00	4.00
31	A3	75r carmine	20.00	12.00
32	A3	80r lt green	20.00	9.00
33	A3	100r brown, *buff*	20.00	9.00
34	A3	150r car, *rose*	30.00	17.50
35	A3	200r dk blue, *lt bl*	30.00	17.50
36	A3	300r dk blue, *sal*	35.00	17.50

For surcharges see Nos. 70-81, 175-179, 213-216, 234.

No. P1 Surcharged in Blue

1894, Aug. *Perf. 13½*

37	N1	25r on 2½r brown	75.00	60.00
a.		Double surcharge, one inverted	175.00	
b.		Perf. 11½	110.00	85.00
c.		Perf. 12½	90.00	67.50
d.		As 'c,' double surcharge, one inverted	140.00	125.00

King Carlos — A5

1898-1903 *Perf. 11½*

Name and Value in Black except 500r

38	A5	2½r gray	.65	.50
39	A5	5r orange	.65	.50
40	A5	10r yellow grn	.65	.50
41	A5	15r violet brn	3.25	1.60
42	A5	15r gray green ('03)	1.60	1.40
43	A5	20r gray violet	.70	.50
44	A5	25r sea green	1.60	.75
45	A5	25r car ('03)	.85	.45
46	A5	50r blue	2.75	1.00
47	A5	50r brown ('03)	8.00	3.75
48	A5	65r dull blue ('03)	8.50	5.75
49	A5	75r rose	11.00	6.00
50	A5	75r red violet ('03)	3.00	2.00
51	A5	80r violet	10.00	3.00
52	A5	100r dk blue, *blue*	2.00	1.40
53	A5	115r org brn, *pink* ('03)	11.00	7.50
54	A5	130r brn, *straw* ('03)	11.00	7.50
55	A5	150r brn, *straw*	11.00	6.00
56	A5	200r red vio, *pink*	7.50	1.75
57	A5	300r dk blue, *rose*	6.50	5.00
58	A5	400r dull bl, *straw* ('03)	12.50	3.50
59	A5	500r blk & red, *bl* ('01)	16.00	5.00
60	A5	700r vio, *yelsh* ('01)	35.00	17.00
		Nos. 38-60 (23)	165.70	82.35

For surcharges and overprints see Nos. 83-102, 113-117, 159-171, 181-183, 217-218, 221-225.

Stamps of 1886-94 Surcharged in Black or Red

Two types of surcharge:
I — 3mm between numeral and REIS.
II — 4½mm spacing.

1902 *Perf. 12½*

61	A2	65r on 40r choc	12.00	6.50
62	A2	65r on 300r org, I	12.00	6.50
a.		Type II	12.00	6.50
63	A2	115r on 10r green	10.00	5.00
a.		Inverted surcharge	90.00	50.00
b.		Perf. 13½	75.00	45.00
64	A2	115r on 200r gray vio	10.00	5.00
65	A2	130r on 50r blue	13.00	5.00
66	A2	130r on 100r brown	8.50	5.00
67	A2	400r on 20r rose	110.00	65.00
a.		Perf. 13½	175.00	92.50
68	A2	400r on 25r violet	22.50	12.00
69	A2	400r on 5r black (R)	20.00	13.00
a.		Double surcharge	75.00	50.00
		Nos. 61-69 (9)	218.00	123.00

For surcharges see Nos. 172-174, 208-210.

Perf. 11½, 12½, 13½

70	A3	65r on 5r yel, I, perf. 11½	11.00	6.50
a.		Type II	11.00	7.00
71	A3	65r on 10r red vio, I, perf. 12½	7.25	5.50
a.		Type II	7.25	5.50
b.		Perf. 11½, I	12.00	7.00
c.		Perf. 11½, I	12.00	7.00
72	A3	65r on 20r lav, perf. 11½	11.00	6.50
73	A3	65r on 25r green, perf. 12½	15.00	9.00
b.		Perf. 13½	7.00	5.00
74	A3	115r on 80r lt grn, perf. 12½	15.00	9.00
75	A3	115r on 100r brn, *buff*, perf. 12½	15.00	7.25
b.		Perf. 13½	80.00	40.00
76	A3	115r on 150r car, *rose*, perf. 11½	17.50	13.00
a.		Perf. 13½	25.00	15.00
b.		Perf. 12½	24.00	15.00
77	A3	130r on 15r choc, perf. 12½	6.50	5.50
b.		Type II	8.00	4.50
78	A3	130r on 75r carmine, perf. 11½	60.00	50.00
a.		Perf. 13½	70.00	55.00
b.		Perf. 12½	15.00	11.00
79	A3	130r on 300r dk bl, *sal*, perf. 12½	20.00	15.00
a.		Perf. 13½	35.00	12.50
80	A3	400r on 50r lt bl, I, perf. 12½	11.00	5.50
a.		Perf. 11½	32.50	15.00
c.		Type II	9.00	6.00
81	A3	400r on 200r bl, *bl*, perf. 12½	11.00	8.00
a.		Perf. 13½	375.00	225.00
82	N1	400r on 2½r brn, I, perf. 12½	1.75	1.60
a.		Type II	1.75	1.60
		Nos. 70-82 (13)	202.00	142.35

For surcharges see Nos. 175-180, 211-216, 234-235.

Reprints of Nos. 65, 67, 68 and 69 have clean-cut perforation 13½.

For detailed listings of perforation and paper varieties, see *Scott Classic Specialized Catalogue of Stamps and Covers 1840-1940.*

Stamps of 1898 Overprinted — a

1902 *Perf. 11½*

83	A5	15r brown	2.50	1.75
84	A5	25r sea green	2.00	1.00
85	A5	50r blue	4.50	2.00
86	A5	75r rose	7.00	5.25
		Nos. 83-86 (4)	16.00	10.00

For surcharge see No. 116.

No. 48 Surcharged in Black

1905

87	A5	50r on 65r dull blue	6.00	3.00

For surcharge see No. 183.

Stamps of 1898-1903 Overprinted in Carmine or Green — b

1911

88	A5	2½r gray	.60	.50
89	A5	5r orange yel	.60	.50
90	A5	10r light green	.60	.50
91	A5	15r gray green	.85	.70
92	A5	20r gray violet	.90	.75
93	A5	25r car (G)	.90	.75
94	A5	50r brown	3.25	1.75
95	A5	75r lilac	6.75	3.25
96	A5	100r dk blue, *bl*	6.75	3.50
97	A5	115r org brn, *pink*	3.75	1.75
98	A5	130r brn, *straw*	3.75	1.75
99	A5	200r red lil, *pnksh*	4.50	2.40
100	A5	400r dull bl, *straw*	4.50	1.75
101	A5	500r blk & red, *bl*	4.50	2.25
102	A5	700r violet, *yelsh*	4.50	2.50
		Nos. 88-102 (15)	46.70	24.60

Inverted and double overprints of Nos. 88-102 were made intentionally.

For surcharges see Nos. 217-218, 221-222, 224.

King Manuel II — A6

Overprinted in Carmine or Green

1912 *Perf. 11½x12*

103	A6	2½r violet	.75	.50
104	A6	5r black	.75	.50
105	A6	10r gray green	.75	.50
106	A6	20r carmine (G)	.75	.50
107	A6	25r violet brown	.75	.50
108	A6	50r dk blue	1.75	1.40
109	A6	75r bister brown	2.00	1.75
110	A6	100r brown, *lt green*	3.75	2.25
111	A6	200r dk green, *salmon*	3.75	2.40
112	A6	300r black, *azure*	3.75	2.40
		Nos. 103-112 (10)	18.75	12.70

For surcharges see Nos. 219-220, 226-227.

No. 91 Surcharged in Black

1912, June *Perf. 11½*

113	A5	2½r on 15r gray green	6.00	3.75
114	A5	5r on 15r gray green	6.75	3.75
115	A5	10r on 15r gray green	5.25	3.75
		Nos. 113-115 (3)	18.00	11.25

Inverted and double surcharges of Nos. 113-115 were made intentionally.

Nos. 86 and 50 Surcharged in Black and Overprinted in Violet — c

1912

116	A5	25r on 75r rose	110.00	60.00
117	A5	25r on 75r red violet	7.50	6.00
a.		"REUPBLICA"	135.00	70.00
b.		"25" omitted	135.00	70.00
c.		"REPUBLICA" omitted	135.00	70.00

Ceres — A7

With Imprint

1914 Chalky Paper *Perf. 15x14*

Name and Value in Black

118	A7	¼c olive brown	2.00	.90
119	A7	½c black	2.00	.90
120	A7	1c blue green	2.00	.90
121	A7	1½c lilac brown	4.00	2.25
122	A7	2c carmine	7.00	3.25
123	A7	2½c violet	1.40	.60
124	A7	5c blue	3.00	1.60
125	A7	7½c yellow brn	4.00	2.40
126	A7	8c slate	4.00	2.40
127	A7	10c orange brn	4.00	2.40
128	A7	15c brown rose	6.00	2.50
129	A7	20c yel green	3.00	1.60
130	A7	30c brown, *green*	3.00	2.40
131	A7	40c brown, *pink*	3.00	2.40
132	A7	50c orange, *sal*	11.00	8.25
133	A7	1e green, *blue*	8.00	4.75
		Nos. 118-133 (16)	67.40	39.50

1915-22 Ordinary Paper

134	A7	¼c olive brown	.45	.45
135	A7	½c black	.45	.45
136	A7	1c blue green	.45	.45
137	A7	1c yellow green ('18)	.45	.45
138	A7	1½c lilac brown	.45	.45
139	A7	2c carmine	.55	.45
140	A7	2½c dark violet	.55	.45
141	A7	3c orange	27.50	24.00
142	A7	4c dull rose ('21)	.45	.45
143	A7	5c blue	1.75	1.40
144	A7	6c lilac ('21)	.45	.45
145	A7	7c ultra ('21)	.45	.45
146	A7	7½c yellow brn ('20)	.55	.45
147	A7	8c slate	.60	.55
148	A7	10c orange brn ('18)	.55	.45
149	A7	12c olive brown ('21)	1.50	1.00
150	A7	15c plum ('20)	.55	.45
151	A7	15c brown rose ('21)	.55	.45
152	A7	20c yel green ('18)	6.75	5.00
153	A7	30c gray green ('21)	1.00	.65
154	A7	80c pink ('21)	1.75	1.00
155	A7	2e dark violet ('22)	3.50	3.00
		Nos. 134-155 (22)	51.25	42.90

1921-26 *Perf. 12x11½*

156	A7	¼c olive brown ('24)	.45	.45
157	A7	½c black	.45	.45
158	A7	1c blue green ('24)	.45	.45
158C	A7	1½c lilac brown ('24)	.45	.45
158D	A7	2c carmine ('24)	.45	.45
158E	A7	2c gray ('25)	.75	.55
158F	A7	2½c lt violet ('24)	.45	.45
158G	A7	3c orange	.45	.45
158H	A7	4c dull rose	.45	.45
158I	A7	4½c gray	.45	.45
158J	A7	5c blue ('24)	.45	.45
158K	A7	6c lilac	.45	.45
158L	A7	7c ultra	.45	.45
158M	A7	7½c yellow brown ('24)	.55	.45
158N	A7	8c slate ('24)	.55	.45
158O	A7	10c orange brn ('24)	.45	.40
158P	A7	12c olive brn	.75	.60
158Q	A7	12c dp green ('25)	.75	.50
158R	A7	15c plum ('24)	.45	.35
158S	A7	20c yel green	1.75	1.60
158T	A7	24c ultra ('25)	1.60	1.20
158U	A7	25c choc ('25)	1.60	1.20
158V	A7	30c gray grn	.75	.60
158W	A7	40c turq blue	1.20	.70
158X	A7	50c lt violet ('25)	1.40	.70
158Y	A7	60c dk blue ('22)	1.50	1.00
158Z	A7	60c dp rose ('26)	75.00	47.50
159A	A7	80c pink ('22)	1.75	1.00
159B	A7	1e rose ('22)	1.75	1.00
		Nos. 156-159B (29)	97.95	65.20

Glazed Paper

1921-25 *Perf. 12x11½*

159C A7 1e rose 1.75 1.75
159D A7 1e deep blue ('25) 3.25 1.60
159E A7 2e dark violet ('22) 2.25 1.25
159F A7 5e buff ('25) 14.00 11.50
159G A7 10e pink ('25) 30.00 25.00
159H A7 20e pale turq ('25) 100.00 70.00
Nos. 159C-159H (6) 151.25 111.10

For surcharges see Nos. 228-229, 236-239.

Stamps of 1898-1903 Overprinted type "c" in Red or Green

1914 *Perf. 11½, 12*

159 A5 10r yel green (R) 7.50 5.50
160 A5 15r gray green (R) 6.75 5.50
161 A5 20r gray violet (G) 2.75 2.00
163 A5 75r red violet (G) 2.00 1.40
164 A5 100r blue, *blue* (R) 4.50 3.75
165 A5 115r org brn, *pink* (R) *150.00*
167 A5 200r red vio, *pnksh* (G) 2.75 1.75
169 A5 400r dl bl, *straw* (R) 50.00 50.00
170 A5 500r blk & red, *bl* (R) 6.75 6.25
171 A5 700r vio, *yelsh* (G) 35.00 27.00

Inverted and double overprints were made intentionally. No. 165 was not regularly issued. Red overprints on the 20r, 75r, 200r were not regularly issued. The 130r was not regularly issued without surcharge (No. 225).

On Nos. 63-65, 74-76, 78-79, 82

Perf. 11½, 12½, 13½

172 A2 115r on 10r (R) 17.00 17.00
a. Perf. 13½ 17.00 17.00
173 A2 115r on 200r (R) 22.50 22.50
174 A2 130r on 50r (R) 110.00 110.00
175 A3 115r on 80r (R) 210.00 200.00
176 A3 115r on 100r (R) 225.00 175.00
a. Perf. 11½ 300.00 300.00
b. Perf. 13½ 900.00 850.00
177 A3 115r on 150r (G) 225.00 175.00
a. Perf. 12½ 250.00 200.00
b. Perf. 13½ 750.00 700.00
178 A3 130r on 75r (G) 8.25 7.50
a. Perf. 12½ 9.00 7.50
179 A3 130r on 300r (R) 10.50 8.25
a. Perf. 12½ 17.50 16.00
180 N1 400r on 2½r (R) 1.10 4.00
a. Perf. 11½ 5.25
b. Perf. 13½ 1.10 .85
Nos. 172-180 (9) 829.35 719.25

Nos. 85-87 Overprinted in Red or Green

On Stamps of 1902

Perf. 11½, 12

181 A5 50r blue (R) 2.50 2.25
182 A5 75r rose (G) 6.00 4.50

On No. 87

183 A5 50r on 65r dull blue (R) 5.50 1.75
Nos. 181-183 (3) 14.00 10.75

Inverted and double surcharges of Nos. 181-183 were made intentionally.

Common Design Types pictured following the introduction.

Vasco da Gama Issue of Various Portuguese Colonies

Common Design Types CD20-CD27 Srchd.

On Stamps of Macao

1913 *Perf. 12½ to 16*

184 ¼c on ½a blue grn 2.25
185 ½c on la red 2.25 1.75
186 1c on 2a red violet 2.40 1.75
187 2½c on 4a yel green 1.75 1.25
188 5c on 8a dk blue 1.75 1.25
189 7½c on 12a vio brn 8.00 5.50
190 10c on 16a bister brn 2.75 2.00
191 15c on 24a bister 3.75 2.00
Nos. 184-191 (8) 24.90 15.50

On Stamps of Portuguese Africa

Perf. 14 to 15

192 ¼c on 2½r blue grn 1.25 .85
193 ½c on 5r red 1.25 .85
194 1c on 10r red violet 1.25 .85
195 2½c on 25r yel grn 1.25 .85
196 5c on 50r dk blue 1.25 .85
197 7½c on 75r vio brn 7.50 6.75
198 10c on 100r bister brn 3.00 2.00
199 15c on 150r bister 3.50 2.25
Nos. 192-199 (8) 20.25 15.25

On Stamps of Timor

200 ¼c on ½a blue grn 2.25 1.75
201 ½c on 1a red 2.25 1.75
202 1c on 2a red vio 2.40 1.75
203 2½c on 4a yel grn 1.75 1.25
204 5c on 8a dk blue 1.75 1.25
205 7½c on 12a vio brn 8.00 5.50
206 10c on 16a bis brn 2.75 2.00
207 15c on 24a bister 3.75 2.00
Nos. 200-207 (8) 24.90 17.25
Nos. 184-207 (24) 70.05 48.00

Provisional Issue of 1902 Overprinted in Carmine

1915 *Perf. 11½, 12½, 13½*

208 A2 115r on 10r green 2.00 2.00
a. Perf. 12½ 2.50 2.25
209 A2 115r on 200r gray vio 2.25 1.90
210 A2 130r on 100r brown 1.90 1.60
211 A3 115r on 80r lt green 2.50 2.25
212 A3 115r on 100r brn, *buff* 2.25 2.00
a. Perf. 11½ 100.00 90.00
b. Perf. 13½ 16.00 13.50
213 A3 115r on 150r car, *rose* 1.60 1.60
a. Perf. 12½ 3.75 3.25
b. Perf. 13½ 2.60 2.25
214 A3 130r on 15r choc 1.60 1.60
a. Perf. 12½ 8.25 6.75
215 A3 130r on 75r carmine 3.25 2.00
a. Perf. 13½ 5.00 4.25
b. Perf. 12½ 3.25 2.00
216 A3 130r on 300r dk bl, *sal* 2.00 2.00
a. Perf. 13½ 3.75 2.50
Nos. 208-216 (9) 19.35 16.95

Stamps of 1911-14 Surcharged in Black

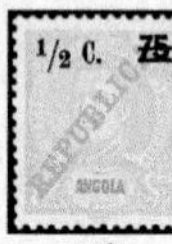

d

e

On Stamps of 1911

1919 *Perf. 11½*

217 A5 (d) ½c on 75r red lilac 3.25 2.60
218 A5 (d) 2½c on 100r blue, *grysh* 3.50 2.60

On Stamps of 1912

Perf. 11½x12

219 A6 (e) ½c on 75r bis brn 2.00 1.50
220 A6 (e) 2½c on 100r brn, *lt grn* 3.50 2.60

On Stamps of 1914

221 A5 (d) ½c on 75r red lil 2.25 1.90
222 A5 (d) 2½c on 100r bl, *grysh* 2.60 2.25
Nos. 217-222 (6) 17.10 13.45

Inverted and double surcharges were made for sale to collectors.

Nos. 163, 98 and Type of 1914 Surcharged in Black

1921

223 A5 (c) 00.5c on 75r *400.00 350.00*
224 A5 (b) 4c on 130r (#98) 3.00 3.00
225 A5 (c) 4c on 130r brn, *straw* 7.50 7.50
a. Without surcharge *240.00*

Nos. 109 and 108 Surcharged with New Values and Bars in Black

226 A6 00.5c on 75r 2.25 1.90
227 A6 1c on 50r 2.50 2.50

Nos. 146 and 150 Surcharged with New Values and Bars in Black

228 A7 00.5c on 7½c 2.50 2.25
229 A7 04c on 15c 3.00 3.00
Nos. 224-229 (6) 20.75 20.15
Nos. 223-229 (7) 420.75 370.15

The 04c surcharge exists on the 15c brown rose, perf 12x11½, No. 158R.

Some authorities question the status of No. 223.

Nos. 81-82 Surcharged

1925 *Perf. 12½*

234 A3 40c on 400r on 200r bl, *bl* 1.50 1.10
a. Perf. 13½ 11.00 7.50
235 N1 40c on 400r on 2½r brn 1.10 1.10
a. Perf. 13½ 1.10 1.10

Nos. 158Y, 159A, 159D-159E Surcharged

1931 *Perf. 12x 11½*

236 A7 50c on 60c deep rose 2.25 2.00
237 A7 70c on 80c pink 4.50 3.00
238 A7 70c on 1e deep blue 4.00 3.00
239 A7 1.40e on 2e dark violet 2.50 2.00
Nos. 236-239 (4) 13.25 10.00

Ceres — A14

Perf. 12x11½

1932-46 **Typo.** **Wmk. 232**

243 A14 1c bister brn .30 .25
244 A14 5c dk brown .35 .30
245 A14 10c dp violet .35 .30
246 A14 15c black .35 .30
247 A14 20c gray .40 .30
248 A14 30c myrtle grn .40 .30
249 A14 35c yel grn ('46) 7.50 4.50
250 A14 40c dp orange .40 .30
251 A14 45c lt blue 1.75 1.25
252 A14 50c lt brown .30 .25
253 A14 60c olive grn 1.00 .30
254 A14 70c orange brn 1.10 .30
255 A14 80c emerald .75 .25
256 A14 85c rose 5.50 2.00
257 A14 1a claret 1.10 .30
258 A14 1.40a dk blue 11.50 1.75
258A A14 1.75a dk blue ('46) 16.00 5.25
259 A14 2a dull vio 5.25 .55
260 A14 5a pale yel grn 10.50 1.75
261 A14 10a olive bis 20.00 5.25
262 A14 20a orange 52.50 5.25
Nos. 243-262 (21) 137.30 31.00
Set, never hinged 175.00

For surcharges see Nos. 263-267, 271-273, 294A-300, J31-J36.

Surcharged in Black

5½mm between bars and new value.

1934

263 A14 10c on 45c lt bl 3.50 2.50
264 A14 20c on 85c rose 3.50 2.50
265 A14 30c on 1.40a dk bl 3.50 2.50
266 A14 70c on 2a dl vio 4.50 3.25
267 A14 80c on 5a pale yel grn 7.00 2.75
Nos. 263-267 (5) 22.00 13.50
Set, never hinged 37.50

See Nos. 294A-300.

Nos. J26, J30 Surcharged in Black

1935 **Unwmk.** *Perf. 11½*

268 D2 5c on 6c lt brown 2.50 1.60
269 D2 30c on 50c gray 2.50 1.60
270 D2 40c on 50c gray 2.50 1.60
Nos. 268-270 (3) 7.50 4.80
Set, never hinged 14.00

No. 255 Surcharged in Black

1938 **Wmk. 232** *Perf. 12x11½*

271 A14 5c on 80c emerald 1.10 .55
272 A14 10c on 80c emerald 1.60 .75
273 A14 15c on 80c emerald 2.25 .75
Nos. 271-273 (3) 4.95 2.05
Set, never hinged 8.25

Vasco da Gama Issue

Common Design Types

Engr.; Name & Value Typo. in Black

Perf. 13½x13

1938, July 26 **Unwmk.**

274 CD34 1c gray green .25 .25
275 CD34 5c orange brn .30 .30
276 CD34 10c dk carmine .40 .30
277 CD34 15c dk violet brn .40 .30
278 CD34 20c slate .40 .30
279 CD35 30c rose violet .55 .40
280 CD35 35c brt green 1.00 .75
281 CD35 40c brown .40 .25
282 CD35 50c brt red vio .55 .25
283 CD36 60c gray black 1.10 .30
284 CD36 70c brown vio 1.10 .30
285 CD36 80c orange 1.10 .30
286 CD36 1a red 1.10 .30
287 CD37 1.75a blue 2.10 1.00
288 CD37 2a brown car 3.25 1.50
289 CD37 5a olive grn 13.50 1.50
290 CD38 10a blue vio 28.00 1.90
291 CD38 20a red brown 40.00 4.25
Nos. 274-291 (18) 95.50 14.45
Set, never hinged 150.00

For surcharges see Nos. 301-304.

Marble Column and Portuguese Arms with Cross — A20

1938, July 29 *Perf. 12½*

292 A20 80c blue green 3.75 2.25
293 A20 1.75a deep blue 20.00 6.00
294 A20 20a dk red brown 60.00 27.00
Nos. 292-294 (3) 83.75 35.25
Set, never hinged 140.00

Visit of the President of Portugal to this colony in 1938.

Stamps of 1932 Surcharged with New Value and Bars

8mm between bars and new value.

1941-45 **Wmk. 232** *Perf. 12x11½*

294A A14 5c on 80c emer ('45) .85 .55
295 A14 10c on 45c lt blue 1.75 1.25
296 A14 15c on 45c lt blue 1.75 1.25
297 A14 20c on 85c rose 1.75 1.25
298 A14 35c on 85c rose 1.75 1.25
299 A14 50c on 1.40a dk blue 1.75 1.25
300 A14 60c on 1a claret 9.00 7.50
Nos. 294A-300 (7) 18.60 14.30
Set, never hinged 32.50

Nos. 285 to 287 Surcharged in Black or Red

1945 **Unwmk.** *Perf. 13½x13*

301 CD36 5c on 80c org .85 .55
302 CD36 50c on 1a red .85 .55
303 CD37 50c on 1.75a bl (R) .85 .55
304 CD37 50c on 1.75a bl .85 .55
Nos. 301-304 (4) 3.40 2.20
Set, never hinged 5.00

Sao Miguel Fort, Luanda — A21

John IV — A22

Designs: 10c, Our Lady of Nazareth Church, Luanda. 50c, Salvador Correia de Sa e Bene vides. 1a, Surrender of Luanda. 1.75a, Diogo Cao. 2a, Manuel Cerveira Pereira. 5a, Stone Cliffs, Yelala. 10a, Paulo Dias de Novais. 20a, Massangano Fort.

Perf. 14½

1948, May **Unwmk.** **Litho.**

305	A21	5c	dk violet	.30	.30
306	A21	10c	dk brown	.75	.30
307	A22	30c	blue grn	.30	.30
308	A22	50c	vio brown	.30	.30
309	A21	1a	carmine	.70	.30
310	A22	1.75a	slate blue	1.00	.45
311	A22	2a	green	1.00	.55
312	A21	5a	gray black	2.50	1.10
313	A22	10a	rose lilac	8.25	1.50
314	A21	20a	gray blue	17.50	5.25
a.			Sheet of 10, #305-314	140.00	100.00
			Never hinged	200.00	
			Nos. 305-314 (10)	32.60	10.35
			Set, never hinged	50.00	

300th anniv. of the restoration of Angola to Portugal. No. 314a sold for 42.50a.

Lady of Fatima Issue
Common Design Type

1948, Dec.

315	CD40	50c	carmine	1.50	.75
316	CD40	3a	ultra	6.00	2.25
317	CD40	6a	red orange	18.00	5.25
318	CD40	9a	dp claret	42.50	9.00
			Nos. 315-318 (4)	68.00	17.25
			Set, never hinged	110.00	

Our Lady of the Rosary at Fatima, Portugal.

Chiumbe River A24

Black Rocks A25

Designs: 50c, View of Luanda. 2.50a, Sa da Bandeira. 3.50a, Mocamedes. 15a, Cubal River. 50a, Duke of Bragança Falls.

1949 **Unwmk.** ***Perf. 13½***

319	A24	20c	dk slate blue	.55	.30
320	A25	40c	black brown	.55	.30
321	A24	50c	rose brown	.55	.30
322	A24	2.50a	blue violet	3.00	.75
323	A24	3.50a	slate gray	3.00	.90
323A	A24	15a	dk green	18.00	2.75
324	A24	50a	dp green	110.00	7.50
			Nos. 319-324 (7)	135.65	12.80
			Set, never hinged	225.00	

Sailing Vessel — A26

1949, Aug. ***Perf. 14***

325	A26	1a	chocolate	6.75	.75
326	A26	4a	dk Prus green	17.50	2.75
			Set, never hinged	37.50	

Centenary of founding of Mocamedes.

UPU Symbols — A27

1949, Oct.

327	A27	4a	dk grn & lt grn	10.50	3.00
			Never hinged	16.00	

75th anniv. of the UPU.

Catalogue values for unused stamps in this section, from this point to the end of the section, are for Never Hinged items.

Stamp of 1870 — A28

1950, Apr. 2 ***Perf. 11½x12***

328	A28	50c	yellow green	1.75	.55
329	A28	1a	red	1.75	.85
330	A28	4a	black	6.25	1.25
a.			Sheet of 3, #328-330	40.00	40.00
			Nos. 328-330 (3)	9.75	2.65

Angola's first philatelic exhibition, marking the 80th anniversary of Angola's first stamps.

No. 330a contains Nos. 328, 329 (inverted), 330, perf. 11½ and sold for 6.50a. All examples carry an oval exhibition cancellation in the margin but the stamps were valid for postage.

Holy Year Issue
Common Design Types

1950, May ***Perf. 13x13½***

331	CD41	1a	dull rose vio	1.60	.35
332	CD42	4a	black	6.00	1.00

Melierax Mechowi A31

Merops Apiaster A32

Designs: 10c, Coracias spatulatus. 15c, Terathopius ecaudatus. 50c, Ceryle maxima. 1a, Buccanodon anchietae. 1.50a, Anastomus lamelligerus. 2a, Bucorvus cafer. 2.50a, Rhynchops flavirostris. 3a, Astur polyzonoides. 3.50a, Otis cafra. 4a, Oriolus notatus. 4.50a, Urolestes melanoleucus. 5a, Lamprocolius phoenicopterus. 6a, Heteropsar acuticaudus. 7a, Urobrachya bocadei. 10a, Alcedo semitorquata 12.50a, Eurocephalus anguitimens. 15a, Neocichla gutturalis. 20a, Lophoceros elegans. 25a, Cinnyricinclus verreauxi. 30a, Chlorophoneus sulfureopectus modestus. 40a, Serpentarius serpentarius. 50a, Agapornis roseicollis.

Photogravure and Lithographed

1951 **Unwmk.** ***Perf. 11½***

Background Color

333	A31	5c	lt blue	.55	.25
334	A32	10c	aqua	.55	.25
335	A32	15c	salmon pink	.75	.25
336	A32	20c	pale yellow	.75	.40
337	A31	50c	gray blue	.75	.25
338	A31	1a	lilac	.75	.25
339	A31	1.50a	gray buff	.75	.25
340	A31	2a	cream	4.00	.25
341	A32	2.50a	gray	1.50	.25
342	A32	3a	lemon yel	1.10	.25
343	A31	3.50a	lt gray	1.50	.25
344	A31	4a	rose buff	1.75	.25
345	A32	4.50a	rose lilac	1.75	.25
346	A31	5a	green	7.50	.55
347	A31	6a	blue	10.50	1.50
348	A31	7a	orange	11.50	2.00
349	A31	10a	lilac rose	45.00	2.75
350	A32	12.50a	slate gray	13.00	3.75
351	A31	15a	pale olive	11.50	3.75
352	A31	20a	pale bis brn	110.00	9.00
353	A31	25a	lilac rose	40.00	6.75
354	A32	30a	pale salmon	40.00	9.00
355	A31	40a	yellow	57.50	11.50
356	A31	50a	turquoise	140.00	22.50
			Nos. 333-356 (24)	502.95	76.45
			Set, hinged	225.00	

Holy Year Extension Issue
Common Design Type

1951, Oct. **Litho.** ***Perf. 14***

357	CD43	4a	orange + label	5.25	1.50

Sheets contain alternate vertical rows of stamps and labels bearing quotations from Pope Pius XII or the Patriarch Cardinal of Lisbon. Stamp without label attached sells for less.

Medical Congress Issue
Common Design Type

Design: Medical examination

1952, June ***Perf. 13½***

358	CD44	1a	vio blue & brn blk	1.50	.50

Head of Christ — A35

1952, Oct. **Unwmk.** ***Perf. 13***

359	A35	10c	dk blue & buff	.25	.25
360	A35	50c	dk ol grn & ol gray	1.10	.35
361	A35	2a	rose vio & cream	3.75	1.30
			Nos. 359-361 (3)	5.10	1.90

Exhibition of Sacred Missionary Art, Lisbon, 1951.

Leopard A36

Sable Antelope A37

Animals: 20c, Elephant. 30c, Eland. 40c, African crocodile. 50c, Impala. 1a, Mountain zebra. 1.50a, Sitatunga. 2a, Black rhinoceros. 2.30a, Gemsbok. 2.50a, Lion. 3a, Buffalo. 3.50a, Springbok. 4a, Brindled gnu. 5a, Hartebeest. 7a, Wart hog. 10a, Defassa waterbuck. 12.50a, Hippopotamus. 15a, Greater kudu. 20a, Giraffe.

1953, Aug. 15 ***Perf. 12½***

362	A36	5c	multicolored	.25	.25
363	A37	10c	multicolored	.25	.25
364	A37	20c	multicolored	.25	.25
365	A37	30c	multicolored	.25	.25
366	A36	40c	multicolored	.25	.25
367	A37	50c	multicolored	.25	.25
368	A37	1a	multicolored	.35	.25
369	A37	1.50a	multicolored	.40	.25
370	A36	2a	multicolored	.40	.25
371	A37	2.30a	multicolored	.45	.25
372	A37	2.50a	multicolored	.50	.25
373	A36	3a	multicolored	.55	.25
374	A37	3.50a	multicolored	.55	.25
375	A37	4a	multicolored	20.00	.40
376	A37	5a	multicolored	1.00	.35
377	A37	7a	multicolored	1.50	.35
378	A37	10a	multicolored	3.00	.35
379	A37	12.50a	multicolored	7.50	3.00
380	A37	15a	multicolored	10.00	3.00
381	A37	20a	multicolored	13.00	1.90
			Nos. 362-381 (20)	60.70	12.60
			Set, hinged	20.00	

Stamp of Portugal and Arms of Colonies — A38

1953, Nov. **Photo.** ***Perf. 13***

Stamp and Arms Multicolored

382	A38	50c	gray & dark gray	1.25	.60

Cent. of Portugal's 1st postage stamps.

Map and Plane — A39

Typographed and Lithographed

1954, May 27 ***Perf. 13½***

383	A39	35c	multicolored	.25	.25
384	A39	4.50e	multicolored	1.10	.65

Visit of Pres. Francisco H C. Lopes.

Sao Paulo Issue
Common Design Type

1954 **Litho.**

385	CD46	1e	bister & gray	.80	.50

Map of Angola — A41

1955, Aug. **Unwmk.** ***Perf. 13½***

386	A41	5c	multicolored	.25	.25
387	A41	20c	multicolored	.25	.25
388	A41	50c	multicolored	.25	.25
389	A41	1e	multicolored	.25	.25
390	A41	2.30e	multicolored	.50	.35
391	A41	4e	multicolored	2.50	.25
392	A41	10e	multicolored	2.50	.25
393	A41	20e	multicolored	4.25	.45
			Nos. 386-393 (8)	10.75	2.30

For overprints see Nos. 593, 598, 604.

Artur de Paiva — A42

1956, Oct. 9 ***Perf. 13½x12½***

394	A42	1e	blk, dk bl & ocher	.60	.30

Cent. of the birth of Col. Artur de Paiva.

Man of Malange — A43

Various Costumes in Multicolor; Inscriptions in Black Brown

1957, Jan. 1 **Photo.** ***Perf. 11½***

Granite Paper

395	A43	5c	gray	.25	.25
396	A43	10c	orange yel	.25	.25
397	A43	15c	lt blue grn	.25	.25
398	A43	20c	pale rose vio	.25	.25
399	A43	30c	brt rose	.25	.25
400	A43	40c	blue gray	.25	.25
401	A43	50c	pale olive	.25	.25
402	A43	80c	lt violet	.45	.40
403	A43	1.50e	buff	2.50	.40
404	A43	2.50e	lt yel grn	3.25	.25
405	A43	4e	salmon	2.00	.25
406	A43	10e	salmon pink	3.00	.50
			Nos. 395-406 (12)	12.95	3.55

Jose M. Antunes — A44

1957, Apr. ***Perf. 13½***

407	A44	1e	aqua & brown	.90	.45

Birth cent. of Father Jose Maria Antunes.

Fair Emblem, Globe and Arms — A45

1958, July **Litho.** ***Perf. 12x11½***

408	A45	1.50e	multicolored	.75	.35

World's Fair, Brussels, Apr. 17-Oct. 19.

Tropical Medicine Congress Issue
Common Design Type

Design: Securidaca longipedunculata.

1958, Dec. 15 ***Perf. 13½***

409	CD47	2.50e	multicolored	3.50	1.10

Medicine Man — A47

Designs: 1.50e, Early government doctor. 2.50e, Modern medical team.

1958, Dec. 18 ***Perf. 11½x12***

410	A47	1e	blue blk & brown	.45	.25
411	A47	1.50e	gray, blk & brown	1.40	.50
412	A47	2.50e	multicolored	2.25	1.10
			Nos. 410-412 (3)	4.10	1.85

75th anniversary of the Maria Pia Hospital, Luanda.

Welwitschia Mirabilis — A48

1959, Oct. 1 Litho. *Perf. 14½*

Various Views of Plant and Various Frames

413	A48	1.50e	lt brn, grn & blk	1.10	.65
414	A48	2.50e	multicolored	1.75	.85
415	A48	5e	multicolored	3.00	1.00
416	A48	10e	multicolored	4.50	2.10
			Nos. 413-416 (4)	10.35	4.60

Centenary of discovery of Welwitschia mirabilis, desert plant.

Map of West Africa, c. 1540, by Jorge Reinel — A49

1960, June 25 *Perf. 13½*

417	A49	2.50e	multicolored	.55	.25

500th anniv. of the death of Prince Henry the Navigator.

Distributing Medicines — A50

1960, Oct. Litho. *Perf. 14½*

418	A50	2.50e	multicolored	.65	.35

10th anniv. of the Commission for Technical Co-operation in Africa South of the Sahara (C.C.T.A.).

Girl of Angola — A51

Various portraits.

1961, Nov. 30 Unwmk. *Perf. 13*

419	A51	10c	multicolored	.25	.25
420	A51	15c	multicolored	.25	.25
421	A51	30c	multicolored	.25	.25
422	A51	40c	multicolored	.25	.25
423	A51	60c	multicolored	.25	.25
424	A51	1.50e	multicolored	.25	.25
425	A51	2e	multicolored	1.00	.25
426	A51	2.50e	multicolored	1.00	.25
427	A51	3e	multicolored	3.50	.30
428	A51	4e	multicolored	1.50	.25
429	A51	5e	multicolored	1.10	.30
430	A51	7.50e	multicolored	1.50	.90
431	A51	10e	multicolored	1.20	.70
432	A51	15e	multicolored	2.00	.90
432A	A51	25e	multicolored	2.40	1.25
432B	A51	50e	multicolored	3.75	2.75
			Nos. 419-432B (16)	20.45	9.35

Sports Issue

Common Design Type

Sports: 50c, Flying. 1e, Rowing. 1.50e, Water polo. 2.50e, Hammer throwing. 4.50e, High jump. 15e, Weight lifting.

1962, Jan. 18 *Perf. 13½*

Multicolored Design

433	CD48	50c	lt blue	.25	.25
434	CD48	1e	olive bister	1.10	.25
435	CD48	1.50e	salmon	.75	.30
436	CD48	2.50e	lt green	.90	.30
437	CD48	4.50e	pale blue	.75	.60
438	CD48	15e	yellow	1.75	1.50
			Nos. 433-438 (6)	5.50	3.20

For overprint see No. 608.

Anti-Malaria Issue

Common Design Type

Design: Anopheles funestus.

1962, April Litho. *Perf. 13½*

439	CD49	2.50e	multicolored	1.75	.90

Gen. Norton de Matos — A54

1962, Aug. 8 Unwmk. *Perf. 14½*

440	A54	2.50e	multicolored	.65	.40

50th anniv. of the founding of Nova Lisboa.

Locusts — A56

1963, June 2 Litho. *Perf. 14*

447	A56	2.50e	multicolored	1.60	.95

15th anniv. of the Intl. Anti-Locust Organ.

Arms of Luanda — A57

Vila de Santo Antonio do Zaire — A58

Coats of Arms (Provinces and Cities): 10c, Massangano. 15c, Sanza-Pombo. 25c, Ambriz. 30c, Muxima. 40c, Ambrizete. 50c, Carmona. 60c, Catete. 70c, Quibaxe. No. 458, Salazar. No. 459, Maquela do Zombo. 1.20e, Bembe. No. 461, Malanje. No. 462, Caxito. 1.80e, Dondo. 2e, Henrique de Carvalho. No. 465, Moçamedes. No. 466, Damba. 3e, Novo Redondo. 3.50e, S. Salvador do Congo. 4e, Cuimba. 5e, Luso. 6.50e, Negage. 7e, Quitexe. 7.50e, S. Filipe de Benguela. 8e, Mucaba. 9e, 31 de Janeiro. 10e, Lobito. 11e, Nova Caipemba. 12.50e, Gabela. 14e, Songo. 15e Sá da Bandeira. 17e, Quimbele. 17.50e, Silva Porto. 20e, Nova Lisboa. 22.50e, Cabinda. 25e, Noqui. 30e, Serpa Pinto. 35e, Santa Cruz. 50e, General Freire.

1963 *Perf. 13½*

Arms in Original Colors; Red and Violet Blue Inscriptions

448	A57	5c	tan	.25	.25
449	A57	10c	lt blue	.25	.25
450	A58	15c	salmon	.25	.25
451	A58	20c	olive	.25	.25
452	A58	25c	lt blue	.25	.25
453	A57	30c	buff	.25	.25
454	A58	40c	gray	.25	.25
455	A57	50c	lt green	.25	.25
456	A58	60c	brt yellow	.25	.25
457	A58	70c	dull rose	.25	.25
458	A57	1e	pale lilac	.65	.25
459	A58	1e	dull yellow	.30	.25
460	A58	1.20e	rose	.30	.25
461	A57	1.50e	pale salmon	.90	.25
462	A58	1.50e	lt green	.75	.25
463	A58	1.80e	yel olive	.75	.55
464	A57	2e	lt yel green	.65	.25
465	A57	2.50e	lt gray	2.50	.30
466	A58	2.50e	dull blue	2.25	.25
467	A57	3e	yel olive	.75	.25
468	A57	3.50e	gray	.90	.25
469	A58	4e	citron	.60	.30
470	A57	5e	citron	.75	.30
471	A58	6.50e	tan	.65	.40
472	A58	7e	rose lilac	.90	.75
473	A57	7.50e	pale lilac	1.00	.75
474	A58	8e	lt aqua	.90	.75
475	A58	9e	yellow	1.10	1.00
476	A57	10e	dp salmon	1.20	.80
477	A58	11e	dull yel grn	1.25	1.25
478	A57	12.50e	pale blue	1.50	1.25
479	A58	14e	lt gray	1.50	1.25
480	A57	15e	lt blue	1.50	1.25
481	A58	17e	pale blue	1.60	1.50
482	A57	17.50e	dull yellow	2.40	2.25
483	A57	20e	lt aqua	2.40	1.75
484	A57	22.50e	gray	2.50	2.40
485	A58	25e	citron	2.10	1.50
486	A57	30e	yellow	3.00	2.50
487	A58	35e	grysh blue	3.25	3.00
488	A58	50e	dp yellow	4.50	2.25
			Nos. 448-488 (41)	47.80	32.80

Pres. Américo Rodrigues Thomaz — A59

1963, Sept. 16 Litho.

489	A59	2.50e	multicolored	.65	.30

Visit of the President of Portugal.

Airline Anniversary Issue

Common Design Type

1963, Oct. 5 Unwmk. *Perf. 14½*

490	CD50	1e	lt blue & multi	1.00	.35

Cathedral of Sá da Bandeira A61

Malange Cathedral A62

Churches: 20c, Landana. 30c, Luanda Cathedral. 40c, Gabela. 50c, St. Martin's Chapel, Baia dos Tigres. 1.50e, St. Peter, Chibia. 2e, Church of Our Lady, Benguela. 2.50e, Church of Jesus, Luanda. 3e, Camabatela. 3.50e, Mission, Cabinda. 4e, Vila Folgares. 4.50e, Church of Our Lady, Lobito. 5e, Church of Cabinda. 7.50e, Cacuso Church, Malange. 10e, Lubango Mission. 12.50e, Huila Mission. 15e, Church of Our Lady, Luanda Island.

1963, Nov. 1 Litho.

Multicolored Design and Inscription

491	A61	10c	gray blue	.25	.25
492	A61	20c	pink	.25	.25
493	A61	30c	lt blue	.25	.25
494	A61	40c	tan	.25	.25
495	A61	50c	lt green	.25	.25
496	A62	1e	buff	.25	.25
497	A61	1.50e	lt vio blue	.25	.25
498	A62	2e	pale rose	.35	.25
499	A61	2.50e	gray	.35	.25
500	A62	3e	buff	.35	.25
501	A61	3.50e	olive	.55	.25
502	A62	4e	buff	.55	.25
503	A62	4.50e	pale blue	.75	.30
504	A61	5e	tan	.75	.30
505	A62	7.50e	gray	1.00	.55
506	A61	10e	dull yellow	1.40	.75
507	A62	12.50e	bister	1.60	1.25
508	A62	15e	pale gray vio	2.40	1.40
			Nos. 491-508 (18)	11.80	7.55

National Overseas Bank Issue

Common Design Type

Design: Antonio Teixeira de Sousa.

1964, May 16 *Perf. 13½*

509	CD51	2.50e	multicolored	.90	.30

Commerce Building and Arms of Chamber of Commerce — A64

1964, Nov. Litho. *Perf. 12*

510	A64	1e	multicolored	.45	.25

Luanda Chamber of Commerce centenary.

ITU Issue

Common Design Type

1965, May 17 Unwmk. *Perf. 14½*

511	CD52	2.50e	gray & multi	1.25	.65

Plane over Luanda Airport — A65

1965, Dec. 3 Litho. *Perf. 13*

512	A65	2.50e	multicolored	1.25	.60

25th anniv. of DTA, Direccao dos Transportes Aereos.

Harquebusier, 1539 — A66

50c, Harquebusier, 1539. 1e, Harquebusier, 1640. 1.50e, Infantry officer, 1777. 2e, Standard bearer, infantry, 1777. 2.50e, Infantry soldier, 1777. 3e, Cavalry officer, 1783. 4e, Cavalry soldier, 1783. 4.50e, Infantry officer, 1807. 5e, Infantry soldier, 1807. 6e, Cavalry officer, 1807. 8e, Cavalry soldier, 1807. 9e, Infantry soldier, 1873.

1966, Feb. 25 Litho. *Perf. 14½*

513	A66	50c	multicolored	.25	.25
514	A66	1e	multicolored	.25	.25
515	A66	1.50e	multicolored	.25	.25
516	A66	2e	multicolored	.25	.25
517	A66	2.50e	multicolored	.40	.25
518	A66	3e	multicolored	.40	.25
519	A66	4e	multicolored	.60	.25
520	A66	4.50e	multicolored	.65	.25
521	A66	5e	multicolored	.65	.30
522	A66	6e	multicolored	1.10	.65
523	A66	8e	multicolored	1.50	1.10
524	A66	9e	multicolored	1.60	1.25
			Nos. 513-524 (12)	7.90	5.30

National Revolution Issue

Common Design Type

Design: St. Paul's Hospital and Commercial and Industrial School.

1966, May 28 Litho. *Perf. 12*

525	CD53	1e	multicolored	.50	.25

Emblem of Holy Ghost Society — A68

1966 Litho. *Perf. 13*

526	A68	1e	blue & multi	.50	.25

Centenary of the Holy Ghost Society.

Navy Club Issue

Common Design Type

Designs: 1e, Mendes Barata and cruiser Dom Carlos I. 2.50e, Capt. Augusto de Castilho and corvette Mindelo.

1967, Jan. 31 Litho. *Perf. 13*

527	CD54	1e	multicolored	.75	.25
528	CD54	2.50e	multicolored	1.00	.50

Fatima Basilica — A70

1967, May 13 Litho. *Perf. 12½x13*

529	A70	50c	multicolored	.45	.25

50th anniv. of the apparition of the Virgin Mary to 3 shepherd children at Fatima.

Angola Map, Manuel Cerveira Pereira — A71

1967, Aug. 15 Litho. *Perf. 12½x13*

530	A71	50c	multicolored	.45	.25

350th anniv. of the founding of Benguela.

Administration Building, Carmona — A72

1967 Litho. *Perf. 12*

531	A72	1e	multicolored	.45	.25

50th anniv. of the founding of Carmona.

Military Order of Valor — A73

50c, Ribbon of the Three Orders. 1.50e, Military Order of Avis. 2e, Military Order of Christ. 2.50e, Military Order of St. John of Espada. 3e, Order of the Empire. 4e, Order of Prince Henry. 5e, Order of Benemerencia. 10e, Order of Public Instruction. 20e, Order for Industrial & Agricultural Merit.

1967, Oct. 31 ***Perf. 14***

532	A73	50c	lt gray & multi	.25	.25
533	A73	1e	lt green & multi	.25	.25
534	A73	1.50e	yellow & multi	.25	.25
535	A73	2e	multicolored	.25	.25
536	A73	2.50e	multicolored	.25	.25
537	A73	3e	lt olive & multi	.35	.25
538	A73	4e	gray & multi	.50	.25
539	A73	5e	multicolored	.60	.25
540	A73	10e	lilac & multi	1.00	.50
541	A73	20e	lt blue & multi	2.25	1.20
			Nos. 532-541 (10)	5.95	3.70

Our Lady of Hope — A74

1e, Belmonte Castle, horiz. 1.50e, St. Jerome's Convent. 2.50e, Cabral's Armada.

1968, Apr. 22 **Litho.** ***Perf. 14***

542	A74	50c	yellow & multi	.25	.25
543	A74	1e	gray & multi	.50	.25
544	A74	1.50e	lt blue & multi	.60	.25
545	A74	2.50e	buff & multi	1.00	.35
			Nos. 542-545 (4)	2.35	1.10

500th anniv. of the birth of Pedro Alvares Cabral, navigator who took possession of Brazil for Portugal.

Francisco Inocencio de Souza Coutinho — A75

1969, Jan. 7 **Litho.** ***Perf. 14***

546 A75 2e multicolored .45 .25

Founding of Novo Redondo, 200th anniv.

Admiral Coutinho Issue

Common Design Type

Design: Adm. Gago Coutinho and his first ship.

1969, Feb. 17 **Litho.** ***Perf. 14***

547 CD55 2.50e multicolored .85 .35

Compass Rose — A77

1969, Aug. 29 **Litho.** ***Perf. 14***

548 A77 1e multicolored .45 .25

500th anniv. of the birth of Vasco da Gama (1469-1524), navigator.

Administration Reform Issue

Common Design Type

1969, Sept. 25 **Litho.** ***Perf. 14***

549 CD56 1.50e multicolored .35 .25

Portal of St. Jeronimo's Monastery — A79

1969, Dec. 1 **Litho.** ***Perf. 14***

550 A79 3e multicolored .45 .25

500th anniv. of the birth of King Manuel I.

Angolasaurus Bocagei — A80

Fossils and Minerals: 1e, Ferrometeorite. 1.50e, Dioptase crystals. 2e, Gondwanidium. 2.50e, Diamonds. 3e, Estromatolite. 3.50e, Procarcharodon megalodon. 4e, Microceratodus angolensis. 4.50e, Moscovite. 5e, Barite. 6e, Nostoceras. 10e, Rotula orbiculus angolensis.

1970, Oct. 31 **Litho.** ***Perf. 13***

551	A80	50c	tan & multi	.25	.25
552	A80	1e	multicolored	.25	.25
553	A80	1.50e	multicolored	.30	.25
554	A80	2e	multicolored	.30	.25
555	A80	2.50e	lt gray & multi	.30	.25
556	A80	3e	multicolored	.35	.25
557	A80	3.50e	blue & multi	.50	.30
558	A80	4e	lt gray & multi	.50	.30
559	A80	4.50e	gray & multi	.50	.30
560	A80	5e	gray & multi	.75	.30
561	A80	6e	pink & multi	1.50	.90
562	A80	10e	lt blue & multi	2.10	1.20
			Nos. 551-562 (12)	7.60	4.80

Marshal Carmona Issue

Common Design Type

1970, Nov. 15 ***Perf. 14***

563 CD57 2.50e multicolored .45 .25

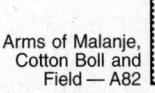

Arms of Malanje, Cotton Boll and Field — A82

1970, Nov. 20 ***Perf. 13***

564 A82 2.50e multicolored .55 .35

Centenary of the municipality of Malanje.

Mail Ships and Angola No. 1 — A83

4.50e, Steam locomotive and Angola No. 4.

1970, Dec. 1 ***Perf. 13½***

565	A83	1.50e	multicolored	.40	.30
566	A83	4.50e	multicolored	1.75	.75

Cent. of stamps of Angola. See No. C36. For overprint see No. 616B.

Map of Africa, Diagram of Seismic Tests — A84

1971, Aug. 22 **Litho.** ***Perf. 13***

567 A84 2.50e multicolored .45 .25

5th Regional Conference of Soil and Foundation Engineers, Luanda, Aug. 22-Sept. 5.

Galleon on Congo River — A85

1972, May 25 **Litho.** ***Perf. 13***

568 A85 1e brt grn & multi .65 .25

4th centenary of the publication of The Lusiads by Luiz Camoens.

Olympic Games Issue

Common Design Type

1972, June 20 ***Perf. 14x13½***

569 CD59 50c multicolored .65 .25

Lisbon-Rio de Janeiro Flight Issue

Common Design Type

1972, Sept. 20 **Litho.** ***Perf. 13½***

570 CD60 1e multicolored .35 .25

WMO Centenary Issue

Common Design Type

1973, Dec. 15 **Litho.** ***Perf. 13***

571 CD61 1e dk gray & multi .45 .25

Radar Station — A89

1974, June 25 **Litho.** ***Perf. 13***

572 A89 2e multicolored .45 .25

Establishment of satellite communications network via Intelsat among Portugal, Angola and Mozambique.

For overprint see No. 616A

Harpa Doris — A90

Designs: Sea shells: 30c, Murex melanamathos. 50c, Venus foliaceo lamellosa. 70c, Lathyrus filosus. 1e, Cymbium cisium. 1.50e, Cassis tesselata. 2e, Cypraea stercoraria. 2.50e, Conus prometheus. 3e, Strombus latus. 3.50e, Tympanotonus fuscatus. 4e, Cardium costatum. 5e, Natica fulminea. 6e, Lyropecten nodosus. 7e, Tonna galea. 10e, Donax rugosus. 25e, Cymatium trigonum. 30e, Olivancilaria acuminata. 35e, Semifusus morio. 40e, Clavatula lineata. 50e, Solarium granulatum.

1974, Oct. 25 **Litho.** ***Perf. 12x12½***

573	A90	25c	shown	.25	.25
574	A90	30c	multicolored	.25	.25
575	A90	50c	multicolored	.30	.25
576	A90	70c	multicolored	.35	.25
577	A90	1e	multicolored	.35	.25
578	A90	1.50e	multicolored	.40	.25
579	A90	2e	multicolored	.40	.25
580	A90	2.50e	multicolored	.45	.25
581	A90	3e	multicolored	.65	.25
582	A90	3.50e	multicolored	.65	.45
583	A90	4e	multicolored	.65	.45
584	A90	5e	multicolored	.75	.45
585	A90	6e	multicolored	1.25	.45
586	A90	7e	multicolored	1.25	.45
587	A90	10e	multicolored	1.00	.45
588	A90	25e	multicolored	2.25	.90
589	A90	30e	multicolored	2.50	.90
590	A90	35e	multicolored	3.00	.90
591	A90	40e	multicolored	3.50	1.10
592	A90	50e	multicolored	5.00	1.75
			Nos. 573-592 (20)	25.20	10.50

For overprints see Nos. 605-607, 617-630.

No. 386 Overprinted in Blue

1974, Dec. 21 **Litho.** ***Perf. 13½***

593 A41 5c multicolored .30 .25

Youth philately.

Republic

Star and Hand Holding Rifle — A91

1975, Nov. 11 **Litho.** ***Perf. 13x13½***

594 A91 1.50e red & multi .50 .25

Independence in 1975.

Diquiche Mask — A92

Design: 3e, Bui ou Congolo mask.

1976, Feb. 6 ***Perf. 13½***

595	A92	50c	lt blue & multi	.25	.25
596	A92	3e	multicolored	.55	.25

Workers — A93

1976, May 1 **Litho.** ***Perf. 12***

597 A93 1e red & multi .35 .25

International Workers' Day.

No. 392 Overprinted

1976, June 15 **Litho.** ***Perf. 13½***

598 A41 10e multicolored 1.10 .75

Stamp Day.

President Agostinho Neto — A94

1976, Nov. 11 **Litho.** ***Perf. 13***

599	A94	50c	yel & dk brown	.25	.25
600	A94	2e	lt gray & plum	.25	.25
601	A94	3e	gray & indigo	.40	.25
602	A94	5e	buff & brown	.40	.25
603	A94	10e	tan & sepia	.55	.25
a.			Souv. sheet of 1, imperf.	4.00	4.00
			Nos. 599-603 (5)	1.85	1.25

First anniversary of independence.

Nos. 393, 588-589, 592 Overprinted

1977, Feb. 9 ***Perf. 13½, 12x12½***

604	A41	20e	multicolored	1.75	.50
605	A90	25e	multicolored	2.25	.60
606	A90	30e	multicolored	2.60	.75
607	A90	50e	multicolored	4.25	1.25
			Nos. 604-607 (4)	10.85	3.10

Overprint in 3 lines on No. 604, in 2 lines on others.

No. 438 Overprinted

1976, Dec. 31 *Perf. 13½*

608	CD48	15e multicolored	2.00	.65

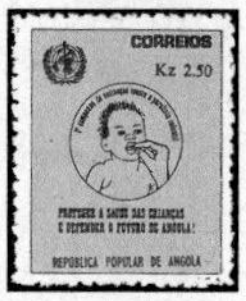

Child and WHO Emblem — A95

1977 Litho. *Perf. 10½*

609	A95	2.50k blk & lt blue	.65	.25

Campaign for vaccination against poliomyelitis.

Map of Africa, Flag of Angola — A96

1977 Photo.

610	A96	6k blk, red & blue	.60	.35

First Congress of Popular Movement for the Liberation of Angola.

Anti-Apartheid Emblem — A97

1979, June 20 Litho. *Perf. 13½*

611	A97	1k multicolored	.25	.25

Anti-Apartheid Year.

Human Rights Emblem — A98

1979, June 15 Litho. *Perf. 13½*

612	A98	2.50k multicolored	.35	.25

Declaration of Human Rights, 30th anniv. (in 1975).

Child Flowers, Globe, IYC Emblem — A99

1980, May 1 Litho. *Perf. 14x14½*

613	A99	3.50k multicolored	.45	.25

International Year of the Child (1979).

Running, Moscow '80 Emblem — A100

1980, Dec. 15 Litho. *Perf. 13½*

614	A100	9k shown	.70	.25
615	A100	12k Swimming, horiz.	.80	.25

22nd Summer Olympic Games, Moscow, July 19-Aug. 3.

5th Anniv. of Independence A101

1980, Nov. 11

616	A101	5.50k multicolored	.45	.25

Nos. 572, 566 Overprinted

1980-81 Litho. *Perf. 13½x13*

616A	A89	2e multi (bar only)	1.25	.25
616B	A83	4.50e multicolored	2.75	1.50

Issued: 2e, 5/17/81; 4.50e, 6/15/80.
See No. C37.

Nos. 577-580, 582-591 Overprinted

1981, June 15 Litho. *Perf. 12x12½*

617	A90	1e multicolored	.25	.25
618	A90	1.50e multicolored	.25	.25
619	A90	2e multicolored	.25	.25
620	A90	2.50e multicolored	.25	.25
621	A90	3.50e multicolored	.25	.25
622	A90	4e multicolored	.30	.25
623	A90	5e multicolored	.35	.25
624	A90	6e multicolored	.40	.25
625	A90	7e multicolored	.55	.25
626	A90	10e multicolored	.65	.30
627	A90	25e multicolored	1.40	.50
628	A90	30e multicolored	1.75	.75
629	A90	35e multicolored	2.00	.90
630	A90	40e multicolored	2.50	1.25
		Nos. 617-630 (14)	11.15	5.95

Man Walking with Canes, Tchibinda Ilunga Statue — A102

1981, Sept. 5 Litho. *Perf. 13½*

631	A102	9k multicolored	.50	.30

Turipex '81 tourism exhibition.

M.P.L.A. Workers' Party Congress — A103

1980, Dec. 23 Litho. *Perf. 14*

632	A103	50 l Millet	.25	.25
633	A103	5k Coffee	.35	.25
634	A103	7.50k Sunflowers	.40	.25
635	A103	13.50k Cotton	.65	.30
636	A103	14k Oil	.80	.35
637	A103	16k Diamonds	.95	.45
		Nos. 632-637 (6)	3.40	1.85

People's Power — A104

1980, Nov. 11

638	A104	40k lt blue & blk	1.75	.65

Natl. Heroes' Day — A105

4.50k, Former Pres. Neto. 50k, Neto, diff.

1980, Sept. 17 *Perf. 14x13½*

639	A105	4.50k multicolored	.25	.25
640	A105	50k multicolored	2.75	.75

Soweto Uprising, 5th Anniv. — A106

1981

641	A106	4.50k multicolored	.35	.25

2nd Central African Games A107

50 l, Bicycling, tennis. 5k, Judo, boxing. 6k, Basketball, volleyball. 10k, Handball, soccer.

1981, Sept. 3 Litho. *Perf. 13½*

642	A107	50 l multicolored	.25	.25
643	A107	5k multicolored	.65	.25
644	A107	6k multicolored	.85	.25
645	A107	10k multicolored	1.40	.35
		Nos. 642-645 (4)	3.15	1.10

Souvenir Sheet

Imperf

646	A107	15k multicolored	*3.00*	*3.00*

Charaxes Kahldeni — A108

1k, Abantis zambesiaca. 5k, Catacroptera cloanthe. 9k, Myrina ficedula, vert. 10k, Colotis danae. 15k, Acraea acrita. 100k, Precis hierta.

1982, Feb. 26 Litho. *Perf. 13½*

647	A108	50 l shown	.25	.25
648	A108	1k multicolored	.25	.25
649	A108	5k multicolored	.40	.25
650	A108	9k multicolored	1.00	.25
651	A108	10k multicolored	1.00	.25
652	A108	15k multicolored	1.25	.40
653	A108	100k multicolored	8.00	3.00
a.		Souvenir sheet	12.00	12.00
		Nos. 647-653 (7)	12.15	4.65

No. 653a contains Nos. 647-653, imperf., and sold for 30k (stamps probably not valid individually).

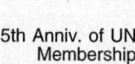

5th Anniv. of UN Membership A109

5.50k, The Silence of the Night, by Musseque Catambor. 7.50k, Cotton picking, Catete.

1982, Sept. 22 Litho.

654	A109	5.50k multicolored	.40	.25
655	A109	7.50k multicolored	.55	.25

20th Anniv. of Engineering Laboratory A110

1982, Dec. 21 Litho. *Perf. 14*

656	A110	9k Lab	.65	.30
657	A110	13k Worker, vert.	.65	.40
658	A110	100k Equipment, vert.	6.75	3.50
		Nos. 656-658 (3)	8.05	4.20

Local Flowers A111

5k, Dichrostachys glomerata. 12k, Amblygonocarpus obtusangulus. 50k, Albizzia versicolor.

1983, Feb. 18 *Perf. 13½*

659	A111	5k multicolored	.40	.25
660	A111	12k multicolored	.75	.30
661	A111	50k multicolored	3.50	1.40
		Nos. 659-661 (3)	4.65	1.95

Women's Org., First Congress — A112

1983 Litho. *Perf. 13½*

662	A112	20k multicolored	1.25	.50

Africa Day — A113

1983, June 30 *Perf. 13*

663	A113	6.5k multicolored	.65	.35

World Communications Year — A114

1983, June 30 Litho. *Perf. 13½*

664	A114	6.5k M'pungi	.75	.35
665	A114	12k Mondu	1.25	.55

BRASILIANA '83 Stamp Exhibition, Rio de Janeiro, July 29-Aug. 7 — A115

Crop-eating insects: 4.50k, Antestiopsis lineaticollis. 6.5k, Stephanoderes hampei ferr. 10k, Zonocerus variegatus.

1983, July 29 Litho. *Perf. 13*

666	A115	4.5k multicolored	.50	.25
667	A115	6.5k multicolored	.55	.35
668	A115	10k multicolored	1.00	.60
		Nos. 666-668 (3)	2.05	1.20

25th Anniv. of Economic Commission for Africa — A116

1983, Aug. 2

669	A116	10k Map, emblem	.70	.50

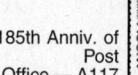

185th Anniv. of Post Office — A117

50 l, Mail collection, vert. 3.5k, Unloading mail plane. 5k, Sorting mail. 15k, Mailing letter, vert. 30k, Post office box delivery.

1983, Dec. 7 Litho. *Perf. 13½*

670	A117	50 l multicolored	.25	.25
671	A117	3.5k multicolored	.35	.25
672	A117	5k multicolored	.55	.40

673 A117	15k multicolored		1.50	.90
674 A117	30k multicolored		2.90	1.60
a.	Min. sheet of 3, #671-672, 674		8.00	8.00
	Nos. 670-674 (5)		5.55	3.40

No. 674a sold for 100k.

Local Butterflies A118

50 l, Parasa karschi. 1k, Diaphone angolensis. 3.5k, Choeropasis jucunda. 6.5k, Hespagarista rendalli. 15k, Euchromia guineensis. 17.5k, Mazuca roseistriga. 20k, Utetheisa callima.

1984, Jan. 20 Litho. *Perf. 13½*

675 A118	50 l multicolored	.25	.25
676 A118	1k multicolored	.30	.25
677 A118	3.5k multicolored	.55	.25
678 A118	6.5k multicolored	.95	.35
679 A118	15k multicolored	1.60	.90
680 A118	17.5k multicolored	1.90	1.00
681 A118	20k multicolored	2.75	1.25
	Nos. 675-681 (7)	8.30	4.25

A119

1984, Apr. 11 Litho. *Perf. 13½*

682 A119	30k multicolored	2.50	1.75

First Natl. Worker's Union Congress, Apr. 11-16.

Local Birds — A120

10.50k, Bucorvus leadbeateri. 14k, Gypohierax angolensis. 16k, Ardea goliath. 19.50k, Pelecanus onocrotalus. 22k, Platalea alba. 26k, Balearica pavonnia.

1984, Oct. 24 Litho. *Perf. 13½*

683 A120	10.50k multicolored	.80	.40
684 A120	14k multicolored	1.00	.50
685 A120	16k multicolored	1.20	.65
686 A120	19.50k multicolored	1.60	.65
687 A120	22k multicolored	1.75	.75
688 A120	26k multicolored	2.50	1.00
	Nos. 683-688 (6)	8.85	3.95

Local Animals — A121

1k, Tragelaphus strepsiceros. 4k, Antidorcas marsupialis angolensis. 5k, Pan troglodytes. 10k, Syncerus caffer. 15k, Hippotragus niger variani. 20k, Orycteropus afer. 25k, Crocuta crocuta.

1984, Nov. 12

689 A121	1k multicolored	.35	.25
690 A121	4k multicolored	.45	.25
691 A121	5k multicolored	.60	.25
692 A121	10k multicolored	1.75	.30
693 A121	15k multicolored	2.10	.45
694 A121	20k multicolored	2.50	.60
695 A121	25k multicolored	3.00	.65
	Nos. 689-695 (7)	10.75	2.75

Angolese Monuments A122

5k, San Pedro da Barra. 12.5k, Nova Oeiras. 18k, M'Banza Kongo. 26k, Massangano. 39k, Escravatura Museum.

1985, Feb. 21 Litho. *Perf. 13½*

696 A122	5k multicolored	.35	.25
697 A122	12.5k multicolored	.90	.50
698 A122	18k multicolored	1.20	.75
699 A122	26k multicolored	1.90	.90
700 A122	39k multicolored	2.60	1.50
	Nos. 696-700 (5)	6.95	3.90

United Workers' Party, 25th Anniv. — A123

1985, May Litho. *Perf. 12*

701 A123	77k XXV, red flags	7.00	4.00

Printed in sheets of 5.

A124

1k, Flags. 11k, Oil drilling platform, Cabinda. 57k, Conference.

1985, May

702 A124	1k multicolored	.25	.25
703 A124	11k multicolored	1.00	.80
704 A124	57k multicolored	2.60	1.25
a.	Strip of 3, #702-704	4.50	4.50

Southern African Development Council, 5th anniv.

Medicinal plants — A125

No. 705, Lonchocarpus sericeus. No. 706, Gossypium. No. 707, Cassia occidentalis. No. 708, Gloriosa superba. No. 709, Cochlospermum angolensis.

Lithographed and Typographed

1985, July 5 *Perf. 11*

705 A125	1k multi	.30	.25
706 A125	4k multi	.40	.30
707 A125	11k multi	1.00	.70
708 A125	25.50k multi	2.00	1.00
709 A125	55k multi	3.50	2.50
	Nos. 705-709 (5)	7.20	4.75

ARGENTINA '85 exhibition.

5th Natl. Heroes Day — A126

Natl. flag and: 10.50k, Portrait of Agostinho Neto, party leader. 36.50k, Neto working.

1985 Litho. *Perf. 13½*

710 A126	10.50k multicolored	12.00	7.50
711 A126	36.50k multicolored	16.00	10.00

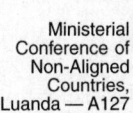

Ministerial Conference of Non-Aligned Countries, Luanda — A127

1985, Sept. 4 Photo. *Perf. 11*

712 A127	35k multicolored	2.50	1.75

UN, 40th Anniv. — A128

1985, Oct. 29 Litho. *Perf. 11*

713 A128	12.50k multicolored	1.25	.75

Industry and Natural Resources A129

1985, Nov. 11

714 A129	50 l Cement Factory	.25	.25
715 A129	5k Logging	.35	.25
716 A129	7k Quartz	.50	.40
717 A129	10k Iron mine	.85	.50
a.	Souvenir sheet of 4, #714-717, imperf.	3.50	3.50
	Nos. 714-717 (4)	1.95	1.40

Natl. independence, 10th anniv.

2nd Natl. Workers' Party Congress (MPLA) — A130

1985, Nov. 28 *Perf. 13½*

718 A130	20k multicolored	1.50	1.00

Demostenes de Almeida Clington Races, 30th Anniv. — A131

Various runners.

1985, Dec. 13

719 A131	50 l multicolored	.25	.25
720 A131	5k multicolored	.40	.25
721 A131	6.50k multicolored	.60	.25
722 A131	10k multicolored	.80	.30
	Nos. 719-722 (4)	2.05	1.05

1986 World Cup Soccer Championships, Mexico — A132

Map, soccer field and various plays.

1986, May 6 Litho. *Perf. 11½x11*

723 A132	50 l multi	.25	.25
724 A132	3.50k multi	.40	.25
725 A132	5k multi	.65	.25
726 A132	7k multi	.80	.25
727 A132	10k multi	1.25	.40
728 A132	18k multi	2.10	.60
	Nos. 723-728 (6)	5.45	2.00

Struggle Against Portugal, 25th Anniv. — A133

1986, May 6 *Perf. 11x11½*

729 A133	15k multicolored	1.40	.50

First Man in Space, 25th Anniv. — A134

50 l, Skylab, US. 1k, Spacecraft. 5k, A. Leonov space-walking. 10k, Lunokhod on Moon. 13k, Apollo-Soyuz link-up.

1986, Aug. 21 Litho. *Perf. 11x11½*

730 A134	50 l multicolored	.25	.25
731 A134	1k multicolored	.25	.25
732 A134	5k multicolored	.40	.25
733 A134	10k multicolored	.90	.35
734 A134	13k multicolored	.95	.40
	Nos. 730-734 (5)	2.75	1.50

Admission of Angola to UN, 10th Anniv. — A135

1986, Dec. 1 Litho. *Perf. 11x11½*

735 A135	22k multi	1.60	1.10

Liberation Movement, 30th Anniv. — A136

Angolese at work, fighting and: No. 736a, "1956." No. 736b, Congress emblem, "1980." No. 736c, Labor Party emblem, "1985."

1986, Dec. 3 *Perf. 11½x11*

736 A136	Strip of 3	1.50	1.50
a.-c.	5k any single	.45	.25

Agostinho Neto University, 10th Anniv. — A137

1986, Dec. 30 Litho. *Perf. 11x11½*

737 A137	50 l Mathematics	.25	.25
738 A137	1k Law	.50	.35
739 A137	10k Medicine	.85	.60
	Nos. 737-739 (3)	1.60	1.20

Tribal Hairstyles — A138

1987, Apr. 15 Litho. *Perf. 11½x11*

740 A138	1k Ouioca	.25	.25
741 A138	1.50k Luanda	.35	.25
742 A138	5k Humbe	.65	.25
743 A138	7k Muila	.80	.25
744 A138	20k Muila, diff.	2.00	.45
745 A138	30k Dilolo	3.75	.80
	Nos. 740-745 (6)	7.80	2.25

Landscapes — A139

Perf. 11½x12, 12x11½

1987, July 7 Litho.

746 A139	50 l Pambala Shore	.25	.25
747 A139	1.50k Dala Waterfalls	.25	.25
748 A139	3.50k Black Stones	.25	.25
749 A139	5k Cuango River	.45	.25
750 A139	10k Luanda coast	.95	.35
751 A139	20k Hills of Leba	1.90	.45
	Nos. 746-751 (6)	4.05	1.80

Nos. 746-747, 749 and 751 horiz.

Lenin — A140

1987, Nov. 25 *Perf. 12x12½*

752	A140	15k multi	1.25	.45

October Revolution, Russia, 70th anniv.

2nd Congress of the Organization of Angolan Women (OMA) — A141

10k, Soldier, nurse, technician, student.

1988, May 30 **Litho.** *Perf. 13x13½*

753	A141	2k shown	.25	.25
754	A141	10k multicolored	.65	.25

Victory Carnival, 10th Anniv. — A142

Various carnival scenes.

1988, June 15 **Litho.** *Perf. 13½x13*

755	A142	5k shown	.40	.25
756	A142	10k multi, diff.	.70	.30

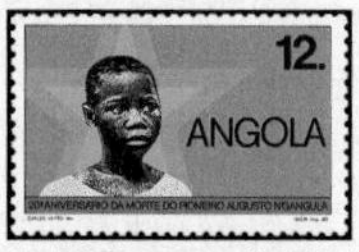

Augusto N'Gangula (1956-1968), Youth Pioneer Killed by Portuguese Colonial Army — A143

Agostinho Neto Pioneers' Organization (OPA), 25th Anniv. — A144

1989, Oct. 2 **Litho.** *Perf. 12x11½*

757	A143	12k multicolored	1.10	.65
758	A144	15k multicolored	1.40	.80

Pioneer Day.

10th Natl. Soccer Championships, Benguela, May 1 — A145

1989, Oct. 16

759	A145	5k shown	.50	.40
760	A145	5k Luanda, 3 years	.50	.40
761	A145	5k Luanda, 5 years	.50	.40
a.		Strip of 3, #759-761	1.60	1.60
		Nos. 759-761 (3)	1.50	1.20

Intl. Fund for Agricultural Development, 10th Anniv. — A146

1990, Feb. 15 **Litho.** *Perf. 11½x12*

762	A146	10k multicolored	1.10	.45

Ingombotas' Houses — A147

Architecture: 2k, Alta Train Station. 5k, National Museum of Anthropology. 15k, Ana Joaquina Palace. 23k, Iron Palace. 36k, Meteorological observatory, vert. 50k, People's Palace.

1990, Feb. 20 *Perf. 12x11½, 11½x12*

763	A147	1k shown	.25	.25
764	A147	2k multicolored	.25	.25
765	A147	5k multicolored	.40	.25
766	A147	15k multicolored	1.10	.60
767	A147	23k multicolored	1.90	.90
768	A147	36k multicolored	3.00	1.25
769	A147	50k multicolored	4.00	1.75
		Nos. 763-769 (7)	10.90	5.25

Luanda and Benguela Railways — A148

Various maps and locomotives.

1990, Mar. 1 *Perf. 12x11½*

770	A148	5k shown	.40	.25
771	A148	12k Garrat T (left)	1.25	.45
772	A148	12k Garrat T (right)	1.25	.45
a.		Pair, #771-772	2.75	2.75
773	A148	14k Mikado	1.25	.75
		Nos. 770-773 (4)	4.15	1.90

Souvenir Sheet

774	A148	25k Diesel electric	3.00	3.00

No. 772a has a continuous design.

Southern Africa Development Coordinating Conf. (SADCC), 10th Anniv. — A149

1990, Apr. 1 **Litho.** *Perf. 14*

775	A149	5k shown	.40	.25
776	A149	9k Floating oil rig	1.00	.45

Pan-African Postal Union (PAPU), 10th Anniv. — A150

10k, Simulated stamp, map.

1990, Apr. 6

777	A150	4k shown	.45	.25
778	A150	10k multicolored	1.00	.65

Paintings by Raul Indipwo — A151

6k, Tres Gracas. 9k, Muxima, vert.

1990, Apr. 24

779	A151	6k multicolored	.45	.25
780	A151	9k multicolored	1.00	.35

Stamp World London 90.

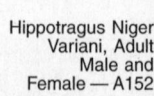

Hippotragus Niger Variani, Adult Male and Female — A152

1990, May 9 *Perf. 14x13½*

781	A152	5k Adult male	1.50	1.50
782	A152	5k shown	1.50	1.50
783	A152	5k Adult female	1.50	1.50
784	A152	5k Female, calf	1.50	1.50
		Nos. 781-784 (4)	6.00	6.00

World Wildlife Fund. Various combinations available in blocks or strips of four.

Rosa de Porcelana — A153

1990, June 2 **Litho.** *Perf. 14*

785	A153	5k shown	.40	.25
786	A153	8k Cravo burro	.80	.35
787	A153	10k Alamandra	.95	.45
		Nos. 785-787 (3)	2.15	1.05

Souvenir Sheet

788	A153	40k Hibiscus	5.00	5.00

Belgica '90.

Miniature Sheet

Intl. Literacy Year A154

Various animals and forest scenes.

1990, July 26 **Litho.** *Perf. 14*

789	A154	Sheet of 30	10.00	10.00
a.-ad.		1k any single	.30	.30
790	A154	5k Zebra	1.00	1.00
791	A154	5k Butterfly	1.00	1.00
792	A154	5k Horse	1.00	1.00
a.		Block of 3, #790-792 + label	4.00	4.00

People's Assembly, 10th Anniv. — A155

1990, Nov. 11 *Perf. 14*

793	A155	10k multicolored	.90	.90

3rd Natl. Labor Congress — A156

1990 **Litho.** *Perf. 13½*

794	A156	14k multicolored	1.00	.50

War of Independence, 30th Anniv. — A157

Uniforms: No. 795, Machete, 1961. No. 796, Rifle, 1962-63. No. 797, Rifle, 1968. No. 798, Automatic rifle, 1972.

1991, Feb. 28 **Litho.** *Perf. 14*

795	A157	6k multicolored	.65	.25
a.		Perf. 13½ vert.	1.20	.75
796	A157	6k multicolored	.65	.25
a.		Perf. 13½ vert.	1.20	.75
797	A157	6k multicolored	.65	.25
a.		Perf. 13½ vert.	1.20	.75
798	A157	6k multicolored	.65	.25
a.		Perf. 13½ vert.	1.20	.75
b.		Bklt. pane of 4, #795a-798a	6.00	
		Nos. 795-798 (4)	2.60	1.00

Musical Instruments — A158

Designs: a, Marimba. b, Mucupela. c, Ngoma la Txina. d, Kissange.

1991, Apr. 5 **Litho.** *Perf. 14*

799	A158	6k Block or strip of 4, #799a-799d	2.50	2.50

Tourism — A159

Designs: 3k, Iona National Park. 7k, Kalandula Waterfalls. 35k, Lobito Bay. 60k, Weltwitschia Mirabilis plant.

1991, June 25 **Litho.** *Perf. 14*

800	A159	3k multi	.25	.25
801	A159	7k multi	.40	.40
802	A159	35k multi	1.90	.80
803	A159	60k multi	3.25	1.50
		Nos. 800-803 (4)	5.80	2.95

Souvenir Sheet

Design: 30k, Map details.

1991, June 25 **Litho.** *Perf. 13¼*

803A	A159	30k multi	*4.00*	*4.00*

Dogs — A160

1991, July 5 **Litho.** *Perf. 14*

804	A160	5k Kabir of dembos	.50	.50
805	A160	7k Ombua	.55	.55
806	A160	11k Kabir massongo	.90	.40
807	A160	12k Kawa tchowe	.90	.50
		Nos. 804-807 (4)	2.85	1.95

1992 Summer Olympics, Barcelona — A161

1991, July 26 *Perf. 13*

808	A161	4k Judo	.25	.25
809	A161	6k Sailing	.25	.25
810	A161	10k Running	.45	.25
811	A161	100k Swimming	3.50	2.25
		Nos. 808-811 (4)	4.45	3.00

Navigation Aids — A162

1991, Nov. 8 **Litho.** *Perf. 12*

812	A162	5k Quadrant	.25	.25
813	A162	15k Astrolabe	.55	.55
814	A162	20k Cross-staff	.75	.40
815	A162	50k Portolano	1.75	1.00
		Nos. 812-815 (4)	3.30	2.20

Iberex '91.

Rays — A163

1992, Mar. 30 Litho. *Perf. 14*

816 A163 40k Myliobatis aquila .90 .30
817 A163 50k Aetobatus narinari .90 .40
818 A163 66k Manta birostris 1.10 .50
819 A163 80k Raja miraletus 1.50 .65
Nos. 816-819 (4) 4.40 1.85

Souvenir Sheet

Perf. 13½

820 A163 25k Manta birostris, diff. 5.00 5.00

Quioca Masks — A164

1992, Apr. 30 Litho. *Perf. 13½*

821 A164 60k Kalelwa .25 .25
822 A164 100k Mukixe Wa Kino .45 .35
823 A164 150k Cikunza .75 .55
824 A164 250k Mukixi Wa Mbwesu 1.20 .70
Nos. 821-824 (4) 2.65 1.85

See Nos. 854-857, 868-871, 883-886, 895-898.

Lubrapex '92 — A165

Medicinal Plants: 200k, Ptaeroxylon obliquum. 300k, Spondias mombin. 500k, Parinari curatellifolia. 600k, Cochlospermum angolense.

1992, May 8 *Perf. 14*

825 A165 200k brown & pale yel .75 .55
826 A165 300k brown & pale yel 1.10 .90
827 A165 500k brown & pale yel 2.00 1.60
828 A165 600k brown & pale yel 2.10 1.75
a. Block or strip of 4, #825-828 6.00 6.00

Evangelization of Angola, 500th Anniv. — A166

150k, King, missionaries. 420k, Ruins of M'banza Congo. 470k, Maxima Church. 500k, Faces of people.

1992, May 10 *Perf. 13½*

829 A166 150k multicolored .55 .45
830 A166 420k multicolored 1.60 1.25
831 A166 470k multicolored 1.75 1.40
832 A166 500k multicolored 2.00 1.60
Nos. 829-832 (4) 5.90 4.70

Traditional Houses — A167

150k, Dimbas. 330k, Cokwe. 360k, Mbali. 420k, Ambwelas. 500k, Upper Zambezi.

Perf. 14, 13½ Vert. (#832A)

1992, May 22

832A A167 150k multi 1.25 1.00
b. Bklt. pane of 4, #832A, 833a-835a 7.50
833 A167 330k multi 1.40 1.10
a. Perf. 13½ vert. 1.60 1.60
834 A167 360k multi 1.60 1.25
a. Perf. 13½ vert. 1.60 1.60
835 A167 420k multi 2.00 1.60
a. Perf. 13½ vert. 2.00 2.00
836 A167 500k multi 2.00 1.60
Nos. 832A-836 (5) 8.25 6.55

Expo '92, Seville.

Agapornis Roseicollis A168

150k, Two birds on branch. 200k, Birds feeding. 250k, Hand holding bird. 300k, Bird on perch.

1992, June 2 *Perf. 12x11½*

837 A168 150k multicolored 1.00 .50
838 A168 200k multicolored 1.40 .65
839 A168 250k multicolored 1.75 .80
840 A168 300k multicolored 2.10 1.00
a. Strip of 4, #837-840 6.50 6.50

Expo '92, Seville.

Souvenir Sheet

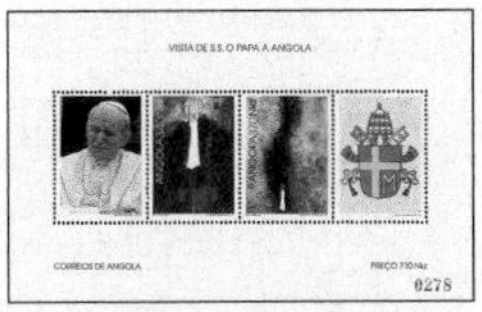

Visit of Pope John Paul II to Angola — A169

Abstract paintings: a, 340k, The Crucifixion. b, 370k, The Resurrection.

1992, June 4 Litho. *Perf. 13½*

841 A169 Sheet of 2, #a.-b. + 2 labels 4.00 4.00

1992 Summer Olympics, Barcelona A170

1992, July 30 *Perf. 14*

842 A170 120k Hurdles .55 .40
843 A170 180k Cycling .80 .55
844 A170 240k Roller hockey .95 .75
845 A170 360k Basketball 1.50 1.10
Nos. 842-845 (4) 3.80 2.80

Native Fishing — A171

1992, Aug. 5 *Perf. 11½x12*

846 A171 65k Building traps .50 .25
847 A171 90k Using nets .65 .35
848 A171 100k Laying traps .80 .40
849 A171 120k Fisherman in boats .95 .50
Nos. 846-849 (4) 2.90 1.50

Souvenir Sheet

Discovery of America, 500th Anniv. — A172

1992, Sept. 18 Litho. *Perf. 12*

850 A172 500k multicolored 4.00 4.00

Genoa '92.

First Free Elections in Angola — A173

Designs: 120k, People voting. 150k, Map, ballot box, peace doves. 200k, People, dove, hand dropping ballot into ballot box.

1992, Oct. 27 Litho. *Perf. 11½x12*

851 A173 120k multicolored .35 .25
852 A173 150k multicolored .40 .30
853 A173 200k multicolored .55 .40
Nos. 851-853 (3) 1.30 .95

Quioca Mask Type of 1992

1992, Nov. 6 *Perf. 13½*

854 A164 72k Cihongo .25 .25
855 A164 80k Mbwasu .35 .25
856 A164 120k Cinhanga .40 .35
857 A164 210k Kalewa .75 .65
Nos. 854-857 (4) 1.75 1.50

Inauguration of Express Mail Service — A174

1992, Dec. 14 Litho. *Perf. 12x11½*

858 A174 450k Truck 1.40 1.20
859 A174 550k Airplane 1.75 1.40

Meteorological Instruments — A175

1993, Mar. 23 Litho. *Perf. 11½x12*

860 A175 250k Weather balloon .95 .80
861 A175 470k Actinometer 1.90 1.40
862 A175 500k Rain gauge 1.90 1.60
Nos. 860-862 (3) 4.75 3.80

Seashells — A176

210k, Trochita trochiformis. 330k, Strombus latus. 400k, Aporrhais pesgallinae. 500k, Fusos aff. albinus.
1000k, Pusionella nifat.

1993, Apr. 6 *Perf. 12x11½*

863 A176 210k multicolored .75 .75
864 A176 330k multicolored 1.10 1.10
865 A176 400k multicolored 1.50 1.50
866 A176 500k multicolored 1.75 1.75
Nos. 863-866 (4) 5.10 5.10

Souvenir Sheet

867 A176 1000k multicolored 4.00 4.00

Quioca Art Type of 1992

1993, June 7 Litho. *Perf. 12*

868 A164 72k Men with vehicles .25 .25
869 A164 210k Cavalier .75 .50
870 A164 420k Airplane 1.50 .90
871 A164 600k Men carrying stretcher 2.00 1.25
Nos. 868-871 (4) 4.50 2.90

Flowering Plants — A177

360k, Sansevieria cylindrica. 400k, Euphorbia tirucalli. 500k, Opuntia ficus-indica. 600k, Dracaena aubryana.

1993, June 28 *Perf. 11½x12*

872 A177 360k multicolored 1.20 .90
873 A177 400k multicolored 1.40 1.00
874 A177 500k multicolored 1.50 1.00
875 A177 600k multicolored 2.00 1.40
Nos. 872-875 (4) 6.10 4.30

Souvenir Sheet

Africa Day A178

1993, May 31 *Perf. 12*

876 A178 1500k Leopard 6.00 6.00

Tribal Pipes — A179

1993, Aug. 16 Litho. *Perf. 11½x12*

877 A179 72k Vimbundi .25 .25
878 A179 200k Vimbundi, diff. .75 .40
879 A179 420k Mutopa 1.40 .90
880 A179 600k Pexi 2.00 1.25
Nos. 877-880 (4) 4.40 2.80

Souvenir Sheet

Union of Portuguese Speaking Capitals — A180

1993, July 30 *Perf. 12x11½*

881 A180 1500k multicolored 5.50 5.50

Turtles — A181

Designs: a, 180k, Chelonia mydas (b). b, 450k, Eretmochelys imbricata. c, 550k, Dermochelys coriacea. d, 630k, Caretta caretta.

1993, July 9 Litho. *Perf. 12½x12*

882 A181 Block of 4, #a.-d. 7.00 7.00

Quioca Art Type of 1992

1993, Sept. 1 Litho. *Perf. 12*

883 A164 300k Leopard .95 .65
884 A164 600k Malhado 1.90 1.25
885 A164 800k Birds 2.50 1.75
886 A164 1000k Chickens 3.25 2.10
Nos. 883-886 (4) 8.60 5.75

Mushrooms — A182

300k, Tricholoma georgii. 500k, Amanita phalloides. 600k, Amanita vaginata. 1000k, Macrolepiota procera.

1993, Dec. 5 Litho. *Perf. 12*

887 A182 300k multicolored .95 .55
a. Perf. 11½ vert. 1.60 1.60
888 A182 500k multicolored 1.60 .95
a. Perf. 11½ vert. 2.40 2.40
889 A182 600k multicolored 1.90 1.20
a. Perf. 11½ vert. 3.25 3.25

890 A182 1000k multicolored 3.25 2.00
a. Perf. 11½ vert. 4.75 4.75
b. Booklet pane of 4, #887a-890a 12.00
Nos. 887-890 (4) 7.70 4.70

A183

Natl. Culture Day: 500k, Cinganji, wood carving of dancer. 1000k, Ohunya yo soma, staff with woman's face. 1200k, Ongende, sculpture of man on donkey. 2200k, Upi, corn pestle.

1994, Jan. 10 Litho. *Perf. 12*

891 A183 500k multicolored .80 .50
892 A183 1000k multicolored 1.50 .95
893 A183 1200k multicolored 2.00 1.25
894 A183 2200k multicolored 3.50 2.25
Nos. 891-894 (4) 7.80 4.95

Hong Kong '94.

Quioca Art Type of 1992

1994, Feb. 21 Litho. *Perf. 12*

895 A164 500k Bird on flower .50 .40
896 A164 2000k Plant with roots 2.25 1.60
897 A164 2500k Feto 2.75 2.00
898 A164 3000k Plant 3.50 2.40
Nos. 895-898 (4) 9.00 6.40

Social Responsibilities of AIDS — A184

500k, Mass of people. 1000k, Witchdoctor receiving AIDS through needle, people being educated. 3000k, Stylized man, woman.

1994, May 5 Litho. *Perf. 12*

899 A184 500k multicolored .55 .40
900 A184 1000k multicolored 1.10 .55
901 A184 3000k multicolored 3.50 2.40
Nos. 899-901 (3) 5.15 3.35

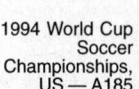

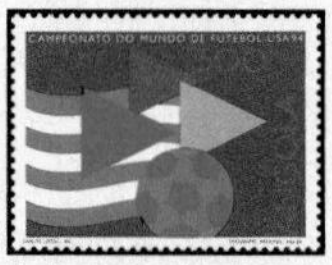
1994 World Cup Soccer Championships, US — A185

500k, Large arrows, small ball. 700k, Small arrows, large ball. 2200k, Ball in goal. 2500k, Ball, foot.

1994, June 17 *Perf. 14*

902 A185 500k multicolored .55 .40
903 A185 700k multicolored .80 .55
904 A185 2200k multicolored 2.50 1.75
905 A185 2500k multicolored 3.00 2.00
Nos. 902-905 (4) 6.85 4.70

Dinosaurs A186

1000k, Brachiosaurus. 3000k, Spinosaurus. 5000k, Ouranosaurus. 10,000k, Lesothosaurus.
19,000k, Lesothosaurus, map of Africa.

1994, Aug. 16 Litho. *Perf. 12*

906 A186 1000k multi .25 .25
907 A186 3000k multi .75 .55
908 A186 5000k multi 1.25 .95
909 A186 10,000k multi 2.50 2.00
Nos. 906-909 (4) 4.75 3.75

Souvenir Sheet

910 A186 19,000k multi 7.50 7.50

PHILAKOREA '94, SINGPEX '94. No. 910 contains one 44x34mm stamp.

Tourism — A187

2000k, Birds. 4000k, Wild animals. 8000k, Native women. 10,000k, Native men.

1994, Sept. 27 Litho. *Perf. 12x11½*

911 A187 2000k multi .50 .40
912 A187 4000k multi .95 .80
913 A187 8000k multi 2.00 1.60
914 A187 10,000k multi 2.50 2.00
Nos. 911-914 (4) 5.95 4.80

Post Boxes — A188

Designs: 5000k, Letters, bundled mail wall box. 7500k, Wall box for letters. 10,000k, Pillar box. 21,000k, Multi-function units.

1994, Oct. 7 *Perf. 14½*

915 A188 5000k multicolored .75 .40
916 A188 7500k multicolored 1.00 .55
917 A188 10,000k multicolored 1.40 .80
918 A188 21,000k multicolored 3.00 1.75
Nos. 915-918 (4) 6.15 3.50

Cotton Pests — A189

Insects: 5000k, Heliothis armigera. 6000k, Bemisia tabasi. 10,000k, Dysdercus. 27,000k, Spodoptera exigua.

1994, Nov. 11 Litho. *Perf. 14*

919 A189 5000k multicolored .80 .40
920 A189 6000k multicolored 1.00 .50
921 A189 10,000k multicolored 1.60 .90
922 A189 27,000k multicolored 4.00 2.10
Nos. 919-922 (4) 7.40 3.90

Intl. Olympic Committee, Cent. — A190

1994, Dec. 15

923 A190 27,000k multicolored 4.50 4.50

Tribal Culture — A191

Designs: 10,000k. Rubbing sticks to start fire. 15,000k, Extracting sap from tree. 20,000k, Smoking tribal pipe. 25,000k, Shooting bow & arrow. 28,000k, Mothers, children. 30,000k, Cave art.

1995, Jan. 6 Litho. *Perf. 14*

924 A191 10,000k multicolored .50 .35
925 A191 15,000k multicolored .75 .50
926 A191 20,000k multicolored 1.00 .65
927 A191 25,000k multicolored 1.25 .80
928 A191 28,000k multicolored 1.25 .90
929 A191 30,000k multicolored 1.50 1.20
Nos. 924-929 (6) 6.25 4.40

Traditional Ceramics — A192

Designs: No. 930, Pitcher with bust of a woman as stopper. No. 931, Cone-shaped vase. No. 932, Bird-shaped vase. No. 933, Pitcher with bust of a man as stopper.

1995, Jan. 2 Litho. *Perf. 14½*

930 A192 (2) 2nd class natl. .55 .25
931 A192 (1) 1st class natl. .80 .35
932 A192 (2) 2nd class intl. 1.10 .55
933 A192 (1) 1st class intl. 1.50 1.25
Nos. 930-933 (4) 3.95 2.40

Rotary Intl., 90th Anniv. — A193

a, Immunizing boy against polio. b, Medical examination. c, Immunizing girl against polio.
No. 936, Dove over map.

1995, Feb. 23 Litho. *Perf. 14*

934 Strip of 3 6.00 6.00
a.-c. A193 27,000k any single 2.00 1.25
935 Strip of 3 6.00 6.00
a.-c. A193 27,000k any single 2.00 1.25

Souvenir Sheet

936 A193 81,000k multicolored 7.50 7.50
a. English inscription 7.50 7.50

No. 934 has Portuguese inscriptions. No. 935 has English inscriptions. Both were issued in sheets of 9 stamps.
No. 936 contains Portuguese inscription in sheet margin.

Rotary Intl., 90th Anniv. A194

Litho. & Embossed

1995, Feb. 23 *Perf. 11½x12*

937 A194 81,000k gold 50.00

World Telecommunications Day — A195

Designs: No. 938, 1957 Sputnik 1. No. 939, Shuttle, Intelsat satellite.

1995 Litho. *Perf. 14*

938 A195 27,000k multicolored 2.00 2.00
939 A195 27,000k multicolored 2.00 2.00
a. Souvenir sheet, #938-939 4.50 4.50

Independence, 20th Anniv. — A196

1995, Nov. 11 Litho. *Perf. 14*

940 A196 2900k multicolored 1.60 1.60

4th World Conference on Women, Beijing — A197

Designs: 375k, Women working in fields. 1106k, Woman teaching, girls with book. 1265k, Woman in industry, career woman. 2900k, Woman in native headdress, vert.
1500k, Native mother, children, vert.

1996, Jan. 29 Litho. *Perf. 14*

941 A197 375k multicolored .25 .25
942 A197 1106k multicolored .80 .80
943 A197 1265k multicolored 1.50 1.50
944 A197 2900k multicolored 3.00 3.00
Nos. 941-944 (4) 5.55 5.55

Souvenir Sheet

945 A197 1500k multicolored 2.75 2.75

UN Assistance Programs A198

Designs: 200k, Boy, highlift moving supplies. 1265k, Supply ship arriving. No. 948, Two high lifts. No. 949, Tractor-trailer traveling past vultures, native girl.
No. 950, Man, ship.

1996 Litho. *Perf. 14*

946 A198 200k multicolored .25 .25
947 A198 1265k multicolored 1.00 1.00
948 A198 2583k multicolored 2.25 2.25
949 A198 2583k multicolored 2.50 2.50
Nos. 946-949 (4) 6.00 6.00

Souvenir Sheet

950 A198 1265k multicolored *6.50 6.50*

Flora and Fauna — A199

1500k, Verdant hawkmoth. 4400k, Water lily. 5100k, Panther toad. 6000k, African wild dog.
1500k: a, Western honey buzzard. b, Bateleuer. c, Common kestrel.
4400k; d, Red-crested turaco. e, Giraffe. f, Elephant.
5100k: g, Hippopotamus. h, Cattle egret. i, Lion.
6000k: j, Helmeted turtle. k, African pygmy goose. l, Egyptian plover.
12,000k, Spotted hyena.

1996, Apr. 20 Litho. *Perf. 14*

951-954 A199 Set of 4 5.00 5.00
955 A199 Sheet of 12, #a.-l. 10.00 10.00

Souvenir Sheet

956 A199 12,000k multicolored 3.00 3.00

Sheets of 12, #a-i.

Birds — A200

Fowl, each 5500k: No. 957a, California quail. b, Greater prairie chicken. c, Painted quail. d, Golden pheasant. e, Roulroul partridge. f, Ceylon sourfowl. g, Himalayan snowcock. h, Temminicks tragopan. i, Lady Amherst's pheasant. j, Great curassow. k, Red-legged partridge. l, Impeyan pheasant.
Hummingbirds, each 5500k: No. 958a, Anna's. b, Blue-throated. c, Broad-tailed. d, Costa's. e, White-eared. f, Calliope. g, Violet-crowned. h, Rufous. i, Crimson topaz. j, Broad-billed. k, Frilled coquette. l, Ruby-throated.
No. 959, 12,000k, Ring-necked pheasant. No. 960, 12,000k, Racquet-tail hummingbird.

1996, Apr. 20

957-958 A200 Set of 2 20.00 20.00

Souvenir Sheets

959-960 A200 Set of 2 5.50 5.50

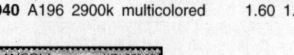

Lubrapex '96 — A201

Wild animals: a, 180k, Lions attacking zebra. b, 450k, Zebras, lions, diff. c, 180k, Zebras grazing, lions stalking. d, 450k, Panthera leo. e, 550k, Cheetah. f, 630k, Cheetah running. g, 550k, Cheetah chasing antilope. h, 630k, Cheetah attacking antelope. i, 180k, Antilope (gnu) being attacked by wild dogs. j, 450k, Antelope, wild dogs. k, 180k, Pack of wild dogs. l, 450k, Licaon pictus. m, 550k, Panthera pardus. n, 630k, Oryx. o, 550k, Oryx, diff. p, 630k, Leopard attacking oryx.

1996, Apr. 27

961 A201 Sheet of 16, #a.-p. 9.00 9.00

Sheets of 6, #a.-f.

Ships — A202

Designs, each 6000k: No. 962a, Styrbjorn, Sweden, 1789. b, Constellation, US, 1797. c, Taureau, France, 1865. d, Bomb Ketch, France, 1682. e, Sardegna, Italy, 1881. f, HMS Glasgow, England, 1867.

No. 963a, Essex, US, 1812. b, HMS Inflexible, England, 1881. c, HMS Minotaur, England, 1863. d, Napoleon, France, 1854. e, Sophia Amalia, Denmark, 1650. f, Massena, France, 1887.

No. 964, 12,000k, HMS Tremendous, England, 1806, vert. No. 965, 12,000k, Royal Prince, England, 1666.

1996, May 4

962-963 A202 Set of 2 12.00 12.00

Souvenir Sheets

964-965 A202 Set of 2 10.00 10.00

UN, 50th Anniv. (in 1995) — A203

Designs: No. 966, Boys pumping water. No. 967, Man, woman with girl.
8000k, Unloading supplies from ship.

1996, Apr. 27 Litho. *Perf. 14*

966 A203 3500k multicolored 1.25 1.25
967 A203 3500k multicolored 1.25 1.25

Souvenir Sheet

968 A203 8000k multicolored 2.75 2.75

Sonangol, 20th Anniv. — A204

Face in traditional mask, costume, native birds, and: No. 969, Oil derricks. No. 970, Oil storage tanks, ship. 2500k, Refinery equipment. 5000k, Cargo shipment, jet.

1996, May 12

969 A204 1000k multicolored .25 .25
970 A204 1000k multicolored .25 .25
971 A204 2500k multicolored 1.60 1.60
972 A204 5000k multicolored 2.75 2.75
Nos. 969-972 (4) 4.85 4.85

Brapex '96 — A205

Designs: No. 973, Slaves in hold. No. 974, Slaves fleeing ship as it's overturned. No. 975, Slave boats approaching ship. No. 976, Slaves talking with captain.
50,000k, like No. 975.

1996, Oct. 19 Litho. *Perf. 14*

973 A205 20,000k multicolored 2.25 2.25
974 A205 20,000k multicolored 2.25 2.25
975 A205 30,000k multicolored 3.00 3.00
976 A205 30,000k multicolored 3.00 3.00
Nos. 973-976 (4) 10.50 10.50

Souvenir Sheet

977 A205 50,000k multicolored 8.00 8.00

Churches — A206

Designs: 5,000k, Mission, Huila. No. 979, Church of the Nazarene. No. 980, Church of Our Lady of Pó Pulo. 25,000k, St. Adriáo Church.

1996, Dec. 6 Litho. *Perf. 14*

978 A206 5,000k multicolored .40 .40
979 A206 10,000k multicolored .90 .90
980 A206 10,000k multicolored .90 .90
981 A206 25,000k multicolored 2.10 2.10
Nos. 978-981 (4) 4.30 4.30

1996 Summer Olympic Games, Atlanta — A207

5,000k, Handball, vert. 10,000k, Swimming. 25,000k, Track & field, vert. 35,000k, Shooting.
65,000k, Basketball.

1996, Dec. 9

982 A207 5,000k multi .60 .60
983 A207 10,000k multi 1.25 1.25
984 A207 25,000k multi 3.25 3.25
985 A207 35,000k multi 4.50 4.50
Nos. 982-985 (4) 9.60 9.60

Souvenir Sheet

986 A207 65,000k multi 6.00 6.00

MPLA (Liberation Movement), 40th Anniv. — A208

1996, Dec. 10 Litho. *Perf. 14*

987 A208 30,000k Dolphins, map *3.50 3.50*

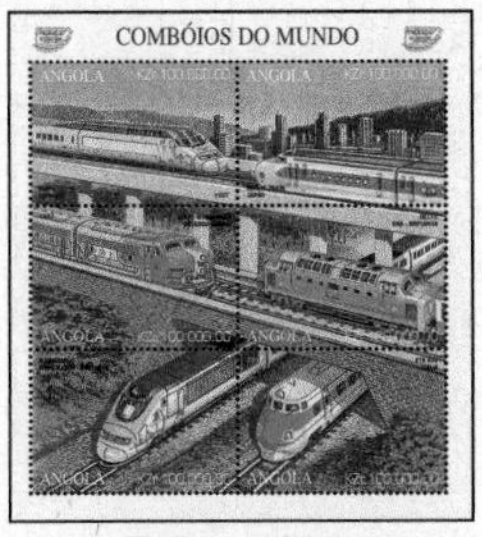

Trains — A209

Trains — A209a

No. 988: a, AVE, Spain. b, Bullet Train, Japan. c, GM F7 Warbonnet, US. d, Deltic, Great Britain. e, Eurostar, France/Great Britain. f, ETR 450, Italy.

No. 989: a, Class E1300, Morocco. b, ICE, Germany. c, X2000, Sweden. d, TGV Duplex, France.

No. 989E, each 250,000k: f, Steam engine. g, Garrat. h, General Electric.

No. 990, 110,000k, Canadian Pacific 4-4-0, Canada. No. 991, 110,000k, Via Rail Canadian, Canada.

1997, May 29 Litho. *Perf. 14*

Sheets of 6, 4 or 3

988 A209 100,000k #a.-f. *8.00 8.00*
989 A209 140,000k #a.-d. *8.00 8.00*
989E A209a Sheet of 3, #f.-h. *14.00 14.00*

Souvenir Sheets

Perf. 13½

990-991 A209 Set of 2 *8.00 8.00*

Nos. 990-991 contain one 38x50 or 50x38mm stamp, respectively.
PACIFIC 97.

Horses A210

No. 992: a, Thoroughbred. b, Palomino, appaloosa. c, Arabians. d, Arabian colt. e, Thoroughbred colt. f, Mustang. g, Mustang, diff. h, Furioso.

No. 993: a, Thoroughbred. b, Arabian, palomino. c, Arabian, chincoteague. d, Pintos. e, Przewalski's horse. f, Thoroughbred colt. g, Arabians. h, New forest pony.

No. 994: a, Selle Francais. b, Fjord. c, Percheron. d, Italian heavy draft. e, Shagya Arab. f, Avelignese. g, Czechoslovakian warmblood. h, New forest pony.

215,000k, Thoroughbreds. 220,000k, Thoroughbreds, diff.

1997, July 5 Litho. *Perf. 14*

Sheets of 8

992 A210 100,000k #a.-h. *8.50 8.50*
993 A210 120,000k #a.-h. *10.00 10.00*
994 A210 140,000k #a.-h. *12.50 12.50*

Souvenir Sheets

995 A210 215,000k multi *6.00 6.00*
996 A210 220,000k multi *6.00 6.00*

PACIFIC 97.

1998 World Cup Soccer Championships, France — A211

Winners holding World Cup trophy: No. 997: a, Uruguay, 1930. b, Germany, 1954. c, Brazil, 1970. d, Argentina, 1986. e, Brazil, 1994.

Winning team pictures: No. 998a, Germany, 1954. b, Uruguay, 1958. c, Italy, 1938. d, Brazil, 1962. e, Brazil, 1970. f, Uruguay, 1930.

220,000k, Angolan team members standing. 250,000k, 1997 Angolan team picture.

1997, July 5 Litho. *Perf. 14*

Sheets of 5 or 6

997 A211 100,000k #a.-e. + label *9.00 9.00*
998 A211 100,000k #a.-f. *10.00 10.00*

Souvenir Sheets

999 A211 220,000k multi *5.50 5.50*
1000 A211 250,000k multi *5.50 5.50*

ENSA (Security System), 20th Anniv. — A212

"Star" emblem, and stylized protection of "egg," each 240,000k: No. 1001, Industry. No. 1002, Recreation. No. 1003, Homes, shelters. No. 1004, Accident prevention.
350,000k, Emblem.

1998 Litho. *Perf. 13½*

1001-1004 A212 Set of 4 *8.00 8.00*

Souvenir Sheet

Perf. 13½x13

1005 A212 350,000k multi *4.00 4.00*

No. 1005 contains one 60x40mm stamp.

GURN (Natl. Unity & Reconciliation Government), 1st Anniv. — A213

Emblem, portion of country map and: 100,000k, a, Sea, swordfish, ships, oil derrick. b, Sea, ships, swordfish. c, Sea, swordfish, ships, mining car on railroad track. d, Sea, power lines.

200,000k: e, Train on track, antelope. f, Mining cars on track, tractor pulling cart. g, Railroad track across rivers, tractor plowing. h, Power lines. i, UR corner of map, crystals. j, Train on track. k, Elephant, tree. l, Trunk of tree, bottom edge of map.

1998

1006 A213 Sheet of 12, #a.-l. 18.00 18.00

Souvenir Sheet

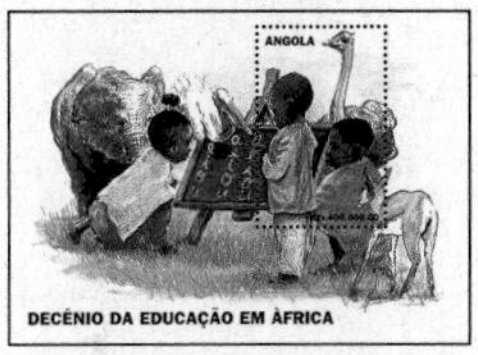

Education in Angola — A214

1998

1007 A214 400,000k multi *6.00 6.00*

Diana, Princess of Wales (1961-97) — A215

Various portraits, each 100,000k, color of sheet margin: No. 1008, pale green. No. 1009, pale yellow.
400,000k, Wearing protective clothing.

1998, May 21 Litho. *Perf. 14*

Sheets of 6, #a.-f.

1008-1009 A215 Set of 2 *20.00 20.00*

Souvenir Sheet

1010 A215 400,000k multi *5.00 5.00*

See No. 1028.

Expo '98, Lisbon — A216

Marine life: No. 1011, 100,000k, Anemones. No. 1012, 100,000k, Sea urchin. No. 1013, 100,000k, Sea horses. No. 1014, 100,000k, Coral (Caravela). No. 1015, 240,000k, Sea slug. No. 1016, 240,000k, Worms (Tunicados).

1998, May 21 *Perf. 13½*

1011-1016 A216 Set of 6 10.00 10.00

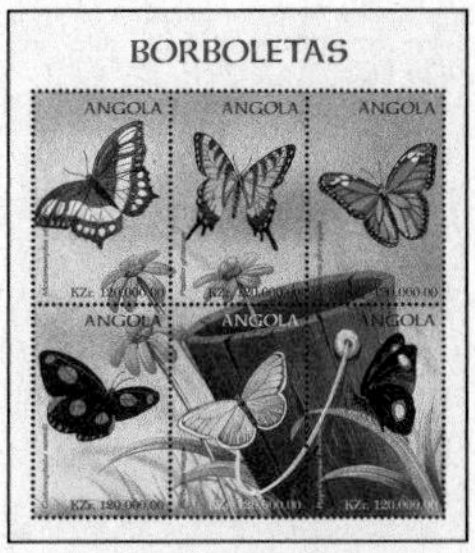

Butterflies — A217

No. 1017, each 120,000k: a, Metamorpha stelene. b, Papilio glaucus. c, Danaus plexippus. d, Catonephele numili. e, Plebejus argus. f, Hypolimnas bolina.

No. 1018, each 120,000k: a, Terinos terpander. b, Bematistes aganice. c, Hebomoia glaucippe. d, Colias eurytheme. e, Pereute leucodrosime. f, Lycaena dispar.

No. 1019, each 120,000k, horiz.: a, Dynastor napolean. b, Zeuxidia amethystus. c, Battus philenor. d, Phoebis philea. e, Danaus chrysippus. f, Glaucopsyche alexis.

Each 250,000k: No. 1020, Euphaedra neophron. No. 1021, Thecla betulae, horiz. No. 1022, Uraneis ucubis, armillaria staminea.

1998, May 21 ***Perf. 14***

Sheets of 6, #a.-f.

1017-1019 A217 Set of 3 *20.00 20.00*

Souvenir Sheets

1020-1022 A217 Set of 3 *16.00 16.00*

Cats and Dogs — A218

Cats, each 140,000k: No. 1023a, British tortoiseshell. b, Chinchilla. c, Russian blue. d, Black Persian (longhair). e, British red tabby. f, Birman.

Dogs, each 140,000k: No. 1024a, West Highland terrier. b, Irish setter. c, Dachshund. d, St. John water dog. e, Shetland sheep dog. f, Dalmatian.

Each 500,000k: No. 1025, Turkish van (swimming cat). No. 1026, Labrador retriever.

1998, May 21 Litho. ***Perf. 14x13½***

Sheets of 6, #a.-f.

1023-1024 A218 Set of 2 *15.00 15.00*

Souvenir Sheets

1025-1026 A218 Set of 2 *12.00 12.00*

Wild Animals — A219

100,000k: a, Panthera leo. b, Hippopotamus amphibius. c, Loxodonta africana. d, Giraffa camelopardalis.

220,000k: e, Syncerus caffer-caffer. f, Gorilla gorilla. g, Ceratotherim simum. h, Oryx gazella.

1998, July 24 Litho. ***Perf. 14***

1027 A219 Sheet of 8, #a.-h. 12.00 12.00

Diana, Princes of Wales Type of 1998

Pictures showing Diana's campaign to ban land mines, each 150,000k: a, With girl. b, With two boys. c, Wearing protective clothing.

1998, Aug. 31 Litho. ***Perf. 14***

1028 A215 Strip of 3, #a.-c. *7.00 7.00*

No. 1028 was issued in sheets of 6 stamps.

Intl. Year of the Ocean — A220

Marine life: No. 1029a, Pagurites. b, Callinectes marginatus. c, Thais forbesi. d, Ostrea tulipa. e, Balanus amohitrite. f, Uca tangeri.

No. 1030: a, Littorina angulifera. b, Semifusus morio. c, Thais coronata. d, Cerithium atratum (red branch). e, Ostrea tulipa. f, Cerithium atratum (green branch).

Each 300,000k: No. 1031, Goniopsis, horiz. No. 1032, Unidentified shell.

1998, Sept. 4 **Sheets of 6**

1029 A220 100,000k #a.-f. *5.00 5.00*

1030 A220 170,000k #a.-f. *7.00 7.00*

Souvenir Sheets

1031-1032 A220 Set of 2 *11.00 11.00*

Souvenir Sheet

Battle Against Polio in Angola A221

1998, Aug. 28 Litho. ***Perf. 13½***

1033 A221 500,000k multicolored *3.75 3.75*

Traditional Boats — A222

Designs: No. 1034, 250,000k, Boat, Bimba. No. 1035, 250,000k, Canoe with sail, Ndongo. 500,000k, Constructing boat, Ndongo.

1998, Sept. 4 ***Perf. 14***

1034-1036 A222 Set of 3 7.50 7.50

Titanic — A223

Views of Titanic, each 350,000k: a, Under tow. b, Stern. c, Starboard side at night. d, At dock.

1998, Sept. 4

1037 A223 Sheet of 4, #a.-d. *9.00 9.00*

No. 1037c is 76x30mm, No. 1037d is 38x61mm.

Angolan Food — A224

Various vegetables, fruits: No. 1038, 100,000k, 4 fruits. No. 1039, 100,000k, Squash sliced in half. No. 1040, 120,000k, Ears of corn. No. 1041, 120,000k, Green beans. No. 1042, 140,000k, Fruit with red seeds sliced in half. No. 1043, 140,000k, Sliced bananas.

1998

1038-1043 A224 Set of 6 7.00 7.00

Portugal '98.

Airplanes A225

No. 1044, IL-62 M. No. 1045, B737 100.

No. 1046: a, Ultralight. b, Gyroplane. c, Business jet. d, onvertible plane (e). e, Chuterplane (a, b, d). f, Twin rotors (e). g, Skycrane. h, Aerospatiale Concorde (i). i, Flying boat.

No. 1047: a, Pedal power (b). b, Sail plane (a, e). c, Aerobatic (f). d, Hang gliding (g). e, Balloon (h). f, Glidercraft (e, i). g, Model airplane. h, Air racing (i). i, Solar cells.

No. 1048, 1,000,000k, Boeing 777. No. 1049, 1,000,000k, Columbia Space Shuttle, vert. No. 1049A, 1,000,000k, Boeing 737-200. No. 1049B, 1,000,000k, Boeing 747-300.

1998-99 Litho. ***Perf. 14***

1044 A225 200,000k multi *1.75 1.75*

1045 A225 200,000k multi *1.75 1.75*

Sheets of 9

1046 A225 150,000k #a.-i. *5.00 5.00*

1047 A225 250,000k #a.-i. *8.00 8.00*

Souvenir Sheets

1048-1049B A225 Set of 4 *26.00 26.00*

Nos. 1048-1049B each contain one 85x28mm stamp.

Issued: Nos. 1049A-1049B, 3/25/99; others 12/24/98.

Dinosaurs — A226

Designs, vert., each 120,000k: No. 1050, Parasaurolophus. No. 1051, Maiasaura. No. 1052, Iguanodon. No. 1053, Elaphosaurus.

No. 1054, vert, 120,000k: a, Brontosaurus. b, Plateosaurus. c, Brachiosaurus. d, Anatosaurus. e, Tyrannosaurus. f, Carnotaurus. g, Corythosaurus. h, Stegosaurus. i, Iguanodon, diff.

No. 1055, 120,000k: a, Hadrosaurus. b, Ouranosaurus. c, Hypsilophodon. d, Brachiosaurus. e, Shunosaurus. f, Amargasaurus. g, Tuojiangosaurus. h, Monoclonius. i, Struthiosaurus.

Each 550,000k: No. 1056, Triceratops, vert. No. 1057, Tyrannosaurus, vert.

1998, Dec. 28

1050-1053 A226 Set of 4 *7.00 6.00*

Sheets of 9, #a.-i.

1054-1055 A226 Set of 2 *17.00 17.00*

Souvenir Sheets

1056-1057 A226 Set of 2 *8.00 8.00*

World Wildlife Fund — A227

Lesser flamingo: a, Facing left. b, Body facing forward. c, Head and neck. d, With wings spread.

Strip of 4

1999 Litho. ***Perf. 14***

1058 A227 300,000k #a.-d. *5.00 5.00*

No. 1058 was issued in sheets of 16 stamps.

Fauna — A228

Designs, each 300,000k: No. 1059, Equis caballus przewalski. No. 1060, Sphenisciformes, vert. No. 1061, Haliaeetus leucocephalus, vert. No. 1062, Anodorhynchus hyacinthinus.

No. 1063, 300,000k: a, Vulpes velox hebes. b, Odocoileus. c, Pongo pygmaeus. d, Leontopitecus rosalia. e, Panthera tigris. f, Tragelaphus eurycerus.

No. 1064, 300,000k: a, Tremarctos ornatus. b, Aphelocoma. c, Otus insularis. d, Balaeniceps rex. e, Lepidochelys kempii. f, Lutra canadensis.

Each 1,000,000k: No. 1065, Ailuropoda melanoleuca, vert. No. 1066, Ursus arctos horribilis.

1999

1059-1062 A228 Set of 4 *5.00 5.00*

Sheets of 6, #a.-f.

1063-1064 A228 Set of 2 *15.00 15.00*

Souvenir Sheets

1065-1066 A228 Set of 2 *12.00 12.00*

These Flora and Fauna stamps, formerly Nos. 1067-1078, were not authorized by Angola postal authorities.

Other items inscribed "Angola" that were not authorized but which have appeared on the market include sheets with the themes of Disney and History of Animation, Millennium, Animals, Trains, Flora, Muhammad Ali & Lennox Lewis, Bruce Lee, Albert Einstein / Moon Landing, Elvis Presley and other entertainers, Great Personalities, John Kennedy and Marilyn Monroe, Martin Luther King, Jr., Payne Stewart, Colin Montgomerie, Babe Ruth, Cardinal John O'Connor, Pope John Paul II / Mother Teresa and Queen Elizabeth II / Winston Churchill.

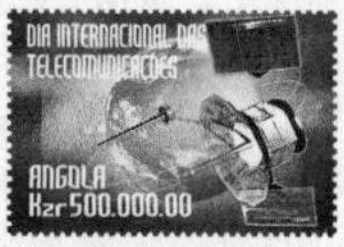

World Telecommunications Day — A230

1999, May 17 Litho. ***Perf. 14***

1079 A230 500,000k multi *.75 .75*

Souvenir Sheet

Waterfalls — A231

a, Andulo. b, Chiumbo. c, Ruacaná. d, Coemba.

1999, June 5 **Sheet of 4**

1080 A231 500,000k #a.-d. *3.00 3.00*

A232

African Men's Basketball Championships — No. 1081: a, Poster. b, Basketball, hoop, tan background. c, Basketball, hoop, green background. d, Welwitschia plant holding basketball.

2,500,000k, Similar to No. 1081c.

1999, July 29 Sheet of 4 ***Perf. 13½***

1081 A232 1,500,000k #a.-d. *4.00 4.00*

Souvenir Sheet

Perf. 13x13½

1082 A232 2,500,000k multi *2.50 2.50*

No. 1082 contains one 40x30mm stamp.

Stamps have one "0" too many in the denominations. Correct denominations would be 1.500.000.00

A233

1999, Aug. 17 ***Perf. 14***

1083 A233 1,000,000k multi *1.25 1.25*

Southern African Development Community. Issued in sheets of 4. Value *$5.*

Tribal Kings — A234

No. 782: a, Ekuikui II. b, Mvemba Nzinga. c, Mwata Yamvu Naweji II. d, Njinga Mbande.
1,000,000k, Mandume Ndemufayo.

1999, Sept. 17 **Sheet of 4**

1084 A234 500,000k #a.-d. *7.50 7.50*

Souvenir Sheet

1085 A234 1,000,000k multi *4.00 4.00*

A235

Queen Mother (b. 1900) — No. 1086: a, With King George VI. b, Wearing brooch. c, Wearing tiara. d, Wearing hat.
500,000k, Wearing academic gown.

Sheet of 4

1999, Sept. 17 **Litho.** ***Perf. 14***

1086 A235 200,000k #a.-d. *8.00 8.00*

Souvenir Sheet

Perf. 13¾

1087 A235 500,000k multi *5.50 5.50*

No. 1087 contains one 38x51mm stamp.

Ships — A236

No. 1088, each 950,000k: a, Egyptian bark, 1300 B.C. b, Flemish carrack, 1480. c, Beagle, 1830. d, North Star, 1852. e, Fram, 1892. f, Unyon Maru, 1909. g, Juan Sebastian de Elcano, 1927. h, Tovarishch, 1933.

No. 1089, each 950,000k: a, Bucentauro, 1728. b, Clermont, 1807. c, Savannah, 1819. d, Dromedary, 1844. e, Iberia, 1881. f, S.S. Gluckauf, 1886. g, City of Paris, 1888. h, Mauretania, 1906.

No. 1090, each 950,000k: a, Gloire, 1859. b, L'Ocean, 1868. c, Dandalo, 1876, stern of HMS Dreadnought, 1906. d, Bow of Dreadnought. e, Bismarck, 1939, stern of USS Cleveland, 1946. f, Bow of Cleveland. g, USS Boston, 1942, stern of USS Long Beach, 1959. h, Bow of Long Beach.

Each 5,000,000k: No. 1091, Chinese junk. No. 1092, Madre de Deus, 1609. No. 1093, Catamaran, 1861. No. 1094, Natchez, 1870.

1999, Sept. 23 **Litho.** ***Perf. 14***

Sheets of 8

1088-1090 A236 Set of 3 *27.00 27.00*

Souvenir Sheets

1091-1094 A236 Set of 4 *22.00 22.00*

Mushrooms — A237

No. 1095, Amanita caesarea. No. 1096, Psalliota xanthoderma. No. 1097, Hygrocybe conica. No. 1098, Boletus chrysenteron. No. 1099, Coprinus comatus. No. 1100, Boletus luteus.

No. 1101: a, Morchella crassipes. b, Boletus rufescens. c, Amanita phalloides. d, Collybia iocephala. e, Tricholoma aurantium. f, Cortinarius violaceus. g, Mycena polygramma. h, Psalliota augusta.

No. 1102: a, Amanita muscaria. b, Boletus aereus. c, Coprinus comatus. d, Amanita rubescens. e, Cortinarius collinitus. f, Boletus satanas. g, Lepiota procera. h, Clitocybe geotropa.

No. 1103: a, Russula nigricans. b, Boletus granulatus. c, Mycena strobilinoides. d, Amanita caesarea. e, Amanita muscaria. f, Boletus, crocipodius. g, Russula virescens. h, Lactarius deliciosus.

No. 1104, Psalliota haemorrhoidaria.

No. 1105, Mycena lilacifolia.

1999, Sept. 23 **Litho.** ***Perf. 14***

1095 A237 1,250,000k multi 1.25 1.00
1096 A237 1,250,000k multi 1.25 1.00
1097 A237 1,250,000k multi 1.25 1.00
1098 A237 1,250,000k multi 1.25 1.00
1099 A237 1,250,000k multi 1.25 1.00
1100 A237 1,250,000k multi 1.25 1.00
Nos. 1095-1100 (6) 7.50 6.00

Sheets of 8

1101 A237 1,000,000k #a-h 8.00 8.00
1102 A237 1,000,000k #a-h 8.00 8.00
1103 A237 1,000,000k #a-h 8.00 8.00

Souvenir Sheets

1104 A237 5,000,000k multi 5.50 5.50
1105 A237 5,000,000k multi 5.50 5.50

A238

First Manned Moon Landing, 30th Anniv. — A239

No. 1107: a, Astronaut spacewalking. b, Mariner 8. c, Viking 10. d, GINGA satellite. e, Soyuz 19. f, Voyager.

No. 1108, vert.: a, Space telescope. b, Space shuttle Atlantis. c, Uhuru satellite. d, Mir space station. e, Gemini 7. f, Venera 7.

No. 1109: a, Mercury, Venus. b, Jupiter. c, Neptune, Pluto. d, Earth, Mars. e, Saturn. f, Uranus.

No. 1110: a, Explorer 17. b, Intelsat 4A. c, GOES-D Satellite. d, Intelsat 2. e, Navstar. f, S.M.S.

No. 1111, 6,000,000k, Lunar rover, vert. No. 1112, 6,000,000k, Apollo 17 astronaut on moon, vert. No. 1113, 12,000,000k, Neil Armstrong, vert. No. 1114, 12,000,000k, Space shuttle Columbia. No. 1115, 12,000,000k, SBS-4, vert.

Perf. 13¾ (A238), 14 (A239)

1999, Nov. 15 **Litho.**

Sheets of 6, #a.-f.

1107-1108 A238 3,500,000k 10.00 10.00
1109-1110 A239 3,500,000k 10.00 10.00

Souvenir Sheets

1111-1112 A238 Set of 2 8.00 8.00
1113-1115 A239 Set of 3 16.00 16.00

Hokusai Paintings — A240

No. 1116, each 3,500,000k: a, Night attack. b, Usigafuchi No Kudan. c, Drawing of man and bowl. d, Wildlife. e, Pheasant. f, People on bridge.

No. 1117, each 3,500,000k: a, Tree and shoreline. b, Kabuki theater. c, Hen. d, Cooper. e, Trip to Enoshima. f, Sumida River landscape.

Each 12,000,000k: No. 1118, Yama-uba and Kintori, vert. No. 1119, Woman, vert.

1999, Dec. 13 **Litho.** ***Perf. 13¾***

Sheets of 6, #a.-f.

1116-1117 A240 Set of 2 18.00 18.00

Souvenir Sheets

1118-1119 A240 Set of 2 12.00 12.00

On Dec. 13, the date of issue of these stamps, Angola devalued its currency, with approximately 1,000,000k being the equivalent of 1k after the devaluation.

Souvenir Sheets

PhilexFrance 99 — A241

No. 1120, 4-8-4 Linder Compound express. No. 1121, Hovertrain prototype.

2000, Mar. 13 **Litho.** ***Perf. 13¾***

1120-1121 A241 12k Set of 2 11.00 11.00

A242

Wildlife — A243

1.50k, Zebra. 2k, Fruit bat. 3k, California condor. 5.50k, Lion.

No. 1126, horiz.: a, Equus zebra. b, Ploceus xanthops. c, Lycaon protus. d, Acinonyx jubatus. e, Oryx gazella. f, Nursing Otocyon megalotis. g, Giraffa camelopardalis. h, Canis adustus. i, Perodicticus potto. j, Panthera leo. k, Coracius caudata. l, Pair of Otocyon megalotis.

No. 1127, horiz.: a, Struthio camelus. b, Felis lybica. c, Aepyceros melampus. d, Cercopithecus aethiops. e, Diceros bicornis. f, Papio sp. g, Felis caracal. h, Sagittarius serpentarius. i, Phacochoerus aethiopicus. j, Arctocephalus pusillus. k, Alcedo cristata. l, Hippopotamus amphibius.

No. 1128, 3.50k: a, Deer. b, Turkey. c, Beaver. d, Frog. e, Manatee. f, Trout.

No. 1129, 3.50k: a, Macaque. b, Toucan. c, Bothriopsis bilineata. d, Hyla leucopyliata. e, Tamarin. f, Eagle.

No. 1130, 3.50k, vert.: a, Mountain gorilla. b, Rhinoceros. c, Water buffalo. d, Chameleon. e, Cobra. f, Meerkats.

No. 1131, 3.50k, vert.: a, Kangaroo. b, Koala. c, Kingfishers. d, Frog on tree root. e, Three fish. f, Turtle.

No. 1132, 12k, Sloth. No. 1133, 12k, Lemur, vert. No. 1134, 12k, Cheetah, vert. No. 1135, 12k, Orangutan, vert. No. 1136, 12k, Cercopithecus aethiops, diff. No. 1137, 12k, Loxodonta africana.

2000, Apr. 7 ***Perf. 14***

1122-1125 A242 Set of 4 6.00 6.00
1126 A243 1.50k Sheet of 12, #a-l 9.00 9.00
1127 A243 2k Sheet of 12, #a-l 13.00 13.00

Sheets of 6, #a-f

1128-1131 A242 Set of 4 40.00 40.00

Souvenir Sheets

1132-1135 A242 Set of 4 24.00 24.00
1136-1137 A243 Set of 2 12.00 12.00

Birds of Prey — A244

1.50k, Harpy eagle. 2k, Unidentified bird. 3k, Vulture, vert. 5.50k, King vulture, vert.

No. 1142, 3.50k: a, Accipiter gentilis. b, Surnia ulula. c, Falco peregrinus. d, Otus asio. e, Haliacetus vocifer. f, Herpetotheres cachinnans.

No. 1143, 3.50k: a, Falco sparverius. b, Pulsetrix perspicillata. c, Elemus leucurus. d, Ninox novaseelandiae. e, Polemaetus bellicosus. f, Polyborus plancus.

No. 1144, 6.50k: a, Verreaux's eagle. b, Aguia gigante. c, Aguia peixe.

No. 1145, 6.50k, vert.: a, Aguia despeida. b, Aguia dourada. c, Aguia devoradora de macacos.

No. 1146, 12k, King vulture, diff. No. 1147, 12k, Falcon, vert. No. 1148, 15k, Sagittarius serpentarius. No. 1149, 15k, Aquila chrysaetos.

2000, Apr. 10

1138-1141 A244 Set of 4 5.50 5.50

Sheets of 6, #a-f

1142-1143 A244 Set of 2 19.00 19.00

Sheets of 3, #a-c

1144-1145 A244 Set of 2 18.00 18.00

Souvenir Sheets

1146-1147 A244 Set of 2 12.00 12.00
1148-1149 A244 Set of 2 13.00 13.00

Millennium — A245

Highlights of the 16th Century: a, Paintings by Lai-Ji. b, The Last Judgment, by Luca Signorelli. c, Garden of Earthly Delights by Hieronymus Bosch. d, The Prince, written by Niccolò Machiavelli. e, Utopia, written by Sir Thomas More. f, Martin Luther. g, Charles I of Spain becomes Holy Roman Emperor Charles V. h, The School of Athens, by Raphael. i, Juan Sebastián de Elcano circumnavigates globe. j, Henry VIII of England. k, Spanish conquest of Aztecs and Incas. l, Placentia Cathedral. m, Potatoes introduced to Europe. n, Heliocentric theory of Copernicus. o, Portuguese reach Japan. p, Death of Albrecht Dürer (60x40mm). q, Bartolomé de Las Casas promotes rights for Indians.

2000, Oct. 2 **Litho.** ***Perf. 12¾x12½***

1150 A245 2.50k Sheet of 17, #a-q, + label 24.00 24.00

War Damage in Angola — A246

Designs: No. 1151, 3k, B.N.A. Building, Kuito. No. 1152, 3k, Kunje St., Kuito. No. 1153, 4k, Post office. No. 1154, 4k, Police headquarters. No. 1155, 5k, Apartment house. No. 1156, 5k, Independence Square. No. 1157, 6k, Child waving from upper floor of apartment house. No. 1158, 6k, Building, man carrying pack.

2000, Sept. 29 **Litho.** ***Perf. 14***

1151-1158 A246 Set of 8 18.00 18.00

The Popes of the Millennium — A247

No. 1159, 3k: a, Nicholas II, 1059-61. b, Paschal II, 1099-1118. c, Sergius IV, 1009-1012. d, Victor II, 1055-57. e, Victor III, 1086-87. f, Urban III, 1185-87.

No. 1160, 3k: a, Innocent II, 1130-43. b, John XIII, 965-72. c, Agapetus II, 946-55. d, John XV, 985-96. e, John XVIII, 1003-09. f, Lucius II, 1144-45.

No. 1161, 3k: a, Celestine II, 1143-44. b, Clement II, 1046-47. c, Clement III, 1187-91. d, Gelasius II, 1118-19. e, Benedict VII, 974-83. f, Gregory V, 996-99.

No. 1162, 12k, Leo IX, 1049-54. No. 1163, 12k, Gregory VII, 1073-85. No. 1164, 12k, Leo XIII, 1878-1903.

2000, Oct. 2 ***Perf. 12x12¼***

Sheets of 6, #a-f

1159-1161 A247 Set of 3 27.00 27.00

Souvenir Sheets

1162-1164 A247 Set of 3 18.00 18.00

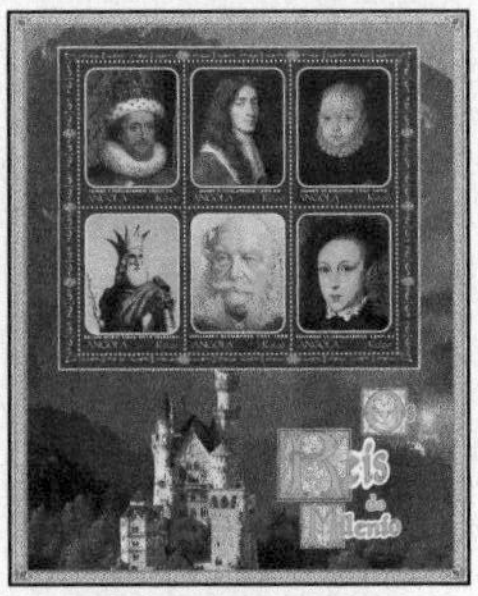

Monarchs — A248

No. 1165, 3k: a, Henry II, King of Germany and Holy Roman Emperor, 1002-24. b, Marina Mniszek, wife of false Russian czar Dmitri, 1605-06. c, Ivan IV of Russia, 1533-84. d, Ivan III of Russia, 1462-1505.

No. 1166, 3k: a, Charles II of Great Britain, 1660-85. b, Lady Jane Grey of England, 1533. c, Leopold III of Belgium, 1934-51. d, Louis XV of France, 1715-74.

No. 1167, 3k: a, James I of Great Britain, 1603-25. b, James II of Great Britain, 1685-88. c, James IV of Scotland, 1567-1625. d, Brian Boru of Ireland, 1002-14. e, Wilhelm I, King of Prussia and German Emperor, 1861-88. f, Edward VI of England, 1547-53.

No. 1168, 12k, Feodor I of Russia, 1584-98. No. 1169, 12k, False Russian czar Dmitri, 1605-06. No. 1170, 12k, William IV of Great Britain, 1830-37

2000, Oct. 2 **Sheets of 4, #a-d**

1165-1166 A248 Set of 2 12.50 12.50
1167 A248 Sheet of 6, #a-f 9.50 9.50

Souvenir Sheets

1168-1170 A248 Set of 3 18.00 18.00

Children's Drawings A249

Various designs. Denominations: 3k, 4k, 5k.

2000, Nov. 7 ***Perf. 14***

1171-1173 A249 Set of 3 4.75 4.75

Post Office Buildings A250

Designs: No. 1174, 5k , Former Secretary of Communications Building, Luanda. No. 1175, 5k, Mbanza Congo Post Office. No. 1176, 5k, Namibe Post Office. No. 1177, 8k, Facade of Luanda Post Office. No. 1178, 8k, Luanda Post Office, diff. No. 1179, 8k, Lobito Post Office.

2000, Sept. 29 **Litho.** ***Perf. 14***

1174-1179 A250 Set of 6 8.50 8.50

National Radio and Television, 25th Anniv. — A251

No. 1180, 9.50k: a, Woman at computer in newsroom. b, Reporter with tape recorder reporting on tank battle. c, Rescuing victims from airplane crash.

No. 1181, 9.50k: a, People and equipment in newsroom. b, Cameraman filming tank battle. c, Refugees.

No. 1182, 20k, Reporter with tape recorder. No. 1183, 20k, Cameraman, vert.

Perf. 13¼x13½, 13½x13¼

2000, Dec. 7 **Sheets of 3, #a-c**

1180-1181 A251 Set of 2 12.00 12.00

Souvenir Sheets

1182-1183 A251 Set of 2 8.00 8.00

Souvenir Sheet

Independence, 25th Anniv. — A252

No. 1184: a, Tank, rifle, dove. b, Dove, hoe, tractor.

2001, Feb. 13 **Litho.** ***Perf. 14¼x14***

1184 A252 12k Sheet of 2, #a-b 5.00 5.00

Africa Day — A253

Designs: No. 1185, 10k, Shown. No. 1186, 10k, Xylophone.

30k, Map, musical instruments, native with mask, elephant, satellite dishes and computer.

2001, May 25 ***Perf. 13x13¼***

1185-1186 A253 Set of 2 4.00 4.00

Souvenir Sheet

1187 A253 30k multi 6.00 6.00

Flowers — A254

Butterfly and: 8k, Nicolaia speciosa. 9k, Allamanda cathartica. No. 1190, 10k, Welwitschia mirabilis. No. 1191, 10k, Tagetes patula.

30k, Welwitschia mirabilis.

2001, June 9

1188-1191 A254 Set of 4 7.75 7.75

Souvenir Sheet

1192 A254 30k multi 6.50 6.50

Belgica 2001 Intl. Stamp Exhibition, Brussels (No. 1192).

Souvenir Sheet

Total Solar Eclipse, June 21 A255

2001, June 21

1193 A255 30k multi 6.50 6.50

Fish — A256

Designs: 11k, Protopterus annectens. 17k, Protopterus amphibius. 18k, Tilapia ruweti.

36k, Tilapia rendalli.

Perf. 13½x13¼

2001, Sept. 28 **Litho.**

1194-1196 A256 Set of 3 *7.75 7.75*

Souvenir Sheet

Perf. 13x13¼

1197 A256 36k multi *6.00 6.00*

Traditional Dances and Costumes A257

Designs: No. 1198, 11k, Massemba. No. 1199, 11k, Ovambo Efundula. 17k, Macolo Batuque. No. 1201, 18k, Humbi Puberty. No. 1202, 18k, Mukixi.

36k, Carneval.

2001, Nov. 12 ***Perf. 13x13¼***

1198-1202 A257 Set of 5 *11.00 11.00*

Souvenir Sheet

1203 A257 36k multi *5.50 5.50*

Souvenir Sheet

Handmade Weaving — A258

No. 1204: a, 17k, Banda. b, 18k, Kijinga.

2001, Dec. 7

1204 A258 Sheet of 2, #a-b *5.25 5.25*

Minerals — A259

Designs: No. 1205, 11k, Hematite. No. 1206, 11k, Malachite. No. 1207, 18k, Psilomelane. No. 1208, 18k, Diamond.

2001, Dec. 14 ***Perf. 13½x13¼***

1205-1208 A259 Set of 4 *8.50 8.50*

Masks — A260

Designs: 10k, Mwana Mpwevo. No. 1210, 11k, Mukixi. No. 1211, 11k, Mbunda. 17k, Mwana Pwo. 18k, Likisi-Cinganji.

36k, Ndemba, horiz.

2002, Jan. 8 ***Perf. 13¼x13½***

1209-1213 A260 Set of 5 *10.00 10.00*

Souvenir Sheet

Perf. 13x13¼

1214 A260 36k multi *5.50 5.50*

2002 World Cup Soccer Championships, Japan and Korea — A261

Two players and: 35k, Ball in air. 37k, Ball on ground.

2002, June 28 ***Perf. 13x13¼***

1215-1216 A261 Set of 2 *11.00 11.00*
1216a Souvenir sheet, #1215-1216 *10.00 10.00*

Meeting of African Committee of International Socialists — A262

Designs: No. 1217, 10k, Fight against poverty (red and orange map of Africa). No. 1218, 10k, Abolition of the death penalty (man with target on chest). No. 1219, 10k, End to violence against women (stylized woman). No. 1220, 10k, Fight against poverty (masks). No. 1221, 10k, Annulment of foreign debt (map of Africa with dollar sign)

2002, July 12

1217-1221 A262 Set of 5 *7.50 7.50*
1221a Souvenir sheet, #1218-1221 *6.00 6.00*

National Peace and Reconciliation A263

2002, Oct. 9

1222 A263 35k multi *2.75 2.75*

Reptiles — A264

Designs: 21k, Pithon anchietae. 35k, Lacerta sp. 37k, Naja nigricollis. 40k, Crocodylus niloticus.

2002, Oct. 15 ***Perf. 13x13¼***

1223-1226 A264 Set of 4 *10.00 10.00*

Lighthouses and Buoys — A265

Designs: No. 1227, 45k, Tafe. No. 1228, 45k, Red buoy, Luanda Bay. No. 1229, 45k, Green buoy, Luanda Bay. No. 1230, 45k, Cabeça da Cobra. No. 1231, 45k, Barra do Dande. No. 1232, 45k, Moita Seca.

2002, Nov. 22

1227-1232 A265 Set of 6 *20.00 20.00*

Souvenir Sheet

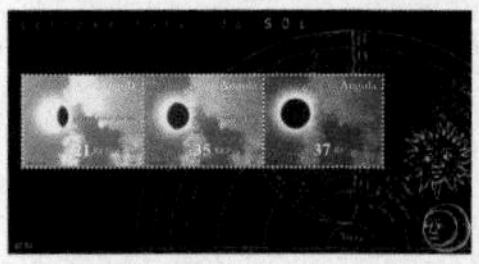

Dec. 4, 2002 Total Solar Eclipse A266

No. 1233: a, 21k, Sun partially eclipsed. b, 35k, Sun mostly eclipsed. c, 37k, Sun totally eclipsed.

2002, Dec. 4

1233 A266 Sheet of 3, #a-c *7.00 7.00*

Angola - Italy Friendship — A267

António Manuel, Prince of N'Funta and Ambassador of Congo to Rome (d. 1608), and: 35k, Lion. 45k, Plaque with Italian inscription.

2002, Dec. 6

1234-1235 A267 Set of 2 *6.00 6.00*
1235a Souvenir sheet, #1234-1235 *6.00 6.00*

Pottery — A268

Designs: 27k, Omolingui. 45k, Mulondo. 47k, Ombya yo Tuma.
51k, Sanga.

2002, Dec. 7 **Litho.**
1236-1238 A268 Set of 3 *8.50 8.50*

Souvenir Sheet

1239 A268 51k multi *4.00 4.00*

United Nations 3rd Meeting on Science, Technology and Development A269

2003, May 30 ***Perf. 13x13¼***
1240 A269 50k multi *3.75 3.75*

Powered Flight, Cent. — A270

2003, Aug. 21 **Litho.** ***Perf. 13x13½***
1241 A270 25k multi *1.90 1.90*

Printed in sheets of 3 stamps + label.

Poets — A271

Designs: No. 1242, 27k, António Jacinto (1924-91) and poem. No. 1243, 45k, Agostinho Neto (1922-79) and poem.
No. 1244: a, 27k, Jacinto. b, 45k, Neto.

2003, Sept. 18 **Litho.** ***Perf. 13x13¼***
1242-1243 A271 Set of 2 *5.00 5.00*

Souvenir Sheet

1244 A271 Sheet of 2, #a-b 5.00 5.00

Hippotragus Niger — A272

Designs: 27k, Pair with curved horns. 45k, Pair with straight horns. 47k, With herd in background.

2003, Oct. 9
1245-1247 A272 Set of 3 *8.50 8.50*

Women's Hairstyles — A273

No. 1248: a, Mbunda. b, Soyo. c, Huila. d, Humbi. e, Cabinda. f, Quipungu.

2003, Nov. 10 ***Perf. 13¼x13***
1248 A273 25k Sheet of 6, #a-f *10.00 10.00*

Whales — A274

Designs: 27k, Balaenoptera edeni. 45k, Cephalorhynchus heavisidii.
No. 1251: a, 47k, Giobiocephaia melaena.

2003, Dec. 5 ***Perf. 14¾x14¼***
1249-1250 A274 Set of 2 *5.00 5.00*

Souvenir Sheet

1251 A274 Sheet, #1249, 1251a *5.50 5.50*

Christmas — A275

No. 1252, 27k: a, The Ascension, attributed to Jorge Afonso. b, Adoration of the Shepherds, by André Reinoso.
No. 1253, 45k: a, Adoration of the Shepherds, detail showing Holy Family, by Josefa de Obidos. b, Adoration of the Shepherds, detail showing angels, by de Obidos.

2003, Dec. 5 ***Perf. 13¼x13¾***

Horiz. Pairs, #a-b

1252-1253 A275 Set of 2 *10.00 10.00*
1253c Souvenir sheet, #1252a-1252b, 1253a-1253b *10.00 10.00*

Chess A276

No. 1254: a, Chess pieces. b, Chess pieces and board.

2003, Dec. 10
1254 A276 45k Horiz. pair, #a-b *6.50 6.50*

Eagles — A277

Designs: No. 1255, 20k, Aquila rapax. No. 1256, 20k, Polemaetus bellicosus. No. 1257, 25k, Haliaeetus vocifer. No. 1258, 25k, Terathopius ecaudatus.
45k, Aquila verreauxi.

2003, Dec. 10 ***Perf. 14¾x14¼***
1255-1258 A277 Set of 4 *6.50 6.50*

Souvenir Sheet

1259 A277 45k multi *3.25 3.25*

Election of Pope John Paul II, 25th Anniv. A278

No. 1260: a, Portrait. b, Pope waving.

2003, Dec. 15 ***Perf. 13¼x13¾***
1260 A278 27k Horiz. pair, #a-b, + central label *4.00 4.00*

Flora — A279

Designs: No. 1261, 27k, Psidium guayava. No. 1262, 27k, Adansonia digitata. No. 1263, 45k, Cymbopogon citratus. No. 1264, 45k, Carica papaya.

2004, Aug. 17 **Litho.** ***Perf. 14x13½***
1261-1264 A279 Set of 4 *6.00 6.00*
1264a Souvenir sheet, #1261-1264 *6.00 6.00*

2004 Summer Olympics, Athens — A280

Designs: No. 1265, 27k, Handball. No. 1266, 27k, Basketball. No. 1267, 45k, Track. No. 1268, 45k, Volleyball.

2004, Sept. 30 ***Perf. 13¾***
1265-1268 A280 Set of 4 *6.00 6.00*

Marine Mammals A281

No. 1269: a, Megaptera novaeangliae. b, Cephalorhynchus heavisidii. c, Tursiops truncatus.
99k, Megaptera novaeangliae, diff.

2004, Oct. 9 ***Perf. 14x13½***
1269 Horiz. strip of 3 *4.00 4.00*
a.-b. A281 27k Either single *1.10 1.10*
c. A281 45k multi *1.75 1.75*

Souvenir Sheet

1270 A281 99k multi *4.00 4.00*

A sheetlet of eight hexagonal 15k depicting the national birds of South African Postal Operators Association (SAPOA) countries was produced in extremely limited quantities. Sheetlet inscribed Angola, value $300.

Trains — A282

Designs: No. 1271, 27k, shown. No. 1272, 27k, Benguela Locomotive 225. No. 1273, 27k, Moçamedes locomotive.

2004, Nov. 30 ***Perf. 13¾***
1271-1273 A282 Set of 3 *3.25 3.25*

Fire Fighting — A283

Telephone, emergency number and: No. 1274, 27k, Fire fighter with hose. No. 1275, 27k, Fire truck. 45k, Fire truck, diff.

2004, Nov. 30
1274-1276 A283 Set of 3 *4.00 4.00*
1276a Souvenir sheet, #1274-1276 *4.00 4.00*

FIFA (Fédération Internationale de Football Association), Cent. — A284

2004, Dec. 7
1277 A284 45k multi *1.90 1.90*

Christmas — A285

No. 1278: a, 27k, Magi. b, 45k Holy Family.

2004, Dec. 14 **Litho.** ***Perf. 13¾***
1278 A285 Horiz. pair, #a-b *3.00 3.00*

Worldwide Fund for Nature (WWF) — A286

No. 1279 — Colobus angolensis: a, Pair of adults. b, Adult and juvenile. c, Close-up of adult's face. d, Adult on rock.

2004, Dec. 29 **Litho.** ***Perf. 13¾***
1279 A286 27k Block of 4, #a-d *4.00 4.00*

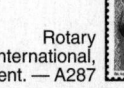

Rotary International, Cent. — A287

Woman and: 45k, City. 51k, Ostriches.

2005, Feb. 23 **Litho.** ***Perf. 13x13¼***
1280-1281 A287 Set of 2 *4.00 4.00*
1281a Souvenir sheet, #1280-1281 *4.00 4.00*

Basketry — A288

Designs: No. 1282, 27k, Kinda Kya Kuzambuila. No. 1283, 27k, Ngyendu. No. 1284, 45k, Ngombo Ya Cisuka. No. 1285, 45k, Silo.
90k, Kinda Kya Kuzambuila, diff.

2005, Sept. 6 **Litho.** ***Perf. 12x12½***
1282-1285 A288 Set of 4 *12.00 12.00*

Souvenir Sheet

1286 A288 90k multi *20.00 20.00*

Expo 2005, Aichi, Japan.

Independence, 30th Anniv. — A289

Designs: 27k, Capanda Hydroelectric Dam. 45k, Presidents Agostinho Neto and José Eduardo dos Santos, Angolan flag and dove.

2005, Nov. 8 **Litho.** ***Perf. 12x12½***
1287-1288 A289 Set of 2 *5.50 5.50*

Souvenir Sheet

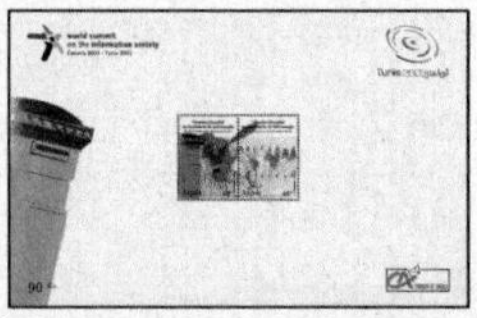

World Summit on the Information Society, Tunis — A290

No. 1289: a, Mail box, map of Africa, dish antenna, Angolan. b, Computer, world map, dish antenna.

2005, Nov. 14 **Litho.** ***Perf. 12***
1289 A290 45k Sheet of 2, #a-b *20.00 20.00*

Souvenir Sheet

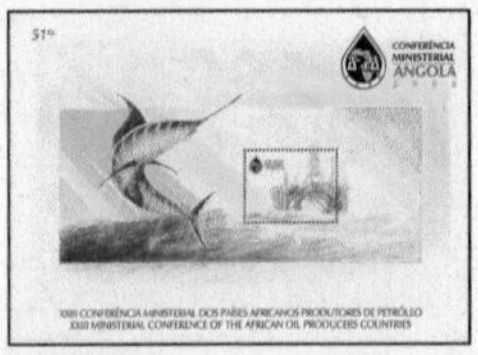

23rd Ministerial Conference of the African Oil Producing Countries — A291

Design: 51p, Off-shore oil rig.

2006, Apr. 24 Litho. ***Perf. 12x12½***
1294 A291 51k multi — —

Four additional stamps were issued in this set. The editors would like to examine any examples.

A292

2006 World Cup Soccer Championships, Germany — A293

2006, Aug. 30 ***Perf. 12x11¾***
1295 A292 45k shown *3.00 3.00*
1296 A293 45k shown *3.00 3.00*

Souvenir Sheet

1297 A293 90k Player dribbling *4.50 4.50*

Nos. 1295-1297 lack country name.

Community of Portuguese Language Nations, 10th Anniv. — A294

Anniversary emblem, emblem of 2006 Lubrapex Intl. Stamp Exhibition and: 27k, Dogs. No. 1299, 45k, Vultures. No. 1300, 45k, Parrots.

2006, Oct. 30 Litho. ***Perf. 12x11¾***
1298-1300 A294 Set of 3 *6.00 6.00*

Nos. 1298-1300 lack country name.

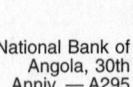

National Bank of Angola, 30th Anniv. — A295

Designs: No. 1301, 27k, Bird in flight, people in boat, ship, Katanga cross currency. No. 1302, 27k, Men, cowrie shells. No. 1303, 45k, Early automobile, coins. No. 1304, 45k, Buildings, banknotes.
90k, Dome, luggage

2006, Nov. 7
1301-1304 A295 Set of 4 *7.50 7.50*

Souvenir Sheet

1305 A295 90k multi *7.00 7.00*

José Sayovo, First Angolan Paralympian Gold Medalist — A296

2006, Dec. 29 Litho. ***Perf. 12x11¾***
1306 A296 45k multi *1.10 1.10*

Peace, 5th Anniv. — A297

2007, Apr. 20 Litho. ***Perf. 13x13½***
1307 A297 51k multi *1.75 1.75*

52nd Venice Art Biennale — A298

Designs: 65k, Entire painting. 155k, Painting detail.

2007, Apr. 20 ***Perf. 13x13½***
1308 A298 65k multi *1.90 1.90*

Souvenir Sheet

Perf. 13½x13

1309 A298 155k multi *4.50 4.50*

No. 1309 contains one 60x40mm stamp.

Souvenir Sheet

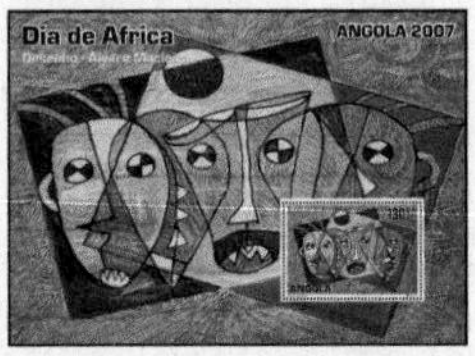

Africa Day A299

2007, Apr. 20 ***Perf. 13½x13***
1310 A299 130k multi *3.75 3.75*

Scouting, Cent. A300

No. 1311: a, 30k, Scouts sitting in fleur-de-lis pattern. b, 30k, Scouts sitting at desks. c, 55k, Scouts sitting on ground. d, 65k, Scouts saluting.
130k, Group of scouts standing on steps.

2007, June 1 ***Perf. 13x13½***
1311 A300 Sheet of 4, #a-d *5.50 5.50*

Souvenir Sheet

Perf. 13½x13

1312 A300 130k multi *4.00 4.00*

No. 1312 contains one 60x40mm stamp.

Souvenir Sheet

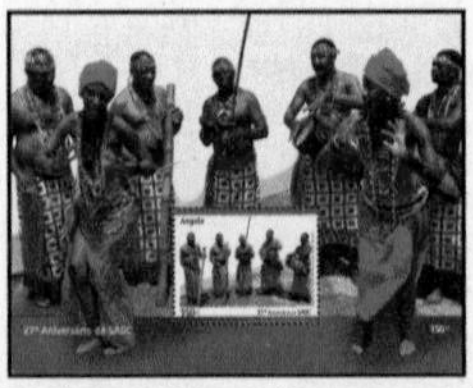

Southern African Development Community, 27th Anniv. — A301

2007, Aug. 17 ***Perf. 12½x13***
1313 A301 150k multi *8.00 8.00*

Souvenir Sheet

Sports A302

Perf. 13¼ Syncopated

2007, Sept. 20
1314 A302 130k multi *4.00 4.00*

Souvenir Sheet

World Post Day A303

No. 1315 — Post office at: a, Malange. b, Huamba.

2007, Oct. 9 ***Perf. 12¾x13½***
1315 A303 45k Sheet of 2, #a-b *2.75 2.75*

Sea Turtles A304

No. 1316: a, 27k, Caretta caretta. b, 27k, Chelonia mydas. c, 45k, Eretmochelys imbricata. d, 45k, Lepidochelys olivacea.
130k, Dermochelys coriacea, vert.

2007, Nov. 11 ***Perf. 13x13¼***
1316 A304 Sheet of 4, #a-d *4.50 4.50*

Souvenir Sheet

Perf. 13¼ Syncopated

1317 A304 130k multi *4.00 4.00*

No. 1317 contains one 38x39mm stamp.

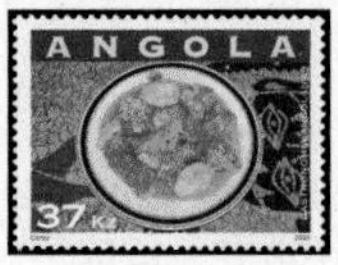

Angolan Cuisine — A305

Various unnamed Angolan dishes: 37k, 40k, 59k, 153k.

2008, May 30 ***Perf. 13x13½***
1318-1320 A305 Set of 3 *7.00 7.00*

Souvenir Sheet

1321 A305 153k multi *13.00 13.00*

Water Resources A306

Designs: No. 1322, 37k, Kuebe River. No. 1323, 37k, Kuanza Rapids. No. 1324, 40k, Kuanza River. No. 1325, 40k, Mouth of Mbridge River.
153k, Kalandula Waterfalls.

2008, June 30 ***Perf. 13x13½***
1322-1325 A306 Set of 4 *8.00 8.00*

Souvenir Sheet

1326 A306 153k multi *8.00 8.00*

Miniature Sheet

Lwini Fund, 10th Anniv. A307

No. 1327: a, 37k, Land mine removal, vert. b, 40k, Wooden box and books. c, 40k, Princess Diana and Angolan woman. d, 59k, Children in wheelchairs. e, 59k, Men making baskets.

Perf. 13½x13, 13x13½ (37k)

2008, June 30
1327 A307 Sheet of 5, #a-e, + label *10.00 10.00*

Water Jugs — A308

Designs: No. 1328, 37k, Jug with head on top. No. 1329, 37k, Two-handled jug. No. 1330, 40k, Jug with handle and spout. No. 1331, 40k, Jug with woman on top.

2008, July 30 ***Perf. 13½x13***
1328-1331 A308 Set of 4 *8.50 8.50*

Mangroves on Chiloango River — A309

Designs: No. 1332, 37k, Roots. No. 1333, 37k, Trees along river. 59k, Roots, diff.

2008, Aug. 30 ***Perf. 13x13½***
1332-1334 A309 Set of 3 *7.00 7.00*

Miniature Sheet

2008 Summer Olympics, Beijing — A310

No. 1335: a, Basketball. b, Handball. c, Running. d, Canoeing.

2008, Sept. 20 ***Perf. 12¾x13½***
1335 A310 30k Sheet of 4, #a-d *5.00 5.00*

Coffee — A311

Designs: 37k, Coffee berries. No. 1337, 45k, Woman picking berries, horiz. No. 1338, 45k, Tree with berries.

Perf. 13¼x13, 13x13¼

2009, Dec. 7 **Litho.**

Granite Paper

1336-1338 A311 Set of 3 *4.00 4.00*

Pres. Antonio Agostinho Neto (1922-79) — A312

Pres. Neto: 40k, Behind lectern. 50k, In army uniform.
150k, Pres. Neto with school children, horiz.

2009, Dec. 7 **Granite Paper**
1339-1340 A312 Set of 2 *2.75 2.75*

Souvenir Sheet

1341 A312 150k multi *4.25 4.25*

Souvenir Sheet

Pope Benedict XVI A313

2009, Dec. 7 ***Perf. 13¼x13***

Granite Paper

1342 A313 100k multi + label *4.00 4.00*

2010 Africa Cup of Nations Soccer Tournament, Angola — A314

Stadiums in: No. 1343, 40k, Benguela. No. 1344, 40k, Cabinda. No. 1345, 50k, Luanda. No. 1346, 50k, Huilá.

2010, Jan. 8 ***Perf. 13x13¼***

Granite Paper

1343-1346 A314 Set of 4 *5.00 5.00*

Africa Day — A315

Designs: 40k, People from Uige and Zaire Provinces. 60k, People from Lunda and Moxico Provinces.
120k, People from Luanda Province.

2010 ***Perf. 13x13¼***

1348-1349 A315 Set of 2 2.75 2.75

Souvenir Sheet

Perf. 13¼ Syncopated

1350 A315 120k multi 3.75 3.75

Expo 2010, Shanghai. No. 1350 contains one 50x39mm stamp.

African Women's Day — A316

Designs: No. 1351, 60k, Kwanhama woman. No. 1352, 60k, Quipungo woman.
150k, Mucubal woman.

2010 ***Perf. 13¼x13***

1351-1352 A316 Set of 2 3.25 3.25

Souvenir Sheet

Perf. 13¼ Syncopated

1353 A316 150k multi 4.00 4.00

Expo 2010, Shanghai. No. 1353 contains one 39x50mm stamp.

Intl. Children's Day — A317

Children, flowers and wildlife with background color of: No. 1354, 40k, Green. No. 1355, 40k, Orange. No. 1356, 60k, Blue. No. 1357, 60k, Green.
150k, Orange.

2010 ***Perf. 13x13¼***

1354-1357 A317 Set of 4 5.00 5.00

Souvenir Sheet

Perf. 13¼ Syncopated

1358 A317 150k multi 4.25 4.25

Expo 2010, Shanghai. No. 1358 contains one 50x39mm stamp.

Organization of Petroleum Exporting Countries, 50th Anniv. — A318

50th anniversary emblem with Angolan flag and: 40k, Antelope. 50k, Statue. 60k, Offshore oil drilling platform.
150k, Off-shore oil drilling platform and other equipment.

2010, Oct. ***Perf. 13x13¼***

1359-1361 A318 Set of 3 3.25 3.25

Souvenir Sheet

Perf. 13½ Syncopated

1362 A318 150k multi 3.25 3.25

No. 1362 contains one 50x39mm stamp.

Portuguese Agency for External Investment and Commerce, 20th Anniv. — A319

2010, Nov. ***Perf. 13x13¼***

1363 A319 60k multi 1.40 1.40

Worldwide Fund for Nature (WWF) — A320

No. 1364: a, Two Cercopithecus cephus, one on rock at left. b, Three Cercopithecus ascanius. c, Two Cercopithecus ascanius. d, Two Cercopithecus cephus, one on branch at right.
350k, Cercopithecus cephus and Cercopithecus ascanius, vert.

2011, Aug. 31 ***Perf. 13x13¼***

1364 Strip of 4, #a-d 9.00 9.00
a.-d. A320 100k Any single 2.25 2.25
e. Souvenir sheet of 8, 2 each #1364a-1364d 18.00 18.00

Souvenir Sheet

Perf. 13¼

1365 A320 350k multi 7.50 7.50

No. 1365 contains one 39x45mm stamp.

A321

A322

A323

Southern African Development Community, 31st Anniv. — A324

Design: 150k, Emblem and map of Africa, diff.

2011, Aug. 12 ***Perf. 13x13¼***

1366 A321 50k multi 1.10 1.10
1367 A322 50k multi 1.10 1.10
1368 A323 50k multi 1.10 1.10
1369 A324 50k multi 1.10 1.10
Nos. 1366-1369 (4) 4.40 4.40

Souvenir Sheet

Perf. 13½

1370 A324 150k multi 3.25 3.25

Peonies — A325

No. 1371: a, Paeonia daurica. b, Paeonia mlokosewitschii. c, Paeonia veitchii. d, Paeonia broteri.
350k, Paeonia officinalis salmonea.

2011, Apr. 31 ***Perf. 13¼x13***

1371 Horiz. strip of 4 9.00 9.00
a.-d. A325 100k Any single 2.25 2.25
e. Souvenir sheet of 4, #1371a-1371d 9.00 9.00

Souvenir Sheet

Perf. 13½

1372 A325 350k multi 7.50 7.50

China 2011 International Stamp Exhibition, Wuxi. No. 1372 contains one 39x45mm stamp.

National Bank of Angola, 35th Anniv. — A326

Emblem and: 40k, Ornamental planter. 50k, Crest on exterior wall. No. 1375, 60k, Roof ornament. No. 1376, 60k, Windows near corner of building.
150k, Aerial view of building.

2011, Nov. 4 ***Perf. 13x13¼***

1373-1376 A326 Set of 4 4.50 4.50

Souvenir Sheet

Perf. 13x13¼ Syncopated

1377 A326 150k multi 3.25 3.25

No. 1377 contains one 50x39mm stamp.

Fauna, Flora and Mushrooms A344

Designs: No. 1420, 300k, Adult and juvenile Diceros bicornis. No. 1421, 300k, Adult Diceros bicornis facing right. No. 1422, 300k, One Ceratotherium simum. No. 1423, 300k, Two Ceratotherium simum. No. 1424, 300k, Head of Giraffa camelopardalis angolensis. No. 1425, 300k, Front view of Giraffa camelopardalis angolensis drinking water. No. 1426, 300k, Side view of Giraffa camelopardalis angolensis with head lowered. No. 1427, 300k, Six adult and juvenile Giraffa camelopardalis angolensis. No. 1428, 300k, Galagoides demidoff. No. 1429, 300k, Allenopithecus nigroviridis. No. 1430, 300k, Lophocebus aterrimus. No. 1431, 300k, Colobus angolensis. No. 1432, 300k, Hypsignathus monstrosus. No. 1433, 300k, Mops condylurus. No. 1434, 300k, Epomops franqueti. No. 1435, 300k, Epomophorus crypturus. No. 1436, 300k, Acinonyx jubatus. No. 1437, 300k, Panthera pardus pardus. No. 1438, 300k, Caracal caracal. No. 1439, 300k, Panthera leo bleyenberghi. No. 1440, 300k, Loxodonta africana walking left. No. 1441, 300k, Loxodonta africana facing right. No. 1442, 300k, Two Loxodonta africana with hindquarters touching. No. 1443, 300k, Two Loxodonta africana facing right. No. 1444, 300k, Stenella attenuata. No. 1445, 300k, Stenella longirostris. No. 1446, 300k, Stenella frontalis. No. 1447, 300k, Lagenodelphis hosei. No. 1448, 300k, Globicephala macrorhynchus. No. 1449, 300k, Megaptera novaeangliae. No. 1450, 300k, Eubalaena australis. No. 1451, 300k, Kogia breviceps. No. 1452, 300k, Treron calvus. No. 1453, 300k, Oena capensis. No. 1454, 300k, Columba guinea. No. 1455, 300k, Streptopelia capicola. No. 1456, 300k, Bubo africanus. No. 1457, 300k, Bubo leucostictus. No. 1458, 300k, Otus senegalensis. No. 1459, 300k, Scotopelia peli. No. 1460, 300k, Agapornis pullarius. No. 1461, 300k, Poicephalus meyeri reichenowi. No. 1462, 300k, Poicephalus robustus. No. 1463, 300k, Poicephalus rueppellii. No. 1464, 300k, Halcyon senegalensis. No. 1465, 300k, Corythornis cristatus. No. 1466, 300k, Ispidina picta. No. 1467, 300k, Ceryle rudis. No. 1468, 300k, Merops variegatus. No. 1469, 300k, Merops albicollis. No. 1470, 300k, Merops bullockoides. No. 1471, 300k, Merops nubicoides. No. 1472, 300k, Dendropicos fuscescens. No. 1473, 300k, Campethera abingoni. No. 1474, 300k, Dendropicos elliotii. No. 1475, 300k, Chloropicus xantholophus. No. 1476, 300k, Tockus leucomelas. No. 1477, 300k, Bycanistes fistulator. No. 1478, 300k, Lophoceros alboterminatus. No. 1479, 300k, Bucorvus leadbeateri. No. 1480, 300k, Sylvietta ruficapilla. No. 1481, 300k, Acrocephalus gracilirostris. No. 1482, 300k, Sylvietta rufescens. No. 1483, 300k, Hylia prasina. No. 1484, 300k, Tricholaema leucomelas and Pogoniulus subsulphureus. No. 1485, 300k, Pogoniulus chrysoconus. No. 1486, 300k, Trachyphonus vaillantii. No. 1487, 300k, Lybius minor. No. 1488, 300k, Centropus monachus. No. 1489, 300k, Chrysococcyx klaas. No. 1490, 300k, Chrysococcyx caprius. No. 1491, 300k, Clamator glandarius. No. 1492, 300k, Ardea purpurea. No. 1493, 300k, Pelecanus onocrotalus. No. 1494, 300k, Hydroprogne caspia. No. 1495, 300k, Sarkidiornis melanotos. No. 1496, 300k, Haliaeetus vocifer. No. 1497, 300k, Aquila nipalensis. No. 1498, 300k, Aquila rapax. No. 1499, 300k, Gypohierax angolensis. No. 1500, 300k, Papilio phorcas congoanus. No. 1501, 300k, Hypolycaena antifaunus. No. 1502, 300k, Charaxes numenes. No. 1503, 300k, Charaxes eupale. No. 1504, 300k, Barbus fasciolatus. No. 1505, 300k, Schilbe mystus. No. 1506, 300k, Trachinus araneus. No. 1507, 300k, Synodontis woosnami and Chelonia mydas. No. 1508, 300k, Euspira grossularia. No. 1509, 300k, Tonna galea. No. 1510, 300k, Cardium costatum. No. 1511, 300k, Marginella glabella. No. 1512, 300k, Osteolaemus tetraspis, head at LL. No. 1513, 300k, Osteolaemus tetraspis, head at LR. No. 1514, 300k, Crocodylus niloticus, head at right. No. 1515, 300, Crocodylus niloticus, head at left. No. 1516, 300k, Dendroaspis jamesoni. No. 1517, 300k, Bitis caudalis. No. 1518, 300k, Bitis arietans. No. 1519, 300k, Naja anchietae. No. 1520, 300k, Caretta caretta. No.1521, 3 00k, Dermochelys coriacea. No. 1522, 300k, Lepidochelys olivacea. No. 1523, 300k, Eretmochelys imbricata. No. 1524, 300k, Diplodocus longus and amethyst. No. 1525, 300k, Rhamphorhynchus longicaudus and pyroxenite. No. 1526, 300k, Hatzegopteryx thambema and quartz. No. 1527, 300k, Yangchuanosaurus shangyouensis, atacamite and libethenite. No. 1528, 300k, Adult Diceros bicornis facing left. No. 1529, 300k, Hippotragus niger variani. No. 1530, 300k, Lycaon pictus. No. 1531, 300k, Gyps africanus. No. 1532, 300k, Laelia purpurata "Miss Scarlet." No. 1533, 300k, Cymbidium "Sandy Tiger." No. 1534, 300k, Laeliocattleya "Trick or Treat Sweety." No. 1535, 300k, Brassolaeliocattleya Momilani Rainbow "The Gypsy." No. 1536, 300k, Amanita muscaria. No. 1537, 300k, Coprinellus micaceus. No. 1538, 300k, Amanita rubescens. No. 1539, 300k, Agaricus xanthodermus.

No. 1540, 1200k, Adult and juvenile Ceratotherium simum. No. 1541, 1200k, Giraffa camelopardalis angolensis, diff. No. 1542, 1200k, Ceratopithecus ascanius. No. 1543, 1200k, Cistugo seabrae. No. 1544, 1200k, Leptailurus serval. No. 1545, 1200k, Loxodonta africana facing left. No. 1546, 1200k, Steno bredanensis. No. 1547, 1200k, Balaenoptera musculus. No. 1548, 1200k, Spilopelia senegalensis. No. 1549, 1200k, Bubo lacteus. No. 1550, 1200k, Psittacus erithacus. No. 1551, 1200k, Halcyon leucocephala. No. 1552, 1200k, Merops malimbicus. No. 1553, 1200k, Campethera bennettii. No. 1554, 1200k, Bycanistes bucinator. No. 1555, 1200k, Hyliota flavigaster. No. 1556, 1200k, Trachyphonus purpuratus. No. 1557, 1200k, Chrysococcyx cupreus. No. 1558, 1200k, Netta rufina. No. 1559, 1200k, Terathopius ecaudatus. No. 1560, 1200k, Junonia sophia. No. 1561, 1200k, Synodontis nigromaculatus. No. 1562, 1200k, Architectonica perspectiva. No. 1563, 1200k, Crocodylus niloticus, diff. No. 1564, 1200k, Bitis caudalis, diff. No. 1565, 1200k, Chelonia mydas. No. 1566, 1200k, Austroraptor cabazai and rhodochrosite. No. 1567, 1200k, Mecistops cataphractus. No. 1568, 1200k, Laelia anceps "SanBar Bounty." No. 1569, 1200k, Gliophorus psittacinus.

2018, Dec. 10 **Litho.** ***Perf. 13x13¼***

1420-1539 A344 Set of 120 235.00 235.00

Souvenir Sheets

1540-1569 A344 Set of 30 235.00 235.00

A345

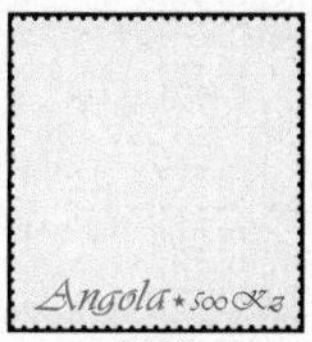

A346

A347

Personalized Stamps — A348

2019, May 15 Litho. ***Perf. 12¾x13¼***

1570 A345 500k multi		3.00	3.00
1571 A346 500k multi		3.00	3.00
1572 A347 500k multi		3.00	3.00

Perf. 13¼x12¾

1573 A348 500k multi		3.00	3.00
Nos. 1570-1573 (4)		12.00	12.00

The vignette portions of Nos. 1570-1573 could be personalized.

First Man on the Moon, 50th Anniv. A349

No. 1574: a, Apollo 11 Lunar Module approaching Moon's surface. b, Neil Armstrong's first step on the Moon. c, Armstrong and Buzz Aldrin on Moon. d, Lunar Module leaving Moon.

1200k, Armstrong and U.S. flag on Moon.

Litho. With Foil Application

2019, May 15 ***Perf. 13¼***

1574 A349 300k Sheet of 4, #a-d	7.25	7.25

Souvenir Sheet

1575 A349 1200k multi	7.25	7.25

No. 1575 contains one 45x51mm stamp.

A350

No. 1576, 300k, The Floor Scrapers, by Gustave Caillebotte (1848-94). No. 1577, 300k, The Luncheon on the Grass, by Edouard Manet (1832-83). No. 1578, 300k, Pont Boieldieu in Rouen, Rainy Weather, by Camille Pissarro (1830-1903). No. 1579, 300k, Dance at Le Moulin de la Galette, by Pierre-Auguste Renoir (1841-1919).

No. 1580, 300k, Oshkosh Striker 8x8 fire truck. No. 1581, 300k, 1980 Seagrave fire truck. No. 1582, 300k, Spartan KME fire truck. No. 1583, 300k, American LaFrance Pioneer fire truck.

No. 1584, 300k, U-127 class 4-6-0 locomotive. No. 1585, 300k, London North Eastern Railway class A4 2509 Silver Link. No. 1586, 300k, London North Eastern Railway class A3 4472 Flying Scotsman. No. 1587, 300k, South African class 25NC 4-8-4 locomotive.

No. 1588, 300k, South African class 33-400 locomotive. No. 1589, 300k, South African class GMA 4-8-2+2-8-4 locomotive. No. 1590, 300k, South African class 43-000 locomotive. No. 1591, 300k, South African class 26 4-8-4 locomotive.

No. 1592, 300k, Prototype Russian rescue vehicle, vert. No. 1593, 300k, 1991 Land Rover Defender ambulance, vert. No. 1594, 300k, RMMV Survivor R, vert. No. 1595, 300k, Scania P 93ML fire truck, vert.

No. 1596, 300k, BMW R1200GS motorcycle, vert. No. 1597, 300k, KTM 950 Adventure motorcycle, vert. No. 1598, 300k, Suzuki TL1000R motocycle, vert. No. 1599, 300k, 2009 Yamaha R1 motorcycle, vert.

No. 1600, 300k, Fairchild Republic A-10 Thunderbolt II, vert. No. 1601, 300k, McDonnell Douglas F/A-18 Hornet, vert. No. 1602, 300k, Alenia Aermacchi M-346 Master, vert. No. 1603, 300k, Lockheed F-117 Nighthawk, vert.

No. 1604, 300k, Pres. John F. Kennedy (1917-63) and Apollo mission emblem, vert. No. 1605, 300k, Apollo 11 Command and Service Modules, Apollo 11 emblems and "50," vert. No. 1606, 300k, Saturn V SA-506 rocket, vert. No. 1607, Neil Armstrong (1930-2012), first man on Moon, vert.

No. 1608, 300k, Thalassa and flag of Netherlands, vert. No. 1609, 300k, Juan Sebastián de Elcano and flag of Spain, vert. No. 1610, 300k, Christian Radich and flag of Norway, vert. No. 1611, 300k, Gorch Fock and flag of Germany, vert.

No. 1612, 300k, Portland Head Lighthouse, Maine, and flag of United States, vert. No. 1613, 300k, Portland Bill Lighthouse, and flag of Great Britain, vert. No. 1614, 300k, Slettnes Lighthouse, and flag of Norway, vert. No. 1615, 300k, Rubjerg Knude Lighthouse, and flag of Denmark, vert.

No. 1616, 300k, Equus quagga and flag of Botswana, vert. No. 1617, 300k, Loxodonta africana and flag of Central African Republic, vert. No. 1618, 300k, Aquila chrysaetos and flag of Egypt, vert. No. 1619, 300k, Panthera leo and flag of Kenya, vert.

No. 1620, 300k, World map, child and parched land, vert. No. 1621, 300k, Sea level measurement posts, vert. No. 1622, 300k, Corals in acidified ocean, vert. No. 1623, 300k, Polar bears on ice, vert.

No. 1624, 300k, Egyptian Mau cat, vert. No. 1625, 300k, Siamese cat, vert. No. 1626, 300k, Russian Blue cat and flag of Russia, vert. No. 1627, 300k, Japanese bobtail cats, vert.

No. 1628, 300k, Cyclostoma purum, vert. No. 1629, 300k, Tegula gallina, vert. No. 1630, 300k, Calyptraea spirata and Labyrinthus plicatus, vert. No. 1631, 300k, Hindsia nivea and Micrarionta kelletti, vert.

No. 1632, 300k, Ichthyosaurus communis, vert. No. 1633, 300k, Liopleurodon ferox, vert. No. 1634, 300k, Eromangasaurus australis, vert. No. 1635, 300k, Dinichthys terrelli, vert.

No. 1636, 300k, Parasaurolophus walkeri, vert. No. 1637, 300k, Ceratops horridus, vert. No. 1638, 300k, Tyrannosaurus rex and Charles Darwin (1809-82), naturalist, vert. No. 1639, 300k, Darwin, map and dinosaur skeleton, vert.

No. 1640, 300k, Two Girl Scouts and tent, vert. No. 1641, 300k, Boy and Girl Scout at campfire, vert. No. 1642, 300k, Boy and Girl Scout with map and flag, vert. No. 1643, 300k, Three Scouts and campfire, vert.

No. 1644, 300k, Pope John Paul II (1920-2005) with arms raised, vert. No. 1645, 300k, Pope John Paul II holding cross, vert. No. 1646, 300k, Pope John Paul II and bishop, vert. No. 1647, 300k, Pope John Paul II standing in automobile, vert.

No. 1648, 300k, Princess Diana (1961-97) in wedding dress, vert. No. 1649, 300k, Princess Diana with Indian children, vert. No. 1650, 300k, Princess Diana riding horse, vert. No. 1651, 300k, Princess Diana holding roses, coat of arms, vert.

No. 1652, 300k, Nelson Mandela (1918-2013), President of South Africa, prison and his prisoner number, vert. No. 1653, 300k, Nobel medal, Mandela wearing tribal costume, vert. No. 1654, 300k, Mandela and election campaign crowd, vert. No. 1655, 300k, Mandela casting ballot, flag and coat of arms of South Africa, vert.

No. 1656, 300k, Mohandas K. Gandhi (1869-1948), Indian nationalist leader, his signature and Taj Mahal, vert. No. 1657, 300k, Taj Mahal, Gandhi holding walking stick, vert. No. 1658, 300k, Gandhi, flag and emblem of India, vert. No. 1659, 300k, Gandhi and crowd, vert.

No. 1660, 300k, Henri Dunant (1828-1910), founder of International Red Cross, and Red Cross volunteers and flag, vert. No. 1661, 300k, Dodge WC54 ambulance and Red Cross tent, vert. No. 1662, 300k, Barkas V 901/2 ambulance and AW139 helicopter, vert. No. 1663, 300k, World War I Red Cross nurses, vert.

No. 1664, 300k, Sick child and mosquito, vert. No. 1665, 300k, Child, hand with hypodermic needle and mosquito, vert. No. 1666, 300k, Children under mosquito netting, vert. No. 1667, 300k, Man spraying insecticide, mosquito, vert.

No. 1668, 300k, Rotary International emblem and Rotary founder Paul P. Harris (1868-1947), seated, vert. No. 1669, 300k, Rotary International emblem and Harris, standing, vert. No. 1670, 300k, Rotary International emblem, Harris and his wife, Jean (1881-1963), vert. No. 1671, 300k, Rotary International emblem, Harris and Luther Burbank (1849-1926), botanist.

No. 1672, 300k, 2018 Nobel laureates in Physiology or Medicine, Tasuku Honjo and James P. Allison, vert. No. 1673, 300k, 2018 Nobel laureates in Chemistry, George P. Smith, Frances H. Arnold, and Sir Gregory P. Winter, vert. No. 1674, 300k, 2018 Nobel laureates in Physics, Arthur Ashkin, Gérard A. Mourou, and Donna T. Strickland, vert. No. 1675, 300k, 2018 Nobel laureates in Economics, William D. Nordhaus and Paul M. Romer, vert.

No. 1676, 300k, Magnus Carlsen, World chess champion, flag and reversed map of Norway, vert. No. 1677, 300k, Fabiano Caruana, second-ranked chess player in world, flag and map of United States, vert. No. 1678, 300k, Ding Liren, fourth-ranked chess player in world, flag and map of People's Republic of China, vert. No. 1679, 300k, Sergey Karjakin, youngest chess player to achieve Grand Master status, flag and map of Russia, vert.

No. 1680, 300k, Omakola, vert. No. 1681, 300k, Tambor falante, vert. No. 1682, 300k, Lamelofone, vert. No. 1683, 300k, Mucupela, vert.

No. 1684, 300k, Pig with tulip, vert. No. 1685, 300k, Pig with pear, vert. No. 1686, 300k, Pig balancing on ball, vert. No. 1687, 300k, Pig jumping rope, vert.

No. 1688, 1200k, Water Lilies, by Claude Monet (1840-1926). No. 1689, 1200k, Mount Arlington, New Jersey 1939 Model VC fire truck. No. 1690, 1200k, Great Western Railway class 7800 locomotive. No. 1691, 1200k, South African class 19D 4-8-2 locomotive. No. 1692, 1200k, Canadair CL-415 firefighting airplane, vert. No. 1693, 1200k, Gilera CX motorcycle, vert. No. 1694, 1200k, Dornier Alpha Jet and Lockheed Martin F-35 Lightning II, vert. No. 1695, 1200k, Apollo 11 Command, Service and Lunar Modules and medal, vert. No. 1696, 1200k, Dar Mlodziedzy and flag of Poland, vert. No. 1697, 1200k, Split Rock Lighthouse, Minnesota, and flag of United States, vert. No. 1698, 1200k, Hippotragus niger and flag of Angola, vert. No. 1699, 1200k, Thermometer and changing landscape, vert. No. 1700, 1200k, Peterbald cat, vert. No. 1701, 1200k, Succinea putris, Fusus kelletii, and Labyrinthus leucodon, vert. No. 1702, 1200k, Helicoprion beswsonowi, vert. No. 1703, 1200k, Darwin and Stegosaurus stenops, vert. No. 1704, 1200k, Two Scouts, tent and lantern, vert. No. 1705, 1200k, Pope John Paul II holding cross, diff., vert. No. 1706, 1200k, Princess Diana and Queen Elizabeth II, vert. No. 1707, 1200k, Mandela standing in automobile, vert. No. 1708, 1200k, Gandhi holding microphone, vert. No. 1709, 1200k, Dunant and horse-drawn ambulance, vert. No. 1710, 1200k, Plasmodium malariae and medical worker, vert. No. 1711, 1200k, Rotary International emblem and bust of Harris, vert. No. 1712, 1200k, Dove and 2018 Nobel Peace laureates, Denis Mukwege and Nadia Murad, vert. No. 1713, 1200k, Shakhriyar Mamedyarov, third-ranked chess player in world, flag and map of Azerbaijan, vert. No. 1714, 1200k, Balafon and marimba, vert. No. 1715, 1200k, Pig blowing bubbles, vert.

Perf. 13x13¼, 13¼x13

2019, May 15 Litho.

1576-1687 A350	Set of 112	200.00	200.00

Souvenir Sheets

1688-1715 A350	Set of 28	200.00	200.00

A351

Luanda Biennale A352

No. 1716: a, Star gateway at Armed Forces Museum, Luanda. b, Cathedral of the Holy Savior, Luanda. c, Luanda Waterfront. d, Marimba players.

500k, Monument to the Unknown Soldier, Luanda.

Perf. 12¾x13¼

2019, Sept. 18 Litho.

1716 A351 300k Sheet of 4, #a-d	6.50	

Souvenir Sheet

Perf. 13¼x12¾

1717 A352 500k multi	2.75	2.75

Flag of India and Mohandas K. Gandhi (1869-1948), Indian Nationalist Leader — A353

2019, Dec. 20 Litho. ***Perf. 13¼x13***

1718 A353 300k multi	1.25	1.25

No. 1718 was printed in sheets of 10 + 2 central labels.

A354

Designs: No. 1719, 300k, Two Canis mesomelas eating. No. 1720, 300k, Two Canis mesomelas on grass. No. 1721, 300k, One Canis mesomelas on rock. No. 1722, 300k, Canis adustas.

No. 1723, 300k, Atelerix frontalis on ground facing right, Latin name at UR in white. No. 1724, 300k, Atelerix frontalis on ground facing right, Latin name at UR in black. No. 1725, 300k, Atelerix frontalis on log facing right, Latin name in UR in black. No. 1726, 300k, Atelerix frontalis facing left.

No. 1727, 300k, Smutsia temminckii facing left. No. 1728, 300k, Smutsia temminckii facing right. No. 1729, 300k, Phataginus tricuspis facing left. No. 1730, 300k, Phataginus tricuspis facing right.

No. 1731, 300k, Two Aonyx capensis. No. 1732, 300k, One Aonyx capensis facing left. No. 1733, 300k, Head of Aonyx capensis. No. 1734, 300k, Three Hydrictis maculicollis.

No. 1735, 300k, One seated Vulpes chama. No. 1736, 300k, One standing Vulpes chama. No. 1737, 300k, Two Vulpes chama. No. 1738, 300k, Three Vulpes chama.

No. 1739, 300k, Oreotragus oreotragus. No. 1740, 300k, Kobus ellipsiprymnus. No. 1741, 300k, Damaliscus lunatus. No. 1742, 300k, Hippotragus equinus.

No. 1743, 300k, Head of Hippopotamus amphibius in water, hippopotami in background. No. 1744, 300k, Three Hippopotamus amphibius walking through shallow water. No. 1745, 300k, One Hippopotamus amphibius on land. No. 1746, Two Hippopotamus amphibius standing in water.

No. 1747, 300k, Male Panthera leo facing left. No. 1748, 300k, Male Panthera leo carrying food in mouth. No. 1749, 300k, Female Panthera leo. No. 1750, 300k, Three Panthera leo cubs.

No. 1751, 300k, One Panthera pardus resting on rock. No. 1752, 300k, Adult and juvenile Panthera pardus on tree limb. No. 1753, 300k, One Panthera pardus resting on tree limb. No. 1754, 300k, One Panthera pardus standing.

No. 1755, 300k, Caracal aurata standing at left, head at right. No. 1756, 300k, Head of Caracal aurata at left, standing at right. No. 1757, 300k, Caracal aurata facing right. No. 1758, 300k, Caracal aurata facing left.

No. 1759, 300k, One Trichechus senegalensis, Latin name at UL in one line. No. 1760, 300k, Two Trichechus senegalensis, Latin name at LL. No. 1761, 300k, Two Trichechus senegalensis, Latin name at LR. No. 1762, 300k, One Trichechus senegalensis, Latin name in UL in two lines.

No. 1763, 300k, Two Orcinus orca. No. 1764, 300k, One Orcinus orca facing right with open mouth. No. 1765, 300k, One Orcinus orca facing left with open mouth. No. 1766, 300k, Three Orcinus orca.

No. 1767, 300k, Caprimulgus natalensis. No. 1768, 300k, Caprimulgus pectoralis. No. 1769, 300k, Caprimulgus europaeus. No. 1770, 300k, Caprimulgus rufigena.

No. 1771, 300k, Actophilornis africanus in water, facing left, Latin name at top center. No. 1772, 300k, Actophilornis africanus in water facing left, Latin name at UR in two lines. No. 1773, 300k, Actophilornis africanus near water, facing left, Latin name at UL. No. 1774, 300k, Actophilornis africanus in flight.

No. 1775, 300k, Terathopius ecaudatus. No. 1776, 300k, Stephanoaetus coronatus. No. 1777, 300k, Aquilla verreauxii. No. 1778, 300k, Haliaeetus vocifer.

No. 1779, 300k, Junonia sophia. No. 1780, 300k, Graphium angolanus. No. 1781, 300k, Papilio zalmoxis. No. 1782, 300k, Papilio antimachus.

No. 1783, 300k, Connochaetes taurinus, Cameia National Park. No. 1784, 300k, Diceros bicornis, Iona National Park. No. 1785, 300k, Panthera leo, Bicuar National Park. No. 1786, 300k, Lycaon pictus, Quissama National Park.

No. 1787, 300k, Giraffa giraffa angolensis and Rio Cuanza. No. 1788, 300k, Smutsia temminckii and Quissama National Park. No.

1789, 300k, Antidorcas marsupialis angolensis and Iona National Park. No. 1790, 300k, Epomophorus angolensis and Tundavala Gap.

No. 1791, 300k, SDD6A locomotive. No. 1792, 300k, GE C30ACi locomotive. No. 1793, 300k, GE U20C locomotive. No. 1794, 300k, CKD8F locomotive.

No. 1795, 300k, Pan troglodytes, vert. No. 1796, 300k, Cercopithecus ascanius, vert. No. 1797, 300k, Cercopithecus neglectus, vert. No. 1798, 300k, Papio ursinus, vert.

No. 1799, 300k, One Orycteropus afer facing forward, vert. No. 1800, 300k, One Orycteropus afer facing right, vert. No. 1801, 300k, One Orycteropus afer behind rock, facing right, vert. No. 1802, 300k, Two Orycteropus afer, vert.

No. 1803, 300k, Crocuta crocuta facing left, vert. No. 1804, 300k, Crocuta crocuta facing right, vert. No. 1805, 300k, Crocuta crocuta in water, vert. No. 1806, 300k, Four Crocuta crocuta, vert.

No. 1807, 300k, Equus quagga chapmani on its back, vert. No. 1808, 300k, Three Equus quagga chapmani, vert. No. 1809, 300k, Adult nursing juvenile Equus quagga chapmani, vert. No. 1810, 300k, Two adult Equus quagga chapmani, vert.

No. 1811, 300k, Lycaon pictus pictus facing right, vert. No. 1812, 300k, Lycaon pictus pictus running in shallow water, vert. No. 1813, 300k, Two Lycaon pictus pictus at play, vert. No. 1814, 300k, Two Lycaon pictus pictus eating dead animal, vert.

No. 1815, 300k, Lepus capensis on hind legs, facing left, vert. No. 1816, 300k, Lepus capensis facing right, with front legs bent, vert. No. 1817, 300k, Lepus capensis facing right, with front legs straight, vert. No. 1818, 300k, Lepus capensis drinking water, vert.

No. 1819, 300k, Pterocles bicinctus facing right, vert. No. 1820, 300k, Pterocles bicinctus facing left, vert. No. 1821, 300k, Pterocles burchelli facing right, vert. No. 1822, 300k, Pterocles burchelli facing left, vert.

No. 1823, 300k, Gold (ouro), vert. No. 1824, 300k, Bayldonite, vert. No. 1825, 300k, Quartz, vert. No. 1826, 300k, Kaolinite (caulinta), vert.

No. 1827, 300k, Back of Chokwe chair (encosto da cadeira Chokwe), vert. No. 1828, 300k, Chokwe mask (máscara Chokwe), vert. No. 1829, 300k, Ceramic vessel (vaso de cerâmica), vert. No. 1830, 300k, Top of scepter (topo de ceptro), vert.

No. 1831, 300k, Rat with tuba, vert. No. 1832, 300k, Rat carrying barrel, vert. No. 1833, 300k, Rat playing with top, vert. No. 1834, 300k, Rat delivering mail to mailbox, vert.

No. 1835, 1200k, Canis mesomelas, vert. No. 1836, 1200k, Atelerix frontalis, vert. No. 1837, 1200k, Smutsia temminckii, vert. No. 1838, 1200k, Aonyx capensis, vert. No. 1839, 1200k, Vulpes chama, vert. No. 1840, 1200k, Hippotragus niger variani, vert. No. 1841, 1200k, Hippopotamus amphibius, vert. No. 1842, 1200k, Panthera leo, vert. No. 1843, 1200k, Panthera pardus, vert. No. 1844, 1200k, Caracal aurata, vert. No. 1845, 1200k, Trichechus senegalensis, vert. No. 1846, 1200k, Orcinus orca, vert. No. 1847, 1200k, Caprimulgus rufigena, vert. No. 1848, 1200k, Actophilornis africanus, vert. No. 1849, 1200k, Polemaetus bellicosus, vert. No. 1850, 1200k, Eurema hecabe, vert. No. 1851, 1200k, Hippotragus niger, Cangandala National Park, vert. No. 1852, 1200k, Aviceda cuculoides and Calandula Falls, vert. No. 1853, 1200k, SDD6 Diesel locomotive. No. 1854, 1200k, Cercopithecus mitis, vert. No. 1855, 1200k, Orycteropus afer, diff., vert. No. 1856, 1200k, Two Crocuta crocuta, vert. No. 1857, 1200k, Equus quagga chapmani standing, vert. No. 1858, 1200k, Lycaon pictus pictus, diff., vert. No. 1859, 1200k, Lepus capensis, diff., vert. No. 1860, 1200k, Pterocles namaqua, vert. No. 1861, 1200k, Opal, vert. No. 1862, 1200k, Chikwe statue, vert. No. 1863, 1200k, Rat holding gift, vert.

Perf. 13x13¼, 13¼x13

2019, Dec. 20 — Litho.

1719-1834	A354	Set of 116	145.00	145.00

Souvenir Sheets

1835-1863	A354	Set of 29	145.00	145.00

SEMI-POSTAL STAMPS

Angolan Red Cross — SP1

No. B1, Mother and child. No. B2, Zebra and foal.

1991, Sept. 19 — Litho. — *Perf. 14*

B1	SP1	20k +5k multi		1.25	1.25
B2	SP1	40k +5k multi		2.25	2.25

AIR POST STAMPS

Plane Over Globe

Common Design Type

Perf. 13½x13

1938, July 26 — Engr. — Unwmk.

Name and Value in Black

C1	CD39	10c	red orange	.60	.40
C2	CD39	20c	purple	.60	.40
C3	CD39	50c	orange	.60	.40
C4	CD39	1a	ultra	.60	.40
C5	CD39	2a	lilac brn	1.25	.40
C6	CD39	3a	dk green	2.50	.60
C7	CD39	5a	red brown	6.00	.90
C8	CD39	9a	rose carmine	9.25	1.90
C9	CD39	10a	magenta	12.50	3.00
			Nos. C1-C9 (9)	33.90	8.40
			Set, Never Hinged	47.50	

No. C7 exists with overprint "Exposicao Internacional de Nova York, 1939-1940" and Trylon and Perisphere. Value; used & unused $110., never hinged, $160.

AP2

1947, Aug. — Litho. — *Rough Perf. 10½*

C10	AP2	1a	red brown	16.00	5.25
C11	AP2	2a	yellow grn	18.00	6.75
C12	AP2	3a	orange	18.00	6.75
C13	AP2	3.50a	orange	32.50	6.75
C14	AP2	5a	olive grn	110.00	30.00
C15	AP2	6a	rose	110.00	29.00
C16	AP2	9a	red	375.00	300.00
C17	AP2	10a	green	250.00	115.00
C18	AP2	20a	blue	350.00	125.00
C19	AP2	50a	black	450.00	300.00
C20	AP2	100a	yellow	625.00	575.00
			Nos. C10-C20 (11)	2,355.	1,500.

Planes Circling Globe — AP3

1949, May 1 — Photo. — *Perf. 11½*

C21	AP3	1a	henna brown	.75	.25
C22	AP3	2a	red brown	1.50	.25
C23	AP3	3a	plum	2.00	.25
C24	AP3	6a	dull green	4.00	.85
C25	AP3	9a	violet brown	5.50	2.25
			Nos. C21-C25 (5)	13.75	3.85
			Set, Never Hinged	21.00	

Catalogue values for unused stamps in this section, from this point to the end of the section, are for Never Hinged items.

Cambambe Dam — AP4

Designs: 1.50e, Oil refinery, vert. 3e, Salazar Dam. 4e, Capt. Teófilo Duarte Dam. 4.50e, Craveiro Lopes Dam. 5e, Cuango Dam. 6e, Quanza River Bridge. 7e, Capt. Teófilo Duarte Bridge. 8.50e, Oliveira Salazar Bridge. 12.50e, Capt. Silva Carvalho Bridge.

Perf. 11½x12, 12x11½

1965, July 12 — Litho. — Unwmk.

C26	AP4	1.50e	multicolored	2.50	.25
C27	AP4	2.50e	multicolored	1.50	.25
C28	AP4	3e	multicolored	2.50	.25
C29	AP4	4e	multicolored	1.00	.25
C30	AP4	4.50e	multicolored	1.00	.25
C31	AP4	5e	multicolored	1.60	.25
C32	AP4	6e	multicolored	1.60	.25
C33	AP4	7e	multicolored	2.50	.25
C34	AP4	8.50e	multicolored	3.25	1.40
C35	AP4	12.50e	multicolored	3.75	1.60
			Nos. C26-C35 (10)	21.20	5.00

Stamp Centenary Type

Design: 2.50e, Boeing 707 jet & Angola #2.

1970, Dec. 1 — Litho. — *Perf. 13½*

C36	A83	2.50e multicolored	1.40	.35
a.		Souv. sheet of 3, #565-566, C36	13.00	13.00

No. C36a sold for 15e.

No. C36 Ovptd.

1980, June 15 — Litho. — *Perf. 13½*

C37	A83	2.50e multicolored	1.40	.45

POSTAGE DUE STAMPS

D1

1904 — Unwmk. — Typo. — *Perf. 11½x12*

J1	D1	5r	yellow grn	.50	.45
J2	D1	10r	slate	.50	.45
J3	D1	20r	yellow brn	.95	.50
J4	D1	30r	orange	.95	.50
J5	D1	50r	gray brown	1.15	.85
J6	D1	60r	red brown	11.50	5.50
J7	D1	100r	lilac	2.25	2.75
J8	D1	130r	dull blue	2.25	2.75
J9	D1	200r	carmine	13.50	7.50
J10	D1	500r	gray violet	12.00	6.00
			Nos. J1-J10 (10)	45.55	27.25
			Set, never hinged	100.00	

Postage Due Stamps of 1904 Overprinted in Carmine or Green

1911

J11	D1	5r	yellow grn	.35	.30
J12	D1	10r	slate	.35	.30
J13	D1	20r	yellow brn	.35	.30
J14	D1	30r	orange	.50	.30
J15	D1	50r	gray brown	.50	.30
J16	D1	60r	red brown	1.55	1.00
J17	D1	100r	lilac	1.60	1.00
J18	D1	130r	dull blue	1.75	1.40
J19	D1	200r	carmine (G)	2.25	1.40
J20	D1	500r	gray violet	2.60	2.60
			Nos. J11-J20 (10)	11.80	8.90
			Set, never hinged	70.00	

D2

1921 — *Perf. 11½*

J21	D2	½c	yellow green	.35	.30
J22	D2	1c	slate	.35	.30
J23	D2	2c	orange brown	.35	.30
J24	D2	3c	orange	.35	.30
J25	D2	5c	gray brown	.35	.30
J26	D2	6c	lt brown	.45	.30
J27	D2	10c	red violet	.65	.50
J28	D2	13c	dull blue	1.10	.95
J29	D2	20c	carmine	1.10	.95
J30	D2	50c	gray	1.10	.95
			Nos. J21-J30 (10)	6.15	5.15
			Set, never hinged	8.00	

For surcharges see Nos. 268-270.

Catalogue values for unused stamps in this section, from this point to the end of the section, are for Never Hinged items.

Stamps of 1932 Surcharged in Black

1948 — Wmk. 232 — *Perf. 12x11½*

J31	A14	10c	on 20c gray	.50	.30
J32	A14	20c	on 30c myrtle grn	.95	.50
J33	A14	30c	on 50c lt brown	1.30	.80
J34	A14	40c	on 1a claret	1.90	1.20
J35	A14	50c	on 2a dull vio	3.25	2.10
J36	A14	1a	on 5a pale yel grn	3.50	2.50
			Nos. J31-J36 (6)	11.40	7.40

Common Design Type

Photogravure and Typographed

1952 — Unwmk. — *Perf. 14*

Numeral in Red, Frame Multicolored

J37	CD45	10c	red brown	.35	.25
J38	CD45	30c	olive green	.35	.25
J39	CD45	50c	chocolate	.35	.25
J40	CD45	1a	dk vio blue	.95	.50
J41	CD45	2a	red brown	1.15	.65
J42	CD45	5a	black brown	1.15	.65
			Nos. J37-J42 (6)	4.30	2.55

NEWSPAPER STAMP

N1

1893 — Typo. — Unwmk. — *Perf. 11½*

P1	N1	2½r brown	4.00	1.60
a.		Perf. 12½	4.00	1.40
b.		Perf. 13½	3.50	1.40

No. P1 was also used for ordinary postage. For surcharges see Nos. 37, 82, 180, 235.

POSTAL TAX STAMPS

Pombal Issue

Common Design Types

1925, May 8 — Unwmk. — *Perf. 12½*

RA1	CD28	15c lilac & black	1.10	1.10
RA2	CD29	15c lilac & black	1.10	1.10
RA3	CD30	15c lilac & black	1.10	1.10
		Nos. RA1-RA3 (3)	3.30	3.30

"Charity" — PT1

1929 — Litho. — *Perf. 11*

Without Gum

RA4	PT1	50c dark blue	8.25	2.25

Coat of Arms — PT2

1939 — Without Gum — *Perf. 10½*

RA5	PT2	50c turq green	3.50	.35
RA6	PT2	1a red	5.50	2.25

A 1.50a, type PT2, was issued for fiscal use. Value, $7.50.

Catalogue values for unused stamps in this section, from this point to the end of the section, are for Never Hinged items.

Old Man — PT3

Designs: 1e, Boy. 1.50e, Girl.

Imprint: "Foto-Lito-E.G.A.-Luanda"
Heads in dark brown

1955 Unwmk. *Perf. 13*

RA7	PT3	50c dk ocher	.50	.25
RA8	PT3	1e orange ver	.75	.60
RA9	PT3	1.50e brt yel grn	1.00	.60
		Nos. RA7-RA9 (3)	2.25	1.45

A 2.50e, type PT3 showing an old woman, was issued for revenue use. Value $2.

See Nos. RA16, RA19-RA21, RA25-RA27.

No. RA7 Surcharged in Red or Black

1957-58 Head in dark brown

RA11	PT3	10c on 50c dk ocher (R)	.35	.30
RA12	PT3	10c on 50c dk ocher ('58)	.35	.30
RA13	PT3	30c on 50c dk ocher	.35	.30
		Nos. RA11-RA13 (3)	1.05	.90

Mother and Child — PT4

Design: 30c, Boy and girl.

1959 Litho. *Perf. 13*

RA14	PT4	10c orange & blk	.30	.25
RA15	PT4	30c slate & blk	.30	.25

Type of 1955 Redrawn

Design: 1e, Boy.

1961, Nov. *Perf. 13*

RA16	PT3	1e salmon pink & dk brn	.35	.30

Denomination in italics.

Yellow, White and Black Men — PT5

1962, July 1 Typo. *Perf. 10½*
Without Gum

RA17	PT5	50c multicolored	.35	.25
RA18	PT5	1e multicolored	.50	.25

Issued for the Provincial Settlement Committee (Junta Provincial do Povoamento). The tax was used to promote Portuguese settlement in Angola, and to raise educational and living standards of recent immigrants.

Denominations higher than 1e were used for revenue purposes.

Head Type of 1955

Designs: 50c, Old man. 1e, Boy. 1.50e, Girl.

Without Imprint
Heads in dark brown

1964-65 Litho. *Perf. 11½*

RA19	PT3	50c orange	.35	.25
RA20	PT3	1e dull red org ('65)	.35	.25
RA21	PT3	1.50e yel grn ('65)	.35	.35
		Nos. RA19-RA21 (3)	1.05	.85

No. RA20 is the second redrawing of 1e, with bolder lettering. Space between "Assistencia" and denomination on RA20-RA21 is ½mm; on the 1955 issue space is 2¼mm and 1¾mm, respectively.

Map of Angola, Industrial and Farm Workers — PT6

1965, Sept. 1 Litho. *Perf. 13*

RA22	PT6	50c multicolored	.25	.25
RA23	PT6	1e multicolored	.30	.25

The 2e was used for revenue purposes. Value 50c.

Head Type of 1955

Designs: 50c, Old man. 1e, Boy. 1.50e, Girl.

Imprint: "I.N.A." or "INA" (1e)

1966 Heads in dark brown

RA25	PT3	50c dull orange	.30	.25
RA26	PT3	1e dull brick red	.30	.25
RA27	PT3	1.50e lt yel grn	.35	.35
		Nos. RA25-RA27 (3)	.95	.85

Woman Planting Tree — PT7

1972 Litho. *Perf. 13*

RA28	PT7	50c shown	.25	.25
RA29	PT7	1e Workers	.30	.25
RA30	PT7	2e Produce	.30	.25
		Nos. RA28-RA30 (3)	.85	.75

POSTAL TAX DUE STAMPS

Pombal Issue
Common Design Types

1925, May 8 Unwmk. *Perf. 12½*

RAJ1	CD28	30c lilac & black	1.10	1.10
RAJ2	CD29	30c lilac & black	1.10	1.10
RAJ3	CD30	30c lilac & black	1.10	1.10
		Nos. RAJ1-RAJ3 (3)	3.30	3.30

See note after Portugal No. RAJ4.

ANGRA

'aŋ-grə

LOCATION — An administrative district of the Azores, consisting of the islands of Terceira, Sao Jorge and Graciosa.
GOVT. — A district of Portugal
AREA — 275 sq. mi.
POP. — 70,000 (approx.)
CAPITAL — Angra do Heroismo

1000 Reis = 1 Milreis

King Carlos — A1

1892-93 Typo. Unwmk. *Perf. 12½*

1	A1	5r yellow	5.00	2.10
a.		Perf 11½	15.50	8.50
b.		Perf 13½	4.25	2.10
2	A1	10r redsh violet	5.00	2.10
a.		Perf 13½	5.00	3.00
3	A1	15r chocolate	5.00	3.50
a.		Perf 13½	5.00	3.50
4	A1	20r lavender	5.00	3.50
a.		Perf 13½	5.00	3.50
5	A1	25r green	7.00	1.40
a.		Perf 13½	12.00	6.50
b.		Perf 11½	8.50	3.50
7	A1	50r blue	11.50	6.50
a.		Perf 13½	15.50	7.00
8	A1	75r carmine	12.00	7.00
9	A1	80r yellow green	15.50	13.00
10	A1	100r brown, *yel*, perf 13½ ('93)	52.50	17.50
a.		Perf 12½	200.00	135.00
11	A1	150r car, *rose* ('93)	67.50	47.50
a.		Perf 13½	77.50	57.50
12	A1	200r dk blue, *bl* ('93)	67.50	47.50
		Never hinged	120.00	
a.		Perf 13½	77.50	57.50
13	A1	300r dk blue, *sal* ('93)	67.50	47.50
		Never hinged	120.00	
a.		Perf 13½	77.50	57.50
		Nos. 1-13 (12)	321.00	199.10

Reprints of 50r, 150r, 200r and 300r, made in 1900, are perf. 11½ and ungummed. Value, each $75. Reprints of all values, made in 1905, have shiny white gum and clean-cut perf. Value, each $30.

King Carlos — A2

Name and Value in Black except Nos. 26 and 35

1897-1905 *Perf. 11½*

14	A2	2½r gray	.75	.50
15	A2	5r orange	.75	.50
a.		Diagonal half used as 2½r on newspaper or circular		*28.00*
16	A2	10r yellow grn	.75	.50
17	A2	15r brown	11.50	5.75
18	A2	15r gray grn ('99)	1.40	.70
19	A2	20r gray violet	3.00	1.50
20	A2	25r sea green	4.25	1.40
21	A2	25r car rose ('99)	.75	.70
22	A2	50r dark blue	7.00	2.10
23	A2	50r ultra ('05)	17.00	11.50
24	A2	65r slate bl ('98)	2.10	.70
25	A2	75r rose	4.25	2.10
26	A2	75r gray brn & car, *straw* ('05)	15.50	10.50
27	A2	80r violet	3.00	1.40
28	A2	100r dk blue, *bl*	3.50	2.00
29	A2	115r org brn, *pink* ('98)	3.50	2.10
30	A2	130r gray brn, *straw* ('98)	3.50	2.10
31	A2	150r lt brn, *straw*	3.50	2.00
32	A2	180r sl, *pnksh* ('98)	4.25	3.50
33	A2	200r red vio, *pnksh*	7.75	5.00
34	A2	300r blue, *rose*	10.50	7.00
35	A2	500r blk & red, *bl*	21.00	14.00
a.		Perf. 12½	32.00	18.50
		Nos. 14-35 (22)	129.50	77.55

Azores stamps were used in Angra from 1906 to 1931, when they were superseded by those of Portugal.

ANGUILLA

aŋ-gwi-lə

LOCATION — In the West Indies southeast of Puerto Rico
GOVT. — British territory
AREA — 60 sq. mi.
POP. — 10,663 (est. 1997)
CAPITAL — The Valley

Anguilla separated unilaterally from the Associated State of St. Kitts-Nevis-Anguilla in 1967, formalized in 1980 following direct United Kingdom intervention some years before. A British Commissioner exercises executive authority.

100 Cents = 1 Eastern Caribbean Dollar

Catalogue values for all unused stamps in this country are for Never Hinged items.

St. Kitts-Nevis Nos. 145-160 Overprinted

On Type A14

On Type A15

Wmk. 314

1967, Sept. 4 Photo. *Perf. 14*

1	A14	½c blue & dk brn	75.00	21.00
2	A15	1c multicolored	85.00	9.00
3	A14	2c multicolored	75.00	2.90
4	A14	3c multicolored	75.00	7.00
5	A15	4c multicolored	90.00	5.25
6	A15	5c multicolored	375.00	40.00
7	A15	6c multicolored	160.00	16.00
8	A15	10c multicolored	90.00	9.00
9	A14	15c multicolored	180.00	14.00
10	A15	20c multicolored	375.00	21.00
11	A14	25c multicolored	300.00	40.00
12	A15	50c multicolored	*5,500.*	*725.00*
13	A14	60c multicolored	*6,500.*	*1,850.*
14	A14	$1 multicolored	*4,500.*	*625.00*
15	A15	$2.50 multicolored	*3,500.*	*375.00*
16	A14	$5 multicolored	*4,000.*	*400.00*
		Nos. 1-16 (16)	25,880.	4,160.

Counterfeit overprints exist.

Mahogany Tree, The Quarter — A1

Designs: 2c, Sombrero Lighthouse. 3c, St. Mary's Church. 4c, Valley Police Station. 5c, Old Plantation House, Mt. Fortune. 6c, Valley Post Office. 10c, Methodist Church, West End. 15c, Wall-Blake Airport. 20c, Plane over Sandy Ground. 25c, Island Harbor. 40c, Map of Anguilla. 60c, Hermit crab and starfish. $1, Hibiscus. $2.50, Coconut harvest. $5, Spiny lobster.

Perf. 12½x13

1967-68 Litho. Unwmk.

17	A1	1c orange & multi	.25	.80
18	A1	2c gray green & blk	.25	1.00
19	A1	3c emerald & blk	.25	.25
20	A1	4c brt blue & blk	.25	.25
21	A1	5c lt blue & multi	.25	.25
22	A1	6c ver & black	.25	.25
23	A1	10c multicolored	.25	.25
24	A1	15c multicolored	2.10	.25
25	A1	20c multicolored	1.25	1.75
26	A1	25c multicolored	.60	.25
27	A1	40c blue & multi	1.00	.50
28	A1	60c yellow & multi	4.50	4.00
29	A1	$1 lt green & multi	1.75	2.75
30	A1	$2.50 multicolored	2.00	5.50
31	A1	$5 multicolored	2.75	3.50
		Nos. 17-31 (15)	17.70	21.55

Issued: 1c, 5c, 10c, 20c, 25c, 40c, 11/27/67; 3c, 4c, 15c, 60c, $1, $5, 2/10/68; 2c, 6c, $2.50, 3/21/68.

For overprints see Nos. 53-67, 78-82.

Sailboats — A2

Designs: 15c, Boat building. 25c, Schooner Warspite. 40c, Yacht Atlantic Star.

1968, May 11 *Perf. 14*

32	A2	10c rose & multi	.35	.25
33	A2	15c olive & multi	.40	.25
34	A2	25c lilac rose & multi	.60	.25
35	A2	40c dull blue & multi	.65	.35
		Nos. 32-35 (4)	2.00	1.10

Purple-throated Carib — A3

Anguillan Birds: 15c, Bananaquit. 25c, Black-necked stilt, horiz. 40c, Royal tern, horiz.

1968, July 8

36	A3	10c dull yel & multi	.75	.25
37	A3	15c yel green & multi	1.00	.25
38	A3	25c multicolored	1.40	.25
39	A3	40c multicolored	1.75	.35
		Nos. 36-39 (4)	4.90	1.10

Girl Guide Badge — A4

10c, Girl Guide badge, horiz. 25c, Badge and Headquarters, horiz. 40c, Merit Badges.

1968, Oct. 14 *Perf. 13x13½, 13½x13*

40	A4	10c lt green & multi	.25	.25
41	A4	15c lt blue & multi	.25	.25
42	A4	25c multicolored	.25	.25
43	A4	40c multicolored	.30	.25
		Nos. 40-43 (4)	1.05	1.00

Anguillan Girl Guides, 35th anniversary.

Three Kings — A5

Christmas: 10c, Three Kings seeing Star, vert. 15c, Holy Family, vert. 40c, Shepherds seeing Star. 50c, Holy Family and donkey.

1968, Nov. 18

44	A5	1c lilac rose & black	.25	.25
45	A5	10c blue & black	.25	.25
46	A5	15c brown & black	.25	.25
47	A5	40c brt ultra & black	.25	.25
48	A5	50c green & black	.30	.25
		Nos. 44-48 (5)	1.30	1.25

Bagging Salt — A6

Salt Industry: 15c, Packing salt. 40c, Salt pond. 50c, Loading salt.

1969, Jan. 4 *Perf. 13*

49	A6	10c red & multi	.25	.25
50	A6	15c lt blue & multi	.30	.25
51	A6	40c emerald & multi	.30	.25
52	A6	50c purple & multi	.35	.25
		Nos. 49-52 (4)	1.20	1.00

Nos. 17-31 Overprinted

1969, Jan. 9 *Perf. 12½x13*

53	A1	1c orange & multi	.25	.25
54	A1	2c gray green & blk	.25	.25
55	A1	3c emerald & blk	.25	.25
56	A1	4c brt blue & blk	.25	.25
57	A1	5c lt blue & multi	.25	.25
58	A1	6c vermilion & blk	.25	.25
59	A1	10c multicolored	.25	.25
60	A1	15c multicolored	.25	.30
61	A1	20c multicolored	.30	.35
62	A1	25c multicolored	.40	.50
63	A1	40c blue & multi	.70	*.70*
64	A1	60c yellow & multi	.80	*.80*
65	A1	$1 lt green & multi	1.25	*1.50*
66	A1	$2.50 multicolored	3.75	*4.50*
67	A1	$5 multicolored	8.25	*9.50*
		Nos. 53-67 (15)	17.45	19.90

Crucifixion, School of Quentin Massys — A7

Easter: 40c, The Last Supper, ascribed to Roberti.

1969, Mar. 31 Litho. *Perf. 13½*

68	A7	25c multicolored	.25	.25
69	A7	40c multicolored	.35	.25

Amaryllis — A8

1969, June 10 *Perf. 14*

70	A8	10c shown	.25	.25
71	A8	15c Bougainvillea	.35	.35
72	A8	40c Hibiscus	.55	.55
73	A8	50c Cattleya orchid	1.75	1.25
		Nos. 70-73 (4)	2.90	2.40

Turban and Star Shells — A9

Sea Shells: 15c, Spiny oysters. 40c, Scotch, royal and smooth bonnets. 50c, Triton trumpet.

1969, Sept. 22

74	A9	10c multicolored	.25	.25
75	A9	15c multicolored	.35	.30
76	A9	40c multicolored	.70	.35
77	A9	50c multicolored	.80	.40
		Nos. 74-77 (4)	2.10	1.30

No. 17 Ovptd.

No. 25 Ovptd.

No. 26 Ovptd.

No. 27 Ovptd.

No. 28 Ovptd.

1969, Oct. 27 *Perf. 12½x13*

78	A1	1c orange & multi	.25	.25
79	A1	20c multicolored	.25	.25
80	A1	25c multicolored	.25	.25
81	A1	40c blue & multi	.50	.25
82	A1	60c yellow & multi	.75	.30
		Nos. 78-82 (5)	2.00	1.30

Red Goatfish — A10

Designs: 15c, Blue-striped grunts. 40c, Mutton grouper. 50c, Banded butterfly-fish.

1969, Dec. 1 *Perf. 14*

83	A10	10c multicolored	.40	.25
84	A10	15c multicolored	.50	.25
85	A10	40c multicolored	.95	.45
86	A10	50c multicolored	1.25	.60
		Nos. 83-86 (4)	3.10	1.55

Morning Glory — A11

1970, Feb. 23

87	A11	10c shown	.40	.25
88	A11	15c Blue petrea	.55	.25
89	A11	40c Hibiscus	.75	.30
90	A11	50c Flamboyant	.95	.35
		Nos. 87-90 (4)	2.65	1.15

The Way to Calvary, by Tiepolo A12

Easter: 20c, Crucifixion, by Masaccio, vert. 40c, Descent from the Cross, by Rosso Fiorentino, vert. 60c, Jesus Carrying the Cross, by Murillo.

1970, Mar. 26 *Perf. 13½*

91	A12	10c multicolored	.25	.25
92	A12	20c multicolored	.25	.25
93	A12	40c multicolored	.30	.25
94	A12	60c multicolored	.40	.30
		Nos. 91-94 (4)	1.20	1.05

Anguilla Map, Scout Badge — A13

Designs: 15c, Cub Scouts practicing first aid. 40c, Monkey bridge. 50c, Scout Headquarters, The Valley, and Lord Baden-Powell.

1970, Aug. 10 *Perf. 13*

95	A13	10c multicolored	.25	.25
96	A13	15c multicolored	.25	.25
97	A13	40c multicolored	.30	.25
98	A13	50c multicolored	.40	.30
		Nos. 95-98 (4)	1.20	1.05

Anguilla Boy Scouts, 40th anniversary.

Boat Building — A14

Designs: 2c, Road construction. 3c, Blowing Point dock. 4c, Radio announcer. 5c, Cottage Hospital extension. 6c, Valley secondary school. 10c, Hotel extension. 15c, Sandy Ground. 20c, Supermarket and movie house. 25c, Bananas and mangoes. 40c, Wall-Blake airport. 60c, Sandy Ground jetty. $1, Administration building. $2.50, Cow and calf. $5, Sandy Hill Bay.

1970, Nov. 23 Litho. *Perf. 14*

99	A14	1c multicolored	.30	*.40*
100	A14	2c multicolored	.30	*.40*
101	A14	3c multicolored	.30	.25
102	A14	4c multicolored	.30	*.50*
103	A14	5c multicolored	.50	.50
104	A14	6c multicolored	.40	*.50*
105	A14	10c multicolored	.40	.30
106	A14	15c multicolored	.40	.30
107	A14	20c multicolored	.75	.30
108	A14	25c multicolored	.40	*1.00*
109	A14	40c multicolored	4.00	3.00
110	A14	60c multicolored	.70	*3.00*

111	A14	$1 multicolored	1.25	1.25
112	A14	$2.50 multicolored	1.75	*4.00*
113	A14	$5 multicolored	3.75	4.00
		Nos. 99-113 (15)	15.50	19.70

Adoration of the Shepherds, by Guido Reni — A15

Christmas: 20c, Virgin and Child, by Benozzo Gozzoli. 25c, Nativity, by Botticelli. 40c, Santa Margherita Madonna, by Mazzola. 50c, Adoration of the Kings, by Tiepolo.

1970, Dec. 11 ***Perf. 13½***

114	A15	1c multicolored	.25	.25
115	A15	20c multicolored	.25	.25
116	A15	25c multicolored	.30	.25
117	A15	40c multicolored	.45	.35
118	A15	50c multicolored	.50	.40
		Nos. 114-118 (5)	1.75	1.50

Angels Weeping over the Dead Christ, by Guercino A16

Easter: 10c, Ecce Homo, by Correggio, vert. 15c, Christ Appearing to St. Peter, by Carracci, vert. 50c, The Supper at Emmaus, by Caravaggio.

1971, Mar. 29

119	A16	10c pink & multi	.25	.25
120	A16	15c lt blue & multi	.25	.25
121	A16	40c yel green & multi	.40	.25
122	A16	50c violet & multi	.50	.25
		Nos. 119-122 (4)	1.40	1.00

Hypolimnas Misippus — A17

Butterflies: 15c, Junonia lavinia. 40c, Agraulis vanillae. 50c, Danaus plexippus.

1971, June 21 ***Perf. 14x14½***

123	A17	10c multicolored	2.00	1.00
124	A17	15c multicolored	2.00	1.25
125	A17	40c multicolored	2.50	1.50
126	A17	50c multicolored	2.50	2.00
		Nos. 123-126 (4)	9.00	5.75

Magnanime and Aimable in Battle — A18

Ships: 15c, HMS Duke and Agamemnon against Glorieux. 25c, HMS Formidable and Namur against Ville de Paris. 40c, HMS Canada. 50c, HMS St. Albans and wreck of Hector.

1971, Aug. 30 **Litho.** ***Perf. 14***

127	A18	10c multicolored	1.10	1.10
128	A18	15c multicolored	1.40	1.40
129	A18	25c multicolored	1.50	1.50
130	A18	40c multicolored	1.60	1.60
131	A18	50c multicolored	1.75	1.75
a.		Strip of 5, #127-131	8.25	8.25
		Nos. 127-131 (5)	7.35	7.35

West Indies sea battles.

Ansidei Madonna, by Raphael — A19

Christmas: 25c, Mystic Nativity, by Botticelli. 40c, Virgin and Child, School of Seville, inscribed Murillo. 50c, Madonna of the Iris, ascribed to Dürer.

1971, Nov. 29 ***Perf. 14x13½***

132	A19	20c green & multi	.30	.30
133	A19	25c blue & multi	.30	.30
134	A19	40c lilac rose & multi	.35	*.40*
135	A19	50c violet & multi	.40	*.60*
		Nos. 132-135 (4)	1.35	*1.60*

Map of Anguilla and St. Maarten, by Jefferys, 1775 — A20

Maps of Anguilla by: 15c, Samuel Fahlberg, 1814. 40c, Thomas Jefferys, 1775, horiz. 50c, Capt. E. Barnett, 1847, horiz.

1972, Jan. 24 ***Perf. 14x13½, 13½x14***

136	A20	10c lt blue & multi	.25	.25
137	A20	15c lt green & multi	.35	.30
138	A20	40c lt green & multi	.55	.40
139	A20	50c lt ultra & multi	.80	.40
		Nos. 136-139 (4)	1.95	1.35

Jesus Buffeted, Stained-glass Window — A21

Easter (19th cent. Stained-glass Windows, Bray Church): 15c, Jesus Carrying the Cross. 25c, Crucifixion. 40c, Descent from the Cross. 50c, Burial.

1972, Mar. 14 ***Perf. 14x13½***

140	A21	10c multicolored	.30	.30
141	A21	15c multicolored	.35	.35
142	A21	25c multicolored	.35	.35
143	A21	40c multicolored	.40	.40
144	A21	50c multicolored	.50	.50
a.		Strip of 5, #140-144	2.50	2.50
		Nos. 140-144 (5)	1.90	1.90

Spear Fishing — A22

Sandy Ground A23

2c, Loblolly tree, vert. 4c, Ferry, Blowing Point, vert. 5c, Agriculture. 6c, St. Mary's Church, vert. 10c, St. Gerard's Church. 15c, Cottage Hospital. 20c, Public Library. 25c, Sunset, Blowing Point. 40c, Boat building. 60c, Hibiscus. $1, Man-o-war bird. $2.50, Frangipani. $5, Brown pelican. $10, Green-back turtle.

1972-75 ***Perf. 13½***

145	A22	1c shown	.25	.50
146	A23	2c multicolored	.25	.50
147	A23	3c shown	.25	.50
148	A23	4c multicolored	1.75	.25
149	A23	5c multicolored	.25	*1.25*
150	A23	6c multicolored	.35	.25
151	A23	10c multicolored	.35	.50
152	A22	15c multicolored	.35	.40
153	A23	20c multicolored	.35	.45
154	A23	25c multicolored	.50	*2.00*
155	A22	40c multicolored	5.00	1.25
156	A22	60c multicolored	4.25	4.25
157	A23	$1 multicolored	10.00	8.50
158	A23	$2.50 multicolored	6.00	*11.00*
159	A23	$5 multicolored	18.00	*19.00*
160	A22	$10 multicolored	17.00	20.00
		Nos. 145-160 (16)	64.90	70.60

Issued: $10, 5/20/75; others 10/30/72.
For overprints see Nos. 229-246.

Common Design Types pictured following the introduction.

Silver Wedding Issue, 1972
Common Design Type

Design: Queen Elizabeth II, Prince Philip, schooner and dolphin.

Perf. 14x14½

1972, Nov. 20 **Photo.** **Wmk. 314**

161	CD324	25c olive & multi	.55	*.75*
162	CD324	40c maroon & multi	.55	*.75*

Flight into Egypt — A24

20c, Star of Bethlehem. 25c, Nativity. 40c, Three Kings. 50c, Adoration of the Kings.

Perf. 13½

1972, Dec. 4 **Litho.** **Unwmk.**

163	A24	1c shown	.25	.25
164	A24	20c multicolored	.25	.25
165	A24	25c multicolored	.25	.25
166	A24	40c multicolored	.25	.25
167	A24	50c multicolored	.25	.25
a.		Vert. strip of 4, #164-167	1.40	1.40
		Nos. 163-167 (5)	1.25	1.25

Christmas.

Betrayal of Jesus — A25

10c, Man of Sorrow. 20c, Jesus Carrying Cross. 25c, Crucifixion. 40c, Descent from Cross. 50c, Resurrection.

1973, Mar. 26

168	A25	1c shown	.25	.25
169	A25	10c multicolored	.25	.25
170	A25	20c multicolored	.25	.25
171	A25	25c multicolored	.25	.25
172	A25	40c multicolored	.25	.25
173	A25	50c multicolored	.25	.35
a.		Souvenir sheet of 6	1.10	*1.50*
b.		Vert. strip of 5, #169-173	1.00	1.00
		Nos. 168-173 (6)	1.50	1.60

Easter. No. 173a contains 6 stamps similar to Nos. 168-173 with bottom panel in lilac rose.

Santa Maria — A26

20c, Old West Indies map. 40c, Map of voyages. 70c, Sighting land. $1.20, Columbus landing.

1973, Sept. 10

174	A26	1c multicolored	.25	.25
175	A26	20c multicolored	1.60	1.60
176	A26	40c multicolored	1.90	1.90
177	A26	70c multicolored	2.00	2.00
178	A26	$1.20 multicolored	2.75	2.75
a.		Souvenir sheet of 5, #174-178	8.00	8.00
b.		Horiz. strip of 4, #175-178	8.00	8.00
		Nos. 174-178 (5)	8.50	8.50

Discovery of West Indies by Columbus.

Princess Anne's Wedding Issue
Common Design Type

1973, Nov. 14 **Wmk. 314** ***Perf. 13½***

179	CD325	60c blue grn & multi	.25	.25
180	CD325	$1.20 lilac & multi	.30	.30

Wedding of Princess Anne and Capt. Mark Phillips, Nov. 14, 1973.

Adoration of the Shepherds, by Guido Reni — A27

Paintings: 10c, Virgin and Child, by Filippino Lippi. 20c, Nativity, by Meester Van de Brunswijkse Diptiek. 25c, Madonna of the Meadow, by Bellini. 40c, Virgin and Child, by Cima. 50c, Adoration of the Kings, by Geertgen Tot Sint Jans.

1973, Dec. 2 **Unwmk.**

181	A27	1c multicolored	.25	.25
182	A27	10c multicolored	.25	.25
183	A27	20c multicolored	.25	.25
184	A27	25c multicolored	.25	.25
185	A27	40c multicolored	.25	.25
186	A27	50c multicolored	.25	.25
a.		Souvenir sheet of 6, #181-186	1.50	1.50
b.		Horiz. strip of 5, #182-186	1.00	1.00
		Nos. 181-186 (6)	1.50	1.50

Christmas.

Crucifixion, by Raphael — A28

Easter (Details from Crucifixion by Raphael): 15c, Virgin Mary and St. John. 20c, The Two Marys. 25c, Left Angel. 40c, Right Angel. $1, Christ on the Cross.

1974, Mar. 30

187	A28	1c lilac & multi	.25	.25
188	A28	15c gray & multi	.25	.25
189	A28	20c salmon & multi	.25	.25
190	A28	25c yel green & multi	.25	.25
191	A28	40c orange & multi	.25	.25
192	A28	$1 lt blue & multi	.25	.25
a.		Souvenir sheet of 6, #187-192	1.50	*1.75*
b.		Vert. strip of 5, #188-192	1.00	1.00
		Nos. 187-192 (6)	1.50	1.50

Churchill Making Victory Sign — A29

20c, Roosevelt, Churchill, US, British flags. 25c, Churchill broadcasting during the war. 40c, Blenheim Palace. 60c, Churchill Statue & Parliament. $1.20, Chartwell.

1974, June 24

193	A29	1c multicolored	.25	.25
194	A29	20c multicolored	.25	.25
195	A29	25c multicolored	.25	.25
196	A29	40c multicolored	.30	.30
197	A29	60c multicolored	.35	.35
198	A29	$1.20 multicolored	.50	.50
a.		Souvenir sheet of 6, #193-198	1.75	1.75
b.		Horiz. strip of 5, #194-198	2.00	2.00
		Nos. 193-198 (6)	1.90	1.90

Sir Winston Spencer Churchill (1874-1965).

UPU Emblem, Map of Anguilla A30

1974, Aug. 27

199	A30	1c black & ultra	.25	.25
200	A30	20c black & orange	.25	.25
201	A30	25c black & yellow	.25	.25
202	A30	40c black & brt lilac	.25	.25
203	A30	60c black & lt green	.30	.30

204	A30	$1.20 black & blue	.45	.45
a.		Souvenir sheet of 6	1.60	*2.00*
b.		Horiz. strip of 5, #200-204	1.50	1.50
		Nos. 199-204 (6)	1.75	1.75

UPU, centenary. No. 204a contains one each of Nos. 199-204 with second row (40c, 60c, $1.20) perf. 15 at bottom.

Fishermen Seeing Star — A31

Christmas: 20c, Nativity. 25c, King offering gift. 40c, Star over map of Anguilla. 60c, Family looking at star. $1.20, Two angels with star and "Peace."

1974, Dec. 16 Litho. *Perf. 14½*

205	A31	1c brt blue & multi	.25	.25
206	A31	20c dull grn & multi	.25	.25
207	A31	25c gray & multi	.25	.25
208	A31	40c car & multi	.25	.25
209	A31	60c dp blue & multi	.25	.25
210	A31	$1.20 ultra & multi	.25	.25
a.		Souvenir sheet of 6, #205-210	1.60	*2.25*
b.		Horiz. strip of 5, #206-210	1.25	1.25
		Nos. 205-210 (6)	1.50	1.50

Virgin Mary, St. John, Mary Magdalene — A32

Paintings from Isenheim Altar, by Matthias Grunewald: 10c, Crucifixion. 15c, John the Baptist. 20c, St. Sebastian and Angels. $1, Burial of Christ, horiz. $1.50, St. Anthony, the Hermit.

1975, Mar. 25 *Perf. 13½*

211	A32	1c multicolored	.25	.25
212	A32	10c multicolored	.25	.25
213	A32	15c multicolored	.25	.25
214	A32	20c multicolored	.25	.25
215	A32	$1 multicolored	.25	*.35*
216	A32	$1.50 multicolored	.30	*.45*
a.		Souvenir sheet of 6	1.60	*2.00*
b.		Horiz. strip of 5, #212-216	1.25	1.25
		Nos. 211-216 (6)	1.55	1.80

Easter. No. 216a contains 6 stamps similar to Nos. 211-216 with simulated perforations.

Statue of Liberty, N.Y. Skyline — A33

10c, Capitol, Washington, DC. 15c, Congress voting independence. 20c, Washington, map & his battles. $1, Boston Tea Party. $1.50, Bicentennial emblem, historic US flags.

1975, Nov. 10

217	A33	1c multicolored	.25	.25
218	A33	10c multicolored	.25	.25
219	A33	15c multicolored	.25	.25
220	A33	20c multicolored	.25	.25
221	A33	$1 multicolored	.50	.40
222	A33	$1.50 multicolored	.60	*.60*
a.		Souvenir sheet of 6	1.75	*2.50*
b.		Horiz. strip of 5, #218-222	2.00	*2.00*
		Nos. 217-222 (6)	2.10	2.00

American Bicentennial. No. 222a contains one each of Nos. 217-222 with second row (20c, $1, $1.50) perf. 15 at bottom.

Virgin and Child with St. John, by Raphael — A34

Paintings, Virgin and Child by: 10c, Cima. 15c, Dolci. 20c, Durer. $1, Bellini. $1.50, Botticelli.

1975, Dec. 8 *Perf. 14x13½*

223	A34	1c ultra & multi	.25	.25
224	A34	10c Prus blue & multi	.25	.25
225	A34	15c plum & multi	.25	.25
226	A34	20c car rose & multi	.25	.25
227	A34	$1 brt grn & multi	.30	.25
228	A34	$1.50 blue grn & multi	.45	.40
a.		Souvenir sheet of 6, #223-228	2.25	*2.75*
b.		Horiz. strip of 5, #224-228	1.75	1.50
		Nos. 223-228 (6)	1.75	1.65

Christmas.

Nos. 145-146, 148, 150-160 Surcharged and/or Overprinted

(a)

(b)

1976 Litho. *Perf. 13½*

229	A22 (a)	1c #145		.35	*.50*
230	A22 (b)	2c on 1c #145		.35	*.50*
231	A23 (a)	2c #146		7.75	1.75
232	A22 (b)	3c on 40c #155		.90	.75
233	A23 (a)	4c #148		1.10	*1.25*
234	A22 (b)	5c on 40c #155		.35	*.65*
235	A23 (a)	6c #150		.35	*.65*
236	A23 (b)	10c on 20c #153		.35	*.65*
237	A23 (a)	10c #151		8.25	5.50
238	A22 (a)	15c #152		.35	*1.25*
239	A23 (a)	20c #153		.35	*.60*
240	A23 (a)	25c #154		.35	*.60*
241	A22 (a)	40c #155		1.10	.80
242	A22 (a)	60c #156		.75	.80
243	A23 (a)	$1 #157		6.75	2.50
244	A23 (a)	$2.50 #158		2.25	2.50
245	A23 (a)	$5 #159		8.50	*10.00*
246	A22 (a)	$10 #160		3.25	*7.00*
		Nos. 229-246 (18)		43.40	38.25

Nos. 229-246 exist with second "o" of "Constitution" in italic type. Value, set *$175.*

Flowering Trees — A35

1976, Feb. 16 *Perf. 13½x14*

247	A35	1c Almond	.25	.25
248	A35	10c Clusia rosea	.25	.25
249	A35	15c Calabash	.25	.25
250	A35	20c Cordia	.25	.25
251	A35	$1 Papaya	.50	.40
252	A35	$1.50 Flamboyant	.70	.55
a.		Souvenir sheet of 6, #247-252	2.50	2.50
b.		Horiz. strip of 5, #248-252	2.50	2.50
		Nos. 247-252 (6)	2.20	1.95

The Three Marys — A36

Designs: 10c, Crucifixion. 15c, Two soldiers. 20c, Annunciation. $1, Altar tapestry, 1470, Monastery of Rheinau, Switzerland, horiz. $1.50, "Noli me Tangere" (Jesus and Mary Magdalene). Designs of vertical stamps show details from tapestry shown on $1 stamp.

1976, Apr. 5 *Perf. 14x13½, 13½x14*

253	A36	1c multicolored	.25	.25
254	A36	10c multicolored	.25	.25
255	A36	15c multicolored	.25	.25
256	A36	20c multicolored	.25	.25
257	A36	$1 multicolored	.45	.45
258	A36	$1.50 multicolored	.55	.55
a.		Souvenir sheet of 6	2.25	*2.75*
b.		Horiz. strip of 5, #254-258	2.25	2.25
		Nos. 253-258 (6)	2.00	2.00

Easter. No. 258a contains 6 stamps similar to Nos. 253-258 with simulated perforations.

Le Desius and La Vaillante Approaching Anguilla A37

Sailing Ships: 3c, Sailboat leaving Anguilla for Antigua to get help. 15c, HMS Lapwing in battle with frigate Le Desius and brig La Vaillante. 25c, La Vaillante aground off St. Maarten. $1, Lapwing. $1.50, Le Desius burning.

1976, Nov. 8 Litho. *Perf. 13½x14*

259	A37	1c multicolored	.25	.25
260	A37	3c multicolored	1.40	.50
261	A37	15c multicolored	1.50	.70
262	A37	25c multicolored	1.50	.95
263	A37	$1 multicolored	2.00	1.40
264	A37	$1.50 multicolored	2.25	1.90
a.		Souvenir sheet of 6, #259-264	7.75	7.75
b.		Strip of 5, #260-264	9.50	9.50
		Nos. 259-264 (6)	8.90	5.70

Bicentenary of Battle of Anguilla between French and British ships.

Christmas Carnival A38

Children's Paintings: 3c, 3 children dreaming of Christmas gifts. 15c, Caroling. 25c, Candlelight procession. $1, Going to Church on Christmas Eve. $1.50, Airport, coming home for Christmas.

1976, Nov. 22

265	A38	1c multicolored	.25	.25
266	A38	3c multicolored	.25	.25
267	A38	15c multicolored	.25	.25
268	A38	25c multicolored	.25	.25
269	A38	$1 multicolored	.30	.30
270	A38	$1.50 multicolored	.40	.40
a.		Souvenir sheet of 6, #265-270	2.25	2.25
b.		Strip of 5, #266-270	1.75	1.75
		Nos. 265-270 (6)	1.70	1.70

Christmas. For overprints and surcharges see Nos. 305-310a.

Prince Charles and HMS Minerva, 1973 — A39

Designs: 40c, Prince Philip landing at Road Bay, 1964. $1.20, Homage to Queen at Coronation. $2.50, Coronation regalia and map of Anguilla.

1977, Feb. 9

271	A39	25c multicolored	.25	.25
272	A39	40c multicolored	.25	.25
273	A39	$1.20 multicolored	.25	.25
274	A39	$2.50 multicolored	.35	.30
a.		Souvenir sheet of 4, #271-274	1.00	*1.50*
		Complete booklet, 2 each #271-274	3.00	
		Complete booklet, 2 each #271-274 with vert. selvage at right	5.00	
		Nos. 271-274 (4)	1.10	1.05

25th anniv. of reign of Queen Elizabeth II.

The booklets with thin vert. selvage at right were from a separate printing.

For overprints see Nos. 297-300.

Yellow-crowned Night Heron — A40

Designs: 2c, Great barracuda. 3c, Queen conch. 4c, Spanish bayonet (Yucca). 5c, Trunkfish. 6c, Cable and telegraph building. 10c, American sparrow hawk. 15c, Ground orchids. 20c, Parlorfish. 22c, Lobster fishing boat. 35c, Boat race. 50c Sea bean (flowers). $1, Sandy Island with palms. $2.50, Manchineel (fruit). $5, Ground lizard. $10, Red-billed tropic bird.

1977-78 Litho. *Perf. 13½x14*

275	A40	1c multicolored	.35	*1.00*
276	A40	2c multicolored	.35	*2.50*
277	A40	3c multicolored	2.00	*3.50*
278	A40	4c multicolored	.40	*.70*
279	A40	5c multicolored	1.75	*.45*
280	A40	6c multicolored	.35	*.45*
281	A40	10c multicolored	5.50	4.50
282	A40	15c multicolored	3.75	2.00
283	A40	20c multicolored	3.75	1.00
284	A40	22c multicolored	.60	*1.00*
285	A40	35c multicolored	1.50	1.00
286	A40	50c multicolored	1.00	.90
287	A40	$1 multicolored	.70	.90
288	A40	$2.50 multicolored	1.10	1.00
289	A40	$5 multicolored	2.25	2.25
290	A40	$10 multicolored	9.00	6.50
		Nos. 275-290 (16)	34.35	29.65

Issued: Nos. 275-280, 290, 4/18/77; others 2/20/78.

For overprints and surcharges see Nos. 319-324, 337-342, 387-390, 402-404, 407-415, 417-423.

Crucifixion, by Quentin Massys A41

Easter (Paintings): 3c, Betrayal of Christ, by Ugolino. 22c, Way to Calvary, by Ugolino. 30c, The Deposition, by Ugolino. $1, Resurrection, by Ugolino. $1.50, Crucifixion, by Andrea del Castagno.

1977, Apr. 25

291	A41	1c multicolored	.25	.25
292	A41	3c multicolored	.25	.25
293	A41	22c multicolored	.25	.25
294	A41	30c multicolored	.35	.30
295	A41	$1 multicolored	.60	.55
296	A41	$1.50 multicolored	.90	.80
a.		Souvenir sheet of 6, #291-296	2.50	2.50
b.		Strip of 5, #292-296	2.50	2.50
		Nos. 291-296 (6)	2.60	2.40

Nos. 271-274, 274a Overprinted

1977, Oct. 26 Litho. *Perf. 13½x14*

297	A39	25c multicolored	.25	.25
298	A39	40c multicolored	.25	.25
299	A39	$1.20 multicolored	.40	*.50*
300	A39	$2.50 multicolored	.75	*1.00*
a.		Souvenir sheet of 4	1.40	*2.00*
		Nos. 297-300 (4)	1.65	2.00

Visit of Queen Elizabeth II to West Indies.

Suzanne Fourment in Velvet Hat, by Rubens — A42

Rubens Paintings: 40c, Helena Fourment with her Children. $1.20, Rubens with his wife. $2.50, Marchesa Brigida Spinola-Doria.

1977, Nov. 1 *Perf. 14x13½*

301	A42	25c black & multi	.25	.25
302	A42	40c black & multi	.30	.30
303	A42	$1.20 multicolored	.80	.80
304	A42	$2.50 black & multi	1.10	*1.35*
a.		Souvenir sheet of 4, #301-304	2.50	*2.75*
		Nos. 301-304 (4)	2.45	2.70

Peter Paul Rubens, 400th birth anniv. Nos. 301-304 printed in sheets of 5 stamps and blue label with Rubens' portrait.

For overprint, see Nos. 311-314.

Nos. 265-270b Ovptd. & Srchd.

1977, Nov. 7 *Perf. 13½x14*

305	A38	1c multicolored	.25	.25
306	A38	5c on 3c multi	.25	.25
307	A38	12c on 15c multi	.25	.25
308	A38	18c on 25c multi	.30	.30

309	A38	$1 multicolored	.60	.60
310	A38	$2.50 on $1.50 multi	1.25	1.25
a.		Souvenir sheet of 6, #305-310	3.50	3.50
b.		Strip of 5, #306-310	3.00	3.00
		Nos. 305-310 (6)	2.90	2.90

Christmas. Stamps and souvenir sheets have "1976" and old denomination obliterated with variously shaped rectangles.

Nos. 301-304a Ovptd. in Gold

1978, Mar. 6 ***Perf. 14x13½***

311	A42	25c black & multi	.25	.25
312	A42	40c black & multi	.25	.25
313	A42	$1.20 black & multi	.60	.60
314	A42	$2.50 black & multi	.70	.70
a.		Souvenir sheet of 4, #311-314	2.25	*2.50*
		Nos. 311-314 (4)	1.80	1.80

Buckingham Palace — A43

Designs: 50c, Coronation procession. $1.50, Royal family on balcony. $2.50, Royal coat of arms.

1978, Apr. 6 ***Perf. 14***

315	A43	22c multicolored	.25	.25
316	A43	50c multicolored	.25	.25
317	A43	$1.50 multicolored	.40	.40
318	A43	$2.50 multicolored	.60	.60
a.		Souvenir sheet of 4, #315-318	1.60	1.60
		Complete booklet, 2 each #315-318	3.25	
		Complete booklet, 2 each #315-318 with thin vert. selvage at right	4.00	
		Nos. 315-318 (4)	1.50	1.50

25th anniv. of coronation of Queen Elizabeth II.

The booklets with thin vert. selvage at right were from a separate printing.

Nos. 284-285 and 288 Ovptd. and Surcharged

1978, Aug. 14 Litho. *Perf. 13½x14*

319	A40	22c multicolored	.50	.50
320	A40	35c multicolored	.70	.70
321	A40	$1.50 on $2.50 multi	1.30	1.30
		Nos. 319-321 (3)	2.50	2.50

Valley Secondary School, 25th anniv. Surcharge on No. 321 includes heavy bar over old denomination.

Nos. 286-287, 289 Ovptd. and Surcharged

1978, Aug. 14

322	A40	50c multicolored	1.00	1.00
323	A40	$1 multicolored	1.25	1.25
324	A40	$1.20 on $5 multi	2.00	2.00
		Nos. 322-324 (3)	4.25	4.25

Road Methodist Church, centenary. Surcharge on No. 324 includes heavy bar over old denomination.

Mother and Child — A44

Christmas: 12c, Christmas masquerade. 18c, Christmas dinner. 22c, Serenade. $1, Star over manger. $2.50, Family going to church.

1978, Dec. 11 Litho. *Perf. 13½*

325	A44	5c multicolored	.25	.25
326	A44	12c multicolored	.25	.25
327	A44	18c multicolored	.25	.25
328	A44	22c multicolored	.25	.25
329	A44	$1 multicolored	.30	.30
330	A44	$2.50 multicolored	.60	.60
a.		Souvenir sheet of 6, #325-330	2.00	*2.25*
		Nos. 325-330 (6)	1.90	1.90

Type A44 in Changed Colors with IYC Emblem and Inscription

1979, Jan. 15 Litho. *Perf. 13½*

331	A44	5c multicolored	.25	.25
332	A44	12c multicolored	.25	.25
333	A44	18c multicolored	.25	.25
334	A44	22c multicolored	.25	.25
335	A44	$1 multicolored	.30	.30
336	A44	$2.50 multicolored	.50	.50
a.		Souvenir sheet of 6, #331-336	2.75	*3.25*
		Nos. 331-336 (6)	1.80	1.80

Intl. Year of the Child. For overprint see No. 416

Nos. 275-278, 280-281 Surcharged

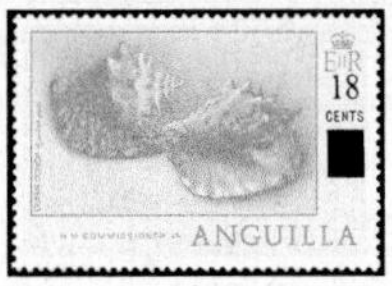

1979, Feb. 8 Litho. *Perf. 13½x14*

337	A40	12c on 2c multi	*.60*	.50
338	A40	14c on 4c multi	*.50*	*.60*
339	A40	18c on 3c multi	*1.10*	*.90*
340	A40	25c on 6c multi	*.70*	*.55*
341	A40	38c on 10c multi	*2.75*	*1.10*
342	A40	40c on 1c multi	*3.00*	*1.10*
		Nos. 337-342 (6)	8.65	4.75

No. 338 exists with surcharge inverted. Value, *$30.*

Valley Methodist Church — A45

Church Interiors: 12c, St. Mary's Anglican Church, The Valley. 18c, St. Gerard's Roman Catholic Church, The Valley. 22c, Road Methodist Church. $1.50, St. Augustine's Anglican Church, East End. $2.50, West End Methodist Church.

1979, Mar. 30 Litho. *Perf. 14*

343	A45	5c multicolored	.25	.25
344	A45	12c multicolored	.25	.25
345	A45	18c multicolored	.25	.25
346	A45	22c multicolored	.25	.25
347	A45	$1.50 multicolored	.40	.40
348	A45	$2.50 multicolored	.60	.60
a.		Souvenir sheet of 6	2.25	2.25
b.		Strip of 6, #343-348	2.00	2.00
		Nos. 343-348 (6)	2.00	2.00

Easter. No. 348a contains Nos. 343-348 in 2 horizontal rows of 3.

US No. C3a — A46

No. 350, Cape of Good Hope #1. No. 351, Penny Black. No. 352, Germany #C36. No. 353, US #245. No. 354, Great Britain #93.

1979, Apr. 23 Litho. *Perf. 14*

349	A46	1c multicolored	.25	.25
350	A46	1c multicolored	.25	.25
351	A46	22c multicolored	.25	.25
352	A46	35c multicolored	.25	.25
353	A46	$1.50 multicolored	.50	.50
354	A46	$2.50 multicolored	.75	.75
a.		Souvenir sheet of 6, #349-353	2.00	*2.75*
		Complete booklet, 2 each #349-354	4.50	
		Nos. 349-354 (6)	2.25	2.25

Sir Rowland Hill (1795-1879), originator of penny postage.

Wright's Flyer A — A47

History of Aviation: 12c, Louis Bleriot landing at Dover, 1909. 18c, Vickers Vimy, 1919. 22c, Spirit of St. Louis, 1927. $1.50, LZ127 Graf Zeppelin, 1928. $2.50, Concorde, 1979.

1979, May 21 Litho. *Perf. 14*

355	A47	5c multicolored	.25	.25
356	A47	12c multicolored	.30	.25
357	A47	18c multicolored	.35	.25
358	A47	22c multicolored	.40	.30
359	A47	$1.50 multicolored	.95	.95
360	A47	$2.50 multicolored	3.50	1.50
a.		Souvenir sheet of 6, #355-360	6.50	6.50
		Nos. 355-360 (6)	5.75	3.50

Map of Anguilla, Map and View of Sombrero Island — A48

Map of Anguilla, Map and View of: 12c, Anguillita Island. 18c, Sandy Island. 25c, Prickly Pear Cays. $1, Dog Island. $2.50, Scrub Island.

1979 Litho. *Perf. 14*

361	A48	5c multicolored	.25	.25
362	A48	12c multicolored	.25	.25
363	A48	18c multicolored	.25	.25
364	A48	25c multicolored	.25	.25
365	A48	$1 multicolored	.45	*.55*
366	A48	$2.50 multicolored	.70	*.95*
a.		Souvenir sheet of 6, #361-366	3.00	3.00
		Nos. 361-366 (6)	2.15	2.50

Anguilla's Outer Islands.

Red Poinsettia — A49

35c, Kalanchoe. $1.50, Cream poinsettia. $2.50, White poinsettia.

1979, Oct. 22 Litho. *Perf. 14½*

367	A49	22c shown	.25	.25
368	A49	35c multicolored	.25	.25
369	A49	$1.50 multicolored	.40	.40
370	A49	$2.50 multicolored	.65	.65
a.		Souvenir sheet of 4, #367-370	2.50	2.50
		Nos. 367-370 (4)	1.55	1.55

Christmas.

Booths and Frames — A50

Designs: 50c, Earls Court Exhibition Hall. $1.50, Penny Black, Great Britain #2. $2.50, Exhibition emblem.

1979, Dec. 10 Litho. *Perf. 13*

371	A50	35c multicolored	.25	.25
372	A50	50c multicolored	.25	.25
373	A50	$1.50 multicolored	.40	.40
374	A50	$2.50 multicolored	.70	.70
b.		Souvenir sheet of 4, #371-374	1.75	1.75
		Complete booklet, 2 each #371-374	4.00	
		Nos. 371-374 (4)	1.60	1.60

Perf. 14½

371a	A50	35c	.25	.25
372a	A50	50c	.25	.25
373a	A50	$1.50	.45	.45
374a	A50	$2.50	.80	.80
c.		Souvenir sheet of 4, #371-374	2.00	2.00
		Nos. 371a-374a (4)	1.75	1.75

London 1980 Intl. Stamp Exhibition, May 6-14, 1980.

Lake Placid and Olympic Rings — A51

Olympic Rings and: 18c, Ice Hockey. 35c, Figure skating. 50c, Bobsledding. $1, Downhill skiing. $2.50, Luge.

1980, Jan. Litho. *Perf. 13½, 14½*

375	A51	5c multicolored	.25	.25
376	A51	18c multicolored	.25	.25
377	A51	35c multicolored	.25	.25
378	A51	50c multicolored	.30	.25
379	A51	$1 multicolored	.45	*.65*
380	A51	$2.50 multicolored	.80	*1.10*
a.		Souvenir sheet of 6, #375-380	2.25	*3.00*
		Nos. 375-380 (6)	2.30	2.75

13th Winter Olympic Games, Lake Placid, NY, Feb. 12-24.

Salt Field — A52

12c, Tallying salt. 18c, Unloading salt flats. 22c, Storage pile. $1, Bagging and grinding. $2.50, Loading onto boats.

1980, Apr. 14 Litho. *Perf. 14*

381	A52	5c multicolored	.25	.25
382	A52	12c multicolored	.25	.25
383	A52	18c multicolored	.25	.25
384	A52	22c multicolored	.25	.25
385	A52	$1 multicolored	.40	.40
386	A52	$2.50 multicolored	.85	.85
a.		Souvenir sheet of 6, #381-386	2.25	2.25
		Nos. 381-386 (6)	2.25	2.25

Salt industry.

Nos. 281, 288 Overprinted

1980, Apr. 16 ***Perf. 13½x14***

387	A40	10c multicolored	3.25	.30
388	A40	$2.50 multicolored	3.25	2.00

Nos. 283, 289 Overprinted

1980, Apr. 16 ***Perf. 13½x14***

389	A40	20c multicolored	2.50	.30
390	A40	$5 multicolored	5.00	3.00

Rotary International, 75th anniversary.

Big Ben, Great Britain No. 643, London 1980 Emblem A53

Designs: $1.50, Canada No. 756. $2.50, Statue of Liberty, US No. 1632.

1980, May
391 A53 50c multicolored .45 .45
392 A53 $1.50 multicolored .65 .65
393 A53 $2.50 multicolored 1.15 1.15
a. Souvenir sheet of 3, #391-393 2.25 2.25
Nos. 391-393 (3) 2.25 2.25

London 1980 International Stamp Exhibition, May 6-14.

Queen Mother Elizabeth, 80th Birthday — A54

1980, Aug. 4 Litho. *Perf. 14*
394 A54 35c multicolored .55 .35
395 A54 50c multicolored .70 .40
396 A54 $1.50 multicolored 1.25 1.00
397 A54 $3 multicolored 1.50 1.50
a. Souvenir sheet of 4, #394-397 5.00 4.25
Nos. 394-397 (4) 4.00 3.25

Pelicans — A55

22c, Great gray herons. $1.50, Swallows. $3, Hummingbirds.

1980, Nov. 10 Litho. *Perf. 14*
398 A55 5c multicolored .40 .25
399 A55 22c multicolored 1.10 .30
400 A55 $1.50 multicolored 2.40 .95
401 A55 $3 multicolored 3.00 2.10
a. Souvenir sheet of 4, #398-401 12.00 12.00
Nos. 398-401 (4) 6.90 3.60

Christmas. For overprints see Nos. 405-406.

Nos. 275, 278, 280-290, 334, 400-401 Overprinted

Perf. 13½x14, 14 (A55)

1980, Dec. 18 Litho.
402 A40 1c #275 .25 .80
403 A40 2c on 4c #278 .25 .80
404 A40 5c on 15c #282 1.25 .80
405 A55 5c on $1.50 #400 1.25 .80
406 A55 5c on $3 #401 1.25 .80
407 A40 10c #281 1.90 .80
408 A40 12c on $1 #287 .30 .80
409 A40 14c on $2.50 #288 .30 .80
410 A40 15c #282 1.50 .80
411 A40 18c on $5 #289 .35 .80
412 A40 20c #283 .35 .80
413 A40 22c #284 .35 .80
414 A40 25c on 15c #282 1.50 .95
415 A40 35c #285 .40 *.95*
416 A44 38c on 22c #334 .40 *.95*
417 A40 40c on 1c #275 .40 *.95*
418 A40 50c #286 .45 *1.10*
419 A40 $1 #287 .60 *1.40*
420 A40 $2.50 #288 1.50 *3.50*
421 A40 $5 #289 2.75 *4.50*
422 A40 $10 #290 5.50 *6.50*
423 A40 $10 on 6c #280 5.50 *6.50*
Nos. 402-423 (22) 28.30 36.90

Petition for Separation, 1825 — A56

22c, Referendum ballot, 1967. 35c, Airport blockade, 1967. 50c, Anguilla flag. $1, Separation celebration, 1980.

1980, Dec. 18 *Perf. 14*
424 A56 18c multicolored .25 .25
425 A56 22c multicolored .25 .25
426 A56 35c multicolored .30 .30
427 A56 50c multicolored .35 .35
428 A56 $1 multicolored .60 *.80*
a. Souvenir sheet of 5, #424-428 1.75 *2.00*
Nos. 424-428 (5) 1.75 1.95

Separation from St. Kitts-Nevis.

Nelson's Dockyard, by R. Granger Barrett — A57

Ship Paintings: 35c, Agamemnon, Vanguard, Elephant, Captain and Victory, by Nicholas Pocock. 50c, Victory, by Monamy Swaine. $3, Battle of Trafalgar, by Clarkson Stanfield. $5, Lord Nelson, by L.F. Abbott and Nelson's arms.

1981, Mar. 2 Litho. *Perf. 14*
429 A57 22c multicolored 2.10 .90
430 A57 35c multicolored 2.40 1.25
431 A57 50c multicolored 2.75 1.50
432 A57 $3 multicolored 3.75 *5.50*
Nos. 429-432 (4) 11.00 9.15

Souvenir Sheet
433 A57 $5 multicolored 4.75 4.75

Lord Horatio Nelson (1758-1805), 175th death anniversary (1980).

Minnie Mouse — A58

Easter: Various Disney characters in Easter outfits.

1981, Mar. 30 Litho. *Perf. 13½*
434 A58 1c multicolored .25 .25
435 A58 2c multicolored .25 .25
436 A58 3c multicolored .25 .25
437 A58 5c multicolored .25 .25
438 A58 7c multicolored .25 .25
439 A58 9c multicolored .25 .25
440 A58 10c multicolored .25 .25
441 A58 $2 multicolored 1.50 1.50
442 A58 $3 multicolored 2.00 2.00
Nos. 434-442 (9) 5.25 5.25

Souvenir Sheet
443 A58 $5 multicolored 5.50 5.50

Prince Charles, Lady Diana, St. Paul's Cathedral — A59

$2.50, Althorp. $3, Windsor Castle. $5, Buckingham Palace.

1981, June 15 Litho. *Perf. 14*
444 A59 50c shown .25 .25
a. Souvenir sheet of 2 .30 .30
b. Wmk. 380 .25 .25
c. Booklet pane of 4 #444b 1.00 1.00
445 A59 $2.50 multicolored .45 .60
a. Souvenir sheet of 2 1.60 1.60
446 A59 $3 multicolored .55 .75
a. Souvenir sheet of 2 2.00 2.00
b. Wmk. 380 1.25 1.25
c. Booklet pane of 4 #446b 5.00 5.00
Complete booklet, #444c, 446c 6.00
Nos. 444-446 (3) 1.25 1.60

Souvenir Sheet
447 A59 $5 multicolored 1.50 1.50

Royal Wedding. Nos. 444a-446a contain stamps in different colors.

Boys Climbing Tree — A60

10c, Boys sailing boats. 15c, Children playing instruments. $3, Children with animals. $4, Boys playing soccer, vert.

1981 Litho. *Perf. 14*
448 A60 5c multicolored .25 .25
449 A60 10c multicolored .30 .30
450 A60 15c multicolored .40 *.45*
451 A60 $3 multicolored 2.75 *3.50*
Nos. 448-451 (4) 3.70 4.50

Souvenir Sheet
452 A60 $4 multicolored 4.25 4.25

UNICEF, 35th anniv.
Issued: 5c-15c, July 31; $3-$4, Sept. 30.

"The Children were Nestled all Snug in their Beds" — A61

Christmas: Scenes from Walt Disney's The Night Before Christmas.

1981, Nov. 2 Litho. *Perf. 13½*
453 A61 1c multicolored .25 .25
454 A61 2c multicolored .25 .25
455 A61 3c multicolored .25 .25
456 A61 5c multicolored .30 .25
457 A61 7c multicolored .30 .25
458 A61 10c multicolored .30 .25
459 A61 12c multicolored .30 .25
460 A61 $2 multicolored 3.25 2.10
461 A61 $3 multicolored 3.25 2.50
Nos. 453-461 (9) 8.45 6.35

Souvenir Sheet
462 A61 $5 multicolored 7.00 7.00

Red Grouper A62

No. 473

5c, Ferries, Blowing Point. 10c, Racing boats. 15c, Majorettes. 20c, Launching boat, Sandy Hill. 25c, Coral. 30c, Little Bay cliffs. 35c, Fountain Cave. 40c, Sandy Isld. 45c, Landing, Sombrero. 60c, Seine fishing. 75c, Boat race, Sandy Ground. $1, Bagging lobster, Island Harbor. $5, Pelicans. $7.50, Hibiscus. $10, Queen triggerfish.

1982, Jan. 1 Litho. *Perf. 14*
463 A62 1c multi .25 *.90*
464 A62 5c multi .35 *.90*
465 A62 10c multi .25 *.90*
466 A62 15c multi .25 *.90*
467 A62 20c multi .45 *.90*
468 A62 25c multi 1.75 .90
469 A62 30c multi .35 *1.10*
470 A62 35c multi 1.75 1.25
471 A62 40c multi .35 *1.10*
472 A62 45c multi .55 *1.25*
473 A62 50c on 45c, #472 .60 .55
474 A62 60c multi 3.50 3.50
475 A62 75c multi 1.10 *2.50*
476 A62 $1 multi 2.50 2.50
477 A62 $5 multi 18.00 18.00
478 A62 $7.50 multi 14.00 *20.00*
479 A62 $10 multi 18.00 *20.00*
Nos. 463-479 (17) 64.00 *77.15*

For overprints & surcharges see Nos. 507-510, 546A-546D, 578-582, 606-608, 640-647.

Easter — A63

Butterflies on flowers: 10c, Zebra, anthurium. 35c, Caribbean buckeye. 75c, Monarch, allamanda. $3, Red rim, orchid. $5, Flambeau, amaryllis.

1982, Apr. 5
480 A63 10c multicolored 1.00 .25
481 A63 35c multicolored 1.75 .55
482 A63 75c multicolored 2.00 .80
483 A63 $3 multicolored 3.50 2.40
Nos. 480-483 (4) 8.25 4.00

Souvenir Sheet
484 A63 $5 multicolored 5.75 5.75

Princess Diana, 21st Birthday — A64

Designs: Portraits, 1961-1981.

1982, May 17
485 A64 10c 1961 .60 .25
486 A64 30c 1968 1.35 .25
487 A64 40c 1970 .70 .30
488 A64 60c 1974 .70 .40
489 A64 $2 1981 1.10 1.50
490 A64 $3 1981 5.00 2.10
a. Souvenir sheet of 6, #485-490 9.75 9.75
Complete booklet, 4 each #485, 487-489 10.00
Nos. 485-490 (6) 9.45 4.80

Souvenir Sheet
491 A64 $5 1981 9.75 9.75

For overprints see Nos. 639A-639G.

1982 World Cup — A65

Various Disney characters playing soccer.

1982, Aug. 3 Litho. *Perf. 11*
492 A65 1c multicolored .25 .25
493 A65 3c multicolored .25 .25
494 A65 4c multicolored .25 .25
495 A65 5c multicolored .25 .25
496 A65 7c multicolored .25 .25
497 A65 9c multicolored .25 .25
498 A65 10c multicolored .25 .25
499 A65 $2.50 multicolored 2.50 2.25
500 A65 $3 multicolored 2.50 2.25
Nos. 492-500 (9) 6.75 6.25

Souvenir Sheet
Perf. 14
501 A65 $5 multicolored 8.00 8.00

Scouting Year — A66

1982, July 5
502 A66 10c Pitching tent .60 .50
503 A66 35c Marching band 1.00 .70
504 A66 75c Sailing 1.40 1.25
505 A66 $3 Flag bearers 3.75 2.75
Nos. 502-505 (4) 6.75 5.20

Souvenir Sheet
506 A66 $5 Camping 6.25 6.25

Nos. 465, 474-475, 477 Overprinted

1982, Oct. 18 Litho. *Perf. 14*
507 A62 10c multicolored .30 .30
508 A62 60c multicolored .70 .70
509 A62 75c multicolored .90 .90
510 A62 $5 multicolored 5.00 5.00
Nos. 507-510 (4) 6.90 6.90

12th Commonwealth Games, Brisbane, Australia, Sept. 30-Oct. 9.

Christmas A67

Scenes from Walt Disney's Winnie the Pooh.

1982, Nov. 29

511	A67	1c multicolored	.25	.25
512	A67	2c multicolored	.25	.25
513	A67	3c multicolored	.25	.25
514	A67	5c multicolored	.40	.25
515	A67	7c multicolored	.40	.25
516	A67	10c multicolored	.50	.25
517	A67	12c multicolored	.60	.30
518	A67	20c multicolored	1.35	.35
519	A67	$5 multicolored	8.50	8.50
		Nos. 511-519 (9)	12.50	10.65

Souvenir Sheet

520	A67	$5 multicolored	11.50	11.50

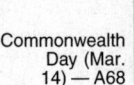

Commonwealth Day (Mar. 14) — A68

10c, Carnival procession. 35c, Flags. 75c, Economic cooperation. $2.50, Salt pond.
$5, Map showing Commonwealth.

1983, Feb. 28 Litho. *Perf. 14*

521	A68	10c multicolored	.25	.25
522	A68	35c multicolored	.45	.50
523	A68	75c multicolored	.85	1.00
524	A68	$2.50 multicolored	5.25	5.25
		Nos. 521-524 (4)	6.80	7.00

Souvenir Sheet

525	A68	$5 multicolored	7.00	7.00

Easter — A69

Ten Commandments.

1983, Mar. 31 Litho. *Perf. 14*

526	A69	1c multicolored	.25	.25
527	A69	2c multicolored	.25	.25
528	A69	3c multicolored	.25	.25
529	A69	10c multicolored	.25	.25
530	A69	35c multicolored	.55	.30
531	A69	60c multicolored	1.00	.50
532	A69	75c multicolored	1.10	.55
533	A69	$2 multicolored	2.75	2.10
534	A69	$2.50 multicolored	3.00	2.10
535	A69	$5 multicolored	4.25	3.25
		Nos. 526-535 (10)	13.65	9.80

Souvenir Sheet

536	A69	$5 Moses Taking Tablets	4.50	4.50

Local Turtles and World Wildlife Fund Emblem A70

1983, Aug. 10 Litho. *Perf. 13½*

537	A70	10c Leatherback	*5.00*	*2.10*
538	A70	35c Hawksbill	*8.25*	*3.25*
539	A70	75c Green	*12.00*	*4.75*
540	A70	$1 Loggerhead	*13.50*	*6.50*
		Nos. 537-540 (4)	38.75	16.60

Souvenir Sheet

541	A70	$5 Leatherback, diff.	*30.00*	*8.25*

1983, Aug. 10 Litho. *Perf. 12*

537a	A70	10c Leatherback	*3.50*	*2.40*
538a	A70	35c Hawksbill	*11.00*	*4.75*
539a	A70	75c Green	*14.50*	*10.50*
540a	A70	$1 Loggerhead	*22.00*	*13.00*
		Nos. 537a-540a (4)	51.00	30.65

Manned Flight Bicentenary — A71

10c, Montgolfiere, 1783. 60c, Blanchard & Jeffries, 1785. $1, Giffard's airship, 1852. $2.50, Lilienthal's glider, 1890.
$5, Wright Brothers' plane, 1909.

1983, Aug. 22 *Perf. 14*

542	A71	10c multicolored	.60	.40
543	A71	60c multicolored	1.90	.90
544	A71	$1 multicolored	2.00	1.10
545	A71	$2.50 multicolored	3.00	3.00
		Nos. 542-545 (4)	7.50	5.40

Souvenir Sheet

546	A71	$5 multicolored	6.50	*6.50*

Nos. 465, 471, 476-477 Overprinted

10c, Racing boats. 40c, Sandy Isld. $1, Bagging lobster, Island Harbor. $5, Pelicans.

1983, Oct. 24 Litho. *Perf. 14*

546A	A62	10c multicolored	.30	.25
546B	A62	40c multicolored	.45	.35
546C	A62	$1 multicolored	1.00	.65
546D	A62	$5 multicolored	7.75	3.75
		Nos. 546A-546D (4)	9.50	5.00

Jiminy Cricket — A72

Various Disney productions: 2c, Jiminy Cricket, kettle. 3c, Jiminy Cricket, toys. 4c, Mickey and Morty. 5c, Scrooge McDuck. 6c, Minnie and Goofy. 10c, Goofy and Elf. $2, Scrooge McDuck, diff. $3, Disney characters.
$5, Scrooge McDuck.

1983, Nov. 14 *Perf. 13½*

547	A72	1c shown	.25	.25
548	A72	2c multicolored	.25	.25
549	A72	3c multicolored	.25	.25
550	A72	4c multicolored	.25	.25
551	A72	5c multicolored	.25	.25
552	A72	6c multicolored	.25	.25
553	A72	10c multicolored	.25	.25
554	A72	$2 multicolored	4.50	3.25
555	A72	$3 multicolored	5.00	3.00
		Nos. 547-555 (9)	11.25	8.00

Souvenir Sheet

556	A72	$5 multicolored	8.00	8.00

Boys' Brigade Centenary A73

10c, Anguilla company, banner. $5, Marching with drummer.

1983, Sept. 12 Litho. *Perf. 14*

557	A73	10c multicolored	.50	.35
558	A73	$5 multicolored	3.75	3.25
a.		Souvenir sheet of 2, #557-558	4.75	4.75

1984 Olympics, Los Angeles A74

Mickey Mouse Competing in Decathlon.

1984, Feb. 20 Litho. *Perf. 14*

559	A74	1c 100-meter run	.25	.25
560	A74	2c Long jump	.25	.25
561	A74	3c Shot put	.25	.25
562	A74	4c High jump	.25	.25
563	A74	5c 400-meter run	.25	.25
564	A74	6c Hurdles	.25	.25
565	A74	10c Discus	.25	.25
566	A74	$1 Pole vault	3.25	3.00
567	A74	$4 Javelin	6.75	4.75
		Nos. 559-567 (9)	11.75	9.50

Souvenir Sheet

568	A74	$5 1500-meter run	12.50	12.50

1984, Apr. 24 *Perf. 12½x12*

559a	A74	1c	.25	.25
560a	A74	2c	.25	.25
561a	A74	3c	.25	.25
562a	A74	4c	.25	.25
563a	A74	5c	.25	.25
564a	A74	6c	.25	.25
565a	A74	10c	.25	.25
566a	A74	$1	4.75	3.75
567a	A74	$4	6.25	*9.50*
		Nos. 559a-567a (9)	12.75	15.00

Souvenir Sheet

568a	A74	$5 With Olympic rings emblem	11.00	11.00

Nos. 559a-567a inscribed with Olympic rings emblem. Printed in sheets of 5 plus label.

Easter — A75

Ceiling and Wall Frescoes, La Stanze della Segnatura, by Raphael (details).

1984, Apr. 19 Litho. *Perf. 13½x14*

569	A75	10c Justice	.25	.25
570	A75	25c Poetry	.30	.30
571	A75	35c Philosophy	.40	.40
572	A75	40c Theology	.40	.40
573	A75	$1 Abraham & Paul	.90	.90
574	A75	$2 Moses & Matthew	1.75	1.75
575	A75	$3 John & David	2.50	2.50
576	A75	$4 Peter & Adam	3.00	3.00
		Nos. 569-576 (8)	9.50	9.50

Souvenir Sheet

577	A75	$5 Astronomy	5.25	5.25

Nos. 463, 469, 477-479 Surcharged

1984 Litho. *Perf. 14*

578	A62	25c on $7.50 #478	.85	.45
579	A62	35c on 30c #469	.70	.55
580	A62	60c on 1c #463	.75	.60
581	A62	$2.50 on $5 #477	3.75	1.90
582	A62	$2.50 on $10 #479	2.75	1.90
		Nos. 578-582 (5)	8.80	5.40

Issue dates: 25c, May 17, others, Apr. 24.

Ausipex '84 — A76

Australian stamps.

1984, July 16 Litho. *Perf. 13½*

583	A76	10c No. 2	.60	.45
584	A76	75c No. 18	1.75	1.40
585	A76	$1 No. 130	2.25	1.90
586	A76	$2.50 No. 178	3.50	3.50
		Nos. 583-586 (4)	8.10	7.25

Souvenir Sheet

587	A76	$5 Nos. 378, 379	6.75	6.75

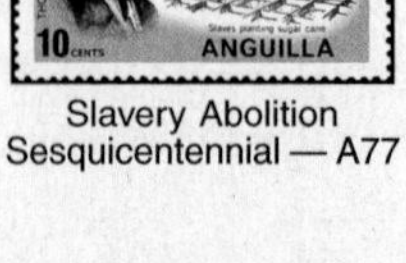

Slavery Abolition Sesquicentennial — A77

Abolitionists and Vignettes: 10c, Thomas Fowell Buxton, planting sugar cane. 25c, Abraham Lincoln, cotton field. 35c, Henri Christophe, armed slave revolt. 60c, Thomas Clarkson, addressing Anti-Slavery Society. 75c, William Wilberforce, Slave auction. $1, Olaudah Equiano, slave raid on Benin coast. $2.50, General Gordon, slave convoy in Sudan. $5, Granville Sharp, restraining ship captain from boarding slave.

1984, Aug. 1 *Perf. 12*

588	A77	10c multicolored	.25	.25
589	A77	25c multicolored	.45	.45
590	A77	35c multicolored	.55	.55
591	A77	60c multicolored	.70	.70
592	A77	75c multicolored	.90	.90
593	A77	$1 multicolored	1.00	1.00
594	A77	$2.50 multicolored	1.90	1.90
595	A77	$5 multicolored	3.75	3.75
a.		Miniature sheet of 8, #588-595	9.50	*11.00*
		Nos. 588-595 (8)	9.50	9.50

For overprints see Nos. 688-695a.

Christmas A78

Various Disney characters and celebrations.

Perf. 14, 12½x12 ($2)

1984, Nov. 12 Litho.

596	A78	1c multicolored	.25	.25
597	A78	2c multicolored	.25	.25
598	A78	3c multicolored	.25	.25
599	A78	4c multicolored	.25	.25
600	A78	5c multicolored	.25	.25
601	A78	10c multicolored	.25	.25
602	A78	$1 multicolored	3.75	3.00
603	A78	$2 multicolored	4.75	*5.00*
604	A78	$4 multicolored	6.00	*9.50*
		Nos. 596-604 (9)	16.00	19.00

Souvenir Sheet

605	A78	$5 multicolored	8.50	8.50

Nos. 464-465, 477 Ovptd. or Srchd.

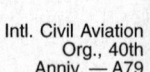

1984, Aug. 13

606	A62	5c #464	.35	.25
607	A62	20c on 10c #465	.50	.30
608	A62	$5 #477	7.00	4.25
		Nos. 606-608 (3)	7.85	4.80

Intl. Civil Aviation Org., 40th Anniv. — A79

60c, Icarus, by Hans Erni. 75c, Sun Princess, by Sadiou Diouf. $2.50, Anniv. emblem, vert.
$5, Map of the Caribbean.

1984, Dec. 3 Litho. *Perf. 14*

609	A79	60c multicolored	.90	*1.00*
610	A79	75c multicolored	1.40	*1.60*
611	A79	$2.50 multicolored	4.00	*4.25*
		Nos. 609-611 (3)	6.30	*6.85*

Souvenir Sheet

612	A79	$5 multicolored	6.00	*7.00*

Audubon Birth Bicent. — A80

Illustrations by artist and naturalist J. J. Audubon (1785-1851) — 10c, Hirundo rustica. 60c, Mycteria americana. 75c, Sterna dougallii. $5, Pandion haliaetus.
No. 617, Vireo solitarus, horiz. No. 618, Piranga ludoviciana, horiz.

1985, Apr. 30 Litho. *Perf. 14*

613 A80 10c multicolored 1.25 1.00
614 A80 60c multicolored 2.10 2.10
615 A80 75c multicolored 2.10 2.10
616 A80 $5 multicolored 7.75 7.75
Nos. 613-616 (4) 13.20 12.95

Souvenir Sheets

617 A80 $4 multicolored 7.00 7.00
618 A80 $4 multicolored 7.00 7.00

Queen Mother 85th Birthday — A81

Photographs: 10c, Visiting the children's ward at King's College Hospital. $2, Inspecting Royal Marine Volunteer Cadets at Deal. $3, Outside Clarence House in London. $5, In an open carriage at Ascot.

1985, July 2

619 A81 10c multicolored .25 .25
620 A81 $2 multicolored 1.00 1.00
621 A81 $3 multicolored 1.75 1.75
Nos. 619-621 (3) 3.00 3.00

Souvenir Sheet

622 A81 $5 multicolored 2.75 2.75

Nos. 619-621 printed in sheetlets of 5.

Birds — A82

5c, Brown pelican. 10c, Turtle dove. 15c, Man-o-war. 20c, Antillean crested hummingbird. 25c, White-tailed tropicbird. 30c, Caribbean elaenia. No. 629, 35c, Black-whiskered vireo. No. 629A, 35c, Lesser Antillean bullfinch ('86). 40c, Yellow-crowned night heron. 45c, Pearly-eyed thrasher. 50c, Laughing bird. 65c, Brown booby. 80c, Gray kingbird. $1, Audubon's shearwater. $1.35, Roseate tern. $2.50, Bananaquit. $5, Belted kingfisher. $10, Green heron.

1985-86 Litho. *Perf. 13½x14*

623 A82 5c multi 3.00 2.00
624 A82 10c multi 3.00 2.00
625 A82 15c multi 3.00 2.00
626 A82 20c multi 3.00 2.00
627 A82 25c multi 3.00 2.50
628 A82 30c multi 3.00 2.50
629 A82 35c multi 13.00 10.00
629A A82 35c multi 3.00 2.50
630 A82 40c multi 3.00 2.50
631 A82 45c multi 3.00 2.50
632 A82 50c multi 3.00 2.50
633 A82 65c multi 3.00 2.50
634 A82 80c multi 4.00 *5.00*
635 A82 $1 multi 4.00 *5.00*
636 A82 $1.35 multi 3.00 *5.00*
637 A82 $2.50 multi 10.00 *11.00*
638 A82 $5 multi 7.75 *13.50*
639 A82 $10 multi 13.00 *17.50*
Nos. 623-639 (18) 87.75 92.50

Issued: 25c, 65c, $1.35, $5, 7/22; 45c, 50c, 80c, $1, $10, 9/30; 5c-20c, 30c, No. 629, 40c, $2.50, 11/11; No. 629A, 3/10.

For overprints & surcharges see Nos. 678-682, 713-716, 723-739, 750-753, 764-767, 783-786.

Nos. 485-491 Overprinted

1985, Oct. 31 Litho. *Perf. 14*

639A A64 10c multicolored .25 .25
639B A64 30c multicolored .25 .25
639C A64 40c multicolored .30 .30
639D A64 60c multicolored .45 .45
639E A64 $2 multicolored 1.50 1.50
639F A64 $3 multicolored 3.50 3.50
h. Souv. sheet of 6, #639A-639F 4.25 4.25
Complete booklet, 4 each #639A, 639C-639E 11.00
Nos. 639A-639F (6) 6.25 6.25

Souvenir Sheet

639G A64 $5 multicolored 4.50 4.50

Nos. 464, 469, 475 and 477 Ovptd.

1985, Oct. 14 Litho. *Perf. 14*

640 A62 5c multicolored .45 .25
641 A62 30c multicolored .75 .55
642 A62 75c multicolored 1.10 .90
643 A62 $5 multicolored 10.50 10.50
Nos. 640-643 (4) 12.80 12.20

Nos. 465 and 469 Ovptd. or Srchd.

1985, Nov. 18

644 A62 10c multicolored .65 .25
645 A62 35c on 30c multi 1.40 .50

Nos. 476, 469 Srchd. or Ovptd.

1985, Nov. 18

646 A62 $1 multicolored 2.25 1.25
647 A62 $5 on 30c multi 6.75 6.75

Brothers Grimm A83

Christmas: Disney characters in Hansel and Gretel.

1985, Nov. 11 Litho. *Perf. 14*

648 A83 5c multicolored .55 .55
649 A83 50c multicolored 1.75 .80
650 A83 90c multicolored 2.25 1.25
651 A83 $4 multicolored 4.00 4.00
Nos. 648-651 (4) 8.55 6.60

Souvenir Sheet

652 A83 $5 multicolored 8.00 8.00

Mark Twain (1835-1910), Author A84

Disney characters in Huckleberry Finn.

1985, Nov. 11

653 A84 10c multicolored .70 .35
654 A84 60c multicolored 2.25 1.10
654A A84 $1 multicolored 3.00 1.60
655 A84 $3 multicolored 4.00 4.00
Nos. 653-655 (4) 9.95 7.05

Souvenir Sheet

656 A84 $5 multicolored 9.00 9.00

Christmas. No. 654A printed in sheets of 8.

Statue of Liberty Centennial A85

10c, Danmark, Denmark. 20c, Eagle, USA. 60c, Amerigo Vespucci, Italy. 75c, Sir Winston Churchill, G.B. $2, Nippon Maru, Japan. $2.50, Gorch, Germany.

$5, Statue of Liberty, vert.

1985, Nov. 25

657 A85 10c multicolored .85 .70
658 A85 20c multicolored 1.25 .95
659 A85 60c multicolored 1.60 1.60
660 A85 75c multicolored 1.60 1.50
661 A85 $2 multicolored 1.60 *3.00*
662 A85 $2.50 multicolored 2.10 *3.00*
Nos. 657-662 (6) 9.00 10.75

Souvenir Sheet

663 A85 $5 multicolored 9.00 9.00

Easter — A86

Stained glass windows.

1986, Mar. 27 Litho. *Perf. 14*

664 A86 10c multicolored .25 .25
665 A86 25c multicolored .50 .50
666 A86 45c multicolored .90 .90
667 A86 $4 multicolored 4.25 *5.25*
Nos. 664-667 (4) 5.90 6.90

Souvenir Sheet

668 A86 $5 multi, horiz. 7.00 7.00

Halley's Comet — A87

A88

Designs: 5c, Johannes Hevelius (1611-1687), Mayan temple observatory. 10c, US Viking probe landing on Mars, 1976. 60c, Theatri Cosmicum (detail), 1668. $4, Sighting, 1835. $5, Comet over Anguilla.

1986, Mar. 24

669 A87 5c multicolored .45 .45
670 A87 10c multicolored .50 .50
671 A87 60c multicolored 1.50 1.10
672 A87 $4 multicolored 6.25 6.25
Nos. 669-672 (4) 8.70 8.30

Souvenir Sheet

673 A88 $5 multicolored 5.50 *6.25*

Queen Elizabeth II, 60th Birthday
Common Design Type

20c, Inspecting guards, 1946. $2, Garter Ceremony, 1985. $3, Trooping the color.
$5, Christening, 1926.

1986, Apr. 21

674 CD339 20c multicolored .25 .25
675 CD339 $2 multicolored 1.50 1.50
676 CD339 $3 multicolored 2.25 2.25
Nos. 674-676 (3) 4.00 4.00

Souvenir Sheet

677 CD339 $5 multicolored 4.00 4.00

Nos. 623, 631, 635, 637 and 639 Ovptd.

1986, May 22 *Perf. 13½x14*

678 A82 5c multicolored .90 *1.10*
679 A82 45c multicolored 2.00 .75
680 A82 $1 multicolored 3.50 1.60
681 A82 $2.50 multicolored 3.50 *4.25*
682 A82 $10 multicolored 10.00 *11.00*
Nos. 678-682 (5) 19.90 18.70

Wedding of Prince Andrew and Sarah Ferguson — A89

1986, July 23 Litho. *Perf. 14*

683 A89 10c Couple .25 .25
684 A89 35c Andrew .30 .30
685 A89 $2 Sarah 1.10 *1.60*
686 A89 $3 Couple, diff. 1.75 *2.75*
Nos. 683-686 (4) 3.40 *4.90*

Souvenir Sheet

687 A89 $6 Westminster Abbey 5.25 *6.00*

Perf. 12

683a A89 10c Couple .40 .25
684a A89 35c Andrew .65 .30
685a A89 $2 Sarah 1.60 1.25
686a A89 $3 Couple, diff. 2.00 1.90
Nos. 683a-686a (4) 4.65 3.70

Souvenir Sheet

687a A89 $6 Westminster Abbey 5.25 *6.00*

Nos. 588-595 Overprinted

1986, Sept. 29 Litho. *Perf. 12*

688 A77 10c multicolored .65 .35
689 A77 25c multicolored 1.00 .55
690 A77 35c multicolored 1.25 .65
691 A77 60c multicolored 2.00 .95
692 A77 75c multicolored 2.00 1.25
693 A77 $1 multicolored 2.00 1.40
694 A77 $2.50 multicolored 3.50 *5.00*
695 A77 $5 multicolored 4.75 *6.50*
a. Miniature sheet, #688-695 19.00 *20.00*
Nos. 688-695 (8) 17.15 16.65

Ships — A90

1986, Nov. 29 Litho. *Perf. 14*

696 A90 10c Trading Sloop 1.75 .45
697 A90 45c Lady Rodney 3.25 .60
698 A90 80c West Derby 4.50 3.00
699 A90 $3 Warspite 7.75 6.00
Nos. 696-699 (4) 17.25 10.05

Souvenir Sheet

700 A90 $6 Boat Race Day, vert. 20.00 20.00

Christmas.

Discovery of America, 500th Anniv. (in 1992) — A91

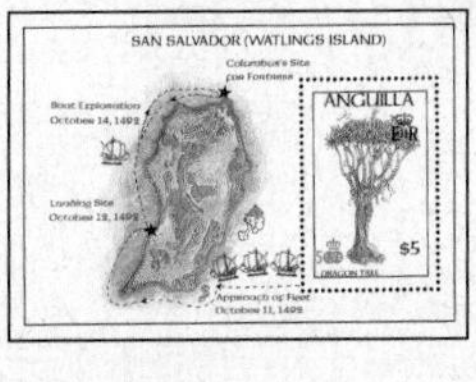

Dragon Tree A92

5c, Christopher Columbus, astrolabe. 10c, Aboard ship. 35c, Santa Maria. 80c, Ferdinand, Isabella. $4, Indians. No. 707, Caribbean manatee.

1986, Dec. 22

701 A91 5c multi .85 .85
702 A91 10c multi 1.40 .90
703 A91 35c multi 2.75 1.60
704 A91 80c multi, horiz. 2.00 *2.25*
705 A91 $4 multi 4.50 *5.00*
Nos. 701-705 (5) 11.50 10.60

Souvenir Sheets

706 A92 $5 shown 9.00 9.00
707 A92 $5 multi, horiz. 9.00 9.00

Butterflies — A93

10c, Monarch. 80c, White peacock. $1, Zebra. $2, Caribbean buckeye.
$6, Flambeau.

1987, Apr. 14 Litho. *Perf. 14*

708	A93	10c multicolored	2.00	.90
709	A93	80c multicolored	5.50	2.75
710	A93	$1 multicolored	6.50	3.25
711	A93	$2 multicolored	10.00	*11.00*
		Nos. 708-711 (4)	24.00	17.90

Souvenir Sheet

712	A93	$6 multicolored	20.00	20.00

Easter.

Nos. 629A, 631, 634 and 639 Ovptd in Red

1987, May 25 Litho. *Perf. 13½x14*

713	A82	35c on No. 629A	2.25	1.00
714	A82	45c on No. 631	2.25	1.10
715	A82	80c on No. 634	3.25	1.60
716	A82	$10 on No. 639	12.00	*16.00*
		Nos. 713-716 (4)	19.75	*19.70*

Separation from St. Kitts and Nevis, 20th Anniv. — A94

10c, Old goose iron, electric iron. 35c, Old East End School, Albena Lake-Hodge Comprehensive College. 45c, Old market place, People's Market. 80c, Old ferries & modern ferry at Blowing Point. $1, Old & new cable & wireless offices. $2, Public meeting at Burrowes Park, House of Assembly.

1987, May 25 *Perf. 14*

717	A94	10c multicolored	.75	.50
718	A94	35c multicolored	.85	.65
719	A94	45c multicolored	1.00	.80
720	A94	80c multicolored	2.25	1.00
721	A94	$1 multicolored	1.75	1.25
722	A94	$2 multicolored	2.50	*2.75*
a.		Souvenir sheet of 6, #717-722	12.50	12.50
		Nos. 717-722 (6)	9.10	6.95

Nos. 623, 625-628, 629A-639 Ovptd. in Red or Srchd. in Red & Black

1987, Sept. 4 Litho. *Perf. 13½x14*

723	A82	5c No. 623	3.50	3.00
724	A82	10c on 15c No. 625	3.50	3.00
725	A82	15c No. 625	3.50	3.00
726	A82	20c No. 626	3.50	3.00
727	A82	25c No. 627	3.50	3.00
728	A82	30c No. 628	3.50	3.00
729	A82	35c No. 629A	3.50	3.00
730	A82	40c No. 630	3.50	3.00
731	A82	45c No. 631	3.50	3.00
732	A82	50c No. 632	3.50	3.00
733	A82	65c No. 633	3.75	3.25
734	A82	80c No. 634	3.50	3.00
735	A82	$1 No. 635	4.00	*4.00*
736	A82	$1.35 No. 636	4.75	4.75
737	A82	$2.50 No. 637	5.50	*6.50*
738	A82	$5 No. 638	7.50	*9.00*
739	A82	$10 No. 639	11.00	*13.50*
		Nos. 723-739 (17)	75.00	74.00

Cricket World Cup — A95

Various action scenes.

1987, Oct. 5 *Perf. 14*

740	A95	10c multicolored	1.75	.90
741	A95	35c multicolored	2.50	.90
742	A95	45c multicolored	2.50	.95
743	A95	$2.50 multicolored	5.00	*7.50*
		Nos. 740-743 (4)	11.75	10.25

Souvenir Sheet

744	A95	$6 multicolored	15.00	15.00

Sea Shells, Crabs — A96

10c, West Indian top shell. 35c, Ghost crab. 50c, Spiny Caribbean vase. $2, Great land crab.
$6, Queen conch.

1987, Nov. 2

745	A96	10c multicolored	1.75	.70
746	A96	35c multicolored	2.25	1.10
747	A96	50c multicolored	4.00	2.10
748	A96	$2 multicolored	6.00	*10.50*
		Nos. 745-748 (4)	14.00	14.40

Souvenir Sheet

749	A96	$6 multicolored	14.00	14.00

Christmas.

Nos. 629A, 635-636 and 639 Ovptd. in Scarlet

1987, Dec. 14 Litho. *Perf. 13½x14*

750	A82	35c multicolored	.30	.30
751	A82	$1 multicolored	.70	.75
752	A82	$1.35 multicolored	1.00	1.00
753	A82	$10 multicolored	7.00	*8.50*
		Nos. 750-753 (4)	9.00	10.55

Easter (Lilies) — A97

30c, Crinum erubescens. 45c, Hymenocallis caribaea. $1, Crinum macowanii. $2.50, Hemerocallis fulva.
$6, Lilium longiflorum.

1988, Mar. 28 Litho. *Perf. 14*

754	A97	30c multicolored	.65	.35
755	A97	45c multicolored	.85	.35
756	A97	$1 multicolored	2.25	1.00
757	A97	$2.50 multicolored	2.50	*4.00*
		Nos. 754-757 (4)	6.25	5.70

Souvenir Sheet

758	A97	$6 multicolored	5.75	*7.25*

1988 Summer Olympics, Seoul — A98

1988, July 25 Litho. *Perf. 14*

759	A98	35c 4x100-Meter relay	.70	.35
760	A98	45c Windsurfing	.80	.50
761	A98	50c Tennis	2.25	1.60
762	A98	80c Basketball	5.00	4.25
		Nos. 759-762 (4)	8.75	6.70

Souvenir Sheet

763	A98	$6 Women's 200 meters	5.75	5.75

Nos. 629A, 634-635 and 637 Ovptd.

1988, Dec. 14 Litho. *Perf. 13½x14*

764	A82	35c multicolored	1.90	.85
765	A82	80c multicolored	2.75	1.75
766	A82	$1 multicolored	2.75	2.10
767	A82	$2.50 multicolored	4.75	*5.75*
		Nos. 764-767 (4)	12.15	10.45

Marine Life — A99

35c, Common sea fan. 80c, Coral crab. $1, Grooved brain coral. $1.60, Old wife.
$6, West Indies spiny lobster.

1988, Nov. 28 Litho. *Perf. 14*

768	A99	35c multicolored	1.50	.45
769	A99	80c multicolored	2.25	.95
770	A99	$1 multicolored	3.25	1.60
771	A99	$1.60 multicolored	3.50	*4.50*
		Nos. 768-771 (4)	10.50	7.50

Souvenir Sheet

772	A99	$6 multicolored	6.75	6.75

Christmas.

Lizards A100

1989, Feb. 20 Litho. *Perf. 13½x14*

773	A100	45c Wood slave	1.50	.70
774	A100	80c Slippery back	2.40	1.25
775	A100	$2.50 Iguana	5.50	*6.50*
		Nos. 773-775 (3)	9.40	8.45

Souvenir Sheet

776	A100	$6 Tree lizard	16.00	16.00

Easter — A101

Paintings: 35c, Christ Crowned with Thorns, by Hieronymous Bosch (c. 1450-1516. 80c, Christ Bearing the Cross, by David. $1, The Deposition, by David. $1.60, Pieta, by Rogier van der Weyden (1400-1464). $6, Crucified Christ with the Virgin Mary and Saints, by Raphael.

1989, Mar. 23 Litho. *Perf. 14x13½*

777	A101	35c multicolored	.50	.35
778	A101	80c multicolored	.90	.75
779	A101	$1 multicolored	1.00	.80
780	A101	$1.60 multicolored	1.60	*2.25*
		Nos. 777-780 (4)	4.00	4.15

Souvenir Sheet

781	A101	$6 multicolored	4.50	*5.00*

University of the West Indies, 40th Anniv. — A102

1989, Apr. 24 Litho. *Perf. 14x13½*

782	A102	$5 Coat of arms	3.50	*4.50*

Nos. 634-636 and 638 Ovptd.

1989, July 3 Litho. *Perf. 13½X14*

783	A82	80c multicolored	2.75	1.25
784	A82	$1 multicolored	2.75	1.60
785	A82	$1.35 multicolored	3.25	2.50
786	A82	$5 multicolored	9.25	*12.00*
		Nos. 783-786 (4)	18.00	17.35

Christmas A103

Well-known and historic houses: 5c, Lone Star, 1930. 35c, Whitehouse, 1906. 45c, Hodges House. 80c, Warden's Place.
$6, Wallblake House, 1787.

1989, Dec. 4 Litho. *Perf. 13½x14*

787	A103	5c multicolored	.45	*1.10*
788	A103	35c multicolored	.75	.55
789	A103	45c multicolored	.90	.65
790	A103	80c multicolored	1.60	2.10
		Nos. 787-790 (4)	3.70	4.40

Souvenir Sheet

791	A103	$6 multicolored	5.00	5.00

Fish — A104

5c, Blear eye. 10c, Redman. 15c, Speckletail. 25c, Grunt. 30c, Amber jack. 35c, Red hind. 40c, Goatfish. 45c, Old wife. 50c, Butter fish. 65c, Shell fish. 80c, Yellowtail snapper. $1, Katy. $1.35, Mutton grouper. $2.50, Doctor fish. $5, Angelfish. $10, Barracuda.

1990, Apr. 2 Litho. *Perf. 13½x14*

792	A104	5c multicolored	1.10	*1.50*
793	A104	10c multicolored	1.10	*1.50*
794	A104	15c multicolored	1.10	.90
795	A104	25c multicolored	1.25	1.10
796	A104	30c multicolored	1.25	1.10
797	A104	35c multicolored	1.25	1.10
798	A104	40c multicolored	1.50	1.10
799	A104	45c multicolored	1.50	.80
800	A104	50c multicolored	1.75	1.25
801	A104	65c multicolored	2.25	1.25
802	A104	80c multicolored	2.10	1.50
803	A104	$1 multicolored	2.25	1.50
804	A104	$1.35 multicolored	2.50	2.25
805	A104	$2.50 multicolored	4.00	*4.75*
806	A104	$5 multicolored	5.75	*7.75*
807	A104	$10 multicolored	9.25	*11.50*
		Nos. 792-807 (16)	39.90	40.85

Inscribed "1992"

792a	A104	5c Blear eye	.90	1.25
793a	A104	10c Redman	.90	1.25
797a	A104	35c Red hind	1.00	1.00
		Nos. 792a-797a (3)	2.80	3.50

For overprints and surcharge see Nos. 821-824, 849. For booklet see No. 890.

Easter — A105

35c, Last Supper. 45c, Trial. $1.35, Calvary. $2.50, Empty tomb.
$6, The Resurrection.

1990, Apr. 2 ***Perf. 14x13½***

811	A105	35c multicolored	1.25	.25
812	A105	45c multicolored	1.25	.35
813	A105	$1.35 multicolored	3.00	3.00
814	A105	$2.50 multicolored	3.75	3.75
		Nos. 811-814 (4)	9.25	7.35

Souvenir Sheet

815	A105	$6 multicolored	11.50	11.50

See Nos. 834-838.

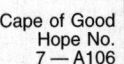

Cape of Good Hope No. 7 — A106

Stamps of Great Britain and exhibition emblem: 25c, No. 1, vert. 50c, No. 2, vert. $2.50, No. 93. $6, Nos. 1-2.

1990, Apr. 30 ***Perf. 14***

816	A106	25c multicolored	1.00	.40
817	A106	50c multicolored	1.75	.70
818	A106	$1.50 shown	3.00	3.00
819	A106	$2.50 multicolored	4.00	*4.75*
		Nos. 816-819 (4)	9.75	8.85

Souvenir Sheet

820	A106	$6 multicolored	13.00	*15.00*

Stamp World London '90, Penny Black 150th anniv.

Nos. 803-806 Overprinted

a

b

c

d

$1, Katy. $1.35, Mutton grouper. $2.50, Doctor fish. $5, Angelfish.

1990, Sept. 24 **Litho.** ***Perf. 13½x14***

821	A104(a)	$1 multi	2.25	1.40
822	A104(b)	$1.35 multi	2.50	1.60
823	A104(c)	$2.50 multi	6.00	6.00
824	A104(d)	$5 multi	11.50	*11.50*
		Nos. 821-824 (4)	22.25	*20.50*

Birds — A107

10c, Laughing gull. 35c, Brown booby. $1.50, Bridled tern. $3.50, Brown pelican.
$6, Least tern.

1990, Dec. 3 ***Perf. 14***

825	A107	10c multicolored	.95	.55
826	A107	35c multicolored	1.60	.55
827	A107	$1.50 multicolored	2.25	2.75
828	A107	$3.50 multicolored	5.00	5.00
		Nos. 825-828 (4)	9.80	8.85

Souvenir Sheet

829	A107	$6 multicolored	10.00	*11.50*

Christmas.

Flags — A108

50c, Mermaid. 80c, New Anguilla official. $1, Three dolphins. $5, Governor's official.

1990, Nov. 5 **Litho.** ***Perf. 13½x14***

830	A108	50c multicolored	1.75	.65
831	A108	80c multicolored	2.75	1.25
832	A108	$1 multicolored	2.90	1.50
833	A108	$5 multicolored	8.25	*9.50*
		Nos. 830-833 (4)	15.65	12.90

Nos. 811-815 Inscribed or Overprinted

1991, Apr. 30 **Litho.** ***Perf. 14x13½***

834	A105	35c like #811	1.25	.75
835	A105	45c like #812	1.50	.75
836	A105	$1.35 like #813	3.00	3.00
837	A105	$2.50 like #814	4.75	*5.25*
		Nos. 834-837 (4)	10.50	9.75

Souvenir Sheet

838	A105	$6 like #815	13.50	13.50

Easter. "1990" obliterated by black bar in souvenir sheet margin.

Christmas A109

5c, Angel, vert. 35c, Santa, vert. $1, Palm trees, poinsettias.
$5, Homes, holly.

Perf. 14x13½, 13½x14

1991, Dec. **Litho.**

839	A109	5c multicolored	.75	*.90*
840	A109	35c multicolored	2.00	.75
841	A109	80c shown	3.00	2.75
842	A109	$1 multicolored	3.00	2.75
		Nos. 839-842 (4)	8.75	7.15

Souvenir Sheet

843	A109	$5 multicolored	10.00	10.00

Easter A110

Designs: 35c, Church, angels holding palms, vert. 45c Church, angels singing, vert. 80c, Village. $1, People going to church, vert. $5, People at beach, sailboats.

1992 **Litho.** ***Perf. 14***

844	A110	35c multicolored	1.00	.65
845	A110	45c multicolored	1.25	.65
846	A110	80c multicolored	2.25	1.10
847	A110	$1 multicolored	2.25	1.60
848	A110	$5 multicolored	6.25	*12.00*
		Nos. 844-848 (5)	13.00	16.00

No. 796 Surcharged

1992, June 10 **Litho.** ***Perf. 13½x14***

849	A104	$1.60 on 30c #796	4.00	2.75

No. 849 inscribed "1992."

Independence, 25th Anniv. — A111

80c, Official seal, flag. $1, Official seal. $1.60, Flags, airport. $2, First seal.
$10, Nos. 1, 8-11, 15-16.

1992, Aug. 10 **Litho.** ***Perf. 14***

850	A111	80c multicolored	2.50	1.50
851	A111	$1 multicolored	2.50	1.50
852	A111	$1.60 multicolored	4.75	4.75
853	A111	$2 multicolored	4.75	4.75
		Nos. 850-853 (4)	14.50	12.50

Souvenir Sheet

854	A111	$10 multicolored	15.00	15.00

No. 854 contains one 85x85mm stamp.
For booklet see No. 970.

Sailboat Racing A112

Designs: 20c, On course. 35c, Stylized boat poster. 45c, Start of race. No. 858, Blue Bird, 1971, vert. No. 859, Construction plans for Blue Bird, vert. $1, Stylized boat poster, diff. $6, Like Nos. 855 & 857.

Perf. 13½x14, 14x13½

1992, Oct. 12 **Litho.**

855	A112	20c multicolored	1.90	.60
856	A112	35c multicolored	2.40	.50
857	A112	45c multicolored	2.75	.50
858	A112	80c multicolored	3.75	*4.25*
859	A112	80c multicolored	3.75	*4.25*
a.		Pair, #858-859	8.00	*10.00*
860	A112	$1 multicolored	3.75	2.50
		Nos. 855-860 (6)	18.30	12.60

Souvenir Sheet

861	A112	$6 multicolored	10.00	*12.50*

No. 861 contains one 96x31mm stamp.

Discovery of America, 500th Anniv. — A113

80c, Landfall. $1, Columbus, vert. $2, Fleet. $3, Pinta.
$6, Map of voyage, vert.

1992, Dec. 15 **Litho.** ***Perf. 14***

862	A113	80c multicolored	3.00	1.75
863	A113	$1 multicolored	3.00	1.75
864	A113	$2 multicolored	4.75	*5.50*
865	A113	$3 multicolored	5.50	*7.00*
		Nos. 862-865 (4)	16.25	16.00

Souvenir Sheet

866	A113	$6 multicolored	15.00	15.00

Christmas A114

Various Christmas trees and: 20c, Mucka Jumbie on stilts. 70c, Masquerading house to house. $1.05, Christmas baking, old oven style. $2.40, $5, Collecting presents.

1992, Dec. 7

867	A114	20c multicolored	.90	.65
868	A114	70c multicolored	2.00	.95
869	A114	$1.05 multicolored	2.25	1.75
870	A114	$2.40 multicolored	4.25	*6.00*
		Nos. 867-870 (4)	9.40	9.35

Souvenir Sheet

871	A114	$5 Sheet of 1 + 3 labels	7.00	7.00

Labels on No. 871 are similar to Nos. 867-869, but without denomination.

Easter — A115

Children's drawings: 20c, Kite flying. 45c, Cliff top village service. 80c, Morning devotion on Sombrero. $1.50, Hilltop church service. $5, Good Friday kites.

1993, Mar. 29 **Litho.** ***Perf. 14***

872	A115	20c multicolored	1.75	.90
873	A115	45c multicolored	2.75	.90
874	A115	80c multicolored	4.00	2.10
875	A115	$1.50 multicolored	4.50	*7.00*
		Nos. 872-875 (4)	13.00	10.90

Souvenir Sheet

876	A115	$5 multicolored	9.00	9.00

No. 876 contains one 42x56mm stamp.

Native Industries A116

20c, Salt. 80c, Tobacco, $1, Cotton. $2, Sugar cane.

1993, June 23 **Litho.** ***Perf. 14***

877	A116	20c multicolored	3.25	1.10
878	A116	80c multicolored	3.00	1.75
879	A116	$1 multicolored	3.00	1.75
880	A116	$2 multicolored	4.25	*6.50*
		Nos. 877-880 (4)	13.50	11.10

Souvenir Sheet

881	A116	$6 Fishing	14.00	14.00

Coronation of Queen Elizabeth II, 40th Anniv. — A117

Designs: 80c, Lord Great Chamberlain presents the spurs of chivalry. $1, The benediction. $2, Queen Elizabeth II, coronation photograph. $3, St. Edward's Crown. $6, Queen, Prince Philip in Gold State Coach.

1993, Aug. 16 **Litho.** ***Perf. 14***

882	A117	80c multicolored	2.25	1.00
883	A117	$1 multicolored	2.50	1.10
884	A117	$2 multicolored	3.25	3.25
885	A117	$3 multicolored	3.75	*4.75*
		Nos. 882-885 (4)	11.75	10.10

Souvenir Sheet

886	A117	$6 multicolored	14.00	*16.00*

Anguilla Carnival A118

20c, Pan musician. 45c, Pirates. 80c, Stars. $1, Playing mas. $2, Masqueraders. $3, Commandos.
$5, Carnival fantasy.

1993, Aug. 23 **Litho.** ***Perf. 14***

887	A118	20c multicolored	.70	.50
888	A118	45c multicolored	1.25	.50
889	A118	80c multicolored	2.40	1.10
890	A118	$1 multicolored	2.40	1.25
		Booklet, 5 ea #796, 890	14.00	

891 A118 $2 multicolored 3.75 *5.50*
892 A118 $3 multicolored 4.00 *6.25*
Nos. 887-892 (6) 14.50 15.10

Souvenir Sheet

893 A118 $5 multicolored 14.00 14.00

Christmas — A119

Traditional Christmas customs: 20c, Mucka Jumbies. 35c, Serenaders. 45c, Baking. $3, Five-fingers Christmas tree. $4, Mucka Jumbies and serenaders.

1993, Dec. 7 Litho. *Perf. 14x13½*

894 A119 20c multicolored 1.10 .90
895 A119 35c multicolored 1.50 .90
896 A119 45c multicolored 1.75 .90
897 A119 $3 multicolored 5.75 *8.00*
Nos. 894-897 (4) 10.10 10.70

Souvenir Sheet

Perf. 14

898 A119 $4 multicolored 5.75 5.75

No. 898 contains one 54x42mm stamp.

Mail Delivery — A120

Designs: 20c, Traveling Branch mail van, Sandy Ground, horiz. 45c, Mail boat, Betsy R, The Forest. 80c, Old post office, horiz. $1, Mail by jeep, Island Harbor. $4, New post office, 1993, horiz.

1994, Feb. 11 Litho. *Perf. 14*

899 A120 20c multicolored 2.00 .95
900 A120 45c multicolored 2.75 .95
901 A120 80c multicolored 3.50 1.90
902 A120 $1 multicolored 3.50 1.90
903 A120 $4 multicolored 5.50 *8.75*
Nos. 899-903 (5) 17.25 14.45

Royal Visits — A121

45c, Princess Alexandra. 50c, Princess Alice. 80c, Prince Philip. $1, Prince Charles. $2, Queen Elizabeth II.

1994, Feb. 18

904 A121 45c multicolored 2.00 .80
905 A121 50c multicolored 2.25 .80
906 A121 80c multicolored 3.00 1.75
907 A121 $1 multicolored 3.50 1.75
908 A121 $2 multicolored 4.75 *5.50*
a. Souvenir sheet of 4, #904-908 15.00 15.00
Nos. 904-908 (5) 15.50 10.60

Easter — A122

Stained glass windows: 20c, Crucifixion. 45c, Empty tomb. 80c, Resurrection. $3, Risen Christ with disciples.

1994, Apr. 6 Litho. *Perf. 14x15*

909 A122 20c multicolored .90 .65
910 A122 45c multicolored 1.10 .80
911 A122 80c multicolored 2.10 1.10
912 A122 $3 multicolored 5.50 *6.25*
Nos. 909-912 (4) 9.60 8.80

Christmas — A123

Designs: 20c, Adoration of the shepherds. 30c, Magi, shepherds. 35c, The Annunciation. 45c, Nativity Scene. $2.40, Flight into Egypt.

1994, Nov. 22 Litho. *Perf. 14*

913 A123 20c multicolored 1.00 .80
914 A123 30c multicolored 1.25 .80
915 A123 35c multicolored 1.25 .80
916 A123 45c multicolored 1.50 .80
917 A123 $2.40 multicolored 5.00 *6.00*
Nos. 913-917 (5) 10.00 9.20

1994 World Cup Soccer Championships, US — A124

Soccer player and: 20c, Pontiac Silverdome, Detroit. 70c, Foxboro Stadium, Boston. $1.80, RFK Memorial Stadium, Washington. $2.40, Soldier Field, Chicago.
$6, Two players.

1994, Oct. 3 Litho. *Perf. 13½x14*

918 A124 20c multicolored 1.00 .50
919 A124 70c multicolored 1.50 1.10
920 A124 $1.80 multicolored 3.00 *3.25*
921 A124 $2.40 multicolored 3.50 *4.00*
Nos. 918-921 (4) 9.00 8.85

Souvenir Sheet

922 A124 $6 multicolored 13.00 13.00

Easter A125

Turtle dove: 45c, One on tree branch. 50c, One on nest, one on branch. $5, Mother with young.

1995, Apr. 10 Litho. *Perf. 14*

923 A125 20c multicolored .70 .60
924 A125 45c multicolored 1.10 .90
925 A125 50c multicolored 1.25 1.10
926 A125 $5 multicolored 7.00 *10.00*
Nos. 923-926 (4) 10.05 12.60

UN, 50th Anniv. A126

Secretaries general and: 20c, Trygve Lie (1946-53), general assembly. 80c, UN flag, UN headquarters with "50" (no portrait). $1, Dag Hammarskjold (1953-61), charter, U Thant (1961-71). $5, UN complex, New York, vert. (no portrait).

Perf. 13½x14, 14x13½

1995, June 26 Litho.

927 A126 20c multicolored .40 .40
928 A126 80c multicolored .80 .80
929 A126 $1 multicolored 1.00 1.00
930 A126 $5 multicolored 5.00 5.00
Nos. 927-930 (4) 7.20 7.20

Caribbean Development Bank, 25th Anniv. — A127

Designs: 45c, Emblem, map of Anguilla. $5, Local headquarters along waterfront.

1995, Aug. 15 Litho. *Perf. 13½x14*

931 A127 45c multicolored 2.50 2.50
932 A127 $5 multicolored 4.75 4.75
a. Pair, #931-932 7.50 7.50

Whales A128

20c, Blue whale. 45c, Right whale, vert. $1, Sperm whale. $5, Humpback whale.

Perf. 13½x14, 14x13½

1995, Nov. 24 Litho.

933 A128 20c multicolored 2.75 .95
934 A128 45c multicolored 3.00 .80
935 A128 $1 multicolored 3.75 2.10
936 A128 $5 multicolored 8.50 *10.50*
Nos. 933-936 (4) 18.00 14.35

Christmas — A129

10c, Palm tree. 25c, Fish net floats. 45c, Sea shells. $5, Fish.

1995, Dec. 12 *Perf. 14½*

937 A129 10c multicolored .80 .80
938 A129 25c multicolored 1.10 .65
939 A129 45c multicolored 1.25 .65
940 A129 $5 multicolored 9.50 *12.00*
Nos. 937-940 (4) 12.65 14.10

Corals — A130

20c, Deep water gorgonia. 80c, Common sea fan. $5, Venus sea fern.

1996, June 21 Litho. *Perf. 14x14½*

941 A130 20c multicolored 2.00 .95
942 A130 80c multicolored 3.25 1.40
943 A130 $5 multicolored 9.00 *11.00*
Nos. 941-943 (3) 14.25 13.35

A131

1996 Summer Olympic Games, Atlanta: 20c, Running. 80c, Javelin, wheelchair basketball. $1, High jump. $3.50, Olympic torch, Greek, US flags.

1996, Dec. 12 Litho. *Perf. 14*

944 A131 20c multicolored .95 .75
945 A131 80c multicolored 3.25 1.50
946 A131 $1 multicolored 2.25 1.50
947 A131 $3.50 multicolored 6.00 6.00
Nos. 944-947 (4) 12.45 9.75

A132

Battle for Anguilla, bicent.: 60c, Sandy Hill Fort, HMS Lapwing. 75c, French troops destroy church, horiz. $1.50, HMS Lapwing defeats Valiant, Decius, horiz. $4, French troops land, Rendezvous Bay.

1996, Dec. 12

948 A132 60c multicolored 1.25 1.25
949 A132 75c multicolored 1.25 1.25
950 A132 $1.50 multicolored 2.50 2.50
951 A132 $4 multicolored 4.00 *5.00*
Nos. 948-951 (4) 9.00 10.00

Fruits and Nuts — A133

10c, Gooseberry. 20c, West Indian cherry. 40c, Tamarind. 50c, Pomme-surette. 60c, Sea almond. 75c, Sea grape. 80c, Banana. $1, Genip. $1.10, Coco plum. $1.25, Pope. $1.50, Papaya. $2, Sugar apple. $3, Soursop. $4, Pomegrante. $5, Cashew. $10, Mango.

1997, Apr. 30 Litho. *Perf. 14*

952 A133 10c multicolored .50 *.75*
953 A133 20c multicolored .60 *.40*
954 A133 40c multicolored .75 *.40*
955 A133 50c multicolored 1.00 .50
956 A133 60c multicolored 1.00 .60
957 A133 75c multicolored 1.25 .80
958 A133 80c multicolored 1.25 .90
959 A133 $1 multicolored 1.50 1.25
960 A133 $1.10 multicolored 1.50 *1.75*
961 A133 $1.25 multicolored 1.75 *1.90*
962 A133 $1.50 multicolored 2.00 *2.25*
963 A133 $2 multicolored 2.50 *3.00*
964 A133 $3 multicolored 4.00 *4.00*
965 A133 $4 multicolored 5.25 *5.50*
966 A133 $5 multicolored 6.25 *6.50*
967 A133 $10 multicolored 10.00 *10.50*
Nos. 952-967 (16) 41.10 41.00

Iguanas — A134

World Wildlife Fund: a, 20c, Baby iguanas emerging from eggs, juvenile iguana. b, 50c, Adult on rock. c, 75c, Two iguanas on tree limbs. d, $3, Adult up close, adult on tree branch.

1997, Oct. 13 Litho. *Perf. 13½x14*

968 A134 Strip of 4, #a.-d. 10.00 10.00

Diana, Princess of Wales (1961-97) — A135

Designs: a, 15c, In red & white. b, $1, In yellow. c, $1.90, Wearing tiara. d, $2.25, Wearing blouse with Red Cross emblem.

1998, Apr. 14 Litho. *Perf. 14*

969 A135 Strip of 4, #a.-d. 9.50 9.50

No. 969 was issued in sheets of 16 stamps.

Fountain Cavern Carvings — A136

30c, Rainbow Deity (Juluca). $1.25, Lizard. $2.25, Solar Chieftan. $2.75, Creator.

1997, Nov. 17 Litho. *Perf. 14x14½*

970 A136 30c multicolored .55 .55
Booklet, 5 ea #851, 970 12.00
971 A136 $1.25 multicolored 1.25 1.25
972 A136 $2.25 multicolored 2.10 2.10
973 A136 $2.75 multicolored 2.75 2.75
Nos. 970-973 (4) 6.65 6.65

1998 Intl. Arts Festival — A137

Paintings: 15c, "Treasure Island." 30c, "Posing in the Light." $1, "Pescadores de Anguilla." $1.50, "Fresh Catch." $1.90, "The Bell Tower of St. Mary's."

1998, Aug. 24 Litho. *Perf. 14*

974 A137 15c multi .65 .65
975 A137 30c multi, vert. .80 .80
976 A137 $1 multi, vert. 1.40 1.40
Booklet, 5 ea #975-976 10.00

977 A137 $1.50 multi 1.40 *1.60*
978 A137 $1.90 multi, vert. 1.75 *2.00*
Nos. 974-978 (5) 6.00 6.45

Christmas
A138

Paintings of "Hidden beauty of Anguilla": 15c, Woman cooking over open fire, girl seated on steps. $1, Person looking over fruits and vegetables. $1.50, Underwater scene. $3, Cacti growing along shore.

1998, Nov. 18

979 A138 15c multicolored .50 .50
980 A138 $1 multicolored 1.00 1.00
981 A138 $1.50 multicolored 1.40 1.40
982 A138 $3 multicolored 2.10 2.10
Nos. 979-982 (4) 5.00 5.00

Royal Air Force, 80th Anniv. — A139

Designs: 30c, Sopwith Camel, Bristol F2B. $1, Supermarine Spitfire II, Hawker Hurricane Mk1. $1.50, Avro Lancaster. $1.90, Harrier GR7, Panavia Tornado F3.

1998, Dec. 31 Litho. *Perf. 13½*
Granite Paper (No. 983)

983 A139 30c multicolored 1.25 .60
984 A139 $1 multicolored 2.00 1.00
985 A139 $1.50 multicolored 2.50 2.25
986 A139 $1.90 multicolored 4.00 3.25
Booklet, 5 ea #983-984 16.50
Nos. 983-986 (4) 9.75 7.10

University of the West Indies, 50th Anniv.
A140

Designs: $1.50, Anguilla campus. $1.90, Anguilla campus, torchbearer, University arms.

1998, Dec. 31 Litho. *Perf. 13¼*
Granite Paper (#988)

987-988 A140 Set of 2 3.00 *3.50*

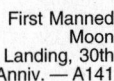

First Manned Moon Landing, 30th Anniv. — A141

Designs: 30c, Lift-off of Apollo 11, Command and Service Modules in lunar orbit. $1, Buzz Aldrin on Moon, footprint. $1.50, Lunar Module leaving Moon. $1.90, Splashdown.

1999, May 6 Litho. *Perf. 13¾*

989 A141 30c multi .80 .50
990 A141 $1 multi 1.40 .90
991 A141 $1.50 multi 1.50 1.75
992 A141 $1.90 multi 2.50 *3.25*
Nos. 989-992 (4) 6.20 6.40

Heroes of Anguilla's Revolution — A142

Designs: 30c, Albena Lake Hodge (1920-85). $1, Collins O. Hodge (1926-78). $1.50, Edwin W. Rey (1906-80). $1.90, Walter G. Hodge (1920-89).

1999, July 5 *Perf. 14½x14¼*

993 A142 30c multi .50 .30
994 A142 $1 multi .90 .60
995 A142 $1.50 multi 1.25 *1.25*
996 A142 $1.90 multi 1.90 *2.00*
Nos. 993-996 (4) 4.55 4.15

Modern Architecture
A143

Designs: No. 997, 30c, Library and resource center. No. 998, 65c, Parliamentary building and court house. No. 999, $1, Caribbean Commercial Bank. No. 999A, $1.50, Police headquarters. No. 1000, $1.90, Post office.

1999 Litho. *Perf. 14x14½*

997-1000 A143 Set of 5 7.50 *7.50*

Christmas and Millennium Celebrations
A144

Designs: 30c, Fireworks display and barbecue. $1, Globe, musicians. $1.50, Family dinner. $1.90, Decorated tree.

1999 Litho. *Perf. 13¼*

1001 A144 30c multi .55 .50
1002 A144 $1 multi 1.40 .90
1003 A144 $1.50 multi 2.10 2.10
1004 A144 $1.90 multi 2.25 *3.75*
Nos. 1001-1004 (4) 6.30 7.25

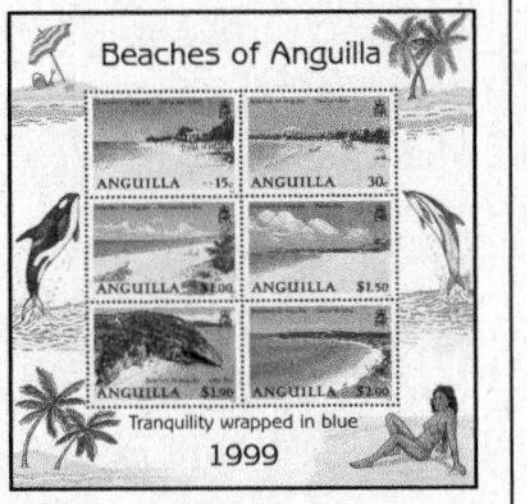

Beaches
A145

1005, 15c, Shoal Bay. 1006, 30c, Maundys Bay. 1007, $1, Rendezvous Bay. 1008, $1.50, Meads Bay. 1009, $1.90, Little Bay. 1010, $2, Sandy Ground.

1999 *Perf. 12*

1005-1010 A145 Set of 6 8.25 8.25
1010a Sheet of 6, #1005-1010 8.25 8.25
1010b As "a," with show emblem in margin 8.25 8.00

The Stamp Show 2000, London (No. 1010b). Issued: No. 1010b, 5/22/00.

Easter
A146

Toys: 25c, Banjo. 30c, Top. $1.50, Slingshot. $1.90, Roller. $2.50, Killy ban.

No. 1016: a, 75c, Rag doll. b, $1, Kite. c, $1.25, Cricket ball. d, $4, Pond boat.

2000 *Perf. 13¼*

1011 A146 25c multi .25 .25
1012 A146 30c multi .35 .35
1013 A146 $1.50 multi 1.25 1.25
1014 A146 $1.90 multi 1.60 *2.25*
1015 A146 $2.50 multi 2.60 *3.00*
Nos. 1011-1015 (5) 6.05 7.10

Souvenir Sheet

1016 A146 Sheet of 4, #a-d 6.25 6.25

100th Test Match at Lord's Ground — A147

$2, Lanville Harrigan. $4, Cardigan Connor. $6, Lord's Ground, horiz.

2000, May 5 Litho. *Perf. 13¾x13¼*

1017-1018 A147 Set of 2 7.75 7.75

Souvenir Sheet

1018A A147 $6 multi 12.00 12.00

Prince William, 18th Birthday
A148

Prince William and: 30c, Queen Elizabeth II, Princes Philip and Charles. $1, Princess Diana, Princes Harry and Charles. $1.90, Princes Harry and Charles. $2.25, Princes Charles and Harry, in winter wear.

$8, Prince William, vert.

2000, July 20 *Perf. 13¼*

1019-1022 A148 Set of 4 9.25 9.25

Souvenir Sheet

1023 A148 $8 multicolored 9.50 9.50

Queen Mother, 100th Birthday
A149

Queen Mother and: 30c, Prince William. $1.50, Anguilla shoreline. $1.90, Clarence House. $5, Castle of Mey.

2000, Aug. 4

1024-1027 A149 Set of 4 8.75 8.75

Intl. Arts Festival — A150

Artwork: 15c, Anguilla Montage, by Weme Caster. 30c, Serenity, by Damien Carty. 65c, Inter-island Cargo, by Paula Walden. $1.50, Rainbow City Where Spirits Find Form, by Fiona Percy. $1.90, Sailing Silver Seas, by Valerie Carpenter.

$7, Historic Anguilla, by Melsadis Fleming.

2000, Sept. 21 *Perf. 14¼x14½*

1028-1032 A150 Set of 5 5.75 5.75

Souvenir Sheet

Perf. 14¼

1033 A150 $7 multi 7.25 7.25

No. 1033 contains one 43x28mm stamp.

Christmas — A151

Flower and Garden Show flower arrangements by: 15c, Rowena Carty. 25c, Yvonda Hodge. 30c, Carty, diff. $1, Simon Rogers. $1.50, Lady Josephine Gumbs. $1.90, Carty, diff.

2000, Nov. 22 *Perf. 13¼*

1034-1039 A151 Set of 6 6.75 6.75

Natl. Bank of Anguilla, 15th Anniv.
A152

Designs: 30c, Soccer team in annual primary school tournament. $1, Sponsored sailboat, De Chan, vert. $1.50, Bank's crest, vert. $1.90, New bank building.

2000, Nov. 27

1040-1043 A152 Set of 4 5.25 5.25

Ebenezer Methodist Church, 170th Anniv.
A153

Church in: 30c, Sepia tones. $1.90, Full color.

2000, Dec. 4

1044-1045 A153 Set of 2 2.75 2.75

UN Women's Human Rights Campaign
A154

Designs: 25c, Soroptimist Day Care Center. 30c, Britannia Idalia Gumbs, vert. $2.25, Woman, vert.

2001 Litho. *Perf. 13¼*

1046-1048 A154 Set of 3 4.00 4.00

American Revolution, 225th Anniv. — A155

Designs: 30c, John Paul Jones, USS Ranger. $1, George Washington, Battle of Yorktown. $1.50, Thomas Jefferson, Submission of Declaration of Independence. $1.90, John Adams, Adams and Benjamin Franklin signing peace treaty.

2001, July 4 Litho. *Perf. 13¼*

1049-1052 A155 Set of 4 8.75 8.75

Birds — A156

Designs: 30c, White-cheeked pintail. $1, Black-faced grassquits, vert. $1.50, Brown noddy. $2, Black-necked stilts, vert. $3, Snowy plovers.

No. 1058: a, 25c, Snowy egret. b, 65c, Red-billed tropicbird. $1.35, Greater yellowlegs. $2.25, Sooty tern.

2001, Aug. 7

1053-1057 A156 Set of 5 14.00 14.00

Souvenir Sheet

1058 A156 Sheet of 4, #a-d 11.00 11.00

Year of Dialogue Among Civilizations — A157

2001, Oct. 9 *Perf. 13¼x13*

1059 A157 $1.90 multi 3.00 3.00

Christmas
A158

Musical instruments: 15c, Triangle. 25c, Maracas. 30c, Guiro, vert. $1.50, Marimba. $1.90, Tambu, vert. $2.50, Bath pan, vert.

No. 1066, vert.: a, 75c, Banjo. b, $1, Quatro. c, $1.25, Ukulele. d, $3, Cello.

2001, Nov. 5 Litho. *Perf. 13¼*

1060-1065 A158 Set of 6 10.00 10.00

Souvenir Sheet

1066 A158 Sheet of 4, #a-d 9.00 9.00

Sombrero Lighthouse
A159

Designs: 30c, Lighhouse in 1960s, vert. $1.50, Comparison of old and new lighthouses. $1.90, New lighthouse, 2001, vert.

2002, Apr. 2 Litho. *Perf. 13¼*
1067-1069 A159 Set of 3 7.00 7.00

Social Security Board, 20th Anniv. — A160

Social Security: 30c, Community service, vert. 75c, Benefits all ages, vert. $2.50, Benefits employees.

2002, May 28 Litho. *Perf. 13¼*
1070-1072 A160 Set of 3 5.00 5.00

Royal Navy Ships — A161

Designs: 30c, HMS Antrim, 1967. 50c, HMS Formidable, 1939. $1.50, HMS Dreadnought, 1906. $2, HMS Warrior, 1860.
$7, HMS Ark Royal, 1981, vert.

2002, June 24 Litho. *Perf. 13¼*
1073-1076 A161 Set of 4 6.25 6.25

Souvenir Sheet

1077 A161 $7 multi 10.00 10.00

Reign of Queen Elizabeth II, 50th Anniv. — A162

Designs: 30c, Holding baby. $1.50, Wearing white dress. $1.90, Wearing tiara. $5, Wearing yellow hat.
$8, At desk.

2002, Oct. 14 Litho. *Perf. 13¼*
1078-1081 A162 Set of 4 8.50 8.50

Souvenir Sheet

1082 A162 $8 multi 10.00 *10.00*

Pan-American Health Organization, Cent. — A163

Designs: 30c, The Valley Health Center. $1.50, Emblem, "100."

2002, Nov. 11
1083-1084 A163 Set of 2 2.75 2.75

Ships — A164

15c, Finance. 30c, Tiny Gull. 65c, Lady Laurel. 75c, Spitfire. $1, Liberator. $1.35, Excelsior. $1.50, Rose Millicent. $1.90, Betsy R. $2, Sunbeam R. $2.25, New London. $3, Ismay. $10, Warspite.

2003, June 10 Litho. *Perf. 14*

1085	A164	15c multi	.50	.50
1086	A164	30c multi	.60	.30
1087	A164	65c multi	1.00	.65
1088	A164	75c multi	1.00	.75
1089	A164	$1 multi	1.25	1.00
1090	A164	$1.35 multi	1.50	1.50
1091	A164	$1.50 multi	1.75	1.60
1092	A164	$1.90 multi	2.00	1.90
1093	A164	$2 multi	2.25	2.00
1094	A164	$2.25 multi	3.00	2.50
1095	A164	$3 multi	3.25	3.25
1096	A164	$10 multi	10.00	*11.00*
	Nos. 1085-1096 (12)		28.10	26.95

Artifacts — A165

Designs: 30c, Stone pestle. $1, Frog-shaped shell ornament. $1.50, Pottery. $1.90, Mask.

2003, Aug. 18 Litho. *Perf. 13¼*
1097-1100 A165 Set of 4 5.75 5.75

Hotels — A166

Designs: 75c, Frangipani Beach Club. $1, Pimms, Cap Juluca. $1.35, Cocoloba Beach Resort. $1.50, Malliouhana Hotel. $1.90, Carimar Beach Club. $3, Covecastles.

2003 Litho. *Perf. 13¼*
1101-1106 A166 Set of 6 9.50 9.50

2002 International Arts Festival A167

Paintings: 15c, Eudice's Garden, by Eunice Summer. 30c, Hammocks, by Lisa Davenport. $1, Conched Out, by Richard Shaffett. $1.50, Island Rhythms, by Carol Gavin. $1.90, Party at the Beach, by Jean-Pierre Ballagny. $3, Shoal Bay Before Luis, by Jacqueline Mariethoz, vert.

Perf. 13½x13¼, 13¼x13½
2004, Aug. 23 Litho.
1107-1112 A167 Set of 6 12.50 12.50

2004 Summer Olympics, Athens — A168

2004 Athens Olympics emblem and: 30c, Runners. $1, Yachting. $1.50, Gymnastics. $1.90, Acropolis, Pierre de Coubertin, Dimitrios Vikelas, horiz.

Perf. 13½x13¼, 13¼x13½
2004, Sept. 20 Litho.
1113-1116 A168 Set of 4 7.00 7.00

Goats A169

Various goats: 30c, 50c, $1, $1.50, $1.90, $2.25. $1, $1.90 are vert.

Perf. 13¼x13½, 13½x13¼
2004, Oct. 4
1117-1122 A169 Set of 6 10.50 10.50

Development of the Telephone — A170

Types of telephones: 30c, Cordless. $1, Touch-tone. $1.50, Cellular. $1.90, Rotary dial, horiz. $3.80, Magneto.

Perf. 13¼x13, 13x13¼
2004, Nov. 8 Litho.
1123-1127 A170 Set of 5 8.75 8.75

Christmas A171

Santa Claus: 30c, Baking with rock oven. $1.50, Climbing coconut tree. $1.90, With string band. $3.80, Delivering gifts by donkey.
$8, Delivering gifts by boat.

2004, Nov. 15 *Perf. 13x13¼*
1128-1131 A171 Set of 4 7.25 7.25

Souvenir Sheet

1132 A171 $8 multi 7.50 7.50

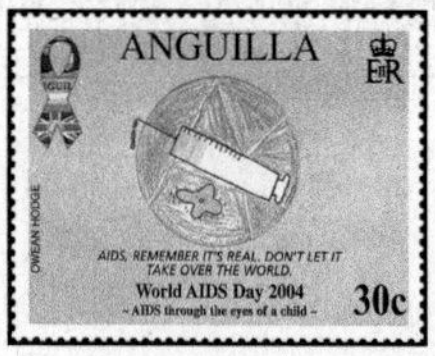

World AIDS Day A172

Children's drawings by: 30c, Owean Hodge. $1.50, Lydia Fleming. $1.90, Nina Rodriguez.
No. 1136: a, 15c, Kenswick Richardson. b, 75c, Toniquewah Ruan. c, $1, Elizabeth Anne Orchard. d, $2, Tricia Watty-Beard.

2005, Jan. 18 *Perf. 13*
1133-1135 A172 Set of 3 5.00 5.00

Souvenir Sheet

1136 A172 Sheet of 4, #a-d 5.00 5.00

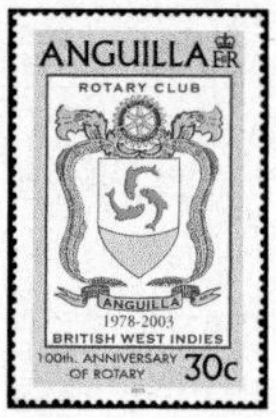

Rotary International, Cent. — A173

Designs: 30c, Emblem of Anguilla Rotary Club. $1, Pelican and palm tree. $1.50, Rotary International founder Paul Harris. $1.90, Children at playground.

Perf. 14¾x14¼
2005, Mar. 23 Litho.
1137-1140 A173 Set of 4 4.75 4.75

Dogs — A174

Designs: 30c, Dog in field. $1.50, Two dogs sitting, vert. $1.90, Dog sitting, vert. $2.25, Dog.

Perf. 14¼x14¾, 14¾x14¼
2005, June 1
1141-1144 A174 Set of 4 5.50 5.50

Commercial Airplanes A175

Designs: 30c, Air Anguilla Cessna 402. 40c, LIAT DHC Dash 8. 60c, Winair Foxtrot-DHC Twin Otter. $1, Anguilla Airways Piper Aztec. $1.50, St. Thomas Air Transport Piper Aztec. $1.90, Carib Air Service Piper Aztec.

2006, Mar. 13 Litho. *Perf. 13¼*
1145-1150 A175 Set of 6 7.00 7.00

Butterflies A176

Designs: 30c, Appias drusillia. $1.50, Danaus plexippus megalippe. $1.90, Phoebis sennae. $2.75, Papilio demoleus.
No. 1155: a, 40c, Aphrissa statira. b, 60c, Eurema elathea. c, $1, Danaus plexippus megalippe, diff. d, $3, Agraulis vanillae.

2006, Oct. 9 Litho. *Perf. 13¼*
1151-1154 A176 Set of 4 7.25 7.25

Miniature Sheet

1155 A176 Sheet of 4, #a-d 5.75 5.75

Anguilla Soroptomist Club, 25th Anniv. — A177

Designs: $1.90, Soroptomist International emblem. $2.75, Alecia Ballin.

2007, Jan. 29
1156-1157 A177 Set of 2 5.25 5.25

Bronze Devotional Medallions From El Buen Consuelo Shipwreck — A178

Medallions depicting: 30c, St. Bruno. $1.50, Our Lady of Sorrows. $1.90, Five Wounds of Jesus. $2.75, Virgin and Child.

2007, Mar. 19 Litho. *Perf. 13¼*
1158-1161 A178 Set of 4 6.25 6.25

Anguilla Revolution, 40th Anniv. — A179

Participants: 30c, Hyacinth Carty. $1, Edward Duncan. $1.50, Connell Harrigan. $1.90, Rev. Leonard Carty. $2.25, Jeremiah Gumbs. $3.75, Atlin Harrigan.

2007, July 18 Litho. *Perf. 13¼*
1162-1167 A179 Set of 6 10.00 10.00

Historical Architecture A180

Designs: 30c, Building with lean-to and gabled roof, by Melsadis Fleming. $1, Building with lean-to and gabled roof, by Daryl Thompson. $1.25, Building with double-hipped roof, by Fleming. $1.50, Building with hipped roof, by Susan Croft. $1.90, Building with double-gabled roof, by Fleming. $2.40, Building with double-hipped roof, by Fleming, diff. $2.75, Building with hipped roof, by Fleming. $3.75, Building with gabled roof, by Fleming.

2008, Oct. 6 *Perf. 14x14¾*
1168-1175 A180 Set of 8 10.00 10.00

Traditional Household Items — A181

Designs: 30c, Three-legged pot. $1, Mortar and pestle. $1.50, Gas and coal irons. $1.90, Oil and gas lamps. $2, Coal pots. $2.25, Enamel and aluminum utensils.

2009, June 18 ***Perf. 13¼***

1176-1181	A181	Set of 6	6.75 6.75

Wild Flowers — A182

Designs: 30c, Tabebulia heterophylla. $1, Argemone mexicana. $1.50, Catharanthus roseus. $1.90, Datura stramonium. $2, Centrosena virginiatum. $2.25, Tetramicra canaliculata.

2009, Sept. 12

1182-1187	A182	Set of 6	6.75 6.75

Endemic Flora and Fauna A183

Designs: $1.50, Sombrero Island ground lizard. $2, Little Scrub Island ground lizard. $2.25, Anguilla bush.

2010, Aug. 10 ***Perf. 13¼***

1188-1190	A183	Set of 3	4.50 4.50

Wedding of Prince William and Catherine Middleton — A184

Designs: $4, Couple. $5, Couple, horiz. $6, Couple, diff. $10, Couple and royal arms, horiz.

2011, June 20 **Litho.** ***Perf. 13¼***

1191-1194	A184	Set of 4	18.50 18.50

Anguilla Revolutionary Coins A185

Designs: 15c, 1967 Liberty dollar counterstruck on Panamanian balboa. 40c, 1967 Liberty dollar counterstruck on Mexican peso. $2.50, Obverse and reverse of 1968 silver $25 coin commemorating first year of Independence. $5, Ship, reverse of 1969 $4 coin.

2012, Feb. 28 ***Perf. 13½x13¼***

1195-1198	A185	Set of 4	6.00 6.00

Royal Anguilla Police Force, 40th Anniv. A186

Designs: 30c, Old Valley Police Station. $1, Police on parade. $1.50, Police headquarters. $1.90, Past and present police crests. $5, Lt. Col. Claudius M. Roberts, first Chief of Police, vert.

2012, Nov. 26 ***Perf. 13¼***

1199-1203	A186	Set of 5	7.25 7.25

Methodism on Anguilla, 200th Anniv. A187

Designs: 40c, Old Methodist Manse, Sandy Ground. 65c, Map of Anguilla, 200th anniversary emblem. $10, Montage of Ebenezer and Bethel Churches, by Aileen Lamond-Smith.

2013, Nov. 11 **Litho.** ***Perf. 13¼***

1204-1206	A187	Set of 3	8.25 8.25

Ship Captains — A188

Captains: 15c, George Richardson (1919-2003). 50c, James Woods (1908-98). 75c, Fritz Ericson Hughes (1891-1970). $1.35, Christopher John Connor (1925-94). $2, Herchel Gumbs (1884-1965). $2.25, Zilphus Fleming (1915-92). $2.50, Walter Hodge (1920-89). $5, John Franklin (1912-98).

2013, Nov. 25 **Litho.** ***Perf. 13¼***

1207-1214	A188	Set of 8	11.00 11.00
1214a		Sheet of 8, #1207-1214	11.00 11.00

See Nos. 1219-1226.

Secondary Education, 60th Anniv. — A189

Designs: 15c, Boy's shirt and tie, 1950s. $1.35, Girl's uniform, 1950s. $2, James T. Thom, first principal of Valley Secondary School. $2.50, Valley Secondary School crest.

2013, Dec. 31 **Litho.** ***Perf. 13¼***

1215-1218	A189	Set of 4	4.50 4.50

Ship Captains Type of 2013

Designs: 50c, Harry S. Franklin (1926-2006). 65c, John A. Edwards (1910-75). 75c, Amos Richardson (1924-2004). 80c, George Joshua Gumbs (1926-2012). $2, Ivan Richardson (1917-67). $2.50, Edward Camile Connor (1910-2000). $3, Henry E. Richardson (1890-1990). $6, Malcolm C. Wathey (1905-84).

2014, July 7 **Litho.** ***Perf. 13¼***

1219-1226	A188	Set of 8	12.00 12.00
1226a		Souvenir sheet of 8, #1219-1226	12.00 12.00

Day Around the Island Boat Race Winning Sailboats — A190

Designs: 50c, Real Deal, champion in 2011, 2012. 60c, Superstar, champion in 2004, 2007, 2009, horiz. 80c, Nathalie, champion in 1993, 1994, 1995. $1.35, UFO, champion in 1997, 1998, 2003, 2005, horiz. $3, De Tree, champion in 2001, 2006, 2008, 2010, 2013, horiz. $10, De Chan, champion in 1982-84, 1986, 1991-92, 1996, 2002.

No. 1233: a, 15c, Sonic, champion in 2014. b, 40c, Satellite, champion in 2000. c, 65c, Viagra, champion in 1999. d, 75c, Saga Boy, champion in 1990. e, $4, Wasp, champion in 1987.

2015, May 29 **Litho.** ***Perf. 13¼***

1227-1232	A190	Set of 6	12.00 12.00

Souvenir Sheet

1233	A190	Sheet of 5, #a-e	4.50 4.50

Summer Festival — A191

Designs: 50c, Calypso Show. $1, August Monday Beach Party, horiz. $1.40, Jouvert, horiz. $1.80, Woman in butterfly costume, horiz. $2.10, Parade, horiz. $3, Queen Show.

2016, Aug. 2 **Litho.** ***Perf. 13¼***

1234-1239	A191	Set of 6	7.25 7.25

National Symbols A192

Designs: 50c, Ground lizard (national animal). 75c, White cedar flowers (national flower). $1.40, Peas and rice (national dish). $1.80, Turtle doves (national bird). $2.10, Boat racing (national sport). $3, Turquoise, white and orange (national colors). $5, White cedar tree (national tree), vert. $10, National flag.

2016, Oct. 10 **Litho.** ***Perf. 13¼***

1240-1247	A192	Set of 8	18.50 18.50

ANJOUAN

'an-jü-wän

LOCATION — One of the Comoro Islands in the Mozambique Channel between Madagascar and Mozambique.
GOVT. — French colony.
AREA — 89 sq. mi.
POP. — 20,000 (approx. 1912)
CAPITAL — Mossamondu

See Comoro Islands.

100 Centimes = 1 Franc

Navigation and Commerce — A1

Perf. 14x13½

1892-1907 **Typo.** **Unwmk.**

Name of Colony in Blue or Carmine

1	A1	1c black, *blue*	1.75	1.75
2	A1	2c brown, *buff*	2.75	1.75
3	A1	4c claret, *lav*	5.50	4.00
4	A1	5c green, *grnsh*	9.50	6.25
5	A1	10c blk, *lavender*	11.50	6.75
6	A1	10c red ('00)	37.50	30.00
7	A1	15c blue, quadrille paper	17.00	11.50
8	A1	15c gray, *lt gray* ('00)	32.50	22.50
9	A1	20c red, *green*	17.50	11.00
10	A1	25c black, *rose*	17.50	14.00
11	A1	25c blue ('00)	32.50	22.50
12	A1	30c brn, *bister*	35.00	22.50
13	A1	35c blk, *yel* ('06)	18.00	10.00
14	A1	40c red, *straw*	37.50	32.50
15	A1	45c blk, *gray grn* ('07)	150.00	115.00
16	A1	50c car, *rose*	45.00	32.50
17	A1	50c brn, *az* ('00)	32.50	32.50
18	A1	75c vio, *orange*	37.50	27.50
19	A1	1fr brnz grn, *straw*	90.00	77.50
		Nos. 1-19 (19)	631.00	482.00

Perf. 13½x14 stamps are counterfeits.

Issues of 1892-1907 Surcharged in Black or Carmine

1912

20	A1	5c on 2c brn, *buff*	1.25	1.25
21	A1	5c on 4c cl, *lav* (C)	1.40	*1.50*
a.		Pair, one without surcharge	*1,000.*	*1,100.*
22	A1	5c on 15c blue (C)	1.40	1.40
a.		Pair, one without surcharge	*1,100.*	*1,000.*
23	A1	5c on 20c red, *green*	1.40	1.40
a.		Pair, one without surcharge	*1,100.*	*1,100.*
24	A1	5c on 25c blk, *rose* (C)	1.50	*1.75*
25	A1	5c on 30c brn, *bis* (C)	2.00	*2.10*
26	A1	10c on 40c red, *straw*	2.00	*2.25*
27	A1	10c on 45c black, *gray green* (C)	2.40	2.40
28	A1	10c on 50c car, *rose*	6.00	*6.50*
29	A1	10c on 75c vio, *org*	4.00	*4.50*
30	A1	10c on 1fr brnz grn, *straw*	5.50	*5.75*
a.		Pair, one without surcharge	*1,250.*	*1,200.*
		Nos. 20-30 (11)	28.85	30.80

Two spacings between the surcharged numerals are found on Nos. 20-30. See the *Scott Classic Specialized Catalogue of Stamps and Covers* for detailed listings.

Nos. 20-30 were available for use in Madagascar and the Comoro archipelago.

The stamps of Anjouan were superseded by those of Madagascar, and in 1950 by those of Comoro Islands.

ANNAM & TONKIN

a-'nam and 'tän-'kin

LOCATION — In French Indo-China bordering on the China Sea on the east and Siam on the west.
GOVT. — French Protectorate
AREA — 97,503 sq. mi.
POP. — 14,124,000 (approx. 1890)
CAPITAL — Annam: Hue; Tonkin: Hanoi

For administrative purposes, the Protectorates of Annam, Tonkin, Cambodia, Laos and the Colony of Cochin-China were grouped together and were known as French Indo-China.

100 Centimes = 1 Franc

Catalogue values for unused stamps are for examples without gum as most stamps were issued in that condition.

Stamps of French Colonies, 1881-86 Handstamped Surcharged in Black

Perf. 14x13½

1888, Jan. 21			**Unwmk.**
1	A9 1c on 2c brn, *buff*	47.50	*50.00*
a.	Inverted surcharge	200.00	*200.00*
b.	Sideways surcharge	200.00	*210.00*
2	A9 1c on 4c claret, *lav*	37.50	45.00
a.	Inverted surcharge	200.00	*210.00*
b.	Double surcharge	275.00	225.00
c.	Sideways surcharge	200.00	*210.00*
3	A9 5c on 10c blk, *lav*	47.50	37.50
a.	Inverted surcharge	200.00	200.00
b.	Double surcharge	225.00	225.00
4	A9 5c on 2c brn, *buff*	*8,500.*	

Hyphen between "A" and "T"

7	A9 1c on 2c brn, *buff*	325.00	*425.00*
a.	Inverted surcharge	750.00	*775.00*
b.	Sideways surcharge	750.00	*775.00*
c.	Pair, Nos. 1, 7	9,000.	
8	A9 1c on 4c claret, *lav*	525.00	*625.00*
9	A9 5c on 10c blk, *lav*	220.00	*240.00*

A 5c on 2c with surcharge in blue was prepared but not issued.

In these surcharges there are different types of numerals and letters.

There are numerous other errors in the placing of the surcharges, including double one inverted, double both inverted, double one sideways, and pair one without surcharge. Such varieties command substantial premiums.

These stamps were superseded in 1892 by those of Indo-China.

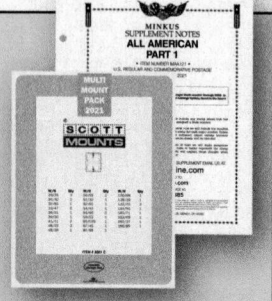

ANTIGUA

an-'tēg-ˌwˌə

LOCATION — In the West Indies, southeast of Puerto Rico
GOVT. — Independent state
AREA — 171 sq. mi.
POP. — 64,246 (est. 1999)
CAPITAL — St. John's

Antigua was one of the presidencies of the former Leeward Islands colony until becoming a Crown Colony in 1956. It became an Associated State of the United Kingdom in 1967 and an independent nation on November 1, 1981, taking the name of Antigua and Barbuda.

Antigua stamps were discontinued in 1890 and resumed in 1903. In the interim, stamps of Leeward Islands were used. Between 1903-1956, stamps of Antigua and Leeward Islands were used concurrently.

12 Pence = 1 Shilling
20 Shillings = 1 Pound
100 Cents = 1 Dollar (1951)

Catalogue values for unused stamps in this country are for Never Hinged items, beginning with Scott 96.

Watermark

Wmk. 5 — Star

Values for unused stamps are for examples with original gum as defined in the catalogue introduction. Any exceptions will be noted. Very fine examples of Nos. 1-8, 11, 18-20 will have perforations touching the design on at least one frameline due to the narrow spacing of the stamps on the plates. Stamps with perfs clear of the framelines on all four sides are extremely scarce and will command higher prices.

Queen Victoria — A1

Rough Perf. 14-16

1862 Engr. Unwmk.

1 A1 6p blue green 950.00 600.00
a. Perf. 11-13 8,500.
b. Perf. 11-13x14-16 3,750.
c. Perf. 11-13 compound with 14-16 3,750.

There is a question whether Nos. 1a-1c ever did postal duty.

Values for No. 1 are for stamps with perfs. cutting into the design. Values for No. 1b are for examples without gum.

1863-67 Wmk. 5

2 A1 1p dull rose 135.00 60.00
a. Vert. pair, imperf. btwn. 37,500.
b. Imperf., pair 2,750.
c. 1p lilac rose 150.00 82.50
3 A1 1p vermilion ('67) 275.00 32.50
a. Horiz. pair, imperf. btwn. 37,500.
4 A1 6p green 775.00 30.00
a. 6p yellow green 4,750. 120.00
b. Pair, imperf. btwn. —

1872 Wmk. 1 *Perf. 12½*

5 A1 1p lake 220.00 22.50
6 A1 1p vermilion 225.00 26.50
7 A1 6p blue green 600.00 12.50

Queen Victoria — A2

1873-79 *Perf. 14*

8 A1 1p lake 250.00 12.50
a. Half used as ½p on cover *9,500.*

Typo.

9 A2 2½p red brown ('79) 700.00 210.00
10 A2 4p blue ('79) 290.00 18.00

Engr.

11 A1 6p blue green ('76) 450.00 22.50

1882-87 Typo. Wmk. 2

12 A2 ½p green 5.00 *20.00*
13 A2 2½p red brown 225.00 67.50
14 A2 2½p ultra ('87) 8.50 *17.00*
15 A2 4p blue 350.00 19.00
16 A2 4p brown org ('87) 2.50 *3.75*
17 A2 1sh violet ('86) 190.00 175.00

Engr.

18 A1 1p carmine ('84) 2.60 *4.50*
19 A1 6p deep green 77.50 *150.00*

No. 18 was used for a time in St. Christopher and is identified by the "A12" cancellation.

1884 *Perf. 12*

20 A1 1p rose red 65.00 20.00

Seal of the Colony — A3

King Edward VII — A4

1903 Typo. Wmk. 1 *Perf. 14*

21 A3 ½p blue grn & blk 4.00 *7.50*
a. Bluish paper ('09) 100.00 100.00
22 A3 1p car & black 14.00 1.50
a. Bluish paper ('09) 92.50 92.50
23 A3 2p org brn & vio 8.25 *27.50*
24 A3 2½p ultra & black 18.00 *25.00*
25 A3 3p ocher & gray green 12.00 *24.00*
26 A3 6p black & red vio 35.00 *60.00*
27 A3 1sh violet & ultra 57.50 *70.00*
28 A3 2sh pur & gray green 95.00 *125.00*
29 A3 2sh6p red vio & blk 30.00 *75.00*
30 A4 5sh pur & gray green 115.00 *165.00*
Nos. 21-30 (10) 388.75 *580.50*

The 2½p, 1sh and 5sh exist on both ordinary and chalky paper.

1908-20 Wmk. 3

31 A3 ½p green 5.25 *5.25*
32 A3 1p scarlet ('15) 8.00 3.75
33 A3 2p org brn & dull vio ('12) 5.25 *35.00*
34 A3 2½p ultra 24.00 *19.00*
35 A3 3p ocher & grn ('12) 7.00 *21.00*
36 A3 6p blk & red vio ('11) 8.25 *47.50*
37 A3 1sh vio & ultra 27.50 *80.00*
38 A3 2sh vio & green ('12) 110.00 *130.00*
Nos. 31-38 (8) 195.25 *341.50*

Nos. 33, 35 to 38 are on chalky paper.
For overprints see Nos. MR1-MR3.

George V — A6

1913

41 A6 5sh violet & green 100.00 *160.00*

St. John's Harbor — A7

1921-29 Wmk. 4

42 A7 ½p green 3.25 .60
43 A7 1p rose red 4.50 .60
44 A7 1p dp violet ('23) 8.75 1.75
45 A7 1½p orange ('22) 6.50 6.00
46 A7 1½p rose red ('26) 10.00 2.00
47 A7 1½p fawn ('29) 3.25 .75
48 A7 2p gray 4.50 .90
49 A7 2½p ultra ('27) 17.00 5.00
50 A7 2½p orange ('23) 2.75 *20.00*

Chalky Paper

51 A7 3p violet, *yel* ('25) 16.00 8.00
52 A7 6p vio & red vio 8.50 6.00
53 A7 1sh black, *emer* ('29) 6.50 5.00
54 A7 2sh vio & ultra, *blue* ('27) 12.00 *65.00*
55 A7 2sh6p blk & red, *blue* ('27) 52.50 *47.50*
56 A7 3sh grn & vio ('22) 52.50 *105.00*
57 A7 4sh blk & red ('22) 52.50 *77.50*
Nos. 42-57 (16) 261.00 *351.60*

Wmk. 3

Chalky Paper

58 A7 3p violet, *yel* 5.00 *15.00*
59 A7 4p black & red, *yel* ('22) 2.50 *6.50*
60 A7 1sh black, *emerald* 4.75 *10.50*
61 A7 2sh vio & ultra, *bl* 14.50 *37.50*
62 A7 2sh6p blk & red, *bl* 19.00 *70.00*
63 A7 5sh grn & red, *yel* ('22) 9.25 *60.00*
64 A7 £1 vio & black, *red* ('22) 300.00 *425.00*
Nos. 58-64 (7) 355.00 *624.50*

Old Dockyard, English Harbour A8

Govt. House, St. John's A9

Nelson's "Victory," 1805 — A10

Sir Thomas Warner's Ship, 1632 — A11

Perf. 12½

1932, Jan. 27 Engr. Wmk. 4

67 A8 ½p green 4.75 *8.75*
68 A8 1p scarlet 6.50 *9.00*
69 A8 1½p lt brown 4.75 *5.50*
70 A9 2p gray 9.00 *27.50*
71 A9 2½p ultra 8.75 *9.75*
72 A9 3p orange 8.75 *14.00*
73 A10 6p violet 16.00 14.00
74 A10 1sh olive green 21.00 *32.50*
75 A10 2sh6p claret 57.50 *82.50*
76 A11 5sh red brown & black 125.00 *160.00*
Nos. 67-76 (10) 262.00 *363.50*
Set, never hinged 650.00

Tercentenary of the colony.
Forged cancellations abound, especially dated "MY 18 1932."

Common Design Types pictured following the introduction.

Silver Jubilee Issue
Common Design Type

1935, May 6 *Perf. 13½x14*

77 CD301 1p car & blue 2.25 *4.00*
78 CD301 1½p gray blk & ultra 2.50 1.50
79 CD301 2½p blue & brn 6.50 1.75
80 CD301 1sh brt vio & ind 9.00 *16.00*
Nos. 77-80 (4) 20.25 *23.25*
Set, never hinged 32.50

Coronation Issue
Common Design Type

1937, May 12 *Perf. 11x11½*

81 CD302 1p carmine .50 *2.75*
82 CD302 1½p brown .35 *2.50*
83 CD302 2½p deep ultra 1.00 *2.75*
Nos. 81-83 (3) 1.85 *8.00*
Set, never hinged 2.75

English Harbour A14

Nelson's Dockyard A15

Fort James A16

St. John's Harbor A17

1938-51 Engr. *Perf. 12½*

84 A14 ½p yel green .30 *1.50*
85 A15 1p scarlet 2.25 2.50
86 A15 1½p red brown ('43) 1.80 *2.75*
87 A14 2p gray .70 *1.00*
88 A15 2½p ultra ('43) .75 *.90*
89 A16 3p pale orange ('44) .75 *1.10*
90 A17 6p purple 2.75 1.25
91 A17 1sh brown & blk 3.50 2.00
92 A16 2sh6p dp claret ('42) 16.00 20.00
93 A17 5sh grayish olive green ('44) 9.00 11.00
94 A15 10sh red vio ('48) 11.00 *35.00*
95 A16 £1 Prussian blue ('48) 22.50 *60.00*
Nos. 84-95 (12) 71.30 *139.00*
Set, never hinged 105.00

See Nos. 107-113, 115-116, 118-121, 136-142, 144-145.
For overprint see Nos. 125-126.

Catalogue values for unused stamps in this section, from this point to the end of the section, are for Never Hinged items.

Peace Issue
Common Design Type

1946, Nov. 1 Wmk. 4 *Perf. 13½x14*

96 CD303 1½p brown .25 .25
97 CD303 3p dp orange .25 *.55*

Silver Wedding Issue
Common Design Types

1949, Jan. 3 Photo. *Perf. 14x14½*

98 CD304 2½p bright ultra .55 *2.75*

Engraved; Name Typographed
Perf. 11½x11

99 CD305 5sh dk brown olive 13.00 13.00

UPU Issue
Common Design Types
Perf. 13½, 11x11½

1949, Oct. 10 Wmk. 4
Engr.; Name Typo. on 3p and 6p

100 CD306 2½p deep ultra .40 *.70*
101 CD307 3p orange 1.60 *3.25*
102 CD308 6p purple .80 *2.25*
103 CD309 1sh red brown .80 *1.50*
Nos. 100-103 (4) 3.60 *7.70*

University Issue
Common Design Types
Perf. 14x14½

1951, Feb. 16 Engr. Wmk. 4

104 CD310 3c chocolate & blk .45 *1.75*
105 CD311 12c purple & blk .90 *2.00*

Coronation Issue
Common Design Type

1953, June 2 *Perf. 13½x13*

106 CD312 2c dk green & blk .40 *.75*

Types of 1938 with Portrait of Queen Elizabeth II

Martello Tower — A24

Perf. 13x13½, 13½x13

1953-56 Wmk. 4

107	A16	½c dk red brn ('56)	.35	*.35*
108	A14	1c gray	.30	*1.75*
109	A15	2c deep green	.30	.25
110	A15	3c yellow & blk	.50	.25
111	A14	4c rose red (shades)	1.25	.25
112	A15	5c dull vio & blk	2.40	.45
113	A16	6c orange	2.40	.25
114	A24	8c deep blue	2.60	.25
115	A17	12c violet	2.60	.25
116	A17	24c chocolate & blk	4.50	.25
117	A24	48c dp bl & rose lil	9.50	3.25
118	A16	60c claret	8.50	.75
119	A17	$1.20 olive green	3.75	.90
120	A15	$2.40 magenta	17.00	11.50
121	A16	$4.80 greenish blue	22.00	*27.50*
		Nos. 107-121 (15)	77.95	*48.20*

See No. 143. For overprint see No. 125-126.

West Indies Federation

Common Design Type

Perf. 11½x11

1958, Apr. 22 Engr. Wmk. 314

122	CD313	3c green	1.50	.30
123	CD313	6c blue	1.90	*2.75*
124	CD313	12c carmine rose	2.40	.75
		Nos. 122-124 (3)	5.80	3.80

Nos. 110 and 115 Overprinted in Red or Black: "Commemoration Antigua Constitution 1960"

Perf. 13x13½, 13½x13

1960, Jan. 1 Wmk. 4

125	A15	3c yellow & black	.25	.25
126	A17	12c violet (Blk)	.25	.25

Constitutional reforms effective Jan. 1, 1960.

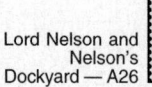

Lord Nelson and Nelson's Dockyard — A26

Perf. 11½x11

1961, Nov. 14 Wmk. 314

127	A26	20c brown & lilac	1.60	1.60
128	A26	30c dk blue & green	1.75	*2.75*

Completion of the restoration of Lord Nelson's headquarters, English Harbour.

Stamp of 1862 and Royal Mail Steam Packet in English Harbour — A27

1962, Aug. 1 Engr. *Perf. 13*

129	A27	3c dull green & pur	.70	.25
130	A27	10c dull green & ultra	.80	.25
131	A27	12c dull green & blk	.90	.25
132	A27	50c dull grn & brn org	1.50	*2.25*
		Nos. 129-132 (4)	3.90	3.00

Centenary of first Antigua postage stamp.

Freedom from Hunger Issue

Common Design Type

Perf. 14x14½

1963, June 4 Photo. Wmk. 314

133	CD314	12c green	.35	.35

Red Cross Centenary Issue

Common Design Type

1963, Sept. 2 Litho. *Perf. 13*

134	CD315	3c black & red	.25	*.75*
135	CD315	12c ultra & red	.75	*1.25*

Types of 1938-53 with Portrait of Queen Elizabeth II

Perf. 13x13½, 13½x13

1963-65 Engr. Wmk. 314

136	A16	½c brown ('65)	2.50	.85
137	A14	1c gray ('65)	1.25	1.00
138	A15	2c deep green	.70	.30
139	A15	3c orange yel & blk	.40	.30
140	A14	4c brown red	.35	*3.00*
141	A15	5c dull vio & black	.30	.25
142	A16	6c orange	.60	.35
143	A24	8c deep blue	.35	.25
144	A17	12c violet	1.00	.25
145	A17	24c choc & black	5.00	.80
		Nos. 136-145 (10)	12.45	7.35

For surcharge see No. 152.

Shakespeare Issue

Common Design Type

Perf. 14x14½

1964, Apr. 23 Photo. Wmk. 314

151	CD316	12c red brown	.35	.25

No. 144 Surcharged with New Value and Bars

Perf. 13½x13

1965, Apr. 1 Engr. Wmk. 314

152	A17	15c on 12c violet	.30	.30

ITU Issue

Common Design Type

Perf. 11x11½

1965, May 17 Litho. Wmk. 314

153	CD317	2c blue & ver	.25	.25
154	CD317	50c orange & vio bl	1.20	1.10

Intl. Cooperation Year Issue

Common Design Type

1965, Oct. 25 *Perf. 14½*

155	CD318	4c blue grn & claret	.25	.25
156	CD318	15c lt vio & green	.30	.25

Churchill Memorial Issue

Common Design Type

1966, Jan. 24 Photo. *Perf. 14*

Design in Black, Gold and Carmine Rose

157	CD319	½c bright blue	.25	*2.00*
158	CD319	4c green	.30	.25
159	CD319	25c brown	1.25	.30
160	CD319	35c violet	1.25	.50
		Nos. 157-160 (4)	3.05	3.05

Royal Visit Issue

Common Design Type

1966, Feb. 4 Litho. *Perf. 11x12*

Portraits in Black

161	CD320	6c violet blue	1.75	1.10
162	CD320	15c dark car rose	1.75	1.50

World Cup Soccer Issue

Common Design Type

1966, July 1 Wmk. 314 *Perf. 14*

163	CD321	6c multicolored	.25	*.60*
164	CD321	35c multicolored	.55	.25

WHO Headquarters Issue

Common Design Type

1966, Sept. 20 *Perf. 14*

165	CD322	2c multicolored	.25	.25
166	CD322	15c multicolored	.90	.30

Nelson's Dockyard — A35

Designs: 1c, Old post office, St. John's. 2c, Health Center. 3c, Teachers' Training College. 4c, Martello Tower, Barbuda. 5c, Ruins of officers quarters, Shirley Heights. 6c, Government House, Barbuda. 10c, Princess Margaret School. 15c, Air terminal. 25c, General post office. 35c, Clarence House. 50c, Government House. 75c, Administration building. $1, Court House, St. John's. $2.50, Magistrates' Court. $5, St. John's Cathedral.

Perf. 11½x11

1966, Nov. 1 Engr. Wmk. 314

167	A35	½c green & blue	.25	*1.10*
168	A35	1c purple & rose	.25	.30
169	A35	2c slate & org	.25	.25
170	A35	3c rose red & blk	.30	.30
171	A35	4c dull vio & brn	1.00	.25
172	A35	5c vio bl & olive	.25	.25
173	A35	6c dp org & pur	1.00	.30
174	A35	10c brt grn & rose red	.25	.25
175	A35	15c brn & blue	1.50	.25
		Complete booklet, 4 ea. #172, 174, 175	11.00	
176	A35	25c slate & brn	.55	.25
177	A35	35c dp rose & sep	1.50	.55
178	A35	50c green & black	2.00	*2.25*
179	A35	75c Prus bl & vio blue	3.50	2.25
180	A35	$1 dp rose & olive	8.00	2.50
181	A35	$2.50 black & rose	6.50	*8.00*
182	A35	$5 ol grn & dl vio	9.00	6.50
		Nos. 167-182 (16)	36.10	25.55

For surcharge see No. 231.

1969 *Perf. 13½*

167a	A35	½c	.25	*2.25*
168a	A35	1c	.25	*1.25*
169a	A35	2c	.25	*.65*
170a	A35	3c	.25	.25
171a	A35	4c	.25	.25
172b	A35	5c	.25	.25
173a	A35	6c	.25	*.90*
174b	A35	10c	.25	.25
175b	A35	15c	.55	.25
176a	A35	25c	.45	.25
177a	A35	35c	.60	*1.00*
178a	A35	50c	.75	*2.25*
180a	A35	$1	1.25	*5.00*
181a	A35	$2.50	1.50	*8.00*
182a	A35	$5	11.50	*24.00*
		Nos. 167a-182a (15)	18.60	*46.80*

The ½c, 3c, 6c are on ordinary paper. The 15c through $5 on glazed paper. The others exist on both papers.

UNESCO Anniversary Issue

Common Design Type

1966, Dec. 1 Litho. *Perf. 14*

183	CD323	4c "Education"	.25	.25
184	CD323	25c "Science"	.40	.25
185	CD323	$1 "Culture"	1.25	*2.00*
		Nos. 183-185 (3)	1.90	*2.50*

Independent State

Flag of Antigua, Spiny Lobster, Maps of Antigua and Barbuda — A37

Designs: 15c, 35c, Flag of Antigua. 25c, Flag and Premier's Office Building.

1967, Feb. 27 Photo. *Perf. 14*

186	A37	4c multicolored	.25	.25
187	A37	15c multicolored	.25	.25
188	A37	25c multicolored	.25	.25
189	A37	35c multicolored	.25	.25
		Nos. 186-189 (4)	1.00	1.00

Antigua's independence, Feb. 27, 1967.

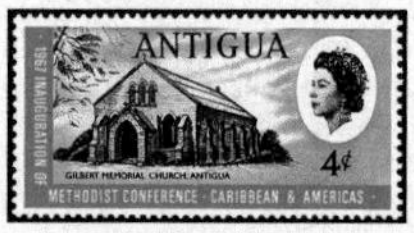

Gilbert Memorial Church, Antigua A38

25c, Nathaniel Gilbert's House. 35c, Map of the Caribbean and Central America.

Perf. 14x13½

1967, May 18 Photo. Wmk. 314

190	A38	4c brt red & black	.25	.25
191	A38	25c emerald & black	.25	.25
192	A38	35c ultra & black	.25	.25
		Nos. 190-192 (3)	.75	.75

Attainment of autonomy by the Methodist Church in the Caribbean and the Americas, and the opening of headquarters near St. John's, Antigua, May 1967.

Antiguan and British Royal Arms — A39

1967, July 21 *Perf. 14½x14*

193	A39	15c dark green & multi	.25	.25
194	A39	35c deep blue & multi	.25	.25

Granting of a new coat of arms to the State of Antigua; 300th anniv. of the Treaty of Breda.

Sailing Ship, 17th Century — A40

Design: 6c, 35c, Map of Barbuda from Jan Blaeu's Atlas, 1665.

Perf. 11½x11

1967, Dec. 14 Engr. Wmk. 314

195	A40	4c dark blue	.35	.25
196	A40	6c deep plum	.35	*1.25*
197	A40	25c green	.50	.25
198	A40	35c black	.50	.30
		Nos. 195-198 (4)	1.70	*2.05*

Resettlement of Barbuda, 300th anniv.

Dow Hill Antenna — A41

Designs: 15c, Antenna and rocket blasting off. 25c, Nose cone orbiting moon. 50c, Re-entry of space capsule.

Perf. 14½x14

1968, Mar. 29 Photo. Wmk. 314

199	A41	4c dk blue, org & black	.25	.25
200	A41	15c dk blue, org & black	.25	.25
201	A41	25c dk blue, org & black	.25	.25
202	A41	50c dk blue, org & black	.25	*.35*
		Nos. 199-202 (4)	1.00	*1.10*

Dedication of the Dow Hill tracking station in Antigua for the NASA Apollo project.

Beach and Sailfish — A42

Designs: ½c, 50c, Limbo dancer, flames and dancing girls. 15c, Three girls on a beach and water skier. 35c, Woman scuba diver, corals and fish.

1968, July 1 Photo. *Perf. 14*

203	A42	½c red & multi	.25	.25
204	A42	15c sky blue & multi	.25	.25
205	A42	25c blue & multi	.30	.25
206	A42	35c brt blue & multi	.30	.25
207	A42	50c multicolored	.50	*1.10*
		Nos. 203-207 (5)	1.60	*2.10*

Issued for tourist publicity.

St. John's Harbor, 1768 — A43

St. John's Harbor: 15c, 1829. 25c, Map of deep-sea harbor, 1968. 35c, Dock, 1968. 2c, Like $1.

Engr. & Litho.; Engr. ($1)

1968, Oct. 31 Wmk. 314 *Perf. 13*

208	A43	2c dp car & lt blue	.25	*.30*
209	A43	15c sepia & yel grn	.35	.25
210	A43	25c dk blue & yel	.45	.25
211	A43	35c dp green & sal	.50	.25
212	A43	$1 black	.85	*1.75*
		Nos. 208-212 (5)	2.40	*2.80*

Opening of St. John's deep-sea harbor.

Mace and Parliament — A44

Mace and: 15c, Mace bearer. 25c, House of Representatives, interior. 50c, Antigua coat of arms and great seal.

1969, Feb. 3 Photo. *Perf. 12½*

213	A44	4c crimson & multi	.25	.25
214	A44	15c crimson & multi	.25	.25
215	A44	25c crimson & multi	.25	.25
216	A44	50c crimson & multi	.30	*1.40*
		Nos. 213-216 (4)	1.05	*2.15*

300th anniversary of Antigua Parliament.

CARIFTA Cargo — A45

4c, 15c, Ship, plane and trucks, horiz.

Perf. 13½x13, 13x13½

1969, Apr. 14 Litho. Wmk. 314

217 A45 4c blk & brt lilac rose .25 .25
218 A45 15c blk & brt grnsh blue .25 .25
219 A45 25c bister & black .25 .25
220 A45 35c tan & black .25 .25
Nos. 217-220 (4) 1.00 1.00

1st anniv. of CARIFTA (Caribbean Free Trade Area).

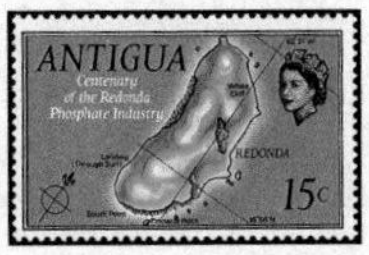

Map of Redonda Island — A46

25c, View of Redonda from the sea & seagulls.

1969, Aug. 1 Photo. *Perf. 13x13½*

221 A46 15c ultra & multi .25 .25
222 A46 25c multicolored .25 .25
223 A46 50c salmon & multi .40 *.60*
Nos. 221-223 (3) .90 *1.10*

Centenary of Redonda phosphate industry.

Adoration of the Kings, by Gugliemo Marcillat — A47

Christmas: 10c, 50c, Holy Family, by anonymous German artist, 15th century.

1969, Oct. 15 Litho. *Perf. 13x14*

224 A47 6c bister brn & multi .25 .25
225 A47 10c fawn & multi .25 .25
226 A47 35c gray olive & multi .25 .25
227 A47 50c gray blue & multi .30 .25
Nos. 224-227 (4) 1.05 1.00

Arms of Antigua — A48

Coil Stamps

Wmk. 314 upright

1970, Jan. 30 Photo. *Perf. 14½x14*

228 A48 5c bright blue .25 .25
a. Wmk. 373 ('77) *7.00*
229 A48 10c bright green .25 .25
a. Wmk. 373, invtd. ('77) — *2.00*
230 A48 25c deep magenta .25 .25
a. Wmk. 373 ('77) *12.50*
Nos. 228-230 (3) .75 .75

Glazed Paper

1973, Mar. 5 Wmk. 314 sideways

228b A48 5c bright blue 1.00 *2.00*
229b A48 10c bright green 1.00 *2.00*
230b A48 25c deep magenta 1.25 *1.75*
Nos. 228b-230b (3) 3.25 *5.75*

No. 176 Surcharged

1970, Jan. 2 Engr. *Perf. 11½x11*

231 A35 20c on 25c slate & brn .35 .25

Sikorsky S-38 — A49

Aircraft: 20c, Dornier DO-X. 35c, Hawker Siddeley 748. 50c, Douglas C-124C Globemaster II. 75c, Vickers VC 10.

1970, Feb. 16 Litho. *Perf. 14½*

232 A49 5c brt green & multi .60 .25
233 A49 20c ultra & multi 1.00 .25
234 A49 35c blue grn & multi 1.25 .25
235 A49 50c blue & multi 1.25 *1.50*
236 A49 75c vio blue & multi 1.60 *2.25*
Nos. 232-236 (5) 5.70 *4.50*

40th anniversary of air service.

Dickens and Scene from "Pickwick Papers" — A50

Charles Dickens (1812-1870), English novelist and Scene from: 5c, "Nicholas Nickleby." 35c, "Oliver Twist." $1, "David Copperfield."

Wmk. 314

1970, May 19 Litho. *Perf. 14*

237 A50 5c olive & sepia .25 .25
238 A50 20c aqua & sepia .25 .25
239 A50 35c violet & sepia .25 .25
240 A50 $1 scarlet & sepia .60 *.75*
Nos. 237-240 (4) 1.35 *1.50*

Carib Indian and War Canoe — A51

Ships: 1c, Columbus and "Nina." 2c, Sir Thomas Warner's arms and sailing ship. 3c, Viscount Hood and "Barfleur." 4c, Sir George Rodney and "Formidable." 5c, Capt. Horatio Nelson and "Boreas." 6c, King William IV and "Pegasus." 10c, Blackbeard (Edward Teach) and pirate ketch. 15c, Capt. Collingwood and "Pelican." 20c, Admiral Nelson and "Victoria." 25c, Paddle steamer "Solent" and Steam Packet Company emblem. 35c, King George V and corvette "Canada." 50c, Cruiser "Renown" and royal badge. 75c, S.S. "Federal Maple" and maple leaf. $1, Racing yacht "Sol-Quest" and Gallant 53 class emblem. $2.50, Missile destroyer "London" and her emblem. $5, Tug "Pathfinder" and arms of Antigua.

Wmk. 314 Sideways

1970, Aug. 19 Litho. *Perf. 14*

241 A51 ½c ocher & multi .25 *1.25*
242 A51 1c Prus bl & multi .30 *1.25*
243 A51 2c yel grn & multi .35 *3.00*
244 A51 3c ol bis & multi .35 *3.00*
245 A51 4c bl gray & multi .40 *2.75*
246 A51 5c fawn & multi .50 .40
247 A51 6c rose lil & multi 1.40 *4.25*
248 A51 10c brn org & multi .80 .25
249 A51 15c ultra & multi 7.00 1.00
250 A51 20c ol grn & multi 1.15 .40
251 A51 25c olive & multi 1.25 .40
252 A51 35c dull red brn & multi 1.60 .80
253 A51 50c lt brn & multi 3.50 *5.75*
254 A51 75c beige & multi 4.50 *5.75*
255 A51 $1 Prus green & multi 4.50 1.75
256 A51 $2.50 gray & multi 6.25 *7.25*
257 A51 $5 yel & multi 2.75 *6.00*
Nos. 241-257 (17) 36.85 *45.25*

1972-74 Wmk. 314 Upright

241a A51 ½c .30 *.45*
242a A51 1c .40 *1.25*
244a A51 3c .80 *1.75*
245a A51 4c .55 *2.00*
246a A51 5c .60 .40
247a A51 6c .90 *2.75*
248a A51 10c .60 *.60*
249a A51 15c 6.25 .90
254a A51 75c 6.25 3.00
255a A51 $1 2.75 1.75
256a A51 $2.50 2.50 *6.50*
257a A51 $5 3.50 *10.00*
Nos. 241a-257a (12) 25.40 *31.35*

For surcharge see No. 368.

1975, Jan. 21 Wmk. 373

257b A51 $5 yellow & multi 4.00 *12.00*

Nativity, by Albrecht Dürer — A52

Christmas: 10c, 50c, Adoration of the Magi, by Albrecht Dürer.

Engr. & Litho.

1970, Oct. 28 *Perf. 13½x14*

258 A52 3c brt grnsh blue & blk .25 .25
259 A52 10c pink & plum .25 .25
260 A52 35c brick red & black .25 .25
261 A52 50c lilac & violet .30 .25
Nos. 258-261 (4) 1.05 1.00

Private, 4th West India Regiment, 1804 — A53

Military Uniforms: ½c, Drummer Boy, 4th King's Own Regiment, 1759. 20c, Grenadier Company Officer, 60th Regiment, The Royal American, 1809. 35c, Light Company Officer, 93rd Regiment, The Sutherland Highlanders, 1826-1834. 75c, Private, 3rd West India Regiment, 1851.

Perf. 14x13½

1970, Dec. 1 Litho. Wmk. 314

262 A53 ½c lake & multi .25 .25
263 A53 10c brn org & multi .45 .25
264 A53 20c Prus grn & multi .90 .25
265 A53 35c dl pur & multi 1.10 .25
266 A53 75c dk ol grn & multi 2.25 *2.75*
a. Souv. sheet, #262-266 + label 6.50 *7.00*
Nos. 262-266 (5) 4.95 *3.75*

See Nos. 274-278, 283-287, 307-311, 329-333.

Market Woman Voting — A54

Voting by: 20c, Businessman. 35c, Mother (and child). 50c, Workman.

Perf. 14½x14

1971, Feb. 1 Photo. Wmk. 314

267 A54 5c brown .25 .25
268 A54 20c olive black .25 .25
269 A54 35c rose magenta .25 .25
270 A54 50c violet blue .25 .25
Nos. 267-270 (4) 1.00 1.00

Adult suffrage, 20th anniversary.

Last Supper, from The Small Passion, by Dürer — A55

Woodcuts by Albrecht Dürer: 35c, Crucifixion from Eichstatt Missal. 75c, Resurrection from The Great Passion.

Perf. 14x13½

1971, Apr. 7 Litho. Wmk. 314

271 A55 5c gray, red & black .25 .25
272 A55 35c gray, violet & black .25 .25
273 A55 75c gray, gold & black .25 .25
Nos. 271-273 (3) .75 .75

Easter.

Uniform Type of 1970

Military Uniforms: ½c, Private, Suffolk Regiment, 1704. 10c, Grenadier, South Staffordshire, 1751. 20c, Fusilier, Royal Northumberland, 1778. 35c, Private, Northamptonshire. 1793, 75c, Private, East Yorkshire, 1805.

1971, July 12 Litho. Wmk. 314

274 A53 ½c gray grn & multi .25 .25
275 A53 10c bluish blk & multi .45 .25
276 A53 20c dk pur & multi 1.15 .25
277 A53 35c dk ol & multi 1.40 .25
278 A53 75c brown & multi 1.75 *2.75*
a. Souv. sheet, #274-278 + label 7.00 *8.00*
Nos. 274-278 (5) 5.00 *3.75*

Virgin and Child, by Veronese — A56

Christmas: 5c, 50c, Adoration of the Shepherds, by Bonifazio Veronese.

1971, Oct. 4 *Perf. 14x13½*

279 A56 3c multicolored .25 .25
280 A56 5c multicolored .25 .25
281 A56 35c multicolored .25 .25
282 A56 50c multicolored .40 .30
Nos. 279-282 (4) 1.15 1.05

Uniform Type of 1970

Military Uniforms: ½c, Officer, King's Own Borderers Regiment, 1815. 10c, Sergeant, Buckinghamshire Regiment, 1837. 20c, Private, South Hampshire Regiment, 1853. 35c, Officer, Royal Artillery, 1854. 75c, Private, Worcestershire Regiment, 1870.

1972, July 1

283 A53 ½c ol brn & multi .25 .25
284 A53 10c dp grn & multi .60 .25
285 A53 20c brt vio & multi 1.10 .25
286 A53 35c mar & multi 1.35 .30
287 A53 75c dk vio bl & multi 1.75 *3.00*
a. Souvenir sheet of 5, #283-287 + label 7.50 *8.50*
Nos. 283-287 (5) 5.05 *4.05*

Reticulated Helmet Cowrie — A57

Sea Shells: 5c, Measled cowrie. 35c, West Indian fighting conch. 50c, Hawkwing conch.

1972, Aug. 1 *Perf. 14½x14*

288 A57 3c multicolored .55 .25
289 A57 5c ver & multi .55 .25
290 A57 35c lt vio & multi 1.60 .25
291 A57 50c rose red & multi 1.75 *2.75*
Nos. 288-291 (4) 4.45 *3.50*

St. John's Cathedral, 1745-1843 A58

Christmas: 50c, Interior of St. John's. 75c, St. John's rebuilt.

1972, Nov. 6 Litho. *Perf. 14*

292 A58 35c org brn & multi .25 .25
293 A58 50c vio & multi .30 .30
294 A58 75c multicolored .50 *.55*
a. Souv. sheet, #292-294, perf 15 1.00 *1.25*
Nos. 292-294 (3) 1.05 *1.10*

Silver Wedding Issue, 1972

Common Design Type

1972, Nov. 20 Photo. *Perf. 14x14½*

295 CD324 20c ultra & multi .25 .25
296 CD324 35c steel blue & multi .25 .25

Map of Antigua, Batsman Driving Ball — A60

Designs: 35c, Batsman and wicketkeeper. $1, Emblem of Rising Sun Cricket Club.

1972, Dec. 15 *Perf. 13½x14*

297 A60 5c multicolored .25 .25
298 A60 35c multicolored .75 .30
299 A60 $1 multicolored 2.25 *2.50*
a. Souvenir sheet of 3, #297-299 5.25 *6.25*
Nos. 297-299 (3) 3.25 *3.05*

Rising Sun Cricket Club, St. John's, 50th anniv.

Map of Antigua and Yacht — A61

1972, Dec. 29 *Perf. 14½*

300 A61 35c shown .25 .25
301 A61 50c Racing yachts .25 .25
302 A61 75c St. John's G.P.O. .35 .25
303 A61 $1 Statue of Liberty .40 .25
a. Souvenir sheet of 2, #301, 303 1.10 *1.25*
Nos. 300-303 (4) 1.25 *1.00*

Opening of Antigua and Barbuda Information Office in New York City.

Window with Episcopal Coat of Arms — A62

Stained glass windows from Cathedral of St. John: 35c, Crucifixion. 75c, Arm of Rt. Rev. D.G. Davis, 1st bishop of Antigua.

1973, Apr. 16 Litho. *Perf. 13½*

304 A62 5c yellow & multi .25 .25
305 A62 35c brt lilac & multi .25 .25
306 A62 75c blue & multi .30 .25
Nos. 304-306 (3) .80 .75

Easter.

Uniform Type of 1970

Military Uniforms: ½c, Private, Col. Zacharia Tiffin's Regiment, 1701. 10c, Private, 63rd Regiment, 1759. 20c, Officer, 35th Sussex Regiment, 1828. 35c, Private, 2nd West India Regiment, 1853. 75c, Sergeant, Princess of Wales Regiment, Hertfordshire, 1858.

Perf. 14x13½

1973, July 1 **Wmk. 314**

307 A53 ½c dp ultra & multi .25 .25
308 A53 10c rose lilac & multi .35 .25
309 A53 20c gray & multi .50 .25
310 A53 35c multicolored .70 .25
311 A53 75c multicolored 1.50 1.25
a. Souv. sheet, #307-311 + label 4.00 3.75
Nos. 307-311 (5) 3.30 2.25

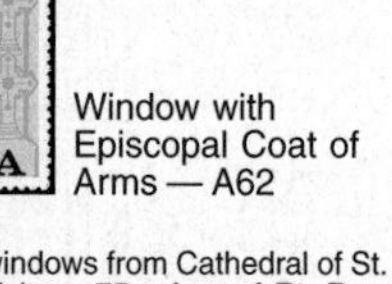

Butterfly Costumes A63

Designs: 20c, Carnival revelers. 35c, Costumed group. 75c, Carnival Queen.

Perf. 13½x14

1973, July 30 **Unwmk.**

312 A63 5c multicolored .25 .25
313 A63 20c multicolored .25 .25
314 A63 35c multicolored .25 .25
315 A63 75c multicolored .30 .25
a. Souvenir sheet of 4, #312-315 1.10 *1.25*
Nos. 312-315 (4) 1.05 1.00

Carnival, July 29-Aug. 7.

Virgin of the Porridge, by David — A64

Christmas: 5c, Adoration of the Kings, by Stomer. 20c, Virgin of the Grand Duke, by Raphael. 35c, Nativity with God the Father and Holy Ghost, by Tiepolo. $1, Madonna and Child, by Murillo.

Perf. 14½

1973, Oct. 15 Photo. **Unwmk.**

316 A64 3c brt blue & multi .25 .25
317 A64 5c emerald & multi .25 .25
318 A64 20c gold & multi .25 .25
319 A64 35c violet & multi .25 .25
320 A64 $1 red & multi .35 *.55*
a. Souvenir sheet of 5, #316-320 1.40 *1.60*
Nos. 316-320 (5) 1.35 *1.55*

Princess Anne and Mark Phillips — A65

Design: $2, different border.

1973, Nov. 14 Litho. *Perf. 13½*

321 A65 35c dull ultra & multi .25 .25
322 A65 $2 yel grn & multi .25 .25
a. Souvenir sheet of 2, #321-322 .65 .65

Wedding of Princess Anne and Capt. Mark Phillips.

Nos. 321-322 were issued in sheets of 5 plus label.

Nos. 321-322 and 322a Ovptd.

1973, Dec. 15 Litho. *Perf. 13½*

323 A65 35c multicolored .25 .25
324 A65 $2 multicolored .40 .40
a. Souvenir sheet of 2, #323-324 .65 .65

Visit of Princess Anne and Mark Phillips to Antigua, Dec. 16. Same overprint in sheet margins of Nos. 323-324 and 324a.

Overprint lithographed. Also exists typographed.

Arms of Antigua and U.W.I. — A66

Designs: 20c, Dancers. 35c, Antigua campus. 75c, Chancellor Sir Hugh Wooding.

1974, Feb. 18 **Wmk. 314**

325 A66 5c multicolored .25 .25
326 A66 20c multicolored .25 .25
327 A66 35c multicolored .25 .25
328 A66 75c multicolored .25 .25
Nos. 325-328 (4) 1.00 1.00

University of the West Indies, 24th anniv.

Uniform Type of 1970

Military Uniforms: ½c, Officer, 59th Foot, 1797. 10c, Gunner, Royal Artillery, 1800. 20c, Private, 1st West India Regiment, 1830. 35c, Officer, Gordon Highlanders, 1843. 75c, Private, Royal Welsh Fusiliers, 1846.

1974, May 1 *Perf. 14x13½*

329 A53 ½c dull grn & multi .25 .25
330 A53 10c ocher & multi .40 .25
331 A53 20c multicolored .75 .25
332 A53 35c gray bl & multi .90 .25
333 A53 75c dk gray & multi 1.25 *1.75*
a. Souvenir sheet of 5, #329-333 3.25 2.50
Nos. 329-333 (5) 3.55 2.75

English Mailman and Coach, Helicopter A67

UPU, Cent.: 1c, English bellman, 1846; Orinoco mailboat, 1851; telecommunications satellite. 2c, English mailtrain guard, 1852; Swiss post passenger bus, 1906; Italian hydrofoil. 5c, Swiss messenger, 16th century; Wells Fargo coach, 1800; Concorde. 20c, German postillion, 1820; Japanese mailmen, 19th century; carrier pigeon. 35c, Contemporary Antiguan mailman; radar station; aquaplane. $1, Medieval French courier; American train, 1884; British Airways jet.

1974, July 15 Litho. *Perf. 14½*

334 A67 ½c multicolored .25 .25
335 A67 1c multicolored .25 .25
336 A67 2c multicolored .25 .25
337 A67 5c multicolored .55 .40
338 A67 20c multicolored .30 .25
339 A67 35c multicolored .40 .25
340 A67 $1 multicolored 1.50 *2.00*
a. Souvenir sheet of 7, #334-340 + label, perf. 13 4.00 3.00
Nos. 334-340 (7) 3.50 3.65

For surcharges see Nos. 365-367.

Traditional Steel Band — A68

Carnival 1974 (Steel Bands): 5c, Traditional players, vert. 35c, Modern steel band. 75c, Modern players, vert.

1974, Aug. 1, Wmk. 314 *Perf. 14*

341 A68 5c rose red, dk red & blk .25 .25
342 A68 20c ocher, brn & blk .25 .25
343 A68 35c yel grn, grn & blk .25 .25
344 A68 75c dl bl, dk bl & blk .25 *1.00*
a. Souvenir sheet of 4, #341-344 .75 *1.25*
Nos. 341-344 (4) 1.00 *1.75*

For surcharge see No. 364.

Soccer — A69

Designs: Games' emblem and soccer.

1974, Sept. 23 Unwmk. *Perf. 14½*

345 A69 5c multicolored .25 .25
346 A69 35c multicolored .25 .25
347 A69 75c multicolored .25 .25
348 A69 $1 multicolored .30 .30
a. Souvenir sheet of 4 1.10 1.10
Nos. 345-348 (4) 1.05 1.05

World Cup Soccer Championship, Munich, June 13-July 7. Nos. 345-348 issued in sheets of 5 plus label showing Soccer Cup. No. 348a contains one each of Nos. 345-348, perf. 13½, and 2 labels.

For overprints and surcharges see Nos. 361-363.

Winston Churchill (1874-1965) at Harrow — A70

Designs: 35c, St. Paul's during bombing and Churchill portrait. 75c, Churchill's coat of arms and catafalque. $1, Churchill during Boer war, warrant for arrest and map of his escape route.

1974, Oct. 20 Unwmk. *Perf. 14½*

349 A70 5c multicolored .25 .25
350 A70 35c multicolored .25 .25
351 A70 75c multicolored .25 *.60*
352 A70 $1 multicolored .30 *1.00*
a. Souvenir sheet of 4, #349-352 1.10 *1.60*
Nos. 349-352 (4) 1.05 *2.10*

Virgin and Child, by Giovanni Bellini — A71

Christmas — Paintings of the Virgin and Child: 1c, Raphael. 2c, Van der Weyden. 3c, Giorgione. 5c, Andrea Mantegna. 20c, Alvise Vivarini. 35c, Bartolommeo Montagna. 75c, Lorenzo Costa.

1974, Nov. 18 Litho. *Perf. 14½*

353 A71 ½c shown .25 .25
354 A71 1c multicolored .25 .25
355 A71 2c multicolored .25 .25
356 A71 3c multicolored .25 .25
357 A71 5c multicolored .25 .25
358 A71 20c multicolored .25 .25
359 A71 35c multicolored .25 .25
360 A71 75c multicolored .35 *1.00*
a. Souv. sheet, #357-360, perf 13½ 1.00 *1.50*
Nos. 353-360 (8) 2.10 2.75

Nos. 346-348 Overprinted

No. 344 Surcharged and Overprinted

1974, Oct. 16 Litho. *Perf. 14½, 14*

361 A69 35c multicolored .30 .30
362 A69 75c multicolored .45 .35
363 A69 $1 multicolored .55 .45
364 A68 $5 on 75c multi 1.75 *2.50*
Nos. 361-364 (4) 3.05 *3.60*

Earthquake of Oct. 8, 1974.

Nos. 338-340 and 254a Surcharged

1974-75 Wmk. 314 *Perf. 14½*

365 A67 50c on 20c 1.25 *2.00*
366 A67 $2.50 on 35c 2.75 *6.00*
367 A67 $5 on $1 6.00 *7.50*

Perf. 14

368 A51 $10 on 75c 2.75 *8.00*
Nos. 365-368 (4) 12.75 *23.50*

Carib War Canoe, English Harbour — A72

Designs (Nelson's Dockyard): 15c, Raising ship, 1770. 35c, Lord Nelson and "Boreas." 50c, Yachts arriving for Sailing Week, 1974. $1, "Anchorage" in Old Dockyard, 1970.

1975, Mar. 17 Unwmk. *Perf. 14½*

369 A72 5c multicolored .30 .25
370 A72 15c multicolored .90 .25
371 A72 35c multicolored 1.25 .25
372 A72 50c multicolored 1.50 *1.75*
373 A72 $1 multicolored 1.75 *2.10*
Nos. 369-373 (5) 5.70 *4.60*

Souvenir Sheet

Perf. 13½

373A A72 Sheet of 5, #369-373 6.00 6.00

Stamps in No. 373A are 43x28mm.

Lady of the Valley Church — A73

Churches of Antigua: 20c, Gilbert Memorial. 35c, Grace Hill Moravian. 50c, St. Phillip's. $1, Ebenezer Methodist.

1975, May 19 Litho. *Perf. 14½*

374 A73 5c multicolored .25 .25
375 A73 20c multicolored .25 .25
376 A73 35c multicolored .25 .25
377 A73 50c multicolored .25 .25
378 A73 $1 multicolored .25 .45
a. Souvenir sheet of 3, #376-378, perf. 13½ 1.00 *1.40*
Nos. 374-378 (5) 1.25 1.45

Antigua, Senex's Atlas, 1721, and Hevelius Sextant, 1640 — A74

Maps of Antigua: 20c, Jeffery's Atlas, 1775, and 18th century engraving of ship. 35c, Barbuda and Antigua, 1775 and 1975. $1, St. John's and English Harbour, 1973.

1975, July 21 **Wmk. 314**

379 A74 5c multicolored .35 .25
380 A74 20c multicolored .65 .25
381 A74 35c multicolored .85 .25

382 A74 $1 multicolored 1.75 *2.10*
a. Souvenir sheet of 4, #379-382 4.50 3.50
Nos. 379-382 (4) 3.60 2.85

Bugler and Sunset — A75

Nordjamb 75 Emblem and: 20c, Black and white Scouts, tents and flags. 35c, Lord Baden-Powell and tents. $2, Dahomey dancers.

Unwmk.

1975, Aug. 26 Litho. *Perf. 14*
383 A75 15c multicolored .30 .25
384 A75 20c multicolored .35 .25
385 A75 35c multicolored .50 .30
386 A75 $2 multicolored 2.00 2.25
a. Souvenir sheet of 4, #383-386 4.00 4.00
Nos. 383-386 (4) 3.15 3.05

Nordjamb 75, 14th Boy Scout Jamboree, Lillehammer, Norway, July 29-Aug. 7.

Eurema Elathea — A76

Butterflies: 1c, Danaus plexippus. 2c, Phoebis philea. 5c, Marpesia petreus thetys. 20c, Eurema proterpia. 35c, Papilio polydamas. $2, Vanessa cardui.

1975, Oct. 30 Litho. *Perf. 14*
387 A76 ½c multicolored .25 .25
388 A76 1c multicolored .25 .25
389 A76 2c multicolored .25 .25
390 A76 5c multicolored .30 .25
391 A76 20c multicolored 1.25 .50
392 A76 35c multicolored 1.75 .75
393 A76 $2 multicolored 5.00 *8.00*
a. Miniature sheet of 4, #390-393 9.50 *10.00*
Nos. 387-393 (7) 9.05 *10.25*

Virgin and Child, by Correggio — A77

Christmas: Virgin and Child paintings.

1975, Nov. 17 Unwmk.
394 A77 ½c shown .25 .25
395 A77 1c El Greco .25 .25
396 A77 2c Durer .25 .25
397 A77 3c Antonello .25 .25
398 A77 5c Bellini .25 .25
399 A77 10c Durer .25 .25
400 A77 35c Bellini .40 .25
401 A77 $2 Durer .75 *.90*
a. Souvenir sheet of 4, #398-401 .200 2.00
Nos. 394-401 (8) 2.65 2.65

West Indies Team — A78

Designs: 5c, Batsman I.V.A. Richards and cup, vert. 35c, Bowler A.M.E. Roberts and cup, vert.

1975, Dec. 15 Litho. *Perf. 14*
402 A78 5c multicolored 1.10 .25
403 A78 35c multicolored 2.00 .55
404 A78 $2 multicolored 4.25 *7.75*
Nos. 402-404 (3) 7.35 *8.55*

World Cricket Cup, victory of West Indies team.

A number of unissued items, imperfs., part perfs., missing color varieties, etc., were made available when the Format International inventory was liquidated. Imperfs of some or all of the Antigua stamps in the following sets are included: #405-422, 503-507, 515-517, 703-707, 745-749, 755-759, 808-816, 819-826, 905-909, 934-937.
See footnote after #962.

Antillean Crested Hummingbird A79

Irrigation System, Diamond Estate — A80

Designs: 1c, Imperial parrot. 2c, Zenaida dove. 3c, Loggerhead kingbird. 4c, Red-necked pigeon. 5c, Rufous-throated solitaire. 6c, Orchid tree. 10c, Bougainvillea. 15c, Geiger tree. 20c, Flamboyant. 25c, Hibiscus. 35c, Flame of the Woods. 50c, Cannon at Fort James. 75c, Premier's Office. $1, Potworks Dam. $5, Government House. $10, Coolidge International Airport.

1976, Jan. 19 Litho. *Perf. 15*
405 A79 ½c multicolored .35 *.60*
406 A79 1c multicolored 1.25 .50
407 A79 2c multicolored 1.25 .50
408 A79 3c multicolored 1.25 .55
409 A79 4c multicolored 1.25 *2.00*
410 A79 5c multicolored 1.75 .25
411 A79 6c multicolored .30 *2.00*
412 A79 10c multicolored .30 .25
413 A79 15c multicolored .35 .25
414 A79 20c multicolored .35 .35
415 A79 25c multicolored .35 .25
416 A79 35c multicolored .35 .35
417 A79 50c multicolored .50 .50
418 A79 75c multicolored .60 *1.75*
419 A79 $1 multicolored .75 *.95*

Perf. 13½x14
420 A80 $2.50 rose & multi 1.50 *4.50*
421 A80 $5 lilac & multi 2.50 *5.50*
422 A80 $10 multicolored 4.25 *7.50*
Nos. 405-422 (18) 19.20 *28.55*

Inscribed "1978"

1978
405a A79 ½c multicolored .90 *1.10*
406a A79 1c multicolored 1.50 1.10
407a A79 2c multicolored 1.50 1.10
408a A79 3c multicolored 1.50 1.10
409a A79 4c multicolored 1.75 1.10
410a A79 5c multicolored 2.00 .90
411a A79 6c multicolored .35 *1.25*
412a A79 10c multicolored .35 .35
413a A79 15c multicolored .30 .35
414a A79 20c multicolored .30 *1.00*
415a A79 25c multicolored .35 *.55*
416a A79 35c multicolored .35 *.55*
417a A79 50c multicolored .55 *1.00*
418a A79 75c multicolored .55 *1.10*
419a A79 $1 multicolored .75 *1.25*

Perf. 13½x14
420a A80 $2.50 rose & multi 1.75 *5.50*
421a A80 $5 lilac & multi 1.90 *6.50*
422a A80 $10 multicolored 6.50 *8.50*
Nos. 405a-422a (18) 23.15 *34.30*

For overprints see Nos. 607-617.

Some Antigua issues from the 1970s were overprinted "Redonda." Other stamps inscribed "Redonda," but lacking any mention of Antigua, were also created in the 1970s and 1980s. These stamps are not listed because Redonda is uninhabited and has no need for stamps of its own.

Privates, Clark's Illinois Regiment — A81

1c, Riflemen, Pennsylvania Militia. 2c, Decorated American powder horn. 5c, Water bottle of Maryland troops. 35c, "Liberty Tree" and "Rattlesnake" flags. $1, American privateer Montgomery. $2.50, Congress Flag. $5, Continental Navy sloop Ranger.

1976, Mar. 17 Litho. *Perf. 14½*
423 A81 ½c multicolored .25 .25
424 A81 1c multicolored .25 .25
425 A81 2c multicolored .25 .25
426 A81 5c multicolored .25 .25
427 A81 35c multicolored .45 .25
428 A81 $1 multicolored 1.25 .30
429 A81 $5 multicolored 2.25 2.75
Nos. 423-429 (7) 4.95 4.30

Souvenir Sheet

Perf. 13
430 A81 $2.50 multicolored 1.90 1.90

American Bicentennial.

High Jump, Olympic Rings — A82

Olympic Rings and: 1c, Boxing. 2c, Pole vault. 15c, Swimming. 30c, Running. $1, Bicycling. $2, Shot put.

1976, July 12 Litho. *Perf. 14½*
431 A82 ½c yellow & multi .25 .25
432 A82 1c purple & multi .25 .25
433 A82 2c emerald & multi .25 .25
434 A82 15c brt blue & multi .25 .25
435 A82 30c olive & multi .30 .25
436 A82 $1 orange & multi .40 .25
437 A82 $2 red & multi 1.10 1.10
a. Souvenir sheet of 4 2.25 2.25
Nos. 431-437 (7) 2.80 2.60

21st Olympic Games, Montreal, Canada, July 17-Aug. 1. No. 437a contains one each of Nos. 434-437, perf. 13½.

Water Skiing — A83

Water Sports: 1c, Sailfish sailing. 2c, Snorkeling. 20c, Deep-sea fishing. 50c, Scuba diving. $2, Swimming.

1976, Aug. 26 *Perf. 14*
438 A83 ½c yel grn & multi .25 .25
439 A83 1c sepia & multi .25 .25
440 A83 2c gray & multi .25 .25
441 A83 20c multicolored .25 .25
442 A83 50c brt vio & multi .40 .40
443 A83 $2 lt gray & multi 1.10 1.10
a. Souvenir sheet of 3, #441-443 2.00 2.00
Nos. 438-443 (6) 2.50 2.50

French Angelfish A84

1976, Oct. 4 Litho. *Perf. 13½x14*
444 A84 15c shown .45 .25
445 A84 30c Yellowfish grouper .70 .25
446 A84 50c Yellowtail snappers .85 .45
447 A84 90c Shy hamlet 1.30 .75
Nos. 444-447 (4) 3.30 1.70

The Annunciation — A85

Christmas: 10c, Flight into Egypt. 15c, Three Kings. 50c, Shepherds and star. $1, Kings presenting gifts to Christ Child.

1976, Nov. 15 Litho. *Perf. 14*
448 A85 8c multicolored .25 .25
449 A85 10c multicolored .25 .25
450 A85 15c multicolored .25 .25
451 A85 50c multicolored .25 .25
452 A85 $1 multi .25 .25
Nos. 448-452 (5) 1.25 1.25

Mercury and UPU Emblem — A86

Designs: 1c, Alfred Nobel, symbols of prize categories. 10c, Viking spacecraft. 50c, Vivi Richards (batsman) and Andy Roberts (bowler). $1, Alexander G. Bell, telephones, 1876 and 1976. $2, Schooner Freelance.

1976, Dec. 28 Litho. *Perf. 14*
453 A86 ½c multicolored .25 .25
454 A86 1c multicolored .25 .25
455 A86 10c multicolored .35 .25
456 A86 50c multicolored 3.50 1.75
457 A86 $1 multicolored .90 *1.75*
458 A86 $2 multicolored 2.10 *4.00*
a. Souvenir sheet of 4, #455-458 8.25 8.25
Nos. 453-458 (6) 7.35 8.25

Special 1976 Events: UN Postal Admin., 25th anniv. (½c); Nobel Prize, 75th anniv. (1c); Viking Space Mission to Mars (10c); World Cricket Cup victory (50c); Telephone cent. ($1); Operation Sail, American Bicent. ($2).

Royal Family — A87

Designs: 10c, Queen Elizabeth, Prince Philip and their children. 30c, Elizabeth II and Prince Philip touring Antigua. 50c, Queen enthroned. 90c, Queen wearing crown. $2.50, Queen and Prince Charles. $5, Queen and Prince Philip.

1977, Feb. 7 *Perf. 13½x14*
459 A87 10c multicolored .25 .25
460 A87 30c multicolored .25 .25
461 A87 50c multicolored .25 .25
462 A87 90c multicolored .25 .25
463 A87 $2.50 multicolored .25 *.50*
Nos. 459-463 (5) 1.25 1.50

Souvenir Sheet
464 A87 $5 multicolored .70 *.85*
Complete booklet, 6 #461 var., 1 #464 var., self-adhesive and in changed colors 3.75

Reign of Queen Elizabeth II, 25th anniv.
Nos. 459-463 were printed in sheets of 40. Sheets of 5 plus label, perf. 12, probably were not sold by the Antigua Post Office.
For overprints see Nos. 477-482.

Scouts Camping — A88

Boy Scout Emblem and: 1c, Scouts on hike. 2c, Rock climbing. 10c, Cutting logs. 30c, Map and compass reading. 50c, First aid. $2, Scouts on raft.

1977, May 23 Litho. *Perf. 14*
465 A88 ½c multicolored .25 .25
466 A88 1c multicolored .25 .25
467 A88 2c multicolored .25 .25
468 A88 10c multicolored .25 .25
469 A88 30c multicolored .30 .25
470 A88 50c multicolored .50 .35
471 A88 $2 multicolored 1.00 *2.00*
a. Souvenir sheet of 3, #469-471 3.25 *3.75*
Nos. 465-471 (7) 2.80 3.60

Caribbean Boy Scout Jamboree, Jamaica.

Carnival Queen Holding Horseshoe — A89

30c, Carnival Queen in feather costume. 50c, Butterfly costume. 90c, Carnival Queen with ornaments. $1, Carnival King, Queen.

1977, July 18 Litho. *Perf. 14*

472	A89	10c multicolored	.25	.25
473	A89	30c multicolored	.25	.25
474	A89	50c multicolored	.25	.25
475	A89	90c multicolored	.35	.30
476	A89	$1 multicolored	.40	.40
a.		Souvenir sheet of 4, #473-476	1.50	*1.75*
		Nos. 472-476 (5)	1.50	1.45

21st Summer Carnival.

Nos. 459-464 Overprinted

Perf. 13½x14, 12

1977, Oct. 17 Litho.

477	A87	10c multicolored	.25	.25
478	A87	30c multicolored	.25	.25
479	A87	50c multicolored	.25	.25
480	A87	90c multicolored	.30	.30
481	A87	$2.50 multicolored	.45	.40
		Nos. 477-481 (5)	1.50	1.45

Souvenir Sheet

482	A87	$5 multicolored	1.75	1.75

Visit of Queen Elizabeth II, Oct. 28.

Virgin and Child, by Cosimo Tura — A90

Virgin and Child by: 1c, $2, Carlo Crivelli (different). 2c, 25c, Lorenzo Lotto (different). 8c, Jacopo da Pontormo. 10c, Tura.

1977, Nov. 15 Litho. *Perf. 14*

483	A90	½c multicolored	.25	.25
484	A90	1c multicolored	.25	.25
485	A90	2c multicolored	.25	.25
486	A90	8c multicolored	.25	.25
487	A90	10c multicolored	.25	.25
488	A90	25c multicolored	.25	.25
489	A90	$2 multicolored	.50	*1.00*
a.		Souvenir sheet of 4, #486-489	1.40	*2.50*
		Nos. 483-489 (7)	2.00	*2.50*

Christmas.

Pineapple — A91

10th anniv. of Statehood: 15c, Flag of Antigua. 50c, Police band. 90c, Prime Minister V. C. Bird. $2, Coat of Arms.

1977, Dec. 28 Litho. *Perf. 13x13½*

490	A91	10c multicolored	.25	.25
491	A91	15c multicolored	.50	.25
492	A91	50c multicolored	2.00	.75
493	A91	90c multicolored	.50	.75
494	A91	$2 multicolored	.90	*1.50*
a.		Souv. sheet, #491-494, perf 14	3.50	3.50
		Nos. 490-494 (5)	4.15	3.50

Wright Glider III, 1902 — A92

1c, Flyer I in air, 1903. 2c, Weight and derrick launch system and Wright engine, 1903. 10c, Orville Wright, vert. 50c, Flyer III, 1905. 90c, Wilbur Wright, vert. $2, Wright Model B, 1910. $2.50, Flyer I, 1903, on ground.

1978, Mar. 28 *Perf. 14*

495	A92	½c multicolored	.25	.25
496	A92	1c multicolored	.25	.25
497	A92	2c multicolored	.25	.25
498	A92	10c multicolored	.35	.25
499	A92	50c multicolored	.55	.25
500	A92	90c multicolored	.80	.30
501	A92	$2 multicolored	.80	.80
		Nos. 495-501 (7)	3.25	2.35

Souvenir Sheet

502	A92	$2.50 multicolored	2.10	*2.75*

1st powered flight by Wright brothers, 75th anniv.

Sunfish Regatta — A93

Sailing Week 1978: 50c, Fishing and work boat race. 90c, Curtain Bluff race. $2, Powerboat rally. $2.50, Guadeloupe-Antigua race.

1978, Apr. 29 Litho. *Perf. 14½*

503	A93	10c multicolored	.30	.25
504	A93	50c multicolored	.40	.25
505	A93	90c multicolored	.70	.40
506	A93	$2 multicolored	1.25	.75
		Nos. 503-506 (4)	2.65	1.65

Souvenir Sheet

507	A93	$2.50 multicolored	2.25	2.25

25th Anniv. of the Coronation of Queen Elizabeth II — A94

Designs: 10c, Elizabeth II and Prince Philip. 30c, Coronation. 50c, State coach. 90c, Elizabeth II and Archbishop. $2.50, Elizabeth II. $5, Elizabeth II, Prince Philip, Prince Charles and Princess Anne as children.

1978, June 2 Litho. *Perf. 14, 12*

508	A94	10c multicolored	.25	.25
509	A94	30c multicolored	.25	.25
510	A94	50c multicolored	.25	.25
511	A94	90c multicolored	.25	.25
512	A94	$2.50 multicolored	.30	.30
		Nos. 508-512 (5)	1.30	1.30

Souvenir Sheet

513	A94	$5 multicolored	1.25	1.25

25th anniv. of coronation of Queen Elizabeth II.

Nos. 508-512 were printed in sheets of 50 (2 panes of 25), perf. 14, and in sheets of 3 plus label, perf. 12, with frames in changed colors.

Glass Coach A95

Royal Coaches: 50c, Irish state coach. $5, Coronation coach.

1978, June 2 Litho. *Imperf.*

Self-adhesive

514		Souvenir booklet	2.50
a.	A95	Bklt. pane, 3 each 25c, 50c	1.00
b.	A95	Bklt. pane, 1 $5	1.40

25th anniversary of coronation of Queen Elizabeth II. No. 514 contains 2 booklet panes printed on peelable paper backing showing royal processions.

Soccer — A96

Designs: Various soccer scenes. Stamps in souvenir sheet horizontal.

1978, Aug. 18 Litho. *Perf. 15*

515	A96	10c multicolored	.25	.25
516	A96	15c multicolored	.25	.25
517	A96	$3 multicolored	1.60	*1.75*
		Nos. 515-517 (3)	2.10	2.25

Souvenir Sheet

518		Sheet of 4	3.75	3.75
a.		A96 25c multicolored	.25	.25
b.		A96 30c multicolored	.40	.40
c.		A96 50c multicolored	.70	.70
d.		A96 $2 multicolored	2.00	2.00

11th World Cup Soccer Championship, Argentina, June 1-25.

Purple Wreath — A97

1978, Oct. Litho. *Perf. 14*

519	A97	25c shown	.25	.25
520	A97	50c Sunflowers	.40	.25
521	A97	90c Frangipani	.70	.30
522	A97	$2 Passionflower	1.50	*1.75*
		Nos. 519-522 (4)	2.85	2.55

Souvenir Sheet

523	A97	$2.50 Red hibiscus	2.00	*2.50*

St. Ildefonso Receiving Chasuble, by Rubens — A98

Christmas: 25c, Flight of St. Barbara, by Rubens. $2, Madonna and Child with Ss. Joseph and John and a Dono, by Sebastiano del Piombo. $4, Annunciation, by Rubens.

1978, Oct. 30 Litho. *Perf. 14*

524	A98	8c multicolored	.25	.25
525	A98	25c multicolored	.25	.25
526	A98	$2 multicolored	.65	.55
		Nos. 524-526 (3)	1.15	1.05

Souvenir Sheet

527	A98	$4 multicolored	1.90	1.90

No. 526 is incorrectly attributed to Rubens.

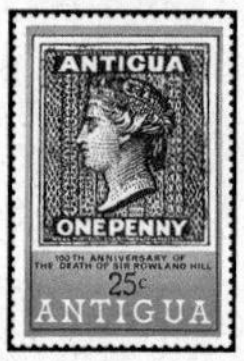

Antigua #2 — A99

Designs: 50c, Great Britain Penny Black, 1840. $1, Woman posting letter in pillar box, and coach. $2, Mail train, ship, plane and Concorde. $2.50, Rowland Hill.

1979, Aug. 27 Litho. *Perf. 14*

528	A99	25c multicolored	.25	.25
529	A99	50c multicolored	.25	.25
530	A99	$1 multicolored	.35	.25
531	A99	$2 multicolored	.85	.50
		Nos. 528-531 (4)	1.70	1.25

Souvenir Sheet

532	A99	$2.50 multicolored	1.15	1.15

Sir Rowland Hill (1795-1879), originator of penny postage.

Nos. 528-531 were printed in sheets of 50 (2 panes of 25), perf. 14, and in sheets of 5 plus label, perf. 12, with frames in changed colors.

For overprints, see Nos. 571A-571D.

Crucifixion, by Durer — A100

Designs (after Dürer): 10c, Deposition. $2.50, Crucifixion. $4, Man of Sorrows.

1979, Mar. 15

533	A100	10c multicolored	.25	.25
534	A100	50c multicolored	.50	.25
535	A100	$4 multicolored	1.10	1.10
		Nos. 533-535 (3)	1.85	1.60

Souvenir Sheet

536	A100	$2.50 multicolored	1.25	1.25

Easter.

Child Playing with Sailboat — A101

IYC emblem, child's hand holding toy: 50c, Rocket. 90c, Automobile. $2, Train. $5, Plane.

1979, Apr. 9 Litho. *Perf. 14*

537	A101	25c multicolored	.25	.25
538	A101	50c multicolored	.25	.25
539	A101	90c multicolored	.40	.30
540	A101	$2 multicolored	1.00	1.00
		Nos. 537-540 (4)	1.90	1.80

Souvenir Sheet

541	A101	$5 multicolored	1.90	1.90

International Year of the Child.

Yellowjacks A102

Sport Fish: 50c, Bluefin tunas. 90c, Sailfish. $2.50, Barracuda. $3, Wahoos.

1979, May Litho. *Perf. 14½*

542	A102	30c multicolored	.30	.25
543	A102	50c multicolored	.40	.30
544	A102	90c multicolored	.85	.40
545	A102	$3 multicolored	2.50	2.00
		Nos. 542-545 (4)	4.05	2.95

Souvenir Sheet

546	A102	$2.50 multicolored	2.25	2.25

Capt. Cook and his Birthplace at Marton — A103

Capt. James Cook (1728-1779) and: 50c, HMS Endeavour. 90c, Marine timekeeper. $2.50, HMS Resolution. $3, Landing at Botany Bay.

1979, July 2 Litho. *Perf. 14*

547	A103	25c multicolored	.55	.30
548	A103	50c multicolored	.85	.40
549	A103	90c multicolored	.60	*.75*
550	A103	$3 multicolored	1.45	*2.75*
		Nos. 547-550 (4)	3.45	*4.20*

Souvenir Sheet

551	A103	$2.50 multicolored	2.75	2.75

Holy Family — A104

Stained-glass Windows: 25c, Flight into Egypt. 50c, Shepherd and star. $3, Angel with trumpet. $4, Three Kings offering gifts.

1979, Oct. 1 Litho. *Perf. 14*

552	A104	8c multicolored	.25	.25
553	A104	25c multicolored	.25	.25
554	A104	50c multicolored	.30	.30
555	A104	$4 multicolored	.80	*2.25*
		Nos. 552-555 (4)	1.60	*3.05*

Souvenir Sheet

Perf. 12x12½

556	A104	$3 multicolored	1.25	*1.75*

Christmas.

Javelin, Olympic Rings — A105

1980, Feb. 7 Litho. *Perf. 14*

557	A105	10c shown	.25	.25
558	A105	25c Running	.30	.30
559	A105	$1 Pole vault	.50	.50
560	A105	$2 Hurdles	.60	1.50
		Nos. 557-560 (4)	1.65	2.55

Souvenir Sheet

561	A105	$3 Boxing, horiz.	1.25	1.25

22nd Summer Olympic Games, Moscow, July 19-Aug. 3.

Disney Characters and IYC Emblem — A106

Transportation scenes: ½c, Mickey, plane. 1c, Donald, car. 2c, Goofy driving taxi. 3c, Mickey, Minnie in sidecar. 4c, Huey, Dewey and Louie. 5c, Grandma Duck. 10c, Mickey in jeep. $1, Chip and Dale sailing. $4, Donald on train.

$2.50, Goofy in glider.

½c, 2c, 3c, 4c, 5c, $1, $2.50, horiz.

1980, Mar. 24 Litho. *Perf. 11*

562	A106	½c multicolored	.25	.25
563	A106	1c multicolored	.25	.25
564	A106	2c multicolored	.25	.25
565	A106	3c multicolored	.25	.25
566	A106	4c multicolored	.25	.25
567	A106	5c multicolored	.25	.25
568	A106	10c multicolored	.25	.25
569	A106	$1 multicolored	1.25	1.50
570	A106	$4 multicolored	3.00	6.00
		Nos. 562-570 (9)	6.00	9.25

Souvenir Sheet

571	A106	$2.50 multicolored	7.50	7.50

Nos. 528-531 in Changed Colors & Overprinted

1980, May 6 Litho. *Perf. 12*

571A	A99	25c multicolored	.35	.35
571B	A99	50c multicolored	.45	.45
571C	A99	$1 multicolored	.75	.75
571D	A99	$2 multicolored	3.00	3.00
		Nos. 571A-571D (4)	4.55	4.55

London '80 Intl. Stamp Exhib., May 6-14.

For overprints see Barbuda Nos. 423-426.

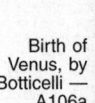

Birth of Venus, by Botticelli — A106a

10c, David, by Donatello. 50c, Reclining Couple, sarcophagus, Cerveteri. 90c, The Garden of Earthly Delights, by Hieronymus Bosch. $1, Portinari Altarpiece, by Hugo van der Goes. $4, Eleanora of Toledo and her Son Giovanni de Medici, by Bronzino. $5, The Holy Family, by Rembrandt.

Perf. 13½x14, 14x13½

1980, June 23 Litho.

572	A106a	10c multi, vert.	.25	.25
573	A106a	30c multi	.40	.25
574	A106a	50c multi	.55	.40
575	A106a	90c multi	.70	.70
576	A106a	$1 multi	.80	.80
577	A106a	$4 multi, vert.	2.00	3.00
		Nos. 572-577 (6)	4.70	5.40

Souvenir Sheet

Perf. 14

578	A106a	$5 multicolored	3.00	3.00

Anniversary Emblem, Intl. Headquarters, Evanston, IL — A107

50c, Antigua club banner. 90c, Map of Antigua. $3, Paul. P. Harris, emblem.

$5, Emblems, Antigua flags.

1980, July 21 Litho. *Perf. 14*

579	A107	30c shown	.35	.25
580	A107	50c multicolored	.40	.40
581	A107	90c multicolored	.60	.60
582	A107	$3 multicolored	1.90	2.75
		Nos. 579-582 (4)	3.25	4.00

Souvenir Sheet

583	A107	$5 multicolored	2.00	2.00

Rotary International, 75th anniv.

A108

1980, Sept. 15

584	A108	10c multicolored	.25	.25
585	A108	$2.50 multicolored	1.25	1.50

Souvenir Sheet

Perf. 12

586	A108	$3 multicolored	1.25	2.00

Queen Mother Elizabeth, 80th birthday.

A109

No. 587, Ringed Kingfisher. No. 588, Plain pigeon. No. 889, Green-throated carib. No. 890, Black-necked stilt.

No. 591, Roseate tern.

1980, Nov. 3 Litho. *Perf. 14*

587	A109	10c multicolored	.90	.30
588	A109	30c multicolored	1.25	.50
589	A109	$1 multicolored	1.75	1.75
590	A109	$2 multicolored	2.50	3.75
		Nos. 587-590 (4)	6.40	6.30

Souvenir Sheet

591	A109	$2.50 multicolored	6.75	6.75

Maleficent and Diablo A110

Christmas: Various scenes from Walt Disney's Sleeping Beauty. $4 vert.

1980, Dec. 23 *Perf. 11, 13½x14 ($4)*

592	A110	½c multicolored	.25	.25
593	A110	1c multicolored	.25	.25
594	A110	2c multicolored	.25	.25
595	A110	4c multicolored	.25	.25
596	A110	8c multicolored	.25	.25
597	A110	10c multicolored	.25	.25
598	A110	25c multicolored	.30	.30
599	A110	$2 multicolored	2.25	2.25
600	A110	$2.50 multicolored	2.50	2.50
		Nos. 592-600 (9)	6.55	6.55

Souvenir Sheet

601	A110	$4 multicolored	6.50	6.50

Sugar-cane Railway Diesel Locomotive No. 15 — A111

50c, Narrow-gauge steam locomotive. 90c, Diesels #1, #10. $3, Hauling sugar-cane.

$2.50, Sugar factory, train yard.

1981, Jan. 12 *Perf. 14*

602	A111	25c shown	.25	.25
603	A111	50c multicolored	.40	.40
604	A111	90c multicolored	.75	.75
605	A111	$3 multicolored	2.10	2.10
		Nos. 602-605 (4)	3.50	3.50

Souvenir Sheet

606	A111	$2.50 multicolored	2.60	2.60

Nos. 411-412, 414-422 Overprinted

1981, Mar. 31 Litho.

607	A79	6c multicolored	.25	.25
608	A79	10c multicolored	.25	.25
609	A79	20c multicolored	.25	.25
610	A79	25c multicolored	.25	.25
611	A79	35c multicolored	.30	.30
612	A79	50c multicolored	.50	.50
613	A79	75c multicolored	.60	.60
614	A79	$1 multicolored	.85	1.25
615	A80	$2.50 multicolored	1.50	2.25
616	A80	$5 multicolored	2.60	3.75
617	A80	$10 multicolored	5.25	7.00
		Nos. 607-617 (11)	12.60	16.65

Pipes of Pan, by Picasso — A112

Paintings by Pablo Picasso (1881-1973): 50c, Seated Harlequin. 90c, Paulo as Harlequin. $4, Mother and Child. $5, Three Musicians.

1981, May 5 Litho. *Perf. 14*

618	A112	10c multicolored	.25	.25
619	A112	50c multicolored	.40	.40
620	A112	90c multicolored	.75	.75
621	A112	$4 multicolored	2.10	2.10
		Nos. 618-621 (4)	3.50	3.50

Souvenir Sheet

Perf. 14x14½

622	A112	$5 multicolored	2.25	2.75

Royal Wedding Issue

Common Design Type

1981, June 16 Litho. *Perf. 14*

623	CD331a	25c Couple	.25	.25
624	CD331a	50c Glamis Castle	.25	.25
625	CD331a	$4 Charles	.80	.80
		Nos. 623-625 (3)	1.30	1.30

Souvenir Sheet

626	CD331	$5 Glass coach	1.25	1.25
627	CD331	Booklet	4.00	
a.		Pane of 6 (2x25c, 2x$1, 2x$2), Charles	2.50	
b.		Pane of 1, $5, Couple	1.50	

No. 627 contains imperf., self-adhesive stamps.

Nos. 623-625 also printed in sheets of 5 plus label, perf. 12 in changed colors.

For surcharges see Nos. 792, 795, 802, 805.

Campfire Sing — A113

1981, Oct. 28 Litho. *Perf. 15*

628	A113	10c Irene Joshua	.25	.25
629	A113	50c shown	.40	.25
630	A113	90c Sailing	.65	.55
631	A113	$2.50 Milking cow	1.60	2.00
		Nos. 628-631 (4)	2.90	3.05

Souvenir Sheet

632	A113	$5 Flag raising	5.25	5.25

Girl Guides, 50th anniv.

A114

10c, Arms. 50c, Flag. 90c, Prime Minister Bird. $2.50, St. John's Cathedral, horiz.

$5, Map.

1981, Nov. 1 Litho. *Perf. 15*

633	A114	10c multicolored	.30	.25
634	A114	50c multicolored	.85	.50
635	A114	90c multicolored	.55	.55
636	A114	$2.50 multicolored	1.40	2.25
		Nos. 633-636 (4)	3.10	3.55

Souvenir Sheet

637	A114	$5 multicolored	4.25	3.25

Independence.

No. 637 contains one 41x41mm stamp.

A115

Christmas (Virgin and Child Paintings by): 8c, Holy Night, by Jacques Stella (1596-1657). 30c Julius Schnorr von Carolsfeld (1794-1872). $1, Alonso Cano (1601-1667). $3, Lorenzo de Credi (1459-1537). $5, Holy Family, by Pieter von Avont (1600-1652).

1981, Nov. 16

638	A115	8c multicolored	.30	.25
639	A115	30c multicolored	.50	.25
640	A115	$1 multicolored	1.20	1.20
641	A115	$3 multicolored	1.75	3.25
		Nos. 638-641 (4)	3.75	4.95

Souvenir Sheet

642	A115	$5 multicolored	3.75	4.50

On No. 639, the artist's name is misspelled as "Carolfeld."

Intl. Year of the Disabled — A116

1981, Dec. 1 Litho. *Perf. 15*

643	A116	10c Swimming	.25	.25
644	A116	50c Discus	.30	.30
645	A116	90c Archery	.45	.55
646	A116	$2 Baseball	1.00	1.40
		Nos. 643-646 (4)	2.00	2.50

Souvenir Sheet

647	A116	$4 Basketball	4.50	3.25

1982 World Cup Soccer — A117

Designs: Various soccer players.

1982, Apr. 15 Litho. *Perf. 14*

648	A117	10c multicolored	.30	.25
649	A117	50c multicolored	.45	.30
650	A117	90c multicolored	.90	.65
651	A117	$4 multicolored	3.00	3.50
		Nos. 648-651 (4)	4.65	4.70

Souvenir Sheet

652	A117	$5 multicolored	6.75	7.50

Also issued in sheetlets of 5 + label in changed colors, perf. 12.

A118

No. 653, A-300 Airbus. No. 654, Hawker-Siddeley 748. No. 655, De Havilland Twin Otter DCH6. No. 656, Britten-Norman Islander.
No. 657, Jet, horiz.

1982, June 17 Litho. *Perf. 14½*

653	A118	10c multicolored	.25	.25
654	A118	50c multicolored	.35	.35
655	A118	90c multicolored	.65	.65
656	A118	$2.50 multicolored	1.75	1.75
		Nos. 653-656 (4)	3.00	3.00

Souvenir Sheet

657	A118	$5 multicolored	4.00	4.00

Coolidge Intl. Airport opening.

A119

No. 658, Cordia, vert. No. 659, Golden spotted mongoose. No. 660, Corallita, vert. No. 661, Bulldog bats.
No. 662, Caribbean monk seals.

1982, June 28 Litho. *Perf. 14½*

658	A119	10c multicolored	.35	.25
659	A119	50c multicolored	.70	.40
660	A119	90c multicolored	1.10	.75
661	A119	$3 multicolored	2.50	*3.25*
		Nos. 658-661 (4)	4.65	*4.65*

Souvenir Sheet

662	A119	$5 multicolored	7.75	7.75

Charles Darwin's death centenary.

Princess Diana Issue
Common Design Type

90c, Greenwich Palace. $1, Wedding. $4, Diana.
$5, Diana, diff.

1982, July 1 Litho. *Perf. 14½x14*

663	CD332	90c multicolored	.70	.50
664	CD332	$1 multicolored	.80	.60
665	CD332	$4 multicolored	3.00	2.50
		Nos. 663-665 (3)	4.50	3.60

Souvenir Sheet

666	CD332	$5 multicolored	3.75	3.75

For overprints and surcharges see Nos. 672-675, 797, 799, 803, 806.

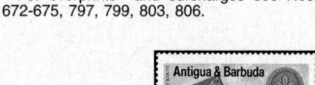

Scouting Year — A120

Independence Day celebration: 10c, Decorating buildings. 50c, Helping woman. 90c, Princess Margaret. $2.20, Cub Scout giving directions.
$5, Baden-Powell.

1982, July 15 *Perf. 14*

667	A120	10c multicolored	.30	.25
668	A120	50c multicolored	.60	.45
669	A120	90c multicolored	.85	.65
670	A120	$2.20 multicolored	1.50	*2.50*
		Nos. 667-670 (4)	3.25	*3.85*

Souvenir Sheet

671	A120	$5 multicolored	5.75	5.75

Nos. 663-666 Overprinted

1982, Aug. 30 Litho. *Perf. 14½x14*

672	CD332	90c multicolored	.45	.45
673	CD332	$1 multicolored	.55	.55
674	CD332	$4 multicolored	1.90	1.90
		Nos. 672-674 (3)	2.90	2.90

Souvenir Sheet

675	CD332	$5 multicolored	2.60	2.60

For surcharges see Nos. 798, 800, 804, 807.

Roosevelt Driving by "The Little White House" — A121

25c, Washington as blacksmith. 45c, Churchill, Roosevelt, Stalin. 60c, Washington crossing Delaware, vert. $1, Roosevelt on train, vert. $3, Roosevelt, vert.
No. 682, Washington, vert. No. 683, Eleanor and Franklin.

1982, Sept. 20 *Perf. 15*

676	A121	10c shown	.25	.25
677	A121	25c multicolored	.40	.25
678	A121	45c multicolored	1.40	.35
679	A121	60c multicolored	.95	.35
680	A121	$1 multicolored	1.35	.90
681	A121	$3 multicolored	1.30	*2.50*
		Nos. 676-681 (6)	5.65	*4.60*

Souvenir Sheets

682	A121	$4 multicolored	3.50	3.50
683	A121	$4 multicolored	3.50	3.50

George Washington's 250th birth anniv. and Franklin D. Roosevelt's birth centenary.

Christmas A122

Raphael Paintings: 10c, Annunciation. 30c, Adoration of the Magi. $1, Presentation at the Temple. $4, Coronation of the Virgin.
$5, Marriage of the Virgin.

1982, Nov. Litho. *Perf. 14*

684	A122	10c multicolored	.25	.25
685	A122	30c multicolored	.25	.25
686	A122	$1 multicolored	.50	.50
687	A122	$4 multicolored	2.25	2.25
		Nos. 684-687 (4)	3.25	*3.25*

Souvenir Sheet

688	A122	$5 multicolored	3.25	3.25

500th Birth Anniv. of Raphael A123

45c, Galatea taking Reins of Dolphins, vert. 50c, Sea Nymphs carried by Tritons, vert. 60c, Winged Angel Steering Dolphins. $4, Cupids Shooting Arrows.
$5, Galatea.

1983, Jan. 28. Litho. *Perf. 14½*

689	A123	45c multicolored	.30	.30
690	A123	50c multicolored	.40	.40
691	A123	60c multicolored	.45	.45
692	A123	$4 multicolored	2.00	2.00
		Nos. 689-692 (4)	3.15	3.15

Souvenir Sheet

693	A123	$5 multicolored	3.00	3.00

A124

1983, Mar. 14 *Perf. 14*

694	A124	25c Pineapple crop	.25	.25
695	A124	45c Carnival	.25	.25
696	A124	60c Tourists, sailboat	.35	.35
697	A124	$3 Control Tower	1.00	*1.50*
		Nos. 694-697 (4)	1.85	2.35

Commonwealth Day.

World Communications Year — A125

15c, TV screen, camera. 50c, Police radio, car. 60c, Long distance phone call. $3, Dish antenna, planets.
$5, Comsat satellite.

1983, Apr. 5 Litho. *Perf. 14*

698	A125	15c multicolored	.50	.25
699	A125	50c multicolored	2.10	1.25
700	A125	60c multicolored	2.10	1.40
701	A125	$3 multicolored	4.00	*5.00*
		Nos. 698-701 (4)	8.70	7.90

Souvenir Sheet

702	A125	$5 multicolored	2.75	*3.25*

Imperforates
See note following No. 404.

Bottlenose Dolphin — A126

50c, Finback whale. 60c, Bowhead whale. $3, Spectacled porpoise.
$5, Unicorn whale.

1983, May 9 Litho. *Perf. 15*

703	A126	15c shown	.75	.25
704	A126	50c multicolored	1.60	1.25
705	A126	60c multicolored	1.75	1.25
706	A126	$3 multicolored	3.25	*4.25*
		Nos. 703-706 (4)	7.35	7.00

Souvenir Sheet

707	A126	$5 multicolored	8.50	8.50

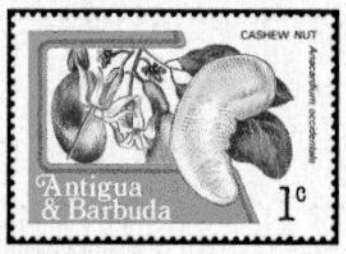

Cashew Nut — A127

1983, July 11 *Perf. 14*

708	A127	1c	shown	.25	*1.10*
709	A127	2c	Passion fruit	.25	*1.10*
710	A127	3c	Mango	.25	*1.10*
711	A127	5c	Grapefruit	.25	*1.10*
712	A127	10c	Pawpaw	.40	.25
713	A127	15c	Breadfruit	.75	.25
714	A127	20c	Coconut	.45	.25
715	A127	25c	Oleander	.75	.35
716	A127	30c	Banana	.55	.40
717	A127	40c	Pineapple	.75	.40
718	A127	45c	Cordia	.85	.55
719	A127	50c	Cassia	.90	.60
720	A127	60c	Poui	1.75	1.00
721	A127	$1	Frangipani	2.25	1.50
722	A127	$2	Flamboyant	3.50	*3.75*
723	A127	$2.50	Lemon	3.75	*6.00*
724	A127	$5	Lignum vitae	5.00	*12.00*
725	A127	$10	Arms	8.00	*17.00*
			Nos. 708-725 (18)	30.65	*48.70*

1985 *Perf. 12½x12*

708a	A127	1c	.25	*1.10*
709a	A127	2c	.25	*1.10*
710a	A127	3c	.25	*1.10*
711a	A127	5c	.30	*1.10*
712a	A127	10c	.35	.25
713a	A127	15c	.50	.25
714a	A127	20c	.60	.25
715a	A127	25c	.60	.25
716a	A127	30c	.70	.30
717a	A127	40c	.75	.30
718a	A127	45c	.80	.45
719a	A127	50c	1.20	.45
720a	A127	60c	1.75	1.10
721a	A127	$1	2.00	1.25
722a	A127	$2	3.75	*4.25*
723a	A127	$2.50	4.25	*6.00*
724a	A127	$5	6.75	*12.00*
725a	A127	$10	11.00	*17.00*
		Nos. 708a-725a (18)	36.05	*48.50*

Issue dates: $2-$5, Dec; others Mar.

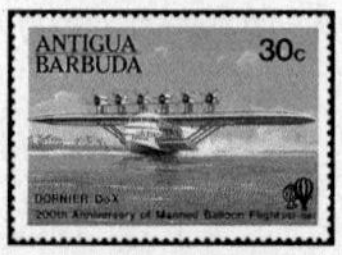

Manned Flight Bicentenary A128

30c, Dornier DoX. 50c, Supermarine S-6B. 60c, Curtiss F9C, USS Akron. $4, Pro Juventute balloon.
$5, Graf Zeppelin.

1983, Aug. 15 *Perf. 15*

726	A128	30c multicolored	1.00	.30
727	A128	50c multicolored	1.25	.60
728	A128	60c multicolored	1.40	.75
729	A128	$4 multicolored	3.25	*5.75*
		Nos. 726-729 (4)	6.90	*7.40*

Souvenir Sheet

730	A128	$5 multicolored	3.50	3.50

Christmas A129

Raphael Paintings: 10c, Angel flying with scroll. 30c, Angel, diff. $1, Inscribing tablet. $4, Angel showing tablet.
$5, Vision of Ezekiel.
10c, 30c, $1, $4, Sybils and Angels details.

1983, Oct. 4 Litho. *Perf. 14*

731	A129	10c multicolored	.35	.25
732	A129	30c multicolored	.65	.40
733	A129	$1 multicolored	1.50	1.25
734	A129	$4 multicolored	2.75	*4.75*
		Nos. 731-734 (4)	5.25	*6.65*

Souvenir Sheet

735	A129	$5 multicolored	1.60	*2.10*

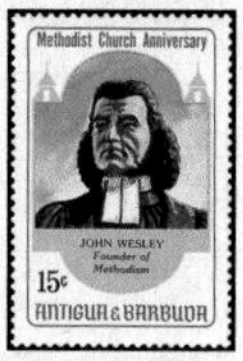

Methodist Church, Anniv. — A130

Designs: 15c, John Wesley founder of Methodism. 50c, Nathaniel Gilbert, Antiguan founder. 60c, St. John's Methodist Church Steeple. $3, Ebenezer Methodist Church.

1983, Nov. Litho. *Perf. 14*

736	A130	15c multicolored	.25	.25
737	A130	50c multicolored	.75	.45
738	A130	60c multicolored	.80	.60
739	A130	$3 multicolored	2.25	*3.75*
		Nos. 736-739 (4)	4.05	*5.05*

1984 Olympics, Los Angeles — A131

1984, Jan. Litho. *Perf. 15*

740	A131	25c Discus	.25	.25
741	A131	50c Gymnastics	.30	.25
742	A131	90c Hurdling	.60	*.60*
743	A131	$3 Bicycling	4.00	*3.00*
		Nos. 740-743 (4)	5.15	*4.10*

Souvenir Sheet

744	A131	$5 Volleyball, horiz.	3.50	*4.00*

Booker Vanguard A132

1984, June 4 Litho. *Perf. 15*

745	A132	45c shown	1.00	.45
746	A132	50c Canberra	1.20	.70
747	A132	60c Yachts	1.40	.90
748	A132	$4 Fairwind	3.00	*6.75*
		Nos. 745-748 (4)	6.60	*8.80*

Souvenir Sheet

749	A132	$5 Man-of-war, vert.	2.75	*3.50*

Local Flowers — A133

1984, June 25 Litho. *Perf. 15*

755	A133	15c multicolored	.50	.25
756	A133	50c multicolored	1.00	.75
757	A133	60c multicolored	1.00	1.00
758	A133	$3 multicolored	3.50	*5.50*
		Nos. 755-758 (4)	6.00	*7.50*

Souvenir Sheet

759	A133	$5 multicolored	3.50	3.50

US Presidents — A134

1984, July 18 Litho. *Perf. 14*

760	A134	10c Lincoln	.25	.25
761	A134	20c Truman	.25	.25
762	A134	30c Eisenhower	.30	.25
763	A134	40c Reagan	.50	.45
764	A134	90c Lincoln, diff.	.90	.80
765	A134	$1.10 Truman, diff.	1.25	1.10
766	A134	$1.50 Eisenhower, diff.	1.60	*1.75*
767	A134	$2 Reagan, diff.	1.75	*2.00*
		Nos. 760-767 (8)	6.80	6.85

Slavery Abolition Sesquicentennial A135

40c, Moravian Mission. 50c, Antigua Courthouse, 1823. 60c, Sugar cane planting. $3, Boiling House, Delaps' Estate.
$5, Willoughby Bay.

1984, Aug. 1

768	A135	40c multicolored	.85	.45
769	A135	50c multicolored	.90	.60
770	A135	60c multicolored	1.00	.70
771	A135	$3 multicolored	3.75	*4.75*
		Nos. 768-771 (4)	6.50	6.50

Souvenir Sheet

772	A135	$5 multicolored	6.25	6.25

Song Birds — A136

40c, Rufous-sided towhee. 50c, Parula warbler. 60c, House wren. $2, Ruby-crowned kinglet. $3, Yellow-shafted flicker.
$5, Yellow-breasted chat.

1984, Aug. 15 *Perf. 15*

773	A136	40c multicolored	1.65	.70
774	A136	50c multicolored	1.50	.90
775	A136	60c multicolored	1.75	1.75
776	A136	$2 multicolored	2.00	*3.50*
777	A136	$3 multicolored	2.25	*4.75*
		Nos. 773-777 (5)	9.15	*11.60*

Souvenir Sheet

778	A136	$5 multicolored	4.75	*5.75*

AUSIPEX '84 — A137

$1, Grass skiing. No. 780, $5, Australian rules football. No. 781, $5, Boomerang.

1984, Sept. 21 *Perf. 15*

779	A137	$1 multicolored	1.25	1.50
780	A137	$5 multicolored	4.00	4.75

Souvenir Sheet

781	A137	$5 multicolored	3.25	3.25

The Blue Dancers, by Degas — A137a

Paintings by Correggio: 25c, Virgin and Infant with Angels and Cherubs. 60c, The Four Saints. 90c, Saint Catherine. $3, The Campori Madonna. No. 790, St. John the Baptist.
Paintings by Degas: 50c, The Pink Dancers. 70c, Two Dancers. $4, Dancers at the Bar. No. 791, Folk Dancers.

1984, Oct. Litho. *Perf. 15*

782	A137a	15c multicolored	.35	.25
783	A137a	25c multicolored	.40	.25
784	A137a	50c multicolored	.85	.50
785	A137a	60c multicolored	.85	.40
786	A137a	70c multicolored	1.05	.70
787	A137a	90c multicolored	1.05	.75
788	A137a	$3 multicolored	2.40	*4.00*
789	A137a	$4 multicolored	2.60	*4.50*
		Nos. 782-789 (8)	9.55	*11.35*

Souvenir Sheets

790	A137a	$5 multicolored	3.00	3.00
791	A137a	$5 multi, horiz.	3.00	3.00

Nos. 623-626, 663-666, 672-675, 694-697 Surcharged in Black or Gold

(CD331)

(A124)

(CD332)

1984, June *Perf. 14, 14½x14*

792	CD331	$2 on 25c #623	3.00	*3.50*
793	A124	$2 on 25c #694	2.25	*1.50*
794	A124	$2 on 45c #695	2.25	*1.50*
795	CD331	$2 on 50c #624	3.00	*3.50*
796	A124	$2 on 60c #696	2.25	*2.75*
797	CD332	$2 on 90c #663 (G)	2.50	*2.75*
798	CD332	$2 on 90c #672 (G)	2.50	*2.75*
799	CD332	$2 on $1 #664 (G)	2.50	*2.75*
800	CD332	$2 on $1 #673 (G)	2.50	*2.75*
801	A124	$2 on $3 #697	2.25	*1.50*
802	CD331	$2 on $4 #625	3.00	*3.50*
803	CD332	$2 on $4 #665 (G)	2.50	*2.75*
804	CD332	$2 on $4 #674 (G)	2.50	*2.75*
		Nos. 792-804 (13)	33.00	*34.25*

Souvenir Sheets

805	CD331	$2 on $5 #626	8.00	8.00
806	CD332	$2 on $5 #666	6.75	6.75
807	CD332	$2 on $5 #675	6.75	6.75

Nos. 797-800, 803-804 exist with silver surcharge.

Christmas 1984 and 50th Anniv. of Donald Duck — A138

Scenes from various Donald Duck comics.

1984, Nov. Litho. *Perf. 11*

808	A138	1c multicolored	.25	.25
809	A138	2c multicolored	.25	.25
810	A138	3c multicolored	.25	.25
811	A138	4c multicolored	.25	.25
812	A138	5c multicolored	.25	.25
813	A138	10c multicolored	.25	.25
814	A138	$1 multicolored	1.75	1.10
815	A138	$2 multicolored	2.00	*2.75*
816	A138	$5 multicolored	3.75	*5.50*
		Nos. 808-816 (9)	9.00	10.85

Souvenir Sheets

Perf. 14

817	A138	$5 multi, horiz.	6.75	6.75
818	A138	$5 Donald on beach	6.75	6.75

20th Century Leaders — A139

No. 819, John F. Kennedy (1917-1963), vert. No. 820, Winston Churchill (1874-1965), vert. No. 821, Mahatma Gandhi (1869-1948), vert. No. 822, Mao Tse-Tung (1883-1976), vert. No. 823, Kennedy in Berlin. No. 824, Churchill in Paris. No. 825, Gandhi in Great Britain. No. 826, Mao in Peking.
No. 827, Flags of Great Britain, India, China, USA.

1984, Nov. 19 Litho. *Perf. 15*

819	A139	60c multicolored	1.15	*1.40*
820	A139	60c multicolored	1.15	*1.40*
821	A139	60c multicolored	1.15	*1.40*
822	A139	60c multicolored	1.15	*1.40*
823	A139	$1 multicolored	1.25	*1.60*
824	A139	$1 multicolored	1.25	*1.60*
825	A139	$1 multicolored	1.25	*1.60*
826	A139	$1 multicolored	1.25	*1.60*
		Nos. 819-826 (8)	9.60	*12.00*

Souvenir Sheet

827	A139	$5 multicolored	9.25	9.25

Statue of Liberty Centennial A140

25c, Torch on display, 1885. 30c, Restoration, 1984-1986, vert. 50c, Bartholdi supervising construction, 1876. 90c, Statue on Liberty Island. $1, Dedication Ceremony, 1886, vert. $3, Operation Sail, 1976, vert.
$5, Port of New York.

1985, Jan. 7

828	A140	25c multicolored	.25	.25
829	A140	30c multicolored	.25	.25
830	A140	50c multicolored	.40	.30
831	A140	90c multicolored	.70	.50
832	A140	$1 multicolored	1.50	1.10
833	A140	$3 multicolored	2.00	*2.75*
		Nos. 828-833 (6)	5.10	5.15

Souvenir Sheet

834	A140	$5 multicolored	4.50	4.50

Traditional Scenes — A141

15c, Ceramics, Arawak pot shard. 50c, Tatooing, body design. 60c, Harvesting Manioc, god Yocahu. $3, Caribs in battle, war club.
$5, Tainos worshiping.

1985, Jan. 21

835	A141	15c multicolored	.30	.25
836	A141	50c multicolored	.40	.40
837	A141	60c multicolored	.55	.50
838	A141	$3 multicolored	1.75	*2.50*
		Nos. 835-838 (4)	3.00	*3.65*

Souvenir Sheet

839	A141	$5 multicolored	2.75	2.75

Invention of the Motorcycle, Cent. — A142

10c, Triumph 2HP Jap, 1903. 30c, Indian Arrow, 1949. 60c, BMW R100RS, 1976. $4, Harley Davidson Model II, 1916.
$5, Laverda Jota, 1975.

1985, Mar. 7 *Perf. 14*

840	A142	10c multicolored	.60	.40
841	A142	30c multicolored	1.10	.50
842	A142	60c multicolored	1.40	1.25
843	A142	$4 multicolored	5.50	*7.25*
		Nos. 840-843 (4)	8.60	9.40

Souvenir Sheet

844	A142	$5 multicolored	6.00	*7.00*

John J. Audubon, 200th Birth Anniv. — A143

90c, Horned grebe. $1, Least petrel. $1.50, Great blue heron. $3, Double-crested cormorant.
$5, White-tailed tropic bird, vert.

1985, Mar. 25 *Perf. 14*

845	A143	90c multicolored	1.75	1.10
846	A143	$1 multicolored	2.00	1.10
847	A143	$1.50 multicolored	2.75	*3.00*
848	A143	$3 multicolored	4.50	*5.75*
		Nos. 845-848 (4)	11.00	*10.95*

Souvenir Sheet

849	A143	$5 multicolored	10.00	10.00

See Nos.910-914.

Butterflies A144

25c, Polygrapha cyanea. 60c, Leodonta dysoni. 90c, Junea doraete. $4, Prepona xenagoras.
$5, Caerois gerdrudtus.

1985, Apr. 16 *Perf. 14*

850	A144	25c multicolored	1.25	.25
851	A144	60c multicolored	2.25	1.10
852	A144	90c multicolored	3.00	1.25
853	A144	$4 multicolored	7.50	*10.00*
		Nos. 850-853 (4)	14.00	12.60

Souvenir Sheet

854	A144	$5 multicolored	6.50	6.50

Cessna 172 — A145

90c, Fokker DVII. $1.50, Spad VII. $3, Boeing 747.
$5, Twin Otter, Coolidge Intl. Airport.

1985, Apr. 30

855	A145	30c shown	1.25	.25
856	A145	90c multicolored	2.50	1.25
857	A145	$1.50 multicolored	3.50	3.25
858	A145	$3 multicolored	5.25	*7.00*
		Nos. 855-858 (4)	12.50	*11.75*

Souvenir Sheet

859	A145	$5 multicolored	5.25	5.25

40th anniv. of the ICAO. Nos. 855, 858-859 show the ICAO and UN emblems.

Maimonides (1135-1204), Judaic Philosopher and Physician — A146

1985, June 17 Litho. *Perf. 14*

860	A146	$2 yellow green	3.75	3.25

Souvenir Sheet

861	A146	$5 deep brown	6.75	5.00

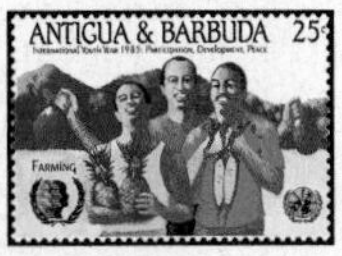

Intl. Youth Year — A147

25c, Agriculture. 50c, Hotel management. 60c, Environmental studies. $3, Windsurfing.
$5, Youths, national flag.

1985, July 1

862	A147	25c multicolored	.25	.25
863	A147	50c multicolored	.35	.30
864	A147	60c multicolored	1.00	.75
865	A147	$3 multicolored	2.10	*5.00*
		Nos. 862-865 (4)	3.70	*6.30*

Souvenir Sheet

866	A147	$5 multicolored	3.25	3.25

Queen Mother, 85th Birthday — A148

Designs: 90c, $1, Attending a church service. No. 867A, $1.50, Touring the London Gardens, children in a sandpit. $2.50, $3, Photograph (1979). $5, With Prince Edward at the wedding of Prince Charles and Lady Diana Spencer.

Perf. 14, 12x12½ (90c, $1, $3)

1985, July 15

866A	A148	90c multi ('86)	.55	.55
867	A148	$1 multi	.60	.60
867A	A148	$1 multi ('86)	.60	.60
868	A148	$1.50 multi	.90	.90
869	A148	$2.50 multi	1.40	1.40
869A	A148	$3 multi ('86)	1.60	1.60
		Nos. 866A-869A (6)	5.65	5.65

Souvenir Sheet

870	A148	$5 multicolored	4.00	4.00

Nos. 866A, 867A, 869A issued in sheets of 5 plus label on Jan. 13, 1986.

Marine Life — A149

15c, Fregata magnificens. 45c, Diploria labyrinthi-formis. 60c, Oreaster reticulatus. $3, Gymnothorax moringa.
$5, Acropora palmata.

1985, Aug. 1 ***Perf. 14***

871	A149	15c multicolored	1.00	.25
872	A149	45c multicolored	2.00	.85
873	A149	60c multicolored	2.25	1.60
874	A149	$3 multicolored	7.00	*8.50*
		Nos. 871-874 (4)	12.25	*11.20*

Souvenir Sheet

875	A149	$5 multicolored	8.75	8.75

Johann Sebastian Bach — A150

1985, Aug. 26 **Litho.** ***Perf. 14***

876	A150	25c Bass trombone	1.10	.40
877	A150	50c English horn	1.40	.90
878	A150	$1 Violino piccolo	2.75	1.50
879	A150	$3 Bass rackett	6.00	*6.75*
		Nos. 876-879 (4)	11.25	9.55

Souvenir Sheet

880	A150	$5 Portrait	5.75	5.75

Girl Guides, 75th Anniv. — A151

Public service and growth-oriented activities: 15c, Public service. 45c, Guides meeting. 60c, Lord and Lady Baden-Powell. $3, Nature study.
$5, Barn swallow.

1985, Sept. 10

881	A151	15c multicolored	.75	.25
882	A151	45c multicolored	1.25	.40
883	A151	60c multicolored	1.60	.60
884	A151	$3 multicolored	4.25	4.25
		Nos. 881-884 (4)	7.85	5.50

Souvenir Sheet

885	A151	$5 multicolored	5.50	*8.00*

State Visit of Elizabeth II, Oct. 24 — A152

1985, Oct. 24 **Litho.** ***Perf. 14½***

886	A152	60c National flags	.90	.45
887	A152	$1 Elizabeth II, vert.	1.35	.90
888	A152	$4 HMY Britannia	3.25	*6.50*
		Nos. 886-888 (3)	5.50	*7.85*

Souvenir Sheet

889	A152	$5 Map of Antigua	3.50	3.50

Mark Twain A153

Disney characters in Roughing It: 25c, Cowboys and Indians. 50c, Canoeing. $1.10, Pony Express. $1.50, Buffalo hunt in Missouri. $2, Nevada silver mine.
$5, Stagecoach on Kansas plains.

1985, Nov. 4 ***Perf. 14***

890	A153	25c multicolored	1.00	.25
891	A153	50c multicolored	1.25	.40
892	A153	$1.10 multicolored	2.00	1.25
893	A153	$1.50 multicolored	2.50	*3.50*
894	A153	$2 multicolored	3.25	*4.25*
		Nos. 890-894 (5)	10.00	9.65

Souvenir Sheet

895	A153	$5 multicolored	8.75	8.75

Jacob and Wilhelm Grimm, Fabulists and Philologists A154

Disney characters in Spindle, Shuttle and Needle.

1985, Nov. 11

896	A154	30c multicolored	1.00	.35
897	A154	60c multicolored	1.50	.70
898	A154	70c multicolored	1.75	1.25
899	A154	$1 multicolored	2.00	1.60
900	A154	$3 multicolored	4.50	*7.00*
		Nos. 896-900 (5)	10.75	*10.90*

Souvenir Sheet

900A	A154	$5 multicolored	8.75	8.75

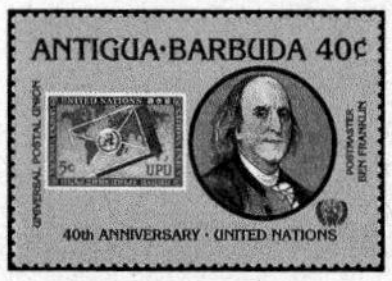

UN 40th Anniv. A155

Stamps of UN and portraits: 40c, No. 18 and Benjamin Franklin. $1, No. 391 and George Washington Carver, agricultural chemist. $3, No. 299 and Charles Lindbergh. $5, Marc Chagall, artist, vert.

1985, Nov. 18 ***Perf. 13½x14***

901	A155	40c multicolored	.90	.50
902	A155	$1 multicolored	1.75	1.25
903	A155	$3 multicolored	4.25	*7.00*
		Nos. 901-903 (3)	6.90	*8.75*

Souvenir Sheet

Perf. 14x13½

904	A155	$5 multicolored	6.75	6.75

Christmas — A156

Religious paintings: 10c, Madonna and Child, by De Landi. 25c, Madonna and Child, by Bonaventura Berlingheiri (d. 1244). 60c, The Nativity, by Fra Angelico (1400-1455). $4, Presentation in the Temple, by Giovanni di Paolo Grazia (c.1403-1482). $5, The Nativity, by Antoniazzo Romano.

1985, Dec. 30 ***Perf. 15***

905	A156	10c multicolored	.30	.25
906	A156	25c multicolored	.60	.25
907	A156	60c multicolored	.85	.45
908	A156	$4 multicolored	1.90	*4.00*
		Nos. 905-908 (4)	3.65	*4.95*

Souvenir Sheet

909	A156	$5 multicolored	3.50	*3.75*

Audubon Type of 1985

Illustrations of North American ducks: 60c, Mallard. 90c, Dusky duck. $1.50, Common pintail. $3, Widgeon.
$5, Common eider.

1986, Jan. 6 ***Perf. 12½x12***

910	A143	60c multicolored	1.90	1.00
911	A143	90c multicolored	2.40	1.50
912	A143	$1.50 multicolored	3.00	3.50
913	A143	$3 multicolored	4.00	*5.75*
		Nos. 910-913 (4)	11.30	11.75

Souvenir Sheet

Perf. 14

914	A143	$5 multicolored	7.25	7.25

1986 World Cup Soccer Championships, Mexico — A157

1986, Mar. 17 **Litho.** ***Perf. 14***

915	A157	30c shown	1.30	.25
916	A157	60c Heading the ball	1.50	.60
917	A157	$1 Referee	1.90	1.40
918	A157	$4 Goal	5.25	*7.50*
		Nos. 915-918 (4)	9.95	9.75

Souvenir Sheet

919	A157	$5 Action	7.50	7.50

Nos. 916-917 vert.
For overprints see Nos. 963-967.

A158

Halley's Comet A159

Designs: 5c, Edmond Halley, Greenwich Observatory. 10c, Me 163B Komet. German WWII fighter plane. 60c, Montezuma sighting comet, 1517. $4, Pocahontas saving Capt. John Smith's life, 1607 sighting as sign for Powhatan Indians to raid Jamestown. $5, Comet over Antigua.

1986, Mar. 24

920	A158	5c multicolored	.30	.25
921	A158	10c multicolored	.35	.25
922	A158	60c multicolored	1.40	.50
923	A158	$4 multicolored	4.25	*5.75*
		Nos. 920-923 (4)	6.30	6.75

Souvenir Sheet

924	A159	$5 multicolored	4.50	4.50

For overprints see Nos. 973-977.

Queen Elizabeth II, 60th Birthday
Common Design Type

60c, Wedding, 1947. $1, Trooping the color. $4, Visiting Scotland.
$5, Held by Queen Mary, 1927.

1986, Apr. 21

925	CD339	60c multicolored	.40	.45
926	CD339	$1 multicolored	.60	.60
927	CD339	$4 multicolored	1.75	*1.90*
		Nos. 925-927 (3)	2.75	2.95

Souvenir Sheet

928	CD339	$5 multicolored	2.75	*3.25*

Boats — A160

30c, Tugboat. 60c, Fishing boat. $1, Sailboat 2056. $4, Lateen-rigged sailboat.
$5, Boatbuilding.

1986, May 15

929	A160	30c multicolored	.25	.25
930	A160	60c multicolored	.45	.30
931	A160	$1 multicolored	.80	.50
932	A160	$4 multicolored	3.00	3.00
		Nos. 929-932 (4)	4.50	4.05

Souvenir Sheet

933	A160	$5 multicolored	3.25	*4.00*

A number of unissued items, imperfs., part perfs., missing color varieties, etc., were made available when the Format International inventory was liquidated. Imperfs of some or all of the Antigua stamps in the following sets are included: Nos. 405-422, 503-507, 515-517, 703-707, 745-749, 755-759, 808-816, 819-826, 905-909, 934-937.

See footnote after No. 962.

AMERIPEX '86 — A161

American trains.

1986, May 22 ***Perf. 15***

934	A161	25c Hiawatha	1.10	.30
935	A161	50c Grand Canyon	1.35	.60
936	A161	$1 Powhattan Arrow	1.75	1.75
937	A161	$3 Empire State	3.00	*5.50*
		Nos. 934-937 (4)	7.20	*8.15*

Souvenir Sheet

938	A161	$5 Daylight	8.00	*10.00*

Wedding of Prince Andrew and Sarah Ferguson
Common Design Type

1986, July 23 ***Perf. 14***

939	CD340	45c Couple	.30	.30
940	CD340	60c Prince Andrew	.45	.45
941	CD340	$4 Princes Andrew, Philip	2.75	*3.75*
		Nos. 939-941 (3)	3.50	*4.50*

Souvenir Sheet

942	CD340	$5 Couple, diff.	3.50	*4.25*

Conch Shells — A162

15c, Say fly-specked cerith. 45c, Gmelin smooth scotch bonnet. 60c, Linne West Indian crown conch. $3, Murex ciboney.
$5, Atlantic natica.

1986, Aug. 6 **Litho.** ***Perf. 15***

943	A162	15c multicolored	.75	.35
944	A162	45c multicolored	1.75	1.25
945	A162	60c multicolored	1.90	1.90
946	A162	$3 multicolored	5.75	*9.50*
		Nos. 943-946 (4)	10.15	*13.00*

Souvenir Sheet

947	A162	$5 multicolored	7.25	*8.00*

Flowers — A163

10c, Water lily. 15c, Queen of the night. 50c, Cup of gold. 60c, Beach morning glory. 70c, Golden trumpet. $1, Air plant. $3, Purple wreath. $4, Zephyr lily.
No. 956, Dozakie. No. 957, Four o'clock.

1986, Aug. 25 Litho. *Perf. 15*

948	A163	10c multicolored	.30	.25
949	A163	15c multicolored	.30	.25
950	A163	50c multicolored	.50	.45
951	A163	60c multicolored	.65	.55
952	A163	70c multicolored	.75	.65
953	A163	$1 multicolored	.85	1.10
954	A163	$3 multicolored	1.90	*2.75*
955	A163	$4 multicolored	2.40	*3.50*
		Nos. 948-955 (8)	7.65	*9.50*

Souvenir Sheets

956	A163	$4 multicolored	2.75	*3.25*
957	A163	$5 multicolored	3.50	*4.00*

Fungi — A164

10c, Hygrocybe occidentalis scarletina. 50c, Trogia buccinalis. $1, Collybia subpruinosa. $4, Leucocoprinus brebissonii.
$5, Pyrrhoglossum pyrrhum.

1986, Sept. 15

958	A164	10c multicolored	.30	.25
959	A164	50c multicolored	.65	.55
960	A164	$1 multicolored	1.35	1.25
961	A164	$4 multicolored	3.25	*4.50*
		Nos. 958-961 (4)	5.55	6.55

Souvenir Sheet

962	A164	$5 multicolored	11.00	11.00

An unissued $3 stamp and No. 961 inscribed "4$" were made available when the Format International inventory was liquidated.

Nos. 915-919 Ovptd. in Gold in 2 or 3 lines

1986, Sept. 15 *Perf. 14*

963	A157	30c multicolored	1.10	.35
964	A157	60c multicolored	1.60	.70
965	A157	$1 multicolored	2.00	1.10
966	A157	$4 multicolored	3.50	*4.50*
		Nos. 963-966 (4)	8.20	6.65

Souvenir Sheet

967	A157	$5 multicolored	5.00	5.00

Automobile, Cent. — A165

Carl Benz and classic automobiles: 10c, 1933 Auburn Speedster. 15c, 1986 Mercury Sable. 50c, 1959 Cadillac. 60c, 1950 Studebaker. 70c, 1939 Lagonda V-12. $1, 1930 Adler Standard. $3, 1956 DKW. $4, 1936 Mercedes 500K.
No. 972, 1921 Mercedes Knight. No. 972A, 1896 Daimler.

1986, Oct. 20

968	A165	10c multicolored	.25	.25
968A	A165	15c multicolored	.30	.25
969	A165	50c multicolored	.55	.25
970	A165	60c multicolored	.70	.30
970A	A165	70c multicolored	.80	.40
970B	A165	$1 multicolored	1.10	.55
970C	A165	$3 multicolored	2.75	2.75
971	A165	$4 multicolored	3.25	3.25
		Nos. 968-971 (8)	9.70	8.00

Souvenir Sheets

972	A165	$5 multicolored	4.25	4.25
972A	A165	$5 multicolored	4.25	4.25

Nos. 920-924 Ovptd. in Black or Silver

1986, Oct. 22 Litho. *Perf. 14*

973	A158	5c multicolored	4.75	.25
974	A158	10c multicolored	.25	.25
975	A158	60c multicolored	1.25	.60
976	A158	$4 multicolored	5.50	4.00
		Nos. 973-976 (4)	11.75	5.10

Souvenir Sheet

977	A159	$5 multicolored (S)	6.00	*6.50*

Christmas A166

Disney characters as children: 25c, Mickey. 30c, Mickey, Minnie. 40c, Aunt Matilda, Goofy. 60c, Goofy, Pluto. 70c, Pluto, Donald, Daisy. $1.50, Stringing popcorn. $3, Grandma Duck, Minnie. $4, Donald, Pete. No. 986, Playing with presents. No. 987, Reindeer.

1986, Nov. 4 *Perf. 11*

978	A166	25c multicolored	.55	.25
979	A166	30c multicolored	.70	.30
980	A166	40c multicolored	.75	.35
981	A166	60c multicolored	.90	.65
982	A166	70c multicolored	1.10	1.00
983	A166	$1.50 multicolored	1.75	*2.25*
984	A166	$3 multicolored	2.75	*4.25*
985	A166	$4 multicolored	3.25	*4.25*
		Nos. 978-985 (8)	11.75	*13.30*

Souvenir Sheets

Perf. 14

986	A166	$5 multicolored	6.50	*7.00*
987	A166	$5 multicolored	6.50	*7.00*

Nos. 985 printed in sheets of 8.

Coat of Arms A167

Natl. Flag A168

1986, Nov. 25 Litho. *Perf. 14x14½*

988	A167	10c bright blue	1.00	.90
989	A168	25c orange	1.75	1.25

Marc Chagall (1887-1985), Artist — A169

Designs: No. 990, The Profile, 1957. No. 991, Portrait of the Artist's Sister, 1910. No. 992, Bride with Fan, 1911. No. 993, David in Profile, 1914. No. 994, Fiancee with Bouquet, 1977. No. 995, Self-portrait with Brushes, 1909. No. 996, The Walk, 1973. No. 997, Candles, 1938. No. 998, Fall of Icarus, 1975. No. 999, Myth of Orpheus, 1977.

1987, Mar. 30 Litho. *Perf. 13½x14*

990	A169	10c multicolored	.45	.25
991	A169	30c multicolored	.60	.30
992	A169	40c multicolored	.80	.35
993	A169	60c multicolored	.90	.40
994	A169	90c multicolored	1.00	.55
995	A169	$1 multicolored	1.00	.60
996	A169	$3 multicolored	2.50	2.50
997	A169	$4 multicolored	2.75	2.75

Size: 110x95mm

Imperf

998	A169	$5 multicolored	5.75	5.75
999	A169	$5 multicolored	5.75	5.75
		Nos. 990-999 (10)	21.50	19.20

A170

America's Cup — A171

30c, Canada I, 1981. 60c, Gretel II, 1970. $1, Sceptre, 1958. $3, Vigilant, 1893.
$5, Australia II, Liberty, 1983.

1987, Feb. 5 *Perf. 15*

1000	A170	30c multicolored	.55	.25
1001	A170	60c multicolored	.70	.35
1002	A170	$1 multicolored	1.00	1.00
1003	A170	$3 multicolored	2.50	*3.00*
		Nos. 1000-1003 (4)	4.75	*4.60*

Souvenir Sheet

1004	A171	$5 multicolored	5.00	5.00

Fish, World Wildlife Fund — A172

Marine Birds — A173

15c, Bridled burrfish. 30c, Brown noddy. 40c, Nassau grouper. 50c, Laughing gull. 60c, French angelfish. $1, Porkfish. $2, Royal tern. $3, Sooty tern.
No. 1013, Banded butterfly fish. No. 1014, Brown booby.

1987, Feb. 23 Litho. *Perf. 14*

1005	A172	15c multicolored	3.00	.45
1006	A173	30c multicolored	6.00	.50
1007	A172	40c multicolored	3.75	.60
1008	A173	50c multicolored	6.75	1.40
1009	A172	60c multicolored	4.00	1.40
1010	A172	$1 multicolored	4.00	1.60
1011	A173	$2 multicolored	9.00	5.50
1012	A173	$3 multicolored	9.00	7.50
		Nos. 1005-1012 (8)	45.50	18.95

Souvenir Sheets

1013	A172	$5 multicolored	10.00	10.00
1014	A173	$5 multicolored	10.00	10.00

The 30c, 50c, $2, $3 and Nos. 1013-1014 do not picture the WWF emblem.
For overprints see Nos. 1137-1139A.

Statue of Liberty, Cent. — A174

Photographs by Peter B. Kaplan: 15c, Lee Iacocca. 30c, Statue at dusk. 45c, Crown, head. 50c, Iacocca, torch. 60c, Crown observatory. 90c, Interior restoration. $1, Head. $2, Statue at sunset. $3, Men on scaffold, flag. $5, Statue at night.

1987, Apr. 20 *Perf. 14*

1015	A174	15c multicolored	.25	.25
1016	A174	30c multicolored	.25	.25
1017	A174	45c multicolored	.35	.35
1018	A174	50c multicolored	.40	.40
1019	A174	60c multicolored	.40	.40
1020	A174	90c multicolored	.55	.55
1021	A174	$1 multicolored	.65	.65
1022	A174	$2 multicolored	1.25	*1.50*
1023	A174	$3 multicolored	1.40	*2.00*
1024	A174	$5 multicolored	2.40	*3.50*
		Nos. 1015-1024 (10)	7.90	*9.85*

Nos. 1015-1018, 1021-1022, 1024 vert.

A175

Transportation Innovations — A175a

10c, Spirit of Australia, 1978. 15c, Siemens' Electric locomotive, 1879. 30c, USS Triton, 1960. 50c, Trevithick, 1801. 60c, USS New Jersey, 1942. 70c, Draisine bicycle, 1818. 90c, SS United States, 1952. $1.50, Cierva C-4, 1923. $2, Curtiss NC-4, 1919. $3, Queen Elizabeth II, 1969.

1987, Apr. 19 *Perf. 15*

1025	A175	10c multi	.85	.25
1026	A175a	15c multi	1.10	.30
1027	A175	30c multi	1.10	.35
1028	A175a	50c multi	1.25	.45
1029	A175	60c multi	1.25	.50
1030	A175a	70c multi	1.25	.65
1031	A175	90c multi	1.25	.75
1032	A175a	$1.50 multi	1.90	*2.50*
1033	A175a	$2 multi	2.10	*2.75*
1034	A175	$3 multi	3.25	*4.25*
		Nos. 1025-1034 (10)	15.30	*12.75*

Reptiles and Amphibians A176

30c, Eleutherodactylus martinicensis. 60c, Thecadactylus rapicauda. $1, Anolis bimaculatus leachi. $3, Geochelone carbonaria.
$5, Ameiva griswoldi.

1987, June 15 *Perf. 14*

1035	A176	30c multicolored	.50	.25
1036	A176	60c multicolored	.75	.35
1037	A176	$1 multicolored	1.00	.65
1038	A176	$3 multicolored	2.00	*2.75*
		Nos. 1035-1038 (4)	4.25	4.00

Souvenir Sheet

1039	A176	$5 multicolored	5.00	5.00

Entertainers — A177

1987, May 11

1040	A177	15c Grace Kelly	.90	.30
1041	A177	30c Marilyn Monroe	2.75	.60
1042	A177	45c Orson Welles	.90	.40
1043	A177	50c Judy Garland	.90	.45
1044	A177	60c John Lennon	4.00	1.00
1045	A177	$1 Rock Hudson	1.50	.90
1046	A177	$2 John Wayne	2.50	1.75
1047	A177	$3 Elvis Presley	9.00	4.25
		Nos. 1040-1047 (8)	22.45	9.65

No. 1047 Overprinted

1987, Sept. 9 Litho. *Perf. 14*

1047A	A177	$3 multicolored	7.50	5.50

1988 Summer Olympics, Seoul — A178

10c, Basketball. 60c, Fencing. $1, Women's gymnastics. $3, Soccer.
$5, Boxing glove.

1987, Mar. 23

1048	A178	10c multicolored	.50	.30
1049	A178	60c multicolored	.75	.40
1050	A178	$1 multicolored	1.05	1.00
1051	A178	$3 multicolored	2.50	*4.00*
		Nos. 1048-1051 (4)	4.80	*5.70*

Souvenir Sheet

1052	A178	$5 multicolored	4.25	*4.75*

16th World Scout Jamboree, Australia, 1987-88 — A179

10c, Campfire, red kangaroo. 60c, Kayaking, blue-winged kookaburra. $1, Obstacle course, ring-tailed rock wallaby. $3, Field kitchen, koalas.
$5, Flags.

1987, Nov. 2 Litho. *Perf. 15*

1053	A179	10c multicolored	.70	.25
1054	A179	60c multicolored	1.40	.65
1055	A179	$1 multicolored	1.15	.75
1056	A179	$3 multicolored	1.75	*3.50*
		Nos. 1053-1056 (4)	5.00	*5.15*

Souvenir Sheet

1057	A179	$5 multicolored	3.50	3.50

US Constitution Bicent. — A180

Designs: 15c, Virginia House of Burgesses exercising right of freedom of speech. 45c, Connecticut state seal. 60c, Delaware state seal. $4, Gouverneur Morris (1752-1816), principal writer of the Constitution, vert. $5, Roger Sherman (1721-1793), jurist and statesman, vert.

1987, Nov. 16 Litho. *Perf. 14*

1058	A180	15c multicolored	.25	.25
1059	A180	45c multicolored	.25	.25
1060	A180	60c multicolored	.30	.30
1061	A180	$4 multicolored	2.25	2.25
		Nos. 1058-1061 (4)	3.05	3.05

Souvenir Sheet

1062	A180	$5 multicolored	3.25	3.25

A181

Christmas (Paintings): 45c, Madonna and Child, by Bernardo Daddi (1290-1355). 60c, Joseph, detail from The Nativity, by Sano Di Pietro (1406-1481). $1, Mary, detail from Di Pietro's The Nativity. $4, Music-making Angel, by Melozzo Da Forli (1438-1494). $5, The Flight into Egypt, by Di Pietro.

1987, Dec. 1

1063	A181	45c multicolored	.35	.25
1064	A181	60c multicolored	.45	.35
1065	A181	$1 multicolored	.75	.55
1066	A181	$4 multicolored	2.00	*3.25*
		Nos. 1063-1066 (4)	3.55	*4.40*

Souvenir Sheet

1067	A181	$5 multicolored	3.00	3.00

A182

No. 1068, Wedding portrait. No. 1069, Elizabeth II, c. 1970. No. 1070, Christening of Charles, 1948. No. 1071, Elizabeth II, c. 1980.
No. 1072, Royal family, c. 1951.

1988, Feb. 8 Litho. *Perf. 14*

1068	A182	25c multi	.25	.25
1069	A182	60c multi	.50	.40
1070	A182	$2 multi	1.10	1.10
1071	A182	$3 multi	1.60	1.60
		Nos. 1068-1071 (4)	3.45	3.35

Souvenir Sheet

1072	A182	$5 multi	2.75	2.75

40th wedding anniv. of Queen Elizabeth II and Prince Philip.

Tropical Birds — A183

10c, Great blue heron, vert. 15c, Ringed kingfisher. 50c, Bananaquit. 60c, Purple gallinule. 70c, Blue-hooded euphonia. $1, Caribbean parakeet, vert. $3, Troupial. $4, Hummingbird. No. 1081, Roseate flamingo, vert. No. 1082, Brown pelicans, vert.

1988, Mar. 1

1073	A183	10c multicolored	.55	.40
1074	A183	15c multicolored	.60	.40
1075	A183	50c multicolored	1.10	.50
1076	A183	60c multicolored	1.10	.50
1077	A183	70c multicolored	1.25	.55
1078	A183	$1 multicolored	1.50	.70
1079	A183	$3 multicolored	3.00	*3.50*
1080	A183	$4 multicolored	3.00	*3.50*
		Nos. 1073-1080 (8)	12.10	10.05

Souvenir Sheets

1081	A183	$5 multicolored	4.50	4.50
1082	A183	$5 multicolored	4.50	4.50

Salvation Army A184

25c, Day-care, Antigua. 30c, Penicillin inoculation, Indonesia. 40c, Day-care Center, Bolivia. 45c, Rehabilitation, India. 50c, Training the blind, Kenya. 60c, Infant care, Ghana. $1, Job training, Zambia. $2, Food distribution, Sri Lanka.
$5, General Eva Burrows.

1988, Mar. 7

1083	A184	25c multicolored	.80	.45
1084	A184	30c multicolored	.80	.45
1085	A184	40c multicolored	.90	.55
1086	A184	45c multicolored	.90	.55
1087	A184	50c multicolored	1.10	1.10
1088	A184	60c multicolored	1.25	1.25
1089	A184	$1 multicolored	1.50	1.75
1090	A184	$2 multicolored	2.25	*3.25*
		Nos. 1083-1090 (8)	9.50	*9.35*

Souvenir Sheet

1091	A184	$5 multicolored	5.00	5.00

A185

Discovery of America, 500th Anniv. (in 1992) — A186

Anniv. emblem and: 10c, Fleet. 30c, View of fleet in harbor from Paino Indian village. 45c, Caravel anchored in harbor, Paino village. 60c, Columbus, 3 Indians in canoe. 90c, Indian, parrot, Columbus. $1, Columbus in longboat. $3, Spanish guard, fleet in harbor. $4, Ships under full sail. No. 1100, Stone cross given to Columbus by Queen Isabella. No. 1101, Gold excelente.

1988, Mar. 14 Litho. *Perf. 14*

1092	A185	10c multicolored	.75	.35
1093	A185	30c multicolored	.75	.40
1094	A185	45c multicolored	.85	.40
1095	A185	60c multicolored	.85	.40
1096	A185	90c multicolored	1.50	.90
1097	A185	$1 multicolored	1.50	.90
1098	A185	$3 multicolored	2.50	*3.25*
1099	A185	$4 multicolored	2.75	*3.25*
		Nos. 1092-1099 (8)	11.45	9.85

Souvenir Sheets

1100	A186	$5 multicolored	4.50	4.50
1101	A186	$5 multicolored	4.50	4.50

Paintings by Titian — A187

Details: 30c, Bust of Christ. 40c, Scourging of Christ. 45c, Madonna in Glory with Saints. 50c, The Averoldi Polyptych. $1, Christ Crowned with Thorns. $2, Christ Mocked. $3, Christ and Simon of Cyrene. $4, Crucifixion with Virgin and Saints. No. 1110, Ecce Homo. No. 1111, Noli Me Tangere.

1988, Apr. 11 Litho. *Perf. 13½x14*

1102	A187	30c shown	.45	.25
1103	A187	40c multicolored	.55	.30
1104	A187	45c multicolored	.55	.30
1105	A187	50c multicolored	.55	.45
1106	A187	$1 multicolored	.85	.65
1107	A187	$2 multicolored	1.05	*1.25*
1108	A187	$3 multicolored	1.75	*2.00*
1109	A187	$4 multicolored	2.10	*2.75*
		Nos. 1102-1109 (8)	7.85	*7.95*

Souvenir Sheets

1110	A187	$5 multicolored	3.75	3.75
1111	A187	$5 multicolored	3.75	3.75

Sailing Week — A188

30c, Canada I, 1980. 60c, Gretel II, Australia, 1970. $1, Sceptre, GB, 1958. $3, Vigilant, US, 1893.
$5, Australia II, 1983.

1988, Apr. 18 *Perf. 15*

1112	A188	30c multicolored	.25	.25
1113	A188	60c multicolored	.45	.45
1114	A188	$1 multicolored	.60	.60
1115	A188	$3 multicolored	1.25	*2.25*
		Nos. 1112-1115 (4)	2.55	*3.55*

Souvenir Sheet

1116	A188	$5 multicolored	2.75	*3.25*

Walt Disney Animated Characters and Epcot Center, Walt Disney World A189

25c, The Living Seas. 30c, World of Motion. 40c, Spaceship Earth. 60c, Universe of Energy. 70c, Journey to Imagination. $1.50, The Land. $3, Communicore. $4, Horizons.
No. 1125, Epcot Center. No. 1126, The Contemporary Resort Hotel.

1988, May 3 *Perf. 14x13½, 13½x14*

1116A	A189	1c like 25c	.25	.25
1116B	A189	2c like 30c	.25	.25
1116C	A189	3c like 40c	.25	.25
1116D	A189	4c like 60c	.25	.25
1116E	A189	5c like 70c	.25	.25
1116F	A189	10c like $1.50	.25	.25
1117	A189	25c multi	.45	.25
1118	A189	30c multi	.45	.25
1119	A189	40c multi	.55	.25
1120	A189	60c multi	.75	.35
1121	A189	70c multi	.85	.40
1122	A189	$1.50 multi	1.60	1.60
1123	A189	$3 multi	2.25	*2.75*
1124	A189	$4 multi	2.25	*2.75*
		Nos. 1116A-1124 (14)	10.65	10.10

Souvenir Sheets

1125	A189	$5 multi	4.00	4.00
1126	A189	$5 multi	4.00	4.00

30c, 40c, $1.50, $3 and No. 1126 are vert.

Flowering Trees — A190

1988, May 16 *Perf. 14*

1127	A190	10c Jacaranda	.30	.25
1128	A190	30c Cordia	.30	.25
1129	A190	50c Orchid tree	.45	.40
1130	A190	90c Flamboyant	.55	.50
1131	A190	$1 African tulip tree	.65	.60
1132	A190	$2 Potato tree	1.25	*1.60*
1133	A190	$3 Crepe myrtle	1.50	*2.00*
1134	A190	$4 Pitch apple	1.75	*2.75*
		Nos. 1127-1134 (8)	6.75	*8.35*

Souvenir Sheets

1135	A190	$5 Cassia	3.25	*3.75*
1136	A190	$5 Chinaberry	3.25	*3.75*

Nos. 1135-1136 are continuous designs.

Nos. 1011-1012, 1014 and 1013 Ovptd. in Black for Philatelic Exhibitions

a

b

c

d

1988, May 9 Litho. *Perf. 14*

1137	A173 (a)	$2 multi	8.00	8.00
1138	A173 (b)	$3 multi	8.50	8.50

Souvenir Sheets

1139	A173 (c)	$5 multi	14.00	14.00
1139A	A172 (d)	$5 multi	14.00	14.00

1988 Summer Olympics, Seoul — A192

40c, Gymnastic rings, vert. 60c, Weight lifting, vert. $1, Water polo. $3, Boxing.
$5, Torch-bearer, vert.

1988, June 10

1140	A192	40c multicolored	.35	.30
1141	A192	60c multicolored	.40	.30
1142	A192	$1 multicolored	.80	.45
1143	A192	$3 multicolored	1.60	*2.25*
		Nos. 1140-1143 (4)	3.15	*3.30*

Souvenir Sheet

1144	A192	$5 multicolored	3.50	3.50

Butterflies A193

1c, Monarch. 2c, Jamaican clearwing. 3c, Yellow-barred ringlet. 5c, Cracker. 10c, Jamaican mestra. 15c, Mimic. 20c, Silver spot. 25c, Zebra. 30c, Fiery sulphur. 40c, Androgeus swallowtail. 45c, Giant brimstone. 50c, Orbed sulphur. 60c, Blue-backed skipper. $1, Common white skipper. $2, Baracoa skipper. $2.50, Mangrove skipper. $5, Silver king. $10, Pygmy skipper. $20, Parides lycimenes.

1988-90 Litho. *Perf. 14*

1145	A193	1c multi	.50	*1.10*
1146	A193	2c multi	.65	*1.10*
1147	A193	3c multi	.65	*1.10*
1148	A193	5c multi	.80	*1.10*
1149	A193	10c multi	.95	.35
1150	A193	15c multi	1.25	.35

1151	A193	20c	multi	1.40	.35
1152	A193	25c	multi	1.40	.35
1153	A193	30c	multi	1.40	.35
1154	A193	40c	multi	1.40	.35
1155	A193	45c	multi	1.40	.35
1156	A193	50c	multi	1.50	.45
1157	A193	60c	multi	1.60	.60
1158	A193	$1	multi	2.00	1.00
1159	A193	$2	multi	3.00	3.50
1160	A193	$2.50	multi	4.00	4.75
1161	A193	$5	multi	5.00	7.00
1161A	A193	$10	multi	7.00	*12.00*
1162	A193	$20	multi	18.00	*21.00*
	Nos. 1145-1162 (19)			53.90	*57.15*

Issued: $20, Feb. 19, 1990; others, Aug. 29.

John F. Kennedy — A194

30c, First family. 60c, Motorcade, Mexico. $1, Funeral procession. $4, Aboard PT109.
$5, Taking Oath of Office.

1988, Nov. 22 Litho. *Perf. 14*

1162A	A194	1c	like 30c	.25	.25
1162B	A194	2c	like $4	.25	.25
1162C	A194	3c	like $1	.25	.25
1162D	A194	4c	like 60c	.25	.25
1163	A194	30c	multi	.35	.25
1164	A194	60c	multi	.70	.40
1165	A194	$1	multi	.75	.75
1166	A194	$4	multi	2.25	*3.25*
	Nos. 1162A-1166 (8)			5.05	*5.65*

Souvenir Sheet

1167	A194	$5	multi	3.75	3.75

Miniature Sheet

Christmas, Mickey Mouse 60th Anniv. — A195

Walt Disney characters: No. 1168: a, Morty and Ferdie. b, Goofy. c, Chip-n-Dale. d, Huey and Dewey. e, Minnie Mouse. f, Pluto. g, Mickey Mouse. h, Donald Duck and Louie.
No. 1169, Goofy driving Mickey and Minnie in a horse-drawn carriage. No. 1170, Characters on roller skates, caroling.

1988, Dec. 1 *Perf. 13½x14, 14x13½*

1168	A195	Sheet of 8	9.00	9.00
a.-h.		$1 any single	.95	.95

Souvenir Sheets

1169	A195	$7 multicolored	5.25	5.25
1170	A195	$7 multi, horiz.	5.25	5.25

1988, Dec. 1 Litho. *Perf. 14*

1171	A195	10c	like No. 1168e	.25	.25
1172	A195	25c	like No. 1168f	.25	.25
1173	A195	30c	like No. 1168g	.30	.30
1174	A195	70c	like No. 1168h	.60	.60
	Nos. 1171-1174 (4)			1.40	1.40

Arawak Indian Whip Dance — A196

UPAE and discovery of America emblems and: a, Five adults. b, Eight adults. c, Seven adults. d, Three adults, three children.

1989, May 16 Litho. *Perf. 14*

1175	Strip of 4	5.00	5.00
a.-d.	A196 $1.50 any single	.90	.90

Souvenir Sheet

1176	A196	$6	Arawak chief	4.00	4.00

Discovery of America 500th anniv. (in 1992), pre-Columbian societies and customs.

Jet Flight, 50th Anniv. — A197

Various jet aircraft: 10c, DeHavilland Comet 4. 30c, Messerschmitt Me262. 40c, Boeing 707. 60c, Canadair F-86 Sabre. $1, Lockheed F-104 Starfighter. $2, McDonnell Douglas DC-10. $3, Boeing 747. $4, McDonnell F-4 Phantom.
No. 1185, Grumman F-14 Tomcat. No. 1186, Concorde.

1989, May 29 Litho. *Perf. 14x13½*

1177	A197	10c	multicolored	1.10	.35
1178	A197	30c	multicolored	1.60	.35
1179	A197	40c	multicolored	1.60	.35
1180	A197	60c	multicolored	1.90	.50
1181	A197	$1	multicolored	2.10	.75
1182	A197	$2	multicolored	3.00	2.75
1183	A197	$3	multicolored	3.25	*4.25*
1184	A197	$4	multicolored	3.25	*4.25*
	Nos. 1177-1184 (8)			17.80	*13.55*

Souvenir Sheets

1185	A197	$7	multicolored	6.00	*7.00*
1186	A197	$7	multicolored	6.00	*7.00*

Caribbean Cruise Ships — A198

25c, TSS Festivale. 45c, M.S. Southward. 50c, M.S. Sagafjord. 60c, MTS Daphne. 75c, M.V. Cunard Countess. 90c, M.S. Song of America. $3, M.S. Island Princess. $4, S.S. Galileo.
No. 1195, S.S. Norway. No. 1196, S.S. Oceanic.

1989, June 20 Litho. *Perf. 14*

1187	A198	25c	multi	1.30	.35
1188	A198	45c	multi	1.50	.35
1189	A198	50c	multi	1.50	.35
1190	A198	60c	multi	1.50	.40
1191	A198	75c	multi	1.75	1.00
1192	A198	90c	multi	2.00	1.10
1193	A198	$3	multi	4.00	*5.50*
1194	A198	$4	multi	4.00	*6.00*
	Nos. 1187-1194 (8)			17.55	*15.05*

Souvenir Sheets

1195	A198	$6	multi	4.50	*5.50*
1196	A198	$6	multi	4.50	*5.50*

Paintings by Hiroshige A199

Designs: 25c, *Fish Swimming by Duck Half-submerged in Stream.* 45c, *Crane and Wave.* 50c, *Sparrows and Morning Glories.* 60c, *Crested Blackbird and Flowering Cherry.* $1, *Great Knot Sitting among Water Grass.* $2, *Goose on a Bank of Water.* $3, *Black Paradise Flycatcher and Blossoms.* $4, *Sleepy Owl Perched on a Pine Branch.* No. 1205, *Bullfinch Flying Near a Clematis Branch.* No. 1206, *Titmouse on a Cherry Branch.*

1989, July 3 *Perf. 14x13½*

1197	A199	25c	multicolored	.90	.30
1198	A199	45c	multicolored	1.10	.40
1199	A199	50c	multicolored	1.25	.40
1200	A199	60c	multicolored	1.25	.50
1201	A199	$1	multicolored	1.60	.65
1202	A199	$2	multicolored	2.50	2.50
1203	A199	$3	multicolored	3.00	3.00
1204	A199	$4	multicolored	3.00	3.00
	Nos. 1197-1204 (8)			14.60	10.75

Souvenir Sheets

1205	A199	$5	multicolored	6.00	6.00
1206	A199	$5	multicolored	6.00	6.00

Hirohito (1901-1989) and enthronement of Akihito as emperor of Japan.

PHILEXFRANCE '89 — A200

Walt Disney characters, French landmarks: 1c, Helicopter over the Seine. 2c, Arc de Triomphe. 3c, Painting Notre Dame Cathedral. 4c, Entrance to the Metro. 5c, Fashion show. 10c, Follies. No. 1213, Shopping stalls on the Seine. $6, Sidewalk cafe, Left Bank. No. 1215, Hot air balloon *Ear Force One.* No. 1216, Dining.

1989, July 7 *Perf. 14x13½*

1207	A200	1c	multicolored	.25	.25
1208	A200	2c	multicolored	.25	.25
1209	A200	3c	multicolored	.25	.25
1210	A200	4c	multicolored	.25	.25
1211	A200	5c	multicolored	.25	.25
1212	A200	10c	multicolored	.25	.25
1213	A200	$5	multicolored	7.50	7.50
1214	A200	$6	multicolored	7.50	7.50
	Nos. 1207-1214 (8)			16.50	16.50

Souvenir Sheets

1215	A200	$5	multicolored	6.25	6.25
1216	A200	$5	multicolored	6.25	6.25

1990 World Cup Soccer Championships, Italy — A201

Natl. flag, various actions of a defending goalie.

1989, Aug. 21 *Perf. 14*

1217	A201	15c	multicolored	.75	.25
1218	A201	25c	multicolored	.80	.25
1219	A201	$1	multicolored	1.25	1.00
1220	A201	$4	multicolored	2.50	*4.75*
	Nos. 1217-1220 (4)			5.30	*6.25*

Souvenir Sheets

1221	A201	$5	2 players, horiz.	3.75	*4.25*
1222	A201	$5	3 players, horiz.	3.75	*4.25*

For overprints see Nos. 1344-1349.

Mushrooms A202

10c, Lilac fairy helmet. 25c, Rough psathyrella, vert. 50c, Golden tops. 60c, Blue cap, vert. 75c, Brown cap, vert. $1, Green gill, vert. $3, Red pinwheel. $4, Red chanterelle.
No. 1231, Slender stalk. No. 1232, Paddy straw mushroom.

1989, Oct. 12 Litho. *Perf. 14*

1223	A202	10c	multi	.75	.35
1224	A202	25c	multi	1.05	.30
1225	A202	50c	multi	1.50	.50
1226	A202	60c	multi	1.50	.60
1227	A202	75c	multi	1.75	1.10
1228	A202	$1	multi	1.75	1.25
1229	A202	$3	multi	2.75	*3.75*
1230	A202	$4	multi	2.75	*3.75*
	Nos. 1223-1230 (8)			13.80	11.60

Souvenir Sheets

1231	A202	$6	multi	8.50	8.50
1232	A202	$6	multi	8.50	8.50

Nos. 1224, 1226-1228, 1231 vert.

Wildlife — A203

25c, Hutia. 45c, Caribbean monk seal. 60c, Mustache bat, vert. $4, Manatee, vert.
$5, West Indies giant rice rat.

1989, Oct. 19 Litho. *Perf. 14*

1233	A203	25c	multi	.80	.35
1234	A203	45c	multi	2.25	.75
1235	A203	60c	multi	1.50	.75
1236	A203	$4	multi	3.25	*5.25*
	Nos. 1233-1236 (4)			7.80	*7.10*

Souvenir Sheet

1237	A203	$5	multi	8.50	*9.00*

American Philatelic Soc. Emblem, Stamps on Stamps and Walt Disney Characters Promoting Philately — A204

Designs: 1c, Israel #150, printing press. 2c, Italy #1238, first day cancel. 3c, US #143L4, Pony Express recruits. 4c, Denmark #566, early radio broadcast. 5c, German Democratic Republic #702, television. 10c, Great Britain #1, stamp collector. $4, Japan #1414, integrated circuits. $6, Germany #B667, boom box. No. 1246, US #1355, C3a, and Jenny biplane over Disneyland, horiz. No. 1247, US #940, 1421 and stamps for the wounded.

1989, Nov. 2 *Perf. 13½x14, 14x13½*

1238	A204	1c	multicolored	.25	.25
1239	A204	2c	multicolored	.25	.25
1240	A204	3c	multicolored	.25	.25
1241	A204	4c	multicolored	.25	.25
1242	A204	5c	multicolored	.25	.25
1243	A204	10c	multicolored	.25	.25
1244	A204	$4	multicolored	4.00	*5.50*
1245	A204	$6	multicolored	5.00	*6.50*
	Nos. 1238-1245 (8)			10.50	*13.50*

Souvenir Sheets

1246	A204	$5	multicolored	5.50	*6.50*
1247	A204	$5	multicolored	5.50	*6.50*

Locomotives and Walt Disney Characters A205

25c, John Bull, 1831. 45c, Atlantic, 1832. 50c, William Crook's, 1861. 60c, Minnetonka, 1869. $1, Thatcher Perkins, 1863. $2, Pioneer, 1848. $3, Peppersass, 1869. $4, Gimbels Flyer.
No. 1256, #6100 Class S-1 & 1835 Thomas Jefferson. No. 1257, Jupiter & #119.

Perf. 14x13½, 13½x14
1989, Nov. 17

1248	A205	25c	multi	.85	.40
1249	A205	45c	multi	.95	.40
1250	A205	50c	multi	.95	.40
1251	A205	60c	multi	.95	.60
1252	A205	$1	multi	1.20	.75
1253	A205	$2	multi	1.75	2.25
1254	A205	$3	multi	2.25	*3.75*
1255	A205	$4	multicolored	2.40	*3.75*
	Nos. 1248-1255 (8)			11.30	12.30

Souvenir Sheets

1256	A205	$6	multi	12.00	12.00
1257	A205	$6	multi	12.00	12.00

New York World's Fair, 50th anniv., and World Stamp Expo '89, Washington, DC.

1st Moon Landing, 20th Anniv. — A206

10c, Apollo 11 liftoff. 45c, Aldrin walking on Moon. $1, Eagle ascending from Moon. $4, Recovery after splashdown.
$5, Armstrong.

1989, Nov. 24 Litho. *Perf. 14*

1258	A206	10c	multicolored	.55	.25
1259	A206	45c	multicolored	1.40	.25
1260	A206	$1	multicolored	1.60	.85
1261	A206	$4	multicolored	2.50	*4.50*
	Nos. 1258-1261 (4)			6.05	*5.85*

Souvenir Sheet

1262	A206	$5	multicolored	5.50	5.50

Nos. 1258-1259 and 1262, vert.

Souvenir Sheet

Smithsonian Institution, Washington, DC — A207

1989, Nov. 17 Litho. *Perf. 14*

1263 A207 $4 multicolored 3.00 3.00

World Stamp Expo '89.

Christmas — A208

Religious paintings: 10c, *The Small Cowper Madonna.* 25c, *Madonna of the Goldfinch.* 30c, *The Alba Madonna.* 50c, *Bologna Altarpiece* (attendant). 60c, *Bologna Altarpiece* (heralding angel). 70c, *Bologna Altarpiece* (archangel). $4, *Bologna Altarpiece* (saint holding ledger). No. 1271, *Madonna of Foligno.* No. 1272, *The Marriage of the Virgin.* No. 1273, *Bologna Altarpiece* (Madonna and Child).

Bologna Altarpiece by Giotto. Other paintings by Raphael.

1989, Dec. 11 Litho. *Perf. 14*

1264 A208 10c multicolored .35 .25
1265 A208 25c multicolored .45 .25
1266 A208 30c multicolored .45 .25
1267 A208 50c multicolored .70 .40
1268 A208 60c multicolored .75 .45
1269 A208 70c multicolored .85 .50
1270 A208 $4 multicolored 2.75 *4.25*
1271 A208 $5 multicolored 2.75 *4.25*
Nos. 1264-1271 (8) 9.05 *10.60*

Souvenir Sheets

1272 A208 $5 multicolored 5.00 *6.00*
1273 A208 $5 multicolored 5.00 *6.00*

America Issue — A210

UPAE, discovery of America 500th anniv. emblems and marine life: 10c, Star-eyed hermit crab. 20c, Spiny lobster. 25c, Magnificent banded fanworm. 45c, Cannonball jellyfish. 60c, Red-spiny sea star. $2, Peppermint shrimp. $3, Coral crab. $4, Branching fire coral. No. 1283, Common sea fan. No. 1284, Portuguese man-of-war.

1990, Mar. 26 Litho. *Perf. 14*

1275 A210 10c multicolored .50 .25
1276 A210 20c multicolored .75 .25
1277 A210 25c multicolored .80 .25
1278 A210 45c multicolored .95 .30
1279 A210 60c multicolored 1.10 .50
1280 A210 $2 multicolored 1.90 2.25
1281 A210 $3 multicolored 2.10 *3.50*
1282 A210 $4 multicolored 2.10 *3.50*
Nos. 1275-1282 (8) 10.20 *10.80*

Souvenir Sheets

1283 A210 $5 multicolored 4.25 4.25
1284 A210 $5 multicolored 4.25 4.25

Orchids — A211

No. 1285, Vanilla mexicana. No. 1286, Epidendrum ibaguense. No. 1287, Epidendrum secundum. No. 1288, Maxillaria conferta. No. 1289, Oncidium altissimum. No. 1290, Spiranthes lanceolata. No. 1291, Tonopsis utricularioides. No. 1292, Epidendrum nocturnum.

No. 1293, Octomeria graminifolia. No. 1294, Rodriguezia lanceolata.

1990, Apr. 17 *Perf. 14*

1285 A211 15c multicolored .80 .35
1286 A211 45c multicolored 1.10 .35
1287 A211 50c multicolored 1.25 .40
1288 A211 60c multicolored 1.40 .40
1289 A211 $1 multicolored 1.50 .85
1290 A211 $2 multicolored 2.00 2.25
1291 A211 $3 multicolored 2.25 3.25
1292 A211 $5 multicolored 3.25 *4.25*
Nos. 1285-1292 (8) 13.55 12.10

Souvenir Sheets

1293 A211 $6 multicolored 4.00 4.00
1294 A211 $6 multicolored 4.00 4.00

EXPO '90, Osaka.

Fish — A212

10c, Flamefish. 15c, Coney. 50c, Squirrelfish. 60c, Sergeant major. $1, Yellowtail snapper. $2, Rock beauty. $3, Spanish hogfish. $4, Striped parrotfish.

No. 1303, Blackbar soldierfish. No. 1304, Foureye butterflyfish.

1990, May 21 *Perf. 14*

1295 A212 10c multicolored .80 .45
1296 A212 15c multicolored 1.10 .45
1297 A212 50c multicolored 1.50 .55
1298 A212 60c multicolored 1.60 .55
1299 A212 $1 multicolored 1.75 .75
1300 A212 $2 multicolored 2.50 *2.75*
1301 A212 $3 multicolored 3.00 *3.50*
1302 A212 $4 multicolored 3.25 *3.50*
Nos. 1295-1302 (8) 15.50 *12.50*

Souvenir sheets

1303 A212 $5 multicolored 5.50 5.50
1304 A212 $5 multicolored 5.50 5.50

Victoria and Elizabeth II — A213

1990, May 3 Litho. *Perf. 15x14*

1305 A213 45c green 1.00 .30
1306 A213 60c bright rose 1.40 .50
1307 A213 $5 bright ultra 4.00 *5.25*
Nos. 1305-1307 (3) 6.40 *6.05*

Souvenir Sheet

1308 A213 $6 black 5.00 *6.00*

Penny Black, 150th anniv.

Royal Mail Transport A214

Designs: 50c, Steam packet *Britannia,* 1840. 75c, Railway mail car, 1892. $4, *Centaurus* seaplane, 1938. $6, Subway, 1927.

1990, May 3 *Perf. 13½*

1309 A214 50c red & deep green 1.25 .30
1310 A214 75c red & vio brn 1.50 1.00
1311 A214 $4 red & brt ultra 4.00 *5.25*
Nos. 1309-1311 (3) 6.75 6.55

Souvenir Sheet

1312 A214 $6 red & black 5.50 *6.25*

Stamp World London '90.

Miniature Sheet

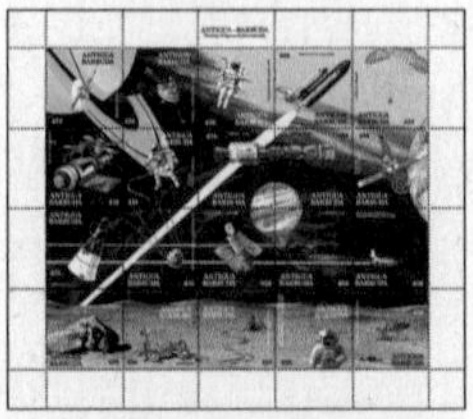

Space Achievements — A215

Designs: a, *Voyager 2* passing Saturn. b, *Pioneer 11* photographing Saturn. c, Manned maneuvering unit. d, *Columbia* space shuttle. e, Splashdown of Apollo 10 command module. f, *Skylab.* g, Ed White space walking, Gemini 4 mission. h, Apollo module, Apollo-Soyuz mission. i, Soyuz module, Apollo-Soyuz mission. j, *Mariner 1* passing Venus. k, Gemini 4 module. l, *Sputnik.* m, Hubble Space Telescope. n, X-15 rocket plane. o, Bell X-1 breaking sound barrier. p, Astronaut, Apollo 17 mission. r, American lunar rover. r, Lunar module, Apollo 14 mission. s, First men on the Moon, Apollo 11 mission. t, Lunokhod, Soviet lunar rover.

1990, June 11 Litho. *Perf. 14*

1313 A215 Sheet of 20 16.00 16.00
a.-t. 45c any single .75 .75

Mickey Production Studios A216

Walt Disney characters in Hollywood: 45c, Minnie Mouse reading script. 50c, Director Mickey Mouse, take 1 of Minnie. 60c, Make-up artist Daisy Duck. $1, Clarabelle as Cleopatra. $2, Mickey, Goofy, Donald Duck. $3, Goofy destroying set. $4, Mickey, Donald editing film. No. 1322, Mickey directs surfing film. No. 1323, Minnie, Daisy, Clarabelle in musical.

1990, Sept. 3 Litho. *Perf. 14x13½*

1314 A216 25c shown .70 .25
1315 A216 45c multicolored .80 .25
1316 A216 50c multicolored .90 .25
1317 A216 60c multicolored 1.10 .30
1318 A216 $1 multicolored 1.25 .60
1319 A216 $2 multicolored 1.75 2.10
1320 A216 $3 multicolored 2.25 3.25
1321 A216 $4 multicolored 2.25 3.25
Nos. 1314-1321 (8) 11.00 10.25

Souvenir Sheets

1322 A216 $5 multicolored 4.50 4.50
1323 A216 $5 multicolored 4.50 4.50

A217

1990, Aug. 27 Litho. *Perf. 14*

1324 A217 15c multicolored .40 .25
1325 A217 35c multi, diff. .65 .25
1326 A217 75c multi, diff. 1.10 .65
1327 A217 $3 multi, diff. 2.00 *3.00*
Nos. 1324-1327 (4) 4.15 *4.15*

Souvenir Sheet

1328 A217 $6 multi, diff. 5.00 5.00

Queen Mother, 90th birthday.

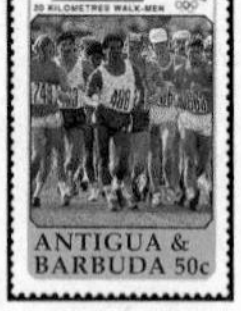

A218

No. 1329, 20-Kilometer Walk. No. 1330, Triple jump. No. 1331, 10,000 meter run. No. 1332, Javelin.

No. 1333, Opening ceremony, Los Angeles, 1984.

1990, Oct. 1 Litho. *Perf. 14*

1329 A218 50c multicolored .90 .30
1330 A218 75c multicolored 1.10 .60
1331 A218 $1 multicolored 1.35 .70
1332 A218 $5 multicolored 3.50 *5.50*
Nos. 1329-1332 (4) 6.85 *7.10*

Souvenir Sheet

1333 A218 $6 multicolored 5.75 *7.25*

1992 Summer Olympics, Barcelona.

Intl. Literacy Year — A219

Walt Disney characters in scenes from books by Charles Dickens: 15c, Huey and Dewey, Christmas Stories. 45c, Donald Duck, Bleak House. 50c, Dewey, Bad Pete, Oliver Twist. 60c, Daisy Duck, Old Curiosity Shop. $1, Little Nell. $2, Scrooge McDuck, Pickwick Papers. $3, Mickey and Minnie Mouse, Dombey and Son. $5, Minnie, Our Mutual Friend. No. 1342, Mickey and friends, David Copperfield. No. 1343, Pinocchio, Oliver Twist.

1990, Oct. 15 Litho. *Perf. 14*

1334 A219 15c multicolored .75 .25
1335 A219 45c multicolored 1.00 .35
1336 A219 50c multicolored 1.10 .40
1337 A219 60c multicolored 1.25 .45
1338 A219 $1 multicolored 1.40 .70
1339 A219 $2 multicolored 2.00 2.25
1340 A219 $3 multicolored 2.25 3.25
1341 A219 $5 multicolored 2.75 *4.25*
Nos. 1334-1341 (8) 12.50 11.90

Souvenir Sheets

1342 A219 $6 multicolored 6.00 6.00
1343 A219 $6 multicolored 6.00 6.00

Nos. 1217-1222 Overprinted

1990, Nov. 11

1344 A201 15c multicolored .85 .30
1345 A201 25c multicolored .85 .30
1346 A201 $1 multicolored 1.75 1.50
1347 A201 $4 multicolored 3.50 *5.00*
Nos. 1344-1347 (4) 6.95 *7.10*

Souvenir Sheets

1348 A201 $5 on #1221 5.50 5.50
1349 A201 $5 on #1222 5.50 5.50

Overprint on Nos. 1348-1349 is 32x13mm.

Birds — A220

10c, Pearly-eyed thrasher. 25c, Purple-throated carib. 50c, Common yellowthroat. 60c, American kestrel. $1, Yellow-bellied sapsucker. $2, Purple gallinule. $3, Yellow-crowned night heron. $4, Blue-hooded euphonia.

No. 1358, Brown pelican. No. 1359, Frigate bird.

1990, Nov. 19

1350 A220 10c multicolored .50 .35
1351 A220 25c multicolored .60 .40
1352 A220 50c multicolored .70 .45
1353 A220 60c multicolored 1.10 .75
1354 A220 $1 multicolored 1.25 .80
1355 A220 $2 multicolored 2.25 *2.50*
1356 A220 $3 multicolored 2.50 *3.00*
1357 A220 $4 multicolored 2.75 *3.25*
Nos. 1350-1357 (8) 11.65 *11.50*

Souvenir Sheets

1358 A220 $6 multicolored 7.00 *8.75*
1359 A220 $6 multicolored 7.00 *8.75*

Christmas A221

Paintings: 25c, Madonna and Child with Saints by del Piombo. 30c, Virgin and Child with Angels by Grunewald, vert. 40c, Holy Family and a Shepherd by Titian. 60c, Virgin and Child by Fra Filippo Lippi, vert. $1, Jesus,

St. John and Two Angels by Rubens. $2, Adoration of the Shepherds by Catena. $4, Adoration of the Magi by Giorgione. $5, Virgin and Child Adored by a Warrior by Catena. No. 1368, Allegory of the Blessings of Jacob by Rubens, vert. No. 1369, Adoration of the Magi by Fra Angelico, vert.

Perf. 14x13½, 13½x14

1990, Dec. 10 Litho.

1360	A221	25c multicolored	.85	.40
1361	A221	30c multicolored	.85	.40
1362	A221	40c multicolored	1.00	.45
1363	A221	60c multicolored	1.25	.50
1364	A221	$1 multicolored	1.50	1.00
1365	A221	$2 multicolored	2.25	*2.50*
1366	A221	$4 multicolored	3.50	*5.00*
1367	A221	$5 multicolored	3.50	*5.00*
		Nos. 1360-1367 (8)	14.70	*15.25*

Souvenir Sheets

1368	A221	$6 multicolored	4.25	4.25
1369	A221	$6 multicolored	4.25	4.25

Peter Paul Rubens (1577-1640), Painter A222

Entire paintings or different details from: 25c, Rape of the Daughters of Leucippus. 45c, $2, $4, Bacchanal. 50c, $1, $3, Rape of the Sabine Women. 60c, Battle of the Amazons. No. 1378, Rape of Hippodameia. No. 1379, Battle of the Amazons.

1991, Jan. 21 Litho. *Perf. 14*

1370	A222	25c multicolored	1.00	.30
1371	A222	45c multicolored	1.25	.45
1372	A222	50c multicolored	1.25	.50
1373	A222	60c multicolored	1.50	.65
1374	A222	$1 multicolored	1.75	1.00
1375	A222	$2 multicolored	2.00	*2.50*
1376	A222	$3 multicolored	2.50	*3.75*
1377	A222	$4 multicolored	2.75	*4.75*
		Nos. 1370-1377 (8)	14.00	*13.90*

Souvenir Sheets

1378	A222	$6 multicolored	4.50	*5.25*
1379	A222	$6 multicolored	4.50	*5.25*

World War II Milestones A223

Designs: 10c, US troops enter Germany, Sept. 11, 1944. 15c, All axis forces surrender in North Africa, May 12, 1943. 25c, US troops invade Kwajalein, Jan. 31, 1944. 45c, Roosevelt and Churchill meet in Casablanca, Jan. 14, 1943. 50c, Marshal Badoglio signs agreement with allies, Sept. 1, 1943. $1, Mountbatten appointed Supreme Allied Commander, Southeast Asia Command, Aug. 25, 1943. $2, Major Greek tactical victory, Koritza, Nov. 22, 1940. $4, Britain and USSR sign mutual assistance pact, July 12, 1941. $5, Operation Torch, Nov. 8, 1942. No. 1389, Japanese attack on Pearl Harbor, Dec. 7, 1941. No. 1390, American bombing attack on Schweinfurt, Oct. 14, 1943.

1991, Mar. 11 Litho. *Perf. 14*

1380	A223	10c multicolored	1.10	.60
1381	A223	15c multicolored	1.25	.50
1382	A223	25c multicolored	1.25	.50
1383	A223	45c multicolored	2.50	.65
1384	A223	50c multicolored	1.50	.65
1385	A223	$1 multicolored	2.75	1.50
1386	A223	$2 multicolored	3.00	2.75
1387	A223	$4 multicolored	3.00	*4.00*
1388	A223	$5 multicolored	3.25	*4.00*
		Nos. 1380-1388 (9)	19.60	*15.15*

Souvenir Sheets

1389	A223	$6 multicolored	6.75	*7.25*
1390	A223	$6 multicolored	6.75	*7.25*

Cog Railways of the World — A224

Designs: 25c, Prince Regent, Middleton Colliery, 1812. 30c, Snowdon Mountain Railway, Wales. 40c, 1st Railcar at Hell Gate, Manitou and Pike's Peak Railway. 60c, PNKA Rack Railway, Amberawa, Java. $1, Green Mountain Railway, Mt. Desert Island, Maine, 1883. $2, Cog locomotive, Pike's Peak, 1891. $4, Vitznau-Rigi Cog Railway, Lake Lucerne. $5, Leopoldina Railway, Brazil. No. 1399, Electric Cog Donkey Engines, Panama Canal. No. 1400, Gornergratbahn, 1st electric cog railway in Switzerland, vert.

1991, Mar. 18 Litho. *Perf. 14*

1391	A224	25c multicolored	1.10	.35
1392	A224	30c multicolored	1.25	.35
1393	A224	40c multicolored	1.25	.45
1394	A224	60c multicolored	1.50	.50
1395	A224	$1 multicolored	2.00	.75
1396	A224	$2 multicolored	2.75	2.75
1397	A224	$4 multicolored	3.25	*4.25*
1398	A224	$5 multicolored	3.25	*4.25*
		Nos. 1391-1398 (8)	16.35	*13.65*

Souvenir Sheets

1399	A224	$6 multicolored	7.00	7.00
1400	A224	$6 multicolored	7.00	7.00

Butterflies A225

10c, Zebra. 35c, Southern daggertail. 50c, Red anartia. 75c, Malachite. $1, Polydamas swallowtail. $2, Orion. $4, Mimic. $5, Cracker. Caterpillars: No. 1409, Monarch, vert. No. 1410, Painted lady, vert.

1991, Apr. 15 Litho. *Perf. 14*

1401	A225	10c multicolored	.70	.35
1402	A225	35c multicolored	1.10	.35
1403	A225	50c multicolored	1.25	.45
1404	A225	75c multicolored	1.50	.85
1405	A225	$1 multicolored	1.75	1.00
1406	A225	$2 multicolored	2.25	*2.50*
1407	A225	$4 multicolored	3.00	*4.00*
1408	A225	$5 multicolored	3.00	*4.00*
		Nos. 1401-1408 (8)	14.55	13.50

Souvenir Sheets

1409	A225	$6 multicolored	7.25	*8.50*
1410	A225	$6 multicolored	7.25	*8.50*

Voyages of Discovery A226

Designs: 10c, Hanno, Phoenicia, c. 450 B.C. 15c, Pytheas, Greece, 325 B.C. 45c, Eric the Red, Viking, A.D. 985. 60c, Leif Erikson, Viking, A.D. 1000. $1, Scylax, Greece, A.D. 518. $2, Marco Polo, A.D. 1259. $4, Queen Hatsheput, Egypt, 1493 B.C. $5, St. Brendan, Ireland, 500 A.D. No. 1419, Columbus, bareheaded. No. 1420, Columbus, wearing hat.

1991, Apr. 22

1411	A226	10c multicolored	.80	.35
1412	A226	15c multicolored	.90	.35
1413	A226	45c multicolored	1.25	.40
1414	A226	60c multicolored	1.40	.55
1415	A226	$1 multicolored	1.75	.90
1416	A226	$2 multicolored	2.25	*2.75*
1417	A226	$4 multicolored	3.00	*4.00*
1418	A226	$5 multicolored	3.00	*4.00*
		Nos. 1411-1418 (8)	14.35	*13.30*

Souvenir Sheets

1419	A226	$6 multicolored	4.25	*4.75*
1420	A226	$6 multicolored	4.25	*4.75*

Discovery of America, 500th anniv. (in 1992).

Paintings by Vincent Van Gogh — A227

Designs: 5c, Portrait of Camille Roulin. 10c, Portrait of Armand Roulin. 15c, Young Peasant Woman with Straw Hat Sitting in the Wheat. 25c, Portrait of Adeline Ravoux. 30c, The Schoolboy (Camille Roulin). 40c, Portrait of Doctor Gachet. 50c, Portrait of a Man. 75c, Two Children. $2, Portrait of Postman Joseph Roulin. $3, The Seated Zouave. $4, L'arlesienne: Madame Ginoux with Books. No. 1432, Self Portrait, November/December 1888. No. 1433, Flowering Garden. No. 1434, Farmhouse in Provence. $6, The Bridge at Trinquetaille.

1991, May 13 *Perf. 13½*

1421	A227	5c multicolored	.60	.75
1422	A227	10c multicolored	.60	.55
1423	A227	15c multicolored	.70	.45
1424	A227	25c multicolored	.80	.45
1425	A227	30c multicolored	.80	.45
1426	A227	40c multicolored	.90	.45
1427	A227	50c multicolored	1.00	.45
1428	A227	75c multicolored	1.60	.75
1429	A227	$2 multicolored	2.50	2.50
1430	A227	$3 multicolored	3.00	2.75
1431	A227	$4 multicolored	3.50	*4.25*
1432	A227	$5 multicolored	3.50	*4.25*
		Nos. 1421-1432 (12)	19.50	*18.05*

Size: 102x76mm

Imperf

1433	A227	$5 multicolored	5.00	*6.00*
1434	A227	$5 multicolored	5.00	*6.00*
1435	A227	$6 multicolored	6.00	*7.00*

Phila Nippon '91 — A228

Walt Disney characters demonstrating Japanese martial arts: 10c, Mickey as champion sumo wrestler, vert. 15c, Goofy using tonfa. 45c, Ninja Donald in full field dress. 60c, Mickey using weapon in kung fu, vert. $1, Goofy tries kendo, vert. $2, Mickey, Donald demonstrating special technique of aikido. $4, Mickey flips Donald with judo throw. $5, Mickey demonstrates yabusame (target shooting from running horse), vert. No. 1444, Mickey using karate. No. 1445, Mickey demonstrating tamashiwara (powerbreaking), vert.

Perf. 13½x14, 14x13½

1991, June 29 Litho.

1436	A228	10c multicolored	.70	.25
1437	A228	15c multicolored	.80	.25
1438	A228	45c multicolored	1.35	.45
1439	A228	60c multicolored	1.75	.60
1440	A228	$1 multicolored	2.25	1.25
1441	A228	$2 multicolored	2.75	3.00
1442	A228	$4 multicolored	3.50	*4.75*
1443	A228	$5 multicolored	3.50	*4.75*
		Nos. 1436-1443 (8)	16.60	*15.30*

Souvenir Sheets

1444	A228	$6 multicolored	5.50	*6.50*
1445	A228	$6 multicolored	5.50	*6.50*

Royal Family Birthday, Anniversary

Common Design Type

1991, July 8 Litho. *Perf. 14*

1446	CD347	10c multicolored	.50	.25
1447	CD347	15c multicolored	.35	.25
1448	CD347	20c multicolored	.35	.25
1449	CD347	40c multicolored	1.00	.30
1450	CD347	$1 multicolored	1.25	.75
1451	CD347	$2 multicolored	1.75	1.75
1452	CD347	$4 multicolored	2.75	2.75
1453	CD347	$5 multicolored	4.50	4.50
		Nos. 1446-1453 (8)	12.45	10.80

Souvenir Sheets

1454	CD347	$4 Elizabeth, Philip	3.75	3.75
1455	CD347	$4 Charles, Diana, sons	5.50	5.50

10c, 40c, $1, $5, No. 1455, Charles and Diana, 10th wedding anniversary. Others, Queen Elizabeth II, 65th birthday.

Walt Disney Characters Playing Golf — A229

Designs: 10c, Daisy Duck teeing off. 15c, Goofy using 3-Wood. 45c, Mickey using 3-Iron. 60c, Mickey missing ball using 6-Iron. $1, Donald trying 8-Iron to get out of pond. $2, Minnie using 9-Iron. $4, Donald digging hole with sand wedge. $5, Goofy trying new approach with putter. No. 1464, Grandma Duck using pitching wedge. No. 1465, Mickey cheering Minnie as she uses her 5-Wood, horiz.

Perf. 13½x14, 14x13½

1991, Aug. 7 Litho.

1456	A229	10c multicolored	.75	.40
1457	A229	15c multicolored	.85	.40
1458	A229	45c multicolored	1.25	.40
1459	A229	60c multicolored	1.75	.50
1460	A229	$1 multicolored	2.00	1.10
1461	A229	$2 multicolored	2.50	*2.75*
1462	A229	$4 multicolored	3.25	*4.00*
1463	A229	$5 multicolored	3.50	*4.00*
		Nos. 1456-1463 (8)	15.85	*13.55*

Souvenir Sheets

1464	A229	$6 multicolored	6.25	*6.50*
1465	A229	$6 multicolored	6.25	*6.50*

1992 Summer Olympics, Barcelona — A230

Archie Comics, 50th anniv.: 10c, Moose receiving gold medal. 25c, Archie, Veronica, Mr. Lodge, polo match, horiz. 40c, Archie & Betty, fencing. 60c, Archie, women's volleyball. $1, Archie, tennis. $2, Archie, marathon race. $4, Archie, judging women's gymnastics, horiz. $5, Archie, Betty, Veronica, basketball. No. 1474, Archie, soccer. No. 1475, Archie, Betty, baseball, horiz.

Perf. 13½x14, 14x13½

1991, Aug. 19

1466	A230	10c multicolored	.65	.30
1467	A230	25c multicolored	1.00	.30
1468	A230	40c multicolored	1.25	.35
1469	A230	60c multicolored	1.50	.45
1470	A230	$1 multicolored	1.75	1.00
1471	A230	$2 multicolored	2.50	2.50
1472	A230	$4 multicolored	3.75	3.75
1473	A230	$5 multicolored	3.75	*5.00*
		Nos. 1466-1473 (8)	16.15	*13.65*

Souvenir Sheets

1474	A230	$6 multicolored	6.00	*6.75*
1475	A230	$6 multicolored	6.00	*6.75*

Charles de Gaulle, Birth Cent. — A231

Charles de Gaulle: 10c, and Pres. Kennedy, families, 1961. 15c, and Pres. Roosevelt, 1945, vert. 45c, and Chancellor Adenauer, 1962, vert. 60c, Liberation of Paris, 1944, vert. $1, Crossing the Rhine, 1945. $2, In Algiers, 1944. $4, and Pres. Eisenhower, 1960. $5, Returning from Germany, 1968, vert. No. 1484, and Churchill at Casablanca, 1943. No. 1485, and Citizens.

1991, Sept. 11 Litho. *Perf. 14*

1476	A231	10c multicolored	.80	.35
1477	A231	15c multicolored	.90	.35
1478	A231	45c multicolored	1.25	.40
1479	A231	60c multicolored	1.50	.50
1480	A231	$1 multicolored	1.75	.90
1481	A231	$2 multicolored	2.50	*3.00*
1482	A231	$4 multicolored	3.25	*4.25*
1483	A231	$5 multicolored	3.25	*4.25*
		Nos. 1476-1483 (8)	15.20	*14.00*

Souvenir Sheets

1484	A231	$6 multicolored	6.75	6.75
1485	A231	$6 multicolored	6.75	6.75

Independence, 10th Anniv. — A232

Designs: 10c, Island maps, government building. $6, Old P. O., St. Johns, #1 & #635.

1991, Oct. 28

1486	A232	10c multicolored	.85	.50

Souvenir Sheet

1487	A232	$6 multicolored	6.75	*8.00*

No. 1487 contains one 50x38mm stamp.

Miniature Sheet

Attack on Pearl Harbor, 50th Anniv. — A233

Designs: No. 1488a, Bow of Nimitz class carrier, Ticonderoga class cruiser. b, Tourist boat to Arizona Memorial. c, USS Arizona Memorial. d, Aircraft salute to missing men. e, White tern. f, Japanese Kate torpedo bombers. g, Japanese Zero fighters. h, Battleship row in flames. i, USS Nevada breaking out. j, Zeros returning to carriers.

1991, Dec. 9 ***Perf. 14½x15***

1488	A233	$1 Sheet of 10, #a.-j.	22.50	22.50

Inscription for No. 1488f incorrectly describes torpedo bombers as Zekes.

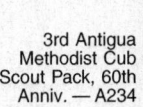

3rd Antigua Methodist Cub Scout Pack, 60th Anniv. — A234

Designs: $2, Lord Robert Baden-Powell, scouts, vert. $3.50, Scouts around campfire. $5, Antigua & Barbuda flag, Jamboree emblem, vert.

1991, Dec. 9 ***Perf. 14***

1489	A234	75c multicolored	1.50	.90
1490	A234	$2 multicolored	6.00	5.00
1491	A234	$3.50 multicolored	5.00	5.00
		Nos. 1489-1491 (3)	12.50	10.90

Souvenir Sheet

1492	A234	$5 multicolored	5.00	5.00

17th World Scout Jamboree, Korea.

Wolfgang Amadeus Mozart, Death Bicent. — A235

Portrait of Mozart and: $1.50, Scene from opera, Don Giovanni. $4, St. Peter's Cathedral, Salzburg.

1991, Dec. 9

1493	A235	$1.50 multicolored	3.50	3.50
1494	A235	$4 multicolored	6.75	6.75

Anniversaries and Events — A236

Designs: $2, Otto Lilienthal's glider No. 5. $2.50, Locomotive cab, vert.

1991, Dec. 9 **Litho.** ***Perf. 14***

1495	A236	$2 multicolored	3.50	2.75
1496	A236	$2.50 multicolored	6.50	4.00

First glider flight, cent. (No. 1495). Trans-Siberian Railway, cent. (No. 1496).

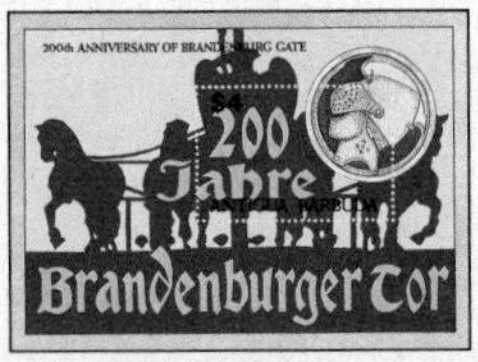

Brandenburg Gate, Bicent. — A237

25c, Demonstrators in autos, German flag. $2, Statue. $3, Portions of decorative frieze.

1991, Dec. 9 **Litho.** ***Perf. 14***

1499	A237	25c multicolored	.25	.25
1500	A237	$2 multicolored	1.10	*1.75*
1501	A237	$3 multicolored	2.00	*3.00*
		Nos. 1499-1501 (3)	3.35	*5.00*

Souvenir Sheet

1502	A237	$4 multicolored	4.75	4.75

Christmas — A238

Paintings by Fra Angelico: 10c, The Annunciation. 30c, Nativity. 40c, Adoration of the Magi. 60c, Presentation in the Temple. $1, Circumcision. $3, Flight into Egypt. $4, Massacre of the Innocents. $5, Christ Teaching in the Temple. No. 1511, Adoration of the Magi, diff. No. 1512, Adoration of the Magi (Cook Tondo).

1991, Dec. 12 ***Perf. 12***

1503	A238	10c multicolored	.40	.25
1504	A238	30c multicolored	.65	.25
1505	A238	40c multicolored	.80	.30
1506	A238	60c multicolored	1.00	.45
1507	A238	$1 multicolored	1.25	.75
1508	A238	$3 multicolored	2.50	*3.00*
1509	A238	$4 multicolored	2.75	*3.50*
1510	A238	$5 multicolored	3.00	*3.75*
		Nos. 1503-1510 (8)	12.35	*12.25*

Souvenir Sheets

1511	A238	$6 multicolored	7.00	*8.00*
1512	A238	$6 multicolored	7.00	*8.00*

Queen Elizabeth II's Accession to the Throne, 40th Anniv.

Common Design Type

Queen Elizabeth II and various island scenes.

1992, Feb. 6 **Litho.** ***Perf. 14***

1513	CD348	10c multicolored	.90	.30
1514	CD348	30c multicolored	1.10	.30
1515	CD348	$1 multicolored	1.25	.75
1516	CD348	$5 multicolored	2.75	*3.75*
		Nos. 1513-1516 (4)	6.00	*5.10*

Souvenir Sheets

1517	CD348	$6 Beach	4.50	*5.00*
1518	CD348	$6 Flora	4.50	*5.00*

Mushrooms — A239

10c, Amanita caesarea. 15c, Collybia fusipes. 30c, Boletus aereus. 40c, Laccaria amethystina. $1, Russula virescens. $2, Tricholoma auratum. $4, Calocybe gambosa. $5, Panus tigrinus.

No. 1527, Auricularia auricula. No. 1528, Clavariadelphus truncatus.

1992 **Litho.** ***Perf. 14***

1519	A239	10c multicolored	.75	.35
1520	A239	15c multicolored	.90	.35
1521	A239	30c multicolored	1.25	.35
1522	A239	40c multicolored	1.25	.45
1523	A239	$1 multicolored	2.00	1.00
1524	A239	$2 multicolored	2.75	2.75
1525	A239	$4 multicolored	3.50	*4.00*
1526	A239	$5 multicolored	3.50	*4.00*
		Nos. 1519-1526 (8)	15.90	*13.25*

Souvenir Sheet

1527	A239	$6 multicolored	6.50	*7.00*
1528	A239	$6 multicolored	6.50	*7.00*

Issued: 10c, 30c, $1, $5, No. 1528, May 18; others, Mar.

Disney Characters at Summer Olympics, Barcelona — A240

Designs: 10c, Mickey presenting gold medal to mermaid for swimming. 15c, Dewey and Huey watching Louie in kayak. 30c, Uncle McScrooge, Donald yachting. 50c, Donald, horse trying water polo. $1, Big Pete weight lifting. $2, Donald, Goofy fencing. $4, Mickey, Donald playing volleyball. $5, Goofy vaulting over horse.

No. 1537, $6, Mickey playing basketball, horiz. No. 1538, $6, Minnie Mouse on uneven parallel bars, horiz. No. 1539, $6, Mickey, Goofy, and Donald judging Minnie's floor exercise, horiz. No. 1540, $6, Mickey running after soccer ball.

1992, Mar. 16 ***Perf. 13***

1529	A240	10c multicolored	.65	.25
1530	A240	15c multicolored	.75	.25
1531	A240	30c multicolored	.95	.30
1532	A240	50c multicolored	1.50	.50
1533	A240	$1 multicolored	1.75	.85
1534	A240	$2 multicolored	2.75	2.75
1535	A240	$4 multicolored	3.50	*4.25*
1536	A240	$5 multicolored	3.50	*4.25*
		Nos. 1529-1536 (8)	15.35	*13.40*

Souvenir Sheets

1537-1540	A240	Set of 4	16.50	16.50

Dinosaurs A241

10c, Pteranodon. 15c, Brachiosaurus. 30c, Tyrannosaurus rex. 50c, Parasaurolophus. $1, Deinonychus. $2, Triceratops. $4, Protoceratops. $5, Stegosaurus.

No. 1549, Apatosaurus. No. 1550, Allosaurus.

1992, Apr. 6 ***Perf. 14***

1541	A241	10c multicolored	.70	.35
1542	A241	15c multicolored	.75	.35
1543	A241	30c multicolored	.95	.35
1544	A241	50c multicolored	1.10	.45
1545	A241	$1 multicolored	1.50	.80
1546	A241	$2 multicolored	2.25	2.25
1547	A241	$4 multicolored	2.50	*3.25*
1548	A241	$5 multicolored	2.50	*3.25*
		Nos. 1541-1548 (8)	12.25	*11.05*

Souvenir Sheets

1549	A241	$6 multicolored	5.50	5.50
1550	A241	$6 multicolored	5.50	5.50

Nos. 1541-1544 are vert.

Easter A242

Paintings: 10c, Supper at Emmaus, by Caravaggio. 15c, The Vision of St. Peter, by Francisco de Zurbaran. 30c, $1, Christ Driving the Money Changers from the Temple, by Tiepolo (detail on $1). 40c, Martyrdom of St. Bartholomew (detail), by Jusepe de Ribera. $2, Crucifixion (detail), by Albrecht Altdorfer. $4, $5, The Deposition (diff. detail), by Fra Angelico. No. 1559, Crucifixion, by Albrecht Altdorfer, vert. No. 1560, The Last Supper, by Vicente Juan Masip.

1992, Apr. 15 ***Perf. 14x13½***

1551	A242	10c multicolored	.55	.25
1552	A242	15c multicolored	.75	.25
1553	A242	30c multicolored	1.00	.35
1554	A242	40c multicolored	1.25	.50
1555	A242	$1 multicolored	2.25	1.00
1556	A242	$2 multicolored	3.25	3.25
1557	A242	$4 multicolored	4.25	*4.75*
1558	A242	$5 multicolored	4.25	*4.75*
		Nos. 1551-1558 (8)	17.55	*15.10*

Souvenir Sheet

Perf. 13½x14

1559	A242	$6 multicolored	5.50	*6.50*
1560	A242	$6 multicolored	5.50	*6.50*

Spanish Art — A243

Designs: 10c, The Miracle at the Well, by Alonso Cano. 15c, The Poet Luis de Gongora y Argote, by Velazquez. 30c, The Painter Francisco Goya, by Vincente Lopez Portana. 40c, Maria de Las Nieves Michaela Fourdiniere, by Luis Paret y Alcazar. $1, Charles III Eating before His Court, by Paret y Alcazar, horiz. $2, A Rain Shower in Granada, by Antonio Munoz Degrain, horiz. $4, Sarah Bernhardt, by Santiago Rusinol y Prats. $5, The Hermitage Garden, by Joaquin Mir Trinxet. No. 1569, Olympus: Battle with the Giants, by Francisco Bayeu y Subias. No. 1570, The Ascent of Monsieur Boucle's Montgolfier Balloon in the Gardens of Aranjuez, by Antonio Carnicero.

1992, May 11

1561	A243	10c multicolored	.45	.25
1562	A243	15c multicolored	.65	.30
1563	A243	30c multicolored	.90	.35
1564	A243	40c multicolored	.90	.50
1565	A243	$1 multicolored	1.50	1.25
1566	A243	$2 multicolored	2.25	*4.00*
1567	A243	$4 multicolored	3.50	*4.00*
1568	A243	$5 multicolored	4.25	*4.50*

Size: 120x95mm

Imperf

1569	A243	$6 multicolored	7.50	*8.50*
1570	A243	$6 multicolored	7.50	*8.50*
		Nos. 1561-1570 (10)	29.40	*32.15*

Granada '92.

Discovery of America, 500th Anniv. — A244

Designs: 15c, San Salvador Island. 30c, Martin Alonzo Pinzon, captain of Pinta. 40c, Columbus, signature, coat of arms. $1, Pinta. $2, Nina. $4, Santa Maria. No. 1577, Sea monster. No. 1578, Map, sailing ship.

1992, May 25 **Litho.** ***Perf. 14***

1571	A244	15c multicolored	.35	.25
1572	A244	30c multicolored	.45	.25
1573	A244	40c multicolored	.60	.35
1574	A244	$1 multicolored	2.25	1.75
1575	A244	$2 multicolored	2.50	*3.00*
1576	A244	$4 multicolored	3.00	*5.75*
		Nos. 1571-1576 (6)	9.15	*11.35*

Souvenir Sheets

1577	A244	$6 multicolored	6.00	*6.75*
1578	A244	$6 multicolored	6.00	*6.75*

World Columbian Stamp Expo '92, Chicago.

Hummel Figurines — A245

Designs 15c, No. 1587a, $1.50, Boy sitting on rock pointing to flower in cap. 30c, No. 1587b, $1.50, Girl sitting on fence. 40c, No. 1587c, $1.50, Boy holding binoculars. 50c, No. 1587d, $1.50, Boy carrying umbrella. $1, No. 1588a, $1.50, Two boys looking up at direction marker. $2, No. 1588b, $1.50, Boy carrying basket on back, walking with stick. $4, No. 1588c, $1.50, Two girls, goat. $5, No. 1588d, $1.50, Boy carrying walking stick.

1993, Jan. 6 **Litho.** ***Perf. 14***

1579	A245	15c multicolored	.40	.25
1580	A245	30c multicolored	.65	.25
1581	A245	40c multicolored	.80	.30
1582	A245	50c multicolored	.90	.40
1583	A245	$1 multicolored	1.50	.75
1584	A245	$2 multicolored	1.75	*2.25*
1585	A245	$4 multicolored	2.75	*3.50*
1586	A245	$5 multicolored	2.75	*3.50*
		Nos. 1579-1586 (8)	11.50	*11.20*

Souvenir Sheets

1587	A245	$1.50 Sheet of 4, #a.-d.	7.00	7.00
1588	A245	$1.50 Sheet of 4, #a.-d.	7.00	7.00

Hummingbirds and Flowers — A246

Designs: 10c, Antillean crested, wild plantain. 25c, Green mango, parrot's plantain. 45c, Purple-throated carib, lobster claws. 60c, Antillean mango, coral plant. $1, Vervain, cardinal's guard. $2, Rufous breasted hermit, heliconia. $4, Blue-headed, red ginger. $5, Green-throated carib, ornamental banana. No. 1597, Bee, jungle flame. No. 1598, Western streamertails, bignonia.

1992, Aug. 10 **Litho.** ***Perf. 14***

1589	A246	10c multicolored	.45	.45
1590	A246	25c multicolored	.60	.30
1591	A246	45c multicolored	.80	.35
1592	A246	60c multicolored	.90	.45
1593	A246	$1 multicolored	1.25	.75
1594	A246	$2 multicolored	2.00	2.00
1595	A246	$4 multicolored	3.25	*5.75*
1596	A246	$5 multicolored	3.50	*5.75*
		Nos. 1589-1596 (8)	12.75	*15.80*

Souvenir Sheets

1597	A246	$6 multicolored	6.00	*6.50*
1598	A246	$6 multicolored	6.00	*6.50*

Genoa '92.

Discovery of America, 500th Anniv. — A247

1992, Aug. 24 Litho. *Perf. 14½*

1599	A247	$1	Coming ashore	1.00	.75
1600	A247	$2	Natives, ships	1.75	*2.10*

Organization of East Caribbean States.

Souvenir Sheet

Madison Square Garden, NYC A248

1992, Oct. 28 Litho. *Perf. 14*

1601	A248	$6	multicolored	5.00	*6.75*

Postage Stamp Mega-Event, Jacob Javits Center, New York City.

Elvis Presley (1935-1977) — A249

Various pictures of Elvis Presley.

1992, Oct. 26 *Perf. 13½x14*

1602	A249	$1	Sheet of 9, #a.-i.	15.00	13.00

Inventors and Pioneers — A250

Designs: 10c, Ts'ai Lun, paper. 25c, Igor I. Sikorsky, 4-engine airplane. 30c, Alexander Graham Bell, telephone. 40c, Johannes Gutenberg, printing press. 60c, James Watt, steam engine. $1, Anton van Leeuwenhoek, microscope. $4, Louis Braille, Braille printing. $5, Galileo, telescope. No. 1607, Phonograph. No. 1608, Steamboat.

1992, Oct. 19 Litho. *Perf. 14*

1603	A250	10c	multicolored	.25	.25
1604	A250	25c	multicolored	1.50	.35
1605	A250	30c	multicolored	.60	.40
1605A	A250	40c	multicolored	.60	.40
1605B	A250	60c	multicolored	3.75	1.00
1605C	A250	$1	multicolored	2.00	1.50
1605D	A250	$4	multicolored	4.50	*5.75*
1606	A250	$5	multicolored	4.75	*5.75*
			Nos. 1603-1606 (8)	17.95	*15.40*

Souvenir Sheet

1607	A250	$6	multicolored	5.75	*6.50*
1608	A250	$6	multicolored	5.75	*6.50*

Christmas — A251

Details from Paintings: 10c, Virgin and Child with Angels, by School of Piero Della Francesca. 25c, Madonna Degli Alberelli, by Giovanni Bellini. 30c, Madonna and Child with St. Anthony Abbot and St. Sigismund, by Neroccio di Landi. 40c, Madonna and the Grand Duke, by Raphael. 60c, The Nativity, by George de la Tour. $1, Holy Family, by Jacob Jordaens. $4, Madonna and Child Enthroned, by Margaritone. $5, Madonna and Child on a Curved Throne, by Byzantine artist. No. 1617, Madonna and Child, by Domenico Ghirlandaio (both names misspelled). No. 1618, The Holy Family, by Pontormo.

1992, Nov. 16 *Perf. 13½x14*

1609	A251	10c	multicolored	.65	.25
1610	A251	25c	multicolored	1.00	.25
1611	A251	30c	multicolored	1.10	.25
1612	A251	40c	multicolored	1.25	.30
1613	A251	60c	multicolored	1.50	.60
1614	A251	$1	multicolored	1.75	1.00
1615	A251	$4	multicolored	3.75	*4.50*
1616	A251	$5	multicolored	3.75	*4.50*
			Nos. 1609-1616 (8)	14.75	*11.65*

Souvenir Sheet

1617	A251	$6	multicolored	5.75	*6.50*
1618	A251	$6	multicolored	5.75	*6.50*

A252

A253

Anniversaries and Events: 10c, Cosmonauts. 40c, Graf Zeppelin, Goodyear blimp. 45c, Right Rev. Daniel C. Davis, St. John's Cathedral. 75c, Konrad Adenauer. $1, Bus Mosbacher, Weatherly. $1.50, Rain forest. No. 1625, Felis tigris. No. 1626, Flag, emblems, plant. No. 1627, Women acting on stage. $2.25, Women carrying baskets of food on their heads. $3, Lions Club emblem, club member. No. 1630, West German, NATO flags. No. 1631, China's Long March Booster Rocket. No. 1632, Dr. Hugo Eckener.

No. 1633, $6, The Hindenburg. No. 1634, $6, Brandenburg Gate, German flag. No. 1635, $6, Monarch butterfly. No. 1636, $6, Hermes Shuttle, Columbus Space Station.

1992, Dec. 14 Litho. *Perf. 14*

1619	A252	10c	multicolored	.80	.50
1620	A252	40c	multicolored	1.75	.55
1621	A253	45c	multicolored	.75	.35
1622	A252	75c	multicolored	.90	.60
1623	A252	$1	multicolored	1.25	.75
1624	A252	$1.50	multicolored	1.75	1.10
1625	A252	$2	multicolored	4.25	2.00
1626	A253	$2	multicolored	2.75	1.50
1627	A253	$2	multicolored	2.50	1.75
1628	A252	$2.25	multicolored	2.50	2.50
1629	A252	$3	multicolored	3.75	3.75
1630	A252	$4	multicolored	5.00	5.00
1631	A252	$4	multicolored	5.50	5.50
1632	A252	$6	multicolored	5.00	5.00
			Nos. 1619-1632 (14)	38.45	30.85

Souvenir Sheets

1633-1636	A252	Set of 4	22.00	*27.50*

Intl. Space Year (Nos. 1619, 1631, 1636). Count Zeppelin, 75th anniv. of death (Nos. 1620, 1632-1633). Diocese of Northeast Caribbean and Aruba District, 150th anniv. (No. 1621). Konrad Adenauer, 25th anniv. of death (Nos. 1622, 1630, 1634). 1962 winner of America's Cup (No. 1623). Earth Summit, Rio (Nos. 1624-1625, 1635). Inter-American Institute for Cooperation on Agriculture, 50th anniv. (No. 1626). Cultural Development, 40th anniv. (No. 1627). WHO Intl. Conf. on Nutrition, Rome (No. 1628). Lions Club, 75th anniv. (No. 1629).

Issued: Nos. 1619, 1621-1623, 1626-1631, 1634, 1636, Nov.; Nos. 1624-1625, 1635, Dec. 14.

Euro Disney, Paris A254

Disney characters: 10c, Golf course. 25c, Davy Crockett Campground. 30c, Cheyenne Hotel. 40c, Santa Fe Hotel. $1, New York Hotel. $2, In car, map showing location. $4, Pirates of the Caribbean. $5, Adventureland.

No. 1645, $6, Mickey Mouse on map with star, vert. No. 1646, $6, Roof turret at entrance, Mickey Mouse in uniform. No. 1646A, $6, Mickey Mouse, colored spots on poster, vert. No. 1646B, $6, Mickey on poster, vert., diff.

1992-93 Litho. *Perf. 14x13½*

1637	A254	10c	multicolored	.70	.25
1638	A254	25c	multicolored	.90	.25
1639	A254	30c	multicolored	.90	.25
1640	A254	40c	multicolored	1.00	.30
1641	A254	$1	multicolored	2.00	.75
1642	A254	$2	multicolored	2.75	2.75
1643	A254	$4	multicolored	3.75	*5.00*
1644	A254	$5	multicolored	3.75	*5.00*
			Nos. 1637-1644 (8)	15.75	*14.55*

Souvenir Sheets
Perf. 13½x14

1645-1646B	A254	Set of 4	17.00	*20.00*

Issued: Nos. 1638-1639, 1642-1643, 1646-1646B, 2/22/93; others, 12/1992.

Miniature Sheets

Louvre Museum, Bicent. — A255

Details or entire paintings, by Peter Paul Rubens: No. 1647a, Destiny of Marie de' Medici. b, Birth of Marie de'Medici. c, Marie's Education. d, Destiny of Marie de'Medici, diff. e, Henry IV Receives the Portrait. f, The Meeting at Lyons. g, The Marriage. h, The Birth of Louis XIII.

No. 1648a, The Capture of Juliers. b, The Exchange of Princesses. c, The Happiness of the Regency. d, The Majority of Louis XIII. e, The Flight from Blois. f, The Treaty of Angouleme. g, The Peace of Angers. h, The Queen's Reconciliation with Her Son.

$6, Helene Fourment Au Carosse.

1993, Mar. 22 Litho. *Perf. 12*

1647	A255	$1	Sheet of 8, #a.-h., + label	7.25	7.25
1648	A255	$1	Sheet of 8, #a.-h., + label	7.25	7.25

Souvenir Sheet
Perf. 14½

1649	A255	$6	multicolored	7.75	7.75

No. 1649 contains one 55x88mm stamp.

Nos. 1647-1649 exist imperf. Values about double those of normal sheets.

Flowers — A256

15c, Cardinal's guard. 25c, Giant granadilla. 30c, Spider flower. 40c, Gold vine. $1, Frangipani. $2, Bougainvillea. $4, Yellow oleander. $5, Spicy jatropha.

No. 1658, Bird lime tree. No. 1659, Fairy lily.

1993, Mar. 15 Litho. *Perf. 14*

1650	A256	15c	multicolored	.95	.30
1651	A256	25c	multicolored	1.10	.30
1652	A256	30c	multicolored	1.10	.35
1653	A256	40c	multicolored	1.10	.35
1654	A256	$1	multicolored	2.10	.90
1655	A256	$2	multicolored	2.75	2.75
1656	A256	$4	multicolored	3.75	*4.50*
1657	A256	$5	multicolored	3.75	*4.50*
			Nos. 1650-1657 (8)	16.60	*13.95*

Souvenir Sheets

1658	A256	$6	multicolored	5.25	*6.50*
1659	A256	$6	multicolored	5.25	*6.50*

Endangered Species — A257

Designs: No. 1660a, St. Lucia parrot. b, Cahow. c, Swallow-tailed kite. d, Everglades kite. e, Imperial parrot. f, Humpback whale. g, Puerto Rican plain pigeon. h, St. Vincent parrot. i, Puerto Rican parrot. j, Leatherback turtle. k, American crocodile. l, Hawksbill turtle.

No. 1662, West Indian manatee.

1993, Apr. 5

1660	A257	$1	Sheet of 12, #a.-l.	15.00	15.00

Souvenir Sheets

1661	A257	$6	like #1660f	4.75	*5.50*
1662	A257	$6	multicolored	4.75	*5.50*

Philatelic Publishing Personalities A258

Portrait, stamp: No. 1663, J. Walter Scott (1842-1919), US "#C3a," Antigua #1. No. 1664, Theodore Champion, France #8, Antigua #1. No. 1665, E. Stanley Gibbons (1856-1913), cover of his first price list and catalogue, Antigua #1. No. 1666, Hugo Michel (1866-1944), Bavaria #1, Antigua #1. No. 1667, Alberto (1877-1944) and Giulio (1902-1987) Bolaffi, Sardinia #1, Great Britain #3. No. 1668, Richard Borek (1874-1947), Brunswick #24, Bavaria #1.

Front pages, Mekeel's Weekly Stamp News: No. 1669a, Jan. 7, 1890. b, Feb. 12, 1993.

1993, June 14

1663	A258	$1.50	multicolored	1.90	1.60
1664	A258	$1.50	multicolored	1.90	1.60
1665	A258	$1.50	multicolored	1.90	1.60
1666	A258	$1.50	multicolored	1.90	1.60
1667	A258	$1.50	multicolored	1.90	1.60
1668	A258	$1.50	multicolored	1.90	1.60
			Nos. 1663-1668 (6)	11.40	9.60

Souvenir Sheet

1669	A258	$3	Sheet of 2, #a.-b.	6.25	*7.00*

Mekeel's Weekly Stamp News, cent. (in 1891; No. 1669).

Miniature Sheets

Coronation of Queen Elizabeth II, 40th Anniv. — A259

No. 1670 — Coronation: a, 30c, Official photograph. b, 40c, Crown of Queen Elizabeth, the Queen Mother. c, $2, Dignataries attending ceremony. d, $4, Queen, Prince Edward.

No. 1671, $1 — First decade, 1953-1963: a, Wedding photograph of Princess Margaret and Antony Armstrong-Jones. b, Queen opening Parliament, Prince Philip. c, Queen holding infant. d, Royal family. e, Queen Elizabeth II, formal portrait. f, Queen, Charles de Gaulle. g, Queen, Pope John XXIII. h, Queen inspecting troops.

No. 1672, $1 — Second decade, 1963-1973: a, Investiture of Charles as Prince of Wales. b, Queen opening Parliament, Prince Philip, diff. c, Queen holding infant, diff. d, Queen, Prince Philip, children. e, Wearing blue robe, diadem. f, Prince Philip, Queen seated. g, Prince Charles, Queen at microphone. h, Queen conversing, model airplane.

No. 1673, $1 — Third decade, 1973-1983: a, Wedding photograph of Prince Charles and Princess Diana. b, Queen opening Parliament, Prince Philip, diff. c, Princess Diana with infant. d, Princess Anne with infant. e, Portrait of Queen. f, Queen waving, Prince Philip. g, Queen, Pope John Paul II. h, Wedding portrait of Mark Phillips and Princess Anne.

No. 1674, $1 — Fourth decade, 1983-1993: a, Wedding photograph of Sarah Ferguson and Prince Andrew. b, Queen opening Parliament, Prince Philip, diff. c, Princess Diana holding infant, diff. d, Sarah Ferguson, infant. e, Queen wearing blue dress. f, Queen waving from carriage, Prince Philip. g, Queen wearing military uniform. h, Queen Mother.

$6, Portrait, by Denis Fildes.

1993, June 2 Litho. *Perf. 13½x14*

1670 A259 Sheet, 2 each #a.-d. 8.50 8.50

Sheets of 8, #a-h

1671-1674 A259 Set of 4 34.00 34.00

Souvenir Sheet

Perf. 14

1675 A259 $6 multicolored 5.00 5.00

No. 1675 contains one 28x42mm stamp.

A260

Wedding of Japan's Crown Prince Naruhito and Masako Owada: Cameo photos of couple and: 40c, Crown Prince. $3, Princess.

$6, Princess wearing white coat, vert.

1993, Aug. 16 Litho. *Perf. 14*

1676 A260 40c multicolored .65 .40
1677 A260 $3 multicolored 2.25 *3.25*

Souvenir Sheet

1678 A260 $6 multicolored 6.00 6.00

Picasso (1881-1973) A261

Paintings: 30c, Cat and Bird, 1939. 40c, Fish on a Newspaper, 1957. $5, Dying Bull, 1934.

$6, Woman with a Dog, 1953.

1993, Aug. 16 Litho. *Perf. 14*

1679 A261 30c multicolored .90 .40
1680 A261 40c multicolored .90 .40
1681 A261 $5 multicolored 3.75 3.75
Nos. 1679-1681 (3) 5.55 4.55

Souvenir Sheet

1682 A261 $6 multicolored 5.75 5.75

Copernicus (1473-1543) — A262

Designs: 40c, Astronomical devices. $4, Photograph of supernova.

$5, Copernicus.

1993, Aug. 16

1683 A262 40c multicolored .65 .50
1684 A262 $4 multicolored 3.25 3.25

Souvenir Sheet

1685 A262 $5 multicolored 5.25 5.25

Willy Brandt (1913-1992), German Chancellor A263

Designs: 30c, Helmut Schmidt, George Leber, Brandt. $4, Brandt, newspaper headlines.

$6, Brandt at Warsaw Ghetto Memorial, 1970.

1993, Aug. 16

1686 A263 30c multicolored .75 .35
1687 A263 $4 multicolored 3.75 3.75

Souvenir Sheet

1688 A263 $6 multicolored 5.50 5.50

Polska '93 — A264

Paintings: $1, Study of a Woman Combing Her Hair, by Wladyslaw Slewinski, 1897. $3, Artist's Wife with Cat, by Konrad Krzyzanowski, 1912.

$6, General Confusion, by S. I. Witkiewicz, 1930, vert.

1993, Aug. 16

1689 A264 $1 multicolored .90 .90
1690 A264 $3 multicolored 2.25 2.25

Souvenir Sheet

1691 A264 $6 multicolored 5.50 5.50

Inauguration of Pres. William J. Clinton — A265

Designs: $5, Pres. Clinton driving car. $6, Pres. Clinton, inauguration ceremony, vert.

1993, Aug. 16

1692 A265 $5 multicolored 3.25 3.25

Souvenir Sheet

1693 A265 $6 multicolored 5.00 5.00

No. 1693 contains one 43x57mm stamp.

1994 Winter Olympics, Lillehammer, Norway — A266

15c, Irina Rodnina, Alexei Ulanov, gold medalists, pairs figure skating, 1972. $5, Alberto Tomba, gold medal, giant slalom, 1988, 1992.

$6, Yvonne van Gennip, Andrea Ehrig, gold, bronze medalists, speedskating, 1988.

1993, Aug. 16

1694 A266 15c multicolored 1.00 .30
1695 A266 $5 multicolored 3.25 3.25

Souvenir Sheet

1696 A266 $6 multicolored 5.50 5.50

1994 World Cup Soccer Championships, US — A267

English soccer players: No. 1697, $2, Gordon Banks. Nos. 1698, $2, Bobby Moore. No. 1699, $2, Peter Shilton. No. 1700, $2, Nobby Stiles. No. 1701, $2, Bryan Robson. No. 1702, $2, Geoff Hurst. No. 1703, $2, Gary Lineker. No. 1704, $2, Bobby Charlton. No. 1705, $2, Martin Peters. No. 1706, $2, John Barnes. No. 1707, $2, David Platt. No. 1708, $2, Paul Gascoigne.

No. 1709, $6, Bobby Moore. No. 1710, $6, Player holding 1990 Fair Play Winners Trophy.

1993, July 30 Litho. *Perf. 14*

1697-1708 A267 Set of 12 18.00 18.00

Souvenir Sheets

1709-1710 A267 Set of 2 10.00 10.00

Nos. 1697-1708 issued in sheets of five plus label identifying player.

Aviation Anniversaries A268

Designs: 30c, Dr. Hugo Eckener, Dr. Wm. Beckers, zeppelin over Lake George, NY. No. 1712, Chicago Century of Progress Exhibition seen from zeppelin. No. 1713, George Washington, Blanchard's balloon, vert. No. 1714, Gloster E.28/39, first British jet plane. $4, Pres. Wilson watching take-off of first scheduled air mail plane. No. 1716, Hindenburg over Ebbets Field, Brooklyn, NY, 1937. No. 1717, Gloster Meteor in combat.

No. 1718, Eckener, vert. No. 1719, Alexander Hamilton, Pres. Washington, John Jay, gondola of Blanchard's balloon. No. 1720, PBY-5.

1993, Oct. 11

1711 A268 30c multicolored 1.00 .60
1712 A268 40c multicolored 1.00 1.00
1713 A268 40c multicolored 1.00 1.00
1714 A268 40c multicolored 1.00 1.00
1715 A268 $4 multicolored 4.00 4.00
1716 A268 $5 multicolored 4.00 4.00
1717 A268 $5 multicolored 4.00 4.00
Nos. 1711-1717 (7) 16.00 15.60

Souvenir Sheets

1718 A268 $6 multicolored 5.25 5.25
1719 A268 $6 multicolored 6.00 6.00
1720 A268 $6 multicolored 6.00 6.00

Dr. Hugo Eckener, 125th anniv. of birth (Nos. 1711-1712, 1716, 1718). First US balloon flight, bicent. (Nos. 1713, 1715, 1719). Royal Air Force, 75th anniv. (Nos. 1714, 1717, 1720).

No. 1720 contains one 57x43mm stamp.

Mickey Mouse Movie Posters — A269

Nos. 1721-1729: 10c, The Musical Farmer, 1932. 15c, Little Whirlwind, 1941. 30c, Pluto's Dream House, 1940. 40c, Gulliver Mickey, 1934. 50c, Alpine Climbers, 1936. $1, Mr. Mouse Takes a Trip, 1940. $2, The Nifty Nineties, 1941. $4, Mickey Down Under, 1948. $5, The Pointer, 1939.

No. 1730, $6, The Simple Things, 1953. No. 1731, $6,The Prince and the Pauper, 1990.

1993, Oct. 25 Litho. *Perf. 13½x14*

1721-1729 A269 Set of 9 15.00 15.00

Souvenir Sheets

1730-1731 A269 Set of 2 13.00 13.00

St. John's Lodge #492, 150th Anniv. — A270

Designs: 10c, W.K. Heath, Grand Inspector 1961-82, vert. 30c, Present Masonic Hall. 40c, 1st Masonic Hall. 60c, J.L.E. Jeffery, Grand Inspector 1953-61, vert.

1993, Aug. 16 Litho. *Perf. 14*

1732-1735 A270 Set of 4 10.00 10.00

First Ford Engine and Benz's First 4-Wheel Car, Cent. — A271

30c, Lincoln Continental. 40c, 1914 Mercedes racing car. $4, 1966 Ford GT40. $5, 1954 Mercedes Benz gull wing coupe, street version.

No. 1740, $6, Mustang emblem. No. 1741, $6, US #1286A, Germany #471.

1993, Oct. 11 Litho. *Perf. 14*

1736-1739 A271 Set of 4 9.00 9.00

Souvenir Sheets

1740-1741 A271 Set of 2 11.00 11.00

Christmas A272

Nos. 1742-1750, Disney characters in The Nutcracker: 10c, 15c, 20c, 30c, 40c, 50c, 60c, $3, $6.

No. 1751, $6, Minnie and Mickey. No. 1752, $6, Mickey, vert.

1993, Nov. 8 *Perf. 14x13½, 13½x14*

1742-1750 A272 Set of 9 13.00 13.00

Souvenir Sheets

1751-1752 A272 Set of 2 11.50 11.50

Fine Art — A273

Paintings by Rembrandt: No. 1753, 15c, Hannah and Samuel. No. 1755, 30c, Isaac & Rebecca (The Jewish Bride). No. 1756, 40c, Jacob Wrestling with the Angel. No. 1760, $5, Moses with the Tablets of the Law.

Paintings by Matisse: No. 1754, 15c, Guitarist. No. 1757, 60c, Interior with a Goldfish Bowl. No. 1758, $1, Portrait of Mlle. Yvonne Landsberg. No. 1759, $4, The Toboggan, Plate XX from Jazz.

No. 1761, $6, The Blinding of Samson by the Philistines, by Rembrandt. No. 1762, $6, The Three Sisters, by Matisse.

1993, Nov. 22 *Perf. 13½x14*

1753-1760 A273 Set of 8 10.50 10.50

Souvenir Sheets

1761-1762 A273 Set of 2 11.50 11.50

A274

Hong Kong '94 — A275

Stamps, fishing boats at Shau Kei Wan: No. 1763, Hong Kong #370, bow of boat. No. 1764, Stern of boat, #1300.

Museum of Qin figures, Shaanxi Province, Tomb of Qin First Emperor: No. 1765a, Inside museum. b, Cavalryman, horse. c, Warriors in battle formation. d, Painted bronze horses, chariot. e, Pekingese dog (not antiquity). f, Chin warrior figures, horses.

1994, Feb. 18 Litho. *Perf. 14*

1763 A274 40c multicolored .70 .70
1764 A274 40c multicolored .70 .70
a. Pair, #1763-1764 1.60 1.60

Miniature Sheet

1765 A275 40c Sheet of 6, #a.-f. 5.75 5.75

Nos. 1763-1764 issued in sheets of 5 pairs. No. 1764a is a continuous design.

New Year 1994 (Year of the Dog) (No. 1765e).

Hong Kong '94 — A276

Disney characters: 10c, Mickey's "Pleasure Junk." 15c, Mandarin Minnie. 30c, Donald, Daisy journey by house boat. 50c, Mickey, Birdman of Mongkok. $1, Pluto encounters a good-luck dog. $2, Minnie, Daisy celebrate Bun Festival. $4, Goofy, the noodle maker. $5, Goofy pulls Mickey in a rickshaw.

No. 1774, $5, Mickey celebrating New Year with Dragon Dance, horiz. No. 1775, $5, View of Hong Kong Harbor, horiz.

1994, Feb. 18 Litho. *Perf. 13½x14*
1766-1773 A276 Set of 8 14.00 14.00

Souvenir Sheets
Perf. 14x13½
1774-1775 A276 $5 Set of 2 11.00 11.00

Sierra Club, Cent. — A277

No. 1776: a, Bactrian camel, emblem UR. b, Bactrian camel, emblem UL. c, African elephant, emblem UL. d, African elephant, emblem UR. e, Leopard, blue background. f, Leopard, emblem UR. g, Leopard, emblem UL. h, Club emblem.

No. 1777: a, Sumatran rhinoceros, lying on ground. b, Sumatran rhinoceros, looking straight ahead. c, Ring-tailed lemur standing. d, Ring-tailed lemur sitting on branch. e, Red-fronted brown lemur on branch. f, Red-fronted brown lemur. g, Red-fronted brown lemur, diff.

No. 1778, $1.50, Sumatran rhinoceros, horiz. No. 1779, $1.50, Ring-tailed lemur, horiz. No. 1780, $1.50, Bactrian camel, horiz. No. 1781, $1.50, African elephant, horiz.

1994, Mar. 1 Litho. *Perf. 14*
1776 A277 $1.50 Sheet of 8, #a.-h. 12.00 12.00
1777 A277 $1.50 Sheet of 8, #a.-g, #1776h 12.00 12.00

Souvenir Sheets
1778-1781 A277 Set of 4 6.50 6.50

New Year 1994 (Year of the Dog) — A278

Small breeds of dogs: No. 1782a, West highland white terrier. b, Beagle. c, Scottish terrier. d, Pekingese. e, Dachshund. f, Yorkshire terrier. g, Pomeranian. h, Poodle. i, Shetland sheepdog. j, Pug. k, Shih tzu. l, Chihuahua.

Large breeds of dogs: No. 1783a, Mastiff. b, Border collie. c, Samoyed. d, Airedale terrier. e, English setter. f, Rough collie. g, Newfoundland. h, Weimaraner. i, English springer spaniel. j, Dalmatian. k, Boxer. l, Old English sheepdog.

No. 1784, $6, Welsh corgi. No. 1785, $6, Labrador retriever.

1994, Apr. 5 *Perf. 14*
1782 A278 50c Sheet of 12, #a.-l. 7.75 7.75
1783 A278 75c Sheet of 12, #a.-l. 11.50 11.50

Souvenir Sheets
1784-1785 A278 Set of 2 11.50 11.50

Orchids — A279

Designs: 10c, Spiranthes lanceolata. 20c, Ionopsis utricularioides. 30c, Tetramicra canaliculata. 50c, Oncidium picturatum. $1, Epidendrum difforme. $2, Epidendrum ciliare. $4, Epidendrum ibaguense. $5, Epidendrum nocturnum.

No. 1794, $6, Encyclia cochleata. No. 1795, $6, Rodriguezia lanceolata.

1994, Apr. 11 *Perf. 14*
1786-1793 A279 Set of 8 17.50 17.50

Souvenir Sheets
1794-1795 A279 Set of 2 11.00 *13.00*

Butterflies — A280

Designs: 10c, Monarch. 15c, Florida white. 30c, Little sulphur. 40c, Troglodyte. $1, Common long-tail skipper. $2, Caribbean buckeye. $4, Polydamas swallowtail. $5, Zebra.

No. 1804, $6, Cloudless sulphur. No. 1805, $6, Hanno blue.

1994, June 27 *Perf. 14*
1796-1803 A280 Set of 8 18.50 18.50

Souvenir Sheets
1804-1805 A280 Set of 2 11.00 *13.00*

Marine Life — A281

No. 1806: a, Bottlenose dolphin. b, Killer whale (a). c, Spinner dolphin (b). d, Ocean sunfish (a). e, Caribbean reef shark, short fin pilot whale (d, f). f, Butterfly fish. g, Moray eel. h, Trigger fish. i, Red lobster (h).

No. 1807, $6, Blue marlin, horiz. No. 1808, $6, Sea horse.

1994, July 21 Litho. *Perf. 14*
1806 A281 50c Sheet of 9, #a.-i. 7.75 7.75

Souvenir Sheets
1807-1808 A281 Set of 2 13.00 13.00

Intl. Year of the Family — A282

1994, Aug. 4
1809 A282 90c multicolored 1.10 1.10

D-Day, 50th Anniv. — A283

Designs: 40c, Short Sunderland attacks U-boat. $2, Lockheed P-38 Lightning attacks train. $3, B-26 Marauders of 9th Air Force.

$6, Hawker Typhoon Fighter Bombers.

1994, Aug. 4
1810-1812 A283 Set of 3 7.00 7.00

Souvenir Sheet
1813 A283 $6 multicolored 7.50 7.50

A284

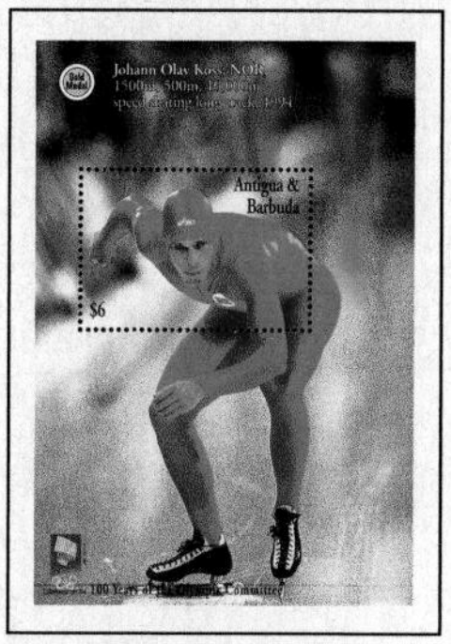

Intl. Olympic Committee, Cent. — A285

Designs: 50c, Edwin Moses, US, hurdles, 1984. $1.50, Steffi Graf, Germany, tennis, 1988. $6, Johann Olav Koss, Norway, speed skating, 1994.

1994, Aug. 4
1814 A284 50c multicolored .40 .30
1815 A284 $1.50 multicolored 2.00 2.00

Souvenir Sheet
1816 A285 $6 multicolored 6.00 6.00

English Touring Cricket, Cent. — A286

35c, M.A. Atherton, England, Wisden Trophy. 75c, I.V.A. Richards, Leeward Islands, vert. $1.20, R.B. Richardson, Leeward Islands, Wisden Trophy.

$3, First English team, 1895.

1994, Aug. 4
1817-1819 A286 Set of 3 6.00 6.00

Souvenir Sheet
1820 A286 $3 multicolored 3.00 3.00

First Manned Moon Landing, 25th Anniv. — A287

No. 1821, $1.50: a, Edwin E. Aldrin, Jr. b, First footprint on Moon. c, Neil A. Armstrong. d, Aldrin descending to lunar surface. e, Aldrin deploys ALSEP (spelled ALSET in error on stamp). f, Aldrin, US flag, Tranquility Base.

No. 1822, $1.50: a, Scientific research, Tranquility Base. b, Plaque on Moon. c, Eagle ascending to docking. d, Command module in lunar orbit. e, US No. C76 made from die carried to Moon. f, Pres. Nixon, Apollo 11 crew.

$6, Armstrong, Aldrin, Postmaster General Blount.

1994, Aug. 4 Sheets of 6, #a-f
1821-1822 A287 Set of 2 22.50 22.50

Souvenir Sheet
1823 A287 $6 multicolored 5.25 5.25

A288

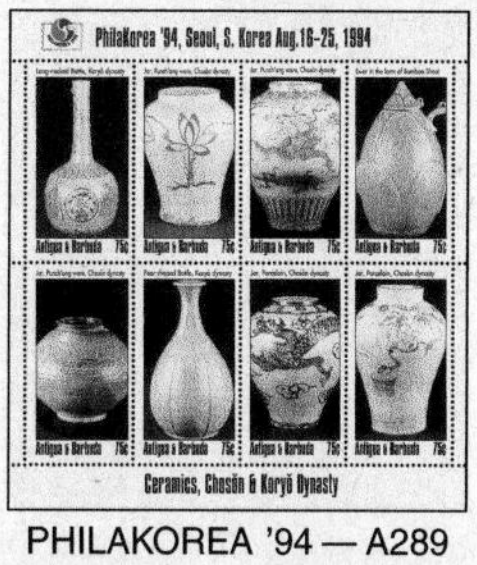

PHILAKOREA '94 — A289

40c, Entrance bridge, Songgwangsa Temple. 90c, Song-op Folk Village, Cheju. $3, Panoramic view, Port Sogwip'o.

Ceramics, Koryo & Choson Dynasties: No. 1827a, Long-necked bottle. b, Jar. c, Jar, diff. d, Ewer in form of bamboo shoot. e, Jar, diff. f, Pear-shaped bottle. g, Porcelain jar with dragon design. h, Porcelain jar with bonsai design.

$4, Ox, ox herder, vert.

1994, Aug. 4 *Perf. 14, 13½ (#1827)*
1824-1826 A288 Set of 3 3.00 3.00
1827 A289 75c Sheet of 8, #a.-h. 6.25 6.25

Souvenir Sheet
1828 A288 $4 multicolored 4.50 4.50

Stars of Country & Western Music — A290

No. 1829, 75c: a, Patsy Cline. b, Tanya Tucker. c, Dolly Parton. d, Anne Murray. e, Tammy Wynette. f, Loretta Lynn. g, Reba McEntire. h, Skeeter Davis.

No. 1830, 75c: a, Travis Tritt. b, Dwight Yoakam. c, Billy Ray Cyrus. d, Alan Jackson. e, Garth Brooks. f, Vince Gill. g, Clint Black. h, Eddie Rabbit.

No. 1831, 75c: a, Hank Snow. b, Gene Autry. c, Jimmie Rogers. d, Ernest Tubb. e, Eddy Arnold. f, Willie Nelson. g, Johnny Cash. h, George Jones.

No. 1832, $6, Kitty Wells, horiz. No. 1833, $6, Hank Williams, Sr. No. 1834, $6, Hank Williams, Jr.

1994, Aug. 18 Litho. *Perf. 14*
Sheets of 8, #a-h
1829-1831 A290 Set of 3 15.50 15.50

Souvenir Sheets
1832-1834 A290 Set of 3 15.50 15.50

1994 World Cup Soccer Championships, US — A291

Designs: 15c, Hugo Sanchez, Mexico. 35c, Juergen Klinsmann, Germany. 65c, Antigua player. $1.20, Cobi Jones, US. $4, Roberto Baggio, Italy. $5, Bwalya Kalusha, Zambia.

No. 1841, $6, FIFA World Cup Trophy, vert. No. 1842, $6, Maldive Islands player, vert.

1994, Sept. 19
1835-1840 A291 Set of 6 13.50 13.50

Souvenir Sheets
1841-1842 A291 Set of 2 8.75 8.75

Order of the Caribbean Community A292

First award recipients: 65c, Sir Shridath Ramphal, statesman, Guyana. 90c, William Demas, economist, Trinidad & Tobago. $1.20, Derek Walcott, writer, St. Lucia.

1994, Sept. 26
1843-1845 A292 Set of 3 3.50 3.50

Herman E. Sieger (1902-54) A293

Germany No. C35, Graf Zeppelin, Sieger.

1994, June 6 Litho. *Perf. 14*
1846 A293 $1.50 multicolored 4.00 4.00

Birds — A294

Designs: 10c, Magnificent frigate birds. 15c, Bridled quail dove. 30c, Magnificent frigate bird hatchling. 40c, Purple-throated carib, vert. No. 1851, $1, Antigua broad-wing hawk, vert. No. 1852, $1, Magnificent frigate bird, vert. $3, Magnificent frigate bird, white head. $4, Yellow warbler.

No. 1855, $6, West Indian Whistling duck. No. 1856, $6, Magnificent frigate bird, diff., vert.

1994, Dec. 12 Litho. *Perf. 14*

1847-1854 A294 Set of 8 11.00 11.00

Souvenir Sheets

1855-1856 A294 Set of 2 9.25 9.25

World Wildlife Fund (Nos. 1847, 1849, 1852-1853).

Christmas — A295

Paintings of Madonnas: 15c, The Virgin and Child by the Fireside, by Robert Campin. 35c, The Reading Madonna, by Giorgione. 40c, Madonna and Child, by Giovanni Bellini. 45c, The Litta Madonna, by da Vinci. 65c, The Virgin and Child Under the Apple Tree, by Lucas Cranach the Elder. 75c, Madonna and Child, by Master of the Female Half-Lengths. $1.20, An Allegory of the Church, by Alessandro Allori. $5, Madonna and Child Wreathed with Flowers, by Jacob Jordaens.

No. 1865, $6, The Virgin Enthroned with Child, by Bohemian Master. No. 1866, $6, Madonna and Child with (painting's) Commissioners, by Palma Vecchio.

1994, Dec. 12 *Perf. 13½x14*

1857-1864 A295 Set of 8 14.00 14.00

Souvenir Sheets

1865-1866 A295 Set of 2 9.50 9.50

Birds — A296

Designs: 15c, Magnificent frigate bird. 25c, Blue-hooded euphonia. 35c, Meadowlark. 40c, Red-billed tropic bird. 45c, Greater flamingo. 60c, Yellow-faced grassquit. 65c, Yellow-billed cuckoo. 70c, Purple-throated carib. 75c, Bananaquit. 90c, Painted bunting. $1.20, Red-legged honeycreeper. $2, Jacana. $5, Greater antillean bullfinch. $10, Caribbean elaenia. $20, Trembler.

1995, Feb. 6 *Perf. 14½x14*

1867	A296	15c multicolored	.25	.25
1868	A296	25c multicolored	.25	.25
1869	A296	35c multicolored	.25	.25
1870	A296	40c multicolored	.30	.30
1871	A296	45c multicolored	.40	.40
1872	A296	60c multicolored	.45	.45
1873	A296	65c multicolored	.60	.60
1874	A296	70c multicolored	.60	.60
1875	A296	75c multicolored	.65	.65
1876	A296	90c multicolored	.80	.80
1877	A296	$1.20 multicolored	1.00	1.00
1878	A296	$2 multicolored	1.75	1.75
1879	A296	$5 multicolored	4.75	4.75
1880	A296	$10 multicolored	9.50	9.50
1881	A296	$20 multicolored	19.00	19.00
		Nos. 1867-1881 (15)	40.55	40.55

See Nos. 2693-2694.

Prehistoric Animals — A297

Designs, vert: 15c, Pachycephalosaurus. 20c, Afrovenator. 65c, Centrosaurus. 90c, Pentaceratops. $1.20, Tarbosaurus. $5, Styracosaur.

No. 1888: a, Kronosaur. b, Ichthyosaur. c, Plesiosaur. d, Archelon. e, Two tyrannosaurs. f, One tyrannosaur. g, One parasaurolophus. h, Two parasaurolophuses. i, Oviraptor. j, Protoceratops with eggs. k, Pteranodon, protoceratops. l, Protoceratops.

No. 1889, $6, Carnotaurus. No. 1890, $6, Corythosaurus.

1995, May 15 Litho. *Perf. 14*

1882-1887 A297 Set of 6 7.50 7.50

1888 A297 75c Sheet of 12, #a.-l. 8.50 8.50

Souvenir Sheets

1889-1890 A297 Set of 2 14.50 14.50

1996 Summer Olympics, Atlanta — A298

Gold medalists: 15c, Al Oerter, US, discus. 20c, Greg Louganis, US, diving. 65c, Naim Suleymanoglu, Turkey, weight lifting. 90c, Louise Ritter, US, high jump. $1.20, Nadia Comaneci, Romania, gymnastics. $5, Olga Bondarenko, USSR, 10,000-meter run.

No. 1897, $6, Lutz Hessilch, Germany, 1000-meter sprint cycling, vert. No. 1898, $6, US team, eight-oared shell, 800-, 1500-meters.

1995, June 6 Litho. *Perf. 14*

1891-1896 A298 Set of 6 7.25 7.25

Souvenir Sheets

1897-1898 A298 Set of 2 13.00 13.00

End of World War II, 50th Anniv. — A299

No. 1899: a, Chiang Kai-Shek. b, Gen. MacArthur. c, Gen. Chennault. d, Brigadier Orde C. Wingate. e, Gen. Stilwell. f, Field Marshall William Slim.

No. 1900: a, Map of Germany showing battle plan. b, Tanks, infantry advance. c, Red Army at gates of Berlin. d, German defenses smashed. e, Airstrikes on Berlin. f. German soldiers give up. g, Berlin falls to Russians. h, Germany surrenders.

$3, Plane, ship, Adm. Chester Nimitz. $6, Gen. Konev at command post outside Berlin, vert.

1995, July 20

1899 A299 $1.20 Sheet of 6, #a.-f. + label 7.00 7.00

1900 A299 $1.20 Sheet of 8, #a.-h. + label 10.50 10.50

Souvenir Sheets

1901 A299 $3 multicolored 4.00 4.00

1902 A299 $6 multicolored 6.00 6.00

UN, 50th Anniv. — A300

No. 1903: a, 75c, Earl of Halifax, signatures. b, 90c, Virginia Gildersleeve. c, $1.20, Harold Stassen.

$6, Franklin D. Roosevelt.

1995, July 20 Litho. *Perf. 14*

1903 A300 Strip of 3, #a.-c. 2.25 *3.00*

Souvenir Sheet

1904 A300 $6 multicolored 4.25 4.25

No. 1903 is a continuous design.

FAO, 50th Anniv. — A301

No. 1905 — Street market scene: a, 75c, Two women, bananas. b, 90c, Women, crates, produce. c, $1.20, Women talking, one with box of food on head.

$6, Tractor.

1995, July 20

1905 A301 Strip of 3, #a.-c. 2.25 *3.00*

Souvenir Sheet

1906 A301 $6 multicolored 4.25 4.25

No. 1905 is a continuous design.

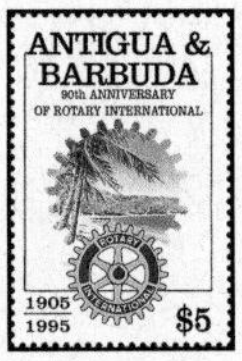

Rotary Intl., 90th Anniv. — A302

1995, July 20

1907 A302 $5 shown 4.50 4.50

Souvenir Sheet

1908 A302 $6 Natl. flag, Rotary emblem 4.50 4.50

Queen Mother, 95th Birthday — A303

No. 1909: a, Drawing. b, White & dark pink hat. c, Formal portrait. d, Blue green hat, dress.

$6, Light blue dress, pearls.

1995, July 20 *Perf. 13½x14*

1909 A303 $1.50 Strip or block of 4, #a.-d. 5.75 5.75

Souvenir Sheet

1910 A303 $6 multicolored 5.75 5.75

No. 1909 was issued in sheets of 2 each.

Sheets of 1909-1910 exist with black frame overprinted in margin, with text "In Memoriam/1900-2002."

Ducks — A304

No. 1911: a, Ring-necked duck. b, Ruddy duck. c, Green-winged teal (d). d, Wood duck. e, Hooded merganser (f). f, Lesser scaup (g). g, West Indian tree duck (h, k, l). h, Fulvous whistling duck (l). i, Bahama pintail. j, Shoveler (i). k, Masked duck (l). l, American widgeon.

$6, Blue-winged teal.

1995, Aug. 31 Litho. *Perf. 14*

1911 A304 75c Sheet of 12, #a.-l. 12.00 12.00

Souvenir Sheet

1912 A304 $6 multicolored 7.50 7.50

Bees — A305

Designs: 90c, Mining bee. $1.20, Solitary bee. $1.65, Leaf-cutter. $1.75, Honey bee.

$6, Solitary mining bee.

1995, Sept. 7

1913-1916 A305 Set of 4 7.50 7.50

Souvenir Sheet

1917 A305 $6 multicolored 6.50 6.50

Domestic Cats — A306

Designs: a, Somali. b, Persian. c, Devon rex. d, Turkish angora. e, Himalayan. f, Maine coon. g, Nonpedigree. h, American wirehair. i, British shorthair. j, American curl. k, Black nonpedigree. l, Birman.

$6, Siberian, vert.

1995, Sept. 7

1918 A306 45c Sheet of 12, #a.-l. 9.00 9.00

Souvenir Sheet

1919 A306 $6 multicolored 7.00 7.00

Tourism — A307

Stylized paintings depicting: a, Caring. b, Marketing. c, Working. d, Enjoying life.

1995, July 31 Litho. *Perf. 14*

1920 A307 $2 Sheet of 4, #a.-d. 6.75 6.75

Greenbay Moravian Church, 150th Anniv. — A308

Designs: 20c, 1st structure, wood & stone. 60c, 1st stone, concrete building, 3/67. 75c, $2, Present structure. 90c, John A. Buckley, 1st minister of African descent. $1.20, John Ephraim Knight, longest serving minister. $6, Front of present structure.

1995, Sept. 4

1921-1926 A308 Set of 6 9.00 9.00

Souvenir Sheet

1927 A308 $6 multicolored 5.50 5.50

Flowers — A309

No. 1928: a, Narcissus. b, Camellia. c, Iris. d, Tulip. e, Poppy. f, Peony. g, Magnolia. h, Oriental lily. i, Rose. j, Pansy. k, Hydrangea. l, Azaleas.

$6, Bird of paradise, calla lily.

1995, Sept. 7

1928 A309 75c Sheet of 12, #a.-l. 9.25 9.25

Souvenir Sheet

1929 A309 $6 multicolored 5.50 5.50

1995 Boy Scout Jamboree, Netherlands A310

No. 1930, $1.20: a, Explorer tent. b, Camper tent. c, Wall tent.

No. 1931, $1.20: a, Trail tarp. b, Miner's. c, Voyager.

No. 1932, $6, Scout with camping equipment, vert. No. 1933, $6, Scout making camp fire.

1995, Oct. 5 Strips of 3, #a-c

1930-1931 A310 Set of 2 9.00 9.00

Souvenir Sheets

1932-1933 A310 Set of 2 10.00 10.00

For overprints see Nos. 1963-1966.

Trains — A311

Designs: 35c, Gabon. 65c, Canadian. 75c, US. 90c, British high-speed. No. 1938, $1.20, French high-speed. No. 1939, $6, American high-speed (Amtrak).

No. 1940: a, Australian diesel. b, Italian high-speed. c, Thai diesel. d, US steam. e, South African steam. f, Natal steam. g, US war train. h, British steam. i, British steam, diff.

No. 1941, $6, Australian diesel, vert. No. 1942, $6, Asian steam, vert.

1995, Oct. 23 Litho. *Perf. 14*

1934-1939 A311 Set of 6 10.50 10.50
1940 A311 $1.20 Sheet of 9, #a.-i. 12.50 12.50

Souvenir Sheets

1941-1942 A311 Set of 2 14.00 14.00

Birds — A312

No. 1943: a, Purple-thoated carib. b, Antillean crested hummingbird. c, Bananaquit (d). d, Mangrove cuckoo. e, Troupial. f, Green-throated carib (e, g). g, Yellow warbler (h). h, Blue-hooded Euphonia. i, Scally-breasted thrasher. j, Burrowing owl (i). k, Caribbean crackle (k). l, Adelaide's warbler.

$6, Purple gallinule.

1995, Aug. 31

1943 A312 75c Sheet of 12, #a.-l. 11.50 11.50

Souvenir Sheet

1944 A312 $6 multicolored 7.50 7.50

Miniature Sheets of 9

Establishment of Nobel Prize Fund, Cent. — A313

No. 1945, $1: a, S.Y. Agnon, literature, 1966. b, Kipling, literature, 1907. c, Aleksandr Solzhenitsyn, literature, 1970. d, Jack Steinberger, physics, 1988. e, Andrei Sakharov, peace, 1975. f, Otto Stern, physics, 1943. g, Steinbeck, literature, 1962. h, Nadine Gordimer, literature, 1991. i, Faulkner, literature, 1949.

No. 1946, $1: a, Hammarskjold, peace, 1961. b, Georg Wittig, chemistry, 1979. c, Wilhelm Ostwald, chemistry, 1909. d, Koch, physiology or medicine, 1945. e, Karl Ziegler, chemistry, 1963. f, Fleming, physiology or medicine, 1945. g, Hermann Staudinger, chemistry, 1953. h, Manfred Eigen, chemistry, 1967. i, Arno Penzias, physics, 1978.

No. 1947, $6, Elie Wiesel, peace, 1986, vert. No. 1948, $6, Dalai Lama, peace, 1989, vert.

Sheets of 9, #a-i, + label

1995, Nov. 8

1945-1946 A313 Set of 2 20.00 20.00

Souvenir Sheets

1947-1948 A313 Set of 2 10.00 10.00

Christmas — A314

Details or entire paintings: 15c, Rest on the Flight into Egypt, by Veronese. 35c, Madonna with The Child, by Van Dyck. 65c, Sacred Conversation Piece, by Veronese. 75c, Vision of Saint Anthony, by Van Dyck. 90c, The Virgin and the Infant, by Van Eyck. No. 1954, The Immaculate Conception, by Tiepolo.

$5, Christ Appearing to His Mother, by Van Der Weyden. $6, Infant Jesus and the Young St. John, by Murillo.

1995, Dec. 18 Litho. *Perf. 13½x14*

1949-1954 A314 Set of 6 7.00 7.00

Souvenir Sheets

1955 A314 $5 multicolored 4.00 4.00
1956 A314 $6 multicolored 5.50 5.50

Elvis Presley (1935-77) — A315

Nos. 1957-1958, Various portraits depicting Presley's life.

1995, Dec. 8 *Perf. 14*

1957 A315 $1 Sheet of 9, #a.-i. 11.00 11.00

Souvenir Sheet

1958 A315 $6 multicolored 7.25 7.25

John Lennon (1940-80), Entertainer — A316

45c, 50c, 65c, 75c, Various portraits of Lennon.

1995, Dec. 8

1959-1962 A316 Set of 4 3.00 3.00

Souvenir Sheet

1962A A316 $6 like 75c 6.75 6.75

Nos. 1959-1962 were each issued in miniature sheets of 16.

No. 1962A has a continuous design.

Nos. 1930-1933 Ovptd.

1995, Dec. 14

1963 A310 $1.20 Strip of 3, #a-c (#1930) 3.50 3.50
1964 A310 $1.20 Strip of 3, #a-c (#1931) 3.50 3.50

Souvenir Sheets

1965 A310 $6 multi (#1932) 6.50 6.50
1966 A310 $6 multi (#1933) 6.50 6.50

Size and location of overprint varies.

Mushrooms — A317

No. 1967, 75c: a, Hygrophoropsis aurantiaca. b, Hygrophorus bakerensis. c, Hygrophorus conicus. d, Hygrophorus miniatus.

No. 1968, 75c: a, Suillus brevipes. b, Suillus luteus. c, Suillus granulatus. d, Suillus caerulescens.

No. 1969, $6, Conocybe filaris. No. 1970, $6, Hygrocybe flavescens.

1996, Apr. 22 Litho. *Perf. 14*

Strips of 4, #a-d

1967-1968 A317 Set of 2 6.25 6.25

Souvenir Sheets

1969-1970 A317 Set of 2 9.00 9.00

Nos. 1967-1968 were each issued in sheets of 12 stamps.

Sailing Ships — A318

Designs: 15c, Resolution. 25c, Mayflower. 45c, Santa Maria. No. 1970D, 75c, Aemilia, Holland, 1630. No. 1970E, 75c, Sovereign of the Seas, England, 1637. 90c, HMS Victory, England, 1765.

No. 1971 — Battleships: a, Aemila, Holland, 1630. b, Sovereign of the Seas, England, 1637. c, Royal Louis, France, 1692. d, HMS Royal George, England, 1715. e, Le Protecteur, France, 1761. f, HMS Victory, England, 1765.

No. 1972 — Ships of exploration: a, Santa Maria. b, Victoria. c, Golden Hinde. d, Mayflower. e, Griffin. f, Resolution.

No. 1973, $6, Grande Hermine. No. 1974, $6 USS Constitution, 1797.

1996, Apr. 25

1970A-1970F A318 Set of 6 3.50 3.50
1971 A318 $1.20 Sheet of 6, #a.-f. 8.50 8.50
1972 A318 $1.50 Sheet of 6, #a.-f. 10.00 10.00

Souvenir Sheets

1973-1974 A318 Set of 2 11.50 11.50

1996 Summer Olympics, Atlanta — A319

Designs: 65c, Florence Griffith Joyner, women's track, vert. 75c, Olympic Stadium, Seoul, 1988. 90c, Allison Jolly, yachting. $1.20, 2000m Tandem cyclying,

No. 1979, 90c — Medalists: a, Wolfgang Nordwig, pole vault. b, Shirley Strong, women's 100m hurdles. c, Sergei Bubka, pole vault. d, Filbert Bayi, 3000m steeplechase. e, Victor Saneyev, triple jump. f, Silke Renk, women's javelin. g, Daley Thompson, decathlon. h, Bob Richards, pole vault. i, Parry O'Brien, shot put.

No. 1980, 90c — Diving medalists: a, Ingrid Kramer, women's platform. b, Kelly McCormick, women's springboard. c, Gary Tobian, men's springboard. d, Greg Louganis, men's diving. e, Michelle Mitchell, women's platform. f, Zhou Jihong, women's platform. g, Wendy Wyland, women's platform. h, Xu Yanmei, women's platform. i, Fu Mingxia, women's platform.

$5, Bill Toomey, decathlon. $6, Mark Lenzi, men's springboard.

1996, May 6

1975-1978 A319 Set of 4 2.50 2.50

Sheets of 9, #a-i

1979-1980 A319 90c Set of 2 12.50 12.50

Souvenir Sheets

1981 A319 $5 multicolored 4.50 4.50
1982 A319 $6 multicolored 5.50 5.50

Sea Birds — A320

No. 1983, 75c: a, Black skimmer. b, Black-capped petrel. c, Sooty tern. d, Royal tern.

No. 1984, 75c: a, Pomarina jaegger. b, White-tailed tropicbird. c, Northern gannet. d, Laughing gull.

$5, Great frigatebird. $6, Brown pelican.

1996, May 13

Vertical Strips of 4, #a-d

1983-1984 A320 Set of 2 5.50 5.50

Souvenir Sheets

1985 A320 $5 multicolored 4.50 4.50
1986 A320 $6 multicolored 5.50 5.50

Nos. 1983-1984 were each issued in sheets of 12 stamps with each strip in sheet having a different order.

Disney Characters In Scenes from Jules Verne's Science Fiction Novels A321

Designs: 1c, Around the World in Eighty Days. 2c, Journey to the Center of the Earth. 5c, Michel Strogoff. 10c, From the Earth to the Moon. 15c, Five Weeks in a Balloon. 20c, Around the World in Eighty Days, diff. $1, The Mysterious Island. $2, From the Earth to the Moon, diff. $3, Captain Grant's Children. $5, Twenty Thousand Leagues Under the Sea.

No. 1997, $6, Twenty Thousand Leagues Under the Sea, diff. No. 1998, $6, Journey to the Center of the Earth, diff.

1996, June 6 Litho. *Perf. 14x13½*

1987-1996 A321 Set of 10 12.50 12.50

Souvenir Sheets

1997-1998 A321 Set of 2 12.50 12.50

Bruce Lee (1940-73), Martial Arts Expert — A322

Various portraits.

1996, June 13 *Perf. 14*

1999 A322 75c Sheet of 9, #a.-i. 6.50 6.50

Souvenir Sheet

2000 A322 $5 multicolored 5.75 5.75

China '96 (No. 1999).

Queen Elizabeth II, 70th Birthday A323

Designs: a, In blue dress, pearls. b, Carrying bouquet of flowers. c, In uniform.

$6, Painting as younger woman.

1996, July 17 *Perf. 13½x14*
2001 A323 $2 Strip of 3, #a.-c. 4.00 4.00

Souvenir Sheet

2002 A323 $6 multicolored 4.75 4.75

No. 2001 was issued in sheets of 9 stamps.

Traditional Cavalry — A324

No. 2003: a, Ancient Egyptian. b, 13th cent. English. c, 16th cent. Spanish. d, 18th cent. Chinese.
$6, 19th cent. French.

1996, July 24 **Litho.** *Perf. 14*
2003 A324 60c Block of 4, #a.-d. 2.50 2.50

Souvenir Sheet

2004 A324 $6 multicolored 4.75 4.75

No. 2003 was issued in sheets of 16 stamps.

UNICEF, 50th Anniv. — A325

Designs: 75c, Girl. 90c, Children. $1.20, Woman holding baby. $6, Girl, diff.

1996, July 30
2005-2007 A325 Set of 3 3.00 3.00

Souvenir Sheet

2008 A325 $6 multicolored 4.50 4.50

Jerusalem, 3000th Anniv. — A326

Site, flower: 75c, Tomb of Zachariah, verbascum sinuatum. 90c, Pool of Siloam, hyacinthus orientalis. $1.20, Hurva Synagogue, ranunculus asiaticus.
$6, Model of Herod's Temple.

1996, July 30
2009-2011 A326 Set of 3 2.25 2.25

Souvenir Sheet

2012 A326 $6 multicolored 6.50 6.50

Radio, Cent. — A327

Entertainers: 65c, Kate Smith. 75c, Dinah Shore. 90c, Rudy Vallee. $1.20, Bing Crosby.
$6, Jo Stafford.

1996, July 30
2013-2016 A327 Set of 4 3.50 3.50

Souvenir Sheet

2017 A327 $6 multicolored 4.50 4.50

Christmas — A328

Details or entire paintings, by Filippo Lippi: 60c, Madonna Enthroned. 90c, Adoration of the Child and Saints. $1, Annunciation. $1.20, Birth of the Virgin. $1.60, Adoration of the Child. $1.75, Madonna and Child.
No. 2024, $6, Madonna and Child, diff. No. 2025, $6, Circumcision.

1996, Nov. 25 *Perf. 13½x14*
2018-2023 A328 Set of 6 7.50 7.50

Souvenir Sheets

2024-2025 A328 Set of 2 10.50 10.50

Disney Pals — A329

Designs: 1c, Goofy, Wilbur. 2c, Donald, Goofy. 5c, Donald, Panchito, Jose Carioca. 10c, Mickey, Goofy. 15c, Dale, Chip. 20c, Pluto, Mickey. $1, Daisy, Minnie at ice cream shop. $2, Daisy, Minnie. $3, Gus Goose, Donald.
No. 2035, $6, Donald, vert. No. 2036, $6, Goofy.

1997, Feb. 17 **Litho.** *Perf. 14x13½*
2026-2034 A329 Set of 9 5.50 5.50

Souvenir Sheets

Perf. 13½x14, 14x13½

2035-2036 A329 Set of 2 9.50 9.50

Salute to Broadway — A330

No. 2037 — Stars, show: a, Robert Preston, The Music Man. b, Michael Crawford, Phantom of the Opera. c, Zero Mostel, Fiddler on the Roof. d, Patti Lupone, Evita. e, Raul Julia, Threepenny Opera. f, Mary Martin, South Pacific. g, Carol Channing, Hello Dolly. h, Yul Brynner, The King and I. i, Julie Andrews, My Fair Lady.
$6, Mickey Rooney, Sugar Babies.

1997 *Perf. 14*
2037 A330 $1 Sheet of 9, #a.-i. 8.00 8.00

Souvenir Sheet

2038 A330 $6 multicolored 5.50 5.50

Butterflies — A331

Designs: 90c, Charaxes porthos. $1.20, Aethiopana honorius. $1.60, Charaxes hadrianus. $1.75, Precis westermanni.
No. 2043, $1.10: a, Charaxes protoclea. b, Byblia ilithyia. c, Black-headed tchagra (bird). d, Charaxes nobilis. e, Pseudacraea boisduvali. f, Charaxes smaragdalis. g, Charaxes lasti. h, Pseudacraea poggei. i, Graphium colonna.
No. 2044, $1.10: a, Carmine bee-eater (bird). b, Pseudacraea eurytus. c, Hypolimnas monteironis. d, Charaxes anticlea. e, Graphium leonidas. f, Graphium illyris. g, Nepheronia argia. h, Graphium policenes. i, Papilio dardanus.
No. 2045, $6, Euxanthe tiberius, horiz. No. 2046, $6, Charaxes lactitinctus, horiz. No. 2047, $6, Euphaedra neophron.

1997, Mar. 10
2039-2042 A331 Set of 4 5.50 5.50

Sheets of 9, #a-i

2043-2044 A331 Set of 2 18.50 18.50

Souvenir Sheets

2045-2047 A331 Set of 3 14.50 14.50

UNESCO, 50th Anniv. A332

World Heritage Sites: 60c, Convent of the Companions of Jesus, Morelia, Mexico. 90c, Fortress, San Lorenzo, Panama, vert. $1, Canaima Natl. Park, Venezuela, vert. $1.20, Huascarán Natl. Park, Peru, vert. $1.60, Church of San Francisco, Guatemala, vert. $1.75, Santo Domingo, Dominican Republic, vert.
No. 2054, vert, each $1.10: a-c, Guanajuato, Mexico. d, Jesuit missions of the Chiquitos, Bolivia. e, Huascarán Natl. Park, Peru. f, Jesuit missions, La Santisima, Paraguay. g, Cartagena, Colombia. h, Old Havana fortification, Cuba.
No. 2055, each $1.65: a, Tikal Natl. Park, Guatemala. b, Rio Platano Reserve, Honduras. c, Ruins of Copán, Honduras. d, Church of El Carmen, Antigua, Guatemala. e, Teotihuacán, Mexico.
No. 2056, $6, Teotihuacán, Mexico, diff. No. 2057, $6, Tikal Natl. Park, Guatemala, diff.

1997, Apr. 10 **Litho.** *Perf. 14*
2048-2053 A332 Set of 6 4.75 4.75
2054 A332 Sheet of 8, #a.-h. + label 8.00 8.00
2055 A332 Sheet of 5, #a.-e. + label 7.50 7.50

Souvenir Sheets

2056-2057 A332 Set of 2 9.75 9.75

Endangered Species — A333

No. 2058, each $1.20: a, Red bishop. b, Yellow baboon. c, Superb starling. d, Ratel. e, Hunting dog. f, Serval.
No. 2059, each $1.65: a, Okapi. b, Giant forest squirrel. c, Masked weaver. d, Common genet. e, Yellow-billed stork. f, Red-headed agama.
No. 2060, $6, Malachite kingfisher. No. 2061, $6, Gray crowned crane. No. 2062, $6, Bat-eared fox.

1997, Apr. 24
2058 A333 Sheet of 6, #a.-f. 7.50 7.50
2059 A333 Sheet of 6, #a.-f. 9.00 9.00

Souvenir Sheets

2060-2062 A333 Set of 3 17.00 17.00

Charlie Chaplin (1889-1977), Comedian, Actor — A334

Various portraits.

1997, Feb. 24 **Litho.** *Perf. 14*
2063 A334 $1 Sheet of 9, #a.-i. 6.75 6.75

Souvenir Sheet

2064 A334 $6 multicolored 5.25 5.25

Paul P. Harris (1868-1947), Founder of Rotary, Intl. — A335

Designs: $1.75, Service above self, James Grant, Ivory Coast, 1994, portrait of Harris.
$6, Group study exchange, New Zealand.

1997, June 12 **Litho.** *Perf. 14*
2065 A335 $1.75 multicolored 1.60 1.60

Souvenir Sheet

2066 A335 $6 multicolored 4.50 4.50

Heinrich von Stephan (1831-97) A336

No. 2067, each $1.75, Portrait of Von Stephan and: a, Kaiser Wilhelm I. b, UPU emblem. c, Pigeon Post.
$6, Von Stephan, Basel messenger, 1400's.

1997, June 12
2067 A336 Sheet of 3, #a.-c. 3.50 3.50

Souvenir Sheet

2068 A336 $6 multicolored 5.00 5.00

PACIFIC 97.

Queen Elizabeth II, Prince Philip, 50th Wedding Anniv. — A337

No. 2069: a, Queen. b, Royal arms. c, Queen, Prince in royal attire. d, Queen, King riding in open carriage. e, Balmoral Castle. f. Prince Philip.
$6, Early portrait of Queen, King in royal attire.

1997, June 12
2069 A337 $1 Sheet of 6, #a.-f. 6.25 6.25

Souvenir Sheet

2070 A337 $6 multicolored 5.25 5.25

Grimm's Fairy Tales — A338

Scenes from "Cinderella", each $1.75: No. 2071: a, Mother, stepsisters. b, Cinderella, fairy godmother. c, Cinderella, Prince Charming.
$6, Prince trying shoe on Cinderella.

1997, June 13 *Perf. 13½x14*
2071 A338 Sheet of 3, #a.-c. 4.75 4.75

Souvenir Sheet

2072 A338 $6 multicolored 5.25 5.25

Chernobyl Disaster, 10th Anniv. — A339

Designs: $1.65, UNESCO. $2, Chabad's Children of Chernobyl.

1997, June 12
2073 A339 $1.65 multicolored 1.50 1.50
2074 A339 $2 multicolored 1.75 1.75

Mushrooms A340

Designs: 45c, Marasmius rotula. 65c, Cantharellus cibarius. 70c, Lepiota cristata. 90c, Auricularia mesenterica. $1, Pholiota alnicola. $1.65, Leccinum aurantiacum.
No. 2081, each $1.75: a, Entoloma serrulatum. b, Panaeolus sphinctrinus. c, Volvariella bombycina. d, Conocybe percincta. e, Pluteus cervinus. f, Russula foetens.
No. 2082, $6, Panellus serotinus. No. 2083, $6, Amanita cothurnata.

1997, Aug. 12 Litho. *Perf. 14*
2075-2080 A340 Set of 6 4.00 4.00
2081 A340 Sheet of 6, #a.-f. 8.00 8.00

Souvenir Sheets

2082-2083 A340 Set of 2 10.00 10.00

Orchids — A341

Designs: 45c, Odontoglossum cervantesii. 65c, Medford star. 75c, Motes resplendent. 90c, Debutante. $1, Apple blossom. $2, Dendrobium.

No. 2090, $1.65: a, Angel lace. b, Precious stones. c, Orange theope butterfly. d, Promenaea xanthina. e, Lycaste macrobulbon. f, Amesiella philippinensis. g, Machu Picchu. h, Zuma urchin.

No. 2091, $1.65: a, Sophia Martin. b, Dog-face butterfly. c, Mini purple. d, Showgirl. e, Mem. Dorothy Bertsch. f, Black II. g, Lee-anum. h, Paphiopedilum macranthum.

No. 2092, $6, Seine. No. 2093, $6, Paphiopedilum gratrixianum.

1997, Aug. 19 Litho. *Perf. 14*
2084-2089 A341 Set of 6 5.75 5.75

Sheets of 8, #a-h

2090-2091 A341 Set of 2 17.00 17.00

Souvenir Sheets

2092-2093 A341 Set of 2 10.00 10.00

1998 World Cup Soccer Championships, France — A342

Designs: 60c, Maradona, Argentina, 1986. 75c, Fritz Walter, W. Germany, 1954. 90c, Zoff, Italy, 1982. $1.20, Moore, England, 1966. $1.65, Alberto, Brazil, 1970. $1.75, Matthäus, W. Germany.

No. 2100, vert: a, Ademir, Brazil, 1950. b, Eusebio, Portugal, 1966. c, Fontaine, France, 1958. d, Schillaci, Italy, 1990. e, Leonidas, Brazil, 1938. f, Stabile, Argentina, 1930. g, Nejedly, Czechoslovakia, 1934. h, Muller, W. Germany, 1970.

No. 2101, $6, Players, W. Germany, 1990. No. 2102, $6, Bebeto, Brazil, vert.

1997, Oct. 6 Litho. *Perf. 14*
2094-2099 A342 Set of 6 5.25 5.25
2100 A342 $1 Sheet of 8, #a.-h., + label 5.25 5.25

Souvenir Sheets

2101-2102 A342 Set of 2 8.50 8.50

Domestic Animals — A343

No. 2103, $1.65 — Dogs: a, Dachshund. b, Staffordshire terrier. c, Sharpei. d, Beagle. e, Norfolk terrier. f, Golden retriever.

No. 2104, $1.65 — Cats: a, Scottish fold. b, Japanese bobtail. c, Tabby manx. d, Bicolor American shorthair. e, Sorrel abyssinian. f, Himalayan blue point.

No. 2105, $6, Siberian husky, vert. No. 2106, $6, Red tabby American shorthair kitten, vert.

1997, Oct. 27 Litho. *Perf. 14*

Sheets of 6, #a-f

2103-2104 A343 Set of 2 18.00 18.00

Souvenir Sheets

2105-2106 A343 Set of 2 10.00 10.00

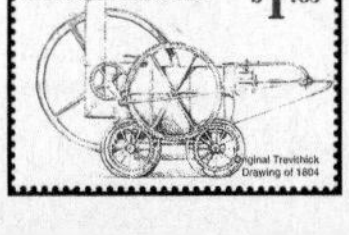

Early Trains — A344

No. 2107, $1.65: a, Original Trevithick drawing, 1804. b, "Puffing Billy," William Hedley, 1860. c, Crampton locomotive, Northern Railway, France, 1858. d, Twenty-five ton locomotive, Lawrence Machine Shop, 1860's. e, First locomotive, "Mississippi," built in England. f, "Coppernob," locomotive by Edward Bury, Furness Railway.

No. 2108, $1.65: a, "Jenny Lind," by David Joy for E.B. Wilson. b, "Atlantic" type locomotive, by Schenectady Locomotive Works, 1899. c, British built tank engine, Japan, by Kisons of Leeds, 1881. d, Express freight locomotive, 4-8-2 type, Pennsylvania Railroad. e, Four-cylinder locomotive, by Karl Golsdorf, Austria. f, "E" series 0-10-0 locomotive, produced by Lugansk Works, Russia, 1930.

No. 2109, $6, "Patente" George Stephenson, 1843. No. 2110, $6, Brunel's Trestle, Lynher River.

1997, Nov. 10 Sheets of 6, #a-f
2107-2108 A344 Set of 2 19.00 19.00

Souvenir Sheets

2109-2110 A344 Set of 2 10.00 10.00

Christmas — A345

Entire paintings or details: 15c, The Angel Leaving Tobias and His Family, by Rembrandt. 25c, The Resurrection, by Martin Knoller. 60c, Astronomy, by Raphael. 75c, Music-making Angel, by Melozzo da Forli. 90c, Amor, by Parmigianino. $1.20, Madonna and Child with Saints John the Baptist, Anthony, Stephen and Jerome, by Rosso Fiorentino.

No. 2117, $6, The Portinari Altarpiece, by Hugo Van Der Goes. No. 2118, $6, The Wedding of Tobiolo, by Gianantonio and Francesco Guardi.

1997, Dec. 2 Litho. *Perf. 14*
2111-2116 A345 $6 Set of 6 3.75 3.75

Souvenir Sheets

2117-2118 A345 $6 Set of 2 9.00 9.00

Diana, Princess of Wales (1961-97) — A346

Various portraits, color of sheet margin: No. 2119, $1.65, Pale green. No. 2120, $1.65, Pale pink.

No. 2121, $6,With her sons (in margin). No. 2122, $6, With Pope John Paul II (in margin).

1998, Jan. 19 Litho. *Perf. 14*

Sheets of 6, #a-f

2119-2120 A346 Set of 2 12.50 12.50

Souvenir Sheets

2121-2122 A346 Set of 2 9.00 9.00

Fish — A347

Designs: 75c, Yellow damselfish. 90c, Barred hamlet. $1, Jewelfish. $1.20, Bluehead wrasse. $1.50, Queen angelfish. $1.75, Queen triggerfish.

No. 2129, $1.65: a, Jack-knife fish. b, Cuban hogfish. c, Sergeant major. d, Neon goby. e, Jawfish. f, Flamefish.

No. 2130, $1.65: a, Rock beauty. b, Yellow-tail snapper. c, Creole wrasse. d, Slender file-fish. e, Squirrel fish. f, Fairy basslet.

No. 2131, $6, Black-capped gramma. No. 2132, $6, Porkfish.

1998, Feb. 19
2123-2128 A347 Set of 6 4.25 4.25

Sheets of 6, #a-f

2129-2130 A347 Set of 2 13.00 13.00

Souvenir Sheets

2131-2132 A347 Set of 2 10.00 10.00

Cedar Hall Moravian Church, 175th Anniv. — A348

Designs: 20c, First church, manse, 1822-40. 45c, Cedar Hall School, 1840. 75c, Hugh A. King, former minister. 90c, Present structure. $1.20, Water tank, 1822. $2, Former manse demolished, 1978.

$6, Present structure, diff.

1998, Mar. 16 Litho. *Perf. 14*
2133-2138 A348 Set of 6 4.00 4.00

Souvenir Sheet

2139 A348 $6 multicolored 4.75 4.75

No. 2139 contains one 50x37mm stamp.

Lighthouses A349

Lighthouse, location: 45c, Trinity, Europa Point, Gibraltar, vert. 65c, Tierra Del Fuego, Argentina. 75c, Point Loma, California, US. 90c, Groenpoint, South Africa, vert. $1, Youghal, County Cork, Ireland, vert. $1.20, Launceston, Tasmania, Australia, vert. $1.65, Point Abino, Ontario, Canada. $1.75, Great Inagua, Bahamas.

$6, Capa Hatteras, North Carolina, US.

1998, Apr. 20
2140-2147 A349 Set of 8 8.00 8.00

Souvenir Sheet

2148 A349 $6 multi, vert. 7.75 7.75

Winnie the Pooh — A350

No. 2149, $1: a, Pooh, Tigger in January. b, Pooh, Piglet in February. c, Piglet in March. d, Tigger, Pooh, Piglet in April. e, Kanga, Roo in May. f, Pooh, Owl in June.

No. 2150, $1,: a, Pooh, Eeyore, Tigger, Piglet in July. b, Pooh, Piglet in August. c, Christopher Robin in September. d, Eeyore in October. e, Pooh, Rabbit in November. f, Pooh, Piglet in December.

No. 2151, $6, Pooh, Rabbit holding blanket, Spring. No. 2152, $6, Pooh holding hand to mouth, Summer. No. 2153, $6, Pooh holding rake, Fall. No. 2154, $6, Eeyore, Pooh, Winter.

1998, May 11 Litho. *Perf. 13½x14*

Sheets of 6, #a-f

2149-2150 A350 Set of 2 13.50 13.50

Souvenir Sheet

2151-2154 A350 Set of 4 19.00 19.00

Thomas Oliver Robinson Memorial High School, Cent. — A351

Designs: 20c, $6, Nellie Robinson (1880-1972), founder, vert. 45c, School picture, 1985. 65c, Former building, 1930-49. 75c, Students with present headmistress, Natalie Hurst. 90c, Ina Loving (1908-96), educator, vert. $1.20, Present building, 1950.

1998, July 23 Litho. *Perf. 14*
2155-2160 A351 Set of 6 4.00 4.00

Souvenir Sheet

2161 A351 $6 multicolored 4.00 4.00

No. 2161 is a continuous design.

Intl. Year of the Ocean — A352

No. 2162 — Marine life, "20,000 Leagues Under the Sea": a, Spotted eagle ray. b, Manta ray. c, Hawksbill turtle. d, Jellyfish. e, Queen angelfish. f, Octopus. g, Emperor angelfish. h, Regal angelfish. i, Porkfish. j, Raccoon butterfly fish. k, Atlantic barracuda. l, Sea horse. m, Nautilus. n, Trumpet fish. o, White tip shark. p, Spanish galleon. q, Black tip shark. r, Long-nosed butterfly fish. s, Green moray eel. t, Captain Nemo. u, Treasure chest. v, Hammer-head shark. w, Divers. x, Lion fish. y, Clown fish.

No. 2163 — Wildlife and birds: a, Maroon tailed conure. b, Cocoi heron. c, Common tern. d, Rainbow lorikeet. e, Saddleback butterfly fish. f, Goatfish, cat shark. g, Blue shark, stingray. h, Majestic snapper. i, Nassau grouper. j, Black-cap gramma, blue tang. k, Stingrays. l, Stingrays, giant starfish.

No. 2164, $6, Fiddler ray. No. 2165, $6, Humpback whale.

1998, Aug. 17
2162 A352 40c Sheet of 25, #a.-y. 8.25 8.25
2163 A352 75c Sheet of 12, #a.-l. 7.75 7.75

Souvenir Sheets

2164-2165 A352 Set of 2 9.75 9.75

Ships — A353

No. 2166, each $1.75: a, Savannah. b, Viking ship. c, Greek warship.

No. 2167, each $1.75: a, Clipper. b, Dhow. c, Fishing cat.

No. 2168, $6, Dory, vert. No. 2169, $6, Baltimore clipper. No. 2170, $6, English warship, 13th cent.

1998, Aug. 18 *Perf. 14x14½*

Sheets of 3, #a-c

2166-2167 A353 Set of 2 7.25 7.25

Souvenir Sheets

Perf. 14

2168-2170 A353 $6 Set of 3 15.00 15.00

CARICOM, 25th Anniv. — A354

1998, Aug. 20 Litho. *Perf. 13½*
2171 A354 $1 multicolored 1.40 1.40

Antique Automobiles A355

No. 2172 $1.65: a, 1911 Torpedo. b, 1913 Mercedes 22. c, 1920 Rover. d, 1956 Mercedes Benz. e, 1934 Packard V12. f, 1924 Opel.

No. 2173, $1.65 — Fords: a, 1896. b, 1903 Model A. c, 1928 Model T. d, 1922 Model T. e, 1929 Blackhawk. f, 1934 Sedan.

No. 2174, $6, 1908 Ford. No. 2175, $6, 1929 Ford.

1998, Sept. 1 *Perf. 14*

Sheets of 6, #a-f

2172-2173 A355 Set of 2 15.00 15.00

Souvenir Sheets

2174-2175 A355 Set of 2 9.00 9.00

Nos. 2174-2175 each contain one 60x40mm stamp.

Aircraft — A356

No. 2176, $1.65: a, NASA Space Shuttle. b, Saab Grippen. c, Eurofighter EF2000. d,

Sukhoi SU 27. e, Northrop B-2. f, Lockheed F-117 Nighthawk.

No. 2177, $1.65: a, Lockheed-Boeing General Dynamics Yf-22. b, Dassault-Breguet Rafale BO 1. c, MiG 29. d, Dassault-Breguet Mirage 2000D. e, Rockwell B-1B Lancer. f, McDonnell-Douglas C-17A.

No. 2178, $6, Sukhoi SU 35. No. 2179, $6, F-18 Hornet.

1998, Sept. 21 **Sheets of 6, #a-f**

2176-2177 A356 Set of 2 14.50 14.50

Souvenir Sheets

2178-2179 A356 Set of 2 10.50 10.50

Inventors and Inventions — A357

No. 2180 $1: a, Rudolf Diesel (1858-1913). b, Internal combustion, diesel engines. c, Zeppelin war balloon, Intrepid. d, Ferdinand von Zeppelin (1838-1917). e, Wilhelm Conrad Röntgen (1845-1923). f, X-ray machine. g, Saturn rocket. h, Wernher von Braun (1912-77).

No. 2181, $1: a, Carl Benz (1844-1929). b, Internal combustion engine, automobile. c, Atomic bomb. d, Albert Einstein. e, Leopold Godowsky, Jr. (1901-83) and Leopold Damrosch Mannes (1899-1964). f, Kodachrome film. g, First turbo jet airplane. h, Hans Pabst von Ohain (1911-98).

No. 2182, $6, Hans Geiger (1882-1945), inventor of the Geiger counter. No. 2183, $6, William Shockley (1910-89), developer of transistors.

1998, Nov. 10 **Litho.** ***Perf. 14***

Sheets of 8, #a-h

2180-2181 A357 Set of 2 16.50 16.50

Souvenir Sheets

2182-2183 A357 Set of 2 10.50 10.50

Nos. 2180b-2180c, 2180f-2180g, 2181b-2181c, 2181f-2181g are 53x38mm.

Diana, Princess of Wales (1961-97) — A358

Designs: a, Peach bar with country name on left side. b, Peach bar with country name on right side.

1998, Nov. 18

2184 A358 $1.20 Pair, #a.-b. 1.10 1.10

No. 2184 was printed in sheets containing 3 pairs.

Gandhi — A359

Portraits: 90c, Up close, later years. $1, Seated with hands clasped. $1.20, Up close, early years. $1.65, Primary school, Rajkot, age 7. $6, With stick, walking with boy (in margin).

1998, Nov. 18

2185-2188 A359 Set of 4 6.00 6.00

Souvenir Sheet

2189 A359 $6 multicolored 5.00 5.00

Picasso — A360

Paintings: $1.20, Figures on the Seashore, 1931, horiz. $1.65, Three Figures Under a Tree, 1907. $1.75, Two Women Running on the Beach, 1922, horiz.

$6, Bullfight, 1900, horiz.

1998, Nov. 18

2190-2192 A360 Set of 3 3.00 3.00

Souvenir Sheet

2193 A360 $6 multicolored 5.00 5.00

1998 World Scouting Jamboree, Chile — A361

90c, Handshake. $1, Scouts hiking. $1.20, Sign.

$6, Lord Baden-Powell.

1998, Oct. 8 **Litho.** ***Perf. 14***

2194-2196 A361 Set of 3 2.25 2.25

Souvenir Sheet

2197 A361 $6 multicolored 4.50 4.50

Organization of American States, 50th Anniv. — A362

1998, Nov. 18 ***Perf. 13½***

2198 A362 $1 multicolored .80 .80

Enzo Ferrari (1898-1988), Automobile Manufacturer A363

No. 2199, each $1.75: a, Top view of Dino 246 GT-GTS. b, Front view of Dino 246 GT-GTS. c, 1977 365 GT4 BB.

$6, Dino 246 GT-GTS.

1998, Nov. 18 ***Perf. 14***

2199 A363 Sheet of 3, #a.-c. 8.00 8.00

Souvenir Sheet

2200 A363 $6 multicolored 8.00 8.00

No. 2200 contains one 92x35mm stamp.

Royal Air Force, 80th Anniv. — A364

No. 2201, each $1.75: a, McDonnell Douglas Phantom FGR1. b, Sepecat Jaguar GR1A. c, Panavia Tornado F3. d, McDonnell Douglas Phantom FGR2.

No. 2202, $6, Eurofighter 2000, Hurricane. No. 2203, $6, Hawk, biplane.

1998, Nov. 18

2201 A364 Sheet of 4, #a.-d. 6.25 6.25

Souvenir Sheets

2202-2203 A364 Set of 2 11.00 11.00

Sea Birds — A365

Designs: 15c, Brown pelican. 25c, Dunlin. 45c, Atlantic puffin. 90c, Pied cormorant.

No. 2208: a, King eider. b, Inca tern. c, Dovekie. d, Ross's bull. e, Brown noddy. f, Marbled murrelet. g, Northern gannet. h, Razorbill. i, Long-tailed jaeger. j, Black guillemot. k, Whimbrel. l, Oystercatcher.

No. 2209, $6, Rhynchops niger. No. 2210, $6, Diomedea exulans.

1998, Nov. 24

2204-2207 A365 Set of 4 2.00 2.00

2208 A365 75c Sheet of 12, #a.-l. 8.50 8.50

Souvenir Sheets

2209-2210 A365 Set of 2 11.00 11.00

Christmas — A366

Dogs with Christmas decorations: 15c, Border collie. 25c, Dalmatian. 65c, Weimaraner. 75c, Scottish terrier. 90c, Long-haired dachshund. $1.20, Golden retriever. $2, Pekingese.

No. 2218, $6, Dalmatian, diff. No. 2219, $6, Jack Russell terrier.

1998, Dec. 10

2211-2217 A366 Set of 7 7.00 7.00

Souvenir Sheet

2218-2219 A366 Set of 2 9.25 9.25

Disney Characters in Water Sports — A367

No. 2220, $1 — Water skiing: a, Goofy, maroon skis. b, Mickey. c, Goofy, Mickey. d, Donald. e, Goofy, blue skis. f, Minnie.

No. 2221, $1 — Surfing: a, Goofy running with board. b, Mickey. c, Donald holding board. d, Donald, riding board. e, Minnie. f, Goofy in water.

No. 2221G, Sailing & sailboarding: h, Mickey wearing cap. i, Mickey, Goofy, counter-balancing boat. j, Goofy sailboarding. k, Mickey, seagull overhead. l, Goofy puffing at sail. m, Mickey sailboarding.

No. 2222, Mickey. No. 2223, Minnie. No. 2224, Goofy. No. 2225, Donald.

1999, Jan. 11 **Litho.** ***Perf. 13½x14***

Sheets of 6, #a-f

2220-2221 A367 Set of 2 11.00 11.00

2221G A367 $1 Sheet of 6, #h.-m. 5.50 5.50

Souvenir Sheets

2222-2225 A367 Set of 4 18.50 18.50

Mickey Mouse, 70th anniv.

Hell's Gate Steel Orchestra, 50th Anniv. — A368

Designs: 20c, Nelson's Dockyard, 1996. 60c, Holiday Inn, Rochester, New York, 1992. 75c, Early years, 1950. 90c, World's Fair, 1964, Eustace Henry (AKA Manning). $1.20, Alston Henry playing double tenor.

No. 2231, $4, Like #2229, vert. No. 2232, $4, The early years, vert.

1999, Feb. 1 **Litho.** ***Perf. 14***

2226-2230 A368 Set of 5 3.25 3.25

Souvenir Sheets

2231-2232 A368 Set of 2 6.75 6.75

Flowers — A369

Designs, vert: 60c, Tulip. 75c, Fuschia. $1.20, Calla lily. $1.65, Sweet pea.

No. 2237: a, Morning glory. b, Geranium. c, Blue hibiscus. d, Marigolds. e, Sunflower. f, Impatiens. g, Petunia. h, Pansy. i, Saucer magnolia.

No. 2238: a, Primrose. b, Bleeding heart. c, Pink dogwood. d, Peony. e, Rose. f, Hellebores. g, Lily. h, Violet. i, Cherry blossoms.

No. 2239, $6, Lily, vert. No. 2240, $6, Zinnias, vert.

1999, Apr. 19 **Litho.** ***Perf. 14***

2233-2236 A369 Set of 4 3.00 3.00

2237 A369 90c Sheet of 9, #a.-i. 6.25 6.25

2238 A369 $1 Sheet of 9, #a.-i. 7.25 7.25

Souvenir Sheets

2239-2240 A369 Set of 2 9.25 9.25

Elle Macpherson, Model — A370

Various portraits, each $1.20.

1999, Apr. 26 ***Perf. 13½***

2241 A370 Sheet of 8, #a.-h. 8.50 8.50

Australia '99 World Stamp Expo.

John Glenn's Space Flight — A371

Space Exploration — A372

No. 2242 — John Glenn, 1962, each $1.75: a, Climbing into Mercury Capsule. b, Formal portrait. c, Having helmet adjusted. d, Entering pressure chamber.

No. 2243, $1.65: a, Luna 2. b, Mariner 2. c, Giotto space probe. d, Rosat. e, Intl. Ultraviolet Explorer. f, Ulysses Space Probe.

No. 2244, $1.65: a, Mariner 10. b, Luna 9. c, Advanced X-ray Astrophysics Facility. d, Magellan Spacecraft. e, Pioneer-Venus 2. f, Infra-red Astronomy Satellite.

No. 2245, $6, Salyut 1, horiz. No. 2246, $6, MIR, horiz.

1999, May 6 **Litho.** ***Perf. 14***

2242 A371 Sheet of 4, #a.-d. 6.50 6.50

Sheets of 6, #a-f

2243-2244 A372 Set of 2 15.00 15.00

Souvenir Sheets

2245-2246 A372 Set of 2 9.00 9.00

Nos. 2245-2246 are incorrectly inscribed.

Prehistoric Animals — A373

Designs: 65c, Brachiosaurus. 75c, Oviraptor, vert. $1, Homotherium. $1.20, Macrauchenia, vert.

No. 2251, each $1.65: a, Leptictidium. b, Ictitherium. c, Plesictis. d, Hemicyon. e, Diacodexis. f, Stylinodon. g, Kanuites. h, Chriacus. i, Argyrolagus.

No. 2252, each $1.65: a, Struthiomimus. b, Corythosaurus. c, Dsungaripterus. d, Compognathus. e, Prosaurolophus. f, Montanoceratops. g, Stegosaurus. h, Deinonychus. i, Ouranosaurus.

No. 2253, each $6, Pteranodon. No. 2254, $6, Eurhinodelphus.

1999, May 26

2247-2250 A373 Set of 4 3.50 3.50

Sheets of 9, #a-i

2251-2252 A373 Set of 2 22.00 22.00

Souvenir Sheets

2253-2254 A373 Set of 2 9.00 9.00

Illustrations on Nos. 2247-2248 are switched.

IBRA'99, World Stamp Exhibition, Nuremberg — A374

Exhibition emblem, Leipzig-Dresden Railway and: No. 2255, $1, Caroline Islands #19. No. 2257, $1.65, Caroline Islands #4.
Emblem, Gölsdorf 4-4-0 and: No. 2256, $1.20, Caroline Islands #16. No. 2258, $1.90, Caroline Islands #8, #10.
$6, Registered label on cover.

1999, June 24 Litho. *Perf. 14*
2255-2258 A374 Set of 4 5.00 5.00

Souvenir Sheet
2259 A374 $6 multicolored 4.75 4.75

Paintings by Hokusai (1760-1849) — A375

No. 2260, $1.65 — Details or entire paintings: a, Asakusa Honganji. b, Dawn at Isawa in Kai Province. c, Samurai with Bow and Arrow (bows level). d, Samurai with Bow and Arrow (bows at different angles). e, Kajikazawa in Kai Province. f, A Great Wave.
No. 2261, $1.65: a, People on the Balcony of the Sazaido. b, Nakahara in Sagami Province. c, Defensive Positions (2 men). d, Defensive Positions (3 men). e, Mount Fuji in Clear Weather. f, Nihonbashi in Edo.
No. 2262, $6, Gotenyama At Shinagawa on Tokaido Highway, vert. No. 2263, $6, A Netsuke Workshop, vert.

1999, June 24 Sheets of 6, #a-f
2260-2261 A375 Set of 2 15.00 15.00

Souvenir Sheets
2262-2263 A375 Set of 2 9.25 9.25

Johann Wolfgang von Goethe (1749-1832), Poet — A376

No. 2264, each $1.75: a, Three archangels in "Faust." b, Portraits of Goethe and Friedrich von Schiller (1759-1805). c, Faust reclining in landscape with spirits.
$6, Profile portrait of Goethe.

1999, June 24 Litho. *Perf. 14*
2264 A376 Sheet of 3, #a.-c. 4.50 4.50

Souvenir Sheet
2265 A376 $6 multicolored 4.50 4.50

Souvenir Sheets

Philexfrance '99, World Philatelic Exhibition — A377

Locomotives: No. 2266, Crampton 1855-69. No. 2267, 232-U1 4-Cylinder Compound 4-6-4, 1949.

1999, June 24 *Perf. 13¾*
2266 A377 $6 multicolored 5.00 5.00
2267 A377 $6 multicolored 5.00 5.00

Wedding of Prince Edward and Sophie Rhys-Jones — A378

No. 2268: a, Sophie. b. Sophie, Edward. c, Edward.
$6, Horse and carriage, couple.

1999, June 24 *Perf. 13½*
2268 A378 $3 Sheet of 3, #a.-c. 6.75 6.75

Souvenir Sheet
2269 A378 $6 multicolored 5.00 5.00

A379

Various white kittens: 35c, 45c, 60c, 75c, 90c, $1.
No. 2276, $1.65: a, One holding paw on another. b, Black & white. c, White kitten, black kitten. d, One with yarn. e, Two in basket. f, One looking up.
No. 2277, $1.65: a, One playing with red yarn. b, Two long-haired. c, Yellow tabby. d, One with mouse. e, Yellow tabby on pillow. f, Black & gray tabby.
No. 2278, $6, Tabby cat carrying kitten. No. 2279, $6, Yellow kitten in tree.

1999, May 25 Litho. *Perf. 14½x14*
2270-2275 A379 Set of 6 3.00 3.00

Sheets of 6
2276-2277 A379 Set of 2 15.00 15.00

Souvenir Sheets
2278-2279 A379 Set of 2 9.25 9.25

Australia '99, World Stamp Expo (Nos. 2276-2279).

A380

UN Rights of the Child Convention, 10th Anniv. — No. 2280: a, Three children. b, Adult hand taking child's hand, silhouette of mother holding infant. c, UN Building, member flags, dove.
$6, Dove.

1999, June 22 *Perf. 14*
2280 A380 $3 Sheet of 3, #a.-c. 6.75 6.75

Souvenir Sheet
2281 A380 $6 multicolored 5.00 5.00

Boats — A381

Designs: 25c, Missa Ferdie. 45c, Sailboats. 60c, Jolly Roger Pirate Ship. 90c, $4, Freewinds. $1.20, Monarch of the Seas.

1999, June 24 Litho. *Perf. 13x11*
2282-2286 A381 Set of 5 3.25 3.25
2286a Souvenir sheet, #2282-2286 3.75 3.75

Souvenir Sheet
Perf. 13¾
2287 A381 $4 multicolored 3.75 3.75

No. 2287 contains one 51x38mm stamp.

A382

Butterflies: 65c, Fiery jewel. 75c, Hewitson's blue hairstreak. $1.20, Scarce bamboo page, horiz. $1.65, Paris peacock, horiz.
No. 2292, horiz.: a, California dog face. b, Small copper. c, Zebra swallowtail. d, White M hairstreak. e, Old world swallowtail. f, Buckeye. g, Apollo. h, Sonoran blue. i, Purple emperor.
No. 2293, $6, Monarch. No. 2294, $6, Cairns birdwing, horiz.

1999, Aug. 16 *Perf. 14*
2288-2291 A382 Set of 4 3.75 3.75
2292 A382 $1 Sheet of 9, #a.-i. 8.50 8.50

Souvenir Sheets
2293-2294 A382 Set of 2 11.00 11.00

Christmas — A383

15c, Madonna and child in a Wreath of Flowers by Peter Paul Rubens. 25c, Shroud of Christ Held by Two Angels, by Albrecht Dürer. 45c, Madonna and Child Enthroned Between Two Saints, by Raphael. 60c, Holy Family with the Lamb, by Raphael. $2, The Transfiguration, by Raphael. $4, Three Putti Holding a Coat of Arms, by Dürer.
$6, The Coronation of the Holy St. Catherine, by Rubens.

1999, Nov. 22 Litho. *Perf. 13¾*
2295-2300 A383 Set of 6 6.50 6.50

Souvenir Sheet
2301 A383 $6 multicolored 5.50 5.50

Famous Elderly People — A384

Designs: a, Katharine Hepburn. b, Martha Graham. c, Eubie Blake. d, Agatha Christie. e, Eudora Welty. f, Helen Hayes. g, Vladimir Horowitz. h, Katharine Graham. i, Pablo Casals. j, Pete Seeger. k, Andres Segovia. l, Frank Lloyd Wright.

2000, Jan. 18 Litho. *Perf. 14*
2302 A384 90c Sheet of 12, #a-l 8.00 8.00

Charlie Chaplin — A385

Designs: a, "Modern Times," street scene. b, "The Gold Rush," with other actor. c, Unidentified film. d, "Modern Times," on gears. e, "The Gold Rush," arms akimbo. f, "The Gold Rush," with cane.

2000, Jan. 18 *Perf. 13¾*
2303 A385 $1.65 Sheet of 6, #a-f 7.25 7.25

Sir Cliff Richard, Rock Musician — A386

2000, Jan. 18 *Perf. 13¼*
2304 A386 $1.65 multi 1.25 1.25

Issued in sheets of 6.

Birds — A387

Designs: 75c, Streamertail. 90c, Yellow-bellied sapsucker. $1.20, Rufous-tailed jacamar. $2, Spectacled owl.
No. 2309, $1.20: a, Ground dove. b, Wood stork. c, Saffron finch. d, Green-backed heron. e, Lovely cotinga. f, St. Vincent parrot. g, Cuban grassquit. h, Red-winged blackbird.
No. 2310, $1.20: a, Scarlet macaw. b, Yellow-fronted amazon. c, Queen-of-Bavaria. d, Nanday conure. e, Jamaican tody. f, Smooth-billed ani. g, Puerto Rican woodpecker. h, Ruby-throated hummingbird.
No. 2311, $6, Vermilion flycatcher. No. 2312, $6, Red-capped manakin, vert.

2000, Apr. 17 Litho. *Perf. 14*
2305-2308 A387 Set of 4 4.00 4.00

Sheets of 8, #a-h
Perf. 13¾x14
2309-2310 A387 Set of 2 15.00 15.00

Souvenir Sheets
Perf. 13¾
2311-2312 A387 Set of 2 9.25 9.25

The Stamp Show 2000, London (Nos. 2309-2312). Size of stamps: Nos. 2309-2310, 48x31mm; No. 2311, 50x38mm; No. 2312, 38x50mm.

Paintings of Anthony Van Dyck A388

No. 2313, $1.20: a, Arthur Goodwin. b, Sir Thomas Wharton. c, Mary Villers (as Venus), Daughter of the Duke of Buckingham. d, Christina Bruce, Countess of Devonshire. e, James Hamilton, 3rd Marquis and 1st Duke of Hamilton. f, Henry Danvers, Earl of Danby.
No. 2314, $1.20: a, Charles I in Robes of State. b, Henrietta Maria. c, Queen Henrietta Maria with Her Dwarf Sir Jeffrey Hudson. d, Charles I in Armor. e, Henrietta Maria in Profile, facing right. f. Queen Henrietta Maria.
No. 2315, $1.20: a, Marie de Raet, Wife of Philippe le Roy. b, Jacomo de Cachiopin. c, Princess Henrietta of Lorraine Attended by a Page. d, Portrait of a Man. e, Portrait of a Woman. f, Philippe le Roy, Seigneur de Ravels.
No. 2316, $5, Charles I on Horseback with Monsieur de St. Antoine. No. 2317, $5, Le Roi a La Chasse (Charles I hunting). No. 2318, $5, Charles I in Three Positions. No. 2319, $5, Charles I and Queen Henrietta.
No. 2320, $6, Portrait of Two Young English Gentlemen, Sons of the Duke of Lenox. No. 2321, $6, George, Lord Digby, and William, Lord Russell.
Illustration reduced.

2000, May 15 ***Perf. 13¾***

Sheets of 6, #a-f

2313-2315 A388 Set of 3 15.00 15.00

Souvenir Sheets

2316-2319 A388 Set of 4 15.50 15.50
2320-2321 A388 Set of 2 9.25 9.25

Butterflies — A389

No. 2322, $1.65: a, Orange theope. b, Sloane's urania. c, Gold-drop helicopis. d, Papilio velovis. e, Graphium androcles. f, Cramer's mesene.

No. 2323, $1.65, horiz.: a, Euploea miniszeki. b, Doris. c, Evenus coronata. d, Anchisiades swallowtail. e, White-spotted tadpole. f, Morpho patroclus.

No. 2324, $1.65, horiz.: a, Mesosemia loruhama. b, Bia actorion. c, Ghost brimstone. d, Blue tharops. e, Catasticta manco. f, White-tailed page.

No. 2325, $6, Reakirt's blue. No. 2326, $6, Graphium encelades, horiz. No. 2327, $6, Graphium milon, horiz.

Illustration reduced.

2000, May 29 ***Perf. 14***

Sheets of 6, #a-f

2322-2324 A389 Set of 3 22.50 22.50

Souvenir Sheets

2325-2327 A389 Set of 3 14.00 14.00

Prince William, 18th Birthday A390

Prince William — No. 2328: a, With checked shirt, waving. b, In jacket and white shirt. c, With arms clasped. d, In striped shirt, waving.

$6, With Prince Harry, Princess Diana and unidentified man.

2000, June 21 ***Perf. 14***

2328 A390 $1.65 Sheet of 4, #a-d 4.75 4.75

Souvenir Sheet

Perf. 13¾

2329 A390 $6 multi 4.25 4.25

100th Test Cricket Match at Lord's Ground — A391

90c, Richie Richardson. $5, Viv Richard. $6, Lord's Ground, horiz.

2000, June 26 ***Perf. 14***

2330-2331 A391 Set of 2 4.50 4.50

Souvenir Sheet

2332 A391 $6 multi 4.50 4.50

Souvenir Sheet

2000 Summer Olympics, Sydney — A392

Designs: a, Cyclist. b, Diver. c, Italian flag, Flaminio Stadium, Rome. d, Ancient Greek javelin thrower.

2000, June 26

2333 A392 $2 Sheet of 4, #a-d 6.00 6.00

First Zeppelin Flight, Cent. A393

No. 2334: a, LZ-1. b, LZ-2. c, LZ-3. $6, LZ-7.

2000, June 26 ***Perf. 13½***

2334 A393 $3 Sheet of 3, #a-c 6.75 6.75

Souvenir Sheet

Perf. 14¼

2335 A393 $6 multi 4.25 4.25

No. 2334 contains three 45x27mm stamps.

Cats A394

No. 2336: a, Long-haired blue & white. b, Snow shoe. c, Persian. d, Chocolate lynx point. e, Brown & white sphynx. f, White tortoiseshell.

$6, Lavender tortie.

2000, May 29 **Litho.** ***Perf. 14***

2336 A394 $1.65 Sheet of 6, #a-f 7.50 7.50

Souvenir Sheet

2337 A394 $6 multi 4.50 4.50

Souvenir Sheet

Public Railways, 175th Anniv. — A395

No. 2338: a, Locomotion No. 1, George Stephenson. b, John Bull.

2000, June 26

2338 A395 $3 Sheet of 2, #a-b 4.50 4.50

The Stamp Show 2000, London.

Souvenir Sheet

Johann Sebastian Bach (1685-1750) — A396

2000, June 26

2339 A396 $6 multi 4.25 4.25

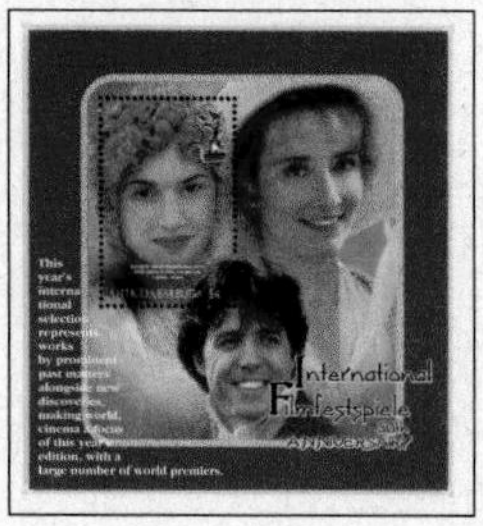

Berlin Film Festival, 50th Anniv. A397

No. 2340: a, Une Femme Est Une Femme. b, Carmen Jones. c, Die Ratten. d, Die Vier im Jeep. e, Lilies of the Field. f, Invitation to the Dance.

$6, Sense and Sensibility.

2000, June 26

2340 A397 $1.65 Sheet of 6, #a-f 7.25 7.25

Souvenir Sheet

2341 A397 $6 multi 4.50 4.50

Flowers — A398

Designs: 45c, Epidendrum pseudepidndrum. 65c, Odontoglossum cervantesii. 75c, Cattleya dowiana. 90c, Beloperone guttata. $1, Colliandra haematocephala. $1.20, Brassavola nodosa.

No. 2348, $1.65: a, Masdevallia coccinea. b, Paphinia cristata. c, Vanilla planifolia. d, Cattleya forbesii. e, Lycaste skinneri. f, Cattleya percivaliana.

No. 2349, $1.65: a, Anthurium andreanum. b, Doxantha unguiscati. c, Hibiscus rosa-sinensis. d, Canna indica. e, Heliconius umilis. f, Strelitzia reginae.

No. 2350, $1.65: a, Pseudocalymna alliaceum. b, Datura candida. c, Ipomoea tuberosa. d, Allamanda cathartica. e, Aspasia epidendroides. f, Maxillaria cucullata.

No. 2351, $6, Strelitzia reginae. No. 2352, $6, Cattleya leopoldii. No. 2353, $6, Rossioglossum grande.

2000, May 29 **Litho.** ***Perf. 14***

2342-2347 A398 Set of 6 3.50 3.50

Sheets of 6, #a-f

2348-2350 A398 Set of 3 22.50 22.50

Souvenir Sheets

2351-2353 A398 Set of 3 13.00 13.00

Dogs — A399

Designs: 90c, Boxer. $1, Wire-haired pointer (inscribed Alaskan malamute). $2, Alaskan malamute (inscribed Wire-haired pointer). $4, Saluki.

No. 2358: a, Bearded collie. b, Cardigan Welsh corgi. c, Saluki. d, Basset hound. e, Standard poodle. f, Boston terrier.

$6, Cavalier King Charles Spaniel.

2000, May 29

2354-2357 A399 Set of 4 5.50 5.50
2358 A399 $1.65 Sheet of 6, #a-f 7.00 7.00

Souvenir Sheet

2359 A399 $6 multi 4.50 4.50

Space Achievements — A400

No. 2360, $1.65: a, Sputnik 1. b, Explorer 1. c, Mars Express. d, Luna 1. e, Ranger 7. f, Mariner 4.

No. 2361, $1.65: a, Mariner 10. b, Soho. c, Mariner 2. d, Giotto. e, Exosat. f, Pioneer.

No. 2362, $6, Hubble Space Telescope. No. 2363, $6, Vostok 1.

2000, June 26 **Sheets of 6, #a-f**

2360-2361 A400 Set of 2 14.00 14.00

Souvenir Sheets

2362-2363 A400 Set of 2 9.00 9.00

World Stamp Expo 2000, Anaheim.

Apollo-Soyuz Mission, 25th Anniv. — A401

No. 2364: a, Alexei Leonov. b, Soyuz 19. c, Valeri Kubasov.

$6, Leonov and Thomas Stafford.

2000, June 26

2364 A401 $3 Sheet of 3, #a-c 6.50 6.50

Souvenir Sheet

2365 A401 $6 multi 4.25 4.25

Souvenir Sheet

Albert Einstein (1879-1955) — A402

2000, June 26 ***Perf. 14¼***

2366 A402 $6 multi 4.25 4.25

Girls' Brigade — A403

Designs: 20c, Outreach program to Sunshine Home for Girls. 60c, Ullida Rawlins Gill, Intl. vice-president, vert. 75c, Officers and girls. 90c, Raising the flag, vert. $1.20, Members with 8th Antigua Company flag.

$5, Emblem, vert.

2000, July 13 ***Perf. 14***

2367-2371 A403 Set of 5 2.75 2.75

Souvenir Sheet

2372 A403 $5 multi 3.75 3.75

A404

Queen Mother, 100th Birthday A405

No. 2373: a, As child. b, In 1940. c, With Princess Anne, 1951. d, In Canada, 1989.

$6, Inspecting the troops. $20, In gardens.

Litho., Margin Embossed

2000, Aug. 4 ***Perf. 14***

2373 A404 $2 Sheet of 4, #a-d, + label 6.00 6.00

Souvenir Sheet

Perf. 13¾

2374 A404 $6 multi 4.50 4.50

Without Gum

Litho. & Embossed

Die Cut 8¾x9

2375 A405 $20 gold & multi

No. 2374 contains one 38x51mm stamp.

See Nos. 2536-2537.

Popes A406

No. 2376, $1.65: a, Alexander VI, 1492-1503, hands clasped. b, Benedict XIII, 1724-30. c, Boniface IX, 1389-1404. d, Alexander VI, no hands. e, Clement VIII, 1592-1605. f, Clement VI, 1342-52.

No. 2377, $1.65: a, John Paul II, 1978-present. b, Benedict XV, 1914-22. c, John XXIII, 1958-63. d, Pius XI, 1922-39. e, Pius XII, 1939-58. f, Paul VI, 1963-78.

No. 2378, $6, Pius II, 1458-1464. No. 2379, $6, Pius VII, 1800-23.

2000, Aug. 21 **Litho.** ***Perf. 13¾***

Sheets of 6, #a-f

2376-2377 A406 Set of 2 15.00 15.00

Souvenir Sheets

2378-2379 A406 Set of 2 9.25 9.25

Monarchs — A407

No. 2380, $1.65: a, Donaldbane of Scotland, 1093-97. b, Duncan I of Scotland, 1034-40. c, Duncan II of Scotland, 1094. d, Macbeth of Scotland, 1040-57. e, Malcolm III of Scotland, 1057-93. f, Edgar of Scotland, 1097-1107.

No. 2381, $1.65: a, Charles I of Great Britain, 1625-49. b, Charles II of Great Britain, 1660-85. c, Charles Edward Stuart, the "Young Pretender," 1720-1788. d, James II of Great Britain, 1685-89. e, James II of Scotland, 1437-60. f, James III of Scotland, 1460-88.

No. 2382, $6, Robert I of Scotland, 1306-29. No. 2383, $6, Anne of Great Britain, 1702-14.

Illustration reduced.

2000, Aug. 21

Sheets of 6, #a-f

2380-2381 A407 Set of 2 15.00 15.00

Souvenir Sheets

2382-2383 A407 Set of 2 9.25 9.25

Millennium (#2385) — A408

No. 2384 — Chinese paintings: a, Admonitions of the Instructress to the Court Ladies, attributed to Ku K'ai-chih. b, Ink drawing on silk, 3rd cent. B.C. c, Ink and color drawing on silk, 2nd cent. B.C. d, Scholars of the Northern Qi Collating Texts (detail), attributed to Yang Zihua. e, Spring Outing (detail), attributed to Zhan Ziqian. f, Portrait of the Emperors (detail), attributed to Yen Liben. g, Sailing Boats and a Riverside Mansion, attributed to Li Sixun. h, Two Horses and a Groom (detail), by Han Kan. i, King's Portrait (detail), attributed to Wu Daozi. j, Court Ladies Wearing Flowered Headdresses (detail), attributed to Zhou Fang. k, Wintry Groves and Layered Banks, by Dong Yuan. l, Mount Kuanglu, by Jing Hao. m, Pheasant and Small Birds by a Jujube Shrub, by Huang Jucai. n, Deer Among Red Maples, by anonymous painter. o, Wintry Groves and Layered Banks, diff., by Dong Yuan. p, Literary Gathering, by Han Huang (60x40mm). q, Sketches of Birds and Insects (detail), by Huang Quan.

Perf. 12¾x12½

2000, Aug. 21 **Litho.**

2384 A408 25c Sheet of 17, #a-q, + label 5.00 5.00

Highlights of 1250-1300: a, Expansion of the Inquisition. b, Chartres Cathedral. c, Sculptures in Naumburg Cathedral. d, 1st English Parliament. e, The Madonna in Majesty (Maestà), by Cimabue. f, Marco Polo. g Divine wind. h, Death of St. Thomas Aquinas. i, Arezzo Cathedral. j, Margaret, Queen of Scotland. k, Jewish exodus from England. l, Fall of Acre to Muslims. m, Moses de León writes much of The Zohar. n, German Civil War. o, Death of Kublai Khan. p, Dante writes La Vita Nuova (60x40mm). q, Chao Meng-fu paints Autumn Colors on the Quiao and Hua Mountains.

2000, Aug. 21

2385 A408 60c Sheet of 17, #a-q + label 9.00 9.00

Battle of Britain, 60th Anniv. A409

No. 2386, $1.20: a, Bristol Blenheim. b, Winston Churchill. c, Bristol Blenheim and barrage balloon. d, Heinkel. e, Spitfire. f, German rescue vessel. g, Messerschmitt 109. h, RAF air and sea rescue launch.

No. 2387, $1.20: a, German lookout. b, Children being evacuated. c, Youngsters evacuated from hospitals. d, Hurricane. e, Rescue workers. f, British political cartoon. g, King George VI and Queen Elizabeth inspect wreckage. h, Barrage balloon over Tower Bridge.

No. 2388, $6, Spitfires. No. 2389, $6, Junkers 87B.

2000, Oct. 16 **Litho.** ***Perf. 14***

Sheets of 8, #a-h

2386-2387 A409 Set of 2 14.50 14.50

Souvenir Sheets

2388-2389 A409 Set of 2 9.25 9.25

Rainforest Fauna — A410

Designs: 75c, Agouti. 90c, Capybara. $1.20, Basilisk lizard. $2, Heliconid butterfly.

No. 2394, $1.65: a, Green violet-ear hummingbird. b, Harpy eagle. c, Three-toed sloth. d, White uakari monkey. e, Anteater. f, Coati.

No. 2395, $1.75: a, Red-eyed tree frog. b, Black spider monkey. c, Emerald toucanet. d, Kinkajou. e, Spectacled bear. f, Tapir.

No. 2396, $6, Keel-billed toucan, horiz. No. 2397, $6, Scarlet macaw, horiz.

2000, Sept. 25 **Litho.** ***Perf. 14***

2390-2393 A410 Set of 4 3.75 3.75

Sheets of 6, #a-f

2394-2395 A410 Set of 2 15.00 15.00

Souvenir Sheets

2396-2397 A410 Set of 2 9.25 9.25

Submarines A411

Designs: 65c, Sea Cliff. 75c, Beaver Mark IV. 90c, Reef Ranger. $1, Cubmarine. $1.20, Alvin. $3, Argus.

No. 2404, $2: a, Revenge. b, Walrus. c, Los Angeles. d, Daphne. e, USS Ohio. f, USS Skipjack.

No. 2405, $6, Trieste. No. 2406, $6, German Type 209.

2000, Oct. 2

2398-2403 A411 Set of 6 5.50 5.50

2404 A411 $2 Sheet of 6, #a-f 8.75 8.75

Souvenir Sheets

2405-2406 A411 Set of 2 9.00 9.00

Paintings from the Prado A412

No. 2407, $1.65: a, Three men. b, Man's head. c, Three women. d, Man on white horse. e, Man on brown horse. f, Man leading horse. a-c from Family Portrait, by Adriaen Thomasz Key. d-f from The Devotion of Rudolf I, by Peter Paul Rubens and Jan Wildens.

No. 2408, $1.65: a, Seated man. b, Man with sash. c, Group of men. d, Laureated figure. e, Men working at anvil. f, Two workers. a-c from The Defense of Cadiz Against the English by Francisco de Zurbaran. d-f from Vulcan's Forge, by Diego Velázquez

No. 2409, $1.65: a, Mandolin player. b, Woman with fan. c, Two men. d, Bald man. e, Two Magi. f, Jesus, Mary and Joseph. a-c from The Concert, by Vicente Palmaroli y Gonzalez. d-f from The Adoration of the Magi, by Juan Bautista Maino

No. 2410, $6, The Seller of Fans, by José del Castillo. No. 2411, $6, Portrati of a Family in a Garden, by Jan van Kessel, the Younger. No. 2412, $6, The Deliverance of St. Peter, by José de Ribera, horiz.

Illustration reduced.

2000, Oct. 6 ***Perf. 12x12¼, 12¼x12***

Sheets of 6, #a-f

2407-2409 A412 Set of 3 20.00 20.00

Souvenir Sheets

2410-2412 A412 Set of 3 13.00 13.00

España 2000 Intl. Philatelic Exhibition.

Christmas — A413

Designs (background): 25c, No. 2417a, Angels, full body (blue). 45c, No. 2417b, Angel's heads (orange). 90c, No. 2417c, Angel's heads (blue). $5, No. 2417d, Angels, full body (yellow).

2000, Dec. 4 ***Perf. 14***

2413-2416 A413 Set of 4 4.50 4.50

2417 A413 $1.75 Sheet of 4, #a-d 5.25 5.25

Souvenir Sheet

2418 A413 $6 Jesus 4.50 4.50

Rijksmuseum, Amsterdam, Bicent. (in 2000) — A414

No. 2419, $1: a, Dr. Ephraim Bueno, by Rembrandt. b, Woman Writing a Letter, by Frans van Mieris, the Elder. c, Mary Magdalene, by Jan van Scorel. d, Portrait of a Woman (inscribed Anna Coddle), by Maarten van Heemskerck. e, Cleopatra's Banquet, by Gerard Lairesse. f, Titus van Rijn in Friar's Habit, by Rembrandt.

No. 2420, $1.20: a, Saskia van Uylenburgh, by Rembrandt. b, In the Month of July, by Paul Joseph Constantin Gabriel. c, Maria Trip, by Rembrandt. d, Still Life with Flowers, by Jan van Huysum. e, Hesje van Cleyburgh, by Rembrandt. f, Girl in a White Kimono, by George Hendrik Breitner.

No. 2421, $1.65: a, Man and woman at spinning wheel, by Pieter Pietersz. b, Self-portrait, by Rembrandt. c, Jeremiah Lamenting the Destruction of Jerusalem, by Rembrandt. d, The Jewish Bride, by Rembrandt. e, Tobit and Anna with a Kid, by Rembrandt. f, The Prophetess Anna, by Rembrandt.

No. 2422, $6, Doubting Thomas, by Hendrick ter Brugghen. No. 2423, $6, Still Life with Cheeses, by Floris van Dijck. No. 2424, $6, Isaac Blessing Jacob, by Govert Flinck.

2001, Jan. 15 **Litho.** ***Perf. 13¾***

Sheets of 6, #a-f

2419-2421 A414 Set of 3 17.00 17.00

Souvenir Sheets

2422-2424 A414 Set of 3 13.50 13.50

Pokémon A415

No. 2425: a, Starmie. b, Misty. c, Brock. d, Geodude. e, Krabby. f, Ash.

2001, Feb. 13

2425 A415 $1.75 Sheet of 6, #a-f 7.25 7.25

Souvenir Sheet

2426 A415 $6 Charizard 4.25 4.25

Mushrooms — A416

Designs: 25c, Blue-toothed entoloma. 90c, Common morel. $1, Red cage fungus. $1.75, Fawn shield-cap.

No. 2431, $1.65: a, Lilac bonnet. b, Silky volvar. c, Poplar field cap. d, St. George's mushroom. e, Red-stemmed tough shank. f, Fly agaric.

No. 2432, $1.65: a, Copper trumpet. b, Meadow mushroom. c, Green-gilled parasol. d, Panther. e, Death cap. f, King bolete.

No. 2433, $6, Yellow parasol. No. 2434, Mutagen milk cap.

2001, Mar. 26 ***Perf. 13¾x13¼***

2427-2430 A416 Set of 4 3.00 3.00

Sheets of 6, #a-f

2431-2432 A416 Set of 2 15.00 15.00

Souvenir Sheets

2433-2434 A416 Set of 2 9.25 9.25

Hong Kong 2001 Stamp Exhibition (2431-2434).

Population and Housing Census — A417

Map of Antigua with various graphs. Denominations: 15c, 25c, 65c, 90c.

2001, Apr. 2 ***Perf. 13¾***

2435-2438 A417 Set of 4 1.50 1.50

Souvenir Sheet

2439 A417 $6 Map, emblem 4.50 4.50

Phila Nippon '01, Japan — A418

Designs: 45c Two women facing right, from Yuna (Bath-house Women). 60c, Woman facing left, from Yuna. 65c, Two women, from Yuna. 75c, Man with stringed instrument at top, from Hikone Screen. $1, Woman with stringed instrument at bottom, from Hikone Screen. $1.20, Two people, from Hikone Screen.

No. 2446 — Namban Screen, by Naizen Kano, each $1.65: a, Ship's stern. b, Ship's bow. c, Man with closed umbrella. d, Man with open umbrella.

No. 2447 — Merry Making Under the Cherry Blossoms, by Naganobu Kano, each $1.65: a, Steps. b, Tree. c, Four people near building. d, Four people, mountains. e, Three people. f, One person.

No. 2448, $6, Visiting a Shrine on a Rainy Night, by Harunobu Suzuki. No. 2449, $6, Courtesan on a Veranda Upstairs, by Kokan Shiba. No. 2450, $6, Daruma, by Tsujo Kano.

2001, May 28 Litho. ***Perf. 14¼x14***

2440-2445 A418 Set of 6 3.50 3.50

2446 A418 Sheet of 4, #a-d 5.00 5.00

2447 A418 Sheet of 6, #a-f 7.50 7.50

Souvenir Sheets

Perf. 13¾

2448-2450 A418 Set of 3 12.50 12.50

Nos. 2448-2450 each contain one 38x51mm stamp.

No. 2449 is incorrectly inscribed. It actually depicts "Courtesan on a Veranda Upstairs," by Kokan.

Orchids — A419

Designs: 45c, Hintleya burtii. 75c, Neomoovea irrovata. 90c, Comparettia speciosa. $1, Cypripedium crapeanum.

No. 2455, $1.20, vert.: a, Trichoceuos muralis. b, Dracula rampira. c, Psychopsis papilio. d, Lycaste clenningiana. e, Telipogon nevuosus. f, Masclecallia ayahbacana.

No. 2456, $1.65, vert.: a, Rhyncholaelia glanca. b, Oncidium barbatum. c, Phaius tankervillege. d, Ghies brechtiana. e, Angraecum leonis. f, Cychnoches loddigesti.

No. 2457, $1.65, vert.: a, Cattleya dowiana. b, Dendrobium cruentum. c, Bulbophyllum lobbi. d, Chysis laevis. e, Ancistrochilus rothschildicanus. f, Angraecum sororium.

No. 2458, $6, Trichopilia fragrans, vert. No. 2459, $6, Symphalossum sanguinem, vert.

2001, June 11 ***Perf. 14***

2451-2454 A419 Set of 4 2.40 2.40

Sheets of 6, #a-f

2455-2457 A419 Set of 3 19.00 19.00

Souvenir Sheets

2458-2459 A419 Set of 2 9.00 9.00

Souvenir Sheets

I Love Lucy A420

Designs: No. 2460, $6, Fred and Ricky. No. 2461, $6, Lucy and Ethel. No. 2462, $6, Lucy and fireplace. No. 2463, $6, Lucy and open door.

2001, Mar. 5 Litho. ***Perf. 13¾***

2460-2463 A420 Set of 4 18.00 18.00

See Nos. 2522-2525.

Marine Life and Birds — A421

Designs: 25c, Yellowtail damselfish. 45c, Indigo hamlet. 65c, Great white shark. No. 2467, 90c, Bottlenose dolphin. No. 2468, 90c, Palette surgeonfish. $1, Octopus.

No. 2470, $1.20: a, Common dolphin. b, Franklin's gull. c, Rock beauty. d, Bicolor angelfish. e, Beaugregory. f, Banded butterflyfish.

No. 2471, $1.20: a, Common tern. b, Flying fish. c, Queen angelfish. d, Blue-striped grunt. e, Porkfish. f, Blue tang.

No. 2472, $1.65: a, Dugong. b, White-tailed tropicbird. c, Bull shark and Spanish grunt. d, Manta ray. e, Green turtle. f, Spanish grunt.

No. 2473, $1.65: a, Red-footed booby. b, Bottlenose dolphin. c, Hawksbill turtle. d, Monk seal. e, Bull shark and coral. f, Lemon shark.

No. 2474, $5, Sailfish. No. 2475, $5, Beaugregory and brown pelican, vert. No. 2476, $6, Hawksbill turtle. No. 2477, $6, Queen triggerfish.

2001, June 11 ***Perf. 14***

2464-2469 A421 Set of 6 3.25 3.25

Sheets of 6, #a-f

2470-2473 A421 Set of 4 24.00 24.00

Souvenir Sheets

2474-2477 A421 Set of 4 16.00 16.00

Ship Freewinds A422

Designs: 30c, Maiden voyage anniversary in Antigua. 45c, In St. Barthelemy. 75c, In Caribbean at sunset. 90c, In Bonaire. $1.50, In Bequia.

No. 2483, $4, With lights on during eclipse. No. 2484, $4, In Curacao.

2001, June 15

2478-2482 A422 Set of 5 3.00 3.00

Souvenir Sheets

2483-2484 A422 Set of 2 6.00 6.00

Toulouse-Lautrec Paintings — A423

No. 2485: a, Monsieur Georges-Henri Manuel Standing. b, Monsieur Louis Pascal. c, Roman Coolus. d, Monsieur Fourcade.

$5, Dancing at the Moulin de la Galette.

2001, July 3 ***Perf. 13¾***

2485 A423 $2 Sheet of 4, #a-d 6.00 6.00

Souvenir Sheet

2486 A423 $5 multi 3.75 3.75

Giuseppe Verdi (1813-1901), Opera Composer — A424

No. 2487: a, Verdi in hat. b, Character and score from Don Carlos. c, Conductor and score for Aida. d, Musicians and score for Rigoletto.

2001, July 3 ***Perf. 14***

2487 A424 $2 Sheet of 4, #a-d 6.00 6.00

Souvenir Sheet

2488 A424 $5 Verdi, score 3.75 3.75

Marlene Dietrich A425

No. 2489: a, With cigarette. b, On sofa. c, Color photograph. d, With piano.

2001, July 3 ***Perf. 13¾***

2489 A425 $2 Sheet of 4, #a-d 6.00 6.00

Queen Victoria (1819-1901) — A426

No. 2490: a, Blue dress. b, Red hat. c, Crown. d, Crown and blue sash.

2001, July 3 ***Perf. 14***

2490 A426 $2 Sheet of 4, #a-d 6.00 6.00

Souvenir Sheet

2491 A426 $5 As old woman 3.75 3.75

Queen Elizabeth II, 75th Birthday A427

No. 2492: a, At birth, 1926. b, In 1938. c, In 1939. d, At coronation, 1953. e, In 1956. f, In 1985.

2001, July 3

2492 A427 $1 Sheet of 6, #a-f 3.75 3.75

Souvenir Sheet

2493 A427 $6 In 1940 4.50 4.50

Photomosaic of Queen Elizabeth II — A428

2001, July 3 Litho. ***Perf. 14***

2494 A428 $1 multi .75 .75

Queen Elizabeth II, 75th birthday. Issued in sheets of 8.

Monet Paintings A429

No. 2495, horiz.: a, Water Lilies. b, Rose Portals, Giverny. c, The Water Lily Pond, Harmony in Green. d, The Artist's Garden, Irises.

$5, Jerusalem Artichokes.

2001, July 3 ***Perf. 13¾***
2495 A429 $2 Sheet of 4, #a-d 6.00 6.00

Souvenir Sheet

2496 A429 $5 multi 3.75 3.75

Endangered Animals — A430

Designs: 25c, Collared peccary. 30c, Baird's tapir. 45c, Agouti. 75c, Bananaquit. 90c, Six-banded armadillo. $1, Roseate spoonbill.

No. 2503, each $1.80: a, Mouse opossum. b, Magnificent black frigatebird. c, Northern jacana. d, Painted bunting. e, Haitian solenodon. f, St. Lucia iguana.

No. 2504, each $2.50: a, West Indian iguana. b, Scarlet macaw. c, Cotton-topped tamarin. d, Kinkajou.

No. 2505, $6, Ocelot, vert. No. 2506, $6, King vulture, vert.

2001, Sept. 10 ***Perf. 14***
2497-2502 A430 Set of 6 2.50 2.50
2503 A430 Sheet of 6, #a-f 8.00 8.00
2504 A430 Sheet of 4, #a-d 7.00 7.00

Souvenir Sheets

2505-2506 A430 Set of 2 9.00 9.00

Rudolph Valentino (1895-1926), Actor — A431

No. 2507, $1: a, Blood and Sand. b, Eyes of Youth. c, All Night. d, Last known photo of Valentino. e, Camille. f, Cobra.

No. 2508, $1: a, The Son of the Sheik. b, The Young Rajah. c, The Eagle. d, The Sheik. e, A Sainted Devil. f, Monsieur Beaucaire.

No. 2509, $6, The Four Horsemen of the Apocalypse. No. 2510, $6, Valentino with Natasha Rambova.

2001, Oct. 2 ***Perf. 13¾***

Sheets of 6, #a-f

2507-2508 A431 Set of 2 9.00 9.00

Souvenir Sheets

2509-2510 A431 Set of 2 9.00 9.00

Scenes From Shirley Temple Movies A432

No. 2511, $1.65 — Scenes from Baby, Take a Bow, with Temple: a, In polka-dot dress. b, With man on steps. c, With man holding gun. d, With woman.

No. 2512, $1.80, horiz. — Scenes from The Little Princess, with Temple: a, With man. b, Washing floor. c, With woman and child. d, With old woman.

No. 2513, $1.50 — Scenes from The Little Princess, with Temple: a, With woman. b, In pink dress. c, Holding doll. d, On throne. e, With man. f, With birthday cake.

No. 2514, $1.65, horiz. — Scenes from Baby, Take a Bow, with Temple: a, With woman and five children. b, With arms around man. c, Being tucked in bed. d, With man. e, Standing with man and woman. f, Looking in cradle.

No. 2515, $6, In polka-dot dress, from Baby, Take a Bow. No. 2516, With soldiers, from The Little Princess.

2001, Oct. 2 **Sheets of 4, #a-d**
2511-2512 A432 Set of 2 10.50 10.50

Sheets of 6, #a-f

2513-2514 A432 Set of 2 14.00 14.00

Souvenir Sheets

2515-2516 A432 Set of 2 8.00 8.00

Nobel Prizes, Cent. A433

No. 2517, $1.50 — Chemistry laureates: a, Melvin Calvin, 1961. b, Linus C. Pauling, 1954. c, Vincent du Vigneaud, 1955. d, Richard Synge, 1952. e, Archer Martin, 1952. f, Alfred Werner, 1913.

No. 2518, $1.50 — Chemistry laureates: a, Robert F. Curl, Jr., 1996. b, Alan J. Heeger, 2000. c, Michael Smith, 1993. d, Sidney Altman, 1989. e, Elias James Corey, 1990. f, William Francis Giauque, 1949.

No. 2519, $6, Ernest Rutherford, Chemistry, 1908. No. 2520, $6, International Red Cross, Peace, 1944. No. 2521, $6, Ernst Otto Fischer, Chemistry, 1973.

2001, Nov. 29 ***Perf. 14***

Sheets of 6, #a-f

2517-2518 A433 Set of 2 13.50 13.50

Souvenir Sheets

2519-2521 A433 Set of 3 13.50 13.50

I Love Lucy Type of 2001

Designs: No. 2522, $6, Fred at desk. No. 2523, $6, Lucy and Fred. No. 2524, $6, Lucy, closed door. No. 2525, $6, Fred and Ricky at desk, horiz.

2001 ***Perf. 13¾***
2522-2525 A420 Set of 4 18.00 18.00

Christmas — A434

Paintings: 25c, Madonna and Child with Angels, by Filippo Lippi. 45c, Madonna of Corneto Tarquinia, by Lippi. 50c, Madonna and Child, by Domenico Ghirlandaio. 75c, Madonna and Child, by Lippi. $4, Madonna del Ceppo, by Lippi.

$6, Madonna Enthroned with Angels and Saints, by Lippi.

2001, Dec. 4 **Litho.** ***Perf. 14***
2526-2530 A434 Set of 5 4.50 4.50

Souvenir Sheet

2531 A434 $6 multi 4.50 4.50

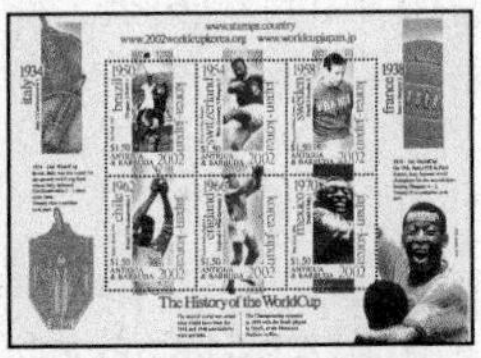

2002 World Cup Soccer Championships, Japan and Korea — A435

No. 2532, $1.50: a, Scene from final game, 1950. b, Ferenc Puskas, 1954. c, Raymond Kopa, 1958. d, Mauro, 1962. e, Gordon Banks, 1966. f, Pelé, 1970.

No. 2533, $1.50: a, Daniel Passarella, 1978. b, Karl-Heinz Rummenigge, 1982. c, World Cup trophy, 1986. d, Diego Maradona, 1990. e, Roger Milla, 1994. f, Zinedine Zidane, 1998.

No. 2534, $6, Head from Jules Rimet Cup, 1930. No. 2535, $6, Head and globe from World Cup trophy, 2002.

2001, Dec. 17 ***Perf. 13¾x14¼***

Sheets of 6, #a-f

2532-2533 A435 Set of 2 12.00 12.00

Souvenir Sheets

Perf. 14¼

2534-2535 A435 Set of 2 8.00 8.00

Queen Mother Type of 2000 Redrawn

No. 2536, each $2: a, As child. b, In 1940. c, With Princess Anne, 1951. d, In Canada, 1989.

$6, Inspecting the troops.

2001, Dec. ***Perf. 14***

Yellow Orange Frames

2536 A404 Sheet of 4, #a-d, + label 6.00 6.00

Souvenir Sheet

Perf. 13¾

2537 A404 $6 multi 4.50 4.50

Queen Mother's 101st birthday. No. 2537 contains one 38x51mm stamp with a darker appearance than that found on No. 2374. Sheet margins of Nos. 2536-2537 lack embossing and gold arms found on Nos. 2373-2374.

US Civil War A436

No. 2538: a, Battle of Nashville. b, Battle of Atlanta. c, Battle of Spotsylvania. d, Battle of the Wilderness. e, Battle of Chickamauga Creek. f, Battle of Gettysburg. g, Battle of Chancellorsville. h, Battle of Fredericksburg. i, Battle of Antietam. j, Second Battle of Bull Run. k, Battle of Five Forks. l, Seven Days' Battle. m, Battle of Bull Run. n, Battle of Shiloh. o, Battle of Seven Pines. p, Battle of Fort Sumter. q, Battle of Chattanooga. r, Surrender at Appomattox.

No. 2539, vert.: a, Gen. Ulysses S. Grant. b, Pres. Abraham Lincoln. c, Confederate Pres. Jefferson Davis. d, Gen. Robert E. Lee. e, Gen. George A. Custer. f, Adm. Andrew Hull Foote. g, General Thomas "Stonewall" Jackson. h, Gen. J.E.B. Stuart. i, Gen. George G. Meade. j, Gen. Philip H. Sheridan. k, Gen. James Longstreet. l, Gen. John S. Mosby.

No. 2540, $6, Monitor. No. 2541, $6, Merrimack.

2002, Jan. 28 ***Perf. 14¾***
2538 A436 45c Sheet of 18, #a-r 10.00 10.00
2539 A436 50c Sheet of 12, #a-l 8.00 8.00

Souvenir Sheets

Perf. 14½x14¾ (#2540), 13¾

2540-2541 A436 Set of 2 11.00 11.00

No. 2541 contains one 50x38mm stamp.

Reign of Queen Elizabeth II, 50th Anniv. A437

No. 2542: a, Striped dress. b, Green patterned dress. c, Orange patterned dress. d, White jacket.

$6, Queen with Princess Margaret.

2002, Feb. 6 ***Perf. 14¼***
2542 A437 $2 Sheet of 4, #a-d 7.00 7.00

Souvenir Sheet

2543 A437 $6 multi 4.50 4.50

United We Stand — A438

2002, Feb. 11 ***Perf. 13½x13¼***
2544 A438 $2 multi 1.50 1.50

Printed in sheets of 4.

Cricket Player Sir Vivian Richards, 50th Birthday — A439

Designs: 25c, Raising bat. 30c, Receiving gift. 50c, With arms raised. 75c, At bat. $1.50, Wearing sash, with woman. $1.80, Standing next to photograph of himself.

No. 2551, $6, Holding sword. No. 2552, $6, With Antigua color guard.

2002, Mar. 7 ***Perf. 13½x13¼***
2545-2550 A439 Set of 6 4.00 4.00

Souvenir Sheets

2551-2552 A439 Set of 2 9.00 9.00

Flora and Fauna — A440

Designs: 50c, Thick-billed parrot. 75c, Lesser long-nosed bat. $1.50, Montserrat oriole. $1.80, Miss Perkin's blue butterfly.

No. 2557, 90c: a, Quetzals. b, Two-toed sloth. c, Lovely cotinga. d, Giant hairstrak butterfly. e, Magenta-throated woodstar. f, Bull's-eye silk moth. g, Golden toads. h, Collared peccaries. i, Tamandua anteater.

No. 2558, $1: a, St. Lucia parrot. b, Cuban kite. c, West Indian whistling duck. d, Poey's sulphur butterfly. e, Scarlet ibis. f, Black-capped petrel. g, St. Lucia whiptail. h, Cuban Solenodon. i, False androgeus swallowtail butterfly.

No. 2559, $6, Margay. No. 2560, $6, Olive Ridley turtle.

2002, Apr. 8 ***Perf. 14***
2553-2556 A440 Set of 4 3.50 3.50

Sheets of 9, #a-i

2557-2558 A440 Set of 2 14.00 14.00

Souvenir Sheets

2559-2560 A440 Set of 2 9.00 9.00

Antigua Community Players, 50th Anniv. — A441

Various photos: 20c, 25c, 30c, 75c, 90c, $1.50, $1.80.

No. 2568, $4, Former Pres. Edie Hill-Thibou, vert. No. 2569, $4, Acting Pres. and Music Director Yvonne Maginley, vert.

Perf. 13½x13¾

2002, June 11 **Litho.**
2561-2567 A441 Set of 7 4.25 4.25

Souvenir Sheets

Perf. 14

2568-2569 A441 Set of 2 6.00 6.00

Endangered Animals — A442

No. 2570, each $1.50: a, Red-billed tropicbird. b, Brown pelican. c, Magnificent frigatebird. d, Ground lizard. e, West Indian whistling duck. f, Antiguan racer snake. g, Spiny lobster. h, Hawksbill turtle. i, Queen conch.

2002, July 12 *Perf. 14*
2570 A442 Sheet of 9, #a-i 12.00 12.00

2002 Winter Olympics, Salt Lake City — A443

Designs: No. 2571, $2, Cross-country skiing. No. 2572, $2, Pairs figure skating.

2002, July 15 *Perf. 13½x13¼*
2571-2572 A443 Set of 2 3.50 3.50
2572a Souvenir sheet, #2571-2572 3.50 3.50

First Solo Transatlantic Flight, 75th Anniv. — A444

No. 2573, each $2.50: a, Charles Lindbergh and The Spirit of St. Louis. b, Arrival at Le Bourget Airport, Paris. c, Lindbergh receiving hero's welcome, New York.
$6, Lindbergh in airplane.

2002, July 15 *Perf. 13¼x13½*
2573 A444 Sheet of 3, #a-c 5.75 5.75

Souvenir Sheet

2574 A444 $6 multi 4.50 4.50

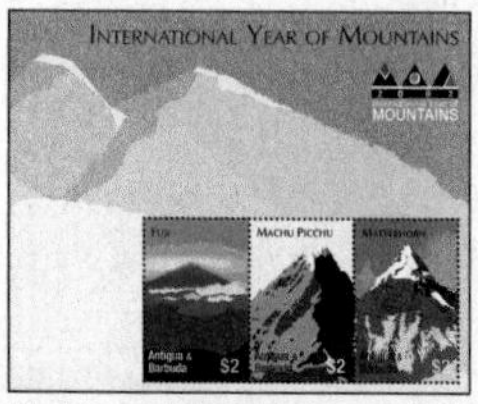

Intl. Year of Mountains — A445

No. 2575: a, Mt. Fuji. b, Machu Picchu. c, Matterhorn.

2002, July 15 *Perf. 13½x13¼*
2575 A445 $2 Sheet of 3, #a-c 4.50 4.50

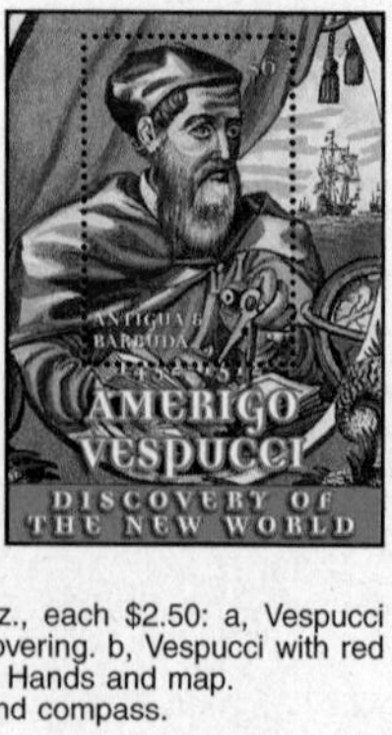

Amerigo Vespucci (1454-1512), Explorer A446

No. 2576, horiz., each $2.50: a, Vespucci with gray head covering. b, Vespucci with red head covering. c, Hands and map.
$6, Vespucci and compass.

Perf. 13¼x13½, 13½x13¼
2002, July 15
2576 A446 Sheet of 3, #a-c 6.00 6.00

Souvenir Sheet

2577 A446 $6 multi 4.50 4.50

Princess Diana (1961-97) — A447

No. 2578: a, Wearing seven-strand pearl necklace. b, Wearing tiara and white dress. c, Wearing hat. d, Wearing earrings and black dress. e, Wearing tiara, no dress seen. f, Wearing earrings, no dress seen.
$6, Wearing white dress.

2002, July 29 *Perf. 14*
2578 A447 $1.80 Sheet of 6, #a-f 7.50 7.50

Souvenir Sheet

2579 A447 $6 multi 4.50 4.50

Presidents John F. Kennedy and Ronald Reagan — A448

No. 2580, $1.50, horiz.: a, John, Robert and Edward Kennedy. b, Kennedy with Danny Kaye. c, Kennedy addressing nation. d, With wife, Jacqueline. e, Shaking hands with young Bill Clinton. f, Family members at funeral.
No. 2581, $1.50, horiz.: a, Reagan with wife, Nancy, and Pope John Paul II. b, As George Gipp in movie *Knute Rockne, All American.* c, With Gen. Matthew Ridgeway at Bitburg Cemetery. d, With Vice-president George H. W. Bush and Mikhail Gorbachev. e, With Presidents Ford, Carter, and Nixon. f, On horseback, with Queen Elizabeth II.
No. 2582, $6, Kennedy and flag. No. 2583, $6, Reagan.

2002, July 29 **Litho.**

Sheets of 6, #a-f

2580-2581 A448 Set of 2 13.50 13.50

Souvenir Sheets

2582-2583 A448 Set of 2 9.00 9.00

Elvis Presley (1935-77) — A449

2002, Aug. 20 *Perf. 13¾*
2584 A449 $1 multi 1.25 1.25

Printed in sheets of 9.

Teddy Bears, Cent. A450

No. 2585: a, Cheerleader bear. b, Figure skater bear. c, Ballet dancer bear. d, Aerobics instructor bear.

2002, Aug. 26
2585 A450 $2 Sheet of 4, #a-d 7.00 7.00

Pokémon A451

No. 2586: a, Croconau. b, Mantine. c, Feraligatr. d, Quilfish. e, Remoraid. f, Quagsire.
$6, Chinchou.

2002, Aug. 26
2586 A451 $1.50 Sheet of 6, #a-f 6.75 6.75

Souvenir Sheet

2587 A451 $6 multi 4.50 4.50

Lee Strasberg (1901-82), Movie Actor and Director — A452

2002, Sept. 16 *Perf. 14*
2588 A452 $1 multi .75 .75

Printed in sheets of 9.

Charlie Chaplin (1889-1977), Actor — A453

No. 2589: a, Wearing bowler hat, facing forward. b, Wearing suit and vest. c, Wearing top hat. d, Wearing bowler hat, profile. e, Wearing bow tie and suit. f, With hand at chin.
$6, Wearing bowler hat, diff.

2002, Sept. 16
2589 A453 $1.80 Sheet of 6, #a-f 8.25 8.25

Souvenir Sheet

2590 A453 $6 multi 4.50 4.50

Marlene Dietrich (1901-92), Actress — A454

No. 2591: a, With hands at side of face. b, Wearing top hat. c, Faciing forward. d, With hand on chin. e, Wearing black hat. f, Wearing gloves.
$6, Facing forward, diff.

2002, Sept. 16
2591 A454 $1.50 Sheet of 6, #a-f 6.75 6.75

Souvenir Sheet

2592 A454 $6 multi 4.50 4.50

Bob Hope A455

No. 2593: a, Wearing red cap. b, Wearing hat with strap. c, Wearing top hat. d, Wearing black cap. e, Wearing camouflage. f, Wearing white cap.

2002, Sept. 16
2593 A455 $1.50 Sheet of 6, #a-f 7.50 7.50

Ferrari Race Cars — A456

Designs: 20c, 1957 801. 25c, 1959 256 F1. 30c, 1960 246P F1. 90c, 1966 246 F1. $1, 1971 312 B2. $1.50, 1969 312 F1. $2, 1997 F310B. $4, 2002 F2002.

2002, Oct. 14 **Litho.**
2594-2601 A456 Set of 8 7.75 7.75

Independence, 21st Anniv. — A457

Designs: 25c, Flag. 30c, Arms, vert. $1.50, Mt. St. John's Hospital nearing completion. $1.80, Parliament Building.
No. 2606, $6, Prime Minister Lester B. Bird, vert. No. 2607, $6, Sir Vere C. Bird, vert.

2002, Oct. 31 *Perf. 14*
2602-2605 A457 Set of 4 3.50 3.50

Souvenir Sheets

2606-2607 A457 Set of 2 9.00 9.00

Nos. 2606-2607 each contain one 38x50mm stamp.

Second Round of World Cup Soccer Championships — A458

No. 2608, $1.65: a, Pyo Lee. b, Ji Sung Park. c, Jung Hwan Ahn. d, Filippo Inzaghi. e, Paolo Maldini. f, Damiano Tommasi.

No. 2609, $1.65: a, Juan Valeron. b, Iker Casillas. c, Fernando Hierro. d, Gary Kelly. e, Damien Duff. f, Matt Holland.

No. 2610, $3: a, South Korean coach Guus Hiddink. b, Chul Sang Yoo.

No. 2611, $3: a, Francesco Totti. b, Italy coach Giovanni Trapattoni.

No. 2612, $3: a, Spain coach Jose Antonio Camacho. b, Carlos Gamarra.

No. 2613, $3: a, Robbie Keane. b, Ireland coach Mick McCarthy.

2002, Nov. 4 *Perf. 13½x13¼*

Sheets of 6, #a-f

2608-2609 A458 Set of 2 15.00 15.00

Souvenir Sheets, #a-b

2610-2613 A458 Set of 4 18.00 18.00

Christmas A459

Designs: 25c, Coronation of the Virgin, by Domenico Ghirlandaio. 45c, Adoration of the Magi (detail), by Ghirlandaio. 75c, Annunciation (detail), by Simone Martini, vert. 90c, Adoration of the Magi (detail, diff.) by Ghirlandaio. $5, Madonna and Child, by Giovanni Bellini.

$6, Madonna and Child, by Martini.

2002, Nov. 18 *Perf. 14*

2614-2618 A459 Set of 5 5.50 5.50

Souvenir Sheet

2619 A459 $6 multi 4.50 4.50

Worldwide Fund for Nature (WWF) — A460

Antiguan racer snake: a, Head. b, Snake with head near tail. c, Snake and dried leaves. d, Snake on rocks.

2002, Nov. 25

2620 Strip of 4 3.75 3.75

a.-d. A460 $1 Any single .90 .90

Printed in sheets of 4 strips.

Flora & Fauna A461

No. 2621, $1.50: a, Magnificent frigatebird. b, Sooty tern. c, Bananaquit. d, Yellow-crowned night heron. e, Greater flamingo. f, Belted kingfisher.

No. 2622, $1.50: a, Killer whale. b, Sperm whale. c, Minke whale. d, Blainville's beaked whale. e, Blue whale. f, Cuvier's beaked whale.

No. 2623, $1.80: a, Hieroglyphic moth. b, Hypocrita dejanira. c, Snowy eupseudosoma moth. d, Composia credula. e, Giant silkworm moth. f, Diva moth.

No. 2624, $1.80: a, Epidendrum fragrans. b, Dombeya. c, Yellow poul. d, Milky wave plant. e, Cinderella plant. f, Coral orchid.

No. 2625, $5, Snowy egret. No. 2626, $5, Rothschildia orizaba. No. 2627, $6, Humpback whale. No. 2628, $6, Ionopsis utricularoides.

2002, Nov. 25 **Litho.**

Sheets of 6, #a-f

2621-2624 A461 Set of 4 32.50 32.50

Souvenir Sheets

2625-2628 A461 Set of 4 19.00 19.00

Souvenir Sheet

Pan-American Health Organization, Cent. — A462

No. 2629: a, Dr. Margaret O'Garro. b, Nurse Ineta Wallace. c, Public Health Worker Vincent Edwards.

2002, Dec. 2

2629 A462 $1.50 Sheet of 3, #a-c 3.50 3.50

Souvenir Sheets

Science Fiction A463

No. 2630, $6, Writings of Nostradamus. No. 2631, $6, *2001: A Space Odyssey*, by Arthur C. Clarke. No. 2632, $6, Are We Alone?

2002, Dec. 12 *Perf. 13¾*

2630-2632 A463 Set of 3 13.50 13.50

A464

20th World Scout Jamboree, Thailand — A465

No. 2633, horiz.: a, Lord Robert Baden-Powell. b, Ernest Thompson Seton, first Chief Scout. c, First black troop.

No. 2634: a, Brownie with broad neckerchief "X." b, Brownie with narrow neckerchief "X." c, Brownie with incomplete neckerchief "X."

No. 2635, Seton. No. 2636, Scout salute.

2002, Dec. 12 **Litho.** *Perf. 14*

2633 A464 $3 Sheet of 3, #a-c 7.00 7.00

2634 A465 $3 Sheet of 3, #a-c 7.00 7.00

Souvenir Sheet

2635 A464 $6 multi 4.50 4.50

2636 A465 $6 multi 4.50 4.50

Ram, by Liu Jiyou — A466

2003, Feb. 10 *Perf. 13¾*

2637 A466 $1.80 multi 1.40 1.40

New Year 2003 (Year of the Ram). Issued in sheets of 4.

A467

Coronation of Queen Elizabeth II, 50th Anniv. — A468

No. 2638, each $3: a, In uniform. b, With tan jacket. c, With white dress and hat.

$6, With white dress.

2003 **Litho.** *Perf. 14*

2638 A467 Sheet of 3, #a-c 6.75 6.75

Souvenir Sheet

2639 A467 $6 multi 4.50 4.50

Miniature Sheet

Litho. & Embossed

Perf. 13¼x13

2640 A468 $20 gold & multi 17.50 17.50

Issued: Nos. 2638-2639, 5/14; No. 2640, 2/10.

Paintings of Lucas Cranach the Elder (1472-1553) A469

Designs: 75c, Lucretia. 90c, Venus and Cupid. $1, Judith with the Head of Holofernes, c. 1530. $1.50, Portrait of a Young Lady.

No. 2645: a, Portrait of the Wife of a Jurist. b, Portrait of a Jurist. c, Johannes Cuspinian. d, Portrait of Anna Cuspinian.

$6, Judith with the Head of Holofernes, c. 1532.

2003, Apr. 30 **Litho.** *Perf. 14¼*

2641-2644 A469 Set of 4 3.25 3.25

2645 A469 $2 Sheet of 4, #a-d 6.00 6.00

Souvenir Sheet

2646 A469 $6 multi 4.50 4.50

Paintings of Yoshitoshi Taiso (1839-92) — A470

Designs: 25c, A High Class Maid Training in a Samurai Household. 50c, A Castle-Toppler Known as "Keisei": A Beautiful Woman Able to Seduce a Ruler So That He Forgets the Affairs of the State. $1, Stylish Young Geisha Battling a Snowstorm on Her Way to Work. $5, A Lady in Distress Being Treated With Moxa.

No. 2651: a, A Lady of the Imperial Court Wearing Four Layers of Robes. b, Young Mother Adoring Her Infant Son. c, Lady-in-waiting Looking Amused Over a Veranda in the Household of a Great Lord. d, A High-ranking Courtesan Known as "Oiran" Waiting For a Private Assignation.

$6, A Girl Teasing Her Cat.

2003, Apr. 30

2647-2650 A470 Set of 4 5.00 5.00

2651 A470 $2 Sheet of 4, #a-d 6.00 6.00

Souvenir Sheet

2652 A470 $6 multi 4.50 4.50

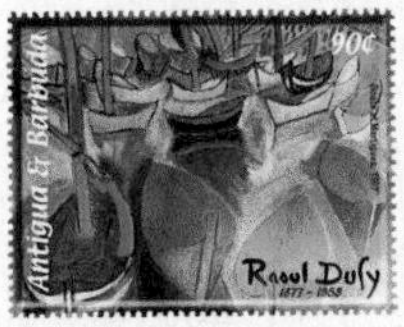

Paintings of Raoul Dufy (1877-1953) A471

Designs: 90c, Boats at Martigues. $1, Harvesting. $1.80, Sailboats in the Port of Le Havre. $5, The Big Bather, vert.

No. 2657: a, The Beach and the Pier at Trouville. b, Port With Sailing Ships. c, Black Cargo. d, Nice, the Bay of Anges.

No. 2658, $6, The Interior With an Open Window. No. 2659, $6, Vence.

2003, Apr. 30

2653-2656 A471 Set of 4 6.50 6.50

2657 A471 $2 Sheet of 4, #a-d 6.00 6.00

Size: 96x76mm

Imperf

2658-2659 A471 Set of 2 9.00 9.00

Prince William, 21st Birthday A472

No. 2660: a, With yellow and black shirt. b, With polo helmet. c, With blue shirt.

$6, In suit.

2003, May 14 *Perf. 14*

2660 A472 $3 Sheet of 3, #a-c 7.00 7.00

Souvenir Sheet

2661 A472 $6 multi 4.50 4.50

Salvation Army in Antigua, Cent. — A473

Designs: 30c, Emblem, Tamarind tree, Parham, vert. 90c, Salvation Army Pre-school, vert. $1, Meals on Wheels. $1.50, St. John's Citadel Band. $1.80, Salvation Army Citadel.

$6, Tamarind tree, Parham, vert.

2003, May 19 ***Perf. 14¼***
2662-2666 A473 Set of 5 4.25 4.25

Souvenir Sheet

2667 A473 $6 multi 4.50 4.50

Antigua & Barbuda Scouts Association, 90th Anniv. — A474

Designs: 30c, First Anglican Scout troop, 1931. $1, National Scout Camp, 2002. $1.50, Woodbadge Training Course, 2000, horiz. $1.80, Men visiting National Scout Camp, 1986, horiz.

No. 2672: a, Edris George. b, Theodore George. c, Edris James.

$6, Scout with semaphore flags.

2003, June 9 ***Perf. 14***
2668-2671 A474 Set of 4 3.75 3.75
2672 A474 90c Sheet of 3, #a-c 2.25 2.25

Souvenir Sheet

2673 A474 $6 multi 4.75 4.75

Tour de France Bicycle Race, Cent. A475

No. 2674, $2: a, Cesar Garin, 1903. b, Henri Cornet, 1904. c, Louis Trousselier, 1905. d, René Pottier, 1906.

No. 2675, $2: a, Lucien Petit-Breton, 1907. b, Petit-Breton, 1908. c, François Faber, 1909. d, Octave Lapize, 1910.

No. 2676, $2: a, Gustave Garrigou, 1911. b, Odile Defraye, 1912. c, Philippe Thys, 1913. d, Thys, 1914.

No. 2677, $6, Pierre Giffard. No. 2678, $6, Henri Desgrange. No. 2679, $6, Comte de Dion.

2003, June 9 ***Perf. 13¼***

Sheets of 4, #a-d

2674-2676 A475 Set of 3 18.00 18.00

Souvenir Sheets

2677-2679 A475 Set of 3 13.50 13.50

Caribbean Community, 30th Anniv. — A476

2003, July 4 ***Perf. 14***
2680 A476 $1 multi .80 .80

Intl. Year of Fresh Water A477

No. 2681, horiz.: a, Chutes de Carbet and rocks. b, Chutes de Carbet and foliage at left and right. c, Rocks at base of Chutes de Carbet.

$6, Ocho Rios Waterfall.

2003, July 14 ***Perf. 13¼***
2681 A477 $2 Sheet of 3, #a-c 5.25 5.25

Souvenir Sheet

2682 A477 $6 multi 5.00 5.00

General Motors Automobiles — A478

No. 2683, $2 — Cadillacs: a, 1955 Eldorado convertible. b, 1937 Series 60. c, 1959 Eldorado. d, 2002 Eldorado.

No. 2684, $2 — Chevrolet Corvettes: a, 1954 convertible. b, 1964 Sting Ray. c, 1964 Sting Ray convertible. d, 1998 convertible.

No. 2685, $6, 1953 Cadillac Eldorado. No. 2686, $6, 1956 Corvette convertible.

2003, July 14 ***Perf. 13¼x13½***

Sheets of 4, #a-d

2683-2684 A478 Set of 2 12.00 12.00

Souvenir Sheets

2685-2686 A478 Set of 2 9.00 9.00

Cadillac, cent.; Corvette, 50th anniv.

History of Aviation A479

No. 2687, $2: a, First Wright Brothers flight, 1903. b, First free flight in helicopter by Paul Cornu, 1907. c, First landing on ship, by E. B. Ely. d, Curtiss A-1, first hydroplane, 1911.

No. 2688, $2: a, Bell X-5, 1951. b, Convair XFY-1, 1954. c, North American X-15, 1959. d, Alexei Leonov, first man to walk in space, 1965.

No. 2689, $2: a, Concorde, 1969. b, Martin X-24, 1969. c, Apollo-Soyuz space mission, 1975. d, Mars probe Viking, 1976.

No. 2690, $6, Boeing Model 200 Monomail, 1930. No. 2691, $6, Breaking of sound barrier by Bell X-1, 1947. No. 2692, $6, Grumman X-29, 1984.

2003, July 28 ***Perf. 14***

Sheets of 4, #a-d

2687-2689 A479 Set of 3 20.00 20.00

Souvenir Sheets

2690-2692 A479 Set of 3 13.50 13.50

Bird Type of 1995

Designs: $5, Montezuma oropendola. $10, Green jay.

2003, Aug. 11 **Litho.** ***Perf. 15x14***
2693 A296 $5 multi 3.75 3.75
2694 A296 $10 multi 7.50 7.50

Circus Performers — A480

No. 2695, $1.80 — Clowns: a, Apes. b, Mo Lite. c, Gigi. d, "Buttons" McBride.

No. 2696, $1.80 — Perfomers: a, Chun Group. b, Casselly Sisters. c, Oliver Groszer. d, Keith Nelson.

2003, Sept. 1 ***Perf. 14***

Sheets of 4, #a-d

2695-2696 A480 Set of 2 11.00 11.00

Christmas — A481

Designs: 25c, Madonna and Child, by Bartolomeo Vivarini. 30c, Holy Family, by Pompeo Girolamo Batoni. 45c, Madonna and Child, by Benozzo Gozzoli. 50c, Madonna and Child (Calci Parish Church), by Gozzoli. 75c, Madonna and Child Giving Blessings, by Gozzoli. 90c, Madonna and Child, by Master of the Female Half-figures. $2.50, Benois Madonna, by Leonardo da Vinci.

$6, The Virgin and Child with Angels, by Rosso Fiorentino.

2003, Nov. 10 **Litho.** ***Perf. 14¼***
2697-2703 A481 Set of 7 4.25 4.25

Souvenir Sheet

2704 A481 $6 multi 4.50 4.50

Orchids A482

No. 2705, $2.50, vert.: a, Psychopsis papilio. b, Amesiella philippinensis. c, Maclellanara Pagan Dove Song. d, Phalaenopsis Little Hal.

No. 2706, $2.50: a, Daeliocattleya Amber Glow. b, Hygrochilus parishii. c, Dendrobium crystallinum. d, Disa hybrid.

$5, Cattleya deckeri.

2003, Dec. 8 ***Perf. 13½***

Sheets of 4, #a-d

2705-2706 A482 Set of 2 17.50 17.50

Souvenir Sheet

2707 A482 $5 multi 5.00 5.00

Birds A483

No. 2708, $2.50, vert.: a, Blue and gold macaw. b, Green-winged macaw. c, Green-naped lorikeet. d, Lesser sulfur-crested cockatoo.

No. 2709, $2.50: a, Severe macaw. b, Blue-headed parrot. c, Budgerigar. d, Sun conure.

$5, Bald ibis.

2003, Dec. 8 **Sheets of 4, #a-d**

2708-2709 A483 Set of 2 19.50 19.50

Souvenir Sheet

2710 A483 $5 multi 5.00 5.00

Butterflies — A484

No. 2711, $2: a, Esmerelda. b, Tiger pierid. c, Blue night. d, Charaxes nobilis.

No. 2712, $2.50: a, Orange-barred sulphur. b, Scarce bamboo page. c, Charaxes latona. d, Hewitson's blue hairstreak.

$5, Diaethia meridionalis.

2003, Dec. 8 **Sheets of 4, #a-d**

2711-2712 A484 Set of 2 17.50 17.50

Souvenir Sheet

2713 A484 $5 multi 5.00 5.00

Sharks A485

No. 2714: a, Bull. b, Gray reef. c, Black tip. d, Leopard.

$5, Great white.

2003, Dec. 8
2714 A485 $2 Sheet of 4, #a-d 7.50 7.50

Souvenir Sheet

2715 A485 $5 multi 4.50 4.50

New Year 2004 (Year of the Monkey) A486

No. 2716, each $1.50: a, Monkey with black face and white chest. b, Monkey with brown face and white chest. c, Monkey with black, gray and yellow face. d, Red brown monkey on branch.

2004, Jan. 19 ***Perf. 14***
2716 A486 Sheet of 4, #a-d 5.00 5.00

Arthur and Friends A487

No. 2717, each $1.50: a, Binky. b, Buster. c, Francine. d, D.W. e, Sue Ellen. f, Muffy.

No. 2718, each $1.80: a, Binky. b, Muffy. c, Francine. d, Buster.

No. 2719, each $2.50: a, Arthur hitting baseball. b, Sue Ellen. c, Binky. d, Arthur with foot on home plate.

2004, Feb. 16 ***Perf. 13¼***
2717 A487 Sheet of 6, #a-f 6.75 6.75

Sheets of 4, #a-d

2718-2719 A487 Set of 2 13.00 13.00

Paintings by Ren Xiong (1820-57) — A488

No. 2720, each $1.50: a, Purple hills. b, Cliffside waves. c, Hills at left, trees, Chinese text at right. d, House and tree.

No. 2721, each $1.50: a, Rocky pinnacles. b, Rocks at left and right. c, Hills, trees and bridge, Chinese text at top right. d, Waterfall at right, Chinese text at top left. e, Waterfalls, Chinese text at left. f, Rocks and flowers, Chinese text at top left.

No. 2722, each $1.50: a, Bird on flowering tree. b, Bird in tree.

2004, Feb. 16
2720 A488 Sheet of 4, #a-d 4.50 4.50
2721 A488 Sheet of 6, #a-f 6.75 6.75
2722 A488 Sheet of 2, #a-b 4.00 4.00

Paintings by Pablo Picasso A489

No. 2723: a, Woman with a Flower. b, Marie-Thérèse Seated. c, The Red Armchair (Marie-Thérèse) Seated. d, The Dream (Marie-Thérèse) Seated.
$5, Bust of a Girl (Marie-Thérèse).

2004, Mar. 8 ***Perf. 14¼***
2723 A489 $2 Sheet of 4, #a-d 6.50 6.50

Imperf
2724 A489 $5 shown 4.00 4.00

No. 2723 contains four 38x50mm stamps.

Paintings by Norman Rockwell A490

No. 2725: a, Freedom of Speech. b, Freedom to Worship. c, Freedom from Want. d, Freedom from Fear.
$5, Painting for cover of Apr. 1, 1961 Saturday Evening Post.

2004, Mar. 8
2725 A490 $2 Sheet of 4, #a-d 6.00 6.00

Imperf
2726 A490 $6 shown 4.50 4.50

No. 2725 contains four 38x50mm stamps.

Paintings by Paul Gauguin (1848-1903) A491

Designs: 25c, Vaite Goupil, vert. 30c, Autoportrait prés de Golgotha, vert. 75c, Le Moulin David à Pont-Aver. $2.50, Moisson en Bretagne, vert.
$4, Cavaliers sur la Plage.

2004, Mar. 8 **Litho.** ***Perf. 14¼***
2727-2730 A491 Set of 4 3.00 3.00

Imperf
Size: 77x63mm
2731 A491 $4 multi 4.75 4.75

Paintings by Joan Miró (1893-1983) A492

Designs: 75c, The Smile of Flaming Wings. 90c, The Bird's Song in the Dew of the Moon. $1, Dancer II, vert. $4, Painting, 1954, vert.
No. 2736, $2 — Painting Based on a Collage, description in: a, LL. b, LR. c, UL. d, UR.
$5, Bather. $6, Flame in Space and Nude Woman, vert.

2004, Mar. 8 **Litho.** ***Perf. 14¼***
2732-2735 A492 Set of 4 5.50 5.50
2736 A492 $2 Sheet of 4, #a-d 6.50 6.50

Imperf
Size: 102x83mm
2737 A492 $5 multi 4.00 4.00

Size: 83x102mm
2738 A492 $6 multi 5.00 5.00

Wedding of Prince Felipe de Borbón of Spain and Letizia Ortiz — A493

Designs: 30c, Couple. 50c, Couple, diff. 75c, Letizia. 90c, Prince Felipe. $1, Couple, diff. No. 2744, $5, Couple, diff.
No. 2745: a, Spanish royal family. b, Flags and Prince Felipe in uniform. c, Prince Felipe, his grandfather, Juan de Borbón y Battenberg, and his father, King Juan Carlos. d, Letizia, Prince Felipe, King Juan Carlos and Queen Sophia, horiz. e, Similar to 75c. f, Similar to 90c.
No. 2746, $5, Couple, diff. No. 2747, $5, Similar to #2745a. No. 2748, $5, Similar to #2745c. No. 2749, $6, Letizia, map of Europe. No. 2750, $6, Similar to #2745b. No. 2751, $6, Similar to #2745d, horiz.

2004, May 21 ***Perf. 13¼***
2739-2744 A493 Set of 6 6.50 6.50
2745 A493 $1.80 Sheet of 6, #a-f 8.50 8.50

Souvenir Sheets
2746-2751 A493 Set of 6 25.00 25.00

Election of Pope John Paul II, 25th Anniv. (in 2003) A494

No. 2752: a, Pope with Mother Teresa. b, Pope in the Holy Land. c, Pope meeting with Pres. George W. Bush. d, Pope waving, dark background. e, Pope waving, light background.

2004, June 17 ***Perf. 14***
2752 A494 $1.80 Sheet of 5, #a-e 7.25 7.25

Inscription of "2000" on No. 2752a is incorrect.

Intl. Year of Peace A495

No. 2753 Dove and: a, Intl. Year of Peace emblem. b, Earth. c, UN emblem.

2004, June 17
2753 A495 $3 Sheet of 3, #a-c 6.75 6.75

2004 Summer Olympics, Athens — A496

Designs: $1, Poster for 1964 Tokyo Olympics. $1.65, Commemorative medal for 1964 Tokyo Olympics. $1.80, Fencing, horiz. $2, Wrestlers, horiz.

2004, June 17 ***Perf. 14¼***
2754-2757 A496 Set of 4 5.00 5.00

European Soccer Championships, Portugal — A497

No. 2758: a, Milan Galic. b, Slava Metreveli. c, Igor Netto. d, Parc des Princes.
$6, 1960 USSR team.

2004, June 17 ***Perf. 14***
2758 A497 $2 Sheet of 4, #a-d 7.50 7.50

Souvenir Sheet
Perf. 14¼
2759 A497 $6 multi 5.00 5.00

No. 2758 contains four 28x42mm stamps.

Locomotives, Signals and Stations — A498

No. 2760, $1: a, Evening Star. b, Indian Railways XC Pacific. c, German Kriegslokomotive. d, Bulleid Light Pacific. e, G. W. R. copper cap chimney. f, Tallylyn Railway. g, Preservation volunteers. h, N. E. R. Y7 0-4-0T. h, Breda 0-4-0 WT, locomotive shed, Asmara, Eritrea.
No. 2761, $1, vert.: a, King Class 4-6-0. b, Argentinian 11B Class 2-8-0. c, Baldwin Mikado. d, Round trackside signal with red horizontal band. e, Wooden box with button signal. f, Signal house, signals with red and yellow arms. g, Signal house, signal with two red arms. h, Window of signal house. i, Signal lights.
No. 2762, $1, vert.: a, 2-4-0T on Douglas to Port Erin line, Isle of Man. b, South African Railways 4-8-2S. c, China Railways SY Class 2-8-2. d, St. Pancras Station. e, Ulverston Station. f, Bolton Station. g, Liverpool St. Station. h, Cannon St. Station. i, Malvern Station.
No. 2763, $5, Settle-Carlisle line. No. 2764, $6, Douro Valley Railway. No. 2765, $6, Train over Lake Egridir, Turkey.

2004, June 17 ***Perf. 14***
Sheets of 9, #a-i
2760-2762 A498 Set of 3 21.00 21.00

Souvenir Sheets
2763-2765 A498 Set of 3 14.00 14.00

D-Day, 60th Anniv. — A499

Designs: 30c, Derrick Tysoe. 45c, Lt. Gen. Walter Bedell Smith. $1.50, Les Perry. $3, Maj. Gen. Percy Hobart.
No. 2770, $2: a, Tiger II tank. b, Standartenfuhrer Kurt Meyer. c, Canadian infantry. d, British infantry.
No. 2771, $2: a, Hamilcar disgorges Tetrarch tank. b, Horsa glider unloads cargo. c, Beachheads established. d, Liberation begins.
No. 2772, $6, Sherman tank. No. 2773, $6, Mulberry Harbor.

2004, July 26 ***Perf. 14¼***
Stamp + Label (#2766-2769)
2766-2769 A499 Set of 4 4.00 4.00

Sheets of 4, #a-d
2770-2771 A499 Set of 2 12.00 12.00

Souvenir Sheets
2772-2773 A499 Set of 2 9.00 9.00

Miniature Sheet

Queen Juliana of the Netherlands (1909-2004) — A500

No. 2774 — Netherlands flag and: a, Juliana. b, Juliana and Prince Bernhard. c, Juliana and Princess Beatrix. d, Juliana and Princess Irene. e, Juliana and Princess Margriet. f, Juliana and Princess Christina.

2004, June 17 **Litho.** ***Perf. 13¼***
2774 A500 $2 Sheet of 6, #a-f 9.00 9.00

Miniature Sheet

National Basketball Association Players — A501

No. 2775: a, Mike Bibby, Sacramento Kings. b, Jim Jackson, Houston Rockets. c, Tracy McGrady, Houston Rockets. d, Chris Webber, Sacramento Kings. e, Peja Stojakovic, Sacramento Kings. f, Yao Ming, Houston Rockets.

2004, Nov. 8 ***Perf. 12***
2775 A501 $1.50 Sheet of 6, #a-f 6.75 6.75

FIFA (Fédération Internationale de Football Association), Cent. — A502

No. 2776: a, Zinedine Zidane. b, Roberto Baggio. c, Franz Beckenbauer. d, Ossie Ardiles.
$6, Jimmy Greaves.

2004, Nov. 8 ***Perf. 12¾x12½***
2776 A502 $2 Sheet of 4, #a-d 6.00 6.00

Souvenir Sheet
2777 A502 $6 multi 4.50 4.50

Miniature Sheet

John Denver (1943-97), Singer — A503

No. 2778, each $1.50: a, At microphone. b, Tuning guitar. c, With arm extended. d, Facing left, playing guitar.

2004, Nov. 22 ***Perf. 14***
2778 A503 Sheet of 4, #a-d 4.50 4.50

Miniature Sheet

George Herman "Babe" Ruth (1895-1948), Baseball Player — A504

No. 2779, each $1.80: a, Wearing blue cap. b, Wearing crown. c, Wearing pinstriped cap. d, Holding bat.

2004, Nov. 22
2779 A504 Sheet of 4, #a-d 5.50 5.50

The Family Circus, Comic Strip by Bil and Jeff Keane A505

No. 2780, $2: a, "Billy attackled me too hard," purple panel. b, "His ears came from where his eyes are." c, "Tennessee!" d, "One candy or one bowl?"
No. 2781, $2: a, "If you had wider shoulders, Daddy, you could be a two-seater." b, "Billy attackled me too hard," red panel. c, "Who teepeed the mummies?" d, "Looking out there makes me realize it's indeed the little things that count."
No. 2782, $2: a, "Someday I might travel to another planet, but I'm not sure why." b, "Adam and Eve were lucky. They didn't have any history to learn." c, "My backpack is too full. Will somebody help me stand up?" d, "I tripped because one foot tried to hug the other foot."
No. 2783, $2: a, "If you don't put enough stamps on it the mailman will only take it part way." b, "Gee, Grandma, you have a lot of thoughts on your wall." c, "Shall I play for you pa-rum-pa-pum-pummm. . .?" d, "You have to do that when you're married."
No. 2784, $2: a, Billy. b, Jeffy. c, PJ. d, Dolly.

Perf. 13¼, 14¼(#2784)
2004, Nov. 22 Sheets of 4, #a-d
2780-2784 A505 Set of 5 30.00 30.00

World AIDS Day — A506

2004, Dec. 1 ***Perf. 14***
2785 A506 $2 multi 1.75 1.75

Christmas — A507

Designs: 20c, Madonna in Floral Wreath, by Jan Breughel the Elder and Peter Paul Rubens. 25c, Madonna and Child, by Jan Gossaert. 30c, Santa Claus on skis. 45c, Santa Claus with raised arms. 50c, Santa Claus, reindeer on roof. $1, Floral Wreath with Virgin and Child, by Daniel Seghers. $1.80, Madonna and Child, by Andrea Mantegna.
$6, Madonna in a Floral Wreath, by Seghers.

2004, Dec. 13 ***Perf. 12¼x12***
2786-2792 A507 Set of 7 3.50 3.50

Souvenir Sheet

2793 A507 $6 multi 5.00 5.00

Dogs — A508

Designs: 30c, American pit bull terrier. 90c, Maltese. $1.50, Rottweiler. $3, Australian terrier.
$6, German shepherd, horiz.

2005, May 23 Litho. ***Perf. 12¾***
2794-2797 A508 Set of 4 8.00 8.00

Souvenir Sheet

2798 A508 $6 multi 6.25 6.25

Cats — A509

Designs: 75c, Golden Persian. $1, Calico shorthair. $1.50, Siamese. $3, Tabby Persian.
$5, Turkish.

2005, May 23
2799-2802 A509 Set of 4 6.00 6.00

Souvenir Sheet

2803 A509 $5 multi 5.00 5.00

Insects A510

No. 2804, horiz.: a, Figure-of-eight butterfly. b, Honeybee. c, Migratory grasshopper. d, Hercules beetle.
$5, Cramer's Mesene butterfly.

2005, May 23
2804 A510 $2 Sheet of 4, #a-d 7.75 7.75

Souvenir Sheet

2805 A510 $5 multi 4.50 4.50

Marine Life A511

No. 2806: a, Yellowtail damselfish. b, French angelfish. c, Horseshoe crab. d, Emerald mithrax crab.
$6, Spanish hogfish.

2005, May 23
2806 A511 $2 Sheet of 4, #a-d 7.25 7.25

Souvenir Sheet

2807 A511 $6 multi 5.75 5.75

Prehistoric Animals — A512

No. 2808, $2: a, Mammuthus imperator. b, Brontops. c, Hyracotherium. d, Propaleotherium.
No. 2809, $2.50: a, Ceratosaur. b, Coelurosaurs. c, Ornitholestes. d, Baryonyx.
No. 2810, $3: a, Plateosaurus. b, Yangchuanosaurus. c, Ceolophysis. d, Lystrosaurus.
No. 2811, $4, Triceratops. No. 2812, $5, Stegoasurus, vert. No. 2813, $6, Coelodonta.

2005, May 23

Sheets of 4, #a-d

2808-2810 A512 Set of 3 28.00 28.00

Souvenir Sheets

2811-2813 A512 Set of 3 13.00 13.00

Miniature Sheet

Pres. Ronald Reagan (1911-2004) — A513

No. 2814 — Background colors: a, Gray blue. b, Gray brown. c, Pink. d, White. e, Gray green. f, Buff.

2005, June 15 ***Perf. 14***
2814 A513 $1.50 Sheet of 6, #a-f 7.50 7.50

New Year 2005 (Year of the Rooster) — A514

Mother Hen and Her Brood, by Wang Ning: $1, Detail. $4, Entire painting.

2005, June 15 ***Perf. 14¼***
2815 A514 $1 multi .75 .75

Souvenir Sheet

2816 A514 $4 multi 4.00 4.00

No. 2815 printed in sheets of 4.

Friedrich von Schiller (1759-1805), Writer — A515

No. 2817: a, Bust of Schiller, by C. L. Richter, Central Park, New York. b, Actors in "Kabale und Liebe." c, Schiller's birthplace, Marbach, Germany.
$6, Sculpture of Schiller, by Ernst Rau, Lincoln Park, Chicago.

2005, June 15 ***Perf. 14***
2817 A515 $3 Sheet of 3, #a-c 6.75 6.75

Souvenir Sheet

2818 A515 $6 multi 5.25 5.25

Jules Verne (1828-1905), Writer — A516

No. 2819, vert. — Movie posters for Verne works: a, Monster Island, 1961. b, Journey to the Center of the Earth, 1961. c, From the Earth to the Moon, 1956. d, Sea Devils, 1961.
$5, Michael Strogoff, 1956.

2005, June 15
2819 A516 $2 Sheet of 4, #a-d 6.00 6.00

Souvenir Sheet

2820 A516 $5 multi 3.75 3.75

No. 2819 contains four 28x42mm stamps.

World Cup Soccer Championships, 75th Anniv. — A517

No. 2821, each $1.50 — Uruguayan flag, first place medal and: a, 1930 Uruguay team. b, Hector Castro scoring goal against Argentina. c, Crowd in Estadio Centenario. d, Hector Castro.
$6, Uruguay team celebrating 1930 victory.

2005, June 15 ***Perf. 14¼***
2821 A517 Sheet of 4, #a-d 8.00 8.00

Souvenir Sheet

2822 A517 $6 multi 4.50 4.50

End of World War II, 60th Anniv. A518

No. 2823, $1.50: a, Soldiers in Red Square, Moscow, May 9, 1945. b, Gen. Bernard Law Montgomery. c, Marshal Georgi K. Zhukov. d, Gen. Omar N. Bradley.
No. 2824, $2, horiz.: a, Winston Churchill, Franklin D. Roosevelt and Joseph Stalin at Yalta Summit. b, Raising of US flag on Mount Suribachi. c, Gen. Douglas MacArthur signing Japanese surrender documents. d, Japanese officials at surrender ceremony.

2005, June 15 ***Perf. 14***

Sheets of 4, #a-d

2823-2824 A518 Set of 2 10.50 10.50

Battle of Trafalgar, Bicent. A519

Various ships in battle: 90c, $1, $1.50, $1.80.
$6, The Victory firing during the Battle of Trafalgar.

2005, June 15 ***Perf. 14¼***
2825-2828 A519 Set of 4 6.75 6.75

Souvenir Sheet

2829 A519 $6 multi 7.75 7.75

National Basketball Association Players — A520

Designs: No. 2830, 75c, Ray Allen, Seattle Supersonics. No. 2831, 75c, Lucious Harris, Cleveland Cavaliers. No. 2832, 75c, Dwight Howard, Orlando Magic. No. 2833, 75c, Antonio McDyess, Detroit Pistons. No. 2834, 75c, Emeka Okafor, Charlotte Bobcats.

2005 ***Perf. 14***
2830-2834 A520 Set of 5 3.00 3.00

Pope John Paul II (1920-2005) and Meir Lau, Chief Rabbi of Israel — A521

2005, Oct. 10 ***Perf. 13½x13¼***
2835 A521 $3 multi 4.25 4.25

Printed in sheets of 6.

Albert Einstein (1879-1955), Physicist — A522

No. 2836 — Photograph of Einstein in: a, Brown. b, Olive green. c, Black.

2005, Oct. 10 Litho. ***Perf. 13¼x13½***
2836 A522 $3 Sheet of 3, #a-c 6.75 6.75

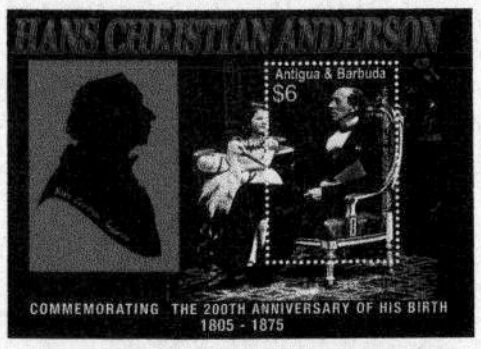

Hans Christian Andersen (1805-75), Author — A523

No. 2837: a, Portrait of Andersen. b, Statue of Andersen, Central Park, New York City. c, Andersen's gravesite.

$6, Andersen seated.

2005, Oct. 10 ***Perf. 13½x13¼***
2837 A523 $3 Sheet of 3, #a-c 6.75 6.75

Souvenir Sheet

2838 A523 $6 multi 5.25 5.25

Rotary International, Cent. — A524

No. 2839, vert.: a, Italy #1372. b, Paul Harris Medallion. c, Paul P. Harris, first Rotary President.

$6, Children.

2005, Oct. 10 ***Perf. 13½x13¼***
2839 A524 $3 Sheet of 3, #a-c 7.25 7.25

Souvenir Sheet

Perf. 13¼x13½

2840 A524 $6 multi 6.00 6.00

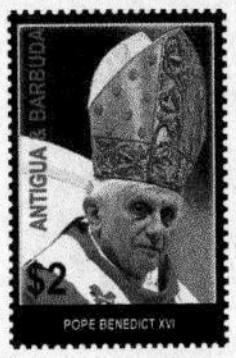

Pope Benedict XVI — A525

2005, Nov. 21 ***Perf. 13½x13¼***
2841 A525 $2 multi 1.75 1.75

Christmas A526

Churches: 25c, Gilbert's Memorial Methodist Church. No. 2843, 30c, People's Church, Barbuda. No. 2844, 30c, Tyrell's Roman Catholic Church. 45c, St. Barnabas Anglican Church. 50c, St. Peter's Anglican Church. No. 2847, 75c, Spring Gardens Moravian Church. No. 2848, 75c, St. Steven's Anglican Church. No. 2849, 90c, Holy Family Catholic Cathedral. No. 2850, 90c, Pilgrim Holiness Church, vert. $1, Ebenezer Methodist Church.

No. 2852, $5, St. John's Cathedral. No. 2853, $5, Worship service, Spring Gardens Moravian Church, vert.

2005, Dec. 19 ***Perf. 12¾***
2842-2851 A526 Set of 10 6.75 6.75

Souvenir Sheets

2852-2853 A526 Set of 2 8.00 8.00

Elvis Presley (1935-77) — A527

Serpentine Die Cut 8¾x9

2005 Litho. & Embossed
2854 A527 $20 gold & multi 16.00 16.00

National Parks — A528

Designs: No. 2855, 20c, Joiner's Loft, Nelson's Dockyard Natl. Park. No. 2856, 20c, Pay Office, Nelson's Dockyard Natl. Park, vert. No. 2857, 30c, Admiral's House Museum, Nelson's Dockyard Natl. Park. No. 2858, 30c, Bakery, Nelson's Dockyard Natl. Park. No. 2859, 75c, Devil's Bridge Natl. Park. No. 2860, 75c, View from Shirley Heights Lookout, Nelson's Dockyard Natl. Park. No. 2861, 90c, Green Castle Hill Natl. Park. No. 2862, 90c, Fort Berkeley, Nelson's Dockyard Natl. Park. No. 2863, $1.50, Pigeon Point Beach, Nelson's Dockyard Natl. Park. No. 2864, $1.50, Half Moon Bay Natl. Park. $1.80, Cannon at Ft. Berkeley.

No. 2866, $5, Codrington Lagoon Natl. Park. No. 2867, $5, Museum, Nelson's Dockyard Natl. Park, vert.

2006, Jan. 9 ***Perf. 14***
2855-2865 A528 Set of 11 7.00 7.00

Souvenir Sheets

2866-2867 A528 Set of 2 9.50 9.50

National Parks of the United States A529

No. 2868: a, Yellowstone. b, Olympic. c, Glacier. d, Grand Canyon. e, Yosemite. f, Great Smoky Mountains.

$6, Mount Rainier.

2006, Jan. 6 ***Perf. 14¼***
2868 A529 $1.50 Sheet of 6, #a-f 7.50 7.50

Souvenir Sheet

Perf. 14

2869 A529 $6 multi 4.75 4.75

No. 2868 contains six 50x38mm stamps.

Moravian Church Antigua Conference, 250th Anniv. — A530

Designs: 30c, Bishop John Ephraim Knight. $1, John Andrew Buckley. $1.50, Old Spring Gardens Moravian Church, horiz.

No. 2873, $5, Sandbox tree. No. 2874, $5, Westerby Memorial. No. 2875, $5, Spring Gardens Teachers College, horiz.

2006, Apr. 3 ***Perf. 12¾***
2870-2872 A530 Set of 3 2.25 2.25

Souvenir Sheets

2873-2875 A530 Set of 3 13.00 13.00

Marilyn Monroe (1926-62), Actress — A531

2006, Apr. 10 ***Perf. 13¼***
2876 A531 $3 multi 2.25 2.25

Printed in sheets of 4.

Queen Elizabeth II, 80th Birthday A532

No. 2877: a, As young woman (black and white photo). b, Wearing pearl necklace. c, Wearing white blouse. d, Wearing crown.

$6, Wearing crown, diff.

2006, Apr. 10
2877 A532 $2 Sheet of 4, #a-d 6.50 6.50

Souvenir Sheet

2878 A532 $6 multi 4.75 4.75

2006 Winter Olympics, Turin A533

Designs: No. 2879, 75c, Austria #715. No. 2880, 75c, Poster for 1972 Sapporo Winter Olympics, vert. No. 2881, 90c, Austria #714. No. 2882, 90c, Japan #1103, vert. $2, Austria #717. $3, Poster for 1964 Innsbruck Winter Olympics, vert.

2006, May 11 Litho. ***Perf. 14¼***
2879-2884 A533 Set of 6 7.00 7.00

Miniature Sheets

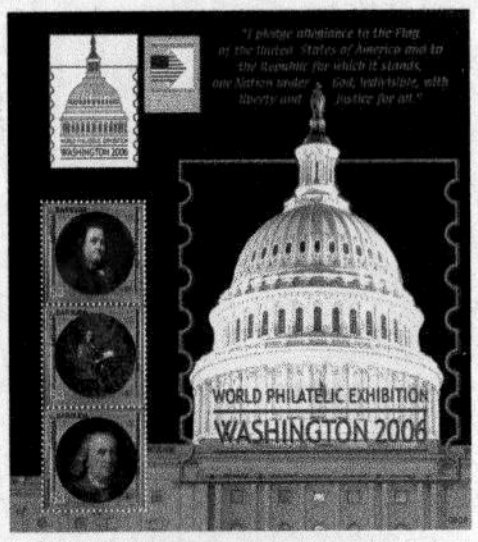

A534

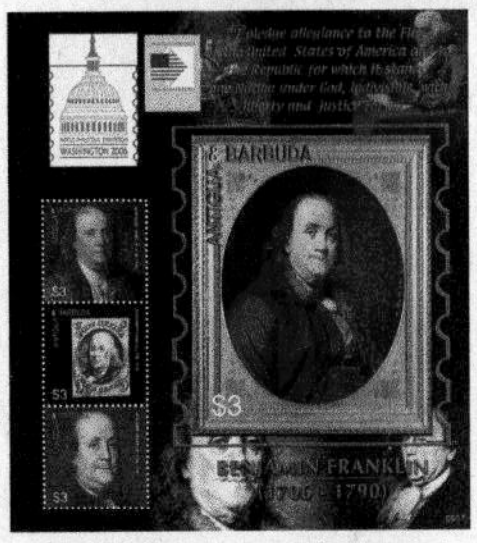

Washington 2006 World Philatelic Exhibition — A535

No. 2885: a, Framed circular portrait of Benjamin Franklin wearing red jacket with fur collar. b, Framed circular portrait of Franklin seated. c, Framed circular portrait of Franklin wearing gray jacket.

No. 2886: a, Unframed portrait of Franklin wearing jacket with fur collar. b, US #1. c, Unframed portrait of Franklin wearing black coat. d, Framed oval portrait like #2885a (73x87mm).

2006, May 29 ***Perf. 11½***
2885 A534 $3 Sheet of 3, #a-c 7.50 7.50

Perf. 11½, Imperf. (#2886d)

2886 A535 $3 Sheet of 4, #a-d 9.50 9.50

Miniature Sheet

Wolfgang Amadeus Mozart (1756-91), Composer — A536

No. 2887: a, Mozart's viola. b, Mozart at age 11. c, Young Mozart. d, Mozart in Verona, 1770.

2006, July 3 ***Perf. 12¾***
2887 A536 $3 Sheet of 4, #a-d 11.00 11.00

Miniature Sheet

Posters of Elvis Presley Movies A537

No. 2888: a, Charro! b, Follow That Dream. c, G.I. Blues. d, Blue Hawaii.

2006, July 12 ***Perf. 13¼***
2888 A537 $3 Sheet of 4, #a-d 10.00 10.00

Antigua and Barbuda Girl Guides, 75th Anniv. — A538

Designs: 25c, Leaders after garbage collection race, 2002. 30c, Girl Guides color party, horiz. 45c, Uniformed and non-uniformed members. 50c, Girl Guides marching band,

horiz. $1, Leeward Islands leaders training camp, 1946.
No. 2894, $5, Assistant Commissioner Lisa Simon. No. 2895, $5, Girl Guides gathering at Fort James, 1935, horiz. No. 2896, $5, Enrollment ceremony, 2006, horiz.

2006, July 17 *Perf. 12¾*
2889-2893 A538 Set of 5 2.75 2.75

Souvenir Sheets
2894-2896 A538 Set of 3 12.50 12.50

Leeward Islands Air Transport, 50th Anniv. — A539

Designs: 30c, HS-748 Hawker Siddely Avro. No. 2898, 50c, BN2 Islanders. No. 2899, 50c, BN2 Norman Islander. No. 2900, 50c, Beechcraft Twin Bonanza, vert. $1.50, BAC 111, HS-748. $2.50, DH8-300 de Havilland.
$5, Sir Frank Delisle, LIAT founder, and Beechcraft Twin Bonanza, vert.

2006, Oct. 2 **Litho.** *Perf. 14¼*
2897-2902 A539 Set of 6 6.25 6.25

Souvenir Sheet
2903 A539 $5 multi 5.25 5.25

Independence, 25th Anniv. — A540

Designs: 30c, Pineapple. $1, Flag. $1.50, Coat of arms.
No. 2907: a, One magnificent frigatebird. b, Two fallow deer. c, One fallow deer. d, Two magnificent frigatebirds.
$5, New Parliament Building, vert.

2006, Oct. 30 *Perf. 12¾*
2904-2906 A540 Set of 3 2.50 2.50
2907 A540 25c Sheet of 4, #a-d 1.50 1.50

Souvenir Sheet
2908 A540 $5 multi 5.50 5.50
No. 2908 contains one 38x50mm stamp.

Civil Rights Leaders — A541

No. 2909, $2: a, Dalai Lama. b, Pres. Abraham Lincoln. c, Susan B. Anthony. d, Harriet Tubman.
No. 2910, $2: a, Mahatma Gandhi. b, Nelson Mandela. c, Rosa Parks.
$5, Dr. Martin Luther King, Jr.

2006, Nov. 20 *Perf. 12, 12½ (#2910)*
2909 Horiz. strip of 4 8.00 8.00
a.-d. A541 $2 Any single 1.75 1.75
2910 A541 $2 Sheet of 3, #a-c 5.00 5.00

Souvenir Sheet
2911 A541 $5 multi 5.50 5.50

Rembrandt (1606-69), Painter — A542

Designs: 50c, Landscape with the Baptism of the Eunuch. 75c, Landscape with a Coach. $1, River Landscape with Ruins. $2, Landscape with a Castle.
No. 2916, $2: a, The Holy Family (Joseph at table). b, The Good Samaritan Arriving at the Inn. c, Rebecca Taking Leave of Her Family. d, The Holy Family (Madonna and Child).
No. 2917, $2 — Samson Posting the Riddle to the Wedding Guests: a, Woman with beads in hair. b, Three men. c, Two men. d, Woman holding glass.
No. 2918, $5, Self-portrait. No. 2919, $5, Rembrandt's Mother.

2006, Dec. 20 *Perf. 12¼x12*
2912-2915 A542 Set of 4 5.00 5.00

Sheets of 4, #a-d
2916-2917 A542 Set of 2 13.50 13.50

Imperf

Size: 70x100mm
2918-2919 A542 Set of 2 9.00 9.00

Betty Boop A543

No. 2920, vert. — Background color: a, Yellow. b, Green. c, Red violet. d, Orange. e, Blue green. f, Purple.
No. 2921: a, Text, "Betty Boop" and stars. b, Betty Boop and cat.

2006, Dec. 20 *Perf. 14¼*
2920 A543 $1.50 Sheet of 6, #a-f 7.50 7.50

Souvenir Sheet
2921 A543 $3 Sheet of 2 5.00 5.00

Space Achievements — A544

No. 2922: a, JSC Shuttle mission simulator. b, STS-1 prime crew in classroom. c, STS-1 Columbia on launch pad. d, Launch of Columbia. e, Columbia landing at Edwards Air Force Base. f, Columbia on runway.
No. 2923, $3: a, Molniya 8K78M launch vehicle. b, Luna 9 flight apparatus. c, Moon images transmitted by Luna 9. d, Luna 9 capsule.
No. 2924, $3: a, Apollo crew boards transfer van. b, Handshake after Apollo-Soyuz linkup. c, Display of Apollo-Soyuz plaque. d, Recovery of Apollo command module.
No. 2925, $6, Artist's conception of NASA spaceship to orbit Moon. No. 2926, $6, Calipso Satellite. No. 2927, $6, Space Station Mir.

2006 *Perf. 12¾*
2922 A544 $2 Sheet of 6, #a-f 10.00 10.00

Sheets of 4, #a-d
2923-2924 A544 Set of 2 21.00 21.00

Souvenir Sheets
2925-2927 A544 Set of 3 16.00 16.00

Christmas — A545

Ornaments: 30c, Ball. 90c, Star. $1, Bell. $1.50, Christmas tree.
No. 2932: a, Ball. b, Star. c, Bell. d, Christmas tree.
$6, Santa Claus at beach.

2006 *Perf. 13½*
2928-2931 A545 Set of 4 3.00 3.00
2932 A545 $2 Sheet of 4, #a-d 6.75 6.75

Souvenir Sheet
2933 A545 $6 multi 6.00 6.00

Scouting, Cent. A546

Scout emblem at: $4, UL. $6, LR.

2007, Jan. 18 *Perf. 13½*
2934 A546 $4 multi 4.00 4.00

Souvenir Sheet
2935 A546 $6 multi 6.00 6.00
No. 2934 was printed in sheets of 3.

Christopher Columbus (1451-1506), Explorer — A547

Designs: 75c, Map of North and South America, Columbus on bended knee. 90c, Portrait of Columbus. $2, Portrait, diff. $3, Portrait, diff.
$6, Columbus and ships.

2007, Jan. 18 *Perf. 13¼*
2936-2939 A547 Set of 4 7.00 7.00

Souvenir Sheet
2940 A547 $6 multi 6.00 6.00

Miniature Sheets

Pres. John F. Kennedy (1917-63) — A548

No. 2941, $3: a, Wearing naval ensign dress uniform. b, With crew. c, On PT-109. d, Wearing light jacket in South Pacific.
No. 2942, $3: a, Campaigning on crutches. b, Wearing t-shirt. c, With John F. Fitzgerald and Joseph P. Kennedy. d, Celebrating victory with sister.

Sheets of 4, #a-d

2007, Jan. 18 **Litho.**
2941-2942 A548 Set of 2 22.00 22.00

Mushrooms — A549

No. 2943: a, Cantharellus cibarius. b, Auricularia auricula-judae. c, Mycena acicula. d, Peziza vesiculosa.
$6, Pleurotus djamor.

2007, Apr. 2 **Litho.** *Perf. 14¼*
2943 A549 $2 Sheet of 4, #a-d 9.00 9.00

Souvenir Sheet
2944 A549 $6 multi 6.50 6.50

Butterflies — A550

Designs: 75c, Figure-of-eight. 90c, Tiger pierid. $1, Purple mort bleu. $4, Mosaic.
No. 2949: a, Small lacewing. b, Clorinde. c, Common morpho. d, White peacock.
$5, Grecian shoemaker.

2007, Apr. 2
2945-2948 A550 Set of 4 8.00 8.00
2949 A550 $2 Sheet of 4, #a-d 7.00 7.00

Souvenir Sheet
2950 A550 $5 multi 6.50 6.50

Flowers — A551

Designs: 75c, Allamanda. 90c, Bidens sulphurea. $1, Alstromeria caryophyflacea. $4, Bougainvillea.
No. 2955, $2, horiz.: a, Canna limbata. b, Gazania rigens. c, Gloriosa rothschildiana. d, Hibiscus sinensis.
No. 2956, $3, horiz.: a, Oncidium flexuosum. b, Paphiopedilum pinocchio. c, Cattleyopsis lindenii. d, Cattleyopsis cubensis.
No. 2957, $6, Caesalpinia pulcherrima. No. 2958, $6, Osmoglossum pulchellum.

2007, Apr. 2
2951-2954 A551 Set of 4 8.00 8.00

Sheets of 4, #a-d
2955-2956 A551 Set of 2 20.00 20.00

Souvenir Sheets
2957-2958 A551 Set of 2 12.00 12.00

Cricket Players — A552

Designs: 25c, Kenneth Benjamin. 30c, Anderson Roberts. 90c, Ridley Jacobs. $1, Curtly Ambrose. $1.50, Richard Richardson.
$5, Sir Vivian Richards.

2007, Apr. 5 *Perf. 12¾*
2959-2963 A552 Set of 5 3.75 3.75

Souvenir Sheet
2964 A552 $5 multi 6.00 6.00

Wedding of Queen Elizabeth II and Prince Philip, 60th Anniv. — A553

No. 2965: a, Couple. b, Wedding sandals.
$6, Couple, vert.

2007, May 1 *Perf. 14*
2965 A553 $1.50 Pair, #a-b 3.00 3.00

Souvenir Sheet
2966 A553 $6 multi 6.00 6.00
No. 2965 was printed in sheets containing three of each stamp.

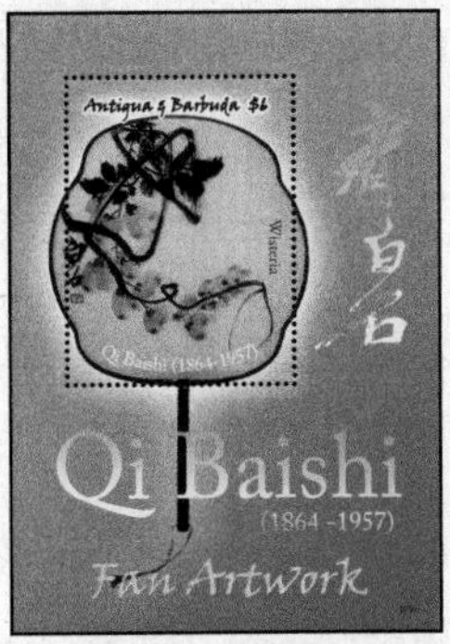

Painted Fans by Qi Baishi (1864-1957) — A554

No. 2967, horiz.: a, Camellias and butterfly. b, Two Shrimp and Arrowhead Leaves. c, Gourd and Ladybug. d, Bird. e, Landscape. f, Five Shrimp.
No. 2968: a, Chrysanthemums. b, Maple Leaves.
$6, Wisteria.

2007, May 1 *Perf. 14¼*

2967	A554	$1.50 Sheet of 6, #a-f	7.50	7.50
2968	A554	$3 Sheet of 2, #a-b	6.00	6.00

Souvenir Sheet

2969	A554	$6 multi	6.00	6.00

Miniature Sheet

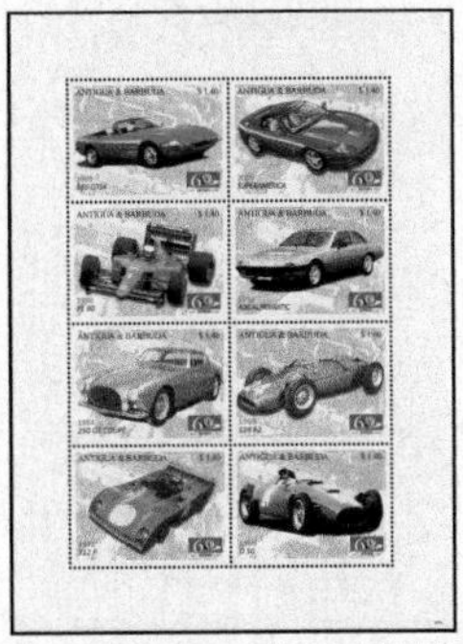

Ferrari Automobiles — A555

No. 2970: a, 1969 365 GTS4. b, 2005 Superamerica. c, 1990 F1 90. d, 1976 400 Automatic. e, 1954 250 GT Coupe. f, 1960 156 F2. g, 1972 312 P. h, 1956 D 50.

2007, June 4 *Perf. 13¼*

2970	A555	$1.40 Sheet of 8, #a-h	10.00	10.00

Concorde — A556

No. 2971, $1.50 — Concorde O1: a, On ground, red frame. b, In air, green frame. c, On ground, blue violet frame. d, In air, red frame. e, On ground, green frame. f, In air, blue violet frame.
No. 2972, $1.50 — Concorde in flight and: a, Millennium Wheel, green denomination. b, Sydney Opera House, black denomination. c, Millennium Wheel, red violet denomination. d, Sydney Opera House, red orange denomination. e, Millennium Wheel, black denomination. f, Sydney Opera House, blue denomination.

2007, June 20 *Perf. 12¾*

Sheets of 6, #a-f

2971-2972	A556	Set of 2	17.50	17.50

First Helicopter Flight, Cent. — A557

No. 2973, horiz.: a, NH 90. b, BO 105, black denomination at LR. c, NH 90. d, AS-61 over water. e, BO 105, black denomination at LL. f, AS-61 from below.
$6, UH-1 Iroquois.

2007, June 20 *Perf. 12¾*

2973	A557	$1.50 Sheet of 6, #a-f	9.25	9.25

Souvenir Sheet

2974	A557	$6 multi	6.75	6.75

Pope Benedict XVI — A558

2007, July 30 *Perf. 13¾*

2975	A558	$1.40 multi	1.50	1.50

Printed in sheets of 8.

Miniature Sheet

Elvis Presley (1935-77) — A559

No. 2967 — Presley: a, Wearing black jacket. b, Facing left, wearing striped shirt, brown background. c, Wearing jacket and holding guitar. d, Facing forward, wearing striped shirt, brown background. e, Wearing red shirt. f, Holding guitar, purple background.

2007, July 30 *Perf. 13¼*

2976	A559	$1.50 Sheet of 6, #a-f	11.00	11.00

Princess Diana (1961-97) — A560

No. 2977 — Princess Diana wearing: a, Beige suit. b, Lilac dress. c, Purple jacket with black-edged collar. d, Hat.
$6, White robe.

2007, July 30

2977	A560	$2 Sheet of 4, #a-d	7.50	7.50

Souvenir Sheet

2978	A560	$6 multi	5.75	5.75

Flora — A561

Designs: 15c, Bird of paradise. 20c, Seaside mahoe. 30c, Hibiscus. 50c, Agave. 70c, Barringtonia tree. 75c, Coconut tree. 90c, Mesquite tree, horiz. $1, Tamarind tree. $1.50, Black willow flowers, horiz. $1.80, Baobab tree, horiz. $2, Petrea volubilis. $2.50, Opuntia cochenillifera, horiz. $5, Locust fruit, horiz. $10, Barbuda black warri. $20, Castor oil plant.

Perf. 12½x13¼, 13¼x12½

2007, Oct. 1 **Litho.**

2979	A561	15c multi	.25	.25
2980	A561	20c multi	.25	.25
2981	A561	30c multi	.30	.25
2982	A561	50c multi	.45	.40
2983	A561	70c multi	.70	.55
2984	A561	75c multi	.75	.60
2985	A561	90c multi	.90	.70
2986	A561	$1 multi	1.00	.75
2987	A561	$1.50 multi	1.40	1.10
2988	A561	$1.80 multi	1.75	1.40
2989	A561	$2 multi	2.25	1.50
2990	A561	$2.50 multi	2.75	1.90
2991	A561	$5 multi	5.00	3.75
2992	A561	$10 multi	8.00	7.50
2993	A561	$20 multi	19.00	15.00
		Nos. 2979-2993 (15)	44.75	35.90

Miniature Sheet

Intl. Holocaust Remembrance Day — A562

No. 2994 — United Nations delegates, each $1.40: a, John W. Ashe, Antigua & Barbuda. b, Alfred Capelle, Marshall Islands. c, Masao Nakayama, Micronesia. d, Gilles Noghes, Monaco. e, Baatar Choisuren, Mongolia. f, Filipe Chidumo, Mozambique. g, Marlene Moses, Nauru. h, Franciscus Majoor, Netherlands.

2007, Oct. 25 *Perf. 13¼*

2994	A562	Sheet of 8, #a-h	10.00	10.00

Christmas A563

Designs: 30c, Stylized map of Antigua & Barbuda, sailboat, candy canes. 90c, Dancers, sailboat, decorated palm tree. $1, Decorated cake. $1.50, Woman in costume.

2007, Nov. 5 *Perf. 14¾x14*

2995-2998	A563	Set of 4	2.75	2.75

Hospice and Palliative Care — A564

Emblem of Hospice Antigua & Barbuda and: No. 2999, 30c, Clock. No. 3000, 30c, Hands.

2007, Dec. 27 *Perf. 13¼*

2999-3000	A564	Set of 2	.85	.85

National Heroes — A565

Designs: No. 3001, 90c, King Court (1691-1736), slave rebellion leader. No. 3002, 90c, Dame Georgianna E. (Nellie) Robinson (1880-1972), educator. $1, Sir Vivian Richards, cricket player. $1.50, Sir Vere Cornwall Bird, Sr. (1909-99), first Prime Minister.

2008, Mar. 7 **Litho.** *Perf. 12¾*

3001-3004	A565	Set of 4	4.00	4.00

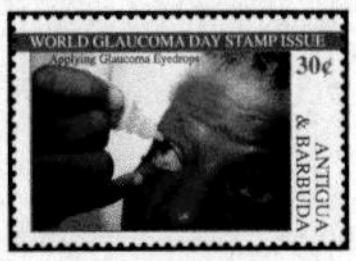

World Glaucoma Day — A566

Designs: 30c, Person applying glaucoma eyedrops. 50c, Normal and glaucomatous optic nerves. $1, Braille writing.

2008, Mar. 7 *Perf. 13¼*

3005-3007	A566	Set of 3	2.25	2.25

32nd America's Cup Yacht Races, Off Valencia, Spain — A567

No. 3008 — Various yachts with text "32nd America's Cup" in: a, $1.20, Yellow. b, $1.80, White. c, $3, Blue. d, $5, Orange.

2008, Mar. 25 *Perf. 12½*

3008	A567	Block of 4, #a-d	8.25	8.25

Miniature Sheet

2008 Summer Olympics, Beijing — A568

No. 3009, each $1.40: a, Pierre de Coubertin. b, Poster for 1896 Athens Olympic Games. c, Spiridon Louis, 1896 marathon gold medalist. d, Paul Masson, 1896 cycling gold medalist.

2008, Mar. 25 *Perf. 12¾*

3009	A568	Sheet of 4, #a-d	4.25	4.25

2008 World Stamp Championship, Israel — A569

2008, May 14 *Imperf.*

3010	A569	$6 multi	4.75	4.75

Visit of Pope Benedict XVI to United States — A570

2008, June 18 *Perf. 13¼*

3011	A570	$2 multi	1.75	1.75

Printed in sheets of 4.

Miniature Sheet

Army Induction of Elvis Presley, 50th Anniv. A571

No. 3012 — Presley wearing: a, Dress uniform and cap. b, Dress uniform, no cap. c, Army fatigues and cap. d, Dress uniform with shoulder insignia and cap.

2008, June 18
3012 A571 $2 Sheet of 4, #a-d 6.50 6.50

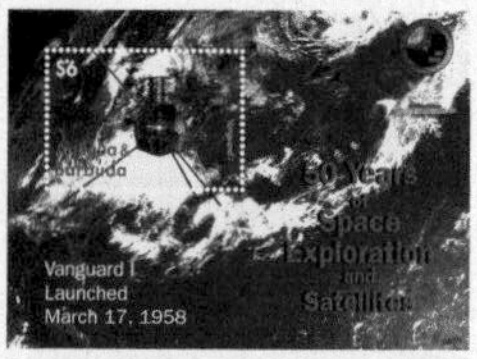

Space Achievements — A572

No. 3013, $1.50, vert. — Vanguard I: a, Against black background, with five rods showing. b, Against white and green background. c, Against black background, with six rods showing.
No. 3014, $1.50: a, Explorer III and equipment, vert. b, Explorer III and Earth, vert. c, Diagram of Van Allen radiation belts.
No. 3015, $2, vert. — Vanguard I and: a, Black background. b, Multicolored background.
No. 3016, $2, vert. — Explorer III and: a, Red and green background. b, Black background.
No. 3017, $6, Vanguard I. No. 3018, $6, Explorer III.

2008, July 29 ***Perf. 13¼***
Horiz. Strips of 3, #a-c
3013-3014 A572 Set of 2 9.00 9.00
Pairs, #a-b
3015-3016 A572 Set of 2 8.00 8.00
Souvenir Sheets
3017-3018 A572 Set of 2 12.00 12.00

Nos. 3013-3014 were each printed in sheets containing two strips. Nos. 3015-3016 were each printed in sheets containing two pairs.

Miniature Sheets

Muhammad Ali, Boxer — A573

No. 3019 — Ali with words or letters in background: a, "ws" at UR. b, "learned" above denomination. c, "is so ugly" at UR. d, "should donate" at UR. e, "greates" at UR. f, "hat" at UR.
No. 3020 — Ali, each $2: a, Hitting punching bag. b, Wearing robe. c, With bare shoulders. d, Wearing protective headgear.

2008, Sept. 29 ***Perf. 11½***
3019 A573 $1.50 Sheet of 6, #a-f 7.50 7.50
Perf. 13¼
3020 A573 Sheet of 4, #a-d 6.50 6.50

No. 3020 contains four 37x50mm stamps.

Star Trek A574

No. 3021: a, Capt. James Kirk and Mr. Spock. b, Chief Engineer Scott, Dr. Leonard McCoy, Kirk and Spock. c, Lt. Uhura, Spock. d, Actors on planetary city set. e, Uhura. f, Scott.
No. 3022: a, McCoy. b, Spock. c, Kirk. d, Hikaru Sulu.

2008, Sept. 29 ***Perf. 11½***
3021 A574 $1.50 Sheet of 6, #a-f 8.00 8.00
Perf. 13¼
3022 A574 $2 Sheet of 4, #a-d 7.50 7.50

No. 3022 contains four 50x37mm stamps.

Miniature Sheet

Pres. John F. Kennedy (1917-63) — A575

No. 3023 — Kennedy: a, Looking right. b, Looking forward, curtains in background. c, Looking forward, smiling with teeth showing. d, Looking right with hand at chin.

2008, Dec. 18 ***Perf. 13¼***
3023 A575 $2 Sheet of 4, #a-d 6.75 6.75

Miniature Sheet

Marilyn Monroe (1926-62), Actress — A576

No. 3024 — Monroe wearing: a, Orange sweater, with arm raised. b, Orange sweater, arms at side. c, Pink sweater. d, Purple sweater.

2008, Dec. 18
3024 A576 $2 Sheet of 4, #a-d 8.50 8.50

Christmas A577

Stained-glass windows: 30c, Holy Family. 90c, Infant Jesus in manger. $1, Madonna and Child, vert. $1.50, Sts. Elizabeth and John the Baptist, vert.

2009, Jan. 2 ***Perf. 14¾x14, 14x14¾***
3025-3028 A577 Set of 4 3.00 3.00

Miniature Sheet

China 2009 World Stamp Exhibition — A578

No. 3029: a, Baseball. b, Beach volleyball. c, Artistic gymnastics. d, Judo.

2009, Jan. 5 ***Perf. 11¼x11½***
3029 A578 $1.40 Sheet of 4, #a-d 4.50 4.50

Miniature Sheet

Pres. Abraham Lincoln (1809-65) — A579

No. 3030: a, Lincoln's first inaugural address, 1861. b, Lincoln, flag. c, Lincoln's second inaugural address, 1865. d, Lincoln at right, crowd at second inaugural.

2009, Jan. 5 ***Perf. 11½x11¼***
3030 A579 $2 Sheet of 4, #a-d 7.25 7.25

Inauguration of US Pres. Barack Obama — A580

Pres. Obama facing: $2.75, Right. $10, Left.

2009, Jan. 20 ***Perf. 12¼x11¾***
3031 A580 $2.75 multi 2.75 .275
Souvenir Sheet
Perf. 13¼x13½
3032 A580 $10 multi 7.75 7.75

No. 3031 was printed in sheets of 4. No. 3032 contains one 37x51mm stamp.

New Year 2009 (Year of the Ox) — A581

2009, Jan. 26 ***Perf. 11½x12***
3033 A581 $1 multi 1.25 1.25

Printed in sheets of 4.

A582

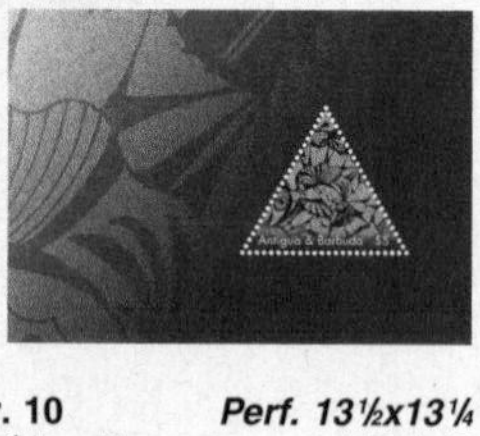

A583

2009, Apr. 10 ***Perf. 13½x13¼***
3034 A582 $1 multi 1.10 1.10
Souvenir Sheet
Perf. 13
3035 A583 $5 multi 4.75 4.75

No. 3034 was printed in sheets of 8.

Miniature Sheet

Elvis Presley (1935-77) — A584

No. 3036 — Presley wearing: a, Hat. b, Suit with handkerchief in pocket. c, Black shirt and pants. d, Pink, white and black windbreaker. e, Blue shirt and lei. f, Suit without handkerchief.

2009, Apr. 14 ***Perf. 14x14¼***
3036 A584 $1.50 Sheet of 6, #a-f 7.75 7.75

Miniature Sheets

A585

China 2009 World Stamp Exhibition — A586

No. 3037 — Landmarks in China: a, Bell Tower, Xian. b, St. Sophia Church, Harbin. c, Great Hall of the People, Chongqing. d, Fenghua Bridge, Tianjin.
No. 3038 — First emperor of China: a, Qin Shi Huang (259-210 B.C.). b, Horses of Terracotta Army. c, Soldiers of Terracotta Army. d, Excavated Terracotta Army.

2009, June 29 **Litho.** ***Perf. 12***
3037 A585 $1.40 Sheet of 4, #a-d 5.50 5.50
Perf. 12½x12¾
3038 A586 $1.40 Sheet of 4, #a-d 5.50 5.50

A587

2009, July 9 ***Perf. 14x15***
3039 A587 $4 multi 3.50 3.50

Miniature Sheets

Dogs A588

No. 3040, $2.50 — Labrador retrievers: a, Puppy in canoe. b, Two puppies at window. c, Two puppies with stick. d, Puppy in bucket.
No. 3041, $2.50 — Dachshunds: a, Dog and carrying case. b, Dog and flowers. c, Two dogs in flower box. d, Dog near flower pot.

2009, Aug. 13 ***Perf. 12***
Sheets of 4, #a-d
3040-3041 A588 Set of 2 21.00 21.00

A589

Michael Jackson (1958-2009), Singer — A590

No. 3042 — Jackson: a, Holding microphone, wearing black coat with gold trim. b, Wearing black coat with gold trim, not holding microphone. c, Wearing red and black shirt. d, Wearing jacket with eagle and shield.
No. 3043 — Jackson: a, Wearing black pants, white above red orange frame at top of stamp. b, Wearing pants with buckles along leg, white above red orange frame at top of stamp. c, As "b," with black above red orange frame. d, As "a," with black above red orange frame.
$6, Jackson singing.

2009 Litho. *Perf. 11¼x11½*
3042 A589 $2.50 Sheet of 4, #a-d 9.50 9.50

Perf. 12x11½
3043 A590 $2.50 Sheet of 4, #a-d 9.50 9.50

Souvenir Sheet
Perf. 13¼
3044 A590 $6 multi 4.75 4.75

Issued: Nos. 3042-3043, 9/30; No. 3044, 12/3. No. 3044 contains one 37x50mm stamp.

Meeting of US Pres. Barack Obama and Pope Benedict XVI
A591

No. 3045, vert.: a, Pres. Obama. b, Pope Benedict XVI. c, Michelle Obama.
$6, Pope Benedict XVI and Pres. Obama.

2009, Nov. 4 *Perf. 11¼x11½*
3045 A591 $2.75 Sheet of 3, #a-c 7.50 7.50

Souvenir Sheet
Perf. 11½x12
3046 A591 $6 multi 5.75 5.75

Chinese Aviation, Cent.
A592

No. 3047 — Aerobatic team: a, Six airplanes with blue, white and red contrails. b, Six airplanes flying right in double triangle formation. c, Six airplanes flying left in diagonal line formation. d, Five airplanes.
$6, J-7GB.

2009, Nov. 12 *Perf. 14*
3047 A592 $2 Sheet of 4, #a-d 6.75 6.75

Souvenir Sheet
Perf. 14¼
3048 A592 $6 multi 5.00 5.00

Aeropex 2009 Intl. Philatelic Exhibition, Biejing. No. 3048 contains one 50x37mm stamp.

First Man on the Moon, 40th Anniv.
A593

No. 3049: a, Apollo 11 patch, US flag on Moon. b, Lunar Module on Moon. c, Passive seismic experiment package. d, Apollo 11 on launch pad.
$6, Apollo 11 Command and Service Modules.

2009, Nov. 13 *Perf. 12¾x12½*
3049 A593 $2.50 Sheet of 4, #a-d 9.50 9.50

Souvenir Sheet
Perf. 12¾x13
3050 A593 $6 multi 5.50 5.50

Intl. Year of Astronomy.

Souvenir Sheets

A594

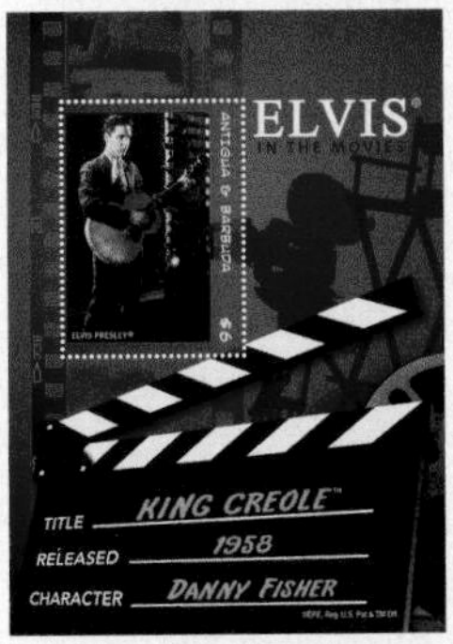

A595

A596

Elvis Presley (1935-77) — A597

2009, Nov. 26 *Perf. 13¼*
3051 A594 $6 multi 5.50 5.50
3052 A595 $6 multi 5.50 5.50
3053 A596 $6 multi 5.50 5.50
3054 A597 $6 multi 5.50 5.50
Nos. 3051-3054 (4) 22.00 22.00

Worldwide Fund for Nature (WWF) — A598

No. 3055 — Caribbean coots: a, Pair in water. b, Pair taking off. c, Pair and chick. d, Adult and chick.

2009, Dec. 3 *Perf. 13¼*
3055 Strip of 4 7.50 7.50
a.-d. A598 $2.65 Any single 1.75 1.75
e. Miniature sheet, 2 each #3055a-3055d 20.00 20.00

Christmas — A599

Christmas light displays: 90c, Candles. $1, Palm tree and reindeer. $1.80, Bells. $3, Nativity scene, horiz.

2009, Dec. 3 *Perf. 14x14¾, 14¾x14*
3056-3059 A599 Set of 4 5.00 5.00

Sir Vere Cornwall Bird, Sr. (1909-99), First Chief Minister, Premier and Prime Minister — A600

Bird: 30c, In chair. 75c, With blue, white and red stripes in background. 90c, Wearing red hat. $1.50, With building in background.
No. 3064: a, Like 75c. b, Like 30c. c, Like 90c. d, Like $1.50.
$6, Bird, map of Antigua with flag.

2009, Dec. 8 *Perf. 11¼x11½*
3060-3063 A600 Set of 4 3.00 3.00
3064 A600 $2.50 Sheet of 4, #a-d 8.00 8.00

Souvenir Sheet
Perf. 12x11½
3065 A600 $6 multi 5.00 5.00

Birds — A601

Designs: $1.20, Glossy ibis. $1.80, Green-winged teal. No. 3068, $3, California clapper rail. $5, Cattle egret, vert.
No. 3070: a, Green heron. b, Common ground dove. c, White-tailed hawk. d, Black-faced grassquit.
No. 3071, $3: a, Bananaquit. b, Osprey.

Perf. 11½x11¼, 11¼x11½
2009, Dec. 8
3066-3069 A601 Set of 4 7.75 7.75

Perf. 11½x12
3070 A601 $2.50 Sheet of 4, #a-d 9.00 9.00

Souvenir Sheet
3071 A601 $3 Sheet of 2, #a-b 5.50 5.50

Souvenir Sheet

New Year 2010 (Year of the Tiger)
A602

No. 3072 — Chinese bronze tigers of: a, Western Han Dynasty. b, Shang Dynasty.

2010, Jan. 4 *Perf. 11½x12*
3072 A602 $5 Sheet of 2, #a-b 7.75 7.75

Ferrari Automobiles and Their Parts — A603

No. 3073, $1.25: a, Engine of 1960 246 P F1. b, 1960 246 P F1.
No. 3074, $1.25: a, Engine of 1964 158 F1. b, 1964 158 F1.
No. 3075, $1.25: a, Interior of 1966 365P Speciale. b, 1966 365P Speciale.
No. 3076, $1.25: a, Air foil and rear wheel of 1968 312 F1-68. b, 1968 312 F1-68.

2010, Feb. 22 *Perf. 12*
Vert. Pairs, #a-b
3073-3076 A603 Set of 4 8.25 8.25

Nos. 3073-3076 exist imperf. Value, set of pairs *$25.*

Whales and Dolphins — A604

Designs: $1.20, Risso's dolphin. $1.80, Common dolphin. $3, Humpback whale. $5, Sperm whale.
No. 3081: a, Shortsnout dolphin. b, Spotted dolphin. c, Cuvier's beaked whale. d, Shortfin pilot whale. e, Gulf Stream beaked whale. f, Rough-toothed dolphin.

2010, Feb. 23 Litho.
3077-3080 A604 Set of 4 10.00 10.00
3081 A604 $2 Sheet of 6, #a-f 11.00 11.00

Miniature Sheets

A605

A606

Princess Diana (1961-97) — A607

No. 3082 — Diana wearing: a, White dress. b, Pink dress. c, Lilac suit. d, White dress, holding flowers.
No. 3083 — Diana wearing tiara and: a, White dress, two earrings visible. b, Red dress, earring with black stone. c, Red dress, pearl earring. d, White dress with high collar.
No. 3084 — Diana wearing: a, Lei. b, Lilac dress. c, Blue and white dress and hat. d, Red orange hat and dress.

2010 Litho. *Perf. 12x11½*
3082 A605 $2 Sheet of 4, #a-d 6.50 6.50
3083 A606 $2.75 Sheet of 4, #a-d 8.25 8.25
3084 A607 $2.75 Sheet of 4, #a-d 8.25 8.25
Nos. 3082-3084 (3) 23.00 23.00

Issued: No. 3082, 2/23; Nos. 3083-3084, 5/10.

Butterflies A608

Designs: $1.20, Common buckeye. $1.80, Red postman. $3, Red admiral. $5, Zebra longwing.

No. 3089: a, Orange sulfur. b, Blue morpho. c, Queen butterfly. d, Zebra swallowtail. e, Malachite. f, Gatekeeper butterfly.

2010, Apr. 14 ***Perf. 14***

3085-3088 A608 Set of 4 10.00 10.00

Perf. 14¾x14

3089 A608 $2 Sheet of 6, #a-f 10.50 10.50

No. 3089 contains six 40x30mm stamps.

Sharks — A609

Designs: $1.20, Nurse shark. $1.80, Caribbean reef shark. $3, Tiger shark. $5, Whale shark.

No. 3094: a, Caribbean sharpnose shark. b, Blacktip shark. c, Oceanic whitetip shark. d, Bull shark.

2010, Apr. 14 ***Perf. 14***

3090-3093 A609 Set of 4 10.50 10.50

Perf. 14¾x14

3094 A609 $2.75 Sheet of 4, #a-d 10.00 10.00

No. 3094 contains four 40x30mm stamps.

Pope John Paul II (1920-2005) — A610

2010, May 10 ***Perf. 11¼x11½***

3095 A610 $2.75 multi 2.10 2.10

Printed in sheets of 4, with each stamp having slight differences in background.

Boy Scouts of America, Cent. A611

No. 3096, $2.50: a, Scout at lectern. b, Scouts canoeing.

No. 3097, $2.50: a, Statue of Liberty giving Scout salute. b, Scouts using map and compass.

2010, May 10 ***Perf. 13¼***

Pairs, #a-b

3096-3097 A611 Set of 2 7.50 7.50

Nos. 3096 and 3097 each were printed in sheets containing two pairs.

Girl Guides, Cent. A612

No. 3098: a, Rainbows. b, Brownies. c, Guides. d, Senior Section.

$6, Girl Guides, diff.

2010, May 10 ***Perf. 11½x12***

3098 A612 $2.75 Sheet of 4, #a-d 8.50 8.50

Souvenir Sheet

Perf. 11½

3099 A612 $6 multi 4.75 4.75

Miniature Sheet

Expo 2010, Shanghai — A613

No. 3100: a, Dancers, Shanghai Intl. Culture and Art Festival. b, China National Grand Theater, Beijing. c, Rice terraces, Guangxi Province, China. d, Dance performance, Beijing.

2010, May 10 ***Perf. 11½***

3100 A613 $1.50 Sheet of 4, #a-d 4.50 4.50

Miniature Sheet

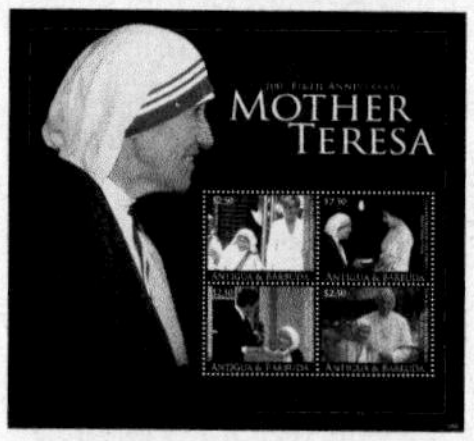

Mother Teresa (1910-97), Humanitarian — A614

No. 3101 — Mother Teresa and: a, Princess Diana. b, Queen Elizabeth II. c, Pres. Ronald Reagan. d, Pope John Paul II.

2010, May 10 ***Perf. 11½x12***

3101 A614 $2.50 Sheet of 4, #a-d 7.50 7.50

Miniature Sheet

Pres. John F. Kennedy (1917-63) — A615

No. 3102: a, Sitting in limousine. b, Standing. c, Sitting in rocking chair. d, Behind microphones.

2010, May 10 ***Perf. 11¼x11½***

3102 A615 $2.75 Sheet of 4, #a-d 8.25 8.25

Miniature Sheet

Awarding of Nobel Peace Prize to Pres. Barack Obama A616

No. 3103 — Pres. Obama: a, Holding diploma and medal, blue curtain in background. b, At lectern, with hand closed. c, At lectern, with hand open. d, Holding diploma and medal.

2010, May 10 ***Perf. 12x11½***

3103 A616 $2.75 Sheet of 4, #a-d 8.25 8.25

Miniature Sheets

A617

Pres. Abraham Lincoln (1809-65) — A618

Various photographs of Lincoln.

2010, May 10 ***Perf. 11¼x11½***

3104 A617 $2.75 Sheet of 4, #a-d 8.25 8.25

3105 A618 $2.75 Sheet of 4, #a-d 8.25 8.25

Miniature Sheets

A619

Elvis Presley (1935-77) — A620

No. 3106: a, Wearing rhinestone-studded jacket, microphone in front of mouth. b, Wearing black open-neck shirt. c, Two portraits. d, Wearing white jacket with lapels and pockets with dark trim.

No. 3107: a, Presley holding guitar, parts of "E" and "L" in background. b, Presley holding guitar, parts of "L" and "V" in background. c, Presley holding guitar, parts of "V" and "7" in background. d, Three portraits.

2010, May 10 ***Perf. 13¼***

3106 A619 $2.75 Sheet of 4, #a-d 8.25 8.25

3107 A620 $2.75 Sheet of 4, #a-d 8.25 8.25

Miniature Sheet

Chinese Zodiac Animals A621

No. 3108: a, Rat. b, Ox. c, Tiger. d, Rabbit. e, Dragon. f, Snake. g, Horse. h, Goat. i, Monkey. j, Cock. k, Dog. l, Pig.

2010, Jan. 4 **Litho.** ***Perf. 12¼***

3108 A621 60c Sheet of 12, #a-l 5.50 5.50

Miniature Sheet

The Three Stooges A622

No. 3109: a, Moe and Larry with cowboy hats, Curly with pick. b, Moe, Larry and Curly in painter's coveralls. c, Moe and Larry in surgical garb examining Curly. d, Moe and Larry squeezing Curly's neck in giant nutcracker.

2010, Sept. 27 **Litho.** ***Perf. 11½x12***

3109 A622 $2.50 Sheet of 4, #a-d 7.50 7.50

2010 World Cup Soccer Championships, South Africa — A623

No. 3110: a, Maximiliano Pereira. b, John Heitinga. c, Edinson Cavani. d, Mark Van Bommel. e, Martin Caceres. f, Giovanni van Bronckhorst.

No. 3111, $3.50: a, Netherlands Coach Bert van Marwijk. b, Netherlands flag on soccer ball.

No. 3112, $3.50: a, Uruguay Coach Oscar Tabarez. b, Uruguay flag on soccer ball.

2010, Oct. 18 ***Perf. 12***

3110 A623 $1.50 Sheet of 6, #a-f 7.75 7.75

Souvenir Sheets of 2, #a-b

3111-3112 A623 Set of 2 11.00 11.00

Henri Dunant (1828-1910), Founder of Red Cross — A624

No. 3113 — Red Cross, scenes from Battle of Solferino and portrait of Dunant in: a, Blue green. b, Brown. c, Lilac. d, Blue gray.

$6, Red Cross, Battle of Solferino, Dunant in lilac.

2010, Dec. 20

3113 A624 $2.50 Sheet of 4, #a-d 8.00 8.00

Souvenir Sheet

3114 A624 $6 multi 4.75 4.75

Cats
A625

No. 3115: a, California spangled cat. b, Siamese cat. c, British shorthair cat. d, Norwegian forest cat. e, Egyptian Mau cat. f, American curl longhair cat.
$6, Manx cat.

2010, Dec. 20
3115 A625 $2.50 Sheet of 6, #a-f 13.00 13.00

Souvenir Sheet

3116 A625 $6 multi 5.00 5.00

No. 3115 contains six 30x40mm stamps.

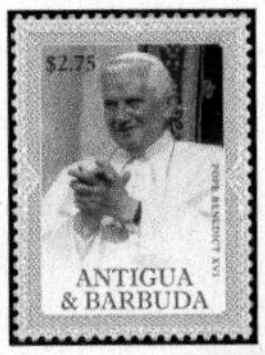

A626

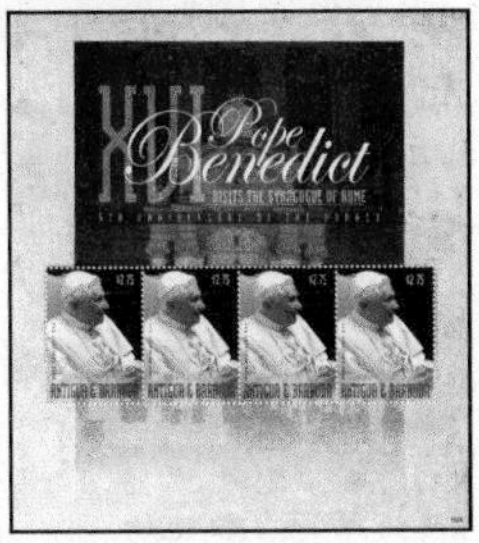

Pope Benedict XVI
A627

No. 3118 — Pope Benedict XVI and: a, Buff area below "G" in "Antigua," brown area below "U" in "Antigua." b, Red brown area below "IG" of "Antigua," buff area below first "A" in "Antigua." c, Dark brown areas below "ANTIG" of "Antigua." d, Buff areas below first and second "A" of "Antigua."

2010, Dec. 20 **Litho.** ***Perf. 12***
3117 A626 $2.75 multi 2.10 2.10
3118 A627 $2.75 Sheet of 4, #a-d 8.50 8.50

No. 3117 issued in sheets of 4.

Souvenir Sheet

New Year 2011 (Year of the Rabbit)
A628

No. 3119: a, Rabbit. b, Chinese character for "rabbit."

2011, Jan. 3
3119 A628 $4 Sheet of 2, #a-b 6.00 6.00

Pandas
A629

No. 3120: a, Panda with mouth open. b, Head of panda. c, Panda eating, large leaf partially covering head. d, Panda eating, diff.
$5, Panda, diff.

2011, Jan. 3
3120 A629 $2 Sheet of 4, #a-d 7.00 7.00

Souvenir Sheet

3121 A629 $5 multi 4.25 4.25

Beijing 2010 Intl. Philatelic Exhibition.

Christmas 2010 — A630

Designs: 30c, Casini Madonna, by Tommaso Masaccio. 75c, Madonna of the Stars, by Tintoretto. 90c, Wall mosaic, Basilica of Sant'Apollinaire Nuovo, Ravenna, Italy. $1.50, The Annunciation, by Fra Angelico.

2011, Jan. 17 ***Perf. 12¾x12½***
3122-3125 A630 Set of 4 2.60 2.60

Engagement of Prince William and Catherine Middleton
A631

Design: No. 3126, Couple.
No. 3127: a, Prince William. b, Middleton.
No. 3128, $6, Prince William wearing striped shirt and necktie, vert. No. 3129, $6, Prince William wearing white shirt and bow tie, vert.

2011, Feb. 14 ***Perf. 13 Syncopated***
3126 A631 $2.50 multi 1.90 1.90
3127 A631 $2.50 Horiz. pair, #a-b 3.75 3.75

Souvenir Sheets

3128-3129 A631 Set of 2 9.00 9.00

No. 3126 printed in sheets of 4. No. 3127 printed in sheets of 2 pairs.

Miniature Sheets

A632

Mohandas K. Gandhi (1869-1948), Indian Nationalist — A633

No. 3130 — Gandhi and: a, Qutub Minar Tower, Delhi. b, Asoka pillar. c, Hyderabad Mosque. d, Taj Mahal.
No. 3131 — Crowd and: a, Profile of Gandhi, robe visible. b, Gandhi looking forward. c, Profile of Gandhi, robe not visible. d, Gandhi looking right.

2011, Mar. 1 ***Perf. 12***
3130 A632 $2.75 Sheet of 4, #a-d 8.25 8.25
3131 A633 $2.75 Sheet of 4, #a-d 8.25 8.25

2011 Indipex Intl. Philatelic Exhibition, New Delhi

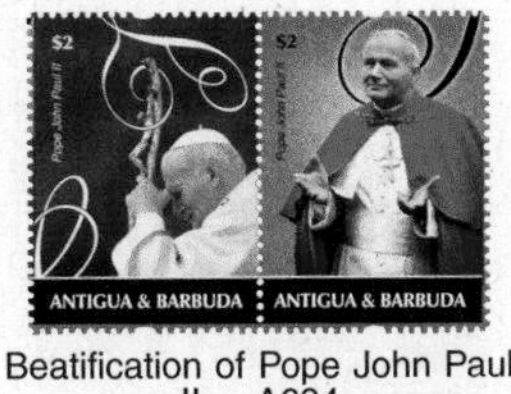

Beatification of Pope John Paul II — A634

No. 3132 — Pope John Paul II: a, Holding crucifix. b, Wearing red stole.
$6, Head of Pope John Paul II.

2011, Apr. 4 ***Perf. 13 Syncopated***
3132 A634 $2 Pair, #a-b 3.00 3.00

Souvenir Sheet
Perf. 12

3133 A634 $6 multi 4.50 4.50

Miniature Sheets

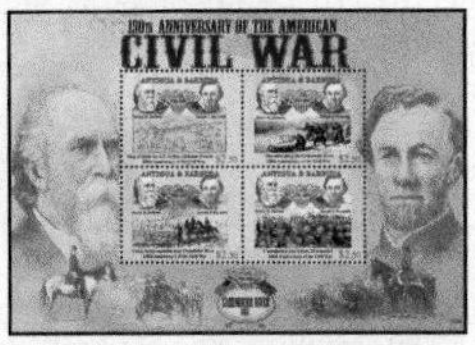

United States Civil War, 150th Anniv.
A635

No. 3134, $2.50 — Eagle, shield, flags, Generals Henry R. Jackson and Joseph J. Reynolds of Battle of Greenbrier River, Oct. 3, 1861, and: a, Battle map by A. T. McRae, Quitman Guards. b, Skirmish along the Greenbrier river. c, Union forces assembling near Greenbrier River. d, Battle scene.
No. 3135, $2.50 — Eagle, shield, flags, Confederate Secretary of the navy Stephen Mallory, Union Lt. Commander Alexander Murray of Battle of Cockle Creek, Oct. 5, 1861, and: a, Warships of the Atlantic Blockading Squadron. b, Flotilla of Union warships. c, Confederate privateers near Delaware Bay. d, USS Minnesota.
No. 3136, $2.50 — Eagle, shield, flags, Confederate Brigadier General Richard H. Anderson, Union Colonel Harvey Brown of Battle of Santa Rosa Island, Oct. 9, 1861, and: a, Fort Pickens. b, Drawing of Fight at Santa Rosa Island, by John Volck. c, Boats cutting off confederate dispatch galley. d, Col. Brown commanding 3rd U.S. Infantry.

Sheets of 4, #a-d

2011, Apr. 4 ***Perf. 12***
3134-3136 A635 Set of 3 22.50 22.50

Mushrooms — A636

No. 3137: a, Tylopilus potamogeton. b, Amanita campinaranae. c, Cantharellus altratus. d, Tylopilus orsonianus. e, Boletellus ananas. f, Amanita craseoderma.
No. 3138: a, Amanita cyanopus. b, Phyllobolites miniatus. c, Chroogomphus jamaicensis. d, Coltricia cf. montagnei.
No. 3139, $6, Austroboletus rostrupii. No. 3140, $6, Austroboletus festivus.

2011, May 9 **Litho.**
3137 A636 $2 Sheet of 6, #a-f 10.00 10.00
3138 A636 $2.50 Sheet of 4, #a-d 7.50 7.50

Souvenir Sheets

3139-3140 A636 Set of 2 9.00 9.00

1997 Visit of Princess Diana To Barbuda — A637

Designs: No. 3141, $10, Princess Diana, her sons, family friend and airplane. No. 3142, $10, Princess Diana.
$50, Princess Diana, horiz.

2011, July 12 ***Perf. 12***
3141-3142 A637 Set of 2 17.00 17.00

Souvenir Sheet

3143 A637 $50 multi 37.50 37.50

Nos. 3141-3142 each were issued in sheets of 5.

Wedding of Prince William and Catherine Middleton — A638

No. 3144, $2.50 — a, Prince William wearing cap. b, Middleton, name at left in one line. c, Couple.
No. 3145, $2.50 — a, Prince William waving. b, Middleton, name at top in two lines. c, Couple kissing.
$6, Couple, diff.

2011, Aug. 15 ***Perf. 13x13¼***
3144 A638 Sheet of 4, #3144a-3144b, 2 #3144c 7.50 7.50
3145 A638 Sheet of 4, #3145a-3145b, 2 #3145c 7.50 7.50

Souvenir Sheet
Perf. 12

3146 A638 $6 multi 4.50 4.50

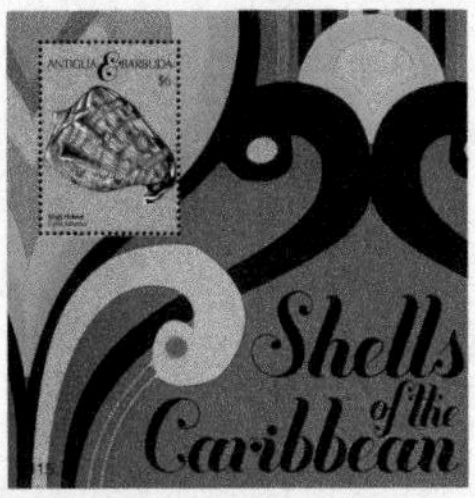

Shells
A639

No. 3147: a, Bleeding tooth nerite. b, Pen shell. c, Banded tulip shell. d, Chank shell. e, Flame helmet. f, Atlantic partridge tun.
No. 3148: a, Pink conch. b, Sunrise tellin. c, Flamingo tongue. d, Queen's helmet.
No. 3149, $6, King's helmet. No. 3150, $6, Triton's trumpet, horiz.

Perf. 13¼x13, 13x13¼

2011, Aug. 15
3147 A639 $2 Sheet of 6, #a-f 9.00 9.00
3148 A639 $2.75 Sheet of 4, #a-d 8.25 8.25

Souvenir Sheets

3149-3150 A639 Set of 2 9.00 9.00

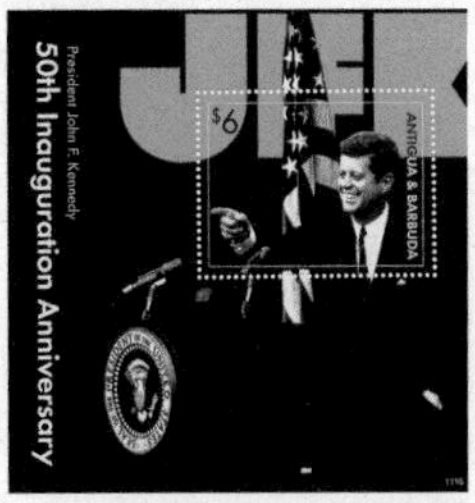

Pres. John F. Kennedy (1917-63) — A640

No. 3151, vert. — Pres. Kennedy: a, Inspecting Mercury capsule, Feb. 22, 1962. b, On Cape Canaveral tour, Nov. 16, 1963. c, At Saturn rocket briefing, Nov. 16, 1963. d, At Cape Canaveral, pointing, Nov. 16, 1963.
$6, Kennedy and flag.

2011, Sept. 9 ***Perf. 12***
3151 A640 $2.75 Sheet of 4, #a-d 8.25 8.25

Souvenir Sheet
Perf. 12¾

3152 A640 $6 multi 4.50 4.50

No. 3151 contains four 30x40mm stamps.

Pres. Barack Obama, 50th Birthday
A641

No. 3153 — Pres. Obama: a, Looking right, wearing dark tie and flag lapel pin. b, Wearing light patterned tie, standing in front of microphone. c, Wearing dark patterned tie, standing in front of microphones. d, Looking left.
$6, Pres. Obama, diff.

2011, Sept. 9 ***Perf. 13 Syncopated***
3153 A641 $2.75 Sheet of 4, #a-d 8.25 8.25

Souvenir Sheet

3154 A641 $6 multi 5.00 5.00

Princess Diana (1961-97) — A642

No. 3155 — Princess Diana: a, Seated on sofa. b, Wearing beige and white dress. c, Wearing white dress. d, With Prince Charles.
$6, Princess Diana, horiz.

2011, Sept. 9 ***Perf. 12***
3155 A642 $2.75 Sheet of 4, #a-d 8.25 8.25

Souvenir Sheet

Perf. 12¾

3156 A642 $6 multi 4.50 4.50

No. 3156 contains one 51x38mm stamp.

First Man in Space, 50th Anniv.
A643

No. 3157, $2.75: a, Liftoff of Vostok 1. b, Russian tracking ship named after Yuri Gagarin. c, Vostok 1 mission emblem. d, Alan Shepard, first American astronaut.
No. 3158, $2.75: a, Map of Gagarin's flightpath. b, Vostok 8K72K rocket. c, Gagarin, first cosmonaut. d, Virgil "Gus" Grissom, American astronaut, and rocket.
No. 3159, $6, Gagarin, diff. No. 3160, $6, Vostok spacecraft and Earth.

Sheets of 4, #a-d

2011, Sept. 9 ***Perf. 12***
3157-3158 A643 Set of 2 16.50 16.50

Souvenir Sheets

3159-3160 A643 Set of 2 9.00 9.00

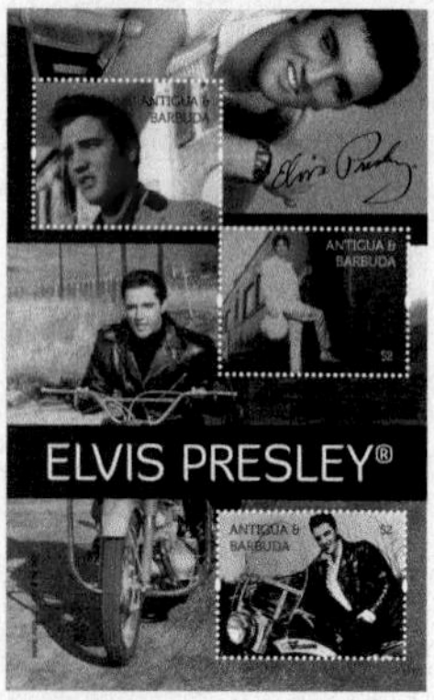

A644

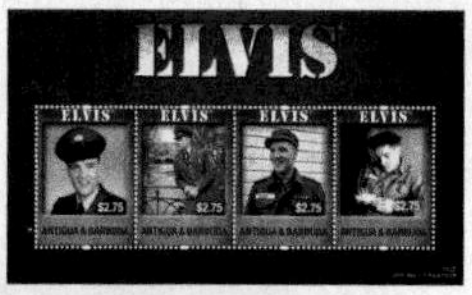

A645

A646

Elvis Presley (1935-77) — A647

No. 3161 — Presley: a, With building in background. b, On train steps. c, On motorcycle.
No. 3162 — Presley wearing: a, Army dress uniform. b, Dress uniform, standing next to railing. c, Battle fatigues. d, Battle fatigues, reading letter.
No. 3163 — Presley wearing: a, Glasses and red shirt. b, Suit, facing right. c, Sequined suit, facing forward. d, Suit, facing left.
No. 3164 — Presley: a, On stage. b, Wearing sweater.

2011, Sept. 9 ***Perf. 13 Syncopated***
3161 A644 $2 Sheet of 3, #a-c 4.50 4.50
3162 A645 $2.75 Sheet of 4, #a-d 8.25 8.25
3163 A646 $2.75 Sheet of 4, #a-d 8.25 8.25
Nos. 3161-3163 (3) 21.00 21.00

Souvenir Sheet

3164 A647 $3 Sheet of 2, #a-b 4.50 4.50

Miniature Sheets

A648

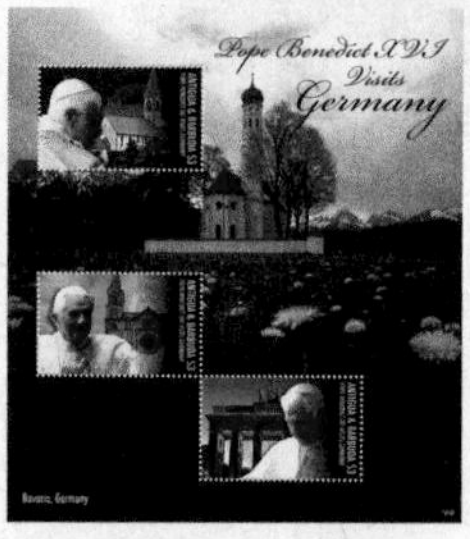

Visit of Pope Benedict XVI to Germany
A649

No. 3165 — Pope Benedict XVI: a, With church spires behind head. b, With arm extended, crucifix visible, hand in front of church steeple. c, With mountain behind head, chuch steeple and building with flowers at right.
No. 3166 — Pope Benedict XVI: a, Facing right, church with red roof at right. b, With arm extended, no crucifix visible, chuch at right.c, With Brandenburg Gate at left.

2011, Aug. 3 **Litho.** ***Perf. 12***
3165 A648 $3 Sheet of 3, #a-c 6.75 6.75
3166 A649 $3 Sheet of 3, #a-c 6.75 6.75

Fish
A650

No. 3167, $3.50: a, Queen angelfish. b, Ocean surgeonfish. c, Rock beauty. d, Gray angelfish.
No. 3168, $3.50: a, Foureye butterflyfish. b, French grunt. c, French angelfish. d, Spotfin butterflyfish.
No. 3169, $9, Great barracuda (80x30mm). No. 3170, $9, Banded butterflyfish (40x40mm).

Sheets of 4, #a-d

2011, Sept. 30 ***Perf. 12***
3167-3168 A650 Set of 2 21.00 21.00

Souvenir Sheets

3169-3170 A650 Set of 2 13.50 13.50

Hu Jintao, President of People's Republic of China — A651

Pres. Hu and flag of People's Republic of China: $3, At lower left. $6, In background.

2011, Oct. 24
3171 A651 $3 multi 2.25 2.25

Souvenir Sheet

3172 A651 $6 multi 4.50 4.50

China 2011 Intl. Philatelic Exhibition, Wuxi (No. 3172).

Christmas — A652

Paintings: 30c, Madonna and Child with Angels, by Giottino. 75c, The Annunciation and Two Saints, by Simone Martini. $1.50, Paradise, by Giusto de' Menabuoi. $3, Madonna, by Vitale da Bologna.

2011, Nov. 15 ***Perf. 14***
3173-3176 A652 Set of 4 4.25 4.25

Miniature Sheet

Chinese Zodiac Animals
A653

No. 3177: a, Rat. b, Ox. c, Tiger. d, Rabbit. e, Dragon. f, Snake. g, Horse. h, Sheep. i, Monkey. j, Rooster. k, Dog. l, Boar.

Litho. With Foil Application

2011, Nov. 15 ***Perf. 13 Syncopated***
3177 A653 65c Sheet of 12, #a-l 5.75 5.75

Pres. Abraham Lincoln (1809-65) — A654

No. 3178: a, Lincoln without beard. b, Campaign poster for Lincoln and Hannibal Hamlin. c, Eyes and nose of Lincoln. d, Linoln with beard.
$6, Lincoln, vert.

2011, Dec. 19 **Litho.** ***Perf. 12***
3178 A654 $2.75 Sheet of 4, #a-d 8.25 8.25

Souvenir Sheet

3179 A654 $6 multi 4.50 4.50

No. 3179 contains one 30x50mm stamp.

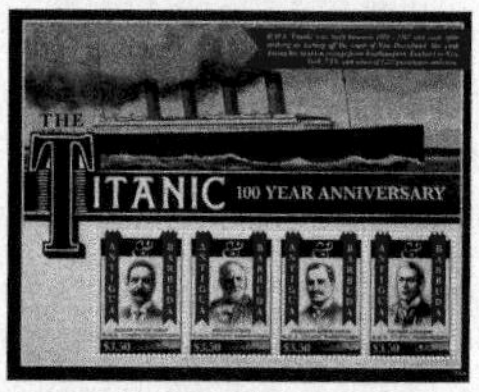

Sinking of the Titanic, Cent.
A655

No. 3180 — Titanic passengers: a, Joseph Bruce Ismay (1862-1937), chairman of White Star Line. b, William Stead (1849-1912), journalist. c, Benjamin Guggenheim (1865-1912), businessman. d, Thomas Andrews (1873-1912), naval architect of Titanic.
$9, Titanic, horiz.

2012, Jan. 25
3180 A655 $3.50 Sheet of 4, #a-d 10.50 10.50

Souvenir Sheet

3181 A655 $9 multi 6.75 6.75

No. 3181 contains one 50x30mm stamp.

Reign of Queen Elizabeth II, 60th Anniv.
A656

No. 3182 — Queen Elizabeth II as young girl: a, At piano. b, Color photograph, looking left. c, In meadow, looking right. d, Near house and flowers.
$9, Queen Elizabeth II and flowers, vert.

2012, Mar. 26
3182 A656 $3.50 Sheet of 4, #a-d 10.50 10.50

Souvenir Sheet

3183 A656 $9 multi 6.75 6.75

First Wedding Anniversary of the Duke and Duchess of Cambridge — A657

No. 3184 — Duke and Duchess, rose and background color of: a Dark red violet. b, Red. c, Rose. d, Pink.
No. 3185: a, Rose and Duke of Cambridge. b, Rose and Duchess of Cambridge.

2012, May 3 ***Perf. 13 Syncopated***
3184 A657 $3.50 Sheet of 4, #a-d 10.50 10.50

Souvenir Sheet

3185 A657 $4.50 Sheet of 2, #a-b 6.75 6.75

Miniature Sheet

2012 Summer Olympics, London — A658

No. 3186: a, Rhythmic gymnastics. b, Hurdles. c, Judo. d, Three runners.

2012, June 18 ***Perf. 12***
3186 A658 $2.20 Sheet of 4, #a-d 6.50 6.50

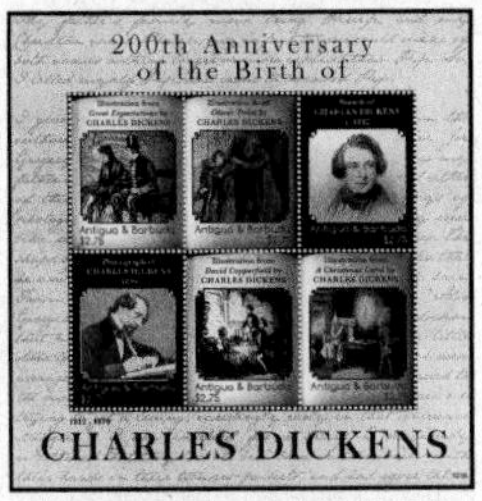

200th Anniversary of the Birth of
CHARLES DICKENS

Charles Dickens (1812-70), Writer — A659

No. 3187: a, Illustration from *Great Expectations.* b, Illustration from *Oliver Twist.* c, Sketch of Dickens. d, Photograph of Dickens. e, Illustration from *David Copperfield.* f, Illustration from *A Christmas Carol.*

$9, Illustration from *A Tale of Two Cities,* horiz.

2012, July 30 ***Perf. 14***

3187 A659 $2.75 Sheet of 6, #a-f 12.50 12.50

Souvenir Sheet

Perf. 12

3188 A659 $9 multi 6.75 6.75

Princess Diana (1961-97) — A660

No. 3189 — Princess Diana wearing: a, White gown, denomination at UL. b, White jacket, denomination at UL. c, Red dress. d, White dress and necklace, denomination at UR.

$9, Princess Diana and school children.

2012, July 30 ***Perf. 14***

3189 A660 $3.50 Sheet of 4, #a-d 10.50 10.50

Souvenir Sheet

3190 A660 $9 multi 6.75 6.75

Miniature Sheet

Seahorses — A661

Various seahorses.

2012, Sept. 24 ***Perf. 14***

3191 A661 $3 Sheet of 5, #a-e 11.50 11.50

War of 1812 A662

No. 3192: a, HMS Shannon Leading Her Prize The American Frigate Chesapeake into Halifax Harbor, by Louis Haghe. b, Action Between USS Constitution and HMS Guerriere, by Michele F. Corne. c, Portrait of Pres. James Madison, by John Vanderlyn. d, Portrait of Pres. Andrew Jackson, by Ralph E. W. Earl. e, The U.S. Capitol After Burning by the British, by George Munger. f, Battle of Lake Erie, by William H. Powerll.

$9, A View of the Bombardment of Fort McHenry, Near Baltimore, by John Bower.

2012, Nov. 12 ***Perf. 12***

3192 A662 $2.75 Sheet of 6, #a-f 12.50 12.50

Souvenir Sheet

3193 A662 $9 multi 6.75 6.75

Christmas — A663

Paintings: 30c, Adoration of the Child, by Antonio da Correggio. 75c, Madonna and Child with Two Angels, by Fra Filippo Lippi. $1.50, Virgin and Child, by Peter Paul Rubens. $2, Madonna and Child, by Parmigianino. $3, The Grand Duke's Madonna, by Raphael. $3.25, Adoration of the Magi, by Sandro Botticelli.

2012, Nov. 19 ***Perf. 12¾***

3194-3199 A663 Set of 6 8.00 8.00

Miniature Sheet

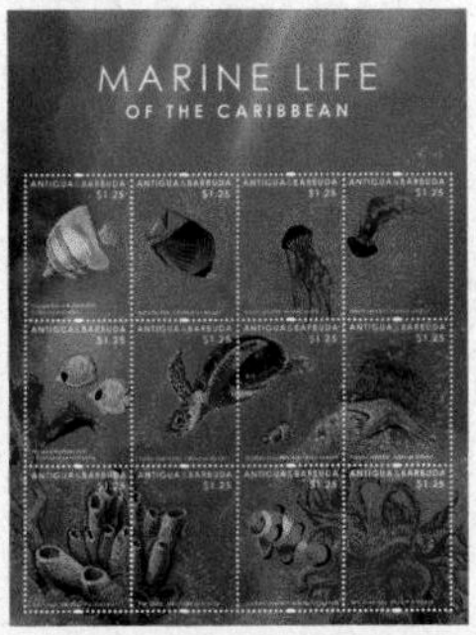

Marine Life A664

No. 3200: a, Copperband butterflyfish. b, Butterfly fish. c, Moon jellyfish, tentacles at bottom. d, Moon jellyfish, tentacles at top. e, Masked butterflyfish. f, Head of Green sea turtle. g, Rear of Green sea turtle, Ocellaris clownfish. h, Forbes sea star. i, Fan coral, red coral at left. j, Fan coral at left. k, Ocellaris clownfish and sea anemone. l, Sea anemone.

2012, Dec. 3 ***Perf. 13 Syncopated***

3200 A664 $1.25 Sheet of 12, #a-l 11.50 11.50

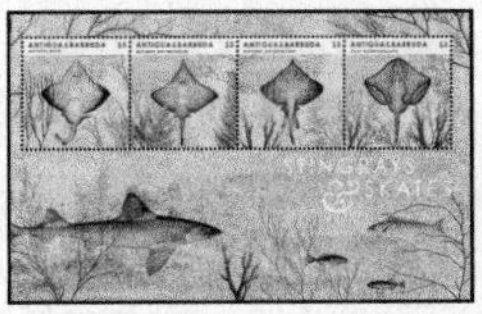

Stingrays and Skates A665

No. 3201: a, Dipturus batis. b, Dipturus oxyrhynchus without long appendages near tail. c, Dipturus oxyrhynchus with long appendages near tail. d, Raja microocellata.

$9, Leucoraja naevus, vert.

2012, Dec. 3 ***Perf. 13¾***

3201 A665 $3 Sheet of 4, #a-d 9.00 9.00

Souvenir Sheet

Perf. 12¾

3202 A665 $9 multi 6.75 6.75

No. 3202 contains one 38x51mm stamp.

Turtles A666

No. 3203: a, Chelonia mydas. b, Trachemys decorata. c, Dermochelys coriacea. d, Chelonoidis carbonaria.

$9, Chelus fimbriatus.

2012, Dec. 3 ***Perf. 14***

3203 A666 $3.50 Sheet of 4, #a-d 10.50 10.50

Souvenir Sheet

Perf. 12

3204 A666 $9 multi 6.75 6.75

Paintings by Raphael A667

No. 3205: a, Andrea Navagero. b, La Muta. c, Self-portrait. d, La Fornarina.

$9, Portrait of a Cardinal.

2013, Feb. 20 ***Perf. 12½***

3205 A667 $3.25 Sheet of 4, #a-d 9.75 9.75

Souvenir Sheet

3206 A667 $9 multi 6.75 6.75

Souvenir Sheets

Elvis Presley (1935-77) — A668

Presley: No. 3207, $9, Standing in front of sign depicting him playing guitar, purple frame. No. 3208, $9, Wearing suit and tie, black frame. No. 3209, $9, Holding microphone, red frame. No. 3210, $9, With guitar on back, looking at music stand, red frame. No. 3211, $9, With Pres. Richard M. Nixon, gray frame.

2013, Feb. 20

3207-3211 A668 Set of 5 34.00 34.00

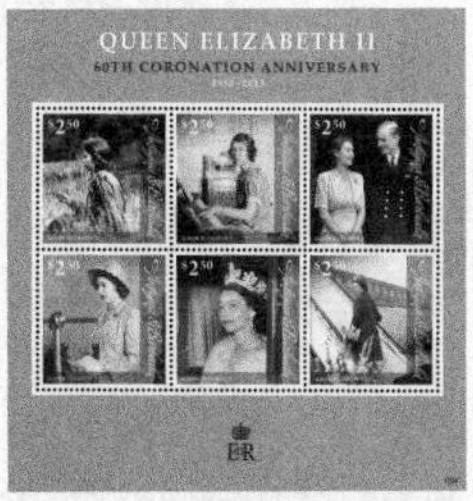

Coronation of Queen Elizabeth II, 60th Anniv. — A669

No. 3212 — Queen Elizabeth II: a, As young woman in field. b, As young woman at piano. c, With Prince Philip. d, Behind microphone. e, Wearing tiara. f, Boarding ariplane.

$9, Queen Eliazbeth II wearing hat, vert.

2013, May 13 **Litho.** ***Perf. 13¾***

3212 A669 $2.50 Sheet of 6, #a-f 11.50 11.50

Souvenir Sheet

Perf. 12½

3213 A669 $9 multi 6.75 6.75

No. 3213 contains one 38x51mm stamp.

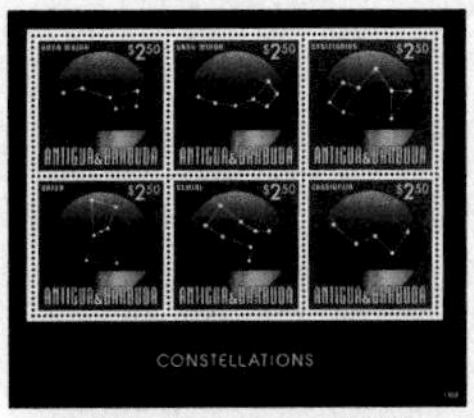

Constellations — A670

No. 3214: a, Ursa Major. b, Ursa Minor. c, Sagittarius. d, Orion. e, Gemini. f, Cassiopeia.

$9, Canis Major, vert.

2013, May 13 **Litho.** ***Perf. 13¾***

3214 A670 $2.50 Sheet of 6, #a-f 11.50 11.50

Souvenir Sheet

Perf. 12½

3215 A670 $9 multi 6.75 6.75

No. 3215 contains one 38x51mm stamp.

Election of Pope Francis A671

No. 3216 — Pope Francis: a, Waving, orange background. b, Behind microphone, cardinal in background. c, Waving, behind lectern and microphone. d, Facing right, waving, cardinals in background.

$9, Pope Francis waving, diff.

Perf. 13¼x12½

2013, June 19 **Litho.**

3216 A671 $3.25 Sheet of 4, #a-d 9.75 9.75

Souvenir Sheet

Perf. 13½

3217 A671 $9 multi 6.75 6.75

No. 3217 contains one 38x51mm stamp.

Dolphins A672

No. 3218: a, Bottlenose dolphins. b, Spotted dolphins. c, Striped dolphins. d, Fraser's dolphins.

$9, Pygmy killer whale.

Perf. 12½x13¼

2013, June 19 **Litho.**

3218 A672 $3.25 Sheet of 4, #a-d 9.75 9.75

Souvenir Sheet

Perf. 12½x12

3219 A672 $9 multi 6.75 6.75

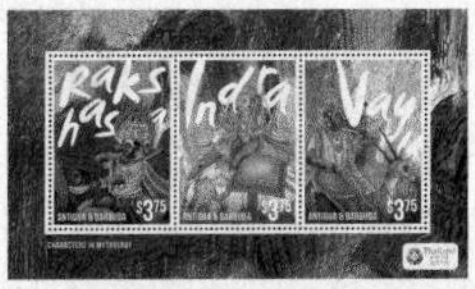

Mythological Beings of Asia — A673

No. 3220: a, Rakshasa. b, Indra. c, Vayu.

$9, Garuda.

2013, Oct. 28 **Litho.** ***Perf. 12½***

3220 A673 $3.75 Sheet of 3, #a-c 8.50 8.50

Souvenir Sheet

3221 A673 $9 multi 6.75 6.75

Thailand 2013 World Stamp Exhibition, Bangkok.

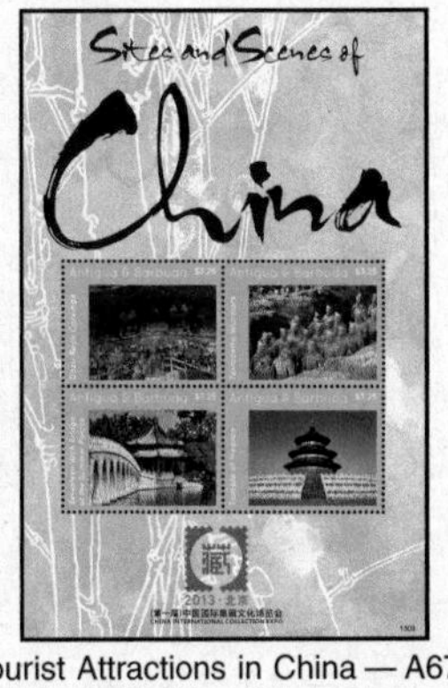

Tourist Attractions in China — A674

No. 3222: a, Dazu Rock Carvings. b, Terracotta warriors. c, Seventeen-arch bridge at Summer Palace. d, Temple of Heaven.
No. 3223: a, Forbidden City. b, Potala Palace.

2013, Oct. 28 Litho. *Perf. 14*

3222 A674 $3.25 Sheet of 4, #a-d 9.75 9.75

Souvenir Sheet

3223 A674 $4.75 Sheet of 2, #a-b 7.00 7.00

2013 China International Collection Expo, Beijing.

Dogs
A675

No. 3224: a, Chow chow. b, Japanese chin. c, Poodle. d, French bulldog.
$9, Toy spaniel.

2013, Oct. 28 Litho. *Perf. 14*

3224 A675 $3.25 Sheet of 4, #a-d 9.75 9.75

Souvenir Sheet

Perf. 12

3225 A675 $9 multi 6.75 6.75

Birth of Prince George of Cambridge — A676

No. 3226 — Duke and Duchess of Cambridge with Prince George: a, Duke holding Prince. b, Duchess holding Prince, Duke waving. c, Duke holding Prince, head of prince visible. d, Duchess holding Prince, shoulder of Duke visible.
$9, Duke and Duchess of Cambridge with Prince George, diff.

2013, Oct. 28 Litho. *Perf. 13¾*

3226 A676 $3.25 Sheet of 4, #a-d 9.75 9.75

Souvenir Sheet

3227 A676 $9 multi 6.75 6.75

Animals of South America
A677

No. 3228: a, Black howler. b, South American tapir. c, Spectacled bear, d, Maned wolf.
$9, Toco toucan.

2013, Nov. 18 Litho. *Perf. 12½x12*

3228 A677 $3.25 Sheet of 4, #a-d 9.75 9.75

Souvenir Sheet

3229 A677 $9 multi 6.75 6.75

2013 Brasiliana World Stamp Exhibition, Rio de Janeiro.

Christmas — A678

Paintings: 30c, Holy Family, by Alessandro Buonvicino. 75c, Christ Blessing, by Girolamo Romani (Il Romanino). 90c, Madonna, by Correggio. $1.50, The Adoration of the Shepherds, by Girolamo Savoldo. $3, Madonna and Child, by Giovanni da Pordenone.

2013, Dec. 2 Litho. *Perf. 12½*

3230-3234 A678 Set of 5 4.75 4.75

New Year 2014 (Year of the Horse) A679

No. 3235 — Various paintings of horses, by Liu Jiyu (1918-83), with: a, Artist's name at UL, "Year of the Horse" in red at LL. b, Artist's name at LL, "Year of the Horse" in red at UR. c, Artist's name at LL, no "Year of the Horse" inscription. d, Artist's name at UL, "Year of the Horse" in tan at LL.
No. 3236, horiz. — Various paintings of horses, by Liu Jiyu, with "Year of the Horse" at: a, LR. b, LL.

2013, Dec. 2 Litho. *Perf. 14*

3235 A679 $3.25 Sheet of 4, #a-d 9.75 9.75

Souvenir Sheet

Perf. 12

3236 A679 $3.50 Sheet of 2, #a-b 5.25 5.25

A680

A681

Nelson Mandela (1918-2013), President of South Africa — A682

No. 3237 — Mandela: a, Behind microphone. b, Wearing blue shirt with circular designs. c, Sitting in chair. d, With cap lifted. e, Wearing black shirt. f, Wearing sunglasses.
No. 3238 — Mandela: a, Wearing black-and-white patterned shirt, with red ribbon near collar. b, Wearing black-and-white patterned shirt, no red ribbon. c, Wearing white shirt and jacket with leopard-skin pattern. d, Waving. e, Wearing black, white and red patterned shirt, with red ribbon near collar. f, Wearing tasseled cap.
$9, Mandela with people in background. $13.50, Mandela, diff.

2013, Dec. 15 Litho. *Perf. 13¾*

3237 A680 $2.50 Sheet of 6, #a-f 11.00 11.00

3238 A681 $2.50 Sheet of 6, #a-f 11.00 11.00

Souvenir Sheets

3239 A681 $9 multi 6.75 6.75

Litho.; Margin Embossed With Foil Application

Imperf

3240 A682 $13.50 multi 10.00 10.00

Characters From *Downton Abbey* Television Series — A683

No. 3241: a, Mrs. Hughes. b, Miss O'Brein. c, Thomas Barrow. d, William Mason.
$9, Mrs. Patmore and Daisy, horiz.

2014, Mar. 24 Litho. *Perf. 14*

3241 A683 $3.25 Sheet of 4, #a-d 9.75 9.75

Souvenir Sheet

3242 A683 $9 multi 6.75 6.75

Parrots
A684

No. 3243, $4.75: a, Eclectus parrot. b, Blue-and-yellow macaw. c, Black-capped lory. d, Sun parakeet.
No. 3244, $4.75: a, Blue-and-yellow macaw, leg near beak. b, Lilac-crowned Amazon. c, Saint Vincent Amazon. d, Indian ring-necked parakeet.
No. 3245, $9.50: a, Scarlet macaw. b, Yellow-headed Amazon.
No. 3246, $9.50: a, Rainbow lorikeet. b, Hyacinth macaw.

2014, June 23 Litho. *Perf. 14*

Sheets of 4, #a-d

3243-3244 A684 Set of 2 28.00 28.00

Souvenir Sheets of 2, #a-b

3245-3246 A684 Set of 2 28.00 28.00

A685

A686

A687

Aloe Vera
A688

No. 3247: a, Plant in pot. b, Plant (no pot and plus signs). c, Close-up of plant.
No. 3248: a, Plant and roots. b, Plant diagonally. c, Close-up of plant, diff.
No. 3249: a, Plant (no plus signs). b, Plant and plus signs.
No. 3250: a, Plant (no plus signs), diff. b, Plant cut into pieces and plus signs.

2014, June 23 Litho. *Perf. 13¾*

3247 A685 $4.75 Sheet of 4, #3247a-3247b, 2 #3247c 14.00 14.00

3248 A686 $4.75 Sheet of 4, #3248a-3248b, 2 #3248c 14.00 14.00

Souvenir Sheets

3249 A687 $9.50 Sheet of 2, #a-b 14.00 14.00

3250 A688 $9.50 Sheet of 2, #a-b 14.00 14.00

Christmas — A689

Paintings by Raphael: $2.25, Holy Family Below the Oak. $3.50, Madonna with the Blue Diadem. No. 3253, $5, Incoronazione della Vergine, detta Pala Oddi. No. 3254, $5, Aldobrandini Madonna.

2014, Dec. 29 Litho. *Perf. 14¼*

3251-3254 A689 Set of 4 12.00 12.00

New Year 2015 (Year of the Ram)
A690

No. 3255 — Ram with: a, Orange horns (at right). b, Red horns (at left). c, Green horns (at left). d, Olive horns at right.
$10, Ram with red horns at right.

2015, Jan. 2 Litho. *Perf. 14*

3255 A690 $3.25 Sheet of 4, #a-d 9.75 9.75

Souvenir Sheet

Perf.

3256 A690 $10 multi 7.50 7.50

No. 3256 contains one 38mm diameter stamp.

Rare Stamps
A691

No. 3257: a, Canada #3. b, Livingston, Alabama #51X1. c, Belgium #123B.
$10, Canada #387a, horiz.

2015, Jan. 2 Litho. *Perf. 13¼x12½*

3257 A691 $3.50 Sheet of 3, #a-c 7.75 7.75

Souvenir Sheet

Perf. 12½x13¼

3258 A691 $10 multi 7.50 7.50

Hummingbirds — A692

No. 3259, $3.25: a, Broad-tailed hummingbird, flower at LL. b, Broad-billed hummingbird, beak at right. c, Rufous-tailed hummingbird. d, Allen's hummingbird in flight.

No. 3260, $3.25: a, Allen's hummingbird on perch. b, Broad-tailed hummingbird, flower at UR. c, Broad-billed hummingbird, beak and flower at left. d, Ruby-throated hummingbird.

No. 3261, $5: a, Ruby-throated hummingbird on branch. b, Buff-bellied hummingbird.

No. 3262, $5: a, Anna's hummingbird. b, Calliope hummingbird.

Perf. 14, 12 (#3262)

2015, Jan. 2 Litho.

Sheets of 4, #a-d

3259-3260 A692 Set of 2 19.50 19.50

Souvenir Sheets of 2, #a-b

3261-3262 A692 Set of 2 15.00 15.00

Macaws A693

No. 3263, $3.25: a, Red-shouldered macaw. b, Hyacinth macaw. c, Blue-and-yellow macaw. d, Military macaw.

No. 3264, $3.25, vert.: a, Blue-headed macaw. b, Blue-throated macaw. c, Catalina macaw. d, Miligold macaw.

No. 3265, $5, vert.: a, Harlequin macaw. b, Scarlet macaw.

No. 3266, $5, vert.: a, Great green macaw. b, Green-winged macaw.

Perf. 14, 12 (#3264)

2015, Jan. 2 Litho.

Sheets of 4, #a-d

3263-3264 A693 Set of 2 19.50 19.50

Souvenir Sheets of 2, #a-b

3265-3266 A693 Set of 2 15.00 15.00

Ducks and Geese A694

No. 3267, $3.25: a, Hartlaub's ducks. b, Wood ducks. c, Common shelducks. d, Mallards.

No. 3268, $3.25: a, Ruddy shelducks. b, White-backed duck and eggs in nest. c, Knob-billed ducks. d, Fulvous whistling ducks.

No. 3269, $5: a, Egyptian geese. b, Chiloé wigeons.

No. 3270, $5: a, White-face whistling ducks. b, Red-billed teals.

2015, Jan. 2 Litho. *Perf. 14*

Sheets of 4, #a-d

3267-3268 A694 Set of 2 19.50 19.50

Souvenir Sheets of 2, #a-b

3269-3270 A694 Set of 2 15.00 15.00

Corals A695

No. 3271, $3.25: a, Purple wide-mesh sea fans. b, Orange wide-mesh sea fan. c, Brain coral with green spots. d, Brain coral with red spots.

No. 3272, $3.25: a, Solitary disk coral. b, Antler coral. c, Common mushroom coral. d, Common lettuce coral.

No. 3273: a, Elkhorn coral. b, Orage cup coral.

$10, Great star coral, vert.

2015, Jan. 2 Litho. *Perf. 14*

Sheets of 4, #a-d

3271-3272 A695 Set of 2 19.50 19.50

3273 A695 $5 Sheet of 2, #a-b 7.50 7.50

Souvenir Sheet

Perf. 12½

3274 A695 $10 multi 7.50 7.50

No. 3274 contains oner 38x51mm stamp.

Prince George of Cambridge — A696

No. 3275 — Prince George in hands of: a, Duchess of Cambridge. b, Duke of Cambridge.

No. 3276, $9.50, Prince George, black panel at bottom. No. 3277, $9.50, Prince George, Duchess of Cambridge, red panel at bottom.

Perf. 13 Syncopated

2015, Jan. 2 Litho.

3275 A696 $3.25 Pair, #a-b 5.00 5.00

Souvenir Sheets

3276-3277 A696 Set of 2 14.00 14.00

No. 3275 was printed in sheets containing three pairs.

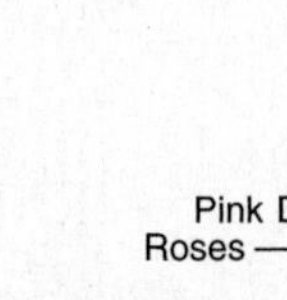

Julie Mango Tree — A697

2015, Jan. 16 Litho. *Perf. 13¾*

3278 A697 25c multi .25 .25

Pink Desert Roses — A698

2015, Feb. 24 Litho. *Perf. 14*

3279 A698 $2.20 multi 1.75 1.75

Souvenir Sheet

Perf. 12

3280 A698 $10 Pink desert roses, diff. 7.50 7.50

No. 3279 was printed in sheets of 8 + central label.

Valentina Tereshkova, First Woman in Space — A699

No. 3281: a, Space capsule and Earth, conical section of capsule at left. b, Space capsule and Earth, conical section of capsule at bottom. c, Tereshkova. d, Rocket lift-off.

$10, Capsule, diff.

2015, Mar. 24 Litho. *Perf. 14*

3281 A699 $3.25 Sheet of 4, #a-d 9.75 9.75

Souvenir Sheet

Perf. 12¾

3282 A699 $10 multi 7.50 7.50

No. 3282 contains one 51x38mm stamp.

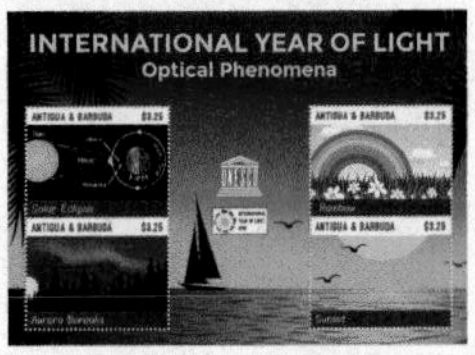

International Year of Light — A700

No. 3283: a, Solar eclipse. b, Rainbow. c, Aurora Borealis. d, Sunset.

$10, Sunlight.

2015, Mar. 24 Litho. *Perf. 12¾*

3283 A700 $3.25 Sheet of 4, #a-d 9.75 9.75

Souvenir Sheet

Perf.

3284 A700 $10 multi 7.50 7.50

No. 3284 contains one 38mm diameter stamp.

Paintings by Vincent van Gogh (1853-90) — A701

No. 3285: a, Cafén Terrace at Night, 1888. b, Self-portrait, 1889. c, Vincent's Bedroom in Arles, 1888. d, Starry Night, 1889. e, Vase with 12 Sunflowers, 1888. f, Interior of a Restaurant, 1887.

$10, Postman Joseph Roulin, 1888.

2015, Mar. 24 Litho. *Perf. 12¾*

3285 A701 $3.15 Sheet of 6, #a-f 14.00 14.00

Souvenir Sheet

3286 A701 $10 multi 7.50 7.50

A702

Horses in Art A703

No. 3287 — Various unattributed paintings depicting: a, Roundup of wild horses. b, Rider on horse, woman tending to two horses. c, Brown horse facing left. d, White horse and attendant facing left. e, Horse and colt. f, White horse facing right.

No. 3288 — Various unattributed paintings depicting: a, Horses and jockeys at race track. b, Horses and riders at seashore. c, Horse and jockey with race track grandstand in background. d, Horse and fence.

No. 3289, $10, Black horse with clipped tail facing left. No. 3290, $10, Rider on galloping horse beside running dogs.

2015, Mar. 24 Litho. *Perf. 12¾*

3287 A702 $3.15 Sheet of 6, #a-f 14.00 14.00

3288 A703 $3.25 Sheet of 4, #a-d 9.75 9.75

Souvenir Sheets

3289-3290 A703 Set of 2 15.00 15.00

Landscapes — A704

Designs: 30c, White sand beach, Barbuda. 75c, Aerial view of St. John's, Antigua. 90c, English Harbor, Antigua. $1, Pink sand beach, Barbuda. $1.50, Green Island.

2015, Apr. 20 Litho. *Perf. 13¼x12½*

3291-3295 A704 Set of 5 3.50 3.50

Flag of Antigua and Barbuda A705

Coat of Arms of Antigua and Barbuda A706

2015, Apr. 20 Litho. *Perf. 13¼x12½*

3296 A705 $50 multi 37.50 37.50

3297 A706 $100 multi 75.00 75.00

Queen Elizabeth II, Longest-Reigning British Monarch — A707

No. 3298 — Queen Elizabeth II: a, As young woman. b, Wearing tiara. c, Wearing hat. d, Wearing blue dress. e, Wearing green dress. f, Wearing pink jacket.

No. 3299 — Queen Elizabeth II: a, As child. b, As older woman wearing white hat.

2015, July 8 Litho. *Perf. 14*

3298 A707 $3.15 Sheet of 6, #a-f 14.00 14.00

Souvenir Sheet

Perf. 12

3299 A707 $5 Sheet of 2, #a-b 7.50 7.50

Souvenir Sheets

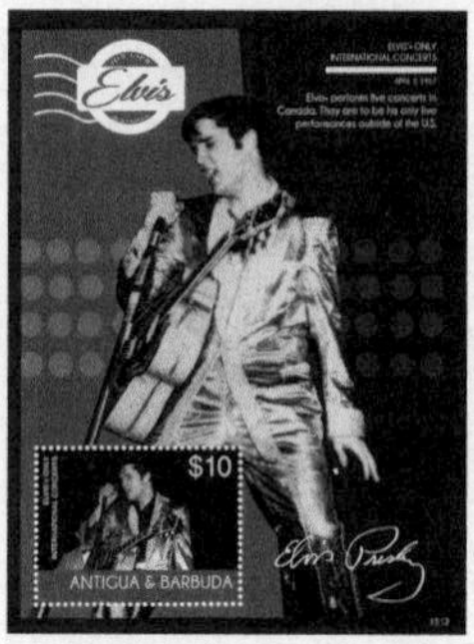

Elvis Presley (1935-77) — A708

Various photographs of Presley with panel at bottom of stamp in: No. 3300, $10, Dull green. No. 3301, $10, Purple. No. 3302, $10, Orange. No. 3303, $10, Salmon.

2015, Aug. 31 Litho. *Perf. 14*
3300-3303 A708 Set of 4 30.00 30.00

Battle of Waterloo, 200th Anniv. — A709

No. 3304: a, King William II of the Netherlands. b, Portrait of the Duke of Wellington. c, Emperor Napoleon in His Study at the Tuileries. d, Gebhard Lebrecht von Blücher.
$10, The Battle of Waterloo, horiz.

2015, Dec. 1 Litho. *Perf. 12x12½*
3304 A709 $3.25 Sheet of 4, #a-d 9.75 9.75

Souvenir Sheet
Perf. 13½
3305 A709 $10 multi 7.50 7.50

No. 3305 contains one 51x38mm stamp.

Christmas — A710

Paintings by Sandro Botticelli: 90c, The Virgin Adoring the Sleeping Christ Child. $2.25, Madonna and Child with St. John the Baptist. $3.50, Madonna and Child. $5, Madonna and Child with an Angel.

2015, Nov. 3 Litho. *Perf. 12½*
3306-3309 A710 Set of 4 8.75 8.75

Gemstones — A711

No. 3310: a, Diamond. b, Sapphire. c, Aquamarine. d, Topaz. e, Turquoise. f, Emerald.
$10, Opal.

2015, Dec. 28 Litho. *Perf. 13¾*
3310 A711 $3.15 Sheet of 6, #a-f 14.00 14.00

Souvenir Sheet
3311 A711 $10 multi 7.50 7.50

World War I Events of 1915 A712

No. 3312: a, Zeppelins. b, Sinking of British steamer Andex. c, Diagrams of torpedoed RMS Lusitania. d, Fokker airplane. e, Serbian refugees. f, Evacuation of Gallipoli.
$10, Soldier wearing gas mask.

2015, Dec. 28 Litho. *Perf. 12*
3312 A712 $3.15 Sheet of 6, #a-f 14.00 14.00

Souvenir Sheet
3313 A712 $10 multi 7.50 7.50

New Horizons Space Probe A713

No. 3314: a, New Horizons above Earth, Jan. 19, 2006. b, New Horizons near Asteroid 2002 JF 56, June 12, 2006. c, Voyager 2 flying by Neptune, Summer, 1989. d, New Horizons crossing Neptune orbit, Aug. 25, 2014.
$10, Rocket launch.

2015, Dec. 28 Litho. *Perf. 14*
3314 A713 $3.25 Sheet of 4, #a-d 9.75 9.75

Souvenir Sheet
3315 A713 $10 multi 7.50 7.50

Miniature Sheet

New Year 2016 (Year of the Monkey) A714

No. 3316 — Stone figurines: a, Monkey holding ball. b, Monkey on pedestal. c, Two monkeys. d, Monkey in tree.

2016, Jan. 28 Litho. *Perf. 14*
3316 A714 $2 Sheet of 4, #a-d 6.00 6.00

Visit of Pope Francis to New York City A715

No. 3317 — Pope Francis in front of: a, Flags, teeth visible. b, United Nations Building and flags, waving. c, As "a," waving hand. d, As "b," no hands visible. e, As "a," teeth not visible. f, As "b", waving with hand raised above head.
$10, Pope Francis waving, flags.

2016, Jan. 28 Litho. *Perf. 14*
3317 A715 $3.15 Sheet of 6, #a-f 14.00 14.00

Souvenir Sheet
Perf. 12
3318 A715 $10 multi 7.50 7.50

Paintings A716

No. 3319, $3.50 — Details of *Consequences of War,* by Peter Paul Rubens: a, Left portion. b, Center portion. c, Right portion.
No. 3320, $3.50: a, *The Death of General Wolfe,* by Benjamin West. b, *Lady with an Ermine,* by Leonardo da Vinci. c, *An Old Man and His Grandson,* by Domenico Ghirlandaio.
No. 3321, $10, The Tempest, by Giorgione. No. 3322, $10, The Virgin and Child with St. Anne, by Leonardo.

2016, Feb. 2 Litho. *Perf. 12½*
Sheets of 3, #a-c
3319-3320 A716 Set of 2 15.50 15.50

Size: 100x100mm
Imperf
3321-3322 A716 Set of 2 15.00 15.00

Klingons From *Star Trek* A717

No. 3323: a, Klingon holding tangled Christmas lights. b, Three Klingons caroling. c, Klingon snowman. d, Klingon as Santa Claus. e, Klingon family and Christmas stocking. f, Two Klingon holding mugs.
$10, Klingon as Santa Claus, vert.

2016, Feb. 15 Litho. *Perf. 12½*
3323 A717 $3.15 Sheet of 6, #a-f 14.00 14.00

Souvenir Sheet
Perf. 11¼x11½
3324 A717 $10 multi 7.50 7.50

No. 3324 contains one 30x50mm stamp.

Mushrooms — A718

No. 3325: a, Weeping bolete. b, Saffron milk cap. c, Black trumpet. d, Parasol mushroom. e, Green-cracking russula. f, Common puffball.
No. 3326, vert.: a, Red-capped scaber stalk. b, Porcino. c, Fly agaric. d, Psilocybe cubensis.
$10, Chanterelle, vert.

2016, May 11 Litho. *Perf. 14*
3325 A718 $3.15 Sheet of 6, #a-f 14.00 14.00
3326 A718 $3.25 Sheet of 4, #a-d 9.75 9.75

Souvenir Sheet
Perf. 12
3327 A718 $10 multi 7.50 7.50

Marine Mammals — A719

No. 3328: a, Sperm whale. b, Dugong. c, Spinner dolphins. d, Harbor porpoise. e, Humpback whale. f, West Indian manatee.
No. 3329: a, California sea lion. b, Polar bear. c, Northern fur seal. d, Harp seal.
$10, Walruses, horiz.

2016, May 25 Litho. *Perf. 13¾*
3328 A719 $3.15 Sheet of 6, #a-f 14.00 14.00
3329 A719 $3.25 Sheet of 4, #a-d 9.75 9.75

Souvenir Sheet
Perf. 14
3330 A719 $10 multi 7.50 7.50

No. 3330 contains one 40x30mm stamp.

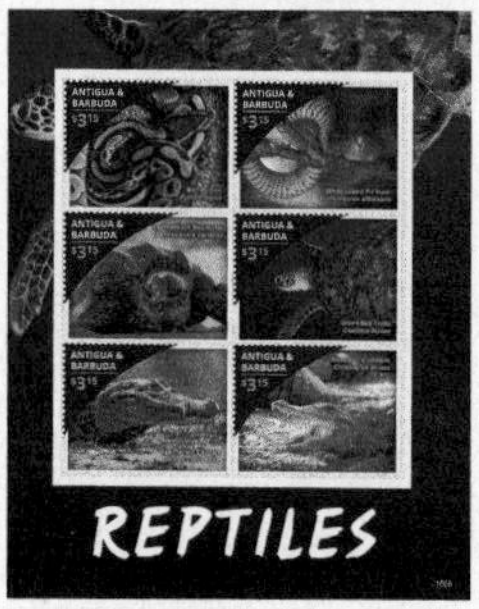

Reptiles A720

No. 3331: a, Ball python. b, White-lipped pit viper. c, Leatherback sea turtle. d, Green sea turtle. e, Spectacled caiman. f, American crocodile.
No. 3332: a, Carolina anole. b, Dwarf yellow-headed gecko. c, Little striped whiptail. d, Giant girdled lizard.
$10, Panther chameleon.

2016, May 25 Litho. *Perf. 14*
3331 A720 $3.15 Sheet of 6, #a-f 14.00 14.00

Perf. 12
3332 A720 $3.25 Sheet of 4, #a-d 9.75 9.75

Souvenir Sheet
3333 A720 $10 multi 7.50 7.50

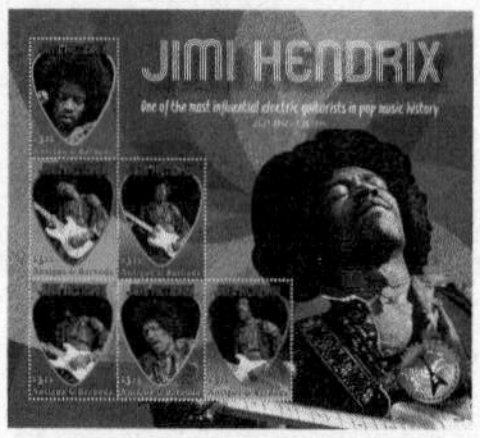

Jimi Hendrix (1942-70), Rock Musician — A721

No. 3334 — Various photographs of Hendrix, as shown.
$10, Hendrix, diff.

2016, May 25 Litho. *Perf. 14*
3334 A721 $3.15 Sheet of 6, #a-f 14.00 14.00

Souvenir Sheet
Perf. 12
3335 A721 $10 multi 7.50 7.50

No. 3335 contains one 30x50mm stamp.

A722

A723

A724

Atlantic Goliath Grouper A725

2016, June 8 Litho. *Perf. 12*

3336	Strip of 4	9.75	9.75
a.	A722 $3.25 multi	2.40	2.40
b.	A723 $3.25 multi	2.40	2.40
c.	A724 $3.25 multi	2.40	2.40
d.	A725 $3.25 multi	2.40	2.40
e.	Miniature sheet of 8, 2 each #3336a-3336d	19.50	19.50

Worldwide Fund for Nature (WWF).

William Shakespeare (1564-1616), Writer — A726

No. 3337 — Various scenes from *Hamlet*: a, Hamlet and Claudius. b, Hamlet holding sword. c, Hamlet and Ophelia. d, Hamlet holding skull.
$10, Shakespeare.

2016, July 22 Litho. *Perf. 14*

3337 A726 $3.25 Sheet of 4, #a-d 9.75 9.75

Souvenir Sheet

Perf. 13¾

3338 A726 $10 multi 7.50 7.50

No. 3338 contains one 35x35mm stamp.

Sergei Korolev (1907-66), Rocket Engineer — A727

No. 3339: a, Statue depicting Korolev, Moscow. b, Luna 3 and Moon. c, Sputnik 1. d, Vostok 1.
$14, Soyuz TMA-ISS rocket launch.

2016, July 29 Litho. *Perf. 14*

3339 A727 $4 Sheet of 4, #a-d 12.00 12.00

Souvenir Sheet

Perf. 12

3340 A727 $14 multi 10.50 10.50

Queen Elizabeth II, 90th Birthday A728

No. 3341: a, Queen Elizabeth II wearing pink jacket and hat. b, Royal coat of arms. c, Queen Elizabeth II wearing blue jacket and hat. d, Queen's royal cypher.
No. 3342, vert.: a, Queen's flag. b, Queen Elizabeth II wearing white and apple green hat.

2016, July 29 Litho. *Perf. 13¾*

3341 A728 $4 Sheet of 4, #a-d 12.00 12.00

Souvenir Sheet

Perf. 12½

3342 A728 $7 Sheet of 2, #a-b 10.50 10.50

No. 3342 contains two 38x51mm stamps.

Souvenir Sheets

Elvis Presley (1935-77) — A729

Inscriptions: No. 3343, $14, First top-billed film. No. 3344, $14, Last Ed Sullivan appearance. No. 3345, $14, Graceland welcomes Scatter. No. 3346, $14, Performs at Messick High School, horiz.

Perf. 13¼x13, 13x13¼

2016, Aug. 16 Litho.

3343-3346 A729 Set of 4 42.00 42.00

Statue of Liberty, 130th Anniv. A730

No. 3347 — Various depictions of the Statue of Liberty, as shown.
$14, Statue of Liberty, diff.

2016, Aug. 29 Litho. *Perf. 14*

3347 A730 $3.15 Sheet of 6, #a-f 14.00 14.00

Souvenir Sheet

Perf.

3348 A730 $14 multi 10.50 10.50

No. 3348 contains one 33x44mm oval stamp.

Characters From *Star Trek* Television Series — A731

No. 3349: a, Captain Kirk. b, Spock. c, Uhura. d, Chekov. e, McCoy. f, Scotty.
No. 3350, $7, horiz.: a, Captain Kirk, diff. b, Mirror Captain Kirk.
No. 3351, $7, horiz.: a, Spock, diff. b, Mirror Spock.

2017, Jan. 9 Litho. *Perf. 14*

3349 A731 $3 Sheet of 6, #a-f 13.50 13.50

Souvenir Sheets of 2, #a-b

Perf. 12½

3350-3351 A731 Set of 2 21.00 21.00

Nos. 3350-3351 each contain two 51x38mm stamps.

Christmas A732

Designs: No. 3352, $5.50, Christmas tree. No. 3353, $5.50, Snowflake. No. 3354, $10, Reindeer. No. 3355, $10, Angel.

2017, Jan. 23 Litho. *Perf. 12½*

3352-3355 A732 Set of 4 23.00 23.00

A733

A734

New Year 2017 (Year of the Rooster) A735

No. 3357: a, Two roosters, pale mauve background. b, One rooster, brown background. c, One rooster, head pointing left, white background. d, One rooster, head pointing right, white background with flowers.
No. 3358 — Rooster facing: a, Right. b, Left. c, Right, streak of color at LL. b, Left, streak of color at LR.

2017, Jan. 23 Litho. *Perf. 12*

3356 A733 $5.50 multi 4.25 4.25

Miniature Sheets

Perf. 12½

3357 A734 $5.50 Sheet of 4, #a-d 16.50 16.50
3358 A735 $5.50 Sheet of 4, #a-d 16.50 16.50

No. 3356 comes in sheets of 4.

A736

A737

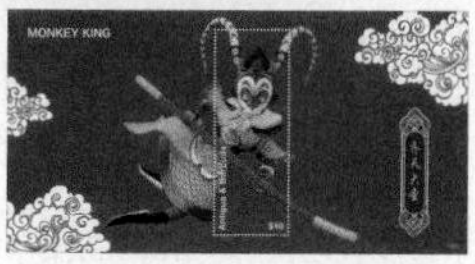

Monkey King A738

No. 3359 — Various scenes from *The Monkey King*, as shown.

2017, Mar. 15 Litho. *Perf. 12½*

3359 A736 $5.50 Sheet of 4, #a-d 16.50 16.50

Souvenir Sheets

3360 A737 $10 multi 7.50 7.50

Perf. 14

3361 A738 $10 multi 7.50 7.50

Zeppelins — A739

No. 3362: a, Spotlight on Zeppelin. b, Zeppelins and airplanes. c, Zeppelin crash in ocean, ship in background. d, Zeppelin on fire.
No. 3363: a, Z2. b, LZ 127.

2017, Apr. 5 Litho. *Perf. 14*

3362 A739 $5.50 Sheet of 4, #a-d 16.50 16.50

Souvenir Sheet

Perf. 12

3363 A739 $7.50 Sheet of 2, #a-b 11.00 11.00

Count Ferdinand von Zeppelin (1838-1917).
No. 3363 contains two 50x30mm stamps.

Miniature Sheet

Acheivements of Pres. John F. Kennedy (1917-63) — A740

No. 3364: a, Kennedy signing copy of *Why England Slept*, 1940 (35x70mm). b, Kennedy at his inauguration, 1961 (70x35mm). c, Kennedy wearing naval uniform (35x70mm). d, Kennedy as child wearing police uniform (35x35mm). e, Kennedy graduating from Harvard, 1940 (35x35mm).

2017, June 3 Litho. *Perf. 13¾*

3364 A740 $3.50 Sheet of 5, #a-e 13.00 13.00

First Man in Space, 55th Anniv. (in 2016) A741

No. 3365: a, Vostok mission patch. b, Yuri Gagarin in military uniform. c, Gagarin in space suit. d, Vostok 1 capsule. e, Vostok mission patch with "CCCP." f, Coin depicting Gagarin.
No. 3366: a, Nose of Vostok 1 at lift-off. b, Vostok 1 engines and exhaust at lift-off.

2017, June 3 Litho. *Perf. 14*
3365 A741 $3 Sheet of 6, #a-f 13.50 13.50

Souvenir Sheet
Perf. 13¼
3366 A741 $8 Sheet of 2, #a-b 12.00 12.00

No. 3366 contains two 35x35mm stamps.

Miniature Sheets

A742

Elvis Presley (1935-77) — A743

No. 3367 — Presley wearing: a, Suit and tie. b, Shirt and tie. c, Black and blue shirt d, Jacket and striped shirt.
No. 3368 — Presley: a, Wearing striped jacket. b, Holding guitar. c, Wearing striped shirt, color photograph. d, Wearing sweater. e, Wearing shirt and tie. f, Wearing ribbed shirt, black-and-white photograph.

2017, July 25 Litho. *Perf. 14*
3367 A742 $3.50 Sheet of 4, #a-d 10.50 10.50
3368 A743 $3.50 Sheet of 6, #a-f 15.50 15.50

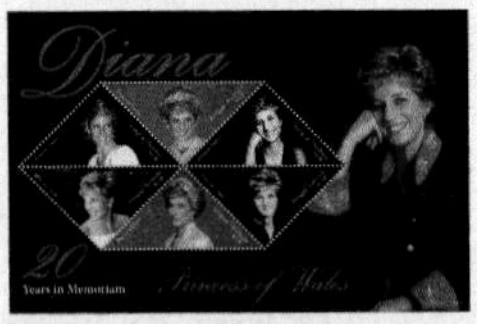

Princess Diana (1961-97) — A744

No. 3369 — Princess Diana wearing: a, White dress covering shoulders. b, Tiara and necklace. c, Black dress, hand touching face. d, White dress not covering shoulders. e, Tiara and gown. f, Collared jacket.
No. 3370 — Princess Diana wearing: a, Black and white hat. b, Pink hat.

2017, July 25 Litho. *Perf. 12*
3369 A744 $3.50 Sheet of 6, #a-f 15.50 15.50

Souvenir Sheet
3370 A744 $3.50 Sheet of 2, #a-b 5.25 5.25

Paintings by Edgar Degas (1834-1917) — A745

No. 3371: a, At the Cafe des Ambassadeurs. b, Young Woman with Ibis. c, The Orchestra at the Opera. d, Visit to a Museum.
No. 3372: a, The Green Dancer. b, Ballet Dancers on the Stage. c, Ballet Class.

2017, July 25 Litho. *Perf. 14*
3371 A745 $5.50 Sheet of 4, #a-d 16.50 16.50

Souvenir Sheet
3372 A745 $5 Sheet of 3, #a-c 11.00 11.00

Piping Plovers A746

No. 3373 — Plover: a, Facing left, beak open. b, In flight. c, Walking left, beak closed.
$10, Head of plover, vert.

2017, July 25 Litho. *Perf. 14*
3373 A746 $5 Sheet of 3 11.00 11.00

Souvenir Sheet
3374 A746 $10 multi 7.50 7.50

Horses A747

No. 3375: a, Two Icelandic horses running left. b, New Forest pony. c, Camargue horse. d, Hutsul horse. e, Two Icelandic horses standing. f, Orlov trotter.
No. 3376: a, Morgan horse. b, Arabian horse. c, Lippizan horse.

2017, July 28 Litho. *Perf. 12½x13¼*
3375 A747 $4 Sheet of 6, #a-f 18.00 18.00

Souvenir Sheet
3376 A747 $7.50 Sheet of 3, #a-c 17.00 17.00

A748

Fallow Deer A749

No. 3377: a, Buck looking over shoulder. b, Profile of Buck. c, Doe in green foilage. d, Doe in field.
No. 3378: a, Fawn. b, Doe in grass by tree. c, Buck profile in tall grass.

2017, Aug. 1 Litho. *Perf. 14*
3377 A748 $7.50 Sheet of 4, #a-d 22.50 22.50

Souvenir Sheet
3378 A749 $7 Sheet of 3, #a-c 15.50 15.50

Macaws A750

No. 3379: a, Blue-and-yellow macaw facing right. b, Scarlet macaw facing right, on branch. c, Blue-and-yellow macaw facing left. d, Scarlet macaw facing left on branch. e, Head of Blue-and-yellow macaw. f, Scarlet macaw faing right, diff.
No. 3380: a, Military macaw. b, Scarlet macaw in flight. c, Blue-and-yellow macaw in flight.

2017, Aug. 1 Litho. *Perf. 14*
3379 A750 $4 Sheet of 6, #a-f 18.00 18.00

Souvenir Sheet
3380 A750 $7 Sheet of 3, #a-c 15.50 15.50

Miniature Sheets

A751

Hawksbill Turtles A752

Various photographs of Hawksbill turtles, as shown.

2017, Aug. 1 Litho. *Perf. 14*
3381 A751 $7 Sheet of 4, #a-d 21.00 21.00
3382 A752 $7 Sheet of 4, #a-d 21.00 21.00

Miniature Sheets

Fruits and Vegetables — A753

No. 3383: a, Apple bananas. b, Malay apples. c, Sapodillas. d, Eggplants.
No. 3384: a, Papayas. b, Cacao pods. c, Spanish limes. d, Avocados.

2017, Aug. 1 Litho. *Perf. 14*
3383 A753 $7 Sheet of 4, #a-d 21.00 21.00

Perf. 13¾
3384 A753 $7 Sheet of 4, #a-d 21.00 21.00

No. 3384 contains four 35x35mm stamps.

Jellyfish A754

No. 3385: a, Pacific sea nettle (40x60mm). b, Moon jellyfish (40x30mm). c, Black sea nettle, blue background (40x30mm). d, Sea nettle jellyfish (40x30mm). e, Black sea nettle, black lilac background (40x30mm).
No. 3386, vert.: a, Blue bubbler (30x40mm). b, Brown jellyfish (30x40mm). c, Lion's mane jellyfish (30x40mm).
No. 3387, vert.: a, Barrel jellyfish (30x40mm). b, Spotted jellyfish (30x40mm).

2017, Aug. 1 Litho. *Perf. 14*
3385 A754 $5 Sheet of 5, #a-e 18.50 18.50
3386 A754 $7 Sheet of 3, #a-c 15.50 15.50

Souvenir Sheet
3387 A754 $7.50 Sheet of 2, #a-b 11.00 11.00

Animals A755

No. 3388: a, Prehensile-tailed porcupine. b, San Clemente Island fox. c, Jaguarundi. d, Grevy's zebra.
$15, Snowy owl.

2017, Aug. 14 Litho. *Perf. 12½*
3388 A755 $6 Sheet of 4, #a-d 18.00 18.00

Souvenir Sheet
3389 A755 $15 multi 11.00 11.00

Miniature Sheets

Paintings by Norman Rockwell (1894-1978) — A756

No. 3390: a, $4, Boy in Dining Car (30x40mm). b, $4, Breaking Home Ties (30x40mm). c, $4, Homecoming Marine (30x40mm). d, $4, Retribution (30x40mm). e, $10, Triple Self-portrait (60x80mm).
No. 3391: a, $4, Russian Schoolroom (30x40mm). b, $4, Southern Justice (Murder in Mississippi) (30x40mm). c, $4, The Circus Barker (30x40mm). d, $4, The Love Song (30x40mm). e, $10, Little Boy Writing a Letter (60x80mm).
No. 3392: a, $4, The Problem We All Live With (30x40mm). b, $4, The Scoutmaster (30x40mm). c, $4, They Remembered Me (30x40mm). d, $4, We, Too, Have a Job to Do (30x40mm). e, $10, The Runaway (60x80mm).

2017, Aug. 22 Litho. *Perf. 14*
Sheets of 5, #a-e
3390-3392 A756 Set of 3 57.50 57.50

Miniature Sheet

Seadragons — A757

No. 3393: a, Weedy seadragon facing left. b, Weedy seadragon facing right. c, Weedy seadragon facing right, diff. d, Leafy seadragon.

2017, Aug. 22 Litho. *Perf. 14*
3393 A757 $7 Sheet of 4, #a-d 21.00 21.00

Seahorses — A758

No. 3394: a, Thorny seahorse. b, Thorny seahorse and coral. c, Yellow seahorse.

2017, Aug. 22 Litho. *Perf. 12*
3394 A758 $7 Sheet of 3, #a-c 15.50 15.50

Horses A759

No. 3395: a, Icelandic horses walking to left. b, New Forest pony. c, Camargue horse. d, Hutsul horse. e, Icelandic horses standing. f, Orlov trotter.
No. 3396: a, Morgan horse. b, Arabian horse. c, Lipizzan horse.

Perf. 12½x13¼

2017, Sept. 26 Litho.

3395 A759 $4 Sheet of 6, #a-f 18.00 18.00

Souvenir Sheet

3396 A759 $7.50 Sheet of 3, #a-c 17.00 17.00

Miniature Sheet

New Year 2018 (Year of the Dog) A760

No. 3397: a, Rottweiler at left. b, English bulldog at right. c, English bulldog at left. d, Rottweiler at right.

2017, Nov. 7 Litho. ***Perf. 14***

3397 A760 $7 Sheet of 4, #a-d 21.00 21.00

Muhammad Ali (1942-2016), Boxer — A761

No. 3398 — Ali with: a, One hand visible, punching bag at right. b, Both hands visible, punching bag at left. c, Both hands visible, punching bag at right.
$12, Ali, fist by chin.

2018, Jan. 23 Litho. ***Perf. 13¼x12½***

3398 A761 $7 Sheet of 3, #a-c 15.50 15.50

Souvenir Sheet

Perf. 13¼

3399 A761 $12 multi 9.00 9.00

No. 3399 contains one 38x51mm stamp.

Miniature Sheet

Marine Mammals — A762

No. 3400: a, $2, Killer whale. b, $3, Humpback whale. c, $4, Sperm whale. d, $5, False killer whales. e, $6, Spinner dolphins. f, $7, Bottlenose dolphin.

2018, May 8 Litho. ***Perf. 14***

3400 A762 Sheet of 6, #a-f 20.00 20.00

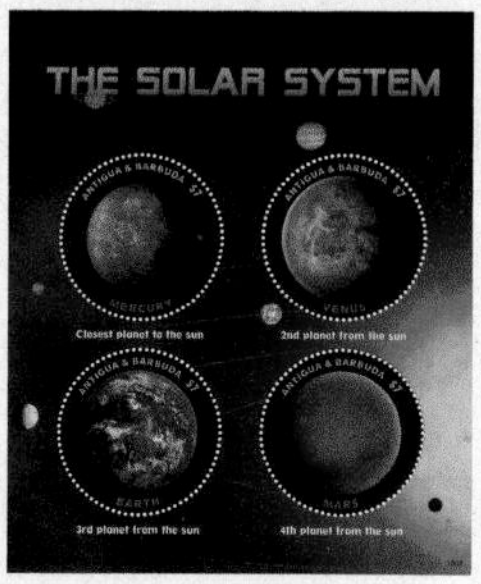

Solar System A763

No. 3401, $7: a, Mercury. b, Venus. c, Earth. d, Mars.
No. 3402: a, $6, Jupiter. b, $6, Neptune. c, $8, Saturn. d, $8, Uranus.
$12, Sun.

2018, May 9 Litho. ***Perf.***

Sheets of 4, #a-d

3401-3402 A763 Set of 2 42.00 42.00

Souvenir Sheet

3403 A763 $12 multi 9.00 9.00

Caribbean Reef Octopus — A764

No. 3404 — Various photographs of octopus: a, $6. b, $7. c, $8. d, $9.
$10, Octopus, diff.

2018, May 29 Litho. ***Perf. 14***

3404 A764 Sheet of 4, #a-d 22.50 22.50

Souvenir Sheet

Perf. 12½

3405 A764 $10 multi 7.50 7.50

No. 3405 contains one 51x38mm stamp.

Coronation of Queen Elizabeth II, 65th Anniv. — A765

No. 3406: a, $3, Coronation pen (35x35mm). b, $3, Coronation glove (35x35mm). c, $5, Diamond diadem (35x35mm). d, $6, Imperial State Crown (35x35mm). e, $6, Coronation gown and Robe of State (35x70mm).
No. 3407: a, Gold State Coach (40x30mm). b, Queen Elizabeth II and Prince Philip (40x30mm).

2018, May 29 Litho. ***Perf. 13¾***

3406 A765 Sheet of 5, #a-e 17.00 17.00

Souvenir Sheet

Perf. 14

3407 A765 $6.50 Sheet of 2, #a-b 9.75 9.75

Miniature Sheet

Visit to Vatican City of Pres. Donald Trump A766

No. 3408 — Pope Francis and: a, $4, Pres. Trump, shaking hands (40x30mm). b, $4, Melania Trump (40x30mm). c, $4, Ivanka Trump (40x30mm). d, $4, Pres Trump, standing (40x30mm). e, $6, Trump family and Jared Kushner (80x30mm).
$10, Trump family and Kushner.

2018, July 25 Litho. ***Perf. 14***

3408 A766 Sheet of 5, #a-e 16.50 16.50

Souvenir Sheet

Perf. 14

3409 A766 $10 multi 7.50 7.50

No. 3409 contains one 40x30mm stamp.

Miniature Sheet

Scalloped Hammerhead Sharks — A767

No. 3410 — Various photographs of sharks: a, $4. b, $5. c, $6. d, $7.

2018, July 25 Litho. ***Perf. 12***

3410 A767 Sheet of 4, #a-d 16.50 16.50

Corals and Sponges A768

No. 3411: a, $1, Elkhorn coral. b, $2, Azure vase sponge. c, $3, Giant barrel sponge. d, $4, Branching fire coral. e, $5, Staghorn coral. f, $6, Branching vase sponge.
$10, Pillar coral, vert.

2018, July 25 Litho. ***Perf. 14***

3411 A768 Sheet of 6, #a-f 15.50 15.50

Souvenir Sheet

Perf. 12½

3412 A768 $10 multi 7.50 7.50

No. 3412 contains one 38x51mm stamp.

Flowers A769

No. 3413: a, $2, Desert rose. b, $3, White frangipani. c, $4, Heliconia. d, $5, Red hibiscus. e, $6, Bougainvillea. f, $7, White oleander.
$12, Dagger log, vert.

2018, July 25 Litho. ***Perf. 14***

3413 A769 Sheet of 6, #a-f 20.00 20.00

Souvenir Sheet

Perf. 12

3414 A769 $12 multi 9.00 9.00

No. 3414 contains one 30x50mm stamp.

Engagement of Prince Harry and Meghan Markle — A770

No. 3415: a, Couple, Prince Harry waving. b, Hands of couple. c, Couple, Prince Harry touching suit button.
$10, Couple, horiz.

2018, Aug. 22 Litho. ***Perf. 14***

3415 A770 $5.50 Sheet of 3, #a-c 12.50 12.50

Souvenir Sheet

Perf. 12½

3416 A770 $10 multi 7.50 7.50

No. 3416 contains one 51x38mm stamp.

Muhammad Ali (1942-2016), Boxer — A771

No. 3417 — Ali boxing against: a, George Foreman, 1974. b, Joe Frazier, 1975. c, Earnie Shavers, 1977. d, Leon Spinks, 1978.
$10, Ali with arms raised, horiz.

2018, Aug. 22 Litho. ***Perf. 14***

3417 A771 $6 Sheet of 4, #a-d 18.00 18.00

Souvenir Sheet

3418 A771 $10 multi 7.50 7.50

Air Mail Centenary — A772

No. 3419: a, Charles Lindbergh in plane cockpit. b, 1929 Antigua air mail postmark. c, Antigua stamps on air mail cover. d, Linbergh and the Spirit of St. Louis.
$10, Sikorsky S-38A.

2018, Aug. 22 Litho. ***Perf. 14***

3419 A772 $5.50 Sheet of 4, #a-d 16.50 16.50

Souvenir Sheet

Perf. 12½

3420 A772 $10 multi 7.50 7.50

No. 3420 contains one 51x38mm stamp.

Miniature Sheet

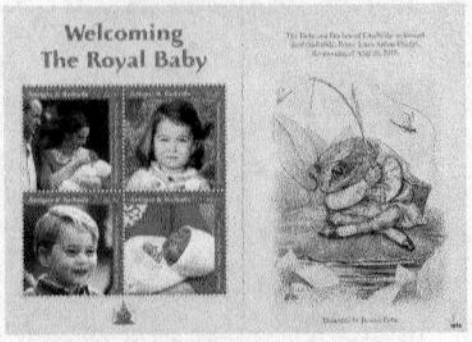

Birth of Prince Louis of Cambridge — A773

No. 3421: a, Duke and Duchess of Cambridge with Prince Louis. b, Princess Charlotte of Cambridge. c, Prince George of Cambridge. d, Prince Louis of Cambridge in arms of his mother.

2018, Aug. 28 Litho. *Perf. 13¾*

3421	A773 $5.50 Sheet of 4, #a-d		16.50	16.50

Wedding of Prince Harry and Meghan Markle A774

No. 3422: a, Groom, lamp in background. b, Bride, lamp in background. c, Groom, tile floor in background. d, Bride, tile floor in background.

$10, Bride and groom on steps, horiz.

2018, Aug. 28 Litho. *Perf. 12*

3422	A774 $5 Sheet of 4, #a-d	15.00	15.00

Souvenir Sheet

Perf. 12½

3423	A774 $10 multi	7.50	7.50

No. 3423 contains one 102x38mm stamp.

Magnificent Frigatebirds — A775

No. 3424 — Frigatebird: a, $5, On perch. b, $5, In flight. c, $6, Facing left. b, $6, Facing right.

$10, Two birds.

2018, Oct. 1 Litho. *Perf. 14*

3424	A775 Sheet of 4, #a-d	16.50	16.50

Souvenir Sheet

3425	A775 $10 multi	7.50	7.50

No. 3425 contains one 80x30mm stamp.

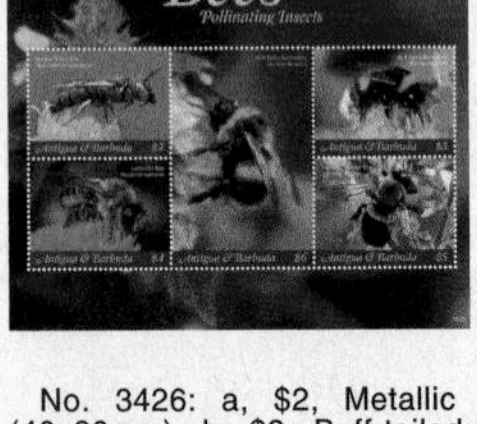

Bees A776

No. 3426: a, $2, Metallic green bee (40x30mm). b, $3, Buff-tailed bumblebee (40x30mm). c, $4, Leafcutter bee (40x30mm). d, $5, Eastern carpenter bee (40x30mm). e, $6, Buff-tailed bumblebee, diff. (40x60mm).

$10, Honeybee, vert.

2018, Oct. 1 Litho. *Perf. 14*

3426	A776 Sheet of 5, #a-e	15.00	15.00

Souvenir Sheet

Perf. 12½

3427	A776 $10 multi	7.50	7.50

No. 3427 contains one 38x51mm stamp.

Miniature Sheets

United States Presidents — A777

No. 3428: a, 1c, George Washington. b, 2c, John Adams. c, 3c, Thomas Jefferson. d, 4c, James Madison. e, 5c, James Monroe. f, 6c, John Quincy Adams. g, 7c, Andrew Jackson. h, 8c, Martin Van Buren. i, 9c, William Henry Harrison. j, 10c, John Tyler. k, 11c, James Knox Polk. l, $5, Seal of the President of the United States.

No. 3429: a, 12c, Zachary Taylor. b, 13c, Millard Fillmore. c, 14c, Fanklin Pierce. d, 15c, James Buchanan. e, 16c, Abraham Lincoln. f, 17c, Andrew Johnson. g, 18c, Ulysses S. Grant. h, 19c, Rutherford B. Hayes. i, 20c, James Garfield. j, 21c, Chester A. Arthur. k, 22c, Grover Cleveland. l, $4, White House.

No. 3430: a, 23c, Benjamin Harrison. b, 24c, Grover Cleveland. c, 25c, William McKinley. d, 26c, Theodore Roosevelt. e, 27c, William Howard Taft. f, 28c, Woodrow Wilson. g, 29c, Warren G. Harding. h, 30c, Calvin Coolidge. i, 31c, Herbert Hoover. j, 32c, Franklin D. Roosevelt. k, 33c, Harry S. Truman. l, $3, U.S. Capitol.

No. 3431: a, 34c, Dwight D. Eisenhower. b, 35c, John F. Kennedy. c, 36c, Lyndon B. Johnson. d, 37c, Richard M. Nixon. e, 38c, Gerald R. Ford. f, 39c, Jimmy Carter. g, 40c, Ronald Reagan. h, 41c, George H. W. Bush. i, 42c, Bill Clinton. j, 43c, George W. Bush. k, 44c, Barack Obama. l, 45c, Donald Trump.

2018, Nov. 1 Litho. *Perf. 13¾*

3428	A777 Sheet of 12, #a-l	4.25	4.25
3429	A777 Sheet of 12, #a-l	4.50	4.50
3430	A777 Sheet of 12, #a-l	4.50	4.50
3431	A777 Sheet of 12, #a-l	3.50	3.50
	Nos. 3428-3431 (4)	16.75	16.75

A778

New Year 2019 (Year of the Pig) A779

No. 3432: a, Red pig. b, Black pig.

2018, Nov. 1 Litho. *Perf. 14*

3432	A778 $3 Pair, #a-b	4.50	4.50

Souvenir Sheet

Perf. 13¾

3433	A779 $6 multi	4.50	4.50

No. 3432 was printed in sheets containing two pairs.

Miniature Sheet

Flowers A780

No. 3434: a, $2, Lobster claw plant. b, $3, Easter lily. c, $4, Flamingo flower. d, $5, Red frangipani. e, $6, False bird of paradise. f, $7, Flaming torch.

2018, Nov. 1 Litho. *Perf. 14*

3434	A780 Sheet of 6, #a-f	20.00	20.00

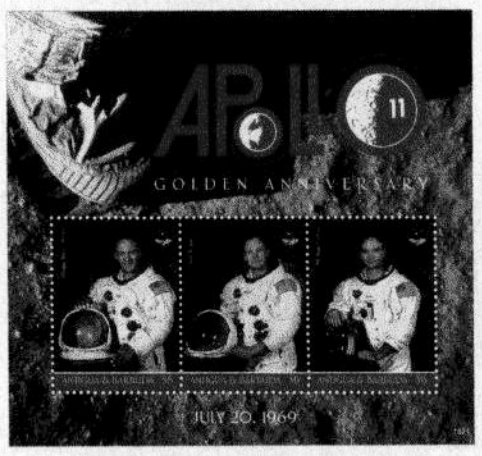

First Man on the Moon, 50th Anniv. (in 2019) A781

No. 3435 — Apollo 11 astronauts: a, Edwin "Buzz" Aldrin, Jr. b, Neil Armstrong. c, Michael Collins.

$10, Footprint on Moon.

2018, Nov. 1 Litho. *Perf. 12*

3435	A781 $6 Sheet of 3, #a-c	13.50	13.50

Souvenir Sheet

Perf. 12½

3436	A781 $10 multi	7.50	7.50

No. 3436 contains one 38x51mm stamp.

Classic Stamps A782

Most expensive variety of the illustrated stamp: No. 3437, $6, United States #7X1. No. 3438, $6, United States #11X6. No. 3439, $6, United States #1. No. 3440, $6, United States #2. No. 3441, $6, United States #5. No. 3442, $6, United States #85E. No. 3443, $6, United States #85F. No. 3444, $6, United States #120b. No. 3445, $6, United States #121b. No. 3446, $6, United States #181. No. 3447, $6, United States #292. No. 3448, $6, United States #294a. No. 3449, $6, United States #295a. No. 3450, $6, United States #C3a. No. 3451, $6, United States #C15. No. 3452, $6, Confederate States #36X1. No. 3453, $6, Confederate States #51X1. No. 3454, $6, Confederate States #62X6. No. 3455, $6, Confederate States #86X5. No. 3456, $6, Canal Zone #157a, No. 3457, $6, Hawaii #3. No. 3458, $6, Argentina #10. No. 3459, $6, Australian States - New South Wales #2s. No. 3460, $6, Australian States - Queensland #3. No. 3461, $6, Australian States - Tasmania #8. No. 3462, $6, Australian States - Western Australia #3a. No. 3463, $6, Austria #226a. No. 3464, $6, Barbados #21c. No. 3465, $6, Belgium #1. No. 3466, $6, Belgium #123B. No. 3467, $6, Bermuda #X1. No. 3468, $6, Bermuda #1b. No. 3469, $6, Brazil #1c. No. 3470, $6, British Central Africa #31. No. 3471, $6, British Central Africa #71. No. 3472, $6, British Central Africa #72. No. 3473, $6, British Guiana #1. No. 3474, $6, British Guiana #7. No. 3475, $6, British Guiana #13. No. 3476, $6, Canadian Provinces - New Brunswick #5. No. 3477, $6, Canadian Provinces - Newfoundland #9. No. 3478, $6, Canadian Provinces - Newfoundland #C1. No. 3479, $6, Canadian Provinces - Nova Scotia #6b. No. 3480, $6, Canada #1. No. 3481, $6, Canada #2. No. 3482, $6, Canada #3. No. 3483, $6, Canada #387a, No. 3484, $6, Cape of Good Hope #7b. No. 3485, $6, Ceylon #5. No. 3486, $6, Ceylon #7a. No. 3487, $6, Ceylon #218. No. 3488, $6, China #83. No. 3489, $6, Denmark #1. No. 3490, $6, Dominica #14. No. 3491, $6, Falkland Islands #151a. No. 3492, $6, Finland #2a. No. 3493, $6, France #9a. No. 3494, $6, France #19a. No. 3495, $6, German States - Bavaria #1b. No. 3496, $6, German States - Brunswick #9f. No. 3497, $6, German States - Lubeck #1. No. 3498, $6, German States - Saxony #1a. No. 3499, $6, Gibraltar #30a. No. 3500, $6, Gold Coast #24. No. 3501, $6, Great Britain #1c. No. 3502, $6, Great Britain #2c. No. 3503, $6, Great Britain #92. No. 3504, $6, Honduras #178. No. 3505, $6, Hong Kong #1a. No. 3506, $6, India #A3. No. 3507, $6, India #6c. No. 3508, $6, Italian States - Tuscany #23. No. 3509, $6, Italian States - Two Sicilies #8. No. 3510, $6, Jamaica #83a. No. 3511, $6, Kenya, Uganda and Tanzania #41D. No. 3512, $6, Malta #65. No. 3513, $6, Mauritius #2. No. 3514, $6, Mauritius #15. No. 3515, $6, Mexico #C74. No. 3516, $6, Nevis #13. No. 3517, $6, New Zealand #123a. No. 3518, $6, Niger Coast Protectorate #34. No. 3519, $6, Northern Nigeria #18A. No. 3520, $6, Norway #1. No. 3521, $6, Peru #1. No. 3522, $6, Reunion #1. No. 3523, $6, Romania #4. No. 3524, $6, Rhodesia #118c. No. 3525, $6, St. Helena #1. No. 3526, $6, Sierra Leone #63A. No. 3527, $6, Spain #8a. No. 3528, $6, Sweden #2. No. 3529, $6, Switzerland #1L1. No. 3530, $6, Switzerland #2L1. No. 3531, $6, Switzerland #3L1a. No. 3532, $6, Switzerland #4. No. 3533, $6, Switzerland #5. No. 3534, $6, Transvaal #3a. No. 3535, $6, Trinidad "Lady McLeod" stamp. No. 3536, $6, Uruguay #5d.

Die Cut Perf. 9x9½, 10¾ (#3449, 3482, 3512, 3515)

2018, Nov. 1 Embossed

On Gold-Faced Paper

3437-3536	A782 Set of 100	450.00	450.00

Christmas 2018 — A783

Designs: 90c, Ornaments on Christmas tree. $2.25, Decorated Christmas tree. $3.50, Candles. $5, Christmas stocking and gifts near fireplace.

2019, Jan. 8 Litho. *Perf. 12¾*

3537-3540	A783 Set of 4	8.75	8.75

A784

Designs: 10c, Team running. 30c, Team holding banner. 90c, Team on boat. $1.50, Team holding oars. $100, Team holding flares.

$10, Team holding flares, diff.

2019, Mar. 20 Litho. *Perf. 14*

3541-3545	A784 Set of 5	76.00	76.00
3543a	Souvenir sheet of 6, 2 each #3541-3543	2.00	2.00

Souvenir Sheet

Perf. 12

3546	A784 $10 multi	7.50	7.50

Team Antigua Island Girls, 13th place finishers in Talisker Whisky Atlantic Challenge.

Team Antigua Island Girls rowed from the Canary Islands to Antigua in 47 days, 8 hours and 25 minutes. No. 3546 contains one 50x30mm stamp.

Miniature Sheet

Mohandas K. Gandhi (1869-1948), Indian Nationalist Leader — A785

No. 3547 — Various photographs of Gandhi on 1930 Salt March with "Mahatma Gandhi": a, $4, At UL, in black, reading up (40x30mm). b, $4, At UL, in white, reading horizontally (40x30mm). c, $4, At UR, in black, reading down (Gandhi holding walking stick, 40x30mm). d, $4, At UR, in black, reading down (Gandhi's walking stick not visible, 40x30mm). e, $5, Gandhi bending down to touch salt (40x60mm).

2019, June 11 Litho. *Perf. 14*
3547 A785 Sheet of 5, #a-e 15.50 15.50

Souvenir Sheet

Elvis Presley (1935-77) — A786

Inscriptions: $11, "I can sing this song all day." $12, "Started a revolution, ended up a king," horiz. $13, "It Happened at the World's Fair." $14, Elvis's iconic sunglasses.

2019, June 11 Litho. *Perf. 14*
3548-3551 A786 Set of 4 37.00 37.00

Miniature Sheet

Roses A787

No. 3552: a, $3, Pink roses and butterfly. b, $3, White roses and pink buds. c, $4, Yellow roses. d, $4, Pale yellow roses. e, $5, White roses and butterflies. f, $5, Pink roses.

2019, June 1 Litho. *Perf. 14*
3552 A787 Sheet of 6, #a-f 18.00 18.00

2019 China World Stamp Exhibition, Wuhan — A788

No. 3553 — Sights in Cherry Blossom Park, Wuhan: a, $4, Cherry blossoms, pagoda. b, $5, Lanterns and cherry blossoms. c, $6, Cherry blossoms. d, $7, Pagoda, cherry trees, lake.
$14, Pagoda, cherry trees, vert.

2019, June 1 Litho. *Perf. 14*
3553 A788 Sheet of 4, #a-d 16.50 16.50

Souvenir Sheet

3554 A788 $14 multi 10.50 10.50

Pres. Franklin D. Roosevelt (1882-1945) — A789

No. 3555 — Roosevelt: a, At 1933 Presidential inauguration. b, Working on stamp collection, 1936. c, With wife, Eleanor, 1939. d, Making radio address, 1939. e, Signing declaration of war, 1941. f, With Winston Churchill, 1941.
$14, Official Presidential portrait, by Frank O. Salisbury, vert.

2019, June 1 Litho. *Perf. 14*
3555 A789 $4 Sheet of 6, #a-f 18.00 18.00

Souvenir Sheet
Perf. 12½

3556 A789 $14 multi 10.50 10.50

No. 3556 contains one 38x51mm stamp.

Miniature Sheet

Beans A790

No. 3557: a, $3, Vanilla bean and orchid. b, $3, Bowl of vanilla ice cream. c, $4, Cocoa bean. d, $4, Chocolate bar. e, $5, Coffee beans. f, $5, Cup of coffee.

2019, June 11 Litho. *Perf. 14*
3557 A790 Sheet of 6, #a-f 18.00 18.00

Sea Birds A791

No. 3558: a, $1, Brown pelican. b, $2, White-tailed tropicbird. c, $3, Cory's shearwater. d, $4, Brown boobies. e, $5, Red-footed booby. f, $6, Masked boobies.
No. 3559: a, $7.50, Magnificent frigatebird chick. b, $8.50, Male Magnificent frigatebird.

2019, June 11 Litho. *Perf. 14*
3558 A791 Sheet of 6, #a-f 15.50 15.50

Souvenir Sheet
Perf. 12½

3559 A791 Sheet of 2, #a-b 12.00 12.00

No. 3559 contains two 51x38mm stamps.

Beaches A792

No. 3560: a, $2, Darkwood Beach, Antigua. b, $3, Ffryes Beach, Antigua. c, $4, Galley Bay Beach, Antigua. d, $5, Pink Sand Beach, Barbuda. e, $6, Turners Beach, Antigua. f, $7, Valley Church Beach, Antigua.
No. 3561: a, $8, Galleon Beach, Antigua. b, $9, Princess Diana Beach, Barbuda.

2019, June 11 Litho. *Perf. 14*
3560 A792 Sheet of 6, #a-f 20.00 20.00

Souvenir Sheet

3561 A792 Sheet of 2, #a-b 12.50 12.50

Miniature Sheet

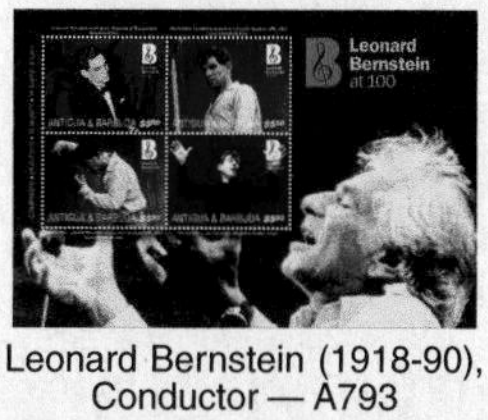

Leonard Bernstein (1918-90), Conductor — A793

No. 3562 — Bernstein: a, Wearing jacket and bow tie. b, Standing near microphone stand. c, Wearing white shirt, conducting. d, Wearing black shirt, conducting.

2019, June 17 Litho. *Perf. 14*
3562 A793 $5.50 Sheet of 4, #a-d 16.50 16.50

Miniature Sheet

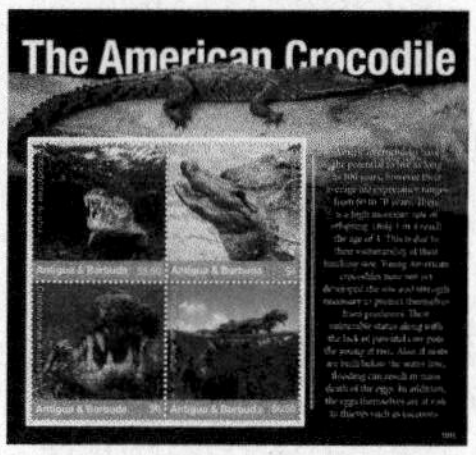

American Crocodiles — A794

No. 3563 — Various photographs of crocodiles with denominations of: a, $4. b, $5.50. c, $6. d, $6.50.

2020, Jan. 15 Litho. *Perf. 13¾*
3563 A794 Sheet of 4, #a-d 16.50 16.50

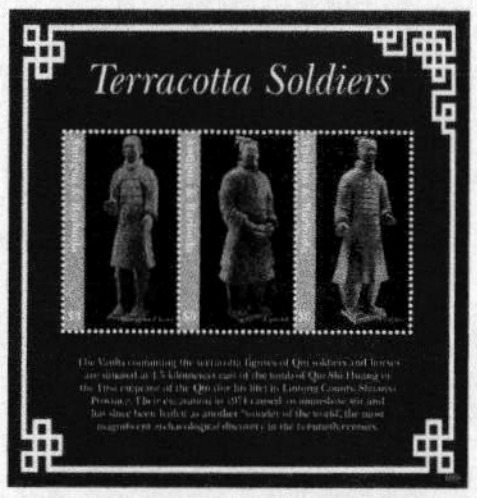

Terracotta Soldiers, People's Republic of China — A795

No. 3564: a, $3, Armored figure. b, $5, General. c, $6, Officer.
$10, Head of statue.

2020, Jan. 15 Litho. *Perf. 12*
3564 A795 Sheet of 3, #a-c 10.50 10.50

Souvenir Sheet

3565 A795 $10 multi 7.50 7.50

Flamingos — A796

No. 3566 — Various photographs of Phoenicopterus ruber with denominations of: a, $2. b, $3. c, $4. d, $5.
$14, Phoenicopterus ruber feeding chick, vert.

2020, May 20 Litho. *Perf. 13¾*
3566 A796 Sheet of 4, #a-d 10.50 10.50

Souvenir Sheet
Perf. 12

3567 A796 $14 multi 10.50 10.50

No. 3567 contains one 30x50mm stamp.

Turkey Vultures A797

No. 3568 — Cathartes aura: a, $1, In flight. b, $1, Landing. c, $1.50, Standing in tall grass. d, $2, Head.
$14, Cathartes aura on roof, vert.

2020, May 20 Litho. *Perf. 12*
3568 A797 Sheet of 4, #a-d 4.25 4.25

Souvenir Sheet

3569 A797 $14 multi 10.50 10.50

Sheep A798

No. 3570 — Various photographs of heads of Merino sheep with denominations of: a, $3. b, $4. c, $5.
$14, Blackface sheep.

2020, May 20 Litho. *Perf. 13¾*
3570 A798 Sheet of 3, #a-c 9.00 9.00

Souvenir Sheet

3571 A798 $14 multi 10.50 10.50

Mallard Ducks A799

No. 3572 — Mallard duck: a, $4, Facing right. b, $5, Facing right, diff. c, $6, In flight. d, $7, Facing left.
$14, Mallard duck in flight, diff.

2020, May 20 Litho. *Perf. 14*
3572 A799 Sheet of 4, #a-d 16.50 16.50

Souvenir Sheet
Perf. 12½

3573 A799 $14 multi 10.50 10.50

No. 3573 contains one 51x38mm stamp.

Spotted Cleaner Shrimp A800

No. 3574 — Various depictions of spotted cleaner shrimp: a, $4. b, $5. c, $6. d, $7.
$14, Spotted cleaner shrimp, vert.

2020, May 20 Litho. *Perf. 14*
3574 A800 Sheet of 4, #a-d 16.50 16.50

Souvenir Sheet
Perf. 12½

3575 A800 $14 multi 10.50 10.50

No. 3575 contains one 38x51mm stamp.

Seashells — A801

No. 3576 — Various unnamed seashells with frame color of: a, $3, Light blue. b, $3, Brown rose. c, $4, Lilac. d, $4, Yellow brown. e, $5, Salmon. f, $5, Blue green.
$14, Conch shell, black frame.

2020, May 20 Litho. *Perf. 13¾*
3576 A801 Sheet of 6, #a-f 18.00 18.00

Souvenir Sheet

3577 A801 $14 multi 10.50 10.50

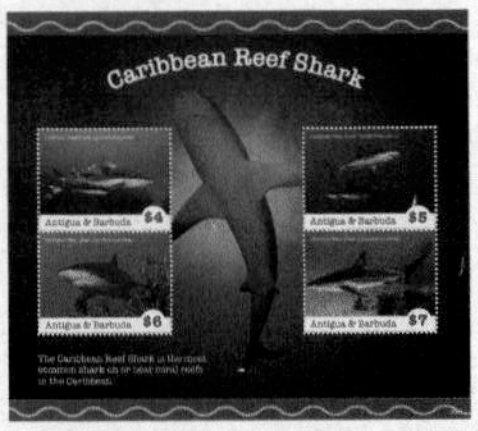

Caribbean Reef Sharks — A805

No. 3584 — Various depictions of Caribbean reef sharks: a, $4. b, $5. c, $6. d, $7.
$14, Caribbean reef shark, diff.

2020, June 3 Litho. *Perf. 14*
3584 A805 Sheet of 4, #a-d 16.50 16.50

Souvenir Sheet

3585 A805 $14 multi 10.50 10.50

No. 3585 contains one 80x30mm stamp.

Dorje Chang Buddha III, Religious Leader — A806

2020, Dec. 21 Litho. *Perf. 13¼*
3586 A806 $5 multi 3.75 3.75

Miniature Sheet

Tribute to Workers During the COVID-19 Pandemic — A807

No. 3587: a, Health care worker with syringe and bottle. b, Gloved hand holding Earth. c, Person holding "Thank You" sign. d, Earth, gloved hand, hypodermic needle, vaccine vial.

2020, Dec. 21 Litho. *Perf. 14*
3587 A807 $5 Sheet of 4, #a-d 15.00 15.00

Miniature Sheet

Victory in Europe (V-E Day), 75th Anniv. A808

No. 3588: a, General Dwight D. Eisenhower (1890-1969). b, Neville Chamberlain (1869-1940), British Prime Minister. c, V-E Day celebrations in France. d, Franklin D. Roosevelt (1882-1945), U.S. President. e, Winston Churchill (1874-1965), British Prime Minister.

2020, Dec. 21 Litho. *Perf. 12*
3588 A808 $4.50 Sheet of 5, #a-e 17.00 17.00

Paintings by Raphael (1483-1520) — A809

No. 3589 — Paintings in the Room of the Segnatura, Apostolic Palace, Vatican City: a, Cardinal and Theological Virtues, 1511. b, The Parnassua, 1509-11. c, Disputation of the Holy Sacrament, 1509. d, Ceiling of the Selling Room, 1508.
$25, The School of Athens, 1511.

2020, Dec. 21 Litho. *Perf. 14*
3589 A809 $5 Sheet of 4, #a-d 15.00 15.00

Souvenir Sheet
Perf. 12

3590 A809 $25 multi 18.50 18.50

No. 3590 contains one 50x30mm stamp.

Ludwig van Beethoven (1770-1827), Composer — A810

No. 3591 — Portrait of Beethoven by: a, Carl Traugott Riedel. b, Christian Horneman. c, Joseph Willibrord Mähler. d, Ferdinand Schimon.
$25, Portrait of Beethoven by Joseph Karl Stieler.

2020, Dec. 21 Litho. *Perf. 14*
3591 A810 $5 Sheet of 4, #a-d 15.00 15.00

Souvenir Sheet
Perf. 12½

3592 A810 $25 multi 18.50 18.50

No. 35920 contains one 38x51mm stamp.

Visit to the United Kingdom of Pres. Donald Trump A811

No. 3593: a, $5, Pres. Trump (30x40mm). b, $5, Queen Elizabeth II (30x40mm). c, $10, Pres. Trump and Queen Elizabeth II (60x40mm).
$25, Pres. Trump and wife, Melania, Queen Elizabeth II, Prince Charles and his wife, the Duchess of Cornwall, horiz.

2020, Dec. 21 Litho. *Perf. 14*
3593 A811 Sheet of 3, #a-c 15.00 15.00

Souvenir Sheet
Perf. 12

3594 A811 $25 multi 18.50 18.50

No. 3594 contains one 80x30mm stamp.

Sea Otters A812

No. 3595 — Various photograhphs of sea otters, as shown.
$14, Sea otter, vert.

2020, Dec. 21 Litho. *Perf. 13¾*
3595 A812 $5.50 Sheet of 4, #a-d 16.50 16.50

Souvenir Sheet
Perf. 12½

3596 A812 $14 multi 10.50 10.50

No. 3596 contains one 38x51mm stamp.

A813

Working Dogs A814

No. 3597: a, Police dog. b, Sled dogs. c, Herd dog. d, Guide dog.
$14, Military dog, vert.

2020, Dec. 21 Litho. *Perf. 13¾*
3597 A813 $5.50 Sheet of 4, #a-d 16.50 16.50

Souvenir Sheet
Perf. 12

3598 A814 $14 multi 10.50 10.50

Manatees — A815

No. 3599 — Manatee with denomination in: a, $5, Black (40x30mm). b, $5, White (40x30mm). c, $6, Black (80x30mm).
$12, Manatee, vert.

2020, Dec. 21 Litho. *Perf. 14*
3599 A815 Sheet of 3, #a-c 12.00 12.00

Souvenir Sheet
Perf. 12

3600 A815 $12 multi 9.00 9.00

No. 3600 contains one 30x50mm stamp.

Miniature Sheet

Birth of Archie Mountbatten-Windsor — A816

No. 3601: a, $4, Duke and Duchess of Sussex. b, $5, Duke and Duchess of Sussex, holding son, Archie. c, $6, Duke and Duchess of Sussex holding son, Archie, diff. d, $7, Duke and Duchess of Sussex holding son, Archie, diff.

2021, Apr. 28 Litho. *Perf. 14*
3601 A816 Sheet of 4, #a-d 16.50 16.50

Miniature Sheet

New Year 2021 (Year of the Ox) A817

No. 3602 — Color of ox: a, Red. b, Violet. c, Pale yellow. d, Orange.

2021, Apr. 11 Litho. *Perf. 13¾*
3602 A817 $5.50 Sheet of 4, #a-d 16.50 16.50

Miniature Sheet

Arrival in Massachusetts of the Pilgrims, 400th Anniv. (in 2020) — A818

No. 3603: a, The Mayflower at sea. b, The First Thanksgiving at Plymouth, painting by Jennie A. Brownscombe (reversed image). c, Mayflower Compact. d, Embarkation of the Pilgrims, painting by Robert Walter Weir.

2021, Apr. 28 Litho. *Perf. 14*
3603 A818 $5 Sheet of 4, #a-d 15.00 15.00

Miniature Sheet

United Nations, 75th Anniv. (in 2020) A819

No. 3604: a, United Nations Headquarters, Chrysler Building, and other New York City buildings. b, United Nations General Assembly Hall. c, United Nations Security Council Hall. d, United Nations Headquarters.

2021, Apr. 28 Litho. *Perf. 14*
3604 A819 $5.50 Sheet of 4, #a-d 16.50 16.50

Miniature Sheet

St. John Paul II (1920-2005) — A820

No. 3605: a, St. John Paul II holding papal ferula in Munich, 1980. b, Painting depicting Pope John Paul II. c, Pope John Paul II and Pres. Ronald Reagan. d, Pope John Paul II and Cardinal Joseph Ratzinger (later Pope Benedict XVI).

2021, Apr. 28 Litho. *Perf. 14*
3605 A820 $5 Sheet of 4, #a-d 15.00 15.00

Miniature Sheet

Metropolitan Museum of Art, 150th Anniv. (in 2020) — A821

No. 3606: a, Hippopotamus sculpture (Museum's mascot). b, Opening reception. c, Ticket counter. d, European Sculpture Court.

2021, Apr. 28 Litho. *Perf. 14*
3606 A821 $5.50 Sheet of 4, #a-d 16.50 16.50

A822

Morgan Plus 4 Automobiles, 70th Anniv. (in 2020) — A823

No. 3607: a, Black 2018 Morgan Plus 4. b, White 1952 Morgan Plus 4. c, Green 1956 Morgan Plus 4. d, Black 1956 Morgan Plus 4 (reversed image).
$14, White 1957 Morgan Plus 4.

2021, Apr. 28 Litho. *Perf. 14*
3607 A822 $5.50 Sheet of 4, #a-d 16.50 16.50

Souvenir Sheet
Perf. 12½
3608 A823 $14 multi 10.50 10.50

A824

Range Rover, 50th Anniv. (in 2020) A825

No. 3609: a, White 2007 Land Range Rover. b, 2014 Range Rover Evoque. c, 2016 Land Range Rover. d, Yellow 2007 Land Range Rover.
$14, 2013 Land Range Rover.

2021, Apr. 28 Litho. *Perf. 14*
3609 A824 $5.50 Sheet of 4, #a-d 16.50 16.50

Souvenir Sheet
Perf. 12½
3610 A825 $14 multi 10.50 10.50

A826

Audi Quattro Automobiles, 40th Anniv. (in 2020) — A827

No. 3611: a, 1988 Audi 80 Quattro. b, 1991 Audi Quattro. c, 1985 Audi Quattro. d, 1986 Audi Quattro.
$14, 1987 Audi Quattro.

2021, Apr. 28 Litho. *Perf. 14*
3611 A826 $5.50 Sheet of 4, #a-d 16.50 16.50

Souvenir Sheet
Perf. 12½
3612 A827 $14 multi 10.50 10.50

A828

Mini Cooper Automobiles, 20th Anniv. (in 2020) — A829

No. 3613: a, 1993 Mini Cooper. b, 2019 Mini JCW F57. c, 2019 Mini John Cooper. d, 2008 Mini JCP W50.
$14, 1990 Mini Cooper.

2021, Apr. 28 Litho. *Perf. 14*
3613 A828 $5.50 Sheet of 4, #a-d 16.50 16.50

Souvenir Sheet
Perf. 12½
3614 A829 $14 multi 10.50 10.50

Rabbits A830

No. 3615: a, Netherland Dwarf rabbit. b, Omilteme Cottontail rabbit. c, Desert Cottentail rabbit. d, Satin rabbit.
$14, Fee de Marbourg rabbit, vert.

2021, Apr. 28 Litho. *Perf. 14*
3615 A830 $5.50 Sheet of 4, #a-d 16.50 16.50

Souvenir Sheet
3616 A830 $14 multi 10.50 10.50

Marine Life A831

No. 3617: a, Squirrelfish. b, American eel. c, Smallmouth grunt. d, Blue tang.
$14, Southern stingray.

2021, Apr. 28 Litho. *Perf. 14*
3617 A831 $5.50 Sheet of 4, #a-d 16.50 16.50

Souvenir Sheet
3618 A831 $14 multi 10.50 10.50

Flowers A832

No. 3619: a, Yellow allamanda. b, Hawaiian hibiscus. c, Blue plumbago. d, Frangipani.
$14, Oleander.

2021, Apr. 28 Litho. *Perf. 14*
3619 A832 $5.50 Sheet of 4, #a-d 16.50 16.50

Souvenir Sheet
3620 A832 $14 multi 10.50 10.50

Joseph R. Biden, Jr., 46th President of the United States — A833

No. 3621 — Pres. Biden: a, And Vice-President Kamala Harris. b, And wife, Jill. c, Taking oath of office. d, And microphones. e, Sitting at desk.
$14.60, Pres. Biden wearing protective face mask, vert.

2021, Aug. 9 Litho. *Perf. 14*
3621 A833 $4.60 Sheet of 5, #a-e 17.00 17.00

Souvenir Sheet
Perf. 12½
3622 A833 $14.60 multi 11.00 11.00

No. 3622 contains one 38x51mm stamp.

Queen Elizabeth II, 95th Birthday A834

No. 3623 — Queen Elizabeth II: a, Wearing uniform and hat. b, Wearing tiara. c, Wearing scarf. d, Without head covering.
$14, Queen Elizabeth II in 1952, horiz.

2021, Aug. 9 Litho. *Perf. 12½*
3623 A834 $4.95 Sheet of 4, #a-d 15.00 15.00

Souvenir Sheet
Perf. 14
3624 A834 $14 multi 10.50 10.50

No. 3624 contains one 40x30mm stamp.

Dedication of the Lincoln Memorial, Cent. (in 2022) — A835

No. 3625 — Washington, D. C. attractions: a, Statue of Abraham Lincoln, by Daniel Chester French. b, Washington Monument. c, Untied States Capitol. d, White House. e, Jefferson Memorial. f, National World War II Memorial.
$14, Lincoln Memorial.

2021 Litho. *Perf. 14*
3625 A835 $3.35 Sheet of 6, #a-f 15.00 15.00

Souvenir Sheet
Perf. 12
3626 A835 $15 multi 11.00 11.00

Issued: No. 3625, 10/8; No. 3626, 9/30. No. 3626 contains one 50x30mm stamp.

Miniature Sheet

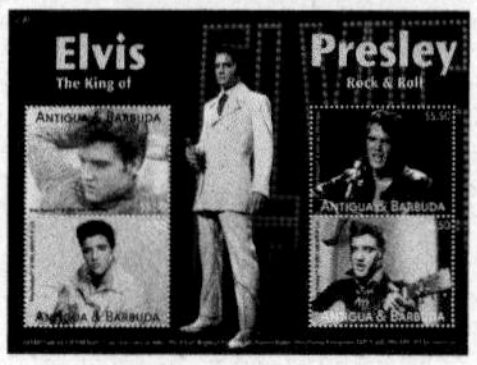

Elvis Presley (1935-77) — A836

No. 3627 — Presley: a, Wearing sweater. b, With microphone at mouth level. c, Holding guitar. d, With microphone above head.

2021, Oct. 8 Litho. *Perf. 14*
3627 A836 $5.50 Sheet of 4, #a-d 16.50 16.50

Hummingbirds — A837

No. 3628 — Photographs of various hummingbirds with denomination of: a, $3.50. b, $4. c, $4.50. d, $5. 3, $5.50.
$14, Hummingbird, horiz.

2021, Oct. 8 Litho. *Perf. 14*
3628 A837 Sheet of 5, #a-e 17.00 17.00

Souvenir Sheet
3629 A837 $14 multi 10.50 10.50

Tropical Fruits A838

No. 3630: a, Starfruits. b, Coconut. c, Passionfruits. d, Papayas. e, Dragonfruits. f, Pineapples.
No. 3631, vert.: a, Lychees. b, Mangos.

2021, Oct. 8 Litho. *Perf. 14*
3630 A838 $4 Sheet of 6, #a-f 18.00 18.00

Souvenir Sheet
3631 A838 $8 Sheet of 2, #a-b 12.00 12.00

Mushrooms — A839

No. 3632: a, $2.50, Saffron milk cap. b, $3.50, Chanterelle. c, $4.50, Penny bun. d, $4.50, Fly agaric. e, $5.50, Honey fungus.
$14.50, Yellow morel, vert.

2021, Oct. 8 Litho. *Perf. 14*
3632 A839 Sheet of 5, #a-e 15.50 15.50

Souvenir Sheet
Perf. 12½
3633 A839 $14.50 multi 11.00 11.00

No. 3633 contains one 38x51mm stamp.

Duke and Duchess of Cambridge, 10th Anniv. of Wedding — A840

No. 3634 — Various photographs of Duke and Duchess of Cambridge, with Duke at: a, Right, wearing white shirt. b, Left, wearing suit and red tie. c, Right, seated in red chair. d, Left, wearing blue shirt. e, Right, kissing Duchess at wedding. f, Right, wearing suit and red tie.

$14, Duke and Duchess of Cambridge in carriage on wedding day.

2021, Oct. 8 Litho. *Perf. 14*

3634	A840	$4	Sheet of 6, #a-f	18.00	18.00

Souvenir Sheet

Perf. 12½

3635	A840	$14	multi	10.50	10.50

No. 3635 contains one 51x38mm stamp.

Duke and Duchess of Sussex, First Anniv. of Wedding A841

No. 3636 — Various photographs of Duke and Duchess of Sussex, with Duke at: a, Left, in coach, wearing uniform with cap on wedding day. b, Right, wearing suit and blue sweater. c, Left, wearing suit and tie. d, Left, wearing uniform without cap, on wedding day.

$14, Duke and Duchess of Sussex holding hands.

2021, Oct. 8 Litho. *Perf. 14*

3636	A841	$5.50	Sheet of 4, #a-d	16.50	16.50

Souvenir Sheet

Perf. 12½

3637	A841	$14	multi	10.50	10.50

No. 3637 contains one 51x38mm stamp.

Prince Philip (1921-2021) — A842

No. 3638 — Prince Philip: a, At ceremony with Queen Elizabeth II, in uniform. b, Wearing bow tie and medal. c, With Princess Elizabeth on wedding day. d, Wearing striped shirt and tie, facing left. e, Wearing striped shirt and tie, facing right.

$14, Coffin of Prince Philip being brought into St. George's Chapel.

2021, Oct. 8 Litho. *Perf. 14*

3638	A842	$4.50	Sheet of 5, #a-e	17.00	17.00

Souvenir Sheet

3639	A842	$14	multi	10.50	10.50

2020 Summer Olympics, Tokyo — A843

No. 3640: a, Rhythmic gymnastics and "2." b, Field hockey and "0." c, Equestrian and "2." d, Diving and "0."

2021, Dec. 1 Litho. *Perf. 14*

3640	A843	$5.50	Sheet of 4, #a-d	16.50	16.50

The 2020 Summer Olympics were postponed until 2021 because of the COVID-19 pandemic.

WAR TAX STAMPS

No. 31 and Type A3 Overprinted in Black or Red

1916-18 Wmk. 3 *Perf. 14*

MR1	A3	½p	green	4.75	3.75
MR2	A3	½p	green (R) ('17)	1.60	*3.50*
MR3	A3	1½p	orange ('18)	1.75	*1.75*
			Nos. MR1-MR3 (3)	8.10	*9.00*

ARGENTINA

ˌär-jən-ˈtē-nə

LOCATION — In South America
GOVT. — Republic
AREA — 1,084,120 sq. mi.
POP. — 36,737,664 (est. 1999)
CAPITAL — Buenos Aires

100 Centavos = 1 Peso (1858, 1992)
100 Centavos = 1 Austral (1985)

Catalogue values for unused stamps in this country are for Never Hinged items, beginning with Scott 587 in the regular postage section, Scott B12 in the semi-postal section, Scott C59 in the airpost section, Scott CB1 in the airpost semi-postal section and Scott O79 in the officials section.

Watermarks

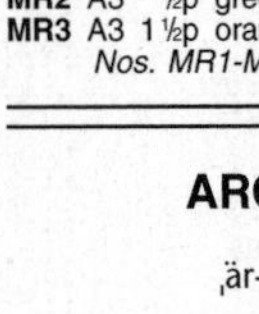

Wmk. 84 — Italic RA

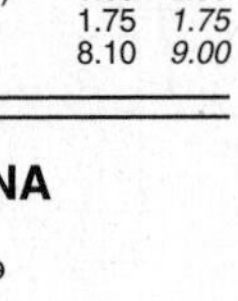

Wmk. 85 — Small Sun, 4½mm

Wmk. 86 — Large Sun, 6mm

Wmk. 87 — Honeycomb

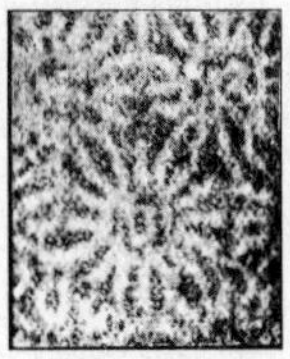

Wmk. 88 — Multiple Suns

Wmk. 89 — Large Sun

In this watermark the face of the sun is 7mm in diameter, the rays are heavier than in the large sun watermark of 1896-1911 and the watermarks are placed close together, so that parts of several frequently appear on one stamp. This paper was intended to be used for fiscal stamps and is usually referred to as "fiscal sun paper."

Wmk. 90 — RA in Sun

In 1928 watermark 90 was slightly modified, making the diameter of the Sun 9mm instead of 10mm. Several types of this watermark exist.

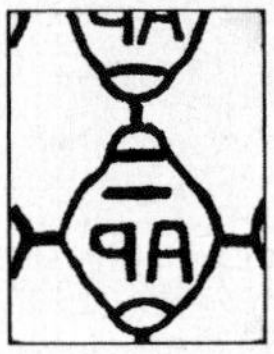

Wmk. 205 — AP in Oval

The letters "AP" are the initials of "AHORRO POSTAL." This paper was formerly used exclusively for Postal Savings stamps.

Wmk. 287 — Double Circle and Letters in Sheet

Wmk. 288 — RA in Sun with Straight Rays

Wmk. 365 — Argentine Arms, "Casa de Moneda de la Nacion" & "RA" Multiple

Values for Unused
Unused values for Nos. 5-17 are for examples without gum. Examples with original gum command higher prices. Unused values of Nos. 1-4B and stamps after No. 17 are for examples with original gum as defined in the catalogue introduction.

Argentine Confederation

Symbolical of the Argentine Confederation — A1

Unwmk.

1858, May 1 Litho. *Imperf.*

1	A1	5c	red	1.75	*40.00*
a.			Colon after "5"	2.50	*32.50*
b.			Colon after "V"	2.50	*32.50*
2	A1	10c	green	5.00	*90.00*
f.			Diagonal half used as 5c on cover		*1,000.*
3	A1	15c	blue	18.00	*250.00*
c.			Horiz. third used as 5c on cover		*10,000.*
			Nos. 1-3 (3)	24.75	*380.00*

There are nine varieties of Nos. 1, 2 and 3. Counterfeits and forged cancellations of Nos. 1-3 are plentiful.

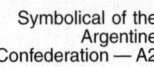

Symbolical of the Argentine Confederation — A2

1860, Jan.

4	A2	5c	red	6.00	*100.00*
4A	A2	10c	green	8.50	—
4B	A2	15c	blue	40.00	—
			Nos. 4-4B (3)	54.50	

Nos. 4A and 4B were never placed in use. Some compostitions of Nos. 4-4B contain 8 different types across the sheet. Other settings exist with minor variations. Counterfeits and forged cancellations of Nos. 4-4B are plentiful.

Argentine Republic

Seal of the Republic — A3

Broad "C" in "CENTAVOS," Accent on "U" of "REPUBLICA"

1862, Jan. 11

5	A3	5c	rose	49.00	37.50
6	A3	10c	green	175.00	80.00
7	A3	15c	blue	350.00	225.00
a.			Without accent on "U"	*8,000.*	*5,000.*
b.			Tete beche pair	*150,000.*	*120,000.*
d.			15c ultramarine	500.00	350.00
e.			Diagonal third used as 5c on cover		*12,000.*

No. 6g is printed on white wove paper.

Only one used example of No. 7b is known. It has faults. Two unused examples are known. One is sound with origional gum, the other is in a block, without gum, and has tiny faults.

No. 7u is known only used in Mendoza.

Broad "C" in "CENTAVOS," No Accent on "U"

1863

7C	A3	5c	rose	20.00	*24.00*
i.			5c rose lilac	200.00	250.00
7F	A3	10c	yellow green	1,000.	250.00

Narrow "C" in "CENTAVOS," No Accent on "U"

1864
7H A3 5c rose red 225.00 32.50

The so-called reprints of 10c and 15c are counterfeits. They have narrow "C" and straight lines in shield. Nos. 7C and 7H have been extensively counterfeited.

Rivadavia Issue

Bernardino Rivadavia
A4 A5

Rivadavia — A6

1864-67 Engr. Wmk. 84 *Imperf.*
Clear Impressions

8 A4 5c brown rose *2,500. 250.*
a. 5c brick red ('67) *2,500. 250.*
9 A5 10c green *3,000. 1,750.*
10 A6 15c blue *13,500. 6,500.*

Perf. 11½
Dull to Worn Impressions

11 A4 5c brown rose ('65) 40.00 15.00
11B A4 5c lake 100.00 22.50
12 A5 10c green 150.00 70.00
a. Diagonal half used as 5c on cover *2,000.*
b. Vert. half used as 5c on cover *3,000.*
c. Horiz. pair, imperf vert. *5,000.*
13 A6 15c blue 450.00 150.00

1867-72 Unwmk. *Imperf.*
14 A4 5c carmine ('72) 350. 100.
15 A4 5c rose, thin white paper 350. 100.
15A A5 10c green, medium white paper *3,000. 3,200.*
16 A6 15c blue, medium white paper *3,000. 2,700.*

Nos. 15A-16 issued without gum.

1867 *Perf. 11½*
17 A4 5c carmine 1,000. 200.00

Rivadavia
A7

Manuel Belgrano
A8

Jose de San Martin — A9

Groundwork of Horizontal Lines

1867-68 *Perf. 12*
18 A7 5c vermilion 225.00 17.50
18A A8 10c green 50.00 7.50
b. Diag. half used as 5c on cover *2,500.*
19 A9 15c blue 100.00 22.50

Groundwork of Crossed Lines

20 A7 5c vermilion 15.00 1.25
21 A9 15c blue 120.00 15.00

See Nos. 27, 33-34, 39 and types A19, A33, A34, A37. For surcharges and overprints see Nos. 30-32, 41-42, 47-51, O6-O7, O26.

Gen. Antonio G. Balcarce
A10

Mariano Moreno
A11

Carlos Maria de Alvear
A12

Gervasio Antonio Posadas
A13

Cornelio Saavedra — A14

1873
22 A10 1c purple 6.00 2.25
a. 1c gray violet 10.00 2.25
23 A11 4c brown 6.00 .75
a. 4c red brown 15.00 2.00
24 A12 30c orange 140.00 25.00
a. Vert. pair, imperf horiz. *4,000.*
25 A13 60c black 160.00 5.00
26 A14 90c blue 60.00 3.00
Nos. 22-26 (5) 372.00 36.00

For overprints see Nos. O5, O12-O14, O19-O21, O25, O29.
Four examples of No. 24a are known. Three examples of No. 26 are known on cover.

1873 Laid Paper
27 A8 10c green 325.00 32.50

Nos.18, 18A Surcharged in Black

Nos. 30-31

No. 32

1877, Feb. Wove Paper
30 A7 1c on 5c vermilion 75.00 25.00
a. Inverted surcharge 1,000. 300.00
31 A7 2c on 5c vermilion 125.00 75.00
a. Inverted surcharge 1,200. 750.00
32 A8 8c on 10c green 160.00 40.00
b. Inverted surcharge 2,500. 1,000.
Nos. 30-32 (3) 360.00 140.00

Varieties also exist with double and triple surcharges, surcharge on reverse, 8c on No. 27, all made clandestinely from the original cliches of the surcharges.
Forgeries of these surcharges include the inverted and double varieties.

1876-77 *Rouletted*
33 A7 5c vermilion 200.00 85.00
34 A7 8c lake ('77) 35.00 .65

Belgrano
A17

Dalmacio Vélez Sarsfield
A18

San Martín — A19

1878 *Rouletted*
35 A17 16c green 12.00 1.10
36 A18 20c blue 20.00 2.25
37 A19 24c blue 30.00 3.50
Nos. 35-37 (3) 62.00 6.85

See No. 56. For overprints see Nos. O9-O10, O15-O17, O22, O28.

Vicente Lopez
A20

Alvear
A21

1877-80 *Perf. 12*
38 A20 2c yellow green 5.00 .75
39 A7 8c lake ('80) 4.50 .75
a. 8c brown lake *52.50* .75
40 A21 25c lake ('78) 30.00 6.00
Nos. 38-40 (3) 39.50 7.50

No. 38 measures 19.9 mm x 25.3 mm. No. 38a measaures 19.8 mm x 25.3 mm.
For overprints see Nos. O4, O11, O18, O24.

No. 18 Surcharged in Black

Large "P"

Small "P"

1882
41 A7 ½c on 5c ver 2.75 2.75
a. Double surcharge 100.00 100.00
b. Inverted surcharge 50.00 50.00
c. "PROVISORIO" omitted 110.00 110.00
d. Fraction omitted 100.00
e. "PROVISOBIO" 50.00 50.00
f. Pair, one without surcharge 250.00
g. Small "P" in "PROVISORIO" 2.75 2.75
h. As "a," small "P" in "PROVISORIO" 50.00 50.00
i. As "b," small "P" in "PROVISORIO" 75.00 75.00
j. As "d," small "P" in "PROVISORIO" 30.00 30.00

Perforated across Middle of Stamp

42 A7 ½c on 5c ver 6.00 6.00
a. "PROVISORIQ" 50.00 50.00
b. Large "P" in "PROVISORIO" 40.00 30.00

A23

1882 Typo. *Perf. 12½*
43 A23 ½c brown 2.25 1.50
a. Imperf., pair 100.00 80.00
44 A23 1c red 15.00 6.00
45 A23 12c ultra 90.00 14.00

Perf. 14¼
44A A23 1c red 3.50 1.50
45A A23 12c ultra 65.00 12.00

Engr.
46 A23 12c grnsh blue 225.00 16.00
Nos. 43-46 (6) 400.75 51.00

See type A29. For overprints see Nos. O2, O8, O23, O27.

No. 21 Surcharged in Red

a

b

c

1884 Engr. *Perf. 12*
47 A9 (a) ½c on 15c blue 3.00 2.00
a. Groundwork of horiz. lines 150.00 90.00
b. Inverted surcharge 35.00 25.00
48 A9 (b) 1c on 15c blue 22.50 16.50
a. Groundwork of horiz. lines 13.00 11.50
b. Inverted surcharge 100.00 62.50
c. Double surcharge 50.00 40.00
d. Triple surcharge 400.00

Nos. 20-21 Surcharged in Black

49 A7 (a) ½c on 5c ver 5.00 4.50
a. Inverted surcharge 200.00 150.00
b. Date omitted 200.00 —
c. Pair, one without surcharge 500.00
d. Double surcharge 550.00
50 A9 (a) ½c on 15c blue 15.00 12.00
a. Groundwork of horiz. lines 50.00 35.00
b. Inverted surcharge 90.00 70.00
c. Pair, one without surcharge 400.00
51 A7 (c) 4c on 5c ver 12.00 9.00
a. Inverted surcharge 35.00 28.00
b. Double surcharge 700.00 350.00
c. Pair, one without surcharge but with "4" in manuscript 750.00 650.00
d. Pair, one without surcharge 400.00
Nos. 47-51 (5) 57.50 44.00

A29

1884-85 Engr. *Perf. 12*
52 A29 ½c red brown 1.50 .65
a. Horiz. pair, imperf vert. *1,200.*
53 A29 1c rose red 7.00 .65
a. Horiz. pair, imperf vert. *300.00 250.00*
54 A29 12c deep blue 35.00 1.50
a. 12c grnsh blue ('85) 50.00 1.50
b. Horiz. pair, imperf vert. *300.00 250.00*
Nos. 52-54 (3) 43.50 2.80

For overprints see Nos. O1, O3, O9.

San Martin Type of 1878

1887 Engr.
56 A19 24c blue 20.00 1.40

Justo Jose de Urquiza A30

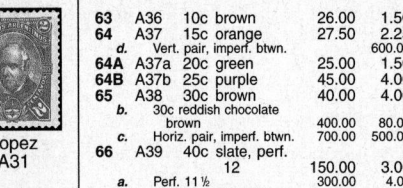

Lopez A31

Miguel Juarez Celman A32

Rivadavia (Large head) A33

Rivadavia (Small head) A34

Domingo F. Sarmiento A35

Nicolas Avellaneda — A36

San Martin — A37

Julio A. Roca — A37a

Belgrano — A37b

Manuel Dorrego A38

Moreno A39

Bartolome Mitre — A40

CINCO CENTAVOS.
A33 — Shows collar on left side only.
A34 — Shows collar on both sides. Lozenges in background larger and clearer than in A33.

1888-90 Litho. *Perf. 11½*

57	A30	½c blue	1.75	.75
b.		Vert. pair, imperf. horiz.	200.00	200.00
c.		Horiz. pair, imperf. vert.	200.00	200.00
58	A31	2c yel grn	20.00	10.00
b.		Vert. pair, imperf. horiz.	130.00	
c.		Horiz. pair, imperf. vert.	250.00	
59	A32	3c blue green	3.50	1.50
b.		Horiz. pair, imperf. vert.	60.00	
c.		Horiz. pair, imperf. btwn.	130.00	
d.		Vert. pair, imperf. btwn.	25.00	25.00
60	A33	5c carmine	18.00	.75
b.		Vert. pair, imperf. horiz.	175.00	
61	A34	5c carmine	26.00	2.25
b.		Vert. pair, imperf. btwn.	*200.00*	
c.		Vert. pair, imperf. horiz.		400.00
62	A35	6c red	50.00	20.00
b.		Vert. pair, imperf. btwn.	*150.00*	
c.		Perf. 12	100.00	50.00
63	A36	10c brown	26.00	1.50
64	A37	15c orange	27.50	2.25
d.		Vert. pair, imperf. btwn.		600.00
64A	A37a	20c green	25.00	1.50
64B	A37b	25c purple	45.00	4.00
65	A38	30c brown	40.00	4.00
b.		30c reddish chocolate brown	400.00	80.00
c.		Horiz. pair, imperf. btwn.	700.00	500.00
66	A39	40c slate, perf. 12	150.00	3.00
a.		Perf. 11½	300.00	4.00
b.		Horiz. pair, imperf. btwn. (#66)		800.00
67	A40	50c blue	350.00	20.00
		Nos. 57-67 (13)	782.75	71.50

In this issue there are several varieties of each value, the difference between them being in the relative position of the head to the frame.

Imperf., Pairs

57a	A30	½c	85.00	67.50
58a	A31	2c	100.00	
59a	A32	3c	45.00	27.50
61a	A34	5c		*100.00*
62a	A35	6c	*150.00*	150.00
63a	A36	10c	*55.00*	
64c	A37	15c		*200.00*
65a	A38	30c	*325.00*	*225.00*

Urquiza A41

Velez Sarsfield A42

Miguel Juarez Celman A43

Rivadavia (Large head) A44

Sarmiento A45

Juan Bautista Alberdi A46

1888-89 Engr. *Perf. 11½, 11½x12*

68	A41	½c ultra	.75	.45
a.		Vert. pair, imperf. horiz.	—	—
b.		Imperf., pair	30.00	—
69	A42	1c brown	1.50	.75
a.		Vert. pair, imperf. horiz.	65.00	
b.		Vert. pair, imperf. btwn.	—	
c.		Imperf., pair	30.00	
d.		Horiz. pair, imperf. btwn.	100.00	
70	A43	3c blue green	6.00	1.75
71	A44	5c rose	4.50	.75
a.		Imperf., pair	50.00	—
72	A45	6c blue black	3.00	.90
b.		Perf. 11½x12	15.00	4.50
73	A46	12c blue	8.75	3.75
a.		Imperf., pair	45.00	
b.		bluish paper	9.50	3.75
c.		Perf. 11½	14.00	3.00
		Nos. 68-73 (6)	24.50	8.35

Nos. 69-70 exist with papermakers' watermarks.

See No. 77, types A50, A61. For surcharges see Nos. 83-84.

Jose Maria Paz A48

Santiago Derqui A49

Rivadavia (Small head) A50

Avellaneda A51

Moreno A53

Mitre A54

Gervasio Antonio de Posadas — A55

1890 Engr. *Perf. 11½*

75	A48	¼c green	.65	.45
76	A49	2c violet	1.50	.75
a.		2c purple	2.00	.75
b.		2c slate	2.00	.75
c.		Horiz. pair, imperf. btwn.	30.00	25.00
d.		Imperf., pair	37.50	
e.		Perf. 11½x12	9.00	.75
77	A50	5c carmine	3.50	.45
a.		Imperf., pair	70.00	32.50
b.		Perf. 11½x12	10.00	1.25
c.		Vert. pair, imperf. btwn.	75.00	60.00
d.		Horiz. pair, imperf. btwn.	75.00	60.00
78	A51	10c brown	4.50	.75
b.		Imperf., pair	150.00	
c.		Vert. pair, imperf. btwn.	225.00	
80	A53	40c olive green	8.00	1.50
a.		Imperf., pair	55.00	
b.		Horiz. pair, imperf. btwn.		*250.00*
81	A54	50c orange	9.00	1.50
a.		Imperf., pair	80.00	
b.		Perf. 11½x12	40.00	3.00
82	A55	60c black	20.00	4.50
a.		Imperf., pair	—	
b.		Vert. pair, imperf. btwn.	125.00	100.00
		Nos. 75-82 (7)	47.15	9.90

Type A50 differs from type A44 in having the head smaller, the letters of "Cinco Centavos" not as tall, and the curved ornaments at sides close to the first and last letters of "Republica Argentina."

Lithographed Surcharge on No. 73 in Black or Red

1890 *Perf. 11½x12*

83	A46	¼c on 12c blue	.75	.75
a.		Perf. 11½	50.00	40.00
b.		Double surcharge	75.00	47.50
c.		Inverted surcharge	100.00	
84	A46	¼c on 12c blue (R)	.75	.75
a.		Double surcharge	55.00	50.00
b.		Perf. 11½	8.00	6.00

Surcharge is different on Nos. 83 and 84.

Nos. 83-84 exist as pairs, one without surcharge. These were privately produced.

Rivadavia A57

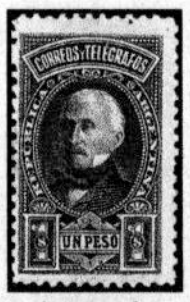
Jose de San Martin A58

Gregorio Araoz de Lamadrid A59

Admiral Guillermo Brown A60

1891 Engr. *Perf. 11½*

85	A57	8c carmine rose	1.50	.65
a.		Imperf., pair	130.00	
86	A58	1p deep blue	50.00	12.00
87	A59	5p ultra	325.00	45.00
88	A60	20p green	500.00	100.00
		Nos. 85-88 (4)	876.50	157.65

A 10p brown and a 50p red were prepared but not issued. Values: 10p $1,500 for fine, 50p $1,200 with rough or somewhat damaged perfs.

Velez Sarsfield — A61

1890 *Perf. 11½*

89	A61	1c brown	1.25	.65
b.		Horiz. pair, imperf. btwn.		*550.00*

Type A61 is a re-engraving of A42. The figure "1" in each upper corner has a short horizontal serif instead of a long one pointing downward. In type A61 the first and last letters of "Correos y Telegrafos" are closer to the curved ornaments below than in type A42. Background is of horizontal lines (cross-hatching on No. 69).

"Santa Maria," "Nina" and "Pinta" — A62

1892, Oct. 12 Wmk. 85 *Perf. 11½*

90	A62	2c light blue	8.50	3.00
a.		Double impression	225.00	
91	A62	5c dark blue	9.50	4.00

Discovery of America, 400th anniv. Counterfeits of Nos. 90-91 are litho.

Rivadavia A63

Belgrano A64

San Martin — A65

1892-95 Wmk. 85 *Perf. 11½*

92	A63	½c dull blue	1.00	.35
a.		½c bright ultra	80.00	40.00
93	A63	1c brown	.65	.50
94	A63	2c green	1.00	.35
95	A63	3c org ('95)	1.75	.35
96	A63	5c carmine	1.75	.35
b.		5c green (error)	700.00	700.00
98	A64	10c car rose	13.50	.60
99	A64	12c dp bl ('93)	10.00	.60
100	A64	16c gray	16.50	.65
101	A64	24c gray brown	16.50	.65
102	A64	50c blue green	27.50	.75
103	A65	1p lake ('93)	12.00	1.00
a.		1p red brown	20.00	5.00
104	A65	2p dark green	27.50	3.50
105	A65	5p dark blue	37.50	3.50
		Nos. 92-105 (13)	167.15	13.15

Perf. 12

92E	A63	½c dull blue	6.00	1.00
93E	A63	1c brown	10.00	2.00
94E	A63	2c green	10.00	3.00
95E	A63	3c org ('95)	30.00	5.00
96E	A63	5c carmine	35.00	1.00
98E	A64	10c car rose	21.00	3.50
99E	A64	12c dp bl ('93)	40.00	4.00
100E	A64	16c gray	40.00	4.00
101E	A64	24c gray brown	30.00	17.00
102E	A64	50c blue green	30.00	6.00
104E	A65	2p dark green	125.00	40.00
		Nos. 92E-104E (11)	377.00	86.50

Perf. 11½x12

92F	A63	½c dull blue	18.00	10.00
93F	A63	1c brown	15.00	8.00
94F	A63	2c green	40.00	15.00
95F	A63	3c org ('95)	55.00	22.50
96F	A63	5c carmine	20.00	4.00
98F	A64	10c car rose	30.00	7.50
99F	A64	12c dp bl ('93)	60.00	27.50
100F	A64	16c gray	60.00	27.50
102F	A64	50c blue green	60.00	10.00
103F	A64	1p red brown	60.00	10.00
104F	A65	2p dark green	175.00	75.00
		Nos. 92F-104F (11)	593.00	217.00

The high values of this and succeeding issues are frequently punched with the word "INUTILIZADO," parts of the letters showing on each stamp. These punched stamps sell for only a small fraction of the catalogue values.

Examples of No. 95 in yellow shades are changelings.

Reprints of No. 96b have white gum. The original stamp has yellowish gum. Value $125.

Imperf., Pairs

92b	A63	½c	60.00
93a	A63	1c	60.00
94a	A63	2c	30.00
96a	A63	5c	30.00
98a	A64	10c	60.00
99a	A64	12c	60.00

100a	A64	16c	60.00	
101a	A64	24c	60.00	
102a	A64	50c	60.00	
103b	A65	1p	60.00	
105a	A65	5p	150.00	

Nos. 102a, 103b and 105a exist only without gum; the other imperfs are found with or without gum, and values are the same for either condition.

Vertical Pairs, Imperf. Between

92c	A63	½c	125.00	
93b	A63	1c	100.00	
94b	A63	2c	50.00	
95a	A63	3c	250.00	
96c	A63	5c	45.00	—
98b	A64	10c	100.00	
99b	A64	12c	100.00	

Horizontal Pairs, Imperf. Between

93c	A63	1c	110.00	
94c	A63	2c	55.00	
96d	A63	5c	55.00	45.00
98c	A64	10c	110.00	

1896-97 Wmk. 86 *Perf. 11½*

106	A63	½c slate	.65	.30
a.		½c gray blue	2.00	.35
b.		½c indigo	.65	.30
107	A63	1c brown	.65	.30
108	A63	2c yellow green	.65	.30
109	A63	3c orange	.65	.30
110	A63	5c carmine	.65	.30
a.		Imperf., pair	100.00	
111	A64	10c carmine rose	10.00	.30
112	A64	12c deep blue	5.00	.30
a.		Imperf., pair	—	
113	A64	16c gray	13.50	.90
114	A64	24c gray brown	13.50	1.25
a.		Imperf., pair	100.00	—
115	A64	30c orange ('97)	13.50	.70
116	A64	50c blue green	13.50	.70
117	A64	80c dull violet	20.00	.90
118	A65	1p lake	30.00	1.60
119	A65	1p20c black ('97)	13.50	3.50
120	A65	2p dark green	20.00	10.00
121	A65	5p dark blue	135.00	13.50
		Nos. 106-121 (16)	290.75	35.15

Perf. 12

106E	A63	½c slate	2.00	1.00
a.		½c gray blue	10.00	4.00
b.		½c indigo	10.00	4.00
107E	A63	1c brown	1.75	1.00
108E	A63	2c yellow green	2.50	1.00
109E	A63	3c orange	45.00	2.00
110E	A63	5c carmine	3.50	1.00
111E	A64	10c car rose	15.00	1.00
112E	A64	12c deep blue	11.00	2.00
113E	A64	16c gray	35.00	5.50
114E	A64	24c gray brown	52.50	11.00
115E	A64	30c orange ('97)	52.50	2.00
116E	A64	50c blue green	65.00	.80
117E	A64	80c dull violet	65.00	22.50
118E	A65	1p lake	65.00	3.50
119E	A65	1p20c black ('97)	65.00	22.50
121E	A65	5p dark blue	800.00	20.00
		Nos. 106E-121E (15)	1,281.	96.80

Perf. 11½x12

106F	A63	½c slate	20.00	11.00
107F	A63	1c brown	30.00	25.00
108F	A63	2c yellow green	20.00	11.00
109F	A63	3c orange	13.00	8.00
110F	A63	5c carmine	26.00	4.50
111F	A64	10c car rose	45.00	18.00
112F	A64	12c deep blue	47.50	15.00
113F	A64	16c gray	60.00	20.00
115F	A64	30c org ('97)	—	75.00
116F	A64	50c blue green	—	75.00
117F	A64	80c dull violet	—	75.00
119F	A65	1p20c black ('97)	100.00	60.00
		Nos. 106F-119F (12)	361.50	397.50

Vertical Pairs, Imperf. Between

106c	A63	½c	200.00	
107a	A63	1c	125.00	
108a	A63	2c	125.00	
109a	A63	3c	200.00	
110b	A63	5c	125.00	125.00
112b	A64	12c	125.00	100.00

Horizontal Pairs, Imperf. Between

107b	A63	1c	125.00	
108b	A63	2c	125.00	
110c	A63	5c	125.00	80.00
111a	A64	10c	125.00	
112c	A64	12c	125.00	

Allegory, Liberty Seated
A66 A67

1899-1903 *Perf. 11½*

122	A66	½c yel brn	.40	.30
123	A66	1c green	.60	.30
124	A66	2c slate	.60	.30
125	A66	3c org ('01)	.80	.50
126	A66	4c yel ('03)	1.40	.60
127	A66	5c car rose	.60	.30
128	A66	6c blk ('03)	.90	.60
129	A66	10c dk grn	1.40	.40
130	A66	12c dull blue	.95	.60
131	A66	12c ol grn ('01)	.95	.60
132	A66	15c sea grn ('01)	2.50	.60
132B	A66	15c dl blue ('01)	2.50	.60
133	A66	16c orange	8.00	8.00
134	A66	20c claret	1.90	.30
135	A66	24c violet	4.00	1.00
136	A66	30c rose	7.25	.60
137	A66	30c ver ('01)	4.00	.50
a.		30c scarlet	47.50	3.00
138	A66	50c brt blue	4.50	.50
139	A67	1p bl & blk	15.00	1.25
a.		Center inverted	*2,000.*	*1,000.*
140	A67	5p org & blk	57.50	11.00
		Punch cancellation		3.00
a.		Center inverted	*2,750.*	*2,500.*
141	A67	10p grn & blk	70.00	18.00
		Punch cancellation		3.00
a.		Center inverted	*5,000.*	
		Punch cancellation		675.00
142	A67	20p red & blk	200.00	35.00
		Punch cancellation		3.00
a.		Center invtd. (punch cancel)		*4,000.*
		Nos. 122-142 (22)	385.75	81.85

Nos. 139-142 used are valued with violet oval or black boxed parcel cancels. Examples with letter cancels are worth ⅓rd more.

Perf. 12

122E	A66	½c yellow brown	1.50	1.20
123E	A66	1c green	2.00	.60
124E	A66	2c slate	1.50	.60
125E	A66	3c orange ('01)	3.50	1.75
126E	A66	4c yellow ('03)	10.00	3.50
127E	A66	5c carmine rose	5.25	.60
128E	A66	6c black ('03)	8.50	2.00
129E	A66	10c dark green	8.50	1.75
130E	A66	12c dull blue	8.00	2.00
131E	A66	12c ol grn ('01)	8.50	2.00
132E	A66	15c sea grn ('01)	17.00	1.75
133E	A66	16c orange	10.00	9.50
134E	A66	20c claret	12.00	9.50
135E	A66	24c violet	11.00	8.50
136E	A66	30c rose	28.00	3.50
137E	A66	30c ver ('01)	60.00	4.00
a.		30c scarlet	47.50	3.00
138E	A66	50c brt blue	27.50	3.50
139E	A67	1p bl & blk	500.00	160.00
		Nos. 122E-139E (18)	722.75	216.25

Perf. 11½x12

122F	A66	½c yellow brown	25.00	15.00
		Never hinged	37.50	
		On cover, single franking		20.00
123F	A66	1c green	25.00	15.00
		Never hinged	37.50	
		On cover		1.00
124F	A66	2c slate	12.00	3.00
		Never hinged	18.00	
		On cover		1.00
125F	A66	3c orange ('01)	47.50	18.00
		Never hinged	72.50	
		On cover		1.50
127F	A66	5c carmine rose	12.00	6.00
		Never hinged	18.00	
		On cover		1.00
128F	A66	6c black ('03)	32.50	20.00
		Never hinged	47.50	
		On cover		2.00
129F	A66	10c dark green	30.00	6.50
		Never hinged	45.00	
		On cover		1.50
130F	A66	12c dull blue	50.00	15.00
		Never hinged	75.00	
		On cover		2.00
131F	A66	12c ol grn ('01)	50.00	10.00
		Never hinged	75.00	
		On cover		2.00
132F	A66	15c sea grn ('01)	50.00	8.00
		Never hinged	75.00	
		On cover		2.50
134F	A66	20c claret	60.00	12.00
		Never hinged	90.00	
		On cover		1.00
135F	A66	24c violet	50.00	10.00
		Never hinged	75.00	
		On cover		5.00
136F	A66	30c rose	120.00	20.00
		Never hinged	175.00	
		On cover		5.00
137F	A66	30c ver ('01)	140.00	25.00
		Never hinged	210.00	
		On cover		5.00
138F	A66	50c brt blue	120.00	20.00
		Never hinged	175.00	
		On cover		10.00
		Nos. 122F-138F (15)	824.00	203.50

Imperf., Pairs

122a	A66	½c	35.00	
123a	A66	1c	50.00	
124a	A66	2c	17.50	
125a	A66	3c	325.00	
127a	A66	5c	17.50	
128a	A66	6c	60.00	
129a	A66	10c	50.00	
132a	A66	15c	50.00	

Vertical Pairs, Imperf. Between

122b	A66	½c	10.00	9.50
123b	A66	1c	10.00	9.50
124b	A66	2c	5.00	4.50
125b	A66	3c	325.00	200.00
126a	A66	4c	400.00	275.00
127b	A66	5c	4.50	2.50
128b	A66	6c	13.50	10.00
129b	A66	10c	85.00	
132c	A66	15c	15.00	10.00

Horizontal Pairs, Imperf. Between

122c	A66	½c	30.00	19.00
123c	A66	1c	47.50	27.50
124c	A66	2c	10.00	5.00
125c	A66	3c	325.00	200.00
126b	A66	4c	400.00	
127c	A66	5c	10.00	5.00
128c	A66	6c	17.00	10.00
129c	A66	10c	17.00	10.00
132d	A66	15c	40.00	23.00
138a	A66	50c	165.00	

River Port of Rosario — A68

1902, Oct. 26 *Perf. 11½, 11½x12*

143	A68	5c deep blue	4.75	2.00
a.		Imperf., pair	95.00	
b.		Vert. pair, imperf. btwn.	60.00	
c.		Horiz. pair, imperf. btwn.	90.00	

Completion of port facilities at Rosario.

San Martin
A69 A70

1908-09 Typo. *Perf. 13½x12½*

144	A69	½c violet	.50	.30
145	A69	1c brnsh buff	.50	.30
146	A69	2c chocolate	.60	.30
147	A69	3c green	.65	.40
148	A69	4c redsh violet	1.25	.40
149	A69	5c carmine	.60	.30
150	A69	6c olive bister	.75	.40
151	A69	10c gray green	1.75	.30
152	A69	12c yellow buff	1.00	.60
153	A69	12c dk blue ('09)	1.75	.30
155	A69	20c ultra	1.25	.30
156	A69	24c red brown	3.50	.60
157	A69	30c dull rose	6.00	.60
158	A69	50c black	6.00	.50
159	A70	1p sl bl & pink	18.00	2.50
		Nos. 144-159 (15)	44.10	8.10

The 1c blue was not issued. Value $500.

Wmk. 86 appears on ½, 1, 6, 20, 24 and 50c. Other values have similar wmk. with wavy rays.

Stamps lacking wmk. are from outer rows printed on sheet margin.

Perf. 13½

146A	A69	2c chocolate	1.20	.25
147A	A69	3c green	2.00	1.00
148A	A69	4c redsh violet	1.30	.50
149A	A69	5c carmine	1.00	.30
151A	A69	10c gray green	6.25	2.25
152A	A69	12c yellow buff	1.20	.70
153A	A69	12c dk blue ('09)	4.25	1.00
154A	A69	15c apple green	.60	.50
156A	A69	24c red brown	4.75	1.30
157A	A69	30c dull rose	9.50	1.30
159A	A70	1p sl bl & pink	20.00	3.00

Pyramid of May — A71

Nicolas Rodriguez Pena and Hipolito Vieytes — A72

Meeting at Pena's Home — A73

Designs: 3c, Miguel de Azcuenaga (1754-1833) and Father Manuel M. Alberti (1763-1811). 4c, Viceroy's house and Fort Buenos Aires. 5c, Cornelio Saavedra (1759-1829). 10c, Antonio Luis Beruti (1772-1842) and French distributing badges. 12c, Congress building. 20c, Juan Jose Castelli (1764-1812) and Domingo Matheu (1765-1831). 24c, First council. 30c, Manuel Belgrano (1770-1820) and Juan Larrea (1782-1847). 50c, First meeting of republican government, May 25, 1810. 1p, Mariano Moreno (1778-1811) and Juan Jose Paso (1758-1833). 5p, Oath of the Junta. 10p, Centenary Monument. 20p, Jose Francisco de San Martin (1778-1850).

Inscribed "1810 1910"

Various Frames

1910, May 1 Engr. *Perf. 11½*

160	A71	½c bl & gray bl	.30	.25
161	A72	1c bl grn & blk	.30	.30
b.		Horiz. pair, imperf. btwn.	*65.00*	
162	A73	2c olive & gray	.25	.30
163	A72	3c green	.70	.40
164	A73	4c dk blue & grn	.70	.40
165	A71	5c carmine	.40	.25
166	A73	10c yel brn & blk	1.10	.50
167	A73	12c brt blue	1.10	.50
168	A72	20c gray brn & blk	3.25	.60
169	A73	24c org brn & bl	1.75	1.25
170	A72	30c lilac & blk	1.75	1.00
171	A71	50c car & blk	4.50	1.25
172	A72	1p brt blue	9.50	3.25
173	A73	5p orange & vio	72.50	35.00
		Punch cancel		5.00
174	A71	10p orange & blk	90.00	62.50
		Punch cancel		10.00
175	A71	20p dp blue & ind	150.00	100.00
		Punch cancel		15.00
		Nos. 160-175 (16)	338.10	207.75

Centenary of the republic.

Center Inverted

160a	A71	½c	*1,000.*	
161a	A72	1c	*1,000.*	
162a	A73	2c	*800.00*	
164a	A73	4c	*650.00*	
167a	A73	12c	*1,000.*	
171a	A71	50c	*1,000.*	
173a	A73	5p	*750.00*	

Domingo F. Sarmiento — A87

1911, May 15 Typo. *Perf. 13½*

176	A87	5c gray brn & blk	.80	.40

Domingo Faustino Sarmiento (1811-88), pres. of Argentina, 1868-74.

Agriculture — A88

Size: 19x25mm

Wmk. 86, without Face

1911 Engr. *Perf. 12*

177	A88	5c vermilion	.40	.25
178	A88	12c deep blue	5.00	.50

Size: 18x23mm

Wmk. 86, with Face

1911 Typo. *Perf. 13½x12½*

179	A88	½c violet	.50	.30
180	A88	1c brown ocher	.30	.30
181	A88	2c chocolate	.30	.25
a.		Perf. 13½	15.00	4.00
b.		Imperf., pair	*40.00*	
182	A88	3c green	.50	.50
183	A88	4c brown violet	.50	.30
184	A88	10c gray green	.50	.30
185	A88	20c ultra	4.50	.95
186	A88	24c red brown	6.50	3.75
187	A88	30c claret	3.50	.50
188	A88	50c black	8.00	.80
		Nos. 179-188 (10)	25.10	7.95

The 5c dull red is a proof. In this issue Wmk. 86 comes: straight rays (4c, 20c, 24c) and wavy rays (2c). All other values exist with both forms.

Wmk. 87 (Horiz. or Vert.)

1912-14 *Perf. 13½x12½*

189	A88	½c violet	.30	.30
190	A88	1c ocher	.30	.30
191	A88	2c chocolate	.50	.30
192	A88	3c green	.50	.50
193	A88	4c brown violet	.50	.60
194	A88	5c red	.40	.30
195	A88	10c deep green	1.75	.30
196	A88	12c deep blue	.60	.30
197	A88	20c ultra	3.25	.50
198	A88	24c red brown	6.50	2.00
199	A88	30c claret	5.50	7.00
200	A88	50c black	10.00	.90
		Nos. 189-200 (12)	30.10	13.30

See Nos. 208-212. For overprints see Nos. OD1-OD8, OD47-OD54, OD102-OD108, OD146-OD152, OD183-OD190, OD235-OD241, OD281-OD284, OD318-OD323.

Perf. 13½

189a	A88	½c	1.00	.50
190a	A88	1c	1.00	.50
191a	A88	2c	1.00	.50
192a	A88	3c	150.00	30.00
193a	A88	4c	2.50	1.25
194a	A88	5c	.90	.50
196a	A88	12c	3.50	1.50
197a	A88	20c	9.00	.90
		Nos. 189a-197a (8)	168.90	35.65

A89

1912-13 *Perf. 13½*

201 A89 1p dull bl & rose 10.00 1.10
Punch cancel .35
202 A89 5p slate & ol grn 19.00 7.00
Punch cancel 1.00
203 A89 10p violet & blue 75.00 17.50
Punch cancel 1.40
204 A89 20p blue & claret 210.00 80.00
Punch cancel 2.00
Nos. 201-204 (4) 314.00 105.60

1915 Unwmk. *Perf. 13½x12½*

208 A88 1c ocher 1.50 .30
209 A88 2c chocolate 1.50 .30
212 A88 5c red 1.50 .30
Nos. 208-212 (3) 4.50 .90

Only these denominations were printed on paper without watermark.

Other stamps of the series are known unwatermarked but they are from the outer rows of sheets the other parts of which are watermarked.

Francisco Narciso de Laprida A90

Declaration of Independence A91

A92 A92a
Jose de San Martin

Perf. 13½, 13½x12½

1916, July 9 Litho. Wmk. 87

215 A90 ½c violet .60 .30
216 A90 1c buff .50 .30

Perf. 13½x12½

217 A90 2c chocolate .60 .30
218 A90 3c green .60 .60
219 A90 4c red violet .60 .60

Perf. 13½

220 A91 5c red .50 .30
a. Imperf., pair 40.00
221 A91 10c gray green 1.50 .30
222 A92 12c blue .90 .35
223 A92 20c ultra .70 .70
224 A92 24c red brown 2.75 1.40
225 A92 30c claret 2.75 1.60
226 A92 50c gray black 6.75 1.60
227 A92a 1p slate bl & red 10.00 10.00
Punch cancel .50
a. Imperf., pair 325.00
228 A92a 5p black & gray grn 100.00 80.00
Punch cancel 15.00
229 A92a 10p violet & blue 150.00 135.00
Punch cancel 9.00
230 A92a 20p dull blue & cl 150.00 100.00
Punch cancel 7.00
a. Imperf., pair 650.00
Nos. 215-230 (16) 428.75 333.35

Cent. of Argentina's declaration of independence of Spain, July 9, 1816.

The watermark is either vert. or horiz. on Nos. 215-220, 222; only vert. on No. 221, and only horiz. on Nos. 223-230.

For overprints see Nos. OD9, OD55-OD56, OD109, OD153, OD191-OD192, OD285, OD324.

A93

A94

A94a

1917 *Perf. 13½*

231 A93 ½c violet .60 .60
a. Imperf. pair 70.00
232 A93 1c buff .60 .30
a. Imperf, pair 70.00
233 A93 2c brown .60 .30
a. Imperf, pair 70.00
234 A93 3c lt green 1.00 .30
a. imperf, pair 70.00
235 A93 4c red violet 1.50 .60
a. Imperf, pair 70.00
236 A93 5c red 1.25 .50
Never hinged 1.90
a. Imperf, pair 15.00
237 A93 10c gray green 4.00 .50
a. Imperf, pair 70.00
Nos. 231-237 (7) 9.55 3.10

Perf. 13½x12½

231B A93 ½c violet .30 .30
232B A93 1c buff .40 .40
233B A93 2c brown .40 .40
234B A93 3c lt green 1.00 .30
235B A93 4c red violet 2.00 .50
236B A93 5c red .30 .30
237B A93 10c gray green 3.00 .25
Nos. 231B-237B (7) 7.40 2.45

Perf. 13½

238 A94 12c blue 1.00 .25
239 A94 20c ultra 2.50 .30
240 A94 24c red brown 6.00 3.00
241 A94 30c claret 6.00 1.50
242 A94 50c gray black 6.00 .60
243 A94a 1p slate bl & red 6.00 .60
244 A94a 5p blk & gray grn 19.00 3.00
Punch cancel 1.50
245 A94a 10p violet & blue 47.50 12.00
Punch cancel 1.50
246 A94a 20p dull blue & cl 90.00 50.00
Punch cancel 1.50
a. Center inverted 1,500. 1,500.
Nos. 231-246 (16) 193.55 74.35

The watermark is either vert. or horiz. on Nos. 231-236, 238 and 231B-236B, 238B; only vert. on No. 237 and 237B, and only horiz. on Nos. 239-246.

All known examples of No. 246a are off-center to the right.

See Nos. 292-300, 304-307A, 310-314, 318, 322.

For overprints see Nos. OD10-OD20, OD57-OD71, OD74, OD110-OD121, OD154-OD159, OD161-OD162, OD193-OD207, OD209-OD211, OD242-OD252, OD254-OD255, OD286-OD290, OD325-OD328, OD330.

Juan Gregorio Pujol — A95

1918, June 15 Litho. *Perf. 13½*

247 A95 5c bister & gray .60 .35

Cent. of the birth of Juan G. Pujol (1817-61), lawyer and legislator.

1918-19 Unwmk. *Perf. 13½*

248 A93 ½c violet .30 .25
249 A93 1c buff .30 .25
a. Imperf., pair 35.00
250 A93 2c brown .30 .25
251 A93 3c lt green .50 .25
252 A93 4c red violet .50 .25
253 A93 5c red .80 .25
254 A93 10c gray green .80 .25
255 A94 12c blue 1.25 .25
256 A94 20c ultra 2.00 .25
257 A94 24c red brown 2.40 .25
258 A94 30c claret 3.00 .35
259 A94 50c gray black 8.00 1.25
Nos. 248-259 (12) 20.15 4.10

Perf. 13½x12½

248B A93 ½c violet .70 .50
249B A93 1c buff .70 .50
250B A93 2c brown .70 .50
251B A93 3c lt green .90 .50
252B A93 4c red violet .90 .50
253B A93 5c red .60 .50
254B A93 10c gray green 2.00 .50
Nos. 248B-254B (7) 6.50 3.50

The stamps of this issue sometimes show letters of papermakers' watermarks.

There were two printings, in 1918 and 1923, using different ink and paper.

1920 Wmk. 88

264 A93 ½c violet .50 .25
265 A93 1c buff .50 .25
266 A93 2c brown .50 .25
267 A93 3c green 2.00 1.00
268 A93 4c red violet 2.50 1.50
269 A93 5c red .50 .25
270 A93 10c gray green 6.00 .30

Perf. 13½

264A A93 ½c violet .80 .30
265A A93 1c buff .80 .30
266A A93 2c brown 1.00 .30
267A A93 3c green 2.00 1.00
269A A93 5c red 4.00 .30
270A A93 10c gray green 55.00 15.00
271 A94 12c blue 3.00 .30
272 A94 20c ultra 4.25 .40
274 A94 30c claret 15.00 3.00
275 A94 50c gray black 10.00 3.00
Nos. 264-275 (17) 108.35 27.70

Belgrano's Mausoleum A96

Creation of Argentine Flag A97

Gen. Manuel Belgrano — A98

1920, June 18

280 A96 2c red 1.00 .30
a. Perf. 13½x12½ 3.00 1.00
281 A97 5c rose & blue 1.00 .30
282 A98 12c green & blue 2.00 1.00
Nos. 280-282 (3) 4.00 1.60

Belgrano (1770-1820), Argentine general, patriot and diplomat.

Gen. Justo Jose de Urquiza — A99

1920, Nov. 11

283 A99 5c gray blue .60 .35

Gen. Justo Jose de Urquiza (1801-70), pres. of Argentina, 1854-60. See No. 303.

Bartolome Mitre — A100

1921, June 26 Unwmk.

284 A100 2c violet brown .50 .35
285 A100 5c light blue .50 .35

Bartolome Mitre (1821-1906), pres. of Argentina, 1862-65.

Allegory, Pan-America — A101

1921, Aug. 25 *Perf. 13½*

286 A101 3c violet 1.50 .35
287 A101 5c blue 2.00 .35
288 A101 10c vio brown 3.00 .50
289 A101 12c rose 3.50 1.00
Nos. 286-289 (4) 10.00 2.20

Inscribed "Buenos Aires-Agosto de 1921" A102

Inscribed "Republica Argentina" A103

1921, Oct. *Perf. 13½x12½*

290 A102 5c rose 1.25 .35
291 A103 5c rose 7.00 10.50

Perf. 13½

290A A102 5c rose 6.00 .50
291A A103 5c rose 7.00 .60

1st Pan-American Postal Cong., Buenos Aires, Aug., 1921.

See Nos. 308-309, 319. For overprints see Nos. OD72, OD160, OD208, OD253, OD329.

1920 Wmk. 89 *Perf. 13½x12½*

292 A93 ½c violet 1.60 .80
293 A93 1c buff 4.50 1.50
294 A93 2c brown 4.00 .50
297 A93 5c red 5.00 .35
298 A93 10c gray green 5.00 .35

Perf. 13½

294A A93 2c brown 7.00 1.50
297A A93 5c red 52.50 9.00
298A A93 10c gray green 40.00 2.00
299 A94 12c blue *6,000.* 200.00
300 A94 20c ultra 12.00 1.50

1920 Wmk. 89

303 A99 5c gray blue 500.00 400.00

1922-23 Wmk. 90 *Perf. 13½*

304 A93 ½c violet .60 .25
305 A93 1c buff 1.00 .30
306 A93 2c brown 1.00 .30
307 A93 3c green .60 .40
307A A93 4c red violet 1.50 1.00
308 A102 5c rose 10.00 3.00
309 A103 5c red 5.00 .80
310 A93 10c gray green 9.00 1.00
311 A94 12c blue 1.00 .40
312 A94 20c ultra 2.00 .50
313 A94 24c red brown 20.00 10.00
314 A94 30c claret 10.00 1.00

Perf. 13½x12½

304B A93 ½c violet .50 .30
305B A93 1c buff .50 .30
306B A93 2c brown .50 .30
307B A93 3c green 1.00 .80
307C A93 4c red violet 22.50 10.00
308B A102 5c rose 6.00 1.00
309B A103 5c red .60 .30
310B A93 10c gray green 2.25 .25
Nos. 304-310B (20) 95.55 32.20

Paper with Gray Overprint RA in Sun

1922-23 Unwmk. *Perf. 13½*

318 A93 2c brown 10.00 2.50
319 A103 5c red 15.00 2.50
322 A94 20c ultra 50.00 5.00

Perf. 13½x12½

318A A93 2c brown 10.00 2.50
319A A103 5c red 8.50 2.50

A104

San Martín — A105

With Period after Value

Perf. 13½x12½

1923, May Litho. Wmk. 90

323 A104 ½c red violet .50 .30
324 A104 1c buff .80 .30
325 A104 2c dark brown .60 .30
326 A104 3c lt green .80 .40
327 A104 4c red brown .80 .40
328 A104 5c red .80 .30
329 A104 10c dull green 7.00 .30
330 A104 12c deep blue .70 .30
331 A104 20c ultra 2.00 .30
332 A104 24c lt brown 5.00 3.00
333 A104 30c claret 16.00 .80
334 A104 50c black 62.00 7.00

Perf. 13½

323A A104 ½c red violet .80 .30
324A A104 1c buff 1.50 .30
325A A104 2c dark brown 41.00 .30
326A A104 3c lt green 3.00 1.00
327A A104 4c red brown 3.00 1.00
328A A104 5c red 3.00 .30
329A A104 10c dull green 10.00 1.00
330A A104 12c deep blue 12.50 3.00
331A A104 20c ultra 11.00 .70
332A A104 24c lt brown 20.00 5.00
333A A104 30c claret 20.00 3.00
334A A104 50c black 8.00 1.00

Without Period after Value

Perf. 13½

Wmk. 87

335 A105 1p blue & red 10.00 .80
336 A105 5p gray lil & grn 30.00 6.00
Punch cancel 1.00
337 A105 10p clar & blue 90.00 15.00
Punch cancel 2.00

338 A105 20p sl & brn lake 120.00 45.00
Punch cancel 1.25
Nos. 323-338 (28) 480.80 97.40

Nos. 335-338 and 353-356 canceled with round or oval killers in purple (revenue cancellations) sell for one-fifth to one-half as much as postally used copies.

For overprints see Nos. 399-404.

Design of 1923
Without Period after Value

Perf. 13½x12½

1923-24 Litho. Wmk. 90

340 A104 ½c red violet .50 .30
341 A104 1c buff .50 .30
342 A104 2c dk brown .50 .30
343 A104 3c green .60 .30
a. Imperf., pair 60.00
344 A104 4c red brown .80 .30
345 A104 5c red .50 .30
346 A104 10c dull green .50 .30
347 A104 12c deep blue .80 .30
348 A104 20c ultra 1.00 .30
349 A104 24c lt brown 4.00 1.25
350 A104 25c purple 2.00 .40
351 A104 30c claret 4.00 .40
352 A104 50c black 6.00 .40

Perf. 13½

340B A104 ½c red violet 180.00 60.00
345B A104 5c red 75.00 30.00
346B A104 10c dull green 75.00 30.00
349B A104 24c lt brown 150.00 50.00
353 A105 1p blue & red 6.00 .70
354 A105 5p dk vio & grn 35.00 2.00
355 A105 10p claret & blue 75.00 8.00
356 A105 20p slate & lake 120.00 15.00
Nos. 340-356 (21) 737.70 200.85

1931-33 Typo.

343b A104 3c 3.00 .50
345a A104 5c 4.50 .50
346a A104 10c 7.50 .50
347a A104 12c 15.00 3.50
348a A104 20c 55.00 3.50
350a A104 25c 40.00 2.00
351a A104 30c 25.00 1.50
Nos. 343b-351a (7) 150.00 12.00

The typographed stamps were issued only in coils and have a rough impression with heavy shading about the eyes and nose. Nos. 343 and 346 are known without watermark.

Nos. 341-345, 347-349, 351a may be found in pairs, one with period.

See note after No. 338. See Nos. 362-368. For overprints see Nos. OD21-OD33, OD75-OD87, OD122-OD133, OD163-OD175, OD212-OD226, OD256-OD268, OD291-OD304, OD331-OD345.

Rivadavia — A106

1926, Feb. 8 ***Perf. 13½***

357 A106 5c rose .60 .35

Presidency of Bernardino Rivadavia, cent.

Rivadavia
A108

San Martin
A109

General Post Office, 1926
A110

General Post Office, 1826
A111

1926, July 1 ***Perf. 13½x12½***

358 A108 3c gray green .50 .30
359 A109 5c red .50 .30

Perf. 13½

360 A110 12c deep blue 1.25 .40
361 A111 25c chocolate 3.25 .80
a. "1326" for "1826" 15.00 10.00
Nos. 358-361 (4) 5.50 1.80

Centenary of the Post Office.

For overprints see Nos. OD34, OD88, OD134, OD227-OD228, OD269, OD305, OD346.

Type of 1923-31 Issue
Without Period after Value

1927 Wmk. 205 ***Perf. 13½x12½***

362 A104 ½c red violet .70 .60
a. Pelure paper 2.75 2.50
363 A104 1c buff .70 .60
364 A104 2c dark brown .70 .35
a. Pelure paper 1.00 .70
365 A104 5c red 1.00 .35
a. Period after value 15.00 9.00
b. Pelure paper 1.00 .70
366 A104 10c dull green 6.00 3.50
367 A104 20c ultra 60.00 6.00

Perf. 13½

368 A105 1p blue & red 45.00 8.50
Nos. 362-368 (7) 114.10 19.90

Arms of Argentina and Brazil — A112

Wmk. RA in Sun (90)

1928, Aug. 27 ***Perf. 12½x13***

369 A112 5c rose red 1.50 .40
370 A112 12c deep blue 2.50 .70

Cent. of peace between the Empire of Brazil and the United Provinces of the Rio de la Plata.

Allegory, Discovery of the New World
A113

"Spain" and "Argentina"
A114

"America" Offering Laurels to Columbus — A115

1929, Oct. 12 Litho. ***Perf. 13½***

371 A113 2c lilac brown 2.00 .40
372 A114 5c light red 2.00 .40
373 A115 12c dull blue 6.00 1.00
Nos. 371-373 (3) 10.00 1.80

Discovery of America by Columbus, 437th anniv.

Spirit of Victory Attending Insurgents
A116

March of the Victorious Insurgents
A117

Perf. 13½x12½ (A116), 12½x13 (A117)

1930

374 A116 ½c violet gray 1.00 .50
375 A116 1c myrtle green 1.00 .50
376 A117 2c dull violet 1.00 .50
377 A116 3c green 1.00 .50
378 A116 4c violet 1.00 .70
379 A116 5c rose red 1.00 .30
380 A116 10c gray black 1.00 .70
381 A117 12c dull blue 1.75 .80
382 A117 20c ocher 2.00 1.00
383 A117 24c red brown 6.50 2.50
384 A117 25c green 7.50 2.50
385 A117 30c deep violet 9.50 3.50
386 A117 50c black 13.00 6.25
387 A117 1p sl bl & red 25.00 10.00
388 A117 2p black & org 37.50 14.00
389 A117 5p dull grn & blk 100.00 35.00
390 A117 10p dp red brn & dull blue 140.00 47.50
391 A117 20p yel grn & dl bl 260.00 125.00
392 A117 50p dk grn & vio 900.00 800.00
Nos. 374-390 (17) 349.75 126.75

Revolution of 1930.

Nos. 387-392 with oval (parcel post) cancellation sell for less.

For overprint see No. 405.

1931 ***Perf. 12½x13***

393 A117 ½c red violet 1.00 .50
394 A117 1c gray black 1.50 1.00
395 A117 3c green 1.50 .70
396 A117 4c red brown 1.00 .50
397 A117 5c red .80 .50
a. Plane omitted, top left corner 10.00 8.00
398 A117 10c dull green 1.90 .80
Nos. 393-398 (6) 7.70 4.00

Revolution of 1930.

Stamps of 1924-25 Overprinted in Red or Green

1931, Sept. 6 ***Perf. 13½, 13½x12½***

399 A104 3c green .50 .50
400 A104 10c dull green .70 .70
401 A104 30c claret (G) 5.00 3.25
402 A104 50c black 5.00 3.25

Overprinted in Blue

403 A105 1p blue & red 6.00 3.25
404 A105 5p dk violet & grn 60.00 22.50

No. 388 Overprinted in Blue

Perf. 12½x13

405 A117 2p black & orange 12.00 8.00
Nos. 399-405 (7) 89.20 41.45

1st anniv. of the Revolution of 1930.
See Nos. C30-C34.

Refrigeration Compressor — A118

Perf. 13½x12½

1932, Aug. 29 Litho.

406 A118 3c green 1.25 .50
407 A118 10c scarlet 2.25 .40
408 A118 12c gray blue 7.50 1.10
Nos. 406-408 (3) 11.00 2.00

6th Intl. Refrigeration Congress.

Port of La Plata
A119

Pres. Julio A. Roca
A120

Municipal Palace — A121

Cathedral of La Plata — A122

Dardo Rocha — A123

Perf. 13½x13, 13x13½ (10c)

1933, Jan.

409 A119 3c green & dk brn .50 .30
410 A120 10c orange & dk vio .70 .30
411 A121 15c dk bl & dp bl 2.50 1.50
412 A122 20c violet & yel brn 2.25 1.00
413 A123 30c dk grn & vio brn 14.00 7.00
Nos. 409-413 (5) 19.95 10.10

50th anniv. of the founding of the city of La Plata, Nov. 19th, 1882.

Christ of the Andes
A124

Buenos Aires Cathedral
A125

1934, Oct. 1 ***Perf. 13x13½, 13½x13***

414 A124 10c rose & brown 1.00 .30
415 A125 15c dark blue 3.00 .60

32nd Intl. Eucharistic Cong., Oct. 10-14.

"Liberty" with Arms of Brazil and Argentina
A126

Symbolical of "Peace" and "Friendship"
A127

1935, May 15 ***Perf. 13x13½***

416 A126 10c red 1.00 .30
417 A127 15c blue 2.00 .60

Visit of Pres. Getulio Vargas of Brazil.

Belgrano
A128

Sarmiento
A129

Urquiza
A130

Louis Braille
A131

San Martin
A132

Brown
A133

Moreno
A134

Alberdi
A135

Nicolas Avellaneda
A136

Rivadavia
A137

Mitre
A138

Bull (Cattle Breeding)
A139

Martin Güemes A140

Agriculture A141

Merino Sheep (Wool) — A142

Sugar Cane — A143

Oil Well (Petroleum) — A144

Map of South America
A145 A146

Fruit A147

Iguacu Falls (Scenic Wonders) A148

Grapes (Vineyards) A149

Cotton A150

Two types of A140:
Type I — Inscribed Juan Martin Guemes.
Type II — Inscribed Martin Güemes.

Perf. 13, 13½x13, 13x13½

1935-51 Litho. Wmk. 90

418 A128 ½c red violet .30 .25
419 A129 1c buff .30 .25
a. Typo. 2.00 .25
420 A130 2c dark brown .50 .25
421 A131 2½c black ('39) .40 .25
422 A132 3c green .60 .25
423 A132 3c lt gray ('39) .60 .25
424 A134 3c lt gray ('46) .50 .25
425 A133 4c lt gray .60 .25
426 A133 4c sage grn ('39) .50 .25
427 A134 5c yel brn, typo. .80 .25
a. Tete beche pair, typo. 20.00 10.00
b. Booklet pane of 8, typo.
c. Booklet pane of 4, typo. 5.00
d. Litho. 5.00 .50
428 A135 6c olive green .50 .25
429 A136 8c orange ('39) .50 .25
430 A137 10c car, perf. 13½ (typo.) 4.00 .25
a. Perf. 13½x13 3.00 .35
431 A137 10c brown ('42) .40 .25
432 A138 12c brown 1.00 .25
433 A138 12c red ('39) .40 .25
434 A139 15c slate bl ('36) 1.50 .25
435 A139 15c pale ultra ('39) 3.00 .25
436 A140 15c lt gray bl (II) ('42) 50.00 3.00
437 A140 20c lt ultra (I) 1.00 .25
438 A140 20c lt ultra (II) ('36) 1.00 .25
439 A140 20c bl gray (II) ('39) 3.00 .25
439A A139 20c dk bl & pale bl, ('42) 22x33mm 1.00 .25
440 A139 20c blue ('51) 1.00 .25
a. Typo. .35 .35
441 A141 25c car & pink ('36) 1.25 .25
442 A142 30c org brn & yel brown ('36) 1.00 .25
443 A143 40c dk vio ('36) 1.00 .25
444 A144 50c red & org ('36) 1.00 .25
445 A145 1p brn blk & lt bl ('36) 25.00 1.00
446 A146 1p brn blk & lt bl ('37) 16.00 .30
a. Chalky paper 100.00 2.00
447 A147 2p brn lake & dk ultra ('36) 2.50 .25
448 A148 5p ind & ol grn ('36) 4.00 .25
449 A149 10p brn lake & blk 15.00 1.25
450 A150 20p bl grn & brn ('36) 25.00 3.00
Nos. 418-450 (34) 165.15 15.80

See Nos. 485-500, 523-540, 659, 668. For overprints see Nos. O37-O41, O43-O51, O53-O56, O58-O78, O108, O112, OD35-OD46, OD89-OD101, OD135-OD145, OD176-OD182C, OD229-OD234F, OD270-OD280, OD306-OD317, OD347-OD357.

No. 439A exists with attached label showing medallion. Value $42.50 unused, $22.50 used.

Souvenir Sheet

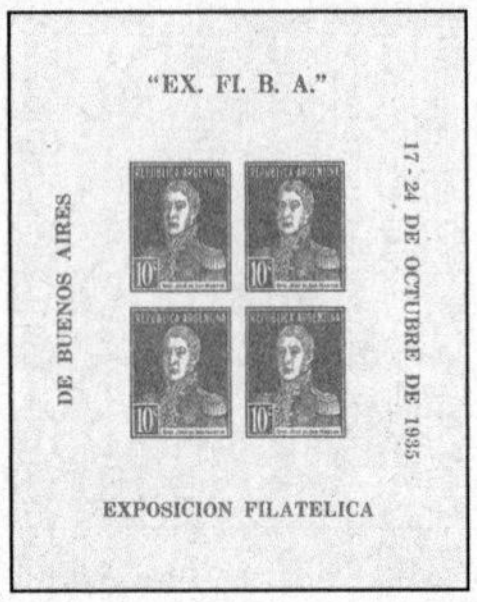

A151

Without Period after Value

1935, Oct. 17 Litho. *Imperf.*

452 A151 Sheet of 4 75.00 35.00
a. 10c dull green 16.50 7.50

Phil. Exhib. at Buenos Aires, Oct. 17-24, 1935. The stamps were on sale during the 8 days of the exhibition only. Sheets measure 83x101mm.

Plaque — A152

1936, Dec. 1 ***Perf. 13x13½***

453 A152 10c red .80 .40

Inter-American Conference for Peace.

Domingo Faustino Sarmiento — A153

1938, Sept. 5

454 A153 3c sage green .50 .50
455 A153 5c red .50 .50
456 A153 15c deep blue 2.25 .70
457 A153 50c orange 4.25 1.00
Nos. 454-457 (4) 7.50 2.70

50th anniv. of the death of Domingo Faustino Sarmiento, pres., educator and author.

"Presidente Sarmiento" — A154

1939, Mar. 16

458 A154 5c greenish blue .80 .35

Final voyage of the training ship "Presidente Sarmiento."

Allegory of the UPU A155

Coat of Arms A157

Post Office, Buenos Aires — A156

Iguacu Falls — A158

Bonete Hill, Nahuel Huapi Park A159

Allegory of Modern Communications A160

Argentina, Land of Promise A161

Lake Frias, Nahuel Huapi Park A162

Perf. 13x13½, 13½x13

1939, Apr. 1 Photo.

459 A155 5c rose carmine 1.00 .25
460 A156 15c grnsh black 1.00 .40
461 A157 20c brt blue 1.00 .25
462 A158 25c dp blue grn 2.00 .40
463 A159 50c brown 3.00 1.00
464 A160 1p brown violet 6.50 2.75
465 A161 2p magenta 27.50 17.50
466 A162 5p purple 62.50 52.50
Nos. 459-466 (8) 104.50 75.05

Universal Postal Union, 11th Congress.

Souvenir Sheets

A163

A164

1939, May 12 Wmk. 90 ***Imperf.***

467 A163 Sheet of 4 15.00 7.50
a. 5c rose carmine (A155) 2.00 1.50
b. 20c bright blue (A157) 2.00 1.50
c. 25c deep blue green (A158) 2.00 1.50
d. 50c brown (A159) 2.00 1.50
468 A164 Sheet of 4 15.00 7.50

Issued in four forms:

a. Unsevered horizontal pair of sheets, type A163 at left, A164 at right 30.00 16.00
b. Unsevered vertical pair of sheets, type A163 at top, A164 at bottom 30.00 15.00
c. Unsevered block of 4 sheets, type A163 at left, A164 at right 65.00 65.00
d. Unsevered block of 4 sheets, type A163 at top, A164 at bottom 65.00 65.00

11th Cong. of the UPU and the Argentina Intl. Phil. Exposition (C.Y.T.R.A.).
No. 468 contains Nos. 467a-467d.

Family and New House — A165

Perf. 13½x13

1939, Oct. 2 Litho. Wmk. 90

469 A165 5c bluish green .50 .35

1st Pan-American Housing Congress.

Bird Carrying Record A166

Head of Liberty and Arms of Argentina A167

Record and Winged Letter — A168

Perf. 13x13½, 13½x13 (#472)

1939, Dec. 11 Photo.

470 A166 1.18p indigo 14.00 10.00
471 A167 1.32p bright blue 14.00 10.00
472 A168 1.50p dark brown 52.50 35.00
Nos. 470-472 (3) 80.50 55.00

These stamps were issued for the recording and mailing of flexible phonograph records.

Map of the Americas — A169

1940, Apr. 14 ***Perf. 13x13½***

473 A169 15c ultramarine 1.00 .35

50th anniv. of the Pan American Union.

Souvenir Sheet

Reproductions of Early Argentine Stamps — A170

Wmk. RA in Sun (90)

1940, May 25 Litho. *Imperf.*

474 A170 Sheet of 5		25.00	10.00
a.	5c dark blue (Corrientes A2)	2.50	1.75
b.	5c red (Argentina A1)	2.50	1.75
c.	5c dark blue (Cordoba #1)	2.50	1.75
d.	5c red (Argentina A3)	2.50	1.75
e.	10c dark blue (Buenos Aires A1)	2.50	1.75

100th anniv. of the first postage stamp.

General Domingo French and Colonel Antonio Beruti — A171

1941, Feb. 20 *Perf. 13½x13*

475 A171 5c dk gray blue & lt blue .60 .35

Issued in honor of General French and Colonel Beruti, patriots.

Marco M. de Avellaneda — A172

1941, Oct. 3 *Perf. 13x13½*

476 A172 5c dull slate blue .60 .35

Avellaneda, (1814-41), army leader and martyr.

Statue of Gen. Julio Roca — A173

1941, Oct. 19 Photo. Wmk. 90

477 A173 5c dark olive green .50 .35

Dedication of a monument to Lt. Gen. Julio Argentino Roca (1843-1914).

Carlos Pellegrini and Bank of the Nation — A174

1941, Oct. 26 *Perf. 13½x13*

478 A174 5c brown carmine .60 .35

Founding of the Bank of the Nation, 50th anniv.

Gen. Juan Lavalle — A175

1941, Dec. 5 *Perf. 13x13½*

479 A175 5c bright blue .60 .35

Gen. Juan Galo de Lavalle (1797-1841).

National Postal Savings Bank — A176

1942, Apr. 5 Litho. *Perf. 13½x13*

480 A176 1c pale olive .60 .35

Jose Manuel Estrada — A177

1942, July 13 *Perf. 13x13½*

481 A177 5c brown violet .60 .35

Jose Estrada (1842-1894), writer and diplomat.

Exists imperf. Value, pair $45.

No. 481 exists with label, showing medallion, attached. Value, pair $11.

Types of 1935-51

Perf. 13, 13x13½, 13½x13

1942-50 Litho. Wmk. 288

485	A128	½c	brown violet	10.00	2.00
486	A129	1c	buff ('50)	.40	.30
487	A130	2c	dk brown ('50)	.40	.25
488	A132	3c	lt gray	16.00	1.25
489	A134	3c	lt gray ('49)	.30	.25
490	A137	10c	red brn ('49)	2.50	.25
491	A138	12c	red	.50	.25
492	A140	15c	lt gray blue (II)	1.00	.25
493	A139	20c	dk sl bl & pale bl	4.50	.30
494	A141	25c	dull rose ('49)	1.00	.25
495	A142	30c	org brn ('49)	1.50	.25
496	A143	40c	violet ('49)	10.00	1.00
497	A144	50c	red & org ('49)	10.00	.50
498	A146	1p	brn blk & lt bl	10.00	.40
499	A147	2p	brn lake & bl ('49)	22.50	3.00
500	A148	5p	ind & ol grn ('49)	65.00	4.00
			Nos. 485-500 (16)	155.60	14.50

No. 493 measures 22x33mm.

Post Office, Buenos Aires — A178

Inscribed: "Correos y Telegrafos."

1942, Oct. 5 Litho. *Perf. 13*

503 A178 35c lt ultra 10.00 .35

See Nos. 541-543.

Proposed Columbus Lighthouse — A179

1942, Oct. 12 Wmk. 288

504 A179 15c dull blue 10.00 .50

Wmk. 90

505 A179 15c dull blue 70.00 8.00

450th anniv. of the discovery of America by Columbus.

Jose C. Paz — A180

1942, Dec. 15 Wmk. 288

506 A180 5c dark gray .50 .35

Cent. of the birth of Jose C. Paz, stateman and founder of the newspaper La Prensa.

Books and Argentine Flag — A181

1943, Apr. 1 Litho. *Perf. 13*

507 A181 5c dull blue .50 .35

1st Book Fair of Argentina.

Arms of Argentina Inscribed "Honesty, Justice, Duty" — A182

1943-50 Wmk. 288 *Perf. 13*

Size: 20x26mm

508 A182 5c red ('50) 6.00 .35

Wmk. 90

509	A182	5c	red	.60	.35
a.			5c dull red, unsurfaced paper	8.00	.35
510	A182	15c	green	.60	.35

Perf. 13x13½

Size: 22x33mm

511 A182 20c dark blue .95 .35

Nos. 508-511 (4) 8.15 1.40

Change of political organization, 6/4/43.

Independence House, Tucuman — A183

1943-51 Wmk. 90 *Perf. 13*

512 A183 5c blue green 1.00 .35

Wmk. 288

513 A183 5c blue green ('51) .50 .35

Restoration of Independence House.

Liberty Head and Savings Bank — A184

1943, Oct. 25 Wmk. 90

514 A184 5c violet brown .50 .35

Wmk. 288

515 A184 5c violet brown 60.00 8.00

1st conference of National Postal Savings.

Port of Buenos Aires in 1800 — A185

1943, Dec. 11 Wmk. 90

516 A185 5c gray black .50 .35

Day of Exports.

Warship, Merchant Ship and Sailboat — A186

1944, Jan. 31 *Perf. 13*

517 A186 5c blue .60 .35

Issued to commemorate Sea Week.

Arms of Argentine Republic — A187

1944, June 4

518 A187 5c dull blue .60 .35

1st anniv. of the change of political organization in Argentina.

St. Gabriel A188

Cross at Palermo A189

1944, Oct. 11

519 A188 3c yellow green .70 .35

520 A189 5c deep rose .80 .35

Fourth national Eucharistic Congress.

Allegory of Savings — A190

1944, Oct. 24

521 A190 5c gray .50 .35

20th anniv. of the National Savings Bank.

Reservists — A191

1944, Dec. 1

522 A191 5c blue .50 .35

Day of the Reservists.

Types of 1935-51

Perf. 13x13½, 13½x13

1945-47 Litho. Unwmk.

523	A128	½c	brown vio ('46)	.25	.25
524	A129	1c	yellow brown	.25	.25
525	A130	2c	sepia	.25	.25
526	A132	3c	lt gray (San Martin)	2.50	.25
527	A134	3c	lt gray (Moreno) ('46)	.25	.25
528	A135	6c	olive grn ('47)	.50	.35
529	A137	10c	brown ('46)	2.00	.30
530	A140	15c	lt gray bl (II)	1.25	.25
531	A139	20c	dk sl bl & pale bl	3.00	.25
532	A141	25c	dull rose	2.50	.25
533	A142	30c	orange brown	1.00	.25
534	A143	40c	violet	2.00	.35
535	A144	50c	red & orange	3.00	.25
536	A146	1p	brn blk & lt bl	4.50	.25
537	A147	2p	brown lake & bl	35.00	1.00
538	A148	5p	ind & ol grn ('46)	60.00	4.00
539	A149	10p	dp cl & int blk	17.50	2.50
540	A150	20p	bl grn & brn ('46)	15.00	2.50
			Nos. 523-540 (18)	150.75	13.75

No. 531 measures 22x33mm.

Post Office Type Inscribed

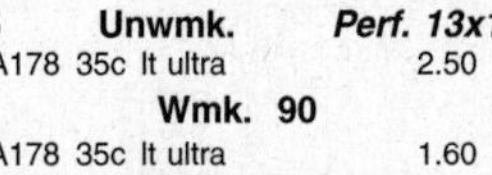

1945 Unwmk. *Perf. 13x13½*

541 A178 35c lt ultra 2.50 .35

Wmk. 90

542 A178 35c lt ultra 1.60 .35

Wmk. 288

543 A178 35c lt ultra .50 .35

Nos. 541-543 (3) 4.60 1.05

Nos. 541 and 543 exist imperf. Value, each, pair $10.

Bernardino Rivadavia
A192 A193

Mausoleum of Rivadavia — A194

Perf. 13½x13

1945, Sept. 1 Litho. Unwmk.

544 A192 3c blue green .40 .35
545 A193 5c rose .40 .35
546 A194 20c blue .50 .35
Nos. 544-546 (3) 1.30 1.05

Cent. of the death of Bernardino Rivadavia, Argentina's first president.

No. 546 exists imperf. Value, pair $20.

No. 546 exists with mute label attached. Value, pair, $4.50.

San Martin — A195

1945-46 Wmk. 90 Typo. or Litho.

547 A195 5c carmine .35 .35
a. Litho. ('46) .35 .35

Wmk. 288

548 A195 5c carmine, litho. 125.00 30.00

Unwmk.

549 A195 5c carmine ('46) 1.50 .35
a. Litho. ('46) .35 .35

Nos. 547 and 547a exist imperf. Values, pairs: No. 547, $17.50; No. 547a, $10.

For overprints see Nos. O42, O57.

Monument to Army of the Andes, Mendoza — A196

1946, Jan. 14 Litho. *Perf. 13½x13*

550 A196 5c violet brown .40 .35

Issued to honor the Unknown Soldier of the War for Independence.

Franklin D. Roosevelt — A197

1946, Apr. 12

551 A197 5c dark blue .35 .35

A198

Liberty Administering Presidential Oath.

1946, June 4 *Perf. 13x13½*

552 A198 5c blue .35 .35

Inauguration of Pres. Juan D. Perón, 6/4/46.

Argentina Receiving Popular Acclaim — A199

1946, Oct. 17 *Perf. 13½x13*

553 A199 5c rose violet .80 .30
554 A199 10c blue green 1.25 .40
555 A199 15c dark blue 1.75 .60
556 A199 50c red brown 2.25 .50
557 A199 1p carmine rose 3.00 1.20
Nos. 553-557 (5) 9.05 3.00

First anniversary of the political organization change of Oct. 17, 1945.

Coin Bank and World Map — A200

1946, Oct. 31 Unwmk.

558 A200 30c dk rose car & pink .60 .35

Universal Day of Savings, October 31, 1946.

Argentine Industry — A201

1946, Dec. 6 *Perf. 13x13½*

559 A201 5c violet brown .50 .35

Day of Argentine Industry, Dec. 6.

International Bridge Connecting Argentina and Brazil — A202

1947, May 21 Litho. *Perf. 13½x13*

560 A202 5c green .40 .35

Opening of the Argentina-Brazil International Bridge, May 21, 1947.

Map of Argentine Antarctic Claims — A203

1947-49 Unwmk. *Perf. 13x13½*

561 A203 5c violet & lilac 1.00 .35
562 A203 20c dk car rose & rose 2.00 .35

Wmk. 90

563 A203 20c dk car rose & rose 4.00 .35

Wmk. 288

564 A203 20c dk car rose & rose ('49) 7.00 .50
Nos. 561-564 (4) 14.00 1.55

1st Argentine Antarctic mail, 43rd anniv.

Nos. 561 and 563 exist imperf. Values, pairs: No. 561, $13.50; No. 563, $27.50.

Justice — A204

1947, June 4 Unwmk.

565 A204 5c brn vio & pale yel .35 .35

1st anniversary of the Peron government.

Icarus Falling — A205

1947, Sept. 25 *Perf. 13½x13*

566 A205 15c red violet .40 .35

Aviation Week.

Training Ship Presidente Sarmiento — A206

1947, Oct. 5 *Perf. 13x13½*

567 A206 5c blue .50 .35

50th anniv. of the launching of the Argentine training frigate "Presidente Sarmiento."

Cervantes and Characters from Don Quixote — A207

Perf. 13½x13

1947, Oct. 12 Photo. Wmk. 90

568 A207 5c olive green .40 .35

400th anniv. of the birth of Miguel de Cervantes Saavedra, playwright and poet.

Exists imperf. Value, pair $10.

Gen. Jose de San Martin — A208

Perf. 13½x13

1947-49 Unwmk. Litho.

569 A208 5c dull green .40 .35

Wmk. 288

570 A208 5c dull green ('49) .40 .35

Transfer of the remains of Gen. Jose de San Martin's parents.

Nos. 569 and 570 exist imperf. Value for pair, each $10.

School Children — A209

1947-49 Unwmk. *Perf. 13x13½*

571 A209 5c green .30 .35

Wmk. 90

574 A209 20c brown .50 .35

Wmk. 288

575 A209 5c green ('49) .50 .35
Nos. 571-575 (3) 1.30 1.05

Argentine School Crusade for World Peace.

Nos. 571 and 574 exist imperf. Value for pair, each $10.

Statue of Araucanian Indian — A210

1948, May 21 Wmk. 90

576 A210 25c yellow brown .35 .35

American Indian Day, Apr. 19.

No. 576 exists imperf. Value, pair $10.

Cap of Liberty — A211

1948, July 16

577 A211 5c ultra .35 .35

Revolution of June 4, 1943, 5th anniv.

Manual Stop Signal — A212

1948, July 22

578 A212 5c chocolate & yellow .35 .35

Traffic Safety Day, June 10.

No. 578 exists imperf. Value, pair $10.

Post Horn and Oak Leaves — A213

1948, July 22 Unwmk.

579 A213 5c lilac rose .45 .35

200th anniversary of the establishment of regular postal service on the Plata River.

No. 579 exists imperf. Value, pair $10.

Argentine Farmers — A214

Perf. 13x13½

1948, Sept. 20 Wmk. 288

580 A214 10c red brown .35 .35

Agriculture Day, Sept. 8, 1948.

Liberty and Symbols of Progress — A215

Perf. 13x13½

1948, Nov. 23 Photo. Wmk. 287

581 A215 25c red brown .50 .35

3rd anniversary of President Juan D. Peron's return to power, October 17, 1945.

No. 581 exists imperf. Value, pair $10.

Souvenir Sheets

A216

15c, Mail coach. 45c, Buenos Aires in 18th cent. 55c, 1st train, 1857. 85c, Sailing ship, 1767.

1948, Dec. 21 Unwmk. *Imperf.*

582 A216 Sheet of 4 12.00 5.00
a. 15c dark green 1.00 .75
b. 45c orange brown 1.00 .75
c. 55c lilac brown 1.00 .75
d. 85c ultramarine 1.00 .75

A217

Designs: 85c, Domingo de Basavilibaso (1709-75). 1.05p, Postrider. 1.20p, Sailing ship, 1798. 1.90p, Courier in the Andes, 1772.

583	A217	Sheet of 4	32.50	20.00
a.		85c brown	4.75	3.25
b.		1.05p dark green	4.75	3.25
c.		1.20p dark blue	4.75	3.25
d.		1.90p red brown	4.75	3.25

200th anniversary of the establishment of regular postal service on the Plata River.

Winged Wheel — A218

Perf. 13½x13

1949, Mar. 1 **Wmk. 288**

584	A218 10c blue		.50	.35

Railroad nationalization, 1st anniv.

Liberty — A219

1949, June 20 **Engr.** **Wmk. 90**

585	A219 1p red & red violet	1.25	.35

Ratification of the Constitution of 1949.

Allegory of the UPU — A220

1949, Nov. 19

586	A220 25c dk grn & yel grn	.40	.35

75th anniv. of the UPU.

Catalogue values for unused stamps in this section, from this point to the end of the section, are for Never Hinged items.

Gen. Jose de San Martin — A221

San Martin at Boulogne sur Mer — A222

Mausoleum of San Martin — A223

20c, 50c, 75c, Different portraits of San Martin. 1p, House where San Martin died.

Engr., Photo. (25c, 1p, 2p)

1950, Aug. 17 **Wmk. 90** ***Perf. 13½***

587	A221	10c indigo & dk pur	.50	.35
588	A221	20c red brn & dk brn	.50	.35
589	A222	25c brown	.50	.35
590	A221	50c dk green & ind	.80	.35
591	A221	75c choc & dk grn	1.20	.35
a.		Souv. sheet of 4, #587, 588, 590, 591, imperf.	6.00	3.00
592	A222	1p dark green	2.75	.40
593	A223	2p dp red lilac	3.25	.50
		Nos. 587-593 (7)	9.50	2.65

Death cent. of General Jose de San Martin.

Map Showing Antarctic Claims — A224

1951, May 21 **Litho.** ***Perf. 13x13½***

594	A224 1p choc & lt blue	1.40	.35

For overprint see No. O52.
No. 594 exists imperf. Value, pair $25.

Pegasus and Train A225

Communications Symbols A226

Design: 25c, Ship and dolphin.

1951, Oct. 17 **Photo.** ***Perf. 13½***

595	A225	5c dark brown	1.60	.35
596	A225	25c Prus green	3.25	.35
597	A226	40c rose brown	3.75	.35
		Nos. 595-597 (3)	8.60	1.05

Close of Argentine Five Year Plan.

Woman Voter and "Argentina" — A227

1951, Dec. 14 ***Perf. 13½x13***

598	A227 10c brown violet	.85	.35

Granting of women's suffrage.

Eva Peron
A228 A229

Litho. or Engraved (#605)

1952, Aug. 26 **Wmk. 90** ***Perf. 13***

599	A228	1c orange brown	.40	.25
600	A228	5c gray	.40	.25
601	A228	10c rose lilac	.40	.25
602	A228	20c rose pink	.40	.25
603	A228	25c dull green	.45	.25
604	A228	40c dull violet	.55	.25
605	A228	45c deep blue	.55	.25
606	A228	50c dull brown	.80	.25

Photo.

607	A229	1p dark brown	1.20	.30
608	A229	1.50p deep green	4.50	.30
609	A229	2p brt carmine	1.20	.30
610	A229	3p indigo	1.90	.30
		Nos. 599-610 (12)	12.75	3.20

For overprints see Nos. O79-O85.
Nos. 599, 601-604 and 606 exist imperf. Value for set of 6 pairs, $235.

Inscribed: "Eva Peron"

1952-53 ***Perf. 13x13½***

611	A229	1p dark brown	1.20	.35
612	A229	1.50p deep green	2.40	.35
613	A229	2p brt car ('53)	2.40	.40
614	A229	3p indigo	4.50	.90

Engr.

Perf. 13½x13

Size: 30x40mm

615	A229	5p red brown	6.00	2.00
616	A228	10p red	9.50	4.00
617	A229	20p green	21.00	8.50
618	A228	50p ultra	47.50	20.00
		Nos. 611-618 (8)	94.50	36.50

For overprints see Nos. O86-O93.

Indian Funeral Urn — A230

1953, Aug. 28 **Photo.** ***Perf. 13x13½***

619	A230 50c blue green	.85	.35

Founding of Santiago del Estero, 400th anniv.

Rescue Ship "Uruguay" A231

1953, Oct. 8 ***Perf. 13½***

620	A231 50c ultra	1.50	.50

50th anniv. of the rescue of the Antarctic expedition of Otto C. Nordenskjold.

Planting Argentine Flag in the Antarctic — A232

1954, Jan. 20 **Engr.** ***Perf. 13½x13***

621	A232 1.45p blue	1.60	.50

50th anniv. of Argentina's 1st antarctic p.o. and the establishing of the La Hoy radio p.o. in the South Orkneys.

Wired Communications A233

Television A234

Perf. 13x13½, 13½x13

1954, Apr. **Photo.** **Wmk. 90**

622	A233	1.50p shown	.55	.35
623	A233	3p Radio	2.25	.35
624	A234	5p shown	3.25	.40
		Nos. 622-624 (3)	6.05	1.10

Intl. Plenipotentiary Conf. of Telecommunications, Buenos Aires, 1952.

Pediment, Buenos Aires Stock Exchange — A235

1954, July 13 ***Perf. 13½x13***

625	A235 1p dark green	1.00	.35

Cent. of the establishment of the Buenos Aires Stock Exchange.

Eva Peron — A236

1954 **Wmk. 90**

626	A236 3p dp car rose	3.50	.50

Wmk. 288

627	A236 3p dp car rose	250.00	50.00

2nd anniv. of the death of Eva Peron.

Jose de San Martin A237

Wheat A238

Industry — A238a

Eva Peron Foundation Building — A239

Cliffs of Humahuaca A240

Gen. Jose de San Martin — A241

Designs: 50c, Buenos Aires harbor. 1p, Cattle ranch (Ganaderia). 3p, Nihuil Dam. 5p, Iguacu Falls, vert. 20p, Mt. Fitz Roy, vert.

Engraved (#632, 638-642), Photogravure (#634-637)

Perf. 13½, 13x13½ (80c), 13½x13 (#639, 641-642)

1954-59 **Wmk. 90**

628	A237	20c brt red, typo.	.35	.25
629	A237	20c red, litho. ('55)	1.10	.25
630	A237	40c red, litho. ('56)	.45	.25
631	A237	40c brt red, typo. ('55)	.45	.25
632	A239	50c blue ('56)	.45	.25
633	A239	50c bl, litho. ('59)	.35	.25
634	A238	80c brown	.45	.25
635	A239	1p brown ('58)	.45	.25
636	A238a	1.50p ultra ('58)	.45	.25
637	A239	2p dk rose lake	.55	.25
638	A239	3p violet brn ('56)	.55	.25
639	A240	5p gray grn ('55)	9.00	.25
a.		Perf. 13½	10.00	.35
640	A240	10p yel grn ('55)	9.00	.25
641	A240	20p dull vio ('55)	12.00	.50
a.		Perf. 13½	16.00	.50

642 A241 50p ultra & ind ('55) 14.00 1.50
a. Perf. 13½ 15.00 1.00
Nos. 628-642 (15) 49.60 5.25

See Nos. 699-700. For similar designs inscribed "Republica Argentina" see Nos. 823-827, 890, 935, 937, 940, 990, 995, 1039, 1044, 1048.
For overprints see Nos. O94-O106, O142, O153-O157.

Allegory — A242

1954, Aug. 26 Typo. *Perf. 13½*
643 A242 1.50p slate black 1.00 .35

Cent. of the establishment of the Buenos Aires Grain Exchange.

Clasped Hands and Congress Medal — A243

1955, Mar. 21 Photo. *Perf. 13½x13*
644 A243 3p red brown 1.75 .35

Issued to publicize the National Productivity and Social Welfare Congress.

Allegory of Aviation — A244

1955, June 18 Wmk. 90 *Perf. 13½*
645 A244 1.50p olive gray 1.25 .35

Commercial aviation in Argentina, 25th anniv.

Argentina Breaking Chains — A245

1955, Oct. 16 Litho.
647 A245 1.50p olive green .95 .35

Liberation Revolution of Sept. 16, 1955.

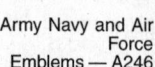

Army Navy and Air Force Emblems — A246

Perf. 13½x13
1955, Dec. 31 Photo. Wmk. 90
648 A246 3p blue 1.00 .35

"Brotherhood of the Armed Forces."

Justo Jose de Urquiza — A247

1956, Feb. 3 *Perf. 13½*
649 A247 1.50p dk grn, lt grn .95 .35

Battle of Caseros, 104th anniversary.

No. 649 exists imperf. Value, pair $30.

Coin and Die — A248

1956, July 28 Engr. *Perf. 13½x13*
650 A248 2p multicolored .65 .35

75th anniversary of the Argentine Mint.

1856 Stamp of Corrientes A249

Juan G. Pujol A250

Design: 2.40p, Stamp of 1860-78.

1956, Aug. 21
651 A249 40c dk grn & blue .35 .35
652 A249 2.40p brn & lil rose .60 .35

Photo.
653 A250 4.40p brt blue 1.40 .35
a. Souv. sheet, #651-653, imperf. 9.75 6.00
Nos. 651-653 (3) 2.35 1.05

Centenary of Argentine postage stamps.
No. 653a for the Argentine stamp cent. and Philatelic Exhib. for the Cent. of Corrientes Stamps, Oct. 12-21. The 4.40p is photo., the other two stamps and border litho. Colors of 40c and 2.40p differ slightly from engraved stamps.

Felling Trees, La Pampa A251

Maté Herb and Gourd, Misiones A252

1p, Cotton plant and harvest, Chaco.

1956, Sept. 1 *Perf. 13½*
654 A251 50c ultra 1.00 .35
655 A251 1p magenta 1.00 .35
656 A252 1.50p green 1.00 .35
Nos. 654-656 (3) 3.00 1.05

Elevation of the territories of La Pampa, Chaco and Misiones to provinces.

"Liberty" — A253

Perf. 13½
1956, Sept. 15 Wmk. 90 Photo.
657 A253 2.40p lilac rose 1.00 .35

1st anniv. of the Revolution of Liberation.

Florentino Ameghino — A254

1956, Nov. 30
658 A254 2.40p brown .85 .35

Issued to honor Florentino Ameghino (1854-1911), anthropologist.

For overprint see No. O110.

Adm. Brown Type of 1935-51

Two types:
I. Background lines touch the left cheek, bust and lower frame in direct contact.
II. Background lines don't touch the left cheek, white line separates bust from frame line.

Size: 19½-20½x26-27mm
1956 Litho. *Perf. 13*
659 A133 20c dull purple (I) .60 .35
a. Type II .60 .35
b. Size 19½x25¼mm (I) .75 .35

For overprint see No. O108.

Benjamin Franklin — A255

1956, Dec. 22 Photo. *Perf. 13½*
660 A255 40c intense blue .90 .35

250th anniv. of the birth of Benjamin Franklin.

Frigate "Hercules" A256

Guillermo Brown A257

1957, Mar. 2
661 A256 40c brt blue .50 .35
662 A257 2.40p gray black .80 .35
Nos. 661-662,C63-C65 (5) 3.00 1.75

Admiral Guillermo (William) Brown (1777-1857), founder of the Argentine navy.

Roque Saenz Pena (1851-1914) — A258

1957, Apr. 1
663 A258 4.40p grnsh gray .90 .35

Roque Saenz Pena, pres. 1910-14.
For overprint see No. O111.

Church of Santo Domingo, 1807 — A259

1957, July 6 Wmk. 90
664 A259 40c brt blue green .60 .35

150th anniv. of the defense of Buenos Aires.

"La Portena" — A260

1957, Aug. 31 Wmk. 90 *Perf. 13½*
665 A260 40c pale brown 1.00 .35

Centenary of Argentine railroads.

Esteban Echeverria — A261

1957, Sept. 2 *Perf. 13x13½*
666 A261 2p claret .60 .35

Esteban Echeverria (1805-1851), poet.
For overprint see No. O109.

"Liberty" — A262

1957, Sept. 28 *Perf. 13½*
667 A262 40c carmine rose .65 .35

Constitutional reform convention.

Portrait Type of 1935-51

1957, Oct. 28 Litho. *Perf. 13½*
Size: 16½x22mm
668 A128 5c Jose Hernandez .60 .35

For overprint see No. O112.

Oil Derrick and Hands Holding Oil — A263

Perf. 13½
1957, Dec. 21 Wmk. 90 Photo.
669 A263 40c bright blue .90 .35

50th anniv. of the national oil industry.
No. 669 exists imperf. Value, pair $30.

Museum, La Plata — A264

1958, Jan. 11
670 A264 40c dark gray .60 .35

City of La Plata, 75th anniversary.

A265

A266

40c, Locomotive & arms of Argentina & Bolivia. 1p, Map of Argentine-Bolivian boundary & plane.

1958, Apr. 19 Wmk. 90 *Perf. 13½*
671 A265 40c slate & dp car .80 .35
672 A266 1p dark brown .80 .35

Argentine-Bolivian friendship. No. 671 for the opening of the Jacuiba-Santa Cruz railroad; No. 672, the exchange of presidential visits.

Symbols of the Republic — A267

1958, Apr. 30 Photo. & Engr.

673 A267 40c multicolored .55 .50
674 A267 1p multicolored .70 .50
675 A267 2p multicolored 1.25 .50
Nos. 673-675 (3) 2.50 1.50

Transmission of Presidential power.

Flag Monument — A268

1958, June 21 Litho. Wmk. 90

676 A268 40c blue & violet bl .60 .35

1st anniv. of the Flag Monument of Rosario.
Exists imperf. Value, pair $40.

Map of Antarctica — A269

1958, July 12 *Perf. 13½*

677 A269 40c car rose & blk .95 .35

International Geophysical Year, 1957-58.
Exists imperf. Value, pair $80.

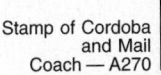

Stamp of Cordoba and Mail Coach — A270

1958, Oct. 18

678 A270 40c pale blue & slate .65 .35
Nos. 678,C72-C73 (3) 1.75 1.05

Centenary of Cordoba postage stamps.

"Slave" by Michelangelo and UN Emblem A271

Engraved and Lithographed

1959, Mar. 14 Wmk. 90 *Perf. 13½*

679 A271 40c violet brn & gray .60 .35

10th anniv. (in 1958) of the signing of the Universal Declaration of Human Rights. No UN Emblem (error) Value, $200.
Exists imperf. Value, pair $50.

Orchids and Globe — A272

1959, May 23 Photo. *Perf. 13½*

680 A272 1p dull claret .75 .35

1st International Horticulture Exposition.
Exists imperf. Value, pair $50.

Pope Pius XII — A273

1959, June 20 Engr. *Perf. 13½*

681 A273 1p yellow & black .65 .35

Pope Pius XII, 1876-1958.
Exists imperf. Value, pair $50.

William Harvey — A274

1p, Claude Bernard. 1.50p, Ivan P. Pavlov.

1959, Aug. 8 Litho. Wmk. 90

682 A274 50c green .35 .35
683 A274 1p dark red .35 .35
684 A274 1.50p brown .45 .35
Nos. 682-684 (3) 1.15 1.05

21st Intl. Cong. of Physiological Sciences, Buenos Aires.

Type of 1958 and

Domestic Horse A275

Jose de San Martin A276

Tierra del Fuego A277

Inca Bridge, Mendoza A278

Ski Jumper — A279

Mar del Plata — A280

Designs: 10c, Cayman. 20c, Llama. 50c, Puma. No. 690, Sunflower. 3p, Zapata Slope, Catamarca. 12p, 23p, 25p, Red Quebracho tree. 20p, Nahuel Huapi Lake. 22p, "Industry" (cogwheel and factory).
Two overall paper sizes for 1p, 5p:
I — 27x37½mm or 37½x27mm.
II — 27x39mm or 39x27mm.

Perf. 13x13½

1959-70 Litho. Wmk. 90

685 A275 10c slate green .40 .35
686 A275 20c dl red brn ('61) .40 .35
687 A275 50c bister ('60) .40 .35
688 A275 50c bis, typo. ('60) .40 .35
689 A275 1p rose red .40 .35

Perf. 13½

690 A278 1p brn, photo., I ('61) .35 .35
a. Paper II ('69) 1.10 .35
690B A278 1p brown, I 1.10 .70
691 A276 2p rose red ('61) .45 .35
692 A276 2p red, typo. (19½ x 26mm) ('61) .55 .35
a. Redrawn (19½ x 25mm) 4.50 .35
693 A277 3p dk bl, photo. ('60) .35 .35
694 A276 4p red, typo ('62) 1.10 .35
694A A276 4p red ('62) .65 .35
695 A277 5p gray brn, photo., I .35 .35
e. 5p dark brown, paper II ('70) 10.00 5.50
695A A276 8p ver ('65) 2.25 .35
695B A276 8p red, typo. ('65) .35 .35
695C A276 10p ver ('66) .65 .35
695D A276 10p red, typo. ('66) .65 .35

Photo.

696 A278 10p lt red brn ('60) .55 .35
697 A278 12p dk brn vio ('62) 1.10 .35
697A A278 12p dk brn, litho. ('64) 13.00 .40
698 A278 20p Prus grn ('60) 3.25 .35
698A A276 20p red, typo. ('67) .35 .35
699 A238a 22p ultra ('62) 2.25 .35
700 A238a 22p ultra, litho. ('62) 27.50 .35
701 A278 23p green ('65) 5.50 .35
702 A278 25p dp vio ('66) 2.25 .35
703 A278 25p pur, litho. ('66) 6.50 .35
704 A279 100p blue ('61) 9.00 .35
705 A280 300p dp vio ('62) 5.50 .35
Nos. 685-705 (29) 87.55 10.55

Imperf and imperf between examples of some numbers exist.
See Nos. 882-887, 889, 892, 923-925, 928-930, 938, 987-989, 991.
For overprints and surcharges see Nos. 1076, C82-C83, O113-O118, O122-O124, O126-O141, O143-O145, O163.
The 300p remained on sale as a 3p stamp after the 1970 currency exchange.

Symbolic Sailboat — A281

1959, Oct. 3 Litho. *Perf. 13½*

706 A281 1p blk, red & bl .60 .35

Red Cross sanitary education campaign.

Child Playing with Doll — A282

1959, Oct. 17

707 A282 1p red & blk .60 .35

Issued for Mother's Day, 1959.

Buenos Aires 1p Stamp of 1859 — A283

1959, Nov. 21 Wmk. 90 *Perf. 13½*

708 A283 1p gray & dk bl .60 .35

Issued for the Day of Philately.

Bartolomé Mitre and Justo José de Urquiza — A284

1959, Dec. 12 Photo. *Perf. 13½*

709 A284 1p purple .60 .35

Treaty of San Jose de Flores, centenary.
Exists imperf. Value, pair $40.

WRY Emblem — A285

1960, Apr. 7 Litho. Wmk. 90

710 A285 1p bister & car .60 .35
711 A285 4.20p apple grn & dp claret .60 .35

World Refugee Year, July 1, 1959-June 30, 1960. See No. B25.

Abraham Lincoln — A286

1960, Apr. 14 Photo. *Perf. 13½*

712 A286 5p ultra .70 .35

Sesquicentennial (in 1959) of the birth of Abraham Lincoln.
Exists imperf. Value, pair $70.

Cornelio Saavedra and Cabildo, Buenos Aires — A287

"Cabildo" and: 2p, Juan José Paso. 4.20p, Manuel Alberti and Miguel Azcuénaga. 10.70p, Juan Larrea and Domingo Matheu.

Perf. 13½

1960, May 28 Wmk. 90 Photo.

713 A287 1p rose lilac .50 .35
714 A287 2p bluish grn .50 .35
715 A287 4.20p gray & grn .60 .35
716 A287 10.70p gray & ultra .90 .35
Nos. 713-716,C75-C76 (6) 3.70 2.10

150th anniversary of the May Revolution.
Souvenir sheets are Nos. C75a and C76a.

Luis Maria Drago — A288

1960, July 8

717 A288 4.20p brown .60 .35

Centenary of the birth of Dr. Luis Maria Drago, statesman and jurist.
Exists imperf. Value, pair $40.

Juan Bautista Alberdi — A289

1960, Sept. 10 Wmk. 90 *Perf. 13½*

718 A289 1p green .60 .35

150th anniversary of the birth of Juan Bautista Alberdi, statesman and philosopher.
Exists imperf. Value, pair $40.

Map of Argentina and Antarctic Sector — A290

1960, Sept. 24 Litho. *Perf. 13½*

719 A290 5p violet 1.00 .35

National census of 1960.
Exists imperf. Value, pair $70.

Caravel and Emblem — A291

1960, Oct. 1 Photo.

720 A291 1p dk olive grn .60 .35
721 A291 5p brown .95 .35
Nos. 720-721,C78-C79 (4) 3.30 1.40

8th Congress of the Postal Union of the Americas and Spain.

Virgin of Luján, Patroness of Argentina — A292

1960, Nov. 12 Wmk. 90 *Perf. 13½*
722 A292 1p dark blue .85 .35

First Inter-American Marian Congress.
Exists imperf. Value, pair $30.

Argentine Boy Scout Emblem — A293

1961, Jan. 17 Litho.
723 A293 1p car rose & blk .60 .35

International Patrol Encampment of the Boy Scouts, Buenos Aires.
Exists imperf. Value, pair $70.

"Shipment of Cereals," by Quinquela Martin — A294

1961, Feb. 11 Photo. *Perf. 13½*
724 A294 1p red brown .60 .35

Export drive: "To export is to advance."
Exists imperf. Value, pair $40.

Naval Battle of San Nicolás — A295

1961, Mar. 2 *Perf. 13½*
725 A295 2p gray .60 .35

Naval battle of San Nicolas, 150th anniv.
Exists imperf. Value, pair $67.50.

Mariano Moreno by Juan de Dios Rivera — A296

1961, Mar. 25 *Perf. 13½*
726 A296 2p blue .60 .35

Mariano Moreno (1778-1811), writer, politician, member of the 1810 Junta.
Exists imperf. Value, pair $40.

Emperor Trajan Statue — A297

1961, Apr. 11
727 A297 2p slate green .60 .35

Visit of Pres. Giovanni Gronchi of Italy to Argentina, April 1961.
Exists imperf. Value, pair $40.

Rabindranath Tagore — A298

1961, May 13 Photo. *Perf. 13½*
728 A298 2p purple, *grysh* 1.20 .35

Centenary of the birth of Rabindranath Tagore, Indian poet.

San Martin Statue, Madrid — A299

1961, May 24 Wmk. 90
729 A299 1p olive gray .60 .35

Unveiling of a statue of General José de San Martin in Madrid.
Exists imperf. Value, pair $40.

Manuel Belgrano — A300

1961, June 17 *Perf. 13½*
730 A300 2p violet blue .85 .35

Erection of a monument by Hector Rocha, to General Manuel Belgrano in Buenos Aires.
Exists imperf. Value, pair $40.

Explorers, Sledge and Dog Team — A301

1961, Aug. 19 Photo. Wmk. 90
731 A301 2p black 1.10 .35

10th anniversary of the General San Martin Base, Argentine Antarctic.
Exists imperf. Value, pair $75.

Spanish Conquistador and Sword — A302

1961, Aug. 19 Litho.
732 A302 2p red & blk 1.00 .35

First city of Jujuy, 400th anniversary.
Exists imperf. Value, pair $40.

Sarmiento Statue by Rodin, Buenos Aires — A303

1961, Sept. 9 Photo.
733 A303 2p violet .60 .35

Domingo Faustino Sarmiento (1811-88), political leader and writer.
Exists imperf. Value, pair $40.

Symbol of World Town Planning — A304

1961, Nov. 25 Litho. *Perf. 13½*
734 A304 2p ultra & yel .60 .35

World Town Planning Day, Nov. 8.

Manuel Belgrano Statue, Buenos Aires — A305

1962, Feb. 24 Photo.
735 A305 2p Prus blue .60 .35

150th anniversary of the Argentine flag.
Exists imperf. Value, pair $40.

Grenadier, Flag and Regimental Emblem — A306

1962, Mar. 31 Wmk. 90 *Perf. 13½*
736 A306 2p carmine rose .85 .35

150th anniversary of the San Martin Grenadier Guards regiment.
Exists imperf. Value, pair $40.

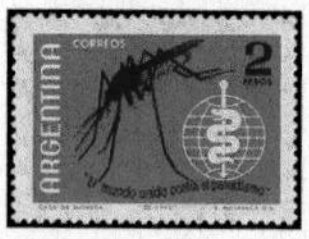

Mosquito and Malaria Eradication Emblem — A307

1962, Apr. 7 Litho.
737 A307 2p vermilion & blk .60 .35

WHO drive to eradicate malaria.

Church of the Virgin of Lujàn — A308

1962, May 12 *Perf. 13½*
738 A308 2p org brn & blk .60 .35

75th anniversary of the pontifical coronation of the Virgin of Lujan.

Bust of Juan Jufrè — A309

1962, June 23 Photo.
739 A309 2p Prus blue .60 .35

Founding of San Juan, 4th cent.
Exists imperf. Value, pair $40.

"Soaring into Space" — A310

1962, Aug. 18 Litho. *Perf. 13½*
740 A310 2p maroon, blk & bl .60 .35

Argentine Air Force, 50th anniversary.
Exists imperf. Value, pair $40.

Juan Vucetich — A311

1962, Oct. 6 Photo. Wmk. 90
741 A311 2p green .60 .35

Juan Vucetich (1864-1925), inventor of the Argentine system of fingerprinting.
Exists imperf. Value, pair $40.

Domingo F. Sarmiento — A312

Design: 4p, Jose Hernandez.

1962-66 Photo. *Perf. 13½*
742 A312 2p deep green .75 .35

Litho.
742A A312 2p lt green ('64) .75 .35

Photo.
742B A312 4p dull red ('65) .75 .35

Litho.
742C A312 4p rose red ('66) 1.75 .35
Nos. 742-742C (4) 4.00 1.40

No. 742A exists imperf. Value, pair $40.
See No. 817-819. For overprints see Nos. O119-O121, O125, O149.

February 20th Monument, Salta — A313

1963, Feb. 23 Photo. Wmk. 90
743 A313 2p dark green .90 .35

150th anniversary of the Battle of Salta, War of Independence.
Exists imperf. Value, pair $40.

Gear Wheels — A314

1963, Mar. 16 Litho. *Perf. 13½*
744 A314 4p gray, blk & brt rose .85 .35

Argentine Industrial Union, 75th anniv.
Exists imperf. Value, pair $40.

National College, Buenos Aires — A315

1963, Mar. 16 Wmk. 90
745 A315 4p dull org & blk .90 .35

National College of Buenos Aires, cent.
Exists imperf. Value, pair $40.

Child Draining Cup — A316

1963, Apr. 6
746 A316 4p multicolored .60 .35

FAO "Freedom from Hunger" campaign.
Exists imperf. Value, pair $40.

Frigate "La Argentina," 1817, by Emilio Biggeri — A317

1963, May 18 **Photo.**
747 A317 4p bluish green 1.10 .35

Issued for Navy Day, May 17.
Exists imperf. Value, pair $40.

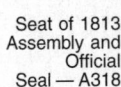

Seat of 1813 Assembly and Official Seal — A318

1963, July 13 **Litho.** ***Perf. 13½***
748 A318 4p lt blue & blk .85 .35

150th anniversary of the 1813 Assembly.
Exists imperf. Value, pair $40.

Battle of San Lorenzo, 1813 — A319

1963, Aug. 24
749 A319 4p grn & blk, *grnsh* .85 .35

Sesquicentennial of the Battle of San Lorenzo.

Queen Nefertari Offering Papyrus Flowers, Abu Simbel — A320

1963, Sept. 14 ***Perf. 13½***
750 A320 4p ocher, blk & bl grn .85 .35

Campaign to save the historic monuments in Nubia.
Exists imperf. Value, pair $40.

Government House, Buenos Aires — A321

1963, Oct. 12 **Wmk. 90** ***Perf. 13½***
751 A321 5p rose & brown .85 .35

Inauguration of President Arturo Illia.
Exists imperf. Value, pair $40.

"Science" — A322

1963, Oct. 16 **Litho.**
752 A322 4p org brn, bl & blk .90 .35

10th Latin-American Neurosurgery Congress.
Exists imperf. Value, pair $40.

Francisco de las Carreras, Supreme Court Justice — A323

1963, Nov. 23 **Photo.** ***Perf. 13½***
753 A323 5p bluish green .60 .35

Centenary of judicial power.
Exists imperf. Value, pair $40.

Blackboards A324

1963, Nov. 23 **Litho.**
754 A324 5p red, blk & bl .60 .35

Issued to publicize "Teachers for America" through the Alliance for Progress program.
Exists imperf. Value, pair $40.

Kemal Atatürk — A325

1963, Dec. 28 **Photo.** ***Perf. 13½***
755 A325 12p dark gray .85 .35

25th anniversary of the death of Kemal Atatürk, president of Turkey.
Exists imperf. Value, pair $40.

"Payador" by Juan Carlos Castagnino — A326

1964, Jan. 25 **Litho.**
756 A326 4p ultra, blk & lt bl .85 .35

Fourth National Folklore Festival.
Exists imperf. Value, pair $40.

Maps of South Georgia, South Orkney and South Sandwich Islands — A327

4p, Map of Argentina & Antarctic claims, vert.

1964, Feb. 22 **Wmk. 90** ***Perf. 13½***
Size: 33x22mm
757 A327 2p lt & dk bl & bister 1.60 .30
Size: 30x40mm
758 A327 4p lt & dk bl & ol grn 2.25 .30
Nos. 757-758,C92 (3) 6.85 1.35

Argentina's claim to Antarctic territories, 60th anniv.
Exist imperf. Value, set of 3 pairs, $150.

Jorge Newbery in Cockpit — A328

1964, Feb. 23 **Photo.**
759 A328 4p deep green .90 .35

Newbery, aviator, 50th death anniv.
Exists imperf. Value, pair $40.

John F. Kennedy — A329

1964, Apr. 14 **Engr.** **Wmk. 90**
760 A329 4p claret & dk bl .85 .35

President John F. Kennedy (1917-63).
Exists imperf. Value, pair $100.

José Brochero by José Cuello — A330

1964, May 9 **Photo.** ***Perf. 13½***
761 A330 4p light sepia .85 .35

50th anniversary of the death of Father Jose Gabriel Brochero.
Exists imperf. Value, pair $50.

Soldier of Patricios Regiment — A331

1964, May 29 **Litho.** **Wmk. 90**
762 A331 4p blk, ultra & red 1.00 .35

Issued for Army Day. Later Army Day stamps, inscribed "Republica Argentina," are of type A340a.
Exists imperf. Value, pair $40.

Pope John XXIII — A332

1964, June 27 **Engr.**
763 A332 4p orange & blk .60 .35

Issued in memory of Pope John XXIII.
Exists imperf. Value, pair $50.

University of Cordoba Arms — A333

1964, Aug. 22 **Litho.** **Wmk. 90**
764 A333 4p blk, ultra & yel .60 .35

350th anniv. of the University of Cordoba.

Pigeons and UN Building, NYC — A334

1964, Oct. 24 ***Perf. 13½***
765 A334 4p dk blue & lt blue .60 .35

Issued for United Nations Day.
Exists imperf. Value, pair $40.

Joaquin V. Gonzalez — A335

1964, Nov. 14 **Photo.**
766 A335 4p dk rose carmine .85 .35

Centenary (in 1963) of the birth of Joaquin V. Gonzalez, writer.
Exists imperf. Value, pair $40.

Julio Argentino Roca — A336

1964, Dec. 12 ***Perf. 13½***
767 A336 4p violet blue .60 .35

General Julio A. Roca, (1843-1914), president of Argentina, (1880-86, 1898-1904).
Exists imperf. Value, pair $40.

Market at Montserrat Square, by Carlos Morel — A337

1964, Dec. 19 **Photo.**
768 A337 4p sepia .60 .35

19th century Argentine painter Carlos Morel.
Exists imperf. Value, pair $40.

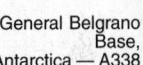

General Belgrano Base, Antarctica — A338

4p, Icebreaker General San Martin.

1965 ***Perf. 13½***
769 A338 2p dull purple .75 .35
770 A338 4p ultra 1.50 .35

Issued to publicize the natl. territory of Tierra del Fuego, Antarctic and South Atlantic Isles.
Issue dates: 4p, Feb. 27; 2p, June 5.
No. 769 exists imperf. Value, pair $50.

Girl with Piggy Bank — A339

1965, Apr. 3 **Litho.**
771 A339 4p red org & blk .60 .35

National Postal Savings Bank, 50th anniv.
Exists imperf. Value, pair $40.

Sun and Globe — A340

1965, May 29
772 A340 4p blk, org & dl bl .75 .30
Nos. 772,C98-C99 (3) 3.25 1.15

International Quiet Sun Year, 1964-65.
Exists imperf. Value, pair $40.

Hussar of Pueyrredon Regiment — A340a

1965, June 5 **Wmk. 90** ***Perf. 13½***
773 A340a 8p dp ultra, blk & red 1.00 .50

Issued for Army Day. See Nos. 796, 838, 857, 893, 944, 958, 974, 1145.
Exists imperf. Value, pair $50.

Ricardo Rojas (1882-1957) — A341

Portraits: No. 775, Ricardo Guiraldes (1886-1927). No. 776, Enrique Larreta (1873-1961). No. 777, Leopoldo Lugones (1874-1938). No. 778, Roberto J. Payro (1867-1928).

1965, June 26 **Photo.**

774 A341 8p brown .60 .35
775 A341 8p brown .60 .35
776 A341 8p brown .60 .35
777 A341 8p brown .60 .35
778 A341 8p brown .60 .35
Nos. 774-778 (5) 3.00 1.75

Issued to honor Argentine writers. Printed se-tenant in sheets of 100 (10x10); 2 horizontal rows of each design with Guiraldes in top rows and Rojas in bottom rows.

Nos. imperf. Value, strip of 5, $250.

Hipolito Yrigoyen — A342

1965, July 3 **Litho.**

779 A342 8p pink & black .60 .35

Hipolito Yrigoyen (1852-1933), president of Argentina 1916-22, 1928-30.

Children Looking Through Window A343

1965, July 24 **Photo.**

780 A343 8p salmon & blk .85 .35

International Seminar on Mental Health. Exists imperf. Value, pair $40.

Child's Funerary Urn and 16th Century Map — A344

1965, Aug. 7 **Litho.**

781 A344 8p lt grn, dk red, brn & ocher .60 .35

City of San Miguel de Tucuman, 400th anniv. Exists imperf. Value, pair $40.

Cardinal Cagliero — A345

1965, Aug. 21 **Photo.**

782 A345 8p violet .55 .35

Juan Cardinal Cagliero (1839-1926), missionary to Argentina and Bishop of Magida. Exists imperf. Value, pair $40.

Dante Alighieri — A346

1965, Sept. 16 **Wmk. 90** ***Perf. 13½***

783 A346 8p light ultra .85 .35

Dante Alighieri (1265-1321), Italian poet. Exists imperf. Value, pair $40.

Clipper "Mimosa" and Map of Patagonia — A347

1965, Sept. 25 **Litho.**

784 A347 8p red & black .60 .35

Centenary of Welsh colonization of Chubut, and the founding of the city of Rawson. Exists imperf. Value, pair $40.

A348

Design: Map of Buenos Aires, cock and compass Emblem of federal police.

1965, Oct. 30 **Photo.** ***Perf. 13½***

785 A348 8p carmine rose .60 .35

Issued for Federal Police Day. Exists imperf. Value, pair $40.

Child's Drawing of Children — A349

1965, Nov. 6 **Litho.** **Wmk. 90**

786 A349 8p lt yel grn & blk .60 .35

Public education law, 81st anniversary. Exists imperf. Value, pair $40.

Church of St. Francis, Catamarca — A350

1965, Dec. 8

787 A350 8p org yel & red brn .60 .35

Brother Mamerto de la Asuncion Esquiu, preacher, teacher and official of 1885 Provincial Constitutional Convention.

Ruben Dario — A351

Litho. and Photo.

1965, Dec. 22 ***Perf. 13½***

788 A351 15p bl vio, *gray* .60 .35

Ruben Dario (pen name of Felix Ruben Garcia Sarmiento, 1867-1916), Nicaraguan poet, newspaper correspondent and diplomat. Exists imperf. Value, pair $40.

"The Orange Seller" — A352

Pueyrredon Paintings: No. 790, "Stop at the Grocery Store." No. 791, "Landscape at San Fernando" (sailboats). No. 792, "Bathing Horses at River Plata."

1966, Jan. 29 **Photo.** ***Perf. 13½***

789 A352 8p bluish green .80 .50
790 A352 8p bluish green .80 .50
791 A352 8p bluish green .80 .50
792 A352 8p bluish green .80 .50
a. Block of 4, #789-792 + 2 labels 4.00 4.00

Prilidiano Pueyrredon (1823-1870), painter.

Sun Yat-sen, Flags of Argentina and China — A353

1966, Mar. 12 **Wmk. 90** ***Perf. 13½***

793 A353 8p dk red brown .95 .35

Dr. Sun Yat-sen (1866-1925), founder of the Republic of China. Exists imperf. Value, pair $100.

Souvenir Sheet

Rivadavia Issue of 1864 — A354

Wmk. 90

1966, Apr. 20 **Litho.** ***Imperf.***

794 A354 Sheet of 3 1.90 1.10
a. 4p gray & red brown .35 .35
b. 5p gray & green .35 .35
c. 8p gray & dark blue .35 .35

2nd Rio de la Plata Stamp Show, Buenos Aires, Mar. 16-24. Exists with flags omitted (error). Value, $150.

People of Various Races and WHO Emblem A355

1966, Apr. 23 ***Perf. 13½***

795 A355 8p brown & black .60 .35

Opening of the WHO Headquarters, Geneva. Exists imperf. Value, pair $40.

Soldier Type of 1965

Army Day: 8p, Cavalryman, Guemes Infernal Regiment.

1966, May 28 **Litho.**

796 A340a 8p multicolored 1.00 .35

Exists imperf. Value, pair $40.

Coat of Arms — A356

Arms: a, National. b, Buenos Aires. c, La Rioja. d, Catamarca. e, Cordoba. f, Corrientes. g, Chaco. h, Chubut. i, Entre Rios. j, Formosa. k, Jujuy. l, La Pampa. m, Federal Capital. n, Mendoza. o, Misiones. p, Neuquen. q, Salta. r, San Juan. s, San Luis. t, Santa Cruz. u, Santa Fe. v, Santiago del Estero. w, Tucuman. x, map of Rio Negro. y, Map of Tierra del Fuego, Antarctica, South Atlantic Islands.

1966, July 30 **Wmk. 90** ***Perf. 13½***

797 Sheet of 25 35.00
a.-y. A356 10p black & multi 1.00 1.00

150th anniv. of Argentina's Declaration of Independence. Exists imperf. Value, sheet $2,000.

Three Crosses, Caritas Emblem — A357

1966, Sept. 10 **Litho.** ***Perf. 13½***

798 A357 10p ol grn, blk & lt bl .60 .35

Caritas, charity organization.

Hilario Ascasubi (1807-75) — A358

Portraits: No. 800, Estanislao del Campo (1834-80). No. 801, Miguel Cane (1851-1905). No. 802, Lucio V. Lopez (1848-94). No. 803, Rafael Obligado (1851-1920). No. 804, Luis Agote (1868-1954), M.D. No. 805, Juan B. Ambrosetti (1865-1917), naturalist and archaeologist. No. 806, Miguel Lillo (1862-1931), botanist and chemist. No. 807, Francisco P. Moreno (1852-1919), naturalist and paleontologist. No. 808, Francisco J. Muñiz (1795-1871), physician.

1966 **Photo.** **Wmk. 90**

799 A358 10p dk blue green .65 .40
800 A358 10p dk blue green .65 .40
801 A358 10p dk blue green .65 .40
802 A358 10p dk blue green .65 .40
803 A358 10p dk blue green .65 .40
804 A358 10p deep violet .65 .40
805 A358 10p deep violet .65 .40
806 A358 10p deep violet .65 .40
807 A358 10p deep violet .65 .40
808 A358 10p deep violet .65 .40
Nos. 799-808 (10) 6.50 4.00

Nos. 799-803 issued Sept. 17 to honor Argentine writers. Printed se-tenant in sheets of 100 (10x10); 2 horizontal rows of each portrait. Nos. 804-808 issued Oct. 22 to honor Argentine scientists; 2 horizontal rows of each portrait. Scientists set has value at upper left, frame line with rounded corners.

Anchor — A359

1966, Oct. 8 **Litho.**

809 A359 4p multicolored .60 .35

Argentine merchant marine. Exists imperf. Value, pair $40.

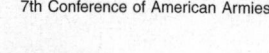

Flags and Map of the Americas — A360

1966, Oct. 29 ***Perf. 13½***

810 A360 10p gray & multi .60 .35

7th Conference of American Armies.

Argentine National Bank — A361

1966, Nov. 5 **Photo.**

811 A361 10p brt blue green .60 .35

75th anniv. of the Argentine National Bank. Exists imperf. Value, pair $40.

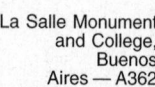

La Salle Monument and College, Buenos Aires — A362

1966, Nov. 26 **Litho.** ***Perf. 13½***

812 A362 10p brown org & blk .60 .35

75th anniv. of the Colegio de la Salle, Buenos Aires, and to honor Saint Jean Baptiste de la Salle (1651-1719), educator. Exists imperf. Value, pair $125.

Map of Argentine Antarctica and Expedition Route — A363

1966, Dec. 10 **Wmk. 90**

813 A363 10p multicolored 1.00 .35

1965 Argentine Antarctic expedition, which planted the Argentine flag on the South Pole. Exists imperf. Value, pair $70.

See No. 851.

Juan Martin de Pueyrredon — A364

1966, Dec. 17 **Photo.** ***Perf. 13½***

814 A364 10p dull red brn .60 .35

Issued to honor Juan Martin de Pueyrredon (1777-1850), Governor of Cordoba and of the United Provinces of the River Plata.

Gen. Juan de Las Heras — A365

1966, Dec. 17 **Engr.**

815 A365 10p black .60 .35

Issued to honor Gen. Juan Gregorio de Las Heras (1780-1866), Peruvian field marshal and aide-de-camp to San Martin.

Inscribed "Republica Argentina" Types of 1955-61 and

Jose Hernandez — A366

Trout Leaping in National Park — A366a

Designs: 50p, Gen. Jose de San Martin. 90p, Guillermo Brown. 500p, Red deer in forest.

Two overall paper sizes for 6p, 50p (No. 827) and 90p:

I — 27x37 ½mm
II — 27x39mm

Perf. 13½

1965-68 **Wmk. 90** **Photo.**

817	A366	6p	rose red, litho, I ('67)	1.75	.30
818	A366	6p	rose red ('67), II	6.50	.35
819	A366	6p	brn, 15x22mm ('68)	.35	.30
823	A238a	43p	dk car rose	8.50	.35
824	A238a	45p	brn ('66)	4.25	.30
825	A238a	45p	brn, litho ('67)	9.50	.35
826	A241	50p	dk bl, 29x40mm	10.00	.45
827	A241	50p	dk bl, 22x31 ½mm, I ('67)	5.25	.35
a.			Paper II	2.25	.30
828	A366	90p	ol bis, I ('67)	3.50	.35
a.			Paper II	14.00	.35

Engr.

829	A495	500p	yellow grn ('66)	3.00	.30
829A	A366a	1,000p	vio bl ('68)	9.50	.35
			Nos. 817-829A (11)	62.10	3.75

The 500p and 1,000p remained on sale as 5p and 10p stamps after the 1970 currency exchange.

See Nos. 888, 891, 939, 992, 1031, 1045-1047. For surcharge and overprints see Nos. 1077, O153-O158, O162.

Pre-Columbian Pottery — A367

1967, Feb. 18 **Litho.** ***Perf. 13½***

830 A367 10p multicolored .60 .35

20th anniv. of UNESCO. Exists imperf. Value, pair $40.

"The Meal" by Fernando Fader — A368

1967, Feb. 25 **Photo.** **Wmk. 90**

831 A368 10p red brown .60 .35

Issued in memory of the Argentine painter Fernando Fader (1882-1935). Exists imperf. Value, pair $40.

Col. Juana Azurduy de Padilla (1781-1862), Soldier — A369

Famous Argentine Women: No. 833, Juana Manuela Gorriti, writer. No. 834, Cecilia Grierson (1858-1934), physician. No. 835, Juana Paula Manso (1819-75), writer and educator. No. 836, Alfonsina Storni (1892-1938), writer and educator.

1967, May 13 **Photo.** ***Perf. 13½***

832	A369	6p	dark brown	.65	.25
833	A369	6p	dark brown	.65	.25
834	A369	6p	dark brown	.65	.25
835	A369	6p	dark brown	.65	.25
836	A369	6p	dark brown	.65	.25
			Nos. 832-836 (5)	3.25	1.25

Printed se-tenant in sheets of 100 (10x10); 2 horizontal rows of each portrait.

Schooner "Invencible," 1811 — A370

1967, May 20 **Litho.**

837 A370 20p multicolored 1.25 .35

Issued for Navy Day. Exists imperf. Value, pair $50.

Soldier Type of 1965

Army Day: 20p, Highlander (Arribeños Corps).

1967, May 27

838 A340a 20p multicolored .90 .35

Exists imperf. Value, pair $50.

Souvenir Sheet

Manuel Belgrano and José Artigas A371

1967, June 22 ***Imperf.***

839	A371	Sheet of 2	1.10	.65
a.		6p gray & brown	.35	.25
b.		22p brown & gray	.35	.25

Third Rio de la Plata Stamp Show, Montevideo, Uruguay, June 18-25.

Peace Dove and Valise — A372

1967, Aug. 5 **Litho.** ***Perf. 13½***

840 A372 20p multicolored .60 .35

Issued for International Tourist Year 1967.

PADELAI Emblem — A373

1967, Aug. 12 **Litho.**

841 A373 20p multicolored .55 .35

75th anniv. of the Children's Welfare Association (Patronato de la Infancia-PADELAI).

Stagecoach and Modern City — A374

1967, Sept. 23 **Wmk. 90** ***Perf. 13½***

842 A374 20p rose, yel & blk .60 .35

Centenary of Villa Maria, Cordoba.

San Martin by Ibarra — A375

"Battle of Chacabuco" by P. Subercaseaux — A376

1967, Sept. 30 **Litho.**

843 A375 20p blk brn & pale yel .70 .35

Engr.

844 A376 40p blue black 1.10 .35

Battle of Chacabuco, 150th anniversary.

Exhibition Rooms — A377

1967, Oct. 11 **Photo.**

845 A377 20p blue gray .60 .35

Government House Museum, 10th anniv.

Pedro L. Zanni, Fokker and 1924 Flight Route — A378

1967, Oct. 21 **Litho.** ***Perf. 13½***

846 A378 20p multicolored .60 .35

Issued for Aviation Week and to commemorate the 1924 flight of the Fokker seaplane "Province of Buenos Aires" from Amsterdam, Netherlands, to Osaka, Japan.

Training Ship General Brown, by Emilio Biggeri — A379

1967, Oct. 28 **Wmk. 90**

847 A379 20p multicolored 1.25 .35

Issued to honor the Military Naval School.

Ovidio Lagos and Front Page — A380

1967, Nov. 11 **Photo.**

848 A380 20p sepia .50 .35

Centenary of La Capital, Rosario newspaper. Imperf pair $40.

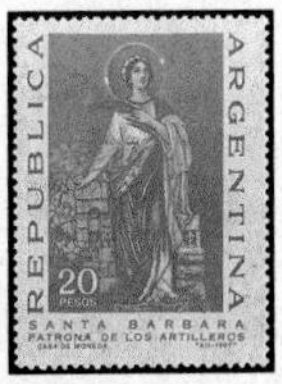

St. Barbara — A381

1967, Dec. 2 ***Perf. 13½***

849 A381 20p rose red .60 .35

St. Barbara, patron saint of artillerymen.

Portrait of his Wife, by Eduardo Sivori — A382

1968, Jan. 27 **Photo.** ***Perf. 13½***

850 A382 20p blue green .60 .30

Eduardo Sivori (1847-1918), painter.

Antarctic Type of 1966 and

Admiral Brown Scientific Station — A383

Planes over Map of Antarctica A384

6p, Map showing radio-postal stations 1966-67.

1968, Feb. 17 Litho. Wmk. 90

851 A363 6p multicolored .65 .30
852 A383 20p multicolored .90 .30
853 A384 40p multicolored 1.50 .50
Nos. 851-853 (3) 3.05 1.10

Issued to publicize Argentine research projects in Argentine Antarctica.

The Annunciation, by Leonardo da Vinci — A385

1968, Mar. 23 Photo. *Perf. 13½*

854 A385 20p lilac rose .60 .35

Issued for the Day of the Army Communications System and its patron saint, Gabriel. Exists imperf. Value, pair $40.

Man in Wheelchair and Factory — A386

1968, Mar. 23 Litho.

855 A386 20p green & black .60 .35

Day of Rehabilitation of the Handicapped.

Children and WHO Emblem — A387

1968, May 11 Wmk. 90 *Perf. 13½*

856 A387 20p dk vio bl & ver .60 .35

20th anniv. of WHO.

Soldier Type of 1965

Army Day: 20p, Uniform of First Artillery Regiment "General Iriarte."

1968, June 8 Litho.

857 A340a 20p multicolored 1.00 .35

Frigate "Libertad," Painting by Emilio Biggeri — A388

1968, June 15 Wmk. 90

858 A388 20p multicolored 1.40 .35

Issued for Navy Day. Exists imperf. Value, pair $40.

Guillermo Rawson and Old Hospital — A389

1968, July 20 Photo. *Perf. 13½*

859 A389 6p olive bister .60 .35

Cent. of Rawson Hospital, Buenos Aires.

Student Directing Traffic for Schoolmates A390

1968, Aug. 10 Litho. *Perf. 13½*

860 A390 20p lt bl, blk, buff & car .80 .35

Traffic safety and education.

O'Higgins Joining San Martin at Battle of Maipu, by P. Subercaseaux — A391

1968, Aug. 15 Engr.

861 A391 40p bluish black .90 .35

Sesquicentennial of the Battle of Maipu.

Osvaldo Magnasco (1864-1920), Lawyer, Professor of Law and Minister of Justice — A392

1968, Sept. 7 Photo. *Perf. 13½*

862 A392 20p brown .65 .35

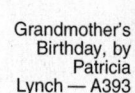

Grandmother's Birthday, by Patricia Lynch — A393

The Sea, by Edgardo Gomez — A394

1968, Sept. 21 Litho.

863 A393 20p multicolored .60 .35
864 A394 20p multicolored .60 .35

The designs were chosen in a competition among kindergarten and elementary school children.

Mar del Plata at Night — A395

1968, Oct. 19 Litho. *Perf. 13½*

865 A395 20p black, ocher & bl 1.40 .25
Nos. 865,C113-C114 (3) 4.00 1.10

4th Plenary Assembly of the Intl. Telegraph and Telephone Consultative Committee, Mar del Plata, Sept. 23-Oct. 25.

Frontier Gendarme A396

Patrol Boat A397

1968, Oct. 26

866 A396 20p multicolored .60 .35
867 A397 20p blue, vio bl & blk .60 .35

No. 866 honors the Gendarmery; No. 867 the Coast Guard.

Aaron de Anchorena and Pampero Balloon — A398

1968, Nov. 2 Photo.

868 A398 20p blue & multi .60 .35

22nd Aeronautics and Space Week.

St. Martin of Tours, by Alfredo Guido — A399

1968, Nov. 9 Litho.

869 A399 20p lilac & dk brn .60 .35

St. Martin of Tours, patron saint of Buenos Aires.

Municipal Bank Emblem — A400

1968, Nov. 16

870 A400 20p multicolored .60 .35

Buenos Aires Municipal Bank, 90th anniv.

Anniversary Emblem — A401

1968, Dec. 14 Wmk. 90 *Perf. 13½*

871 A401 20p car rose & dk grn .60 .35

ALPI (Fight Against Polio Assoc.), 25th anniv.

Shovel and State Coal Fields Emblem A402

Pouring Ladle and Army Manufacturing Emblem A403

1968, Dec. 21 Litho.

872 A402 20p orange, bl & blk .60 .35
873 A403 20p dl vio, dl yel & blk .60 .35

Issued to publicize the National Coal and Steel industry at the Rio Turbio coal fields and the Zapla blast furnaces.

Woman Potter, by Ramon Gomez Cornet — A404

1968, Dec. 21 Photo. *Perf. 13½*

874 A404 20p carmine rose .75 .40

Centenary of the Witcomb Gallery.

View of Buenos Aires and Rio de la Plata by Ulrico Schmidl A405

1969, Feb. 8 Litho. Wmk. 90

875 A405 20p yellow, blk & ver .75 .35

Ulrico Schmidl (c. 1462-1554) who wrote "Journey to the Rio de la Plata and Paraguay."

Types of 1955-67

Designs: 50c, Puma. 1p, Sunflower. 3p, Zapata Slope, Catamarca. 5p, Tierra del Fuego. 6p, José Hernandez. 10p, Inca Bridge, Mendoza. 50p, José de San Martin. 90p, Guillermo Brown. 100p, Ski jumper.

Photo.; Litho. (50c, 3p, 10p)

1969-70 Wmk. 365 *Perf. 13½*

882 A275 50c bister ('70) 1.00 .60
883 A277 5p brown 1.40 .90
884 A279 100p blue 26.00 8.00

Unwmk.

885 A278 1p brown ('70) .40 .25
886 A277 3p dk blue ('70) .65 .25
a. Wmk. 90 10.00 3.00
887 A277 5p brown ('70) .75 .25
888 A366 6p red brn, 15x22mm ('70) .90 .25
889 A278 10p dull red ('70) .50 .25
a. Wmk. 90 475.00 60.00
890 A241 50p dk bl, 22x31½mm ('70) 1.50 .25
891 A366 90p ol brn, 22x32mm ('70) 4.00 .50
892 A279 100p blue ('70) 12.50 1.00
Nos. 882-892 (11) 49.60 12.50

For surcharges see Nos. 1076-1077.

Soldier Type of 1965

Army Day: 20p, Sapper (gastador) of Buenos Aires Province, 1856.

Wmk. 365

1969, May 31 Litho. *Perf. 13½*

893 A340a 20p multicolored 1.10 .35

Frigate Hercules, by Emilio Biggeri — A406

1969, May 31

894 A406 20p multicolored 1.75 .35

Issued for Navy Day.

"All Men are Equal" — A407

1969, June 28 Wmk. 90

895 A407 20p black & ocher .60 .35

International Human Rights Year.

ILO Emblem — A408

1969, June 28 Litho. Wmk. 365

896 A408 20p lt green & multi .60 .35

50th anniv. of the ILO. Exists imperf. Value, pair $100.

Pedro N. Arata (1849-1922), Chemist — A409

Portraits: No. 898, Miguel Fernandez (1883-1950), zoologist. No. 899, Angel P. Gallardo (1867-1934), biologist. No. 900, Cristobal M. Hicken (1875-1933), botanist. No. 901, Eduardo Ladislao Holmberg, M.D. (1852-1937), natural scientist.

1969, Aug. 9 Wmk. 365 *Perf. 13½*

897 A409 6p Arata .70 .45
898 A409 6p Fernandez .70 .45
899 A409 6p Gallardo .70 .45
900 A409 6p Hicken .70 .45
901 A409 6p Holmberg .70 .45
Nos. 897-901 (5) 3.50 2.25

Argentine scientists. See No. 778 note.

Radar Antenna, Balcarce Station and Satellite — A410

1969, Aug. 23 Wmk. 99

902 A410 20p yellow & blk .60 .35

Communications by satellite through Intl. Telecommunications Satellite Consortium (INTELSAT). Exists imperf. Value, pair $40.
See No. C115.

Nieuport 28, Flight Route and Map of Buenos Aires Province — A411

1969, Sept. 13 Litho. Wmk. 90

903 A411 20p multicolored .60 .35

50th anniv. of the first Argentine airmail service from El Palomar to Mar del Plata, flown Feb. 23-24, 1919, by Capt. Pedro L. Zanni.

Military College Gate and Emblem A412

1969, Oct. 4 Wmk. 365 *Perf. 13½*

904 A412 20p multicolored .60 .35

Cent. of the National Military College, El Palomar (Greater Buenos Aires).

Gen. Angel Pacheco — A413

1969, Nov. 8 Photo. Wmk. 365

905 A413 20p deep green .60 .35

Gen. Angel Pacheco (1795-1869).

La Farola, Logotype of La Prensa — A414

Design: No. 907, Bartolomé Mitre & La Nacion logotype.

1969, Nov. 8 Litho. *Perf. 13½*

906 A414 20p orange, yel & blk .95 .35
907 A414 20p brt green & blk .95 .35

Cent. of newspapers La Prensa and La Nacion.

Julian Aguirre — A415

Musicians: No. 909, Felipe Boero. No. 910, Constantino Gaito. No. 911, Carlos Lopez Buchardo. No. 912, Alberto Williams.

Wmk. 365

1969, Dec. 6 Photo. *Perf. 13½*

908 A415 6p Aguirre .85 .35
909 A415 6p Boero .85 .35
910 A415 6p Gaito .85 .35
911 A415 6p Buchardo .85 .35
912 A415 6p Williams .85 .35
Nos. 908-912 (5) 4.25 1.75

Argentine musicians. See No. 778 note.

Lt. Benjamin Matienzo and Nieuport Plane — A416

1969, Dec. 13 Litho.

913 A416 20p multicolored .75 .35

23rd Aeronautics and Space Week.

High Power Lines and Map — A417

Design: 20p, Map of Santa Fe Province and schematic view of tunnel.

1969, Dec. 13

914 A417 6p multicolored .60 .35
915 A417 20p multicolored 1.40 .35

Completion of development projects: 6p for the hydroelectric dams on the Limay and Neuquen Rivers, the 20p the tunnel under Rio Grande from Sante Fe to Parana. Set exists imperf.©

Lions Emblem A418

1969, Dec. 20 Wmk. 365 *Perf. 13½*

916 A418 20p black, emer & org .95 .35

Argentine Lions Intl. Club, 50th anniv.

Madonna and Child, by Raul Soldi — A419

1969, Dec. 27 Litho.

917 A419 20p multicolored .90 .35

Christmas 1969.

Manuel Belgrano, by Jean Gericault — A420

The Creation of the Flag, Bas-relief by Jose Fioravanti — A421

Perf. 13½

1970, July 4 Unwmk. Photo.

918 A420 20c deep brown .55 .35

Litho. *Perf. 12½*

919 A421 50c bister, blk & bl .85 .55

Gen. Manuel Belgrano (1770-1820), Argentine patriot.

San Jose Palace — A422

1970, Aug. 9 Litho. *Perf. 13½*

920 A422 20c yellow grn & multi .60 .35

Gen. Justo Jose de Urquiza (1801-70), pres. of Argentina, 1854-60.

Schooner "Juliet" — A423

1970, Aug. 8 Unwmk.

921 A423 20c multicolored 1.25 .40

Issued for Navy Day.

Receiver of 1920 and Waves — A424

1970, Aug. 29

922 A424 20c lt blue & multi .70 .35

50th anniv. of Argentine broadcasting.

Types of 1955-67 Inscribed "Republica Argentina" and

Belgrano A425

Lujan Basilica A426

Designs: 1c, Sunflower. 3c, Zapata Slope, Catamarca. 5c, Tierra del Fuego. 8c, No. 931, Belgrano. 10c, Inca Bridge, Mendoza. 25c, 50c, 70c, Jose de San Martin. 65c, 90c, 1.20p, San Martin. 1p, Ski jumper. 1.15p, 1.80p, Adm. Brown.

1970-73 Photo. Unwmk. *Perf. 13½*

923 A278 1c dk green ('71) .35 .35
924 A277 3c car rose ('71) .35 .35
925 A277 5c Prus blue ('71) .35 .35
926 A425 6c deep blue .35 .35
927 A425 8c green ('72) .35 .35
928 A278 10c dull red ('71) .45 .35
929 A278 10c brn, litho. ('71) .90 .35
930 A278 10c org brn ('72) .35 .35
931 A425 10c brown ('73) .35 .35
932 A426 18c yel & dk brn, litho ('73) .35 .35
933 A425 25c brown ('71) .50 .35
934 A425 50c scarlet ('72) 1.40 .35
935 A241 65c brn, 22x31½mm, paper II ('71) 1.25 .35
936 A425 70c dk blue ('73) .35 .35
937 A241 90c emer, 22x31½mm ('72) 3.25 .35
938 A279 1p brn, 22½x29½mm ('71) 6.00 .35
939 A366 1.15p dk bl, 22½x32mm ('71) 1.25 .35
940 A241 1.20p org, 22x31½mm ('73) 1.40 .35
941 A366 1.80p brown ('73) .45 .35
Nos. 923-941 (19) 20.00 6.65

The imprint "Casa de Moneda de la Nacion" (in capitals) appears on 3c, 5c, Nos. 928-929; 65c, 90c, 1p, 1.20p.

On type A425 only the 6c is inscribed "Ley 18.188" below denomination.

Fluorescent paper was used in printing the 25c, 50c, and 70c. The 3c, 5c, 8c, No. 931 and 65c were issued on both ordinary and fluorescent paper.

See Nos. 987-996, 1032-1038, 1042-1043, 1089-1107. For overprint and surcharge see Nos. 1010, 1078.

Soldier Type of 1965

Galloping messenger of Field Army, 1879.

1970, Oct. 17 Litho. *Perf. 13½*

944 A340a 20c multicolored 1.10 .35

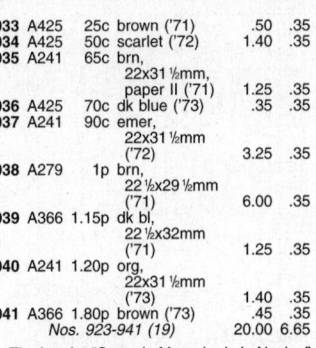

Dome of Cathedral of Cordoba — A430

1970, Nov. 7 Unwmk.

945 A430 50c gray & blk 1.00 .35

Bishopric of Tucuman, 400th anniv. See No. C131.

People Around UN Emblem — A431

1970, Nov. 7

946 A431 20c tan & multi .60 .35

25th anniversary of the United Nations.

State Mint and Medal — A432

1970, Nov. 28 Unwmk. *Perf. 13½*

947 A432 20c gold, grn & blk .60 .35

Inauguration of the State Mint Building, 25th anniversary.

St. John Bosco and Dean Funes College — A433

1970, Dec. 19 Litho.

948 A433 20c olive & blk .60 .35

Honoring the work of the Salesian Order in Patagonia.

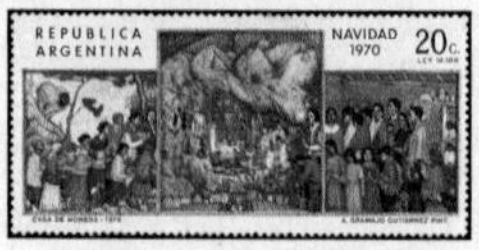

Nativity, by Horacio Gramajo Gutierrez
A434

1970, Dec. 19

949 A434 20c multicolored .80 .35

Christmas 1970.

Argentine Flag, Map of Argentine Antarctica — A435

1971, Feb. 20 Litho. ***Perf. 13½***

950 A435 20c multicolored 1.50 .50

Argentine South Pole Expedition, 5th anniv.

Phosphorescent Sorting Code and Albert Einstein
A436

1971, Apr. 30 Unwmk. ***Perf. 13½***

951 A436 25c multicolored .70 .35

Electronics in postal development.

Symbolic Road Crossing
A437

1971, May 29 Litho.

952 A437 25c blue & blk .60 .35

Inter-American Regional Meeting of the Intl. Federation of Roads, Buenos Aires, 3/28-31.

Elias Alippi — A438

Actors: No. 954, Juan Aurelio Casacuberta. No. 955, Angelina Pagano. No. 956, Roberto Casaux. No. 957, Florencio Parravicini. See No. 778 note.

1971, May 29 Litho.

953	A438	15c Alippi		.60	.35
954	A438	15c Casacuberta		.60	.35
955	A438	15c Pagano		.60	.35
956	A438	15c Casaux		.60	.35
957	A438	15c Parravicini		.60	.35
		Nos. 953-957 (5)		3.00	1.75

Soldier Type of 1965

Army Day, May 29: Artilleryman, 1826.

1971, July 3 Unwmk. ***Perf. 13½***

958 A340a 25c multicolored 1.50 .35

Bilander "Carmen," by Emilio Biggeri — A439

1971, July 3

959 A439 25c multicolored 1.50 .35

Navy Day

Peruvian Order of the Sun — A440

1971, Aug. 28

960 A440 31c multicolored .90 .35

Sesquicentennial of Peru's independence.

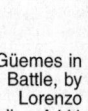

Güemes in Battle, by Lorenzo Gigli — A441

Design: No. 962, Death of Güemes, by Antonio Alice.

1971, Aug. 28 Size: 39x29mm

961 A441 25c multicolored .75 .35

Size: 84x29mm

962 A441 25c multicolored .75 .35

Sesquicentennial of the death of Martin Miguel de Güemes, leader in Gaucho War, Governor and Captain General of Salta Province.

Stylized Tulip — A442

1971, Sept. 18

963 A442 25c tan & multi .60 .35

3rd Intl. and 8th Natl. Horticultural Exhib.

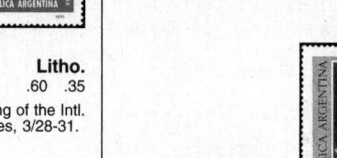

Father Antonio Saenz, by Juan Gut — A443

1971, Sept. 18

964 A433 25c gray & multi .60 .35

Sesquicentennial of University of Buenos Aires, and to honor Father Antonio Saenz, first Chancellor and Rector.

Fabricaciones Militares Emblem
A444

1971, Oct. 16 Unwmk. ***Perf. 13½***

965 A444 25c brn, gold, bl & blk .60 .35

30th anniv. of military armament works.

Cars and Trucks — A445

Design: 65c, Tree converted into paper.

1971, Oct. 16

966	A445	25c dull bl & multi	.65	.35
967	A445	65c green & multi	1.60	.35
		Nos. 966-967,C134 (3)	3.25	1.05

Nationalized industries.

Luis C. Candelaria and his Plane, 1918 — A446

1971, Nov. 27

968 A446 25c multicolored .60 .35

25th Aeronautics and Space Week.

Observatory and Nebula of Magellan
A447

1971, Nov. 27

969 A447 25c multicolored .90 .35

Cordoba Astronomical Observatory, cent.

Christ in Majesty — A448

1971, Dec. 18 Litho.

970 A448 25c blk & multi .55 .35

Christmas 1971. Design is from a tapestry by Horacio Butler in Basilica of St. Francis, Buenos Aires.

Mother and Child, by J. C. Castagnino — A449

1972, May 6 Unwmk. ***Perf. 13½***

971 A449 25c fawn & black .65 .35

25th anniv. (in 1971) of UNICEF.

Mailman's Bag — A450

1972, Sept. 2 Litho. ***Perf. 13½***

972 A450 25c lemon & multi .60 .35

Bicentenary of appointment of first Argentine mailman.

Adm. Brown Station, Map of Antarctica
A451

1972, Sept. 2

973 A451 25c blue & multi .90 .35

10th anniv. (in 1971) of Antarctic Treaty.

Soldier Type of 1965

Army Day: 25c, Sergeant, Negro and Mulatto Corps, 1806-1807.

1972, Sept. 23

974 A340a 25c multicolored .90 .35

Brigantine "Santisima Trinidad"
A452

1972, Sept. 23

975 A452 25c multicolored 1.10 .35

Navy Day. See No. 1006.

Oil Pump — A453

1972, Sept. 30 Litho. ***Perf. 13½***

976 A453 45c multicolored 1.00 .35

50th anniv. of the organ. of the state oil fields (Yacimientos Petroliferos Fiscales).

Sounding Balloon — A454

1972, Sept. 30

977 A454 25c multicolored .60 .35

Cent. of Natl. Meteorological Service.

Trees and Globe
A455

1972, Oct. 14 ***Perf. 13x13½***

978 A455 25c bl, blk & lt bl .85 .35

7th World Forestry Congress, Buenos Aires, Oct. 4-18.

Arms of Naval School, Frigate "Presidente Sarmiento" — A456

1972, Oct. 14

979 A456 25c gold & multi .95 .35

Centenary of Military Naval School.

Early Balloon and Plane, Antonio de Marchi — A457

1972, Nov. 4 ***Perf. 13½***

980 A457 25c multicolored .70 .35

Aeronautics and Space Week, and in honor of Baron Antonio de Marchi (1875-1934), aviation pioneer.

Bartolomé Mitre — A458

1972, Nov. 4 **Engr.**

981 A458 25c dark blue .75 .35

Pres. Bartolome Mitre (1821-1906), writer, historian, soldier.

Flower and Heart — A459

1972, Dec. 2 **Litho.** ***Perf. 13½***

982 A459 90c lt bl, ultra & blk .75 .35

"Your heart is your health," World Health Day.

"Martin Fierro," by Juan C. Castagnino A460

"Spirit of the Gaucho," by Vicente Forte A461

1972, Dec. 2 **Litho.** ***Perf. 13½***

983 A460 50c multicolored .50 .35

984 A461 90c multicolored .75 .40

Intl. Book Year 1972, and cent. of publication of the poem, Martin Fierro, by Jose Hernandez (1834-86).

Iguacu Falls and Tourist Year Emblem A462

1972, Dec. 16 ***Perf. 13x13½***

985 A462 45c multicolored .60 .35

Tourism Year of the Americas.

King, Wood Carving, 18th Century — A463

1972, Dec. 16 ***Perf. 13½***

986 A463 50c multicolored .70 .35

Christmas 1972.

Types of 1955-73 Inscribed "Republica Argentina" and

Moon Valley, San Juan Province — A463a

Designs: 1c, Sunflower. 5c, Tierra del Fuego. 10c, Inca Bridge, Mendoza. 50c, Lujan Basilica. 65c, 22.50p, San Martin. 1p, Ski jumper. 1.15p, 4.50p, Guillermo Brown. 1.80p, Manuel Belgrano.

Litho.; Photo. (1c, 65c, 1p)

Perf. 13½, 12½ (1.80p)

1972-75 **Wmk. 365**

987	A278	1c	dk green	.30	.30
988	A277	5c	dark blue	.30	.30
989	A278	10c	bister brn	.35	.30
989A	A426	50c	dull pur ('75)	.30	.30
990	A241	65c	gray brown	4.25	.35
991	A279	1p	brown	4.75	.30
992	A366	1.15p	dk gray bl	1.75	.60
993	A425	1.80p	blue ('75)	.35	.30
994	A366	4.50p	green ('75)	.55	.30
995	A241	22.50p	vio bl ('75)	1.75	.40
996	A463a	50p	multi ('75)	1.60	.30
	Nos. 987-996 (11)			16.25	3.75

Paper size of 1c is 27½x39mm; others of 1972, 37x27, 27x37mm.

Size of 22.50p, 50p: 26½x38½mm.

See Nos. 1050, 1108.

Cock (Symbolic of Police) — A464

1973, Feb. 3 **Litho.** **Unwmk.**

997 A464 50c lt green & multi .60 .35

Sesqui. of Federal Police of Argentina.

First Coin of Bank of Buenos Aires — A465

1973, Feb. 3 ***Perf. 13½***

998 A465 50c purple, yel & brn .60 .35

Sesquicentennial of the Bank of Buenos Aires Province.

DC-3 Planes Over Antarctica A466

1973, Apr. 28 **Litho.** ***Perf. 13½***

999 A466 50c lt blue & multi 1.60 .50

10th anniversary of Argentina's first flight to the South Pole.

Rivadavia's Chair, Argentine Arms and Colors — A467

1973, May 19 **Litho.** ***Perf. 13½***

1000 A467 50c multicolored .60 .35

Inauguration of Pres. Hector J. Campora, May 25, 1973.

San Martin, by Gil de Castro — A468

San Martin and Bolivar — A469

1973, July 7 **Litho.** ***Perf. 13½***

1001 A468 50c lt green & multi .60 .35

1002 A469 50c yellow & multi .60 .35

Gen. San Martin's farewell to the people of Peru and his meeting with Simon Bolivar at Guayaquil July 26-27, 1822.

Eva Peron — A470

1973, July 26 **Litho.** ***Perf. 13½***

1003 A470 70c black, org & bl .60 .35

Maria Eva Duarte de Peron (1919-1952), political leader.

House of Viceroy Sobremonte, by Hortensia de Virgilion — A471

1973, July 28 ***Perf. 13x13½***

1004 A471 50c blue & multi .60 .35

400th anniversary of the city of Cordoba.

Woman, by Lino Spilimbergo — A472

1973, Aug. 28 **Litho.** ***Perf. 13½***

1005 A472 70c multicolored 1.20 .35

Philatelists' Day. See Nos. B60-B61.

Ship Type of 1972

Navy Day: 70c, Frigate "La Argentina."

1973, Oct. 27 **Litho.** ***Perf. 13½***

1006 A452 70c multicolored .80 .35

New and Old Telephones — A473

1973, Oct. 27

1007 A473 70c brt blue & multi .60 .35

Natl. telecommunications system, 25th anniv.

Plume Made of Flags of Participants — A474

1973, Nov. 3 ***Perf. 13½***

1008 A474 70c yellow bis & multi .60 .35

12th Cong. of Latin Notaries, Buenos Aires.

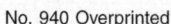

No. 940 Overprinted

1973, Nov. 30 **Photo.**

1010 A241 1.20p orange 1.10 .35

Assumption of presidency by Juan Peron, Oct. 12.

Virgin and Child, Window, La Plata Cathedral — A476

Christmas: 1.20p, Nativity, by Bruno Venier, b. 1914.

1973, Dec. 15 **Litho.** ***Perf. 13½***

1011 A476 70c gray & multi .50 .35

1012 A476 1.20p black & multi 1.00 .35

The Lama, by Juan Battle Planas — A477

Paintings: 50c, Houses in Boca District, by Eugenio Daneri, horiz. 90c, The Blue Grotto, by Emilio Pettoruti, horiz.

1974, Feb. 9 **Litho.** ***Perf. 13½***

1013 A477 50c multicolored .75 .35

1014 A477 70c multicolored .75 .35

1015 A477 90c multicolored .75 .35

Nos. 1013-1015,B64 (4) 2.70 1.40

Argentine painters.

Mar del Plata — A478

1974, Feb. 9

1016 A478 70c multicolored .60 .35

Centenary of Mar del Plata.

Weather Symbols — A479

1974, Mar. 23 **Litho.** ***Perf. 13½***

1017 A479 1.20p multicolored .60 .35

Cent. of intl. meteorological cooperation.

Justo Santa Maria de Oro — A480

1974, Mar. 23

1018 A480 70c multicolored .60 .35

Bicentenary of the birth of Brother Justo Santa Maria de Oro (1772-1836), theologian, patriot, first Argentine bishop.

Belisario Roldan (1873-1922), Writer — A481

1974, June 29 Photo. Unwmk.
1019 A481 70c bl & brn .60 .35

Poster with Names of OAS Members A482

1974, June 29 Litho.
1020 A482 1.38p multicolored .60 .35

Organization of American States, 25th anniv.

ENCOTEL Emblem — A483

1974, Aug. 10 Litho. *Perf. 13*
1021 A483 1.20p blue, gold & blk .70 .35

ENCOTEL, Natl. Post and Telegraph Press.

Flags of Argentina, Bolivia, Brazil, Paraguay, Uruguay — A484

1974, Aug. 16 *Perf. 13½*
1022 A484 1.38p multicolored .60 .35

6th Meeting of Foreign Ministers of Rio de la Plata Basin Countries.

El Chocon Hydroelectric Complex, Limay River — A485

Somisa Steel Mill, San Nicolas — A486

Gen. Belgrano Bridge, Chaco-Corrientes — A487

Perf. 13½, 13x13½ (4.50p)
1974, Sept. 14
1023 A485 70c multicolored .45 .30
1024 A486 1.20p multicolored .75 .30
1025 A487 4.50p multicolored 2.25 .45
Nos. 1023-1025 (3) 3.45 1.05

Development projects.

Brigantine Belgrano, by Emilio Biggeri — A488

1974, Oct. 26 Litho. *Perf. 13½*
1026 A488 1.20p multicolored 1.25 .35

Departure into exile in Chile of General San Martin, Sept. 22, 1822.

Alberto R. Mascias and Bleriot Plane — A489

1974, Oct. 26 Unwmk.
1027 A489 1.20p multicolored .80 .35
a. Wmk 365 — —

Air Force Day, Aug. 10, and to honor Alberto Roque Garcias (1878-1951), aviation pioneer.

Hussar, 1812, by Eleodoro Marenco — A490

1974, Oct. 26
1028 A490 1.20p multicolored .80 .35

Army Day.

Post Horn and Flags — A491

1974, Nov. 23 Unwmk. *Perf. 13½*
1029 A491 2.65p multicolored 1.00 .35
a. Wmk 365 *45.00 22.50*

Centenary of Universal Postal Union.

Franciscan Monastery A492

1974, Nov. 23 Litho.
1030 A492 1.20p multicolored .60 .35

400th anniversary, city of Santa Fe.

Trout Type of 1968

1974 Engr. Unwmk.
1031 A366a 1000p vio bl 5.50 .35

Due to a shortage of 10p stamps a quantity of this 1,000p was released for use as 10p.

Types of 1954-73 Inscribed "Republica Argentina" and

Red Deer in Forest — A495

Congress Building A497

Designs: 30c, 60c, 1.80p, Manuel Belgrano. 50c, Lujan Basilica. 1.20p, 2p, 6p, San Martin (16x22½mm). 2.70p, 7.50p, 22.50p, San Martin (22x31½mm). 4.50p, 13.50p, Guillermo Brown. 10p, Leaping trout.

1974-76 Unwmk. Photo. *Perf. 13½*

1032	A425	30c	brown vio	.40	.35
1033	A426	50c	blk & brn red	.40	.35
1034	A426	50c	bister & bl	.35	.35
1035	A425	60c	ocher	.40	.35
1036	A425	1.20p	red	.40	.35
1037	A425	1.80p	deep blue	.40	.35
1038	A425	2p	dark purple	.50	.40
1039	A241	2.70p	dk bl, 22x31½mm	.40	.35
1040	A366	4.50p	green	2.00	.35
1041	A495	5p	yel green	.50	.35
1042	A425	6p	red orange	.40	.35
1043	A425	6p	emerald	.40	.35
1044	A241	7.50p	grn, 22x31½mm	1.20	.35
1045	A366a	10p	violet blue	2.50	.35
1046	A366	13.50p	scar, 16x22½mm	.60	.35
1047	A366	13.50p	scar, 22x31½mm	1.20	.35
1048	A241	22.50p	dp bl, 22x31½mm	1.20	.60
1049	A497	30p	yel & dk red brn	4.50	.35
1050	A463a	50p	multicolored	1.75	.35
			Nos. 1032-1050 (19)	19.50	6.95

Issued: 10p, 5/74; 30c, 1.20p, 2.70p, 5/15/74; 5p, 11/20/74; 30p, 12/10/74; 2p, 3/1/75; 60c, 7.50p, 4/30/75; 4.50p, 7/21/75; 1.80p, Nos. 1042, 1047, 22.50p, 8/14/75; No. 1046, 10/10/75; No. 1034, 10/30/75; No. 1043, 11/6/75; 50p, 2/76.

Fluorescent paper was used in printing No. 1036, 2p, Nos. 1044 and 1047. The 30p was issued on both ordinary and fluorescent paper.

See No. 829. For type of A495 overprinted see No. 1144.

Miniature Sheet

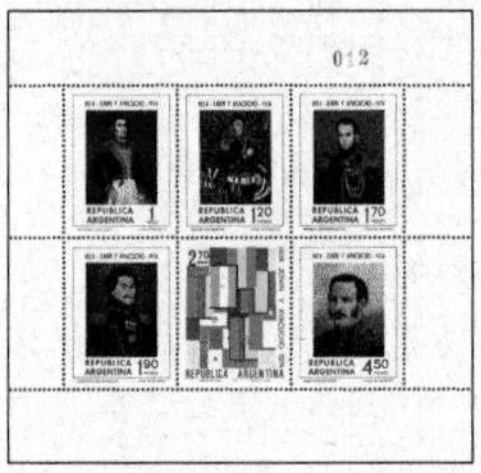

A498

1974, Dec. 7 Litho. *Perf. 13½*
1052 A498 Sheet of 6 4.50 3.00
a. 1p Mariano Necochea .50 .25
b. 1.20p Jose de San Martin .50 .25
c. 1.70p Manuel Isidoro Suarez .50 .25
d. 1.90p Juan Pascual Pringles .50 .25
e. 2.70p Latin American flags .50 .25
f. 4.50p Jose Felix Bogado .50 .25

Sesqui. of Battles of Junin and Ayacucho.

Dove, by Vito Campanella A499

St. Anne, by Raul Soldi — A500

1974, Dec. 21 Litho. *Perf. 13½*
1053 A499 1.20p multicolored .90 .35
1054 A500 2.65p multicolored .90 .35

Christmas 1974.

Boy Looking at Stamp — A501

1974, Dec. 21
1055 A501 1.70p black & yel .60 .35

World Youth Philately Year.

Space Monsters, by Raquel Forner — A502

Argentine modern art: 4.50p, Dream, by Emilio Centurion.

1975, Feb. 22 Litho. *Perf. 13½*
1056 A502 2.70p multi 1.00 .30
1057 A502 4.50p multi 1.95 .40

Indian Woman and Cathedral, Catamarca — A503

Tourist Publicity: No. 1059, Carved chancel and street scene. No. 1060, Logging operations and monastery yard. No. 1061, Painted pottery and power station. No. 1062, Farm cart and colonial mansion. No. 1063, Perito Moreno glacier and spinning mill. No. 1064, Lake Lapataia and scientific surveyor. No. 1065, Los Alerces National Park and oil derrick.

1975 Litho. *Perf. 13½*
Unwmk., Wmk 365 (6p)

1058	A503	1.20p	shown	.50	.35
1059	A503	1.20p	Jujuy	.50	.35
1060	A503	1.20p	Salta	.50	.35
1061	A503	1.20p	Santiago del Estero	.50	.35
1062	A503	1.20p	Tucuman	.50	.35
1063	A503	6p	Santa Cruz	.90	.35
1064	A503	6p	Tierra del Fuego	.90	.35
1065	A503	6p	Chubut	.90	.35
			Nos. 1058-1065 (8)	5.20	2.80

Issue dates: 1.20p, Mar. 8; 6p, Dec. 20.

"We Have Been Inoculated" — A504

1975, Apr. 26 Unwmk. *Perf. 13½*
1066 A504 2p multi .70 .35

Children's inoculation campaign (child's painting).

Hugo A. Acuña and South Orkney Station A505

Designs: No. 1068, Francisco P. Moreno and Lake Nahuel Huapi. No. 1069, Lt. Col. Luis Piedra Buena and cutter, Luisito. No. 1070, Ensign José M. Sobral and Snow Hill House. No. 1071, Capt. Carlos M. Moyano and Cerro del Toro (mountain).

1975, June 28 Litho. *Perf. 13*
1067 A505 2p grnsh bl & multi .60 .35
1068 A505 2p yel grn & multi .60 .35
1069 A505 2p lt vio & multi .60 .35

1070 A505 2p gray bl & multi .60 .35
1071 A505 2p pale grn & multi .60 .35
Nos. 1067-1071 (5) 3.00 1.75

Pioneers of Antarctica.

Frigate "25 de Mayo" — A506

1975, Sept. 27 Unwmk. *Perf. 13½*
1072 A506 6p multi 1.10 .35

Navy Day 1975.

Eduardo Bradley and Balloon — A507

1975, Sept. 27 Wmk. 365
1073 A507 6p multi .70 .35

Air Force Day.

Declaration of Independence, by Juan M. Blanes — A508

1975, Oct. 25
1074 A508 6p multi .95 .35

Sesquicentennial of Uruguay's declaration of independence.

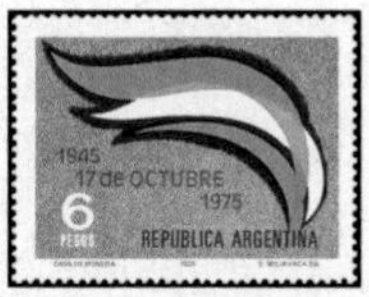

Flame — A509

1975, Oct. 17 Unwmk.
1075 A509 6p gray & multi .60 .35

Loyalty Day, 30th anniversary of Pres. Peron's accession to power.

No. 886 Surcharged

No. 891 Surcharged

No. 932 Surcharged

1975 Lithographed, Photogravure
1076 A277 6c on 3p .50 .35
a. On #886a 50.00
1077 A366 30c on 90p .60 .35
1078 A426 5p on 18c .70 .35
Nos. 1076-1078 (3) 1.80 1.05

Issued: 6c, 10/30; 30c, 11/20; 5p, 10/24.

A510

Design: International Bridge, flags of Argentina & Uruguay.

1975, Oct. 25 Litho. Wmk. 365
1081 A510 6p multi .60 .35

Post Horn, Surcharged A511

1975, Nov. 8
1082 A511 10p on 20c multi .75 .35

Introduction of postal code. Not issued without surcharge.

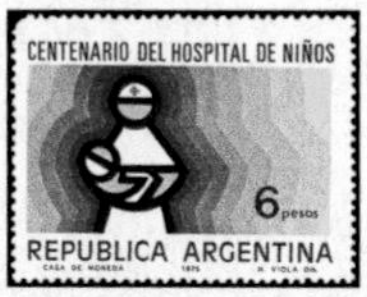

Nurse Holding Infant — A512

1975, Dec. 13 Litho. *Perf. 13½*
1083 A512 6p multi .95 .35

Children's Hospital, centenary.

Nativity, Nueva Pompeya Church — A513

1975, Dec. 13 Litho. Unwmk.
1084 A513 6p multicolored .70 .35

Christmas 1975.

Types of 1970-75 and

Church of St. Francis, Salta — A515

Designs: 3p, No. 1099, 60p, 90p, Manuel Belgrano. 12p, 15p, 20p, 30p, No. 1100, 100p, 110p, 120p, 130p, San Martin. 15p, 70p, Guillermo Brown. 300p, Moon Valley (lower inscriptions italic). 500p, Adm. Brown Station, Antarctica.

1976-78 Photo. Unwmk. *Perf. 13½*
1089 A425 3p slate .50 .30
1090 A425 12p rose red .45 .30

Perf. 12½x13
Litho. Wmk. 365
1091 A425 12p rose red .60 .30
1092 A425 12p emerald .60 .30

Perf. 13½
Photo. Unwmk.
1093 A425 12p emer ('77) .60 .30
1094 A425 15p rose red .50 .30
1095 A425 15p vio bl ('77) .60 .30
1097 A425 20p rose red ('77) .60 .30
1098 A425 30p rose red ('77) .60 .30
1099 A425 40p dp grn 1.75 .30
1100 A425 40p rose red ('77) .60 .30
1101 A425 60p dk bl ('77) 2.50 .30
1102 A425 70p dk bl ('77) 2.50 .35
1103 A425 90p emer ('77) 1.25 .30
1104 A425 100p red 1.75 .30
1105 A425 110p rose red ('78) .60 .30
1106 A425 120p rose red ('78) .60 .30
1107 A425 130p rose red ('78) .85 .30

Litho.
1108 A463a 300p multi 5.00 .35
a. Wmk 365 17.50 5.00
1109 A515 500p multi ('77) 8.50 .35
a. Wmk 365 120.00 14.00
1110 A515 1000p multi ('77) 6.75 8.00
Nos. 1089-1110 (21) 37.70 14.15

Fluorescent paper was used in printing both 12p rose red, 15p rose red, 20p, 30p, 40p rose red, 100p, 110p, 120p, 130p.

No. 1099 and the 300p were issued on both ordinary and fluorescent paper.

Nos. 1108 and 1109 exist imperf. Values, pairs: No. 1108 $250; No. 1109 $120.

See Nos. B73-B74.

A516

1976 Photo. Unwmk. *Perf. 13½*
1112 A516 12c gray & blk .35 .30
1113 A516 50c gray & grn .35 .30
1114 A516 1p red & blk .35 .30
1115 A516 4p bl & blk .35 .30
1116 A516 5p org & blk .40 .30
1117 A516 6p dp brn & blk .40 .30
1118 A516 10p gray & vio bl .70 .30
1119 A516 27p lt grn & blk .50 .30
1120 A516 30p lt bl & blk 2.50 .30
1121 A516 45p yel & blk 1.40 .30
1122 A516 50p dl grn & blk 1.40 .30
1123 A516 100p brt grn & red 1.40 .30

Perf. 13x12½
1976 Litho. Wmk. 365
1124 A516 5p org & blk .45 .30
1125 A516 27p lt grn & blk 1.00 .30
1126 A516 45p yel & blk 1.40 .30
Nos. 1112-1126 (15) 12.95 4.50

The 1p, 6p, 10p, 50p and No. 1116 were issued on both ordinary and fluorescent paper.

Jet and Airlines Emblem A517

Perf. 13x13½
1976, Apr. 24 Litho. Unwmk.
1130 A517 30p bl, lt bl & dk bl 1.35 .35

Argentine Airlines, 25th anniversary.

Frigate Heroina & Map of Falkland Islands A518

1976, Apr. 26
1131 A518 6p multi 3.25 .40

Argentina's claim to Falkland Islands.

Louis Braille — A519

Wmk. 365
1976, May 22 Engr. *Perf. 13½*
1132 A519 19.70 deep blue .60 .30

Sesquicentennial of the invention of the Braille system of writing for the blind by Louis Braille (1809-1852).

Private, 7th Infantry Regiment — A520

1976, May 29 Litho. Unwmk.
1133 A520 12p multi .70 .35

Army Day.

Schooner Rio de la Plata, by Emilio Biggeri — A521

1976, June 19
1134 A521 12p multi .95 .35

Navy Day.

Dr. Bernardo Houssay A522

Argentine Nobel Prize Winners:

10p, Bernardo Houssay, medicine and physiology, 1947. 15p, Luis F. Leloir, chemistry, 1970. 20p, Carlos Saavedra Lamas, peace, 1936.

1976, Aug. 14 Litho. *Perf. 13½*
1135 A522 10p org & blk .60 .35
1136 A522 15p yel & blk .60 .35
1137 A522 20p ocher & blk .60 .35
Nos. 1135-1137 (3) 1.80 1.05

Rio de la Plata International Bridge — A523

1976, Sept. 18 Litho. *Perf. 13½*
1138 A523 12p multi .95 .35

Inauguration of International Bridge connecting Puerte Unzue, Argentina, and Fray Bentos, Uruguay.

Pipelines & Cooling Tower, Gen. Mosconi Plant — A524

1976, Nov. 20 Litho. *Perf. 13½*
1139 A524 28p multi .70 .35

Pablo Teodoro Fels & Bleriot Monoplane, 1910 — A525

1976, Nov. 20
1140 A525 15p multi .75 .35

Air Force Day.

Nativity — A526

1976, Dec. 18 Litho. *Perf. 13½*
1141 A526 20p multi .90 .35

Christmas. Painting by Edith Chiapetto.

Water Conference Emblem — A527

1977, Mar. 19 Litho. *Perf. 13½*
1142 A527 70p multi .90 .35

UN Water Conf., Mar del Plata, Mar. 14-25.

Dalmacio Velez Sarsfield A528

1977, Mar. 19 Engr.

1143 A528 50p blk & red brn .95 .35

Dalmacio Velez Sarsfield (1800-1875), author of Argentine civil code.

Red Deer Type of 1974 Surcharged

1977, July 30 Photo. *Perf. 13½*

1144 A495 100p on 5p brn 1.60 .35

Sesquicentennial of Uruguayan postal service. Not issued without surcharge.

Soldier, 16th Lancers — A529

1977, July 30

1145 A529 30p multi 1.10 .35

Army Day.

Schooner Sarandi, by Emilio Biggeri — A530

1977, July 30

1146 A530 30p multi 1.10 .50

Navy Day.

Soccer Games' Emblem — A531

70p, Argentina '78 emblem, flags & soccer field.

1977, May 14

1147 A531 30p multi .70 .35
1148 A531 70p multi 1.00 .35

11th World Cup Soccer Championship, Argentina, June 1-25, 1978.

The Visit, by Horacio Butler — A532

Consecration, by Miguel P. Caride — A533

1977, Mar. 26 Litho.

1149 A532 50p multi .75 .35
1150 A533 70p multi 1.00 .35

Argentine artists.

Sierra de la Ventana A534

Views: No. 1152, Civic Center, Santa Rosa. No. 1153, Skiers, San Martin de los Andes. No. 1154, Boat on Lake Fonck, Rio Negro.

1977, Oct. 8 Litho. *Perf. 13x13½*

1151 A534 30p multi .60 .35
1152 A534 30p multi .60 .35
1153 A534 30p multi .60 .35
1154 A534 30p multi .60 .35
Nos. 1151-1154 (4) 2.40 1.40

Guillermo Brown, by R. del Villar — A535

1977, Oct. 8 *Perf. 13½*

1155 A535 30p multi .60 .35

Adm. Guillermo Brown (1777-1857), leader in fight for independence, bicentenary of birth.

Jet — A536

Double-decker, 1926 — A537

1977 Litho. *Perf. 13½*

1156 A536 30p multi .55 .35
1157 A537 40p multi .65 .35

50th anniversary of military plane production (30p); Air Force Day (40p).
Issue dates: 30p, Dec. 3; 40p, Nov. 26.

Adoration of the Kings — A538

1977, Dec. 17

1158 A538 100p multi 1.25 .35

Christmas 1977.

Historic City Hall, Buenos Aires A539

Chapel of Rio Grande Museum, Tierra del Fuego A540

5p, 20p, La Plata Museum. 10p, Independence Hall, Tucuman. 40p, City Hall, Salta. No. 1165, City Hall, Buenos Aires. 100p, Columbus Theater, Buenos Aires. 200p, flag Monument, Rosario. 280p, 300p, Chapel of Rio Grande Museum, Tierra del Fuego. 480p, 520p, 800, Ruins of Jesuit Mission Church of San Ignacio, Misiones. 500p, Candonga Chapel, Cordoba. 1000p, G.P.O., Buenos Aires. 2000p, Civic Center, Bariloche, Rio Negro.

Three types of 10p: I. Nine vertical window bars; small imprint "E. MILIAVACA Dib." II. Nine bars; large imprint "E. MILIAVACA DIB." III. Redrawn; 5 bars; large imprint.

1977-81 Photo. Unwmk. *Perf. 13½*
Size: 32x21mm, 21x32mm

1159 A540 5p gray & blk .40 .30
1160 A540 10p lt ultra & blk, I .40 .30
a. Type II .60 .35
1161 A540 10p lt bl & blk, III .40 .30
1162 A540 20p citron & blk, litho. .40 .30
1163 A539 40p gray bl & blk .50 .30
1164 A539 50p yel & blk .60 .30
1165 A540 50p citron & blk .85 .30
1166 A540 100p org & blk, litho. .50 .35
a. Wmk. 365 100.00 18.00
1167 A540 100p red org & blk .50 .30
1168 A540 100p turq & blk .40 .30
1169 A539 200p lt bl & blk .85 .30
1170 A540 280p rose & blk 11.00 1.00
1171 A540 300p lemon & blk 1.40 .30
1172 A540 480p org & blk 1.75 .30
1173 A540 500p yel grn & blk .60 .30
1174 A540 520p org & blk 1.20 .35
1175 A540 800p rose lil & blk 2.10 .35
1176 A540 1000p lem bis & blk 1.75 .50
1177 A540 1000p gold & blk, 40x29mm 3.00 .30
1178 A540 2000p multi 1.40 .50
Nos. 1159-1178 (20) 30.00 7.25

Nos. 1161, 1163, 1165, 1167, 1169, 1171, 1173, 1176, 1177 were issued on both ordinary and fluorescent paper. No. 1174 was issued only on fluorescent paper. All others were issued only on ordinary paper.

Issued: No. 1164, 5/30/77; 280p, 12/15/77; No. 1160, 3/14/78; 480p, 5/22/78; 5p, 7/25/78; 20p, 500p, 9/8/78; No. 1166, 9/20/78; No. 1177, 9/28/78; 520p, 9/30/78; 300p, 10/5/78; 40p, 12/1/78; No. 1161, 1979; No. 1165, 1/8/79; 800p, 3/20/79; No. 1167, 4/25/79; 200p, 6/23/79; No. 1176, 12/15/79; 2000p, 6/25/80; No. 1168, 5/26/81.

For overprints see Nos. 1253, 1315.

Soccer Games' Emblem — A544

1978, Feb. 10 Photo. *Perf. 13½*

1179 A544 200p yel grn & bl 1.10 .35
a. Wmk 365 *100.00 75.00*

11th World Cup Soccer Championship, Argentina, June 1-25.

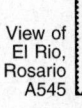

View of El Rio, Rosario A545

Designs (Argentina '78 Emblem and): 100p, Rio Tercero Dam, Cordoba. 150p, Cordillera Mountains, Mendoza. 200p, City Center, Mar del Plata. 300p, View of Buenos Aires.

1978, May 6 Litho. *Perf. 13*

1180 A545 50p multi .45 .45
1181 A545 100p multi .45 .45
1182 A545 150p multi .75 .50
1183 A545 200p multi .75 .50
1184 A545 300p multi 1.40 .60
Nos. 1180-1184 (5) 3.80 2.50

Sites of 11th World Cup Soccer Championship, June 1-25.

Children A546

1978, May 20

1185 A546 100p multi .60 .35

50th anniversary of Children's Institute.

Labor Day, by B. Quinquela Martin — A547

Design: No. 1187, Woman's torso, sculpture by Orlando Pierri.

1978, May 20 *Perf. 13½*

1186 A547 100p multi .75 .35
1187 A547 100p multi .75 .35

Argentina, Hungary, France, Italy and Emblem — A548

Stadium A549

Teams and Argentina '78 Emblem: 200p, Poland, Fed. Rep. of Germany, Tunisia, Mexico. 300p, Austria, Spain, Sweden, Brazil. 400p, Netherlands, Iran, Peru, Scotland.

1978 Litho. *Perf. 13*

1188 A548 100p multi .45 .45
1189 A548 200p multi 1.00 .45
1190 A548 300p multi 1.40 .55
1191 A548 400p multi 1.75 .55
Nos. 1188-1191 (4) 4.60 2.00

Souvenir Sheet

Lithographed and Engraved

Perf. 13½

1192 A549 700p buff & blk 3.00 3.00

11th World Cup Soccer Championship, Argentina, June 1-25. Issued: Nos. 1188-1191, 6/6; No. 1192, 6/3.

Stadium Type of 1978 Inscribed in Red

Lithographed and Engraved

1978, Sept. 2 *Perf. 13½*

1193 A549 1000p buff, blk & red 4.50 4.50

Argentina's victory in 1978 Soccer Championship. No. 1193 has margin similar to No. 1192 with Rimet Cup emblem and text added in red.

Young Tree Nourished by Old Trunk, UN Emblem A550

1978 Sept. 2 Litho.

1194 A550 100p multi .60 .35

Technical Cooperation among Developing Countries Conf., Buenos Aires, Sept. 1978.

Emblems of Buenos Aires & Bank — A551

1978, Sept. 16

1195 A551 100p multi .60 .35

Bank of City of Buenos Aires, centenary.

General Savio & Steel Production A552

1978, Sept. 16
1196 A552 100p multi .60 .35

Gen. Manuel N. Savio (1892-1948), general manager of military heavy industry.

San Martin — A553

1978, Oct. **Engr.**
1197 A553 2000p grnsh blk 4.25 .50

1979 **Wmk. 365**
1198 A553 2000p grnsh blk 5.75 1.00

Gen Jose de San Martin (1778-1850), soldier and statesman. See No. 1292.

Globe & Argentine Flag — A554

1978, Oct. 7 **Litho.** ***Perf. 13½***
1199 A554 200p multi 1.00 .35

12th Intl. Cancer Cong., Buenos Aires, Oct. 5-11.

Chessboard, Queen & Pawn — A555

1978, Oct. 7
1200 A555 200p multi 4.50 .65

23rd National Chess Olympics, Buenos Aires, Oct. 25-Nov. 12.

Correct Positioning of Stamps — A557

50p, Use correct postal code number.

1978 **Photo.** ***Perf. 13½***
1201 A557 20p ultra .60 .35
1203 A557 50p carmine .60 .35

No. 1201 issued on both ordinary and fluorescent paper.

A558

A559

1978-82 **Photo.** ***Perf. 13½***
1204 A558 150p bl & ultra .65 .35
1205 A558 180p bl & ultra .65 .35
1206 A558 200p bl & ultra .90 .35
1207 A559 240p ol bis & bl ('79) .65 .35
1208 A559 260p blk & lt bl ('79) .65 .35
1209 A559 290p brn & lt bl ('79) .80 .35
1210 A559 310p mag & bl ('79) .80 .35
1211 A559 350p ver & bl ('79) 1.00 .35
1212 A559 450p ultra & bl .90 .35
1213 A559 600p grn & bl ('80) 2.00 .35
1214 A559 700p blk & bl ('80) 1.20 .35
1215 A559 800p red & bl ('81) .80 .35
1216 A559 1100p gray & bl ('81) 1.60 .35
1217 A559 1500p blk & bl ('81) .90 .35
1218 A559 1700p grn & bl ('82) .90 .35
Nos. 1204-1218 (15) 14.40 5.25

No. 1204 issued on fluorescent and ordinary paper. No. 1206 issued only on fluorescent paper.
For overprint see No. 1338.

Balsa "24" — A561

Ships: 200p, Tug Legador. 300p, River Parana tug No. 34. 400p, Passenger ship Ciudad de Parana.

1978, Nov. 4 **Litho.** ***Perf. 13½***
1220 A561 100p multi .45 .30
1221 A561 200p multi .70 .30
1222 A561 300p multi 1.00 .30
a. Pair, #1221-1222 2.00
1223 A561 400p multi 1.30 .60
a. Pair, #1220, 1223 2.00
Nos. 1220-1223 (4) 3.45 1.50

20th anniversary of national river fleet. Issued on fluorescent paper.

View and Arms of Bahia Blanca — A562

1978, Nov. 25 **Litho.** ***Perf. 13½***
1224 A562 20p multi .75 .35

Sesquicentennial of Bahia Blanca.

"Spain," (Queen Isabella and Columbus) by Arturo Dresco — A563

1978, Nov. 25
1225 A563 300p multi 3.00 .60

Visit of King Juan Carlos and Queen Sofia of Spain to Argentina, Nov. 26.

Virgin and Child, San Isidro Cathedral — A564

1978, Dec. 16
1226 A564 200p gold & multi 1.00 .35

Christmas 1978.

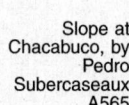

Slope at Chacabuco, by Pedro Subercaseaux A565

Painting: 1000p, The Embrace of Maipu (San Martin and O'Higgins), by Pedro Subercaseaux, vert.

1978, Dec. 16 **Litho.** ***Perf. 13½***
1227 A565 500p multi 2.25 .35
1228 A565 1000p multi 3.75 .35

José de San Martin, 200th birth anniversary.

Adolfo Alsina — A566

Design: No. 1230, Mariano Moreno.

1979, Jan. 20
1229 A566 200p lt bl & blk .75 .35
1230 A566 200p yel red & blk .75 .35

Adolfo Alsina (1828-1877), political leader, vice-president; Mariano Moreno (1778-1811), lawyer, educator, political leader.

Argentina No. 37 and UPU Emblem A567

1979, Jan. 20
1231 A567 200p multi .75 .35

Centenary of Argentina's UPU membership.

Still-life, by Carcova A568

Painting: 300p, The Laundresses, by Faustino Brughetti.

1979, Mar. 3
1232 A568 200p multi .90 .30
1233 A568 300p multi .90 .35

Ernesto de la Carcova (1866-1927) and Faustino Brughetti (1877-1956), Argentine painters.

Balcarce Earth Station — A569

1979, Mar. 3
1234 A569 200p multicolored .90 .35

Third Inter-American Telecommunications Conference, Buenos Aires, March 5-9.

Stamp Collecting — A570

1979
1235 A570 30p multicolored .60 .35

Printed on ordinary and fluorescent paper.

European Olive — A571

1979, June 2 **Litho.** ***Perf. 13½***
1236 A571 100p shown .85 .35
1237 A571 200p Tea .85 .35
1238 A571 300p Sorghum 1.60 .45
1239 A571 400p Common flax 1.60 .55
Nos. 1236-1239 (4) 4.90 1.70

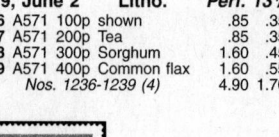

Laurel and Regimental Emblem — A572

1979, June 9
1240 A572 200p gold & multi .70 .35

Founding of Subteniente Berdina Village in memory of Sub-lieutenant Rodolfo Hernan Berdina, killed by terrorists in 1975.

"75" and Automobile Club Emblem A573

1979, June 9
1241 A573 200p gold & multi .60 .35

Argentine Automobile Club, 75th anniv.

Exchange Building and Emblem A574

1979, June 9
1242 A574 200p bl, blk & gold .60 .35

Grain Exchange, 125th anniversary.

Cavalry Officer, 1817 — A575

1979, July 7 **Litho.** ***Perf. 13½***
1243 A575 200p multi 1.25 .35

Army Day.

Corvette Uruguay and Navy Emblem A576

Design: No. 1245, Hydrographic service ship & emblem.

1979 ***Perf. 13***
1244 A576 250p multi 1.65 .35
1245 A576 250p multi 1.65 .35

Navy Day; Cent. of Naval Hydrographic Service. Issued: No. 1244, July 28; No. 1245, July 7.

Tree and Man — A577

1979, July 28 ***Perf. 13½***
1246 A577 250p multi .85 .35

Protection of the Environment Day, June 5.

"Spad" Flying over Andes, and Vicente Almandos Almonacid
A578

1979, Aug. 4

1247 A578 250p multi 1.00 .35

Air Force Day.

Gen. Julio A. Roca Occupying Rio Negro, by Juan M. Blanes — A579

1979, Aug. 4

1248 A579 250p multi 1.00 .35

Conquest of Rio Negro Desert, centenary.

Rowland Hill — A580

1979, Sept. 29 Litho. *Perf. 13½*

1249 A580 300p gray red & blk .90 .35

Sir Rowland Hill (1795-1879), originator of penny postage.

Viedma Navarez Monument — A581

1979, Sept. 29

1250 A581 300p multi 1.10 .35

Viedma and Carmen de Patagones towns, bicentenary.

Pope Paul VI — A582

Design: No. 1252, Pope John Paul I.

1979, Oct. 27 Engr. *Perf. 13½*

1251 A582 500p black 1.25 .35

1252 A582 500p sepia 1.25 .35

No. 1169 Overprinted in Red

1979, Nov. 10 Photo. *Perf. 13½*

1253 A539 200p lt blue & blk .90 .35

Rosario Philatelic Society, 75th anniversary.

A583

1979, Nov. 10 Litho.

1254 A583 300p multi 1.00 .35

Frontier resettlement.

A584

1979, Dec. 1 Litho. *Perf. 13½*

1255 A584 300p multi 1.00 .35

Military Geographic Institute centenary.

Christmas 1979 — A585

1979, Dec. 1

1256 A585 300p multi .90 .40

General Mosconi Birth Centenary A586

1979, Dec. 15 Engr. *Perf. 13½*

1257 A586 1000p blk & bl 1.75 .50

Rotary Emblem and Globe — A587

1979, Dec. 29 Litho.

1258 A587 300p multi 2.00 .35

Rotary International, 75th anniversary.

Child and IYC Emblem — A588

Family, by Pablo Menicucci A589

1979, Dec. 29

1259 A588 500p lt bl & sepia 1.00 .35

1260 A589 1000p multi 1.75 .35

International Year of the Child.

Microphone, Waves, ITU Emblem — A590

1980, Mar. 22 Litho. *Perf. 13x13½*

1261 A590 500p multi 1.65 .35

Regional Administrative Conference on Broadcasting by Hectometric Waves for Area 2, Buenos Aires, Mar. 10-29.

Guillermo Brown — A591

1980 Engr. *Perf. 13½*

1262 A591 5000p black 5.25 .35

See No. 1372.

Argentine Red Cross Centenary A592

1980, Apr. 19 Litho. *Perf. 13½*

1263 A592 500p multi .80 .35

OAS Emblem — A593

1980, Apr. 19

1264 A593 500p multi .80 .35

Day of the Americas, Apr. 14.

Dish Antennae, Balcarce A594

No. 1266, Hydroelectric Station, Salto Grande. No. 1267, Bridge, Zarate-Brazo Largo.

1980, Apr. 26 Litho. & Engr.

1265 A594 300p shown .75 .35

1266 A594 300p multicolored .75 .35

1267 A594 300p multicolored .75 .35

Nos. 1265-1267 (3) 2.25 1.05

Capt. Hipolito Bouchard, Frigate "Argentina" — A595

1980, May 31 Litho. *Perf. 13x13½*

1268 A595 500p multicolored 1.40 .35

Navy Day.

"Villarino," San Martin, by Theodore Gericault — A596

1980, May 31

1269 A596 500p multicolored 1.40 .35

Return of the remains of Gen. Jose de San Martin to Argentina, centenary.

Buenos Aires Gazette, 1810, Signature A597

1980, June 7 *Perf. 13½*

1270 A597 500p multicolored .80 .35

Journalism Day.

Miniature Sheet

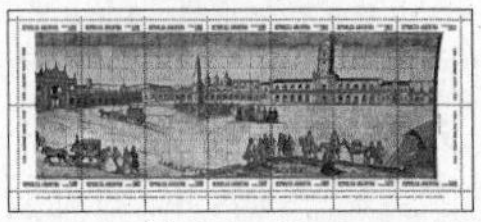

Coaches in Victoria Square — A598

1980 June 14

1271 A598 Sheet of 14 21.00 17.50

a.-n. 500p any single .90 .50

Buenos Aires, 400th anniv. No. 1271 shows ceramic mural of Victoria Square by Rodolfo Franco in continuous design. See No. 1285.

Gen. Pedro Aramburu — A599

1980, July 12 Litho. *Perf. 13½*

1272 A599 500p yel & blk .90 .35

Gen. Pedro Eugenio Aramburu (1903-1970), provisional president, 1955.

Army Day — A600

1980, July 12

1273 A600 500p multicolored 1.10 .35

Gen. Juan Gregorio de Las Heras (1780-1866), Hero of 1817 War of Independence A601

Grandees of Argentina Bicentenary: No. 1275, Rivadavia. No. 1276, Brig. Gen Jose Matias Zapiola (1780-1874), naval commander and statesman.

1980, Aug. 2 Litho. *Perf. 13½*

1274 A601 500p tan & blk .80 .35

1275 A601 500p multicolored .80 .35

1276 A601 500p lt lilac & blk .80 .35

Nos. 1274-1276 (3) 2.40 1.05

Avro "Gosport" Biplane, Maj. Francisco de Artega — A602

1980, Aug. 16 *Perf. 13*
1277 A602 500p multicolored .85 .40

Air Force Day. Artega (1882-1930) was first director of Military Aircraft Factory where Avro "Gosport" was built (1927).

University of La Plata, 75th Anniversary A603

1980, Aug. 16 *Perf. 13½*
1278 A603 500p multi .80 .35

Souvenir Sheets

A604

A605

No. 1279: a, King penguin. b, Bearded penguin. c, Adelie penguins. d, Papua penguins. e, Sea elephants. f, Puerto Soledad, 1829. g, Puerto Soledad harbor, 1829. h, Fur seals. i, Giant petrels. j, Blue-eyed cororants. k, Stormy petrels. l, Antarctic doves.

No. 1280: Letters a-e and h-l are the same as No. 1279. f, South Orkneys Argentine Base, towers and buildings. g, South Orkneys Argentine Base, buildings and mountains.

1980, Sept. 27 **Litho.** *Perf. 13½*
1279 A604 Sheet of 12 23.00 20.00
a.-l. 500p, any single .75 .60
1280 A605 Sheet of 12 23.00 20.00
f.-g. 500p, any single .75 .60

75th anniv. of Argentina's presence in the South Orkneys and 150th anniv. of political and military command in the Falkland Islands. Nos. 1279-1280 each contain 12 stamps (4x3) with landscape designs in center of sheets. Silhouettes of Argentine exploration ships in margins. No. 1280 contains Nos. 1279a-1279e, 1279h-1279m, 1280a-1280b.

Anti-smoking Campaign — A608

1980, Oct. 11
1282 A608 700p multi 1.10 .40

National Census — A609

1980, Sept.
1283 A609 500p blk & bl 1.40 .35

Madonna and Child (Congress Emblem) A610

1980, Oct. 1 **Litho.**
1284 A610 700p multi 1.10 .35

National Marian Cong., Mendoza, Oct. 8-12

Mural Type of 1980
Miniature Sheet

1980, Oct. 25
1285 Sheet of 14 21.00 17.50
a.-n. A598 500p, any single .65 .50

Buenos Aires, 400th anniv./Buenos Aires '80 Stamp Exhib., Oct. 24-Nov. 2. No. 1285 shows ceramic mural Arte bajo la Ciudad by Alfredo Guido in continuous design.

Technical Military Academy, 50th Anniversary — A611

1980, Nov. 1
1286 A611 700p multi 1.00 .35

Amateur Radio Operation — A612

1980, Nov. 1
1287 A612 700p multi 1.00 .35

Medal — A613

Lujan Cathedral Floor Plan — A614

1980, Nov. 29 **Litho.** *Perf. 13½*
1288 A613 700p multi 1.00 .35
1289 A614 700p olive & brn 1.00 .35

Christmas 1980. 150th anniv. of apparition of Holy Virgin to St. Catherine Laboure, Paris (No. 1288), 350th anniv. of apparition at Lujan.

150th Death Anniversary of Simon Bolivar — A615

1980, Dec. 13
1290 A615 700p multi 1.00 .40

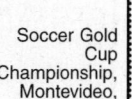

Soccer Gold Cup Championship, Montevideo, 1980 — A616

1981, Jan. 3 **Litho.**
1291 A616 1000p multi 1.35 .40

San Martin Type of 1978

1981, Jan. 20 **Engr.** *Perf. 13½*
1292 A553 10,000p dark blue 7.75 .35

Landscape in Lujan, by Marcos Tiglio — A617

Paintings: No. 1304, Expansion of Light along a Straight Line, by Miguel Angel Vidal, vert.

1981, Apr. 11 **Litho.**
1303 A617 1000p multi 1.10 .45
1304 A617 1000p multi 1.10 .45

Intl. Sports Medicine Congress, June 7-12 — A618

1981, June 6 **Litho.** *Perf. 13½*
1305 A618 1000p bl & dk brn 1.00 .35

Esperanza Base, Antarctica A619

Cargo Plane, Map of Vice-Commodore Marambio Island — A620

Perf. 13½, 13x13½ (No. 1308)

1981, June 13
1306 A619 1000p shown 1.60 .75
1307 A619 2000p Almirante Irizar 3.00 .85
1308 A620 2000p shown 2.90 1.35
Nos. 1306-1308 (3) 7.50 2.95

Antarctic Treaty 20th anniv.

Antique Pistols (Military Club Centenary) A621

1981, June 27 *Perf. 13½*
1309 A621 1000p Club building 1.10 .35
1310 A621 2000p shown 1.10 .35

Gen. Juan A. Alvarez de Arenales (1770-1831) — A622

Famous Men: No. 1312, Felix G. Frias (1816-1881), writer. No. 1313, Jose E. Uriburu (1831-1914), statesman.

1981, Aug. 8 **Litho.** *Perf. 13½*
1311 A622 1000p multi .90 .35
1312 A622 1000p multi .90 .35
1313 A622 1000p multi .90 .35
Nos. 1311-1313 (3) 2.70 1.05

Naval Observatory Centenary — A623

1981, Aug. 15 **Litho.** *Perf. 13x13½*
1314 A623 1000p multi 1.25 .35

No. 1176 Overprinted in Red

1981, Aug. 15 **Photo.** *Perf. 13½*
1315 A540 1000p lem & blk 2.00 .35

50th anniv. of Bahia Blanca Philatelic and Numismatic Society.

St. Cayetano, Stained-glass Window, Buenos Aires — A624

1981, Sept. 5 **Litho.** *Perf. 13½*
1316 A624 1000p multi .95 .35

St. Cayetano, founder of Teatino Order, 500th birth anniv.

Pablo Castaibert (1883-1909) and his Monoplane (Air Force Day) — A625

1981, Sept. 5 *Perf. 13x13½*
1317 A625 1000p multi 1.35 .40

Intl. Year of the Disabled A626

1981, Sept. 10 *Perf. 13½*
1318 A626 1000p multi 1.00 .35

22nd Latin-American Steelmakers' Congress, Buenos Aires, Sept. 21-23 — A627

1981, Sept. 19
1319 A627 1000p multi .85 .35

Army Regiment No. 1 (Patricios), 175th Anniv. — A628

1981, Oct. 10 **Litho.** *Perf. 13½*
1320 1500p Natl. arms .75 .35
1321 1500p shown .75 .35
a. A628 Pair, #1320-1321 2.00 2.00

A629

San Martin as artillery Captain in Battle of Bailen, 1808.

1981, Oct. 5

1322 Sheet of 8 + 4 labels 6.75 6.75
a. A629 1000p multi .50 .35
b. A629 1500p multi .65 .55

Espamer '81 Intl. Stamp Exhib. (Americas, Spain, Portugal), Buenos Aires, Nov. 13-22.

No. 1322 contains 2 each se-tenant pairs with label between.

A630

1981, Oct. 5

1323 A630 1000p multi 7.00 .40

Anti-indiscriminate whaling.

Espamer '81 Emblem and Ship — A631

1981

1324 A631 1300p multi 1.25 .40

No. 1324 Overprinted in Blue

1981, Nov. 7 Photo. *Perf. 13½*

1325 A631 1300p multi 1.75 .40

Postal Administration philatelic training course.

Soccer Players A632

Designs: Soccer players.

1981, Nov. 13 Litho.

1326 A632 Sheet of 4 + 2 labels 9.00 9.00
a. 2000p multi 1.50 1.25
b. 3000p multi 1.75 1.50
c. 5000p multi 2.00 1.75
d. 15,000p multi 2.25 2.00

Espamer '81.

"Peso" Coin Centenary A633

2000p, Patacon, 1881. 3000p, Argentine Oro, 1881.

1981, Nov. 21

1327 A633 2000p multicolored .80 .35
1328 A633 3000p multicolored .80 .35

Christmas 1981 — A634

1981, Dec. 12

1329 A634 1500p multi 2.60 .50

Traffic Safety — A635

1000p, Observe traffic lights, vert. 2000p, Drive carefully, vert. 3000p, Cross at white lines. 4000p, Don't shine headlights.

1981, Dec. 19 Litho.

1330 A635 1000p multicolored 1.90 .40
1331 A635 2000p multicolored 1.00 .50
1332 A635 3000p multicolored 1.50 .45
1333 A635 4000p multicolored 1.50 .65
Nos. 1330-1333 (4) 5.90 2.00

Francisco Luis Bernardez, Ciuda Laura — A636

Writers and title pages from their works: 2000p, Lucio V. Mansilla, Excursion a los indios ranqueles. 3000p, Conrado Nale Roxlo, El Grillo. 4000p, Victoria Ocampo, Sur.

1982, Mar. 20 Litho.

1334 A636 1000p shown 2.00 .40
1335 A636 2000p multi 1.00 .40
1336 A636 3000p multi 1.00 .50
1337 A636 4000p multi 2.00 .30
Nos. 1334-1337 (4) 6.00 1.60

No. 1218 Overprinted

1982, Apr. 17 Photo. *Perf. 13½*

1338 A559 1700p green & blue .95 .35

Argentina's claim on Falkland Islands.

Robert Koch — A637

1982, Apr. 17 Litho. Wmk. 365

1339 A637 2000p multi 1.40 .35

TB bacillus centenary and 25th Intl. Tuberculosis Conference.

American Airforces Commanders' 22nd Conf. — A638

1982, Apr. 17

1340 A638 2000p multi 1.50 .35

Stone Carving, City Founder's Signature (Don Hernando de Lerma) — A639

1982, Apr. 17

1341 A639 2000p multi 1.75 .40

Souvenir Sheet

1342 A639 5000p multi 3.25 3.25

City of Salta, 400th anniv. No. 1342 contains one 43x30mm stamp.

Naval Center Centenary — A640

1982, Apr. 24 *Perf. 13x13½*

1343 A640 2000p multi 1.00 .35

Chorisia Speciosa — A641

200p, Zinnia peruviana. 300p, Ipomoea purpurea. 400p, Tillandsia aeranthos. 800p, Oncidium bifolium. 1000p, Erythrina cristagalli. 2000p, Jacaranda mimosi-folia. 3000p, Bauhinia candicans. 5000p, Tecoma stans. 10,000p, Tabebuia ipe. 20,000p, Passiflora coerulea. 30,000p, Aristolochia littoralis. 50,000p, Oxalis enneaphylla.

1982 Unwmk. Photo. *Perf. 13½*

1344 A641 200p multi .40 .30
1345 A641 300p multi .40 .30
1346 A641 400p multi .40 .30
1347 A641 500p shown .35 .30
1348 A641 800p multi .35 .30
1349 A641 1000p multi .40 .30
1350 A641 2000p multi .40 .30
1351 A641 3000p multi .90 .30
1352 A641 5000p multi .85 .30
1353 A641 10,000p multi 1.40 .30
1354 A641 20,000p multi 1.75 .40
1355 A641 30,000p multi 2.50 .45
1356 A641 50,000p multi 5.00 .75
Nos. 1344-1356 (13) 15.10 4.60

Nos. 1344-1346, 1348-1350 issued on fluorescent paper. Nos. 1353-1356 issued on ordinary paper. Others issued on both fluorescent and ordinary paper.

Issued: 500p, 2000p, 5000p, 10,000p, 5/22; 200p, 300p, 1000p, 20,000p, 9/25; 400p, 800p, 30,000p, 50,000p, 12/4; 3000p, 12/18.

See Nos. 1429-1443A, 1515-1527, 1683-1691. For overprint see No. 1382.

10th Death Anniv. of Gen. Juan C. Sanchez — A641a

1982, May 29 Litho. Wmk. 365

1364 A641a 5000p grn & blk 1.10 .40

Luis Vernet, First Commander — A641b

1982, June 12

1365 A641b 5000p org & blk 2.00 1.10

Size: 83x28mm

1366 A641b 5000p Map 1.25 .90
a. Pair, Nos. 1365-1366 3.25 2.75

153rd Anniv. of Malvinas Political and Military Command District.

Compare with No. 1411.

Visit of Pope John Paul II — A641c

1982, June 12

1367 A641c 5000p multi 2.25 .55

Organ Grinder, by Aldo Severi (b. 1928) — A641d

3000p, Still Life, by Santiago Cogorno (b. 1915).

1982, July 3 Wmk. 365

1368 A641d 2000p shown 1.00 .40
1369 A641d 3000p multi 1.00 .40

Guillermo Brown Type of 1980 and

Jose de San Martin — A641e

Litho. and Engr.

1982 Unwmk. *Perf. 13½*

1372 A591 30,000p blk & bl 4.00 .70
1376 A641e 50,000p sepia & car 7.75 1.00

Issue dates: 30,000p, June; 50,000p, July.

Scouting Year — A641f

Wmk. 365

1982, Aug. 7 Litho. *Perf. 13½*

1380 A641f 5000p multi 2.60 .50

Alconafta Fuel Campaign — A641g

1982, Aug. 7 Wmk. 365

1381 A641g 2000p multi 1.10 .40

No. 1352 Overprinted

1982, Aug. 7 Photo. Unwmk.

1382 A641 5000p multi 2.60 1.00

Rio III Central Nuclear Power Plant, Cordoba A642

Wmk. 365

1982, Sept. 4 Litho. *Perf. 13½*
1383 A642 2000p shown .70 .40
1384 A642 2000p Control room .70 .40

Namibia Day — A643

1982, Sept. 4
1385 A643 5000p Map 1.20 .35

Formosa Cathedral A644

Churches and Cathedrals of the Northeast: 2000p, Our Lady of Itati, Corrientes, vert. 3000p, Resistencia Cathedral, Chaco, vert. 10,000p, St. Ignatius Church ruins, Misiones.

1982, Sept. 18 Litho. & Engr.
1386 A644 2000p dk grn & blk .70 .65
1387 A644 3000p dk brn & brn .70 .65
1388 A644 5000p dk bl & brn 1.25 .65
1389 A644 10,000p dp org & blk 1.25 .65
Nos. 1386-1389 (4) 3.90 2.60

Tension Sideral, by Mario Alberto Agatiello — A645

Sculpture (Espamer '81 and Juvenex '82 Exhibitions): 3000p, Sugerencia II, by Eduardo Mac Entyre. 5000p, Storm, by Carlos Silva.

1982, Oct. 2 Litho. *Perf. 13½*
1390 A645 2000p multi 2.25 .40
1391 A645 3000p multi 2.25 .40
1392 A645 5000p multi 2.25 .45
Nos. 1390-1392 (3) 6.75 1.25

Santa Fe Bridge — A646

1982, Oct. 16 Litho. & Engr.
1393 A646 2000p bl & blk 1.25 .40

2nd Southern Cross Games, Santa Fe and Rosario, Nov. 26-Dec. 5.

10th World Men's Volleyball Championship A647

1982, Oct. 16 Litho. Wmk. 365
1394 A647 2000p multi .75 .35
1395 A647 5000p multi 1.00 .35

Los Andes Newspaper Centenary A648

Design: Army of the Andes Monument, Hill of Glory, Mendoza.

1982, Oct. 30
1396 A648 5000p multi .85 .40

A649

1982, Oct. 30 Wmk. 365
1397 A649 5000p Signs .90 .40

50th Anniv. of Natl. Roads, Administration.

A650

A650a

La Plata City Cent., each 2500p: No. 1400: a, Cathedral, diff. b, Head, top. c, Observatory. d, City Hall, diff. e, Head, bottom. f, University.

1982, Nov. 20 Litho.
1398 A650 5000p Cathedral 1.10 .50
1399 A650 5000p City Hall 1.10 .50
1400 A650a Sheet of 6 4.00 4.00
a.-f. 2500p Any single .35 .25

Well, Natl. Hydrocarbon Congress Emblem A651

1982, Nov. 20
1401 A651 5000p multi 1.40 .40

Oil Discovery, Comodoro Rivadavia, 75th anniv.

Jockey Club of Buenos Aires Centenary — A652

Design: No. 1403, Carlos Pellegrini, first president.

1982, Dec. 4 Litho.
1402 A652 5000p Emblem 1.25 .40
1403 A652 5000p multi 1.25 .40

Christmas — A653

3000p, St. Vincent de Paul. 5000p, St. Francis of Assisi.

1982, Dec. 18 *Perf. 13½*
1404 A653 3000p multi 2.25 1.00

Size: 29x38mm

1405 A653 5000p multi 1.60 .50

Pedro B. Palacios (1854-1917), Writer — A654

Writers: 2000p, Leopoldo Marechal (1900-1970). 3000p, Delfina Bunge de Galvez (1881-1952). 4000p, Manuel Galvez (1882-1962). 5000p, Evaristo Carriego (1883-1912).

1983, Mar. 26 Litho. *Perf. 13½*
1406 A654 1000p multi .75 .40
1407 A654 2000p multi .75 .40
1408 A654 3000p multi .75 .40
1409 A654 4000p multi .75 .40
1410 A654 5000p multi .75 .40
a. Strip of 5, #1406-1410 4.00 4.00

Recovery of the Malvinas (Falkland Islands) A655

20,000p, Map, flag.

1983, Apr. 9 Litho. *Perf. 13½*
1411 A655 20,000p multi 2.00 .60

Compare No. 1411 with No. 1366.

Telecommunications Systems — A656

No. 1412, SITRAM, No. 1413, ARPAC network.

1983, Apr. 16 Wmk. 365
1412 A656 5000p multi 1.50 .65
1413 A656 5000p multi 1.50 .65

Naval League Emblem — A657

1983, May 14 Litho. *Perf. 13½*
1414 A657 5000p multi .90 .40

Navy Day and 50th anniv. of Naval League.

Allegory, by Victor Rebuffo — A658

1983, May 14
1415 A658 5000p multi .90 .40

Natl. Arts Fund, 25th Anniv.

75th Anniv. of Colon Opera House, Buenos Aires — A659

1983, May 28 Wmk. 365
1416 A659 5000p Main hall 1.00 .40
1417 A659 10000p Stage 1.25 .40

Protected Species A660

1p, Chrysocyon brachtyurus. 1.50p, Ozotocerus bezoarticus. 2p, Myrmecophaga tridactyla. 2.50p, Leo onca.

1983, July 2 Litho. *Perf. 13½*
1418 A660 1p multicolored 1.20 .40
1419 A660 1.50p multicolored 1.75 .40
1420 A660 2p multicolored 1.90 .40
1421 A660 2.50p multicolored 2.00 .40
Nos. 1418-1421 (4) 6.85 1.60

City of Catamarca, 300th Anniv. — A661

Foundation of the City of Catamarca, by Luis Varela Lezana (1900-1982).

1983, July 16 Litho. *Perf. 13½*
1422 A661 1p multi .75 .40

Mamerto Esquiu (1826-1883) — A662

1983, July 16
1423 A662 1p multi .75 .40

Bolivar, by Herrera Toro — A663

Bolivar, Engraving by Kepper — A664

Perf. 13 (A663), 13½ (A664)

1983 Unwmk.
1424 A663 1p multi .55 .50
1425 A664 2p blk & maroon .75 .65
1426 A664 10p San Martin 4.00 .75
Nos. 1424-1426 (3) 5.30 1.90

Issue dates: 1p, 2p, July 23. 10p, Aug. 20.
See Nos. 1457-1462B.

Gen. Toribio de Luzuriaga (1782-1842) — A665

1983, Aug. 20 Litho. *Perf. 13½*

1427 A665 1p multi .85 .40

50th Anniv. of San Martin National Institute — A666

1983, Aug. 20 Engr. Unwmk.

1428 A666 2p sepia .85 .40

Flower Type of 1982 in New Currency

1983-85 Photo. *Perf. 13½*

1429	A641	5c like #1347	.70	.30
1430	A641	10c like #1349	.35	.30
1431	A641	20c like #1350	.35	.30
1432	A641	30c like #1351	.55	.30
1433	A641	40c Eichhornia crassipes	.35	.30
1434	A641	50c like #1352	.35	.30
1435	A641	1p like #1353	.40	.30
1435A	A641	1.80p Mutisia retusa	.40	.30
1436	A641	2p like #1354	.50	.30
1437	A641	3p like #1355	.55	.30
1438	A641	5p like #1356	.55	.30
1439	A641	10p Alstroemeria aurantiaca	1.50	.80
1440	A641	20p like #1345	.55	.30
1441	A641	30p Embothrium coccineum	2.75	.30
1442	A641	50p like #1346	.85	.40
1443	A641	100p like #1348	2.40	.30
1443A	A641	300p Cassia carnaval	2.75	.50
		Nos. 1429-1443A (17)	15.85	5.90

Issued: 20p, 8/27/84; 50p, 10/19/84; 100p, 12/84; 300p, 6/15/85.

Nos. 1429, 1433, 1435A issued on fluorescent paper. Nos. 1443, 1443A issued on ordinary paper. Others issued on both ordinary and fluorescent paper.

No. 1440 has denomination at UL.

For overprint and surcharge see Nos. 1489, 1530.

Intl. Rotary South American Regional Conference, Buenos Aires, Sept. 25-28 — A667

1983, Sept. 24 Litho.

1444 A667 1p multi 1.25 .40

9th Pan American Games, Caracas, Aug. 13-28 — A668

1983, Sept. 24

1445 A668 1p Track .65 .40
1446 A668 2p Emblem .90 .40

World Communications Year — A669

1983, Oct. 8 *Perf. 13½*

1447 A669 2p multi .85 .40

Squash Peddler by Antonio Berni (1905-1981) — A670

2p, Figure in Yellow by Luis Seoane (1910-79).

1983, Oct. 15 *Perf. 13½*

1448 A670 1p multi .80 .40
1449 A670 2p multi .80 .40

World Communications Year — A671

Designs: 1p, Wagon, 18th cent. 2p, Post chaise, 19th cent. 4p, Steam locomotive, 1857. 5p, Tramway, 1910.

1983, Nov. 19 Litho. *Perf. 13½*

1450 A671 1p multi .90 .40
1451 A671 2p multi .90 .40
1452 A671 4p multi 1.25 .40
1453 A671 5p multi 1.25 .40
Nos. 1450-1453 (4) 4.30 1.60

World Communications Year — A672

2p, General Post Office.

1983, Nov. 26 Litho. *Perf. 12½x12*

1454 A672 2p multicolored .65 .40

Return to Elected Government — A673

1983, Dec. 10 Photo. *Perf. 13½*

1455 A673 2p Coin, 1813 .90 .40

Eudyptes Crestatus — A674

Designs: b, Diomedea exulans. c, Diomedea melanophris. d, Eudyptes chrysolophus. e, Luis Piedra Buena. f, Carlos Maria Moyano. g, Luis Py. h, Augusto Lasserre. i, Phoebetria palpebrata. j, Hydrurga leptonyx. k, Lobodon carcinophagus. l, Leptonychotes weddelli.

1983, Dec. 10 Litho.

1456 A674 Sheet of 12 12.50 12.50
a.-l. 2p any single .40 .25

Southern pioneers and fauna. Margin depicts various airplanes and emblems.

Bolivar Type of 1983

Famous men: 10p, Angel J. Carranza (1834-99), historian. No. 1458, 500p, Guillermo Brown. No. 1459, Estanislao del Campo (1834-80), poet. 30p, Jose Hernandez (1834-86), author. 40p, Vicente Lopez y Planes (1784-1856), poet and patriot. 50p, San Martin. 200p, Belgrano.

1983-85 Litho. & Engr. *Perf. 13½*

1457	A664	10p pale bl & dk bl	.65	.40
1458	A664	20p dk bl & blk	.65	.40
1459	A664	20p dl brn ol & ol blk	.65	.40
1460	A664	30p pale bl & bluish blk	.75	.40
1461	A664	40p lt bl grn & blk	1.25	.40
1462	A664	50p Prus grn & choc	3.00	1.50
1462A	A664	200p int bl & blk	2.60	1.00
1462B	A664	500p brn & int bl	2.50	.50
		Nos. 1457-1462B (8)	12.05	5.00

Issued: No. 1458, 10/6; 10p, No. 1459, 30p, 40p, 3/23/85; 50p, 4/23/85; 200p, 11/2/85; 500p, 5/2/85.

Christmas 1983 — A675

Nativity Scenes: 2p, Tapestry, by Silke. 3p, Stained-glass window, San Carlos de Bariloche's Wayn Church, vert.

1983, Dec. 17 Litho. *Perf. 13½*

1463 A675 2p multi .65 .35
1464 A675 3p multi 1.25 .45

Centenary of El Dia Newspaper — A676

4p, Masthead, printing roll.

1984, Mar. 24 Litho.

1465 A676 4p multicolored .70 .40

Alejandro Carbo Teachers' College Centenary A677

1984, June 2 Litho. *Perf. 13½*

1466 A677 10p Building .70 .40

1984 Olympics A678

Designs: No. 1468, Weightlifting, discus, shot put. No. 1469, Javelin, fencing. No. 1470, Bicycling, swimming.

1984, July 28 Litho. *Perf. 13½*

1467 A678 5p shown .65 .45
1468 A678 5p multicolored .65 .45
1469 A678 10p multicolored 1.10 .55
1470 A678 10p multicolored 1.10 .55
Nos. 1467-1470 (4) 3.50 2.00

Rosario Stock Exchange Centenary — A679

1984, Aug. 11

1471 A679 10p multicolored .75 .40

Wheat — A680

1984, Aug. 11

1472 A680 10p shown .85 .40
1473 A680 10p Corn .85 .40
1474 A680 10p Sunflower .85 .40
Nos. 1472-1474 (3) 2.55 1.20

18th FAO Regional Conference for Latin America and Caribbean (No. 1472); 3rd Natl. Corn Congress (No. 1473); World Food Day (No. 1474).

Wildlife Protection A681

No. 1475, Hippocamelus bisulcus. No. 1476, Vicugna vicugna. No. 1477, Aburria jacutinga. No. 1478, Mergus octosetaceus. No. 1479, Podiceps gallardoi.

1984, Sept. 22 Litho. *Perf. 13½*

1475 A681 20p multicolored 1.25 .80
1476 A681 20p multicolored 1.25 .80
1477 A681 20p multicolored 1.25 .80
1478 A681 20p multicolored 1.25 .80
1479 A681 20p multicolored 1.25 .80
Nos. 1475-1479 (5) 6.25 4.00

First Latin American Theater Festival, Cordoba, Oct. — A682

1984, Oct. 13 Litho. *Perf. 13½*

1480 A682 20p Mask .65 .40

Intl. Eucharistic Congress, 50th Anniv. — A683

Apostles' Communion, by Fra Angelico.

1984, Oct. 13

1481 A683 20p multicolored .70 .40

Glaciares Natl. Park (UNESCO World Heritage List) — A684

1984, Nov. 17 Litho.

1482 A684 20p Sea .90 .50
1483 A684 30p Glacier 1.40 .50

City of Puerto Deseado Centenary A685

No. 1485, Ushuaia centenary.

1984, Nov. 17 *Perf. 13½*

1484 A685 20p shown .95 .50
1485 A685 20p multicolored .95 .50

Childrens' Paintings, Christmas 1984 — A686

1984, Dec. 1 Litho. *Perf. 13½*

1486	A686	20p Diego Aguero	.80	.40
1487	A686	30p Leandro Ruiz	1.00	.40
1488	A686	50p Maria Castillo, vert.	1.10	.40
		Nos. 1486-1488 (3)	2.90	1.20

No. 1439 Overprinted

1984, Dec. 1 Photo. *Perf. 13½*

1489	A641	10p multicolored	.70	.45

Buenos Aires Philatelic Center, 50th anniv.

Vista Del Jardin Zoologico, by Fermin Eguia — A687

Paintings: No. 1491, El Congreso Iluminado, by Francisco Travieso. No. 1492, Galpones (La Boca), by Marcos Borio.

1984, Dec. 15 *Perf. 13½*

1490	A687	20p multi	.75	.50
1491	A687	20p multi, vert.	.75	.50
1492	A687	20p multi, vert.	.75	.50
		Nos. 1490-1492 (3)	2.25	1.50

Gen. Martin Miguel de Guemes (1785-1821) A688

1985, Mar. 23 Litho. *Perf. 13½*

1493	A688	30p multicolored	.75	.50

ARGENTINA '85 Exhibition A689

First airmail service from: 20p, Buenos Aires to Montevideo, 1917. 40p, Cordoba to Villa Dolores, 1925. 60p, Bahia Blanca to Comodoro Rivadavia, 1929. 80p, Argentina to Germany, 1934. 100p, naval service to the Antarctic, 1952.

1985, Apr. 27

1494	A689	20p Bleriot Gnome	.40	.40
1495	A689	40p Junker F-13L	.65	.40
1496	A689	60p Latte 25	.95	.40
1497	A689	80p L.Z. 127 Graf Zeppelin	1.20	.60
1498	A689	100p Consolidated PBY Catalina	1.60	.60
		Nos. 1494-1498 (5)	4.80	2.40

Central Bank, 50th Anniv. — A690

80p, Bank Building, Buenos Aires.

1985, June 1

1499	A690	80p multicolored	.95	.50

Jose A. Ferreyra (1889-1943), Director of Munequitas Portenas A691

Famous directors and their films: No. 1501, Leopoldo Torre Nilsson (1924-1978), scene from Martin Fierro.

1985, June 1

1500	A691	100p shown	1.00	.50
1501	A691	100p multi	1.00	.50

Carlos Gardel (1890-1935), Entertainer — A692

Paintings: No. 1502, Gardel playing the guitar on stage, by Carlos Alonso (b. 1929). No. 1503, Gardel in a wide-brimmed hat, by Hermenegildo Sabat (b. 1933). No. 1504, Portrait of Gardel in an ornamental frame, by Aldo Severi (b. 1928) and Martiniano Arce (b. 1939).

1985, June 15

1502	A692	200p multi	1.75	.75
1503	A692	200p multi	1.75	.75
1504	A692	200p multi	1.75	.75
		Nos. 1502-1504 (3)	5.25	2.25

The Arrival, by Pedro Figari — A693

A Halt on the Plains, by Prilidiano Pueyrredon — A693a

Oil paintings (details): 30c, The Wagon Square, by C. B. de Quiros.

1985, July 6 Litho. *Perf. 13½*

1505	A693	20c multi	1.20	.50
1506	A693	30c multi	1.60	.50

Souvenir Sheet

Perf. 12

1507	A693a	Sheet of 2	4.00	4.00
a.		20c Pilgrims, vert.	.40	.40
b.		30c Wagon	.45	.45

ARGENTINA '85. No. 1507 contains one 30x40mm and one 40x30mm stamp. See No. 1542.

Buenos Aires to Montevideo, 1917 Teodoro Fels Flight — A694

Historic flight covers: No. 1509, Villa Dolores to Cordoba, 1925. No. 1510, Buenos Aires to France, 1929 St. Exupery flight. No. 1511, Buenos Aires to Bremerhaven, 1934 Graf Zeppelin flight. No. 1512, 1st Antarctic flight, 1952.

1985, July 13 *Perf. 12x12½*

1508	A694	10c emer & multi	.75	.40
1509	A694	10c ultra & multi	.75	.40
1510	A694	10c lt choc & multi	.75	.40
1511	A694	10c chnt & multi	.75	.40
1512	A694	10c ap grn & multi	.75	.40
		Nos. 1508-1512 (5)	3.75	2.00

ARGENTINA '85.

Illuminated Fruit, by Fortunato Lacamera (1887-1951) A695

Paintings: 20c, Woman with Bird, by Juan del Prete, vert.

1985, Sept. 7 *Perf. 13½*

1513	A695	20c multi	1.10	.60
1514	A695	30c multi	1.25	.60

Flower Types of 1982-85

Designs: 1a, Begonia micranthera var. hieronymi. 5a, Gymnocalycium bruchii.

1985-88 Photo. *Perf. 13½*

1515	A641	½c like #1356	.95	.25
1516	A641	1c like #1439	.55	.25
1517	A641	2c like #1345	.55	.25
1518	A641	3c like #1441	.55	.25
1519	A641	5c like #1346	.55	.25
1520	A641	10c like #1348	.95	.25
1521	A641	20c like #1347	.75	.25
1522	A641	30c like #1443A	1.50	.30
1523	A641	50c like #1344	2.00	.30
1524	A641	1a multi	1.50	.35
1525	A641	2a like #1351	1.10	.25
1526	A641	5a multi	6.50	2.50

Size: 15x23mm

1527	A641	8½c like #1349	.55	.25
		Nos. 1515-1527 (13)	18.00	5.70

Issued: ½c, 1c, 12/16; 2c, 8½c, 30c, 9/18; 3c, 5c, 10c, 50c, 1a, 9/7; 20c, 10/17; 5a, 3/21/87; 2a, 12/5/88.

No. 1435 Surcharged

1986, Nov. 4 Photo. *Perf. 13½*

1530	A641	10c on 1p No. 1435	1.25	.50

Folk Musical Instruments — A699

1985, Sept. 14 Litho. *Perf. 13½*

1531	A699	20c Frame drum	.85	.60
1532	A699	20c Long flute	.85	.60
1533	A699	20c Jew's harp	.85	.60
1534	A699	20c Pan flutes	.85	.60
1535	A699	20c Musical bow	.85	.60
		Nos. 1531-1535 (5)	4.25	3.00

Juan Bautista Alberdi (1810-1884), Historian, Politician — A700

Famous men: 20c, Nicolas Avellaneda (1836-1885), President in 1874. 30c, Fr. Luis Beltran (1784-1827), military and naval engineer. 40c, Ricardo Levene (1885-1959), historian, author.

1985, Oct. 5

1536	A700	10c multi	.35	.35
1537	A700	20c multi	.60	.35
1538	A700	30c multi	.85	.50
1539	A700	40c multi	1.60	.60
		Nos. 1536-1539 (4)	3.40	1.80

Type of 1985 and

Skaters — A701

Deception, by J. H. Rivoira — A702

1985, Oct. 19 Litho. *Perf. 13½*

1540	A701	20c multi	1.00	.40
1541	A702	30c multi	1.10	.40

Size: 147x75mm

Imperf

1542	A693a	1a multi	3.50	3.50

IYY. No. 1542 is inscribed in silver with the UN 40th anniversary and IYY emblems.

Provincial Views — A703

Designs: No. 1543, Rock Window, Buenos Aires. No. 1544, Forclaz Windmill, Entre Rios. No. 1545, Lake Potrero de los Funes, San Luis. No. 1546, Mission church, north-east province. No. 1547, Penguin colony, Punta Tombo, Chubut. No. 1548, Water Mirrors, Cordoba.

1985, Nov. 23 *Perf. 13½*

1543	A703	10c multi	.95	.40
1544	A703	10c multi	.95	.40
1545	A703	10c multi	.95	.40
1546	A703	10c multi	.95	.40
1547	A703	10c multi	.95	.40
1548	A703	10c multi	.95	.40
		Nos. 1543-1548 (6)	5.70	2.40

Christmas 1985 — A704

Designs: 10c, Birth of Our Lord, by Carlos Cortes. 20c, Christmas, by Hector Viola.

1985, Dec. 7

1549	A704	10c multi	.65	.40
1550	A704	20c multi	1.40	.75

Natl. Campaign for the Prevention of Blindness A705

1985, Dec. 7

1551	A705	10c multi	.75	.40

Rio Gallegos City, Cent. — A716

1985, Dec. 21 Litho. *Perf. 13½*

1552	A716	10c Church	1.75	.50

Natl. Grape Harvest Festival, 50th Anniv. — A717

1986, Mar. 15

1553	A717	10c multi	.75	.40

Exists with Wmk. 365, Value $20.

Historical Architecture in Buenos Aires — A718

Designs: No. 1554, Valentin Alsina House, Italian Period, 1860-70. No. 1555, House on Cerrito Street, French influence, 1880-1900. No. 1556, House on the Avenida de Mayo y Santiago del Estero, Art Nouveau, 1900-10. No. 1557, Customs Building, academic architecture, 1900-15. No. 1558, Isaac Fernandez Blanco Museum, house of architect Martin Noel, natl. restoration, 1910-30. Nos. 1554-1556 vert.

1986, Apr. 19

1554 A718 20c multi .85 .50
1555 A718 20c multi .85 .50
1556 A718 20c multi .85 .50
1557 A718 20c multi .85 .50
1558 A718 20c multi .85 .50
Nos. 1554-1558 (5) 4.25 2.50

Antarctic Bases, Pioneers and Fauna A719

Designs: a, Base, Jubany. b, Arctocephalus gazella. c, Otaria byronia. d, Gen. Belgrano Base. e, Daption capensis. f, Diomedia melanophris. g, Apterodytes patagonica. h, Macronectes giganteus. i, Hugo Alberto Acuna (1885-1953). j, Spheniscus magellanicus. k, Gallinago gallinage. l, Capt. Agustin del Castillo (1855-89).

1986, May 31

1559 A719 Sheet of 12 20.00 20.00
a.-l. 10c any single .90 .85

Famous People — A720

Designs: No. 1560, Dr. Alicia Moreau de Justo, human rights activist. No. 1561, Dr. Emilio Ravignani (1886-1954), historian. No. 1562, Indira Gandhi.

1986, July 5 Litho. *Perf. 13½*

1560 A720 10c multi .65 .50
1561 A720 10c multi .65 .50
1562 A720 30c multi 1.75 1.00
Nos. 1560-1562 (3) 3.05 2.00

Statuary, Buenos Aires — A721

20c, Fountain of the Nereids, by Dolores Lola Mora (1866-1936). 30c, Lamenting at Work, by Rogelio Yrurtia (1879-1950), horiz.

1986, July 5

1563 A721 20c multi 1.25 .45
1564 A721 30c multi 1.25 .45

Famous Men — A722

Designs: No. 1565, Francisco N. Laprida (1786-1829), politician. No. 1566, Estanislao Lopez (1786-1838), brigadier general. No. 1567, Francisco Ramirez (1786-1821), general.

1986, Aug. 9 Litho. *Perf. 13*

1565 A722 20c dl yel, brn & blk .75 .50
1566 A722 20c dl yel, brn & blk .75 .50
1567 A722 20c dl yel, brn & blk .75 .50
Nos. 1565-1567 (3) 2.25 1.50

Fr. Ceferino Namuncura (1886-1905) — A723

1986, Aug. 30 *Perf. 13½*

1568 A723 20c multi .85 .40

Miniature Sheets

Natl. Team Victory, 1986 World Cup Soccer Championships, Mexico — A724

Designs: No. 1569a-1569d, Team. Nos. 1569e-1569h, Shot on goal. Nos. 1570a-1570d, Action close-up. Nos. 1570e-1570h, Diego Maradona holding soccer cup.

1986, Nov. 8 Litho. *Perf. 13½*

1569 A724 Sheet of 8 14.50 *14.50*
a.-h. 75c any single 1.45 *1.45*
1570 A724 Sheet of 8 14.50 *14.50*
a.-h. 75c any single 1.45 *1.45*

San Francisco (Cordoba), Cent. — A725

20c, Municipal Building.

1986, Nov. 8

1571 A725 20c multicolored .75 .45

Trelew City (Chubut), Cent. — A726

20c, Old railroad station, 1865.

1986, Nov. 22 Litho. *Perf. 13½*

1572 A726 20c multicolored .75 .45

Mutualism Day — A727

1986, Nov. 22

1573 A727 20c multicolored 1.00 .50

Christmas A728

Designs: 20c, Naif retable, by Aniko Szabo (b. 1945). 30c, Everyone's Tree, by Franca Delacqua (b. 1947).

1986, Dec. 13 Litho. *Perf. 13½*

1574 A728 20c multicolored 1.20 .60
1575 A728 30c multicolored 1.40 .60

Santa Rosa de Lima, 400th Birth Anniv. — A729

1986, Dec. 13

1576 A729 50c multicolored 2.10 .85

Rio Cuarto Municipal Building — A730

No. 1578, Court Building, Cordoba.

1986, Dec. 20

1577 A730 20c shown 1.15 .45
1578 A730 20c multicolored 1.15 .45

Rio Cuarto City, bicent. Court Building, Cordoba, 50th anniv.

Antarctic Treaty, 25th Anniv. — A731

1987, Mar. 7 Litho. *Perf. 13½*

1579 A731 20c Marine biologist 1.25 .50
1580 A731 30c Ornithologist 1.75 .50

Souvenir Sheet

Perf. 12

1581 Sheet of 2 5.75 5.75
a. A731 20c like No. 1579 2.00 1.50
b. A731 30c like No. 1580 3.00 2.00

No. 1581 contains 2 stamps, size: 40x50mm. Exist imperf. Value $500.

Natl. Mortgage Bank, Cent. — A732

1987, Mar. 21 *Perf. 13½*

1582 A732 20c multicolored 1.05 .50

Natl. Cooperative Associations Movement A733

1987, Mar. 21

1583 A733 20c multicolored 1.05 .50

Second State Visit of Pope John Paul II — A734

Engr., Litho. (No. 1585)

1987, Apr. 4 *Perf. 13½*

1584 A734 20c shown .50 .35
1585 A734 80c Papal blessing 1.90 .90

Souvenir Sheet

Perf. 12

1586 A734 1a like 20c 3.75 3.00

No. 1586 contains one 40x50mm stamp.

Intl. Peace Year — A735

30c, Pigeon, abstract sculpture by Victor Kaniuka.

1987, Apr. 11 Litho.

1587 A735 20c multicolored .95 .40
1588 A735 30c multicolored .95 .40

Low Handicap World Polo Championships A736

Polo Players, painting by Alejandro Moy.

1987, Apr. 11

1589 A736 20c multicolored 1.10 .40

Miniature Sheet

ICOM '86 — A737

Designs: a, Emblem. b, Family crest, National History Museum, Buenos Aires. c, St. Bartholomew, Enrique Larreta Museum of Spanish Art, Buenos Aires. d, Zoomorphic club, Patagonian Museum, San Carlos de Bariloche. e, Supplication, anthropomorphic sculpture, Natural Sciences Museum, La Plata. f, Wrought iron lattice from the house of J. Urquiza, president of the Confederation of Argentina, Entre Rios History Museum, Parana. g, St. Joseph, 18th cent. wood figurine, Northern History Museum, Salta. h, Funerary urn, Provincial Archaeological Museum, Santiago del Estero.

1987, May 30

1590 A737 Sheet of 8 6.00 6.00
a.-h. 25c any single .60 .60

Intl. Council of Museums, 14th general conf.

Natl. College of Monserrat, Cordoba, 300th Anniv. — A738

1987, July 4 *Imperf.*

1591 A738 1a multicolored 2.25 2.25

Monserrat '87 Philatelic Exposition.

Fight Drug Abuse — A739

The Proportions of Man, by da Vinci.

1987, Aug. 15		*Perf. 13½*	
1592 A739 30c multicolored		1.40	.50

Famous Men — A740

Portraits and quotations: 20c, Jorge Luis Borges (1899-1986), writer. 30c, Armando Discepolo (1887-1971), playwright. 50c, Carlos A. Pueyrredon (1887-1962), professor, Legion of Honor laureate.

1987, Aug. 15		
1593 A740 20c multicolored	.75	.60
1594 A740 30c multicolored	.75	.60
1595 A740 50c multicolored	.75	.60
Nos. 1593-1595 (3)	2.25	1.80

Pillar Boxes

A741 A742

1987	**Photo.**	*Perf. 13½*	
1596 A741 (30c) yel, blk & dark red		1.15	.40
Booklet with 10 stamps		11.50	
1597 A742 (33c) lt blue grn, blk & yel		1.15	.40
Complete booklet, 10 #1597		11.50	

Issue dates: (30c), June 8; (33c), July 13.

The Sower, by Julio Vanzo — A743

1987, Sept. 12		
1598 A743 30c multicolored	1.00	.50

Argentine Agrarian Federation, 75th anniv.

10th Pan American Games, Indianapolis, Aug. 7-25 — A744

1987, Sept. 26		
1599 A744 20c Basketball	1.10	.50
1600 A744 30c Rowing	1.25	.50
1601 A744 50c Yachting	1.40	.50
Nos. 1599-1601 (3)	3.75	1.50

Children Playing Doctor, WHO Emblem A745

1987, Oct. 7		
1602 A745 30c multi	.75	.50

Vaccinate every child campaign.

Heroes of the Revolution — A746

Signing of the San Nicolas Accord, 1852, by Rafael del Villar — A747

Independence anniversaries and historic events: No. 1603, Maj.-Col. Ignacio Alvarez Thomas (1787-1857). No. 1604, Col. Manuel Crispulo Bernabe Dorrego (1787-1829). No. 1606, 18th cent. Spanish map of the Falkland Isls., administered by Jacinto de Altolaguirre.

1987, Oct. 17		
1603 A746 25c shown	.65	.40
1604 A746 25c multi	.65	.40
1605 A747 50c shown	1.25	.50
1606 A747 50c multi	1.25	.50
Nos. 1603-1606 (4)	3.80	1.80

Museum established in the House of the San Nicholas Accord, 50th anniv. (No. 1605); Jacinto de Altolaguirre (1754-1787), governor the Malvinas Isls. for the King of Spain (No. 1606).

Celedonio Galvan Moreno, 1st Director A748

1987, Nov. 21		
1607 A748 50c multicolored	1.05	.50

Postas Argentinas magazine, 50th anniv.

LRA National Radio, Buenos Aires, 50th Anniv. — A749

1987, Nov. 21		
1608 A749 50c multicolored	1.05	.50

Natl. Philatelic Society, Cent. — A750

1987, Nov. 21		
1609 A750 1a Jose Marco del Pont	1.90	.75

Christmas — A751

Tapestries: 50c, *Navidad,* by Alisia Frega. 1a, *Vitral,* by Silvina Trigos.

1987, Dec. 5		
1610 A751 50c multicolored	1.00	.50
1611 A751 1a multicolored	1.40	.75

Natl. Parks A752

1987, Dec. 19	*Perf. 13x13½*	
1612 A752 50c Baritu	1.75	.50
1613 A752 50c Nahuel Huapi	1.75	.50
1614 A752 50c Rio Pilcomayo	1.75	.50
1615 A752 50c Tierra del Fuego	1.75	.50
1616 A752 50c Iguacu	1.75	.50
Nos. 1612-1616 (5)	8.75	2.50

See Nos. 1647-1651, 1715-1719, 1742-1746.

Landscapes in Buenos Aires Painted by Jose Cannella A753

No. 1617, Caminito. No. 1618, Viejo Almacen.

1988-89	**Litho.**	*Perf. 13½*	
1617 A753 5a multi		3.25	1.25
1618 A753 10a multi		6.50	2.50
1618A A753 10a like No. 1618		1.60	.60
1618B A753 50a like No. 1617		1.60	.60
c. Wmk 365		*150.00*	20.00
Nos. 1617-1618B (4)		12.95	4.95

No. 1618 inscribed "Viejo Almacen"; No. 1618A inscribed "El Viejo Almacen."

Issue dates: 5a, No. 1618, 3/15; No. 1618A, 10/20; 50a, 5/30/89.

For overprint see No. 1635.

Minstrel in a Tavern, by Carlos Morel — A754

Paintings: No. 1620, Interior of Curuzu, by Candido Lopez.

1988, Mar. 19	**Litho.**	*Perf. 13½*	
1619 A754 1a shown		1.25	.50
1620 A754 1a multicolored		1.25	.50

See Nos. 1640-1641.

Argentine-Brazilian Economic Cooperation and Integration Program for Mutual Growth — A755

1988, Mar. 19		
1621 A755 1a multicolored	.90	.50

Cities of Alta Gracia and Corrientes, 400th Annivs. — A756

No. 1622, Alta Gracia Church. No. 1623, Chapel of St. Anne, Corrientes.

1988, Apr. 9	**Litho.**	*Perf. 13½*	
1622 A756 1a multicolored		1.25	.50
1623 A756 1a multicolored		1.25	.50

Labor Day A757

Grain Carriers, a tile mosaic by Alfredo Guido, Line D of Nueve de Julio station, Buenos Aires subway: a, (UL). b, (UR). c, (LL). d, (LR).

1988, May 21		
1624 A757 Block of 4	5.00	5.00
a.-d. 50c any single	.75	.75

1988 Summer Olympics, Seoul — A758

1988, July 16	**Litho.**	*Perf. 13½*	
1625 A758 1a Running		.60	.50
1626 A758 2a Soccer		1.40	.75
1627 A758 3a Field hockey		2.00	1.50
1628 A758 4a Tennis		2.25	1.25
Nos. 1625-1628 (4)		6.25	4.00

Mendoza Bank, Cent. — A759

Natl. Gendarmerie, Cent. — A760

1988, Aug. 13		
1629 A759 2a multicolored	1.50	.60
1630 A760 2a multicolored	1.50	.60

Sarmiento and Cathedral School to the North, Buenos Aires — A761

1988, Sept. 10	**Litho.**	*Perf. 13½*	
1631 A761 3a multicolored		1.50	.50

Domingo Faustino Sarmiento (1811-1888), educator, politician.

St. Cayetano, Patron of Workers — A762

El Amor, by Antonio Berni, Pacific Gallery, Buenos Aires A763

3a, Our Lady of Carmen, Cuyo.

1988, Sept. 10		**Litho.**
1632 A762 2a multicolored	.90	.75
1633 A762 3a multicolored	1.60	1.25

Souvenir Sheet

Perf. 12

1634 A763 5a multicolored	3.00	3.00

Liniers Philatelic Circle and the Argentine Western Philatelic Institution (IFADO), 50th annivs.

No. 1634 contains one 40x30mm stamp.

No. 1617 Ovptd.

1988, Oct. 29 Litho. *Perf. 13½*
1635 A753 5a multicolored 7.00 2.00

21st Congress of the Intl. Urology Soc.

Tourism — A763a

3a, Purmamarca, Jujuy. 20a, Ushuaia.

1988, Nov. 1 Litho. *Perf. 13½*
1635A A763a 3a multi .80 .40

Size: 28½x38mm

1635B A763a 20a multi 4.90 2.10

Buenos Aires Subway, 75th Anniv. — A764

5a, Train, c. 1913.

1988, Dec. 17 Litho. *Perf. 13½*
1636 A764 5a multicolored 1.60 .65

Christmas — A765

Frescoes in Ucrania Cathedral, Buenos Aires: No. 1637, *Virgin Patron.* No. 1638, *Virgin of Tenderness.*

1988, Dec. 17
1637 A765 5a multicolored 2.50 .65
1638 A765 5a multicolored 2.50 .65

St. John Bosco (1815-1888), Educator, and Church in Ushuaia A766

1989, Apr. 8 Litho. *Perf. 13½*
1639 A766 5a multicolored 1.15 .50

Dated 1988.

Art Type of 1988

Paintings: No. 1640, *Blancos,* by Fernando Fader (1882-1935). No. 1641, *Rincon de los Areneros,* by Justo Lynch (1870-1953).

1989, Apr. 8
1640 A754 5a multicolored 2.00 .40
1641 A754 5a multicolored 2.00 .40

Holy Week — A767

Sculpture and churches: No. 1642, *The Crown of Thorns,* Calvary of Tandil, and Church of Our Lady Carmelite, Tandil. No. 1643, *Jesus the Nazarene* and Metropolitan Cathedral, Buenos Aires. No. 1644, *Jesus Encounters His Mother* (scene of the crucifixion), La Quebrada Village, San Luis. No. 1645, *Our Lady of Sorrow* and Church of Humahuaca, Jujuy.

1989, Apr. 22 Litho. *Perf. 13½*
1642 A767 2a multicolored .60 .50
1643 A767 2a multicolored .60 .50
1644 A767 3a multicolored .80 .50
1645 A767 3a multicolored .80 .50
a. Block of 4 + 2 labels 3.50 3.00
Nos. 1642-1645 (4) 2.80 2.00

Printed in sheets of 16+4 labels containing blocks of 4 of each design. Labels picture Jesus's arrival in Jerusalem (Palm Sunday).

Prevent Alcoholism A768

1989, Apr. 22
1646 A768 5a multicolored 1.00 .40

Natl. Park Type of 1987

1989, May 6 *Perf. 13x13½*
1647 A752 5a Lihue Calel 1.50 .40
1648 A752 5a El Palmar 1.50 .40
1649 A752 5a Calilegua 1.50 .40
1650 A752 5a Chaco 1.50 .40
1651 A752 5a Los Glaciares 1.50 .40
Nos. 1647-1651 (5) 7.50 2.00

Admission of Argentina to the ITU, Cent. — A769

1989, May 6 *Perf. 13½*
1652 A769 10a multicolored 2.00 .40

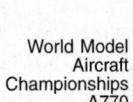

World Model Aircraft Championships A770

No. 1653, F1A glider. No. 1654, F1B rubber band motor. No. 1655, F1C gas motor.

1989, May 27 Litho. *Perf. 13½*
1653 A770 5a multi .80 .35
1654 A770 5a multi .80 .35
1655 A770 10a multi 1.40 .40
Nos. 1653-1655 (3) 3.00 1.10

French Revolution, Bicent. — A771

Designs: 10a, "All men are born free and equal." 15a, French flag and *La Marianne,* by Gandon. 25a, *Liberty Guiding the People,* by Delacroix.

1989, July 1 Litho. *Perf. 13½*
1656 A771 10a shown .85 .50
1657 A771 15a multicolored .85 .50

Souvenir Sheet

Perf. 12

1658 A771 25a multicolored 2.40 2.40

No. 1658 contains one 40x30mm stamp.

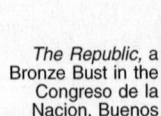

The Republic, a Bronze Bust in the Congreso de la Nacion, Buenos Aires — A772

1989, Aug. 12 Litho. *Perf. 13½*
1659 A772 300a on 50a multi 2.00 .50

Peaceful transition of power (presidential office). Not issued without surcharge.

Immigration to Argentina A773

150a, S.S. Weser, 1889. 200a, Immigrant hotel, 1889.

1989, Aug. 19 *Perf. 13½*
1660 A773 150a multi 2.00 .55
1661 A773 200a multi 2.00 .55

Souvenir Sheet

Perf. 12

1662 Sheet of 2 3.50 3.50
a. A773 150a like No. 1660 1.50 1.50
b. A773 200a like No. 1661 1.50 1.50

No. 1662 contains 40x30mm stamps.

Famous Men — A774

Designs: No. 1663, Fr. Guillermo Furlong (1889-1974), historian, and title page of *The Jesuits.* No. 1664, Dr. Gregorio Alvarez (1889-1986), physician, and title page of *Canto a Chos Malal.* 200a, Brig.-Gen. Enrique Martinez (1789-1870) and lithograph *La Batalla de Maipu,* by Teodoro Gericault.

1989, Oct. 7 Litho. *Perf. 13½*
1663 A774 150a multicolored 1.10 .55
1664 A774 150a multicolored 1.10 .55
1665 A774 200a multicolored 1.10 .55
Nos. 1663-1665 (3) 3.30 1.65

America Issue — A775

Emblem of the Postal Union of the Americas and Spain (PUAS) and pre-Columbian art from Catamarca Province: 200a, Wooden mask from Atajo, Loma Morada. 300a, Urn of the Santa Maria Culture (Phase 3) from Punta de Balastro, Santa Maria Department.

1989, Oct. 14
1666 A775 200a multicolored 1.40 1.20
1667 A775 300a multicolored 2.25 1.30

Federal Police Week — A776

Children's drawings: No. 1668, Diego Molinari, age 13. No. 1669, Carlos Alberto Sarago, age 8. No. 1670, Roxana Andrea Osuna, age 7. No. 1671, Pablo Javier Quaglia, age 9.

1989, Oct. 28 Litho. *Perf. 13½*
1668 A776 100a multi .85 .35
1669 A776 100a multi .85 .35
1670 A776 150a multi 1.40 .50
1671 A776 150a multi 1.40 .50
Nos. 1668-1671 (4) 4.50 1.70

Battle of Vuelta de Obligado, 1845 — A777

1989, Dec. 2 Litho. *Perf. 13x13½*
1672 A777 300a multicolored 1.75 .60

Paintings A778

Cristo de los Cerros, Sculpture by Chipo Cespedes — A779

No. 1673, Gato Frias. No. 1674, Maria Carballido.

1989, Dec. 2 *Perf. 13½*
1673 A778 200a multi 1.35 .50
1674 A778 200a multi 1.35 .50
1675 A779 300a shown 1.35 .50
Nos. 1673-1675 (3) 4.05 1.50

Christmas.

Buenos Aires Port, Cent. A780

1990, Mar. 3 Litho. *Perf. 13½*
1676 A780 Strip of 4 16.00 15.00
a.-d. 200a any single 1.50 .75

Aconcagua Intl. Fair, Mendoza — A781

Design: Aconcagua mountain, Los Horcones Lagoon and fair emblem.

1990, Mar. 3
1677 A781 Pair, #a.-b. 2.50 1.50

Natl. Savings and Insurance Fund, 75th Anniv. — A782

1990, May 5 Litho. *Perf. 13½*
1678 A782 1000a multicolored 1.05 .50

Miniature Sheet

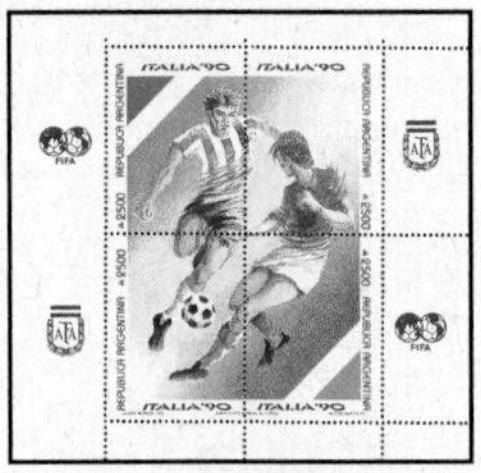

1990 World Cup Soccer Championships, Italy — A783

Designs: a, Athlete's torso (striped jersey). b, Athlete's torso (solid jersey). c, Players' feet, soccer ball. d, Player (knee to waist).

1990, May 5
1679 A783 Sheet of 4 9.00 8.00
a.-d. 2500a multicolored 2.00 1.50

Carlos Pellegrini, Commercial High School Founder, Cent. — A784

1990, June 2 Litho. *Perf. 13½*
1680 A784 2000a multicolored 1.75 .60

Youth Against Drugs — A785

1990, June 2
1681 A785 2000a multicolored 1.75 .60

Intl. Literacy Year — A786

1990, July 14 Litho. *Perf. 13½*
1682 A786 2000a multicolored 1.75 .60

Flower Type of 1982 in New Currency

1989-90 Photo. *Perf. 13½*
1683 A641 10a like #1433 .40 .25
1684 A641 20a like #1440 .35 .25
1685 A641 50a like #1354 .40 .25
1686 A641 100a like #1439 .50 .25
1687 A641 300a like #1345 1.75 .50
1688 A641 500a like #1441 2.75 .75
1689 A641 1000a like #1355 .85 .35
1690 A641 5000a like #1349 4.25 .35
1691 A641 10,000a like #1350 7.00 3.25
Nos. 1683-1691 (9) 18.25 6.20

Issued: 20a, 100a, 300a, 500a, 8/1/89; 10a, 8/24/89; 50a, 8/30/89; 1000, 3/8/90; 5000a, 4/6/90; 10,000a, 7/2/90.

World Basketball Championships A787

1990, Aug. 11 Litho. *Perf. 13½*
1703 A787 2000a multicolored 2.25 1.50

Souvenir Sheet
Perf. 12
1704 A787 5000a Jump ball 6.75 6.00

Postal Union of the Americas and Spain, 14th Congress A788

No. 1705, Arms, seal. No. 1706, Sailing ships. No. 1707, Modern freighter. No. 1708, Van, cargo plane.

1990, Sept. 15 Litho. *Perf. 13½*
1705 A788 3000a multi 2.00 .75
1706 A788 3000a multi 2.00 .75
1707 A788 3000a multi 2.00 .75
1708 A788 3000a multi 2.00 .75
Nos. 1705-1708 (4) 8.00 3.00

America Issue — A789

No. 1709, Iguacu Falls, hamelia erecta. No. 1710, Puerto Deseado, elephant seal.

1990, Oct. 13
1709 A789 3000a multicolored 2.75 1.25
1710 A789 3000a multicolored 2.75 1.25

Natl. Park Type of 1987

1990, Oct. 27 *Perf. 13x13½*
1715 A752 3000a Lanin 2.25 .90
1716 A752 3000a Laguna Blanca 2.25 .90
1717 A752 3000a Perito Moreno 2.25 .90
1718 A752 3000a Puelo 2.25 .90
1719 A752 3000a El Rey 2.25 .90
Nos. 1715-1719 (5) 11.25 4.50

Stamp Day — A790

1990, Oct. 27 *Perf. 13½*
1720 A790 3000a multicolored 1.90 .75

Salvation Army, Cent. — A793

Designs: No. 1722, Natl. University of the Littoral, Santa Fe, cent.

1990, Dec. 1 Litho. *Perf. 13½*
1721 A793 3000a multicolored 2.25 .90
1722 A793 3000a multicolored 2.25 .90
a. Pair, #1721-1722 + label 8.00 7.00

Miniature Sheets

Christmas — A794

Stained glass windows: No. 1723, The Immaculate Conception. No. 1724, The Nativity. No. 1725, Presentation of Jesus at the Temple.

1990, Dec. 1 *Perf. 13½x13*
Sheets of 4
1723 A794 3000a #a.-d. 8.50 7.50
1724 A794 3000a #a.-d. 8.50 7.50
1725 A794 3000a #a.-d. 8.50 7.50

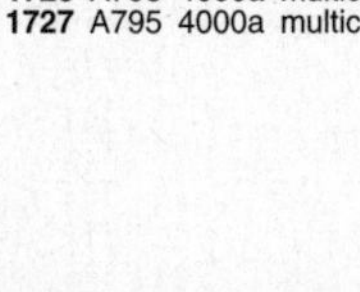

Landscapes A795

Paintings: No. 1726, Los Sauces, by Atilio Malinverno. No. 1727, Paisaje, by Pio Collivadino, vert.

1991, May 4 Litho. *Perf. 13½*
1726 A795 4000a multicolored 1.75 .90
1727 A795 4000a multicolored 1.75 .90

Return of Remains of Juan Manuel de Rosas (1793-1877) — A796

1991, June 1 Litho. *Perf. 13½*
1728 A796 4000a multicolored 1.50 .75

Swiss Confederation, 700th Anniv. — A797

1991, Aug. 3 Litho. *Perf. 13½*
1729 A797 4000a multicolored 1.50 .75

Miniature Sheet

Cartoons — A798

Designs: a, Hernan, the Corsair by Jose Luis Salinas. b, Don Fulgencio by Lino Palacio. c, Medical Rules of Salerno by Oscar Esteban Conti. d, Buenos Aires Undershirt by Alejandro del Prado. e, Girls! by Jose A.G. Divito. f, Langostino by Eduardo Carlos Ferro. g, Mafalda by Joaquin Salvador Lavoro. h, Mort Cinder by Alberto Breccia.

1991, Aug. 3
1730 A798 4000a Sheet of 8, #a.-h. 21.00 19.00

City of La Rioja, 400th Anniv. — A799

1991, Sept. 14 Litho. *Perf. 13½*
1731 A799 4000a multicolored 1.50 .75

First Balloon Flight over the Andes, 75th Anniv. A800

1991, Sept. 14
1732 A800 4000a multicolored 1.50 .75

America Issue — A801

Designs: No. 1733, Magellan's caravel, Our Lady of Victory. No. 1734, Ships of Juan Diaz de Solis.

1991, Nov. 9 Litho. *Perf. 13½*
1733 A801 4000a multicolored 2.00 1.75
1734 A801 4000a multicolored 2.00 1.75

Anniversaries — A802

Designs: a, Johann Heinrich Pestalozzi, Swiss pedagogue and educational reformer, whose Argentine school, the *Colegio Pestalozzi*, was associated with the anti-fascist newspaper *Argentinisches Tageblatt*. b, Leandro N. Alem, founder of Radical People's Party. c, Man with rifle, emblem of Argentine Federal Shooting Club. d, Dr. Nicasio Etchepareborda, emblem of College of Odontology. e, Dalmiro Huergo, emblem of Graduate School of Economics.

1991, Nov. 30
1735 A802 4000a Strip of 5, #a.-e. 9.25 8.00

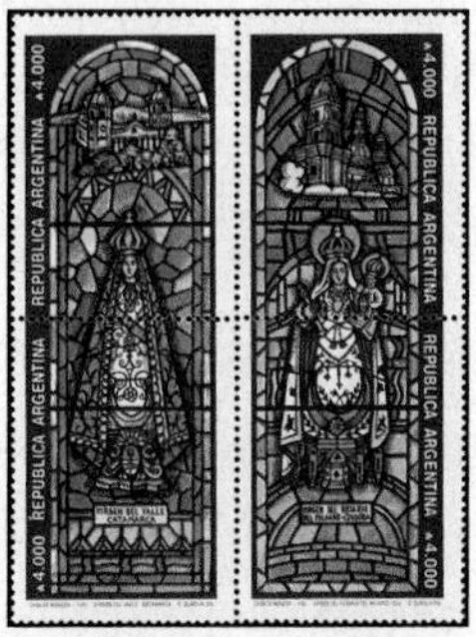

Christmas — A803

Stained glass windows from Our Lady of Lourdes Basilica, Buenos Aires: Nos. 1736a-1736b, Top and bottom portions of Virgin of the Valley, Catamarca. Nos. 1736c-1736d, Top and bottom portions of Virgin of the Rosary of the Miracle, Cordoba.

1991, Nov. 30
1736 A803 4000a Block of 4, #a.-d. 7.00 6.00
e. Sheet of 16, 4 ea #a-d, + 4 labels 30.00 26.00

The four labels of No. 1736a form a nativity scene across the middle of the sheet.

Famous Men — A804

Designs: a, Gen. Juan de Lavalle (1797-1841), Peruvian medal of honor. b, Brig. Gen. Jose Maria del Rosario Ciriaco Paz (1791-1854), medal. c, Marco Manuel de Avellaneda (1813-1841), lawyer. d, Guillermo Enrique Hudson (1841-1922), author.

1991, Dec. 14 Litho. *Perf. 13½*
1737 A804 4000a Block of 4, #a.-d. 6.75 5.75

Birds — A805

No. 1738, Pterocnemia pennata. No. 1739, Morphnus guianensis. No. 1740, Ara chloroptera.

1991, Dec. 28
1738 A805 4000a multicolored 1.90 1.00
1739 A805 4000a multicolored 1.90 1.00
1740 A805 4000a multicolored 1.90 1.00
Nos. 1738-1740 (3) 5.70 3.00

Miniature Sheet

Arbrafex '92, Argentina-Brazil Philatelic Exhibition — A806

Traditional costumes: a, Gaucho, woman. b, Gaucho, horse. c, Gaucho in store. d, Gaucho holding lariat.

1992, Mar. 14 Litho. *Perf. 13½*
1741 A806 38c Sheet of 4, #a.-d. 8.00 7.00

Natl. Park Type of 1987

No. 1742, Alerces. No. 1743, Formosa Nature Reserve. No. 1744, Petrified Forest. No. 1745, Arrayanes. No. 1746, Laguna de los Pozuelos.

1992, Apr. 4 Litho. *Perf. 13x13½*

1742	A752	38c	multicolored	1.75	.50
1743	A752	38c	multicolored	1.75	.50
1744	A752	38c	multicolored	1.75	.70
1745	A752	38c	multicolored	1.75	.50
1746	A752	38c	multicolored	1.75	.50
	Nos. 1742-1746 (5)			8.75	2.70

Mushrooms — A807

10c, Psilocybe cubensis. 25c, Coprinus atramentarius. 50c, Suillus granulatus. 51c, Morchella esculenta. 61c, Amanita muscaria. 68c, Coprinus comatus. 1.77p, Stropharia oeruginosa.

1992-94 Photo. *Perf. 13½*

1748	A807	10c	multi	1.10	.30
1749	A807	25c	multi	1.20	.30
a.	Wmk. 365			30.00	4.00
1750	A807	38c	like #1748	1.20	.30
1751	A807	48c	like #1749	1.50	.60
1752	A807	50c	multi	2.40	.30
1753	A807	51c	multi	1.50	.60
1754	A807	61c	multi	1.90	.75
1755	A807	68c	multi	3.00	.50
1756	A807	1p	like #1754	5.00	.80
1757	A807	1.25p	like #1752	5.00	.50
1758	A807	1.77p	multi	7.50	2.75
1759	A807	2p	like #1753	10.00	2.25
	Nos. 1748-1759 (12)			41.30	9.95

No. 1758 not issued without overprint "Centro Filatelico de Neuquen y Rio Negro 50th Aniversario."

Issued: 38c, 4/4/92; 48c, 51c, 61c, 8/1/92; 1.77p, 11/7/92; 25c, 50c, 8/17/93; 1p, 2p, 8/26/93; 10c, 1/11/94; 68c, 1.25p, 10/10/92; No. 1749a, 1997.

See design A838.

Falkland Islands War, 10th Anniv. — A808

No. 1767, Pucara 1A-58. No. 1768, Cruiser Gen. Belgrano. No. 1769, Soldier and truck.

1992, May 2 Litho. *Perf. 13½*

1767	A808	38c	multicolored	1.85	.80
1768	A808	38c	multicolored	1.85	.80
1769	A808	38c	multicolored	1.85	.80
	Nos. 1767-1769 (3)			5.55	2.40

Miniature Sheet

Preserve the Environment — A809

a, Deer. b, Geese. c, Butterflies. d, Whale.

1992, June 6 Litho. *Perf. 12*
1770 A809 38c Sheet of 4, #a.-d. 9.00 8.00

Paintings by Florencio Molina Campos A810

No. 1771, A La Sombra. No. 1772, Tileforo Areco, vert.

1992, June 6 *Perf. 13½*

1771	A810	38c	multicolored	1.75	.90
1772	A810	38c	multicolored	1.75	.90

Famous Men — A811

Designs: No. 1773, Gen. Lucio N. Mansilla (1792-1871). No. 1774, Jose Manuel Estrada (1842-1894), writer. No. 1775, Brig. Gen. Jose I. Garmendia (1842-1915).

1992, July 4 Litho. *Perf. 13½*

1773	A811	38c	multicolored	1.25	.70
1774	A811	38c	multicolored	1.25	.70
1775	A811	38c	multicolored	1.25	.70
	Nos. 1773-1775 (3)			3.75	2.10

Fight Against Drugs — A812

1992, Aug. 1 *Perf. 13½x13*
1776 A812 38c multicolored 1.60 .70

Col. Jose M. Calaza, 140th Birth Anniv. — A813

1992, Sept. 5 Litho. *Perf. 13½*
1777 A813 38c multicolored 1.50 1.25

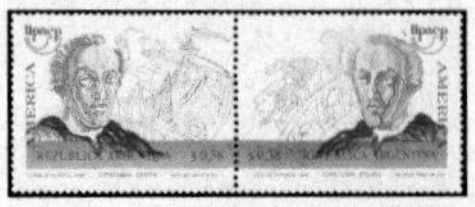

Discovery of America, 500th Anniv. — A814

Designs: a, Columbus, castle, ship. b, Native drawings, Columbus.

1992, Oct. 10 Litho. *Perf. 13½*
1778 A814 38c Pair, #a.-b. 4.50 4.00

Argentine Film Posters — A815

No. 1779, Dios Se Lo Pague, 1948. No. 1780, Las Aguas Bajan Turbias, 1952. No. 1781, Un Guapo Del 900, 1960. No. 1782, La Tregua, 1974. No. 1783, La Historia Oficial, 1984.

1992, Nov. 7 Litho. *Perf. 13½*

1779	A815	38c	multicolored	1.75	.50
1780	A815	38c	multicolored	1.75	.50
1781	A815	38c	multicolored	1.75	.50
1782	A815	38c	multicolored	1.75	.50
1783	A815	38c	multicolored	1.75	.50
	Nos. 1779-1783 (5)			8.75	2.50

Christmas — A816

1992, Nov. 28
1784 A816 38c multicolored 1.50 .60

Miniature Sheet

Iberoprenfil '92 — A817

Lighthouses: a, Punta Mogotes. b, Rio Negro. c, San Antonio. d, Cabo Blanco.

1992, Dec. 5
1785 A817 38c Sheet of 4, #a.-d. 12.00 12.00

A818

Fight Against AIDS — A819

1992, Dec. 12 Litho. *Perf. 13½*

1786	A818	10c	multicolored	2.75	1.00
1787	A819	26c	multicolored	5.25	1.00

Intl. Space Year — A820

1992, Dec. 19
1788 A820 38c multicolored 1.50 .75

Souvenir Sheet

Miraculous Lord Crucifix, 400th Anniv. of Arrival in America — A821

1992, Dec. 26 *Perf. 12*
1789 A821 76c multicolored 4.75 4.50

Jujuy City, 400th Anniv. — A822

1993, Apr. 24 Litho. *Perf. 13½*
1790 A822 38c multicolored 1.50 1.25

Argentina Soccer Assoc., Cent. — A823

1993, Mar. 27
1791 A823 38c multicolored 1.50 .60

Souvenir Sheet

Intl. Philatelic Exhibitions — A824

Designs: a, 38c, City Hall, Poznan, Poland. b, 48c, Statue of Christ the Redeemer, Rio de Janeiro, Brazil. c, 76c, Royal Palace, Bangkok, Thailand.

1993, May 8 Litho. *Perf. 12*
1792 A824 Sheet of 3, #a.-c. 5.75 5.00

Polska '93 (No. 1792a), Brasiliana '93 (No. 1792b), Bangkok '92 (No. 1792c).

Luis C. Candelaria's Flight Over Andes Mountains, 75th Anniv. — A825

1993, June 26 Litho. *Perf. 13x13½*
1793 A825 38c multicolored 1.75 1.50

Order of San Martin, 50th Anniv. — A826

National History Academy, Cent. — A827

1993, May 29 *Perf. 13½*

1794 A826 38c multicolored	1.75	.60
1795 A827 38c multicolored	1.75	.60

Armed Forces Memorial Day — A828

No. 1796, Natl. Gendarmerie. No. 1797, Coast Guard.

1993, June 12

1796 A828 38c multicolored	1.75	.60
1797 A828 38c multicolored	1.75	.60

Paintings A829

Designs: No. 1798, Old House, by Norberto Russo. No. 1799, Pa'las Casas, by Adriana Zaefferer.

1993, Aug. 14 **Litho.** *Perf. 13½*

1798 A829 38c multicolored	1.75	.60
1799 A829 38c multicolored	1.75	.60

Pato A830

1993, Aug. 28 **Litho.** *Perf. 12*

1800 A830 1p multicolored	3.50	1.25

Nut-Bearing Trees — A831

Designs: No. 1801, Enterolobium contortisiliquum. No. 1802, Prosopis alba. No. 1803, Magnolia grandiflora. No. 1804, Erythrina falcata.

1993, Sept. 25 **Litho.** *Perf. 13x13½*

1801 A831 75c multicolored	2.75	1.00
1802 A831 75c multicolored	2.75	1.00
1803 A831 1.50p multicolored	5.25	2.00
1804 A831 1.50p multicolored	5.25	2.00
Nos. 1801-1804 (4)	16.00	6.00

America Issue — A832

Whales: 50c, Eubalaena australis. 75c, Cephalorhynchus commersonii.

1993, Oct. 9 *Perf. 13½*

1805 A832 50c multicolored	2.00	.80
1806 A832 75c multicolored	3.00	1.25

Miniature Sheet

Christmas, New Year — A833

Denomination at: a, UL. b, UR. c, LL. d, LR.

1993, Dec. 4 **Litho.** *Perf. 13½*

1807 A833 75c Sheet of 4, #a.-d.	10.00	8.00

Cave of the Hands, Santa Cruz — A834

1993, Dec. 18

1808 A834 1p multicolored	3.25	3.00

New Emblem, Argentine Postal Service — A835

1994, Jan. 8 *Perf. 11½*

1809 A835 75c multicolored	4.75	4.50

See Nos. 1883A-1884.

A836

Players from: 25c, Germany, 1990. 50c, Brazil, 1970. 75c, 1.50p, Argentina, 1986. 1p, Italy, 1982.

1994, June 11 **Litho.** *Perf. 13½*

1810 A836 25c multicolored	.85	.45
1811 A836 50c multicolored	1.60	.90
1812 A836 75c multicolored	2.50	1.40
1813 A836 1p multicolored	3.75	2.00
Nos. 1810-1813 (4)	8.70	4.75

Souvenir Sheet

Perf. 12

1814 A836 1.50p multicolored	5.25	5.00

No. 1814 contains one 40x50mm stamp with continuous design.

1994 World Cup Soccer Championships, US — A837

Drawings of championships by: No. 1815, Julian Lisenberg. No. 1816, Matias Taylor, vert. No. 1817, Torcuato S. Gonzalez Agote, vert. No. 1818, Maria Paula Palma.

1994, July 23 *Perf. 13½*

1815 A837 75c multicolored	3.25	1.00
1816 A837 75c multicolored	3.25	1.00
1817 A837 75c multicolored	3.25	1.00
1818 A837 75c multicolored	3.25	1.00
Nos. 1815-1818 (4)	13.00	4.00

Issued in sheet containing a block of 4 of each stamp + 4 labels.

A838

Molothrus Badius — A838a

1994-95 **Litho.** *Perf. 13½*

1819 A838 10c like #1748	.35	.25
1820 A838 25c like #1749	.60	.35
1823 A838 50c like #1752	1.25	.60
1828 A838 1p like #1754	2.60	1.25
1832 A838 2p like #1753	5.50	2.50
1835 A838a 9.40p multicolored	26.00	25.00
Nos. 1819-1835 (6)	36.30	29.95

See designs A807, A849.

Issued: 10c, 25c, 50c, 1p, 2p, 6/14/94; 9.40p, 4/12/95.

Wildlife of Falkland Islands — A839

Designs: 25c, Melanodera melanodera. 50c, Pygoscelis papua. 75c, Tachyeres brachypterus. 1p, Mirounga leonina.

1994, Aug 6

1839 A839 25c multicolored	1.00	.55
1840 A839 50c multicolored	1.50	.75
1841 A839 75c multicolored	3.00	1.50
1842 A839 1p multicolored	4.50	2.00
Nos. 1839-1842 (4)	10.00	4.80

City of San Luis, 400th Anniv. — A840

1994, Aug. 20

1843 A840 75c multicolored	4.00	1.50

Province of Tierra del Fuego, Antarctica and South Atlantic Islands — A841

1994, Aug. 20

1844 A841 75c multicolored	3.25	1.50

Argentine Inventors A842

Designs: No. 1845, Ladislao Jose Biro (1899-1985), ball point pen. No. 1846, Raul Pateras de Pescara (1890-1966), helicopter. No. 1847, Quirino Cristiani (1896-1984), animated drawings. No. 1848, Enrique Finochietto (1881-1948), surgical instruments.

1994, Oct. 1

1845 A842 75c multicolored	2.10	2.10
1846 A842 75c multicolored	2.10	2.10
1847 A842 75c multicolored	2.10	2.10
1848 A842 75c multicolored	2.10	2.10
a. Block of 4, #1845-1848	9.50	9.50

Issued in sheets containing 4 No. 1848a + 4 labels.

UNICEF Christmas A843

75c, Bell, red ornament, star.

1994, Nov. 26 **Litho.** *Perf. 11½*

1849 A843 50c shown	2.00	1.25
1850 A843 75c multicolored	2.75	2.50

Take Care of Our Planet — A844

Children's paintings: No. 1851, Boy, girl holding earth, vert. No. 1852, Children outdoors, vert. No. 1853, World as house. No. 1854, People around "world" table.

1994, Dec. 3 *Perf. 13½*

1851 A844 25c multicolored	.95	.50
1852 A844 25c multicolored	.95	.50
1853 A844 50c multicolored	1.50	.80
1854 A844 50c multicolored	1.50	.80
Nos. 1851-1854 (4)	4.90	2.60

Christmas A845

1994, Dec. 10

1855 A845 50c Annunciation	1.75	1.00
1856 A845 75c Madonna & Child	2.50	1.00

Nos. 1855-1856 each issued in sheets of 20 + 5 labels.

12th Pan American Games, Mar del Plata — A846

1995 **Litho.** *Perf. 13½*

1857 A846 75c Running	2.50	.65
1858 A846 75c Cycling	2.50	.65
1859 A846 75c Diving	2.50	.65
1860 A846 1.25p Gymnastics, vert.	3.75	.75
1861 A846 1.25p Soccer, vert.	3.75	.75
Nos. 1857-1861 (5)	15.00	3.45

Issued: No. 1857, 2/18; others, 3/11.

Natl. Constitution A847

Design: 75c, Natl. Congress Dome, woman from statue The Republic Triumphant.

1995, Apr. 8

1862 A847 75c multicolored	2.50	2.25

21st Intl. Book Fair A848

1995, Apr. 8

1863 A848 75c multicolored	2.50	2.25

Birds — A849

5p, Carduelis magellanica. 10p, Zonotrichia capensis.

1995 Litho. *Perf. 13½*

1876 A849 5p multicolored 15.00 15.00
1880 A849 10p multicolored 30.00 30.00

Issued: 5p, 10p, 5/23/95.

A850

1995, Mar. 25 Litho. *Die Cut*

Self-Adhesive

1883A A850 25c multicolored 11.00 1.00
1884 A850 75c multicolored 3.00 1.00
a. Booklet pane, 2 #1883A, 6 #1884 42.00
Complete booklet, #1884a 62.00
b. Booklet pane, 4 #1883A, 12 #1884 82.50
Complete booklet, #1884b 105.00

See Nos. 1921A-1921B.

Argentine Engineers' Center, Cent. — A851

1995, June 3 *Perf. 13½*

1885 A851 75c multicolored 2.50 .60

Jose Marti (1853-95) A852

No. 1887, Antonio Jose de Sucre (1795-1830).

1995, Aug. 12 Litho. *Perf. 13½*

1886 A852 1p multicolored 3.25 3.00
1887 A852 1p multicolored 3.25 3.00

Fauna — A853

Type I

Type II

25c Penguin:

Type I — Penguin 16mm tall, with top of penguin's head barely above blue background circle and eyes below the outer limit of the circle.

Type II — Penguin 17mm tall, with top of penguin's head well above blue background circle and eyes even with the outer limit of the circle.

1995, Sept. 1 Litho. *Perf. 13½*

1888 A853 5c Ostrich .30 .25
1889 A853 25c Penguin, type I .80 .35
1889A A853 25c Penguin, type II — —
1890 A853 50c Toucan 1.50 .35
1891 A853 75c Condor 2.10 .35
1892 A853 1p Owl 4.25 .35
1893 A853 2p Bigua 6.25 .35
1894 A853 2.75p Tero 10.50 .35

Booklet Stamps

Perf. 13½ on 2 or 3 Sides

1895 A853 25c Alligator .80 .40
1896 A853 50c Fox 1.50 .70
1897 A853 75c Anteater 2.25 1.00
1898 A853 75c Deer 2.25 1.00
1899 A853 75c Whale 2.25 1.00
a. Booklet pane, 1 each Nos. 1889, 1890, 1891, 1895-1899 13.50 13.50
Complete booklet, #1899a 14.50
Nos. 1888-1899 (12) 34.75 6.45

See Nos. 1958, 2004-2004A.

Native Heritage A854

a, Cave drawings, shifting sands. b, Stone mask. c, Anthropomorphous vessel. d, Woven textile.

1995, Sept. 9

1900 A854 75c Block of 4, #a.-d. 10.00 9.00

Sunflower, Postal Service Emblem A855

1995, Oct. 7

1901 A855 75c multicolored 8.25 8.00

Juan D. Peron (1895-1974) A856

1995, Oct. 7

1902 A856 75c lt ol bis & dk bl 2.25 .60

Miniature Sheet

Anniversaries — A857

Annivs: a, UN, 50th. b, ICAO, 50th (in 1994). c, FAO, 50th. d, ILO, 75th (in 1994).

1995, Oct. 14 *Perf. 12*

1903 A857 75c Sheet of 4, #a.-d. 10.00 9.00

Christmas and New Year — A858

Designs: Nos. 1904, 1908, Christmas tree, presents. No. 1905, "1996." No. 1906, Champagne glasses. No. 1907, Present.

1995, Nov. 25 Litho. *Perf. 13½*

1904 A858 75c multicolored 2.25 .45

Booklet Stamps

Perf. 13½ on 1 or 2 Sides

1905 A858 75c multicolored 2.50 .75
1906 A858 75c multicolored 2.50 .75
1907 A858 75c multicolored 2.50 .75
1908 A858 75c multicolored 2.50 .75
a. Booklet pane, #1905-1908 + label 10.00
Complete booklet, #1908a 22.00
Nos. 1904-1908 (5) 12.25 3.45

No. 1908a is a continuous design. Ribbon extends from edge to edge on No. 1908 and stops at edge of package on No. 1905.

Miniature Sheet

Motion Pictures, Cent. — A859

Black and white film clips, director: a, The Battleship Potemkin, Sergei Eisenstein (Soviet Union). b, Casablanca, Michael Curtiz (US). c, Bicycle Thief, Vittorio De Sica (Italy). d, Limelights, Charles Chaplin (England). e, The 400 Blows, Francois Truffaut (France). f, Chronicle of the Lonely Child, Leonardo Favio (Argentina).

1995, Dec. 2 *Perf. 13½*

1909 A859 75c Sheet of 6, #a.-f. 26.00 25.00

The Sky — A860

1995, Dec. 16 *Perf. 13½ on 3 Sides*

Booklet Stamps

1910 A860 25c Dirigible .70 .35
1911 A860 25c Kite .70 .35
1912 A860 25c Hot air balloon .70 .35
1913 A860 50c Balloons 1.50 .35
1914 A860 50c Paper airplane 1.50 .35
1915 A860 75c Airplane 2.25 .35
1916 A860 75c Helicopter 2.25 .35
1917 A860 75c Parachute 2.25 .35
a. Booklet pane, #1910-1917 + label 13.00
Complete booklet, No. 1917a 27.00

Nos. 1910-1917 do not appear in Scott number order in No. 1917a, which has a continuous design.

America Issue — A861

Postal vehicles from Postal &Telegraph Museum: No. 1918, Horse & carriage. No. 1919, Truck.

1995, Dec. 16 *Perf. 13½*

1918 A861 75c multicolored 2.75 .75
1919 A861 75c multicolored 2.75 .75

Olympic Games, Cent. — A862

1996, Mar. 30 Litho. *Perf. 13½*

1920 A862 75c Running 2.50 .75
1921 A862 1p Discus 3.50 .90

Type of 1995

Self-Adhesive

Coil Stamps

Country Name and Denomination in Blue

1996 Litho. *Die Cut*

1921A A850 25c multi 7.00 2.00
1921B A850 75c multi 14.00 3.00

Physicians A863

Designs: a, Francisco J. Muniz (1795-1871). b, Ricardo Gutierrez (1838-96). c, Ignacio Pirovano (1844-95). d, Esteban L. Maradona (1895-1995).

1996, Apr. 20 Litho. *Perf. 12*

1922 A863 50c Sheet of 4 7.00 6.00
a.-d. Any single 1.00 1.00

Jerusalem, 3000th Anniv. — A864

7th cent. mosaic maps of city, denomination at: No. 1923, LL. No. 1924, LR.

1996, May 18 Litho. *Perf. 13½*

1923 A864 75c multicolored 1.50 .75
1924 A864 75c multicolored 1.50 .75
a. Pair, #1923-1924 6.50 6.00

No. 1924a is a continuous design and was issued in sheets of 8 + 4 labels.

Endangered Fauna — A865

1996, June 15 Litho. *Perf. 13½*

1925 A865 75c Capybara 2.00 .75
1926 A865 75c Guanaco 2.00 .75
a. Pair, #1925-1926 5.50 5.00

America Issue.

Summer Olympic Games — A866

Designs: 75c, Torch bearer, Buenos Aires, candidate for 2004 Games. 1p, Men's eight with coxswain, Atlanta, 1996.

1996, July 6

1927 A866 75c multicolored 2.25 .70
1928 A866 1p multicolored 2.75 .90

National Parks — A867

Wildlife, national park: No. 1929, Mountain turkey, Diamante. No. 1930, Parrot, San Antonio Nature Reserve. No. 1931, Deer, Otamendi Natl. Reserve. No. 1932, Rabbit, El Leoncito Nature Reserve.

1996, Aug. 24 Litho. *Perf. 13x13½*

1929 A867 75c multicolored 2.50 .70
1930 A867 75c multicolored 2.50 .70
1931 A867 75c multicolored 2.50 .70
1932 A867 75c multicolored 2.50 .70
Nos. 1929-1932 (4) 10.00 2.80

Central Post Office, Buenos Aires — A868

1996, Oct. 5 Litho. ***Die Cut***

Self-Adhesive

Size: 25x35mm

1933 A868 75c multicolored 20.00 8.00

Vignette of No. 1933 is broken by circular and rectangular die cut areas to guard against reuse.

See Nos. 1983-1984.

Carousel Figures A869

Designs: No. 1934, Hand-carved decorative ornaments. No. 1935, Child on carousel horse. No. 1936, Carousel. No. 1937, Heads of horses. No. 1938, Child in airplane. No. 1939, Carousel pig. No. 1940, Boy in car.

1996, Oct. 5 ***Perf. 13½ Horiz.***

Booklet Stamps

1934 A869 25c multicolored .50 .30
1935 A869 25c multicolored .50 .30
1936 A869 25c multicolored .50 .30
1937 A869 50c multicolored 1.00 .60
1938 A869 50c multicolored 1.00 .60
1939 A869 50c multicolored 1.00 .60
1940 A869 75c multicolored 1.50 .70
a. Booklet pane, #1934-1940 7.00
Complete booklet, #1940a 9.00

Sequence of stamps in No. 1940a: No. 1940, 1934, 1937, 1935, 1938, 1936, 1939.

Port Belgrano Naval Base, Cent. — A870

Designs: 25c, LST "San Antonio." 50c, Corvette *Rosales.* 75c, Destroyer *Hercules.* 1p, Aircraft carrier, "25th of May."

1996-97 Litho. ***Perf. 13½***

1941 A870 25c multicolored 1.50 .50
1942 A870 50c multicolored 1.50 .50
1943 A870 75c multicolored 3.00 .75
1944 A870 1p multicolored 3.50 1.00
Nos. 1941-1944 (4) 9.50 2.75

Issued: 25c, 1p, 10/5/96; 50c, 75c, 2/1/97.

Christmas A871

Tapestries: 75c, Nativity, by Gladys Angelica Rinaldi, vert. 1p, Candles, by Norma Bonet de Maekawa.

1996, Nov. 30 Litho. ***Perf. 13½***

1945 A871 75c multicolored 2.00 .75
1946 A871 1p multicolored 2.75 1.00

Exploration of Antarctica A872

Designs: 75c, Melchior Base. 1.25p, Icebreaker ARA Alte. Irizar.

1996, Nov. 30

1947 A872 75c multicolored 2.25 .75
1948 A872 1.25p multicolored 3.25 1.25

National Gallery, Cent. — A873

Paintings of women by: 75c, Paul Gauguin, vert. No. 1950, Edouard Manet, vert. No. 1951, Amedeo Modigiliani, vert. 1.25p, Pablo Picasso.

1996, Dec. 14

1949 A873 75c multicolored 2.25 .70
1950 A873 1p multicolored 3.00 1.00
1951 A873 1p multicolored 3.00 1.00
1952 A873 1.25p multicolored 4.75 1.25
Nos. 1949-1952 (4) 13.00 3.95

Mining Industry A874

1997, Feb. 1 Litho. ***Perf. 13½***

1953 A874 75c Granite 2.00 1.50
1954 A874 1.25p Borax 3.50 3.50

Traditional Costumes A875

1997, Feb. 22 Litho. ***Perf. 13½***

1955 A875 75c multicolored 2.75 2.50

America issue.

Repatriation of the Curved Sword of Gen. San Martin, Cent. — A876

1997, Mar. 15 Litho. ***Perf. 13½***

1956 A876 75c multicolored 2.50 2.25

29th Youth Rugby World Championships A877

1997, Mar. 22

1957 A877 75c multicolored 2.50 2.25

Fauna Type of 1995

1997, Feb. 22 Litho. ***Perf. 13½***

1958 A853 10c Reddish sandpiper 1.60 .35

Buenos Aires-Rio de Janeiro Regatta, 50th Anniv. — A879

1997, Apr. 5 Litho. ***Perf. 13½***

1960 A879 75c Fortuna II 2.50 2.25

Natl. History Museum, Cent. — A880

1997, May 17

1961 A880 75c multicolored 2.50 2.25

La Plata Natl. University, Cent. — A881

1997, May 17

1962 A881 75c multicolored 2.50 2.25

Lighthouses — A882

a, Cabo Virgenes. b, Isla Pingüino. c, San Juan de Salvamento. d, Punta Delgada.

1997, May 31

1963 A882 75c Sheet of 4, #a.-d. 11.00 8.00

Ramón J. Cárcano (1860-1946), Developer of Postal and Telegraph System — A883

1997, May 31

1964 A883 75c multicolored 2.50 2.25

Buenos Aires, Candidate for 2004 Summer Olympics A884

1997, June 21

1965 A884 75c multicolored 2.50 2.25

First Electric Tram in Buenos Aires, Cent. A885

Designs: a, Lacroze Suburban Service Tram Co, 1912. b, Lacroze Urban Service Tram Co., 1907. c, Anglo Argentina Tram Co., 1930. d, Buenos Aires City Transportation Corp., 1942. e, Military Manufacture Tram, 1956. f, South Electric Tram, 1908.

1997, July 12 Sheet of 6

1966 A885 75c #a.-f. + 2 labels 14.00 12.50

Monument to Joaquín V. González (1863-1923), La Rioja — A886

1997, Aug. 9

1967 A886 75c multicolored 2.50 2.25

Musicians and Composers — A887

Paintings: No. 1968, Alberto Ginastera (1916-83), by Carlos Nine. No. 1969, Astor Piazzolla (1921-92), by Carlos Alonso. No. 1970, Anibal Troilo (1914-75), by Hermenegildo Sabat. No. 1971, Atahualpa Yupanqui (b. 1908), by Luis Scafati.

1997, Aug. 9

1968 A887 75c multicolored 2.50 2.00
1969 A887 75c multicolored 2.50 2.00
1970 A887 75c multicolored 2.50 2.00
1971 A887 75c multicolored 2.50 2.00
Nos. 1968-1971 (4) 10.00 8.00

Argentine Authors A888

Designs: No. 1972, Jorge Luis Borges (1899-1986), maze. No. 1973, Julio Cortázar (1914-84), hop scotch game.

1997, Aug. 30 Litho. ***Perf. 13***

1972 A888 1p multicolored 2.75 1.00
1973 A888 1p multicolored 2.75 1.00

Women's Political Rights Law, 50th Anniv. — A889

1997, Sept. 6 Litho. ***Perf. 13½***

1974 A889 75c Eva Perón 3.25 2.00

Mercosur (Common Market of Latin America) — A890

1997, Sept. 27 Litho. ***Perf. 13½***

1975 A890 75c multicolored 2.50 2.25

See Bolivia No. 1019, Brazil No. 2646, Paraguay No. 2564, Uruguay No. 1681.

Launching of Frigate President Sarmiento, Cent. — A891

Designs: No. 1976, Painting of ship by Hugo Leban.

No. 1977: a, Ship. b, Ship's figurehead, vert.

1997, Oct. 4

1976 A891 75c multicolored 2.75 2.50

Souvenir Sheet

Perf. 12

1977 A891 75c Sheet of 2, #a.-b. 5.25 4.00

No. 1977 contains one 40x30mm stamp and one 30x40mm stamp.

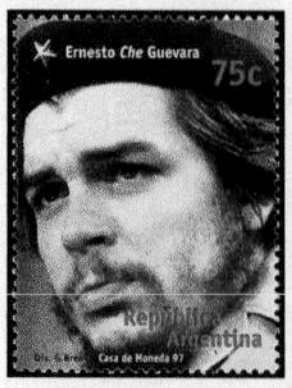

Ernesto "Che" Guevara (1928-67) — A892

1997, Oct. 18

1978 A892 75c multicolored 5.25 5.00

Ecology on Stamps A893

Children's drawings: No. 1979, Animal, by J. Chiapparo, vert. No. 1980, Vicuna, by L.L. Portal, vert. No. 1981, Seal, by A. Lloren. No. 1982, Bird in flight, by J. Saccone.

1997, Nov. 8 Litho. *Perf. 13½*

1979 A893 50c multicolored 1.60 .50
1980 A893 50c multicolored 1.60 .50
1981 A893 75c multicolored 2.25 .75
1982 A893 75c multicolored 2.25 .75
Nos. 1979-1982 (4) 7.70 2.50

Central Post Office, Buenos Aires, Type of 1996

1997, July 24 Litho. *Die Cut*

Self-Adhesive

Size: 23x35mm

1983 A868 25c multicolored *12.00* *.75*
1984 A868 75c multicolored *5.00* *.75*
a. Bklt. pane, 2 #1983, 6 #1984 *55.00*
Complete booklet, #1984a *62.00*

Nos. 1983-1984 are broken at both the top and bottom of each stamp by three lines of wavy die cutting.

Christmas — A893a

Nativity scene tapestries by: Nos. 1984B, 1984G, Mary José. No. 1984C, Elena Aguilar. No. 1984D, Silvia Pettachi. No. 1984E, Ana Escobar. No. 1984F, Alejandra Martinez. No. 1984H, Nidia Martinez.

1997, Nov. 22 Litho. *Perf. 13½*

1984B A893a 75c multicolored 2.50 2.25

Booklet Stamps

Self-Adhesive

Size: 44x27mm

Die Cut

1984C A893a 25c multicolored .75 .50
1984D A893a 25c multicolored 1.00 .50
1984E A893a 50c multicolored 1.50 .75
1984F A893a 50c multicolored 1.50 .75
1984G A893a 75c multicolored 2.00 .75
1984H A893a 75c multicolored 2.00 .75
i. Booklet pane, #1984C-1984H 12.00

Nos. 1984C-1984H are broken at upper right by three die cut chevrons. By its nature, No. 1984Hi is a complete booklet.

Mother Teresa (1910-97) — A893b

1997, Dec. 27

1984J A893b 75c multicolored 2.50 2.25

Dr. Bernardo A. Houssay (1887-1971), 1947 Nobel Prize Winner in Medicine A894

1998, Jan. 31 Litho. *Perf. 13½*

1985 A894 75c multicolored 2.50 2.25

First Ascension of Mount Aconcagua, Cent. — A895

1998, Feb. 14 *Perf. 12*

1986 A895 1.25p multicolored 3.75 3.50

Founding of San Martin de los Andes, Cent. — A896

1998, Mar. 14 Litho. *Perf. 13½*

1987 A896 75c multicolored 2.50 2.25

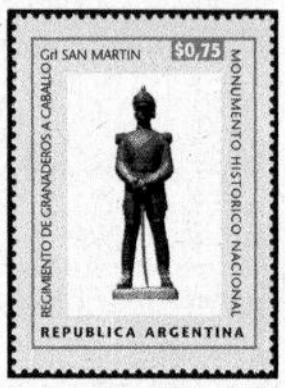

Regimental Quarters of Gen. San Martin's Mounted Grenadiers — A897

Designs: a, Statue. b, Large jar with painting of San Martin. c, Regimental seal. d, Regimental quarters.

1998, Mar. 21 Litho. *Perf. 13½*

1988 A897 75c Block of 4, #a.-d. 9.00 6.00

Protection of the Ozone — A898

1998, Mar. 28 Litho. *Perf. 13½*

1989 A898 75c multicolored 2.50 2.25

America Issue — A899

Letter carriers: No. 1990, Wearing white uniform. No. 1991, Carrying letter bag with shoulder strap.

1998, Apr. 4

1990 A899 75c multicolored 2.75 .75
1991 A899 75c multicolored 2.75 .75

Characters from Stories by Maria Elena Walsh — A900

Designs: No. 1992, El Reino Del Reves. No. 1993, Zoo Loco. No. 1994, Dailan Kifki. No. 1995, Manuelita.

1998, Apr. 17 Litho. *Die Cut*

Booklet Stamps

Self-Adhesive

1992 A900 75c multicolored *3.75 3.00*
1993 A900 75c multicolored *3.75 3.00*
1994 A900 75c multicolored *3.75 3.00*
1995 A900 75c multicolored *3.75 3.00*
a. Complete booklet, #1992-1995 *22.00*

Historic Chapels A901

Designs: No. 1996, San Pedro de Fiambalá, Catamarca. No. 1997, Huacalera, Jujuy. No. 1998, Santo Domingo, La Rioja. No. 1999, Tumbaya, Jujuy.

1998, Apr. 25 Litho. *Perf. 13x13½*

1996 A901 75c multicolored 2.25 2.00
1997 A901 75c multicolored 2.25 2.00
1998 A901 75c multicolored 2.25 2.00
1999 A901 75c multicolored 2.25 2.00
Nos. 1996-1999 (4) 9.00 8.00

White Helmets, A Commitment to Humanity A902

1998, May 23 Litho. *Perf. 13½*

2000 A902 1p multicolored 3.00 2.75

Beginning with No. 2001, many Argentine stamps are inscribed "Correo Oficial," but these are not Official stamps (i.e., for government use only). The addition of "Correo Oficial" distinguishes these stamps, which are products of the Argentine Postal Service, from other stamps from a private post, OCA, which are also inscribed "Republica Argentina."

1998 World Cup Soccer Championships, France — A903

Stylized players representing: a, Argentina. b, Croatia. c, Jamaica. d, Japan.

1998, May 30

2001 A903 75c Block of 4, #a.-d. 8.75 7.75

Journalist's Day — A904

1998, June 20

2002 A904 75c multicolored 2.50 2.25

Creation of Argentine Postal System, 250th Anniv. — A905

a, Corrientes design A2, peso coin. b, Building, post box.

1998, June 27

2003 A905 75c Pair, #a.-b. 5.00 4.50

Fauna Type of 1995

1998 Litho. *Die Cut*

Self-Adhesive (#2004)

2004 A853 60c Picaflor 2.25 2.00

Perf. 13½

2004A A853 3.25p Tero 10.00 5.00

No. 2004 is broken at bottom right by 3 or 5 lines of wavy die cutting.

Issued: 60c, 12/12; 3.25p, 7/22.

Ruins, Mission St. Ignacio — A906

1998, July 25 Litho. *Perf. 13½*

2005 A906 75c multicolored 2.50 2.25

Mercosur.

Cattle — A907

1998, Aug. 1

2006 A907 25c Brahman .80 .70
2007 A907 25c Aberdeen-Angus .80 .70
2008 A907 50c Hereford 1.50 .90
2009 A907 50c Criolla 1.50 .90
2010 A907 75c Holland-Argentina 2.10 1.75
2011 A907 75c Shorthorn 2.10 1.75
Nos. 2006-2011 (6) 8.80 6.70

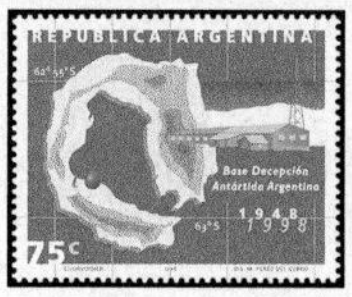

Deception Island Base, Antarctica, 50th Anniv. — A908

1998, Aug. 15 Litho. *Perf. 14½*

2012 A908 75c multicolored 2.60 2.40

State of Israel, 50th Anniv. — A909

1998, Sept. 5 Litho. *Perf. 13½*

2013 A909 75c multicolored 2.50 2.25

Argentina-Japan Friendship Treaty, Cent. — A910

1998, Oct. 3

2014 A910 75c multicolored 2.50 2.25

Post Office Building, Buenos Aires, 70th Anniv. — A911

Designs: No. 2015, Building, clock, tile. No. 2016, Column ornamentation, tile, bench.

1998, Oct. 3

2015 A911 75c multicolored 2.25 2.00
2016 A911 75c multicolored 2.25 2.00
a. Pair, #2015-2016 5.00 4.50

Cartoons — A912

Designs: a, Patoruzu, by Quinterno. b, Matias, by Sendra. c, Clemente, by Caloi. d, El Eternauta, by Oesterheld and López. e, Loco Chavez, by Trillo and Altuna. f, Inodoro Pereyra, by Fontanarrosa. g, Tia Vicenta, by Landrú. h, Gaturro, by Nik.

1998, Oct. 17 Litho. *Perf. 13¾x13¼*

2017 A912 75c Sheet of 8, #a.-h. 24.00 22.00

Dr. Pedro de Elizalde's Children's Hospital, 220th Anniv. — A913

1998, Oct. 24 Litho. *Perf. 13½*

2025 A913 75c multicolored 2.60 2.40

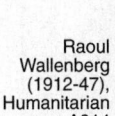

Raoul Wallenberg (1912-47), Humanitarian A914

1998, Nov. 21

2026 A914 75c multicolored 3.00 2.75

Espamer '98 — A915

25c, Spanish flags, arms. 75c, 18th cent. schooner. 75c+75c, Brigantine, gray sails. 1.25p+1.25p, Brigantine, white sails.

1998, Nov. 21 *Die Cut*

Booklet Stamps

Self-Adhesive

2027 A915 25c multicolored 1.10 .75
2028 A915 75c multicolored 3.50 2.00
2029 A915 75c +75c multi 6.75 4.00
2030 A915 1.25p +1.25p multi 11.00 3.25
a. Booklet pane, #2027-2030 23.00

Nos. 2027-2030 are broken at top right of each stamp by four lines of wavy die cutting. No. 2030a is a complete booklet.

Organization of American States, 50th Anniv. — A916

1998, Nov. 28 *Perf. 13½*

2031 A916 75c multicolored 2.50 2.25

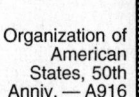

Dinosaurs of Argentina A917

Designs: a, Eoraptor. b, Gasparinisaura. c, Giganotosaurus. d, Patagosaurus.

1998, Nov. 28

2032 A917 75c Sheet of 4, #a.-d. 11.00 10.00

Christmas — A918

1998, Dec. 5

2033 A918 75c multicolored 2.50 2.25

Newspaper El Liberal, Cent. — A919

1998, Dec. 5

2034 A919 75c Juan A. Figueroa 2.50 2.25

La Nueva Provincia, Daily Newspaper, Cent. — A920

1998, Dec. 12

2035 A920 75c Enrique Julio 2.50 2.25

Universal Declaration of Human Rights, 50th Anniv. — A921

1998, Dec. 12

2036 A921 75c multicolored 2.50 2.25

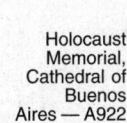

Holocaust Memorial, Cathedral of Buenos Aires — A922

1998, Dec. 12

2037 A922 75c multicolored 2.50 2.25

Southern Cross — A923

Inscriptions: 8.75p, Sur postal express. 17.50p, Sur postal 24.

1999-2000 Litho. *Die Cut*

Self-Adhesive

2038 A923 8.75p bl & silver *27.00* 18.00
2039 A923 17.50p bl & gold *56.00* 37.50

Issued: 8.75p, 7/1/99; 17.50p, 3/2/00. Nos. 2038-2039 are broken at right by five wavy lines of die cutting.

National Fund for the Arts, 40th Anniv. — A925

1999, Mar. 6 Litho. *Perf. 13½*

2042 A925 75c multicolored 2.25 2.00

Intl. Year of the Ocean (in 1998) — A926

1999, Mar. 6

2043 A926 50c Penguin, vert. 1.90 1.60
2044 A926 75c Dolphins 1.90 1.60

Postmen — A927

Designs: 25c, Early postman, city scene. 50c, Early postman, people on bicycles, factory. 75c, Modern postman, city buildings.

1998-2001 Litho. *Die Cut*

Self-Adhesive

2045 A927 25c multicolored *60.00* .75
2046 A927 75c multicolored *30.00* .50
a. Strip of 4, 1 #2045, 3 #2046 *150.00*

Booklet Stamps

Serpentine Die Cut 6

2047 A927 25c multicolored *40.00* 1.00
2048 A927 75c multicolored *15.00* 1.00
a. Bklt. pane, 2 #2047, 6 #2048 *175.00*
Complete booklet, #2048a *180.00*

Serpentine Die Cut 11

2048B A927 25c multi *2.00* .25
2048C A927 75c multi *6.00* .50
d. Booklet pane, 2 #2048B, 6 #2048C *45.00*
Complete booklet, 2 #2048Cd *90.00*
Complete booklet, 4 #2048Cd *180.00*

Size: 21x27mm

Die Cut

2049 A927 25c multicolored 3.50 .50
2050 A927 50c multicolored 3.50 1.00
2051 A927 75c multicolored 3.50 1.75
a. Bklt. pane, 2 ea #2049-2051 21.00
Complete booklet, #2051a 32.00

Nos. 2045-2048C are broken at lower right by five lines of wavy die cutting. Nos. 2049-2051 are broken in center by five wavy lines of die cutting. Nos. 2045-2046 have darker vignettes than Nos. 2047-2048.

Issued: Nos. 2045-2048, 12/9/98. Nos. 2049-2051, 2/2/99. Nos. 2048B-2048C, Feb. 2001.

25th Book Fair — A928

Designs: a, Book. b, Obelisk, readers.

1999, Apr. 17 Litho. *Perf. 13¾x13½*

2052 A928 75c Pair, a.-b. 4.25 3.50

Argentine Rugby Union, Cent. — A929

75c, Player, balls. 1.50p, Old, modern players.

1999, Apr. 24 Litho. *Perf. 13¾x13½*

2054 A929 75c multicolored 2.25 1.90

Souvenir Sheet

2055 A929 1.50p multi + 3 labels 6.75 6.50

Cafes of Buenos Aires — A930

Designs: a, Mug, Giralda Dairy. b, Two glasses, Homero Manzi Cafe. c, Hat hanging on rack, Ideal Sweet Shop. d, Cup and saucer, Tortoni Cafe.

Serpentine Die Cut

1999, Apr. 30 Litho.

Self-Adhesive

2056 Booklet pane of 4 14.00 12.00
a. A930 25c multicolored .60 .50
b.-c. A930 75c multi, each 1.75 1.00
d. A930 1.25p multicolored 3.00 1.25
Complete booklet, #2056 15.00

Argentine Olympic Committee, 75th Anniv. — A931

1999, May 15 *Perf. 14x13¼*

2057 A931 75c Pierre de Coubertin 2.25 1.75

Enrico Caruso (1873-1921), Opera Singer — A932

Designs: a, Portrait of Caruso. b, Singer, various musical instruments. c, Outside of Colon Theatre, Buenos Aires. d, Scene from opera, "El Matrero."

1999, May 15 *Perf. 13½*

2058 A932 75c Sheet of 4, #a.-d. 10.00 9.00

Famous Women — A933

Designs: a, Rosario Vera Penaloza (1873-1950), educator. b, Julieta Lanteri (1862-1932), physician.

1999, June 5 *Perf. 14x13¼*

2059 A933 75c Pair, #a.-b. 4.50 3.90

Souvenir Sheets

Paintings from Natl. Museum of Art, Buenos Aires — A934

No. 2060: a, Anarchy of Year 20, by Luis Felipe Noé. b, Retrato de L.E.S., by Carlos Alonso.

No. 2061: a, Typical Orchestra, by Antonio Berni. b, Untitled, (Woman seated), by Aída Carballo.

1999, June 5 *Perf. 14*

Sheets of 2

2060 A934 75c #a.-b. 5.50 5.00
2061 A934 75c #a.-b. 5.50 5.00

No. 2060b is 40x40mm, No. 2061a, 70x50mm, No. 2061b, 40x50mm.

Carrier Pigeon — A935

1999, June 12 *Perf. 13¾x13½*

2062 A935 75c multicolored 2.50 2.25

Maps — A936

1999, June 12 ***Die Cut***

Self-Adhesive

2063	A936 35c Local highway	1.25	1.20
2064	A936 40c City street	1.35	1.20
2065	A936 50c Regional highway	1.75	1.20
	Nos. 2063-2065 (3)	4.35	3.60

Nos. 2063-2065 are broken at lower left by five wavy lines of die cutting.

Dogs — A937

Designs: a, 25c, Boxer. b, 25c, English sheepdog. c, 50c, Collie. d, 50c, St. Bernard. e, 75c, German shepherd. f, 75c, Siberian husky.

1999, July 24 Litho. ***Perf. 13½***

2066	A937 Sheet of 6, #a.-f.	12.00	10.50

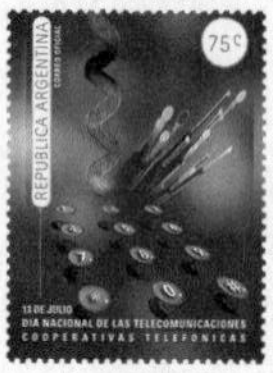

Natl. Telecommunications Day — A938

1999, July 24 ***Perf. 13½x13¾***

2067	A938 75c multicolored	2.25	1.75

Justo José de Urquiza School, Concepcion del Uruguay, 150th Anniv. — A939

1999, Aug. 7 ***Perf. 13¾x13½***

2068	A939 75c multicolored	2.25	1.75

Otto Krause Technical School, Buenos Aires, Cent. — A940

1999, Aug. 7 ***Perf. 13½x13¾***

2069	A940 75c multicolored	2.25	1.75

Bethlehem 2000 Project — A941

1999, Aug. 21 ***Perf. 13½***

2070	A941 75c multicolored	2.25	1.75

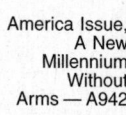

America Issue, A New Millennium Without Arms — A942

No. 2072, Tree of hands, vert.

Perf. 13½x13¾, 13¾x13½

1999, Aug. 21

2071	A942 75c shown	2.25	2.00
2072	A942 75c multicolored	2.25	2.00

National Parks A943

Parks and animals: No. 2073, Mburucuyá, coypu. No. 2074, Quebrada de Los Condoritos, condor. No. 2075, San Guillermo, vicuna. No. 2076, Sierra de las Quijadas, puma. No. 2077, Talampaya, gray fox.

1999, Sept. 25 Litho. ***Perf. 14x13½***

2073	A943 50c multicolored	1.60	1.40
2074	A943 50c multicolored	1.60	1.40
2075	A943 50c multicolored	1.60	1.40
2076	A943 75c multicolored	3.50	1.90
2077	A943 75c multicolored	3.50	1.90
	Nos. 2073-2077 (5)	11.80	8.00

For surcharge, see Nos. 2853A-2854.

Inter-American Development Bank, 40th Anniv. — A944

1999, Oct. 9 Litho. ***Perf. 13½x13¾***

2078	A944 75c multi	2.25	1.75

UPU, 125th Anniv. — A945

1999, Oct. 9 ***Perf. 13¾x13½***

2079	A945 1.50p multi	4.00	3.75

Trees — A946

a, Nothofagus pumilio. b, Prosopis caldenia. c, Schinopsis balansae. d, Cordia trichotoma.

1999, Oct. 16 ***Perf. 13½x13¾***

2080	A946 75c Strip of 4, #a-d	8.75	7.75

Sinking of A.R.A. Fournier, 50th Anniv. — A947

1999, Oct. 16 ***Perf. 13¾x13½***

2081	A947 75c multi	2.25	1.75

Aviation Anniversaries A948

Designs: No. 2082, Late 25 airplane. No. 2083, Parachutists.

1999, Oct. 30 ***Perf. 13¾x13½***

2082	A948 75c multi	2.10	1.90
2083	A948 75c multi	2.10	1.90

First Argentine airmail flight, 70th anniv. (No. 2082), Hundred consecutive jumps by Argentine Parachute Club, 50th anniv.

Souvenir Sheets

Millennium — A949

No. 2084: a, 75c, Head of soccer player. b, 50c, Machine as soccer player.

No. 2085: a, 50c, Cane, vert. b, 75c, Head of Jorge Luis Borges (1899-1986), writer.

No. 2086: a, 50c, Accordion player on bed, vert. b, 75c, Stylized tango dancers.

1999, Oct. 30 ***Perf. 14***

2084	A949 Sheet of 2, #a.-b.	4.50	4.00
2085	A949 Sheet of 2, #a.-b.	4.50	4.00
2086	A949 Sheet of 2, #a.-b.	4.50	4.00

Size of 75c stamps: 40x40mm.

Argentine Soccer Teams — A950

Designs: No. 2087, Banner and flags of River Plate team. No. 2088, Banner of Boca Juniors team, balloons.

River Plate team (red and white team colors) — No. 2089: a, Stadium, emblem, soccer balls. b, Team on field. c, Fans. d, Emblem. e, Trophy. f, Banner in stadium. g, Player, ball.

Boca Juniors team (blue and yellow team colors) — No. 2090: a, Two players, ball. b, Emblem. c, Four players celebrating. d, Fans, balloons. e, Banner in stadium. f, Blurred shot of players in action. g, Blurred shot of players, diff.

1999 ***Perf. 13½x13¼***

2087	A950 75c multi	2.25	2.00
2088	A950 75c multi	2.25	2.00

Self-Adhesive

Die Cut

2089	Pane of 7	39.00	37.50
a.	A950 25c multi	2.50	2.00
b.-c.	A950 50c any single	2.50	2.00
d.-f.	A950 75c any single	5.50	5.50
g.	A950 1.50p multi	11.00	10.00
2090	Pane of 7	39.00	37.50
a.	A950 25c multi	2.50	2.00
b.-c.	A950 50c any single	3.50	2.00
d.-f.	A950 75c any single	5.50	5.00
g.	A950 1.50p multi	11.00	10.00

Issued: Nos. 2087-2088, 11/13; Nos. 2089-2090, 11/15.

Sizes: Nos. 2089a-2089f, 2090a-2090f, 37x27mm; No. 2089g, 2090g, 37x37mm.

Canonization of Brother Héctor Valdivielso Sáez — A951

1999, Nov. 20 ***Perf. 13¾x13½***

2091	A951 75c multi	2.25	1.90

Manuel Belgrano National Naval School, Bicent. — A952

1999, Nov. 27

2092	A952 75c multi	2.25	1.90

Souvenir Sheet

Launch of Corvette Uruguay, 125th Anniv. A953

1999, Nov. 27 Litho. ***Perf. 14***

2093	A953 1.50p multi	7.00	6.75

A954

Christmas — A955

No. 2094, Figurines of Holy Family.

No. 2095: a, Magus. b, Bell. c, Two Magi, camels. d, Leaf. e, Angel with star. f, Nativity scene. g, Star. h, Ornaments.

1999, Dec. 4 ***Perf. 13¾x13½***

2094	A954 75c multi	2.25	1.90

Perf. 14

2095	A955 Sheet of 8	13.50	11.50
a.-b	25c any single	1.00	.80
c.-d.	50c any single	1.60	1.25
e.-h.	75c any single	2.00	1.75

Sizes: Nos. 2095a, 2095b, 2095g, 2095h, 30x30mm.

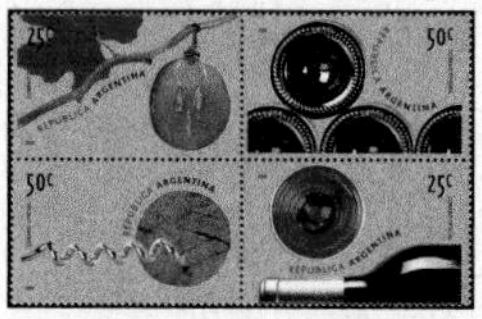

Viticulture — A956

Designs: a, 25c, Grape on vine. b, 50c, Bottoms of wine bottles. c, 50c, Cork and corkscrew. d, 25c, Glass of wine, wine bottle.

2000, Feb. 26 Litho. ***Perf. 13¼***

2096	A956 Block of 4, #a-d	9.50	8.50

World Mathematics Year — A957

2000, Mar. 18 ***Perf. 13¾x13½***

2097	A957 75c multi	2.25	1.90

Birds — A958

a, Leptotila verrauxi. b, Columba picazuro. c, Columbina picni. d, Zenaida auriculata.

2000, Mar. 18 ***Die Cut***

Self-Adhesive

2098	Booklet of 4	11.00	10.00
a.-d.	A958 75c any single	2.50	1.50

Souvenir Sheet

Bangkok 2000 Stamp Exhibition — A959

Designs: a, 25c, Vanda coerulea. b, 75c, Erythrina crista-galli.

2000, Mar. 25 *Perf. 14*
2099 A959 Sheet of 2, #a-b 4.00 3.50

Miniature Sheet

Libraries A960

Designs: a, 25c, National Public Library Protection Commission. b, 50c, Jujuy Public Library. c, 75c, Argentine Library for the Blind. d, 1p, Argentine National Library.

Litho., Litho. & Embossed (#2100c)
2000, Apr. 15 *Perf. 13½*
2100 A960 Sheet of 4, #a-d 7.75 6.75

Gen. Luis Maria Campos Military School, Cent. — A961

2000, Apr. 29 *Perf. 13¾x13½*
2101 A961 75c multi 2.25 1.90

Discovery of Brazil, 500th Anniv. — A962

a, 75c, Pedro Cabral, 1558 map of Brazil coastline. b, 25c, Compass rose and ship.

2000, Apr. 29
2102 A962 Pair, #a-b 4.25 3.75

Souvenir Sheet

The Stamp Show 2000, London A963

Designs: a, 25c, Great Britain #1 and design A1, La Porteña, 1st locomotive in Argentina. b, 75c, Argentina No. 7, mail box.

2000, May 20 *Perf. 14*
2103 A963 Sheet of 2, #a-b 4.00 3.50

91st Intl. Convention of Rotary International, Buenos Aires — A964

2000, June 3 Litho. *Perf. 13½x13¾*
2104 A964 75c multi 2.25 1.90

Stampin' the Future A965

Children's Stamp Design Contest Winners: 25c, Rocío Casado. 50c, Carolina Cáceres, vert. 75c, Valeria A. Pizarro. 1p, Cristina Ayala Castro, vert.

Perf. 13½x13¼, 13¼x13½
2000, June 24
2105-2108 A965 Set of 4 7.50 6.50

America Issue — A966

AIDS Prevention: No. 2109, Handshake. No. 2110, Heart and hands.

2000, July 8 *Perf. 13¾x13½*
2109-2110 A966 75c Set of 2 4.25 3.75

Antoine de Saint-Exupéry (1900-44), Pilot, Writer — A967

Designs: Nos. 2111, 2115, Potez 25. Nos. 2112, 2116, Late 28. No. 2113, Saint-Exupéry. No. 2114, Henri Guillaumet, Vicente A. Almonacid and Jean Mermoz. No. 2117, Map of southern Argentina, tail of Late 25 plane. 1p, Nose of Late 25 plane, cover from 1st airmail flight to Trelew.

2000, July 29 *Perf. 13½*
2111 A967 25c multi 1.40 1.25
2112 A967 50c multi 3.00 2.60

Booklet Stamps
Perf. 14
Size: 30x30mm

2113 A967 25c multi 2.25 .50
2114 A967 50c multi 3.25 1.10

Size: 60x20mm

2115 A967 25c multi 2.25 .50
2116 A967 50c multi 3.25 1.10
a. Booklet pane, #2113-2116 13.00

Size: 40x30mm

2117 A967 50c multi 3.25 1.10
2118 A967 1p multi 4.75 1.75
a. Booklet pane, #2117-2118 8.75
Booklet, #2116a, 2118a 24.00
Nos. 2111-2118 (8) 23.40 9.90

Argentine airmail service, 73rd anniv., Aerofila 2000 Philatelic Exhibition, Buenos Aires (No. 2118a).

President Arturo U. Illia (1900-82) — A968

2000, Aug. 5 *Perf. 13½x13¼*
2119 A968 75c multi 2.25 1.75

José de San Martín (1778-1850) — A969

2000, Aug. 26 *Perf. 13½*
2120 A969 75c multi 2.25 1.75

Dalmacio Vélez Sarsfield (1800-75), Writer of Civil Code — A970

Perf. 13½x13¼
2000, Sept. 23 **Litho.**
2121 A970 75c multi 2.25 1.75

2000 Summer Olympic, Sydney A971

No. 2122: a, Windsurfing. b, Field hockey. c, Volleyball. d, Pole vault.

2000, Sept. 23 *Perf. 13½*
2122 A971 75c Block of 4, #a-d 8.75 7.50

Horses — A972

No. 2123: a, Argentine Petiso. b, Argentine Carriage Horse. c, Peruvian. d, Criolla. e, Argentine Saddle Horse. f, Argentine Polo.
No. 2124: a, Horse-drawn mail coach. b, Horse's head.

2000, Oct. 7 *Perf. 13¾x13½*
2123 Sheet of 6 + 2 labels 9.50 8.00
a.-b. A972 25c Any single 1.10 1.10
c.-d. A972 50c Any single 1.40 4.10
e.-f. A972 75c Any single 2.10 2.10

Souvenir Sheet
Perf. 14

2124 Sheet of 2 4.00 3.50
a. A972 25c multi 1.25 1.25
b. A972 75c mutli 1.75 1.75

España 2000 Intl. Philatelic Exhibition.

Archaeological Artifacts — A973

Designs: 10c, Ceremonial hatchet, Santa Maria culture. 25c, Musical pipes. 50c, Loom, Mapuche culture. 60c, Poncho. 75c, Funerary mask, Tafi culture. 1p, Basket, Mbayá Indians. 2p, Drum, Mapuche culture. 3.25p, Ceremonial mask, Chané culture. 5p, Funerary urn, Belén culture. 9.40p, Rhea-feather costume.

Perf. 13½x13¾ Syncopated
2000 **Litho.**

2125 A973 10c multi .25 .25
2126 A973 25c multi .65 .50
2127 A973 50c multi 1.00 .80
2128 A973 60c multi 1.30 1.00
2129 A973 75c multi 1.60 1.25
2130 A973 1p multi 2.25 1.75
2131 A973 2p multi 4.50 3.00
2132 A973 3.25p multi 8.50 5.50
2133 A973 5p multi 11.00 7.00
2134 A973 9.40p multi 21.00 9.50
Nos. 2125-2134 (10) 52.05 30.55

Issued: 10c, 60c, 11/16; 25c, 50c, 75c, 9.40p, 10/26; 1p, 2p, 9/13; 3.25p, 5p, 8/30.
See Nos. 2495, 2670-2672. For surcharges, see Nos. 2841, 2849.

Natl. Atomic Energy Commission, 50th Anniv. — A974

2000, Nov. 11 **Litho.** *Perf. 13½*
2135 A974 75c multi 2.25 1.75

Fileteado Art Style and the Tango A975

No. 2136: a, Left side of Fileteado design. b, Right side of Fileteado design. c, Musicians. d, Tango dancers.

2000, Nov. 11 *Perf. 13¾x13½*
2136 A975 75c Block of 4, #a-d 11.00 10.00

Organ Donation Campaign — A976

2000, Nov. 25 *Perf. 13½*
2137 A976 75c multi 2.25 1.75

Christmas — A977

2000, Nov. 25
2138 A977 75c multi 2.25 1.75

Medicinal Plants — A978

Designs: No. 2139, 75c, Mirabilis jalapa. No. 2140, 75c, Senna corymbosa. No. 2141, 75c, Eugenia uniflora. No. 2142, 75c, Commelina erecta.

2000, Nov. 25
2139-2142 A978 Set of 4 8.50 7.00

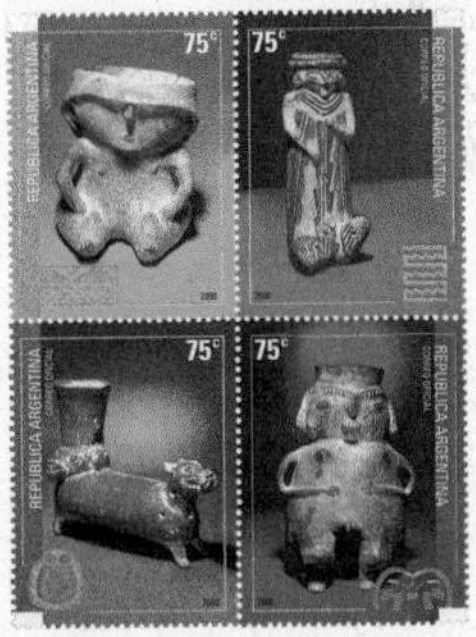

Pre-Columbian Art — A979

Various artifacts. Background colors: a, Bright orange. b, Red orange. c, Green. d, Red violet.

2000, Dec. 9
2143 A979 75c Block of 4, #a-d 12.00 11.00

A979a

Serpentine Die Cut 11¼x11
2001, Feb. 6 Litho. Self-Adhesive
Background Color

2143E A979a 10c blue grn *.85* *.30*
2143F A979a 25c brt green *2.25* *.75*
2143G A979a 60c orange *4.50* *1.90*
2143H A979a 75c red *7.00* *2.00*
2143I A979a 1p blue *9.00* *2.75*
2143J A979a 3p red brn *35.00* *8.50*

2143K A979a 3.25p yel green 30.00 9.00
2143L A979a 5.50p rose 52.50 16.00
Nos. 2143E-2143L (8) 141.10 41.20

Nos. 2143E-2143L are broken at right by five die cut wavy lines. Sold at Unidad Postal outlets. See Nos. 2217-2224A.

Miniature Sheet

Cenozoic Mammals — A980

No. 2144: a, Megaterio (Megatherium americanum). b, Gliptodonte (Doedicurus clavicaudatus). c, Macrauquenia (Macrauchenia patachonica). d, Toxodonte (Toxodon platensis).

2001, Mar. 10 ***Perf. 13¾x13½***
2144 A980 75c Sheet of 4, #a-d 11.00 10.00

Antarctic Bases, 50th Anniv. — A981

Map and: No. 2145, 75c, Cormorant, Base Brown. No. 2146, 75c, Skua, Base San Martín.

Perf. 13¾x13½
2001, Mar. 24 **Litho.**
2145-2146 A981 Set of 2 5.00 4.00

Apiculture — A982

No. 2147: a, Bee on flower. b, Bees on honeycomb. c, Bees, apiarist, and hives. d, Honey, pollen.

2001, Apr. 7 ***Perf. 13½x13¼***
2147 A982 Block of 4 18.00 15.00
a.-d. 75c Any single 3.00 3.00

Souvenir Sheet

Argentine Antarctic Institute, 50th Anniv. — A983

No. 2148: a, Scientist with fossils. b, Scientist with mapping equipment.

2001, Apr. 21 ***Perf. 14***
2148 A983 75c Sheet of 2, #a-b 8.50 8.00

Spain to Argentina Flight of Plus Ultra Seaplane, 75th Anniv. — A984

2001, Apr. 28 ***Perf. 13¾x13½***
2149 A984 75c multi 2.25 1.75

Art in Silver A985

No. 2150: a, Bridle (Freno). b, Stirrups (Estribos). c, Spurs (Espuelas). d, Gaucho's ornament (Rastra).

2001, May 19 Litho. ***Perf. 13¾x13½***
2150 A985 75c Block of 4, #a-d 11.00 10.00

World Youth Soccer Championships A986

Designs: No. 2151, 75c, Player kicking ball. No. 2152, 75c, Goalie catching ball.

2001, June 16
2151-2152 A986 Set of 2 4.50 3.25

Souvenir Sheet

Belgica 2001 Intl. Stamp Exhibition, Brussels — A987

No. 2153: a, 25c, Washerwoman by the Banks of the Belgrano, by Prilidiano Pueyrredón. b, 75c, The Hay Harvest, by Pieter Breughel, the Elder.

2001, June 16 ***Perf. 14***
2153 A987 Sheet of 2, #a-b 4.00 3.50

2001 Census — A988

Perf. 13½x13¾ Syncopated
2001, July 14
2154 A988 75c multi 2.00 1.75

SAC-C Satellite, Birds and Flowers — A989

2001, July 14 ***Perf. 13¾x13½***
2155 A989 75c multi 2.00 1.75

Environmental protection.

Bandoneón Recital — 1990, by Aldo Severi — A990

2001, July 28 ***Perf. 13½x13¾***
2156 A990 75c multi 2.25 1.75

The tango in art.

Souvenir Sheet

Phila Nippon '01, Japan A991

No. 2157: a, Tango dancers, musical score. b, Kabuki dancer.

2001, July 28 ***Perf. 14***
2157 A991 75c Sheet of 2, #a-b 5.50 5.00

Exists imperf. Value, pair $200.

Miniature Sheet

Wild Cats A992

No. 2158: a, 25c, Puma. b, 25c, Jaguar. c, 50c, Jaguarundi and young. d, 50c, Ocelot. e, 75c, Mountain cat. f, 75c, Huiña.

2001, July 28 ***Perf. 13¾x13½***
2158 A992 Sheet of 6, #a-f, +2 labels 11.50 10.00

Enrique Santos Discépolo (1901-51), Tango Lyricist — A993

2001, Aug. 4 ***Perf. 13½x13¾***
2159 A993 75c multi 2.50 2.25

America Issue — UNESCO World Heritage — A994

No. 2160 — Buildings and artifacts from Jesuit Block and Estancias of Cordoba: a, Denomination at UL. b, Denomination at UR.

2001, Aug. 11 ***Perf. 13¾x13½***
2160 A994 75c Horiz. pair, #a-b 9.00 7.50

Prevention of Breast Cancer — A995

2001, Sept. 1 ***Perf. 13½x13¾***
2161 A995 75c multi 2.25 1.75

World Championship Race Cars of Juan Manuel Fangio — A996

No. 2162 — Cars and track layouts: a, Alfa Romeo 159 Alfetta, Barcleona, 1951. b, Mercedes-Benz W196, Reims, France, 1954. c, Lancia-Ferrari D50, Monte Carlo, Monaco, 1956. d, Maserati 250F, Nürburgring, Germany, 1957.

2001, Oct. 6 ***Perf. 13¾x13½***
2162 A996 75c Block of 4, #a-d 11.00 9.00

Politicians A997

Designs: No. 2163, 75c, Roque Sáenz Peña (1851-1914). No. 2164, 75c, Justo José de Urquiza (1801-70).

2001, Oct. 20
2163-2164 A997 Set of 2 4.50 3.50

Bulnesia Sarmientoi — A998

2001, Oct. 20 Litho. ***Perf. 13½x13¾***
2165 A998 75c multi 2.25 1.75

Souvenir Sheet

Hafnia 01 Philatelic Exhibition, Copenhagen — A999

No. 2166: a, 25c, Argentine post rider, 18th cent. b, 75c, European post rider, 17th cent.

2001, Oct. 27 **Litho.** ***Perf. 14***
2166 A999 Sheet of 2, #a-b 4.00 3.50

Items in Argentine Museums A1000

Designs: No. 2167, 75c, Ammonite, skeleton of Carnotaurus sastrei, from Argentine Naural Science Museum. No. 2168, 75c, Letter from Buenos Aires, stagecoach "La Pobladora," from Enrique Udaondo Graphic Museum Complex. No. 2169, 75c, Icons from Averias culture, funerary urn from Las Mercedes culture, from Emilio and Duncan Wagner Museum of Anthropological and Natural Sciences, vert. No. 2170, 75c, Crucifix of Juan Martin de Pueyrredon, and detail, from Pueyrredon Museum, vert.

Perf. 13¾x13½, 13½x13¾
2001, Nov. 10 **Litho.**
2167-2170 A1000 Set of 4 8.50 7.50

Aviators and Their Airplanes
A1001

Designs: No. 2171, 75c, Carola Lorenzini (1899-1941) and Focke Wulf 44-J. No. 2172, 75c, Jean Mermoz (1901-36) and "Arc-en-Ciel."

2001, Nov. 24 ***Perf. 13¾x13½***
2171-2172 A1001 Set of 2 4.50 3.50

No. 2171 exists imperf. Value, pair $150.

Christmas — A1002

2001, Nov. 24 ***Perf. 13½x13¾***
2173 A1002 75c multi 2.25 1.75

Dances
A1003

No. 2174: a, Flamenco. b, Waltz. c, Zamba. d, Tango.

Perf. 13¾x13½

2001, Nov. 29 **Litho.**
2174 Booklet pane of 4 11.00 —
a.-d. A1003 75c Any single 2.00 2.00
Booklet, #2174 11.00

Dancers' Day — A1004

2001, Dec. 1 **Litho.** ***Perf. 13¾x13½***
2175 A1004 75c multi 2.50 2.00

Argentine Television, 50th Anniv. — A1005

No. 2176: a, Television, camera, microphone, test pattern. b, Televisions and videotape reels. c, Television, astronaut and satellite dish. d, Televisions, cables and VCR remote control.

2001, Dec. 1 ***Perf. 13¾x13½***
2176 A1005 75c Block of 4, #a-d 8.75 7.00

Argentina in the Antarctic
A1006

Designs: No. 2177, 75c, Esperanza Base, 50th anniv. No. 2178, 75c, First air and sea courier service, 50th anniv.

2002, Mar. 9
2177-2178 A1006 Set of 2 4.50 3.25

America Issue — Education
A1007

No. 2179: a, School and Argentine flag. b, Children playing hop scotch.

2002, Mar. 23
2179 A1007 75c Vert. pair, #a-b 4.50 3.50

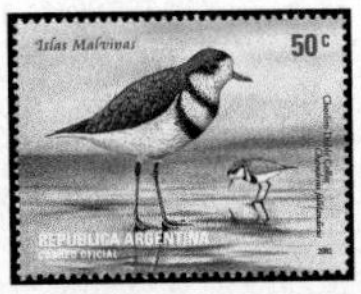

Falkland Islands Birds — A1008

Designs: No. 2180, 50c, Charadrius falklandicus. No. 2181, 50c, Larus scoresbii. No. 2182, 75c, Chloephaga rubidiceps, vert. No. 2183, 75c, Aptenodytes patagonicus, vert.

Perf. 13¾x13½, 13½x13¾

2002, Apr. 13 **Litho.**
2180-2183 A1008 Set of 4 7.00 6.00

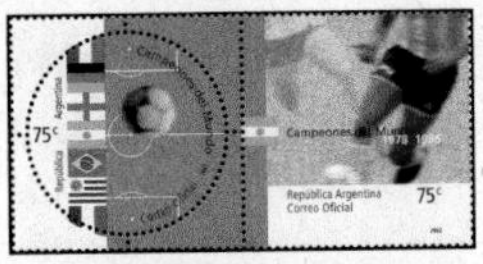

2002 World Cup Soccer Championships, Japan and Korea — A1009

No. 2184: a, Flags, soccer ball and field (38mm diameter). b, Soccer players, years of Argentinian championships.

2002, Apr. 27 **Litho.** ***Perf. 12¾***
2184 A1009 75c Horiz. pair, #a-b 4.00 3.25

See Brazil No. 2840, France No. 2891, Germany No. 2163, Italy No. 2526, Uruguay No. 1946.

Anniversaries — A1010

No. 2185, 25c: a, Rosario riverfront, Ship on Paraná River, arms. b, Rosario riverfront, National Flag Monument.
No. 2186, 50c: a, Mt. Fitzroy, Nahuel Huapi Natl. Park. b, Dr. Francisco P. Moreno.
No. 2187, 75c: a, Flower, aerial view of San Carlos de Bariloche. b, Church and town map.

2002, May 11 **Litho.** ***Perf. 13½x13¾***
Horiz. Pairs, #a-b
2185-2187 A1010 Set of 3 7.50 6.00

Pan-American Health Organization, Cent. — A1011

2002, June 1
2188 A1011 75c multi 2.25 1.75

Doctors
A1012

No. 2189: a, Cosme Mariano Argerich (1758-1820), founder of Military Health Service. b, José María Ramos Mejía (1849-1914), psychiatric educator. c, Salvador Mazza (1886-1946), Chagas' disease specialist. d, Carlos Arturo Gianantonio (1926-95), pediatrician.

Perf. 13¾x13½

2002, June 15 **Litho.**
2189 A1012 50c Block of 4, #a-d 5.00 4.00

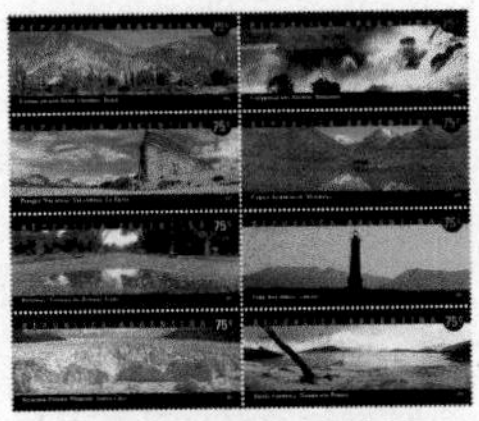

Landscapes — A1013

No. 2190: a, Seven-colored Mountain, Jujuy Province. b, Iguaçu Falls, Misiones Province. c, Talampaya Natl. Park, La Rioja Province. d, Mt. Aconcagua, Mendoza Province. e, Rose Garden, Buenos Aires. f, San Jorge Lighthouse, Chubut. g, Perito Moreno Glacier, Santa Cruz Province. h, Lapataia Bay, Tierra del Fuego Province.

2002, July 29 ***Perf. 14x13½***
2190 A1013 Block of 8 14.00 12.00
a.-h. 75c Any single 1.50 1.50

For surcharge, see No. 2847.

Eva Perón (1919-52) — A1014

No. 2191: a, Official portrait. b, Embossed profile. c, At microphone. d, Painting by Nicolas Garcia Uriburu.

Litho., Litho & Embossed (#2191b)

2002, July 27 ***Perf. 13½x13¾***
2191 Horiz. strip of 4 7.00 6.00
a.-d. A1014 75c Any single 1.25 1.25

Worldwide Fund for Nature (WWF) — A1015

No. 2192: a, Ozotoceros bezoarticus. b, Vicugna vicugna. c, Pudu puda. d, Catagonus wagneri.

2002, July 27 **Litho.** ***Perf. 13¾x13½***
2192 A1015 $1 Block of 4, #a-d 8.50 7.00

Souvenir Sheet

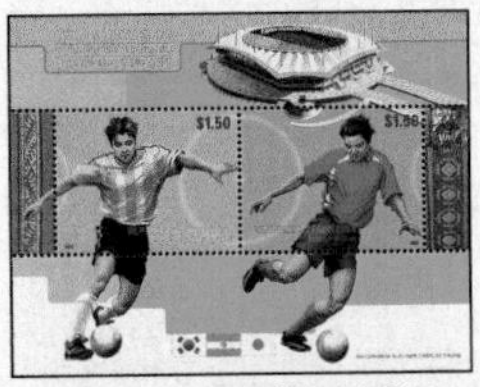

Philakorea 2002 World Stamp Exhibition, Seoul — A1016

No. 2193: a, Argentine soccer player (blue and white shirt). b, Korean soccer player (red shirt).

2002, Aug. 10 ***Perf. 14***
2193 A1016 1.50p Sheet of 2, #a-b 6.50 6.00

Sports — A1016a

10c, Cycling. 25c, Tennis. 50c, Auto racing. 75c, Parachuting. 1p, Horse racing. 2p, Golf. 5p, Sailing.

Perf. 13½x13¾ Syncopated

2002, Sept. 6 **Litho.**

2193C	A1016a	10c	multi	2.40	.35
2193D	A1016a	25c	multi	2.40	.35
2193E	A1016a	50c	multi	2.40	.40
2193F	A1016a	75c	multi	4.25	.75
2193G	A1016a	1p	multi	4.25	1.05
2193H	A1016a	2p	multi	7.00	2.10
2193I	A1016a	5p	multi	10.25	5.25
	Nos. 2193C-2193I (7)			32.95	10.25

Nos. 2193C-2193I were sold only to customers who met certain mailing requirements but could be used on mail by anyone without restrictions.

Valdés Peninsula Tourism — A1017

Whale breaching: a, Head. b, Tail.

2002, Sept. 14 ***Perf. 13½x13¾***
2194 A1017 75c Horiz. pair, #a-b 4.00 3.50

Insects — A1018

Designs: 25c, Edessa meditabunda. 50c, Elaechlora viridis. 75c, Chrysodina aurata. 1p, Steirastoma breve.

2002, Sept. 21 ***Perf. 13¾x13½***
2195-2198 A1018 Set of 4 6.25 5.25

Men's Volleyball World Championships
A1019

Various players with background colors of: No. 2199, 75c, Blue green (shown). No. 2200, 75c, Light blue. No. 2201, 75c, Bright yellow green. No. 2202, 75c, Pale orange.

Perf. 13½x13¾

2002, Sept. 28 **Litho.**
2199-2202 A1019 Set of 4 7.25 6.25

On Nos. 2199-2202 portions of the design were applied by a thermographic process producing a shiny, raised effect.

Argentine Highway Association, 50th Anniv. — A1020

2002, Oct. 5 ***Perf. 13¾x13½***
2203 A1020 75c multi 1.90 1.60

Argentine Personalities
A1021

Designs: No. 2204, 75c, Roberto Arlt (1900-42), novelist. No. 2205, 75c, Beatriz Guido (1924-88), writer. No. 2206, 75c, Niní Marshall (1903-96), actress. No. 2207, 75c, Luis Sandrini (1905-80), actor.

2002, Oct. 19
2204-2207 A1021 Set of 4 7.00 6.00

Immigrant Agricultural Colonies — A1022

Flags of France, Switzerland, Spain and Italy and: a, Hotel for immigrants, mother and son, stamped passport. b, Two immigrants and ship. c, Two immigrants, Provisory Hotel for immigrants, French immigrant instruction book. d, Farmer plowing field, family of immigrants.

2002, Oct. 19 Litho. ***Perf. 13½x13¾***
2208 Horiz. strip of 4 7.00 6.00
a.-d. A1022 75c Any single 1.50 1.50

Argentine Federation of Philatelic Entities, 50th Anniv. — A1023

Designs: No. 2209, 75c, Stamped cover, stagecoach, EXFICEC '56 exhibition cancel, Head of Ceres from Corrientes issue. No. 2210, 75c, ESPAMER '98 Cancel, postman, ship and map, coat of arms.

2002, Nov. 2 ***Perf. 13¾x13½***
2209-2210 A1023 Set of 2 3.50 2.75

Christmas
A1024

2002, Nov. 16
2211 A1024 75c multi 1.75 .50

Folk Musicians — A1025

Designs: No. 2212, 75c, Gustavo "Cuchi" Leguizamón (1917-2000). No. 2213, 75c, Armando Tejada Gómez (1929-92). No. 2214, 75c, Carlos Vega (1898-1966). No. 2215, 75c, Andrés Chazarreta (1876-1960).

2002, Dec. 7 ***Perf. 13½x13¾***
2212-2215 A1025 Set of 4 7.00 6.00

Puppets
A1026

No. 2216: a, Marionette of woman. b, King and fish hand puppets. c, Rod puppet of man. d, Shadow theater.

2002, Dec. 7 ***Perf. 13¾x13½***
2216 Booklet pane of 4 10.00 8.00
a.-d. A1026 75c Any single 2.25 2.00
Booklet, #2216 10.00

Unidad Postal Type of 2001
Perf. 13¾x13½ Syncopated
2002 Litho.
Size: 35x24mm (10p, 35x25mm)
Background Color

2217 A979a 10c blue green .30 .25
2218 A979a 25c brt green .65 .40
2219 A979a 50c tan 1.20 .55
2220 A979a 75c red 1.75 .85
2221 A979a 1p blue 2.75 1.20
2222 A979a 2p gray 5.50 1.75
2223 A979a 3p brown 6.50 2.00
2224 A979a 5p olive bister 10.50 2.60
2224A A979a 10p yellow 21.00 3.50
Nos. 2217-2224A (9) 50.15 13.10

Issue dates: Nos. 2217-2224, 6/02; 10p, 8/16/02.
Nos. 2217-2224A were sold only at Unidad Postal outlets.
For surcharge, see No. 2843.

Communal Vegetable Gardens
A1027

Designs: No. 2225, 75c, Cabbage. No. 2226, 75c, Corn, vert.

Perf. 13¾x13½, 13½x13¾
2003, Mar. 8
2225-2226 A1027 Set of 2 3.50 2.50

Native Handicrafts
A1028

Designs: No. 2227, 75c, Sieve, by Mbyá people, fork and spoon by Wichi people. No. 2228, 75c, Woven waistband of Pilagal'ek people, Bag by Nam Qom people.

2003, Mar. 8 ***Perf. 13¾x13½***
2227-2228 A1028 Set of 2 3.50 2.75

National Parks
A1029

Animals and parks: No. 2229, 50c, Lama guanicoe, Los Cardones National Park. No. 2230, 50c, Piaya cayana, Colonia Benítez Natural Reserve. No. 2231, 50c, Mazama gouazoupira, Copo National Park. No. 2232, 75c, Tinamotis pentlandii, Campo de los Alisos National Park. No. 2233, 75c, Spheniscus magellanicus, Monte León, planned National Park.

2003, Mar. 22 ***Perf. 14x13½***
2229-2233 A1029 Set of 5 7.25 5.50

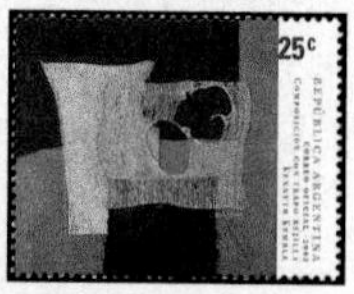

Paintings
A1030

Designs: No. 2234, 25c, Composición con Trapo Rejilla, by Kenneth Kemble. No. 2235, 25c, Pintura, by Roberto Aizenberg, vert. 50c, Pantalla, by Rómulo Macció, vert. No. 2237, 75c, La Giaconda, by Guillermo Roux. No. 2238, 75c, Hacerse Humo, by Antonio Seguí. 1p, San P., by Xul Solar (with attached label).

Perf. 13¾x13½, 13½x13¾
2003, Apr. 12
2234-2239 A1030 Set of 6 9.50 8.00

Nos. 2234-2238 were each printed in sheets of 4; No. 2239 was printed in sheets of 2 + 2 labels.

Argentina, Champions of 2002 Intl. Sporting Events — A1031

Designs: No. 2240, 75c, Women's field hockey. No. 2241, 75c, Soccer for blind players.

Litho., Litho. & Embossed (#2241)
2003, May 3 ***Perf. 13¾x13½***
2240-2241 A1031 Set of 2 3.50 3.00

Comic Strips
A1032

No. 2242: a, 25c, Mago Fafa, by Alberto Bróccoli. b, 25c, Astronaut, by Crist (Cristóbal Reinoso). c, 50c, Hijitus, by Manuel García Ferré. d, 50c, Savarese, by Domingo Mandrafina and Robin Wood. e, 75c, Sónoman, by Oswal (Oswaldo Walter Viola). f, 75c, El Tipito, by Daniel Paz and Rudy (Marcelo E. Rudaeff). g, 75c, La Vaca Aurora, by Domingo Mirco Repetto. h, 75c, Diógenes y el Linyera, by Tabaré (Gómez Laborde), Jorge Guinzberg and Carlos Abrevaya.

2003, May 17 Litho. ***Perf. 13½x13¾***
2242 A1032 Sheet of 8, #a-h 11.50 9.50

Silver Tableware — A1033

No. 2243: a, Soup bowl with lid (sopera). b, Kettle and burner, maté kettle and drinking tube. c, Chocolate pot and jar with handle. d, Sugar bowl (azucarera).

2003, May 24 ***Perf. 13¾x13½***
2243 A1033 75c Block of 4, #a-d 7.00 5.75

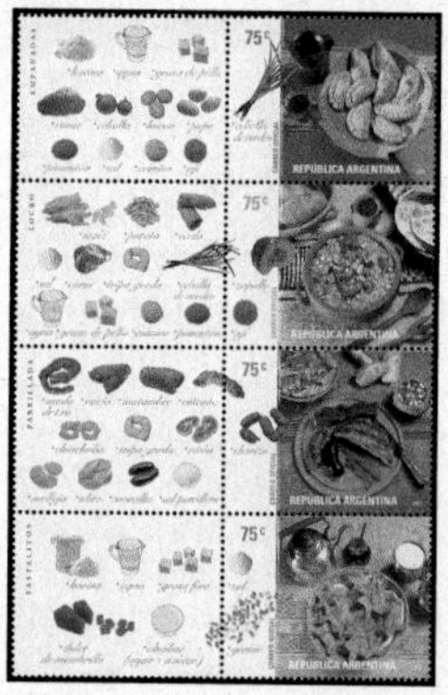

Food
A1034

Designs: Nos. 2244a, 2245a, Empanadas (red denomination). Nos. 2244b, 2245b, Locro (orange denomination) Nos. 2244c, 2246a, Parrillada (green denomination) Nos. 2244d, 2246b, Pastelitos (blue denomination).

2003, June 7 ***Perf. 13¾x13½***
2244 A1034 75c Vert strip of 4, #a-d, + 4 labels 9.50 8.00

Booklet Panes
Perf. 14
2245 A1034 75c Pane of 2, #a-b, + 2 labels *16.00 15.00*
2246 A1034 75c Pane of 2, #a-b, + 2 labels *16.00 15.00*
Complete booklet, #2245-2246 *32.00*

Size of stamps in booklet panes: 40x30mm.

Miniature Sheet

Children's Games — A1035

No. 2247: a, El Elástico. b, La escondida (hide and seek). c, La mancha (tag). d, Martín Pescador.

2003, July 12 ***Perf. 13¾x13½***
2247 A1035 50c Sheet of 4, #a-d 7.50 6.50

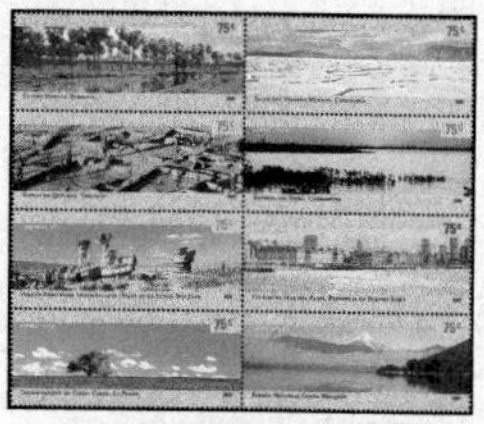

Landscapes — A1036

No. 2248: a, Mbiguá Marsh, Formosa Province. b, Dead Man's Salt Flats, Catamarca Province. c, Quilmes Ruins, Tucumán Province. d, Iberá Marshes, Corrientes Province. e, Ischigualasto Provincial Park, San Juan Province. f, Mar del Plata, Buenos Aires Province. g, Caleu Caleu Department, La Pampa Province. h, Lanín National Park, Nequén Province.

2003, July 19 ***Perf. 14x13¾***
2248 A1036 75c Block of 8, #a-h 14.00 12.00

For surcharge, see No. 2845.

Opening of Nuestra Señora del Rosario Bridge and Roadway, Rosario-Victoria — A1037

No. 2249: a, 25c, Bridge, map of roadway. b, 75c, Bridge and cross-section.

Perf. 13½x13¾
2003, Aug. 23 Litho.
2249 A1037 Horiz. pair, #a-b 6.00 5.00

Argentine History — A1038

Designs: No. 2250, 75c, Dr. Vicente Fidel López (1815-1903), Education minister, headquarters of Province of Buenos Aires Bank. No. 2251, 75c, First page of constitution, medal and signature of Juan Bautista Alberdi. No. 2252, 75c, Emblem and squadron of General San Martín Mounted Grenadiers Regiment. No. 2253, 75c, Presidential sash and staff, Casa Rosada. No. 2254, 75c, Arms of Río Negro Province, vert.

Perf. 13¾x13½, 13½x13¾
2003, Sept. 6
2250-2254 A1038 Set of 5 8.75 7.00

Constitution, 150th anniv. (No. 2251), Revival of General San Martín Mounted Grenadiers Regiment, cent. (No. 2252), Presidential inauguration (No. 2253).

Souvenir Sheet

Bangkok 2003 World Philatelic Exhibition — A1039

No. 2255: a, Quebrada de Humahuacha black demon mask, Argentine flag. b, Phi Ta Khon Festival mask, Thailand flag.

Litho. with Foil Application

2003, Oct. 4 ***Perf. 14***
2255 A1039 75c Sheet of 2, #a-b 4.25 3.50

America Issue — Flora and Fauna — A1040

Designs: No. 2256, 75c, Nothofagus pumilio. No. 2257, 75c, Vultur gryphus.

2003, Oct. 11 Litho. ***Perf. 13¾x13½***
2256-2257 A1040 Set of 2 3.75 3.25

Jubany Base, Antarctica, 50th Anniv. — A1041

2003, Oct. 18
2258 A1041 75c multi 1.90 1.60

Rescue of Swedish Scientific Expedition by A. R. A. Uruguay, Cent. — A1042

Designs: No. 2259, Welcome, (ship and penguins) by Eduardo De Martino.

No. 2260: a, A. R. A. Uruguay. b, A. R. A. Uruguay and Lt. Julián Irízar.

2003, Oct. 18 ***Perf. 13¾x13½***
2259 A1042 75c multi 1.90 1.60

Souvenir Sheet

Perf. 14

2260 A1042 75c Sheet of 2, #a-b 4.50 4.00

No. 2260 contains two 40x30mm stamps.

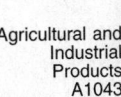

Agricultural and Industrial Products A1043

Designs: No. 2261, 75c, Cattle. No. 2262, 75c, Soybeans. No. 2263, 75c, Aluminum. No. 2264, 75c, Teradi 800 cobalt therapy machine.

2003, Oct. 18 ***Perf. 13¾x13½***
2261-2264 A1043 Set of 4 7.00 6.00

Christmas — A1044

Designs: No. 2265, 75c, Purmamarca clay creche figures. No. 2266, 75c, Gaucho Birth, carved wood creche figures by Eloy López.

2003, Nov. 8 ***Perf. 13½x13¾***
2265-2266 A1044 Set of 2 3.50 1.50

20th Century Architecture A1045

Designs: No. 2267, 75c, Barolo Palace, Buenos Aires, by Mario Palanti, 1923. No. 2268, 75c, Tucumán Province Bank Building, San Miguel de Tucumán, by Alejandro Virasoro, 1928. No. 2269, 75c, Córdoba Province Savings Bank Building, Córdoba, by Jaime Roca, 1929. No. 2270, 75c, Minetti Palace, Rosario, by Juan B. Durand, Leopoldo Schwarz and José Gerbino, 1930.

2003, Nov. 8
2267-2270 A1045 Set of 4 7.00 5.50

Orcadas Base, Antarctica, Cent. — A1046

Designs: No. 2271, Helicopter, Orcadas Base.

No. 2272: a, #127 with 1904 South Orcadas cancel, vert. b, Meteorological observatory and weather vane.

2004, Feb. 21 ***Perf. 13¾x13½***
2271 A1046 75c multi 2.25 2.00

Souvenir Sheet

Perf. 14

2272 A1046 75c Sheet of 2, #a-b 5.50 5.00

No. 2272 contains one 30x40mm and one 40x30mm stamp.

Quebrada de Humahuaca UNESCO World Heritage Site — A1047

No. 2273 — View of Rio Grande Valley and: a, Decorated llama, rock painting, person in front of door. b, Santa Rosa de Lima Church, costumed carnival participants.

2004, Mar. 27 ***Perf. 13½x13¾***
2273 A1047 75c Horiz. pair, #a-b 4.00 3.50

America Issue — Forest Conservation — A1048

No. 2274 — Forest and timeline charting hectares of forest with years: a, 1914, 1956. b, 1989, 2004.

2004, Mar. 27
2274 A1048 75c Horiz. pair, #a-b 4.50 4.00

No. 2274b has large hole in center of stamp.

La Voz del Interior Newspaper, Cent. — A1049

2004, Apr. 17 ***Perf. 13¾x13½***
2275 A1049 75c multi 2.00 1.75

For surcharge, see No. 2846.

Landscapes — A1050

No. 2276: a, Molinos, Salta Province. b, Pampa del Indio Provincial Park, Chaco Province. c, Rio Hondo Dam, Santiago del Estera Province. d, Bridge, Santa Fe de la Vera Cruz, Santa Fe Province. e, San Roque Lake, Córdoba Province. f, El Palmar National Park, Entre Rios Province. g, Potrero de los Funes, San Luis Province. h, Mt. Tronador, Río Negro Province.

2004, Apr. 17 ***Perf. 14x13½***
2276 A1050 75c Block of 8, #a-h 17.00 15.00

FIFA (Fédération Internationale de Football Association), Cent. — A1051

Paintings of soccer players by Rubén Ramonda: No. 2277, 75c, The Tunnel (blue background). No. 2278, 75c, El Picado (orange background).

2004, May 22 Litho. ***Perf. 13¾x13½***
2277-2278 A1051 Set of 2 4.00 3.50

Souvenir Sheet

España 2004 World Philatelic Exhibition — A1052

No. 2279: a, Return of the Fishing Fleet, by Joaquín Sorolla y Bastida. b, A Stop in the Pampas, by Angel Della Valle, vert.

2004, May 22 ***Perf. 14***
2279 A1052 75c Sheet of 2, #a-b 5.50 5.00

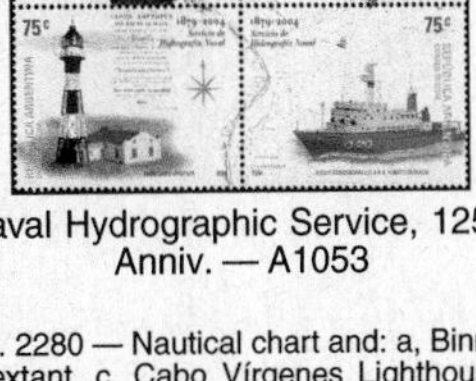

Naval Hydrographic Service, 125th Anniv. — A1053

No. 2280 — Nautical chart and: a, Binnacle. b, Sextant. c, Cabo Vírgenes Lighthouse. d, Oceanographic ship Puerto Deseado.

2004, June 5 ***Perf. 13¾x13½***
2280 A1053 75c Block of 4, #a-d 8.00 7.00

Printed in sheets of four blocks separated by a central column of labels.

Souvenir Sheet

Circus A1054

No. 2281: a, Trained dogs. b, Clown on stilts, trapeze artist. c, Clown juggling on unicycle. d, Bareback rider.

2004, June 12
2281 A1054 50c Sheet of 4, #a-d 8.00 7.00

Characters From Comic Strip "Patoruzito," by Dante Quinterno — A1055

No. 2282: a, 25c, Isidorito. b, 25c, Upita. c, 50c, Patoruzito. d, 50c, Malén. e, 75c, Pamperito. f, 75c, Chacha.

No. 2283: a, Patoruzito (20x60mm). b, Pamperito (20x60mm). c, Isidorito (30x30mm)

No. 2284: a, Malén (30x40mm). b, Upita (30x40mm). c, Chacha (30x40mm)

2004, July 10 Litho. ***Perf. 13½x13¾***
2282 A1055 Sheet of 6 + 2 labels *9.00 7.50*

Booklet Panes

Perf. 14

2283	Booklet pane of 3 + label	*15.00*	*15.00*
a.-c.	A1055 75c Any single	*4.00*	*4.00*
2284	Booklet pane of 3 + label	*15.00*	*15.00*
a.-c.	A1055 75c Any single	*4.00*	*4.00*
	Complete booklet, #2283-2284	*34.00*	

Fish of the Falkland Islands Area — A1056

Designs: No. 2285, 75c, Salilota australis. No. 2286, 75c, Patagonotothen ramsayi. No. 2287, 75c, Dissostichus eleginoides. No. 2288, 75c, Bathyraja griseocauda.

2004, July 17 Litho. ***Perf. 13¾x13½***
2285-2288 A1056 Set of 4 8.00 7.00

Assistance Dogs — A1057

Designs: No. 2289, 75c, Rescue dog. No. 2290, 75c, Seeing-eye dog, vert.

Perf. 13¾x13½, 13½x13¼

2004, July 17
2289-2290 A1057 Set of 2 4.25 3.75

2004 Summer Olympics, Athens — A1058

No. 2291: a, Cycling. b, Judo. c, Swimming. d, Tennis.

2004, Aug. 7 *Perf. 13¾x13½*
2291 A1058 75c Block of 4, #a-d 8.00 7.00

Legends
A1059

Designs: No. 2292, 75c, El Pehuén. No. 2293, 75c, La Yacumama. No. 2294, 75c, La Pachamama. No. 2295, 75c, La Difunta Correa.

2004, Aug. 21
2292-2295 A1059 Set of 4 8.00 7.00

Souvenir Sheet

World Stamp Championship 2004, Singapore — A1060

No. 2296: a, Mangifera indica. b, Syagrus romanzoffiana.

2004, Aug. 21 *Perf. 14*
2296 A1060 75c Sheet of 2, #a-b 4.00 3.50

Centenaries
A1061

Designs: No. 2297, 75c, Agronomy and Veterinary Science Institute for Higher Learning, Buenos Aires. No. 2298, 75c, City of Neuquén. No. 2299, 75c, Philatelic Association of Rosario.

2004, Sept. 11 *Perf. 13¾x13½*
2297-2299 A1061 Set of 3 5.75 5.00

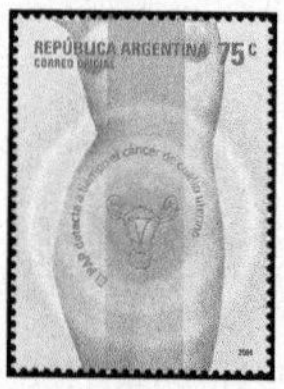

Prevention of Uterine Cancer — A1062

2004, Sept. 18 *Perf. 13½x13¾*
2300 A1062 75c multi 2.00 1.75

Preservation of Water Resources
A1063

No. 2301: a, Hourglass with clean water. b, Hourglass with polluted water.

2004, Sept. 18 *Perf. 13¾x13½*
2301 A1063 75c Vert. tete beche pair, #a-b 3.75 3.25

Landmarks in Argentina — A1063a

Designs: 25c, Ruins of San Ignacio Miní, Misiones Province. 50c, Iruya. 1p, Buenos Aires. 2p, Aconcagua Provincial Park. 3p, Valdes Peninsula. 5p, Mina Clavero. 10p, Ushuaia.

Perf. 13¾x13½ Syncopated

2004, Sept. 24 **Litho.**

2301C	A1063a	25c	multi	.35	.35
2301D	A1063a	50c	multi	.50	.50
2301E	A1063a	1p	multi	1.00	1.00
2301F	A1063a	2p	multi	2.10	2.00
2301G	A1063a	3p	multi	3.00	3.00
2301H	A1063a	5p	multi	5.25	5.00
j.	With label			3.50	3.50
2301I	A1063a	10p	multi	10.00	9.50
	Nos. 2301D-2301I (6)			21.85	21.00

Issued: No. 2301Hj, 5/11/10.
See Nos. 2357, 2586-2587, 2678-2679.

The Nativity
A1064

Virgin Mary
A1065

2004, Oct. 16 **Litho.** *Perf. 13½x13¾*
2302 A1064 75c multi 1.60 .65
2303 A1065 75c multi 1.60 .65

Christmas, Stained glass windows, St. Felicitas Church, Buenos Aires.

Numismatics — A1066

No. 2304 — Halves of 1813 silver 1 real coin and 1813 gold 8 escudos coin: a, Obverse (sun). b, Reverse (coat of arms).

2004, Oct. 23
2304 A1066 75c Horiz. pair, #a-b 3.25 2.75

Andrés Bello and Front Page of Spanish Grammar for Americans
A1067

2004, Nov. 6 *Perf. 13¾x13½*
2305 A1067 75c multi 1.75 1.50

Third Intl. Spanish Language Congress, Rosario.

Buenos Aires Commodities Exchange, 150th Anniv. — A1068

2004, Nov. 6
2306 A1068 75c multi 1.75 1.50

Medicinal Plants — A1069

Designs: No. 2307, 75c, Aloysia citriodora. No. 2308, 75c, Minthostachys mollis. No. 2309, 75c, Lippia turbinata. No. 2310, 75c, Tagetes minuta.

2004, Nov. 20 *Perf. 13½x13¾*
2307-2310 A1069 Set of 4 8.00 7.00

12th Pan-American Scout Jamboree
A1070

2005, Jan. 15 *Perf. 13¾x13½*
2311 A1070 75c multi 1.50 1.10

Argentina — Thailand Diplomatic Relations, 50th Anniv. — A1071

Designs: No. 2312, 75c, Tango dancers, Argentina. No. 2313, 75c, Tom-tom dancers, Thailand.

2005, Feb. 5 *Perf. 13½x13¾*
2312-2313 A1071 Set of 2 3.50 3.00

Paintings by Antonio Berni (1905-81) — A1072

Designs: No. 2314, Woman with a Red Sweater.
No. 2315 — Details from Manifestation: a, 75c, Bearded man, man looking up (40x50mm). b, 75c, Child, two men with hats in foreground, horiz. (50x40mm).

2005, Mar. 12 *Perf. 13½x13¾*
2314 A1072 75c shown 1.50 1.10

Souvenir Sheet
Perf. 14
2315 A1072 Sheet of 2, #a-b 3.50 2.75

Rotary International, Cent. — A1073

2005, Mar. 19 *Perf. 13¾x13½*
2316 A1073 75c multi 1.50 1.00

Writers — A1074

Designs: No. 2317, 75c, Silvina Ocampo (1903-93). No. 2318, 75c, Ezequiel Martínez Estrada (1895-1964).

2005, Mar. 19 *Perf. 13½x13¾*
2317-2318 A1074 Set of 2 4.25 3.75

Argentine Motor Vehicles
A1075

Designs: No. 2319, 75c, Graciela sedan. No. 2320, 75c, Justicialista Sport. No. 2321, 75c, Rastrojero Diesel truck. No. 2322, 75c, Siam Di Tella 1500. No. 2323, 75c, Torino 380 W.

2005, Apr. 9 **Litho.** *Perf. 13¾x13½*
2319-2323 A1075 Set of 5 8.25 7.00

A portion of the design of each stamp is coated with a glossy varnish.

Intl. Year of Physics
A1076

Designs: No. 2324, 75c, José Antonio Balseiro, founder of Balseiro Institute, nuclear reactor. No. 2325, 75c, Albert Einstein, front page of Einstein's theory of relativity.

2005, Apr. 23 **Litho.** *Perf. 13¾x13½*
2324-2325 A1076 Set of 2 3.50 3.00

Balseiro Institute, 50th anniv.

Pope John Paul II (1920-2005)
A1077

Designs: No. 2326, Pope waving.
No. 2327: a, Pope with crucifix, Papal arms. b, Pope and crowd.

2005, Apr. 23 *Perf. 13½x13¾*
2326 A1077 75c shown 2.75 2.50

Souvenir Sheet
Perf. 14
2327 A1077 75c Sheet of 2, #a-b 5.50 4.75

No. 2327 contains two 40x50mm stamps.

General Workers Confederation, 75th Anniv. — A1078

La Capital Newspaper, Mar del Plata, Cent. — A1079

Sunday Blue Law No. 4661, Cent. — A1080

2005, May 21 **Litho.** *Perf. 13½x13¾*

2328	A1078	75c	multi	1.50	1.25
2329	A1079	75c	multi	1.50	1.25
2330	A1080	75c	multi	1.50	1.25
	Nos. 2328-2330 (3)			4.50	3.75

César Milstein (1927-2002), 1984 Nobel Laureate in Physiology or Medicine
A1081

2005, June 4 *Perf. 13¾x13½*
2331 A1081 75c multi 1.60 1.40

Volunteer Firefighters
A1082

Designs: No. 2332, 75c, Orestes Liberti (1860-1936), first commander of volunteer firefighter brigade, horse-drawn fire engine.

No. 2333, 75c, Fire fighters in action, fire truck.

2005, June 4 *Perf. 13½x13¾*
2332-2333 A1082 Set of 2 3.00 2.50

Argentine Red Cross, 125th Anniv. — A1083

2005, June 11 *Perf. 13¾x13½*
2334 A1083 75c multi 1.50 1.10

Juan Filloy (1894-2000), Writer — A1084

2005, July 16
2335 A1084 75c multi 1.50 1.00

Miniature Sheet

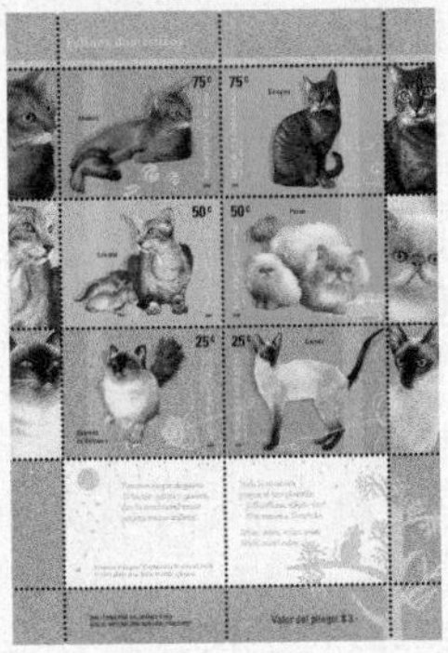

Cats A1085

No. 2336: a, 25c, Birman. b, 25c, Siamese. c, 50c, Oriental. d, 50c, Persian. e, 75c, Abyssinian. f, 75c, European.

2005, July 16
2336 A1085 Sheet of 6, #a-f, + 2 labels 7.50 6.00

Wine Regions A1086

Glass of wine, map, vineyard in: No. 2337, 75c, Salta Province, Torrontés grapes. No. 2338, 75c, Mendoza Province, Malbec grapes. No. 2339, 75c, San Juan Province, Syrah grapes. No. 2340, 75c, Río Negro Province, Merlot grapes.

2005, July 16 *Perf. 14x13½*
2337-2340 A1086 Set of 4 6.25 5.25

Compare Nos. 2337-2340 with Nos. 2370b-2373b. For surcharges, see Nos. 2855-2857.

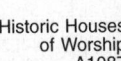

Historic Houses of Worship A1087

Designs: No. 2341, 75c, Our Lady of the Rosary of Candonga Chapel, Sierra Chicas. No. 2342, 75c, Al Ahmad Mosque, Buenos Aires. No. 2343, 75c, Temple of the Israelite Congregation, Buenos Aires. No. 2344, 75c, Vision of the Middle Buddhist Temple, Buenos Aires.

2005, Aug. 6 *Perf. 13¾x13½*
2341-2344 A1087 Set of 4 6.00 4.75

Local Grocery Stores — A1088

Designs: No. 2345, 75c, Pulpería de Cacho di Catarina, Mercedes. No. 2346, 75c, Pulpería El Torito, Baradero. No. 2347, 75c, Pulpería Perucho, General Lavalle. No. 2348, 75c, Pulpería Impini, Larroque.

2005, Sept. 10
2345-2348 A1088 Set of 4 6.00 4.75

Antarctic Science A1089

Designs: No. 2349, Iceberg, Antarctic Treaty emblem

No. 2350: a, Major General Hernán Pujato and members of First Argentine Polar Expedition air crew. b, Divers, raft, iceberg.

2005, Sept. 24 *Perf. 13¾x13½*
2349 A1089 75c multi 1.90 1.60

Souvenir Sheet

Perf. 14

2350 A1089 75c Sheet of 2, #a-b 4.50 4.00

No. 2350 contains two 40x30mm stamps.

Colón Theater Companies, 80th Anniv. — A1090

No. 2351: a, Dancer Julio Bocca, ballet dancers, Colón Theater building. b, Orchestra, choir, opera singers.

2005, Sept. 24 *Perf. 13½x13¾*
2351 A1090 75c Horiz. pair, #a-b 3.00 2.00

Alternative Energy Sources — A1091

Designs: 75c, Solar power. 4p, Wind power.

2005, Oct. 15
2352-2353 A1091 Set of 2 8.25 5.50

Christmas — A1092

Details from altarpiece by Elena Storni: No. 2354, Madonna and Child.

No. 2355: a, The Annunciation, Mary and Elizabeth. b, Nativity. c, Magi. d, Presentation of Jesus in the Temple.

2005, Oct. 15 *Perf. 13½x13¾*
2354 A1092 75c shown 1.50 .50

Souvenir Sheet

Litho. with Foil Application

Perf. 14

2355 A1092 75c Sheet of 4, #a-d 6.00 4.00

No. 2355 contains four 40x40mm stamps.

Fourth Summit of the Americas, Mar del Plata — A1093

2005, Oct. 29 Litho. *Perf. 13¾x13½*
2356 A1093 75c multi 1.50 1.25

Landmarks Type of 2004

Design: Perito Moreno Glacier

Perf. 13¾x13½ Syncopated

2005, Nov. 18
2357 A1063a 4p multi 4.25 3.75

Immigrants to Argentina A1095

Designs: No. 2358, 75c, German immigrants in Cañada de Gómez, bandoneon. No. 2359, 75c, Slovakian immigrants in Buenos Aires, weather indicator. No. 2360, 75c, Welsh immigrants, Chubut Central Railway train, railway lantern. No. 2361, 75c, Jewish settlers, Moisés Ville, wheat.

2005, Nov. 19 *Perf. 13¾x13½*
2358-2361 A1095 Set of 4 6.00 3.75

Boxers — A1096

Designs: No. 2362, 75c, Lius Angel Firpo (1894-1960). No. 2363, 75c, Nicolino Locche (1939-2005).

2005, Dec. 17 *Perf. 13½x13¾*
2362-2363 A1096 Set of 2 3.00 2.00

Argentine Design A1097

Designs: No. 2364, 75c, Image and sound design. No. 2365, 75c, Clothes and textile design, vert. No. 2366, 75c, Industrial design, vert. No. 2367, 75c, Graphic design.

Perf. 13¾x13½, 13½x13¾

2005, Dec. 17
2364-2367 A1097 Set of 4 6.00 4.00

Pres. Bartolomé Mitre (1821-1906) A1098

2006, Jan. 21 *Perf. 13¾x13½*
2368 A1098 75c multi 1.50 1.00

Esquel, Cent. — A1099

2006, Feb. 18
2369 A1099 75c multi 1.50 1.00

Wine Producing Regions — A1100

No. 2370: a, Merlot grapes and wine, Alto Valle, Río Negro (70x30mm). b, Wine flowing from vat (50x30mm).

No. 2371: a, Wine barrels (50x30mm). b, Torrontés grapes and wine, Cafayate, Salta (70x30mm).

No. 2372: a, Grape harvesters (50x30mm). b, Syrah grapes and wine, Valle del Zonda, San Juan (70x30mm).

No. 2373: a, Malbec grapes and wine, Valle del Tupungato, Mendoza (70x30mm). b, Wine in glass and bottle (50x30mm).

2006, Mar. 3 Litho. *Perf. 14*

2370 A1100 Booklet pane of 2 5.25 5.00
a. 50c multi .50 .45
b. 3.50p multi 4.00 3.50
Complete booklet, #2370 6.00
2371 A1100 Booklet pane of 2 5.25 5.00
a. 75c multi .85 .75
b. 3.25p multi 3.50 3.00
Complete booklet, #2371 6.00
2372 A1100 Booklet pane of 2 5.25 5.00
a. 1p multi 1.10 1.00
b. 3p multi 3.50 3.00
Complete booklet, #2372 6.00
2373 A1100 Booklet pane of 2 6.50 6.00
a. 1.25p multi 2.00 1.75
b. 2.75p multi 4.00 3.50
Complete booklet, #2373 6.50
Nos. 2370-2373 (4) 22.25

Compare Nos. 2370b-2373b with Nos. 2337-2340.

Dr. Ramón Carrillo (1906-56), Neurologist A1101

Perf. 13¾x13½

2006, Mar. 11 **Litho.**
2374 A1101 75c multi 1.50 1.00

Musical Instruments — A1102

Designs: 75c, Charango. 3.50p, Drum.

2006, Mar. 11 *Perf. 13½x13¾*
2375-2376 A1102 Set of 2 6.50 5.00

Miniature Sheet

Lighthouses — A1103

No. 2377: a, Primero de Mayo. b, Año Nuevo. c, El Rincón. d, Recalada a Bahía Blanca.

2006, Mar. 18
2377 A1103 75c Sheet of 4, #a-d 5.50 4.25

Souvenir Sheet

Start of Military Dictatorship, 30th Anniv. — A1104

No. 2378: a, Man, left side of Navy Mechanics School. b, Flower, right side of Navy Mechanics School.

2006, Mar. 25 *Perf. 14*
2378 A1104 75c Sheet of 2, #a-b 3.25 2.75

Silver Religious Objects A1105

No. 2379: a, Crown. b, Candelabra. c, Chalice. d, Viaticum.

2006, Apr. 8 *Perf. 13¾x13½*
2379 A1105 75c Block of 4, #a-d 6.00 5.00

Auto Racing A1106

Races and winning automobiles: No. 2380, 75c, Rally Nacional A8, Toyota Corolla WRC. No. 2381, 75c, Turismo Carretera, Ford Falcon. No. 2382, 75c, Turismo Competición 2000, Ford Focus. No. 2383, 75c, Class 3 Turismo Nacional, Ford Escort.

2006, May 6
2380-2383 A1106 Set of 4 6.00 5.00

Miniature Sheet

Dogs A1107

No. 2384: a, 25c, Springer spaniel. b, 25c, Yorkshire terrier. c, 50c, Argentino dog. d, 50c, Miniature schnauzer. e, 75c, Poodle. f. 75c, Chow chow.

2006, May 20
2384 A1107 Sheet of 6 #a-f, + 2 labels 7.75 6.00

A1108

2006 World Cup Soccer Championships — A1109

No. 2386: a, Serbia & Montenegro player. b, Argentina player, blue and white background.
No. 2387: a, Ivory Coast player. b, Netherlands player.

2006, May 20 Litho. *Perf. 13¾x13½*
2385 A1108 4p shown 6.75 6.00

Booklet Panes

Perf. 14¼

2386	Pane of 2	3.50	3.50
a.-b.	A1109 1p Either single	1.50	1.50
2387	Pane of 2	3.50	3.50
a.-b.	A1109 1p Either single	1.50	1.50
	Complete booklet, #2386-2387	8.25	

Souvenir Sheet

2388 A1109 1.50p shown 4.00 3.50

World No Tobacco Day A1110

2006, May 27 Litho. *Perf. 14x13½*
2389 A1110 75c multi 1.50 1.25

Intl. Year of Deserts and Desertification A1111

Designs: No. 2390, 75c, Lizard and plant. No. 2391, 75c, Impression of lizard in sand, dead plant.

Perf. 13¾x13½

2006, June 10 **Litho.**
2390-2391 A1111 Set of 2 3.00 2.50

Famous Men — A1112

Designs: No. 2392, 75c, Tato Bores (1927-96), television actor. No. 2393, 75c, Rodolfo Walsh (1927-77), kidnapped journalist.

2006, June 10 *Perf. 13½x13¾*
2392-2393 A1112 Set of 2 3.00 2.50

Winter Sports A1113

No. 2394: a, Alpine skiing. b, Snowboarding. c, Cross-country skiing. d, Biathlon.

2006, June 17 *Perf. 13¾x13½*
2394 A1113 75c Block of 4, #a-d 6.00 5.00

Tango Dancing A1114

Designs: 75c, Musician. 4p, Dancers.

2006, June 24
2395-2396 A1114 Set of 2 7.00 6.50

See France Nos. 3224-3225.

Patoruzito Riding Pamperito A1115

2006, July 8
2397 A1115 75c multi 1.50 1.25

Endangered Animals — A1116

Designs: No. 2398, 75c, Eubalaena australis. No. 2399, 75c, Hippocamelus bisulcus. No. 2400, 75c, Hippocamelus antisensis. No. 2401, 75c, Panthera onca.

2006, July 8 *Perf. 14x13¾*
2398-2401 A1116 Set of 4 6.50 6.00

For surcharges, see Nos. 2850-2853.

30th Mercosur Common Market Council and Summit of Presidents, Córdoba — A1117

2006, July 22 *Perf. 13¾x13½*
2402 A1117 3.50p multi 5.75 5.00

Souvenir Sheet

First British Invasion of Buenos Aires and Reconquest, Bicent. — A1118

2006, July 22 *Perf. 14*
2403 A1118 1.50p multi 2.75 2.25

Energy Conservation A1119

Winning designs in children's art contest: No. 2404, 75c, Light bulb, house and electrical cord, by Florencia Tovi. No. 2405, 75c, Plant in sunlight, unplugged lamp, by Camila Suárez.

2006, July 22 *Perf. 13¾x13½*
2404-2405 A1119 Set of 2 3.00 2.00

First Postage Stamps of Corrientes, 150th Anniv. — A1120

Designs: 75c, August 21, 1856 Corrientes cancel. 1.50p, Corrientes #1.

Litho. & Embossed

2006, Aug. 19 *Perf. 13¾x13½*
2406 A1120 75c multi 1.50 1.10

Souvenir Sheet

Litho.

Perf. 14

2407 A1120 1.50p multi 2.75 2.25

No. 2407 contains one 40x40mm stamp.

Interjurisdictional Committee on the Colorado River, 50th Anniv. — A1121

Perf. 13½x13¾

2006, Aug. 26 **Litho.**
2408 A1121 75c multi 1.50 1.25

Patricios Infantry Corps, Bicent. — A1122

2006, Sept. 9
2409 A1122 75c multi 1.50 1.10

Grapes, Wines and Vineyards — A1123

Designs: No. 2410, 75c, Syrah grapes and wine, Catamarca vineyards. No. 2411, 75c, Torrontés Riojano grapes and wine, La Rioja vineyards. No. 2412, 75c, Pinot Noir grapes and wine, Neuquén vineyards.

2006, Sept. 16 *Perf. 14x13½*
2410-2412 A1123 Set of 3 4.50 3.25

Compare Nos. 2410-2412 with Nos. 2426b-2428b. For surcharges, see Nos. 2840, 2842, 2844.

Col. Ramón L. Falcón Federal Police Cadet School, Cent. — A1124

2006, Oct. 14 Litho. *Perf. 13¾x13½*
2413 A1124 75c multi 1.50 1.00

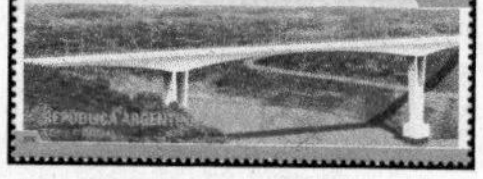

Border Bridges A1125

Designs: No. 2414, 75c, Pres. Tancredo Neves Intl. Bridge. No. 2415, 75c, San Roque González de Santa Cruz Intl. Bridge.

2006, Oct. 14 *Perf. 14x13¾*
2414-2415 A1125 Set of 2 3.00 2.00

For surcharges, see Nos. 2858-2859.

Christmas — A1126

Paintings by Alfredo Guttero: No. 2416, 75c, Madonna and Dove. No. 2417, 75c, The Annunciation, horiz.

Perf. 13½x13¾, 13¾x13½

2006, Oct. 21
2416-2417 A1126 Set of 2 3.00 2.00

Natl. Institute of Agricultural and Cattle Ranching Technology, 50th Anniv. — A1127

Perf. 13¾x13½

2006, Nov. 11 **Litho.**
2418 A1127 75c multi 1.50 1.25

Rock Musicians — A1128

Designs: No. 2419, 75c, Tanguito (1945-72). No. 2420, 75c, Luca Prodan (1953-87). No. 2421, 75c, Miguel Abuelo (1946-88). No. 2422, 75c, Pappo (1950-2005).

2006, Nov. 18 *Perf. 13½x13¾*
2419-2422 A1128 Set of 4 6.00 4.50

Caciques — A1129

Designs: No. 2423, 75c, Valentín Sayhueque (1823-1903), Huilliche cacique. No. 2424, 75c, Casimiro Biguá, Tehuelche cacique.

2006, Dec. 2
2423-2424 A1129 Set of 2 3.00 2.25

Frigate Hercules, Detail From *Battle of Martín García Island*, by Emilio Biggeri A1130

2007, Mar. 10 *Perf. 13¾x13½*
2425 A1130 75c multi 1.50 1.25

Adm. Guillermo Brown (1777-1857).

Wine-Growing Regions — A1131

No. 2426: a, Hand picking bunch of grapes. b, Vineyard, grapes, bottle of Pinot Noir, Neuquén Region (60x30mm).

No. 2427: a, Harvester cutting grapes from vine. b, Vineyard, grapes, bottle of Torrontés Riojano, La Rioja Region (60x30mm).

No. 2428: a, Harvester inspecting grapes on vine. b, Vineyard, grapes, bottle of Syrah, Catamarca Region (60x30mm).

2007, Mar. 10 **Litho.** *Perf. 14*

2426	Booklet pane of 2	7.00	7.00
a.	A1131 75c multi	1.25	1.25
b.	A1131 3.25p multi	5.25	5.25
	Complete booklet, #2426	7.00	
2427	Booklet pane of 2	7.00	7.00
a.	A1131 75c multi	1.25	1.25
b.	A1131 3.25p multi	5.25	5.25
	Complete booklet, #2427	7.00	
2428	Booklet pane of 2	7.00	7.00
a.	A1131 75c multi	1.25	1.25
b.	A1131 3.25p multi	5.25	5.25
	Complete booklet, #2428	7.00	

Complete booklets include a plastic wine bottle spout. Compare Nos. 2426b-2428b with Nos. 2410-2412.

Falkland Islands War, 25th Anniv. — A1132

Map of the Falkland Islands and: No. 2429, 75c, Argentina No. C90 in changed colors with Islas Malvinas cancel. No. 2430, 75c, IAI Dagger fighters. No. 2431, 75c, Battle cruiser ARA General Belgrano. No. 2432, 75c, Decorated war veteran. No. 2433, 75c, War decoration, vert.

Perf. 13¾x13½, 13½x13¾

2007, Mar. 31 **Litho.**
2429-2433 A1132 Set of 5 6.25 5.00

Postal and Telecommunications Workers Federation, 50th Anniv. — A1133

2007, Apr. 14 *Perf. 13¾x13½*
2434 A1133 75c multi 1.50 1.25

Map of Antarctica, Icebreaker Almirante Irízar — A1134

No. 2436 — Antarctic fauna: a, Phalacrocorax atriceps. b, Leptonychotes weddellii. c, Sterna vittata, denomination at UR. d, Sterna vittata, denomination at UL. e, Pygoscelis adeliae. f, Chionis alba. g, Pygoscelis papua, denomination at UR. h, Pygoscelis papua, denomination at UL.

2007, Apr. 21

2435	A1134 4p shown	12.00	10.00
2436	Sheet of 8	6.00	5.00
a.-h.	A1134 75c Any single	.50	.50

Miniature Sheet

Toys A1135

No. 2437: a, Rocking horse. b, Tea set. c, Toy train and stations. d, Toy soldiers.

2007, May 5 **Litho.** *Perf. 13¾x13½*

2437	A1135 Sheet of 4	6.00	5.00
a.-d.	75c Any single	.65	.65

Museums A1136

Designs: 75c, Latin American Art Museum, Buenos Aires. 3.25p, High Mountain Archaeological Museum, Salta.

2007, May 5
2438-2439 A1136 Set of 2 6.50 6.00

Road Safety Year — A1137

2007, May 19 **Litho.** *Perf. 13½x13¾*
2440 A1137 75c red & silver 1.50 1.25

Souvenir Sheet

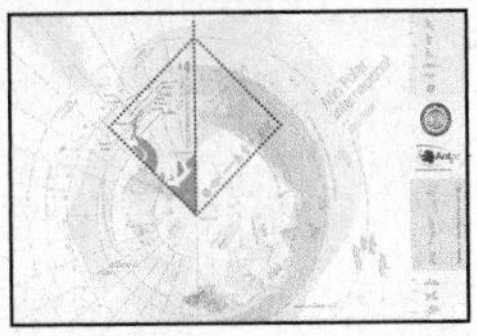

Intl. Polar Year A1138

2007, June 2 *Perf. 14*
2441 A1138 4p multi + label 6.25 6.00

Defense of Buenos Aires From British Attack, Bicent. A1139

Perf. 13¾x13½

2007, June 23 **Litho.**
2442 A1139 75c multi 1.50 1.25

Pierre Auger Observatory A1140

2007, July 14 **Litho.** *Perf. 13½x13¾*
2443 A1140 75c multi 1.50 1.25

St. Joseph Calasanctius (1557-1648) A1141

2007, July 14
2444 A1141 1p multi 1.75 1.50

Souvenir Sheet

Campo del Cielo Meteorite A1142

2007, July 28 *Perf. 14*
2445 A1142 6p multi *10.50 10.00*

No. 2445 was sold with, but unattached to, a booklet cover, and 3-D glasses.

Homero Manzi (1907-51), Political Leader, Tango Lyricist — A1143

Perf. 13½x13¾

2007, Aug. 11 **Litho.**
2446 A1143 1p multi 1.50 1.25

Tourism Along Route 40 — A1144

No. 2447: a, Road to San Carlos de Bariloche (30x30mm). b, El Acay Pass (40x30mm). c, Road to Perito Moreno (70x30mm). d, La Trochita locomotive (40x30mm). e, Lanin Volcano (40x30mm). f, Rio Grande (50x30mm). g, Animals on road, San José Jachal (40x30mm). h, Cuesta de Miranda (50x30mm) i, Nuestra Senora del Tránsito Chapel (30x30mm). j, Quilmes Ruins (30x30mm). k, Road to Oratorio (40x30mm).

2007, Aug. 25 **Litho.** *Perf. 14*

2447	Sheet of 11	14.50	14.00
a.-b.	A1144 50c Either single	.65	.65
c.-k.	A1144 1p Any single	1.25	1.25

Souvenir Sheet

Diplomatic Relations Between Argentina and Germany, 150th Anniv. — A1145

2007, Sept. 8
2448 A1145 4p multi 5.25 5.00

Prevention of Carbon Monoxide Accidents A1146

Children's art by: No. 2449, 1p, Julieta Saavedra Barragán. No. 2450, 1p, Leandro Ventancour. No. 2451, 1p, Efraín Osvaldo Rost, vert. No. 2452, 1p, Camila M. Alvarez Petrone, vert.

Perf. 13¾x13½, 13½x13¾

2007, Sept. 8
2449-2452 A1146 Set of 4 6.00 5.00

San Lorenzo de Almagro Athletic Club, Cent. — A1147

2007, Sept. 22 *Perf. 13½x13¾*
2453 A1147 1p multi 1.50 1.25

Beatification of Ceferino Namuncurá (1886-1905) A1148

2007, Oct. 13 **Litho.** *Perf. 13¾x13½*
2454 A1148 1p multi 1.50 1.25

Contemporary Art — A1149

Designs: No. 2455, 1p, Corrientes Esquina Uruguay, photograph by Horacio Coppola. No. 2456, 1p, 0611, painting by Pablo Siquier. No. 2457, 1p, Diálogo, digital photograph by Liliana Porter, vert. No. 2458, 1p, Imaginando el Estupor, mosaic by Marta Minujin, vert.

Perf. 13¾x13½, 13½x13¾

2007, Oct. 27

2455-2458 A1149 Set of 4 6.00 5.00

Nos. 2455-2458 each were printed in sheets of 4.

Christmas — A1150

Designs: 25c, Adoration of the Magi. 1p, Holy Family.

2007, Nov. 10 *Perf. 13½x14*

2459-2460 A1150 Set of 2 3.00 2.50

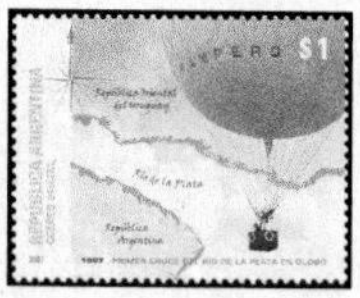

First Balloon Crossing of Río de la Plata, Cent. — A1151

Perf. 13¾x13½

2007, Nov. 24 **Litho.**

2461 A1151 1p multi 1.50 1.25

Discovery of Oil and Gas in Argentina, Cent. — A1152

2007, Nov. 24

2462 A1152 1p multi 1.50 1.25

2007 Presidential Inauguration A1153

2007, Dec. 15 *Perf. 13½x13¾*

2463 A1153 1p multi 1.50 1.25

Festivals — A1154

Designs: No. 2464, 1p, National Chamamé Festival, Corrientes Province. No. 2465, 1p, National Poncho Festival, Catamarca Province. No. 2466, 1p, National Festival of Dressage and Folklore, Jesús María, Cordoba Province. No. 2467, 1p, National Snow Festival, San Carlos de Bariloche, Río Negro Province.

2007, Dec. 15

2464-2467 A1154 Set of 4 6.00 5.00

2008 Summer Olympics, Beijing — A1155

Designs: No. 2468, 50c, Mountain biking. No. 2469, 50c, Taekwondo. 1p, Basketball. 4p, Pole vault.

Perf. 13½x13¾

2008, Mar. 29 **Litho.**

2468-2471 A1155 Set of 4 6.00 5.00

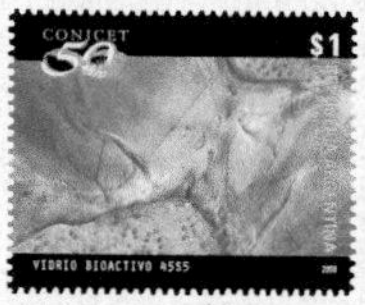

Natl. Scientific and Technical Research Council, 50th Anniv. — A1156

Designs: No. 2472, 1p, Bone tissue bridges with 45S5 bioactive glass particles. No. 2473, 1p, Pollen grain of Polygonum sp. No. 2474, 1p, Remnants of Supernova W44. No. 2475, 1p, Cave paintings, Epuyén River Valley. No. 2476, 1p, Fluidodinamica (fluid dynamics).

2008, Apr. 12 *Perf. 13¾x13½*

2472-2476 A1156 Set of 5 5.75 4.50

Association of Argentine Private Radio Stations, 50th Anniv. — A1157

2008, Apr. 26

2477 A1157 1p multi 1.15 .90

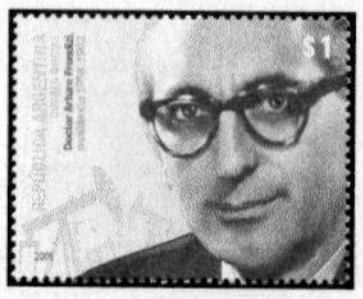

Pres. Arturo Frondizi (1908-95), Oil Pumps A1158

2008, Apr. 26

2478 A1158 1p multi 1.25 1.00

Birds — A1159

Male and female: 1p, Sturnella loyca. 4p, Xanthopsar flavus.

2008, Apr. 26 *Perf. 13½x13¾*

2479-2480 A1159 Set of 2 5.50 5.00

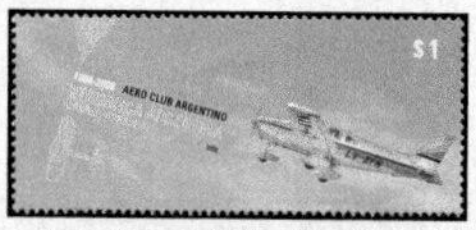

Argentine Aero Club, Cent. — A1160

2008, May 10 *Perf. 14x13½*

2481 A1160 1p multi 1.15 .90

Colón Theater, Buenos Aires, Cent. A1161

2008, May 24

2482 A1161 1p multi 1.15 .90

Aimé Bonpland (1773-1858), Founder of Corrientes Natural Sciences Museum A1162

2008, May 24 *Perf. 13¾x13½*

2483 A1162 1p multi 1.15 .90

Dr. Marcos Sastre (1808-87), Textbook Writer, and Text from Reading Book, Anagnosia A1163

Perf. 13¾x13½

2008, June 21 **Litho.**

2484 A1163 1p multi 1.15 .90

Luciano-Honorato Valette (1880-1957), Antarctic Naturalist — A1164

Disappearance of Rescue Ship ARA Guaraní, 50th Anniv. — A1165

2008, June 28

2485 A1164 1p multi 1.15 .90

2486 A1165 1p multi 1.15 .90

Characters From "The Mail Song," by Maria Elena Walsh A1166

Character From "Big Brother," by Silvia Schujer A1167

Characters From "Letters to Santa Claus," by Luis María Pescetti A1168

Character From "Mammarachos por Carta," by Ricardo Mariño A1169

Perf. 13½x13¾, 13¾x13½

2008, July 26

2487 A1166 1p multi 1.15 .90

2488 A1167 1p multi 1.15 .90

2489 A1168 1p multi 1.15 .90

2490 A1169 1p multi 1.15 .90

Nos. 2487-2490 (4) 4.60 3.60

Children's songs and literature.

Scenes From "The Mail Song," by María Elena Walsh A1170

Scenes From "Mamarrachos por Carta," by Ricardo Mariño — A1171

Characters From "Letters to Santa Claus," by Luis María Pescetti — A1172

Characters From "Big Brother," by Silvia Schujer — A1173

No. 2491: a, Bird holding Argentina #2216b in beak. b, Mailbox. c, Paper airplane, letters. d, Post office, letters. e, Smokestacks behind open envelope with letter. f, Philatelic office, Argentina #2236, #2239 and its adjacent label.

No. 2492: a, Postman holding letter. b, Postman and woman reading letter. c, Bird reading letter. d, Man with pipe. e, Birds on mail box. f, Monkey with banana.

No. 2493: a, Child writing letter to Santa Claus. b, Santa Claus reading letter from child.

No. 2494: a, Girl at table playing card game (40x50mm). b, Boy and mother, horiz. (70x40mm).

2008, July 26 Litho. ***Perf. 13½x13¾***

Booklet Stamps

2491 A1170 Block of 6 7.50 7.50
a.-f. 1p Any single 1.20 1.20
g. Booklet pane, 2 #2491 15.00 15.00
2492 A1171 Block of 6 7.50 7.50
a.-f. 1p Any single 1.20 1.20
g. Booklet pane, 2 #2492 15.00 15.00

Perf. 14¼

2493 A1172 Booklet pane of 2 10.00 10.00
a.-b. 4p Either single 5.00 5.00

Perf. 14

2494 A1173 Booklet pane of 2 10.00 10.00
a.-b. 4p Either single 5.00 5.00
Complete booklet, #2491g, 2492g, 2493, 2494 50.00

Complete booklet is a spiral-bound book containing the four booklet panes, postal cards, text pages and pieces for a children's card game.

Archaeological Artifacts Type of 2000

Design: Jar, Yocavil culture.

Perf. 13½x13¾ Syncopated

2008, Aug. 2
2495 A973 10p multi 7.25 6.75

Souvenir Sheet

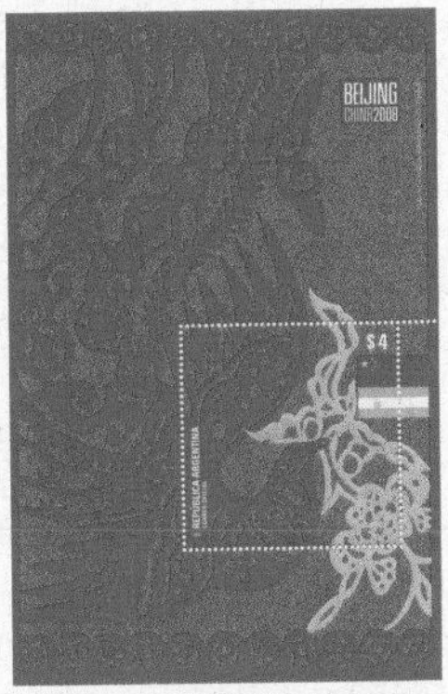

Olympex 2008 World Stamp Exhibition, Beijing — A1174

Litho. With Foil Application

2008, Aug. 2 ***Perf. 14***
2496 A1174 4p multi 3.50 3.00

Immigrants to Argentina A1175

Designs: No. 2497, 1p, Cherry blossoms, koi, immigrants from Japan. No. 2498, 1p, Metal decorative plates and immigrants from Lebanon. No. 2499, 1p, Tiles, guitar and immigrants from Portugal. No. 2500, 1p, Wooden decorative box, embroidered silk, Ugaritic alphabet and immigrants from Syria.

Perf. 13¾x13½

2008, Sept. 20 **Litho.**
2497-2500 A1175 Set of 4 4.25 3.00

Souvenir Sheets

National Flower Festival A1176

Designs: No. 2501, 5p, Gerbera daisy, gardenia and rose (shown). No. 2502, 5p, Carnation, gold-banded lily and delphinium.

2008, Sept. 27 ***Perf. 14***
2501-2502 A1176 Set of 2 8.50 8.50

Nos. 2501-2502 are impregnated with a floral scent.

Souvenir Sheets

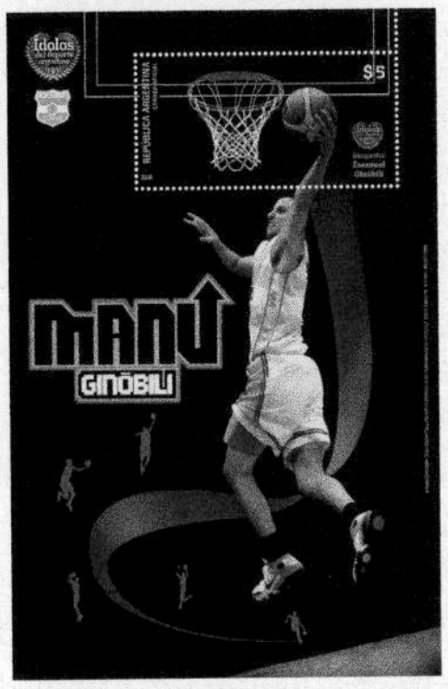

Sports Personalities — A1177

Designs: No. 2503, 5p, Hand of Manu Ginobili, basketball and hoop. No. 2504, 5p, Rugby football kicked by Hugo Porta, goal posts, silhouettes of rugby player kicking ball. No. 2505, 5p, Silhouette of golfer putting, foot of Roberto De Vicenzo, vert. No. 2506, 5p, Juan Manuel Fangio in race car, vert.

2008, Oct. 11 ***Perf. 14***
2503-2506 A1177 Set of 4 27.50 27.50

See Nos. 2541-2544, 2632-2635.

Science Teaching Year — A1178

2008, Oct. 25 ***Perf. 13¾x13½***
2507 A1178 1p multi 1.25 1.00

Flowers A1179

Designs: No. 2508, 1p, Ceiba chodatii. No. 2509, 1p, Nelumbo nucifera.

2008, Oct. 25
2508-2509 A1179 Set of 2 3.00 2.50

See Viet Nam Nos. 3343-3344.

Souvenir Sheet

First Stamps of Argentina, Buenos Aires and Cordoba,150th Anniv. — A1180

No. 2510: a, Cordoba No. 2 (30x30mm). b, Buenos Aires No. 4 (40x30mm). c, Argentina No. 3 (30x40mm).

2008, Nov. 1 ***Perf. 14***
2510 A1180 1p Sheet of 3, #a-c *4.75 4.00*

Christmas — A1181

2008, Nov. 15 ***Perf. 13½x13¾***
2511 A1181 1p multi 1.00 .80

Dances — A1182

Designs: No. 2512, 1p, Malambo sureño dancer, Argentina. No. 2513, 1p, Hoy-nazan dancers, Armenia.

2008, Nov. 22 **Litho.**
2512-2513 A1182 Set of 2 2.25 1.75

See Armenia Nos. 790-791.

El Cronista Comercial Newspaper, Cent. — A1183

2008, Dec. 13 ***Perf. 13¾x13½***
2514 A1183 1p multi 1.00 .80

School of Forestry, 50th Anniv. — A1184

2008, Dec. 13 ***Perf. 13½x3¾***
2515 A1184 1p multi 1.00 .80

Festivals — A1185

Designs: No. 2516, 1p, Chaya Festival, La Rioja Province. No. 2517, 1p, Natl. Grape Harvest Festival, Mendoza Province. No. 2518, 1p, Natl. Cherry Festival, Los Antiguos, Santa Cruz Province. No. 2519, 1p, Natl. Sea Festival, Mar del Plata, Buenos Aires Province.

2009, Feb. 14 ***Perf. 13½x13¾***
2516-2519 A1185 Set of 4 4.25 3.25

Souvenir Sheet

Preservation of Polar Regions and Glaciers — A1186

No. 2520: a, Retreat of Piedras Blancas Glacier. b, Retreat of Argentine Antarctic Territory ice.

2009, Mar. 7 ***Perf. 14***
2520 A1186 5p Sheet of 2, #a-b 7.50 7.00

Bishop Colombres Memorial Experimental Agribusiness, Cent. — A1187

2009, Mar. 21 ***Perf. 13¾x13½***
2521 A1187 1p multi 1.00 .80

Souvenir Sheet

New Year 2009 (Year of the Ox) A1188

Litho. & Embossed, Margin With Foil Application

2009, Apr. 4 ***Perf. 14***
2522 A1188 5p multi 4.50 4.25

China 2009 World Stamp Exhibition, Luoyang.

Holy Cross Exaltation Parish, Puerto Santa Cruz, Cent. — A1189

2009, Apr. 18 Litho. ***Perf. 13½x13¾***
2523 A1189 1p multi 1.00 .80

Argentine Exports A1190

Designs: 1p, Wine. 5p, Agricultural machines.

2009, Apr. 18 ***Perf. 13¾x13½***
2524-2525 A1190 Set of 2 4.50 4.00

Endangered Species — A1191

Designs: No. 2526, 1p, Harpyhaliaetus coronatus. No. 2527, 1p, Chelonoidis chilensis, horiz.

Perf. 13½x13¾, 13¾x13½

2009, Apr. 18
2526-2527 A1191 Set of 2 2.50 2.00

Pres. Raúl Ricardo Alfonsín (1927-2009) A1192

2009, May 9 ***Perf. 13½x13¾***
2528 A1192 1p multi 1.00 .80

Children of the Holy Virgin of the Garden Congregation in Argentina, 150th Anniv. — A1193

2009, May 23

2529 A1193 1p multi 1.00 .80

Raúl Scalabrini Ortiz (1898-1959), Writer — A1194

2009, May 23

2530 A1194 1p multi 1.00 .80

Political and Military Command of the Malvinas (Falkland Islands), 180th Anniv. — A1195

Paintings: 1p, Luis Vernet, governor of the Malvinas, by Luisa Vernet Lavalle Lloveras. 5p, Ship and houses near cliff, by Vernet, map of Malvinas.

2009, June 13 ***Perf. 13½x13¾***

2531 A1195 1p multi 1.00 .85

Souvenir Sheet

Perf. 14

2532 A1195 5p multi 4.00 3.75

No. 2532 contains one 70x30mm stamp.

Water A1196

No. 2533: a, Droplets. b, Drops, clouds and hand, vert.

2009, June 27 ***Perf. 14***

2533 Sheet of 2, unscratched 7.50 7.00
a. A1196 5p multi 3.50 3.50
b. A1196 5p multi, unscratched 3.50 3.50
c. As "b," scratched 3.50

No. 2533b and sheet margin have scratch-off panels.

Flora and Fauna — A1197

Designs: No. 2534, 1p, Polybetes pythagoricus. No. 2535, 1p, Passiflora caerulea.

2009, July 25 ***Perf. 13¾x13½***

2534-2535 A1197 Set of 2 2.10 1.60

Amusement Park Rides — A1198

No. 2536: a, Bumper cars. b, Roller coaster. c, Ferris wheel. d, Ghost train.

2009, Aug. 1

2536 Horiz. strip of 4 + flanking label 3.75 2.75
a.-d. A1198 1p Any single .85 .65

Miniature Sheet

Sheep A1199

No. 2537: a, Merino ram. b, Romney Marsh yearling. c, Corriedale ewe and lamb. d, Hampshire Down ewe and lamb. e, Lincoln ewe. f, Frisian ewe.

2009, Aug. 22

2537 A1199 1p Sheet of 6, #a-f, + 2 labels 6.00 4.50

Soil Erosion A1200

No. 2538 — Erosion by: a, Water. b, Wind.

2009, Sept. 12 ***Perf. 14x13½***

2538 Horiz. pair 1.90 1.60
a.-b. A1200 1p Either single .95 .80

A1201

America Issue, Education For All — A1202

Perf. 13¾x13½

2009, Sept. 12 **Litho.**

2539 A1201 1p multi 1.00 .75
2540 A1202 1p multi 1.00 .75

Sports Personalities Type of 2008

Designs: No. 2541, 5p, Delfo Cabrera running in 1948 Summer Olympics, vert. No. 2542, 5p, Tennis ball and shorts of Guillermo Vilas (38mm diameter). No. 2543, 10p, Field hockey players, stick of Luciana Aymar, vert. No. 2544, 10p, Cyclists chasing Juan Curuchet, vert.

Perf. 14, Perf. (No. 2542)

2009, Sept. 26 **Litho.**

2541-2544 A1177 Set of 4 22.00 20.00

The tennis ball on No 2542 is covered with flocking.

National Technological University, 50th Anniv. — A1203

2009, Oct. 17 ***Perf. 13½x13¾***

2545 A1203 1p multi 1.00 .80

Souvenir Sheets

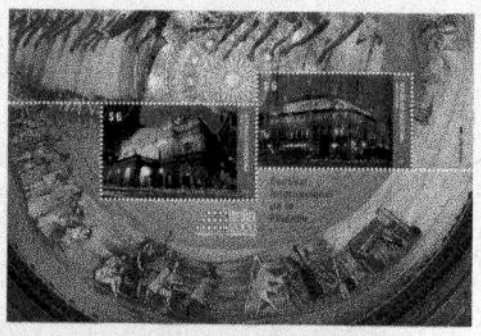

A1204

Italia 2009 Intl. Philatelic Exhibition, Rome — A1205

No. 2546: a, La Scala Theater, Milan. b, Colon Theater, Buenos Aires.

No. 2547: a, Froilán González racing in Ferrari 375 (85x30mm rhomboid) b, Ferrari F60 race car (60x20mm).

2009, Oct. 24 **Litho.** ***Perf. 14***

2546 A1204 6p Sheet of 2, #a-b 7.50 7.00
2547 A1205 6p Sheet of 2, #a-b 7.50 7.00

Intl. Year of Astronomy A1206

Designs: 1p, Telescope, National University of Córdoba Astronomical Observatory.

10p, Galileo Galilei (1564-1642), diagram of solar system orbits.

2009, Oct. 24 **Litho.** ***Perf. 13¾x13½***

2548 A1206 1p multi 1.00 .80

Souvenir Sheet

Perf. 14

2549 A1206 10p multi 7.50 7.25

No. 2549 contains one 80x20mm stamp.

Children's Art — A1207

Winning art in "I Can Slow TB Down" children's stamp design contest: No. 2550, 1p, Boxing gloves hitting "TB," by Alberto Penayo Pardo. No. 2551, 1p, Lungs with bandage, by Candela Alemany Fiandrino. No. 2552, 1p, Boy coughing, doctor holding sign, by Rocío Cabrera, vert. No. 2553, 1p, Hands holding lungs, by Juliana Benzo, vert.

Perf. 13¾x13½, 13½x13¾

2009, Nov. 14 **Litho.**

2550-2553 A1207 Set of 4 7.00 3.25

Christmas — A1208

2009, Nov. 21 ***Perf. 13½x14***

2554 A1208 1p multi 1.00 .45

Historic Buildings A1209

No. 2555, 1p — San Martín Mansion, 1910: a, Exterior. b, Interior.

No. 2556, 1p — Ortiz Basualdo Mansion, 1918: a, Exterior. b, Interior.

No. 2557, 1p — Fernandez-Anchorena Mansion, 1909: a, Exterior. b, Interior.

No. 2558, 1p — Duhau Mansion, 1934: a, Exterior. b, Interior.

Perf. 13¾x13½

2009, Dec. 12 **Litho.**

Horiz. Pairs, #a-b

2555-2558 A1209 Set of 4 7.00 6.00

Nos. 2555-2558 each were printed in sheets containing 8 pairs and 4 labels.

Festivals — A1210

Designs: No. 2559, 1.50p, National Apple Festival, General Roca, Río Negro Province. No. 2560, 1.50p, National Sun Festival, San Juan, San Juan Province. No. 2561, 1.50p, National Students Festival, San Salvador de Jujuy, Jujuy Province. No. 2562, 1.50p, National Tradition Festival, San Antonio de Areco, Buenos Aires Province.

2010, Feb. 20 ***Perf. 13½x13¾***

2559-2562 A1210 Set of 4 5.25 4.25

South American Sails 2010 Regatta — A1211

Designs: 1.50p, Argentine Navy frigate Libertad.

No. 2564: a, Chilean Navy schooner Esmerelda. b, Libertad, diff.

Perf. 13¾x13½ Syncopated

2010, Feb. 20

2563 A1211 1.50p multi 1.25 1.00

Souvenir Sheet

Perf. 14

2564 A1211 6p Sheet of 2, #a-b, + 12 labels 7.75 7.75

No. 2564 contains two 40x50mm stamps.

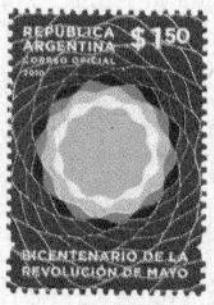

May Revolution, Bicent. — A1212

Perf. 13½x13¾ Syncopated

2010, Mar. 6

2565 A1212 1.50p multi 1.25 .90

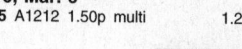

National Symbols — A1213

Designs: No. 2566, 1.50p, Coat of arms. No. 2567, 1.50p, Flag, horiz.

Perf. 13½x13¾, 13¾x13½

2010, Mar. 27

2566-2567 A1213 Set of 2 2.50 1.75

A Culture of Peace A1214

No. 2568: a, Dove. b, Map of South America.

2010, Apr. 24 Litho. ***Perf. 13½x13¾***

2568 A1214 1.50p Horiz. pair, #a-b 2.25 1.75

Buenos Aires City Symphony, Cent. — A1215

2010, Apr. 24 ***Perf. 14x13½***

2569 A1215 1.50p multi 1.25 1.00

Argentine Army, Bicent. — A1216

2010, May 8 ***Perf. 13½x13¾***

2570 A1216 1.50p multi 1.25 1.00

Argentine Naval Command, Bicent. A1217

2010, May 29 ***Perf. 13¾x13½***

2571 A1217 1.50p multi 1.25 1.00

Bicentenary Mural — A1218

No. 2572: a, Cabildo, Buenos Aires (30x50mm). b, General Manuel Belgrano, flag of Argentina on pole, Casa de Tucumán, San Miguel de Tucumán (30x50mm). c, Gen. José de San Martín on horseback, raising sword (40x80mm). d, National Constitution (30x50mm). e, Ships unloading immigrants (30x50mm). f, Sword battle, people voting, "1910," horiz. (70x30mm). g, National Congress, Blind Justice (30x50mm). h, Trolley, film set, bridge, horiz. (40x30mm). i, Palm tree, crowd, banners, men with feet in fountain, baby with umbilical cord (30x60mm). j, Military with guns, cardinal, man smoking cigar, eyes, "the disappeared" in pit (30x40mm). k, Mothers of the Plaza de Mayo holding pictures of the disappeared, May Pyramid statue (40x60mm). l, Motorcyclist, men with briefcases holding cellular phones, man on computer, airplanes (40x60mm).

2010, May 29 Litho. ***Perf. 14***

2572 Sheet of 12 16.00 13.00
a.-l. A1218 1.50p Any single 1.25 1.00

Gazeta de Buenos-Ayres, Bicent. — A1219

2010, June 5 Litho. ***Perf. 13½x13¾***

2573 A1219 1.50p multi 1.25 1.00

A1220

2010 World Cup Soccer Championships, South Africa — A1221

2010 World Cup emblem and stylized player from: No. 2574, 1.50p, Nigeria. No. 2575, 1.50p, Greece, vert. 5p, South Korea. 7p, Argentina, vert.

No. 2578, 5p, Argentina player sliding to kick ball. No. 2579, 5p, Argentina player heading ball into net. No. 2580, 5p, Argentina player making scissor kick. No. 2581, 5p, Goalie making save, vert.

Perf. 13¾x13½, 13½x13¾

2010, June 5

2574-2577 A1220 Set of 4 10.50 9.00

Souvenir Sheets

Perf. 14

2578-2581 A1221 Set of 4 14.00 12.50

Nos. 2578-2579 each contain one 70x40mm stamp, No. 2580 contains one 60x40mm stamp, and No. 2581 contains one 40x60mm stamp.

World Junior Rugby Championships, Argentina A1222

2010, June 19 ***Perf. 13¾x13½***

2582 A1222 1.50p multi 1.25 1.00

Souvenir Sheet

First Government Junta, Bicent. — A1223

2010, July 24 ***Perf. 14***

2583 A1223 5p multi 3.50 3.00

Miniature Sheet

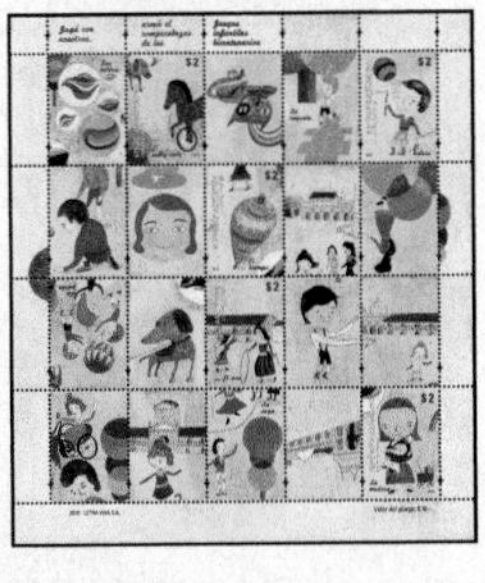

Toys and Games A1224

No. 2584: a, Sulky-cycle (sulky-ciclo). b, Cup and ball (balero). c, Top (trompo). d, Hoop (aro). e, Doll (muñeca).

Perf. 13½x13¾ Syncopated

2010, July 24 Litho.

2584 A1224 2p Sheet of 5, #a-e, + 15 labels 7.75 6.50

The stamps and labels of No. 2584 are puzzle pieces that when separated and rearranged form a picture.

Jorge Luis Borges (1899-1986), Writer — A1225

Perf. 13¾x13½ Syncopated

2010, Aug. 14 Litho.

2585 A1225 7p multi 4.75 4.50

2010 Frankfurt Book Fair. See Germany No. 2585.

Landmarks Type of 2004

Designs: 1.50p, Parana River, Corrientes. 6p, Les Eclaireurs Lighthouse, Tierra del Fuego.

Perf. 13¾x13½ Syncopated

2010 Litho.

2586 A1063a 1.50p multi + label 2.00 1.50
2587 A1063a 6p multi 7.00 6.50

Issued: 1.50p, 5/11; 6p, 2/12.

Mountain Lakes — A1226

Flags of Romania and Argentina and: 1.50p, Lake Ballea, Romania. 7p, Lake Nahuel Huapi, Argentina.

2010, Aug. 14 ***Perf. 13¾x13½***

2588-2589 A1226 Set of 2 6.00 5.00

See Romania Nos. 5201-5202.

Women's Field Hockey World Cup Championships, Rosario A1227

2010, Aug. 28

2590 A1227 1.50p multi 1.25 1.00

Games — A1228

Designs: No. 2591, 1.50p, Truco (card game). No. 2592, 1.50p, Bocce.

2010, Aug. 28 ***Perf. 13½x13¾***

2591-2592 A1228 Set of 2 2.50 1.90

2010 Census — A1229

Perf. 13¾x13½ Syncopated

2010, Sept. 18

2593 A1229 1.50p multi 1.25 1.00

Juan Bautista Alberdi (1810-84), Lawyer and Diplomat — A1230

2010, Sept. 18 ***Perf. 13½x13¾***

2594 A1230 1.50p multi 1.25 1.00

National Library, Bicent. A1231

Perf. 13¾x13½

2010, Sept. 18 Litho.

2595 A1231 1.50p multi 1.25 1.00

Souvenir Sheet

Weather Stations in Austria and Argentina — A1232

No. 2596 — Weather station in: a, Stadtpark, Vienna. b, Buenos Aires Botanical Garden.

2010, Oct. 16 ***Perf. 14***

2596 A1232 5p Sheet of 2, #a-b 7.00 6.25

See Austria No. 2283.

The Child of Bethlehem, by Aldo Severi — A1233

2010, Nov. 13 ***Perf. 13¾x13½***

2597 A1233 1.50p multi 1.25 1.00

Christmas.

Federal Electric Power Council, 50th Anniv. — A1234

2010, Nov. 27 ***Perf. 13½x13¾***

2598 A1234 1.50p multi 1.25 1.00

Souvenir Sheets

Lighthouses — A1235

Portuguese Ceramic Tile — A1236

No. 2599: a, Querandí Lighthouse, Argentina. b, Santa Marta Lighthouse, Portugal.

2010, Sept. 25 ***Perf. 14***

2599 A1235 5p Sheet of 2, #a-b 6.75 6.00
2600 A1236 10p multi 6.75 6.00

Portugal 2010 Intl. Philatelic Exhibition, Lisbon. Portions of the designs of Nos. 2599a-2599b were applied by a thermographic process producing a shiny, raised effect.

World Post Day — A1237

2010, Oct. 9 Litho. ***Perf. 13½x13¾***
2601 A1237 1.50p multi 1.25 1.00

A Song to Work, Sculpture by Rogelio Yrurtia — A1238

2010, Oct. 16 ***Perf. 14x13½***
2602 A1238 1.50p multi 1.25 1.00

Dakar Rally in Argentina — A1239

No. 2603 — Photographs of 2009 and 2010 Rallies: a, Starting line of Rally, Buenos Aires (60x40mm). b, Motorcycle No. 107 (50x50mm). c, Car No. 300 on dirt road (60x40mm). d, Truck No. 502 on dirt road, (50x50mm). e, Vehicles on dirt road (50x50mm). f, Quad No. 251 (40x80mm). g, Quad No. 277 (40x80mm).

No. 2604: a, Car No. 375 on dirt road (60x50mm). b, Two quad riders in sand near hill (60x40mm). c, Car No. 377 in air (60x40mm). d, Motorcycle No. 1 (40x50mm). e, Tree near Laguna del Pescado (40x50mm). f, White clouds over mountain near Tucumán (40x50mm). g, Road and bridge near Jujuy (40x50mm). h, Truck No. 500 in water (70x50mm).

2010, Dec. 11 ***Perf. 14***

2603	Booklet pane of 7	14.00	14.00
a.-e.	A1239 1.50p Any single	1.00	1.00
f.	A1239 5p multi	3.25	3.25
g.	A1239 7p multi	4.50	4.50
2604	Booklet pane of 8	14.00	14.00
a.-g.	A1239 1.50p Any single	1.00	1.00
h.	A1239 10p multi	6.50	6.50
	Complete booklet, #2603-2604 + post card	28.00	

Intl. Year of Forests — A1240

2011, Mar. 19 ***Perf. 13½x13¾***
2605 A1240 2p multi 1.50 1.20

Postal Union of the Americas, Spain and Portugal (UPAEP), Cent. — A1241

2011, Mar. 19 ***Perf. 13¾x13½***
2606 A1241 8p multi 5.00 4.50

Buenos Aires, 2010 World Book Capital A1242

No. 2607 — Stylized buildings spelling: a, "Buenos Aires Capital." b, "Mundial del Libro 2011."

2011, Apr. 16 ***Perf. 14x13½***
2607 Horiz. pair 2.90 2.25
a.-b. A1242 2p Either single 1.40 1.10

A1243

Antarctic Treaty, 50th Anniv. A1244

Designs: 2p, Iceberg and Antarctic Treaty emblem.

No. 2609: a, Pygoscelis papua. b, Scientist and equipment.

2011, Apr. 16 ***Perf. 13¾x13½***
2608 A1243 2p multi 1.40 1.00

Souvenir Sheet

Perf. 14

2609 A1244 8p Sheet of 2, #a-b 8.50 8.00

34th Antarctic Treaty Consultative Meeting, Buenos Aires.

Mariano Moreno (1778-1811), Politician A1245

2011, May 21 ***Perf. 13¾x13½***
2610 A1245 2p multi 1.40 1.00

World Blood Donor Day — A1246

Perf. 13¾x13½ Syncopated

2011, May 21
2611 A1246 5p multi 3.25 2.50

Year of Decent Labor, Health and Safety for Workers A1247

2011, June 4 ***Perf. 13¾x13½***
2612 A1247 2p multi 1.40 1.00

Pres. Domingo Faustino Sarmiento (1811-88) — A1248

2011, June 25 ***Perf. 13½x13¾***
2613 A1248 2.50p multi 1.75 1.50

May Pyramid, Buenos Aires, Bicent. — A1249

2011, June 25 ***Perf. 13½x14***
2614 A1249 2.50p multi 1.75 1.50

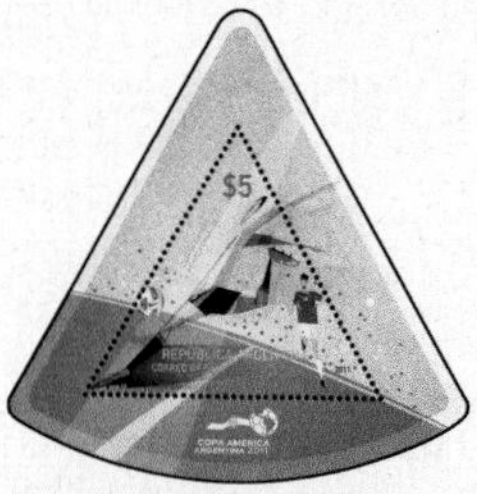

America Cup Soccer Tournament — A1250

No. 2615 — Players from Group A teams: a, Argentina and Bolivia. b, Colombia and Costa Rica.

No. 2616 — Players from Group B teams: a, Venezuela and Brazil. b, Paraguay and Ecuador.

No. 2617 — Players from Group C teams: a, Peru and Uruguay. b, Mexico and Chile.

2011, June 25 ***Perf. 14***

2615	Wheel with 2 sheets	9.00	9.00
a.-b.	A1250 5p Either sheet	4.50	4.50
2616	Wheel with 2 sheets	9.00	9.00
a.-b.	A1250 5p Either sheet	4.50	4.50
2617	Wheel with 2 sheets	9.00	9.00
a.-b.	A1250 5p Either sheet	4.50	4.50
	Nos. 2615-2617 (3)	27.00	27.00

Nos. 2615a-2615b, 2616a-2616b and 2617a-2617b are attached to wheels with a metal grommet at the center of the wheels.

Launch of SAC-D/Aquarius Satellite — A1251

2011, July 23 Litho. ***Perf. 13¾x13½***
2618 A1251 2.50p multi 1.75 1.50

Mailboxes A1252

Designs: No. 2619, 2.50p, Corneta type mailbox, cancel. No. 2620, 2.50p, Pillar box, handwritten letter, vert.

Perf. 13¾x13½, 13½x13¾

2011, Aug. 20
2619-2620 A1252 Set of 2 3.50 3.00

Festivals — A1253

Designs: No. 2621, 2.50p, National Beer Festival, Villa General Belgrano. No. 2622, 2.50p, National Horse Festival, San Cristóbal. No. 2623, 2.50p, Foreign Communities Fair, Comodoro Rivadavia. No. 2624, 2.50p, National Tea Festival, Campo Viera.

2011, Sept. 10 ***Perf. 13½x13¾***
2621-2624 A1253 Set of 4 7.00 6.00

Orchids A1254

Designs: No. 2625, 2.50p, Zygopetalum maxillare. No. 2626, 2.50p, Sacoila lanceolata, vert.

Perf. 13¾x13½, 13½x13¾

2011, Sept. 24
2625-2626 A1254 Set of 2 5.50 5.00

Train on the Clouds A1255

No. 2627: a, Train cars, bridge (yellow orange panel). b, Locomotive, bridge (blue panel). c, Train on curved bridge (orange panel). d, Train on curved bridge, diff. (red panel).

2011, Sept. 24 ***Perf. 14***
2627 Sheet of 4 16.00 15.00
a.-d. A1255 5p Any single 4.00 3.75

Argentine Pediatric Society, Cent. — A1256

2011, Oct. 22 ***Perf. 13¾x13½***
2628 A1256 2.50p multi 1.75 1.50

Miniature Sheet

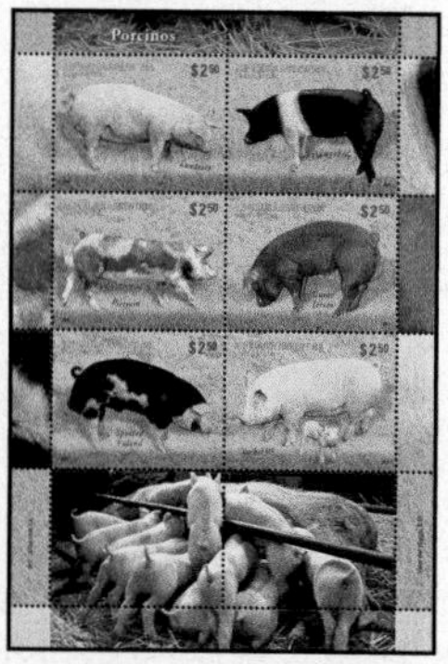

Pig Breeds A1257

No. 2629: a, Landrace. b, Hampshire. c, Pietrain. d, Duroc Jersey. e, Spotted Poland. f, Yorkshire.

2011, Oct. 29 **Litho.**
2629 A1257 2.50p Sheet of 6, #a-f, + 2 labels 10.00 9.00

Christmas — A1258

Litho. With Glitter Affixed

2011, Oct. 29 ***Perf. 13¾ Syncopated***

2630 A1258 2.50p multi 1.75 .75

Souvenir Sheet

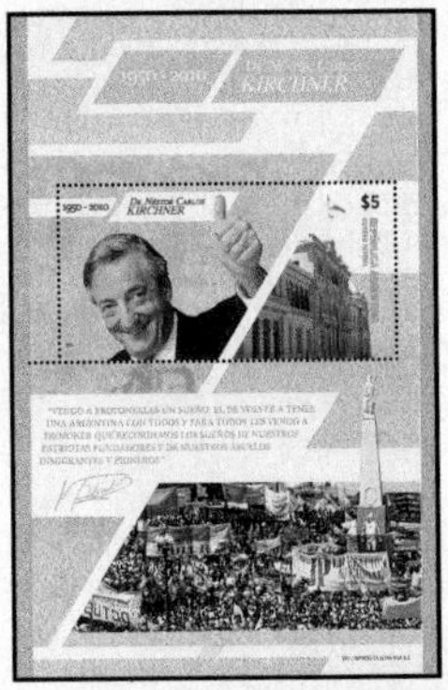

Pres. Néstor Carlos Kirchner (1950-2010), and Casa Rosada — A1259

2011, Nov. 26 **Litho.** ***Perf. 14***

2631 A1259 5p multi 3.25 3.00

Sports Personalities Type of 2008

Souvenir Sheets

Designs: No. 2632, 10p, Horse and mallet of Adolfo Cambiaso, polo player, vert. No. 2633, 10p, Chessboard and Miguel Najdorf (1910-97), chess player, vert. (50x60mm). No. 2634, 10p, Sailboard of Carlos Espinola, sailboarder, vert. (50x60mm). No. 2635, 10p, Roller skates of Nora Vega, roller skater (60x40mm).

2011, Nov. 12

2632-2635 A1177 Set of 4 25.00 24.00

Rights of the Child — A1260

Winning art in children's stamp design contest by: No. 2636, 2.50p, Nicolás Agustín Bernachea (blue panels). No. 2637, 2.50p, Sofía Panagópulo (pink panels). No. 2638, 2.50p, Ezequiel Catalano Segesso (yellow green panels). No. 2639, 2.50p, Laura Florencia Martinessi (orange panels).

2011, Nov. 26 ***Perf. 13½x13¾***

2636-2639 A1260 Set of 4 7.00 6.00

Souvenir Sheet

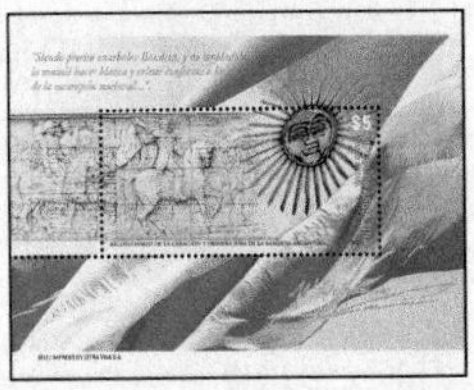

Creation of Argentine Flag and Pledge of Allegiance, Bicent. — A1261

2012, Mar. 3 **Litho.** ***Perf. 14***

2640 A1261 5p multi 3.00 2.75

First Argentine Flight Landing at South Pole, 50th Anniv. — A1262

2012, Mar. 3 **Litho.** ***Perf. 13¾x13½***

2641 A1262 2.50p multi 1.60 1.40

Monument to Gen. Manuel Belgrano, Buenos Aires, and Argentine Flag — A1263

2012, Mar. 31 ***Perf. 14x13¾***

2642 A1263 2.50p multi 1.60 1.40

Argentine Claims of Sovereignty Over British South Atlantic Islands A1264

Argentine flag and map of: No. 2643, 2.50p, Falkland Islands (Isla Gran Malvina and Isla Soledad). No. 2644, 2.50p, South Georgia (Isla San Pedro). No. 2645, 2.50p, South Sandwich Islands (Islas Traverse, Islas Candelaria, Isla Saunders, Isla Jorge, Isla Blanca and Grupo Tule del Sur), vert. (28x67mm).

Perf. 13¾x13½, 13¾x14 (#2645)

2012, Mar. 31

2643-2645 A1264 Set of 3 5.00 4.00

Presidential Staff and Argentine Flag — A1265

2012, Apr. 14 ***Perf. 13½x13¾***

2646 A1265 2.50p multi 1.60 1.40

Presidential mandate of Cristina Fernández Kirchner for 2011-15.

Monument to Gen. José de San Martín, First Deed of Río Gallegos Town Council — A1266

2012, Apr. 14 ***Perf. 14x13¾***

2647 A1266 2.50p multi 1.60 1.40

Río Gallegos Town Council, cent.

Alernative Energies — A1267

Designs: 2.50p, Biogas, biomass and biocombustibles. 9.50p, Solar, wind and hydroelectric energy.

2012, Apr. 28 **Litho.** ***Perf. 14x13½***

2648-2649 A1267 Set of 2 7.00 6.50

Argentine Natural History Museum, Bicent. — A1268

Museum emblem and: No. 2650, 2.50p, Skeleton of Dahlia the Elephant. No. 2651, 2.50p, Skull of Bonatitan reigi (dinosaur). No. 2652, 2.50p, Agrias narcissus butterflies, horiz. No. 2653, 2.50p, Display in Hall of Birds, horiz.

Perf. 13½x13¾, 13¾x13½

2012, Apr. 28

2650-2653 A1268 Set of 4 6.50 5.50

Intl. Year of Cooperatives A1269

2012, June 16 ***Perf. 13¾x13½***

2654 A1269 2.50p multi 1.60 1.40

Passage of Sáenz Peña Universal Male Suffrage Law, Cent. — A1270

2012, June 16 ***Perf. 13½x13¾***

2655 A1270 2.50p multi 1.60 1.40

Paintings of Historical Events of 1812 — A1271

Painting of: No. 2656, 2.50p, Jujuy Exodus, by unknown artist. No. 2657, 2.50p, Battle of Tucuman, by Tomas del Villar.

2012, June 16 ***Perf. 13¾x13½***

2656-2657 A1271 Set of 2 4.00 3.50

Argentine School of Military Aviation, Cent. — A1272

2012, July 21 ***Perf. 14x13½***

2658 A1272 2.75p multi 1.75 1.50

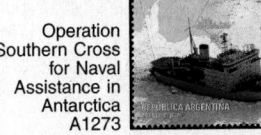

Operation Southern Cross for Naval Assistance in Antarctica A1273

2012, July 21 ***Perf. 13¾x13½***

2659 A1273 5p multi 3.00 2.75

Souvenir Sheet

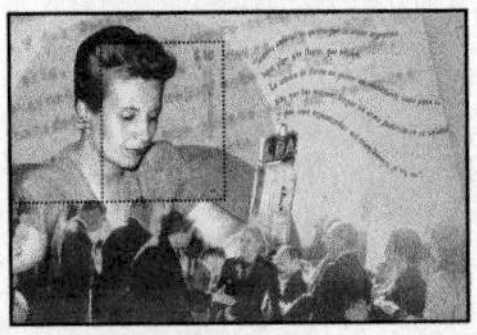

Eva Perón (1919-52) — A1274

2012, Sept. 1 ***Perf. 14***

2660 A1274 10p multi 5.75 5.50

Alzheimer's Disease Awareness — A1275

2012, Sept. 15 ***Perf. 13½x13¾***

2661 A1275 3p multi 1.90 1.75

Festivals — A1276

Designs: No. 2662, 3p, National Artisans Festival, Colón. No. 2663, 3p, Maní National Festival, Hernando. No. 2664, 3p, National Orange Festival, Bella Vista. No. 2665, 3p, National Calf Festival and Branding Day, Ayacucho.

2012, Sept. 25

2662-2665 A1276 Set of 4 7.50 6.50

General San Martín Mounted Grenadiers Regiment, 200th Anniv. — A1277

2012, Oct. 13 ***Perf. 13¾x13½***

2666 A1277 3p multi 1.90 1.60

Christmas — A1278

2012, Nov. 17 ***Perf. 13½x13¾***

2667 A1278 3p multi 1.90 1.60

Miniature Sheet

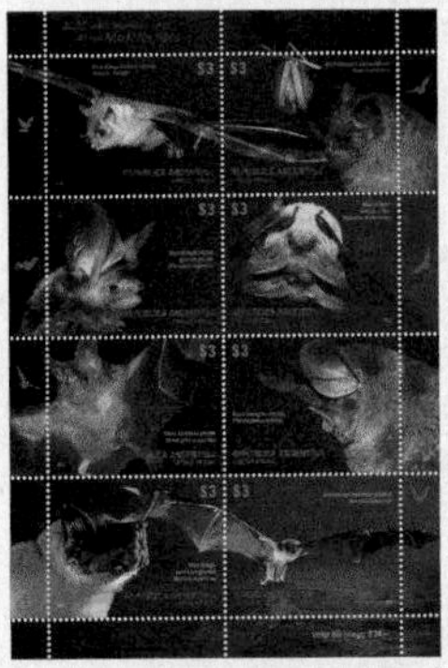

Bats A1279

No. 2668: a, Sturnira lillium in flight. b, Sturnira lillium hanging and close-up of head. c, Histiotus laephotis. d, Histiotus montanus. e, Chrotopterus auritus in flight. f, Head of Chrotopterus auritus. g, Head of Noctilio leporinus. h, Noctilio leporinus in flight.

2012, Dec. 22 ***Perf. 13¾x13½***

2668 A1279 3p Sheet of 8, #a-h 15.00 13.00

Battle of Salta, 200th Anniv. A1280

2013, Feb. 23 ***Perf. 14x13½***

2669 A1280 3.50p multi 2.25 1.90

Archaeological Artifacts Type of 2000

Designs: 30p, Ceremonial hatchet, Tehuelche culture. 40p, Basket with handle, Selk'nam culture. 50p, Basket with handle and lid, Wichi culture.

Perf. 13½x13¾ Syncopated

2013, Mar. 1

2670 A973 30p multi 22.00 22.00

2671 A973 40p multi 22.00 22.00

2672 A973 50p multi 22.00 22.00

Nos. 2670-2672 (3) 66.00 66.00

General Constituent Assembly of 1813, 200th Anniv. — A1281

2013, Mar. 9 ***Perf. 13½x13¾***
2673 A1281 3.50p multi 2.25 2.00

Festivals A1282

Designs: No. 2674, 3.50p, National Folklore Festival, Cosquín. No. 2675, 3.50p, National Trout Festival, Junín de los Andes. No. 2676, 3.50p, National Lemon Festival, Tafí Viejo, vert. No. 2677, 3.50p, National Petroleum Festival, Comodoro Rivadavia, vert.

Perf. 13¾x13½, 13½x13¾
2013, Mar. 23
2674-2677 A1282 Set of 4 8.00 7.00

Landmarks Type of 2004

Designs: 3.50p, Cancha de Bochas, Ischigualasto National Park. 30p, Hill of Seven Colors, Jujuy.

Perf. 13¾x13½ Syncopated
2013, Mar.
2678 A1063a 3.50p multi 1.75 1.75
2679 A1063a 30p multi 15.50 15.00

Souvenir Sheet

Partido de Esteban Echeverría Area of Buenos Aires, Cent. — A1283

No. 2680: a, Door on building built in 1789. b, Plaza and flags, horiz.

2013, Apr. 13 **Litho.** ***Perf. 14***
2680 A1283 Sheet of 2 4.75 4.25
a.-b. 5p Either single 2.25 2.10

National University of Córdoba, 400th Anniv. — A1284

2013, Apr. 27 ***Perf. 14x13½***
2681 A1284 3.50p multi 2.00 1.75

Election of Pope Francis A1285

No. 2682 — Arms of Pope Francis and: a, Pope Francis, flags of Vatican City, Italy and Argentina. b, Pope Francis in profile, flags of Vatican City and Argentina. c, Pope Francis waving, flags of Vatican City and Argentina. d, Pope Francis holding cross, flags of Vatican City and Argentina.

2013, May 2 ***Perf. 13¾x13½***
2682 Vert. strip of 4 16.00 15.00
a.-b. A1285 3.50p Either single 1.50 1.50
c. A1285 10p multi 4.25 4.25
d. A1285 14p multi 6.00 6.00

See Italy No. 3179, Vatican City Nos. 1523-1526.

African Union, 50th Anniv. — A1286

2013, June 1 **Litho.** ***Perf. 13½x13¾***
2683 A1286 4p multi 1.75 1.50

Villa Carlos Paz, Cent. — A1287

2013, July 27 **Litho.** ***Perf. 13¾x13½***
2684 A1287 4p multi 1.75 1.50

Souvenir Sheet

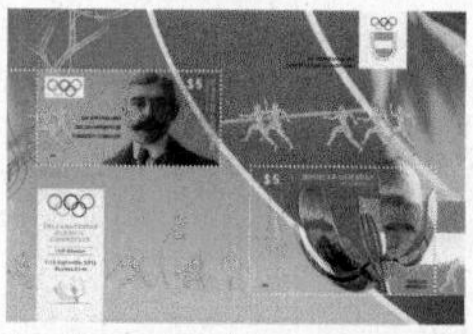

125th Session of the International Olympic Committee, Buenos Aires — A1288

No. 2685: a, Runners, Pierre de Coubertin (1863-1937), founder of Intl. Olympic Committee (60x30mm). b, Gymnast, flag of Argentina, *Floralis Generica,* sculpture by Eduardo Catalano (60x40mm).

2013, Sept. 14 **Litho.** ***Perf. 14***
2685 A1288 5p Sheet of 2, #a-b 4.50 4.00

Birds — A1289

Designs: No. 2686, 4p, Furnarius rufus. No. 2687, 4p, Podiceps gallardoi. No. 2688, 4p, Campephilus magellanicus, vert. No. 2689, 4p, Gubernatrix cristata, vert.

Perf. 13¾x13½, 13½x13¾
2013, Oct. 19 **Litho.**
2686-2689 A1289 Set of 4 7.50 6.50

A1290

A1291

A1292

Winning Designs in "Right to Identity" Children's Art Contest — A1293

2013, Oct. 22 **Litho.** ***Perf. 13¾x13½***
2690 A1290 4p multi 1.60 1.40
2691 A1291 4p multi 1.60 1.40

Perf. 13½x13¾
2692 A1292 4p multi 1.60 1.40
2693 A1293 4p multi 1.60 1.40
Nos. 2690-2693 (4) 6.40 5.60

Sergeant Juan Bautista Cabral (c. 1789-1813), Hero in Battle of San Lorenzo — A1294

San Martín Regiment of Mounted Grenadiers in Battle of San Lorenzo — A1295

2013, Nov. 9 **Litho.** ***Perf. 13½x13¾***
2694 A1294 4p multi 1.60 1.40

Perf. 14x13½
2695 A1295 4p multi 1.60 1.40

Battle of San Lorenzo, 200th anniv.

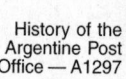

Campaign Against Discrimination — A1296

No. 2696 — Stylized people with joined hands and background color of: a, 4p, White. b, 13p, Black.

2013, Nov. 9 **Litho.** ***Perf. 13½x13¾***
2696 A1296 Horiz. pair, #a-b 6.25 5.75

America Issue.

History of the Argentine Post Office — A1297

No. 2697: a, Queen Juana of Castile, coat of arms, postal runner, map of Peru (opening of first post office in Lima, Peru, 1514) (30x30mm). b, Manuel Belgrano, Mariano Moreno, Cabildo, Buenos Aires (Post Office of the May Revolution, 1810) (30x40mm). c, President Juan Perón, and his wife, Eva (creation of Post Office and Telecommunications Secretariat, 1949) (30x40mm). d, Mail box, postal workers, flag of Argentina (renationalization of Postal Service, 10th anniv., 2013) (30x40mm). e, Pres. Nelson Kirchner, people with flags, mail boxes (renationalization of Postal Service, 2003) (63mm diameter).

Litho., Litho. With Foil Application (10p)

2013, Nov. 19 ***Perf. 14***
2697 Miniature sheet of 5 11.00 9.75
a.-d. A1297 5p Any single 1.75 1.60
e. A1297 10p multi 3.50 3.25

Souvenir Sheet

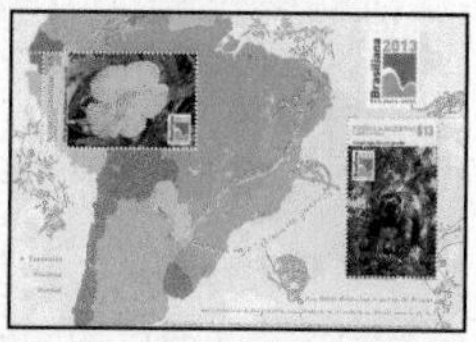

Brasiliana 2013 Intl. Philatelic Exhibition, Rio de Janeiro — A1298

No. 2698: a, 4p, Dolichandra unguis-cati. b, 13p, Alouatta guariba, vert.

2013, Nov. 23 **Litho.** ***Perf. 14***
2698 A1298 Sheet of 2, #a-b 6.00 5.50

Argentine National Anthem, 200th Anniv. — A1299

Perf. 13½x13¾
2013, Nov. 30 **Litho.**
2699 A1299 4p multi 1.50 1.25

Christmas — A1300

Perf. 13½x13¾
2013, Nov. 30 **Litho.**
2700 A1300 4p multi 1.50 1.25

New Laws, Policies, and Regulations Affecting Argentina Society — A1301

Designs; 25c, New national idenification cards (resolution 1800/09). 50c, Marriage equality (law 26,618). 1p, Soccer balls (free television broadcasts of local soccer games). 2p, Airplane, oil well, envelope and mail box (nationalization of industries). 5p, Flasks and chemical symbols (law 26,421 establishing program to support Network of Argentinian Researchers and Scientists Abroad). 10p, Family, hands, roof (establishment of Pro.Cre.Ar. loan program). 30p, End of Impunity laws and reopening of criminal trials of Argentina's military dictatorship (law 25,779). 40p, Mandatory open primary elections with obligatory voting. 50p, Open digital television.

Perf. 13½x13¾ Syncopated
2014, Jan. 20 **Litho.**
2701 A1301 25c multi .35 .35
2702 A1301 50c multi .35 .35
2703 A1301 1p multi .35 .35
2704 A1301 2p multi .55 .55
2705 A1301 5p multi 1.40 .90
2706 A1301 10p multi 2.75 1.90
2707 A1301 30p multi 8.50 5.75
2708 A1301 40p multi 11.00 7.50
2709 A1301 50p multi 14.00 9.00
Nos. 2701-2709 (9) 39.25 26.65

New Laws, Policies and Regulations Affecting Argentina Society — A1302

Designs: 25c, Nationalization of pension funds (law 26,425). 50c, Argentina Connected national telecommunications plan. 1p, Argentina-Bolivia pipeline integration. 2p, Latin American integration (Union of South American Nations). 3p, Creation of universities. 4p, Law regulating audiovisual communication services (law 26,522). 5p, Argentina Works Program. 6p, National Assisted Fertilization

Act (law 26,862). 10p, National child allowance decrees (Decree 1602/09). 30p, Suffrage for 16-year-olds (law 26,774). 50p, Restructuring of national debt.

Perf. 13½x13¾ Syncopated

2014				Litho.	
2710	A1302	25c multi		.35	.25
2711	A1302	50c multi		.35	.25
2712	A1302	1p multi		.35	.25
2713	A1302	2p multi		.55	.30
2714	A1302	3p multi		.80	.40
2715	A1302	4p multi		1.10	.50
2716	A1302	5p multi		1.40	.60
2717	A1302	6p multi		1.60	.75
2718	A1302	10p multi		2.75	1.25
2719	A1302	30p multi		8.00	3.75
2719A	A1302	50p multi		13.00	12.00
	Nos. 2710-2719A (11)			30.25	20.30

Issued: No. 2710-2719, 1/20; 50p, 8/25.

Jorge A. Newbery (1875-1914), Pilot, Airplane and Hot Air Balloon A1303

2014, Mar. 5 Litho. *Perf. 13¾x13½*
2720 A1303 4.50p multi 1.50 1.25

Hugo Chávez (1954-2013), President of Venezuela A1304

Chávez: No. 2721, 10p, Waving, wearing presidential sash. No. 2722, 10p, Holding map of South America.

2014, Mar. 5 Litho. *Perf. 13¾x13½*
2721-2722 A1304 Set of 2 5.75 5.25

America Issue.

Argentine Presence in the Antarctic, 110th Anniv. — A1305

No. 2724 — Latin American Antarctic Progam Administrators emblem and: a, Scientific researcher and penguin (30x60mm). b, Plesiosaurs (60x30mm).

Perf. 13¾x13½
2014, Mar. 25 Litho.
2723 A1305 4.50p shown 1.50 1.25

Souvenir Sheet

Perf. 14
2724 Sheet of 2 3.25 3.00
a.-b. A1305 6p Either single 1.50 1.50

25th reunion of Latin American Antarctic Program Administrators, Buenos Aires (No. 2724).

Flora and Fauna of Iguazu Falls Area — A1306

No. 2725: a, Doxocopa linda mileta (40x40mm). b, Billbergia zebrina (30x40mm). c, Iguazu Falls and Toco toucan (70x40mm). d, Iguazu Falls (90x30mm)

Litho. & Silk-Screened
2014, Apr. 14 *Perf. 14*
2725 Miniature sheet of 4 9.75 9.00
a.-b. A1306 8p Either single 2.00 2.00
c.-d. A1306 10p Either single 2.50 2.50

Souvenir Sheet

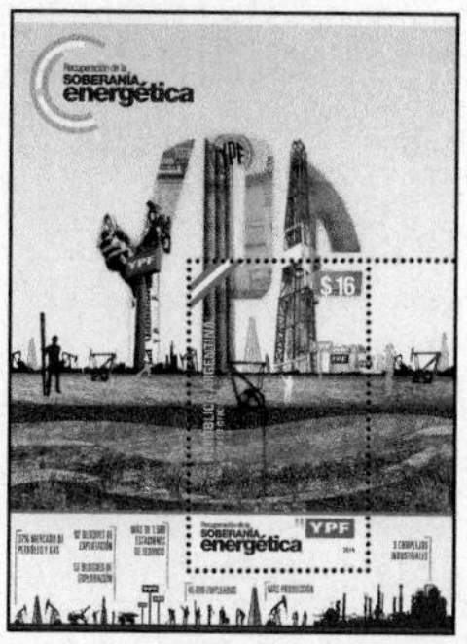

Renationalization of YPF Energy Company — A1307

2014, May 5 Litho. *Perf. 14*
2726 A1307 16p multi 4.25 4.00

Battle of Montevideo, 200th Anniv. — A1308

2014, May 19 Litho. *Perf. 14x13½*
2727 A1308 4.50p multi 1.40 1.10

National University of Tucuman, Cent. — A1309

2014, May 26 Litho. *Perf. 14x13½*
2728 A1309 4.50p multi 1.40 1.10

2014 World Cup Soccer Championships, Brazil — A1310

No. 2729 — Shirts and schedules of Group F teams: a, Argentina. b, Bosnia & Herzegovina. c, Iran. d, Nigeria.

2014, May 12 Litho. *Perf. 13½x13¾*
2729 Horiz. strip of 4 *33.00 32.00*
a.-d. A1310 10p Any single *8.00 7.50*

No. 2729 was quickly withdrawn from sale.

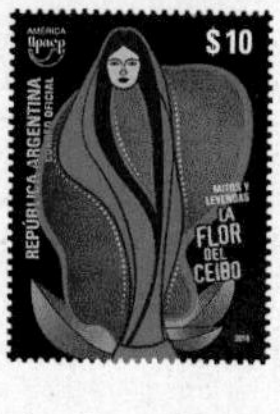

Myths and Legends — A1311

Designs: No. 2733, 10p, La Flor del Ceibo (the Ceibo flower). No. 2734, 10p, El Viento Zonda (the Zonda wind).

Perf. 13½x13¾
2014, June 30 Litho.
2733-2734 A1311 Set of 2 5.50 5.00

America Issue.

El Enterriano, by Eleodoro Ergasto Marenco (1914-96) — A1312

2014, July 14 Litho. *Perf. 13½x13¾*
2735 A1312 5p multi 1.50 1.25

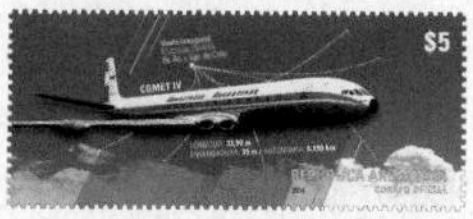

Commercial Aircraft — A1313

Designs: No. 2736, 5p, Comet IV. No. 2737, 5p, Boeing 747-200. No. 2738, 5p, Boeing 737-800NG. No. 2739, 5p, Airbus 340-300.

2014, July 21 Litho. *Perf. 14x13½*
2736-2739 A1313 Set of 4 6.00 5.00

Souvenir Sheet

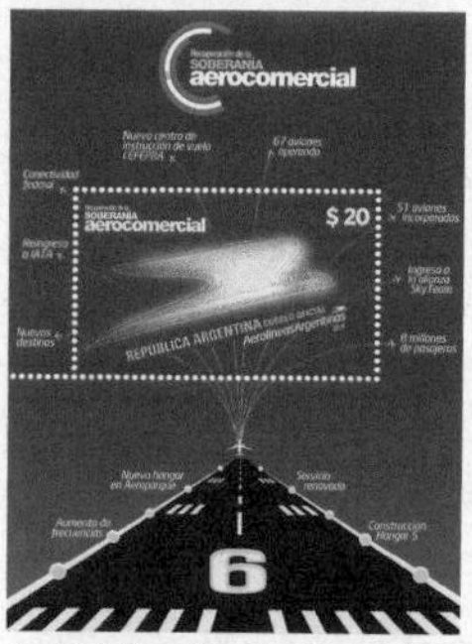

Control of Aerolíneas Argentinas by Argentine Government, 6th Anniv. — A1314

Litho. & Silk-Screened
2014, July 21 *Perf. 14*
2740 A1314 20p multi 5.25 5.00

Souvenir Sheet

PhilaKorea 2014 Intl. Philatelic Exhibition, Seoul — A1315

No. 2741: a, Bird in flight (29mm diameter). b, Three birds (38mm diameter)

Litho. & Silk-Screened With Foil Application
2014, Aug. 11 *Perf.*
2741 A1315 15p Sheet of 2, #a-b 7.50 7.25

Luis Alberto Spinetta (1950-2012), Rock Musician — A1316

Perf. 13½x13¾
2014, Sept. 22 Litho.
2742 A1316 10p multi 2.60 2.40

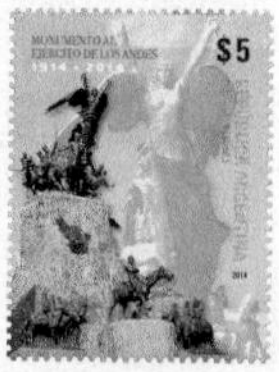

Monument to the Army of the Andes, Cent. — A1317

Perf. 13½x13¾
2014, Sept. 25 Litho.
2743 A1317 5p multi 1.50 1.25

Festivals — A1318

Designs: No. 2744, 5p, Cuevas de las Manos Festival, Perito Moreno. No. 2745, 5p, National Mate Festival, Paraná. No. 2746, 5p, 70th National Agriculture Festival, Esperanza. No. 2747, 5p, National Steam Train Festival, El Maitén.

Perf. 13½x13¾
2014, Sept. 29 Litho.
2744-2747 A1318 Set of 4 5.75 4.75

Souvenir Sheet

1813 Coins of the United Provinces of the River Plate — A1319

No. 2748: a, Gold 8-escudo and silver 8-real coins. b, Silver coins, horiz.

2014, Oct. 14 Litho. *Perf. 14*
2748 A1319 6p Sheet of 2, #a-b 3.50 3.00

Julio Cortázar (1914-84), Writer — A1320

Prize-winning art in Cortázar stamp design contest by: No. 2749, 5p, Gastón Martino. No. 2750, 5p, José Rivadulla. No. 2751, 5p, Lucía Valentina Piuzzi, vert. No. 2752, 5p, Ana Gauna, vert.

Perf. 13¾x13½, 13½x13¾
2014, Oct. 20 Litho.
2749-2752 A1320 Set of 4 5.75 4.75

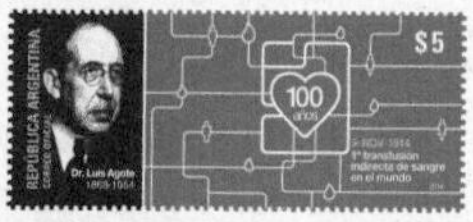

Non-Direct Blood Transfusions by Dr. Luis Agote, Cent. — A1321

2014, Nov. 10 Litho. *Perf. 14x13½*
2753 A1321 5p multi 1.50 1.25

Nativity, by Raúl Soldi (1905-94) — A1322

Perf. 13½x13¾
2014, Nov. 21 Litho.
2754 A1322 10p multi 2.60 2.40

Christmas. See Vatican City No. 1581.

Movie Stars — A1323

Designs: No. 2755, 5p, Tita Merello (1904-2002), actress. No. 2756, 5p, Alfredo Alcón (1930-2014), actor.

Perf. 13½x13¾

2014, Nov. 25 **Litho.**
2755-2756 A1323 Set of 2 2.90 2.40

Mar del Plata Intl. Film Festival, 60th anniv.

Nelson Mandela (1918-2013), President of South Africa — A1324

Perf. 13¾x13½

2014, Dec. 15 **Litho.**
2757 A1324 10p multi 2.60 2.40

Antarctopelta Oliveroi A1325

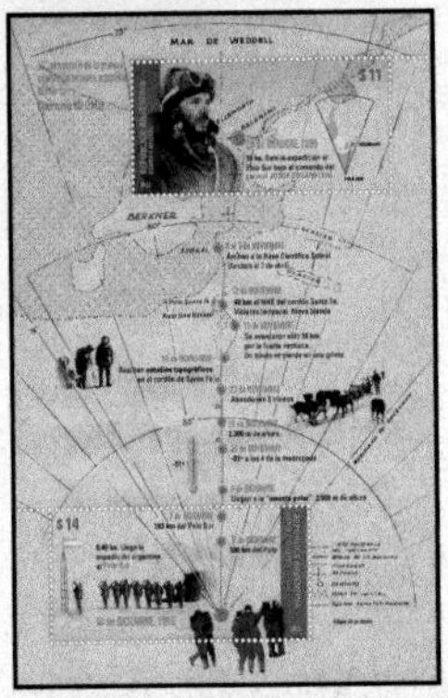

First Argentine Expedition to the South Pole, 50th Anniv. — A1326

No. 2759: a, 11p, Map and Col. Jorge Edgard Leal, expedition leader. b, 14p, Expedition members saluting flag of Argentina.

2015, Mar. 9 **Litho.** ***Perf. 13¾x13½***
2758 A1325 6p multi 1.60 1.40

Souvenir Sheet

Perf. 14

2759 A1326 Sheet of 2, #a-b 6.00 5.75

Argentine exploration and science projects in Antarctica.

Festivals — A1327

Designs: No. 2760, 6p, National Festival of the Longest Night, Ushuaia. No. 2761, 6p, National Drum Festival, Frías. No. 2762, 6p, National Chocolate Festival, Bariloche. No. 2763, 6p, National Cotton Festival, Presidencia Roque Sáenz Peña.

2015, Apr. 27 **Litho.** ***Perf. 13½x13¾***
2760-2763 A1327 Set of 4 6.50 5.50

Miniature Sheet

Trees A1328

No. 2764: a, Handroanthus impetiginosus. b, Araucaria araucana. c, Salix humboldtiana. d, Cercidium praecox.

2015, Apr. 27 **Litho.** ***Perf. 13½x13¾***
2764 A1328 6p Sheet of 4, #a-d 6.50 5.50

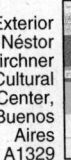

Souvenir Sheet

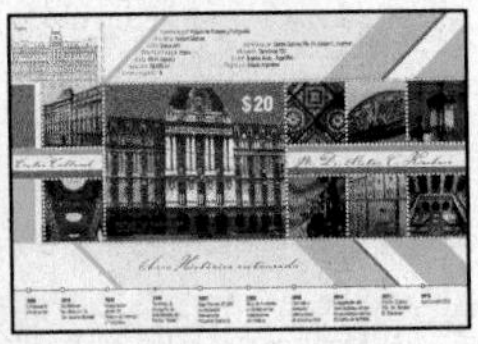

Exterior of Néstor Kirchner Cultural Center, Buenos Aires A1329

2015, May 26 **Litho.** ***Perf. 14***
2765 A1329 20p multi + 6 labels 4.75 4.50

Free Peoples Congress, 200th Anniv. — A1330

Perf. 13½x13¾

2015, June 29 **Litho.**
2766 A1330 10p multi 2.50 2.25

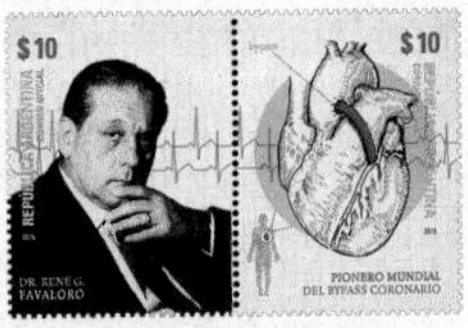

A1331

No. 2767: a, Dr. René G. Favaloro (1923-2000), cardiac surgeon. b, Heart with bypass pioneered by Dr. Favaloro.

2015, July 13 **Litho.** ***Perf. 13½x13¾***
2767 A1331 10p Horiz. pair, #a-b 5.00 4.50

International Telecommunication Union, 150th Anniv. — A1332

2015, Aug. 21 **Litho.** ***Perf. 14x13½***
2768 A1332 10p multi 2.50 2.25

United Nations, 70th Anniv. — A1333

Perf. 13¾x13½

2015, Aug. 31 **Litho.**
2769 A1333 10p multi 2.50 2.25

Souvenir Sheet

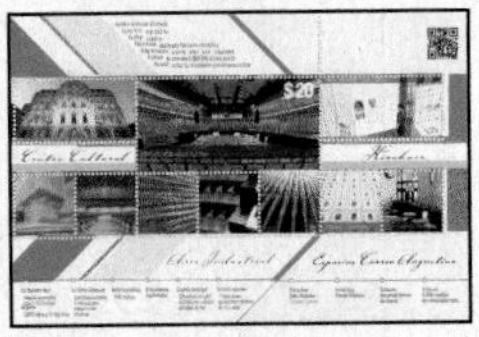

Interior of Nestor Kirchner Cultural Center, Buenos Aires A1334

2015, Sept. 14 **Litho.** ***Perf. 14***
2770 A1334 20p multi + 9 labels 4.50 4.25

Miniature Sheet

Birds A1335

No. 2771: a, Ramphastos dicolorus. b, Ramphastos toco. c, Pteroglossus bailloni. d, Selenidera maculirostris.

Perf. 13¾x13½

2015, Sept. 22 **Litho.**
2771 A1335 7p Sheet of 4, #a-d 7.00 6.00

Miniature Sheet

Mammals — A1336

No. 2772: a, Lama pacos. b, Lama guanicoe. c, Vicugna vicugna. d, Lama glama.

Perf. 13¾x13½

2015, Sept. 22 **Litho.**
2772 A1336 7p Sheet of 4, #a-d 7.00 6.00

A1337

A1338

A1339

A1340

Gustavo Cerati (1959-2014), Rock Musician A1341

2015, Oct. 9 **Litho.** ***Perf. 13¾x13½***
2773 A1337 7p multi 1.75 1.50
2774 Horiz. strip of 4 9.50 8.50
a. A1338 10p multi 2.10 2.10
b. A1339 10p multi 2.10 2.10
c. A1340 10p multi 2.10 2.10
d. A1341 10p multi 2.10 2.10

Souvenir Sheet

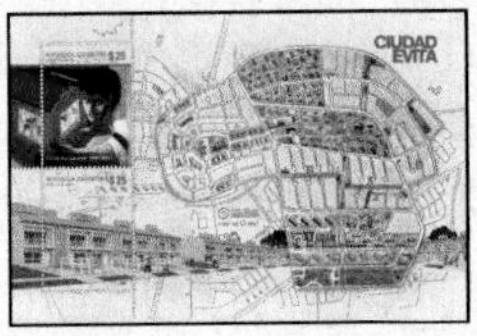

Ciudad Evita A1342

No. 2775: a, Man and house. b, Apartment complex.

Litho. (Sheet Margin Litho. & Embossed)

2015, Oct. 13 ***Perf. 14***
2775 A1342 25p Sheet of 2, #a-b 11.00 10.50

Christmas — A1343

2015, Nov. 2 **Litho.** ***Perf. 13½x13¾***
2776 A1343 10p multi 2.40 2.10

Souvenir Sheet

Pres. Juan D. Perón (1895-1974) — A1344

2015, Nov. 17 **Litho.** ***Perf. 14***
2777 A1344 29p multi 6.25 6.00

2015 Inauguration of Pres. Mauricio Macri — A1345

2016, May 9 **Litho.** ***Perf. 13½x14***
2778 A1345 8p multi 1.75 1.25

Campaign Against Human Trafficking — A1346

No. 2779 — Inscription starting with: a, "Yo le digo. . ." b, "Explotación. . ."

2016, May 23 **Litho.** ***Perf. 13½x13¾***
2779 A1346 8p Horiz. pair, #a-b 3.25 2.75

America Issue.

Argentine Naval Aviation, Cent. — A1347

2016, June 6 Litho. *Perf. 14x13½*

2780 A1347 10p multi 2.10 1.75

Rubén Darío (1867-1916), Poet — A1348

Perf. 13¾x13½

2016, June 10 Litho.

2781 A1348 20p multi 4.00 3.50

Independence, 200th Anniv. — A1349

Perf. 13½x13¾ Syncopated

2016, June 27 Litho.

2782 A1349 10p multi 2.10 1.75

Open Cabildo of Buenos Aires of May 25, 1810 A1350

Battle of Tucumán and Members of the Second Triumvirate, 1812 — A1351

Argentine Declaration of Independence, 200th Anniv. — A1352

2016, July 7 Litho. *Perf. 14*

2783 Sheet of 3 7.00 6.50
- *a.* A1350 10p multi 2.00 1.90
- *b.* A1351 10p multi 2.00 1.90
- *c.* A1352 10p multi 2.00 1.90

Road to Argentine Independence.

A1353

Coats of Arms — A1354

No. 2784 — Arms of: a, Argentina. b, Corrientes Province. c, Chaco Province. d, Formosa Province. e, Misiones Province. f, Catamarca Province. g, Jujuy Province. h, La Rioja Province. i, Salta Province. j, Santiago del Estero Province. k, Tucumán Province. l, Mendoza Province. m, San Juan Province. n, San Luis Province. o, Autonomous City of Buenos Aires. p, Buenos Aires Province. q, Córdoba Province. r, Entre Ríos Province. s, La Pampa Province. t, Santa Fe Province. u, Chubut Province. v, Neuquén Province. w, Río Negro Province. x, Santa Cruz Province. y, Tierra del Fuego, Antarctica and Southern Atlantic Islands Province.

2016, July 7 Litho. *Perf. 14*

2784 Sheet of 25 50.00 45.00
- *a.* A1353 10p multi 2.00 2.00
- *b.-y.* A1354 10p Any single 2.00 2.00
- *z.* Booklet pane of 25, #2784a-2784y — —
- Complete booklet, #2784z —

Souvenir Sheet

July 9, 1816, Bas-relief by Lola Mora — A1355

No. 2785: a, Deputies at Congress of Tucumán, facing right. b, Three deputies, facing left, behind table.

2016, July 7 Litho. *Perf. 14*

2785 A1355 10p Sheet of 2, #a-b, + label 4.25 3.50

Fruits — A1356

Designs: 1p, Prunus persica. 2p, Malus domestica. 5p, Citrus limon. 8p, Prunus salicina. 10p, Prunus avium. 30p, Vitis vinifera. 35p, Vaccinum spp. 40p, Pyrus communis. 50p, Citrus sinensis. 100p, Citrullus lanatus.

Perf. 13½x13¾ Syncopated

2016-19 Litho.

2786	A1356	1p	multi	.30	.30
2787	A1356	2p	multi	.30	.30
2788	A1356	5p	multi	.85	.85
2789	A1356	8p	multi	1.35	1.25
2790	A1356	10p	multi	1.75	1.60
2791	A1356	30p	multi	5.00	4.75
2791A	A1356	35p	sil & multi	2.25	2.10
2792	A1356	40p	multi	7.00	6.50
2793	A1356	50p	multi	8.25	8.00
2794	A1356	100p	multi	16.50	16.00
	Nos. 2786-2794 (10)			43.55	41.65

Issued: 1p, 2p, 5p, 7/22; 8p, 10p, 30p, 100p, 8/4; 40p, 50p, 7/26; 35p, 2019.

Vegetables — A1357

Designs: 1p, Daucus carota. 2p, Cynara cardunculus. 3p, Zea mays. 4p, Lycopersicum esculentum. 5p, Asparagus officinalis. 8p, Solanum melongena. 10p, Solanum tuberosum. 30p, Capsicum annuum. 35p, Brasica oleracea var. Itálica. 50p, Cucurbita maxima. 100p, Allium cepa.

Perf. 13½x13¾ Syncopated

2016-19 Litho.

2795	A1357	1p	multi	.35	.30
2796	A1357	2p	multi	.35	.30
2797	A1357	3p	multi	.50	.45
2798	A1357	4p	multi	.70	.65
2799	A1357	5p	multi	.90	.85
2800	A1357	8p	multi	1.50	1.25
2801	A1357	10p	multi	1.80	1.60
2802	A1357	30p	multi	5.25	4.75
2802A	A1357	35p	sil & multi	2.25	2.10
2803	A1357	50p	multi	8.75	8.25
2804	A1357	100p	multi	17.50	16.00
	Nos. 2795-2804 (11)			39.85	36.50

Issued: 1p, 4p, 8p, 50p, 100p, 8/4; 2p, 3p, 7/22; 5p, 10p, 30p, 7/26; 35p, 2019.

Miniature Sheet

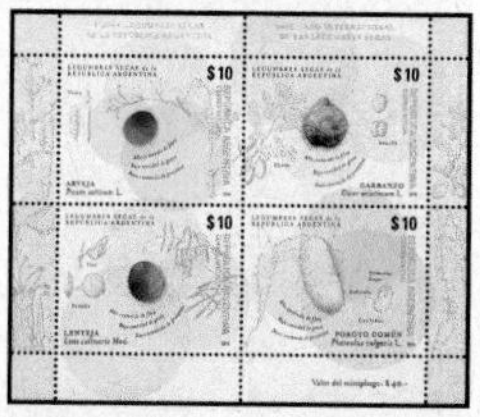

International Year of Pulses — A1358

No. 2805: a, Pisum sativum. b, Cicer arietinum. c, Lens culinaris. d, Phaseolus vulgaris.

Perf. 13¾x13½

2016, Aug. 16 Litho.

2805 A1358 10p Sheet of 4, #a-d 7.25 6.25

Miniature Sheet

Aves Argentina, Cent. — A1359

No. 2806: a, Heliomaster furcifer. b, Hylocharis chrysura. c, Sappho sparganura. d, Chlorostilbon lucidus.

Perf. 13¾x13½

2016, Sept. 19 Litho.

2806 A1359 11p Sheet of 4, #a-d 8.00 7.00

Souvenir Sheet

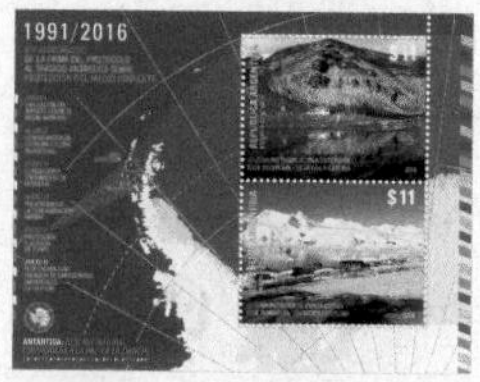

Signing of the Protocol to the Antarctic Treaty on Environmental Protection, 25th Anniv. — A1360

No. 2807: a, Base Decepción. b, Base Primavera.

2016, Oct. 4 Litho. *Perf. 14*

2807 A1360 11p Sheet of 2, #a-b 4.00 3.50

Canonization of St. José Gabriel del Rosario Brochero (1840-1914) — A1361

2016, Oct. 17 Litho. *Perf. 14x13½*

2808 A1361 11p gold & multi 2.00 1.60

Russian Tea and Tea Service A1362

Argentinian Mate and Mate Service A1363

Perf. 13½x13¾

2016, Nov. 14 Litho.

2809 A1362 11p gold & multi 6.25 6.00

2810 A1363 11p gold & multi 6.25 6.00

See Russia No. 7784.

Sloop Nuestra Señora del Carmen, Flags of Greece and Argentina — A1364

2016, Dec. 5 Litho. *Perf. 13½x13¾*

2811 A1364 11p multi 2.00 1.60

Remembrance of Greek soldiers who fought for independence for Argentina.

Christmas — A1365

No. 2812 — Angels, by Norah Borges: a, Angel facing right. b, Angel facing left.

Perf. 13½x13¾

2016, Dec. 13 Litho.

2812 A1365 11p Horiz. pair, #a-b 4.00 3.50

Winning Designs in Children's "Healthy Feelings and Values" Art Contest — A1366

Art by: No. 2813, 11p, Guadalupe Sotelo. No. 2814, 11p, Victoria Figueroa Fernández. No. 2815, 11p, Morena Gianella Oliva, horiz.

Perf. 13½x13¾, 13¾x13½

2016, Dec. 19 Litho.

2813-2815 A1366 Set of 3 6.00 5.25

Butterflies A1367

Designs: 11p, Strymon eurytulus. 55p, Morpho epistrophus argentinus.

2017, Jan. 23 Litho. *Perf. 13¾x13½*

2816-2817 A1367 Set of 2 10.50 10.00

José Luis Cabezas (1961-97), Murdered Photojournalist A1368

2017, May 9 Litho. *Perf. 13¾x13½*

2818 A1368 13p multi 2.40 2.10

Pedro Bonifacio Palacios (1854-1917), Poet — A1369

2017, May 15 Litho. ***Perf. 13¾x13½***
2819 A1369 13p multi 2.40 2.10

Marist Brothers, 200th Anniv. A1370

2017, May 22 Litho. ***Perf. 14x13½***
2820 A1370 13p multi 2.40 2.10

Battle of Humahuaca, 200th Anniv. — A1371

Perf. 13½x13¾
2017, June 26 Litho.
2821 A1371 16p multi 2.75 2.50

Roberto Fontanarrosa (1944-2007), Cartoonist — A1372

A1373

Cartoons by Fontanarrosa — A1374

No. 2823: a, Front and profile views of Boogie (70x40mm). b, Dog with Inodoro Pereyra holding flowers (40x60mm). c, Inodoro Pereyra talking with Eulogia (60x60mm). d, Dog of Inodoro Pereyra speaking (40x60mm). e, Boogie holding binoculars (50x40mm).

No. 2824: a, Man holding ball talking to soccer player (80x60mm). b, Man with pens in shirt pocket talking (50x80mm). c, Creator of Frankenstein monster talking to another man (80x60mm).

2017, July 31 Litho. ***Perf. 13½x13¾***
2822 A1372 16p multi 2.90 2.50

Booklet Stamps
Perf. 14

2823 A1373 Booklet pane of 5 21.00 —
a.-d. 16p Any single 3.50 3.50
e. 32p black & silver 6.75 6.75
2824 A1374 Booklet pane of 3 23.00 —
a.-b. 16p Either single 3.50 3.50
c. 68p black & silver 15.00 15.00
Complete booklet 44.00

Complete booklet contains Nos. 2823, 2824 and No. 2822 in a stamp mount and four post cards. It sold for 250p.

First Air Mail Flight from Buenos Aires to Montevideo, Uruguay, Cent. — A1375

2017, Oct. 2 Litho. ***Perf. 14x13½***
2825 A1375 32p multi 4.75 4.50

Souvenir Sheet

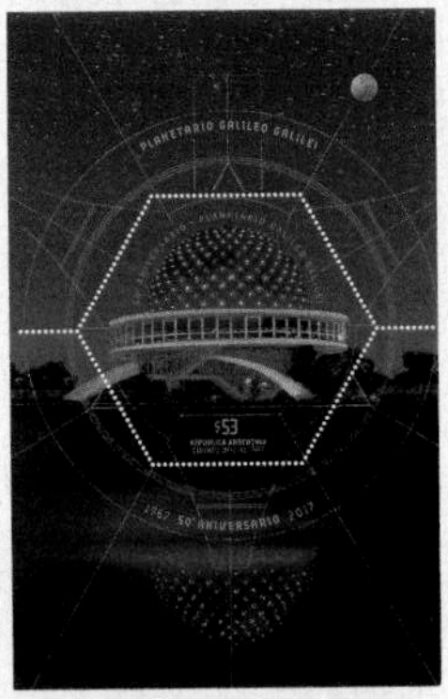

Galileo Galilei Planetarium, Buenos Aires, 50th Anniv. — A1376

Litho. & Silk-Screened
2017, Oct. 31 ***Perf. 14***
2826 A1376 53p multi 7.75 7.50

Argentina Men's Tennis Team, Winners of 2016 Davis Cup — A1377

Designs: 32p, Davis Cup. 53p, Davis Cup held by player's hands, horiz.

2017, Nov. 6 Litho. ***Perf. 13½x13¾***
2827 A1377 32p multi 4.75 4.50

Souvenir Sheet
Perf. 14

2828 A1377 53p multi 7.75 7.50

No. 2828 contains one 40x30mm stamp.

Sandro (Roberto Sánchez-Ocampo) (1945-2010), Singer — A1378

No. 2830: a, Hands of Sandro and guitar (70x40mm). b, Head of Sandro (40x50mm).

Perf. 13¾x13½
2017, Nov. 21 Litho.
2829 A1378 32p multi 4.75 4.50

Souvenir Sheet
Litho. & Silk-Screened
Perf. 14

2830 A1378 Sheet of 2 12.50 12.00
a. 32p multi 4.50 4.50
b. 53p multi 9.50 7.50

Pres. Hipólito Yrigoyen (1852-1933) A1379

Perf. 13½x13¾
2017, Dec. 11 Litho.
2831 A1379 16p multi 2.50 2.25

A1380

A1381

Cartoons by Quino A1382

No. 2833: a, Girl mailing letter (40x60mm). b, Girl walking (30x50mm).

2017, Dec. 11 Litho. ***Perf. 14x13½***
2832 A1380 32p multi 4.75 4.50

Booklet Stamps

2833 A1381 Booklet pane of 2 13.00 —
a. 32p black & gold 5.00 5.00
b. 53p black & gold 7.25 7.25
2834 A1382 85p Booklet pane of 1 13.00 —
Complete booklet, #2833-2834 26.00

Christmas.

Souvenir Sheet

Crossing of the Andes of San Martín's Army, 200th Anniv. A1383

2017, Dec. 26 Litho. ***Perf. 14***
2835 A1383 53p multi 7.75 7.50

Souvenir Sheet

Renewable Energy — A1384

No. 2836: a, Solar-powered building, biofuel plant, bicycle and automobile at fuel pump. b, Dam and wind generators.

2018, Jan. 15 Litho. ***Perf. 14***
2836 A1384 16p Sheet of 2, #a-b 5.00 4.50

Souvenir Sheet

Astor Piazzolla (1921-92), Tango Composer — A1385

No. 2837: a, 45p, Piazzolla's hand on bandoneon keys. b, 75p, Piazzolla playing bandoneon.

2018, May 8 Litho. ***Perf. 14***
2837 A1385 Sheet of 2, #a-b 10.00 9.75

Souvenir Sheet

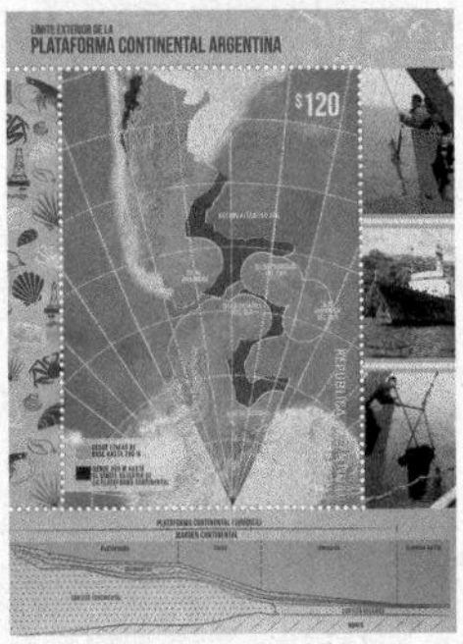

Map of Continental Shelf Off Argentina and Antarctica — A1386

2018, Sept. 10 Litho. ***Perf. 14***
2838 A1386 120p sil & multi 8.50 8.25

National Gendarmerie, 80th Anniv. — A1387

Perf. 13½x13¾
2018, Dec. 12 Litho.
2839 A1387 50p multi 3.75 3.50

Nos. 2125, 2190, 2217, 2248, 2275 and 2410-2412 Surcharged in Silver and Black

Methods and Perfs. As Before

2018

2840 A1123 2p on 75c #2411 *.55 .55*
2841 A973 5p on 10c #2125 *1.50 1.50*
2842 A1123 10p on 75c #2410 *2.90 2.90*
2843 A979a 25p on 10c #2217 *7.00 7.00*
2844 A1123 40p on 75c #2412 *11.50 11.50*

Blocks of 8

2845 A1036 25p on 75c #2248 *55.00 55.00*
a.-h. Any single *7.00 7.00*
2846 A1050 50p on 75c #2276 *115.00 115.00*
a.-h. Any single *14.50 14.50*
2847 A1013 100p on 75c #2190 *230.00 230.00*
a.-h. Any single *29.00 29.00*
Nos. 2840-2847 (8) *423.45 423.45*

Placement of surcharge varies.

Nos. 2076-2077, 2129, 2232, 2337, 2339, 2340, 2398-2401, and 2414-2415 Surcharged in Silver and Black With Added "UP" Inscription

Methods and Perfs. As Before

2018

2848 A1029 1p on 75c #2232 *.40 .40*
2849 A973 2p on 75c #2129 *.55 .55*
2850 A1116 10p on 75c #2398 *2.90 2.90*
2851 A1116 10p on 75c #2399 *2.90 2.90*
2852 A1116 10p on 75c #2400 *2.90 2.90*
2853 A1116 10p on 75c #2401 *2.90 2.90*
2853A A943 30p on 75c #2076 *9.50 9.50*

2854 A943 30p on 75c #2077 8.50 8.50
2855 A1086 30p on 75c #2337 8.50 8.50
2856 A1086 30p on 75c #2339 8.50 8.50
2857 A1086 30p on 75c #2340 8.50 8.50
2858 A1125 100p on 75c #2414 29.00 29.00
2859 A1125 100p on 75c #2415 29.00 29.00
Nos. 2848-2859 (13) 114.05 114.05

Placement of surcharge varies.

A1388

Landmarks and Wildlife of Tierra del Fuego, Antarctica and South Atlantic Islands
A1389

Designs: No. 2860, Les Eclaireurs Lighthouse. No. 2861, Pygoscelis papua. No. 2862, Brown Base. No. 2863, Hydrurga leptonyx.

2019, Jan. 28 Litho. *Perf. 13¾x13½*

2860 A1388 170p multi 14.50 14.50
2861 A1388 180p multi 15.50 15.50

Inscribed "UP" at Lower Left

2862 A1389 170p multi 14.50 14.50
2863 A1389 180p multi 15.50 15.50
Nos. 2860-2863 (4) 60.00 60.00

Eighth International Congress of the Spanish Language, Córdoba, Argentina — A1390

No. 2864: a, 35p, Spanish language books making "ñ." b, 145p, Jorge Luis Borges (1899-1986), writer.

Perf. 13½x13¾

2019, Mar. 25 Litho.

2864 A1390 Horiz. pair, #a-b 14.50 14.00

Souvenir Sheet

Icebreaker A.R.A. Almirante Irízar — A1391

No. 2865: a, 40p, Icebreaker and raft (40x30mm). b, 160p, Icebreaker (40x50mm).

Litho. & Silk-Screened

2019, Apr. 29 *Perf. 13¾*

2865 A1391 Sheet of 2, #a-b 16.00 16.00

Souvenir Sheet

Marambio Base, Antarctica, 50th Anniv. — A1392

No. 2866: a, 40p, Construction of Marambio Base in 1969, DHC-2 Beaver, Fokker F-27. b, 160p, Hercules C-130 and DHC-6 Twin Otter over Marambio Base.

Litho. & Silk-Screened

2019, Apr. 29 *Perf. 14*

2866 A1392 Sheet of 2, #a-b 16.00 16.00

Diplomatic Relations Between Argentina and Israel, 70th Anniv. — A1393

2019, May 27 Litho. *Perf. 13½x13¾*

2867 A1393 100p gold & multi 8.00 7.50

New Year 2019 (Year of the Pig) A1394

Litho. & Embossed

2019, May 27 *Perf.*

2868 A1394 200p gold & multi 16.00 15.00

A1395

National Parks — A1396

Designs: No. 2869, Calilegua National Park. No. 2870, Los Cardones National Park. No. 2871, Río Pilcomayo National Park.No. 2872, El Palmar National Park. No. 2873, Ciervo de los Pantanos National Park. No. 2874, Talampaya National Park. No. 2875, Quebrada del Condorito National Park. No. 2876, Tierra del Fuego National Park. No. 2877, Iguazú National Park. No. 2878, Patagonia National Park. No. 2879, Nahuel Huapi National Park. No. 2880, Perito Moreno National Park. No. 2880A, Lihué Calel National Park.

No. 2881, Campos del Tuyú National Park. No. 2882, Aconquija National Park. No. 2883, El Impenetrable National Park. No. 2884, Sierra de las Quijadas National Park. No. 2885, El Rey National Park. No. 2886, El Leoncito National Park. No. 2887, Pre-Delta National Park. No. 2888, Los Glaciares National Park. No. 2889, Lanín National Park. No. 2889A, Monte León National Park. No. 2889B, Los Alerces National Park. No. 2889C, Iberá National Park.

Perf. 13¾x13½ Syncopated

2019-22 Litho.

2869 A1395 1p multi .40 .35
2870 A1395 2p multi .40 .35
2871 A1395 5p multi .40 .35
2872 A1395 10p multi .85 .80
2873 A1395 20p multi 1.60 1.50
2874 A1395 30p multi 2.40 2.25
2875 A1395 40p multi 3.25 3.00
2876 A1395 50p multi 4.00 3.75
2877 A1395 100p multi 8.00 7.75
2878 A1395 200p multi 16.00 15.50
2879 A1395 300p multi 24.00 23.00
2880 A1395 400p multi 32.00 30.00
2880A A1395 500p multi ('22) 8.50 8.50
Nos. 2869-2880A (13) 101.80 97.10

Inscribed "UP" at Lower Left

2881 A1396 1p multi .40 .35
2882 A1396 2p multi .40 .35
2883 A1396 5p multi .40 .35
2884 A1396 10p multi .85 .80
2885 A1396 20p multi 1.60 1.50
2886 A1396 40p multi 3.25 3.00
2887 A1396 50p multi 4.00 3.75
2888 A1396 100p multi 8.00 7.50
2889 A1396 200p multi 16.00 15.50
2889A A1396 300p multi 24.00 23.00
2889B A1396 400p multi 32.00 30.00
2889C A1396 500p multi ('22) 8.50 8.50
Nos. 2881-2889C (12) 99.40 94.60

Issued: Nos. 2880A, 2889C, 5/15/22, others, 6/7/19. See Nos. 2913-2924.

Buses — A1397

Designs: No. 2890, 50p, Chevrolet bus used on Line 45, 1942. No. 2891, 50p, Mercedes-Benz 312 bus used on Line 159, 1961.

2019, July 29 Litho. *Perf. 13¾x13½*

2890-2891 A1397 Set of 2 8.25 7.50

A1398

Carlos Gardel (1890-1935), Tango Singer — A1399

Perf. 13½x13¾

2019, Aug. 27 Litho.

2892 A1398 100p gold & multi 6.00 5.50

Souvenir Sheet

Perf. 14

2893 A1399 225p gold & multi 13.00 12.50

Angel Villoldo (1861-1919), Tango Musician A1400

Street Lamp and Tango Dancers A1401

Tango Score and Don Filatango, Mascot of 2019 International Philatelic Exhibition, Buenos Aires — A1402

Statue of Carlos Gardel (1890-1935), Tango Singer — A1403

Sign From Boedo Neighborhood, Buenos Aires — A1404

Perf. 13¾x13½

2019, Aug. 28 Litho.

2894 Booklet pane of 5 15.00 14.00
a. A1400 50p gold & multi 2.50 2.25
b. A1401 50p gold & multi 2.50 2.25
c. A1402 50p gold & multi 2.50 2.25
d. A1403 50p gold & multi 2.50 2.25
e. A1404 50p gold & multi 2.50 2.25
Complete booklet, #2894 15.00 14.00

Tango seritage of Barracas, Caminito, San Telmo, Downtown and Boedo neighborhoods of Buenos Aires.

Mohandas K. Gandhi (1869-1948), Indian Nationalist Leader A1405

Perf. 13¾x13½

2019, Sept. 30 Litho.

2895 A1405 235p multi 13.00 13.00

Souvenir Sheet

Solo 1925-28 Buenos Aires-Washington D.C. Journey of A. F. Tschiffely (1895-1954) With Horses Mancha and Gato — A1406

2019, Oct. 7 Litho. *Perf. 13¾x14*

2896 A1406 180p multi 8.50 8.00

Southern Fuegian Railway (Train at the End of the World), Ushuaia A1407

Various trains: 195p, 225p, 235p.

2019, Oct. 15 Litho. *Perf. 13¾x13½*

2897-2899 A1407 Set of 3 30.00 30.00

Estudiantes de la Plata Soccer Team, Winners of 1968 Intercontinental Cup — A1408

2019, Nov. 11 Litho. *Perf. 13½x14*

2900 A1408 125p multi 6.00 6.00

Souvenir Sheet

Mercado de Abasto, Buenos Aires, Designed by Viktor Sulcic (1895-1973) — A1409

2019, Nov. 25 Litho. *Perf. 14*
2901 A1409 270p multi 12.50 12.50

Joint Issue between Argentina and Slovenia. See Slovenia No. 1365.

Loss of ARA San Juan Submarine, 2nd Anniv. — A1410

2019, Nov. 15 Litho. *Perf. 14x13½*
2902 A1410 35p multi 1.75 1.50

La Nacion Newspaper, 150th Anniv. — A1411

2019, Dec. 4 Litho. *Perf. 14x13½*
2903 A1411 80p multi 3.75 3.50

Christmas A1412

2019, Dec. 9 Litho. *Perf. 13¾x13½*
2904 A1412 80p multi 3.75 3.50

A gritty substance covers parts of the vignette of No. 2904. Values are for stamps with surrounding selvage.

Transmission of Presidential Power — A1413

2020, Oct. 8 Litho. *Perf. 13½x13*
2905 A1413 55p multi 1.60 1.40

Souvenir Sheet

Gen. Manuel Belgrano (1770-1820) — A1414

2020, Oct. 12 Litho. *Perf. 14*
2906 A1414 125p multi 3.50 3.25

Ludwig van Beethoven (1770-1827), Composer — A1415

2020, Oct. 26 Litho. *Perf. 13½x13¾*
2907 A1415 90p multi 2.60 2.40

New Year 2020 (Year of the Rat) — A1416

No. 2908: a, Rats, horse, dog, rooster, and dragon. b, Rats, pig and monkey. c, Rats, rabbit and snake. d, Rats, tiger and goat. e, Rats with red envelopes.
320p, Rat.

2020, Nov. 2 Litho. *Perf. 13¾x13½*
2908 Booklet pane of 5 8.50 —
a.-e. A1416 55p Any single 1.60 1.60

Souvenir Sheet

Litho. With Foil Application

Perf.

2909 A1416 320p gold & multi 10.50 10.50

No. 2909 contains one 63mm diameter stamp.

Souvenir Sheet

First Raising of Argentine Flag in the Falkland Islands, 200th Anniv. — A1417

2020, Nov. 6 Litho. *Perf. 14*
2910 A1417 90p multi 2.25 2.25

Souvenir Sheet

Apparition of the Virgin Mary in Catamarca Valley, 400th Anniv. — A1418

2020, Nov. 30 Litho. *Perf. 14*
2911 A1418 90p multi 2.50 2.25

Souvenir Sheet

Chrismas — A1419

No. 2912 — Details from Nativity Tympanum, by Gabriel Cercato: a, Angel in sky. b, Nativity scene.

2020, Dec. 9 Litho. *Perf. 14*
2912 A1419 55p Sheet of 2, #a-b 2.75 2.60

National Parks Type of 2019 With Microprinted "CORREOARGENTINO" and Denomination Above Large Denomination at Lower Right

Designs: No. 2913, Calilegua National Park. No. 2914, Los Cardones National Park. No. 2915, Río Pilcomayo National Park. No. 2916, El Palmar National Park. No. 2917, Ciervo de los Pantanos National Park. No. 2918, Talampaya National Park. No. 2919, Quebrada del Condorito National Park. No. 2920, Tierra del Fuego National Park. No. 2921, Iguazú National Park. No. 2922, Patagonia National Park. No. 2923, Nahuel Huapi National Park. No. 2924, Perito Moreno National Park.

Perf. 13¾x13½ Syncopated

2020 ? Litho.

2913	A1395	1p	multi	.30	.25
2914	A1395	2p	multi	.30	.25
2915	A1395	5p	multi	.30	.25
2916	A1395	10p	multi	.30	.25
2917	A1395	20p	multi	.60	.55
2918	A1395	30p	multi	.85	.75
2919	A1395	40p	multi	1.20	1.10
2920	A1395	50p	multi	1.50	1.40
2921	A1395	100p	multi	2.90	2.60
2922	A1395	200p	multi	5.75	5.25
2923	A1395	300p	multi	8.75	8.00
2924	A1395	400p	multi	11.50	10.50
	Nos. 2913-2924 (12)			34.25	31.15

UP National Parks Type of 2019 With Microprinted "CORREOARGENTINO" and Denomination Above Large Denomination at Lower Right

Designs: No. 2925, El Impenetrable National Park. No. 2926, Sierra de las Quijadas National Park. No. 2927, El Rey National Park. No. 2928, El Leoncito National Park. No. 2929, Pre-Delta National Park. No. 2930, Los Glaciares National Park. No. 2931, Lanín National Park. No. 2932, Monte León National Park. No. 2933, Los Alerces National Park.

Perf. 13¼x13½ Syncopated

2020 ? Litho.

2925	A1396	5p	sil & multi	.35	.30
2926	A1396	10p	sil & multi	.35	.30
2927	A1396	20p	sil & multi	.65	.60
2928	A1396	40p	sil & multi	1.30	1.10
2929	A1396	50p	sil & multi	1.75	1.50
2930	A1396	100p	sil & multi	3.25	3.00
2931	A1396	200p	sil & multi	6.50	6.00
2932	A1396	300p	sil & multi	9.75	9.00
2933	A1396	400p	sil & multi	13.00	12.00
	Nos. 2925-2933 (9)			36.90	33.80

Adrienne Bolland (1895-1975), First Woman to Fly From Argentina to Chile Over Andes Mountains — A1420

2021, Apr. 5 Litho. *Perf. 14x13½*
2934 A1420 65p gold & multi 1.75 1.50

Bolland's trans-Andean flight, cent.

Federal Police, 200th Anniv. — A1421

2021, Apr. 19 Litho. *Perf. 13¾x13½*
2935 A1421 105p gold & multi 2.50 2.25

Myrmecophaga Tridactyla — A1422

Various depictions of giant anteater with denomination at: No. 2936, 70p, UL. No. 2937, 70p, UR.

2021, May 30 Litho. *Perf. 14x13½*
2936-2937 A1422 Set of 2 3.50 3.00

National Parks A1423

Designs: No. 2938, 70p, El Impenetrable National Park. No. 2939, 70p, Los Alerces National Park.

2021, June 7 Litho. *Perf. 14x13½*
2938-2939 A1423 Set of 2 3.50 3.00

America issue.

Martín Miguel de Güemes (1785-1821), Governor of Salta Province and Military Officer — A1424

Perf. 13½x13¾

2021, June 17 Litho.
2940 A1424 70p gold & multi 1.75 1.50

Ernesto Sabato (1911-2011), Writer — A1425

Perf. 13¾x13½

2021, June 24 Litho.
2941 A1425 110p sil & multi 2.60 2.40

City of Río Grande, Cent. — A1426

2021, July 12 Litho. *Perf. 13¾x13½*
2942 A1426 70p sil & multi 1.75 1.50

1961, Apr. 15

B31 SP16 50c +50c deep blue .50 .25
B32 SP16 1p +1p bluish grn (Brn) .50 .25
B33 SP16 3p +3p hen brn (Bl) .95 .25
B34 SP16 5p +5p dk brn (R) 1.30 .40
Nos. B31-B34 (4) 3.25 1.15

Day of the Americas, Apr. 14.

Cathedral, Cordoba SP17

Stamp of 1862 SP18

Design: 10p+10p, Cathedral, Buenos Aires.

Perf. 13½

1961, Oct. 21 Wmk. 90 Photo.

B35 SP17 2p +2p rose claret .35 .25
B36 SP18 3p +3p green .50 .25
B37 SP17 10p +10p brt blue 1.10 .60
a. Souvenir sheet of 3 3.00 2.00
Nos. B35-B37 (3) 1.95 1.10

1962 International Stamp Exhibition.

No. B37a contains three imperf. stamps similar to Nos. B35-B37 in dark blue.

Flight into Egypt, by Ana Maria Moncalvo — SP19

1961, Dec. 16 Litho.

B38 SP19 2p +1p lilac & blk brn .40 .35
B39 SP19 10p +5p lt & dp clar .80 .35

The surtax was for child welfare.

Mimus Saturninus Modulator — SP20

Design: 12p+6p, Zonotrichia capensis hypoleuca.

1962, Dec. 29 ***Perf. 13½***

B40 SP20 4p +2p bis, brn & bl grn 1.30 .65
B41 SP20 12p +6p gray, yel, grn & brn 2.00 1.25

The surtax was for child welfare. See Nos. B44, B47, B48-B50, CB32, CB35-CB36.

Soccer — SP21

No. B43, Horsemanship.

1963, May 18 ***Perf. 13½***

B42 SP21 4p +2p multi .40 .25
B43 SP21 12p +6p multi .70 .35
a. Dark carmine (jacket) omitted *15.00*
Nos. B42-B43,CB31 (3) 2.30 1.10

4th Pan American Games, Sao Paulo. See No. CB31.

Bird Type of 1962

4p +2p, Pyrocephalus rubineus rubineus.

1963, Dec. 21 Litho.

B44 SP20 4p +2p multi .95 .30

The surtax was for child welfare. See No. CB32.

Fencers — SP22

4p+2p, National Stadium, Tokyo, horiz.

1964, July 18 Wmk. 90 ***Perf. 13½***

B45 SP22 4p +2p red, ocher & brn .35 .35
B46 SP22 12p +6p bl grn & blk .50 .35
Nos. B45-B46,CB33 (3) 2.25 1.40

18th Olympic Games, Tokyo, Oct. 10-25, 1964. See No. CB33.

Bird Type of 1962

4p +2p, Cardinal paroaria coronata.

1964, Dec. 23 Litho.

B47 SP20 4p +2p multi 1.10 .35

The surtax was for child welfare. See No. CB35.

SP22a

Designs: 8p+4p, Belonopterus cayennensis lampronotus. 10p+5p, Amblyramphus holosericeus, horiz. 20p+10p, Chloroceryle amazona.

1966-67 ***Perf. 13½***

B48 SP22a 8p +4p blk, ol, brt grn & red 1.05 .35
B49 SP22a 10p +5p blk, bl, org & grn 1.05 .55
B50 SP22a 20p +10p blk, yel, bl & pink .50 .35
Nos. B48-B50,CB36,CB38-CB39 (6) 6.10 3.50

The surtax was for child welfare.

Issue dates: 8p+4p, Mar. 26, 1966. 10p+5p, Jan. 14, 1967. 20p+10p, Dec. 23, 1967.

Grandmother's Birthday, by Patricia Lynch; Lions Emblem — SP23

Perf. 12½x13½

1968, Dec. 14 Litho. Wmk. 90

B51 SP23 40p + 20p multi .70 .40

1st Lions Intl. Benevolent Phil. Exhib. Surtax for the Children's Hospital Benevolent Fund.

White-faced Tree Duck — SP24

1969, Sept. 20 Wmk. 365 ***Perf. 13½***

B52 SP24 20p + 10p multi .70 .35

Surtax for child welfare. See No. CB40.

Slender-tailed Woodstar (Hummingbird) SP25

1970, May 9 Wmk. 365 ***Perf. 13½***

B53 SP25 20c + 10c multi .65 .40

The surtax was for child welfare. See Nos. CB41, B56-B59, B62-B63.

Dolphinfish — SP26

1971, Feb. 20 Unwmk. ***Perf. 12½***

Size: 75x15mm

B54 SP26 20c + 10c multi .75 .45

Surtax for child welfare. See No. CB42.

Children with Stamps, by Mariette Lydis — SP27

1971, Dec. 18 Litho. ***Perf. 13½***

B55 SP27 1p + 50p multi .75 .35

2nd Lions Intl. Solidarity Stamp Exhib.

Bird Type of 1970

Birds: 25c+10c, Saffron finch. 65c+30c, Rufous-bellied thrush, horiz.

1972, May 6 Unwmk. ***Perf. 13½***

B56 SP25 25c + 10c multi .50 .35
B57 SP25 65c + 30c multi .75 .35

Surtax was for child welfare.

Bird Type of 1970

Birds: 50c+25c, Southern screamer (chaja). 90c+45c, Saffron-cowled blackbird, horiz.

1973, Apr. 28

B58 SP25 50c + 25c multi .75 .35
B59 SP25 90c + 45c multi .95 .55

Surtax was for child welfare.

Painting Type of Regular Issue

Designs: 15c+15c, Still Life, by Alfredo Guttero, horiz. 90c+90c, Nude, by Miguel C. Victorica, horiz.

1973, Aug. 28 Litho. ***Perf. 13½***

B60 A472 15c + 15c multi .50 .35
B61 A472 90c + 90c multi 1.50 1.00

Bird Type of 1970

Birds: 70c+30c, Blue seed-eater. 1.20p+60c, Hooded siskin.

1974, May 11 Litho. ***Perf. 13½***

B62 SP25 70c + 30c multi .85 .35
B63 SP25 1.20p + 60c multi 1.25 .50

Surtax was for child welfare.

Painting Type of 1974

Design: 70c+30c, The Lama, by Juan Batlle Planas.

1974, May 11 Litho. ***Perf. 13½***

B64 A477 70c + 30c multi .45 .35

PRENFIL-74 UPU, Intl. Exhib. of Phil. Periodicals, Buenos Aires, Oct. 1-12.

Plushcrested Jay — SP28

Designs: 13p+6.50p, Golden-collared macaw. 20p+10p, Begonia. 40p+20p, Teasel.

1976, June 12 Litho. ***Perf. 13½***

B65 SP28 7p + 3.50p multi .75 .35
B66 SP28 13p + 6.50p multi .90 .35
B67 SP28 20p + 10p multi 1.10 .40
B68 SP28 40p + 20p multi 1.50 .60
Nos. B65-B68 (4) 4.25 1.70

Argentine philately.

Telegraph, Communications Satellite — SP29

Designs: 20p+10p, Old and new mail trucks. 60p+30p, Old, new packet boats. 70p+35p, Biplane and jet.

1977, July 16 Litho. ***Perf. 13½***

B69 SP29 10p + 5p multi .40 .35
B70 SP29 20p + 10p multi .80 .60
B71 SP29 60p + 30p multi 1.60 .85
B72 SP29 70p + 35p multi 1.80 .90
Nos. B69-B72 (4) 4.60 2.70

Surtax was for Argentine philately.

No. B70 exists with wmk. 365.

Church of St. Francis Type, 1977

Inscribed "EXPOSICION ARGENTINA '77"

1977, Aug. 27

B73 A515 160p + 80p multi 2.50 2.00

Surtax was for Argentina '77 Philatelic Exhibition. Issued in sheets of 4. Value $13.

No. B73 Overprinted with Soccer Cup Emblem

1978, Feb. 4 Litho. ***Perf. 13½***

B74 A515 160p + 80p multi 4.75 4.25
a. Souvenir sheet of 4 23.50 20.00

11th World Cup Soccer Championship, Argentina, June 1-25.

Spinus Magellanicus SP30

Birds: No. B76, Variable seedeater. No. B77, Yellow thrush. No. B78, Pyrocephalus rubineus. No. B79, Great kiskadee.

1978, Aug. 5 Litho. ***Perf. 13½***

B75 SP30 50p + 50p multi 1.75 1.00
B76 SP30 100p + 100p multi 1.75 1.00
B77 SP30 150p + 150p multi 2.75 1.50
B78 SP30 200p + 200p multi 2.75 1.75
B79 SP30 500p + 500p multi 4.75 3.50
Nos. B75-B79 (5) 13.75 8.75

ARGENTINA '78, Inter-American Philatelic Exhibition, Buenos Aires, Oct. 27-Nov. 5. Nos. B75-B79 issued in sheets of 4 with marginal inscriptions commemorating Exhibition and 1978 Soccer Championship. Value, set $62.50.

Caravel "Magdalena," 16th Century SP31

Sailing Ships: 500+500p, 3 master "Rio de la Plata," 17th cent. 600+600p, Corvette "Descubierta," 18th cent. 1500+1500p, Naval Academy yacht "A.R.A. Fortuna," 1979.

1979, Sept. 8 Litho. *Perf. 13½*

B80	SP31	400p +400p multi	3.75	2.25
B81	SP31	500p +500p multi	4.50	2.50
B82	SP31	600p +600p multi	6.50	3.25
B83	SP31	1500p +1500p multi	15.00	8.00
		Nos. B80-B83 (4)	29.75	16.00

Buenos Aires '80, Intl. Philatelic Exhibition, 10/24-11/2/80. Issued in sheets of 4. Value, set $130.

Purmamarca Church — SP32

Churches: 200p + 100p, Molinos. 300p + 150p, Animana. 400p + 200p, San Jose de Lules.

1979, Nov. 3 Litho. *Perf. 13½*

B84	SP32	100p + 50p multi	.50	.35
B85	SP32	200p + 100p multi	.75	.35
B86	SP32	300p + 150p multi	1.05	.35
B87	SP32	400p + 200p multi	1.50	.50
		Nos. B84-B87 (4)	3.80	1.55

Buenos Aires No. 3, Exhibition and Society Emblems — SP33

Argentine Stamps: 750p+750p, type A580. 1000p+1000p, No. 91. 2000p+2000p, type A588.

1979, Dec. 15 Litho. *Perf. 13½*

B88	SP33	250p + 250p	2.10	1.25
B89	SP33	750p + 750p	3.60	2.25
B90	SP33	1000p + 1000p	10.50	6.00
B91	SP33	2000p + 2000p	9.00	6.00
		Nos. B88-B91 (4)	25.20	15.50

PRENFIL '80, Intl. Philatelic Literature and Publications Exhib., Buenos Aires, Nov. 7-16, 1980.

Minuet, by Carlos E. Pellegrini SP34

Paintings: 700p+350p, Media Cana, by Carlos Morel. 800p+400p, Cielito, by Pellegrini. 1000p+500p, El Gato, by Juan Leon Palliere.

1981, July 11 Litho. *Perf. 13½*

B92	SP34	500p + 250p multi	.95	.45
B93	SP34	700p + 350p multi	1.50	.80
B94	SP34	800p + 400p multi	1.50	1.00
B95	SP34	1000p + 500p multi	1.90	1.40
		Nos. B92-B95 (4)	5.85	3.65

Espamer '81 Intl. Stamp Exhib. (Americas, Spain, Portugal), Buenos Aires, Nov. 13-22.

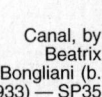

Canal, by Beatrix Bongliani (b. 1933) — SP35

Tapestries: 1000p+500p, Shadows, by Silvia Sieburger, vert. 2000p+1000p, Interpretation of a Rectangle, by Silke R. de Haupt, vert. 4000p+2000p, Tilcara, by Tana Sachs.

1982, July 31 Litho. *Perf. 13½*

B96	SP35	1000p + 500p multi	.65	.40
B97	SP35	2000p + 1000p multi	.85	.50
B98	SP35	3000p + 1500p multi	1.00	.60
B99	SP35	4000p + 2000p multi	1.20	.70
		Nos. B96-B99 (4)	3.70	2.20

Boy Playing Marbles — SP36

No. B101, Jumping rope. No. B102, Hopscotch. No. B103, Flying kites. No. B104, Spinning top.

1983, July 2 Litho. *Perf. 13½*

B100	SP36	20c + 10c shown	.50	.35
B101	SP36	30c + 15c multi	.55	.30
B102	SP36	50c + 25c multi	1.10	.60
B103	SP36	1p + 50c multi	1.50	.70
B104	SP36	2p + 1p multi	2.00	1.00
		Nos. B100-B104 (5)	5.65	2.95

Surtax was for natl. philatelic associations. See Nos. B106-B110.

Compass, 15th Cent. — SP37

ARGENTINA '85 Intl. Stamp Show: b, Arms of Spain, Argentina. c, Columbus' arms. d-f, Columbus' arrival at San Salvador Island. Nos. B105d-B105f in continuous design; ships shown on singles range in size, left to right, from small to large. Surtax was for exhibition.

1984, Apr. 28 Litho. *Perf. 13½*

B105		Block of 6	6.00	4.50
a.-f.	SP37	5p + 2.50p, any single	.80	.45

Children's Game Type of 1983

No. B106, Blind Man's Buff. No. B107, The Loop. No. B108, Leap Frog. No. B109, Rolling the loop. No. B110, Ball Mold.

1984, July 7 Litho. *Perf. 13½*

B106	SP36	2p + 1p multi	.60	.25
B107	SP36	3p + 1.50p multi	.60	.30
B108	SP36	4p + 2p multi	.90	.40
B109	SP36	5p + 2.50p multi	.90	.40
B110	SP36	6p + 3p multi	1.25	.60
		Nos. B106-B110 (5)	4.25	1.95

Butterflies SP38

No. B111, Rothschildia jacobaeae. No. B112, Heliconius erato phyllis. No. B113, Precis evarete hilaris. No. B114, Cyanopepla pretiosa. No. B115, Papilio androgeus.

1985, Nov. 9 Litho. *Perf. 13½*

B111	SP38	5c + 2c multi	1.25	.35
B112	SP38	10c + 5c multi	1.25	.60
B113	SP38	20c + 10c multi	1.75	.75
B114	SP38	25c + 13c multi	2.75	1.50
B115	SP38	40c + 20c multi	3.50	2.25
		Nos. B111-B115 (5)	10.50	5.45

Children's Drawings SP39

No. B116, N. Pastor, vert. No. B117, T. Valleistein. No. B118, J.M. Flores, vert. No. B119, M.E. Pezzuto. No. B120, E. Diehl.

1986, Aug. 30 Litho.

B116	SP39	5c + 2c multi	.35	.25
B117	SP39	10c + 5c multi	.50	.35
B118	SP39	20c + 10c multi	.85	.60
B119	SP39	25c + 13c multi	1.20	.85
B120	SP39	40c + 20c multi	1.75	1.25
		Nos. B116-B120 (5)	4.65	3.30

Surtax for natl. philatelic associations.

Miniature Sheets

Fresh-water Fish — SP40

No. B121: a, Metynnis maculatus. b, Cynolebias nigripinnis. c, Leporinus solarii. d, Aphyocharax rathbuni. e, Corydoras aeneus. f, Thoracocharax securis. g, Cynolebias melanotaenia. h, Cichlasoma facetum.

No. B122: a, Tetragonopterus argenteus. b, Hemigrammus caudovittatus. c, Astyanax bimaculatus. d, Gymnocorymbus ternetzi. e, Hoplias malabaricus. f, Aphyocharax rubripinnis. g, Apistogramma agassizi. h, Pyrrhulina rachoviana.

1987, June 27

B121	SP40	Sheet of 8	5.00	5.00
a.-h.		10c +5c, any single	.35	.35
B122	SP40	Sheet of 8	9.00	9.00
a.-h.		20c +10c, any single	.55	.55

PRENFIL '88, Intl. Philatelic Literature and Media Exhibition, Buenos Aires, Nov. 25-Dec. 2 — SP41

Locomotives and railroad car: No. B123, Yatay locomotive, 1888. No. B124, FCCA electric passenger car, 1914. No. B125, B-15 locomotive, 1942. No. B126, GT-22 No. 200 locomotive, 1988.

1988, June 4 Litho. *Perf. 13½*

B123	SP41	1a +50c multi	1.50	.60
B124	SP41	1a +50c multi	1.50	.60
B125	SP41	1a +50c multi	1.50	.60
B126	SP41	1a +50c multi	1.50	.60
		Nos. B123-B126 (4)	6.00	2.40

Nos. B123-B125 each issued in sheets of 4. Value, set $16.

Horses — SP42

Paintings: No. B127, *The Waiting,* by Gustavo Solari. No. B128, *Mare and Foal,* by E. Castro. No. B129, *Saint Isidor,* by Castro. No. B130, *At Lagoon's Edge,* by F. Romero Carranza. No. B131, *Under the Tail,* by Castro.

1988, Oct. 29 Litho. *Perf. 13½*

B127	SP42	2a +1a multi	2.00	.60
B128	SP42	2a +1a multi	2.00	.60
B129	SP42	2a +1a multi	2.00	.60
B130	SP42	2a +1a multi	2.00	.60
B131	SP42	2a +1a multi	2.00	.60
		Nos. B127-B131 (5)	10.00	3.00

PRENFIL '88 — SP43

Covers of philatelic magazines: No. B132, *Cronaca Filatelica,* Italy. No. B133, *CO-FI,* Brazil. No. B134, *References de la Poste,* France. No. B135, *Postas Argentinas.*

1988, Nov. 26 Litho. *Perf. 13½*

B132	SP43	1a +1a multi	1.25	.40
B133	SP43	1a +1a multi	1.25	.40
B134	SP43	1a +1a multi	1.25	.40
B135	SP43	2a +2a multi	1.25	.40
		Nos. B132-B135 (4)	5.00	1.60

Nos. B132-B135 printed in sheets of 4. Value, set $14.

Souvenir Sheet

ARBRAPEX '88 — SP44

Designs: No. B136a, *Candel Delivery at San Ignacio,* by Leonie Matthis, Cornelio Saavedra Museum, Buenos Aires. No. B136b, *Immaculate Conception,* a statue in the Isaac Fernandez Blanco Museum, Buenos Aires.

1988, Nov. 26 *Perf. 12*

B136	SP44	Sheet of 2	3.50	3.50
a.		2a +2a multi	1.00	.75
b.		3a +3a multi	1.75	1.25

Fish — SP45

Designs: No. B137, Diplomystes viedmensis. No. B138, Haplochiton taeniatus. No. B139, Percichthys trucha. No. B140, Galaxias platei. No. B141, Salmo fario.

1989, June 24 Litho. *Perf. 13½*

B137	SP45	10a +5a multi	1.15	.40
B138	SP45	10a +5a multi	1.15	.40
B139	SP45	10a +5a multi	1.15	.40
B140	SP45	10a +5a multi	1.15	.40
B141	SP45	10a +5a multi	1.15	.40
		Nos. B137-B141 (5)	5.75	2.00

Nos. B137-B141 printed in sheets of 4. Value, set $15.

Discovery of America 500th Anniv. (in 1992) and ESPAMER '90 — SP46

Documents and chronicles: No. B142, Columbus's coat of arms, *Book of Privileges* title page. No. B143, Illustration from *New Chronicle and Good Government,* by Guaman Poma de Ayala. No. B144, Illustration from *Discovery and Conquest of Peru,* by Pedro de Cieza de Leon. No. B145, Illustration from *Travel to the River Plate,* by Ulrico Schmidl.

1989, Sept. 16 Litho. *Perf. 13½*
Yellow, Rose Violet & Black

B142	SP46	100a +50a	2.25	.85
B143	SP46	150a +50a	2.25	.85
B144	SP46	200a +100a	2.25	.85
B145	SP46	250a +100a	2.25	.85
		Nos. B142-B145 (4)	9.00	3.40

Nos. B142-B145 printed in sheets of 4. Value, set $17.

Insects — SP47

Designs: No. B146, *Podisus nigrispinus.* No. B147, *Adalia bipunctata.* No. B148, *Nabis punctipennis.* No. B149, *Hippodamia convergens.* No. B150, *Calleida suturalis.*

1990, June 30 Litho. *Perf. 13½*

B146	SP47	1000a +500a multi	1.40	.95
B147	SP47	1000a +500a multi	1.40	.95
B148	SP47	1000a +500a multi	1.40	.95

B149 SP47 1000a +500a multi 1.40 .95
B150 SP47 1000a +500a multi 1.40 .95
Nos. B146-B150 (5) 7.00 4.75

Nos. B146-B150 printed in sheets of 4. Value, set $24.

Souvenir Sheet

First Natl. Exposition of Aerophilately — SP48

a, Lieut. Marcos A. Zar, Macchi seaplane. b, Capt. Antonio Parodi, Ansaldo SVA biplane.

1990, July 14 Litho. *Perf. 12*
B151 SP48 Sheet of 2 10.00 6.50
a. 2000a +2000a multi 3.00 2.50
b. 3000a +3000a multi 3.00 2.50

Souvenir Sheet

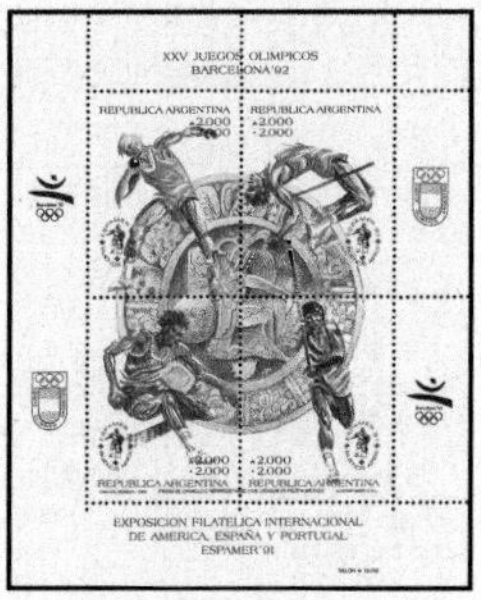

1992 Summer Olympics, Barcelona — SP49

Designs: a, Shot put. b, High jump. c, Hurdles. d, Pole vault.

1990, Dec. 15 Litho. *Perf. 13½*
B152 SP49 Sheet of 4 12.00 12.00
a.-d. 2000a +2000a multi 2.50 2.50

Espamer '91 Philatelic Exhibition.
See No. B155.

Souvenir Sheet

Discovery of America, 500th Anniv. (in 1992) — SP50

Voyage of Alesandro Malaspina, 1789-1794: a, Sailing ship. b, Malaspina. c, Indian, hut. d, Indian, horse, artist drawing.

1990, Oct. 13 Litho. *Perf. 13½*
B153 SP50 Sheet of 4 13.00 12.00
a.-d. 2000a +1000a, any single 2.00 2.00

Espamer '91, Buenos Aires.

Souvenir Sheet

Race Cars and Drivers SP51

Designs: a, Juan Manuel Fangio. b, Juan Manuel Bordeu. c, Carlos Alberto Reutemann. d, Oscar and Juan Galvez.

1991 Litho. *Perf. 13½*
B154 SP51 Sheet of 4 7.50 6.50
a.-d. 2500a +2500a, any single 1.50 1.40

Espamer '91.

1992 Summer Olympics Type of 1990

Souvenir Sheet

Women's gymnastics routines: a, Floor exercise. b, Uneven parallel bars. c, Balance beam. d, Rhythmic gymnastics.

1991, June 29 Litho. *Perf. 13½*
B155 SP49 Sheet of 4 7.50 6.50
a.-d. 2500a +2500a, any single 1.50 1.25

Espamer '91.

Iberoprenfil '92 — SP52

Designs: No. B156, Castor missile. No. B157, Satellite LUSAT 1.

1991, Dec. 28 Litho. *Perf. 13½*
B156 SP52 4000a +4000a multi 3.25 3.25
B157 SP52 4000a +4000a multi 3.25 3.25

Dinosaurs — SP53

No. B158, Carnotaurus. No. B159, Amargasaurus.

1992, May 2 Litho. *Perf. 13½*
B158 SP53 38c +38c multi 2.50 2.50
B159 SP53 38c +38c multi 2.50 2.50
a. Pair, #B158-B159 6.00 6.00

Iberoprenfil '92, Buenos Aires — SP54

Paintings by Raul Soldi (b. 1905): No. B160, The Fiesta. No. B161, Church of St. Anne of Glew.

1992, Sept. 5 Litho. *Perf. 13½*
B160 SP54 76c +76c multi 4.00 3.25
B161 SP54 76c +76c multi 4.00 3.25

Parafil '92 — SP55

1992, Nov. 21 Litho. *Perf. 13½*
B162 SP55 76c +76c multi 4.00 3.25

2nd Argentine-Paraguayan Philatelic Exhibition, Buenos Aires.

Souvenir Sheet

Birds — SP56

a, Egretta thula. b, Amblyramphus holosericeus. c, Paroaria coronata. d, Chloroceryle amazona.

1993, July 17 Litho. *Perf. 13½*
B163 SP56 38c +38c Sheet of 4 9.00 9.00

Souvenir Sheet

Latin American Air Post Philatelic Exhibition — SP57

Designs: a, 25c+25c, Antoine de Saint-Exupery (1940-44), pilot, author. b, 75c+75c, "The Little Prince," vert.

1995, June 3 Litho. *Perf. 12*
B164 SP57 Sheet of 2, #a.-b. 8.00 7.50

For overprint see No. B180.

Souvenir Sheet

Exploration of Antarctica — SP58

75c+25c, Transport ship ARA Bahia Aguirre. 1.25p+75c, Argentine Air Force Hercules C-130.

1995, July 8
B165 SP58 Sheet of 2, #a.-b. 9.50 9.00

Aerofila '96 — SP59

Historic airplanes, pilots: No. B166, "Plus ultra," Ramón Franco Bahamonde (1896-1938). No. B167, 14 Bis, Alberto Santos-Dumont (1873-1932). No. B168, Spirit of St. Louis, Charles A. Lindbergh (1902-1974). No. B169, Buenos Aires, Eduardo A. Olivero (1896-1966).

1996, July 13 Litho. *Perf. 13½*
B166 SP59 25c +25c multi 1.75 1.20
B167 SP59 25c +25c multi 1.75 1.20
B168 SP59 50c +50c multi 3.25 2.40
B169 SP59 50c +50c multi 3.25 2.40
Nos. B166-B169 (4) 10.00 7.20

Ceramic Murals from Buenos Aires Subway SP60

1996, Sept. 21 Litho. *Perf. 13½*
B170 SP60 1p +50c Dragon 4.50 3.75
B171 SP60 1.50p +1p Bird 7.00 5.50

MEVIFIL '97, 1st Intl. Exhibition of Audio-Visual and Philatelic Information Media — SP61

Designs: No. B172, France Type A1. No. B173, Spain Type A3. No. B174, Argentina Type A4. No. B175, Buenos Aires Type A1.

1997, May 10 Litho. *Perf. 13½*
B172 SP61 50c +50c multi 2.50 2.25
B173 SP61 50c +50c multi 2.50 2.25
B174 SP61 50c +50c multi 2.50 2.25
B175 SP61 50c +50c multi 2.50 2.25
a. Block of 4, #B172-B175 11.50 11.50

Issued in sheets of 16 stamps + 4 labels.

Trains SP62

Designs: No. B176, Las Nubes (Train to the Clouds), Salta. No. B177, Historical train, Buenos Aires. No. B178, Old Patagonian Express, Rio Negro-Chubut. No. B179, Southern Fueguino Railway, Tierra Del Fuego.

1997, Sept. 6 Litho. *Perf. 13*
B176 SP62 50c +50c multi 4.00 3.25
B177 SP62 50c +50c multi 4.00 3.25
B178 SP62 50c +50c multi 4.00 3.25
B179 SP62 50c +50c multi 4.00 3.25
Nos. B176-B179 (4) 16.00 13.00

No. B164 Overprinted in Red Violet

1997, Sept. 27 Litho. *Perf. 12*
B180 SP57 Sheet of 2 8.00 7.50

Cartography SP63

Maps of the Buenos Aires area from: 25c+25c, 1546. No. B182, 17th century. No. B183, 1910. 75c+75c, 1999.

Perf. 13¾x13½
1999, Nov. 20 Litho.
B181 SP63 25c + 25c multi 1.00 1.00
B182 SP63 50c + 50c multi 2.00 2.00
B183 SP63 50c + 50c multi 2.00 2.00
B184 SP63 75c + 75c multi 3.00 3.00
a. Block of 4, #B181-B184 14.00 14.00

Methods of Transportation — SP64

No. B185: a, Bicycle. b, Graf Zeppelin. c, Train. d, Trolley.

2000, Oct. 21 Litho. *Perf. 14x13½*
B185 SP64 Block of 4 12.00 11.00
a. 25c +25c multi 1.25 1.20
b.-c. 50c +50c Any single 2.50 2.40
d. 75c +75c multi 3.75 3.50

Cetaceans — SP65

No. B186: a, Burmeister's porpoise (Mariposa espinosa). b, River Plate dolphin. c, Minke whale. d, Humpback whale (Yubarta).

2001, Sept. 15 Litho. *Perf. 14x13½*
B186 Block of 4 16.00 15.00
a. SP65 25c +25c multi 1.10 1.10
b.-c. SP65 50c +50c Any single 2.25 2.25
d. SP65 75c +75c multi 3.25 3.25

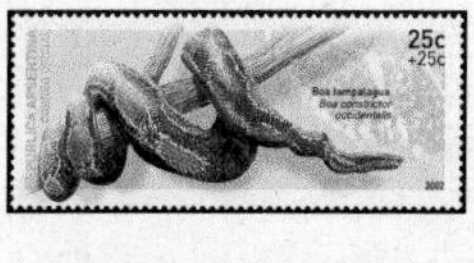

Reptiles SP66

No. B187: a, Boa constrictor occidentalis. b, Caiman yacare. c, Tupinambis merianae. d, Chelonoidis carbonaria.

2002, Aug. 24 Litho. *Perf. 14x13½*
B187 Block of 4 10.00 9.00
a. SP66 25c +25c multi .80 .80
b.-c. SP66 50c +50c Either single 1.35 1.35
d. SP66 75c +75c multi 2.25 2.25

Bicycles SP67

No. B188: a, Velocipede, 1855, Cycling Club champions, 1902. b, Velocipede, 1867, postman with delivery tricycle. c, Coventry Eagle touring bicycle, 1949, cyclists in park. d, Racing bicycle, 1960s, Palermo Velodrome, 1902.

2003, Aug. 9 Litho. *Perf. 14x13¾*

B188	Block of 4	6.50	5.50
a.	SP67 25c+25c multi	.70	.70
b.-c.	SP67 50c+50c Either single	1.20	1.20
d.	SP67 75c+75c multi	1.75	1.75

Ships SP68

No. B189: a, A. R. A. Villarino. b, A. R. A. Pampa. c, A. R. A. Bahia Thetis. d, A. R. A. Cabo de Hornos.

2004, Aug. 21 Litho. *Perf. 14x13½*

B189	Block of 4	6.50	5.25
a.	SP68 25c +25c multi	.55	.55
b.-c.	SP68 50c +50c either single	.85	.85
d.	SP68 75c +75c multi	1.40	1.40

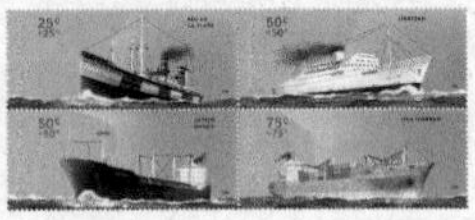
Merchant Ships SP69

No. B190: a, Río de la Plata. b, Libertad. c, Campo Durán. d, Isla Soledad.

2005, Sept. 24 Litho. *Perf. 14x13½*

B190	Block of 4	6.50	5.25
a.	SP69 25c +25c multi	.55	.55
b.-c.	SP69 50c +50c either single	.85	.85
d.	SP69 75c +75c multi	1.40	1.40

River Boats SP70

No. B191: a, Ciudad de Buenos Aires. b, Lambaré. c, Madrid. d, Rawson.

2006, Aug. 19 Litho. *Perf. 14x13½*

B191	Block of 4	6.50	5.25
a.	SP70 25c +25c multi	.55	.55
b.-c.	SP70 50c +50c either single	.85	.85
d.	SP70 75c +75c multi	1.40	1.40

Scouting, Cent. — SP71

No. B192: a, Scouts at campfire. b, Scout saluting near tent. c, Scout saluting, Scout with patrol flag. d, Scouts pulling rope.

2007, July 28 Litho. *Perf. 13½x14*

B192	Horiz. strip of 4	6.50	5.00
a.	SP71 25c +25c multi	.40	.40
b.	SP71 50c +50c multi	.80	.80
c.	SP71 75c +75c multi	1.10	1.10
d.	SP71 1p +1p multi	1.40	1.40

Shells — SP72

Designs: 25c+25c, Calliostoma militaris. 50c+50c, Epitonium fabrizioi. 75c+75c, Odontocymbiola magellanica. 1p+1p, Trophon geversianus.

Perf. 13½x13¾

2008, Aug. 23 Litho.

B193-B196	SP72	Set of 4	5.00	4.00

Astronomical Observatories — SP73

Designs: No. B197, 50c+50c, Radio telescope, Argentine Institute of Radioastronomy. No. B198, 50c+50c, Telescope, La Plata Astronomical Observatory. No. B199, 1p+1p, El Lioncito Astronomical Complex. No. B200, 1p+1p, Telescope, Félix Aguilar Astronomical Observatory.

2009, Aug. 22 Litho. *Perf. 14x13½*

B197-B200	SP73	Set of 4	5.50	4.50

Girl Guides and Girl Scouts, Cent. — SP74

Designs: No. B201, 75c+75c, Girl Scout salute. No. B202, 75c+75c, Hands of five Girl Scouts joined. No. B203, 1p+1p, Hands of Girl Scouts joined, campfire. No. B204, 1p+1p, Hand on shoulder of Girl Scout.

2010, Aug. 21 Litho. *Perf. 13½x14*

B201-B204	SP74	Set of 4	5.50	4.50

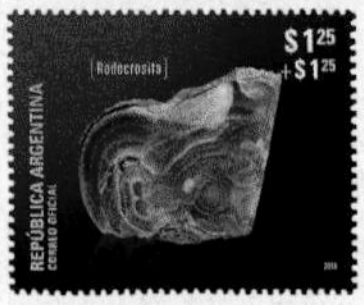
Minerals SP75

Designs: No. B205, 1.25p+1.25p, Rhodochrosite (rodocrisita). No. B206, 1.25p+1.25p, Sulphur (azufre). No. B207, 1.25p+1.25p, Pyrite (pirita). No. B208, 1.25p+1.25p, Quartz (cuarzo).

2011, Aug. 20 *Perf. 13¾x13½*

B205-B208	SP75	Set of 4	7.00	6.50

Minerals Type of 2011

Designs: No. B209, 1.50p+1.50p, Agate (agata). No. B210, 1.50p+1.50p, Amethyst (amatista). No. B211, 1.50p+1.50p, Fluorite (fluorita). No. B212, 1.50p+1.50p, Malachite (malaquita).

2012, Aug. 25

B209-B212	SP75	Set of 4	7.50	6.50

Extreme Sports SP76

Designs: No. B213, 2p+2p, Skiing. No. B214, 2p+2p, Skateboarding. No. B215, 2p+2p, BMX cycling. No. B216, 2p+2p, Surfing.

2013, Dec. 21 Litho. *Perf. 14x13½*

B213-B216	SP76	Set of 4	6.00	5.00

Volcanoes SP77

Designs: No. B217, 5p+5p, Payú Liso. No. B218, 5p+5p, Llullaillaco. No. B219, 5p+5p, Lanín. No. B220, 5p+5p, Maipo.

Perf. 13¾x13½

2014, Aug. 19 Litho.

B217-B220	SP77	Set of 4	10.50	9.50

Clocks and Sundials — SP78

Designs: No. B221, 7p+7p, Los Colosos de Siemens Clock, Buenos Aires. No. B222, 7p+7p, Palacio Fuentes Clock Tower, Rosario. No. B223, 7p+7p, Jesuit Estate Sundial, Alta Gracia. No. B224, 7p+7p, Miroglio Brothers Clock, Buenos Aires.

2015, Dec. 4 Litho. *Perf. 13½x13¾*

B221-B224	SP78	Set of 4	12.50	11.50

Railroad Mail Cars SP79

No. B225: a, Mail car with open door. b, Diagram of interior of mail car. c, Postal workers in mail car and on ground transfering mail. d, Mail car with closed doors.

2016, Aug. 22 Litho. *Perf. 14x13½*

B225	SP79	10p+10p Block of 4, #a-d	13.50	11.00

Ponchos — SP80

Designs: No. B226, 16p+16p, 60-stripe poncho, Litoral region. No. B227, 16p+16p, Cayupán poncho, La Pampa Province. No. B228, 16p+16p, Andino poncho, Catamarca Province. No. B229, 16p+16p, Pilagá poncho, Chaco Province.

Perf. 13½x13¾

2017, Aug. 23 Litho.

B226-B229	SP80	Set of 4	21.00	18.00

Map of Corrientes Province, Mesenger on Horseback, Postman, and Truck — SP81

Post Office Palace, Buenos Aires, and Tile SP82

2018, Dec. 26 Litho. *Perf. 14x13½*

B230	SP81	30p+15p sil & multi	3.25	2.75
B231	SP82	30p+15p sil & multi	3.25	2.75

Mail delivery in Corrientes area, 270th anniv., and Post Office Palace, 90th anniv.

Tango — SP83

Designs: No. B232, 50p+25p, Tango dancers. No. B233, 50p+25p, Bandoneon player.

Perf. 13½x13¾

2019, Aug. 26 Litho.

B232-B233	SP83	Set of 2	9.00	7.50

AIR POST STAMPS

Airplane Circles the Globe AP1

Eagle AP2

Wings Cross the Sea — AP3

Condor on Mountain Crag — AP4

Perforations of Nos. C1-C37 vary from clean-cut to rough and uneven, with many skipped perfs.

Perf. 13x13½, 13½x13

1928, Mar. 1 Litho. Wmk. 90

C1	AP1	5c lt red	1.50	.60
C2	AP1	10c Prus blue	2.50	1.10
C3	AP2	15c lt brown	2.50	1.00
C4	AP1	18c lilac gray	4.00	3.00
a.		18c brown lilac	4.50	3.00
b.		Double impression	375.00	
C5	AP2	20c ultra	3.00	1.00
C6	AP2	24c deep blue	5.00	3.00
C7	AP3	25c brt violet	5.00	1.60
C8	AP3	30c rose red	6.00	1.25
C9	AP4	35c rose	5.00	1.10
C10	AP1	36c bister brn	3.00	1.60
C11	AP4	50c gray black	5.00	.75
C12	AP2	54c chocolate	5.00	2.25
C13	AP2	72c yellow grn	6.00	2.25
a.		Double impression	350.00	
C14	AP3	90c dk brown	11.00	2.00
C15	AP3	1p slate bl & red	13.00	.90
C16	AP3	1.08p rose & dk bl	18.00	5.00
C17	AP4	1.26p dull vio & grn	25.00	10.00
C18	AP4	1.80p blue & lil rose	25.00	10.00
C19	AP4	3.60p gray & blue	50.00	22.00
		Nos. C1-C19 (19)	195.50	70.40

The watermark on No. C4a is larger than on the other stamps of this set, measuring 10mm across Sun.

Zeppelin First Flight

Air Post Stamps of 1928 Overprinted in Blue

1930, May

C20	AP2	20c ultra	10.00	5.00
a.		Inverted overprint	500.00	
C21	AP4	50c gray black	20.00	10.00
a.		Inverted overprint	500.00	
C22	AP3	1p slate bl & red	25.00	12.50
a.		Inverted overprint	850.00	
C23	AP4	1.80p blue & lil rose	70.00	30.00
C24	AP4	3.60p gray & blue	200.00	90.00
		Nos. C20-C24 (5)	325.00	147.50

Overprinted in Green

C25	AP2	20c ultra	13.00	8.00
C26	AP4	50c gray black	15.00	10.00
C27	AP3	90c dark brown	13.00	8.00
C28	AP3	1p slate bl & red	25.00	15.00
C29	AP4	1.80p blue & lil rose	700.00	500.00
a.		Thick paper	1,000.	
		Nos. C25-C29 (5)	766.00	541.00

Air Post Stamps of 1928 Overprinted in Red or Blue

On AP1-AP2

On AP3-AP4

1931

C30	AP1	18c lilac gray	2.00	1.50
C31	AP2	72c yellow green	14.00	10.50
C32	AP3	90c dark brown	14.00	10.50
C33	AP4	1.80p bl & lil rose (Bl)	30.00	22.50
C34	AP4	3.60p gray & blue	57.50	40.00
		Nos. C30-C34 (5)	117.50	85.00

1st anniv. of the Revolution of 1930.

Zeppelin Issue

Nos. C1, C4, C4a, C14 Overprinted in Blue or Red

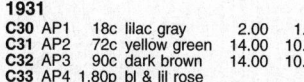

On AP1

On AP3

1932, Aug. 4

C35	AP1	5c lt red (Bl)	3.00	2.00
C36	AP1	18c lilac gray (R)	12.50	9.00
a.		18c brown lilac (R)	100.00	60.00
C37	AP3	90c dark brown (R)	32.50	26.00
		Nos. C35-C37 (3)	48.00	37.00

Plane and Letter AP5

Mercury AP6

Plane in Flight — AP7

Perf. 13½x13, 13x13½

1940, Oct. 23 Photo. Wmk. 90

C38	AP5	30c deep orange	12.00	.40
C39	AP6	50c dark brown	12.00	.40
C40	AP5	1p carmine	5.00	.25
C41	AP7	1.25p deep green	2.00	.25
C42	AP5	2.50p bright blue	4.00	.60
		Nos. C38-C42 (5)	35.00	1.90

Plane and Letter AP8

Mercury and Plane AP9

Perf. 13½x13, 13x13½

1942, Oct. 6 Litho. Wmk. 90

C43	AP8	30c orange	.35	.35
C44	AP9	50c dull brn & buff	.65	.35

No. C43 exists imperf. Value, pair $20.

See Nos. C49-C52, C57, C61.

Plane over Iguaçu Falls AP10

Plane over the Andes AP11

Perf. 13½x13

1946, June 10 Unwmk.

C45	AP10	15c dull red brn	.35	.35
C46	AP11	25c gray green	.35	.35

See Nos. C53-C54.

Allegory of Flight AP12

Astrolabe AP13

Perf. 13½x13, 13x13½

1946, Sept. 25 Litho. Unwmk.

Surface-Tinted Paper

C47	AP12	15c sl grn, *pale grn*	.55	.35
C48	AP13	60c vio brn, *ocher*	.55	.35

Types of 1942

1946-48 Unwmk. *Perf. 13½x13*

C49	AP8	30c orange	1.40	.25
C50	AP9	50c dull brn & buff	2.50	.25
C51	AP8	1p carmine ('47)	1.25	.25
C52	AP8	2.50p brt blue ('48)	5.50	.75
		Nos. C49-C52 (4)	10.65	1.50

No. C51 exists imperf. Value, pair $30.

Types of 1946

1948 Wmk. 90

C53	AP10	15c dull red brn	.35	.35
C54	AP11	25c gray green	.35	.35

Atlas (National Museum, Naples) AP14

Map of Argentine Republic, Globe and Caliper AP15

Perf. 13½x13, 13x13½

1948-49 Photo. Wmk. 288

C55	AP14	45c dk brown ('49)	.40	.25
C56	AP15	70c dark green	.70	.40

4th Pan-American Reunion of Cartographers, Buenos Aires, Oct.-Nov., 1948.

Mercury Type of 1942

1949 Litho. *Perf. 13x13½*

C57	AP9	50c dull brn & buff	.40	.35

Marksmanship Trophy — AP16

1949, Nov. 4 Photo.

C58	AP16	75c brown	.75	.35

World Rifle Championship, 1949.

Catalogue values for unused stamps in this section, from this point to the end of the section, are for Never Hinged items.

Douglas DC-3 and Condor — AP17

Perf. 13x13½

1951, June 20 Wmk. 90

C59	AP17	20c dk olive grn	.75	.35

10th anniversary of the State air lines.

Douglas DC-6 and Condor — AP18

1951, Oct. 17 *Perf. 13½*

C60	AP18	20c blue	.75	.35

End of Argentine 5-year Plan.

Plane-Letter Type of 1942

1951 Litho. *Perf. 13½x13*

C61	AP8	1p carmine	.65	.35

No. C61 exists imperf. Value, pair $20.

Jesus by Leonardo da Vinci (detail, "Virgin of the Rocks") — AP19

Perf. 13½x13

1956, Sept. 29 Photo. Wmk. 90

C62	AP19	1p dull purple	1.00	.35

Issued to express the gratitude of the children of Argentina to the people of the world for their help against poliomyelitis.

Battle of Montevideo AP20

Leonardo Rosales and Tomas Espora AP21

Guillermo Brown — AP22

1957, Mar. 2 *Perf. 13½*

C63	AP20	60c blue gray	.50	.35
C64	AP21	1p brt pink	.60	.35
C65	AP22	2p brown	.60	.35
		Nos. C63-C65 (3)	1.70	1.05

Cent. of the death of Admiral Guillermo Brown, founder of the Argentine navy.

Map of Americas & Arms of Buenos Aires — AP23

1957, Aug. 16

C66	AP23	2p rose violet	.75	.35

Issued to publicize the Inter-American Economic Conference in Buenos Aires.

Modern locomotive — AP24

1957, Aug. 31 Wmk. 90 *Perf. 13½*

C67	AP24	60c gray	.70	.35

Centenary of Argentine railroads.

AP25

No. C68, Globe, Flag,Compass Rose. No. C69, Key.

1957, Sept. 14

C68	AP25	1p multi	.50	.35
C69	AP25	2p multi	.70	.35

1957 International Congress for Tourism.

Birds Carrying Letters — AP26

1957, Nov. 6

C70	AP26	1p bright blue	.60	.35

Issued for Letter Writing Week, Oct. 6-12.

Early Plane — AP27

1958, May 31 *Perf. 13½*

C71	AP27	2p maroon	.60	.35

50th anniv. of the Argentine Aviation Club.

Stamp Anniv. Type

Designs: 80c, Stamp of Buenos Aires and view of the Plaza de la Aduana. 1p, Stamp of 1858 and "The Post of Santa Fe."

1958 Litho. *Perf. 13½*

C72	A270	80c pale bis & sl bl	.55	.35
C73	A270	1p red org & dk bl	.55	.35

Cent. of the 1st postage stamps of Buenos Aires & the Argentine Confederation.

Issue dates: 80c, Oct. 18; 1p, Aug. 23.

Comet Jet over World Map — AP29

1959, May 16 *Perf. 13½*

C74	AP29	5p black & olive	.65	.35

Inauguration of jet flights by Argentine Airlines.

Type of Regular Issue, 1960

"Cabildo" and: 1.80p, Mariano Moreno. 5p, Manuel Belgrano and Juan Jose Castelli.

Perf. 13½

1960, May 28 Wmk. 90 Photo.

C75	A287	1.80p red brown	.50	.35
a.		Souvenir sheet of 3	1.40	.95
C76	A287	5p buff & purple	.70	.35
a.		Souvenir sheet of 3	2.00	1.50

Souvenir sheets are imperf. No. C75a contains one No. C75 and 1p and 2p resembling Nos. 713-714; stamps in reddish brown. No. C76a contains one No. C76 and 4.20p and 10.70p resembling Nos. 715-716; stamps are in green.

Symbolic of New Provinces — AP30

1960, July 8 **Litho.**
C77 AP30 1.80p dp car & blue .60 .35

Elevation of the territories of Chubut, Formosa, Neuquen, Rio Negro and Santa Cruz to provinces.

Type of Regular Issue, 1960

1960, Oct. 1 **Photo.** ***Perf. 13½***
C78 A291 1.80p rose lilac .75 .35
C79 A291 10.70p brt grnsh blue 1.00 .35

UNESCO Emblem — AP31

1962, July 14 **Litho.**
C80 AP31 13p ocher & brown .85 .35

15th anniv. of UNESCO.

Mail Coach — AP32

1962, Oct. 6 **Wmk. 90** ***Perf. 13½***
C81 AP32 5.60p gray brn & blk 1.00 .35

Mailman's Day, Sept. 14, 1962.

No. 695 and Type of 1959 Surcharged in Green

1962, Oct. 31 **Photo.**
C82 A277 5.60p on 5p brown .60 .35
C83 A277 18p on 5p brn, *grnsh* 1.40 .35

UPAE Emblem — AP33

1962, Nov. 24 **Photo.** ***Perf. 13½***
C84 AP33 5.60p dark blue .65 .35

50th anniv. of the founding of the Postal Union of the Americas and Spain, UPAE.

Skylark — AP34

Design: 11p, Super Albatros.

1963, Feb. 9 **Litho.**
C85 AP34 5.60p blue & black .45 .35
C86 AP34 11p blue, blk & red .75 .35

9th World Gliding Championships.

Symbolic Plane — AP35

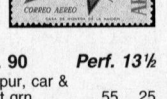

1963-65 **Wmk. 90** ***Perf. 13½***
C87 AP35 5.60p dk pur, car & brt grn .55 .25
C88 AP35 7p black & bis ('64) .75 .25
C88A AP35 7p black & bis ('65) 8.00 1.00
C89 AP35 11p blk, dk pur & grn .80 .25
C90 AP35 18p dk pur, red & vio bl 1.75 .35
C91 AP35 21p brown, red & gray 2.40 .40
Nos. C87-C91 (6) 14.25 2.50

"Argentina" reads down on No. C88, up on No. C88A. See Nos. C101-C104, C108-C111, C123-C126, C135-C141. For overprint and surcharges see Nos. C96, C146-C150.

Type of Regular Issue, 1964

Map of Falkland Islands (Islas Malvinas).

1964, Feb. 22 ***Perf. 13½***
Size: 33x22mm
C92 A327 18p lt & dk bl & ol grn 3.00 .75

UPU Monument, Bern, and UN Emblem — AP36

1964, May 23 **Engr.** ***Perf. 13½***
C93 AP36 18p red & dk brown .85 .35

15th UPU Cong., Vienna, Austria, 5-6/64.

Discovery of America, Florentine Woodcut — AP37

1964, Oct. 10 **Litho.**
C94 AP37 13p tan & black 1.10 .35

Day of the Race, Columbus Day.

Lt. Matienzo Base, Antarctica — AP38

1965, Feb. 27 **Photo.** ***Perf. 13½***
C95 AP38 11p salmon pink .75 .35

Issued to publicize the national territory of Tierra del Fuego, Antarctic and South Atlantic Isles.

No. C88A Overprinted in Silver

1965, Mar. 17 **Litho.**
C96 AP35 7p black & bister .60 .35

1st Rio de la Plata Stamp Show, sponsored jointly by the Argentine and Uruguayan Philatelic Associations, Montevideo, Mar. 19-28.

ITU Emblem — AP39

1965, May 11 **Wmk. 90** ***Perf. 13½***
C97 AP39 18p slate, blk & red .65 .35

Centenary of the ITU.

Ascending Rocket — AP40

Design: 50p, Earth with trajectories and magnetic field, horiz.

1965, May 29 **Photo.** ***Perf. 13½***
C98 AP40 18p red org .90 .30
C99 AP40 50p ultra 1.60 .55

6th Symposium on Space Research, held in Buenos Aires, and to honor the Natl. Commission of Space Research.

Type of 1963-65 Inscribed "Republica Argentina"

1965, Oct. 13 **Litho.** **Wmk. 90**
C101 AP35 12p dk car rose & brn 1.50 .25
C102 AP35 15p vio blue & dk red 1.60 .50
C103 AP35 27.50p dk bl grn & gray 2.75 1.00
C104 AP35 30.50p dk brown & dk bl 3.25 1.50
Nos. C101-C104 (4) 9.10 3.25

Argentine Antarctica Map and Centaur Rocket — AP41

1966, Feb. 19 ***Perf. 13½***
C105 AP41 27.50p bl, blk & dp org 1.40 .85

Launchings of sounding balloons and of a Gamma Centaur rocket in Antarctica during February, 1965.

Sea Gull and Southern Cross — AP42

1966, May 14 ***Perf. 13½***
C106 AP42 12p Prus blue, blk & red .65 .35

50th anniv. of the Naval Aviation School.

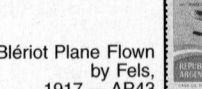

Blériot Plane Flown by Fels, 1917 — AP43

1967, Sept. 2 **Litho.** ***Perf. 13½***
C107 AP43 26p olive, bl & blk .60 .35

Flight by Theodore Fels from Buenos Aires to Montevideo, Sept. 2, 1917, allegedly the 1st intl. airmail flight.

Type of 1963-65 Inscribed "Republica Argentina" Reading Down

1967, Dec. 20 ***Perf. 13½***
C108 AP35 26p brown .65 .25
C109 AP35 40p violet 5.75 .30
C110 AP35 68p blue green 3.75 .45
C111 AP35 78p ultra 1.60 .60
Nos. C108-C111 (4) 11.75 1.60

Vito Dumas and Ketch "Legh II" AP44

1968, July 27 **Litho.** **Wmk. 90**
C112 AP44 68p bl, blk, red & vio bl .90 .40

Issued to commemorate Vito Dumas's one-man voyage around the world in 1943.

Type of Regular Issue and

Assembly Emblem AP45

40p, Globe and map of South America.

1968, Oct. 19 **Litho.** ***Perf. 13½***
C113 A395 40p brt pink, lt bl & blk 1.00 .30
C114 AP45 68p bl, lt bl, gold & blk 1.60 .55

4th Plenary Assembly of the Intl. Telegraph and Telephone Consultative Committee, Mar del Plata, Sept. 23-Oct. 25.

Radar Antenna, Balcarce Station — AP46

Perf. 13½
1969, Aug. 23 **Wmk. 90** **Photo.**
C115 AP46 40p blue gray .95 .35

Communications by satellite through Intl. Telecommunications Consortium (INTELSAT).

Atucha Nuclear Center — AP47

1969, Dec. 13 **Litho.** **Wmk. 365**
C116 AP47 26p blue & multi 2.50 .80

Completion of Atucha Nuclear Center.

Type of 1963-65 Inscribed "Republica Argentina" Reading Down

1969-71 ***Perf. 13½***
C123 AP35 40p violet 6.25 .40
C124 AP35 68p dk blue grn ('70) 2.25 .60

Unwmk.

C125 AP35 26p yellow brn ('71) .40 .35
C126 AP35 40p violet ('71) 3.25 .40
Nos. C123-C126 (4) 12.15 1.75

Old Fire Engine and Fire Brigade Emblem AP48

1970, Aug. 8 **Litho.** **Unwmk.**
C128 AP48 40c green & multi 1.75 .35

Centenary of the Fire Brigade.

Education Year Emblem — AP49

1970, Aug. 29 *Perf. 13½*
C129 AP49 68c blue & blk 1.00 .35

Issued for International Education Year.

Fleet Leaving Valparaiso, by Antonio Abel — AP50

1970, Oct. 17 **Litho.** *Perf. 13½*
C130 AP50 26c multicolored 1.25 .35

150th anniv. of the departure for Peru of the liberation fleet from Valparaiso, Chile.

Sumampa Chapel — AP51

1970, Nov. 7 **Photo.**
C131 AP51 40c multicolored 1.25 .40

Bishopric of Tucuman, 400th anniversary.

Buenos Aires Planetarium AP52

1970, Nov. 28 **Litho.** *Perf. 13½*
C132 AP52 40c multicolored 1.00 .35

Jorge Newbery and Morane Saulnier Plane — AP53

1970, Dec. 19
C133 AP53 26c bl, blk, yel & grn .70 .35

24th Aeronautics and Space Week.

Industries Type of Regular Issue

Design: 31c, Refinery.

1971, Oct. 16 **Litho.** *Perf. 13½*
C134 A445 31c red, blk & yel 1.00 .35

Type of 1963-65 Inscribed "Republica Argentina" Reading Down

1971-74 **Unwmk.**
C135 AP35 45c brown 4.00 .35
C136 AP35 68c red .55 .35
C137 AP35 70c vio blue ('73) 3.00 .50
C138 AP35 90c emerald ('73) 3.00 .50
C139 AP35 1.70p blue ('74) .70 .25
C140 AP35 1.95p emerald ('74) .70 .25
C141 AP35 2.65p dp claret ('74) .70 .25
Nos. C135-C141 (7) 12.65 2.45

Fluorescent paper was used for Nos. C135-C136, C138-C141. The 70c was issued on both papers. Value, 70c on fluorescent paper $5.50

Don Quixote, Drawing by Ignacio Zuloaga — AP54

1975, Apr. 26 **Photo.** *Perf. 13½*
C145 AP54 2.75p yellow, blk & red .85 .35

Day of the Race and for Espana 75 Intl. Philatelic Exhibition, Madrid, Apr. 4-13.

No. C87 Surcharged

1975, Sept. 15 **Litho.** **Wmk. 90**
C146 AP35 9.20p on 5.60p .95 .35
C147 AP35 19.70p on 5.60p 1.40 .45
C148 AP35 100p on 5.60p 6.00 2.25
Nos. C146-C148 (3) 8.35 3.05

No. C87 Surcharged

1975, Oct. 15
C149 AP35 9.20p on 5.60p 1.1 .35
C150 AP35 19.70p on 5.60p 1.75 .60

Argentine State Airline, 50th Anniv. — AP55

No. C151, Junkers JU52-3M. No. C152, Grumman SA-16. No. C153, Fokker F-27. No. C154, Fokker F-28.

1990, Sept. 15 **Litho.** *Perf. 13½*
C151 AP55 2500a multi 1.80 .90
C152 AP55 2500a multi 1.80 .90
C153 AP55 2500a multi 1.80 .90
C154 AP55 2500a multi 1.80 .90
Nos. C151-C154 (4) 7.20 3.60

AIR POST SEMI-POSTAL STAMPS

Catalogue values for unused stamps in this section are for Never Hinged items.

Philatelic Exhibition Type

Designs: No. CB1, Stamp engraving. No. CB2, Proofing stamp die. No. CB3, Sheet of stamps. No. CB4, The letter. No. CB5, Gen. San Martin.

Perf. 13½

1950, Aug. 26 **Wmk. 90** **Photo.**
CB1 SP8 45c + 45c vio bl .35 .25
CB2 SP8 70c + 70c dk brn .65 .40
a. Souv. sheet of 3, #B12, CB1, CB2, imperf. 5.00 3.00
CB3 SP8 1p + 1p cerise 1.40 1.25
CB4 SP8 2.50p + 2.50p ol gray 9.00 6.00
CB5 SP8 5p + 5p dull grn 10.50 7.25
Nos. CB1-CB5 (5) 21.90 15.15

Argentine Intl. Philatelic Exhib., 1950.

Pieta by Michelangelo SPAP2

1951, Dec. 22 *Perf. 13½x13*
CB6 SPAP2 2.45p +7.55p grnsh blk 23.00 14.00

Surtax as for the Eva Peron Foundation.

Flower and Child's Head — SPAP3

1958, Mar. 15 *Perf. 13½*
CB7 SPAP3 1p +50c deep claret .60 .35

Surtax for National Council for Children.

Stamp of 1858 — SPAP4

1958, Mar. 29 **Litho.** **Wmk. 90**
CB8 SPAP4 1p + 50c gray ol & bl .65 .35
CB9 SPAP4 2p + 1p rose lilac & vio .80 .45
CB10 SPAP4 3p + 1.50p green & brown .85 .55
CB11 SPAP4 5p + 2.50p gray ol & car rose 1.50 .90
CB12 SPAP4 10p + 5p gray ol & brn 2.75 1.75
Nos. CB8-CB12 (5) 6.55 4.00

The surtax was for the Intl. Centennial Philatelic Exhibition, Buenos Aires, Apr. 19-27.

Type of Semi-Postal Issue, 1958

Designs: 1p+50c, Flooded area. 5p+2.50p, House and truck under water.

1958, Oct. 4 **Photo.** *Perf. 13½*
CB13 SP11 1p + 50c dull purple .45 .25
CB14 SP11 5p + 2.50p grnsh blue 1.50 .80

The surtax was for victims of a flood in the Buenos Aires district.

Type of Semi-Postal Issue

1959, Sept. 5 **Litho.** *Perf. 13½*
CB15 SP13 2p + 1p Rowing .70 .35
a. Torch missing 170.00 170.00
CB16 SP13 3p + 1.50p Woman diver 1.00 .60
a. Torch missing 170.00 170.00

Bird Type of Semi-Postal Issue

2p+1p, Rufous tinamou. 3p+1.50p, Rhea.

1960, Feb. 6 *Perf. 13½*
CB17 SP14 2p + 1p rose car & sal .70 .35
CB18 SP14 3p + 1.50p slate green .80 .35

The surtax was for child welfare work. See No. CB29.

Buenos Aires Market Place, 1810 — SPAP5

6p+3p, Oxcart water carrier. 10.70p+5.30p, Settlers landing. 20p+10p, The Fort.

1960, Aug. 20 **Photo.** **Wmk. 90**
CB19 SPAP5 2 + 1p rose brown .35 .30
CB20 SPAP5 6 + 3p gray .45 .30
CB21 SPAP5 10.70 + 5.30p blue .80 .50
CB22 SPAP5 20 + 10p bluish grn 1.20 .85
Nos. CB19-CB22 (4) 2.80 1.95

Inter-American Philatelic Exhibition EFIMAYO 1960, Buenos Aires, Oct. 12-24, held to for the sesquicentennial of the May Revolution of 1810.

No. CB22 exists imperf. Value, pair $40.

For overprints see Nos. CB25-CB28.

Seibo, National Flower — SPAP6

#CB24, Copihue, Chile's national flower.

1960, Sept. 10 *Perf. 13½*
CB23 SPAP6 6 + 3p lilac rose .70 .30
CB24 SPAP6 10.70 + 5.30p ver 1.00 .40

The surtax was for earthquake victims in Chile. Nos. CB23-CB24 exist imperf. Value, each pair $40.

Nos. CB19-CB22 Overprinted

1960, Oct. 8
CB25 SPAP5 2 + 1p rose brown .35 .30
CB26 SPAP5 6 + 3p gray .45 .30
CB27 SPAP5 10.70 + 5.30p blue .75 .40
CB28 SPAP5 20 + 10p bluish green 1.50 .75
Nos. CB25-CB28 (4) 3.05 1.75

United Nations Day, Oct. 24, 1960.

Type of Semi-Postal Issue, 1960

Design: Emperor penguins.

1961, Feb. 25 **Photo.** **Wmk. 90**
CB29 SP14 1.80p + 90c gray .60 .35

The surtax was for child welfare work. Exists imperf. Value, pair $50.

Stamp of 1862 — SPAP7

1962, May 19 **Litho.**
CB30 SPAP7 6.50p + 6.50p Prus bl & grnsh bl .95 .65

Opening of the "Argentina 62" Philatelic Exhibition, Buenos Aires, May 19-29. Exists imperf. Value, pair $40.

Type of Semi-Postal Issue, 1963

1963, May 18 **Wmk. 90** *Perf. 13½*
CB31 SP21 11p + 5p Bicycling 1.20 .50

Exists imperf. Value, pair $40.

Type of Semi-Postal Issue, 1962

Design: Pitangus sulphuratus bolivianus.

1963, Dec. 21 *Perf. 13½*
CB32 SP20 11p + 5p multi 1.25 .60

The surtax was for child welfare.

Type of Semi-Postal Issue, 1964

1964, July 18 **Litho.**
CB33 SP22 11p + 5p Sailboat 1.40 .70

Exists imperf. Value, pair $50.

Crutch, Olympic Torch and Rings — SPAP8

1964, Sept. 19 **Litho.** *Perf. 13½*
CB34 SPAP8 18p + 9p bluish grn, blk, red & yel .85 .60

13th "Olympic" games for the handicapped, Tokyo, 1964. Exists imperf. Value, pair $50.

Bird Type of Semi-Postal Issue, 1962

Design: Iridoprocne leucopyga.

1964, Dec. 23 Litho. Wmk. 90
CB35 SP20 18p + 9p multi 1.25 .85

The surtax was for child welfare.

Furnarius Rufus Rufus — SP22a

1966, Mar. 26 ***Perf. 13½***
CB36 SP22a 27.50p + 12.50p bl, ocher, yel & grn 1.10 .85

The surtax was for child welfare.

Coat of Arms SPAP9

1966, June 25 Litho. ***Perf. 13½***
CB37 SPAP9 10p + 10p multi 2.00 1.40

ARGENTINA '66 Philatelic Exhibition held in connection with the sesquicentennial celebration of the Declaration of Independence, Buenos Aires, July 16-23. The surtax was for the Exhibition. Issued in sheets of 4.

Designs: 15p+7p, Thraupis bonariensis. 26p+13p, Ramphastos toco.

1967 Litho. Wmk. 90
CB38 SP22a 15p + 7p blk, bl, grn & yel 1.75 1.00
CB39 SP22a 26p + 13p blk, org, yel & bl .65 .40

The surtax was for child welfare.
Issued: 15p+7p, Jan. 14; 26p+13p, Dec. 23.

Bird Type of Semi-Postal Issue, 1969

Design: Ceophloeus lineatus.

1969, Sept. 20 Wmk. 365 ***Perf. 13½***
CB40 SP24 26p + 13p multi 1.05 .40

The surtax was for child welfare.

Bird Type of Semi-Postal Issue, 1970

Design: Phoenicopterus ruber chilensis.

1970, May 9 Litho. Wmk. 365
CB41 SP25 40c + 20c multi 1.05 .40

The surtax was for child welfare.

Fish Type of Semi-Postal Issue, 1971

Design: Odostethes platensis.

1971, Feb. 20 Unwmk. ***Perf. 12½***
Size: 75x15mm
CB42 SP26 40c + 20c multi .75 .40

The surtax was for child welfare.

OFFICIAL STAMPS

Regular Issues Overprinted in Black — a

1884-87 Unwmk. ***Perf. 12, 14***
O1 A29 ½c brown 40.00 25.00
O2 A23 1c red 15.00 10.00
b. Perf. 12 100.00 80.00
O3 A29 1c red 1.00 .85
b. Double overprint 100.00 100.00
O4 A20 2c green 1.00 .50
b. Double overprint 120.00 120.00
O5 A11 4c brown 1.00 .50
O6 A7 8c lake 1.00 1.00
O7 A8 10c green 100.00 50.00
O8 A23 12c ultra (#45) 10.00 5.00
a. Perf. 14 1,000. 250.00
O9 A29 12c grnsh blue 1.50 1.00
O10 A19 24c blue 2.00 1.50
O11 A21 25c lake 40.00 30.00
O12 A12 30c orange 80.00 70.00
O13 A13 60c black 50.00 40.00
O14 A14 90c blue 40.00 30.00
b. Double overprint 120.00 120.00
Nos. O1-O14 (14) 382.50 265.35

Inverted Overprint

O1a A29 ½c 30.00 20.00
O2a A23 1c Perf. 14 100.00 80.00
c. Perf. 12 75.00 —
O3a A29 1c 3.00 3.00
O4a A20 2c 120.00 100.00
O5a A11 4c 60.00 50.00
O6a A7 8c (Inverted overprint on reverse) *500.00* —
O8b A23 12c Perf. 12 20.00 —
O9a A29 12c 300.00 250.00
O10a A19 24c 10.00 5.00
O13a A13 60c 150.00 120.00
O14a A14 90c 120.00 120.00

1884 ***Rouletted***
O15 A17 16c green 3.00 2.00
a. Double overprint 25.00 —
b. Inverted overprint 300.00
O16 A18 20c blue 15.00 12.00
a. Inverted overprint 120.00 80.00
O17 A19 24c blue 2.50 1.50
a. Inverted overprint 8.00 5.00
b. Double ovpt., one inverted 250.00 —
Nos. O15-O17 (3) 20.50 15.50

Overprinted Diagonally in Red

1885 ***Perf. 12***
O18 A20 2c green 5.00 4.00
a. Inverted overprint 100.00
O19 A11 4c brown 3.00 2.00
a. Inverted overprint 100.00 —
b. Double overprint 100.00 100.00
O20 A13 60c black 50.00 40.00
O21 A14 90c blue 450.00 275.00

1885 ***Rouletted***
O22 A19 24c blue 40.00 20.00

On all of these stamps, the overprint is found reading both upwards and downwards.
Counterfeits exist of No. O21 overprint and others.

Regular Issues Handstamped Horizontally in Black — b

1884 ***Perf. 12, 14***
O23 A23 1c red 100.00 50.00
a. Perf. 12 400.00 300.00
O24 A20 2c green, diagonal overprint 60.00 40.00
a. Horizontal overprint 450.00 300.00
O25 A11 4c brown 25.00 20.00
O26 A7 8c lake 25.00 20.00
O27 A23 12c ultra 60.00 50.00

Overprinted Diagonally

O28 A19 24c bl, rouletted 50.00 35.00
O29 A13 60c black 30.00 15.00

Counterfeit overprints exist.

Liberty Head — O1

Perf. 11½, 12 and Compound

1901, Dec. 1 Engr.
O31 O1 1c gray .50 .25
b. Vert. pair, imperf. horiz. 80.00
c. Horiz. pair, imperf. vert. 100.00
O32 O1 2c orange brown .50 .25
O33 O1 5c red .50 .25
b. Vert. pair, imperf. horiz. 100.00
O34 O1 10c dark green 1.00 .25
O35 O1 30c dark blue 8.00 3.00
O36 O1 50c orange 4.00 2.00
Nos. O31-O36 (6) 14.50 6.00

Imperf, Pairs

O31a O1 1c 80.00
O32a O1 2c 80.00
O33a O1 5c 100.00
O34a O1 10c 80.00
O35a O1 30c 100.00
O36a O1 50c 150.00

Regular Stamps of 1935-51 Overprinted in Black — c

Perf. 13x13½, 13½x13, 13

1938-54 Wmk. RA in Sun (90)
O37 A129 1c buff ('40) .75 .35
O38 A130 2c dk brn ('40) .75 .35
O39 A132 3c grn ('39) 1.75 .75
O40 A132 3c lt gray ('39) .75 .35
O41 A134 5c yel brn .75 .35
O42 A195 5c car ('53) .90 .35
O43 A137 10c carmine .60 .25
O44 A137 10c brn ('39) 1.50 .35
O45 A140 15c lt gray bl, type II ('47) .90 .35
O46 A139 15c slate blue 1.50 .35
O47 A139 15c pale ultra ('39) .90 .35
O48 A139 20c blue ('53) 1.75 .75
O49 A141 25c carmine .75 .35
a. Overprint 11mm 1.50 .35
O49B A143 40c dk violet 3.75 1.20
O50 A144 50c red & org .75 .35
a. Overprint 11mm .75 .35
O51 A146 1p brn blk & lt bl ('40) .90 .35
a. Overprint 11mm 13.50 .75
O52 A224 1p choc & lt bl ('51) 3.00 .35
a. Overprint 11mm 2.25 .35
O53 A147 2p brn lake & dk ultra (ovpt. 11mm) ('54) 3.00 .75
Nos. O37-O53 (18) 24.95 8.25

Overprinted in Black on Stamps and Types of 1945-47

Perf. 13x13½, 13½x13

1945-46 Unwmk.
O54 A130 2c sepia 6.00 5.00
O55 A134 3c lt gray 4.00 4.00
O56 A134 5c yel brn .60 .25
O57 A195 5c dp car .50 .25
O58 A137 10c brown 1.00 .25
a. Double overprint
O59 A140 15c lt gray bl, type II .70 .25
O61 A141 25c dull rose .50 .25
O62 A144 50c red & org 1.00 .25
O63 A146 1p brn blk & lt bl 1.00 .25
O64 A147 2p brn lake & bl .60 .25
O65 A148 5p ind & ol grn .80 .25
O66 A149 10p dp cl & int blk 1.25 .50
O67 A150 20p bl grn & brn 2.50 2.00
Nos. O54-O67 (13) 20.45 13.75

Overprinted in Black on Stamps and Types of 1942-50

Perf. 13, 13x13½

1944-51 Wmk. 288
O73 A132 3c lt gray 6.00 2.00
O74 A134 5c yellow brown 2.00 .50
O75 A137 10c red brown .60 .25
O76 A140 15c lt gray bl, type II 1.00 .25
O77 A144 50c red & org (overprint 11 mm) 8.00 2.00
O78 A146 1p brn blk & lt bl (overprint 11mm) 10.00 5.00
Nos. O73-O78 (6) 27.60 10.00

Catalogue values for unused stamps in this section, from this point to the end of the section, are for Never Hinged items.

Nos. 600-606 Overprinted in Black — d

1953 Wmk. 90 ***Perf. 13***
O79 A228 5c gray .50 .25
O80 A228 10c rose lilac .50 .25
O81 A228 20c rose pink .50 .25
O82 A228 25c dull green .50 .25
O83 A228 40c dull violet .50 .25
O84 A228 45c deep blue .60 .25
O85 A228 50c dull brown .50 .25

Nos. 611-617 Overprinted in Blue — e

Perf. 13x13½, 13½x13
O86 A229 1p dk brown .50 .25
O87 A229 1.50p dp green .60 .25
O88 A229 2p brt carmine .60 .25
O89 A229 3p indigo .60 .35

Size: 30x40mm

O90 A229 5p red brown 1.25 .80
O91 A228 10p red 10.00 7.00
O92 A229 20p green 100.00 90.00
Nos. O79-O92 (14) 117.15 100.65

No. 612 Overprinted in Blue — f

O93 A229 1.50p dp grn 3.00 1.50

Regular Issues of 1954-59 Variously Overprinted in Black or Blue

g

h

Perf. 13½, 13x13½, 13½x13

1955-61 Litho. Wmk. 90
O94 A237(c) 20c red (#629) .50 .25
O95 A237(d) 20c red (#629) .50 .25
O96 A237(d) 40c red, ovpt. 15mm (#630) .50 .25

Engr.

O97 A239(g) 50c bl (#632) .50 .25

Photo.

O98 A239(h) 1p brn (#635) .50 .25
O99 A239(e) 1p brn (Bl, #635) .50 .25
O100 A239(e) 1p brn (Bk, #635) .50 .25

Engr.

O101 A239(h) 3p vio brn (#638) .50 .25
O102 A240(h) 5p gray grn (#639) 1.00 .40
O103 A240(e) 10p yel grn (#640) 1.50 .50
O104 A240(f) 20p dl vio (#641) 3.00 2.00
O105 A240(h) 20p dl vio (#641) 1.50 .80
a. Perf 13½ (#641a) 2.00 1.00
O106 A241(e) 50p ultra & ind (#642) 3.00 1.50
Nos. O94-O106 (13) 14.00 7.20

The overprints on Nos. O99-O100 & O103-O104 are horizontal; that on No. O106 is vertical. On No. O106 overprint measures 23mm.
Issued: No. O102, 1957; Nos. O97, O101, O103, O105, 1958; Nos. O98-O99, O104, 1959; No. O100, 1960; No. O106, 1961.

No. 659 Overprinted Type "d"

1957 Wmk. 90 Litho. ***Perf. 13***
O108 A133 20c dl pur (ovpt. 15mm) .50 .25

Nos. 666, 658 and 663 Variously Overprinted

1957 Photo. ***Perf. 13x13½, 13½***
O109 A261(g) 2p claret .50 .25
O110 A254(e) 2.40p brown .50 .30
O111 A258(c) 4.40p grnsh gray .50 .25
Nos. O109-O111 (3) 1.50 .80

Nos. 668, 685-687, 690-691, 693-705, 742, 742C and Types of 1959-65 Overprinted in Black, Blue or Red Types "e," "g," or

i

j

k

m

n

Lithographed; Photogravure

1960-68 *Perf. 13x13½, 13½*

O112	A128(g)	5c	buff (vert. ovpt.)	.50	.25
O113	A275(j)	10c	sl grn	.50	.30
O114	A275(j)	20c	dl red brn	1.00	.80
O115	A275(i)	50c	bister	.50	.25
O116	A278(k)	1p	brn	.60	.30
O117	A278(j)	1p	brn, photo. (vert. ovpt.)	2.00	.25
O117A	A278(j)	1p	brn, litho., (down)	10.00	2.00
O118	A276(j)	2p	rose red	.50	.25
O119	A312(m)	2p	dp grn	1.00	.25
O120	A312(j)	2p	brt grn (up)	2.00	.30
O121	A312(j)	2p	grn litho. (down)	2.00	1.00
O122	A277(e)	3p	dk bl (horiz.)	.50	.25
O123	A277(j)	3p	dk blue	30.00	10.00
O124	A276(j)	4p	red, litho.	.50	.25
O125	A312(j)	4p	rose red, litho. (down)	1.00	.25
O126	A277(e)	5p	brn (Bl) (horiz.)	.80	.30
O127	A277(e)	5p	brn (Bk) (horiz.)	.60	.25
O128	A277(j)	5p	sepia	1.00	.25
O130	A276(j)	8p	red	.50	.25
O131	A278(i)	10p	lt red brn	.60	.25
O132	A276(j)	10p	vermilion	1.00	.25
O133	A278(j)	10p	brn car (up)	4.00	1.00
O133A	A278(j)	10p	brn car (down)	90.00	30.00
O134	A278(m)	12p	dk brn vio (horiz.)	.50	.25
O135	A278(k)	20p	Prus grn	.60	.30
O136	A278(j)	20p	Prus grn (up)	.60	.25
O137	A276(j)	20p	red, litho.	.60	.30
O138	A276(m)	20p	red, litho. (horiz.)	.80	.30
O139	A278(j)	23p	grn (vert. ovpt.)	1.50	.50
O140	A278(j)	25p	dp vio, photo. (R) (up)	2.50	.80
O141	A278(j)	25p	pur, litho. (R) (down)	2.50	1.00
O142	A241(n)	50p	dk blue	6.00	3.00
O143	A279(m)	100p	bl (horiz. ovpt.)	4.00	2.00
O144	A279(m)	100p	blue (up)	4.00	1.00
O145	A280(m)	300p	dp violet (horiz.)	12.00	8.00
	Nos. O112-O133,O134-O145 (34)			96.70	36.95

The "m" overprint measures 15½mm on 2p; 14½mm on 12p, 100p and 300p; 13mm on 20p.

Issued: Nos. O122, O127, O135, 1961; Nos. O112-O114, O116, O118, 1962; No. O124, 1963; Nos. O119, O134, O143, 1964; Nos. O117, O125, O130, O139, O144, 1965; Nos. O120, O128, O132-O133, O136, O140, O142, O145, 1966; Nos. O121, O129, O137-O138, O141, 1967; No. O117A, 1968.

Nos. 699, 823-825, 827-829, and Type of 1962 Overprinted in Black or Red Types "j," "m," or "o"

o

Inscribed: "Republica Argentina"

Litho., Photo., Engr.

1964-67 **Wmk. 90** *Perf. 13½*

O149	A312(j)	6p	rose red (down)	2.00	1.00
O153	A238a(m)	22p	ultra	1.25	.50
O154	A238a(j)	43p	dk car rose (down)	3.00	1.00
O155	A238a(j)	45p	brn, photo. (up)	3.00	1.00
O156	A238a(j)	45p	brn, litho. (up)	10.00	8.00
O157	A241(j)	50p	dk bl (up) (R)	8.00	1.50
O158	A366(j)	90p	ol bis (up)	10.00	8.00
O162	A495(o)	500p	yel grn	25.00	20.00
	Nos. O149-O162 (8)			62.25	41.00

Issued: No. O153, 1964; No. O155, 1966; Nos. O149, O156-O162, 1967.

Type of 1959-67 Ovptd. Type "j"

1969 **Litho.** **Wmk. 365** *Perf. 13½*

O163	A276	20p	vermilion	1.00	.80

Beginning with No. 2001, many Argentine stamps are inscribed "Correo Official," but are not official stamps.

OFFICIAL DEPARTMENT STAMPS

Regular Issues of 1911-38 Overprinted in Black

Ministry of Agriculture

No. OD1

1913 **Type I** *Perf. 13½x12½*

OD1	A88	2c	choc (#181)	.50	.50
OD2	A88	1c	ocher (#190)	.50	.50
OD3	A88	2c	choc (#191)	1.00	1.00
OD4	A88	5c	red (#194)	1.00	.50
a.			Perf. 13½ (#194a)	4.00	7.50
OD5	A88	12c	dp bl (#196)	10.00	.50
a.			Perf. 13½ (#196a)	10.00	1.00
	Nos. OD2-OD5 (4)			12.50	2.50

1915

OD6	A88	1c	ocher (#208)	1.50	1.00
OD7	A88	2c	chocolate (#209)	1.00	.50
OD8	A88	5c	red (#212)	2.00	1.00
	Nos. OD6-OD8 (3)			4.50	2.50

No. OD9

1916 *Perf. 13½*

OD9	A91	5c	red (#220)	1.00	.50

No. OD11

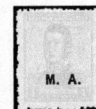

No. OD15

1918

OD10	A94	12c	blue (#238)	3.00	.50
OD11	A93	1c	buff (#249)	.50	.50
OD12	A93	2c	brown (#250)	.50	.50
OD13	A93	5c	red (#253)	.50	.50
OD14	A94	12c	blue (#255)	.50	.50
OD15	A94	20c	ultra (#256)	.50	.50
	Nos. OD10-OD15 (6)			5.50	3.00

1920 *Perf. 13½, 13½x12½ (OD16)*

OD16	A93	1c	buff (#265)	2.00	1.25
OD17	A93	2c	brown (#266A)	8.00	2.00
OD18	A93	5c	red (#269A)	.70	.50
a.			Perf. 13½x12½ (#269)	1.40	.50
	Nos. OD16-OD18 (3)			10.70	3.75

1922 *Perf. 13½*

OD19	A94	12c	blue (#311)	4.00	2.00
OD20	A94	20c	ultra (#312)	100.00	

No. OD23

1923 *Perf. 13½x12½*

OD21	A104	1c	buff (#324)	2.00	1.00
a.			Perf. 13½ (#324A)	10.00	10.00
OD22	A104	2c	dk brn (#325)	.50	.50
OD23	A104	5c	red (#328)	.50	.50
a.			Perf. 13½ (#328A)	2.00	.50
OD24	A104	12c	deep blue (#330)	.80	.50
OD25	A104	20c	ultra (#331)	.80	.50
a.			Perf. 13½ (#331A)	12.00	8.00
	Nos. OD21-OD25 (5)			4.60	3.00

1924

OD26	A104	1c	buff (#341)	.50	.50
a.			Inverted ovpt.	20.00	15.00
OD27	A104	2c	dk brn (#342)	.50	.50
OD29	A104	5c	red (#345)	.50	.50
OD30	A104	10c	dl grn (#346)	1.00	.50
OD31	A104	12c	dp bl (#347)	.50	.50
OD32	A104	20c	dp bl (#348)	.50	.50
a.			Inverted ovpt.	80.00	60.00
	Nos. OD26-OD32 (6)			3.50	3.00

No. OD34

1926

OD34	A110	12c	deep blue (#360)	.50	.50

No. OD28B

Type II

1931-36 *Perf. 13x13½, 13½x13*

OD27B	A104	2c	dk brn (#342)	10.00	6.00
OD28B	A104	3c	green (#343)	.50	.50
OD29B	A104	5c	red (#345)	.50	.50
OD30B	A104	10c	dl grn (#346)	.50	.50
c.			Typo (coil) (#346a)	1.00	1.00
OD32B	A104	20c	ultra (#348)	1.00	.50
c.			Typo (coil) (#348a)	1.00	.50
OD33B	A104	30c	claret (#351)	.50	.50
c.			Typo (coil) (#351a)	1.00	.50

No. OD46

1936-38 **Litho.**

OD35	A129	1c	buff (#419)	.50	.50
OD36	A130	2c	dk brn (#420)	.50	.50
OD37	A132	3c	green (#422)	1.00	.50
OD38	A134	5c	yel brn (#427)	1.00	.50
OD40	A139	15c	lt gray bl (#436)	5.00	1.00
OD41	A140	20c	lt ultra (#437)	6.00	.50
OD42	A140	20c	lt ultra (#438)	.80	.50
OD43	A141	25c	car & pink (#441), perf. 13x13½	.50	.50
OD44	A142	30c	org brn & yel brown (#442)	.50	.50
OD45	A145	1p	brn blk & Lt bl (#445)	10.00	4.00
OD46	A146	1p	brn blk & lt bl (#446)	3.00	1.00
	Nos. OD35-OD46 (11)			28.80	10.00

Typo. *Perf. 13½*

OD38A	A134	5c	yel brn (#427)	1.00	.50
OD39A	A137	10c	carmine (#430)	1.00	.50
b.			Perf. 13½x13 (#430a)	1.00	.50

Ministry of War

No. OD47

1913 **Type I** *Perf. 13½x12½*

OD47	A88	2c	choc (#181)	2.50	.50
OD48	A88	1c	ocher (#190)	.50	.50
OD49	A88	2c	choc (#191)	8.00	.50
a.			Perf. 13½ (#191a)	20.00	20.00
OD50	A88	5c	red (#194)	1.00	.50
a.			Inverted ovpt.	50.00	—
OD51	A88	12c	dp bl (#196)	.50	.50
a.			Perf. 13½ (#196a)	10.00	6.00
	Nos. OD48-OD51 (4)			10.00	2.00

1915

OD52	A88	1c	ocher (#208)	60.00	12.00
OD53	A88	2c	chocolate (#209)	4.00	.50
OD54	A88	5c	red (#212)	8.00	.50
	Nos. OD52-OD54 (3)			72.00	13.00

1916 *Perf. 13½*

OD55	A91	5c	red (#220)	3.00	1.00
OD56	A92	12c	blue (#222)	6.00	1.00

1918

OD57	A93	1c	buff (#232)	2.00	.50
a.			Perf. 13½x12½ (#232B)	10.00	6.00
OD58	A93	2c	brown (#233)	24.00	1.50
a.			Perf. 13½x12½ (#233B)	3.00	.50
OD59	A93	5c	red (#236B) (Perf. 13½x12½)	1.50	.50
OD60	A94	12c	blue (#238)	4.00	1.50
	Nos. OD57-OD60 (4)			31.50	4.00

1918

OD61	A93	1c	buff (#249)	3.00	1.00
a.			Perf. 13½x12½ (#249B)	6.00	5.00
OD62	A93	2c	brown (#250)	.50	.50
a.			Perf. 13½x12½ (#250B)	1.00	.50
OD63	A93	5c	red (#253)	2.00	1.00
a.			Perf. 13½x12½ (#253B)	.50	.50
OD64	A94	12c	blue (#255)	1.50	.50
OD65	A94	20c	ultra (#256)	8.00	1.25
	Nos. OD61-OD65 (5)			15.00	4.25

1920

OD66	A93	2c	brown (#266A)	12.00	6.00
a.			Perf. 13½x12½ (#266)	1.00	.50
OD67	A93	5c	red (#269A)	10.00	6.00
a.			Perf. 13½x12½ (#269)	10.00	6.00
OD68	A94	12c	blue (#271)	2.00	.30
	Nos. OD66-OD68 (3)			24.00	12.30

1921

OD69	A94	12c	blue (#299)	18.00	5.00

No. OD72

1922

OD70	A93	1c	buff (#305)	5.00	.60
OD71	A93	2c	brown (13½x12½) (#306B)	10.00	2.00

OD72 A103 5c red (#309) 5.00 1.00
OD73 A94 20c ultra (#312) 2.00 .50
Nos. OD70-OD73 (4) 22.00 4.10

Perf. 13½x12½

OD74 A93 2c brown (#318A) 10.00 2.00

1923 ***Perf. 13½x12½***

OD75 A104 1c buff (#324) 1.50 .50
a. Inverted ovpt. *20.00* *18.00*
b. Perf. 13½ (#324A) 45.00 24.00
OD76 A104 2c dk brn (#325) .50 .50
a. Perf. 13½ (#325A) 2.00 .50
OD77 A104 5c red (#328) 1.00 .50
a. Inverted ovpt. *20.00* *18.00*
b. Perf. 13½ (#328A) 4.00 4.00
OD78 A104 12c dp bl (#330) 2.00 .50
OD79 A104 20c ultra (#331) 6.00 .50
a. Perf. 13½ (#331A) 6.00 1.00
b. As "a.," inverted ovpt. *20.00* *18.00*
Nos. OD75-OD79 (5) 11.00 2.50

1924

OD80 A104 1c buff (#341) 10.00 3.00
OD81 A104 2c dk brn (#342) 1.00 .50
OD82 A104 3c green (#343) 2.00 .50
OD83 A104 5c red (#345) .50 .50
OD84 A104 10c dl grn (#346) 6.00 .50
OD85 A104 20c ultra (#348) .50 .50
OD86 A104 30c claret (#351) 10.00 1.00
OD87 A105 1p blue & red (#353) 10.00 2.00
Nos. OD80-OD87 (8) 40.00 8.50

No. OD88

1926

OD88 A109 5c red (#359) 3.00 .50

No. OD82B

Type II

1931-36 ***Perf. 13½x12½, 13 (OD87B)***

OD82B A104 3c green (#343) 6.00 1.00
OD83B A104 5c red (#345) 1.25 .50
c. Inverted ovpt. — *60.00*
OD84B A104 10c dl grn (#346) 1.00 .50
c. Typo (coil) (346a) 5.00 1.00
OD85B A104 20c ultra (#348) 1.00 .50
c. Typo (coil) (#348a) 12.00 .50
OD86B A104 30c claret (#351) 1.50 .50
c. Typo (coil) (#351a) 2.00 .50
OD87B A105 1p blue & red (#353) 10.00 2.00
Nos. OD82B-OD87B (6) 20.75 5.00

No. OD90

1936-38 **Litho.**

OD89 A129 1c buff (#419) .50 .50
OD90 A130 2c dk brn (#420) .50 .50
OD91 A132 3c green (#422) 1.00 .50
OD92 A134 5c yel brn (#427) .50 .50
OD93 A137 10c car (#430) .50 .50
OD94 A139 15c slate bl (#434) 1.60 .50
OD95 A140 20c lt ultra (#437) 14.00 .50
OD96 A140 20c lt ultra (#438) 1.00 .50
OD97 A141 25c car & pink (#441) .50 .50
OD98 A142 30c org brn & yel brown (#442) .50 .50
OD99 A144 50c red & org (#444) 1.50 .50
OD100 A145 1p brn blk & lt bl (#445) 4.00 2.00
OD101 A146 1p brn blk & lt bl (#446) 2.00 1.00
Nos. OD89-OD101 (13) 28.10 8.50

Typo. ***Perf. 13½***

OD92B A134 5c yel brn (#427) .50 .50
c. Inverted ovpt. 20.00 15.00
OD93B A137 10c car (#430) 1.00 .50
c. Inverted ovpt. 50.00 35.00
d. Perf. 13½x13 (#430a) 2.00 1.00

Ministry of Finance

No. OD102

1913 **Type I** ***Perf. 13½x12½***

OD102 A88 2c choc (#181) .50 .50
OD103 A88 1c ocher (#190) .50 .50
OD104 A88 2c choc (#191) .50 .50
OD105 A88 5c red (#194) .50 .50
OD106 A88 12c dp bl (#196) .50 .50
a. Perf. 13½ (#196a) 180.00 35.00
Nos. OD103-OD106 (4) 2.00 2.00

1915

OD107 A88 2c choc (#209) .50 .50
OD108 A88 5c red (#212) .50 .50

1916 ***Perf. 13½***

OD109 A91 5c red (#220) .70 .60

1917

OD110 A93 2c brown (#233) .50 .50
OD111 A93 5c red (#236) 8.00 1.00
OD112 A94 12c blue (#238) .50 .50
Nos. OD110-OD112 (3) 9.00 2.00

1918

OD113 A93 2c brown (#250) *100.00*
OD114 A93 5c red (#253) .70 .50
a. Perf. 13½x12½ (#253B) 4.00 .50
OD115 A94 12c blue (#255) .70 .50
OD116 A94 20c ultra (#256) 2.00 1.00
Nos. OD113-OD116 (4) 3.40 102.00

1920

OD117 A93 1c buff (#265) 6.00 3.00
OD118 A93 2c brown (#266) 9.00 5.00
OD119 A93 5c #269 20.00 12.00
a. Perf. 13½ (#269A) 12.00 1.00
OD120 A94 12c blue (#271) (perf. 13½) 3.00 1.00
Nos. OD117-OD120 (4) 38.00 21.00

1922

OD121 A94 20c ultra (#312) 60.00 15.00

1923 ***Perf. 13½x12½, 13½***

OD122 A104 1c buff (#324) *20.00* *10.00*
a. Perf. 13½ (#324A) 10.00 6.00
OD123 A104 2c dk brn (#325) .50 .50
a. Perf. 13½ (#325A) — 12.00
OD124 A104 5c red (#328) .50 .50
a. Inverted ovpt. — *35.00*
b. Perf. 13½ (#328A) 2.00 1.00
OD125 A104 12c dp bl (#330) .70 .50
a. Perf. 13½ (#330A) 5.00 1.00
OD126 A104 20c ultra (#331) .50 .50
a. Perf. 13½ (#331A) 10.00 4.00
Nos. OD122-OD126 (5) 22.20 12.00

1924 ***Perf. 13½x12½***

OD127 A104 2c dk brn (#342) 250.00 250.00
OD128 A104 5c red (#345) 2.00 .50
OD130 A104 12c dp bl (#347) 80.00 35.00
OD131 A104 20c ultra (#348) .50 .50
Nos. OD127-OD131 (4) 332.50 286.00

1926

OD134 A110 12c dp bl (#360) 60.00 25.00

No. OD129B

No. OD133B

1931-36 **Type II**

OD127B A104 3c green (#343) 60.00 30.00
OD129B A104 10c dl grn (#346) .50 .50
c. Typo (coil) (#346a) 1.25 .50
OD131B A104 20c ultra (#348) 2.00 .50
c. Typo (coil) (#348a) 1.00 .50
OD132B A104 30c claret (#351) 1.00 .50
c. Typo (coil) (#351a) 3.00 .50

Perf. 13

OD133B A105 1p blue & red (#353) 2.00 1.00
Nos. OD127B-OD133B (5) 65.50 32.50

No. OD135

1936-38 **Litho.** ***Perf. 13½x13***

OD135 A129 1c buff (#419) .50 .50
OD136 A130 2c dk brn (#420) .50 .50
OD137 A132 3c green (#422) 1.50 1.00
OD138 A134 5c yel brn (#427d) .50 .50
OD139 A137 10c car (#430) .50 .50
OD140 A139 15c slate blue (#434) ('36) 6.00 1.60
a. Inverted ovpt. — 80.00
OD141 A140 20c lt ultra (#437) 5.00 .50
OD142 A140 20c lt ultra (#438) .50 .50
OD143 A142 30c org brn & yel brown (#442) .50 .50
OD144 A145 1p brn blk & lt bl (#445) 10.00 3.00
OD145 A146 1p brn blk & lt bl (#446) 1.20 .80
Nos. OD135-OD145 (11) 26.70 9.90

Typo.

OD138A A134 5c yel brn (#427) .50 .50
b. Inverted ovpt. *50.00* *50.00*
OD139A A137 10c car (#430) 2.00 .50
b. Perf. 13½x13 (#430a) 40.00 1.00

Ministry of the Interior

No. OD147

1913 **Type I** ***Perf. 13½x12½***

OD146 A88 2c choc (#181) 2.00 .50
OD147 A88 1c ocher (#190) .50 .50
OD148 A88 2c choc (#191) 5.00 2.00
OD149 A88 5c red (#194) 3.00 .50
OD150 A88 12c dp bl (#196) 2.50 .50
a. Perf. 13½ (#196a) 10.00 3.00
Nos. OD146-OD150 (5) 13.00 4.00

1915

OD151 A88 2c chocolate (#209) 4.00 1.20
OD152 A88 5c red (#212) 4.00 1.20

1916 ***Perf. 13½***

OD153 A91 5c red (#220) 4.00 1.60

1918

OD154 A93 5c red (#236B) 10.00 1.00
OD155 A93 2c brown (#250) .50 .50
OD156 A93 5c red (#253) .70 .50
a. Perf. 13½x12½ (#253B) 2.00 .50
Nos. OD154-OD156 (3) 11.20 2.00

1920

OD157 A93 1c buff (13½x12½) (#265) *10.00* *3.00*
OD158 A93 5c red (#269) 10.00 2.00

1922 ***Perf. 13½***

OD160 A103 5c red (#309) 20.00 8.00
OD161 A94 12c blue (#311) 5.00 1.00
OD162 A94 20c ultra (#312) *2.00* *2.00*
Nos. OD160-OD162 (3) 27.00 11.00

1923 ***Perf. 13½x12½***

OD163 A104 1c buff (#324) 6.00 1.00
a. Perf. 13½ (#324A) 4.00 2.00
OD164 A104 2c dark brown (#325) .50 .50
a. Perf. 13½ (#325A) 50.00 30.00
OD165 A104 5c red (#328) 1.20 .50
a. Perf. 13½ (#328A) 10.00 1.00
OD166 A104 12c deep blue (#330) 12.00 4.00
a. Perf. 13½ (#330A) 45.00 20.00
OD167 A104 20c ultra (#331) 20.00 2.00
a. Perf. 13½ (#331A) 20.00 10.00
Nos. OD163-OD167 (5) 39.70 8.00

1924

OD168 A104 1c buff (#341) .50 .50
OD169 A104 2c dk brn (#342) 1.00 .50
OD170 A104 3c green (#343) 8.00 2.00
OD171 A104 5c red (#345) 1.00 .50
OD173 A104 12c dp bl (#347) 1.00 .50
OD174 A104 20c ultra (#348) 20.00 8.00
Nos. OD168-OD174 (6) 31.50 12.00

No. OD172B

Type II

1931-36 ***Perf. 13½x12½***

OD170B A104 3c green (#343) 2.00 2.00
OD171B A104 5c red (#345) .75 .50
OD172B A104 10c dull green (#346) 1.00 .50
c. Typo (coil) (#346a) .50 .50
OD174B A104 20c ultra (#348) 2.00 1.00
c. Typo (coil) (#348a) 2.00 1.00
OD175B A104 30c claret (#351) 6.00 1.00
c. Typo (coil) (#351a) 16.00 5.00
Nos. OD170B-OD175B (5) 11.75 5.00

No. OD182A

1936-38 **Litho.** ***Perf. 13½x13***

OD176 A129 1c buff (#419) .50 .50
OD177 A130 2c dk brn (#420) .50 .50
OD178 A132 3c green (#422) 1.00 .50
OD178A A134 5c yel brn (#427d) .50 .50
OD180 A139 15c slate bl (#434) ('36) 1.40 .50
OD181 A140 20c lt ultra (#437) 6.00 1.00
OD182 A140 20c lt ultra (#438) 1.00 .50
OD182A A142 30c org brn & yel brown (#442) .50 .50
OD182B A145 1p brn blk & lt blue (#445) 10.00 6.00
OD182C A146 1p brn blk & lt bl (#446) ('37) 1.25 .50
Nos. OD176-OD182C (10) 22.65 11.00

Typo. ***Perf. 13½***

OD178D A134 5c yel brn (#427) 1.25 .50
e. Inverted ovpt. *75.00*
OD179D A137 10c car (#430) 1.60 .50
e. Perf. 13½x13 (#430a) 1.25 .75

Ministry of Justice and Instruction

No. OD184

1913 **Type I** ***Perf. 13½x12½***

OD183 A88 2c choc (#181) 6.00 2.00
OD184 A88 1c ocher (#190) 8.00 1.00
OD185 A88 2c choc (#191) 6.00 1.00
a. Perf. 13½ (#191a) — 30.00
OD186 A88 5c red (#194) 2.00 .50
OD187 A88 12c dp bl (#196) 3.00 .50
Nos. OD184-OD187 (4) 19.00 3.00

1915

OD188 A88 1c ocher (#208) 2.00 1.00
OD189 A88 2c chocolate (#209) 2.00 .50
OD190 A88 5c red (#212) 6.00 .80
Nos. OD188-OD190 (3) 10.00 2.30

1916 ***Perf. 13½***

OD191 A91 5c red (#220) 3.00 .50
OD192 A92 12c blue (#222) 4.00 1.60

1918

OD193 A93 1c buff (#232) 3.00 1.00
a. Perf. 13½x12½ (#232B) 2.00 1.00
OD194 A93 2c brown (#233) 8.00 8.00
a. Perf. 13½x12½ (#233B) 4.00 1.00
OD195 A93 5c red (#236) 20.00 2.00
a. Perf. 13½x12½ (#236B) 10.00 1.00
OD196 A94 12c blue (#238) 90.00 20.00
Nos. OD193-OD196 (4) 121.00 31.00
OD197 A93 1c buff (#249) .60 .50
a. Perf. 13½x12½ (#249B) 200.00 14.00
OD198 A93 2c brown (#250) .50 .50
a. Perf. 13½x12½ (#250B) 1.00 .50
OD199 A93 5c red (#253) .50 .50
a. Perf. 13½x12½ (#253B) 1.00 .50
OD200 A94 12c blue (#255) .50 .50
OD201 A94 20c ultra (#256) 2.00 1.00
Nos. OD197-OD201 (5) 4.10 3.00

1920 ***Perf. 13½x12½***

OD202 A93 1c buff (#265) 1.50 1.00
OD203 A93 2c brown (#266) 1.00 .50
OD204 A93 5c red (#269) 1.00 .50
a. Perf. 13½ (#269A) 16.00 8.00
OD205 A94 12c blue (perf. 13½) (#271) 2.00 1.00
Nos. OD202-OD205 (4) 5.50 3.00

1922 ***Perf. 13½***

OD206 A93 1c buff (#305) 6.00 2.00
a. Perf. 13½x12½ (#305B) 1.50 .50
OD207 A93 2c brown, (perf. 13½x12½) (#306B) 8.00 2.00

OD208 A103 5c red (#309) 1.50 .50
a. Perf. 13½x12½ (#309B) 1.00 .50
OD209 A94 12c blue (#311) 50.00 16.00
OD210 A94 20c ultra (#312) 8.00 1.25
Nos. OD206-OD210 (5) 73.50 21.75

1922 ***Perf. 13½x12½***
OD211 A93 2c brown (#318A) 7.00 2.00

1923
OD212 A104 1c buff (#324) 1.25 .50
a. Perf. 13½ (#324A) 2.50 1.00
OD213 A104 2c dk brn (#325) .50 .50
a. Perf. 13½ (#325A) 2.00 1.00
b. As "a," inverted ovpt. *25.00 20.00*
OD214 A104 5c red (#328) .50 .50
a. Perf. 13½ (#328A) 2.00 1.00
OD215 A104 12c dp bl (#330) .50 .50
OD216 A104 20c ultra (#331) 1.00 .50
a. Perf. 13½ (#331A) 2.00 1.00
Nos. OD212-OD216 (5) 3.75 2.50

1924
OD218 A104 1c buff (#341) .50 .50
OD219 A104 2c dk brn (#342) .50 .50
OD220 A104 3c green (#343) .60 .50
OD221 A104 5c red (#345) 2.00 2.00
OD222 A104 10c dl grn (#346) 5.00 2.00
OD223 A104 12c dp bl (#347) .50 .50
OD224 A104 20c ultra (#348) .50 .50
Nos. OD218-OD224 (7) 9.60 6.50

1926
OD227 A109 5c red (#359) .50 .50
a. Inverted ovpt. *35.00 30.00*
OD228 A110 12c dp bl (#360) 1.00 .50

No. OD217B

Type II

1931-36 ***Perf. 13½x12½, 13***
OD217B A104 ½c red vio (#340) 10.00 6.00
OD218B A104 1c buff (#341) 1.00 1.00
OD220B A104 3c green (#343) .50 .50
c. Typo (coil) (#343b) .50 .50
OD221B A104 5c red (#345) 2.00 2.00
OD222B A104 10c dl grn (#346) .80 .50
c. Typo (coil) (#346a) 1.00 1.00
OD223B A104 12c dp bl (#347) 6.00 .60
OD224B A104 20c ultra (#348) .50 .50
c. Typo (coil) (#348a) .50 .50
OD225B A104 30c claret (#351) .50 .50
c. Typo (coil) (#351a) 2.50 1.00
OD226B A105 1p blue & red (Perf. 13½) (#353) 2.00 1.25
Nos. OD217B-OD226B (9) 23.30 12.85

No. OD229

1936-38 ***Perf. 13½x13***
OD229 A129 1c buff (#419) .50 .50
OD230 A130 2c dk brn (#420) .50 .50
OD231 A132 3c green (#422) .50 .50
OD232 A134 5c yel brn (#427d) .50 .50
OD234 A139 15c slate bl (#434) 2.00 1.00
OD234A A140 20c lt ultra (#437) .50 .50
OD234B A140 20c lt ultra (#438) .60 .50
OD234C A141 25c car & pink (#441) .50 .50
OD234D A142 30c org brn & yel brn (#442) 1.00 .50
OD234E A145 1p brn blk &l lt bl (#445) 6.00 3.00
OD234F A146 1p brn blk& lt bl (#446) 6.00 2.00
Nos. OD229-OD234F (11) 18.60 10.00

Typo. ***Perf. 13½***
OD232A A134 5c yel brn (#427) .50 .50
OD233 A137 10c car (#430) .50 .50
a. Perf. 13½x13 (#430a) 2.00 .50

Ministry of Marine

No. OD236

1913 **Type I** ***Perf. 13½x12½***
OD235 A88 2c choc (#181) 1.25 .50
a. Perf. 13½ (#181a) 150.00 75.00
OD236 A88 1c ocher (#190) .50 .50
OD237 A88 2c choc (#191) 24.00 .50
OD238 A88 5c red (#194) 3.00 .50
a. Perf. 13½ (#194a) 80.00 16.00
OD239 A88 12c dp bl (#196) .60 .50
Nos. OD236-OD239 (4) 28.10 2.00

1915
OD240 A88 2c chocolate (#209) 6.00 .50
OD241 A88 5c red (#212) 6.00 .50

1918
OD242 A93 1c buff (#232) .70 .50
OD243 A93 2c brown (#233) .70 .50
OD244 A93 5c red (#236) 1.40 .50
a. Perf. 13½ (#236B) 4.00 1.00
Nos. OD242-OD244 (3) 2.80 1.50

1920 ***Perf. 13½***
OD245 A93 1c buff (#249) .50 .50
OD246 A93 2c brown (#250) .70 .50
a. Perf. 13½x12½ (#250) 6.00 2.00
OD247 A93 5c red (#253) 7.00 .50
a. Perf. 13½x12½ (#253B) .60 .50
OD248 A94 12c blue (#255) 2.50 .60
OD249 A94 20c ultra (#256) 16.00 3.00
Nos. OD245-OD249 (5) 26.70 5.10

1920
OD250 A93 1c buff (#265A) (perf. 13½x12½) .50 .50
OD251 A93 2c brown (#266A) .70 .50
a. Perf. 13½x12½ (#266) .80 .50
OD252 A93 5c red (#269A) .80 .50
Nos. OD250-OD252 (3) 2.00 1.50

1922
OD253 A103 5c red (#309) 10.00 2.00
a. Perf. 13½x12½ (#309B) 3.00 .60
OD254 A94 12c blue (#311) 60.00 20.00
OD255 A94 20c ultra (#312) 90.00 16.00
Nos. OD253-OD255 (3) 160.00 38.00

1923 ***Perf. 13½x12½***
OD256 A104 1c buff (#324) .50 .50
a. Perf. 13½ (#324A) 150.00 60.00
OD257 A104 2c dk brn (#325) 2.00 .50
a. Inverted overprint — *75.00*
b. Perf. 13½ (#325A) 24.00 2.00
OD258 A104 5c red (#328) 5.00 .50
a. Inverted overprint — *75.00*
b. Perf. 13½ (#328A) 30.00 5.00
c. As "b," inverted overprint — *75.00*
OD259 A104 12c deep blue (#330) 2.50 .50
a. Perf. 13½ (#330A) 36.00 4.00
OD260 A104 20c ultra (#331) 3.00 .50
a. Perf. 13½ (#331A) 16.00 2.00
Nos. OD256-OD260 (5) 13.00 2.50

1924
OD261 A104 1c buff (#341) 10.00 2.50
OD262 A104 2c dk brn (#342) .50 1.00
OD264 A104 5c red (#345) .50 .50
OD266 A104 20c ultra (#348) 16.00 .50
Nos. OD261-OD266 (4) 27.00 4.50

1926
OD269 A109 5c red (#359) .50 .25

No. OD264B

Type II

1931-36 ***Perf. 13½x12½, 13***
OD263B A104 3c grn (#343) 20.00 1.60
OD264B A104 5c red (#345) 3.00 .50
OD265B A104 10c dl grn (#346) 10.00 2.00
c. Typo (coil) (#346a) 2.00 .50
OD266B A104 20c ultra (#348) 20.00 2.00
c. Typo (coil) (#348a) 10.00 1.00
OD267B A104 30c claret (#351) 8.00 1.60
OD268B A105 1p blue & red (Perf. 13½) (#353) 120.00 60.00

No. OD270

1936-38 ***Perf. 13½x13***
OD270 A129 1c buff (#419) 1.00 .50
OD271 A130 2c dk brn (#420) .50 .50
OD272 A132 3c green (#422) 1.00 1.00
OD273 A134 5c yel brn (#427d) .50 .50
OD275 A139 15c slate bl (#434) ('36) 2.50 .60
OD276 A140 20c lt ultra (#437) 4.00 1.00
OD277 A140 20c lt ultra (#438) 2.00 .50
OD278 A142 30c org brn & yel brn (#442) ('36) 1.50 .50
OD279 A145 1p brn blk & lt bl (#445) ('36) 24.00 16.00
OD280 A146 1p brn blk & lt bl (#446) ('37) 16.00 4.00
Nos. OD270-OD280 (10) 53.00 25.10

Typo. ***Perf. 13½***
OD273A A134 5c yel brn (#427) 1.00 .60
b. Inverted overprint *25.00 25.00*
OD274A A137 10c car (#430) 4.00 .50
b. Perf. 13½x13 (#430a) 1.50 .75

Ministry of Public Works

No. OD281

1913 **Type I** ***Perf. 13½x12½***
OD281 A88 2c choc (#181) 4.00 .50
a. Perf. 13½ (#181a) 20.00 4.00
OD282 A88 1c ocher (#190) 2.00 .50
OD283 A88 5c red (#194) 3.00 .50
OD284 A88 12c dp bl (#196) 20.00 8.00
a. Perf. 13½ (#196a) *15.00 6.00*
Nos. OD282-OD284 (3) 25.00 9.00

1916 ***Perf. 13½***
OD285 A91 5c red (#220) 70.00 20.00

1918 ***Perf. 13½x12½***
OD286 A93 2c brown (#233) *30.00 20.00*
OD287 A93 5c red (#236) *18.00 9.00*

1920 ***Perf. 13½***
OD288 A93 2c brown (#266) *35.00 8.00*
OD289 A93 5c red (#269) 20.00 2.00
OD290 A94 12c blue (#271) *50.00 20.00*
Nos. OD288-OD290 (3) 105.00 30.00

1923 ***Perf. 13½x12½***
OD291 A104 1c buff (#324) .60 .50
a. Perf. 13½ (#324A) 40.00 *15.00*
OD292 A104 2c dk brn (#325) .50 .50
a. Perf. 13½ (#325A) 2.00 2.00
OD293 A104 5c red (#328) 4.00 1.00
a. Perf. 13½ (#328A) 6.00 2.00
OD294 A104 12c dp bl (#330) 4.00 2.00
a. Perf. 13½ (#330A) 4.00 1.00
OD295 A104 20c ultra #331 4.00 .60
a. Perf. 13½ (#331A) 16.00 1.25
Nos. OD291-OD295 (5) 13.10 4.60

1924
OD296 A104 1c buff (#341) .50 .50
OD297 A104 2c dk brn (#342) .50 .50
OD299 A104 5c red (#345) .50 .50
OD301 A104 12c dp bl (#347) 60.00 20.00
OD302 A104 20c ultra (#348) .50 .50
Nos. OD296-OD302 (5) 62.00 22.00

1926
OD305 A109 5c red (#359) .60 .25

No. OD299B

Type II

1931-36 ***Perf. 13½x12½, 13***
OD298B A104 3c grn (#343) .50 .50
c. Typo (coil) (#343b) — 40.00
OD299B A104 5c red (#345) .60 .50
OD300B A104 10c dl grn (#346) .60 .50
c. Typo (coil) (#346a) 4.00 .50
OD301B A104 20c ultra typo (coil) (#348b) *50.00 10.00*
OD303B A104 30c claret (#351) 1.80 .50
OD304B A105 1p blue & red (13½) (#353) 200.00 —
Nos. OD298B-OD304B (6) 253.50 12.00

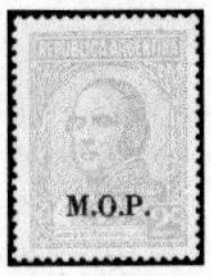

No. OD307

1936-38 ***Perf. 13½x13***
OD306 A129 1c buff (#419) .50 .50
OD307 A130 2c dk brn (#420) .60 .50
OD308 A132 3c green (#422) 2.00 .50
OD309 A134 5c yel brn (#427d) 1.00 .50
OD311 A139 15c slate bl (#434) 3.00 1.00
OD312 A140 20c lt ultra (#437) 6.00 .50
OD313 A140 20c lt ultra (#438) 1.00 .50
OD314 A142 30c org brn & yel brn (#442) ('36) .60 .50
OD315 A144 50c red & org (#444) ('36) 5.00 5.00
OD316 A145 1p brn blk & lt bl (#445) ('36) 10.00 6.00
OD317 A146 1p brn blk & lt bl (#446) ('37) 2.00 1.00
Nos. OD306-OD317 (11) 31.70 16.50

Typo. ***Perf. 13½***
OD309A A134 5c yel brn (#427) 1.25 .50
b. Inverted overprint — *75.00*
OD310 A137 10c car (#430) 4.00 .50
a. Perf. 13½x13 (#430a) 2.00 .50

Ministry of Foreign Affairs and Religion

No. OD318

1913 **Type I** ***Perf. 13½x12½***
OD318 A88 2c choc (#181) 90.00 20.00
OD319 A88 1c ocher (#190) .50 .50
OD320 A88 2c choc (#191) .50 .50
OD321 A88 5c red (#194) 3.00 1.00
OD322 A88 12c dp bl (#196) 1.25 .50
a. Perf. 13½ (#196a) 100.00 40.00
Nos. OD319-OD322 (4) 5.25 2.50

1915
OD323 A88 5c red (#212) 3.00 1.75

1916 ***Perf. 13½***
OD324 A91 5c red (#220) 2.50 .50

1918
OD325 A94 20c ultra (#256) 20.00 8.00

1922
OD326 A93 1c buff, perf. 13½x12½ (#265) 3.00 1.00
OD327 A93 5c red (#269) 1.25 .60

1922-23 ***Perf. 13½x12½***
OD328 A93 2c brn (#306B) 80.00 30.00
OD329 A103 5c red (#309B) *100.00*

Perf. 13½
OD330 A93 12c blue (#311) *100.00*
OD330A A94 20c ultra (#312) *100.00*

1923 ***Perf. 13½x12½***
OD331 A104 1c buff (#324) .60 .50
a. Perf. 13½ (#324A) 25.00 10.00
OD332 A104 2c dk brn (#325) 1.00 .60
a. Perf. 13½ (#325A) 25.00 16.00
OD333 A104 5c red (#328) .50 .50
a. Perf. 13½ (#328A) 6.00 2.00
OD334 A104 12c dp bl (#330) .50 .50
a. Perf. 13½ (#330A) 5.00 2.00
OD335 A104 20c ultra (#331) .50 .50
Nos. OD331-OD335 (5) 3.10 2.60

No. OD344B

1924

OD337 A104 1c buff (#341) .60 .50
OD338 A104 2c dk brn (#342) .50 .50
OD339 A104 3c green (#343) .50 .50
OD340 A104 5c red (#345) .50 .50
OD341 A104 10c dl grn (#346) 8.00 1.00
OD342 A104 12c dp bl (#347) .60 .50
OD343 A104 20c ultra (#348) .60 .50
OD344 A104 30c claret (#351) 4.00 2.00
Nos. OD337-OD344 (8) 15.30 6.00

1926

OD346 A110 12c dp bl (#360) .50 .60

Type II

1931-36 ***Perf. 13½x12½, 13½***

OD336B A104 ½c red vio (#340) 10.00 5.00
OD341B A104 10c dl grn (#346) 1.25 .60
OD343B A104 20c ultra (typo, coil) (#348a) .60 .60
OD344B A104 30c claret (typo, coil) (#351a) .60 .60
OD345B A105 1p blue & red, perf. 13½ (#353) 1.50 1.00
Nos. OD336B-OD345B (5) 13.95 7.80

No. OD347

1935-37 **Typo.** ***Perf. 13x13½***

OD347 A129 1c buff (#419) .50 .50
OD348 A130 2c dk brn (#420) .50 .50
OD349 A132 3c green (#422) .50 .50
OD350 A134 5c yel brn (#427d) .50 .50
OD352 A139 15c slate bl (#434) .70 .50
OD353 A140 20c lt ultra (#437) 3.00 .50
OD354 A140 20c lt ultra (#438) .50 .50
OD355 A142 30c org brn & yel brn (#442) .50 .50
OD356 A145 1p brn blk & lt bl (#445) 20.00 10.00
OD357 A146 1p brn blk & lt bl (#446) 1.50 1.00
Nos. OD347-OD357 (10) 28.20 15.00

Typo. ***Perf. 13½***

OD350B A134 5c yel brn (#427) .60 .50
OD351B A137 10c car (#430) .50 .50
c. Perf. 13½x13 (#430a) 4.00 .50

PARCEL POST STAMPS

PP1

Postal Service Headquarters, Buenos Aires — PP2

2001 **Litho.** ***Serpentine Die Cut 11***

Self-Adhesive

Q1 PP1 1p red & black *20.00 20.00*

Die Cut

Q1A PP1 1p red & black *40.00 20.00*
Q2 PP2 7p blue & black *27.50 20.00*
Q3 PP2 11p brown & black *40.00 30.00*
Nos. Q1-Q3 (3) *87.50 70.00*

Nos. Q1-Q3 were sold only at Unidas Postal outlets. No. Q3 is inscribed "Caja Envio 2."

Stamps of Type PP2 lacking "U.P." in denominations of 7p, 11p, 16p, and 23p were issued in 1999, but were applied by postal workers to packages brought to post offices by customers with large mailings (Grandes Clientes). These stamps were not to be given to any customers purchasing them. Value, set unused $160.

The same sale and use restrictions applied to four other non-denominated stamps for use by "Grandes Clientes," which are inscribed "Caja Normalizada," have blue, brown-violet, gray-green, and ocher frames, and were issued in 1995. Value, set unused $550.

Nos. Q2 and Q3, though inscribed "Grandes Clientes," apparently were available for purchase by any customers, at Unidas Postal outlets.

BUENOS AIRES

The central point of the Argentine struggle for independence. At intervals Buenos Aires maintained an independent government but after 1862 became a province of the Argentine Republic.

8 Reales = 1 Peso

Values of Buenos Aires Nos. 1-8 vary according to condition. Quotations are for fine examples. Very fine to superb specimens sell at much higher prices, and inferior or poor stamps sell at reduced values, depending on the condition of the individual specimen.

Nos. 1-8 are normally found without gum, and the values below are for such items. Examples with original gum sell for higher prices.

Steamship — A1

1858 **Unwmk.** **Typo.** ***Imperf.***

1 A1 1 (in) pesos lt brn *500.00* *300.*
a. Double impression *700.*
2 A1 2 (dos) pesos blue 300.00 150.
b. Diag. half used as 1p on cover *7,500.*
3 A1 3 (tres) pesos grn 1,500. *950.*
a. 3p dark green 2,000. *1,500.*
4 A1 4 (cuatro) pesos ver 5,000. *4,500.*
a. Half used as 2p on cover *25,000.*
b. 4p chestnut brown (error) *30,000.* *40,000.*
5 A1 5 (cinco) pesos org 5,000. *3,000.*
a. 5p ocher 5,000. *3,000.*
b. 5p olive yellow 5,000. *3,000.*

Issued: Nos. 2-5, Apr. 29; No. 1, Oct. 26.

1858, Oct. 26

6 A1 4 (cuatro) reales brown 350.00 300.
a. 4r gray brown 400.00 300.
b. 4r chestnut 350.00 300.

1859, Jan. 1

7 A1 1 (in) pesos blue 200. *200.*
a. 1p indigo 300. *150.*
b. Impression on reverse of stamp in blue *28,500.*
c. Double impression 2,800. *700.*
d. Vert. tête-bêche pair *675,000.*
e. Horiz. tête-bêche pair —
f. Half used as 4r on cover *7,500.*
8 A1 1 (to) pesos blue 600. 450.

No. 7e is valued with faults.

Nos. 1, 2, 3 and 7 have been reprinted on very thick, hand-made paper. The same four stamps and No. 8 have been reprinted on thin, hard, white wove paper.

Counterfeits of Nos. 1-8 are plentiful.

Liberty Head — A2

1859, Sept. 3

9 A2 4r green, *bluish* 400.00 200.00
10 A2 1p blue, fine impression 40.00 25.00
d. Double impression 600.00 400.00
e. Partial double impression 325.00 175.00
11 A2 2p vermilion, fine impression 500.00 200.00
a. 2p red, blurred impression 375.00 125.00
b. Vert. half used as 1p on cover *4,000.*

Both fine and blurred impressions of these stamps may be found. They have generally been called Paris and Local prints, respectively, but the opinion now obtains that the differences are due to the impression and that they do not represent separate issues. Values are for fine impressions. Rough or blurred impressions sell for less.

Many shades exist of Nos. 1-11.

1862, Oct. 4

12 A2 1p rose 350.00 150.00
13 A2 2p blue 350.00 90.00

All three values have been reprinted in black, brownish black, blue and red brown on thin hard white paper. The 4r has also been reprinted in green on bluish paper.

Values are for fine impressions. Rough or blurred impressions sell for less.

No. 13 exists with papermaker's wmk.

CORDOBA

A province in the central part of the Argentine Republic.

100 Centavos = 1 Peso

Arms of Cordoba — A1

Unwmk.

1858, Oct. 28 **Litho.** ***Imperf.***

Laid Paper

1 A1 5c blue 150.
2 A1 10c black *3,000.*

Cordoba stamps were printed on laid paper, but stamps from edges of the sheets sometimes do not show any laid lines and appear to be on wove paper. Counterfeits are plentiful.

CORRIENTES

The northeast province of the Argentine Republic.

1 Real M(oneda) C(orriente) =
12½ Centavos M.C. = 50 Centavos
100 Centavos Fuertes = 1 Peso Fuerte

Nos. 1-2 were issued without gum. Nos. 3-8 were issued both with and without gum (values the same).

Ceres — A1

Unwmk.

1856, Aug. 21 **Typo.** ***Imperf.***

1 A1 1r black, *blue* 100.00 *40.00*

No. 1 used is valued with pen cancellation.

Pen Stroke Through "Un Real"

1860, Feb. 8

2 A1 (3c) black, *blue* 600.00 *120.00*

No. 2 used is valued with pen cancellation.

Ceres — A2

1860-80

3 A2 (3c) black, *blue* 9.50 *30.00*
4 A2 (2c) blk, *yel grn* ('64) 50.00 *100.00*
a. (2c) black, *blue green* 92.50 *150.00*
5 A2 (2c) blk, *yel* ('67) 7.50 *19.00*
6 A2 (3c) blk, *dk bl* ('71) 3.00 *19.00*
7 A2 (3c) blk, *rose red* ('76) 150.00 70.00
a. (3c) black, *lil rose* ('75) 200.00 100.00
8 A2 (3c) blk, *dk rose* ('79) 8.00 *35.00*
a. (3c) black, *red vio* ('77) 75.00 50.00
Nos. 3-8 (6) 228.00 273.00

Pen canceled examples of Nos. 3-8 that do not indicate the town of origin sell for much less.

Printed from settings of 8 varieties, 3 or 4 impressions constituting a sheet. Some impressions were printed inverted and tete beche pairs may be cut from adjacent impressions.

From Jan. 1 to Feb. 24, 1864, No. 4 was used as a 5 centavos stamp but examples so used can only be distinguished when they bear dated cancellations.

The reprints show numerous spots and small defects which are not found on the originals. They are printed on gray blue, dull blue, gray green, dull orange and light magenta papers.

ARMENIA

är-ˈmē-nē-ə

LOCATION — South of Russia bounded by Georgia, Azerbaijan, Iran and Turkey
GOVT. — Republic
AREA — 11,490 sq. mi.
POP. — 3,409,234 (est. 1999)
CAPITAL — Yerevan

With Azerbaijan and Georgia, Armenia made up the Transcaucasian Federation of Soviet Republics.

Stamps of Armenia were replaced in 1923 by those of Transcaucasian Federated Republics.

With the breakup of the Soviet Union on Dec. 26, 1991, Armenia and ten former Soviet republics established the Commonwealth of Independent States.

100 Kopecks = 1 Ruble
100 Luma = 1 Dram (1993)

Catalogue values for unused stamps in this country are for Never Hinged items, beginning with Scott 430 in the regular postage section.

Counterfeits abound of all Armenian stamps through Scott 390, both of the basic stamps and of overprinted and surcharged stamps.

Watermark

Wmk. 171 — Diamonds

Perforations
Perforations are the same as the basic Russian stamps.

National Republic
Russian Stamps of 1902-19 Handstamped

At least thirteen types exist of both framed and unframed overprints ("a" and "c"). The device is the Armenian "H," initial of Hayasdan (Armenia). Inverted and double overprints are found.

Surcharged

Type I — Without periods (two types).
Type II — Periods after 1st "K" and "60."

Black Surcharge

1919 Unwmk. *Perf. 14x14½*

1 A14 60k on 1k orange (II) 2.00 5.00
a. Imperf. (I) 2.00 5.00
b. Imperf. (II) 2.00 3.00

Violet Surcharge

2 A14 60k on 1k orange (II) 5.00 5.00

Handstamped in Violet a

6 A15 4k carmine 5.00 7.00
7 A14 5k claret, imperf. 5.00 7.00
a. Perf. 10.00 10.00
9 A14 10k on 7k lt blue 10.00 15.00
10 A11 15k red brn & bl 5.00 7.00
11 A8 20k blue & car 5.00 7.00
13 A11 35k red brn & grn 5.00 7.00
14 A8 50k violet & green 5.00 7.00
15 A14 60k on 1k orange (II) 5.00 7.00
a. Imperf. (I) 10.00 10.00
b. Imperf. (II) 15.00 15.00
18 A13 5r dk bl, grn & pale bl 20.00 25.00
a. Imperf. 20.00 30.00
19 A12 7r dk green & pink 35.00 40.00
20 A13 10r scar, yel & gray 35.00 40.00

Handstamped in Black

31 A14 2k green, imperf. 4.00 4.00
a. Perf. 10.00 10.00
32 A14 3k red, imperf. 3.00 3.00
a. Perf. 10.00 10.00
33 A15 4k carmine 10.00 10.00
a. Imperf. 15.00 15.00
34 A14 5k claret 1.10 1.10
a. Imperf. 10.00 10.00
36 A15 10k dark blue 2.00 2.00
37 A14 10k on 7k lt blue 1.50 *4.50*
38 A11 15k red brn & bl 4.00 *7.50*
a. Imperf. 8.00 *15.00*
39 A8 20k blue & car 2.00 *5.00*
40 A11 25k green & gray vio 2.00 *5.00*
41 A11 35k red brn & grn 2.00 *4.00*
42 A8 50k violet & green 3.00 *5.00*
43 A14 60k on 1k orange (II) 5.00 5.00
43A A11 70k brown & org 3.00 3.00
b. Imperf. 2.00 *4.00*
44 A9 1r pale brn, dk brn & org 3.00 *5.00*
a. Imperf. 8.00 8.00
45 A12 3½r mar & lt grn, imperf. 3.00 *5.00*
a. Perf. 10.00 10.00
46 A13 5r dk bl, grn & pale bl 8.00 10.00
a. Imperf. 12.00 15.00
47 A12 7r dk green & pink 6.50 6.50
48 A13 10r scar, yel & gray 30.00 *50.00*

Handstamped in Violet c

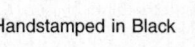

Wove Paper

Unwmk. *Perf.*

62 A14 2k green, imperf. 12.00 12.00
a. Perf. 15.00 15.00
63 A14 3k red, imperf. 2.50 2.50
a. Perf. 15.00 15.00
64 A15 4k carmine 10.00 10.00
65 A14 5k claret 5.00 5.00
a. Imperf. 15.00 15.00
67 A15 10k dark blue 5.00 *10.00*
68 A14 10k on 7k lt bl 3.50 3.50
69 A11 15k red brn & bl 5.00 *10.00*
70 A8 20k blue & car 3.00 *6.00*
71 A11 25k grn & gray vio 25.00 *15.00*
72 A11 35k red brn & grn 15.00 *20.00*
73 A8 50k violet & grn 5.00 *10.00*
74 A14 60k on 1k org (II) 10.00 *12.00*
a. Imperf. (I) 10.00 *12.00*
b. Imperf. (II) 10.00 *12.00*
75 A9 1r pale brn, dk brn & org 12.50 12.50
a. Imperf. 10.00 *12.00*
76 A12 3½r mar & lt grn, imperf. 6.00 6.00
a. Perf. 10.00 10.00
77 A13 5r dk bl, grn & pale bl, imperf. 12.50 12.50
a. Perf. 8.00 8.00
78 A12 7r dk green & pink 30.00 30.00
79 A13 10r scar, yel & gray 50.00 50.00

Imperf

85 A11 70k brown & org 25.00 25.00

Handstamped in Black

Perf.

90 A14 1k orange 10.00 10.00
a. Imperf. 10.00 10.00
91 A14 2k green, imperf. 1.25 *3.00*
a. Perf. 8.00 *10.00*
92 A14 3k red, imperf. 8.00 *12.00*
a. Perf. 1.50 *2.00*
93 A15 4k carmine 3.00 3.00
94 A14 5k claret 1.00 2.00
a. Imperf. 2.00 *5.00*
95 A14 7k light blue 5.00 *8.00*
96 A15 10k dark blue 10.00 *10.00*
97 A14 10k on 7k lt bl 1.25 *5.00*
98 A11 15k red brn & bl 2.00 *5.00*
99 A8 20k blue & car 5.00 *7.00*
100 A11 25k grn & gray vio 2.00 *5.00*
101 A11 35k red brn & grn 3.00 *5.00*
102 A8 50k violet & grn 2.00 *5.00*
102A A14 60k on 1k org, imperf. (I) 20.00 *30.00*
b. Imperf. (II) 4.00 *6.00*
c. Perf. (II) 8.00 8.00
103 A9 1r pale brn, dk brn & org 2.00 *5.00*
a. Imperf. 2.00 *5.00*
104 A12 3½r maroon & lt grn 5.00 *8.00*
a. Imperf. 5.00 8.00
105 A13 5r dk bl, grn & pale bl 7.00 9.00
a. Imperf. 8.00 12.00
106 A12 7r dk green & pink 15.00 *20.00*
107 A13 10r scar, yel & gray 25.00 *50.00*

Imperf

113 A11 70k brown & org 2.50 *4.00*

Handstamped in Violet or Black

Violet Surcharge, Type f

1920 *Perf.*

120 A14 3r on 3k red, imperf. 10.00 15.00
a. Perf. 10.00 15.00
121 A14 5r on 3k red 10.00 10.00
122 A15 5r on 4k car 10.00 *12.00*
123 A14 5r on 5k claret, imperf. 5.00 *12.00*
a. Perf. 12.00 *20.00*
124 A15 5r on 10k dk blue 20.00 *30.00*
125 A14 5r on 10k on 7k lt bl 20.00 *30.00*
126 A8 5r on 20k bl & car 10.00 *15.00*

Imperf

127 A14 5r on 2k green 12.00 12.00
128 A11 5r on 35k red brn & grn 12.00 12.00

Black Surcharge, Type f or Type g (#130)

Perf.

130 A14 1r on 1k orange 10.00 12.00
a. Imperf. 15.00 15.00
131 A14 3r on 3k red 8.00 8.00
a. Imperf. 2.00 5.00
132 A15 3r on 4k carmine 25.00 25.00
133 A14 5r on 2k grn, imperf. 2.50 *3.00*
a. Perf. 5.00 5.00
134 A14 5r on 3k red 12.00 12.00
a. Imperf. 5.00 5.00
135 A15 5r on 4k carmine 4.00 *10.00*
a. Imperf. 10.00 10.00
136 A14 5r on 5k claret 3.50 *4.00*
a. Imperf. 1.50 *2.00*
137 A14 5r on 7k lt blue 3.00 *4.00*
138 A15 5r on 10k dk blue 2.00 *4.00*
139 A14 5r on 10k on 7k lt bl 2.00 *5.00*
140 A11 5r on 14k bl & rose 2.50 2.50
141 A11 5r on 15k red brn & blue 1.00 3.00
a. Imperf. 3.00 6.00
142 A8 5r on 20k bl & car 1.00 *3.00*
a. Imperf. 50.00 50.00
143 A11 5r on 20k on 14k bl & rose 75.00 *100.00*
144 A11 5r on 25k grn & gray vio 10.00 *15.00*

Black Surcharge, Type g or Type f (#148A, 151)

145 A14 10r on 1k org, imperf. 1.10 1.10
a. Perf. *125.00* *125.00*
146 A14 10r on 3k red *175.00* *175.00*
147 A14 10r on 5k claret 18.00 18.00
a. Imperf. 15.00
148 A8 10r on 20k bl & car 15.00 15.00
148A A11 10r on 25k grn & gray vio 10.00 10.00
149 A11 10r on 25k grn & gray vio 5.00 *6.00*
a. Imperf. 10.00 *20.00*
150 A11 10r on 35k red brn & grn 1.50 1.50
151 A8 10r on 50k brn vio & grn 50.00 50.00
152 A8 10r on 50k brn vio & grn 2.00 *3.00*
152A A11 10r on 70k brn & org, imperf. 5.00 5.00
b. Perf. — —
152C A8 25r on 20k bl & car 8.00 *10.00*
153 A11 25r on 25k grn & gray vio 5.00 5.00
154 A11 25r on 35k red brn & grn 20.00 *25.00*
a. Imperf. 4.00 4.00
155 A8 25r on 50k vio & grn 5.00 *8.00*
a. Imperf. 6.00 *8.00*
156 A11 25r on 70k brn & org 8.00 8.00
a. Imperf. 5.00 5.00
157 A9 50r on 1r pale brn, dk brn & org, imperf. 2.00 2.00
a. Perf. 20.00 *25.00*
158 A13 50r on 5r dk bl, grn & lt bl 45.00 45.00
a. Imperf. 50.00 50.00
159 A12 100r on 3½r mar & lt grn 15.00 *18.00*
a. Imperf. 10.00 10.00
160 A13 100r on 5r dk bl, grn & pale bl 15.00 20.00
a. Imperf. 25.00 35.00
161 A12 100r on 7r dk grn & pink 10.00 15.00
a. Imperf. 42.00 42.00
162 A13 100r on 10r scar, yel & gray 15.00 20.00

Wmk. Wavy Lines (168)
Perf. 11½
Vertically Laid Paper

163 A12 100r on 3½r blk & gray *150.00* *150.00*
164 A12 100r on 7r blk & yel *150.00* *150.00*

No. 168

1920 Unwmk. *Imperf.*
Wove Paper

166 A14 (g) 1r on 60k on 1k org (I) 12.00 14.50
168 A14 (f) 5r on 1k orange 12.00 12.00
173 A11 (f) 5r on 35k red brn & grn 15.00 15.00
177 A11 (g) 50r on 70k brn & org 6.00 10.00
179 A12 (g) 50r on 3½r mar & lt grn 20.00 20.00
181 A9 (g) 100r on 1r pale brn, dk brn & org 25.00 25.00

Romanov Issues

Surcharged Types g or f (#185-187, 190) on Stamps of 1913

No. 187

No. 187C

1920 *Perf. 13½*

184 A16 1r on 1k brn org 200.00 200.00
185 A18 3r on 3k rose red 75.00 75.00
186 A19 5r on 4k dull red 10.00 10.00
187 A22 5r on 14k blue grn 40.00 40.00
187A A19 10r on 4k dull red 40.00
187B A26 10r on 35k gray vio & dk grn 100.00
187C A19 25r on 4k dull red 100.00 100.00
188 A26 25r on 35k gray vio & dk grn *100.00* *100.00*
189 A28 25r on 70k yel grn & brn *100.00* *100.00*
190 A31 50r on 3r dk vio — —
190A A16 100r on 1k brn org 125.00 125.00
190B A17 100r on 2k green 125.00 125.00
191 A30 100r on 2r brown 125.00 125.00
192 A31 100r on 3r dk vio 100.00 100.00

On Stamps of 1915, Type g

Thin Cardboard
Inscriptions on Back
Perf. 12

193 A21 100r on 10k blue 20.00
194 A23 100r on 15k brn 20.00
195 A24 100r on 20k ol grn 18.00

On Stamps of 1916, Type f

Perf. 13½

196 A20 5r on 10k on 7k brown 8.00 8.00
197 A22 5r on 20k on 14k bl grn 25.00 35.00

Surcharged Types f or g (#204-205A, 207-207C, 210-211) over Type c

Type c in Violet

Perf.

200	A15	5r on 4k car	50.00	*55.00*
201	A15	5r on 10k dk bl	50.00	50.00
202	A11	5r on 15k red brn & bl	50.00	50.00
203	A8	5r on 20k blue & car	50.00	50.00
204	A11	10r on 25k grn & gray vio	50.00	50.00
205	A11	10r on 35k red brn & grn	55.00	55.00
205A	A8	10r on 50k brn vio & grn	—	—
206	A8	25r on 50k brn vio & grn	150.00	150.00
207	A9	50r on 1r pale brn, dk brn & org, imperf.	50.00	50.00
a.		Perf.	50.00	50.00
207B	A12	100r on 3½r mar & lt grn	100.00	100.00
207C	A12	100r on 7r dk grn & pink	100.00	100.00

Imperf

208	A14	5r on 2k green	50.00	50.00
209	A14	5r on 5k claret	50.00	50.00
210	A11	25r on 70k brn & org	75.00	*75.00*
211	A13	100r on 5r dk bl, grn & pale bl	100.00	*110.00*

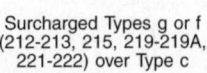

Surcharged Types g or f (212-213, 215, 219-219A, 221-222) over Type c

Type c in Black

Perf.

212	A14	5r on 7k lt bl	150.00	150.00
213	A14	5r on 10k on 7k lt bl	75.00	75.00
214	A11	5r on 15k red brn & bl	50.00	*60.00*
215	A8	5r on 20k blue & car	50.00	50.00
215A	A11	10r on 5r on 25k grn & gray vio	50.00	50.00
216	A11	10r on 35k red brn & grn	50.00	*60.00*
217	A8	10r on 50k brn vio & grn	*50.00*	*50.00*
217A	A9	50r on 1r pale brn, dk brn & org	50.00	*75.00*
b.		Imperf.	40.00	*50.00*
217C	A12	100r on 3½r mar & lt grn	35.00	*40.00*
218	A13	100r on 5r dk bl, grn & pale bl	35.00	*40.00*
a.		Imperf.	35.00	*45.00*
219	A12	100r on 7r dk grn & pink	50.00	50.00
219A	A13	100r on 10r scar, yel & gray	45.00	*55.00*

Imperf

220	A14	1r on 60k on 1k org (I)	50.00	50.00
221	A14	5r on 2k green	20.00	20.00
222	A14	5r on 5k claret	50.00	*50.00*
223	A11	10r on 70k brn & org	50.00	*50.00*
224	A11	25r on 70k brn & org	50.00	*50.00*

Surcharged Types g or f (#233) over Type a

Type a in Violet

Imperf

231	A9	50r on 1r pale brn, dk brn & org	150.00	*175.00*
232	A13	100r on 5r dk bl, grn & pale bl	150.00	*160.00*

Type a in Black

Perf.

233	A8	5r on 20k blue & car	45.00	45.00
233A	A11	10r on 25k grn & gray vio	35.00	35.00
234	A11	10r on 35k red brn & grn	185.00	185.00
235	A12	100r on 3½r mar & lt grn	—	—
a.		Imperf.	—	—

Imperf

237	A14	5r on 2k green	150.00	150.00
237A	A11	10r on 70k brn & org	—	—

Surcharged Type a and New Value

Type a in Violet

Perf.

238	A11	10r on 15k red brn & blue	*30.00*	*30.00*

Type a in Black

239	A8	5r on 20k blue & car	—	—
239A	A8	10r on 20k blue & car	*20.00*	*20.00*
239B	A8	10r on 50k brn red & grn	*30.00*	*40.00*

Imperf

240	A12	100r on 3½r mar & lt grn	*50.00*	*60.00*

Surcharged Type c and New Value

Type c in Black

1920 *Perf.*

241	A15	5r on 4k red	—	—
242	A11	5r on 15k red brn & bl	—	—
243	A8	10r on 20k blue & car	*50.00*	*50.00*
243A	A11	10r on 25k grn & gray vio	50.00	*50.00*
244	A11	10r on 35k red brn & grn	*50.00*	*50.00*
a.		With additional srch. "5r"	100.00	100.00
245	A12	100r on 3½r mar & lt grn	—	—

No. 248

Imperf

247	A14	3r on 3k red	*32.50*	*32.50*
248	A14	5r on 2k green	*30.00*	*30.00*
249	A9	50r on 1r pale brn, dk brn & org	35.00	35.00

Type c in Violet

249A	A14	5r on 2k green	—	—

Russia AR1-AR3 Surcharged

A1 A2 A3

Perf. 14½x15

Wmk. 171

250	A1	60k on 1k red & buff	75.00	75.00
251	A2	1r on 1k red & buff	75.00	75.00
252	A3	5r on 5k green & buff	75.00	75.00
253	A3	5r on 10k brn & buff	75.00	75.00

Russian Semi-Postal Stamps of 1914-18 Srchd. with Armenian Monogram & New Values

On Stamps of 1914

Unwmk. *Perf.*

255	SP5	25r on 1k red brn & dk grn, *straw*	75.00	75.00
256	SP5	25r on 3k mar & gray grn, *pink*	75.00	75.00
257	SP5	50r on 7 dk brn & dk grn, *buff*	125.00	150.00
258	SP5	100r on 1k red brn & dk grn, *straw*	100.00	100.00
259	SP5	100r on 3k mar & gray grn, *pink*	100.00	100.00
260	SP5	100r on 7k dk brn & dk grn, *buff*	100.00	100.00

No. 261

On Stamps of 1915-19

261	SP5	25r on 1k org brn & gray	125.00	125.00
262	SP5	25r on 3k car & gray	90.00	90.00
263	SP5	50r on 10k dk bl & brn	50.00	50.00
264	SP5	100r on 1k org brn & gray	100.00	100.00
265	SP5	100r on 10k dk bl & brn	125.00	125.00

These surcharged semi-postal stamps were used for ordinary postage.

A set of 10 stamps in the above designs was prepared in 1920, but not issued for postal use, though some were used fiscally. Value of set, $30. Reprints abound.

Soviet Socialist Republic

Hammer and Sickle — A7

Mythological Monster — A8

Symbols of Soviet Republics on Designs from old Armenian Manuscripts A9

Ruined City of Ani A10

Mythological Monster — A11

Armenian Soldier — A12

Mythological Monster A13

Soviet Symbols, Armenian Designs A14

Mt. Alagöz and Plain of Shirak — A15

Fisherman on River Aras — A16

Post Office in Erevan and Mt. Ararat — A17

Ruin in City of Ani — A18

Street in Erevan A19

Lake Sevan and Sevan Monastery A20

Mythological Subject from old Armenian Monument A21

Mt. Ararat — A22

1921 **Unwmk.** ***Perf. 11½***

278	A7	1r gray green	1.00	
279	A8	2r slate gray	1.00	
280	A9	3r carmine	1.00	
281	A10	5r dark brown	1.00	
282	A11	25r gray	1.00	5.00
283	A12	50r red	1.00	
284	A13	100r orange	1.00	
285	A14	250r dark blue	1.00	
286	A15	500r brown vio	1.00	
287	A16	1,000r sea green	1.00	
288	A17	2,000r bister	1.00	
289	A18	5,000r dark brown	1.00	
290	A19	10,000r dull red	1.00	
291	A20	15,000r slate blue	75.00	
292	A21	20,000r lake	2.00	
293	A22	25,000r gray blue	6.00	
294	A22	25,000r brown olive	10.00	
		Nos. 278-294 (17)	106.00	

Imperf.

278a	A7	1r	12.00	
279a	A8	2r	1.00	
280a	A9	3r	1.00	
281a	A10	5r	1.00	
282a	A11	25r	1.00	5.00
283a	A12	50r	45.00	
284a	A13	100r	1.00	
285a	A14	250r	1.00	

286a	A15	500r	1.00	
287a	A16	1,000r	1.00	
288a	A17	2,000r	1.00	
289a	A18	5,000r	1.00	
290a	A19	10,000r	1.00	
291a	A20	15,000r	90.00	
292a	A21	20,000r	2.00	
293a	A22	25,000r	5.00	
294a	A22	25,000r	5.00	
		Nos. 278a-294a (17)	170.00	5.00

Except the 25r, Nos. 278-294 were not regularly issued and used. Most examples of Nos. 278-294a on the market are forgeries. Values are for genuine stamps.

For surcharges see Nos. 347-390.

Russian Stamps of 1909-17 Surcharged

Lozenges of Varnish on Face

1921, Aug. Wove Paper *Perf. 13½*

295	A9	5,000r on 1r	*25.00*
296	A12	5,000r on 3½r	*25.00*
297	A13	5,000r on 5r	*25.00*
298	A12	5,000r on 7r	*25.00*
299	A13	5,000r on 10r	*25.00*
		Nos. 295-299 (5)	*125.00*

Nos. 295-299 were not officially issued. Counterfeits abound.

A23

Mt. Ararat & Soviet Star — A24

Soviet Symbols A25

Crane A26

Peasant A27

Harpy A28

Peasant Sowing A29

Soviet Symbols A30

Forging — A31

Plowing — A32

1922 *Perf. 11½*

300	A23	50r green & red	.85
301	A24	300r slate bl & buff	1.00
302	A25	400r blue & pink	1.00
303	A26	500r vio & pale lil	1.00
304	A27	1,000r dull bl & pale bl	1.00
305	A28	2,000r black & gray	1.25
306	A29	3,000r black & grn	1.25
307	A30	4,000r black & lt brn	1.25
308	A31	5,000r blk & dull red	1.25
309	A32	10,000r black & pale rose	1.25
a.		Tête-bêche pair	100.00
		Nos. 300-309 (10)	11.10

Nos. 300-309 were not issued without surcharge.

Stamps of types A23 to A32, printed in other colors than Nos. 300 to 309, are essays.

Nos. 300-309 with Hstmpd. Srch. in Rose, Violet or Black

1922

310	10,000 on 50r (R)	*90.00*	*90.00*
311	10,000 on 50r (V)	*100.00*	*60.00*
312	10,000 on 50r	*25.00*	*35.00*
313	15,000 on 300r (R)	*120.00*	*120.00*
314	15,000 on 300r (V)	*100.00*	*90.00*
315	15,000 on 300r	*25.00*	*35.00*
316	25,000 on 400r (V)	*75.00*	*60.00*
317	25,000 on 400r	*25.00*	*35.00*
318	30,000 on 500r (R)	*120.00*	*120.00*
319	30,000 on 500r (V)	*50.00*	*60.00*
320	30,000 on 500r	*25.00*	*35.00*
321	50,000 on 1,000r (R)	*250.00*	*250.00*
322	50,000 on 1,000r (V)	*200.00*	*200.00*
323	50,000 on 1,000r	*25.00*	*25.00*
324	75,000 on 3,000r	*25.00*	*35.00*
325	100,000 on 2,000r (R)	*250.00*	*275.00*
326	100,000 on 2,000r (V)	*100.00*	*60.00*
327	100,000 on 2,000r	*25.00*	*25.00*
328	200,000 on 4,000r (V)	*35.00*	*35.00*
329	200,000 on 4,000r	*20.00*	*20.00*
330	300,000 on 5,000r (V)	*50.00*	*60.00*
331	300,000 on 5,000r	*20.00*	*20.00*
332	500,000 on 10,000r (V)	*100.00*	*100.00*
333	500,000 on 10,000r	*12.00*	*12.00*
	Nos. 310-333 (24)	*1,867.*	*1,857.*

Forgeries exist.

Goose A33

Armenian Woman at Well A35

Armenian Village Scene — A34

Mt. Ararat — A36

Mt. Ararat — A37

New Values in Gold Kopecks, Handstamped Surcharge in Black

1922 *Imperf.*

334	A33	1(k) on 250r rose	25.00	35.00
335	A33	1(k) on 250r gray	25.00	35.00
336	A34	2(k) on 500r rose	25.00	*35.00*
337	A34	3(k) on 500r gray	25.00	35.00
338	A35	4(k) on 1,000r rose	25.00	35.00
339	A35	4(k) on 1,000r gray	25.00	35.00
340	A36	5(k) on 2,000r gray	25.00	35.00
341	A36	10(k) on 2,000r rose	25.00	35.00
342	A37	15(k) on 5,000r rose	47.50	52.50
343	A37	20(k) on 5,000r gray	25.00	*35.00*
		Nos. 334-343 (10)	272.50	367.50

Nos. 334-343 were issued for postal tax purposes.

Nos. 334-343 exist without surcharge but are not known to have been issued in that condition. Counterfeits exist of both sets.

Regular Issue of 1921 Handstamped with New Values in Black or Red Short, Thick Numerals

1922 *Imperf.*

347	A8	2(k) on 2r (R)	125.00	200.00
350	A11	4(k) on 25r (R)	125.00	125.00
353	A13	10(k) on 100r (R)	*24.00*	*24.00*
354	A14	15(k) on 250r	5.00	5.00
355	A15	20(k) on 500r	18.00	18.00
a.		With "k" written in red	12.00	12.00
357	A22	50(k) on 25,000r bl (R)	500.00	500.00
358	A22	50(k) on 25,000r brn ol (R)	*150.00*	*150.00*
359	A22	50(k) on 25,000r brn ol	—	—
		Nos. 347-358 (7)	947.00	1,022.

Perf. 11½

360	A7	1(k) on 1r, imperf.	*75.00*	*75.00*
a.		Perf.	*50.00*	*50.00*
361	A7	1(k) on 1r (R)	*45.00*	*45.00*
a.		Imperf.	*45.00*	*75.00*
362	A8	2(k) on 2r, imperf.	*47.50*	*60.00*
a.		Perf.	*50.00*	*50.00*
363	A15	2(k) on 500r	*100.00*	*150.00*
a.		Imperf.	*100.00*	*100.00*
364	A15	2(k) on 500r (R)	200.00	200.00
365	A11	4(k) on 25r, imperf.	*30.00*	*30.00*
a.		Perf.	*50.00*	*50.00*
366	A12	5(k) on 50r, imperf.	24.00	*36.00*
a.		Perf.	*100.00*	*100.00*
367	A13	10(k) on 100r	*24.00*	*25.00*
a.		Imperf.	*50.00*	*50.00*
368	A21	35(k) on 20,000r, imperf.	*75.00*	*100.00*
a.		With "k" written in violet	*150.00*	*125.00*
b.		Perf.	*90.00*	*100.00*
c.		As "a," perf.	*90.00*	*100.00*
d.		With "kop" written in violet, imperf.		
		Nos. 360-368 (9)	620.50	721.00

Manuscript Surcharge in Red

Perf. 11½

371	A14	1k on 250r dk bl	*100.00*	*60.00*

Handstamped in Black or Red Tall, Thin Numerals

No. 381

Imperf

377	A11	4(k) on 25r (R)	125.00	125.00
379	A13	10(k) on 100r	90.00	*100.00*
380	A15	20(k) on 500r	7.25	7.25
381	A22	50k on 25,000r bl	*25.00*	*90.00*
a.		Surcharged "50" only	60.00	60.00
382	A22	50k on 25,000r bl (R)	14.50	14.50
382A	A22	50k on 25,000r brn ol	29.00	29.00
382B	A22	50k on 25,000r brn ol (R)	750.00	750.00
		Nos. 377-382A (6)	*290.75*	*365.75*

On Nos. 381, 382 and 382A the letter "k" forms part of the surcharge.

Perf. 11½

383	A7	1(k) on 1r (R)	*40.00*	*40.00*
a.		Imperf.	100.00	
384	A14	1(k) on 250r	100.00	100.00
385	A15	2(k) on 500r	150.00	150.00
a.		Imperf.	150.00	150.00
386	A15	2(k) on 500r (R)	*24.00*	*24.00*
387	A9	3(k) on 3r	40.00	*50.00*
a.		Imperf.	40.00	*50.00*
388	A21	3(k) on 20,000r, imperf.	150.00	*150.00*
a.		Perf.	150.00	150.00
389	A11	4(k) on 25r	100.00	100.00
a.		Imperf.	120.00	120.00
390	A12	5(k) on 50r, imperf.	*45.00*	*50.00*
a.		Perf.	*50.00*	*75.00*
		Nos. 383-390 (8)	*649.00*	*664.00*

Catalogue values for unused stamps in this section, from this point to the end of the section, are for Never Hinged items.

Mt. Ararat — A45

a, 20k. b, 2r. c, 5r.

1992, May 28 Litho. *Perf. 14*

430	A45	Strip of 3, #a.-c.	3.50	3.50

Souvenir Sheet

431	A45	7r Eagle & Mt. Ararat	*45.00*	*45.00*

AT & T Communications System in Armenia — A45a

1992, July 1 Litho. *Perf. 13x13½*

431A	A45a	50k multicolored	4.50	4.50

A46

1992 Summer Olympics, Barcelona: a, 40k, Ancient Greek wrestlers. b, 3.60r, Boxing. c, 5r, Weight lifting. d, 12r, Gymnastics.

1992, July 25 Litho. *Perf. 14*

432	A46	Strip of 4, #a.-d.	3.50	3.50

A47

20k, Natl. flag. 1r, Goddess Waroubini, Orgov radio telescope. 2r, Yerevan Airport. No. 436, Goddess Anahit. No. 437, Runic message, 7th cent B.C. 5r, UPU emblem. 20r, Silver cup.

1992-93 Litho. *Perf. 14½, 15x14½*

433	A47	20k multicolored	.30	.30
434	A47	1r gray green	.30	.30
435	A47	2r blue	.40	.40
436	A47	3r brown	.60	.60
437	A47	3r bronze	.30	.30
438	A47	5r brown black	.90	.90
439	A47	20r gray	.70	.70
		Nos. 433-439 (7)	3.50	3.50

No. 435 is airmail. See Nos. 464-471, 521-524.

Issued: No. 436, 20k, 2r, 5r, 8/25/92; others, 5/12/93.

Religious Artifacts — A50

David of Sassoun, by Hakop Kojoian A50a

40k, Marker. 80k, Gospel page. 3.60r, Bas-relief, 13th cent. 5r, Icon of the Madonna.

1993, May 23 Litho. *Perf. 14*

448 A50 40k multicolored .25 .25
449 A50 80k multicolored .30 .30
450 A50 3.60r multicolored .90 .90
451 A50 5r multicolored 1.75 1.75
Nos. 448-451 (4) 3.20 3.20

Souvenir Sheet

Perf. 14x13½

451A A50a 12r multicolored 8.00 8.00

Scenic Views A51

Designs: 40k, Garni Canyon, vert. 80k, Shaki Waterfall, Zangezur, vert. 3.60r, Arpa River Canyon, vert. 5r, Lake Sevan. 12r, Mount Aragats.

1993, May 24 *Perf. 14*

452 A51 40k multicolored .25 .25
453 A51 80k multicolored .25 .25
454 A51 3.60r multicolored .50 .50
455 A51 5r multicolored .70 .70
456 A51 12r multicolored 1.75 1.75
Nos. 452-456 (5) 3.45 3.45

Yerevan '93 — A52

1993, May 25 *Perf. 14½*

457 A52 10r multicolored .85 .85
a. Min. sheet of 6 + 2 labels 5.50 5.50

For surcharges see Nos. 485-486.

Souvenir Sheet

Noah's Descent from Mt. Ararat, by Hovhannes Aivazovsky — A52a

1993, Aug. 4 Litho. *Perf. 14½*

458 A52a 7r multicolored 4.50 4.50

Religious Relics, Echmiadzin — A53

Designs: 3r, Wooden panel, descent from cross, 9th cent. 5r, Gilded silver reliquary for Holy Cross of Khotakerats. 12r, Cross depicting right hand of St. Karapet, 14th cent. 30r, Reliquary for arm of St. Thaddeus the Apostle, 17th cent. 50r, Gilded silver vessel for consecrated ointment, 1815.

1994, Aug. 4 Litho. *Perf. 14x14½*

459 A53 3d multicolored .25 .25
460 A53 5d multicolored .25 .25
461 A53 12d multicolored .65 .65
462 A53 30d multicolored 1.25 1.25
463 A53 50d multicolored 2.00 2.00
Nos. 459-463 (5) 4.40 4.40

Artifacts and Landmarks Type of 1993

Gods of Van (Urartu): 10 l, Shivini, god of the sun. 50 l, Tayshaba, god of elements. 10d, Khaldi, supreme god.
25d, Natl. arms.

1994, Aug. 4 *Perf. 14½*

464 A47 10 l black & brown .25 .25
465 A47 50 l black & red brown .25 .25
469 A47 10d black & gray .85 .85
471 A47 25d red & bister 2.00 2.00
Nos. 464-471 (4) 3.35 3.35

A54

1994, Dec. 31 Litho. *Perf. 14½x14*

479 A54 16d No. 1a .40 .40

First Armenian postage stamp, 75th anniv.

Early Printing Press — A54a

1994, Dec. 30 Litho. *Perf. 14x14½*

480 A54a 30d multicolored .60 .60

First Armenian periodical, 200th anniv.

Natl. Arms, Stadium — A54b

1994, Dec. 30 Litho. *Perf. 14x14½*

481 A54b 30d multicolored .65 .65

Natl. Olympic Committee.

Olympic Rings — A54c

1994, Dec. 30 Litho. *Perf. 14x14½*

482 A54c 40d multicolored 1.00 1.00

Intl. Olympic Committee, Cent.

A54d

1994, Dec. 31 Litho. *Perf. 14x14½*

483 A54d 50d multi + label 1.00 1.00

Ervand Otian (1869-1926)

A54e

1994, Dec. 31 Litho. *Perf. 14½x14*

484 A54e 50d multi + label 1.00 1.00

Levon Shant (1869-1951).

No. 457 Surcharged in Blue or Red Brown

a

b

1994, Sept. 10 Litho. *Perf. 14*

485 A52(a) 40d on 10r (Bl) 5.50 5.50
486 A52(b) 40d on 10r (RB) 5.50 5.50

Yerevan '94.

A55

Christianity in Armenia: 60d, Cross, 10th-11th cent. No. 488, Kings Abgar & Trdat, 1836. No. 489, St. Bartholomew, St. Thaddeus. 80d, St. Gregory, the Illuminator. 90d, Baptism of the Armenian people, 1892. 400d, Plan of Echmiadzin, c. 1660, engr. by Jakob Peeters.

1995, Apr. 3 Litho. *Perf. 14x15*

487 A55 60d multicolored .65 .65
488 A55 70d multicolored .65 .65
489 A55 70d multicolored .65 .65
490 A55 80d multicolored 1.00 1.00
491 A55 90d multicolored 1.10 1.10
Nos. 487-491 (5) 4.05 4.05

Souvenir Sheet

492 A55 400d multicolored 5.50 5.50

Nos. 488-489 are 45x44mm.

A56

1995, Apr. 3

493 A56 150d gray & black 1.50 1.50

Vazgen I (1908-94), Catholikos of All Armenians.

Armenia Fund — A57

1995, Apr. 27 *Perf. 15x14*

494 A57 90d multicolored .90 .90

UN, 50th Anniv. — A58

1995, Apr. 28

495 A58 90d multicolored .90 .90

Cultural Artifacts — A59

Designs: 30d, Black polished pottery, 14th-13th cent. B.C. 60d, Silver cup, 5th cent. B.C. 130d, Gohar carpet, 1700 A.D.

1995, Apr. 27 *Perf. 15x14*

496 A59 30d multicolored .35 .35
497 A59 60d multicolored .65 .65
498 A59 130d multicolored 1.50 1.50
Nos. 496-498 (3) 2.50 2.50

Birds — A60

1995, Apr. 27 *Perf. 14*

499 A60 40d Milvus milvus .65 .65
500 A60 60d Aquila chrysaetos .95 .95

End of World War II, 50th Anniv. — A61

Designs: No. 501, P. Kitsook, 408th Armenian Rifle Division. No. 502, A. Sargissin, N. Safarian, 89th Taman Armenian Triple Order-Bearer Division. No. 503, B. Chernikov, N. Tavartkeladze, V. Penkovsky, 76th Armenian Alpine Rifle Red Banner (51st Guards) Division. No. 504, S. Zakian, H. Babayan, I. Lyudnikov, 390th Armenian Rifle Division. No. 505, A. Vasillian, M. Dobrovolsky, Y. Grechany, G. Sorokin, 409th Armenian Rifle Division.

No. 506, vert.: a, Marshal Hovhannes Baghramian. b, Adm. Hovhannes Issakov. c, Marshal Hamazasp Babajanian. d, Marshal Sergey Khoudyakov.

No. 507: Return of the Hero, by Mariam Aslamazian.

1995, Sept. 30 Litho. *Perf. 15x14*

501 A61 60d multicolored .60 .60
502 A61 60d multicolored .60 .60
503 A61 60d multicolored .60 .60
504 A61 60d multicolored .60 .60
505 A61 60d multicolored .60 .60
Nos. 501-505 (5) 3.00 3.00

Miniature Sheet

Perf. 15x14½

506 A61 60d Sheet of 4, #a.-d. 3.25 3.25

Souvenir Sheet

Perf. 15x14

507 A61 300d multicolored 4.00 4.00

Authors — A62

Designs: No. 508, Ghevond Alishan (1820-1901). No. 509, Gregor Artsruni (1845-92), vert. No. 510, Franz Werfel (1890-1945), vert.

1995, Oct. 5 Litho. *Perf. 15x14*

508 A62 90d blue & black .85 .85
509 A62 90d cream, blk, gold .85 .85
510 A62 90d blue & maroon .85 .85
Nos. 508-510 (3) 2.55 2.55

Nos. 508-510 issued with se-tenant label.

A64

Prehistoric artifacts: 40d, Four-wheeled carriages, 15th cent. BC. 60d, Bronze model of geocentric solar system, 11-10th cent. BC, vert. 90d, Tombstone, Red Tufa, 7-6th cent. BC, vert.

1995, Dec. 5 *Perf. 14½x15, 15x14½*

512 A64 40d multicolored .40 .40
513 A64 60d multicolored .60 .60
514 A64 90d multicolored .80 .80
Nos. 512-514 (3) 1.80 1.80

A65

Christianity in Armenia — A66

Views of Yerevan: 60d, Brandy distillery, wine cellars. 80d, Abovian Street. 90d, Sports and concert complex. 100d, Baghramian Avenue. 120d, Republic Square.

400d, Panoramic photograph of Yerevan.

1995, Dec. 5 *Perf. 15x14*

515 A65 60d salmon & black .50 .50
516 A65 80d pale org & blk .60 .60
517 A65 90d buff & black .70 .70

Size: 61x24mm

518 A65 100d pale yel bis & blk .80 .80
519 A65 120d dull org & blk 1.00 1.00
Nos. 515-519 (5) 3.60 3.60

Souvenir Sheet

520 A66 400d multicolored 4.25 4.25

No. 464 Surcharged in Green, Red, Blue Violet, or Red Brown

1996, Mar. 30 Litho. ***Perf. 14½***

521 A47 40d on 10l (G) 1.75 1.75
522 A47 100d on 10l (R) 3.50 3.50
523 A47 150d on 10l (BV) 5.00 5.00
524 A47 200d on 10l (RB) 7.00 7.00
Nos. 521-524 (4) 17.25 17.25

Alexsandre Griboyedov (1795-1829), Writer — A67

1996, Apr. 24 Litho. ***Perf. 14x14½***

525 A67 90d multi + label .90 .90

Khrimian Hayrik (1820-1907), Catholicos of All Armenians — A68

1996, Apr. 30 ***Perf. 14½x14***

526 A68 90d brown & blue .90 .90

No. 526 is printed se-tenant with label.

Admiral Lazar Serbryakov (1795-1862) — A69

1996, Apr. 30

527 A69 90d multi + label .90 .90

Armenian Red Cross, 75th Anniv. — A70

1996, May 4 ***Perf. 14x14½***

528 A70 60d multicolored .60 .60

Motion Pictures, Cent. — A71

1996, May 4 ***Perf. 14½x14***

529 A71 60d multicolored .60 .60

No. 529 exists imperf. Value $45.

Endangered Fauna — A72

1996, May 3 ***Perf. 14***

530 A72 40d Carpa aegagrus .70 .70
531 A72 60d Panthera pardus 1.10 1.10

1996 Summer Olympics, Atlanta — A73

Designs: a, 40d, Cyclist. b, 60d, Athletic event. c, 90d, Wrestling.

1996, July 25

532 A73 Strip of 3, #a.-c. 1.90 1.90

Modern Olympic Games, Cent. — A74

1996, July 25 ***Perf. 14x14½***

533 A74 60d multicolored .60 .60

Fridtjof Nansen (1861-1930), Arctic Explorer A75

1996, May 20 Litho. ***Perf. 14x14½***

534 A75 90d multicolored 1.00 1.00

32nd Chess Olympiad, Yerevan — A76

Designs: No. 535, Petrosian-Botvinnik, World Championship match, Moscow, 1963. No. 536, Kasparov-Karpov, World Championship Match, Leningrad, 1986. No. 537, G. Kasparian, first prize winner, Contest of the Shakhmati v SSSR magazine, 1939. No. 538, 32nd Chess Olympiad, Yerevan.

1996, Sept. 15 Litho. ***Perf. 14***

535 A76 40d multicolored .70 .70
536 A76 40d multicolored .70 .55
537 A76 40d multicolored .70 .70
538 A76 40d multicolored .70 .70
a. Booklet pane, #535-538 *3.00*
Complete booklet, 2 #538a *7.50*
Nos. 535-538 (4) 2.80 2.65

No. 538a issued 9/24.
Nos. 535-538 also exist imperf. Value $30.

Tigran Petrosian, World Chess Champion, Chess House, Yerevan — A77

1996, Sept. 20 ***Perf. 14x15***

539 A77 90d multicolored .75 .75

No. 539 also exists imperf. Value $20.

Capra Aegagrus — A78

World Wildlife Fund: 70d, Two running. 100d, One standing. 130d, One holding head down. 350d, Two facing forward.

1996, Oct. 20 Litho. ***Perf. 14½x14***

540 A78 70d multicolored .60 .60
541 A78 100d multicolored .70 .70
542 A78 130d multicolored 1.00 1.00
543 A78 350d multicolored 2.50 2.50
a. Block of 4, #540-543 5.00 5.00
b. Booklet pane, 2 #543a 10.00 10.00
Complete booklet, #543b 12.00 12.00

Issued in sheets of 16 stamps.

Christianity in Armenia, 1700th Anniv. — A79

Armenian churches: No. 544, St. Catherine Church, St. Petersburg, 1780. No. 545, Church of the Holy Mother, Kishinev, 1803. No. 546, Church of the Holy Mother, Samarkand, 1903. No. 547, Armenian Church, Lvov, 1370. No. 548, St. Hripsime Church, Yalta, 1913.

500d, Church of St. Gevorg of Etchmiadzin, Tbilisi, 1805.

1997, Mar. 19 Litho. ***Perf. 14x15***

544 A79 100d multicolored 1.00 1.00
545 A79 100d multicolored 1.00 1.00
546 A79 100d multicolored 1.00 1.00
547 A79 100d multicolored 1.00 1.00
548 A79 100d multicolored 1.00 1.00
Nos. 544-548 (5) 5.00 5.00

Souvenir Sheet

549 A79 500d multicolored 4.00 4.00

First Armenian Printing Press, Etchmiadzin, 225th Anniv. — A80

1997, Mar. 26 Litho. ***Perf. 15x14***

550 A80 70d multicolored 1.00 1.00

Armenian Entertainers A81

Designs: No. 551, Folk singer, Jivani (1846-1909). No. 552, Arno Babajanian (1921-83), composer, vert.

1997, Mar. 26 ***Perf. 15x14, 14x15***

551 A81 90d multicolored .60 .60
552 A81 90d multicolored .60 .60

Paintings from Natl. Gallery of Armenia — A82

Designs: No. 553, "One of my Dreams," by Eghishe Tadevossian. No. 554, "Countryside," by Gevorg Bashinjaghian. No. 555, "Portrait of Natalia Tehumian," by Hakob Hovnatanian. No. 556, "Salomé," by Vardges Sureniants.

1997, May 28 Litho. ***Perf. 15x14***

553 A82 150d multi 1.00 1.00
554 A82 150d multi 1.00 1.00
555 A82 150d multi, vert. 1.00 1.00
556 A82 150d multi, vert. 1.00 1.00
Nos. 553-556 (4) 4.00 4.00

See Nos. 573-575.

Rouben Mamulian (1897-1987), Motion Picture Director — A83

1997, Oct. 8 Litho. ***Perf. 15x14***

557 A83 150d multicolored 1.00 1.00

Moscow '97, World Philatelic Exhibition — A84

170d, St. Basil's Cathedral.

1997, Oct. 17 ***Perf. 14x15***

558 A84 170d multicolored 1.25 1.25

Eghishe Charents (1897-1937), Poet — A85

1997, Oct. 19 ***Perf. 15x14***

559 A85 150d multicolored 1.00 1.00

A86

Europa (Stories and Legends): 170d, Hayk, the Progenitor of the Armenians. 250d, Vahagn, the Dragon Slayer.

1997, Oct. 18 ***Perf. 14x15***

560 A86 170d multicolored *3.00 3.00*
561 A86 250d multicolored *4.00 4.00*

A87

40d, Iris lycotis. 170d, Iris elegantissima.

1997, Dec. 19 Litho. ***Perf. 14***

562 A87 40d multicolored .30 .30
563 A87 170d multicolored 1.20 1.20

Religious Buildings — A88

Designs: No. 564, San Lazzaro, the Mekhitarian Congregation, Venice. No. 565, St. Gregory the Illuminator Cathedral, Anthelias. No. 566, St. Khach Armenian Church, Rostov upon Don. No. 567, St. James Monastery, Jerusalem. No. 568, Nercissian School, Tbilisi.

500d, Lazarian Seminary, Moscow.

1997, Dec. 22 ***Perf. 15x14, 14x15***

564 A88 100d multi, horiz. .70 .70
565 A88 100d multi .70 .70
566 A88 100d multi .70 .70
567 A88 100d multi, horiz. .70 .70

Size: 60x21mm

568 A88 100d multi, horiz. .70 .70
Nos. 564-568 (5) 3.50 3.50

Souvenir Sheet

569 A88 500d multicolored 3.00 3.00

Christianity in Armenia, 1700th anniv. (in 2001).

Christmas — A89

1997, Dec. 26 ***Perf. 14x15***

570 A89 40d multicolored .50 .50

Diana, Princess of Wales (1961-97) — A90

1998, Apr. 8 Litho. ***Perf. 15x14***

571 A90 250d multicolored 2.00 2.00

No. 571 was issued in sheets of 5 + label.

Karabakh Movement, 10th Anniv. — A91

1998, Feb. 20 Litho. *Perf. 13½x14*

572 A91 250d multicolored 2.75 2.75

Paintings from Natl. Gallery of Armenia Type of 1997

Designs: No. 573, "Tartar Women's Dance," by Alexander Bazhbeouk-Melikian. No. 574, "Family. Generations," by Yervand Kochar. No. 575, "Spring in Our Yard," by Haroutiun Kalents.

1998, Feb. 21 *Perf. 15x14, 14x15*

573 A82 150d multi 1.50 1.50
574 A82 150d multi, vert. 1.50 1.50
575 A82 150d multi, vert. 1.50 1.50
Nos. 573-575 (3) 4.50 4.50

1998 World Cup Soccer Championships, France — A92

1998, June 10 Litho. *Perf. 14x15*

576 A92 250d multicolored 2.25 2.25

No. 576 was issued in sheets of 10 and sheets of 8 + 2 labels. Value, sheet of 8 + 2 labels $20. Same, imperf $125.

National Holidays and Festivals — A93

Europa: 170d, Couple jumping over fire, Trndez. 250d, Girls taking part in traditional ceremony, Ascension Day.

1998, June 24 Litho. *Perf. 15x14*

577 A93 170d multicolored *1.50 1.50*
578 A93 250d multicolored *2.50 2.50*

Butterflies — A94

1998, June 26 *Perf. 14*

579 A94 170d Papilio alexanor 1.00 1.00
580 A94 250d Rethera komarovi 1.50 1.50

National Costumes — A95

1998, July 16 Litho. *Perf. 14x13½*

581 A95 170d Ayrarat 1.25 1.25
582 A95 250d Vaspurakan 1.75 1.75

See Nos. 591-592.

Christianity in Armenia, 1700th Anniv. (in 2001) — A96

Churches: a, St. Forty Children's, 1958, Milan. b, St. Sargis, London, 1923. c, St. Vardan Cathedral, 1968, New York. d, St. Hovannes Cathedral, 1902, Paris. e, St. Gregory the Illuminator Cathedral, 1938, Buenos Aires.

1998, Sept. 25 Litho. *Perf. 11½*

583 A96 100d Sheet of 5, #a.-e. 3.00 3.00

Memorial to Armenian Earthquake Victims — A97

1998, Sept. 26 *Perf. 15x14*

584 A97 250d multicolored 2.25 2.25

No. 584 was issued in sheets of 10 and sheets of 8 + 2 labels. Value, sheet of 8 + 2 labels $35.

Minerals — A98

1998, Oct. 23

585 A98 170d Pyrite 1.25 1.25
586 A98 250d Agate 1.75 1.75

See Nos. 616-617.

Valery Bryusov (1873-1924), Writer — A99

1998, Dec. 1 *Perf. 14x15*

587 A99 90d multicolored .75 .75

Souvenir Sheet

Sergei Parajanov, Film Director, 75th Birth Anniv. — A100

1999, Apr. 19 Litho. *Perf. 14x14¾*

588 A100 500d multicolored 4.00 4.00
a. IBRA 99 emblem in margin 4.50 4.50

State Reserves — A101

1999, Apr. 22 *Perf. 14¾x14¼*

589 A101 170d Khosrov *1.50 1.50*
590 A101 250d Kilijan *2.50 2.50*

Europa.

National Costumes Type of 1998

1999, Apr. 20 Litho. *Perf. 14x13½*

591 A95 170d Karin 1.25 1.25
592 A95 250d Zangezour 2.00 2.00

Council of Europe, 50th Anniv. — A102

1999, June 12

593 A102 170d multicolored 4.50 4.50

Cilician Ships — A103

1999, Aug. 12 Litho. *Perf. 14¾x14*

Sail Colors

594 A103 170d orange & blue 1.25 1.25
595 A103 250d red & white 2.00 2.00

With PhilexFrance 99 Emblem at LR

596 A103 250d red & white 2.25 2.25
Nos. 594-596 (3) 5.50 5.50

Domesticated Animals — A104

1999, Aug. 19 *Perf. 13¼x13¾*

597 A104 170d Armenian gampr dog 1.25 1.25
598 A104 250d Van cat 2.00 2.00

With China 1999 World Philatelic Exhibition Emblem at LR

599 A104 250d Van cat 2.50 2.50
Nos. 597-599 (3) 5.75 5.75

Souvenir Sheet

First Pan-Armenian Games — A105

1999, Aug. 28 *Perf. 14¾x14*

600 A105 250d multicolored 3.00 3.00

Souvenir Sheet

Christianity in Armenia, 1700th Anniv. (in 2001) — A106

Churches: a, St. Gregory the Illuminator, Cairo. b, St. Gregory the Illuminator, Singapore. c, St. Khach, Suceava, Romania. d, St. Savior, Worcester, Mass. e, Church of the Holy Mother, Madras, India.

1999, Aug. Litho. *Perf. 13¼x13¾*

601 A106 70d Sheet of 5, #a.-e. + label 7.50 7.50

UPU, 125th Anniv. — A107

1999, Oct. *Perf. 14¾x14¼*

602 A107 270d multicolored 2.25 2.25

Politicians Assassinated Oct. 27, 1999 — A108

Designs: No. 603, Parliament Speaker Karen Demirchyan, Parliament building. No. 604, Prime Minister Vazgen Sargsyan, troops. 540d, Demirchyan, Sargsyan, Yuri Bakhshyan, Ruben Miroyan, Henrik Abrahamyan, Armenak Armenakyan, Leonard Petrossyan and Mikael Kotanyan.

Perf. 14¾x14¼

2000, Feb. 21 Litho.

603 A108 250d multi 2.50 2.00
604 A108 250d multi 2.50 2.00
a. Sheet, 5 each #603-604 *65.00 65.00*

Imperf

Size: 60x44mm

605 A108 540d multi 5.00 5.00

Fish — A109

Designs: 50d, Salmo ischchan. 270d, Barbus goktschaicus.

2000, May 23 Litho. *Perf. 13¼x13¾*

606 A109 50d multi 1.00 1.00
607 A109 270d multi 2.00 2.00

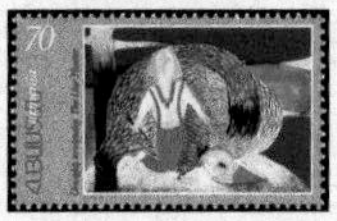

Fairy Tales — A110

70d, The Liar Hunter. 130d, The King and the Peddler.

2000, May 25 *Perf. 14¾x14¼*

608 A110 70d multicolored .65 .65
609 A110 130d multicolored 1.25 1.25

Europa, 2000

Common Design Type

2000, June 19 *Perf. 14¼x14¾*

610 CD17 40d multi *.75 .75*
611 CD17 500d multi *4.00 4.00*

Christianity as State Religion, 1700th Anniv. — A111

No. 612: a, St. Gayane Church, Vagharshapat. b, Etchmiadzin Cathedral, Vagharshapat. c, Church of the Holy Mother, Khor Virap. d, St. Shoghakat Church, Vagharshapat. e, St. Hripsime Church, Vagharshapat.

2000, July 10 Litho. *Perf. 13¼x13¾*

612 A111 70d Sheet of 5, #a-e, + label 4.00 4.00

2000 Summer Olympics, Sydney — A112

Designs: 10d, Basketball. 30d, Tennis. 500d, Weight lifting.

2000, July 11 *Perf. 13½x13¾*

613-615 A112 Set of 3 5.00 5.00

Mineral Type of 1998

Designs: 170d, Quartz. 250d, Molybdenite.

2000, Sept. 4 *Perf. 14¾x14*

616-617 A98 Set of 2 3.25 3.25

A113

2000, Sept. 11 *Perf. 14x14¾*

618 A113 270d multi 2.00 2.00

Nerses Shnorhali (1100-73), poet and musician.

Christmas — A114

2000, Sept. 15

619 A114 170d multi 1.40 1.40

Avetik Issahakian (1875-1957), Poet — A115

2000, Sept. 17 *Perf. 14¾x14*

620 A115 130d multi .90 .90

Musical Instruments — A116

Designs: 170d, Dhol. 250d, Duduk.

2000, Dec. 22 Litho. ***Perf. 14x13¼***
621-622 A116 Set of 2 3.50 3.50

Famous Armenians — A117

No. 623: a, Viktor Hambartsoumian (1908-96), cosmologist. b, Abraham Alikhanov (1904-70), physicist. c, Andranik Iossifian (1905-93), engineer. d, Sargis Saltikov (1905-83), metallurgist. e, Samuel Kochariants (1909-87), nuclear weapons scientist. f, Atrem Mikoyan (1905-70), aircraft designer. g, Norayr Sissakian (1907-66), biologist. h, Ivan Knunyants (1906-90), chemist. i, Nikoghayos Yenikolopian (1924-93), chemist.

No. 624: a, Nikoghayos Adonts (1871-1942), historian. b, Manouk Abeghian (1865-1944), grammarian. c, Hovhannes Toumanian (1869-1923), poet. d, Hrachya Ajarian (1876-1953), linguist. e, Gevorg Emin (1918-98), writer. f, Yervand Lalayan (1864-1931), anthropologist. g, Daniel Varoujan (1884-1915), poet. h, Paruyr Sevak (1924-71), writer. i, William Saroyan (1908-81), writer.

No. 625: a, Hamo Beknazarian (1892-1965), actor. b, Alexandre Tamanian (1878-1936), architect. c, Vahram Papazian (1888-1968), actor. d, Vassil Tahirov (1859-1938), viticulturist. e, Leonid Yengibarov (1935-72), mime. f, Haykanoush Danielian (1893-1958), singer. g, Sergo Hambartsoumian (1910-83) "Strongest man on Earth". h, Hrant Shahinian (1923-96), gymnast. i, Toros Toramanian (1864-1934), architectural historian.

No. 626: a, Komitas (1869-1935), composer. b, Aram Khachatourian (1903-78), composer. c, Martiros Sarian (1880-1972), artist. d, Avet Terterian (1929-94), composer. e, Alexandre Spendiarian (1871-1928), composer. f, Arshile Gorky (1904-48), artist. g, Minas Avetissian (1928-75), artist. h, Levon Orbeli (1882-1958), physiologist. i, Hripsimeh Simonian (1916-98), artist.

2000, Dec. 23 ***Perf. 14¾x14¼***
623 Booklet pane of 9 8.75 8.75
a.-i. A117 110d Any single .90 .90
624 Booklet pane of 9 8.75 8.75
a.-i. A117 110d Any single .90 .90
625 Booklet pane of 9 8.75 8.75
a.-i. A117 110d Any single .90 .90
626 Booklet pane of 9 8.75 8.75
a.-i. A117 110d Any single .90 .90
Booklet, #623-626 45.00

Souvenir Sheet

Battle of Avarayr, 1550th Anniv. A118

No. 627: a, 170d, St. Vardan Mamikonian (388-451). b, 270d, Battle of Avarayr, 451.

2001, June 7 Litho. ***Perf. 14x14¾***
627 A118 Sheet of 2, #a-b 4.50 4.50

Record of Lamentations, by St. Grigor Narekatzi, 1000th Anniv. — A119

2001, June 8 Litho. ***Perf. 14¾x14***
628 A119 25d multi 2.00 2.00

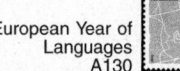

Europa — A120

Designs: 50d, Lake Sevan. 500d, Spandarian Reservoir.

2001, June 9
629-630 A120 Set of 2 *5.75 5.75*

Armenian Admission to Council of Europe — A121

2001, June 11
631 A121 240d multi 2.25 2.25

Worldwide Fund for Nature (WWF) — A122

Sciurus persicus: a, 40d, On branch. b, 50d, Eating. c, 80d, Close-up. d, 120d, Digging.

Perf. 13¼x13¾
2001, Aug. 25 Litho.
632 A122 Block of 4, #a-d 4.00 4.00

Souvenir Sheet

Second Pan-Armenian Games — A123

2001, Aug. 18 Litho. ***Perf. 14¾x14***
633 A123 300d multi 4.00 4.00

Souvenir Sheet

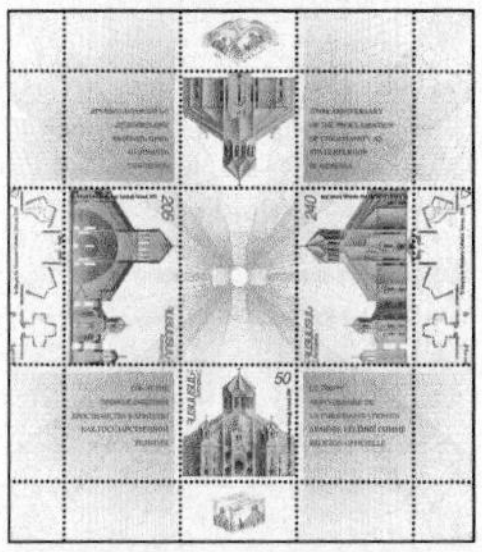

Christianity in Armenia, 1700th Anniv. — A124

Views of St. Gregory the Illuminator Cathedral, Yerevan: a, 50d, Front. b, 205d, Side (45x30mm). c, 240d, Side, diff. (45x30mm).

Perf. 13¾x13¼, 13¼x13¾
2001, Aug. 27
634 A124 Sheet of 3, #a-c, + 6 labels 7.00 7.00
d. As No. 634, with brown inscriptions in margins *65.00 65.00*

Marginal inscriptions on No. 634d read "INTERNATIONAL / PHILATELIC EXHIBITION / ARMENIA '01/ 10-16 September, 2001, Yerevan," in English, Armenian, Russian and French. Souvenir sheet can be formed into a box which shows cathedral from various angles.

Ivan Lazarev (1735-1801) and Institute of Eastern Languages, Moscow — A125

2001, Sept. 26 Litho. ***Perf. 14¾x14***
635 A125 300d multi 8.00 8.00

See Russia No. 6665.

Native Costumes — A126

Man and woman from: 50d, Javakhch. 250r, Artzakh.

2001, Sept. 27 ***Perf. 14x13½***
636-637 A126 Set of 2 3.00 3.00

6th World Wushu Championships A127

2001, Oct. 3 ***Perf. 13¼x13¾***
638 A127 180d black 2.75 2.75

Year of Dialogue Among Civilizations — A128

2001, Oct. 9 ***Perf. 14x14¾***
639 A128 275d multi 6.00 6.00

Commonwealth of Independent States, 10th Anniv. — A129

2001, Nov. 29
640 A129 205d multi 2.25 2.25

European Year of Languages A130

2001, Dec. 21 ***Perf. 14¾x14***
641 A130 350d multi 5.00 5.00

Independence, 10th Anniv. — A131

2001, Dec. 22
642 A131 300d multi 2.75 2.75

Transportation A132

Designs: 180d, Cart. 205d, Phaeton.

2001, Dec. 24 ***Perf. 13½x14***
643-644 A132 Set of 2 3.75 3.75

Medicinal Plants — A133

Designs: 85d, Hypericum perforatum. 205d, Thymus serpyllum.

2001, Dec. 25 ***Perf. 13¼x13¾***
645-646 A133 Set of 2 3.50 3.50

Eagle — A134

2002, Mar. 28 Litho. ***Perf. 14¾x14***
647 A134 10d brown .60 .60
648 A134 25d green .75 .75
649 A134 50d dk blue 1.00 1.00
Nos. 647-649 (3) 2.35 2.35

See Nos. 674-676.

Industries — A135

Designs: 120d, Calendar belt, 2nd cent. B.C., copper smelter. 350d, Containers, 7th cent. B.C., hops, barley, beer kettles.

2002, Apr. 26
650-651 A135 Set of 2 6.50 6.50

National Gallery Artworks — A136

Designs: No. 652, 200d, Lily, by Edgar Chahine. No. 653, 200d, Salomé, sculpture by Hakob Gurjian.

2002, Apr. 29 ***Perf. 14x14¾***
652-653 A136 Set of 2 3.50 3.50

2002 World Cup Soccer Championships, Japan and Korea — A137

2002, May 2 ***Perf. 14¾x14***
654 A137 350d multi 2.75 2.75

Souvenir Sheet

Hovsep Pushman (1877-1906), Artist — A138

2002, May 9
655 A138 650d multi 5.00 5.00

Hovhannes Tevossian (1902-58), Engineer — A139

2002, May 14
656 A139 350d multi 2.75 2.75

Europa — A140

Designs: 70d, Magician's hat. 500d, Clown.

2002, July 30 Litho. ***Perf. 14x14¾***
657-658 A140 Set of 2 *4.00 4.00*

Artemy Aivazian, Composer, Cent. of Birth — A141

2002, July 31 ***Perf. 14¾x14***
659 A141 600d multi 4.75 4.75

Souvenir Sheet

Cathedral of Ani, 1000th Anniv. (in 2001) — A142

Perf. 13¼x13¾
2002, Sept. 24 Litho.
660 A142 550d multi 4.50 4.50

Intl. Year of Mountains — A143

2002-03 ***Perf. 14¾x14***
661 A143 350d multi 3.00 3.00
661a Booklet pane of 3 9.00 9.00

Issued: No. 661, 9/26/02. No. 661a, 2003.

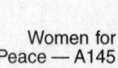

Reptiles — A144

Designs: 170d, Lacerta armeniaca. 220d, Vipera raddei.

2002-03 ***Perf. 13¼x13¾***
662-663 A144 Set of 2 3.50 3.50
663a Booklet pane, 2 each #662-663 7.00 7.00

Issued: Nos. 662-663, 9/27/02. No. 663a, 2003.

Women for Peace — A145

2002, Dec. 20 Litho. ***Perf. 14¾x14***
664 A145 220d multi 2.00 2.00

Alexandrapol — Yeravan Railway, Cent. — A146

2002, Dec. 21
665 A146 350d multi 3.00 3.00

Flowers — A147

Designs: 150d, Galanthus artjuschenkoae. 200d, Merendera mirzoevae.

2002, Dec. 23 ***Perf. 13¼x13¾***
666-667 A147 Set of 2 3.00 3.00
667a Booklet pane, 2 each #666-667 6.00 —
Complete booklet, #661a, 663a, 667a 22.00

Issued: No. 667a, 2003.

Space Research — A148

Designs: 120d, Cosmic ray research. 220d, Orion 1 and Orion 2 space observatories.

2002, Dec. 24 ***Perf. 14¾x14***
668-669 A148 Set of 2 3.00 3.00

Europa — A149

Poster art: 170d, Handle With Care!, by Artak Bagdassaryan. 250d, Armenia, Our Home, by Karen Koyojan.

Perf. 13½x13¼
2003, June 24 Litho.
670-671 A149 Set of 2 3.50 3.50
671a Booklet pane, 4 each #670-671 14.00 14.00

No. 671a was sold with booklet cover, but was unattached to it.

Aram Khatchaturian (1903-78), Composer — A150

Perf. 13½x13¼
2003, June 25 Litho.
672 A150 350d multi 3.00 3.00

Larus Armenicus — A151

2003, June 26 ***Perf. 12½***
673 A151 220d multi 1.60 1.60

Eagle Type of 2002
Perf. 13¼x13½
2003, Sept. 23 Litho.
674 A134 70d red .70 .70
675 A134 300d dk blue 2.50 2.50
676 A134 500d bister brn 5.00 5.00
Nos. 674-676 (3) 8.20 8.20

Souvenir Sheet

Transport Corridor Europe — Caucausus — Asia (TRACECA), 10th Anniv. — A152

2003, Oct. 9 ***Perf. 13***
677 A152 480d multi 6.50 6.50

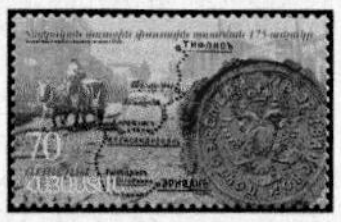
First Armenian Postal Dispatch, 175th Anniv. — A153

2003, Nov. 24 ***Perf. 13¼x13½***
678 A153 70d multi .75 .75

Introduction of Dram Currency, 10th Anniv. — A154

2003, Nov. 25
679 A154 170d multi 1.50 1.50

A155

2003, Nov. 25 ***Perf. 13½x13¼***
680 A155 350d multi 3.25 3.25

Siamanto (1878-1915), poet.

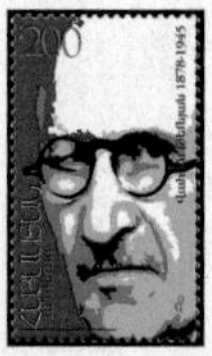
A156

2003, Nov. 27
681 A156 200d multi 2.00 2.00

Vahan Tekeyan (1878-1945), poet.

Neurophysiology A157

2003, Nov. 28 ***Perf. 13¼x13½***
682 A157 120d multi 1.25 1.25

Souvenir Sheet

Third Pan-Armenian Games, Yerevan — A158

2003, Nov. 28
683 A158 350d multi 4.00 4.00

Souvenir Sheet

The Baptism, Miniature From Gospel of Ejmiatsin A159

2003, Nov. 28 ***Perf. 13½x13¼***
684 A159 550d multi 6.50 6.50

A160

Paintings in Museum of Russian Art: 200d, Still Life, by Alexander Shevchenko. 220d, In a Restaurant, by Konstantin Roudakov.

2004, Sept. 6 Litho. ***Perf. 13½x13¼***
685-686 A160 Set of 2 4.00 4.00

A161

2004, Sept. 9
687 A161 350d multi 3.50 3.50

FIFA (Fédération Internationale de Football Association), Cent.

Grapes — A162

Grape color: 170d, Yellow. 220d, Purple.

2004, Sept. 8 ***Perf. 12½***
688-689 A162 Set of 2 4.00 4.00

Souvenir Sheet

Armenian Settlement of New Julfa, 400th Anniv. A163

2004, Sept. 9 ***Perf. 13***
690 A163 590d multi 6.00 6.00

Animated Films — A164

Designs: 70d, Cat and Dog, 1937. 120d, Foxbook, 1975.

2004, Sept. 10 ***Perf. 13¼x13½***
691-692 A164 Set of 2 2.00 2.00

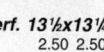

Aramayis Yerzinkyan (1879-1931), Statesman — A165

2004, Sept. 11 ***Perf. 13½x13¼***
693 A165 220d multi 2.50 2.50

Karabakh Horse — A166

2005, Feb. 14 **Litho.** ***Perf. 12½***

694 A166 350d multi 3.50 3.50

Dated 2004.

2004 Summer Olympics, Athens — A167

Hand: 70d, With Olympic Rings. 170d, As runner. 350d, As pistol.

2005, Feb. 14

695-697 A167 Set of 3 *10.00 10.00*

Dated 2004.

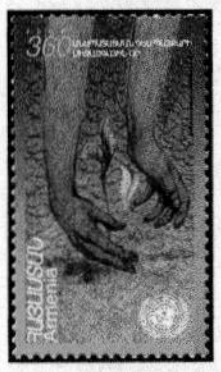

Intl. Day Against Desertification — A168

2005, Feb. 21 ***Perf. 13½x13¼***

698 A168 360d multi 3.25 3.25

Dated 2004.

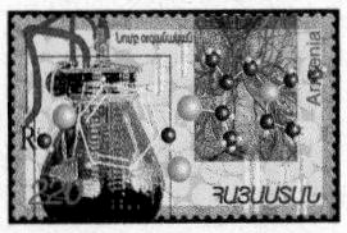

Heart, Molecule and Chemistry Apparatus A169

2005, Feb. 22

699 A169 220d multi 2.25 2.25

Dated 2004.

Michael Nalbandian (1829-66), Writer — A170

2005, Feb. 23

700 A170 220d multi 2.25 2.25

Dated 2004.

Mouratsan (1854-1908), Writer — A171

2005, Feb. 24

701 A171 350d multi 3.50 3.50

Dated 2004.

Tigran Petrosian (1929-84), Chess Champion A172

2005, Feb. 25

702 A172 220d multi 3.00 3.00

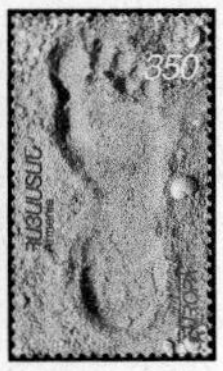

Europa

A173 A174

2005, Mar. 16 ***Perf. 13½x13¼***

703 A173 70d multi 1.50 1.50

704 A174 350d multi 2.50 2.50

Dated 2004.

Souvenir Sheet

Goshavank Monastery — A175

2005, Mar. 17 ***Perf. 12½***

705 A175 480d multi 5.00 5.00

Dated 2004.

Armen Tigranian (1879-1950), Composer A176

2005, Mar. 18 ***Perf. 13¼x13½***

706 A176 220d multi 2.25 2.25

Dated 2004.

A177

2005, Apr. 21 ***Perf. 13½x13¼***

707 A177 350d multi 3.25 3.25

Armenian genocide, 90th anniv.

A178

2005, Apr. 29

708 A178 350d multi 4.00 4.00

End of World War II, 60th anniv.

No. 708 was issued in sheets of 10 and sheets of 8 + 2 labels. Value, sheet of 8 + 2 labels $425.

Anushavan Arzumanian (1904-65), Educator A179

2005, May 2 ***Perf. 13¼x13½***

709 A179 220d multi 2.00 2.00

Dated 2004.

Paintings by Martiros Sarian (1880-1972)

A180 A181

2005, May 10 ***Perf. 13½x13¼***

710 A180 170d Self-portrait 1.50 1.50

711 A181 200d Mount Aragats 1.75 1.75

Mother's Day — A182

2005, Oct. 4 **Litho.** ***Perf. 13¼x13½***

712 A182 350d multi 3.25 3.25

A183

Europa: 70d, Bread. 350d, Porridge.

2005, Oct. 4 ***Perf. 13½x13¼***

713-714 A183 Set of 2 4.00 4.00

714a Booklet pane, 4 each #713-714 16.00 —

No. 714a was sold with booklet cover, but unattached to it.

A184

2005, Oct. 5

715 A184 70d multi .75 .75

Armenian alphabet, 1600th anniv.

A185

2005, Oct. 5

716 A185 70d multi .75 .75

Vardan Ajemian (1905-77), theater director.

A186

2005, Oct. 5

717 A186 170d multi 1.75 1.75

Anania Shirakatsi (605-85), scientist.

Mher Mkrtchian (1930-93), Actor — A187

2005, Oct. 6 ***Perf. 13¼x13½***

718 A187 120d multi 1.10 1.10

Artem Mikoyan (1905-70), Aircraft Designer, and MiG Fighters — A188

2005, Oct. 6

719 A188 350d multi 3.25 3.25

Rugs — A189

Rugs from: 60d, 19th cent. 350d, 1904. 480d, 18th cent.

2005, Oct. 6 ***Perf. 13½x13¼***

720-721 A189 Set of 2 3.50 3.50

Souvenir Sheet

722 A189 480d multi 4.50 4.50

No. 722 contains one 28x42mm stamp.

Armenia Year in Russia A190

2006, Jan. 22 **Litho.** ***Perf. 11¼***

723 A190 350d multi 4.50 4.50

See Russia No. 6938.

Alexander Melik-Pashaev (1905-64), Conductor A191

2006, Mar. 27 ***Perf. 13¼x13½***

724 A191 70d multi .90 .90

Dated 2005.

St. Mary's Russian Orthodox Cathedral, Yerevan — A192

2006, Mar. 27

725 A192 170d multi 2.00 2.00

Dated 2005.

Vakhtang Ananyan (1805-80), Writer — A193

2006, Mar. 27

726 A193 170d multi 2.00 2.00

Dated 2005.

Raphael Patkanian (1830-92), Writer — A194

2006, Mar. 27 ***Perf. 13½x13¼***

727 A194 220d multi 2.25 2.25

Dated 2005.

2006 Winter Olympics, Turin — A195

Mountains and: 120d, 2006 Winter Olympics emblem. 170d, Emblem, map of Italy on snowboard.

2006, Mar. 27 ***Perf. 12½x12¾***

728-729 A195 Set of 2 3.25 3.25

729a Miniature sheet, 5 each #728-729 *30.00 30.00*

Dated 2005.

Spiridon Melikian (1880-1933), Musician — A196

2006, Mar. 28 ***Perf. 13½x13¼***

730 A196 350d multi 3.50 3.50

Dated 2005.

Souvenir Sheet

Miniature Art Depicting Nativity and Adoration of the Magi — A197

2006, Mar. 28 ***Perf. 13¼x13½***

731 A197 480d multi 5.50 5.50

Dated 2005.

Native Costumes — A198

Costumes from: 170d, Sassoun. 200d, Shatakhk.

2006, Mar. 28 ***Perf. 13½x13¼***

732-733 A198 Set of 2 3.50 3.50

Dated 2005.

Insects — A199

Designs: 170d, Porphyrophora hamelii. 350d, Procerus scabrosus fallettianus.

2006, Mar. 28 ***Perf. 12¾x12½***

734-735 A199 Set of 2 5.00 5.00

Dated 2005.

Europa Stamps, 50th Anniv. — A200

Designs: Nos. 736, 740a, 70d, Orange panel and "C." Nos. 737, 740b, 70d, Blue panel and "E." Nos. 738, 740c, 70d, Red panel and "P." Nos. 739, 740d, 70d, Green panel and "T."

2006, Mar. 28 ***Perf. 12¾x12½***

Stamps With "Europa 1956-2006" Inscription

736-739 A200 Set of 4 3.50 3.50

Souvenir Sheet

Stamps Without "Europa 1956-2006" Inscription

740 A200 70d Sheet of 4, #a-d 4.00 4.00

Dated 2005.

Souvenir Sheet

Independence, 15th Anniv. — A201

2006, Sept. 19 **Litho.** ***Perf. 12¾***

741 A201 480d multi 5.00 5.00

World Peace — A202

2006, Oct. 16 ***Perf. 13½x13¼***

742 A202 50d multi .50 .50

Souvenir Sheet

Gospel of Haghpat to Jerusalem — A203

2006, Oct. 16

743 A203 220d multi 2.50 2.50

2006 World Cup Soccer Championships, Germany A204

2006, Oct. 17 ***Perf. 13¼x13½***

744 A204 350d multi 3.75 3.75

Europa — A205

Designs: 200d, Gears and clock hands. 350d, Keys.

2006, Oct. 17

745-746 A205 Set of 2 4.50 4.50

Sergei Merkyurov (1881-1952), Sculptor — A206

2006, Oct. 18

747 A206 230d multi 2.25 2.25

Souvenir Sheet

Armenian General Benevolent Union, Cent. — A207

No. 748: a, Boghos Nubar (1851-1930). b, Signed document. c, Alex Manoogian (1901-96).

2006, Oct. 18 ***Perf. 13½x13¼***

748 A207 120d Sheet of 3, #a-c 3.75 3.75

On Nov. 30, 2006, the Armenian Postal Service was sold to a Dutch-owned firm, HayPost CJSC, affiliated with the Netherlands Postal Corporation. The items illustrated below were released in early 2007 by the stamp producer for the Armenian Postal Service prior to this sale, but as of December 2007, were never put on sale at any HayPost CJSC post office and were not valid for postage. HayPost CJSC acquired the remaining stock of these items from the producer and is negotiating with the Armenian government to place these items on sale and make the items valid for postage. All valid postage stamps from 2007, starting with No. 749 below are inscribed "Post." The items illustrated below do not have this inscription.

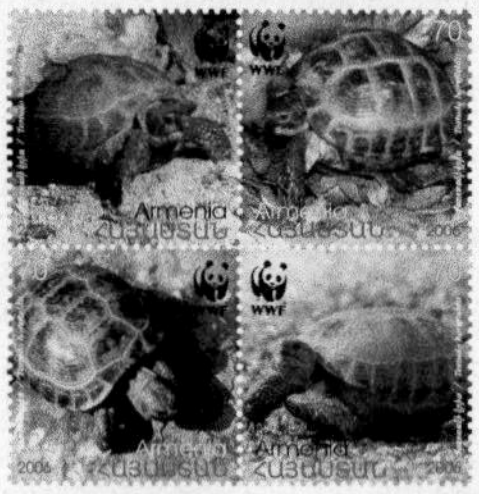

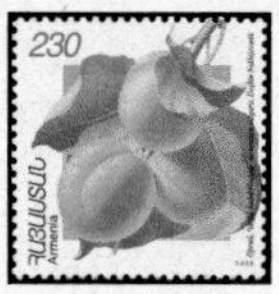

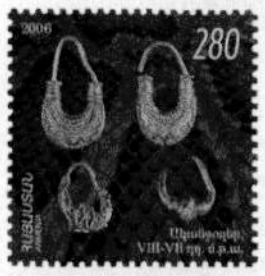

Smile of Reims, France
A208

Nativity, 15th Cent. Miniature, Armenia
A209

2007, May 22 Litho. ***Perf. 13¼x13***
749 A208 70d multi 1.50 1.50
750 A209 350d multi 7.50 7.50

See France Nos. 3335-3336.

Apricot — A210

2007, July 6 ***Perf. 13¼x13¾***
751 A210 350d multi 4.00 4.00

King Tigran the Great (c. 140-55 B.C.) — A211

2007, July 19 ***Perf. 14¾x14***

Background Color

752 A211 50d red .60 .60
753 A211 60d olive green .75 .75
754 A211 70d green .90 .90
755 A211 120d blue 1.50 1.50
Nos. 752-755 (4) 3.75 3.75

See Nos. 780-783. Compare with types A240, A256, A271-A272.

Europa — A212

2007, Sept. 12
756 A212 350d multi 4.00 4.00

Scouting, cent.

Gusan Sheram (1857-1938), Composer — A213

2007, Sept. 13 ***Perf. 14x14¾***
757 A213 280d multi 3.00 3.00

Margar Sedrakyan (1907-73), Cognac Producer — A214

2007, Sept. 14 ***Perf. 14¾x14***
758 A214 170d multi 2.00 2.00

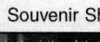

Souvenir Sheet

Genocide Memorial, Tsitsernakaberd — A215

2007, Oct. 9 ***Perf. 14x14¾***
759 A215 480d multi 3.50 3.50

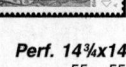

Children's Art — A216

2007, Oct. 24 ***Perf. 14¾x14***
760 A216 35d multi .55 .55

Rural Landscape, by Gevorg Bashinjaghyan (1857-1925)
A217

Kazbek, by Bashinjaghyan
A218

2007, Oct. 24 Litho.
761 A217 160d multi 1.50 1.50
762 A218 220d multi 2.25 2.25

Souvenir Sheet

Fourth Pan-Armenian Games, Yerevan — A219

2007, Oct. 25 ***Perf. 14x14¾***
763 A219 360d multi 3.50 3.50

Jean Garzou (1907-2000), Painter
A220

Seda, by Garzou
A221

2007, Oct. 25 ***Perf. 14¾x14***
764 A220 180d multi 1.75 1.75
765 A221 220d multi 2.25 2.25

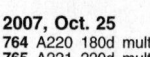

Norayr Sisakyan (1907-66), Biochemist
A222

2007, Oct. 26 ***Perf. 14¾x14***
766 A222 120d multi 1.25 .90

Kamancha — A223

2007, Oct. 27 ***Perf. 14x14¾***
767 A223 110d multi 1.10 .90

Birds — A224

Designs: 120d, Pelecanus crispus. 200d, Aegypius monachus.

2007, Oct. 27 ***Perf. 13¼x13¾***
768-769 A224 Set of 2 4.00 3.00

Matenadaran Ancient Book Depository
A225

2007, Oct. 29 ***Perf. 14¾x14***
770 A225 200d multi 2.00 2.00

Bagrat Nalbandyan (1902-90), Communications Administrator
A226

2007, Oct. 29 Litho.
771 A226 230d multi 2.25 1.75

N. Baghdasaryan (1907-88), Photojournalist — A227

2007, Oct. 31 ***Perf. 14x14¾***
772 A227 200d multi 2.00 1.75

Intl. Solar Year — A228

2007, Nov. 7 ***Perf. 14¾x14***
773 A228 170d multi 1.75 1.25

Busts of Goddesses — A229

Designs: 70d, Greek Goddess Aphrodite. 350d, Armenian Goddess Anahit.

2007, Dec. 14 Litho. ***Perf. 14x113½***
774-775 A229 Set of 2 *5.00 5.00*

See Greece Nos. 2328-2329.

2008 Summer Olympics, Beijing — A230

Perf. 13¼x13¾

2008, June 11 Litho.
776 A230 350d multi 3.50 3.50

Wood Carving — A231

2008, June 17 ***Perf. 14x14¾***
777 A231 120d multi 1.25 1.25

Europa — A232

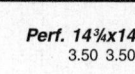

2008, June 18 ***Perf. 14¾x14***
778 A232 350d multi 3.50 3.50

Alexander Shirvanzade (1858-1935), Writer — A233

2008, June 19 ***Perf. 14x14¾***

779 A233 280d multi 2.50 2.50

King Tigran the Great Type of 2007

2008, June 20 ***Perf. 14¾x14***

Background Color

780	A211	10d bright blue	.25	.25
781	A211	20d orange brn	.30	.25
782	A211	50d rose lilac	.60	.40
783	A211	1100d purple	9.00	9.00
		Nos. 780-783 (4)	10.15	9.90

Flowers — A234

Designs: 120d, Anemone fasciculata. 280d, Scabiosa caucasica.

2008, Oct. 9 **Litho.** ***Perf. 13¼x14***

784-785 A234 Set of 2 4.00 4.00

Yerevan State University of Architecture and Construction, 75th Anniv. — A235

2008, Oct. 28 ***Perf. 14¾x14***

786 A235 220d multi 2.25 2.25

William Saroyan (1908-81), Writer — A236

2008, Oct. 29 ***Perf. 14x14¾***

787 A236 350d multi 3.50 3.50

Victor Hambardzumyan (1908-96), Astrophysicist A237

2008, Oct. 20 ***Perf. 14¾x14***

788 A237 120d multi 1.25 1.25

Famous Men A238

No. 789: a, Peyo Yavorov (1878-1914), Bulgarian poet. b, Andranik Ozanian (1865-1927), Armenian general who participated in Balkan Wars.

2008, Nov. 10 ***Perf. 13***

789	Horiz. pair	4.00	4.00
a.	A238 70d multi	.60	.60
b.	A238 350d multi	3.40	3.40

See Bulgaria No. 4492.

Dances — A239

Designs: 70d, Malambo sureño dancer, Argentina. 350d, Hoy-nazan dancers, Armenia.

2009, Apr. 4 ***Perf. 12½x12¾***

790-791 A239 Set of 2 3.75 3.75

See Argentina Nos. 2512-2513.

King Tigran the Great (c. 140-55 B.C.) — A240

2009, Apr. 8 ***Perf. 13¼***

Granite Paper

Background Color

792	A240	10d olive green	.25	.25
793	A240	25d yel bister	.25	.25
794	A240	50d cerise	.45	.45
795	A240	70d brown	.65	.65
796	A240	120d purple	1.10	1.10
797	A240	220d dark blue	2.10	2.10
798	A240	280d dk bl violet	2.60	2.60
799	A240	350d plum	3.25	3.25
		Nos. 792-799 (8)	10.65	10.65

Numerals are in a different font than on Type A211. Compare with types A256, A271-A272.

Van, Ancient Armenian Capital — A241

2009, Apr. 29 ***Perf. 14¾x14***

800 A241 220d multi 1.75 1.75

Europa — A242

2009, July 1 ***Perf. 13¼x13¾***

801 A242 350d multi 2.75 2.75

Intl. Year of Astronomy.

38th Chess Olympiad, Dresden, Germany — A243

Designs: 70d, Chess board, Armenian players holding flag. 280d, Chess pieces, Armenian flag.

2009, July 29 ***Perf. 13¾x13¼***

802-803	A243 Set of 2	3.50	3.50
803a	Miniature sheet of 10, 5 each #802-803	25.00	25.00

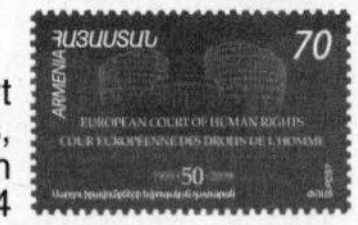

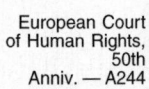

European Court of Human Rights, 50th Anniv. — A244

Perf. 12¾x13¼

2009, Nov. 13 **Litho.**

804 A244 70d multi *15.00 15.00*

Council of Europe, 60th Anniv. — A245

2009, Nov. 13 ***Perf. 13¼x12¾***

805 A245 280d multi *15.00 15.00*

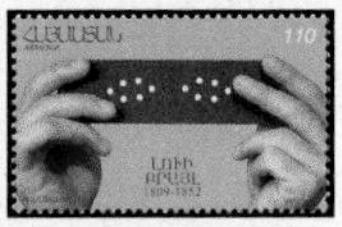

Louis Braille (1809-52), Educator of the Blind — A246

2009, Nov. 24 **Litho.** ***Perf. 14¾x14***

806 A246 110d multi 1.10 1.10

No. 806 was issued in sheets of 10 and sheets of 8 + 2 labels. Value, sheet of 8 + 2 labels $12.

Daniel Varuzhan (1884-1915), Poet — A247

2009, Dec. 8 ***Perf. 13¼x12¾***

807 A247 230d multi 2.00 2.00

Souvenir Sheet

Davit of Sasun Monument, Yerevan, 50th Anniv. — A248

2009, Dec. 11 ***Perf. 14***

808 A248 360d multi 3.00 3.00

Souvenir Sheet

Olympic Champions — A249

No. 809: a, 70d, Hrant Shahinyan, gymnastics, 1952. b, 120d, Igor Novikov, pentathlon, 1956, 1964. c, 160d, Albert Azaryan, gymnastics, 1956, 1960.

2009, Dec. 11 **Litho.**

809 A249 Sheet of 3, #a-c 3.25 3.25

Khachatur Abovyan (1809-48), Writer — A250

2009, Dec. 15 ***Perf. 12¾x13¼***

810 A250 170d multi 1.50 1.50

Animals — A251

Designs: 120d, Lutra lutra meridionalis. 160d, Ursus arctos syriacus.

2009, Dec. 16 ***Perf. 14***

811-812	A251 Set of 2	2.25	2.25
812a	Miniature sheet of 10, 5 each #811-812	12.00	12.00

Paintings in the National Gallery — A252

Designs: No. 813, 200d, Autumn. A Corner in Yerevan, by Sedrak Arakelyan. No. 814, 200d, Panna Paskevich, by Georgi Yakulov.

Perf. 13¼x12¾

2009, Dec. 16 **Litho.**

813-814 A252 Set of 2 3.75 3.75

Vagharshapat Churches on UNESCO World Heritage List — A253

No. 815: a, Zvarnots Church. b, St. Hripsime Church. c, Mother See of Holy Etchmiadzin Church. d, St. Gayane Church.

2009, Dec. 18 ***Perf. 14***

815 A253 70d Sheet of 4, #a-d 6.00 6.00

Christmas — A254

Madonna and Child with: 280d, Country name in white. 650d, Country name in black.

Perf. 13½x13¾

2009, Dec. 18 **Litho.**

816 A254 280d multi 2.50 2.50

No. 816 was issued in sheets of 9 and sheets of 6 + 3 labels.

Souvenir Sheet

Perf. 14

817 A254 650d multi 5.75 5.75

No. 817 contains one 30x60mm stamp.

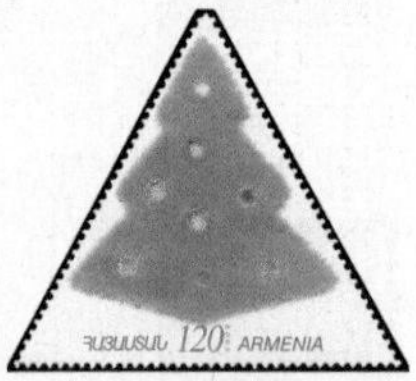

New Year 2010 A255

Litho. with Flocking

2009, Dec. 18 ***Perf. 14***

818 A255 120d multi 7.50 7.50

King Tigran the Great (c. 140-55 B.C.) — A256

2010, Jan. 29 **Litho.** ***Perf. 13x13¼***

Background Color

819	A256	10d cerise	.25	.25
820	A256	25d dark blue	.25	.25
821	A256	50d yel bister	.50	.50
822	A256	70d vermilion	.65	.65
823	A256	100d brown	.85	.85
824	A256	120d maroon	1.00	1.00
825	A256	200d gray	1.75	1.75
826	A256	220d purple	2.00	2.00
827	A256	280d red brown	2.50	2.50
828	A256	650d yel green	6.00	6.00
		Nos. 819-828 (10)	15.75	15.75

Self-Adhesive

Serpentine Die Cut 11¼

829	A256	10d cerise	.25	.25
830	A256	25d dark blue	.25	.25
831	A256	50d yel bister	.40	.40
832	A256	70d vermilion	.55	.55
833	A256	100d brown	.75	.75

834	A256	120d maroon	.90	.90
835	A256	200d gray	1.50	1.50
836	A256	220d purple	1.75	1.75
837	A256	280d red brown	2.10	2.10
838	A256	650d yel green	5.00	5.00
		Nos. 829-838 (10)	13.45	13.45

Type A256 has no lettering below king's neck. The country name is smaller than that found on types A211 and A240. Compare with types A271-A272.

Henrik Kasparyan (1910-95), Chess Player — A257

2010, Feb. 27 ***Perf. 14***

839 A257 870d multi 8.00 8.00

Victory in World War II, 65th Anniv. — A258

2010, May 6 ***Perf. 13¼x12¾***

840 A258 350d multi 2.75 2.75

Cemetery for Russian Officers, Gyumri — A259

2010, Aug. 20 Litho. ***Perf. 13¼x13***

Background Color

841 A259 350d light blue 2.75 2.75

Souvenir Sheet

842 A259 650d maroon 5.75 5.75

Mt. Ararat A260

Flag of Armenia A261

2010, Sept. 21 ***Perf. 12½x13***

843 A260 350d multi 2.75 2.75

Perf. 13¼

844 A261 650d multi 5.00 5.00

Independence Day.

Yerevan and Mt. Ararat A262

Armenian Pavilion at Expo 2010, Shanghai — A263

2010, Sept. 22 ***Perf. 14***

845 A262 280d multi 2.25 2.25

Perf. 12½x13

846 A263 280d multi 2.25 2.25

Expo 2010, Shanghai.

Europa A264

2010, Oct. 8 ***Perf. 13¼***

847 A264 350d multi 2.50 2.50

2010 Youth Olympics, Singapore — A265

2010, Nov. 26 ***Perf. 12½x13***

848 A265 870d multi 6.50 6.50

2010 World Cup Soccer Championships, South Africa — A266

2010, Nov. 26 **Litho.**

849 A266 1100d multi 8.50 8.50

Souvenir Sheet

Olympic Champions — A267

No. 850: a, Vladimir Yengibaryan, boxing gold medalist, 1956. b, Faina Melnik, discus gold medalist, 1972. c, Yuri Vardanyan, weight lifting gold medalist, 1980.

2010, Nov. 26 ***Perf. 13¼***

850 A267 160d Sheet of 3, #a-c 3.75 3.75

Souvenir Sheet

2010 Winter Olympics, Vancouver — A268

No. 851 — Skiers and 2010 Winter Olympics emblem at: a, 350d, Upper left. b, 500d, Center. c, 500d, Upper right.

2010, Nov. 26

851 A268 Sheet of 3, #a-c 11.00 11.00

Arakel Babakhanyan (1860-1932), Historian — A269

2010, Dec. 27 ***Perf. 12½x13***

852 A269 220d multi 1.75 1.75

Raffi (Hakob Melik Hakobyan) (1835-88), Writer — A270

2010, Dec. 27 ***Perf. 13x12½***

853 A270 220d multi 1.75 1.75

King Tigran the Great (c. 140-55 B.C.)

A271 A272

2011, Feb. 1 Litho. ***Perf. 13¼***

Granite Paper

Background Color

854	A271	10d	dark blue	.25	.25
855	A272	35d	gray brn	.30	.30
856	A272	50d	green	.35	.35
857	A272	70d	blue green	.55	.55
858	A272	120d	org brown	.90	.90
859	A272	160d	maroon	1.25	1.25
860	A272	220d	dark red	1.75	1.75
861	A272	280d	purple	2.10	2.10
862	A272	350d	bister	2.75	2.75
863	A272	1100d	dk brown	8.50	8.50
			Nos. 854-863 (10)	18.70	18.70

Nos. 854-863 lack the word "Post." Compare with Types A211, A240 and A256.

Ruben Sevak (1885-1915), Writer — A273

2011, Feb. 2 ***Perf. 13¼***

864 A273 280d multi 2.00 2.00

Dated 2010.

A274

2011, Feb. 2 ***Perf. 13¼***

865 A274 280d multi 2.00 2.00

Vahan Teryan (1885-1920), writer. Dated 2010.

A275

Paintings in National Gallery: No. 866, 450d, Portrait of Actress Khmara, by Haroutyun Kalents. No. 867, 450d, Catholicos Mkrtich Khrimyan, by Vardghes Sourenyants.

2011, Feb. 2 ***Perf. 13x12½***

866-867 A275 Set of 2 6.50 6.50

Dated 2010.

Souvenir Sheet

Pepo, First Armenian Film With Sound, 75th Anniv. (in 2010) — A276

No. 868: a, 170d, Actors Avet Avetisyan and Davit Malyan. b, 200d, Actor Hrachya Nercissyan. c, 500d, Actress Tatiana Makhmuryan.

2011, Feb. 2 ***Perf. 13¼***

868 A276 Sheet of 3, #a-c 6.50 6.50

Dated 2010.

Leonid Yenigbarov (1935-72), Circus Clown — A277

2011, Feb. 2 Litho. ***Perf. 13x12½***

869 A277 220d multi 1.60 1.60

Flora — A278

Designs: No. 870, 280d, Fritillaria armena. No. 871, 280d, Sambucus tigranii.

2011, Feb. 2 ***Perf. 13¼***

870-871 A278 Set of 2 4.00 4.00

Souvenir Sheet

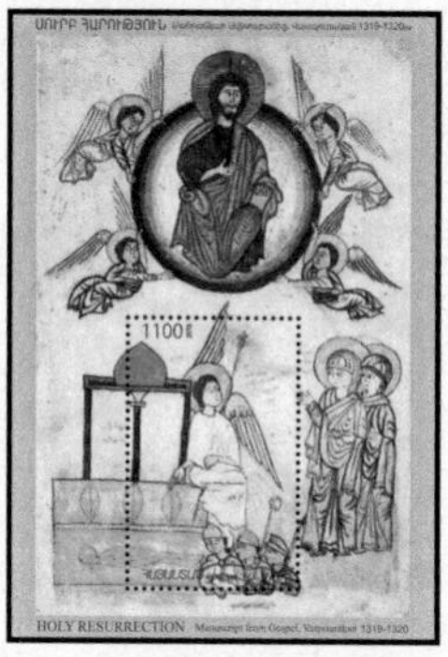

Easter A279

2011, Apr. 15 Litho. ***Perf. 12½x13***

872 A279 1100d multi 7.50 7.50

Andranik Iossifian (1905-93), Designer of Meteorological Satellites A280

First Man in Space, 50th Anniv. A281

2011, Apr. 18 ***Perf. 13x12½***

873 A280 200d multi 1.50 1.50

Perf. 12½x13

874 A281 350d multi 2.50 2.50

Capitals of Belarus and Armenia A282

No. 875 — Buildings and arms of: a, Minsk, Belarus. b, Yerevan, Armenia.

2011, June 1 Litho. ***Perf. 13***

875 A282 200d Horiz. pair, #a-b 3.00 3.00

See Belarus No. 771.

Souvenir Sheet

Communications Regional Commonwealth, 20th Anniv. — A283

2011, June 1
876 A283 200d multi 1.50 1.50

Writers — A284

Designs: 120d, Hovhannes Tumanian (1869-1923). 230d, Valery Bryusov (1873-1924).

2011, June 1 ***Perf. 12¾***
877-878 A284 Set of 2 3.00 3.00
878a Vert. pair, #877-878 3.00 3.00

Nos. 877-878 each were printed in sheets of 9 + label. No. 878a was printed in sheets containing five pairs.
See Russia Nos. 7273-7274.

Souvenir Sheet

Fifth Pan-Armenian Games — A285

2011, Aug. 20
879 A285 380d multi 3.00 3.00

Birds — A286

Designs: 230d, Luscinia svecica. 330d, Parus major.

2011, Sept. 5 ***Perf. 13¼***
880 A286 230d multi 1.75 1.75
881 A286 330d multi 2.75 2.75
a. Horiz. pair, #880-881 4.50 4.50

Independence of Nagorno Karabakh From Azerbaijan, 20th Anniv. — A287

2011, Sept. 13 ***Perf. 13x13¼***
882 A287 330d multi 2.50 2.50

Independence of Armenia, 20th Anniv. — A288

2011, Sept. 13
883 A288 380d multi 3.00 3.00

A289

Design: Fridtjof Nansen (1861-1930), Polar Explorer, Diplomat Assisting in Alleviating Armenian Refugee Crisis.

2011, Nov. 9 ***Perf. 13½***
884 A289 350d olive bister 2.75 2.75

Commonwealth of Independent States, 20th Anniv. — A290

2011, Dec. 1 ***Perf. 13x12½***
885 A290 280d multi 2.10 2.10

Souvenir Sheet

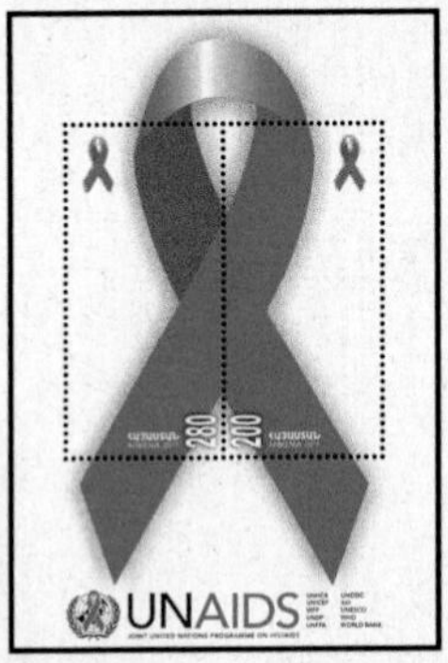

Joint United Nations Program on AIDS A291

No. 886 — AIDS ribbons: a, 200d. b, 280d.

2011, Dec. 1 ***Perf. 13¼***
886 A291 Sheet of 2, #a-b 3.75 3.75

2011 Junior Eurovision Song Contest, Yerevan A292

2011, Dec. 3 ***Perf. 13¼x13***
887 A292 230d multi 1.75 1.75
a. Souvenir sheet of 4 7.00 7.00

No. 887 was printed in sheets of 8.

Europa — A293

Photographs of forest in Dilijan Reserve with denominations at: No. 888, 350d, LL. No. 889, 350d, LR.

2011, Dec. 14 ***Perf. 12½x13***
888-889 A293 Set of 2 5.00 5.00

Intl. Year of Forests.

Grigor Zohrap (1861-1915), Lawyer and Writer — A294

2011, Dec. 23 ***Perf. 13¼x13***
890 A294 170d multi 1.25 1.25

Children A295

No. 891: a, 100d, Girl holding grapes and bird, flag of Armenia. b, 120d, Boy holding wheat stalks, flag of Nagorno Karabakh.

2011, Dec. 27 **Litho.**
891 A295 Horiz. pair, #a-b 1.75 1.75

Youth philately. No. 891 was printed in sheets containing two pairs.

Souvenir Sheet

UNESCO World Heritage Sites — A296

No. 892: a, 230d, Sanahin Monastery. b, 330d, Haghpat Monastery.

2011, Dec. 27 ***Perf. 13¼x13***
892 A296 Sheet of 2, #a-b 5.00 5.00

Christmas and New Year's Day — A297

2011, Dec. 27 ***Perf. 13¼***
893 A297 220d multi 1.75 1.75

Armenian Army, 20th Anniv. — A298

Army coat of arms and: 200d, Soldiers, tank, military vehicle, airplanes. 280d, Armenian flag.

2012, Feb. 9 ***Perf. 13¼x13***
894-895 A298 Set of 2 3.75 3.75

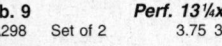

Admission to United Nations, 20th Anniv, — A299

2012, Mar. 23 **Litho.** ***Perf. 13x13¼***
896 A299 350d multi 2.60 2.60

Souvenir Sheet

Yerevan, World Book Capital A300

2012, Apr. 22
897 A300 560d multi 5.00 5.00

Garegin Nzhdeh (1886-1955), Statesman — A301

2012, May 3 ***Perf. 13¼***
898 A301 200d multi 1.60 1.60

Misak Metsarents (1886-1908), Poet — A302

2012, May 3 ***Perf. 13¼x13***
899 A302 280d black 2.10 2.10

Armenian Alphabet — A303

First seven letters of Armenian alphabet in capital and lower-case.

2012, May 14 ***Perf. 13x13¼***
Color of Panel at Left

900	A303	10d	dull rose	.25	.25
901	A303	25d	yel green	.25	.25
902	A303	50d	gray blue	.45	.45
903	A303	70d	dull blue	.50	.50
904	A303	100d	greenish gray	.75	.75
905	A303	120d	dull blue	.95	.95
906	A303	280d	lilac rose	2.10	2.10
			Nos. 900-906 (7)	5.25	5.25

See Nos. 940-946, 983-989, 1066-1072, 1100-1104, 1110-1113, 1140-1142.

Khachkars — A304

Khachkar: 200d, By Master Poghos, Goshavank, 1291. 280d, Arinj, 13th cent.

2012, June 14 ***Perf. 13¼***
907-908 A304 Set of 2 3.50 3.50

Souvenir Sheet

Armenian Olympic Gold Medalists — A305

No. 909: a, Eduard Azaryan. b, Levon Julfalakyan. c, Hoksen Mirzoyan.

2012, June 15
909 A305 160d Sheet of 3, #a-c 3.50 3.50

Souvenir Sheet

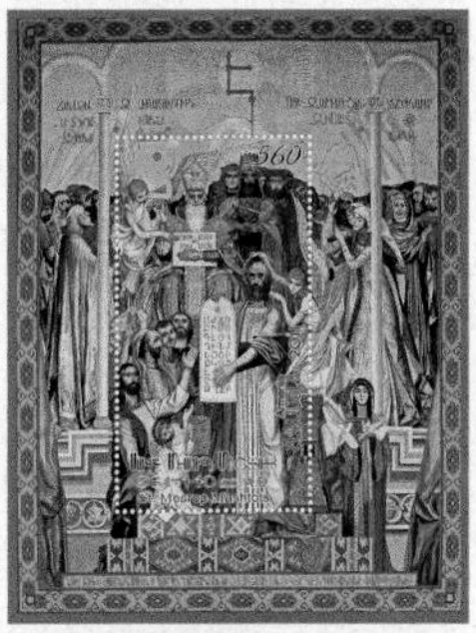

Mesrop Mashtots (361-440), Monk — A306

2012, June 19 *Perf. 14½x14¼*
910 A306 560d multi 3.75 3.75

Hagigadar Monastery A307

2012, Aug. 11 *Perf. 13¼*
911 A307 380d multi 2.75 2.75
a. Souvenir sheet of 2 + 2 labels 5.50 5.50

See Romania No. 5383.

Armenian Membership in Organization for Security and Cooperation in Europe, 20th Anniv. — A308

2012, Sept. 7 *Perf. 13x13¼*
912 A308 330d multi 2.25 2.25

Ancient Artashat, Capital of Kingdom of Armenia, 185 B.C.-120 A.D. — A309

2012, Oct. 30
913 A309 220d multi 1.60 1.60

Mount Ararat and Alexander Misnikyan (1886-1925), Bolshevik Leader — A310

2012, Oct. 30
914 A310 230d multi 1.50 1.50

Samvel Kocharyants (1909-93), Nuclear Physicist — A311

2012, Nov. 30 *Perf. 14x13½*
915 A311 350d multi 2.50 2.50

2012 Summer Olympics, London — A312

2012, Nov. 30 *Perf. 13¼*
916 Horiz. strip of 3 4.50 4.50
a. A312 170d Boxing 1.25 1.25
b. A312 200d Weight lifting 1.40 1.40
c. A312 230d Wrestling 1.75 1.75

Miniature Sheet

Armenian Olympic Gold Medalists — A313

No. 917: a, Hrachya Petikyan, shooting, 1992. b, Israyel Militosyan, weight lifting, 1992. c, Mnatsakan Iskandaryan, boxing, 1992. d, Armen Nazaryan, boxing, 1996.

2012, Nov. 30
917 A313 120d Sheet of 4, #a-d 3.50 3.50

Perch Proshyan (1837-1907), Writer — A314

2012, Dec. 4 **Litho.**
918 A314 170d multi 1.25 1.25

Lusine Zakaryan (1937-92), Opera Singer — A315

2012, Dec. 4 *Perf. 13x13¼*
919 A315 220d multi 1.50 1.50

Religious Treasures of Etchmiadzin — A316

No. 920: a, 200d, Reliquary of Geghard, 1687. b, 220d, Cross with relic, 1746. c, 450d, Reliquary, Argadsz, St. Nshan, 13th cent.

2012, Dec. 4 *Perf. 13¼x13*
920 A316 Horiz. strip of 3, #a-c 6.50 6.50

Ashot Hovhannisyan (1887-1977), First Secretary of Armenian Communist Party — A317

2012, Dec. 5 *Perf. 13x13¼*
921 A317 170d black 1.75 1.75

A318

2012, Dec. 5 *Perf. 13¼x13*
922 A318 280d multi 2.00 2.00

Hovsep Orbeli (1887-1961), President of Armenian Academy of Arts and Sciences.

A319

2012, Dec. 5
923 A319 280d multi 2.00 2.00

Hayk Bzhishkyants (1887-1937), military leader.

Tigran Tchoukhadjian (1837-98), Composer — A320

2012, Dec. 6 **Litho.**
924 A320 330d multi 2.50 2.50

Hayastan All-Armenian Fund, 20th Anniv. — A321

2012, Dec. 12 *Perf. 13x13¼*
925 A321 380d multi 3.00 3.00

Collective Security Treaty Organization, 20th Anniv. — A322

2012, Dec. 17 *Perf. 13¼x13*
926 A322 230d multi 1.75 1.75

Tadevos Minasyants (1912-82), Minister of Communications A323

2012, Dec. 27 *Perf. 13x13¼*
927 A323 170d multi 1.25 1.25

Tatev Monastery — A324

2012, Dec. 27 **Litho.**
928 A324 350d multi 2.50 2.50
a. Sheet of 4 + 2 labels 10.00 10.00

Europa.

Paintings in National Gallery of Armenia — A325

Designs: 220d, Dacha, by Marc Chagall. 280d, Self-portrait, by Rudolf Khachatryan.

2012, Dec. 27 *Perf. 13¼x13*
929-930 A325 Set of 2 3.50 3.50

Souvenir Sheet

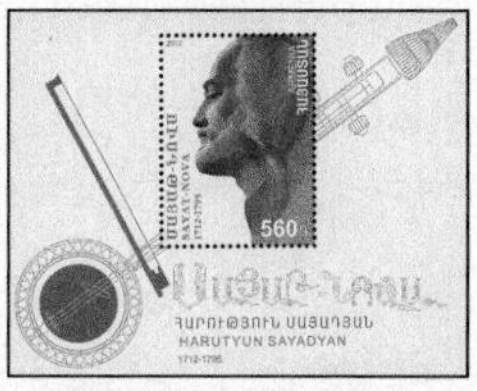

Sayat-Nova (1712-95), Musician — A326

2012, Dec. 27
931 A326 560d multi 4.25 4.25

Children's Art — A327

Designs: 100d, Trees. 120d, Soccer player.

2012, Dec. 28 *Perf. 13¾*
932-933 A327 Set of 2 1.60 1.60

Mammals — A328

Designs: 230d, Allactaga elater. 330d, Ovis orientalis gmelinii.

2012, Dec. 28 *Perf. 12½*
934 A328 230d multi 1.50 1.50
935 A328 330d multi 2.25 2.25
a. Horiz. pair, #934-935 4.00 4.00

Christmas and New Year's Day — A329

2012, Dec. 28 *Perf. 13x13¼*
936 A329 220d multi 1.60 1.60

St. Sargis's Day — A330

2013, Jan. 29 *Perf. 13¼x13*
937 A330 280d multi 1.90 1.90

Souvenir Sheet

Churches — A331

No. 938: a, 160d, Holy Trinity Church, Yerevan. b, 200d, Church of Holy Archangels, St. Etchmiadzin. c, 200d, Church of St. Hakob of Msbin, Gyumri.

2013, Apr. 4 *Perf. 13¼*
938 A331 Sheet of 3, #a-c 4.00 4.00

Brandy Production in Armenia — A332

2013, June 18 *Perf. 13x13¼*
939 A332 300d multi 1.90 1.90

No. 939 was printed in sheets of 8 + 2 labels.

Armenian Alphabet Type of 2012

Second group of seven letters of Armenian alphabet in capital and lower-case.

2013, July 30 *Perf. 13x13¼*

Color of Panel at Left

940	A303	10d olive bister	.25	.25
941	A303	35d salmon rose	.25	.25
942	A303	50d green	.40	.40
943	A303	60d blue	.45	.45
944	A303	70d rose	.55	.55
945	A303	100d greenish blue	.75	.75
946	A303	120d gray blue	.95	.95
		Nos. 940-946 (7)	3.60	3.60

Europa — A333

2013, Aug. 15 **Litho.**
947 A333 350d multi 2.75 2.75
a. Souvenir sheet of 4 11.00 11.00

Johannes Lepsius (1858-1926), Documenter of Armenian Genocide A334

James Bryce (1838-1922), Documenter of Armenian Genocide A335

2013, Aug. 16 ***Perf. 13x13¼***
948 A334 280d multi 2.00 2.00

Perf. 13¼x13
949 A335 330d multi 2.50 2.50

Armenian Genocide, cent. (in 2015).

Souvenir Sheet

Church of St. Grigor, Kecharis Monastery, Tsakhkadsor — A336

2013, Aug. 24 **Litho.** ***Perf. 13¼x13***
950 A336 480d multi 4.00 4.00

Souvenir Sheet

Aurora Mardiganian (1901-94), Writer of Memoir "Ravished Armenia" — A337

Perf. 14¼x14½
2013, Sept. 24 **Litho.**
951 A337 480d multi 4.00 4.00

Souvenir Sheet

Diplomatic Relations Between Armenia and Belarus, 20th Anniv. — A338

2013, Oct. 24 **Litho.** ***Perf. 13***
952 A338 650d multi 5.00 5.00

See Belarus No. 879.

Anton Kochinyan (1913-90), Politician — A339

2013, Oct. 25 **Litho.** ***Perf. 13x13¼***
953 A339 230d multi 1.75 1.75

A340

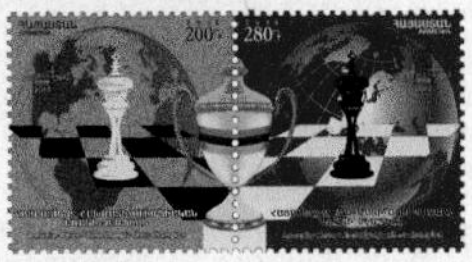

Chess A341

No. 954: a, 200d, Chess pieces and board, stylized globe. b, 280d, Chessboard with rook in background.

No. 955 — Half of trophy, globe, chess pieces and chess board with: a, 200d, Black squares. b, 280d, White squares.

2013, Nov. 6 **Litho.** ***Perf. 13¼***
954 A340 Horiz. pair, #a-b 4.00 4.00
c. Souvenir sheet of 4, 2 each #954a-954b 8.00 8.00
d. Souvenir sheet of 8, 4 each #954a-954b, + 8 labels 17.00 17.00
955 A341 Horiz. pair, #a-b 4.00 4.00
c. Souvenir sheet of 4, 2 each #955a-955b 8.00 8.00
d. Souvenir sheet of 8, 4 each #955a-955b, + 8 labels 17.00 17.00

Armenia as World Chess Team Champion (No. 954); Armenia as 3-time Chess Olympiad champion (No. 955).

Souvenir Sheet

Church of St. Hovhannes, Gandzasar Monastery — A342

2013, Nov. 8 **Litho.** ***Perf. 14¼x14½***
956 A342 560d multi 4.50 4.50

Gyumri, Cultural Capital of Commonwealth of Independent States — A343

2013, Nov. 11 **Litho.** ***Perf. 13x13¼***
957 A343 560d multi + 2 flanking labels 4.50 4.50

Award of the President of Armenia A344

No. 958 — Medal depicting: a, 180d, Eagle. b, 220d, Coat of arms.

2013, Nov. 15 **Litho.** ***Perf. 13¼x13***
958 A344 Horiz. pair, #a-b 3.25 3.25

Ancient Capitals of Armenia — A345

Designs: 160d, Armavir. 170d, Yervandashat.

2013, Nov. 19 **Litho.** ***Perf. 13x13¼***
959-960 A345 Set of 2 2.50 2.50

Beniamin Markarian (1913-85), Astrophysicist A346

2013, Nov. 21 **Litho.** ***Perf. 13x13¼***
961 A346 170d multi 1.25 1.25

Armenian Chairmanship of Council of Europe in 2013 — A347

2013, Nov. 25 **Litho.** ***Perf. 13¼x13***
962 A347 380d multi 3.00 3.00

Paintings — A348

Designs: 230d, Family, by Ara Bekarian. 330d, Portrait of the Painter's Mother, by Stepan Aghajanian.

2013, Nov. 25 **Litho.** ***Perf. 13¼x13***
963-964 A348 Set of 2 4.50 4.50

Mushrooms — A349

Designs: 230d, Macrolepiota rhacodes. 330d, Boletus edulis.

2013, Nov. 25 **Litho.** ***Perf. 12½***
965 A349 230d multi 1.75 1.75
966 A349 330d multi 2.75 2.75
a. Horiz. pair, #965-966 4.50 4.50

Nos. 965-966 each were printed in sheets of 8 + 2 labels. No. 966a was printed in a sheet containing 5 pairs.

Hakop Kojoian (1883-1959), Painter A350

Armenian Herald, by Kojoian A351

2013, Nov. 27 **Litho.** ***Perf. 13¼x13***
967 A350 240d multi 1.75 1.75
968 A351 240d multi 1.75 1.75
a. Horiz. pair, #967-968 3.50 3.50

Nos. 967-968 each were printed in sheets of 8. No. 968a was printed in sheets containing 4 pairs.

Dram Currency, 20th Anniv. — A352

2013, Nov. 29 **Litho.** ***Perf. 13x13¼***
969 A352 380d multi 4.00 4.00

Souvenir Sheet

2014 Winter Olympics, Sochi, Russia — A353

No. 970: a, 350d, Cross-country skiing. b, 1100d, Alpine skiing.

2013, Dec. 2 **Litho.** ***Perf. 13¼***
970 A353 Sheet of 2, #a-b 10.00 10.00

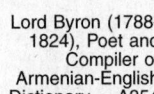

Lord Byron (1788-1824), Poet and Compiler of Armenian-English Dictionary — A354

2013, Dec. 5 **Litho.** ***Perf. 12½***
971 A354 350d multi 2.75 2.75

Telephones in Armenia, Cent. — A355

2013, Dec. 10 **Litho.** ***Perf. 13x13¼***
972 A355 170d multi 1.40 1.40

Vahran Papazian (1888-1968), Actor — A356

2013, Dec. 16 **Litho.** ***Perf. 13x13¼***
973 A356 230d multi 1.75 1.75

Chess — A357

Designs: 100d, Chess pieces and boards. 120d, Chess pieces and board.

2013, Dec. 16 **Litho.** ***Perf. 13x13¼***
974-975 A357 Set of 2 1.75 1.75

Souvenir Sheet

Civil Aviation in Armenia, 80th Anniv. A358

2013, Dec. 16 **Litho.** ***Perf. 13¾***
976 A358 500d multi 3.50 3.50

New Year 2014 — A359

2013, Dec. 16 **Litho.** ***Perf. 13x13¼***
977 A359 220d multi 1.75 1.75

Wine Production in Armenia — A360

2013, Dec. 28 **Litho.** ***Perf. 13x13¼***
978 A360 330d multi + label 2.50 2.50

No. 978 was printed in sheets of 4 + 4 labels. Two different labels were made available on separate sheets.

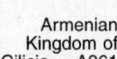

Armenian Kingdom of Cilicia — A361

Designs: 120d, King Levon III, ruler from 1270-89. 240d, Queen Keran, wife of King Levon III.

2013, Dec. 28 **Litho.** ***Perf. 13x13¼***
979-980 A361 Set of 2 2.75 2.75
980a Horiz. pair, #979-980 2.75 2.75

Nos. 979-980 each were printed in sheets of 10. No. 980a was printed in sheets containing two pairs.

Souvenir Sheet

Artsakh Movement (Campaign to Transfer Jurisdiction of Nagorno-Karabakh to Armenia), 25th Anniv. — A362

2013, Dec. 28 Litho. ***Perf. 13x13¼***
981 A362 400d multi 3.00 3.00

Souvenir Sheet

Archaeological Items Found in Areni-1 Cave — A363

No. 982: a, 160d, Matting, c. 3500 B.C. b, 220d, Shoe, c. 3500 B.C.

2013, Dec. 28 Litho. ***Perf. 13¼x13***
982 A363 Sheet of 2, #a-b 3.00 3.00

Armenian Alphabet Type of 2012

Third group of seven letters of Armenian alphabet in capital and lower-case.

2014, May 8 Litho. ***Perf. 13x13¼***
Color of Panel at Left

983	A303	70d	dull bl green	.60	.60
984	A303	120d	rose lilac	1.00	1.00
985	A303	170d	lilac	1.40	1.40
986	A303	220d	gray green	1.75	1.75
987	A303	230d	green blue	1.90	1.90
988	A303	280d	blue	2.25	2.25
989	A303	380d	rose	3.25	3.25
			Nos. 983-989 (7)	12.15	12.15

Intelligence Officers — A364

No. 990: a, Yakov Davtian (1888-1938). b, Ivan Agayants (1911-68). c, Haik Ovakimian (1898-1967). d, Ashot Akopian (1915-81). 350d, Gevork Vartanian (1924-2012).

2014, May 20 Litho. ***Perf. 13x13¼***
990 A364 230d Sheet of 4, #a-d 6.50 6.50

Souvenir Sheet
Perf. 13¼x13½

991 A364 350d multi 2.50 2.50

No. 991 contains one 45x28mm stamp.

Europa — A365

Musical instruments: No. 992, 350d, Pku. No. 993, 350d, Zurna.

2014, May 23 Litho. ***Perf. 13x13¼***
992-993 A365 Set of 2 5.00 5.00

2014 World Cup Soccer Championships, Brazil — A366

2014, June 27 Litho. ***Perf. 13x13¼***
994 A366 380d multi 2.75 2.75

Armenian Kingdom of Cilicia — A367

Map and: No. 995, 240d, Ruins, Ayas. No. 996, 240d, Anamur Fortress. No. 997, 240d, Korikos Fortress.

2014, July 4 Litho. ***Perf. 13x13¼***
995-997 A367 Set of 3 5.00 5.00
997a Souvenir sheet of 6, 2 each #995-997 10.00 10.00

John Kirakossian (1929-85), Historian — A368

2014, July 29 Litho. ***Perf. 13x13¼***
998 A368 330d multi 2.50 2.50

Armenian Genocide Monuments — A369

Monument in: No. 999, 280d, Boston, Massachusetts. No. 1000, 280d, Montevideo, Uruguay, horiz. 380d, Paris, France.

Perf. 13¼x13, 13x13¼
2014, July 29 Litho.
999-1001 A369 Set of 3 7.00 7.00

Souvenir Sheet

Danish Mothers of Armenian Orphans — A370

No. 1002 — Medal and: a, Karen Jeppe (1875-1935). b, Maria Jacobsen (1882-1960).

2014, July 29 Litho. ***Perf. 13¼x13***
1002 A370 200d Sheet of 2, #a-b 3.00 3.00

Famous Men — A371

Building and: No. 1003, 280d, Toros Toramanian (1864-1934), architect. No. 1004, 280d, Nikolay Marr (1864-1934), archaeologist, linguist and architect.

2014, Aug. 13 Litho. ***Perf. 13x13¼***
1003-1004 A371 Set of 2 4.00 4.00

Hounan Avetissian (1914-43), Military Hero — A372

2014, Aug. 15 Litho. ***Perf. 13¼x13***
1005 A372 170d multi 1.25 1.25

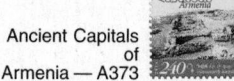

Ancient Capitals of Armenia — A373

Designs: No. 1006, 240d, Dvin. No. 1007, 240d, Tigranakert.

2014, Aug. 21 Litho. ***Perf. 13x13¼***
1006-1007 A373 Set of 2 3.50 3.50

Hamo Sahian (1914-93), Poet — A374

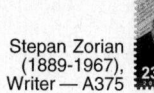

Stepan Zorian (1889-1967), Writer — A375

2014, Sept. 5 Litho. ***Perf. 13x13¼***
1008 A374 220d multi 1.50 1.50
1009 A375 230d multi 1.75 1.75

Flora and Fauna — A376

Designs: 230d, Dianthus gabrielianae. 330d, Upupa epops.

2014, Sept. 23 Litho. ***Perf. 12¾***
1010-1011 A376 Set of 2 4.00 4.00

Souvenir Sheet

Voskan Yerevantsi (1614-74), Book Publisher — A377

Perf. 13¼x13½
2014, Sept. 26 Litho.
1012 A377 650d multi 5.00 5.00

Souvenir Sheet

World War I, Cent. A378

2014, Sept. 29 Litho. ***Perf. 13¼x13***
1013 A378 480d multi 3.50 3.50

Cross Stones (Khachkars) — A379

Designs: No. 1014, 240d, Holy Redeemer khachkar, Urtz, 1279. No. 1015, 240d, Mastara khachkar, 13th cent.

2014, Dec. 12 Litho. ***Perf. 13¼***
1014-1015 A379 Set of 2 3.50 3.50

Souvenir Sheet

Holy Transfiguration Cathedral, Moscow — A380

2014, Dec. 12 Litho. ***Perf. 13¼x13***
1016 A380 870d multi 6.00 6.00

Skier — A381

2014, Dec. 15 Litho. ***Perf. 13¼***
1017 A381 350d multi 2.75 2.75

Dzitoghtyans House Museum, Gyumri — A383

No. 1019: a, Building exterior. b, Dining room.

2014, Dec. 30 Litho. ***Perf. 13x13¼***
1019 A383 280d Horiz. pair, #a-b 4.00 4.00

Shushi — A384

2014, Dec. 30 Litho. ***Perf. 13x13¼***
1020 A384 240d multi 1.75 1.75

Traditional Costumes — A385

Designs: 120d, Man and woman from Yerevan. 230d, Man, woman and child from Gyumri.

2014, Dec. 30 Litho. ***Perf. 13¼x13***
1021-1022 A385 Set of 2 2.75 2.75

A386

A387

Children's Art — A388

2014, Dec. 30 Litho. ***Perf. 13x13¼***
1023 A386 100d multi .75 .75

Perf. 13¼x13

1024 A387 100d multi .75 .75
1025 A388 100d multi .75 .75
Nos. 1023-1025 (3) 2.25 2.25

Forget-me-not — A389

2015, Jan. 29 Litho. *Perf. 13¼x13*

Background Color

1026	A389	70d white	.45	.45
1027	A389	120d pale yellow	.80	.80
1028	A389	240d pale peach	1.50	1.50
1029	A389	280d pale green	1.75	1.75
1030	A389	330d light blue	2.25	2.25
1031	A389	350d dull mauve	2.40	2.40
a.		Souvenir sheet of 1	2.40	2.40
1032	A389	870d pale red vio	5.75	5.75
a.		Souvenir sheet of 1	5.75	5.75
b.		Sheet of 14, 2 each #1026-1032 + central label	30.00	30.00
		Nos. 1026-1032 (7)	14.90	14.90

Armenian Genocide, cent. Nos. 1026-1032 were each printed in sheets of 14 + central label. See Nos. 1048-1050.

Paintings by Panos Terlemezian (1865-1941) — A390

No. 1033: a, 230d, Self-portrait. b, 330d, Mount Sipan from Ktuts Island.

2015, Mar. 3 Litho. *Perf. 13x13¼*
1033 A390 Horiz. pair, #a-b 3.75 3.75

Melkonian Orphanage, Nicosia, Cyprus A391

2015, Apr. 2 Litho. *Perf. 14½x14¼*
1034 A391 350d multi 2.40 2.40

See Cyprus No. 1232.

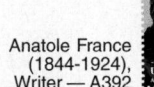

Anatole France (1844-1924), Writer — A392

2015, Apr. 23 Litho. *Perf. 13x13¼*
1035 A392 300d multi 2.25 2.25

Henry Morgenthau, Sr. (1856-1946), U.S. Ambassador to the Ottoman Empire — A393

2015, Apr. 23 Litho. *Perf. 13¼x13*
1036 A393 300d multi 2.25 2.25

Souvenir Sheet

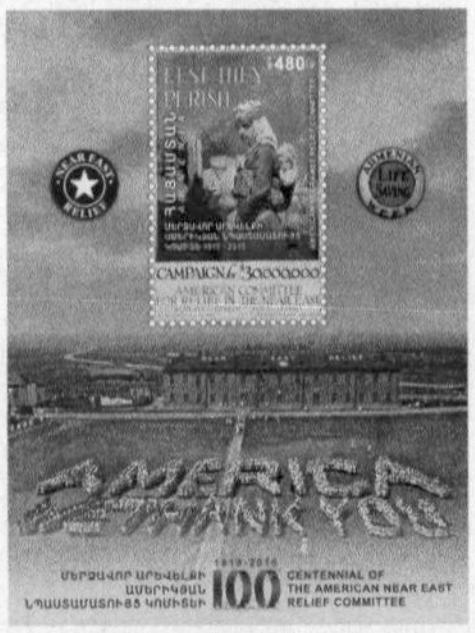

American Committee for Relief in the Near East, Cent. — A394

2015, May 6 Litho. *Perf. 13*
1037 A394 480d multi 3.75 3.75

Victory in World War II, 70th Anniv. — A395

2015, May 8 Litho. *Perf. 13x13¼*
1038 A395 230d multi 1.75 1.75

Eurasian Economic Union — A396

2015, May 12 Litho. *Perf. 13¼x13*
1039 A396 560d multi 4.25 4.25

Missak Manouchian (1906-44), Poet — A397

2015, May 26 Litho. *Perf. 13¼x13*
1040 A397 170d multi 1.40 1.40

Souvenir Sheet

Sixth Pan-Armenian Games — A398

2015, Aug. 5 Litho. *Perf. 13½x13¼*
1041 A398 380d multi 3.25 3.25

Armenian Olympic Committee, 25th Anniv. — A399

2015, Sept. 29 Litho. *Perf. 13¼*
1042 A399 230d multi 1.90 1.90

Souvenir Sheet

Blessing of the Holy Chrism A400

2015, Sept. 29 Litho. *Perf. 13¼x13*
1043 A400 480d multi 3.75 3.75

Constitutional Court, 20th Anniv. — A401

2015, Oct. 8 Litho. *Perf. 13x13¼*
1044 A401 330d multi 2.40 2.40

Lazarev Institute, Moscow, 200th Anniv. — A402

2015, Oct. 23 Litho. *Perf. 13x13¼*
1045 A402 380d multi 3.00 3.00

Resistance to the Armenian Genocide — A403

No. 1046: a, 200d, Resistance in Van, Turkey. b, 280d, Resistance at Mount Musa.

2015, Oct. 29 Litho. *Perf. 13x13¼*
1046 A403 Horiz. pair, #a-b 3.75 3.75

Armenian Genocide Museum and Institute, Yerevan — A404

No. 1047: a, 230d, Museum exterior and displays. b, 280d, Museum interior.

2015, Nov. 21 Litho. *Perf. 13x13¼*
1047 A404 Horiz. pair, #a-b 4.25 4.25

Forget-me-not Type of 2015

2015, Dec. 24 Litho. *Perf. 13¼x13*

Background Color

1048	A389	40d yellow	.35	.35
1049	A389	50d light blue	.40	.40
1050	A389	60d pink	.50	.50
		Nos. 1048-1050 (3)	1.25	1.25

Nos. 1048-1050 were each printed in sheets of 14 + central label.

A405

Children's Art — A406

2015, Dec. 24 Litho. *Perf. 13x13¼*
1051 A405 70d multi .70 .70
1052 A406 70d multi .70 .70

Top — A407

2015, Dec. 28 Litho. *Perf. 13¼*
1053 A407 350d multi 3.50 3.50

Europa.

Flora and Fauna — A408

Designs: 220d, Lynx lynx dinniki. 280d, Sorbus hajastana.

2015, Dec. 28 Litho. *Perf. 12¾*
1054-1055 A408 Set of 2 3.75 3.75

Vladimir Vysotsky (1938-80), Singer — A409

2015, Dec. 30 Litho. *Perf. 13x13¼*
1056 A409 350d multi 2.75 2.75

Armenian State Philharmonia, Yerevan — A410

2015, Dec. 30 Litho. *Perf. 13¼x13*
1057 A410 380d multi 3.00 3.00

Souvenir Sheet

Operation Nemesis — A411

2015, Dec. 30 Litho. *Perf. 13¼x13*
1058 A411 360d multi 2.75 2.75

Operation Nemesis was a series of assassinations of people responsible for the Armenian Genocide.

Souvenir Sheets

A412

Medals and Orders for Fund-raising for Genocide Survivors — A413

No. 1059 — Order inscribed: a, Armenia. b, Servia, Syria, Armenia.

No. 1060 — Medal depicting: a, Two-headed bird. b, Cross.

2015, Dec. 30 Litho. *Perf. 13¼*
1059 A412 280d Sheet of 2, #a-b 4.25 4.25

Perf.
1060 A413 280d Sheet of 2, #a-b 4.25 4.25

Souvenir Sheet

2016 Posteurop Plenary Assembly, Yerevan — A414

2016, Apr. 20 Litho. *Perf. 13¼*
1061 A414 870d multi 6.50 6.50

Souvenir Sheet

2016 World Stamp Show, New York
A415

2016, May 29 Litho. *Perf.*
1062 A415 650d multi 5.00 5.00

Souvenir Sheet

2016 Summer Olympics, Rio de Janeiro — A416

2016, May 29 Litho. *Perf. 13¼*
1063 A416 650d multi 5.00 5.00

Visit to Armenia of Pope Francis
A417

No. 1064: a, 170d, Pope Francis and Yerevan. b, 230d, Pope Francis, cupola of St. Peter's Basilica. c, 380d, Pope Francis, statue of St. Gregory the Illuminator. d, 480d, Pope Francis, Etchmiadzin Cathedral.
870d, Pope Francis, St. Peter's Basilica, Etchmiadzin Cathedral, horiz.

2016, June 24 Litho. *Perf. 13¼*
1064 A417 Sheet of 4, #a-d, + label 12.00 12.00

Souvenir Sheet
Perf. 13¾x14

1065 A417 870d multi 6.50 6.50

No. 1065 contains one 45x33mm stamp.

Armenian Alphabet Type of 2012

Fourth group of seven letters of Armenian alphabet in capital and lower-case.

2016, July 7 Litho. *Perf. 13x13¼*
Color of Panel at Left

1066	A303	70d	salmon pink	.50	.50
1067	A303	120d	apple green	.90	.90
1068	A303	170d	red lilac	1.25	1.25
1069	A303	230d	bister	1.75	1.75
1070	A303	280d	olive	2.10	2.10
1071	A303	330d	lt red brown	2.50	2.50
1072	A303	380d	gray blue	3.00	3.00
			Nos. 1066-1072 (7)	12.00	12.00

2016 European Soccer Championships, France — A418

2016, July 15 Litho. *Perf. 13x13¼*
1073 A418 500d multi 3.75 3.75

A419

Independence, 25th Anniv. — A420

2016, Sept. 21 Litho. *Perf. 13x13¼*
1074 A419 200d multi 1.50 1.50

Perf. 13¼x13

1075 A420 300d multi 2.25 2.25

Tatevik Sazandarian (1916-99), Opera Singer — A421

2016, Oct. 4 Litho. *Perf. 13¼x13*
1076 A421 230d multi 1.75 1.75

Arshak Fetvadjian (1866-1947), Painter — A422

No. 1077: a, 170d, Fetvadjian. b, 230d, Woman Playing the Mandolin, by Fetvadjian.

2016, Oct. 7 Litho. *Perf. 13¼x13*
1077 A422 Pair, #a-b 3.00 3.00

Srbuhi Tyusab (1841-1901), Writer — A423

2016, Oct. 20 Litho. *Perf. 13x13¼*
1078 A423 230d multi 1.75 1.75

Souvenir Sheet

First Bible Printed in Armenian, 350th Anniv. — A424

2016, Nov. 13 Litho. *Perf. 13¼x13*
1079 A424 560d multi 4.25 4.25

Sergey Paradjanov Museum, Yerevan — A425

2016, Nov. 18 Litho. *Perf. 13¼*

1080	Horiz. pair	5.50	5.50
a.	A425 300d Museum exterior	2.50	2.50
b.	A425 380d Museum interior	3.00	3.00

Telbats Koubati — A426

2016, Nov. 28 Litho. *Perf. 13¼x13*
1081 A426 170d multi 1.40 1.40

Europa
A427

No. 1082: a, Dead and living trees. b, City, bicyclist, wind generators.

2016, Dec. 1 Litho. *Perf. 13x13¼*
1082 A427 350d Pair, #a-b 5.25 5.25

Think Green Issue.

Souvenir Sheet

Argentine Boca Juniors Soccer Team, 1977, 2000 and 2003 Intercontinental Soccer Cup Champions — A428

2016, Dec. 12 Litho. *Perf. 14*
1083 A428 500d multi 3.75 3.75

Ancient Capitals of Armenia — A429

Designs: 230d, Bagara, 2nd cent. B.C. 330d, Vagharshapat, 2nd cent. A.D.

2016, Dec. 15 Litho. *Perf. 13x13¼*
1084-1085 A429 Set of 2 4.25 4.25

Armenia on Ancient Maps — A430

Designs: 300d, Babylonian map of the world, 6th cent. B.C. 330d, Map of Ptolemy's Greater Armenia, 2nd cent. A.D.

2016, Dec. 15 Litho. *Perf. 13x13¼*
1086-1087 A430 Set of 2 5.00 5.00

Commonwealth of Independent States, 25th Anniv. — A431

2016, Dec. 21 Litho. *Perf. 13¼x13*
1088 A431 380d multi 3.00 3.00

Stylized Animals — A432

Designs: No. 1089, 100d, Armenian gull. No. 1090, 100d, Van cat. No. 1091, 100d, Armenian mouflon.

2016, Dec. 26 Litho. *Perf. 13¼x13*
1089-1091 A432 Set of 3 2.25 2.25

Children's Philately.

Birds — A433

Designs: 230d, Neophron percnopterus. 280d, Falco tinnunculus.

2016, Dec. 29 Litho. *Perf. 12½*
1092-1093 A433 Set of 2 4.00 4.00

Flowers — A434

Designs: 230d, Tulipa sylvestris. 330d, Orchis tridentata.

2016, Dec. 29 Litho. *Perf. 12½*
1094-1095 A434 Set of 2 4.50 4.50

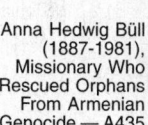

Anna Hedwig Büll (1887-1981), Missionary Who Rescued Orphans From Armenian Genocide — A435

2016, Dec. 30 Litho. *Perf. 13¼x13*
1096 A435 280d multi 2.10 2.10

Armenian Army, 25th Anniv. — A436

No. 1097 — Emblem and: a, Soldiers, tanks, trucks and flag. b, Soldiers and flags.

2017, Jan. 27 Litho. *Perf. 13x13¼*
1097 A436 280d Pair, #a-b 4.25 4.25

No. 1097 was printed in sheets containing two pairs.

Alexander Mantashian (1842-1911), Industrialist and Philanthropist
A437

2017, Mar. 3 Litho. *Perf. 14*
1098 A437 380d multi 3.25 3.25

Souvenir Sheet

Artur Aleksanyan, 2016 Olympic Greco-Roman Wrestling Gold Medalist — A438

2017, May 30 Litho. *Perf.*
1099 A438 480d multi 4.00 4.00

Armenian Alphabet Type of 2012

29th-32nd letters of Armenian alphabet in capital and lower-case.

2017, June 2 Litho. ***Perf. 13x13¼***
Color of Panel at Left

1100 A303 10d gray blue .25 .25
1101 A303 50d olive green .40 .40
1102 A303 70d dull rose .55 .55
1103 A303 100d dull purple .80 .80
Nos. 1100-1103 (4) 2.00 2.00

First Postage Stamps of Republic of Armenia, 25th Anniv. — A439

2017, June 15 Litho. ***Perf. 12½***
1104 A439 100d multi .90 .90

Amberd Castle A440

2017, July 10 Litho. ***Perf. 14***
1105 A440 350d multi 3.00 3.00

Europa.

Hamo Beknazarian (1891-1965), Film Director and Actor — A441

2017, July 13 Litho. ***Perf. 14***
1106 A441 170d multi 1.50 1.50

Paintings by Gabriel Gyurjian (1892-1987) A442

Designs: 170d, Nork. 230d, Dsegh. Sunrise, and Gyurjian.

2017, July 20 Litho. ***Perf. 13x13¼***
1107-1108 A442 Set of 2 3.25 3.25

Helix Nebula — A443

2017, July 27 Litho. ***Perf. 13x13¼***
1109 A443 280d multi 2.25 2.25

Regional Astronomical Center. No. 1109 was printed in sheets of 8 + central label.

Armenian Alphabet Type of 2012

Last group of four letters of Armenian alphabet in capital and lower-case.

2017, Aug. 23 Litho. ***Perf. 13x13¼***
Color of Panel at Left

1110 A303 230d brn rose 1.90 1.90
1111 A303 280d gray lilac 2.40 2.40
1112 A303 330d yellow brown 2.75 2.75
1113 A303 380d dl blue grn 3.25 3.25
Nos. 1110-1113 (4) 10.30 10.30

Independence, 25th Anniv. — A444

No. 1114: a, 200d, National colors of flags and Government House. b, 300d, Nation colors of flag & new building for various governmental ministries.

2017, Oct. 9 Litho. ***Perf. 13x13¼***
1114 A444 Horiz. pair, #a-b 4.25 4.25

Mekhitarist Congregation on St. Lazarus Island, 300th Anniv. — A445

2017, Oct. 23 Litho. ***Perf. 13x13¼***
1115 A445 230d multi 1.90 1.90

Souvenir Sheet

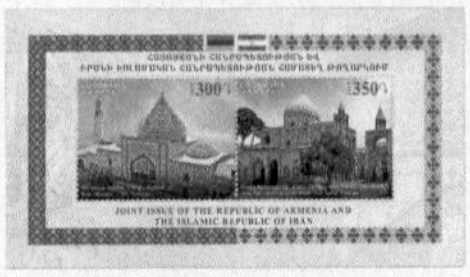

Houses of Worship A446

No. 1116: a, 300d, Blue Mosque, Yerevan. b, 350d, Holy Savior Cathedral, Isfahan, Iran.

2017, Oct. 25 Litho. ***Perf. 13¾x14***
1116 A446 Sheet of 2, #a-b 5.50 5.50

Joint issue between Armenia and Iran. See Iran No. 3178.

Miniature Sheet

Paintings by Ivan Aivazovsky (1817-1900) — A447

No. 1117: a, 170d, Self-portrait, 1874 (29x35mm). b, 220d, Noah's Descent from Mt. Ararat, 1889 (43x25mm). c, 230d, Bayron's Visit to the Mekhitarists on the Island of St. Lazarus, 1899 (43x25mm). d, 380d, Seascape. Mediterranean Seashore, 1892 (43x25mm). e, 450d, The Ninth Wave, 1850 (43x25mm).

Perf. 14x13¾ (170d), 14
2017, Nov. 7 Litho.
1117 A447 Sheet of 5, #a-e 12.00 12.00

Souvenir Sheet

Diplomatic Relations Between Armenia and Russia, 25th Anniv. — A448

No. 1118 — Coat of arms of: a, Armenia ("25" at LL). b, Russia ("25" at LR).

2017, Nov. 21 Litho. ***Perf. 13½***
1118 A448 280d Sheet of 2, #a-b 4.75 4.75

Flag of Armenia and Emblem of Collective Security Treaty Organization A449

2017, Nov. 30 Litho. ***Perf. 13x13¼***
1119 A449 230d multi 1.90 1.90

Collective Security Treaty, 25th anniv., Collective Security Treaty Organization, 15th anniv.

Sergey Aganov (1917-96), Soviet Marshal — A450

2017, Dec. 17 Litho. ***Perf. 13¼x13***
1120 A450 160d multi 1.40 1.40

Ruins of Shirakavan, Capital of Armenia, 890-929 — A451

Map of Kars, Capital of Armenia, 929-61 — A452

2017, Dec. 12 Litho. ***Perf. 13x13¼***
1121 A451 160d multi 1.40 1.40
1122 A452 160d multi 1.40 1.40

Kirk Kerkorian (1917-2015), Businessman and Philanthropist — A453

2017, Dec. 14 Litho. ***Perf. 13¼x13***
1123 A453 380d multi 3.25 3.25

Kutahya Ceramics, 19th Cent. — A454

2017, Dec. 18 Litho. ***Perf. 13x13¼***
1124 A454 170d multi 1.50 1.50

Holy Martyrs of the Armenian Genocide — A455

2017, Dec. 18 Litho. ***Perf. 13½***
1125 A455 450d multi 3.75 3.75

No. 1125 was printed in sheets of 8 + 4 labels.

Yuri Oganessian, Nuclear Physicist Source of Name of Element 118, Oganesson A456

2017, Dec. 28 Litho. ***Perf. 14***
1126 A456 70d multi .70 .70

Ghazanchetsots Cathedral, Shushi — A457

2017, Dec. 28 Litho. ***Perf. 13x13¼***
1127 A457 230d multi 1.90 1.90

Liberation of Shushi, 25th anniv.

Kevork V (1847-1930), Catholicos of Armenian Apostolic Church — A458

2017, Dec. 28 Litho. ***Perf. 13¼x13***
1128 A458 280d multi 2.40 2.40

Dinosaurs A459

Designs: 230d, Pterosaur. 280d, Tyrannosaurus.

2017, Dec. 28 Litho. ***Perf. 13x13¼***
1129-1130 A459 Set of 2 4.50 4.50

Christmas — A460

2017, Dec. 28 Litho. ***Perf. 13¼x13***
1131 A460 220d multi 1.90 1.90

When you turn stamp upside down you see a Christmas tree.

Flora and Fauna — A461

Designs: 230d, Ixiolirion montanum. 330d, Mustela nivalis.

2017, Dec. 29 Litho. ***Perf. 12½***
1132-1133 A461 Set of 2 4.75 4.75

Souvenir Sheet

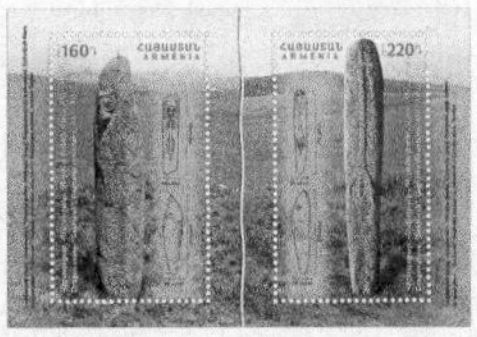

Dragon Stones A462

No. 1134: a, 160d, 360-centimeter tall dragon stone. b, 220d, 375-centimeter tall dragon stone.

2017, Dec. 29 Litho. ***Perf. 14***
1134 A462 Sheet of 2, #a-b 3.25 3.25

Souvenir Sheet

World Cup and Flag of Brazil A463

2017, Dec. 29 Litho. ***Perf. 13½***
1135 A463 480d multi 4.00 4.00

Brazil, five-time World Cup Champion.

Souvenir Sheet

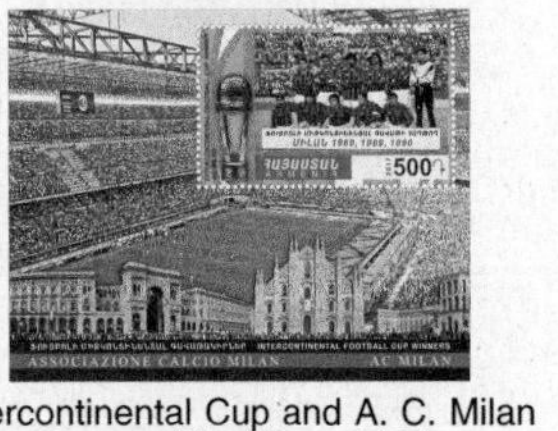

Intercontinental Cup and A. C. Milan Soccer Players — A464

2017, Dec. 29 Litho. ***Perf. 14***
1136 A464 500d multi 4.25 4.25

A. C. Milan, three-time Intercontinental Cup Champion.

Souvenir Sheet

St. Grigor Narekatsi (951-1003), Poet — A465

2017, Dec. 29 Litho. *Perf. 13x13¼*
1137 A465 870d multi 7.50 7.50

Souvenir Sheet

Lavash Bread A466

2017, Dec. 29 Litho. *Perf. 13½*
1138 A466 1100d multi 9.25 9.25

Babken Nersisian (1917-86), Actor — A467

2018, Apr. 4 Litho. *Perf. 14*
1139 A467 170d multi 1.50 1.50

Armenian Alphabet Type of 2012

33rd-35th letters in the Armenian alphabet.

2018, Apr. 5 Litho. *Perf. 13x13¼*
Color of Panel at Left

1140 A303 70d ochre .60 .60
1141 A303 230d gray green 2.00 2.00
1142 A303 330d gray olive 2.75 2.75
Nos. 1140-1142 (3) 5.35 5.35

2018 Winter Olympics, Pyeongchang, South Korea — A468

2018, June 6 Litho. *Perf. 13½*
1143 A468 380d multi 3.25 3.25

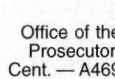

Office of the Prosecutor, Cent. — A469

2018, July 1 Litho. *Perf. 13¾x14*
1144 A469 330d multi 2.75 2.75

2018 World Cup Soccer Championships, Russia — A470

2018, July 25 Litho. *Perf. 13x13¼*
1145 A470 450d multi 4.00 4.00

Armenian General Athletic Union Scouts, Cent. A471

2018, July 26 Litho. *Perf. 14*
1146 A471 330d multi 2.75 2.75

Goris, Cultural Capital of the Commonwealth of Independent States — A472

2018, July 27 Litho. *Perf. 13½*
1147 A472 330d multi 2.75 2.75

Dances A473

No. 1148: a, Hov Arek dancers, Armenia. b, Manipuri dancers, India.

2018, Aug. 29 Litho. *Perf. 13x13¼*
1148 A473 280d Horiz. pair, #a-b 4.75 4.75

See India Nos. 3053-3054.

Armenian Security Bodies, Cent. — A474

2018, Sept. 24 Litho. *Perf. 13x13¼*
1149 A474 170d multi 1.50 1.50

Natural Bridge, Tsakkar — A475

2018, Oct. 2 Litho. *Perf. 13x13¼*
1150 A475 350d multi 3.00 3.00

Europa.

Souvenir Sheet

First Republic of Armenia, Cent. A476

2018, Oct. 4 Litho. *Perf. 13¼*
1151 A476 480d multi 4.25 4.25

Souvenir Sheet

17th Francophone Summit, Yerevan — A477

2018, Oct. 8 Litho. *Perf. 14*
1152 A477 870d multi 7.50 7.50

Souvenir Sheet

Charles Aznavour (1924-2018), Singer — A478

2018, Oct. 11 Litho. *Perf. 13½*
1153 A478 870d multi 7.50 7.50

National Police, Cent. — A479

2018, Oct. 31 Litho. *Perf. 13x13¼*
1154 A479 120d multi 1.10 1.10

Paintings by Hovhannes Zardaryan (1918-92) — A480

Designs: 170d, Spring. 230d, Winter Landscape, and Zardaryan.

2018, Nov. 6 Litho. *Perf. 13x13¼*
1155-1156 A480 Set of 2 3.50 3.50

Shikahogh Reserve A481

2018, Nov. 8 Litho. *Perf. 14*
1157 A481 230d multi 1.90 1.90

A482

2018, Nov. 22 Litho. *Perf. 13x13¼*
1158 A482 100d multi .85 .85

Jamanak, Armenian Language Daily Newspaper of Istanbul, Turkey, 110th anniv.

Dram Currency, 25th Anniv. — A483

2018, Nov. 22 Litho. *Perf. 13¾*
1159 A483 230d multi 1.90 1.90

Values are for stamps with surrounding selvage.

Miniature Sheet

Yerevan, 2800th Anniv. A484

No. 1160: a, 220d, Erebuni Fortress excavations. b, 230d, Buildings on Amiryan Street, 1920. c, 350d, Yerevan Railroad Station. d, 650d, Alexander Spendidaryan National Academic Theater of Opera and Ballet.

2018, Nov. 29 Litho. *Perf. 13¼*
1160 A484 Sheet of 4, #a-d 12.00 12.00

State Award for Global Contribution in Information Technology Sphere — A485

No. 1161: a, 160d, Medal. b, 170d, Trophy.

2018, Nov. 30 Litho. *Perf. 13¼x13*
1161 A485 Horiz. pair, #a-b 2.75 2.75

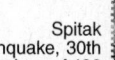

Spitak Earthquake, 30th Anniv. — A486

2018, Dec. 7 Litho. *Perf. 13x13¼*
1162 A486 230d multi 1.90 1.90

George VI (1868-1954), Catholicos of All Armenians — A487

2018, Dec. 10 Litho. *Perf. 13¼x13*
1163 A487 230d multi 1.90 1.90

Prehistoric Animals — A488

Designs: 220d, Argentinosaurus. 280d, Tapejara.

2018, Dec. 14 Litho. *Perf. 13x13¼*
1164-1165 A488 Set of 2 4.25 4.25

Flora and Fauna — A489

Designs: 230d, Punica granatum. 330d, Capoeta capoeta sevangi.

2018, Dec. 19 Litho. *Perf. 12½*
1166-1167 A489 Set of 2 4.75 4.75

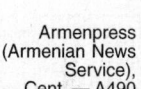

Armenpress (Armenian News Service), Cent. — A490

2018, Dec. 21 Litho. *Perf. 13x13¼*
1168 A490 120d multi 1.10 1.10

Hakob Paronian (1843-91) — A491

2018, Dec. 28 Litho. *Perf. 13¼x13*
1169 A491 230d multi 1.90 1.90

ErAZ 762 — A492

2018, Dec. 28 Litho. *Perf. 13x13¼*
1170 A492 380d multi 3.25 3.25

Anahit A493

Found Dream A494

2018, Dec. 28 Litho. ***Perf. 13¼x13***
1171 A493 100d multi .85 .85

Perf. 12½

1172 A494 230d multi 1.90 1.90

Armenian animated films.

Intercontinental Soccer Cup and Nacional Soccer Players of Uruguay — A495

2018, Dec. 28 Litho. ***Perf. 14***
1173 A495 500d multi 4.25 4.25

Saint Hripsime Cathedral, Vagharshapat, 1400th Anniv. — A496

2018, Dec. 28 Litho. ***Perf. 13½***
1174 A496 870d multi 7.50 7.50

Christmas and New Year — A497

2018, Dec. 28 Litho. ***Perf. 12½***
1175 A497 220d multi 1.90 1.90

New Year 2019 (Year of the Pig) — A498

2018, Dec. 28 Litho. ***Perf. 13x13¼***
1176 A498 330d multi 2.75 2.75

Silva Kaputikyan (1919-2006), Poet — A499

2019, Jan. 22 Litho. ***Perf. 13¼x13***
1177 A499 120d multi 1.10 1.10

8th Century B.C. Seals of the Kingdom of Ararat — A500

Various seals.

2019, Feb. 6 Litho. ***Perf. 13x13¼***
1178 A500 70d multi .60 .60
1179 A500 120d multi 1.00 1.00
1180 A500 230d multi 1.90 1.90
1181 A500 330d multi 2.75 2.75
Nos. 1178-1181 (4) 6.25 6.25

Souvenir Sheet

Hovhannes Toumanian (1869-1923), Poet — A501

2019, Feb. 18 Litho. ***Perf. 13***
1182 A501 1100d multi 9.25 9.25

Calouste Sarkis Gulbenkian (1869-1955), Businessman and Philanthropist — A502

No. 1183 — Gulbenkian and: a, 230d, Jeweled peacock. b, 330d, Ceramic bowl, 18th cent.

2019, Mar. 26 Litho. ***Perf. 13x13¼***
1183 A502 Horiz. pair, #a-b 4.75 4.75

Joint Issue between Armenia & Portugal. See Portugal Nos. 4109-4110.

Mammuthus Trogontherii A503

2019, Mar. 27 Litho. ***Perf. 13x13¼***
1184 A503 230d multi 1.90 1.90

Firefighters and Fire Truck — A504

2019, May 6 Litho. ***Perf. 13x13¼***
1185 A504 330d multi 2.75 2.75

Historic Capitals of Armenia — A505

Designs: 160d, Map of Ani, 10th cent. capital, Ani Cathedral and bowl. 170d, Aerial view and map of Yerevan, 20th cent. capital, and bowl.

2019, May 16 Litho. ***Perf. 13x13¼***
1186-1187 A505 Set of 2 2.75 2.75

Hirundo Rustica — A506

2019, May 21 Litho. ***Perf. 13¼x13***
1188 A506 350d multi 3.00 3.00

Europa.

Mohandas K. Gandhi (1869-1948), Indian Nationalist Leader — A507

2019, May 23 Litho. ***Perf. 13¼x13***
1189 A507 650d multi 5.50 5.50

Henrikh Mkhitaryan, Captain of Armenian National Soccer Team — A508

2019, June 4 Litho. ***Perf. 13½x12¾***
1190 A508 450d multi 4.00 4.00

Yerevan State University, Cent. — A509

2019, June 27 Litho. ***Perf. 13x13¼***
1191 A509 220d multi 1.90 1.90

Emblem of Eurasian Economic Union and Flags of Members as Puzzle Pieces — A510

2019, Aug. 9 Litho. ***Perf. 13½***
1192 A510 330d multi 2.75 2.75

Souvenir Sheet

7th Pan-Armenian Games — A511

2019, Aug. 20 Litho. ***Perf. 13¼***
1193 A511 870d multi 7.50 7.50

Etchmiadzin Cathedral, Vagharshapat A512

2019, Sept. 18 Litho. ***Perf. 13x13¼***
1194 A512 220d multi 1.00 1.00

Aram Khachaturian (1903-78), Composer A513

2019, Sept. 27 Litho. ***Perf. 13x13¼***
1195 A513 380d multi 1.75 1.75

Gevorg Emin (1919-98), Writer — A514

2019, Sept. 30 Litho. ***Perf. 13¼x13***
1196 A514 120d multi .55 .55

History Museum of Armenia — A515

2019, Sept. 30 Litho. ***Perf. 13x13¼***
1197 A515 220d multi 1.00 1.00

Souvenir Sheet

2019 World Congress on Information Technology, Yerevan — A516

2019, Oct. 7 Litho. ***Perf. 13¼***
1198 A516 650d multi 3.00 3.00

First Armenian Postage Stamps, Cent. — A517

2019, Nov. 11 Litho. ***Perf. 13x13¼***
1199 A517 230d multi 1.10 1.10

Fauna — A518

Designs: 230d, Alcedo atthis. 330d, Panthera pardus ciscaucasica.

2019, Nov. 12 Litho. ***Perf. 12½***
1200-1201 A518 Set of 2 2.50 2.50

A519 Chalcedony Seal

A520 Jet Seal

2019, Nov. 27 Litho. ***Perf. 13x13¼***
1202 A519 10d multi .25 .25
1203 A520 50d multi .30 .30

Souvenir Sheet

Komitas (1869-1935), Priest and Composer — A521

2019, Dec. 1 Litho. ***Perf. 13¼x13***
1204 A521 1100d multi 5.00 5.00

Hrachya Hovhannissian (1919-97), Poet — A522

2019, Dec. 11 Litho. ***Perf. 13¼***
1205 A522 120d multi .55 .55

Admiral Ivan Isakov (1894-1967) — A523

2019, Dec. 24 Litho. ***Perf. 13¼x13***
1206 A523 120d multi .75 .75

Daredevils of Sassoun Cartoon Character — A524

2019, Dec. 24 Litho. *Perf. 13x13¼*
1207 A524 120d multi .75 .75

Souvenir Sheet

Peñarol Soccer Team, Winners of 1961, 1966 and 1982 Intercontinental Cup — A525

2019, Dec. 24 Litho. *Perf. 14*
1208 A525 500d multi 3.25 3.25

Airplane and Mount Ararat A526

2019, Dec. 26 Litho. *Perf. 14*
1209 A526 220d multi 1.40 1.40

Snowman Heads — A527

2019, Dec. 26 Litho. *Perf. 13¼*
1210 A527 220d multi 1.40 1.40

Christmas and New Year's Day.

New Year 2020 (Year of the Rat) — A528

2019, Dec. 26 Litho. *Perf. 13¼x13*
1211 A528 230d multi 1.40 1.40

7th Century B.C. Bronze Van Kingdom Throne Decoration — A529

2020, May 26 Litho. *Perf. 13x13¼*
Background Color

1212	A529	10d	orange	.25	.25
1213	A529	50d	greenish blue	.25	.25
1214	A529	70d	rose pink	.30	.30
1215	A529	100d	yellow green	.45	.45
1216	A529	120d	light blue	.55	.55
1217	A529	230d	vermilion	1.10	1.10
1218	A529	330d	plum	1.50	1.50
	Nos. 1212-1218 (7)			4.40	4.40

See Nos. 1236-1237.

Prehistoric Animals — A530

Designs: 230d, Basilosaurus. 280d, Diplodocus.

2020, June 16 Litho. *Perf. 13x13¼*
1219-1220 A530 Set of 2 2.25 2.25

Bullet-riddled Wall With Armenian Inscription A531

2020, June 26 Litho. *Perf. 13x13¼*
1221 A531 280d multi 1.25 1.25

End of World War II, 75th anniv.

Horse-drawn Mail Wagon in Gyumri — A532

2020, July 3 Litho. *Perf. 13x13¼*
1222 A532 350d multi 1.50 1.50

Ancient Postal Routes.
Europa.

Souvenir Sheet

Napoleon Bonaparte (1769-1821), Emperor of France — A533

2020, July 10 Litho. *Perf. 13¼x13*
1223 A533 650d multi 3.00 3.00

Paintings by Jean Jansem (1920-2013) — A534

Designs: 280d, Self-portrait. 330d, Man, Woman and Child.

2020, July 20 Litho. *Perf. 13¼x13*
1224-1225 A534 Set of 2 2.75 2.75

Souvenir Sheet

Henri Verneuil (1920-2002), Film Director — A535

2020, Sept. 1 Litho. *Perf.*
1226 A535 1100d multi 4.75 4.75

Sergo Hambardzumyan (1910-83), Weight Lifter — A536

2020, Sept. 9 Litho. *Perf. 13¼x13*
1227 A536 120d multi .55 .55

Alexander Harutyunyan (1920-2012), Composer — A537

2020, Sept. 11 Litho. *Perf. 13¼*
1228 A537 220d multi .95 .95

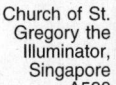

Church of St. Gregory the Illuminator, Singapore A538

2020, Sept. 17 Litho. *Perf. 13x13¼*
1229 A538 120d multi .55 .55

Paintings by Yeghishe Tadevossian (1870-1936) — A539

Designs: 230d, Self-portrait. 330d, Canal and Gondola, horiz.

Perf. 13¼x13, 13x13¼
2020, Nov. 11 Litho.
1230-1231 A539 Set of 2 2.50 2.50

New Year 2021 (Year of the Ox) — A540

2020, Nov. 13 Litho. *Perf. 13¼*
1232 A540 330d multi 1.50 1.50

Diana Apcar (1859-1937), Writer and Honorary Consul to Japan — A541

2020, Nov. 23 Litho. *Perf. 13¼x13*
1233 A541 120d multi .60 .60

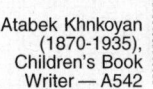

Atabek Khnkoyan (1870-1935), Children's Book Writer — A542

2020, Nov. 25 Litho. *Perf. 13x13¼*
1234 A542 120d multi .60 .60

Lazar Sarian (1920-98), Composer — A543

2020, Nov. 27 Litho. *Perf. 13¼x13*
1235 A543 120d multi .60 .60

Van Kingdom Throne Decoration Type of 2020

2020, Dec. 11 Litho. *Perf. 13x13¼*
Background Color

1236 A529 220d claret 1.10 1.10
1237 A529 280d blue 1.30 1.30

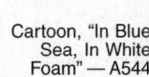

Cartoon, "In Blue Sea, In White Foam" — A544

2020, Dec. 24 Litho. *Perf. 13x13¼*
1238 A544 120d multi .60 .60

Bicycle — A545

2020, Dec. 24 Litho. *Perf. 13x13¼*
1239 A545 220d multi 1.10 1.10

Miniature Sheet

Paintings by Arshile Gorky (1904-48) — A546

No. 1240: a, 220d, Untitled, 1944 (29x35mm). b, 230d, Abstraction, 1936 (35x35mm). c, 350d, Landscape-Table, 1945 (35x35mm). d, 650d, Untitled, 1941 (30x40mm).

Perf. 14x13¾ (220d), 13¼ (230d, 350d), 13¼x13 (650d)
2020, Dec. 25 Litho.
1240 A546 Sheet of 4, #a-d 7.00 7.00

Ophrys Apifera A547

Tomares Romanovi A548

2020, Dec. 28 Litho. *Perf. 12½*
1241 A547 230d multi 1.10 1.10
1242 A548 330d multi 1.60 1.60

Souvenir Sheet

Ludwig van Beethoven (1770-1827), Composer — A549

2020, Dec. 28 Litho. *Perf. 13*
1243 A549 870d multi 4.25 4.25

Hrachya Nersisian (1895-1961), Actor — A550

2020, Dec. 29 Litho. *Perf. 13¼x13*
1244 A550 330d multi 1.60 1.60

Christmas and New Year's Day — A551

2020, Dec. 29 Litho. *Perf. 13x13¼*
1245 A551 240d multi 1.25 1.25

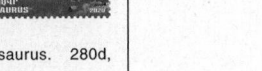

Souvenir Sheet

Printing House of Holy Etchmiadzin, 250th Anniv. — A552

2021, Apr. 16 Litho. *Perf. 13x13¼*
1246 A552 400d multi 1.90 1.90

Tribute to Healthcare Workers in the COVID-19 Pandemic — A553

Background color: 220d, Dark blue. 230d, Orange. 280d, Red. 300d, Violet.

2021, Apr. 16 Litho. *Perf. 13½*
1247-1250 A553 Set of 4 5.00 5.00
1250a Sheet of 8, 2 each #1247-1250 10.00 10.00

Steam Locomotive A554

2021, Apr. 19 Litho. *Perf. 13x13¼*
1251 A554 190d multi .90 .90

Cartoon, "Kikos" — A555

2021, Apr. 21 Litho. *Perf. 13x13¼*
1252 A555 190d multi .90 .90

Armenian College and Philanthropic Academy of Kolkata, 200th Anniv. — A556

2021, Apr. 26 Litho. *Perf. 13¼*
1253 A556 160d multi .80 .80

Bodil Biorn (1871-1960), Missionary and Founder of Orphanage in Alexandropol — A557

2021, May 5 Litho. *Perf. 13½x13*
1254 A557 230d multi 1.10 1.10

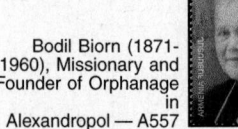

Prehistoric Animals — A558

Designs: 230d, Titanoboa. 280d, Velociraptor.

2021, May 6 Litho. *Perf. 13x13½*
1255-1256 A558 Set of 2 2.50 2.50

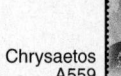

Aquila Chrysaetos A559

2021, May 7 Litho. *Perf. 13x13½*
1257 A559 350d multi 1.75 1.75

Europa.

Ghapama (Stuffed Pumpkin) — A560

2021, May 17 Litho. *Perf. 13½*
1258 A560 300d multi 1.50 1.50

Regional Communications Commonwealth, 30th Anniv. — A561

2021, May 31 Litho. *Perf. 13x13½*
1259 A561 290d multi 1.40 1.40

Characters From Cartoon *Lazy Huri* — A562

2021, June 1 Litho. *Perf. 13½x14*
1260 A562 70d multi .35 .35

2020 European Soccer Championships A563

2021, June 3 Litho. *Perf. 13x13½*
1261 A563 290d multi 1.40 1.40

The 2020 European Soccer Championships were postponed until 2021 because of the COVID-19 pandemic.

2020 Summer Olympics, Tokyo — A564

2021, June 4 Litho. *Perf. 13x13½*
1262 A564 500d multi 2.40 2.40

The 2020 Summer Olympics were postponed until 2021 because of the COVID-19 pandemic.

7th Century B.C. Bronze Van Kingdom Throne Decoration — A565

2021 Litho. *Perf. 13x13¼*

Background Color

1263	A565	10d	scarlet	.25	.25
1264	A565	20d	Turq blue	.25	.25
1265	A565	50d	ol gray	.25	.25
1266	A565	70d	pink	.35	.35
1267	A565	100d	brt green	.55	.55
1268	A565	230d	brn pur	1.25	1.25
1269	A565	290d	dull blue	1.60	1.60
1270	A565	400d	org red	2.25	2.25
1271	A565	450d	dark blue gray	1.90	1.90
1272	A565	1000d	bister yel	5.50	5.50
1273	A565	1600d	bluish violet	8.75	8.75
	Nos. 1263-1273 (11)			22.90	22.90

Issued: 10d, 20d, 50d, 70d, 100d, 230d, 290d, 1000d, 1600d, 6/7; 400d, 8/4; 450d, 12/15.

Souvenir Sheet

Alexander Spendiaryan (1871-1928), Composer — A566

2021, June 14 Litho. *Perf. 13½*
1274 A566 890d multi 4.25 4.25

Pghndzahank Fortress and Akhtala Monastery, Akhtala A567

2021, June 16 Litho. *Perf. 14*
1275 A567 470d multi 2.25 2.25

Edward Mirzoyan (1921-2012), Composer A568

2021, June 18 Litho. *Perf. 13x13½*
1276 A568 230d multi 1.10 1.10

Souvenir Sheet

Arno Babajanyan (1921-83), Composer — A569

2021, July 30 Litho. *Perf. 13¼x13*
1277 A569 1000d gold & multi 5.00 5.00

Clara Barton (1821-1912), Nurse and Founder of American Red Cross — A570

2021, Aug. 26 Litho. *Perf. 13*
1278 A570 230d multi 1.10 1.10

Tourist Sites — A571

Designs: 230d, Lsake Sevan and Hayravank Monastery. 410d, Zorats Karer megaliths. 470d, Mermaid's Hair Waterfall. 710d, Temple of Garni.

2021, Aug. 26 Litho. *Perf. 13½*
1279-1282 A571 Set of 4 8.75 8.75
1282a Souvenir sheet of 8, 2 each #1279-1282 17.50 17.50

Souvenir Sheet

Salome, Painting by Vardges Surenyants (1860-1921) — A572

2021, Sept. 13 Litho. *Perf. 14½*
1283 A572 890d multi 4.25 4.25

National Gallery of Armenia, cent.

Souvenir Sheet

Bombing of Ghazanchetsots Holy Savior Cathedral, 1st Anniv. — A573

No. 1284 — Cathedral: a, 940d, Before bombing. b, 950d, After bombing.

2021, Sept. 14 Litho. *Perf. 13x13½*
1284 A573 Sheet of 2, #a-b 9.00 9.00

Independence, 30th Anniv. — A574

Serpentine Die Cut 13½x14
2021, Sept. 21 Litho.
On Plastic Film
Self-Adhesive
1285 A574 890d multi 4.25 4.25

Alexander Kemurdzhian (1921-2003), Designer of Lunokhod Lunar Rover — A575

2021, Oct. 17 Litho. *Perf. 13x13¼*
1286 A575 230d multi 1.00 1.00

Komitas State Conservatory, Yerevan, Cent. — A576

2021, Oct. 20 Litho. *Perf. 13x13¼*
1287 A576 290d multi 1.25 1.25

Souvenir Sheets

A577

Papal Visits to Armenia A578

No. 1288: a, Pope John Paul II. b, Pope Francis.

No. 1289 — Catholicos Karekin II with: a, 940d, Pope John Paul II. b, 950d, Pope Francis.

2021, Oct. 27 Litho. *Perf. 13¼*

1288 A577 630d Sheet of 2, #a-b 5.25 5.25
1289 A578 Sheet of 2, #a-b 8.00 8.00

2001 visit of Pope John Paul II and 2016 visit of Pope Francis.

Havasi (Armenak Markosyan) (1896-1978), Folk Singer — A579

2021, Dec. 14 Litho. *Perf. 14*

1290 A579 290d multi 1.25 1.25

Communist Party of China, Cent. — A580

2021, Dec. 23 Litho. *Perf. 13¼x13*

1291 A580 390d multi 1.60 1.60

New Year 2022 (Year of the Tiger) — A581

Litho. With Foil Application

2021, Dec. 23 *Perf. 13¾*

1292 A581 500d gold & multi 2.10 2.10

Values are for stamps with surrounding selvage.

Flora and Fauna — A582

Designs: 230d, Hemiechinus auritus. 290d, Ommatotriton ophryticus. 400d, Iris lineolata. 450d, Nymphaea alba.

Perf. 13¼x13¾

2021, Dec. 24 Litho.

1293-1296 A582 Set of 4 5.75 5.75
1296a Sheet of 8, 2 each #1293-1296 11.50 11.50

Souvenir Sheet

Christmas and New Year's Day — A583

2021, Dec. 24 Litho. *Perf.*

1297 A583 890d multi 3,75 3.75

Yerevan Television Tower of Public Television Company of Armenia — A584

2021, Dec. 27 Litho. *Perf. 13¼x13*

1298 A584 400d multi 1.75 1.75

Diplomatic Relations Between Armenia and Egypt, 30th Anniv. — A585

2022, Mar. 22 Litho. *Perf. 13½*

1299 A585 400d multi 1.90 1.90

8th-7th Cent. B.C. Van Kingdom Bronze Winged Figurine — A586

2022, Mar. 28 Litho. *Perf. 13x13¼*

Background Color

1300 A586 10d orange .30 .30
1301 A586 20d sage green .30 .30
1302 A586 50d rose lilac .30 .30
1303 A586 70d blue .30 .30
1304 A586 100d cerise .30 .30
1305 A586 230d Prussian green .60 .60
1306 A586 290d pink .80 .80
1307 A586 400d light blue 1.10 1.10
1308 A586 450d black 1.25 1.25
1309 A586 1000d purple brown 2.75 2.75
1310 A586 1600d deep violet 4.25 4.25
Nos. 1300-1310 (11) 12.25 12.25

See Nos. 1331-1332.

Yeghishe Charents (1897-1937), Poet — A587

2022, Apr. 4 Litho. *Perf. 13¼x13*

1311 A587 400d multi 1.90 1.90

Paintings by Lavinia Bazhbeuk-Melikyan (1922-2005) — A588

Designs: 280d, Self-portrait with Zhilinskaya, 1965. 410d, Cacti, 1964.

2022, Apr. 7 Litho. *Perf. 13¼x13*

1312-1313 A588 Set of 2 3.50 3.50

Prehistoric Animals — A589

Designs: 220d, Triceratops. 280d, Liopleurodon.

2022, Apr. 8 Litho. *Perf. 13x13¼*

1314-1315 A589 Set of 2 2.40 2.40

Tram — A590

2022, Apr. 11 Litho. *Perf. 13½*

1316 A590 170d multi .80 .80

Armenian Army, 30th Anniv. — A591

Litho. & Embossed With Foil Application

2022, Apr. 13 *Perf. 13¼x13*

1317 A591 500d sil & multi 2.40 2.40

2022 Winter Olympics, Beijing — A592

Litho. With Foil Application

2022, Apr. 14 *Perf. 13½*

1318 A592 330d multi 1.90 1.90

Sergey Hambardzumyan (1922-2018), Rector of Yerevan State University — A593

2022, Apr. 21 Litho. *Perf. 13x13¼*

1319 A593 220d multi 1.10 1.10

Astghik, Goddess of Love — A594

2022, May 26 Litho. *Perf. 13½*

1320 A594 350d multi 1.90 1.90

Europa.

Ignacy Lukasiewicz (1822-82), Inventor of Paraffin Lamp — A595

2022, May 31 Litho. *Perf. 13½x13*

1321 A595 160d multi .85 .85

Tserents (Hovsep Shishmanian) (1822-88), Writer — A596

2022, June 1 Litho. *Perf. 13x13½*

1322 A596 290d multi 1.60 1.60

Souvenir Sheet

Armenian National Soccer Team — A597

2022, June 2 Litho. *Perf. 13x13½*

1323 A597 500d multi 2.60 2.60

A598

Design: Winning design in children's stamp design contest with theme of "The Future We Want."

2022, June 7 Litho. *Perf. 13x13½*

1324 A598 290d multi 1.60 1.60

United Nations in Armenia, 30th anniv.

Armenian Presidency of Collective Security Treaty Organization — A599

2022, June 9 Litho. *Perf. 13½*

1325 A599 380d multi 2.00 2.00

Ardem Patapoutian, 2021 Nobel Laureate in Physiology or Medicine — A600

2022, June 14 Litho. *Perf. 13½*

1326 A600 350d multi 2.00 2.00

Khachatur Abovyan Armenian State Pedagogical University, Cent. — A601

2022, June 20 Litho. *Perf. 13½x13*

1327 A601 590d multi 3.50 3.50

Davit Bek Monument, Kapan — A602

2022, July 22 Litho. *Perf. 13½*

1328 A602 380d multi 2.25 2.25

Syunik Rebellion, 300th anniv.

Archag Tchobanian (1872-1954), Writer — A603

2022, July 25 Litho. *Perf. 13¼x13*

1329 A603 320d multi 1.90 1.90

Holy Resurrection Church, Dhaka, Bangladesh — A604

2022, July 25 Litho. *Perf. 13x13½*

1330 A604 320d multi 1.90 1.90

Bronze Winged Figure Type of 2022

2022, July 26 Litho. *Perf. 13x13¼*

Background Color

1331 A586 320d red 1.90 1.90
1332 A586 380d violet 2.25 2.25

Vahagn Davtyan (1922-96), Poet — A605

2022, July 27 Litho. *Perf. 13½x13*
1333 A605 320d multi 1.90 1.90

Souvenir Sheet

St. John the Baptist Church, Shushi A606

No. 1334 — St. John the Baptist Church: a, 940d, Before aerial bombing by Azerbaijan forces. b, 950d, After aerial bombing.

2022, July 27 Litho. *Perf. 13x13½*
1334 A606 Sheet of 2, #a-b 11.00 11.00

Grigor Gurzadyan (1922-2014), Astrophysicist, and Planetary Nebula — A607

2022, July 28 Litho. *Perf. 13x13½*
1335 A607 380d multi 2.25 2.25

Souvenir Sheet

Scene From 1975 Motion Picture *A Bride From the North* A608

2022, July 28 Litho. *Perf. 13x13½*
1336 A608 800d multi 4.50 4.50

Scene From 1972 Cartoon *Vin the Penguin* — A609

2022, July 29 Litho. *Perf. 13x13½*
1337 A609 200d multi 1.10 1.10

Eurasian Economic Commission, 10th Anniv. — A610

2022, Aug. 25 Litho. *Perf. 13½*
1338 A610 160d multi .90 .90

Churches — A611

No. 1339: a, Armenian Apostolic Church of Saint Catherine, St. Petersburg, Russia (lt. blue panel). b, Russian Orthodox Church of St. Michael the Archangel, Gyumri, Armenia (reddish purple panel).

2022, Aug. 30 Litho. *Perf. 13½*
1339 A611 500d Pair, #a-b 5.75 5.75

See Russia No.

Flora and Fauna — A612

Designs: 320d, Lilium armenum. 380d, Astrantia maxima. 500d, Otocolobus manul. 560d, Tichodroma muraria.

2022, Sept. 7 Litho. *Perf. 13½*
1340-1343 A612 Set of 4 10.00 10.00
1343a Souvenir sheet of 8, 2 each #1340-1343 20.00 20.00

Souvenir Sheet

2022 Men's European Boxing Championships, Yerevan — A613

2022, Sept. 8 Litho. *Perf. 13¼x14*
1344 A613 800d multi 4.75 4.75

Souvenir Sheet

Sixth Starmus International Festival, Yerevan — A614

2022, Sept. 8 Litho. *Perf. 13x13½*
1345 A614 500d multi 3.00 3.00

Tourist Sites — A615

Designs: 320d, Geghad Monastic Complex, Kotayk Region. 380d, Lake Sev, Syunik Region. 500d, Trchkan Waterfall, Shirak Region. 560d, Mount Aragats.

2022, Sept. 12 Litho. *Perf. 13½*
1346-1349 A615 Set of 4 10.00 10.00
1349a Souvenir sheet of 8, 2 each #1346-1349 20.00 20.00

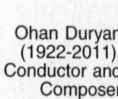

Ohan Duryan (1922-2011), Conductor and Composer A616

2022, Sept. 13 Litho. *Perf. 13x13½*
1350 A616 230d multi 1.30 1.30

2022 World Cup Soccer Championships, Qatar — A617

2022, Sept. 13 Litho. *Perf. 13x13¼*
1351 A617 500d multi 3.00 3.00

Stepanavan "Sochut" Dendropark (Arboretum) A618

2022, Sept. 14 Litho. *Perf. 13x13¼*
1352 A618 380d multi 2.25 2.25

Ghalinjakar Fortress, Berdavan — A619

2022, Sept. 15 Litho. *Perf. 13½*
1353 A619 380d multi 2.25 2.25

Gata — A620

2022, Sept. 16 Litho. *Perf. 13½x13*
1354 A620 380d multi 2.25 2.25

SEMI-POSTAL STAMPS

International Children's Day — SP1

2008, June 1 Litho. *Perf. 14¾x14*
B1 SP1 70d +30d multi + label 1.00 1.00

Surtax (on sheet margin) was for UNICEF.

Marguerite Barankitse, Burundian Humanitarian Awarded 2016 Aurora Prize — SP2

2017, May 26 Litho. *Perf. 12¾x13¼*
B2 SP2 350d +150d multi + label 4.00 4.00

No. B2 was printed in sheets of 3 + 3 labels. The label is on either side of the stamp.

SP3

Insurance Foundation for Servicemen — SP4

No. B4 — Emblem of Insurance Foundation for Servicemen and: a, 350d, Soldier writing. b, 1100d, Soldier in watch tower.

2017, Sept. 18 Litho. *Perf. 13x13¼*
B3 SP3 350d +150d multi + label 4.25 4.25

Souvenir Sheet

B4 SP4 Sheet of 2, #a-b 90.00 90.00

No. B4 was sold with a 10,000d surtax.

Dr. Tom Catena, Recipient of 2017 Aurora Prize SP5

2018, June 4 Litho. *Perf. 14*
B5 SP5 350d +150d multi + label 4.25 4.25

Kyaw Hla Aung, Recipient of 2018 Aurora Prize SP6

2019, Oct. 16 Litho. *Perf. 14*
B6 SP6 350d +150d multi + label 3.25 3.25

Historical and Cultural Landmarks — SP7

Designs: 240d+120d, Agarakadzor Bridge. 300d+120d, Monastery of Marmashen. 350d+120d, Yererouyk Basilica.

2020, Nov. 30 Litho. *Perf. 13x13¼*
B7 SP7 240d +120d multi + label 1.75 1.75
B8 SP7 330d +120d multi + label 2.25 2.25
B9 SP7 350d +120d multi + label 2.25 2.25
Nos. B7-B9 (3) 6.25 6.25

Surtax for preservation of historical and cultural monuments of Armenia.

Mirza Dinnayi, Recipient of 2019 Aurora Prize SP8

2020, Dec. 5 Litho. *Perf. 14*
B10 SP8 350d +150d multi + label 2.40 2.40

Sculptures — SP9

Designs: 120d+500d, Monument to David of Sassoun. 220d+500d, Mountain Dance Sculpture Group. 230d+500d, Monument to Leonid Yengibaryan (1935-72), circus clown. 280d+500d, Monument to Komitas (1869-1935), priest and composer. 300d+500d, Monument to Martiros Sarian (1880-1972), painter. 380d+500d, Monument to Arno Babajanyan (1921-83), composer. 500d+500d, Monument to Mesrop Mashtots (362-440), inventor of Armenian alphabet.

2020, Dec. 22 Litho. *Perf. 13¼*
B11 SP9 120d +500d multi + label 3.00 3.00
B12 SP9 220d +500d multi + label 3.50 3.50
B13 SP9 230d +500d multi + label 3.50 3.50

B14	SP9	280d +500d multi + label	3.75	3.75
B15	SP9	330d +500d multi + label	4.00	4.00
B16	SP9	380d +500d multi + label	4.25	4.25
B17	SP9	500d +500d multi + label	4.75	4.75
a.		Souvenir sheet of 7, #B11-B17 (without attached +500d labels) + 5000d label	34.00	34.00
		Nos. B11-B17 (7)	26.75	26.75

Historical and Cultural Landmarks — SP10

Designs: 230d+120d, Saints Peter and Paul Church, Aghjots Monastery. 290d+120d, Gandzasar Monastery. 330d+120d, Amaras Monastery.

2021, July 20 Litho. *Perf. 13x13¼*

B18	SP10	230d +120d multi + label	1.90	1.90
B19	SP10	290d +120d multi + label	2.10	2.10
B20	SP10	330d +120d multi + label	2.40	2.40
		Nos. B18-B20 (3)	6.40	6.40

Surtax for preservation of historical and cultural monuments of Armenia.

Fartuun Adan and Ilwad Elman, Recipients of 2020 Aurora Prize — SP11

2021, Dec. 8 Litho. *Perf. 14*

B21	SP11	350d +150d multi + label	2.50	2.50

Soldiers SP12

2021, Dec. 13 Litho. *Perf. 13½*

B22	SP12	290d +110d multi + label	2.10	2.10

Surtax for Insurance Foundation for Servicemen.

Historical and Cultural Landmarks — SP13

Designs: 230d+120d, Aghdzk Royal Tomb. 340d+120d, Khoranashat Monastic Complex. 350d+120d, Srvegh Monastery.

2022, June 6 Litho. *Perf. 13x13¼*

B23	SP13	230d +120d multi + label	1.90	1.90
B24	SP13	340d +120d multi + label	2.50	2.50
B25	SP13	350d +120d multi + label	2.50	2.50
		Nos. B23-B25 (3)	6.90	6.90

Surtax for preservation of historical and cultural monuments of Armenia.

AIR POST STAMPS

AP1

Design: 90d, Artiom Katsian (1886-1943), world record holding pilot on range and altitude in 1909.

1995, Dec. 5 Litho. *Perf. 14x15*

C1	AP1	90d multicolored	.75	.75

AP2

1996, Apr. 30 Litho. *Perf. 14x14½*

C2	AP2	90d multicolored	.90	.90

Nelson Stepanian (1913-44), WWII fighter ace.

ARUBA

ə-'rü-bə

LOCATION — West Indies, north of Venezuela
AREA — 78 sq. mi.
POP. — 67,014
CAPITAL — Oranjestad

On Jan. 1, 1986 Aruba, formerly part of Netherlands Antilles, achieved a separate status within the Kingdom of the Netherlands.

100 Cents = 1 Gulden

Catalogue values for all unused stamps in this country are for Never Hinged items.

Used values are for CTO or stamps removed from first day covers. Postally used examples sell for more.

Traditional House — A1

Perf. 14x13

1986-87 Litho. Unwmk.

1	A1	5c shown	.40	.25
2	A1	15c King William III Tower	.90	.40
3	A1	20c Loading crane	.65	.30
4	A1	25c Lighthouse	1.20	.40
5	A1	30c Snake	.80	.65
6	A1	35c Owl	1.20	.65
7	A1	45c Shell	1.00	.65
8	A1	55c Frog	1.20	.65
9	A1	60c Water skier	1.20	.80
10	A1	65c Net fishing	1.15	1.00
11	A1	75c Music box	1.50	1.10
12	A1	85c Pre-Columbian bisque pot	1.50	.80
13	A1	90c Bulb cactus	1.60	1.10
14	A1	100c Grain	1.60	1.10
15	A1	150c Watapana tree	2.40	1.60
16	A1	250c Aloe plant	3.25	3.25
		Nos. 1-16 (16)	21.55	14.70

Issued: 5c, 30c, 60c, 150c, 1/1; 15c, 35c, 65c, 250c, 2/5; 20c, 45c, 75c, 100c, 4/7/87; 25c, 55c, 85c, 90c, 7/17/87.

Independence — A2

25c, Map. 45c, Coat of arms, vert. 55c, Natl. anthem, vert. 100c, Flag.

1986, Jan. 1 *Perf. 14x13, 13x14*

18	A2	25c multicolored	1.75	.60
19	A2	45c multicolored	1.75	1.15
20	A2	55c multicolored	1.75	1.75
21	A2	100c multicolored	2.25	2.25
		Nos. 18-21 (4)	7.50	5.75

Intl. Peace Year — A3

1986, Aug. 29 Litho. *Perf. 14x13*

22	A3	60c shown	2.00	1.25
23	A3	100c Barbed wire	3.50	2.00

Princess Juliana and Prince Bernhard, 50th Wedding Anniv. — A4

1987, Jan. 7 Photo. *Perf. 13x14*

24	A4	135c multicolored	3.50	2.75

State Visit of Queen Beatrix and Prince Claus of the Netherlands — A5

60c, Prince William-Alexander.

1987, Feb. 16 Litho. *Perf. 14x13*

25	A5	55c shown	1.75	1.20
26	A5	60c multicolored	1.75	1.20

Tourism — A6

1987, June 5 Litho.

27	A6	60c Beach and sea	1.75	1.50
28	A6	100c Rock and cacti	2.50	2.00

Aloe Vera Plant — A7

1988, Jan. 27 Litho. *Perf. 13x14*

29	A7	45c Field	1.90	1.00
30	A7	60c Plant	2.00	1.25
31	A7	100c Harvest	2.40	1.50
		Nos. 29-31 (3)	6.30	3.75

Coins — A8

1988, Mar. 16 Litho. *Perf. 13x14*

32	A8	25c 25-cent	1.40	.50
33	A8	55c 50-cent	1.75	1.00
34	A8	65c 5 and 10-cent	2.10	1.35
35	A8	150c 1-florin	3.25	2.40
		Nos. 32-35 (4)	8.50	5.25

Love Issue — A9

135c, Seashells, coastal scenery.

1988, May 4

36	A9	70c shown	1.75	1.00
37	A9	135c multicolored	2.25	2.00

A10

1988, Aug. 24

38	A10	35c shown	1.50	.90
39	A10	100c Emblems	2.50	1.60

Aruba, the 162nd member of the Intl. Olympic Committee (35c), 1988 Summer Olympics, Seoul (100c).

Carnival — A11

1989, Jan. 5 *Perf. 14x13*

40	A11	45c Two children	2.00	1.00
41	A11	60c Girl	2.00	1.00
42	A11	100c Entertainer	2.50	1.50
		Nos. 40-42 (3)	6.50	3.50

Maripampun, Omphalophalmum Rubrum — A12

1989, Mar. 16 Litho. *Perf. 14x13*

43	A12	35c Leaves	1.50	.75
44	A12	55c Pods	1.50	1.00
45	A12	200c Blossom	4.00	3.00
		Nos. 43-45 (3)	7.00	4.75

New Year 1990 — A13

Dande band members playing instruments or singing: 25c, Violin, tambor, cuatro, marimba. 70c, Lead singer, guitar. 150c, Accordion, urri, guitar.

1989, Nov. 16 Litho. *Perf. 13x14*

46	A13	25c multicolored	1.00	.50
47	A13	70c multicolored	1.40	1.00
48	A13	150c multicolored	2.60	2.00
		Nos. 46-48 (3)	5.00	3.50

UPU — A14

1989, June 8 Litho. *Perf. 13x14*

49	A14	250c multicolored	6.00	3.75

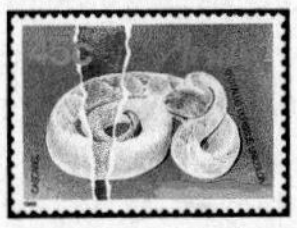

Crotalus durissus unicolor — A15

1989, Aug. 24 *Perf. 14x13*

50	A15	45c shown	1.50	.75
51	A15	55c multi, diff.	1.75	1.00
52	A15	60c multi, diff.	1.75	1.00
		Nos. 50-52 (3)	5.00	2.75

Snake species in danger of extinction.

Man Living in Harmony with Nature — A16

1990, Feb. 7 *Perf. 13x14, 14x13*

53	A16	45c The land	1.50	1.00
54	A16	55c shown	1.75	1.00
55	A16	100c The sea	3.00	2.00
		Nos. 53-55 (3)	6.25	4.00

Environmental protection. Nos. 53, 55 horiz.

Marine Life — A17

Designs: 60c, Giant caribbean anemone, Pederson's cleaning shrimp. 70c, Queen angelfish, red and orange coral. 100c, Banded coral shrimp, fire sponge, yellow boring sponge.

1990, Apr. 4 Litho. *Perf. 14x13*
56 A17 60c multicolored 1.60 1.00
57 A17 70c multicolored 2.10 1.50
58 A17 100c multicolored 3.00 2.50
Nos. 56-58 (3) 6.70 5.00

A18

200c, Character trademark.

1990, May 30 Litho. *Perf. 13x14*
59 A18 35c multicolored 1.50 1.00
60 A18 200c multicolored 4.50 3.25

World Cup Soccer Championships, Italy.

A19

1990, Sept. 12
61 A19 45c Tools 1.40 1.00
62 A19 60c Stone figure 1.60 1.00
63 A19 100c Jar 2.75 1.50
Nos. 61-63 (3) 5.75 3.50

Archeological discoveries.

Landscapes — A20

1991, Jan. 31 Litho. *Perf. 14x13*
64 A20 55c Seashore 1.25 1.00
65 A20 65c Desert 1.50 1.30
66 A20 100c Cactus, ocean view 2.25 2.00
Nos. 64-66 (3) 5.00 4.30

Working Women — A21

Designs: 35c, Taking care of others. 70c, Housewife. 100c, Women in society.

1991, Mar. 28 Litho. *Perf. 13x14*
67 A21 35c multicolored 1.00 .50
68 A21 70c multicolored 1.50 1.25
69 A21 100c multicolored 2.00 1.75
Nos. 67-69 (3) 4.50 3.50

Style of inscriptions varies.

Medicinal Plants — A22

65c, Ocimum sanctum. 75c, Jatropha gossypifolia. 95c, Croton flavens.

1991, May 29
70 A22 65c multicolored 1.50 1.00
71 A22 75c multicolored 1.75 1.25
72 A22 95c multicolored 2.00 1.50
Nos. 70-72 (3) 5.25 3.75

A23

Aruban Handicrafts: 35c, Fish net, wood float, wooden needle. 250c, Straw hat, hat block.

1991, July 31 Litho. *Perf. 13x14*
73 A23 35c lt bl, dk bl & blk 1.00 .75
74 A23 250c pink, lil rose & blk 4.25 3.50

A24

35c, Toucan. 70c, People shaking hands. 100c, Windmill.

1991, Nov. 29 Litho. *Perf. 13x14*
75 A24 35c multicolored 1.00 1.00
76 A24 70c multicolored 1.50 1.00
77 A24 100c multicolored 2.50 2.00
Nos. 75-77 (3) 5.00 4.00

Welcome to Aruba.

Aruba Postal Service, Cent. — A25

60c, Government decree, 1892, vert. 75c, First post office. 80c, Current post office.

Perf. 13x14, 14x13
1992, Jan. 31 Litho.
78 A25 60c multicolored 1.25 1.00
79 A25 75c multicolored 1.50 1.00
80 A25 80c multicolored 2.00 1.50
Nos. 78-80 (3) 4.75 3.50

Equality Day — A26

No. 81, People of five races. No. 82, Woman, man, scales.

1992, Mar. 25 Litho. *Perf. 14x13*
81 A26 100c multicolored 2.00 1.50
82 A26 100c multicolored 2.00 1.50

Discovery of America, 500th Anniv. — A27

1992, July 30 Litho. *Perf. 13x14*
83 A27 30c Columbus 1.50 .50
84 A27 40c Sailing ship 1.50 .75
85 A27 50c Natives, map 1.50 1.00
Nos. 83-85 (3) 4.50 2.25

Natural Bridges in Aruba — A28

Designs: 70c, Seroe Colorado Bridge, south coast. 80c, Natural Bridge, north coast.

1992, Nov. 30 Litho. *Perf. 14x13*
86 A28 70c multicolored 1.50 1.00
87 A28 80c multicolored 1.75 1.00

Express Mail Service — A29

1993, Jan. 29 Litho. *Perf. 13x14*
88 A29 200c multicolored 4.50 3.25

A30

Various rock formations found in Districts of Ayo and Casibari.

1993, Mar. 31 Litho. *Perf. 13x14*
89 A30 50c multicolored 1.00 1.00
90 A30 60c multicolored 1.25 1.00
91 A30 100c multicolored 2.00 1.75
Nos. 89-91 (3) 4.25 3.75

Folklore — A31

40c, String instruments, drum. 70c, Traditional music & games. 80c, Dera Gai song lyrics.

1993, May 28 Litho. *Perf. 13x14*
92 A31 40c multicolored 1.20 1.00
93 A31 70c multicolored 1.30 1.00
94 A31 80c multicolored 1.50 1.50
Nos. 92-94 (3) 4.00 3.50

Sailing Sports — A32

1993, July 30 Litho. *Perf. 13x14*
95 A32 50c Sailboating 1.15 1.00
96 A32 65c Land sailing 1.35 1.00
97 A32 75c Wind surfing 1.50 1.25
Nos. 95-97 (3) 4.00 3.25

Iguana Iguana — A33

Perf. 14x13, 13x14
1993, Sept. 1 Litho.
98 A33 35c Young 1.50 1.00
99 A33 60c Almost grown 1.65 1.25
100 A33 100c Mature, vert. 2.25 2.00
Nos. 98-100 (3) 5.40 4.25

Burrowing Owl — A34

5c, Two adults. 10c, Two adults, young. 35c, Adult with prey, vert. 40c, Adult, vert.

Perf. 14x13, 13x14
1994, Jan. 28 Litho.
101 A34 5c multicolored 1.75 .50
102 A34 10c multicolored 1.75 .75
103 A34 35c multicolored 2.25 1.00
104 A34 40c multicolored 2.25 1.50
Nos. 101-104 (4) 8.00 3.75

World Wildlife Fund.

A35

Intl. Olympic Committee, Cent.: 90c, Baron Pierre de Coubertin (1863-1937), founder of modern Olympics.

1994, Mar. 29 Litho. *Perf. 13x14*
105 A35 50c multicolored 1.25 1.00
106 A35 90c multicolored 1.75 1.40

A36

150c, Mascot, soccer ball.

1994, July 7 Litho. *Perf. 13x14*
107 A36 65c shown 1.50 1.25
108 A36 150c multicolored 3.00 2.50

1994 World Cup Soccer Championships, US.

Wild Fruit — A37

Designs: 40c, Malpighia punicifolia. 70c, Cordia sebestena. 85c, Pithecellobium unguis-cati. 150c, Coccoloba uvifera.

1994, Sept. 28 Litho. *Perf. 13x14*
109 A37 40c multicolored 1.10 1.00
110 A37 70c multicolored 1.50 1.00
111 A37 85c multicolored 1.90 1.50
112 A37 150c multicolored 3.25 2.50
Nos. 109-112 (4) 7.75 6.00

Architectural Landmarks — A38

Designs: 35c, Government building, 1888. 60c, Ecury residence, 1929, vert. 100c, Protestant Church, 1846, vert.

1995, Jan. 27 Litho. *Perf. 14x13*
113 A38 35c multicolored .90 .80

Perf. 13x14
114 A38 60c multicolored 1.50 1.00
115 A38 100c multicolored 2.10 1.90
Nos. 113-115 (3) 4.50 3.70

UN, 50th Anniv. — A39

Designs: 30c, Flags, sea, UN emblem, dove, text from UN charter. 200c, World with flags, doves, UN emblem.

1995, Mar. 29 Litho. *Perf. 13x14*
116 A39 30c multicolored 1.25 .75
117 A39 200c multicolored 3.75 3.25

Interpaso Horses — A40

Designs: 25c, 10-time champion Casanova II, ribbons, horiz. 75c, Paso Fino, horiz. 80c, Horse doing figure 8. 90c, Girl on horse.

1995, May 26 *Perf. 14x13, 13x14*
118 A40 25c multicolored .90 .50
119 A40 75c multicolored 1.60 1.25
120 A40 80c multicolored 1.60 1.50
121 A40 90c multicolored 1.90 1.50
Nos. 118-121 (4) 6.00 4.75

Vegetables — A41

25c, Vigna sinensis. 50c, Cucumis anguria. 70c, Hibiscus esculentus. 85c, Cucurbita moschata.

1995, July 28 Litho. *Perf. 13x14*
122 A41 25c multicolored .85 .50
123 A41 50c multicolored 1.40 1.00
124 A41 70c multicolored 1.50 1.25
125 A41 85c multicolored 1.75 1.50
Nos. 122-125 (4) 5.50 4.25

Turtles — A42

1995, Sept. 27 Litho. *Perf. 14x13*
126 A42 15c Hawksbill 1.75 .55
127 A42 50c Green 2.25 1.00
128 A42 95c Loggerhead 2.40 1.50
129 A42 100c Leatherback 2.75 1.50
Nos. 126-129 (4) 9.15 4.55

Separate Status, 10th Anniv. — A43

Statesmen and politicians: No. 130, Jan Hendrik Albert Eman (1887-1957). No. 131, Juan Enrique Irausquin (1904-62). No. 132, Cornelis Albert Eman (1916-67). No. 133, Gilberto Francois Croes (1938-86).

1996, Jan. 1 Litho. *Perf. 13x14*
130 A43 100c multicolored 1.90 1.50
131 A43 100c multicolored 1.90 1.50
132 A43 100c multicolored 1.90 1.50
133 A43 100c multicolored 1.90 1.50
Nos. 130-133 (4) 7.60 6.00

The 1986 date on No. 133 is in error.

America Issue — A44

National dresswear: 65c, Woman wearing long, full dress, apron, vert. 70c, Man wearing hat, bow tie, white shirt, black pants, vert. 100c, Couple dancing.

Perf. 13x14, 14x13
1996, Mar. 25 **Litho.**
134 A44 65c multicolored 2.25 1.00
135 A44 70c multicolored 2.25 1.00
136 A44 100c multicolored 3.00 1.50
Nos. 134-136 (3) 7.50 3.50

1996 Summer Olympic Games, Atlanta — A45

1996, May 28 Litho. *Perf. 14x13*
137 A45 85c Runners 2.00 1.25
138 A45 130c Cyclist 2.50 2.25

A46

Famous Women: No. 139, Livia (Mimi) Ecury (1920-91), nurse. No. 140, Lolita Euson (1914-94), poet. No. 141, Laura Wernet-Paskel (1911-62), teacher.

1996, Sept. 27 Litho. *Perf. 13x14*
139 A46 60c multicolored 1.50 1.50
140 A46 60c multicolored 1.50 1.50
141 A46 60c multicolored 1.50 1.50
Nos. 139-141 (3) 4.50 4.50

A47

Year of Papiamento 1997: 50c, Sign promoting use of Papiamento language, children playing on beach, people in water, boat. 140c, "Papiamento," sunrise.

1997, Jan. 23 Litho. *Perf. 13x14*
142 A47 50c multicolored 1.00 1.00
143 A47 140c multicolored 2.50 2.50

Mailman on Bicycle, 1936-57 — A48

America issue: 70c, Mailman handing mail to woman, jeep, 1957-88. 80c, Mailman on motor scooter placing mail in mailbox, 1995.

1997, Mar. 27 Litho. *Perf. 14x13*
144 A48 60c multicolored 2.75 1.50
145 A48 70c multicolored 2.75 1.50
146 A48 80c multicolored 2.75 1.50
Nos. 144-146 (3) 8.25 4.50

Aruban Architectrue — A49

30c, Decorated cunucu house. 65c, Steps with "popchi's." 100c, Arends's Building, vert.

1997, May 22 Litho. *Perf. 14x13*
147 A49 30c multicolored .90 .75
148 A49 65c multicolored 1.75 1.25

Perf. 13x14

149 A49 100c multicolored 2.00 1.75
Nos. 147-149 (3) 4.65 3.75

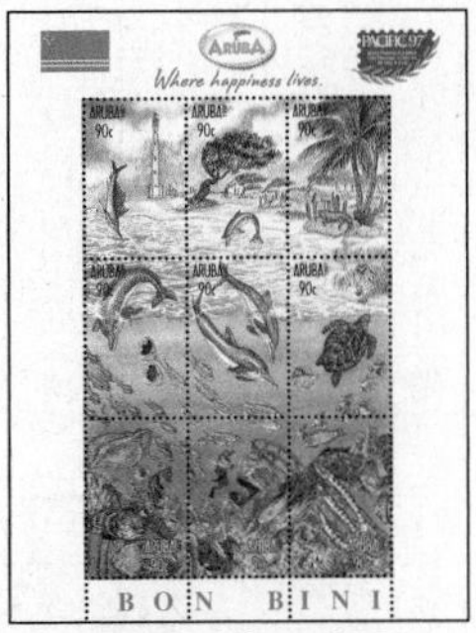

Marine Life — A50

Designs: a, Marlin jumping out of water, lighthouse. b, Dolphin jumping out of water, trees, plants on beach. c, Iguana on rock, beach. d, Dolphin, fish. e, Two dolphins, fish. f, Fish, turtles, owl on beach. g, Various fish among coral. h, Diver, shipwreck, fish, coral. i, Various fish.

1997, May 29 Litho. *Perf. 12½x13*
150 A50 90c Sheet of 9, #a.-i. 27.50 27.50

PACIFIC 97.

Cruise Tourism — A51

Designs: 35c, Ship at pier, tourists walking toward ship. 50c, Ship with gangway lowered, tourists. 150c, Ship out to sea, small boat.

1997, July 24 Litho. *Perf. 14x13*
151 A51 35c multicolored 1.25 .85
152 A51 50c multicolored 1.50 1.10
153 A51 150c multicolored 3.00 2.50
Nos. 151-153 (3) 5.75 4.45

Aruban Wild Flowers — A52

50c, Erythrina velutina. 60c, Cordia dentata. 70c, Tabebuia billbergii. 130c, Guaiacum officinale.

1997, Sept. 25
154 A52 50c multicolored 1.50 1.00
155 A52 60c multicolored 1.75 1.25
156 A52 70c multicolored 2.00 1.25
157 A52 130c multicolored 2.75 2.00
Nos. 154-157 (4) 8.00 5.50

Fort Zoutman, Bicent. — A53

1998, Jan. 13 Litho. *Perf. 14x13*
158 A53 30c sepia & multi 1.00 .75
159 A53 250c gray & multi 4.25 3.75

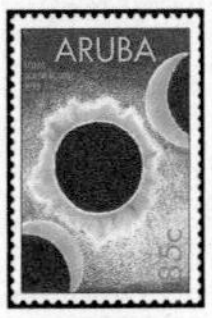

Total Solar Eclipse, 1998 — A54

100c, Map, track of eclipse.

1998, Feb. 26 Litho. *Perf. 13x14*
160 A54 85c shown 2.25 1.50
161 A54 100c multicolored 2.75 1.60

Native Birds — A55

50c, Mimus gilvus. 60c, Falco sparverius. 70c, Icterus icterus. 150c, Coereba flaveola.

Perf. 14x13, 13x14
1998, July 10 **Litho.**
162 A55 50c multi 1.80 1.00
163 A55 60c multi, vert. 2.00 1.25
164 A55 70c multi, vert. 2.25 1.25
165 A55 150c multi 3.25 2.75
Nos. 162-165 (4) 9.30 6.25

World Stamp 1998 — A56

1998, Sept. 8 Litho. *Perf. 14x13*
166 A56 225c multicolored 5.50 4.25

Endangered Animals — A57

Equus asinus: 40c, Two standing on hill. 65c, Three standing, rocks, cacti, tree. 100c, Adult, foal standing among rocks, cacti.

1999, June 21 Litho. *Perf. 14x13*
167 A57 40c multicolored 1.40 .75
168 A57 65c multicolored 1.60 1.25
169 A57 100c multicolored 2.40 2.00
Nos. 167-169 (3) 5.40 4.00

Cacti — A58

Designs: 50c, Opuntia wentiana. 60c, Lemaireocereus griseus. 70c, Cephalocereus lanuginosus. 75c, Cephalocereus lanuginosus (in bloom).

1999, Mar. 31 Litho. *Perf. 14x13*
170 A58 50c multicolored 1.50 1.00
171 A58 60c multicolored 1.75 1.25
172 A58 70c multicolored 1.75 1.25
173 A58 75c multicolored 2.00 1.50
Nos. 170-173 (4) 7.00 5.00

Dogs — A59

Various dogs, background: 40c, Trees. 60c, Cactus, aloe plant, rocks. 80c, Tree, sea. 165c, Sky, clouds.

1999, May 31 Litho. *Perf. 13x14*
174 A59 40c multicolored 1.50 1.00
175 A59 60c multicolored 1.75 1.25
176 A59 80c multicolored 2.00 1.50
177 A59 165c multicolored 3.25 2.75
Nos. 174-177 (4) 8.50 6.50

Discovery of Aruba, 500th Anniv. — A60

1999, Aug. 9 Litho. *Perf. 14x13*
178 A60 150c shown 2.75 2.25
179 A60 175c Abstract paintings 3.25 2.75
a. Souvenir sheet, #178-179 7.00 6.00

Natl. Library, 50th Anniv. — A61

1999, Aug. 20
180 A61 70c shown 1.50 1.50
181 A61 100c Original building 2.25 2.00

Christmas — A62

Coil Stamps

Die Cut Perf. 13x13½

1999, Dec. 1 Self-Adhesive Litho.
182 A62 40c Magi on shore 1.80 1.00
183 A62 70c Magi in desert 2.25 1.25
184 A62 100c Holy Family 2.75 1.75
Nos. 182-184 (3) 6.80 4.00

Tourist Attractions A62a

Reptiles A63

Tourist Attractions: 25c, Guadirikiri Cave. 55c, Cactus landscape. 85c, Hooiberg. 500c, Conchi. Reptiles: 40c, Norops lineatus. 60c, Iguana iguana, vert. 75c, Leptodeira annulata, vert. 150c, Cnemidophorus murinus.

2000 Litho. *Perf. 14x13, 13x14*
185 A62a 25c multi 1.00 .50
186 A63 40c multi 1.25 .75
187 A62a 55c multi 1.40 1.00
188 A63 60c multi 1.40 1.25
189 A63 75c multi 1.60 1.25
190 A62a 85c multi 1.75 1.50
191 A63 150c multi 3.25 2.25
192 A62a 500c multi 8.50 7.25
Nos. 185-192 (8) 20.15 15.75

Issued: 40c, 60c, 75c, 150c, 1/31; 25c, 55c, 85c, 500c, 6/5.

See Nos. 197-204.

America Issue, Campaign Against AIDS — A64

175c, Ribbon on globe, vert.

Perf. 14x13, 13x14

2000, Mar. 2 **Litho.**

193 A64	75c Flags	2.00	2.00
194 A64	175c multicolored	4.00	4.00

Organization Anniversaries A65

Designs: 150c, Aruba Bank N.V., 75th anniv. 165c, Alto Vista Church, 250th anniv.

2000, Apr. 20 **Litho.** ***Perf. 14x13***

195 A65	150c multi	3.00	2.50
196 A65	165c multi	3.25	2.75

Type of 2000

Animals: 5c, Cat. 15c, Shells. 30c, Tortoise. 35c, Mud house, vert. 50c, Rabbit. 100c, Balashi gold smelter, vert. 200c, Parakeet. 250c, Rock crystals.

Perf. 14x13, 13x14 (#200, 202)

2001 **Litho.**

197 A63	5c multi	1.10	.50
198 A62a	15c multi	.50	.40
199 A63	30c multi	1.75	1.00
200 A62a	35c multi	1.00	.95
201 A63	50c multi	1.75	1.00
202 A62a	100c multi	2.50	2.10
203 A63	200c multi	4.50	4.00
204 A62a	250c multi	5.25	4.75
	Nos. 197-204 (8)	18.35	14.70

Issued: 5c, 30c, 50c, 200c, 1/31. 15c, 35c, 100c, 250c, 8/6.

Mascaruba, 40th Anniv. — A66

Actors on stage and audience in: 60c: Background. 150c, Foreground.

2001, Mar. 26 **Litho.** ***Perf. 14x13***

205-206 A66 Set of 2 4.50 4.00

Classic Motor Vehicles — A67

Designs: 25c, 1930 Ford Crown Victoria Leatherback. 40c, 1933 Citroen Commerciale. 70c, 1948 Plymouth pickup truck. 75c, 1959 Ford Edsel.

2001, May 31

207-210 A67 Set of 4 8.00 5.75

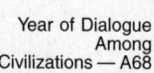

Year of Dialogue Among Civilizations — A68

2001, Oct. 9 **Litho.** ***Perf. 14x13***

211 A68 175c multi 4.00 3.25

Airport Views — A69

Designs: 30c, Dakota Airport, 1950. 75c, Queen Beatrix Airport, 1972. 175c, Queen Beatrix Airport, 2000.

2002, Jan. 31 **Litho.** ***Perf. 14x13***

212-214 A69 Set of 3 6.25 5.00

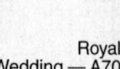

Royal Wedding — A70

Prince Willem-Alexander, Maxima Zorreguieta and: 60c, Royal palace, golden coach. 300c, Bourse of Berlage, New Church.

2002, Feb. 2

215-216 A70 Set of 2 6.50 6.25

Water and Energy Company, 70th Anniv. — A71

Designs: 60c, Faucet and water drop, vert. 85c, Pipeline. 165c, Meter and meter-reading equipment, vert.

Perf. 13x14, 14x13

2002, June 3 **Litho.**

217-219 A71 Set of 3 6.50 6.25

America Issue — Youth, Education and Literacy — A72

Designs: 25c, Hand writing letters with quill pen. 100c, Child looking over wall of letters.

2002, July 15 **Litho.** ***Perf. 14x12¾***

220-221 A72 Set of 2 3.75 2.75

Aruba in World War II — A73

Designs: 60c, Attack on Lago Oil Refinery by German U-boat U-156. 75c, Torpedoing of ships by U-156. 150c, Statue of "Boy" Ecury, Aruban resistance fighter, Aruban militiaman, vert.

Perf. 14x13, 13x14

2002, Sept. 9 **Litho.**

222-224 A73 Set of 3 8.00 5.50

Mud Houses — A74

Various houses with frame color of: 40c, Yellow green. 60c, Blue green. 75c, Red.

2003, Jan. 31 **Litho.** ***Perf. 14x13***

225-227 A74 Set of 3 3.75 3.00

De Trupialen Performing Organization, 50th Anniv. — A75

Designs: 30c, Trupialen Boys' Choir. 50c, Play handbills. 100c, Emblems.

2003, Mar. 31 **Litho.** ***Perf. 14x13***

228-230 A75 Set of 3 3.75 3.00

Orchids — A76

Designs: 75c, Schomburgkia humboldtii. 500c, Brassavola nodosa.

2003, May 30 **Litho.** ***Perf. 14x13***

231-232 A76 Set of 2 11.00 11.00

Butterflies — A77

Designs: 40c, Orange-barred sulphur. 75c, Monarch. 85c, Hairstreak. 175c, Gulf fritillary.

2003, July 31

233-236 A77 Set of 4 8.75 7.00

Endangered Animals — A78

Turtles: 25c, Eretmochelys imbricata, vert. 60c, Dermochelys coriacea. 75c, Chelonia mydas, vert. 150c, Caretta caretta.

Perf. 13x14, 14x13

2003, Sept. 30 **Litho.**

237-240 A78 Set of 4 7.50 6.00

Carnival, 50th Anniv. — A79

Designs: 60c, Masks. 75c, Carnival Queen, vert. 150c, Aruba flag, Carnival participants.

Perf. 14x13, 13x14

2004, Jan. 30 **Litho.**

241-243 A79 Set of 3 4.50 4.50

Birds — A80

Designs: 70c, Sterna sandvicensis. 75c, Pelecanus occidentalis. 80c, Fregata magnificens. 90c, Larus atricilla.

2004, Mar. 31 ***Perf. 13x14***

244-247 A80 Set of 4 7.00 5.00

Fish — A81

Designs: 40c, Parrotfish. 60c, Queen angelfish. 75c, Squirrelfish. 100c, Smallmouth grunt.

2004, May 31 **Litho.** ***Perf. 14x13***

248-251 A81 Set of 4 6.50 5.00

Christmas and New Year's Day — A82

Designs: 50c, Children, Christmas tree, gifts. 85c, Choir, stained glass window, candle, gifts. 125c, Fireworks display.

2004, Dec. 1 **Litho.** ***Perf. 13x14***

252-254 A82 Set of 3 4.00 4.00

Kingdom Statutes, 50th Anniv. — A83

Designs: 160c, Collage of Netherlands Antilles islands. 165c, Kingdom Statute Monument.

2004, Dec. 15 ***Perf. 14x13***

255-256 A83 Set of 2 4.50 4.50

Greetings — A84

Designs: 60c, Sun, flower (Thank you). 75c, Cacti and rabbits (Love). 135c, Fish (Get well soon). 215c, Balloons and flag (Congratulations).

2005, Jan. 31 **Litho.** ***Perf. 14x13***

257-260 A84 Set of 4 7.25 7.25

Drag Racing — A85

Drag racers: 60c, One car going airborne. 85c, One car with chute deployed. 185c, Cars at start line.

2005, Mar. 16

261-263 A85 Set of 3 5.50 5.00

Souvenir Sheet

Reign of Queen Beatrix, 25th Anniv. A86

No. 264: a, 30c, At coronation, 1980. b, 60c, Making speech, 1991. c, 75c, With Nelson Mandela, 1999. d, 105c, Visiting Aruba and the Netherlands Antilles, 1999. e, 215c, Speaking before European Parliament, 2004.

2005, Apr. 30 **Litho.** ***Perf. 13¼x13¾***

264 A86 Sheet of 5, #a-e 7.50 7.50

Sunsets — A87

Designs: 60c, Birds and cacti. 100c, Palm tree. 205c, Pelicans and pilings.

2005, May 31 ***Perf. 13x14***

265-267 A87 Set of 3 5.75 5.75

Birds of Prey — A88

Designs: 60c, Falco sparverius. 75c, Athene cunicularia. 135c, Pandion haliaetus. 200c, Polyborus plancus.

2005, July 29 **Litho.** ***Perf. 14x13***

268-271 A88	Set of 4	8.75	8.75
271a	Souvenir sheet, #268-271	8.75	8.75

A89

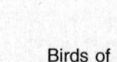

Corals: 60c, Staghorn coral. 75c, Blade fire coral. 100c, Deepwater sea fan. 215c, Smooth brain coral.

2005, Sept. 30 **Litho.** ***Perf. 13x14***

272-275 A89 Set of 4 7.00 7.00

A90

Children and philately: 75c, Girl, stamps. 85c, Boy with magnifying glass and stamp album. 125c, Boy with tongs and stock book.

2005, Oct. 31
276-278 A90 Set of 3 4.75 4.75

Paintings — A91

Designs: 60c, House at Savaneta, by Jean Georges Pandellis. 75c, Haf di Rei, by Mateo Hayde. 185c, Landscape, by Julie Q. Oduber.

2006, Feb. 6 Litho. *Perf. 14x13*
279-281 A91 Set of 3 5.50 5.50

Aruba YMCA, 50th Anniv. — A92

Designs: 75c, YMCA emblem. 205c, Children in playground, horiz.

Perf. 13x14, 14x13
2006, Apr. 3 Litho.
282-283 A92 Set of 2 4.50 4.50

Souvenir Sheet

Washington 2006 World Philatelic Exhibition — A93

No. 284 — Exhibition emblem and: a, Natural Bridge, head of iguana, tree and cactus. b, Cacti, tail of iguana, sailboat, vert.

2006, May 27 Litho. *Perf. 12¾*
284 A93 500c Sheet of 2, #a-b 13.50 13.50

2006 World Cup Soccer Championships, Germany — A94

Designs: 75c, Children's drawing of goalie. 215c, Goalie's gloves and ball.

2006, June 5 Litho. *Perf. 14x13*
285-286 A94 Set of 2 4.50 4.50

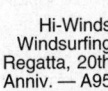

Hi-Winds Windsurfing Regatta, 20th Anniv. — A95

Designs: 60c, Hotel, windsurfers, kitesurfer, and fishing boats. 100c, Kitesurfers, windsurfer and flag in water. 125c, Windsurfers.

2006, July 3 Litho. *Perf. 14x13*
287-289 A95 Set of 3 4.00 4.00

Fire Prevention — A96

Designs: 60c, Fire prevention, safety and extinguishing strategies. 100c, Firemen at house fire. 205c, Fire trucks.

2006, Sept. 29 Litho. *Perf. 14x13*
290-292 A96 Set of 3 5.75 5.75

Arikok National Park — A97

Designs: 75c, Cas di Torto, goat and garden, Cunucu Arikok. 100c, View of Miralamar, vert. 200c, Dunes of Boca Prins.

2006, Oct. 31 Litho. *Perf. 14x13*
293-295 A97 Set of 3 5.25 5.25

Souvenir Sheet

New Year 2007 (Year of the Pig) A98

No. 296: a, 205c, Pig. b, 215c, Dragon, vert.

2007, Feb. 15 Litho. *Perf. 12¾*
296 A98 Sheet of 2, #a-b 6.50 6.50

Casa Cuna Children's Home Foundation, 50th Anniv. — A99

Designs: 50c, Original Casa Cuna building, Luciana Maria Koolman. 125c, Children in hands. 150c, New Casa Cuna building.

2007, Apr. 4 *Perf. 14x13*
297-299 A99 Set of 3 4.50 4.50

Museums in Oranjestad — A100

Designs: 70c, Museum of Antiquities. 85c, Numismatic Museum. 100c, Archaeological Museum. 135c, Historical Museum.

2007, July 2 Litho. *Perf. 14x13*
300-303 A100 Set of 4 5.00 5.00

Souvenir Sheet

Wrecks and Reefs A101

No. 304: a, 200c, Pipeline system of wrecked oil tanker Pedernalis. b, 300c, Convair 400 airplane near Sonesta Island. c, 500c, Sea turtle, wreck of freighter Jane. d, 500c, Fish, wreck of freighter Antilla.

2007, Sept. 3 Litho. *Perf. 14x13*
304 A101 Sheet of 4, #a-d 17.00 17.00

Christmas and New Year's Day — A102

Designs: 70c, Infant and mother. 100c, Girl with toys and gift box. 150c, Boy at New Year's celebration.

2007, Oct. 17
305-307 A102 Set of 3 4.00 4.00

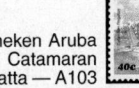

Heineken Aruba Catamaran Regatta — A103

Designs: 40c, Catamarans on beach. 80c, Catamarans racing near race buoy. 125c, Competitor leaning off side of catamaran. 130c, Row of catamarans in race.

2007, Nov. 8
308-311 A103 Set of 4 4.75 4.75

Alto Vista Church — A103a

2007-09 Litho. *Perf. 14x13*

Frame Color

311A	A103a	5c	pink	1.00	1.00
311B	A103a	10c	blue	1.00	1.00
311C	A103a	25c	lt bl grn	1.00	1.00
311D	A103a	50c	yel green	1.00	1.00
311E	A103a	85c	green	1.00	1.00
311F	A103a	90c	lt grnsh bl	1.00	1.00
311G	A103a	100c	salmon	1.00	1.00
311H	A103a	125c	violet	1.50	1.50
311I	A103a	130c	lt blue	1.50	1.50
311J	A103a	135c	beige	1.50	1.50
311K	A103a	140c	violet	1.50	1.50
311L	A103a	200c	dull org	2.00	2.00
311M	A103a	215c	gray	2.50	2.50
311N	A103a	220c	gray	2.50	2.50
	Nos. 311A-311N (14)			17.45	17.45

Issued: 5c, 50c, 85c, 100c, 200c, 7/30/07; 135c, 9/3/08, 90c, 130c, 140c, 220c, 3/9/09. Others, 2007.

Most sets between Nos. 312-465 were printed in sheets containing two sets separated by a row of pictorial tabs. Sets with these tabs command a small premium.

Queen Beatrix, 70th Birthday — A104

Queen Beatrix: 75c, As one-year old with Dutch dignitaries. 125c, With Prince Claus and newborn Crown Prince Willem Alexander. 250c, In royal robes on day of accession to throne. 300c, With family of Crown Prince Willem Alexander.

2008, Jan. 31 *Perf. 13x14*
312-315 A104 Set of 4 9.00 9.00

Aruban Cultural Year — A105

Designs: 80c, Carnival participants. 130c, Organ grinders. 205c, Dera Gai celebration. 275c, Dande musicians visiting home.

2008, Mar. 18 Litho. *Perf. 14x13*
316-319 A105 Set of 4 7.50 7.50

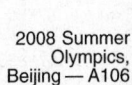

2008 Summer Olympics, Beijing — A106

Designs: 50c, Running. 75c, Synchronized swimming. 100c, Men's rings, vert. 125c, Judo.

2008, Apr. 1 *Perf. 14x13, 13x14*
320-323 A106 Set of 4 4.75 4.75

Athene Cunicularia Arubensis — A107

Aruban burrowing owl: 100c, Entire bird. 150c, Two birds, horiz. 350c, Head of bird.

Perf. 13x14, 14x13
2008, June 2 Litho.
324-326 A107 Set of 3 7.50 7.50

Harley-Davidson Motorcycles A108

Designs: 175c, FRX Super Glide Big Boy. 225c, Knucklehead. 305c, Roadking.

2008, July 4 Litho. *Perf. 14x13*
327-329 A108 Set of 3 8.00 8.00

Aruban Culture — A109

Designs: No. 330, Poem by Federico Oduber. No. 331, 240c, Watapana Magazine covers, vert. No. 332, Henry Habibe and poem by Habibe, vert.

2008, July 8 Litho. *Perf. 13¾*

330 A109 240c multi			6.75	6.75
331 A109 240c multi			6.75	6.75
332 A109 240c multi			6.75	6.75
a.	Souvenir sheet of 5, #330-332, Netherlands #1311, Netherlands Antilles #1187, + etiquette		23.00	23.00
	Nos. 330-332 (3)		20.25	20.25

No. 332a sold for 10g. No. 330 also was available on Netherlands Nos. 1313a and 1313b and Netherlands Antilles No. 1189a.

Flowers A110

No. 333: a, 100c, Calatropis procera. b, 215c, Passiflora foetida.
No. 334: a, 185c, Thespesia populnea. b, 200c, Cryptostegia grandiflora.

2008, Aug. 8 Litho. *Perf. 13½*
333 A110 Pair, #a-b 3.50 3.50
334 A110 Pair, #a-b 4.50 4.50

Drawings by Rembrandt (1606-69) — A111

Designs: 350c, Self-portrait, 1652. 425c, Self-portrait, 1630. 500c, Beggars at door, 1648.

2008, Sept. 30 Litho. *Perf. 13x14*
335-337 A111 Set of 3 14.00 14.00

Aruba in the Past — A112

Designs: 100c, Carting of potable water. 200c, Clay houses. 215c, Processing of aloe resin.

2008, Nov. 3 Litho. *Perf. 14x13*
338-340 A112 Set of 3 5.75 5.75

Louis Braille (1809-52), Educator of the Blind — A113

Designs: 200c, Braille. 215c, Walking stick for the blind.

2009, Jan. 5 Litho. *Perf. 13x14*
341-342 A113 Set of 2 5.50 5.50

Miniature Sheet

Carnival, 55th Anniv. A114

No. 343: a, 75c, Miss Carnival on float. b, 100c, Clown on float. c, 175c, Float with "55" and champagne bottle. d, 225c, Carnival dancers.

2009, Feb. 6 Litho. ***Perf. 13¼x13¾***
343 A114 Sheet of 4, #a-d 8.50 8.50

Caves — A115

Designs: 175c, Tunnel of Love Cave. 200c, Fountain Cave. 225c, Guadirikiri Cave.

2009, Apr. 1 ***Perf. 14x13***
344-346 A115 Set of 3 6.75 6.75

Souvenir Sheet

Global Warming A116

No. 347: a, 200c, Hurricane over map of Caribbean. b, 250c, Map of polar regions, mountains, parched earth. c, 250c, Pollution from industry and vehicles. d, 300c, Fluorescent light bulb, recycling symbols, windmill.

2009, June 2
347 A116 Sheet of 4, #a-d 12.00 12.00

Souvenir Sheet

Architecture — A117

No. 348: a, 175c, California Lighthouse. b, 250c, Plaza Daniel Leo, horiz. c, 275c, Henriquez Building, horiz. d, 325c, Ecury Complex main building.

2009, July 3 ***Perf. 12¾***
348 A117 Sheet of 4, #a-d 11.50 11.50

National Library, 60th Anniv. — A118

Book reader: 185c, Girl. 300c, Woman.

2009, Aug. 20 Litho. ***Perf. 13x14***
349-350 A118 Set of 2 5.75 5.75
350a Vert. pair, #349-350 5.75 5.75

Dolphins — A119

Designs: 125c, Stenella frontalis. 200c, Steno bredanensis. 300c, Two Stenella frontalis. 325c, Group of Steno bredanensis at surface.

2009, Sept. 30 ***Perf. 14x13***
351-354 A119 Set of 4 14.00 14.00

Christmas — A120

Designs: 75c Madonna and Child. 120c, Angel and stars. 125c, Hands, globe, stars, "2009." 210c, Shepherds and sheep.

2009, Oct. 19
355-358 A120 Set of 4 6.00 6.00

Miniature Sheet

Personalized Stamps — A120a

No. 358A: b, Church. c, House. d, Boat. e, Lizard and flower. f, Lighthouse. g, Tree.

2009, Dec. 18 Litho. ***Perf. 13¼x14***
358A A120a (295c) Sheet of 6, #b-g 22.00 22.00

No. 358A sold for 1770c or $20 in U.S. currency. Stamps could be personalized. Butterfly images shown are generic.

Recycling — A121

Various works of art from recycled materials: 90c, Island landscape. 180c, Post office, tree, and animal. 325c, Fish.

2010, Jan. 22 Litho. ***Perf. 13¼***
359-361 A121 Set of 3 6.75 6.75

Historic Airplanes A122

No. 362: a, 250c, Seaplane. b, 500c, Seaplane and lighthouse.

2010, Mar. 26 ***Perf. 13¼x13***
362 A122 Horiz. pair, #a-b 8.50 8.50

Scouting in Aruba, 10th Anniv. A123

No. 363: a, 85c, Scouts observing nature. b, 95c, Scouts building fire. c, 135c, Scout near tent. d, 180c, Scouts playing drums.

2010, Apr. 1 Litho.
363 A123 Block of 4, #a-d 6.50 6.50

End of World War II, 65th Anniv. — A124

No. 364: a, 140c, Large cannon. b, 200c, Beached torpedo. 275c, Equipment and ramp.

2010, May 4 Litho. ***Perf. 13¼x13***
364 A124 Vert. strip of 3, #a-c 7.50 7.50

Parrots A125

No. 365 — Various parrots: a, 85c. b, 90c. c, 180c.

2010, June 2 ***Perf. 13x13¼***
365 A125 Horiz. strip of 3, #a-c 5.00 5.00

Paintings by Vincent Van Gogh A126

No. 366: a, 200c, Self-portrait with Gray Felt Hat. b, 250c, Still Life: Vase with Fifteen Sunflowers. c, 305c, Starry Night. d, 500c, Wheat Field with Crows.

2010, July 29 ***Perf. 13¼x13***
366 A126 Block of 4, #a-d 15.00 15.00

Rum Shops — A127

No. 367: a, 100c, Essoville Rum Shop. b, 200c, Aruba Rum Shop. c, 255c, Caribbean Store.

2010, Sept. 13
367 A127 Vert. strip of 3, #a-c 7.50 7.50

Flowers — A128

No. 368: a, Caesalpinia pulcherrima. b, Dipladenia sanderi. c, Hibiscus. d, Adenium obesum. e, Bougainvillea. f, Ixora. g, Eichhornia crassipes. h, Passiflora caerulea. i, Allamanda cathartica. j, Nerium oleander.

2010, Sept. 29 ***Perf. 14***
368 Block of 10 23.00 23.00
a.-j. A128 200c Any single 2.25 2.25

Houses of Worship A129

No. 369: a, 85c, Synagogue. b, 90c, Church. c, 135c, Church, diff. d, 240c, Church interior.

2010, Oct. 28 ***Perf. 13x13¼***
369 A129 Block of 4, #a-d 6.75 6.75

Birds — A130

No. 370: a, Falco sparverius. b, Icterus icterus. c, Mimus gilvus. d, Egretta alba. e, Aratinga pertinax. f, Pelecanus occidentalis. g, Athene cunicularia arubensis. h, Coerba flaveola. i, Polyborus plancus. j, Colibri thalassinus.

2010, Nov. 17 Litho. ***Perf. 14***
370 Block of 10 23.00 23.00
a.-j. A130 200c Any single 2.25 2.25

Briareus Caribbean Reef Octopus — A131

No. 371 — Various depictions of octopus: a, 100c. b, 175c. c, 255c. d, 300c.

2010, Nov. 30 ***Perf. 13¼x13***
371 A131 Block of 4, #a-d 10.00 10.00

Butterflies — A132

No. 372: a, Zuleika. b, Blue morpho. c, Monarch. d, White peacock. e, Sulphur. f, Zebra. g, Malachite. h, Owl. i, Postman. j, Gulf fritillary.

2010, Dec. 22 ***Perf. 14***
372 Block of 10 23.00 23.00
a.-j. A132 200c Any single 2.25 2.25

Separate Political Status, 25th Anniv. A133

No. 373 — Curved lines and: a, 200c, Star. b, 300c, "Status Aparte." c, 300c, F. B. Tromp, first governor of Aruba, and J. H. A. Eman, first prime minister of Aruba, country name in white at UL. d, 400c, A. J. Booi, first president of Parliament, and G. F. Croes, political party leader, country name in red at LR.

2011, Jan. 1
373 A133 Block of 4, #a-d 14.00 14.00

Flowers — A134

No. 374: a, Catharanthus roseus. b, Echinopsis lageniformis. c, Allamanda cathartica. d, Cordia sebestena. e, Ipomoea pes-caprae. f, Hibiscus rosa-sinensis. g, Cassia fistula. h, Bougainvillea glabra. i, Delonix regia. j, Nerium oleander.

2011, Feb. 16 *Perf. 14*

374	Block of 10	19.00	19.00
a.-j.	A134 160c Any single	1.90	1.90

America Issue — A135

No. 375 — Hands with flags of: a, 200c, Portugal, United States, Cuba and Brazil. b, 250c, Honduras, Canada, Colombia and Chile. c, 350c, United States, Brazil, Aruba and Panama. d, 400c, Suriname, Colombia, Chile and Spain.

No. 376: a, Like No. 375a. b, Like No. 375b. c, Like No. 375c. d, Like No. 375d.

2011, Mar. 23

375	Vert. strip of 4	13.50	13.50
a.	A135 200c multi	2.25	2.25
b.	A135 250c multi	2.75	2.75
c.	A135 350c multi	4.00	4.00
d.	A135 400c multi	4.50	4.50

Miniature Sheet

376	A135 300c Sheet of 4, #a-d	13.50	13.50

Postal Union of the Americas, Spain and Portugal (UPAEP), cent.

Bank Notes — A136

No. 377: a, 1964 Indonesia 25 sen note. b, 1986 Bhutan 2 ngultrum note. c, 1949 Philippines 50 centavo note. d, 1987 Sudan 25 piastre note. e, 1976 Mozambique 100 escudo note. f, 1993 Haiti 25 gourde note. g, 1917 Göttingen 25 pfennig note. h, 1997 Turkey 250,000 lira note. i, 1977 Solomon Islands 10 dollar note. j, 1915 Lille 25 centime note. k, 1985 Egypt 25 piastre note. l, 1976 Albania 100 lek note.

2011, Apr. 4

377	A136 Block of 12	24.00	24.00
a.-l.	167c Any single	2.00	2.00

Maastricht Paper Money Fair.

Peonies A137

No. 378 — Color of flowers: a, Dark red. b, Yellow. c, White. d, Pink.

350c, Pink peony.

2011, May 11 **Litho.** *Perf. 14*

378	A137 110c Sheet of 4, #a-d	5.50	5.50

Souvenir Sheet

379	A137 350c multi	4.25	4.25

Fish — A138

No. 380: a, Holacanthus ciliaris. b, Chaetodon capistratus. c, Sparisoma viride. d, Pomacanthus paru. e, Balistes vetula. f, Lactophrys triqueter. g, Holocentrus rufus. h, Chaetodon striatus. i, Diodon holocanthus. j, Equetus punctatus.

2011, June 15

380	Block of 10	14.00	14.00
a.-j.	A138 120c Any single	1.40	1.40

Chess — A139

No. 381 — Positions of chess pieces at end of 1956 match between Donald Byrne and winner Bobby Fischer: a, White queen on tan square. b, Black king on tan square. c, White knight on tan square, d, Black bishop on tan square. e, White pawn on tan square. f, Black bishop on green square. g, Black knight on tan square. h, Black rook on green square. i, White pawn on green square. j, White king on tan square. k, Black pawn on green square.

2011, July 22

381	Sheet of 15, #a-j, 5 #k + 49 labels	32.50	32.50
a.-k.	A139 180c Any single	2.10	2.10

Mail Boxes of the World — A140

No. 382: a, Dark red rectangular pillar box. b, Orange red Estonian Post mail box. c, Yellow mail box. d, Blue USPS mail box. e, Yellow mail box inscribed "Postbriefkasten." f, Blue mail box with Cyrillic letters. g, Green pillar box with Chinese inscriptions. h, Red mail box inscribed "Brieven Drukwerken." i, Green mail box with two legs. j, Red hexagonal British pillar box.

2011, Aug. 19

382	Block of 10	17.50	17.50
a.-j.	A140 150c Any single	1.75	1.75

Paintings by Jan Vermeer (1632-75) — A141

No. 383: a, Girl with a Red Hat (red frame). b, The Milkmaid (blue frame). c, The Lacemaker (brown frame). d, Girl with a Pearl Earring (red frame).

2011, Sept. 21 **Litho.** *Perf. 14*

383	Vert. strip of 4	11.50	11.50
a.	A141 200c multi	2.25	2.25
b.-c.	A141 250c Either single	2.75	2.75
d.	A141 300c multi	3.50	3.50

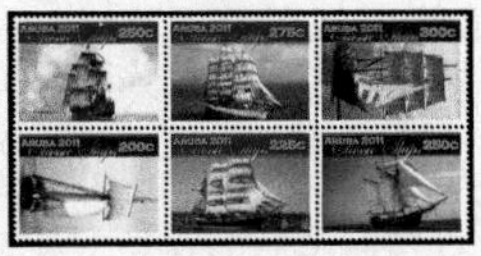

Ships A142

No. 384 — Various tall ships with panel color of: a, 200c, Blue violet. b, 225c, Maroon, horiz. c, 250c, Blue violet, horiz. d, 250c, Maroon, horiz. e, 275c, Maroon, horiz. f, 300c, Blue violet.

2011, Oct. 25

384	A142 Block of 6, #a-f	17.50	17.50

Butterflies — A143

Designs: No. 385, 160c, Diaethria neglecta. No. 386, 160c, Lycaena cupreus lapidicola. No. 387, 160c, Pyrrhogyra edocla. No. 388, 160c, Anartia amathea amathea. No. 389, 160c, Anglais urticae. No. 390, 160c, Morpho aega. No. 391, 160c, Junonia coenia coenia (red violet background). No. 392, 160c, Junonia coenia coenia (dark purple background). No. 393, 160c, Dione juno juno. No. 394, 160c, Lycaena heteronea austin.

2011, Dec. 1

385-394	A143 Set of 10	18.50	18.50

Nos. 385-394 were printed in sheets containing two of each stamp + a central label.

Birds — A144

No. 395: a, Pithecophaga jeffreyi. b, Harpia harpyja. c, Morphnus guaianensis. d, Caracara plancus. e, Lophaetus occipitalis. f, Stephanoaetus coronatus. g, Haliaeetus leucocephalus. h, Vultur gryphus. i, Aquila chrysaetos. j, Falco sparverius.

2012, Jan. 19

395	Block of 10	17.50	17.50
a.-j.	A144 150c Any single	1.75	1.75

Aruban Goats — A145

No. 396: a, Three goats on rocks. b, Two goats on rocks, horiz. c, Goat, horiz. d, Goat and cactus.

2012, Feb. 21

396	Strip of 4	11.00	11.00
a.	A145 175c multi	2.00	2.00
b.	A145 225c multi	2.50	2.50
c.	A145 275c multi	3.00	3.00
d.	A145 300c multi	3.50	3.50

2012 Summer Olympics, London A146

No. 397: a, Torch. b, Swimmer, horiz. c, Hurdler, horiz. d, "Olympia."

2012, Apr. 27

397	A146 500c Block of 4, #a-d	22.50	22.50
e.	Souvenir sheet of 4, #397a-397d	22.50	22.50

Whales — A147

No. 398: a, Delphinapterus leucas. b, Kogia breviceps. c, Balaena mysticetus. d, Orcinus orca. e, Physeter macrocephalus. f, Balaenoptera musculus. g, Globicephala macrorhynchus. h, Mesoplodon europaeus. i, Balaenoptera edeni. j, Megaptera novaeangliae.

2012, May 15

398	Block of 10	14.00	14.00
a.-j.	A147 120c Any single	1.40	1.40

Women's Dresses — A148

No. 399: a, 175c, Woman. b, 200c, Woman with Aruban flag. c, 200c, Two women dancing. d, 250c, Two women, diff.

2012, June 21

399	A148 Block of 4, #a-d	9.25	9.25

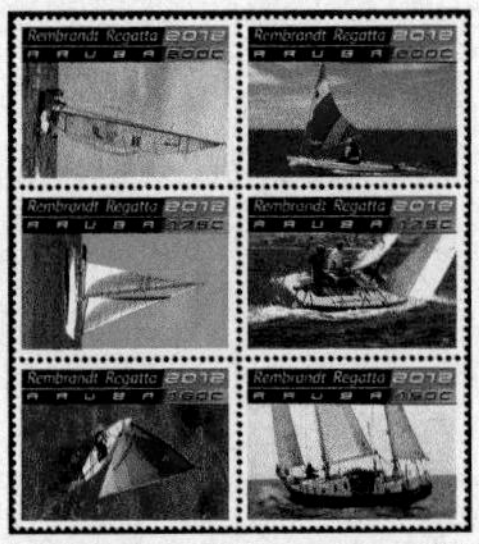

2012 Rembrandt Regatta — A149

No. 400 — Various sailboats: a, 150c, Horiz. b, 150c, Vert. c, 175c, Horiz. d, 175c, Vert. e, 200c, Horiz. f, 200c, Vert.

2012, Aug. 7

400	A149 Block of 6, #a-f	12.00	12.00

A150

A151

A152

A153

A154

A155

A156

Cats — A157

2012, Sept. 20

401	A150 110c multi	1.25	1.25
402	A151 110c multi	1.25	1.25
403	A152 110c multi	1.25	1.25
404	A153 110c multi	1.25	1.25
405	A154 110c multi	1.25	1.25
406	A155 110c multi	1.25	1.25
407	A156 110c multi	1.25	1.25
408	A157 110c multi	1.25	1.25
	Nos. 401-408 (8)	10.00	10.00

Nos. 401-408 were printed in sheets containing two of each stamp and two labels.

Christmas and New Year's Day — A158

No. 409: a, 75c, Ornaments and tree. b, 120c, Gifts and Nativity manger. c, 125c, Candles. d, 210c, Fireworks and champagne flutes.

2012, Oct. 18

409 A158 Block of 4, #a-d 6.00 6.00

A159

A160

A161

A162

A163

A164

A165

A166

A167

Underwater Exploration — A168

2012, Nov. 15

410 Block of 10 11.00 11.00
a. A159 100c multi 1.10 1.10
b. A160 100c multi 1.10 1.10
c. A161 100c multi 1.10 1.10
d. A162 100c multi 1.10 1.10
e. A163 100c multi 1.10 1.10
f. A164 100c multi 1.10 1.10
g. A165 100c multi 1.10 1.10
h. A166 100c multi 1.10 1.10
i. A167 100c multi 1.10 1.10
j. A168 100c multi 1.10 1.10

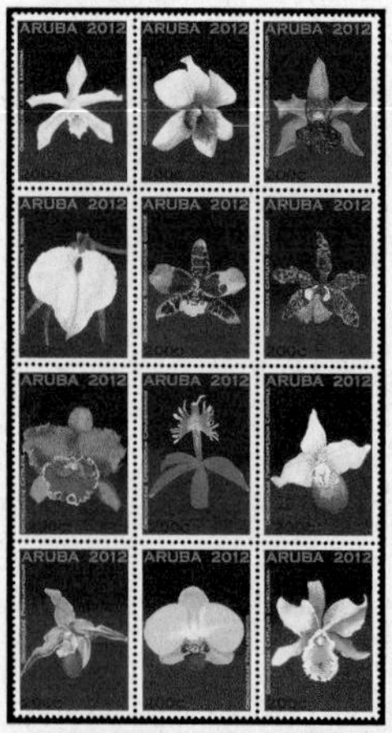

Orchids A169

No. 411: a, Laelia xanthina. b, Dendrobium. c, Dendrobium convolutum. d, Brassavola nodosa. e, Rossioglossum grande. f, Cattleya aclandiae. g, Cattleya. h, Epidendrum cinnabarinum. i, Phragmipedium cardinale. j, Phragmipedium. k, Phalaenopsis. l, Cattleya gaskelliana.

2012, Dec. 20

411 A169 200c Block of 12, #a-l 27.00 27.00

Butterflies — A170

Designs: No. 412, 150c, Graphium sarpedon. No. 413, 150c, Danaus plexippus. No. 414, 150c, Danis danis. No. 415, 150c, Pseudacraea boisduvali. No. 416, 150c, Morpho peleides. No. 417, 150c, Scoptes alphaeus. No. 418, 150c, Jumonia orityа. No. 419, 150c, Palla ussheri. No. 420, 150c, Eryphanis polyxena. No. 421, 150c, Diaethria clymena. No. 422, 150c, Colias eurytheme. No. 423, 150c, Anthocharis cardamis.

2013, Jan. 16

412-423 A170 Set of 12 20.00 20.00

Nos. 412-423 were printed in sheets of 24 containing two of each stamp + a central label.

Wedding Dresses A171

No. 424: a, Brown and green dress. b, Blue gray strapless dress. c, Brown dress with white veil. d, Lilac dress with sash. e, White dress with black ribbon. f, Red dress with gray collar.

2013, Feb. 28

424 A171 200c Block of 6, #a-f 13.50 13.50

Aruban Bank Notes — A172

No. 425: a, 10-florin banknote. b, 25-florin banknote. c, 50-florin banknote. d, 100-florin banknote. e, 500-florin banknote.

2013, Apr. 5

425 Horiz. strip of 5 11.50 11.50
a.-e. A172 200c Any single 2.25 2.25

Printed in sheets containing two tete-beche strips.

A173

A174

A175

A176

Cruise Ships — A177

2013, May 16

426 Horiz. strip of 5 14.00 14.00
a. A173 250c multi 2.75 2.75
b. A174 250c multi 2.75 2.75
c. A175 250c multi 2.75 2.75
d. A176 250c multi 2.75 2.75
e. A177 250c multi 2.75 2.75

No. 426 was printed in sheets containing two tete-beche strips.

A178

Paintings by Frans Hals (c. 1582-1666) A179

Designs: Nos. 427a, 428a, Jester with a Lute. Nos. 427b, 428b, Singing Boy with a Flute.

2013, June 17

427 A178 500c Horiz. pair, #a-b 11.50 11.50

Souvenir Sheet

428 A179 500c Sheet of 2, #a-b 11.50 11.50

Birds A180

No. 429: a, Coereba flaveola. b, Aratinga pertinax arubensis. c, Anas bahamensis. d, Zonotrichia capensis. e, Colinus cristatus. f, Columbigallina passerina. g, Egretta thula. h, Icterus icterus. i, Mimus gilvus. j, Pelecanus occidentalis. k, Sterna eurygnatha. l, Athene cunicularia.

2013, Aug. 1

429 A180 167c Block of 12, #a-l 22.50 22.50

Flowers — A181

No. 430: a, Passiflora. b, Canna. c, Bougainvillea. d, Aramyllis. e, Hibiscus. f, Ipomoea. g, Strelitzia. h, Lillium. i, Allamanda. j, Lantana.

2013, Sept. 5 Litho. *Perf. 14*

430 Block of 10 22.50 22.50
a.-j. A181 200c Any single 2.25 2.25

Printed in sheets containing two blocks that are tete-beche in relationship to each other.

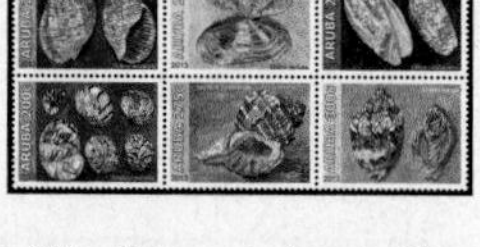
Shells A182

No. 431: a, 200c, Tonna maculosa. b, 200c, Nerita versicolor. c, 250c, Tellina radiata. d, 275c, Cymatium caribbaeum. e, 275c, Oliva caribaeensis. f, 300c, Voluta musica.

2013, Oct. 4 Litho. *Perf. 14*

431 A182 Block of 6, #a-f 17.00 17.00

Nature Photography A183

No. 432: a, Blenchi, by Eddie Thodé. b, Dos Playa, by Lara Kuiperi. c, Iris, by r. Kock. d, Barancanan di Ayo, by Stan Kuiperi. e, Respeta nos Naturalesa, by Joost Howard. f, Un Tesoro, by Bruce Harms. g, Serenidad, by Melissa Sweerts. h, Cactus Landscape, by Lara Kuiperi. i, Palo di Bonchi, by J. Dania. j, Tres Burico, by Lara Kuiperi.

2013, Nov. 12 Litho. *Perf. 14*

432 Block of 10 14,00 14.00
a.-j. A183 120c Any single 1.40 1.40

Wildlife — A184

No. 433: a, Agalychnis calidryas. b, Panthera onca with spotted fur. c, Ara macao. d, Ranitomega benedicta. e, Saimiri sciureus. f, Panthera onca with black fur. g, Ramphastos sulfuratus. h, Saguinus imperator.

2013, Dec. 16 Litho. *Perf. 14*

433 Block of 8 16.00 16.00
a.-h. A184 175c Any single 2.00 2.00

Paintings by Salvador Dalí (1904-89) — A185

No. 435: a, St. James of Compostela, 1957. b, Flores Surrealistas (Gala-Narciso), 1938. c, The Hallucinogenic Toreador, 1968-70. d, The Persistence of Memory, 1931, horiz. e, The Swallow's Tail, 1983, horiz. f, Elephants, 1948, horiz.

2014, Jan. 17 Litho. *Perf. 14*

434 Block of 6 18.00 18.00
a.-f. A185 258c Any single 3.00 3.00

Aruban Carnaval, 60th Anniv. — A186

No. 435: a, 300c, Woman with crown, vert. b, 300c, Woman with mask and feathered headdress, horiz. c, 325c, Woman with headdress, horiz. d, 325c, Woman with headdress and feathers, vert.

2014, Feb. 13 Litho. *Perf. 14*

435 A186 Block of 4, #a-d 14.00 14.00

Automobiles A187

No. 436: a, Ford Thunderbird convertible. b, MG Midget convertible. c, Dodge Challenger. d, Ford Crown Victoria. e, Ford Mustang convertible. f, Chevrolet Corvette Sting Ray.

2014, Mar. 14 Litho. *Perf. 14*

436 Block of 6 15.00 15.00
a.-f. A187 225c Any single 2.50 2.50

Birds of Paradise — A188

No. 437: a, Paradisaea rudolphi. b, Lophorina superba, green background. c, Seleucidis melanoleuca. d, Paradisaea apoda, e, Paradisaea minor. f, Lophorina superba, yellow background. g, Ptiloris victoriae. h, Cicinnurus regius. i, Cicinnurus respublica. j, Parotia carolae.

2014, Apr. 24 Litho. *Perf. 14*

437 Block of 10 27.50 27.50
a.-j. A188 250c Any single 2.75 2.75

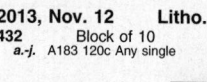

2014 World Cup Soccer Championships, Brazil — A189

No. 438 — World Cup trophy and: a, Player's foot approaching soccer ball. b, Two players attempting to head ball. c, Player making a diving kick. d, Player dribbling ball. e, Penalty kick. f, Soccer field.

2014, May 29 Litho. *Perf. 14*
438 A189 400c Block of 6, #a-f 27.00 27.00

Astronomy — A190

No. 439: a, 350c, Twin planets in circle. b, 350c, Ringed planet. c, 375c, Venus. d, 375c, Star and planets.

2014, June 19 Litho. *Perf. 14*
439 A190 Block of 4, #a-d 16.50 16.50

Miniature Sheets

Attacus Atlas A191

Papilio Cresphontes — A192

No. 440: a, Latin name of moth, "2014," part of wing. b, Head of moth. c, Tip of upper wing. d, Large country name, tip of wing. e, Abdomen of moth, bottom of wing. f, Bottom of wing.

No. 441: a, "2014," "cresphontes," part of wing. b, Parts of wings. c, Edge of top wing. d, Large country name, "Papilio," head of butterfly. e, Abdomen of butterfly. f, Bottom of wing.

2014, Aug. 21 Litho. *Perf. 14*
440 A191 200c Sheet of 6, #a-f 13.50 13.50
441 A192 200c Sheet of 6, #a-f 13.50 13.50

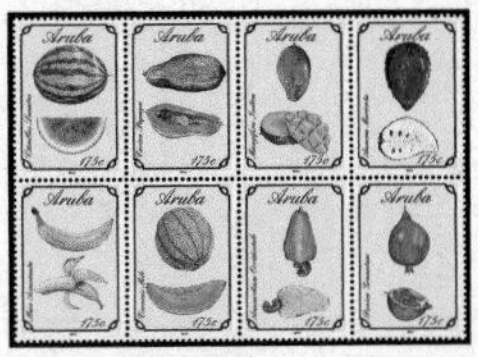

Fruit A193

No. 442: a, Citrullus lanatus. b, Carica papaya. c, Mangifera indica. d, Annona muricata. e, Musa acuminata. f, Cucumis melo. g, Anacardium occidentale. h, Punica granatum.

2014, Sept. 26 Litho. *Perf. 14*
442 A193 175c Block of 8, #a-h 16.00 16.00

Christmas — A194

No. 443 — Ribbon with bow and: a, Bells. b, Gifts, candles, ornaments. c, Stars. d, Ornaments.

2014, Oct. 23 Litho. *Perf. 14*
443 Vert. strip of 4 6.50 6.50
a. A194 85c multi .95 .95
b. A194 130c multi 1.50 1.50
c. A194 135c multi 1.50 1.50
d. A194 220c multi 2.50 2.50

Fishing Boats A195

No. 444: a, 250c, Six boats. b, 275c, Laly. c, 300c, Pikudito and other boats. d, 325c, Phasha and another boat.

2014, Nov. 19 Litho. *Perf. 14*
444 A195 Block of 4, #a-d 13.00 13.00

Dutch Royalty — A196

Designs: No. 445, 300c, King Willem-Alexander. No. 446, 300c, Queen Máxima. No. 447, 300c, King Willem-Alexander and Queen Máxima. No. 448, 300c, King Willem-Alexander, Queen Máxima, Queen Beatrix, Princess Catharina-Amalia, Princess Alexia and Princess Ariane. No. 449, 300c, King Willem-Alexander, Queen Máxima, Princess Catharina-Amalia, Princess Alexia and Princess Ariane waving.

2015, Jan. 30 Litho. *Perf. 14*
445-449 A196 Set of 5 17.00 17.00

Nos. 445-449 were printed in sheets of 10 containing two of each stamp + 2 labels.

Blue Flowers — A197

Designs: No. 450, 200c, Sisyrinchium angustifolium. No. 451, 200c, Lupinus lepidus. No. 452, 200c, Linum lewisii. No. 453, 200c, Amsonia tabernaemontana. No. 454, 200c, Ipomoea learii. No. 455, 200c, Guaiacum officinale. No. 456, 200c, Gentianopsis crinita. No. 457, 200c, Gentiana andrewsii. No. 458, 200c, Campanulastrum americanum. No. 459, 200c, Campanula rotundifolia.

2015, Feb. 26 Litho. *Perf. 14*
450-459 A197 Set of 10 22.50 22.50

Nos. 450-459 were printed in sheets of 20 containing two of each stamp + a central label.

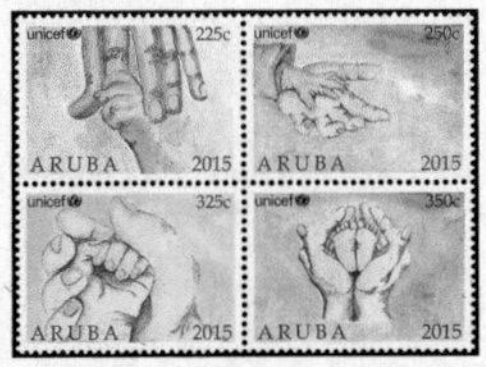

UNICEF A198

No. 460: a, 225c, Child holding finger of adult. b, 250c, Child's hand on adult's hand. c, 325c, Adult hand holding child's hand. d, 350c, Adult's hands holding child's feet.

2015, Mar. 25 Litho. *Perf. 14*
460 A198 Block of 4, #a-d 13.00 13.00

Paintings by Sandro Botticelli (c. 1445-1510) — A199

Paintings or Details: No. 461, The Birth of Venus (De geboorte van Venus). No. 462, The Madonna of the Book (Madonna del Libro). No. 463, Allegorical Portrait of a Woman, Possibly Simonetta Vespucci (Simonetta Vespucci als Maria Lactans). No. 464, The Annunciation (De Blijde Boodschap). No. 465, Madonna of the Magnificat (Madonna del Magnificat).

2015, Mar. 27 Litho. *Perf. 14*
461 A199 275c multi 3.25 3.25
462 A199 275c multi 3.25 3.25
463 A199 275c multi 3.25 3.25
464 A199 275c multi 3.25 3.25
465 A199 275c multi 3.25 3.25
a. Block of 5, #461-465, + label 16.50 16.50
Nos. 461-465 (5) 16.25 16.25

Nos. 461-465 were printed in sheets of 10 containing two of each stamp + 2 labels.

Butterflies — A200

No. 466: a, Colias hyale. b, Carcharodus lavatherae. c, Anthocharis cardamines. d, Carcharodus flocciferus. e, Colias palaeno. f, Euchloe ausonia. g, Gonepteryx cleopatra. h, Heteropterus morpheus. i, Ochlodes venatus. j, Pyrgus fritillarius.

2015, June 30 Litho. *Perf. 14*
466 A200 220c Block of 10, #a-j 24.50 24.50

Cave Art — A201

No. 467: a, 350c, Black spirals in circle. b, 350c, Anthromorphic figure with curved arms and legs. c, 375c, Circles connected by lines. d, 375c, Oval with curved lines and dots.

2015, July 31 Litho. *Perf. 14*
467 A201 Block of 4, #a-d 16.50 16.50

Struthio Camelus A202

No. 468: a, Juvenile facing right, both feet on ground. b, Chick facing right, one foot raised. c, Adult facing left, bending with neck curved. d, Adult facing left with head up. e, Two chicks. f, Head of chick. g, Head of adult. h, Adult facing right. i, Head of adult near chick. j, Adult and juvenile.

2015, Aug. 28 Litho. *Perf. 14*
468 A202 225c Block of 10, #a-j 25.00 25.00

Beaches A203

No. 469 — Various beaches: a, 275c. b, 300c. c, 325c. d, 350c.

2015, Sept. 23 Litho. *Perf. 14*
469 A203 Block of 4, #a-d 14.00 14.00

Historic Buildings A204

No. 470: a, Old Hotel Colombia (red and white building with damaged wall). b, Quinta del Carmen. c, Eloy Arends Building (City Hall) (green and white building). d, Henriquez House (yellow building with red roof and stairway to second floor). e, Wild Family House (red and white building adjacent to parking lot). f, Former Aruba Bank Building (yellow building with red roof, cactus at right). g, Willem III Tower, Fort Zoutman (red and white tower), vert. h, San Nicolas Watertower (brown and yellow tower), vert.

2015, Oct. 16 Litho. *Perf. 14*
470 A204 175c Block of 8, #a-h 16.00 16.00

Tourist Attractions — A205

No. 471: a, Alto Vista Chapel. b, Cruise liner. c, Bushiribana Gold Mill ruins. d, California Lighthouse. e, Double-decker streetcar. f, Rock formations

2015, Nov. 13 Litho. *Perf. 14*
471 A205 250c Block of 6, #a-f 17.00 17.00

Fish — A206

Designs: 90c, Black beauty. 130c, Bluehead wrasse. 205c, Longfin damselfish. 220c, Blue Caribbean tang. 320c, Blackbar soldierfish.

Perf. 13¼x12¾
2016, Feb. 29 Litho.
472-476 A206 Set of 5 11.00 11.00

National Symbols — A207

Aruban: No. 477, 500c, Coat of arms. No. 478, 500c, Flag. No. 479, 500c, National anthem.

Perf. 12¾x13¼
2016, Mar. 16 Litho.
477-479 A207 Set of 3 17.00 17.00
479a Souvenir sheet of 3, #477-479 17.00 17.00

Burrowing Owls — A208

Designs: 140c, Two owls. 200c, One owl. 320c, Three owls. 65c, Owl in flight.

Perf. 13¼x12¾
2016, Mar. 31 Litho.
480-483 A208 Set of 4 15.00 15.00

Butterflies — A209

Designs: 85c, Graphium weiskei. 90c, Papilio glaucus. 100c, Jacoona amrita. 130c, Agrias claudina. 135c, Eunica eurota. 220c, Papilio palinurus. 320c, Arginnis paphia. 420c, Aglais io.

2016, Apr. 29 Litho. *Perf. 12¾x13¼*
484-491 A209 Set of 8 17.00 17.00

Medicinal Plants — A210

Designs: 100c, Aloe vera. 130c, Moringa olifera. 220c, Jatropha gossypiifolia. 250c, Lippia alba. 320c, Croton flavens.

2016, May 31 Litho. *Perf. 12¾x13¼*
492-496 A210 Set of 5 11.50 11.50

2016 Summer Olympics, Rio de Janeiro — A211

Designs: 100c, Synchronized swimming. 130c, Swimming. 220c, Sailing. 500c, Abstract design.

Perf. 13¼x12¾
2016, June 30 Litho.
497-500 A211 Set of 4 11.00 11.00

Vegetables — A212

Designs: 90c, Phaseolus vulgaris. 130c, Capsicum annuum. 205c, Cucumis savitus. 220c, Solanum melongena. 320c, Hibiscus esculentus.

2016, July 29 Litho. *Perf. 12¾x13¼*
501-505 A212 Set of 5 11.00 11.00

Birds — A213

Designs: 50c, Tricolored herons. 85c, Snowy egrets. 90c, Roseate spoonbills. 100c, Blue-winged teals. 130c, Scarlet ibises. 220c, Black skimmers. 250c, Ruby-topaz hummingbird. 325c, Whistling heron.

Perf. 13¼x12¾
2016, Aug. 31 Litho.
506-513 A213 Set of 8 14.00 14.00

Insects — A214

Designs: 50c, Odonata anisoptera. 90c, Blattaria periplaneta. 100c, Formicidae solenopsis. 130c, Tettigonia viridissima. 200c, Apis mellifera. 220c, Musca domestica. 275c, Vespula vulgaris. 320c, Psaltoda moerens.

Perf. 13¼x12¾
2016, Sept. 30 Litho.
514-521 A214 Set of 8 15.50 15.50

Musical Instruments A215

G clef and: 100c, Bongo drums. 140c, Güiro (raspa). 205c, Accordion. 220c, Marimba. 500c, Steelpan drum.

2016, Oct. 31 Litho. *Perf. 13¼x12¾*
522-526 A215 Set of 5 13.00 13.00

Antiques — A216

Designs: 90c, Sewing machine, coffee mill, oil lamp, sadiron. 130c, Sewing machine. 205c, Sadiron. 250c, Phonograph. 325c, Coffee mill and sadiron.

Perf. 13¼x12¾
2016, Nov. 30 Litho.
527-531 A216 Set of 5 11.50 11.50

Souvenir Sheet

New Year 2017 (Year of the Rooster) A217

No. 532: a, 200c, Rooster. b, 420c, Dragon.

2017, Feb. 28 Litho. *Perf. 14x13¼*
532 A217 Sheet of 2, #a-b 7.00 7.00

Miniature Sheet

Underwater Panorama — A218

No. 533: a, 90c, Diver, rays, fish, coral. b, 130c, Sea turtles, fish, tube worm. c, 220c, Fish, coral, starfish. d, 650c, Fish and seaweed.

Perf. 13¾x12¾
2017, Mar. 31 Litho.
533 A218 Sheet of 4, #a-d 12.50 12.50

Houses — A219

Various houses: 85c, 90c, 100c, 130c, 140c, 200c, 220c, 320c.

2017, Apr. 28 Litho. *Perf. 13¼x12¾*
534-541 A219 Set of 8 14.50 14.50

Sports — A220

Designs: 50c, Cycling. 85c, Baseball. 90c, Cross-country biking. 100c, Basketball. 130c, Soccer. 220c, Go-karting. 305c, Skateboarding. 390c, Tennis.

2017, May 31 Litho. *Perf. 13¼x12¾*
542-549 A220 Set of 8 15.50 15.50

Birds — A221

Designs: 85c, Black-crowned night heron. 90c, Purple gallinule. 100c, Saffron finch. 130c, Yellow oriole. 200c, Amazon kingfisher. 220c, American flamingo. 250c, Least bittern. 305c, Yellow-billed cuckoo.

Perf. 12¾x13¼
2017, June 30 Litho.
550-557 A221 Set of 8 15.50 15.50

Postal Services in Aruba, 125th Anniv. — A222

Designs: 90c, Post office, man with wheelbarrow. 130c, Post office. 320c, Mailman on bicycle making delivery. 390c, Motorcyclist and Central Post Office.

2017, July 31 Litho. *Perf. 13¼x12¾*
558-561 A222 Set of 4 10.50 10.50

Communication Devices — A223

Designs: 90c, Radio. 130c, Television, horiz. 220c, Telegraph, horiz. 305c, Typewriter, horiz. 420c, Telephone, horiz.

Perf. 12¾x13¼, 13¼x12¾
2017, Aug. 31 Litho.
562-566 A223 Set of 5 13.00 13.00

Tourist Attractions — A224

Designs: 65c, Anchor and donkey, Seroe Colorado. 90c, Lizard, Hooiberg. 100c, Ayo rock formation. 130c, Windsurfer near shipwreck. 200c, California Lighthouse. 220c, Fisherman and fishing boat. 300c, Fisherman casting net. 320c, Arikok National Park.

Perf. 13¼x12¾
2017, Sept. 29 Litho.
567-574 A224 Set of 8 16.00 16.00

Flowers — A225

Designs: 50c, Plumeria rubra. 90c, Erythrania velutina. 130c, Opuntia wentiana, horiz. 135c, Passiflora foetidal, horiz. 200c, Antigonon leptopus, horiz. 220c, Ixora coccinea, horiz. 305c, Calotropis procera. 320c, Acacia tortuosa.

Perf. 12¾x13¼, 13¼x12¾
2017, Oct. 31 Litho.
575-582 A225 Set of 8 16.50 16.50

Christmas — A226

Designs: 90c, Christmas ornaments and palm trees. 130c, Stocking cap on lighthouse. 220c, Candles, poinsettias, heart. 320c, Christmas gifts and beach umbrella.

Perf. 12¾x13¼
2017, Nov. 30 Litho.
583-586 A226 Set of 4 8.50 8.50

A227

A228

A229

Personalized Stamps — A230

2018, Apr. 24 Litho. *Perf. 13¼x14*
587 A227 130c multi 1.50 1.50
588 A228 130c multi 1.50 1.50
589 A229 130c multi 1.50 1.50
590 A230 130c multi 1.50 1.50
Nos. 587-590 (4) 6.00 6.00

Vignette portions of Nos. 587-590 could be personalized. The vignettes shown for types A227-A230 are generic images.

2018 World Cup Soccer Championships, Russia — A231

Designs: 130c, Two soccer players. 220c, Goalie making save.

2018, June 15 Litho. *Perf. 13¼x13*
591-592 A231 Set of 2 4.00 4.00

Greetings — A232

Designs: 85c, Birthday cake (Happy Birthday). 90c, Hands holding apple (Get Well), vert. 100c, Heart and hands (Valentine), vert. 130c, Orchid (Condolences). 230c, Flowers and hands (Thank You), vert. 650c, Hand and champagne bottle (Congratulations), vert.

Perf. 13¼x12¾, 12¾x13¼

2018, July 31 **Litho.**
593-598 A232 Set of 6 14.50 14.50

Aspects of Aruban Culture — A233

Designs: 90c, Dancers (Celebrations). 130c, Aloe hanging from doorway (Traditions). 220c, Woman in dress (Folklorico Dress). 420c, Fish on plate (Typical food).

Perf. 13¼x12¾

2018, Aug. 31 **Litho.**
599-602 A233 Set of 4 9.75 9.75

Water Sports — A234

Designs: 90c, Windsurfing. 130c, Surfing. 135c, Kitesurfing. 200c, Kayaking. 220c, Bodyboarding. 320c, Parasailing.

Perf. 13¼x12¾

2018, Sept. 28 **Litho.**
603-608 A234 Set of 6 12.50 12.50

Pets — A235

Designs: 90c, Cats. 100c, Dog. 130c, Rabbit. 135c, Fish. 220c, Turtle. 500c, Parrots.

2018, Oct. 31 **Litho.** ***Perf. 13¼x12¾***
609-614 A235 Set of 6 13.00 13.00

Sustainable Energy — A236

Designs: 90c, Wind generators. 100c, Electric car. 130c, Solar panel, vert. 220c, Electric tram, vert. 320c, Bicycle.

Perf. 13¼x12¾, 12¾x13¼

2018, Nov. 30 **Litho.**
615-619 A236 Set of 5 9.75 9.75

65th Aruba Carnaval — A237

Designs: 90c, Musicians and dancers. 130c, Singer in uniform, vert. 220c, Dancer, vert. 420c, Three dancers.

Perf. 13¼x12¾, 12¾x13¼

2019, Mar. 1 **Litho.**
620-623 A237 Set of 4 9.75 9.75

Children at Play — A238

Designs: 90c, Girl jumping rope, girls in sack race. 100c, Girls with hula hoops, boy playing hop scotch. 130c, Boys rolling hoops and tires. 320c, Boys with top and yo-yo.

2019, Apr. 28 **Litho.** ***Perf. 12¾x13¼***
624-627 A238 Set of 4 7.25 7.25

Sports Stars — A239

Designs: No. 628, 220c, Sarah-Quita Offringa, windsurfer. No. 629, 220c, Xander Bogaerts, baseball player. No. 630, 220c, Shanayah Howell, bicycle motocross. No. 631, 220c, Chiara Petrocchi, taekwondo.

Perf. 13¼x12¾

2019, June 28 **Litho.**
628-631 A239 Set of 4 10.00 10.00
631a Souvenir sheet of 4, #628-631 10.00 10.00

Medicinal Plants — A240

Designs: 90c, Origanum vulgare. 130c, Mentha spicata, vert. 220c, Senna alexandrina, vert. 500c, Cymbopogon.

Perf. 13¼x12¾, 12¾x13¼

2019, Aug. 30 **Litho.**
632-635 A240 Set of 4 10.50 10.50

Birds and Their Feathers — A241

Designs: 90c, Falco sparverius. 120c, Athene cunicularia arubensis. 130c, Falco peregrinus. 320c, Caracara cheriway.

2019, Oct. 31 **Litho.** ***Perf. 13¼x12¾***
636-639 A241 Set of 4 7.50 7.50

Archaeology A242

Designs: 100c, Ancient hatchet, potsherd, mortar and pestle. 130c, Archaeologists uncovering artifacts, vert. 220c, Ancinet shell in cross-section, creation of necklace, vert. 320c, Archaeologist unearthing skull, cross-section of burial urn.

Perf. 13¼x12¾, 12¾x13¼

2019, Dec. 9 **Litho.**
640-643 A242 Set of 4 8.75 8.75

Earth Day, 50th Anniv. — A243

Designs: 100c, Hand holding Earth Day 50th anniversary emblem. 130c, Hands holding globe and recycling emblem, horiz. 220c, Hands holding seedling, horiz. 320c, Hands holding globe.

Perf. 12¾x13¼, 13¼x12¾

2020, Apr. 22 **Litho.**
644-647 A243 Set of 4 8.75 8.75

Butterflies — A244

Designs: 90c, Battus polydamas. 130c, Hypna clytemnestra. 220c, Pachliopta aristolochiae. 420c, Papilio rumanzovia.

2020, May 29 **Litho.** ***Perf. 12¾x13¼***
648-651 A244 Set of 4 9.75 9.75

America Issue — A245

Designs: 90c, Building and palm trees. 130c, Yellow building with red roof. 220c, Nicholaas Store. 420c, Green building with date at top.

2020, July 31 **Litho.** ***Perf. 13¼x12¾***
652-655 A245 Set of 4 9.75 9.75

Medical Afflictions — A246

Designs: 90c, Alzheimer's disease. 130c, Cancer, vert. 220c, Diabetes, vert. 320c, Stroke.

Perf. 13¼x12¾, 12¾x13¼

2020, Sept. 21 **Litho.**
656-659 A246 Set of 4 8.50 8.50

Martial Arts — A247

Inscriptions: 100c, Capoeira. 130c, Karate, vert. 220c, Greek wrestling, vert. 320c, Chinese martial art.

Perf. 13¼x12¾, 12¾x13¼

2020, Oct. 30 **Litho.**
660-663 A247 Set of 4 8.75 8.75

Wagons Used in Phosphate Mining — A248

Designs: 90c, Locomotive pulling wagon. 130c, Wagon near miners. 220c, Miners pushing wagon. 420c, Locomotive pulling wagons.

Perf. 13¼x12¾

2020, Nov. 30 **Litho.**
664-667 A248 Set of 4 8.50 8.50

Souvenir Sheet

Fofoti Tree A249

2021, Oct. 14 **Litho.** ***Perf. 13¼x12¾***
668 A249 850c multi 9.50 9.50

America issue.

Agriculture — A250

Designs: 90c, Hands placing plant in ground, butterfly. 220c, Hand watering tomato plants. 320c, Coconut tree and watermelons. 420c, Woman picking fruit from tree.

2021, Nov. 16 **Litho.** ***Perf. 13¼x14***
669-672 A250 Set of 4 12.00 12.00

Fishing — A251

Designs: 100c, Fisherman casting net. 130c, Traditional fishing boat. 420c, Rock fishing. 500c, Deep sea fishing.

2021, Dec. 3 **Litho.** ***Perf. 14x13¼***
673-676 A251 Set of 4 13.00 13.00

Orchids — A252

Designs: 140c, Spathoglottis Big Red Fancy. 200c, Dendrobium nobile. 320c, Vanda Tessellate Blue. 650c, Cattleya habenaria rhodocheila.

2022, Mar. 28 **Litho.** ***Perf. 13¼x14***
677-680 A252 Set of 4 15.00 15.00

Flamingos — A253

Designs: 220c, Flamingo facing forward. 320c, Flamingo with head and wings extended. 420c, Flamingo in flight. 500c, Seven flamingos.

2022, Apr. 29 **Litho.** ***Perf. 13¼x13½***
681-684 A253 Set of 4 16.50 16.50

Miniature Sheet

Winning Pictures in Marine Life Photography Contest — A254

No. 685: a, Green sea turtle. b, Flamingo tongue snail. c, Feather duster worm. d, Ghost crab.

2022, June 8 **Litho.** ***Perf. 13¼x13½***
685 A254 420c Sheet of 4, #a-d 19.00 19.00

Souvenir Sheet

Aruba Postal Service, 130th Anniv. A255

No. 686 — Postal worker, letters and: a, Motorcycle, car, parcels, mailbox with open door. b, Bicycle, ship, car, and airplane. c, Bicycle and pillar box.

2022, Aug. 1 **Litho.** ***Perf. 14x13¾***
686 A255 220c Sheet of 3, #a-c 7.50 7.50

SEMI-POSTAL STAMPS

Surtax for child welfare organizations unless otherwise stated.

Solidarity — SP1

1986, May 7 Litho. *Perf. 14x13*

B1 SP1 30c + 10c shown 1.75 1.00
B2 SP1 35c + 15c Three ropes 1.75 1.00
B3 SP1 60c + 25c One rope 2.50 1.50
Nos. B1-B3 (3) 6.00 3.50

Surtax for social and cultural projects.

Child Welfare — SP2

No. B4, Boy, caterpillar. No. B5, Boy, cocoon. No. B6, Girl, butterfly.

1986, Oct. 29 Litho. *Perf. 14x13*

B4 SP2 45c + 20c multi 2.75 1.00
B5 SP2 70c + 25c multi 2.75 1.75
B6 SP2 100c + 40c multi 3.50 2.25
Nos. B4-B6 (3) 9.00 5.00

Christmas (Child Welfare) — SP3

No. B7, Boy on beach. No. B8, Drawing Christmas tree. No. B9, Child, creche figures.

1987, Oct. 27 Litho. *Perf. 14x13*

B7 SP3 25c +10c multi 1.50 .75
B8 SP3 45c +20c multi 2.00 1.00
B9 SP3 70c +30c multi 2.75 1.50
Nos. B7-B9 (3) 6.25 3.25

Solidarity — SP4

YMCA emblem in various geometric designs.

1988, Aug. 3 Litho. *Perf. 14x13*

B10 SP4 45c +20c shown 2.00 1.00
B11 SP4 60c +25c multi, diff. 2.00 1.50
B12 SP4 100c +50c multi, diff. 2.50 2.00
Nos. B10-B12 (3) 6.50 4.50

11th YMCA world council.
Surtax for social and cultural projects.

Children's Toys (Child Welfare) — SP5

1988, Oct. 26 *Perf. 13x14*

B13 SP5 45c +20c Jacks 2.25 1.00
B14 SP5 70c +30c Top 2.25 1.50
B15 SP5 100c +50c Kite 3.00 2.00
Nos. B13-B15 (3) 7.50 4.50

Child Welfare — SP6

No. B16, Baby spoon. No. B17, Chasing a ball. No. B18, Adult & child holding hands.

1989, Oct. 26 *Perf. 14x13*

B16 SP6 45c +20c multi 2.00 1.00
B17 SP6 60c +30c multi 2.25 1.25
B18 SP6 100c +50c multi 3.00 2.00
Nos. B16-B18 (3) 7.25 4.25

Solidarity — SP7

No. B20, Family, house.

1990, July 25

B19 SP7 55c +25c shown 2.00 1.50
B20 SP7 100c +50c multi 3.50 2.50

Surtax for social and cultural projects.

Child Welfare — SP8

Christmas song: No. B21, Wind surfboards. No. B23, Kites, lizard.

1990, Oct. 24 Litho. *Perf. 13x14*

B21 SP8 45c +20c multi 1.50 1.00
B22 SP8 60c +30c shown 2.00 1.25
B23 SP8 100c +50c multi 3.00 2.25
Nos. B21-B23 (3) 6.50 4.50

Child Welfare — SP9

Literacy: 45c+25c, Discovery of reading. 60c+35c, Pointing to letter. 100c+50c, Child reading.

1991, Oct. 25 Litho. *Perf. 13x14*

B24 SP9 45c +25c multi 1.50 1.25
B25 SP9 60c +35c multi 2.00 1.40
B26 SP9 100c +50c multi 3.00 2.25
Nos. B24-B26 (3) 6.50 4.90

Solidarity — SP10

55c+30c, Girl scouts, flag & emblem. 100c+50c, Hand holding cancer fund emblem, people.

1992, May 27 Litho. *Perf. 14x13*

B27 SP10 55c +30c multi 2.00 1.50
B28 SP10 100c +50c multi 3.50 2.25

Surtax for social and cultural projects.

Postal Services of Aruba, Cent. (Child Welfare) — SP11

Designs: 50c+30c, Heart. 70c+35c, Airplane, letters. 100c+55c, Pigeon with letter in beak, vert.

1992, Oct. 30 Litho. *Perf. 14x13*

B29 SP11 50c +30c multi 1.90 1.25
B30 SP11 70c +35c multi 2.10 1.40

Perf. 13x14

B31 SP11 100c +50c multi 3.00 2.25
Nos. B29-B31 (3) 7.00 4.90

Youth Foreign Study Programs (Child Welfare) — SP12

Abstract designs of: 50c+30c, Landscapes. 75c+40c, Young man, scenes of other countries, vert. 100c+50c, Integrating cultures.

1993, Oct. 27 *Perf. 14x13, 13x14*

B32 SP12 50c +30c multi 1.50 1.25
B33 SP12 75c +40c multi 2.00 1.90
B34 SP12 100c +50c multi 2.50 2.25
Nos. B32-B34 (3) 6.00 5.40

Solidarity — SP13

Intl. Year of the Family: 50c+35c, Family seated, reading, studying. 100c+50c, Family playing in front of house.

1994, May 30 Litho. *Perf. 14x13*

B35 SP13 50c +35c multi 1.50 1.25
B36 SP13 100c +50c multi 2.75 2.50

Surtax for social and cultural projects.

Child Welfare — SP14

Designs: 50c+30c, Children on anchor with umbrella. 80c+35c, Children inside Sun. 100c+50c, Child riding owl.

1994, Oct. 27 Litho. *Perf. 14x13*

B37 SP14 50c +30c multi 2.00 1.50
B38 SP14 80c +35c multi 2.40 2.00
B39 SP14 100c +50c multi 2.50 2.50
Nos. B37-B39 (3) 6.90 6.00

Child Welfare — SP15

Children's drawings: 50c+25c, Children with balloons, house. 70c+35c, Three people with picnic basket on sunny day. 100c+50c, People gardening on sunny day.

1995, Oct. 26 Litho. *Perf. 13x14*

B40 SP15 50c +25c multi 1.75 1.25
B41 SP15 70c +35c multi 2.25 1.75
B42 SP15 100c +50c multi 3.00 2.50
Nos. B40-B42 (3) 7.00 5.50

Solidarity — SP16

El Sol Naciente Lodge, 75th Anniv.: 60c+30c, Masonic emblems. 100c+ 50c, Columns, terrestrial and celestial globes.

1996, July 26 Litho. *Perf. 13x14*

B43 SP16 60c +30c multi 2.50 1.50
B44 SP16 100c +50c multi 3.50 2.50

Surtax for social and cultural projects (Solidarity)

Child Welfare — SP17

Cartoons: 50c+25c, Mother, baby rabbit waiting at school bus stop. 70c+35c, Mother, baby owl, outside school. 100c+50c, Children flying kite.

1996, Oct. 24 Litho. *Perf. 14x13*

B45 SP17 50c +25c multi 1.75 1.25
B46 SP17 70c +35c multi 2.25 1.75
B47 SP17 100c +50c multi 2.50 2.40
Nos. B45-B47 (3) 6.50 5.40

Child Welfare — SP18

Designs: 50c+25c, Girl sitting among aloe plants. 70c+35c, Boy, butterfly, cactus, vert. 100c+50c, Girl swimming under water, fish, coral.

Perf. 14x13, 13x14

1997, Oct. 23 Litho.

B48 SP18 50c +25c multi 1.50 1.25
B49 SP18 70c +35c multi 2.50 2.00
B50 SP18 100c +50c multi 2.50 2.50
Nos. B48-B50 (3) 6.50 5.75

Solidarity — SP19

Service Organizations: 60c+30c, Globe, emblem of Lions Intl., wheelchair balanced on map of Aruba. 100c+50c, Child reading book, emblem of Rotary Intl., woman in rocking chair.

1998, May 29 Litho. *Perf. 14x13*

B51 SP19 60c +30c multi 2.50 1.50
B52 SP19 100c +50c multi 3.50 2.75

Surtax for social and cultural projects.

Child Welfare — SP20

50c+25c, Girl performing traditional ribbon dance. 80c+40c, Boy playing a cuarta. 100c+50c, Two boys playing basketball.

1998, Oct. 22 Litho. *Perf. 13x14*

B53 SP20 50c +25c multi 1.75 1.25
B54 SP20 80c +40c multi 2.50 2.25
B55 SP20 100c +50c multi 3.00 2.50
Nos. B53-B55 (3) 7.25 6.00

Child Welfare — SP21

Designs: 60c+30c, Child on beach with man with fishing net. 80c+40c, Adult reading to children. 100c+50c, Mother, child, vert.

Perf. 14x13, 13x14

1999, Oct. 21 Litho.

B56 SP21 60c +30c multi 1.75 1.50
B57 SP21 80c +40c multi 2.50 2.00
B58 SP21 100c +50c multi 3.00 2.50
Nos. B56-B58 (3) 7.25 6.00

Solidarity — SP22

75c+35c, Children on playground equipment. 100c+50c, Children playing in sand.

2000, Aug. 28 Litho. *Perf. 14x13*

B59-B60 SP22 Set of 2 5.75 4.25

Child Welfare — SP23

Children's art: 60c+30c, House with solar collectors. 80c+40c, House, girl, garbage can. 100c+50c, Flying automobiles.

2000, Oct. 26

B61-B63 SP23 Set of 3 8.00 6.00

Child Welfare — SP24

Intl. Volunteers Year: 40c+20c, Children at crosswalk. 60c+30c, Boys walking dog. 100c+50c, Children depositing trash in can at beach.

2001, Oct. 31 Litho. *Perf. 13x14*

B64-B66 SP24 Set of 3 7.00 5.75

Child Welfare — SP25

Designs: 40c+20c, Boy, iguana and goat. 60c+30c, Girl, hawksbill turtle, red crab, horiz. 100c+50c, Boy, pelicans, parakeet, conch shell.

Perf. 13x14, 14x13

2002, Oct. 31 Litho.

B67-B69 SP25 Set of 3 7.00 5.75

Child Welfare — SP26

Children playing: 40c+20c, Baseball. 60c+30c, Volleyball. 100c+50c, Soccer.

2003, Oct. 31 Litho. *Perf. 14x13*

B70-B72	SP26	Set of 3	6.00	6.00

Children's Welfare — SP27

Children playing: 60c+30c, Maracas. 85c+40c, Steel drum. 100c+50c, Tambourine, wiri.

2004, Oct. 29 Litho. *Perf. 13x14*

B73-B75	SP27	Set of 3	5.50	5.00

ASCENSION

ə-'sen t -shən

LOCATION — An island in the South Atlantic Ocean, 900 miles from Liberia

GOVT. — A part of the British Crown Colony of St. Helena

AREA — 34 sq. mi.

POP. — 1,117 (1993)

In 1922 Ascension was placed under the administration of the Colonial Office and annexed to the British Crown Colony of St. Helena. The only post office is at Georgetown.

12 Pence = 1 Shilling

20 Shillings = 1 Pound

100 Pence = 1 Pound (1971)

Catalogue values for unused stamps in this country are for Never Hinged items, beginning with Scott 50.

Stamps and Types of St. Helena, 1912-22 Overprinted in Black or Red

1922 Wmk. 4 *Perf. 14*

1	A9	½p green & blk	8.00	*29.00*
2	A10	1p green	8.00	*29.00*
3	A10	1½p rose red	21.00	*60.00*
4	A9	2p gray & blk	21.00	16.00
5	A9	3p ultra	16.00	*29.00*
6	A10	8p dl vio & blk	34.00	*62.50*
7	A10	2sh ultra & blk, *blue*	120.00	*150.00*
8	A10	3sh vio & blk	175.00	*200.00*

Wmk. 3

9	A9	1sh blk, *gray grn* (R)	35.00	*60.00*
		Nos. 1-9 (9)	438.00	*635.50*
		Set, never hinged	675.00	

Seal of Colony — A3

1924-33 Typo. Wmk. 4 *Perf. 14*

Chalky Paper

10	A3	½p black & gray	6.75	*19.00*
11	A3	1p green & blk	7.00	*17.00*
12	A3	1½p rose red	10.00	*50.00*
13	A3	2p bluish gray & gray	25.00	13.00
14	A3	3p ultra	10.00	*19.00*
15	A3	4p blk & gray, *yel*	60.00	*100.00*
16	A3	5p ol & lil ('27)	24.00	*29.00*
17	A3	6p rose lil & gray	62.50	*125.00*
18	A3	8p violet & gray	21.00	*52.50*
19	A3	1sh brown & gray	25.00	*62.50*
20	A3	2sh ultra & gray, *blue*	75.00	*115.00*
21	A3	3sh blk & gray, *blue*	110.00	*110.00*
		Nos. 10-21 (12)	436.25	*712.00*
		Set, never hinged	675.00	

View of Georgetown A4

Map of Ascension A5

Sooty Tern Breeding Colony — A9

Designs: 1½p, Pier at Georgetown. 3p, Long Beach. 5p, Three Sisters. 5sh, Green Mountain.

1934, July 2 Engr.

23	A4	½p violet & blk	1.10	1.00
24	A5	1p lt grn & blk	2.25	1.60
25	A4	1½p red & black	2.25	*2.75*
26	A5	2p org & black	2.25	*3.00*
27	A4	3p ultra & blk	2.75	1.90
28	A4	5p blue & black	2.75	*4.00*
29	A5	8p dk brn & blk	5.25	*6.75*
30	A9	1sh car & blk	22.50	12.00
31	A5	2sh6p violet & blk	57.50	50.00
32	A4	5sh brown & blk	62.50	*70.00*
		Nos. 23-32 (10)	161.10	*153.00*
		Set, never hinged	240.00	

Common Design Types pictured following the introduction.

Silver Jubilee Issue

Common Design Type

1935, May 6 *Perf. 11x12*

33	CD301	1½p car & dk blue	3.50	*15.00*
34	CD301	2p blk & ultra	10.00	*37.50*
35	CD301	5p ind & grn	22.50	*32.50*
36	CD301	1sh brn vio & indigo	22.50	*42.50*
		Nos. 33-36 (4)	58.50	*127.50*
		Set, never hinged	100.00	

25th anniv. of the reign of King George V.

Coronation Issue

Common Design Type

1937, May 19 *Perf. 13½x14*

37	CD302	1p deep green	.75	*1.50*
38	CD302	2p deep orange	1.00	.65
39	CD302	3p bright ultra	1.00	.60
		Nos. 37-39 (3)	2.75	*2.75*
		Set, never hinged	3.50	

Georgetown A11

Designs: No. 41, 41A, 2p, 4p, Green Mountain. No. 41D, 6p, 10sh, Three Sisters. 1½p, 2sh6p, Pier at Georgetown. 3p, 5sh, Long Beach.

Perf. 13, 13½ (#41, 44, 45), 14 (#43C)

1938-53 Center in Black

40	A11	½p violet ('44)	.80	*4.00*
		Never hinged	1.50	
a.		Perf. 13½	4.00	*4.00*
		Never hinged	8.00	
41	A11	1p green	30.00	13.50
		Never hinged	45.00	
41A	A11	1p org yel ('42)	.25	*.60*
		Never hinged	.45	
b.		Perf. 14 ('49)	.40	*16.00*
		Never hinged	.70	
c.		Perf. 13½	8.00	*9.00*
		Never hinged	14.50	
41D	A11	1p green ('49)	.35	*1.50*
		Never hinged	.60	
42	A11	1½p red ('44)	.65	*.80*
		Never hinged	1.00	
a.		Perf. 14 ('49)	1.90	*13.50*
		Never hinged	3.75	
b.		Perf. 13½	5.75	1.40
		Never hinged	9.00	
42C	A11	1½p lilac rose ('53)	.30	*6.50*
		Never hinged	.55	
d.		Perf. 14 ('49)	1.35	*1.10*
		Never hinged	2.25	
e.		1½p carmine, perf 14	6.50	6.50
		Never hinged	12.00	
43	A11	2p orange ('44)	.50	.40
		Never hinged	.80	
a.		Perf. 14 ('49)	2.25	*37.50*
		Never hinged	3.50	
b.		Perf. 13½	5.75	1.00
		Never hinged	9.50	
43C	A11	2p red ('49)	.90	*1.90*
		Never hinged	1.50	
44	A11	3p ultra	65.00	30.00
		Never hinged	110.00	
44A	A11	3p black ('44)	.35	*1.00*
		Never hinged	.70	
c.		Perf. 13½ ('40)	13.50	4.00
		Never hinged	21.00	
44B	A11	4p ultra ('44)	3.00	3.00
		Never hinged	5.25	
d.		Perf. 13½	10.00	3.75
		Never hinged	17.50	
45	A11	6p gray blue	7.25	2.50
		Never hinged	13.00	
a.		Perf. 13 ('44)	7.50	7.50
		Never hinged	12.50	
46	A11	1sh dk brn ('44)	3.50	2.00
		Never hinged	5.00	
a.		Perf. 13½	13.00	3.00
		Never hinged	22.50	
47	A11	2sh6p car ('44)	20.00	*37.50*
		Never hinged	30.00	
a.		Perf. 13½	30.00	12.00
		Never hinged	47.50	
b.		Frame printed doubly, one albino	*3,750.*	*5,000.*
		Never hinged	*5,250.*	
48	A11	5sh yel brn ('44)	25.00	45.00
		Never hinged	40.00	
a.		Perf. 13½	62.50	12.00
		Never hinged	100.00	
49	A11	10sh red vio ('44)	45.00	*62.50*
		Never hinged	62.50	
a.		Perf. 13½	65.00	50.00
		Never hinged	120.00	
b.		10sh brt aniline red pur, perf 13	65.00	50.00
		Never hinged	125.00	
		Nos. 40-49 (16)	202.85	*212.70*
		Set, never hinged	315.00	

Catalogue values for unused stamps in this section, from this point to the end of the section, are for Never Hinged items.

Peace Issue

Common Design Type

Perf. 13½x14

1946, Oct. 21 Engr. Wmk. 4

50	CD303	2p deep orange	.40	*1.00*
51	CD303	4p deep blue	.40	*1.00*

Silver Wedding Issue

Common Design Types

1948, Oct. 20 Photo. *Perf. 14x14½*

52	CD304	3p black	.55	.45

Engraved; Name Typographed

Perf. 11½x11

53	CD305	10sh red violet	55.00	50.00

The stamps formerly listed as Nos. 54-56 have been merged into the rest of the George VI definitive series as Nos. 41//43C.

UPU Issue

Common Design Types

Engr.; Name Typo. on Nos. 58, 59

1949, Oct. 10 *Perf. 13½, 11x11½*

57	CD306	3p rose carmine	1.25	*2.00*
58	CD307	4p indigo	4.25	1.50
59	CD308	6p olive	1.60	3.50
60	CD309	1sh slate	4.00	2.00
		Nos. 57-60 (4)	11.10	9.00

Coronation Issue

Common Design Type

1953, June 2 Engr. *Perf. 13½x13*

61	CD312	3p gray & black	1.25	*2.75*

Reservoir — A16

Designs: 1p, Map of Ascension. 1½p, Georgetown. 2p, Map showing Ascension between South America and Africa and cable lines. 2½p, Mountain road. 3p, Yellow-billed tropic bird. 4p, Longfinned tuna. 6p, Waves. 7p, Young green turtles. 1sh, Land crab. 2sh6p, Sooty tern (wideawake). 5sh, Perfect Crater. 10sh, View from Northwest.

1956, Nov. 19 Wmk. 4 *Perf. 13*

Center in Black

62	A16	½p brown	.25	.50
63	A16	1p lilac rose	2.75	2.50
64	A16	1½p orange	.85	1.10
65	A16	2p carmine	3.00	*3.25*
66	A16	2½p org brown	1.50	*3.25*
67	A16	3p blue	3.75	1.10
68	A16	4p turq blue	1.25	*1.75*
69	A16	6p dark blue	1.25	*2.50*
70	A16	7p olive	2.50	1.75
71	A16	1sh scarlet	1.10	*1.60*
72	A16	2sh6p brown violet	30.00	9.00
73	A16	5sh bright green	40.00	19.00
74	A16	10sh purple	55.00	40.00
		Nos. 62-74 (13)	143.20	87.30

Brown Booby — A17

Birds: 1½p, Black tern. 2p, Fairy tern. 3p, Red-billed tropic bird in flight. 4½p, Brown noddy. 6p, Sooty tern. 7p, Frigate bird. 10p, Blue-faced booby. 1sh, Yellow-billed tropic bird. 1sh6p, Red-billed tropic bird. 2sh6p, Madeiran storm petrel. 5sh, Red-footed booby (brown phase). 10sh, Frigate birds. £1, Red-footed booby (white phase).

Perf. 14x14½

1963, May 23 Photo. Wmk. 314

75	A17	1p multicolored	1.15	.30
76	A17	1½p multicolored	1.75	1.00
b.		Blue omitted	130.00	
77	A17	2p multicolored	1.40	.30
78	A17	3p multicolored	1.50	.30
79	A17	4½p multicolored	1.50	.30
80	A17	6p multicolored	1.40	.30
81	A17	7p multicolored	1.40	.30
82	A17	10p multicolored	1.40	.30
83	A17	1sh multicolored	1.40	.30
84	A17	1sh6p multicolored	4.50	2.25
		Complete booklet, 4 each #75, 76, 77, 78, 80 and 84, in blocks of 4	90.00	
85	A17	2sh6p multicolored	8.00	*12.00*
86	A17	5sh multicolored	8.00	*12.00*
87	A17	10sh multicolored	14.50	*14.00*
88	A17	£1 multicolored	22.00	*16.00*
		Nos. 75-88 (14)	69.90	*59.65*

Freedom from Hunger Issue

Common Design Type

1963, June 4 Wmk. 314

89	CD314	1sh6p car rose	1.00	.50

Red Cross Centenary Issue

Common Design Type

1963, Sept. 2 Litho. *Perf. 13*

90	CD315	3p black & red	2.50	1.10
91	CD315	1sh6p ultra & red	4.25	2.25

ITU Issue

Common Design Type

Perf. 11x11½

1965, May 17 Litho. Wmk. 314

92	CD317	3p mag & violet	.50	.40
93	CD317	6p grnsh bl & brn org	1.40	.90

Intl. Cooperation Year Issue

Common Design Type

1965, Oct. 25 Wmk. 314 *Perf. 14½*

94	CD318	1p bl grn & claret	.40	.50
95	CD318	6p lt vio & green	.90	.90

Churchill Memorial Issue

Common Design Type

1966, Jan. 24 Photo. *Perf. 14*

Design in Black, Gold and Carmine Rose

96	CD319	1p bright blue	.50	.50
97	CD319	3p green	1.75	.90
98	CD319	6p brown	2.25	1.50
99	CD319	1sh6p violet	5.50	3.50
		Nos. 96-99 (4)	10.00	6.40

World Cup Soccer Issue

Common Design Type

1966, July 1 Litho. *Perf. 14*

100	CD321	3p multicolored	1.00	.75
101	CD321	6p multicolored	1.50	1.25

WHO Headquarters Issue

Common Design Type

1966, Sept. 20 Litho. *Perf. 14*

102	CD322	3p multicolored	2.10	1.10
103	CD322	1sh6p multicolored	4.50	2.25

Apollo Satellite Station, Ascension — A18

Wmk. 314

1966, Nov. 7 Photo. *Perf. 14*

104 A18 4p purple & black .25 .25
105 A18 8p blue grn & blk .25 .25
106 A18 1sh3p brn ol & blk .25 .25
107 A18 2sh6p brt grnsh blue & black .25 .25
Nos. 104-107 (4) 1.00 1.00

Opening of the Apollo communications satellite-earth station, part of the US Apollo program.

UNESCO Anniversary Issue
Common Design Type

1967, Jan. 3 Litho. *Perf. 14*

108 CD323 3p "Education" 2.50 1.40
109 CD323 6p "Science" 3.50 1.90
110 CD323 1sh6p "Culture" 5.00 2.50
Nos. 108-110 (3) 11.00 5.80

BBC Emblem — A19

Photo.; Gold Impressed

1967, Dec. 1 Wmk. 314 *Perf. 14½*

111 A19 1p ultra & gold .25 .25
112 A19 3p dk green & gold .25 .25
113 A19 6p brt purple & gold .25 .25
114 A19 1sh6p brt red & gold .25 .25
Nos. 111-114 (4) 1.00 1.00

Opening of the British Broadcasting Company's South Atlantic Relay Station on Ascension Island.

Human Rights Flame and Chain — A20

Perf. 14½x14

1968, July 8 Litho. Wmk. 314

115 A20 6p org, car & blk .25 .25
116 A20 1sh6p gray, mag & blk .30 .30
117 A20 2sh6p brt grn, plum & blk .30 .30
Nos. 115-117 (3) .85 .85

International Human Rights Year.

Blackfish — A21

Fish: No. 119, Sailfish. 6p, Oldwife. 8p, Leather jackets. 1sh6p, Yellowtails. 1sh9p, Tuna. 2sh3p, Mako sharks. 2sh11p, Rock hind (jack).

Perf. 13x12½

1968-69 Wmk. 314 Litho.

118 A21 4p brt grnsh bl & blk .30 .25
119 A21 4p red & multi .35 .35
120 A21 6p yel olive & multi .40 .40
121 A21 8p brt rose lil & multi .60 .45
122 A21 1sh6p brown & multi 1.50 *2.00*
123 A21 1sh9p emer & multi 1.00 .95
124 A21 2sh3p ocher & multi 1.50 1.25
125 A21 2sh11p dp org & multi 3.00 2.75
Nos. 118-125 (8) 8.65 8.40

Issue dates: No. 119, 6p, 1sh6p, 2sh11p, Mar. 3, 1969; others, Oct. 23, 1968.
See Nos. 130-133.

Arms of R.N.S. Rattlesnake — A22

Coats of Arms of Royal Naval Ships: 9p, Weston. 1sh9p, Undaunted. 2sh3p, Eagle.

Perf. 14x14½

1969, Oct. 1 Photo. Wmk. 314

126 A22 4p multicolored .65 .50
127 A22 9p multicolored .75 .60
128 A22 1sh9p multicolored 1.25 .75
129 A22 2sh3p multicolored 1.40 .85
a. Min. sheet of 4, #126-129 8.50 8.50
Nos. 126-129 (4) 4.05 2.70

See Nos. 134-137, 152-159, 166-169.

Fish Type of 1968

Deep-sea fish: 4p, Wahoo. 9p, Coalfish. 1sh9p, Dolphinfishes. 2sh3p, Soldierfish.

1970, Apr. 6 Litho. *Perf. 14*

130 A21 4p bluish grn & multi 4.00 2.75
131 A21 9p org & multi 3.00 2.75
132 A21 1sh9p ultra & multi 5.00 3.50
133 A21 2sh3p gray & multi 5.00 3.50
Nos. 130-133 (4) 17.00 12.50

Naval Arms Type of 1969

4p, Penelope. 9p, Carlisle. 1sh6p, Amphion. 2sh6p, Magpie.

Perf. 12½x12

1970, Sept. 7 Photo. Wmk. 314

134 A22 4p ultra, gold & blk 1.25 .30
135 A22 9p lt bl, blk, gold & red 1.50 .55
136 A22 1sh6p grnsh bl, gold & blk 1.60 1.50
137 A22 2sh6p lt grnsh bl, gold & blk 2.25 2.10
a. Miniature sheet of 4, #134-137 12.00 *14.00*
Nos. 134-137 (4) 6.60 4.45

Decimal Currency Issue

Tycho Brahe's Observatory, Quadrant and Supernova, 1572 — A23

Man into Space: ½p, Chinese rocket, 1232, vert. 1p, Medieval Arab astronomers, vert. 2p, Galileo, his telescope and drawing of moon, 1609. 2½p, Isaac Newton, telescope and apple. 3½p, Harrison's chronometer and ship, 1735. 4½p, First American manned orbital flight (Project Mercury, 1962, vert.). 5p, Reflector of Palomar telescope and ring nebula in Lyra, Messier 57. 7½p, Jodrell Bank telescope. 10p, Mariner 7, 1969, and telescopic view of Mars. 12½p, Sputnik 2 and dog Laika, 1957. 25p, Astronaut walking in space, 1965 (Gemini 4; vert.). 50p, US astronauts and moon landing module, 1969. £1, Future space research station.

1971, Feb. 15 Litho. *Perf. 14½*

138 A23 ½p multicolored .25 .25
139 A23 1p multicolored .25 .25
140 A23 1½p multicolored .30 .30
141 A23 2p multicolored .35 .35
142 A23 2½p multicolored 1.10 .90
143 A23 3½p multicolored 2.25 .90
Complete booklet, 4 each #138-143 30.00
144 A23 4½p multicolored 1.50 .95
145 A23 5p multicolored 1.25 .90
146 A23 7½p multicolored 3.50 2.00
147 A23 10p multicolored 3.50 3.25
148 A23 12½p multicolored 4.50 3.50
149 A23 25p multicolored 5.50 3.25
150 A23 50p multicolored 4.50 3.75
151 A23 £1 multicolored 4.50 4.50
Nos. 138-151 (14) 33.25 25.05

For overprints see Nos. 189-191.
Booklet also exists with a date of 5/71 on the back cover. Value, $45.

Arms of H.M.S. Phoenix — A24

Coats of Arms of Royal Naval Ships: 4p, Milford. 9p, Pelican. 15p, Oberon.

1971, Nov. 15 Photo. *Perf. 13½x13*

152 A24 2p gold & multi 1.00 .25
153 A24 4p gold & multi 1.10 .45
154 A24 9p gold & multi 1.50 1.10
155 A24 15p gold & multi 1.60 *2.25*
a. Souvenir sheet of 4, #152-155 7.50 *10.00*
Nos. 152-155 (4) 5.20 *4.05*

Naval Arms Type of 1969

1½p, Lowestoft. 3p, Auckland. 6p, Nigeria. 17½p, Bermuda.

1972, May 22 Litho. *Perf. 14x14½*

156 A22 1½p bl, gold & blk .85 .65
157 A22 3p grnsh bl, gold & blk .95 .70
158 A22 6p grn, gold, blk & bl 1.00 1.00
159 A22 17½p lil, gold, blk & red 1.50 *2.25*
a. Miniature sheet of 4, #156-159 4.25 *6.50*
Nos. 156-159 (4) 4.30 *4.60*

Course of Quest — A25

Designs: 4p, Shackleton and "Quest", horiz. 7½p, Shackleton's cabin and Quest in pack ice, horiz. 11p, Shackleton statue, London, and memorial cairn, South Georgia.

1972, Aug. 2 *Perf. 14*

160 A25 2½p multicolored .55 .50
161 A25 4p multicolored .60 .65
162 A25 7½p multicolored .60 .70
163 A25 11p multicolored .75 .90
a. Souvenir sheet of 4, #160-163 3.00 *5.00*
Nos. 160-163 (4) 2.50 2.75

Sir Ernest Henry Shackleton (1874-1922), explorer of Antarctica.

Silver Wedding Issue, 1972
Common Design Type

Design: Queen Elizabeth II, Prince Philip, land crab and shark.

1972, Nov. 20 Photo. *Perf. 14x14½*

164 CD324 2p violet & multi .25 .25
165 CD324 16p car rose & multi .45 .45

Naval Arms Type of 1969

2p, Birmingham. 4p, Cardiff. 9p, Penzance. 13p, Rochester.

1973, May 28 Litho. Wmk. 314

166 A22 2p blue & multi 2.25 1.40
167 A22 4p yel grn & multi 2.75 1.40
168 A22 9p lt blue & multi 3.25 1.60
169 A22 13p violet & multi 3.75 1.60
a. Min. sheet of 4, #166-169 24.00 15.00
Nos. 166-169 (4) 12.00 6.00

Turtles A26

1973, Aug. 28 *Perf. 13½*

170 A26 4p Green 2.50 1.10
171 A26 9p Loggerhead 3.25 2.25
172 A26 12p Hawksbill 4.50 3.50
Nos. 170-172 (3) 10.25 6.85

Light Infanty Marine Sergeant, 1900 — A27

Uniforms (Royal Marines): 6p, Private, 1816. 12p, Officer, Light Infantry, 1880. 20p, Color Sergeant, Artillery, 1910.

1973, Oct. 31 *Perf. 14½*

173 A27 2p multicolored 1.75 1.50
174 A27 6p lt green & multi 2.75 1.90
175 A27 12p lt blue & multi 3.00 2.75
176 A27 20p lt lilac & multi 3.50 3.00
Nos. 173-176 (4) 11.00 9.15

Departure of the Royal Marines from Ascension, 50th anniv.

Princess Anne's Wedding Issue
Common Design Type

1973, Nov. 14 *Perf. 14*

177 CD325 2p ocher & multi .25 .25
178 CD325 18p multicolored .35 .35

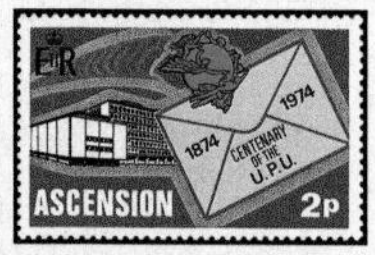

Letter and UPU Emblem — A29

UPU Cent.: 9p, Emblem and Mercury.

Wmk. 314

1974, Mar. 27 Litho. *Perf. 14½*

179 A29 2p multicolored .25 .25
180 A29 9p vio blue & multi .40 .40

Young Churchill and Blenheim Palace — A30

25p, Churchill and UN Headquarters, NYC.

1974, Nov. 30 Litho. Unwmk.

181 A30 5p slate grn & multi .25 .25
182 A30 25p purple & multi .70 .70
a. Souvenir sheet of 2, #181-182 1.75 *2.50*

Sir Winston Churchill (1874-1965).

Skylab over Photograph of Ascension Taken by Skylab 3 — A31

Skylab Space Station: 18p, Command module and photo of Ascension from Skylab 4.

1975, Mar. 20 Wmk. 314 *Perf. 14½*

183 A31 2p multicolored .25 .25
184 A31 18p multicolored .70 .70

US Air Force C-141A Starlifter A32

Aircraft: 5p, Royal Air Force C-130 Hercules. 9p, Vickers VC-10. 24p, U.S. Air Force C-5A Galaxy.

Perf. 13½x14

1975, June 19 Litho. Wmk. 314

185 A32 2p multicolored 1.00 .60
186 A32 5p multicolored 1.50 .75
187 A32 9p multicolored 1.50 1.50
188 A32 24p multicolored 2.50 2.50
a. Souvenir sheet of 4, #185-188 17.00 17.50
Nos. 185-188 (4) 6.50 5.35

Wideawake Airfield, Ascension Island.

Nos. 144, 148-149 Overprinted

1975, Aug. 18 Litho. *Perf. 14½*

189 A23 4½p multicolored .25 .25
190 A23 12½p multicolored .35 .35
191 A23 25p multicolored .50 .50
Nos. 189-191 (3) 1.10 1.10

Apollo Soyuz space test project (Russo-American cooperation), launching July 15; link-up, July 17.

HMS Peruvian and Zenobia Arriving Oct. 22, 1815 — A33

Designs: 5p, Water Supply, Dampiers Drip. 9p, First Landing, Oct. 1815. 15p, The Garden on Green Mountain. All designs after paintings by Isobel McManus.

1975, Oct. 22 Wmk. 373 *Perf. 14½*

192 A33 2p lt blue & multi .25 .25
193 A33 5p lt blue & multi .25 .25
194 A33 9p red & multi .35 .35
195 A33 15p red & multi .65 .65
Nos. 192-195 (4) 1.50 1.50

British occupation, 160th anniv.

Canaries — A34

2p, Fairy tern, vert. 3p, Waxbills. 4p, Black noddy. 5p, Brown noddy. 6p, Common mynah. 7p, Madeira storm petrels. 8p, Sooty terns. 9p, White booby. 10p, Red-footed booby. 15p, Red-throated francolin. 18p, Brown booby. 25p, Red-billed bo'sun bird. 50p, Yellow-billed bo'sun bird. £1, Ascension frigatebird. £2, Boatswain Island Bird Sanctuary and birds.

Perf. 14x14½, 14½x14

1976, Apr. 26 Litho. Wmk. 373

Size: 35x27mm, 27x35mm

196 A34 1p multi .50 *1.75*
197 A34 2p multi .55 *1.75*
198 A34 3p multi .55 *1.75*
199 A34 4p multi, vert. .60 *1.75*
200 A34 5p multi .75 *1.75*
201 A34 6p multi .75 *1.75*
202 A34 7p multi, vert. .75 *1.75*
203 A34 8p multi .75 *1.75*
204 A34 9p multi, vert. .75 *1.75*
205 A34 10p multi .75 *1.75*
206 A34 15p multi, vert. 1.50 *1.75*
207 A34 18p multi, vert. 1.50 *1.75*
208 A34 25p multi 1.60 *1.75*
209 A34 50p multi 2.25 *2.75*
210 A34 £1 multi, vert. 2.75 *3.25*

Perf. 13½

Size: 46x33mm

211 A34 £2 multicolored 5.50 5.00
Nos. 196-211 (16) 21.80 33.75

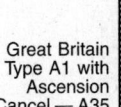

Great Britain Type A1 with Ascension Cancel — A35

9p, Ascension No. 1, vert. 25p, Freighter Southampton Castle.

1976, May 4 *Perf. 13½x14, 14x13½*

212 A35 5p lt brn, car & blk .25 .25
213 A35 9p gray grn, grn & blk .25 .25
214 A35 25p blue & multi .50 .50
Nos. 212-214 (3) 1.00 1.00

Festival of Stamps 1976. See Tristan da Cunha No. 208a for souvenir sheet that contains one each of Ascension No. 214, St. Helena No. 297, and Tristan da Cunha No. 208.

US Base — A36

Designs: 9p, NASA Station, Devil's Ashpit. 25p, Viking satellite landing on Mars.

Wmk. 373

1976, July 4 Litho. *Perf. 13½*

215 A36 8p black & multi .30 .30
216 A36 9p black & multi .40 .40
217 A36 25p black & multi .80 *1.00*
Nos. 215-217 (3) 1.50 1.70

American Bicentennial. No. 215 also for the 20th anniv. of Bahamas Long Range Proving Ground (extension) Agreement.

Queen in Coronation Coach — A37

Designs: 8p, Prince Philip on Ascension Island, 1957, vert. 12p, Queen leaving Buckingham Palace in coronation coach.

Perf. 14x13½, 13½x14

1977, Feb. 7 Litho. Wmk. 373

218 A37 8p multicolored .25 .25
219 A37 12p multicolored .25 .25
220 A37 25p multicolored .30 *.40*
Nos. 218-220 (3) .80 .90

Reign of Queen Elizabeth II, 25th anniv.

Water Pipe in Tunnel — A38

5p, Breakneck Valley wells. 12p, Break tank in pipe line, horiz. 25p, Dam & reservoir, horiz.

1977, June 27 Litho. *Perf. 14½*

221 A38 3p multicolored .25 .25
222 A38 5p multicolored .25 .25
223 A38 12p multicolored .30 .30
224 A38 25p multicolored .50 *.60*
Nos. 221-224 (4) 1.30 1.40

Water supplies constructed by Royal Marines, 1832 and 1881.

Mars Bay Site, 1877 — A39

Designs: 8p, Mars Bay and instrument sites. 12p, Prof. and Mrs. Gill before their tent. 25p, Map of Ascension.

Perf. 13½x14

1977, Oct. 3 Litho. Wmk. 373

225 A39 3p multicolored .25 .25
226 A39 8p multicolored .25 .25
227 A39 12p multicolored .30 *.40*
228 A39 25p multicolored .60 *.70*
Nos. 225-228 (4) 1.40 1.60

Centenary of visit of Prof. David Gill (1843-1914), astronomer, to Ascension.

Elizabeth II Coronation Anniversary Issue

Souvenir Sheet

Common Design Types

Unwmk.

1978, May 21 Litho. *Perf. 15*

229 Sheet of 6 2.00 2.00
a. CD326 25p Lion of England .30 .30
b. CD327 25p Elizabeth II .30 .30
c. CD328 25p Green turtle .30 .30

No. 229 contains 2 se-tenant strips of Nos. 229a-229c, separated by horizontal gutter with commemorative and descriptive inscriptions and showing central part of coronation procession with coach.

East Crater (Broken Tooth) — A40

Volcanoes: 5p, Hollands Crater (Hollow Tooth). 12p, Bears Back. 15p, Green Mountain. 25p, Two Boats village.

1978, Sept. 4 Litho. *Perf. 14½*

230 A40 3p multicolored .25 .25
231 A40 5p multicolored .25 .25
232 A40 12p multicolored .30 .30
233 A40 15p multicolored .40 .40
234 A40 25p multicolored .65 .65
a. Souvenir sheet, 2 each #230-234 3.00 *4.75*
b. Strip of 5, #230-234 2.00 2.00

No. 234b shows panoramic view of volcanic terrain.

Resolution — A41

Capt. Cook's voyages: 8p, Cook's chronometer. 12p, Green turtle. 25p, Cook after Flaxman/Wedgwood medallion.

Litho.; Litho. & Embossed. (25p)

1979, Jan. 8 *Perf. 11*

235 A41 3p multicolored .25 .25
236 A41 8p multicolored .30 .30
237 A41 12p multicolored .55 .55
238 A41 25p multicolored .75 *.85*
Nos. 235-238 (4) 1.85 1.95

St. Mary's Church, Georgetown — A42

Designs: 12p, Old map of Ascension Island. 50p, Ascension, by Rembrandt.

Wmk. 373

1979, May 24 Litho. *Perf. 14½*

239 A42 8p multicolored .25 .25
240 A42 12p multicolored .25 .25
241 A42 50p multicolored .40 *.50*
Nos. 239-241 (3) .90 1.00

Ascension Day.

Landing Cable at Comfortless Cove — A43

Eastern Telegraph Co., 80th anniv.: 8p, Cable Ship Anglia. 12p, Map showing cables across the Atlantic, vert. 15p, Cable-laying ship. 25p, Cable and earth station.

1979, Sept. 15

242 A43 3p rose car & black .25 .25
243 A43 8p dk yel grn & black .25 .25
244 A43 12p yel bister & black .30 .30
245 A43 15p violet & black .40 .40
246 A43 25p deep org & black .50 .50
Nos. 242-246 (5) 1.70 1.70

Ascension No. 45 — A44

1979, Dec. 17 Wmk. 373 *Perf. 14*

247 A44 3p shown .25 .25
248 A44 8p No. 73 .25 .25
249 A44 12p No. 14, vert. .25 .25
250 A44 50p Hill portrait, vert. .45 *.65*
Nos. 247-250 (4) 1.20 1.40

Sir Rowland Hill (1795-1879), originator of penny postage.

Anogramma Ascensionis — A45

6p, Xiphopteris ascensionense. 8p, Sporobolus caespitosus. 12p, Sporobolus durus, vert. 18p, Dryopteris ascensionis, vert. 24p, Marattia purpurascens, vert.

1980, Feb. 18 Litho. *Perf. 14½*

251 A45 3p shown .25 .25
252 A45 6p multicolored .25 .25
253 A45 8p multicolored .25 .25
254 A45 12p multicolored .25 .25
255 A45 18p multicolored .25 .40
256 A45 24p multicolored .30 .55
Nos. 251-256 (6) 1.55 1.95

17th Century Bottle Post, London 1980 Emblem — A46

12p, 36-gun frigate, 19th century. 15p, "Garth Castle," 1863. 50p, "St. Helena," Lockheed C141.

1980, May 1 Wmk. 373 *Perf. 14*

257 A46 8p shown .25 .25
258 A46 12p multicolored .30 .30
259 A46 15p multicolored .35 .35
260 A46 50p multicolored .75 .75
a. Souvenir sheet of 4, #257-260 1.75 *2.25*
Nos. 257-260 (4) 1.65 1.65

London 1980 Intl. Stamp Exhib., May 6-14.

Queen Mother Elizabeth Birthday

Common Design Type

1980, Aug. 11 Litho. *Perf. 14*

261 CD330 15p multicolored .40 .40

Lubbock's Yellowtail — A47

10p, Resplendent angelfish. 25p, Hedgehog butterflyfish. 40p, Marmalade razorfish.

1980, Sept. 15 Litho. *Perf. 13½x14*

262 A47 3p shown .40 .40
263 A47 10p multicolored .50 .50
264 A47 25p multicolored 1.00 .90
265 A47 40p multicolored 1.25 *1.50*
Nos. 262-265 (4) 3.15 *3.30*

Tortoisen, by Thomas Maxon — A48

Map of South Atlantic Ridge and Continental Drift — A49

15p, Wideawake Fair, by Linton Palmer, 1866.

1980, Nov. 17 *Perf. 13½, 14 (60p)*

266 A48 10p multicolored .25 *.40*
267 A48 15p multicolored .30 *.45*
268 A49 60p multicolored .90 *1.25*
Nos. 266-268 (3) 1.45 *2.10*

Royal Geographical Soc., 50th anniv.

Green Mountain Farm, 1881 — A50

Designs: 15p, Two Boats, 1881. 20p, Green Mountain and Two Boats farms, 1981. 30p, Green Mountain Farm, 1981.

1981, Feb. 15 Litho. *Perf. 14*

269 A50 12p multicolored .25 .25
270 A50 15p multicolored .30 .30
271 A50 20p multicolored .30 *.35*
272 A50 30p multicolored .40 *.50*
Nos. 269-272 (4) 1.25 1.40

Cable and Wireless Earth Station — A51

1981, Apr. 27 Litho. *Perf. 14*

273	Sheet of 10	4.00	4.00
a.	A51 15p multicolored	.40	.40

Flight of Columbia space shuttle. Gutter contains story of Ascension and space shuttle; margin shows craft and dish antenna.

Poinsettia A52

2p, Clustererd wax flower. 3p, Kolanchoe, vert. 4p, Yellow pops. 5p, Camel's foot creeper. 8p, White oleander. 10p, Ascension lily, vert. 12p, Coral plant, vert. 15p, Yellow allamanda. 20p, Ascention euphorbia. 30p, Flame of the forest, vert. 40p, Bougainvillea. 50p, Solanum. £1, Ladies petticoat. £2, Red hibiscus.

1981, May 11 Wmk. 373 *Perf. 13½*

274	A52	1p shown	.90	1.10
275	A52	2p multicolored	.70	1.10
276	A52	3p multicolored	.70	1.10
277	A52	4p multicolored	.90	1.10
278	A52	5p multicolored	.90	1.10
279	A52	8p multicolored	.90	1.10
280	A52	10p multicolored	.65	.95
281	A52	12p multicolored	1.75	1.10
282	A52	15p multicolored	.75	.95
		Complete booklet, 4 ea. #275, 276, 280 and 282, in blocks of 4	15.00	
283	A52	20p multicolored	1.10	.95
284	A52	30p multicolored	1.35	1.60
285	A52	40p multicolored	1.35	*3.00*

Size: 42x53mm

286	A52	50p multicolored	1.40	*3.25*
287	A52	£1 multicolored	2.10	*4.00*
288	A52	£2 multicolored	3.25	*6.00*
		Nos. 274-288 (15)	18.70	28.40

1982, Aug. 27 Inscribed "1982"

275a	A52	2p Clustererd wax flower	.60	1.25
276a	A52	3p Kolanchoe, vert.	.60	1.25
280a	A52	10p Ascension lily, vert.	.55	.75
282a	A52	15p Yellow allamanda	.60	.75
283a	A52	20p Ascention euphorbia	1.10	.75
287a	A52	£1 Ladies petticoat	1.75	*2.75*
		Nos. 275a-287a (6)	5.20	7.50

For overprints see Nos. 321-322.

Linschoten's Map of Ascension, 1599. — A53

Maxwell's Map of Ascension, 1793 — A54

Old maps of Ascension: 12p, Maxwell, 1793, diff. 15p, Eckberg & Chapman, 1811. 40p, Campbell, 1819.

1981, May 22 *Perf. 14½*

289	A53	Sheet of 4	.60	.60
a.-d.		5p any single	.25	.25
290	A54	10p shown	.25	.25
291	A54	12p multicolored	.30	.30
292	A54	15p multicolored	.35	.35
293	A54	40p multicolored	.65	.65
		Nos. 289-293 (5)	2.15	2.15

Royal Wedding Issue

Common Design Type

1981, July 22 Wmk. 373 *Perf. 14*

294	CD331	10p Bouquet	.25	.25
295	CD331	15p Charles	.25	.25
296	CD331	50p Couple	.50	.50
		Nos. 294-296 (3)	1.00	1.00

Nos. 294-296 each se-tenant with label.

Man Shining Cannon — A55

1981, Sept. 14 Litho. *Perf. 14*

297	A55	5p shown	.25	.25
298	A55	10p Mountain climbing	.25	.25
299	A55	15p First aid treatment	.25	.25
300	A55	40p Duke of Edinburgh	.35	.35
		Nos. 297-300 (4)	1.10	1.10

Duke of Edinburgh's Awards, 25th anniv.

Scouting Year — A56

10p, Parallel rope walking. 15p, 1st Ascension scout flag. 25p, Radio operators. 40p, Baden-Powell.

1982, Feb. 22 Litho. *Perf. 14*

301	A56	10p multicolored	.25	*.35*
302	A56	15p multicolored	.35	*.50*
303	A56	25p multicolored	.50	*.65*
304	A56	40p multicolored	.65	*.95*
a.		Souvenir sheet of 4	1.60	*2.25*
		Nos. 301-304 (4)	1.75	*2.45*

No. 304a contains stamps in designs of Nos. 301-304 (30x30mm, perf. 14½, diamond-shape).

Sesquicentennial of Charles Darwin's Visit — A57

1982, Apr. 19

305	A57	10p Portrait	.30	*.40*
306	A57	12p Pistols	.35	*.50*
307	A57	15p Rock crab	.45	*.55*
308	A57	40p Beagle	.85	*.95*
		Nos. 305-308 (4)	1.95	*2.40*

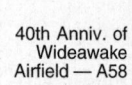

40th Anniv. of Wideawake Airfield — A58

5p, Fairey Swordfish. 10p, North American B25C Mitchell. 15p, Boeing EC-135N Aria. 50p, Lockheed Hercules.

1982, June 15 Litho. *Perf. 14*

309	A58	5p multicolored	.85	.85
310	A58	10p multicolored	1.00	1.00
		Complete booklet, 4 ea. #309 and 310, in blocks of 4	7.75	
311	A58	15p multicolored	1.25	1.25
312	A58	50p multicolored	2.00	2.00
		Nos. 309-312 (4)	5.10	5.10

The cover of the booklet containing Nos. 309 and 310 exists with both brown and blue inscriptions. Same value.

Princess Diana Issue

Common Design Type

Perf. 14½x14

1982, July 1 Wmk. 373

313	CD333	12p Arms	.55	.55
314	CD333	15p Diana	.55	.55
315	CD333	25p Wedding	.90	.90
316	CD333	50p Portrait	1.50	1.50
		Nos. 313-316 (4)	3.50	3.50

Christmas and 50th Anniv. of BBC Overseas Broadcasting A59

Anniv. Emblem and: 5p, Bush House (London headquarters). 10p, Atlantic relay station. 25p, Lord Reith, first director general. 40p, King George V delivering Christmas address, 1932.

1982, Dec. 20 Litho. *Perf. 14*

317	A59	5p multicolored	.25	.25
318	A59	10p multicolored	.25	.25
319	A59	25p multicolored	.60	.60
320	A59	40p multicolored	.90	.90
		Nos. 317-320 (4)	2.00	2.00

Nos. 282a-283a Overprinted

1982 Litho. *Perf. 13½*

321	A52	15p multicolored	.30	.30
322	A52	20p multicolored	.40	.40

12th Commonwealth Games, Brisbane, Australia, Sept. 30-Oct. 9.

A60

7p, Marasmius echinosphaerus. 12p, Chlorophyllum molybdites. 15p, Leucocoprinus cepaestipes. 20p, Lycoperdon marginatum. 50p, Marasmiellus distantifolius.

1983, Mar. 1 *Perf. 14*

323	A60	7p multicolored	.60	.30
324	A60	12p multicolored	.90	.50
325	A60	15p multicolored	1.00	.60
326	A60	20p multicolored	1.25	.70
327	A60	50p multicolored	1.60	*1.75*
		Nos. 323-327 (5)	5.35	*3.85*

View of Georgetown — A61

15p, Farm, Green Mountain. 20p, Boatswain Bird Island. 60p, Telemetry Hill.

1983, May 12 Litho. *Perf. 14*

328	A61	12p shown	.25	.25
329	A61	15p multicolored	.25	.25
330	A61	20p multicolored	.35	.35
331	A61	60p multicolored	.80	.80
		Nos. 328-331 (4)	1.65	1.65

See Nos. 359-362.

Manned Flight Bicentenary A62

Military Aircraft: 12p, Wessex Five helicopter. 15p, Vulcan B2. 20p, Nimrod MR2P. 60p, Victor K2.

1983, Aug. 1 Wmk. 373 *Perf. 14*

332	A62	12p multicolored	.75	.75
333	A62	15p multicolored	.85	.85
334	A62	20p multicolored	.80	.80
335	A62	60p multicolored	1.40	1.40
		Nos. 332-335 (4)	3.80	3.80

Introduced Species — A63

1983, Sept. Litho. Wmk. 373

336	A63	12p Iguanid	.40	.40
337	A63	15p Rabbit	.50	.50
338	A63	20p Cat	.60	.60
339	A63	60p Donkey	1.25	1.25
		Nos. 336-339 (4)	2.75	2.75

Tellina Antonii Philippi — A64

12p, Nodipecten nodosus. 15p, Cypraea lurida oceanica. 20p, Nerita ascensionis gmelin. 50p, Micromelo undatus.

1983, Nov. 28 Litho. *Perf. 14½*

340	A64	7p shown	.25	.25
341	A64	12p multicolored	.30	.30
342	A64	15p multicolored	.40	.40
343	A64	20p multicolored	.50	.50
344	A64	50p multicolored	1.10	1.10
		Nos. 340-344 (5)	2.55	2.55

St. Helena Colony, 150th Anniv. — A65

Designs: First issue inscribed Ascension instead of overprinted.

1984, Jan. 10 Litho. *Perf. 14*

345	A65	12p No. 3	.25	*.40*
346	A65	15p No. 4	.35	*.45*
347	A65	20p No. 6	.45	*.55*
348	A65	60p No. 9	1.00	*1.25*
		Nos. 345-348 (4)	2.05	*2.65*

Souvenir Sheet

Visit of Prince Andrew A66

1984, Apr. 10 *Perf. 14½x14*

349	A66	Sheet of 2	1.50	1.50
a.		12p Andrew	.25	.25
b.		70p In naval uniform	1.10	1.10

Lloyd's List Issue

Common Design Type

12p, Naval semaphore. 15p, "Southampton Castle". 20p, Pier Head. 70p, Dane.

1984, May 28

351	CD335	12p multicolored	.45	.25
352	CD335	15p multicolored	.55	.35
353	CD335	20p multicolored	.65	.45
354	CD335	70p multicolored	1.25	*1.50*
		Nos. 351-354 (4)	2.90	2.55

1984 Coins and Wildlife — A67

12p, One penny, yellowfin tuna. 15p, Two pence, donkeys. 20p, Fifty pence, green turtle. 70p, One pound, sooty terns.

1984, June *Perf. 14*

355	A67	12p multicolored	.70	.70
356	A67	15p multicolored	.90	.90
357	A67	20p multicolored	.90	.90
358	A67	70p multicolored	1.50	*2.00*
		Nos. 355-358 (4)	4.00	4.50

View Type of 1983

12p, Devil's Riding School. 15p, St. Mary's Church. 20p, Two Boats Village. 70p, Ascension Island.

1984, Oct. Litho. Wmk. 373

359	A61	12p multicolored	.25	.25
360	A61	15p multicolored	.30	.30
361	A61	20p multicolored	.45	.45
362	A61	70p multicolored	1.25	1.25
		Nos. 359-362 (4)	2.25	2.25

Trees — A68

7p, Bermuda cypress. 12p, Norfolk Island pine. 15p, Screwpine. 20p, Eucalyptus. 65p, Spore tree.

1985, Mar. 8 Litho. *Perf. 14½x14*

363	A68	7p multicolored	.55	.45
364	A68	12p multicolored	.60	.50
365	A68	15p multicolored	.70	.65
366	A68	20p multicolored	.75	.75
367	A68	65p multicolored	1.90	1.90
		Nos. 363-367 (5)	4.50	4.25

Military Firearms — A69

Large guns and insignia: 12p, Thirty-two pounder small bore muzzle loader, c. 1820; Royal Marines hat plate, c. 1816. 15p, Seven-inch rifled muzzle loader, c. 1866; royal cipher. 20p, Seven-pounder rifled muzzle loader, c. 1877; Royal Artillery badge. 70p, HMS Hood 5.5-inch gun; ship crest.

1985, July 21 Wmk. 373 *Perf. 14½*

368	A69	12p multicolored	.55	.55
369	A69	15p multicolored	.80	.80
370	A69	20p multicolored	.80	.80
371	A69	70p multicolored	2.00	*2.50*
		Nos. 368-371 (4)	4.15	4.65

Queen Mother 85th Birthday
Common Design Type

12p, With Duke of York, Balmoral, 1924. 15p, With Princes Andrew and Edward. 20p, At Ascot. 70p, Christening of Prince Henry, Windsor Castle. 75p, Leaving the QEII, 1968.

Perf. 14½x14

1985, June 7 Wmk. 384

372	CD336	12p multicolored	.50	.50
373	CD336	15p multicolored	.50	.50
374	CD336	20p multicolored	.65	.65
375	CD336	70p multicolored	1.50	1.50
		Nos. 372-375 (4)	3.15	3.15

Souvenir Sheet

376	CD336	75p multicolored	1.50	1.50

Intl. Youth Year, Girl Guides 75th Anniv. — A70

12p, Guides' banner. 15p, First aid. 20p, Camping. 70p, Lady Baden-Powell.

1985, Oct. 4 Wmk. 373

377	A70	12p multicolored	.60	.60
378	A70	15p multicolored	.65	.55
379	A70	20p multicolored	.75	.65
380	A70	70p multicolored	2.00	*2.50*
		Nos. 377-380 (4)	4.00	4.30

Wildflowers — A71

12p, Clerodendrum fragrans. 15p, Shell ginger. 20p, Cape daisy. 70p, Ginger lily.

Wmk. 384

1985, Dec. 6 Litho. *Perf. 14*

381	A71	12p multicolored	.60	.60
382	A71	15p multicolored	.70	.70
383	A71	20p multicolored	.80	.80
384	A71	70p multicolored	1.60	*2.25*
		Nos. 381-384 (4)	3.70	4.35

Halley's Comet — A72

Designs: 12p, Newton's reflector telescope. 15p, Edmond Halley, Old Greenwich Observatory. 20p, Short's Gregorian telescope, comet, 1759. 70p, ICE space probe, Ascension satellite tracking station.

1986, Mar. 7

385	A72	12p multicolored	.60	*.75*
386	A72	15p multicolored	.70	*.85*
387	A72	20p multicolored	.75	*.85*
388	A72	70p multicolored	2.00	*2.75*
		Nos. 385-388 (4)	4.05	*5.20*

Queen Elizabeth II 60th Birthday
Common Design Type

Designs: 7p, Infant photograph, 1926. 15p, 1st worldwide Christmas broadcast, 1952. 20p, Garter Ceremony, Windsor Castle, 1983. 35p, Royal Tour, New Zealand, 1981. £1, Visiting Crown Agents' offices, 1983.

1986, Apr. 21 *Perf. 14x14½*

389	CD337	7p scarlet, blk & sil	.25	.25
390	CD337	15p ultra, blk & sil	.35	.35
391	CD337	20p green & multi	.45	.45
392	CD337	35p violet & multi	.50	.50
393	CD337	£1 rose vio & multi	1.25	*1.75*
		Nos. 389-393 (5)	2.80	3.30

For overprints see Nos. 431-435.

AMERIPEX '86 — A73

1986, May 22 *Perf. 14½*

394	A73	12p No. 183	.35	*.50*
395	A73	15p No. 260	.50	*.60*
396	A73	20p No. 215	.65	*.75*
397	A73	70p No. 310	1.35	*2.00*
		Nos. 394-397 (4)	2.85	*3.85*

Souvenir Sheet

398	A73	75p Statue of Liberty, New York Harbor	3.50	3.50

Statue of Liberty, cent.

Royal Wedding Issue, 1986
Common Design Type

Designs: 15p, Couple kissing. 35p, Andrew in navy uniform, helicopter.

Wmk. 384

1986, July 23 Litho. *Perf. 14*

399	CD338	15p multicolored	.50	.50
400	CD338	35p multicolored	1.10	1.10

Ships — A74

1p, Ganymede, c. 1811. 2p, Kangaroo, c. 1811. 4p, Trinculo, c. 1811. 5p, Daring, c. 1811. 9p, Thais, c. 1811. 10p, Pheasant, 1819. 15p, Myrmidon, 1819. 18p, Atholl, 1825. 20p, Medina, 1830. 25p, Saracen, 1840. 30p, Hydra, c. 1845. 50p, Sealark, 1840. 70p, Rattlesnake, 1868. £1, Penelope, 1889. £2, Monarch, 1897.

1986, Oct. 14 Wmk. 384 *Perf. 14½*

401	A74	1p multicolored	.90	*1.25*
402	A74	2p multicolored	1.00	*1.25*
403	A74	4p multicolored	1.00	*1.25*
404	A74	5p multicolored	1.00	*1.25*
405	A74	9p multicolored	1.10	*1.25*
406	A74	10p multicolored	1.10	*1.25*
407	A74	15p multicolored	1.25	*1.75*
408	A74	18p multicolored	1.25	*1.75*
409	A74	20p multicolored	1.25	*1.75*
410	A74	25p multicolored	1.25	*2.00*
411	A74	30p multicolored	1.25	*2.00*
412	A74	50p multicolored	1.75	*2.75*
413	A74	70p multicolored	2.50	*3.25*
414	A74	£1 multicolored	3.50	*4.25*
415	A74	£2 multicolored	6.50	*8.00*
		Nos. 401-415 (15)	26.60	*35.00*

For surcharges see Nos. 502-504.

Edible Bush Fruits — A75

1987, Jan. 29 *Perf. 14*

416	A75	12p Cape gooseberry	.90	.90
417	A75	15p Prickly pear	1.00	1.00
418	A75	20p Guava	1.10	1.10
419	A75	70p Loquat	2.00	*2.50*
		Nos. 416-419 (4)	5.00	5.50

1st American Manned Orbital Space Flight, 25th Anniv. — A76

15p, Ignition. 18p, Lift-off. 25p, Reentry. £1, Splashdown.
70p, Friendship 7 capsule.

1987, Mar. 30

420	A76	15p multicolored	.85	.85
421	A76	18p multicolored	.95	.95
422	A76	25p multicolored	1.25	1.25
423	A76	£1 multicolored	3.50	3.50
		Nos. 420-423 (4)	6.55	6.55

Souvenir Sheet

424	A76	70p multicolored	2.50	2.50

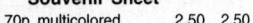

Military Uniforms, 1815-20 — A77

Designs: a, Captains in full dress, 1st landing on Ascenion. b, Surgeon and sailors at campsite. c, Seaman returning from Dampier's Drip with water supply. d, Midshipman at lookout post. e, Commander and surveyor.

1987, June 29

425		Strip of 5	4.00	4.00
a.-e.		A77 25p multicolored	.70	.70

See Nos. 458, 482, 507.

Butterflies — A78

1987, Aug. 10 *Perf. 14½*

426	A78	15p Painted lady	1.10	1.10
427	A78	18p Monarch	1.10	1.10
428	A78	25p Diadem	1.50	1.50
429	A78	£1 Long-tailed blue	4.00	4.00
		Nos. 426-429 (4)	7.70	7.70

See Nos. 436-439, 459-462.

Birds — A79

Designs: a, Ascension frigatebirds (males). b, Brown booby, frigatebird, white boobies. c, Frigatebird, white booby. d, Ascension frigatebirds (females). e, Adult frigatebird feeding young.

1987, Oct. 8 Wmk. 373 *Perf. 14*

430		Strip of 5	11.00	11.00
a.-e.		A79 25p any single	2.00	2.00

No. 430 has continuous design.
See No. 453.

Nos. 389-393 Ovptd. "40TH WEDDING ANNIVERSARY" in Silver

Perf. 14x14½

1987, Dec. 9 Litho. Wmk. 384

431	CD337	7p scar, blk & sil	.25	.25
432	CD337	15p ultra, blk & sil	.30	.30
433	CD337	20p green & multi	.50	.50
434	CD337	35p violet & multi	.75	.75
435	CD337	£1 rose vio & multi	1.50	1.50
		Nos. 431-435 (5)	3.30	3.30

40th wedding anniv. of Queen Elizabeth II and Prince Philip.

Insects Type of 1987

15p, Field cricket. 18p, Bush cricket. 25p, Ladybug. £1, Burnished brass moth.

1988, Jan. 18 *Perf. 14½*

436	A78	15p multicolored	.80	.80
437	A78	18p multicolored	.90	.90
438	A78	25p multicolored	1.25	1.25
439	A78	£1 multicolored	4.25	4.25
		Nos. 436-439 (4)	7.20	7.20

A80

Capt. William Bate (d. 1838), 1st Garrison Commander and Colonial Founder of Ascension: 9p, Bate's Memorial, St. Mary's Church. 15p, Commodore's Cottage, Cross Hill. 18p, North East or Bate's Cottage, 1833. 25p, Landmarks on map. 70p, Bate and 3 soldiers.

1988, Apr. 14 Litho. *Perf. 14*

440	A80	9p multicolored	.30	.30
441	A80	15p multicolored	.50	.50
442	A80	18p multicolored	.60	.60
443	A80	25p multicolored	.85	.85
444	A80	70p multicolored	2.00	2.00
		Nos. 440-444 (5)	4.25	4.25

Australia Bicentennial Emblem and Ships Named HMS Resolution A81

9p, 3-Masted squarerigger, 1667. 18p, 3-Masted squarerigger, 1772. 25p, Navy cruiser, 1892. 65p, Battleship, 1916.

1988, June 23 Litho. *Perf. 14*

445	A81	9p multicolored	1.25	.50
446	A81	18p multicolored	1.75	.80
447	A81	25p multicolored	2.00	1.00
448	A81	65p multicolored	3.00	2.00
		Nos. 445-448 (4)	8.00	4.30

Australia bicentennial.

Nos. 445-448 Overprinted

Wmk. 384

1988, July 30 Litho. *Perf. 14*

449	A81	9p multicolored	.75	.55
450	A81	18p multicolored	1.25	.90
451	A81	25p multicolored	1.25	.95
452	A81	65p multicolored	2.50	2.50
		Nos. 449-452 (4)	5.75	4.90

SYDPEX '88, July 30-Aug. 7.

Bird Type of 1987

Behaviors of the wideawake tern, Sterna fuscata: a, Two adults, flock overhead. b, Nesting (two birds). c, Nesting (three birds). d, Adult and young. e, Tern flapping its wings.

1988, Aug. 15 *Perf. 14*

453		Strip of 5	10.00	10.00
a.-e.		A79 25p any single	1.90	1.90

No. 453 has continuous design.

Lloyds of London, 300th Anniv.
Common Design Type

8p, Lloyd's Coffee House, Tower Street, 1688. 18p, Cable ship Alert, horiz. 25p, Satellite recovery in space, horiz. 65p, Ship Good Hope Castle on fire off Ascension, 1973.

Wmk. 373

1988, Oct. 17 Litho. *Perf. 14*

454 CD341 8p multicolored .40 .40
455 CD341 18p multicolored .85 .85
456 CD341 25p multicolored 1.25 1.25
457 CD341 65p multicolored 2.50 2.50
Nos. 454-457 (4) 5.00 5.00

Military Uniforms Type of 1987

Uniforms of the Royal Marines: a, Marines arrive in Ascension (marines), 1821. b, Semaphore station (officer, marine), 1829. c, Octagonal tank (sergeant), 1831. d, Water pipe tunnel (officers), 1833. e, Constructing barracks (officer), 1834.

1988, Nov. 21

458 Strip of 5 8.50 8.50
a.-e. A77 25p multicolored 1.50 1.50

Insect Type of 1987
Wmk. 384

1989, Jan. 16 Litho. *Perf. 14½*

459 A78 15p Plume moth 1.25 .80
460 A78 18p Green bottle 1.25 .90
461 A78 25p Weevil 1.00 .90
462 A78 £1 Paper wasp 5.00 3.25
Nos. 459-462 (4) 8.50 5.85

Land Crabs, Gecarcinus Lagostoma — A82

1989, Apr. 17

463 A82 15p multicolored .75 .75
464 A82 18p multi, diff. .80 .80
465 A82 25p multi, diff. 1.25 1.25
466 A82 £1 multi, diff. 4.00 4.00
Nos. 463-466 (4) 6.80 6.80

Background designs continuous

467 A82 15p multicolored .55 .55
467A A82 18p multi, diff. .75 .75
467B A82 25p multi, diff. .95 .95
467C A82 £1 multi, diff. 4.00 4.00
d. Souvenir sheet of 4, #467-467C 7.50 7.50

Moon Landing, 20th Anniv.
Common Design Type

Apollo 7: 15p, Tracking Station, Ascension Is. 18p, Launch, Cape Kennedy. 25p, Mission emblem. 70p, Expended Saturn IVB stage. £1, Lunar landing profile for the Apollo 11 mission.

1989, July 20 *Perf. 14x13½*
Size of Nos. 469-470: 29x29mm

468 CD342 15p multicolored .90 .65
469 CD342 18p multicolored 1.00 .75
470 CD342 25p multicolored 1.25 .95
471 CD342 70p multicolored 2.25 2.25
Nos. 468-471 (4) 5.40 4.60

Souvenir Sheet

472 CD342 £1 multicolored 4.00 4.00

Souvenir Sheet

A83

1989, July 7 *Perf. 14x13½*

473 A83 75p Emblems, No. 60 4.25 4.25

Miniature Sheet

World Stamp Expo '89, Washington, DC, and PHILEXFRANCE '89, Paris — A84

The Statue of Liberty and scenes from the centenary celebrations, 1986: a, Operation Sail. b, Face. c, Upper body. d, Three crown points. e, Ships in harbor, view of lower Manhattan. f, Ship in port, New York City.

1989, Aug. 21 Wmk. 373

474 A84 Sheet of 6 5.00 5.00
a.-f. 15p any single .70 .70

Devil's Ashpit Tracking Station — A85

1989, Sept. 30 Wmk. 384 *Perf. 14*

475 Sheet, 5 each #a.-b. 10.50 10.50
a. A85 18p shown .70 .70
b. A85 25p US space shuttle launch 1.10 1.10

Termination of NASA tracking operations, begun in 1965, at the station.

Shells and Mollusks — A86

Designs: 8p, Strombus latus. 18p, Tonna galea. 25p, Harpa doris. £1, Charonia variegata.

Wmk. 384

1989, Nov. 6 Litho. *Perf. 14*

476 A86 8p multicolored .70 .45
477 A86 18p multicolored 1.25 .65
478 A86 25p multicolored 1.75 .90
479 A86 £1 multicolored 4.25 3.50
Nos. 476-479 (4) 7.95 5.50

Donkeys — A87

Perf. 14 on 3 Sides

1989, Nov. 17 Litho. Wmk. 384

Booklet Stamps

480 A87 18p shown *1.50 1.60*
a. Booklet pane of 6 *9.50*
481 A87 25p Green turtle *2.00 1.60*
a. Booklet pane of 4 *8.00*

No. 480a sold for £1.

Military Type of 1987

Royal Navy equipment, c. 1815-1820: a, Seaman's pistol, hat, cutlass. b, Midshipman's belt buckle, button, sword, hat. c, Surgeon's hat, sword, instrument chest. d, Captain's hat, telescope, sword. e, Admiral's epaulet, megaphone, hat, pocket.

1990, Feb. 12 Litho. *Perf. 14*

482 Strip of 5 6.50 6.50
a.-e. A77 25p any single 1.10 1.10

World Wildlife Fund — A88

Frigate birds *(Fregata aquila)*: 9p, Family group. 10p, Chick. 11p, Male in flight. 15p, Female and immature in flight.

Perf. 14½x14

1990, Mar. 5 Litho. Wmk. 373

483 A88 9p multicolored *3.50 1.10*
484 A88 10p multicolored *3.50 1.25*
485 A88 11p multicolored *3.50 1.50*
486 A88 15p multicolored *3.50 2.00*
Nos. 483-486 (4) 14.00 5.85

Great Britain Nos. 1-2 — A89

Exhibition emblem and: 18p, Early Ascension cancellations. 25p, Unloading mail at Wideawake Airfield. £1, Main P.O., Royal Mail van.

1990, May 3 Litho. *Perf. 14*

487 A89 9p shown .50 .50
488 A89 18p multicolored .80 .80
489 A89 25p multicolored 1.10 1.10
490 A89 £1 multicolored 4.00 4.00
Nos. 487-490 (4) 6.40 6.40

Penny Black 150th anniv., Stamp World London '90.

Queen Mother, 90th Birthday
Common Design Types

25p, Portrait, 1940. £1, King, Queen with soldiers.

1990, Aug. 4 Wmk. 384 *Perf. 14x15*

491 CD343 25p multi 1.25 1.25

Perf. 14½

492 CD344 £1 multi 3.50 3.50

Garth Castle, 1910 — A90

Designs: 18p, RMS St. Helena, 1982. 25p, Launching new RMS St. Helena, 1989. 70p, Duke of York launching new RMS St. Helena. £1, New RMS St. Helena.

Wmk. 373

1990, Sept. 13 Litho. *Perf. 14½*

493 A90 9p multicolored 1.25 1.25
494 A90 18p multicolored 1.60 1.60
495 A90 25p multicolored 2.50 2.50
496 A90 70p multicolored 4.25 4.25
Nos. 493-496 (4) 9.60 9.60

Souvenir Sheet

497 A90 £1 multicolored 6.75 6.75

See St. Helena Nos. 535-539, Tristan da Cunha Nos. 482-486.

Christmas — A91

Sculpture (8p) and paintings of Madonna and Child by: 8p, Felici. 18p, Unknown artist. 25p, Gebhard. 65p, Gritti.

1990, Oct. 24 *Perf. 14*

498 A91 8p multicolored 1.00 .80
499 A91 18p multicolored 1.75 1.40
500 A91 25p multicolored 2.50 1.90
501 A91 65p multicolored 4.00 4.00
Nos. 498-501 (4) 9.25 8.10

Nos. 410, 412 & 414 Ovptd. in Silver "BRITISH FOR 175 YEARS"

1991, Feb. 5 Wmk. 384 *Perf. 14½*

502 A74 25p on #410 2.75 2.75
503 A74 50p on #412 3.25 3.25
504 A74 £1 on #414 4.50 4.50
Nos. 502-504 (3) 10.50 10.50

Elizabeth & Philip, Birthdays
Common Design Types

1991, June 18

505 CD345 25p multicolored 1.40 *1.60*
506 CD346 25p multicolored 1.40 *1.60*
a. Pair, #505-506 + label 3.50 3.75

Military Uniforms Type of 1987

Royal Marines Equipment 1821-1844: a, Officer's shako, epaulettes, belt plate, button. b, Officer's cap, sword, epaulettes, belt plate. c, Drum Major's shako with cords, staff. d, Sergeant's shako, chevrons, belt plate, canteen. e, Drummer's drum, sticks, shako.

1991, Aug. 1 Wmk. 373 *Perf. 14*

507 A77 25p Strip of 5, #a.-e. 9.50 9.50

Atlantic Relay Station, 25th Anniv. — A92

15p, BBC Atlantic relay station. 18p, English Bay transmitters. 25p, Satellite receiving station. 70p, Antenna support tower.

1991, Sept. 17 Wmk. 384 *Perf. 14½*

508 A92 15p multi 1.40 1.40
509 A92 18p multi 1.60 1.60
510 A92 25p multi, vert. 2.00 2.00
511 A92 70p multi, vert. 4.50 4.50
Nos. 508-511 (4) 9.50 9.50

Christmas — A93

Designs: 8p, St. Mary's Church, exterior. 18p, St. Mary's Church, interior. 25p, Grotto of Our Lady of Ascension, exterior. 65p, Grotto of Our Lady of Ascension, interior.

1991, Oct. 1 *Perf. 14*

512 A93 8p multicolored .85 .70
513 A93 18p multicolored 1.50 1.25
514 A93 25p multicolored 2.00 1.50
515 A93 65p multicolored 3.75 *4.50*
Nos. 512-515 (4) 8.10 7.95

Fish — A94

1p, Blackfish. 2p, Five finger. 4p, Resplendent angelfish. 5p, Silver fish. 9p, Gurnard. 10p, Blue dad. 15p, Cunning fish. 18p, Grouper. 20p, Moray eel. 25p, Hardback soldierfish. 30p, Blue marlin. 50p, Wahoo. 70p, Yellowfin tuna. £1, Blue shark. £2.50, Bottlenose dolphin.

Wmk. 373

1991, Dec. 10 Litho. *Perf. 14*

516 A94 1p multi .70 .70
517 A94 2p multi 1.00 .75
518 A94 4p multi 1.10 .95
519 A94 5p multi 1.10 .95
520 A94 9p multi 1.50 1.10
521 A94 10p multi 1.50 1.10
522 A94 15p multi 2.00 1.10
523 A94 18p multi 2.00 1.25
524 A94 20p multi 2.00 1.50
525 A94 25p multi 2.00 1.60
526 A94 30p multi 2.00 1.75
527 A94 50p multi 2.50 2.50
528 A94 70p multi 3.25 3.25
529 A94 £1 multi 3.75 3.75
530 A94 £2.50 multi 7.50 7.50
Nos. 516-530 (15) 33.90 29.75

Queen Elizabeth II's Accession to the Throne, 40th Anniv.
Common Design Type

Wmk. 373

1992, Feb. 6 Litho. *Perf. 14*

531 CD349 9p multicolored .45 .45
532 CD349 15p multicolored .75 .75
533 CD349 18p multicolored .90 .90
534 CD349 25p multicolored 1.25 1.25
535 CD349 70p multicolored 2.75 2.75
Nos. 531-535 (5) 6.10 6.10

Discovery of America, 500th Anniv. — A95

9p, STV Eye of the Wind. 18p, STV Soren Larsen. 25p, Pinta, Santa Maria, & Nina. 70p, Columbus, Santa Maria.

Wmk. 373

1992, Feb. 18 Litho. *Perf. 14*

536	A95 9p multicolored		1.40	.65
537	A95 18p multicolored		2.25	.95
538	A95 25p multicolored		2.75	1.25
539	A95 70p multicolored		5.00	2.75
		Nos. 536-539 (4)	11.40	5.60

World Columbian Stamp Expo '92, Chicago and Genoa '92 Intl. Philatelic Exhibitions.

Wideawake Airfield, 50th Anniv. — A96

15p, Control tower. 18p, Nose hangar. 25p, Construction work. 70p, Laying fuel pipeline.

Wmk. 373

1992, May 5 Litho. *Perf. 14*

540	A96 15p multicolored		.95	.95
541	A96 18p multicolored		1.25	1.25
542	A96 25p multicolored		1.50	1.50
543	A96 70p multicolored		3.75	3.75
		Nos. 540-543 (4)	7.45	7.45

Ascension's Participation in Falkland Islands' Liberation, 10th Anniv. — A97

15p, Nimrod Mk.2. 18p, VC10. 25p, Wessex HU Mk.5 helicopter. 65p, Vulcan B2.

No. 548a, 15p + 3p like #544. b, 18p + 4p like #545. c, 25p + 5p like #546. d, 65p + 13p like #547.

Wmk. 373

1992, June 12 Litho. *Perf. 14*

544	A97 15p multicolored		1.25	1.10
545	A97 18p multicolored		1.25	1.10
546	A97 25p multicolored		1.90	1.50
547	A97 65p multicolored		3.00	*4.25*
		Nos. 544-547 (4)	7.40	7.95

Souvenir Sheet

548	A97 Sheet of 4, #a.-d.	8.00	8.00

Surtax for Soldiers,' Sailors,' and Airmen's Families Association.

Christmas — A98

Children's drawings: 8p, Snowman, rocks, candle. 18p, Underwater Santa, Christmas tree. 25p, Hello, bells. 65p, Nativity Scene, angel.

Wmk. 384

1992, Oct. 13 Litho. *Perf. 14*

549	A98 8p multicolored		1.10	.90
550	A98 18p multicolored		1.60	1.25
551	A98 25p multicolored		1.90	1.50
552	A98 65p multicolored		3.50	3.50
		Nos. 549-552 (4)	8.10	7.15

Yellow Canary — A99

15p, Singing male. 18p, Adult male, female. 25p, Young calling for food. 70p, Mixed flock.

Wmk. 373

1993, Jan. 12 Litho. *Perf. 14½*

553	A99 15p multicolored		1.25	1.25
554	A99 18p multicolored		1.40	1.40
555	A99 25p multicolored		1.75	1.75
556	A99 70p multicolored		4.00	4.00
		Nos. 553-556 (4)	8.40	8.40

Royal Air Force, 75th Anniv.

Common Design Type

Designs: 20p, Sopwith Snipe. No. 558, Supermarine Southampton. 30p, Avro Anson. 70p, Vickers Wellington 1C.

No. 561a, Westland Lysander. b, Gloster Meteor. c, DeHavilland Comet. d, British Aerospace Nimrod.

Wmk. 373

1993, Apr. 1 Litho. *Perf. 14*

557	CD350 20p multicolored		2.00	1.50
558	CD350 25p multicolored		2.00	1.50
559	CD350 30p multicolored		2.10	1.60
560	CD350 70p multicolored		3.75	*4.25*
		Nos. 557-560 (4)	9.85	8.85

Souvenir Sheet

561	CD350 25p Sheet of 4, #a.-d.	5.75	5.75

South Atlantic Cable Company, 25th Anniv. — A100

Designs: 20p, Map showing cable route. 25p, Cable ship laying cable. 30p, Map of Ascension. 70p, Cable ship off Ascension.

Perf. 14x14½

1993, June 8 Litho. Wmk. 384

562	A100 20p multicolored		1.10	1.10
563	A100 25p multicolored		1.35	1.35
564	A100 30p multicolored		1.50	1.50
565	A100 70p multicolored		3.50	3.50
		Nos. 562-565 (4)	7.45	7.45

Flowers — A101

Perf. 14x14½

1993, Aug. 3 Litho. Wmk. 384

566	A101 20p Lantana camara		1.50	.75
567	A101 25p Moonflower		1.75	.97
568	A101 30p Hibiscus		1.75	1.10
569	A101 70p Frangipani		4.00	3.50
		Nos. 566-569 (4)	9.00	6.32

Christmas — A102

Designs: 12p, Child mailing Christmas card. 20p, Mail loaded onto Tristar. 25p, Plane in flight. 30p, Mail unloaded at Wideawake Airfield. 65p, Child reading card, Georgetown.

Perf. 14½x14

1993, Oct. 19 Litho. Wmk. 373

570	A102 12p multicolored		.75	.40
571	A102 20p multicolored		1.25	.45
572	A102 25p multicolored		1.40	.50
573	A102 30p multicolored		2.25	2.25
574	A102 65p multicolored		2.75	2.75
a.	Souvenir sheet of 5, #570-574		11.00	11.00
		Nos. 570-574 (5)	8.40	6.35

Stamps from No. 574a show a continuous design, while Nos. 570-574 have white borders on sides.

Prehistoric Aquatic Reptiles — A103

12p, Ichthyosaurus. 20p, Metriorhynchus. 25p, Mosasaurus. 30p, Elasmosaurus. 65p, Plesiosaurus.

1994, Jan. 25 Wmk. 373 *Perf. 14*

575	A103 12p multi		1.00	1.00
576	A103 20p multi		1.25	1.25
577	A103 25p multi		1.50	1.50
578	A103 30p multi		1.50	1.50
579	A103 65p multi		2.75	2.75
		Nos. 575-579 (5)	8.00	8.00

Ovptd. with Hong Kong '94 Emblem

1994, Feb. 18

580	A103 12p on #575		1.00	1.00
581	A103 20p on #576		1.60	1.60
582	A103 25p on #577		1.60	1.60
583	A103 30p on #578		1.75	1.75
584	A103 65p on #579		3.00	3.00
		Nos. 580-584 (5)	8.95	8.95

Green Turtle — A104

20p, Four on beach. 25p, Crawling in sand. No. 587, Crawling from sea. 65p, Swimming.

No. 589a, Side view, crawling from sea. b, Digging nest. c, Hatchlings heading to sea. d, Digging nest, diff.

1994, Mar. 22

585	A104 20p multicolored		2.25	2.25
586	A104 25p multicolored		2.75	2.75
587	A104 30p multicolored		2.75	2.75
588	A104 65p multicolored		4.25	*5.50*
		Nos. 585-588 (4)	12.00	13.25

Souvenir Sheet

589	A104 30p Sheet of 4, #a.-d.	13.50	13.50

Civilian Ships — A105

Ships serving during Falkland Islands War, 1982: 20p, Tug Yorkshireman. 25p, Minesweeper support ship RMS St. Helena. 30p, Oil tanker British ESK. 65p, Cruise liner Uganda, hospital ship.

1994, June 14

590	A105 20p multicolored		2.50	2.50
591	A105 25p multicolored		2.75	2.75
592	A105 30p multicolored		2.75	2.75
593	A105 65p multicolored		5.00	5.00
		Nos. 590-593 (4)	13.00	13.00

Sooty Tern — A106

1994, Aug. 16

594	A106 20p Chick		1.40	1.40
595	A106 25p Juvenile		1.50	1.50
596	A106 30p Brooding adult		1.75	1.75
597	A106 65p Displaying male		2.75	2.75
		Nos. 594-597 (4)	7.40	7.40

Souvenir Sheet

598	A106 £1 Dread	6.50	6.50

Christmas — A107

Donkeys: 12p, Mare with foal. 20p, Young adult. 25p, Foal. 30p, Adult, egrets. 65p, Adult.

1994, Oct. 11 *Perf. 14x14½*

599	A107 12p multicolored		1.25	1.00
600	A107 20p multicolored		1.75	1.40
601	A107 25p multicolored		1.75	1.40
602	A107 30p multicolored		1.90	1.50
603	A107 65p multicolored		3.50	*4.50*
		Nos. 599-603 (5)	10.15	9.80

Flowers — A108

20p, Leonurus japonicus. 25p, Periwinkle. 30p, Four o'clock. 65p, Blood flower.

1995, Jan. 10 *Perf. 14*

604	A108 20p multi, vert.		2.00	2.00
605	A108 25p multi		2.00	2.00
606	A108 30p multi, vert.		2.75	2.75
607	A108 65p multi		3.75	3.75
		Nos. 604-607 (4)	10.50	10.50

Island Scenes, c. 1895 — A109

Designs: 12p, Horse-drawn wagon, Two Boats, Green Mountain. 20p, Island stewards' store. 25p, Royal Navy headquarters, barracks. 30p, Police office. 65p, Pier head.

1995, Mar. 7 Wmk. 384 *Perf. 14½*

608	A109 12p sepia		.70	.70
609	A109 20p sepia		1.00	1.00
610	A109 25p sepia		1.40	1.40
611	A109 30p sepia		2.50	2.50
612	A109 65p sepia		2.75	2.75
		Nos. 608-612 (5)	8.35	8.35

End of World War II, 50th Anniv.

Common Design Types

Designs: 20p, 5.5-inch guns taken from HMS Hood, 1941. 25p, Fairey Swordfish, first aircraft to land at Ascension. 30p, HMS Dorsetshire patrolling South Atlantic. 65p, HMS Devonshire patrolling South Atlantic.

£1, Reverse of War Medal, 1939-45.

1995, May 8 Wmk. 373 *Perf. 14*

613	CD351 20p multicolored		2.25	2.25
614	CD351 25p multicolored		2.50	2.50
615	CD351 30p multicolored		3.00	3.00
616	CD351 65p multicolored		5.00	5.00
		Nos. 613-616 (4)	12.75	12.75

Souvenir Sheet

617	CD352 £1 multicolored	8.75	8.75
	Nos. 613-617 (5)	21.50	21.50

Butterflies — A110

20p, Long-tailed blue. 25p, Painted lady. 30p, Diadem. 65p, African monarch.

£1, Red admiral.

1995, Sept. 1 Wmk. 384

618	A110 20p multi		1.90	1.90
619	A110 25p multi		2.25	2.25
620	A110 30p multi		2.25	2.25
621	A110 65p multi		3.50	3.50
		Nos. 618-621 (4)	9.90	9.90

Souvenir Sheet

622	A110 £1 multi	8.50	8.50

Singapore '95 (No. 622).

Christmas A111

Designs based on children's drawings:

12p, Santa on boat. 20p, Santa on wall. 25p, Santa in chimney. 30p, Santa on dolphin. 65p, South Atlantic run.

1995, Oct. 10 Wmk. 373

623	A111 12p multicolored		1.25	1.25
624	A111 20p multicolored		1.60	1.60
625	A111 25p multicolored		1.75	1.75
626	A111 30p multicolored		2.00	2.00
627	A111 65p multicolored		3.50	3.50
		Nos. 623-627 (5)	10.10	10.10

Mollusks — A112

12p, Cypraea lurida. 25p, Cypraea spurca. 30p, Harpa doris. 65p, Umbraculum umbraculum.

Wmk. 384

1996, Jan. 10 Litho. *Perf. 14*

628	A112 12p multicolored	2.50	2.50
629	A112 25p multicolored	3.00	3.00
630	A112 30p multicolored	3.25	3.25
631	A112 65p multicolored	4.00	4.00
a.	Strip of 4, #628-631	14.00	14.00

Queen Elizabeth II, 70th Birthday
Common Design Type

Various portraits of Queen, scenes of Ascension:

20p, St. Marys Church. 25p, The Residency. 30p, Roman Catholic Grotto. 65p, The Exiles Club.

Wmk. 384

1996, Apr. 22 Litho. *Perf. 13½*

632	CD354	20p multicolored	.80	.80
633	CD354	25p multicolored	.90	.90
634	CD354	30p multicolored	1.10	1.10
635	CD354	65p multicolored	2.50	2.50
		Nos. 632-635 (4)	5.30	5.30

CAPEX '96 — A113

Island transport: 20p, US Army Jeep. 25p, 1924 Citreon 7.5HP two seater. 30p, 1930 Austin Ten-four Tourer. 65p, Series 1 Land Rover.

Wmk. 384

1996, June 8 Litho. *Perf. 14*

636	A113	20p multicolored	1.25	1.25
637	A113	25p multicolored	1.40	1.40
638	A113	30p multicolored	1.50	1.50
639	A113	65p multicolored	2.75	2.75
		Nos. 636-639 (4)	6.90	6.90

Birds and Their Young — A114

1p, Madeiran storm petrel. 2p, Red-billed tropicbird. 4p, Indian mynah. 5p, House sparrow. 7p, Common waxbill. 10p, White tern. 12p, Francolin. 15p, Brown noddy. 20p, Yellow canary. 25p, Black noddy. 30p, Red-footed booby. 40p, Yellow-billed tropicbird. 65p, Brown booby. £1, Masked booby. £2, Sooty tern. £3, Ascension frigate bird.

Wmk. 373

1996, Aug. 12 Litho. *Perf. 13*

640	A114	1p multicolored	.25	*1.00*
641	A114	2p multicolored	.25	*1.00*
642	A114	4p multicolored	.25	*1.00*
643	A114	5p multicolored	.25	*1.00*
644	A114	7p multicolored	.25	*1.00*
645	A114	10p multicolored	.35	*1.25*
646	A114	12p multicolored	.40	*1.50*
647	A114	15p multicolored	.50	*1.50*
648	A114	20p multicolored	.75	*1.50*
649	A114	25p multicolored	.90	*1.50*
650	A114	30p multicolored	1.10	*1.50*
651	A114	40p multicolored	1.50	*2.00*
652	A114	65p multicolored	2.50	*3.25*
a.		Sheet of 1, perf. 14	4.50	*4.50*
653	A114	£1 multicolored	4.00	*4.75*
a.		Souvenir sheet of 1	4.50	*4.50*
654	A114	£2 multicolored	8.25	*9.00*
655	A114	£3 multicolored	10.00	*12.00*
		Nos. 640-655 (16)	31.50	*44.75*

No. 652a for Hong Kong '97. Issued 2/3/97.

No. 653a for return of Hong Kong to China. Issued 7/1/97.

BBC Atlantic Relay Station, 30th Anniv. — A115

Various views of relay station: 20p, 25p, Towers. 30p, Towers, buildings. 65p, Satellite dish, towers, beach.

1996, Sept. 9 Wmk. 384 *Perf. 14*

656	A115	20p multicolored	.85	.85
657	A115	25p multicolored	1.00	1.00
658	A115	30p multicolored	1.10	1.10
659	A115	65p multicolored	2.50	2.50
		Nos. 656-659 (4)	5.45	5.45

Christmas — A116

Santa Claus: 12p, On satellite dish. 20p, Playing golf. 25p, By beach. 30p, On RAF Tristar. 65p, Aboard RMS St. Helena.

Perf. 14x14½

1996, Sept. 23 Litho. Wmk. 373

660	A116	12p multicolored	.50	.50
661	A116	20p multicolored	.90	.90
662	A116	25p multicolored	.90	.90
663	A116	30p multicolored	1.10	1.10
664	A116	65p multicolored	2.50	2.50
		Nos. 660-664 (5)	5.90	5.90

UNICEF, 50th anniv.

A117

20p, Date palm. 25p, Mauritius hemp. 30p, Norfolk Island pine. 65p, Dwarf palm.

Wmk. 373

1997, Jan. 7 Litho. *Perf. 14½*

665	A117	20p multi	.80	.80
666	A117	25p multi	1.00	1.00
667	A117	30p multi	1.15	1.15
668	A117	65p multi	2.25	2.25
		Nos. 665-668 (4)	5.20	5.20

Hong Kong '97.

A118

Flag, ship or aircraft: 12p, Great Britain Red Ensign, tanker Maserk Ascension. 25p, RAF Ensign, Tristar. 30p, NASA emblem, Space Shuttle Atlantis. 65p, Royal Navy White Ensign, HMS Northumberland.

Wmk. 373

1997, Apr. 1 Litho. *Perf. 14½*

669	A118	12p multicolored	1.10	1.10
670	A118	25p multicolored	1.60	1.60
671	A118	30p multicolored	1.75	1.75
672	A118	65p multicolored	3.25	3.25
		Nos. 669-672 (4)	7.70	7.70

Herbs — A119

Designs: a, Solanum sodomaeum. b, Ageratum conyzoides. c, Leonurus sibricus. d, Cerastium vulgatum. e, Commelina diffusa.

Perf. 14x14½

1997, June 7 Litho. Wmk. 373

673	A119	30p Strip of 5, #a.-e.	8.50	8.50

A120

Queen Elizabeth II and Prince Philip, 50th Wedding Anniv.: No. 674, Queen Elizabeth II. No. 675, Prince Philip playing polo. No. 676, Queen petting horse. No. 677, Prince Philip. No. 678, Prince Philip, Queen Elizabeth II. No. 679, Prince Harry, Prince William riding horses.

£1.50, Queen Elizabeth, Prince Philip riding in open carriage.

Wmk. 384

1997, July 10 Litho. *Perf. 13½*

674	A120	20p multicolored	1.50	1.50
675	A120	20p multicolored	1.50	1.50
a.		Pair, #674-675	3.75	3.75
676	A120	25p multicolored	1.60	1.60
677	A120	25p multicolored	1.60	1.60
a.		Pair, #676-677	4.00	4.00
678	A120	30p multicolored	1.75	1.75
679	A120	30p multicolored	1.75	1.75
a.		Pair, #678-679	4.25	4.25
		Nos. 674-679 (6)	9.70	9.70

Souvenir Sheet

680	A120	£1.50 multicolored	7.75	7.75

Birds — A121

Booklet Stamps

Perf. 14 on 3 Sides

1997, Sept. 1 Litho. Wmk. 373

681	A121	15p like #644	2.75	2.75
682	A121	35p like #648	3.50	3.50
a.		Booklet pane, 2 ea #681-682	12.50	
		Complete booklet, #682a	12.50	

Game Fish — A122

12p, Black marlin. 20p, Atlantic sailfish. 25p, Swordfish. 30p, Wahoo. £1, Yellowfin tuna.

Perf. 14x14½

1997, Sept. 3 Litho. Wmk. 373

683	A122	12p multi	.90	.90
684	A122	20p multi	1.40	1.40
685	A122	25p multi	1.50	1.50
686	A122	30p multi	1.60	1.60
687	A122	£1 multi	4.25	4.25
		Nos. 683-687 (5)	9.65	9.65

A123

St. Mary's Church (Christmas): 15p, Interior view. 35p, Stained glass window, Madonna and Child. 40p, Stained glass window, Falklands, 1982. 50p, Stained glass window.

Wmk. 384

1997, Oct. 1 Litho. *Perf. 14*

688	A123	15p multicolored	.90	.90
689	A123	35p multicolored	1.75	1.75
690	A123	40p multicolored	1.90	1.90
691	A123	50p multicolored	2.25	2.25
		Nos. 688-691 (4)	6.80	6.80

A124

Insects: 15p, Cactoblastis cactorum. 35p, Teleonemia scrupulosa. 40p, Neltumius arizonensis. 50p, Algarobius prosopis.

Wmk. 373

1998, Feb. 10 Litho. *Perf. 14*

692	A124	15p multicolored	1.60	1.60
693	A124	35p multicolored	2.10	2.10
694	A124	40p multicolored	2.75	2.75
695	A124	50p multicolored	2.75	2.75
		Nos. 692-695 (4)	9.20	9.20

Diana, Princess of Wales (1961-97)
Common Design Type

a, In polka-dotted dress. b, In yellow blouse. c, With longer hair style. d, Holding flowers.

Perf. 14½x14

1998, Mar. 31 Litho. Wmk. 373

696	CD355	35p Sheet of 4, #a.-d.	5.25	5.25

No. 696 sold for £1.40 + 20p, with surtax from international sales being donated to the Princess Diana Memorial Fund and surtax from national sales being donated to designated local charity.

Royal Air Force, 80th Anniv.
Common Design Type of 1993
Re-inscribed

15p, Fairey Fawn. 35p, Vickers Vernon. 40p, Supermarine Spitfire F-22. 50p, Bristol Britannia C2.

No. 701: a, Blackburn Kangaroo. b, SE5a. c, Curtiss Kittyhawk III. d, Boeing Fortress II (B-17).

Wmk. 384

1998, Apr. 1 Litho. *Perf. 14*

697	CD350	15p multicolored	1.00	1.00
698	CD350	35p multicolored	2.10	2.10
699	CD350	40p multicolored	2.25	2.25
700	CD350	50p multicolored	2.75	2.75
		Nos. 697-700 (4)	8.10	8.10

Souvenir Sheet

701	CD350	50p Sheet of 4, #a.-d.	8.00	8.00

Birds — A125

Wmk. 373

1998, June 15 Litho. *Perf. 14*

702	A125	15p Swallow	1.25	1.25
703	A125	25p House martin	1.75	1.75
704	A125	35p Cattle egret	2.10	2.10
705	A125	40p Swift	2.10	2.10
706	A125	50p Allen's gallinule	2.25	2.25
		Nos. 702-706 (5)	9.45	9.45

Island Sports — A126

Wmk. 373

1998, Aug. 17 Litho. *Perf. 14*

707	A126	15p Cricket	2.50	2.00
708	A126	35p Golf	3.25	2.50
709	A126	40p Soccer	2.50	2.50
710	A126	50p Trapshooting	2.50	2.50
		Nos. 707-710 (4)	10.75	9.50

Christmas A127

Designs: 15p, Children's nativity play. 35p, Santa arriving on Ascension. 40p, Santa arriving at a party. 50p, Carol singers.

Wmk. 373

1998, Oct. 1 Litho. *Perf. 14*

711	A127	15p multicolored	1.10	1.10
712	A127	35p multicolored	1.90	1.90
713	A127	40p multicolored	2.10	2.10
714	A127	50p multicolored	2.10	2.10
		Nos. 711-714 (4)	7.20	7.20

World War II Aircraft — A128

15p, Curtiss C-46 Commando. 35p, Douglas C-47 Dakota. 40p, Douglas C-54 Skymaster. 50p, Consolidated Liberator Mk.V. £1.50, Consolidated Liberator LB-30.

Wmk. 373

1999, Jan. 20 Litho. *Perf. 14*

715	A128	15p multicolored	1.25	1.25
716	A128	35p multicolored	2.00	2.00
717	A128	40p multicolored	2.25	2.25
718	A128	50p multicolored	2.25	2.25
		Nos. 715-718 (4)	7.75	7.75

Souvenir Sheet

719	A128	£1.50 multicolored	11.00	11.00

Winston Churchill, 125th birth anniv.

Australia '99, World Stamp Expo — A129

Union Castle Mail Ships: 15p, SS Glengorm Castle. 35p, SS Gloucester Castle. 40p, SS Durham Castle. 50p, SS Garth Castle. £1, HMS Endeavour.

Perf. 14½x14

1999, Mar. 5 Litho. Wmk. 373

720 A129 15p multicolored 1.25 1.25
721 A129 35p multicolored 2.25 2.25
722 A129 40p multicolored 2.40 2.40
723 A129 50p multicolored 2.40 2.40
Nos. 720-723 (4) 8.30 8.30

Souvenir Sheet

724 A129 £1 multicolored 6.75 6.75

World Wildlife Fund — A130

Fairy tern: No. 725, Two on branch. No. 726, One on branch. No. 727, Adult feeding chick. No. 728, Two in flight.

Wmk. 384

1999, Apr. 27 Litho. *Perf. 14½*

725 A130 10p multicolored .50 .45
726 A130 10p multicolored .50 .45
727 A130 10p multicolored .50 .45
728 A130 10p multicolored .50 .45
a. Sheet of 16, 4 each #725-728 10.00 10.00
Nos. 725-728 (4) 2.00 1.80

Wedding of Prince Edward and Sophie Rhys-Jones

Common Design Type

Perf. 13¾x14

1999, June 19 Litho. Wmk. 384

729 CD356 50p Separate portraits 1.50 1.50
730 CD356 £1 Couple 3.00 3.00

1st Manned Moon Landing, 30th Anniv.

Common Design Type

Designs: 15p, Command and service modules. 35p, Moon from Apollo 11. 40p, Devil's Ashpit Tracking Station. 50p, Lunar module lifts off moon.
£1.50, Looking at earth from moon.

Perf. 14x13¾

1999, July 20 Litho. Wmk. 384

731 CD357 15p multicolored 1.25 1.25
732 CD357 35p multicolored 1.60 1.60
733 CD357 40p multicolored 1.60 1.60
734 CD357 50p multicolored 1.60 1.60
Nos. 731-734 (4) 6.05 6.05

Souvenir Sheet

Perf. 14

735 CD357 £1.50 multicolored 6.75 6.75

No. 735 contains one 40mm circular stamp.

Queen Mother's Century

Common Design Type

Queen Mother: 15p, With King George VI, Winston Churchill. 35p, With Prince Charles. 40p, At Clarence House, 88th birthday. 50p, With drummers at Clarence House.
£1.50, With Titanic.

Wmk. 384

1999, Aug. 20 Litho. *Perf. 13½*

736 CD358 15p multicolored 1.25 1.25
737 CD358 35p multicolored 1.75 1.75
738 CD358 40p multicolored 2.00 2.00
739 CD358 50p multicolored 2.50 2.50
Nos. 736-739 (4) 7.50 7.50

Souvenir Sheet

740 CD358 £1.50 black 8.00 8.00

Christmas — A131

Wmk. 384

1999, Oct. 6 Litho. *Perf. 13¾*

741 A131 15p 3 children 1.10 1.10
742 A131 35p 2 children, hats 2.10 2.10
743 A131 40p 2 children, bed 2.10 2.10
744 A131 50p 4 children 2.10 2.10
Nos. 741-744 (4) 7.40 7.40

Cable and Wireless, Cent. — A132

Perf. 13¼x13¾

1999, Dec. 13 Litho. Wmk. 373

745 A132 15p CS Anglia 1.75 1.75
746 A132 35p CS Cambria 2.50 2.50
747 A132 40p Map 2.50 2.50
748 A132 50p CS Colonia 2.75 2.75
Nos. 745-748 (4) 9.50 9.50

Souvenir Sheet

749 A132 £1.50 CS Seine 8.00 8.00

Turtle Project A133

15p, Young turtles. 35p, Turtle, trail at left. 40p, Turtle with tracking device on beach. 50p, Turtle with tracking device heading to sea.
No. 754: a, Turtle head, rock. b, Like 15p. c, Turtle on beach, sea. d, Turtle in surf.

2000, Mar. 8 Litho. *Perf. 13¾*

750 A133 15p multi 1.10 1.10
751 A133 35p multi 1.90 1.90
752 A133 40p multi 1.90 1.90
753 A133 50p multi 2.10 2.10
Nos. 750-753 (4) 7.00 7.00

Souvenir Sheet

Perf. 14

754 A133 25p Sheet of 4, #a-d 7.50 7.50
e. With Stamp Show 2000 emblem in margin 7.50 7.50

No. 754 contains four 40x26mm stamps. No. 754e issued 5/8.

Prince William, 18th Birthday

Common Design Type

William: 10p, As baby laying on stomach and stuffed animal. 15p, As toddler, vert. 35p, Wearing suit and wearing cap, vert. 40p, Holding flowers, and in parka. 50p, In suit and in checked shirt.

Perf. 13¾x14¼, 14¼x13¾

2000, June 21 Litho. Wmk. 373

Stamps With White Border

755 CD359 15p multi 1.00 1.00
756 CD359 35p multi 1.50 1.50
757 CD359 40p multi 2.25 2.25
758 CD359 50p multi 2.75 2.75
Nos. 755-758 (4) 7.50 7.50

Souvenir Sheet

Stamps Without White Border

Perf. 14¼

759 Sheet of 5 8.00 8.00
a. CD359 10p multi .50 .50
b. CD359 15p multi .75 .75
c. CD359 35p multi 1.50 1.50
d. CD359 40p multi 1.75 1.75
e. CD359 50p multi 2.25 2.25

Forts — A134

Designs: 15p, 1815 fortifications. 35p, Fort Thornton, 1817. 40p, Fort Hayes, 1860. 50p, Fort Bedford, 1940.

Wmk. 373

2000, Aug. 14 Litho. *Perf. 14*

760-763 A134 Set of 4 9.00 9.00

Christmas A135

Carols: 15p, I Saw Three Ships. 25p, Silent Night. 40p, Away in a Manger. 90p, Hark, the Herald Angels Sing.

2000, Oct. 16 Wmk. 384

764-767 A135 Set of 4 12.50 12.50

Souvenir Sheet

New Year 2001 (Year of the Snake) A136

Turtles: a, 25p, Green. b, 40p, Loggerhead.

Wmk. 373

2001, Feb. 1 Litho. *Perf. 14½*

768 A136 Sheet of 2, #a-b 5.00 5.00

Hong Kong 2001 Stamp Exhibition.

Sinking of the Roebuck, Tercentenary — A137

Designs: 15p, Capt. William Dampier. 35p, Drawing of the Roebuck, horiz. 40p, Cave dwelling at Dampier's Drip, horiz. 50p, Map.

2001, Feb. 25 Litho. *Perf. 14*

769-772 A137 Set of 4 11.00 11.00

Discovery of Ascension Island, 500th Anniv. — A138

Designs: 15p, Alfonso de Albuquerque. 35p, Portuguese caravel. 40p, Cantino map. 50p, Rear admiral Sir George Cockburn.

Perf. 14¾x14¼

2001, Mar. 25 Litho. Wmk. 384

773-776 A138 Set of 4 10.50 10.50

The Age of Victoria — A139

Designs: 15p, Great Britain Type A1 with Ascension cancel, vert. 25p, Parade, 1901. 35p, HMS Phoebe. 40p, The Red Lion, 1863. 50p, Queen Victoria, vert. 65p, Sir Joseph Dalton Hooker, botanist, vert.
£1.50, Queen Victoria's Funeral.

Wmk. 373

2001, May 24 Litho. *Perf. 14*

777-782 A139 Set of 6 11.50 11.50

Souvenir Sheet

783 A139 £1.50 multi 9.00 9.00

Souvenir Sheet

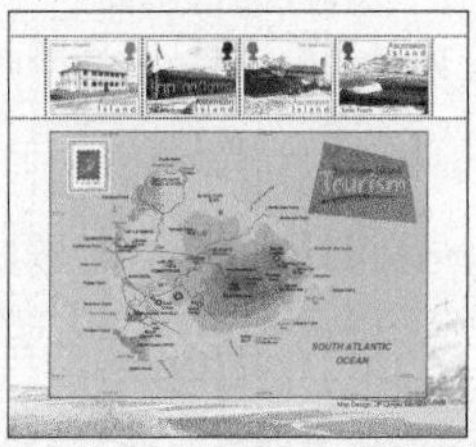

Belgica 2001 Intl. Stamp Exhibition, Brussels — A140

Ascension tourist sites: a, 35p, Islander Hostel. b, 35p, The Residency. c, 40p, The Red Lion. d, 40p, Turtle Ponds.

Wmk. 373

2001, June 9 Litho. *Perf. 14¼*

784 A140 Sheet of 4, #a-d 10.50 10.50

Birdlife International World Bird Festival — A141

Ascension frigate bird: 15p, On rock with wings outstretched. 35p, Chick, with mouth open. 40p, Pair in flight, horiz. 50p, Close-up of bird, horiz.

Perf. 13¾x14¼, 14¼x13¾

2001, Oct. 1 Litho. Wmk. 373

785-788 A141 Set of 4 7.75 7.75

Souvenir Sheet

789 Sheet, #785-788, 789a, perf. 14¼ 8.00 8.00
a. A141 10p Two birds on rock 1.15 1.15

Reign Of Queen Elizabeth II, 50th Anniv. Issue

Common Design Type

Designs: Nos. 790, 794a, 15p, Princess Elizabeth with dog. Nos. 791, 794b, 35p, In 1978. Nos. 792, 794c, 40p, In 1946. Nos. 793, 794d, 50p, In 1998. No. 794e, 60p, 1955 portrait by Annigoni (38x50mm).

Perf. 14¼x14½, 13¾ (#794e)

2002, Feb. 6 Litho. Wmk. 373

With Gold Frames

790 CD360 15p multicolored 1.10 1.10
791 CD360 35p multicolored 1.25 1.25
792 CD360 40p multicolored 1.75 1.75
793 CD360 50p multicolored 2.00 2.00
Nos. 790-793 (4) 6.10 6.10

Souvenir Sheet

Without Gold Frames

794 CD360 Sheet of 5, #a-e 8.00 8.00

Falkland Islands War, 20th Anniv. — A142

Designs: 15p, Troops landing at English Bay. 35p, Weapons testing at Ascension. 40p, HMS Hermes and helicopter. 50p, Vulcan bomber at Wideawake Airfield.

Wmk. 373

2002, June 14 Litho. *Perf. 14*

795-798 A142 Set of 4 6.00 6.00

Queen Mother Elizabeth (1900-2002)

Common Design Type

Designs: 35p, Wearing flowered bonnet (sepia photograph). 40p, Wearing pink hat.
No. 801: a, 50p, Wearing hat (sepia photograph). b, £1, Wearing blue hat.

Wmk. 373

2002, Aug. 5 Litho. *Perf. 14¼*

With Purple Frames

799 CD361 35p multicolored 1.10 1.10
800 CD361 40p multicolored 1.75 1.75

Souvenir Sheet

Without Purple Frames

Perf. 14½x14¼

801 CD361 Sheet of 2, #a-b 6.00 6.00

Flowers and Local Scenes — A143

Designs: 10p, Vinca, Travellers palm. 15p, Mexican poppy, Broken Tooth. 20p, Ascension lily, St. Mary's Church. 25p, Goatweed, Boatswain Bird Island. 30p, Mauritius hemp, Cannon. 35p, Frangipani, Guest House. 40p, Ascension spurge, Wideawake tern. 50p, Lovechaste, Pier head. 65p, Yellowboy, Sisters Peak. 90p, Persian lilac, Two Boats School. £2, Wild currant, Green turtle. £5, Coral tree, Wideawake Airfield.

Wmk. 373

2002, Aug. 28 Litho. *Perf. 14*

802 A143 10p multi .35 .45
803 A143 15p multi .60 .70
804 A143 20p multi .80 .95
805 A143 25p multi 1.00 1.10
806 A143 30p multi 1.25 1.25
807 A143 35p multi 1.50 1.80
808 A143 40p multi 1.60 1.90

809 A143 50p multi 2.00 2.40
810 A143 65p multi 2.75 3.25
811 A143 90p multi 3.50 4.00
812 A143 £2 multi 7.00 8.00
813 A143 £5 multi 18.00 35.00
Nos. 802-813 (12) 40.35 60.80

Christmas — A144

Paintings: 15p, Ecce Ancilla Dominii, by Dante Gabriel Rossetti. 25p, The Holy Family and a Shepherd, by Titian, horiz. 35p, Christ Carrying the Cross, by Ambrogio Bergognone. 75p, Sketch for "The Ascension," by Benjamin West.

Perf. 14x14¼, 14¼x14

2002, Oct. 9 Litho. Wmk. 373
814-817 A144 Set of 4 6.50 6.50

Ariane Downrange Tracking Station — A145

Designs: 35p, Ariane 4 on launchpad, vert. 40p, Map of downrange tracking stations. 65p, Automated Transfer vehicle in space. 90p, Ariane 5 launch, vert.

2003, Jan. 13 Litho. *Perf. 14½*
818-821 A145 Set of 4 9.50 9.50
821a Souvenir sheet, #818-821 9.50 9.50

Head of Queen Elizabeth II
Common Design Type

Wmk. 373

2003, June 2 Litho. *Perf. 13¾*
822 CD362 £3 multi 12.50 12.50
Nos. 822 (1) 12.50 12.50

Coronation of Queen Elizabeth II, 50th Anniv.
Common Design Type

Designs: Nos. 823, 825a, 40p, Queen in carriage. Nos. 824, 825b, £1, Queen with crown at coronation.

Perf. 14¼x14½

2003, June 2 Litho. Wmk. 373

Vignettes Framed, Red Background
823 CD363 40p multicolored 1.75 1.75
824 CD363 £1 multicolored 4.50 4.50

Souvenir Sheet

Vignettes Without Frame, Purple Panel
825 CD363 Sheet of 2, #a-b 6.25 6.25

Prince William, 21st Birthday
Common Design Type

No. 826: a, Color photograph at right. b, Color photograph at left.

Wmk. 373

2003, June 21 Litho. *Perf. 14¼*
826 Horiz. pair 7.25 7.25
a.-b. CD364 75p Either single 3.00 3.00

Powered Flight, Cent. A146

Designs: 15p, Bleriot XI. 20p, Vickers VC-10. 35p, BAe Harrier FRS Mk 1. 40p, Westland Sea King HAS Mk 4. 50p, Rockwell Space Shuttle. 90p, General Dynamics F-16. £1.50, Fairey Swordfish Mk II.

Wmk. 373

2003, Aug. 12 Litho. *Perf. 14*

Stamp + Label
827-832 A146 Set of 6 11.00 11.00

Souvenir Sheet
833 A146 £1.50 multi 8.00 8.00

Democracy, 1st Anniv., and Christmas A147

Dove and: 15p, Casting ballot. 25p, Island council session. 40p, Higher education. £1, Government headquarters.

Wmk. 373

2003, Nov. 1 Litho. *Perf. 14*
834-837 A147 Set of 4 7.00 7.00

Birdlife International — A148

Masked booby: 15p, Adult and chick. 35p, Two adults, vert. 40p, Adult in flight, vert. 50p, Adult with neck and wings extended. 90p, Adult.

Perf. 14¼x13¾, 13¾x14¼

2004, Feb. 6 Litho. Wmk. 373
838-842 A148 Set of 5 10.00 10.00
842a Souvenir sheet, #838-842, perf. 14¼ 10.00 10.00

Royal Horticultural Society, Bicent. — A149

Flora: 15p, Bougainvillea glabra (red flowers). 35p, Bougainvillea glabra (red violet flowers). 40p, Bougainvillea glabra (white flowers). 90p, Bougainvillea spectabilis.
£1.50, Pteris adscensionis.

Wmk. 373

2004, May 25 Litho. *Perf. 14*
843-846 A149 Set of 4 8.00 8.00

Souvenir Sheet
847 A149 £1.50 multi 7.00 7.00

Fish — A150

Designs: 15p, Blue marlin underwater. 35p, Swordfish. 40p, Sailfish. 90p, White marlin.
£1.50, Blue marlin breaching surface.

Wmk. 373

2004, July 26 Litho. *Perf. 13¾*
848-851 A150 Set of 4 8.50 8.50

Souvenir Sheet
852 A150 £1.50 multi 7.25 7.25

The Moon — A151

Designs: 15p, Lunar eclipse from Hummock Point. 25p, Lunar eclipse from Sister's Peak. 35p, Lunar eclipse from Daly's Craggs. £1.25, Moon and birds from Mars Bay.

Wmk. 373

2004, Oct. 28 Litho. *Perf. 13½*
853-856 A151 Set of 4 8.50 8.50
856a Souvenir sheet of 1 6.00 6.00

Merchant Ships — A152

Designs: 15p, MV Ascension. 35p. RMS St. Helena. 40p, RMS Caronia. £1.25, MV Maersk Gannet.

2004, Nov. 26 *Perf. 13¼*
857-860 A152 Set of 4 9.50 9.50

Battle of Trafalgar, Bicent. A153

Designs: 15p, British carronade on sliding carriage. 25p, Royal Marine drummer boy, 1805, vert. 35p, HMS Britannia, vert. 40p, Horatio Nelson, by Jean Frances Rigaud. 50p, HMS Neptune and Santissima Trinidad. 90p, HMS Victory.
No. 867, vert.: a, Horatio Nelson, by Lemuel Francis Abbott. b, HMS Ajax.

Wmk. 373, Unwmkd. (#866)

2005, Apr. 29 Litho. *Perf. 13½*
861-866 A153 Set of 6 9.50 9.50

Souvenir Sheet
867 A153 £1 Sheet of 2, #a-b 8.25 8.25

No. 866 has particles of wood from the HMS Victory embedded in the areas covered by a thermographic process that produces a shiny, raised effect.

Birdlife International A154

Birds: 15p, Fairy tern. 35p, White-tailed tropicbird. 40p, Brown booby. 50p, Brown noddy. £1.25, Red-billed tropicbird.

Wmk. 373

2005, May 27 Litho. *Perf. 13¾*
868-872 A154 Set of 5 10.00 10.00
872a Souvenir sheet, #868-872 10.00 10.00

Tuna Fish — A155

Designs: 35p, Three yellowfin tunas. 40p, Skipjack tunas. 50p, Albacore tunas. £1.25, Bigeye tunas.
£1.50, Yellowfin tuna jumping.

Wmk. 373

2005, July 22 Litho. *Perf. 13¾*
873-876 A155 Set of 4 9.00 9.00

Souvenir Sheet
877 A155 £1.50 multi 6.50 6.50

Pope John Paul II (1920-2005) — A156

Wmk. 373

2005, Aug. 18 Litho. *Perf. 14*
878 A156 40p multi 2.00 2.00

Battle of Trafalgar, Bicent. — A157

Designs: 40p, HMS Victory. 65p, Ships in battle, horiz. 90p, Admiral Horatio Nelson.

Perf. 13¼

2005, Oct. 21 Litho. Unwmk.
879-881 A157 Set of 3 9.50 9.50

Christmas — A158

Stories by Hans Christian Andersen (1805-75): 15p, The Little Fir Tree. 25p, The Mailcoach Passengers. 35p, The Little Match Girl. £1.25, The Snow Man.

2005, Oct. 3 Wmk. 373 *Perf. 14*
882-885 A158 Set of 4 8.50 8.50

Fish — A159

Designs: 20p, Black jack. 35p, Almaco jack. 50p, Horse-eye jack. £1, Rainbow runner.
£1.50, Longfin crevalle jack.

Wmk. 373

2006, Jan. 24 Litho. *Perf. 13¾*
886-889 A159 Set of 4 9.00 9.00

Souvenir Sheet
890 A159 £1.50 multi 6.25 6.25

Queen Elizabeth II, 80th Birthday — A160

"80" and Queen: 20p, As child. 40p, Wearing tiara. 50p, Wearing tiara, diff. £1.30, Wearing hat.
No. 895: a, Wearing tiara, diff. b, Without head covering.

Wmk. 373

2006, Apr. 21 Litho. *Perf. 14¼*
891-894 A160 Set of 4 10.00 10.00

Souvenir Sheet
895 A160 £1 Sheet of 2, #a-b 8.75 8.75

Anniversaries — A161

No. 896, 20p: a, HMS Beagle. b, Charles Darwin.
No. 897, 35p: a, SS Great Britain. b, Isambard Kingdom Brunel.
No. 898, 40p: a, Niña. b, Christopher Columbus.
No. 899, 50p: a, Map with lines of magnetic variation of the compass. b, Edmond Halley.

Perf. 13x13¼

2006, July 24 Litho. Wmk. 373

Horiz. Pairs, #a-b
896-899 A161 Set of 4 13.00 13.00

Darwin's voyage on the Beagle, 175th anniv., birth of Brunel, 200th anniv., death of Columbus, 500th anniv., birth of Halley, 350th anniv.

Greetings A162

Designs: 15p, Long Beach (Greetings from Ascension). 25p, Sunset over lava flow (Merry Christmas). 35p, Dewpond (Seasons Greetings). £1.25, Boatswain Bird Island (Happy New Year).

Wmk. 373

2006, Oct. 30 Litho. *Perf. 14¼*
900-903 A162 Set of 4 9.00 9.00

Worldwide Fund for Nature (WWF) — A163

Resplendent angelfish: 35p, Three fish. 40p, Seven fish. 50p, Three fish, diff. £1.25, Four fish.

Perf. 13¾

2007, Mar. 23 Litho. Unwmk.

904-907 A163 Set of 4 9.00 9.00
907a Sheet, 4 each #904-907 35.00 35.00

Falkland Islands War, 25th Anniv. — A164

Designs: Nos. 908, 913a, 35p, Handley Page Victor K Mk 2 tanker plane. Nos. 909, 912b, 40p, HMS Dumbarton Castle and Chinook helicopter. Nos. 910, 912c, 50p, HMS Fearless, landing craft and helicopters. Nos. 911, 913d, £1.25, Vulcan XM607 leaving Wideawake Airfield.

No. 912: a, 35p, RFA Tidespring refueling HMS Antrim. d, £1.25, Atlantic Conveyor and Harrier jet.

No. 913: b, 40p, Vickers VC 10 transport plane. c, 50p, Nimrod MR2 maritime reconnaisance plane.

2007, May 25 *Perf. 13¼x13*

Stamps With White Frames

908-911 A164 Set of 4 11.50 11.50

Stamps Without White Frames

912 A164 Sheet of 4, #a-d 12.00 12.00
913 A164 Sheet of 4, #a-d 12.00 12.00

Scouting, Cent. — A165

Lord Robert Baden-Powell blowing kudu horn and: 35p, Fleur-de-lis of scouts. 40p, Scouts rescuing turtle. 50p, Scouts on gun of HMS Hood. £1.25, Scouts on Land Rover.

2007, July 9 *Perf. 14*

914-917 A165 Set of 4 12.00 12.00

Mother Teresa (1910-97) and Princess Diana (1961-97) — A166

2007, Aug. 31

918 A166 50p multi 2.25 2.25

Wedding of Queen Elizabeth II and Prince Philip, 60th Anniv.
A167

No. 919: a, 35p, Couple in 1947. b, 90p, Wedding program. c, £1.25, Couple in 2006.

2007, Nov. 20 Litho. *Perf. 14¼*

919 A167 Horiz. strip of 3, #a-c 10.50 10.50

British Ornithological Union Expedition, 50th Anniv. — A168

No. 920, 15p: a, British Ornithological Union base. b, Drawing of extinct rail.

No. 921, 25p: a, Scientist recording sounds of Wideawake tern. b, Wideawake terns.

No. 922, 40p: a, Boatswainbird Island outpost. b, Masked booby.

No. 923, 50p: a, Scientist pushing dinghy in surf. b, Red-footed booby.

2007, Dec. 10 *Perf. 14¼*

Horiz. Pairs, #a-b

920-923 A168 Set of 4 12.00 12.00

Oviparous Creatures A169

Creature and eggs: 15p, Long-tailed blue butterfly. 20p, Ladybird beetle. 25p, Spiny lobster. 30p, Desert locust. 35p, Green turtle. 40p, Land crab. 50p, Red-footed booby. 65p, Coconut palm gecko. 90p, Common waxbill. £1, Yellowtail damselfish. £2.50, Madeiran storm petrel. £5, Red-necked francolin.

2008, Feb. 5 Litho. *Perf. 14¼*

924 A169 15p multi .55 .55
925 A169 20p multi .75 .75
926 A169 25p multi .90 .90
927 A169 30p multi 1.15 1.15
928 A169 35p multi 1.25 1.25
929 A169 40p multi 1.40 1.40
930 A169 50p multi 1.75 1.75
931 A169 65p multi 2.40 2.40
932 A169 90p multi 3.50 3.50
933 A169 £1 multi 3.75 3.75
934 A169 £2.50 multi 9.00 9.00
935 A169 £5 multi 18.00 18.00
Nos. 924-935 (12) 44.40 44.40

Sharks — A170

Designs: 35p, Bluntnose sixgill shark. 40p, Scalloped hammerhead shark. 50p, Shortfin mako shark. £1.25, Whale shark.

£1.50, Bigeye thresher shark.

2008, Mar. 14 Litho. *Perf. 14*

936-939 A170 Set of 4 11.00 10.00
939a Sheet of 16, 4 each #936-939 50.00 50.00

Souvenir Sheet

940 A170 £1.50 multi 6.25 6.25

National Aeronautical and Space Administration, 50th Anniv. — A171

Designs: No. 941, 35p, Bell X-1E airplane. No. 942, 35p, Apollo 11 Moon walk. 40p, Apollo 17 Lunar Rover. 50p, Space Shuttle Columbia. 65p, Hubble Space Telescope. 90p, International Space Station.

2008, May 23 Litho. *Perf. 14*

941-946 A171 Set of 6 12.00 12.00

Royal Air Force, 90th Anniv. — A172

Airplanes: 15p, Sopwith 7F.1 Snipe. 35p, Vickers Wellington Mk 1C. 40p, Supermarine Spitfire Mk IX. 50p, Gloster Meteor F. IV. 65p, BAe Hawk. 90p, Typhoon F-2 Eurofighter.

Unwmk.

2008, June 20 Litho. *Perf. 14*

947-952 A172 Set of 6 14.00 14.00

Botanists and Flowers — A173

Designs: 35p, Valerius Cordus (1515-44), and Cordia sebestena. 40p, Nehemiah Grew (1641-1712), and Grewia occidentalis. 50p, Charles Plumier (1646-1704), and Plumeria rubra. £2, Carl Peter Thunberg (1743-1828), and Thunbergia grandiflora.

2008, Aug. 28 Litho. *Perf. 14*

953-956 A173 Set of 4 13.50 13.50

Christmas A174

Santa Claus: 15p, Holding microphone. 25p, With reindeer in surf. 50p, On inflatable lounger in water. £2, Piloting flying sleigh.

2008, Nov. 22

957-960 A174 Set of 4 11.00 11.00

Longest-Reigning British Monarchs — A175

Designs: 35p, King Henry III and Tower of London. 40p, King James I and Stirling Castle. 50p, King George III and Windsor Castle. 65p, Queen Victoria and Osborne House. £1.25, Queen Elizabeth II and Buckingham Palace.

2008, Dec. 15

961-965 A175 Set of 5 11.00 11.00

Marine Mammals A176

Designs: 35p, Bottlenose dolphins. 40p, Pantropical spotted dolphins. 50p, Sperm whale. £1.25, Gervais' beaked whales.

£2, Humpback whale.

2009, Mar. 23 *Perf. 14x14¾*

966-969 A176 Set of 4 11.50 11.50
969a Sheet, 4 each #966-969 40.00 40.00

Souvenir Sheet

970 A176 £2 multi 9.00 9.00

Naval Aviation, Cent. A177

No. 971, 35p: a, Flight Sub-lieutenant Rex Warneford and Victoria Cross. b, Moraine-Saulnier L destroys Zeppelin LZ-37.

No. 972, 35p: a, Squadron Commander Richard Bell Davies and Victoria Cross. b, Nieuport 10 taking off.

No. 973, 40p: a, Lieutenant Commander Eugene Esmonde and Victoria Cross. b, Fairey Swordfish attacking German warships.

No. 974, 50p: a, Lieutenant Robert Hampton Gray and Victoria Cross. b, Corsair bombing Japanese warships.

2009, May 7 *Perf. 14*

Horiz. Pairs, #a-b

971-974 A177 Set of 4 11.50 11.50

Botany — A178

Designs: No. 975, 35p, Raspberry. No. 976, 35p, Blue water lily. 40p, Prickly pear. 50p, Ascension lily. 65p, Yellowboy. 90p, Joseph Dalton Hooker (1817-1911), botanist.

2009, Sept. 7 *Perf. 14*

975-980 A178 Set of 6 11.00 11.00

Turtle Research and Conservation — A179

No. 981, 15p: a, Early turtle tracking and head of turtle. b, Dr. Archie Carr (1909-87) and map of Ascension.

No. 982, 35p: a, Turtle laying eggs and head of turtle. b, Turtle hatchlings and map of Ascension.

No. 983, 40p: a, Beach raking and head of turtle. b, Population monitoring and map of Ascension.

No. 984, 65p: a, Turtle rescue and head of turtle. b, Turtle rescue and map of Ascension.

2009, Oct. 1 *Perf. 13¾*

Horiz. Pairs, #a-b

981-984 A179 Set of 4 10.00 10.00

Charles Darwin (1809-82), Naturalist A180

Darwin and: 35p, Woodpecker finch. 40p, Marine iguanas. 50p, Galapagos tortoise. £2, Galapagos penguins.

2009, Nov. 9 Unwmk. *Perf. 14*

985-988 A180 Set of 4 12.50 12.50

White-tailed Tropicbird A181

Designs: 35p, Bird in rock crevice. 40p, Bird on rock. 50p, Juvenile in flight. £1.25, Adult in flight.

2009, Dec. 4 Litho. *Perf. 14*

989-992 A181 Set of 4 11.50 11.50
992a Sheet, 4 each #989-992 47.50 47.50

Reef Fish — A182

Designs: 35p, Hardback soldier. 40p, Grouper. 50p, Five fingers. £1.25, Rock bullseye.

£2, Softback soldier.

2010, Mar. 19 *Perf. 13¾*

993-996 A182 Set of 4 11.00 11.00
996a Sheet, 4 each #993-996 47.50 47.50

Souvenir Sheet

997 A182 £2 multi 8.25 8.25

A183

Girl Guides, Cent. A184

Designs: 40p, Girl Guides wearing clown noses. 50p, Girl Guides and fish. 90p, Leaders holding cake. £1.25, Girl Guide climbing rock.

No. 1002: a, Olave Baden-Powell (1889-1977). b, Agnes Baden-Powell (1858-1945). c, Lord Robert Baden-Powell (1857-1941).

2010, Apr. 10 *Perf. 14*

998-1001 A183 Set of 4 11.50 11.50

Souvenir Sheet

1002 A184 £1 Sheet of 3, #a-c 11.50 11.50

Miniature Sheet

Battle of Britain, 70th Anniv. A185

No. 1003: a, Supermarine Spitfire R6803. b, Hawker Hurricane V7383. c, Supermarine Spitfire X4036. d, Hawker Hurricane R4175. e, Supermarine Spitfire R6885. f, Hawker Hurricane V6684. g, Supermarine Spitfire K9998. h, Hawker Hurricane R4118.

2010, May 7 ***Perf. 14***

1003 A185 50p Sheet of 8 #a-h 15.00 15.00

London 2010 Festival of Stamps.

Yellow Canary — A186

Designs: 15p, Juvenile. 35p, Adult male on branch. 60p, Adult female. 90p, Adult male on ground.

2010, Oct. 11 ***Perf. 13¾***

1004-1007 A186 Set of 4 8.25 8.25

1007a Miniature sheet of 16, 4 each #1004-1007 36.00 36.00

Christmas A187

Designs: 15p, Christmas lunch. 40p, Christmas parade. 50p, Christingle. £1.25, Nativity play.

2010, Nov. 17 ***Perf. 14***

1008-1011 A187 Set of 4 8.50 8.50

Rediscovery of the Parsley Fern — A188

Ascension National Park emblem and: 15p, HMS Erebus and HMS Terror approaching Ascension, 1843. 15p, Parsley fern. 35p, Parsley fern in situ. 40p, Parsley fern seedlings in pots. £1, Parsley fern cultivation at Kew Gardens.

2011, Feb. 16 ***Perf. 13¾***

1012-1016 A188 Set of 5 7.00 7.00

Service of Queen Elizabeth II and Prince Philip A189

Designs: 15p, Queen Elizabeth II. 25p, Queen and Prince Philip. 35p, Queen and Prince Philip, diff. 40p, Queen and Prince Philip, diff. 60p, Queen and Prince Philip, diff. £1.25, Prince Philip.

£2, Queen and Prince Philip, diff.

2011, Mar. 23 ***Perf. 13¼***

1017-1022 A189 Set of 6 9.50 9.50

1022a Sheet of 6, #1017-1022, + 3 labels 9.50 9.50

Souvenir Sheet

1023 A189 £2 multi 6.50 6.50

Royal Air Force Search and Rescue, 70th Anniv. A190

Emblem and Sea King helicopter: 35p, On airplane's cargo ramp. 40p, Flying near Ascension. 90p, Approaching HMS Dumbarton Castle. £1, Approaching HMS Spartan submarine.

£2.50, Sea King helicopter in flight.

2011, May 19

1024-1027 A190 Set of 4 8.25 8.25

Souvenir Sheet

1028 A190 £2.50 multi 7.75 7.75

Miniature Sheet

Peonies A191

No. 1029 — Peony color: a, Red. b, Gray lilac. c, Light orange. d, White.

2011, June 22 ***Perf. 13¾***

1029 A191 50p Sheet of 4, #a-d 6.25 6.25

Wedding of Prince William and Catherine Middleton A192

Couple, with Middleton: 35p, Wearing hat. 90p, Without hat. £1.25, Seated in coach in wedding dress.

£2, Couple standing on wedding day, vert.

2011, July 20 ***Perf. 14***

1030-1032 A192 Set of 3 7.75 7.75

Souvenir Sheet

Perf. 14¾x14

1033 A192 £2 multi 6.25 6.25

No. 1033 contains one 29x45mm stamp.

Worldwide Fund for Nature (WWF) — A193

Phaethon aethereus: Nos. 1034, 1038a, 35p, Bird in rock crevice. Nos. 1035, 1038b, 40p, Two birds in flight. Nos. 1036, 1038c, 50p, Adult and juvenile in rock crevice. Nos. 1037, 1038d, £1.25, Bird in flight.

2011, Aug. 31

Stamps With White Frames

1034-1037 A193 Set of 4 7.50 7.50

Stamps Without White Frames

1038 A193 Strip of 4, #a-d 8.00 8.00

Nos. 1038a-1038d were printed in sheets of 16 stamps containing four strips.

Christmas — A194

Pantomimes: 15p, Mother Goose. 40p, Jack and the Beanstalk. 50p, Aladdin. £1.25, Cinderella.

2011, Nov. 16 ***Perf. 14***

1039-1042 A194 Set of 4 6.75 6.75

Reign of Queen Elizabeth II, 60th Anniv. A195

Photographs of Queen Elizabeth II taken in: 15p, 2011. 25p, 1998. 35p, 1988. 40p, 1975. 60p, 1961. £1.25, 1953.

£2, 1977.

2012, Feb. 6 ***Perf. 13¼***

1043-1048 A195 Set of 6 9.00 9.00

1048a Sheet of 6, #1043-1048, + 3 labels 9.00 9.00

Souvenir Sheet

1049 A195 £2 multi 6.00 6.00

Reef Fish — A196

Designs: 35p, Trumpetfish. 40p, Peacock flounder. 90p, Queen triggerfish. £1, Scrawled filefish.

£2, Yellow goatfish.

2012, Apr. 15 **Litho.** ***Perf. 13¾***

1050-1053 A196 Set of 4 8.00 8.00

1053a Sheet, 4 each #1050-1053 32.50 32.50

Souvenir Sheet

1054 A196 £2 multi 6.00 6.00

Sinking of the Titanic, Cent. — A197

Designs: 20p, The departure. 45p, The boat deck. 50p, The iceberg. £1, The sinking.

£2, Abandoning ship.

2012, Aug. 1 ***Perf. 14***

1055-1058 A197 Set of 4 6.50 6.50

Souvenir Sheet

1059 A197 £2 multi 6.00 6.00

Shackleton-Rowett Antarctic Expedition, 90th Anniv. — A198

No. 1060, 45p: a, Sir Ernest Shackleton (36x36mm). b, John Quiller Rowett (18x36mm). c, Frank Wild (36x36mm).

No. 1061, 50p: a, Quest leaving London (36x36mm). b, Quest at Ascension (18x36mm). c, Quest in ice (36x36mm).

2012, Sept. 17 ***Perf. 13¼***

Horiz. Strips of 3, #a-c

1060-1061 A198 Set of 2 8.50 8.50

Christmas A199

Scenes from *A Christmas Carol*, by Charles Dickens: 25c, Ebenezer Scrooge passing Christmas carolers. 40p, Ghost visiting Scrooge. 50p, Scrooge carrying Tiny Tim, vert. £1.25, Scrooge watching boy deliver turkey, vert.

2012, Nov. 15 ***Perf. 13¼x13½***

1062-1065 A199 Set of 4 7.25 7.25

Miniature Sheet

Wideawake Airfield, 70th Anniv. — A200

No. 1066: a, 45p, Wideawake tern. b, 50p, Douglas DC-3 Dakota. c, £1, Eurofighter Typhoon. d, £1.45, Masked booby.

2012, Dec. 5 ***Perf. 13¼***

1066 A200 Sheet of 4, #a-d 13.00 13.00

Aircraft — A201

Designs: 15p, Fairey Swordfish. 20p, North American B-25 Mitchell. 25p, Lockheed C-130K Hercules. 30p, Hawker Siddeley Nimrod MR2. 40p, BAE Sea Harrier FRS1. 45p, Lockheed C-5 Galaxy. 50p, Douglas DC-3 Dakota. 65p, Avro Vulcan. 90p, McDonnell Douglas Phantom F-4. £1, Eurofighter Typhoon. £2.50, Lockheed C-121. £5, Shorts Belfast.

2013, Jan. 15 ***Perf. 13¾***

1067	A201	15p multi	.50	.50
1068	A201	20p multi	.65	.65
1069	A201	25p multi	.80	.80
1070	A201	30p multi	.95	.95
1071	A201	40p multi	1.25	1.25
1072	A201	45p multi	1.40	1.40
1073	A201	50p multi	1.60	1.60
1074	A201	65p multi	2.10	2.10
1075	A201	90p multi	3.00	3.00
1076	A201	£1 multi	3.25	3.25
1077	A201	£2.50 multi	8.00	8.00
1078	A201	£5 multi	16.00	16.00
	Nos. 1067-1078 (12)		39.50	39.50

Items Commemorating British Coronations A202

Coronation of Queen Elizabeth II, 60th Anniv. — A203

Various items commemorating the coronation of: 45p, Queen Victoria. 50p, King Edward VII. 70p, King George V. £1.10, King George VI. £1.25, Queen Elizabeth II.

2013, Feb. 6 ***Perf. 14***

1079-1083 A202 Set of 5 12.00 12.00

Souvenir Sheet

Perf. 14¾x14¼

1084 A203 £2 multi 8.00 8.00

British Settlement of Ascension, Bicent. (in 2015) — A204

Imprisonment of Napoleon Bonaparte on Ascension: 45p, Joséphine Bonaparte at Malmaison, by François Pascal Simon. 50p, Bonaparte at the Bridge of Arcole, by Antoine-Jean Gros. 60p, Napoleon and his General Staff, by Jean-Léon Gérôme. £1.45, Napoleon as First Consul, detail of painting by Jean-Baptiste Isabey.

2013, May 21 *Perf. 13¾*
1085-1088 A204 Set of 4 11.00 11.00

Lady Margaret Thatcher (1925-2013), British Prime Minister — A205

Photographs of Thatcher: 45p, Giving "Victory" sign, 1976. 50p, In cockpit of Sea Harrier jet, 1982. 60p, Holding teacup during visit to Ascension, 1992. £1.45, At Order of the Garter ceremony, 1995.

2013, June 14
1089-1092 A205 Set of 4 11.00 11.00

Ascension Frigatebirds A206

Designs: 20p, Male and female. 45p, Male on egg. 50p, Chick. 60p, Female and chick. £1.10, Juvenile. £1.45, Male in flight.

2013, Aug. 16 *Perf. 13¼x13½*
1093-1098 A206 Set of 6 16.00 16.00

Shallow Marine Surveys Group — A207

Marine life: Nos. 1099, 1103a, 45p, Fire worm. Nos. 1100, 1103b, 50p, Black bar soldier fish. Nos. 1101, 1103c, 60p, Endemic white hawk fish. Nos. 1102, 1103d, £1.45, Atlantic blue tang.
No. 1104a, £1, Anemone, vert.

2013, Aug. 29 *Perf. 13¼x13½*
Stamps With White Frames
1099-1102 A207 Set of 4 11.00 11.00
Stamps Without White Frames
1103 A230 Strip of 4, #a-d 11.00 11.00
Souvenir Sheet
Perf. 13½x13¼
1104 A207 Sheet of 3 (see footnote) 11.00 11.00
a. A207 £1 multi 3.75 3.75

No. 1104 contains No. 1104a, Falkland Islands No. 1107a and South Georgia and South Sandwich Islands No. 485a. This sheet was sold in Ascension, Falkland Islands and South Georgia and South Sandwich Islands.

Churches A208

Stained-Glass Windows A209

Designs: 45p, Grotto of Our Lady Catholic Church. 50p, Window depicting Madonna and Child. 60p, St. Mary's Anglican Church. £1, Window depicting St. Michael.

2013, Nov. 18 **Litho.** *Perf. 13¼*
Stamps With White Frames
1105 A208 45p multi 1.50 1.50
1106 A209 50p multi 1.75 1.75
1107 A208 60p multi 2.00 2.00
1108 A209 £1 multi 3.25 3.25
Nos. 1105-1108 (4) 8.50 8.50
Stamps Without White Frames
1109 Horiz. strip of 4 8.50 8.50
a. A208 45p multi 1.50 1.50
b. A209 50p multi 1.75 1.75
c. A208 60p multi 2.00 2.00
d. A209 £1 multi 3.25 3.25

Christmas.

British Settlement of Ascension, Bicent. (in 2015) — A210

The Napoleonic Years: 50p, Engraving of Napoleon Bonaparte after signing of Treaty of Amiens, 1802. 55p, Napoleon I in Coronation Robes, by François Gérard. 60p, Lord Horatio Nelson, by Lemuel Francis Abbott. £1.60, Napoleon at Wagram, by Emile Jean-Horace Vernet.

2014, Apr. 28 **Litho.** *Perf. 13¾*
1110-1113 A210 Set of 4 12.50 12.50

Royal Christenings — A211

Photograph from christening of: 50p, Queen Elizabeth II, 1926. 55p, Prince Charles, 1948. 60p, Prince William, 1982. £1.60, Prince George, 2013.

2014, May 21 **Litho.** *Perf. 13x13¼*
1114-1117 A211 Set of 4 12.50 12.50

World War I, Cent. — A212

Various poppies: 50p, 55p, 60p, £1.60.

2014, Aug. 4 **Litho.** *Perf. 14¾x14*
1118-1121 A212 Set of 4 12.50 12.50

Royal Marines, 350th Anniv. — A213

Designs: 20p, Duke of York and Albany's Maritime Regiment of Foot on man-of-war, 1664. 50p, Light Infantry and barracks on Ascension, 19th cent. 55p, Light Infantry at Gallipoli, 1915. 60p, Royal Marines Commandos at Eastney, 1970s. 65p, Royal Marines Band Service Bugler at Deal, 1996. £1, Royal Marines Commandos, 2014.

2014, Oct. 28 **Litho.** *Perf. 14*
1122-1127 A213 Set of 6 12.50 12.50

Rosetta Mission — A214

Designs: 35p, Ariane 5 launching Rosetta. 55p, Rosetta spacecraft. 65p, Deploying Philae lander. £1.60, Descent of Philae.
£3, Comet 67P/Churyumov-Gerasimenko.

2014, Dec. 30 **Litho.** *Perf. 14*
1128-1131 A214 Set of 4 9.75 9.75
Souvenir Sheet
1132 A214 £3 multi 9.25 9.25

British Settlement of Ascension, Bicent. — A215

The Napoleonic Wars: 55p, Napoleon Bonaparte on the Borodino Heights, by Vasily V. Vereshchagin. 60p, Napoleon at Fontainebleau, by Paul Delaroche. 65p, Arthur Wellesley, 1st Duke of Wellington, by Thomas Lawrence. £1.60, Napoleon dictating his memoirs in exile.

2015, Apr. 27 **Litho.** *Perf. 13¾*
1133-1136 A215 Set of 4 9.50 9.50

Magna Carta, 800th Anniv. — A216

Designs: 50p, King John examining Magna Carta. 55p, Ascension Government building. 60p, Magistrate's Court, Ascension. £1.60, Arms of Ascension, King John.

2015, June 15 **Litho.** *Perf. 13*
1137-1140 A216 Set of 4 9.50 9.50

Queen Elizabeth II, Longest-Reigning British Monarch — A217

Queen Elizabeth II and events during her reign: 50p, Publications reporting on her coronation, 1953. 55p, First men on the Moon, 1969. 65p, Avro Vulcan (end of Cold War), 1991. £1.60, The Spirit of Chartwell in Diamond Jubilee celebration, 2012.

2015, Sept. 9 **Litho.** *Perf. 14*
1141-1144 A217 Set of 4 9.00 9.00

British Settlement of Ascension, Bicent. — A218

200th anniversary emblem and: 35p, King George III. 50p, Flag of Ascension. 55p, Coat of arms of Ascension. £1.60, Queen Elizabeth II.

2015, Oct. 22 **Litho.** *Perf. 14*
1145-1148 A218 Set of 4 8.50 8.50

William Dampier (1651-1715), Explorer — A219

Designs: 25p, Dampier. 35p, Dampier's ship, HMS Roebuck. £1, Sinking of HMS Roebuck at Ascension Island, 1701. £1.60, Diver and bell of HMS Roebuck.

2015, Dec. 1 **Litho.** *Perf. 14*
1149-1152 A219 Set of 4 8.75 8.75

Worldwide Fund for Nature (WWF) — A220

Red-footed booby: 20p, Bird on rock. 50p, Adult and chick. 55p, Heads of brown and white morphs. £2, Juvenile.

Perf. 13¼x13½
2016, Feb. 22 **Litho.**
Stamps With White Frames
1153-1156 A220 Set of 4 8.75 8.75
Stamps Without White Frames
1157 Strip of 4 9.50 9.50
a. A220 20p multi .60 .60
b. A220 50p multi 1.40 1.40
c. A220 55p multi 1.60 1.60
d. A220 £2 multi 5.75 5.75

Queen Elizabeth II, 90th Birthday — A221

Photograph of Queen Elizabeth II from: 50p, 1951. 55p, 1973. 65p, 1974, £1.60, 1995.
£3, Queen Elizabeth II in 1961.

2016, Apr. 21 **Litho.** *Perf. 14*
1158-1161 A221 Set of 4 8.75 8.75
Souvenir Sheet
1162 A221 £3 multi 8.00 8.00

British Broadcasting Corporation Transmitting Station on Ascension, 50th Anniv. — A222

Designs: 20p, Original control desk. 25p, Klinka Klub and short wave antenna array towers, 1980s. 50p, Atlantic relay station, English Bay. 55p, Current transmitting station. 65p, BBC wind turbines, turtle. £1.60, Current transmitting station main office.

2016, July 3 **Litho.** *Perf. 13½*
1163-1168 A222 Set of 6 9.50 9.50

Scenes from Plays by William Shakespeare (1564-1616) A223

Designs: 50p, Twelfth Night. 55p, Henry V. 65p, Hamlet. £1.60, Romeo and Juliet.

2016, Aug. 8 **Litho.** *Perf. 14*
1169-1172 A223 Set of 4 7.75 7.75

Fish — A224

Designs: 50p, Resplendent angelfish. 55p, White hawkfish. 65p, Ascension wrasse. £1.60, Yellowtail damselfish.

2016, Oct. 17 **Litho.** *Perf. 13¼x13½*
1173-1176 A224 Set of 4 7.25 7.25

Eels — A225

Designs: 20p, Broadbanded moray eel. 35p, Whitespotted moray eel. 50p, Chain moray eel. 55p, Goldtail moray eel. 65p, Brown moray eel. £1.60, Spotted snake eel.

2017, Apr. 12 **Litho.** *Perf. 13¼*
1177-1182 A225 Set of 6 10.00 10.00

70th Wedding Anniversary of Queen Elizabeth II and Prince Philip — A226

Photographs of Queen Elizabeth II and Prince Philip from: 50p, 1947. 55p, 1963. 65p, 1982. £1.60, 2006.

2017, Nov. 20 Litho. *Perf. 13x13¼*

1183-1186 A226 Set of 4 8.00 8.00

Plankton — A227

Designs: 20p, Hyperiid amphipod. 35p, Land crab zoea larva. 50p, Sapphirinid copepod. 55p, Stomatopod shrimp larva. 65p, Gastropod mollusc larva. £1.60, Polychaete worm larva.

2017, Dec. 6 Litho. *Perf. 13¼x13½*

1187-1192 A227 Set of 6 10.50 10.50

Johngarthia Lagostoma A228

Designs: 20p, Female crab with eggs. 35p, Crab in megalops phase. 50p, Juvenile crab. 55p, Crab feeding on moss. 65p, Crab in purple morph stage. £1.60, Crab in yellow morph stage.

2018, Jan. 24 Litho. *Perf. 13½x13¾*

1193-1198 A228 Set of 6 11.00 11.00

Royal Air Force, Cent. — A229

Designs: 20p, Royal Aircraft Factory SE5a. 35p, Hawker Hurricane. 50p, Avro Vulcan. £2, Tornado.

2018, July 2 Litho. *Perf. 13¼x13½*

1199-1202 A229 Set of 4 8.00 8.00

Wedding of Prince Harry and Meghan Markle — A230

Designs: 20p, Engagement photograph. 50p, Couple at dance performance. 55p, Couple at altar. £2, Couple in carriage.

£3, Couple leaving St. George's Chapel on wedding day, vert.

Perf. 13¼x13½

2018, Aug. 14 Litho.

1203-1206 A230 Set of 4 8.50 8.50

Souvenir Sheet

Perf. 13½x13¼

1207 A230 £3 multi 7.75 7.75

Ships — A231

Designs: £1.60, RMS St. Helena I, 1978-90. £2, RMS St. Helena II, 1990-2018.

2018, Oct. 8 Litho. *Perf. 13¼x13¾*

1208-1209 A231 Set of 2 9.25 9.25

Migratory Turtles A232

No. 1210, 65p — Hawksbill turtle and map of: a, South America. b, Ascension Island and Africa.

No. 1211, £1 — Green turtle and map of: a, South America. b, Ascension Island and Africa.

2018, Dec. 5 Litho. *Perf. 13¼x13½*

Horiz. Pairs, #a-b

1210-1211 A232 Set of 2 8.50 8.50

D-Day, 75th Anniv. — A233

Designs: 20p, Troops in door of glider. 35p, Third Infantry Division soldiers on French beach. 50p, Commandos coming ashore. £2, HMS Warspite shelling German batteries.

2019, June 6 Litho. *Perf. 13¼x13½*

1212-1215 A233 Set of 4 7.75 7.75

First Man on the Moon, 50th Anniv. — A234

Designs: 35p, Lunar Module in space. 55p, Astronaut on ladder of Lunar Module. £1, Astronaut on Moon. £1.60, Astronaut and United States flag on Moon.

2019, Dec. 6 Litho. *Perf. 13¼*

1216-1219 A234 Set of 4 9.25 9.25

Island Scenes, Flora and Fauna — A235

Designs: 15p, Bonetta Cemetery. 20p, Ascension Island land crab. 25p, Red Lion Barracks, Green Mountain. 30p, Deadman's Beach. 40p, St. Mary's Church, Georgetown. 50p, Green sea turtle. 60p, Resplendent angelfish. 65p, Ascension donkeys. £1, Ascension lily. £1.30, Ascension Island frigatebirds. £2.50, Boatswainbird Island. £5, Wideawake tern.

Perf. 13¼x13¾

2020, Dec. 22 Litho.

1220	A235	15p	multi	.40	.40
1221	A235	20p	multi	.55	.55
1222	A235	25p	multi	.70	.70
1223	A235	30p	multi	.85	.85
1224	A235	40p	multi	1.10	1.10
1225	A235	50p	multi	1.40	1.40
1226	A235	60p	multi	1.60	1.60
1227	A235	65p	multi	1.75	1.75
1228	A235	£1	multi	2.75	2.75
1229	A235	£1.30	multi	3.50	3.50
1230	A235	£2.50	multi	6.75	6.75
1231	A235	£5	multi	14.00	14.00
	Nos. 1220-1231 (12)			35.35	35.35

Queen Elizabeth II, 95th Birthday — A236

Designs: 15p, Princess Elizabeth, 1932. 20p, Queen Elizabeth II at her coronation. 35p, Queen Elizabeth II with Prince Philip. 65p, Queen Elizabeth II with her dog, 1952. £1, Queen Elizabeth II and Prince Philip, 2015. £1.60, Queen Elizabeth II, 2019.

2021, Apr. 21 Litho. *Perf. 13¼*

1232-1237 A236 Set of 6 11.00 11.00

See Isle of Man No. 2150a.

Blue Belt Program, 5th Anniv. — A237

Part of map of Ascension Island and: Nos. 1238, 1242a, £1, Yellowfin tuna. Nos. 1239, 1242b, £1, Masked booby. Nos. 1240, 1242c, £1, Green turtle. Nos. 1241, 1242d, £1, White-striped cleaner shrimp.

2021, Nov. 9 Litho. *Perf. 13½*

Stamps With White Frames

1238-1241 A237 Set of 4 11.00 11.00

Miniature Sheet

Stamps Without White Frames

1242 A237 £1 Sheet of 4, #a-d 11.00 11.00

Galapagos Sharks — A238

Various photographs of Galapagos sharks: 50p, 55p, 65p, £1.60.

£3, Galapagos shark, diff.

2022, Jan. 31 Litho. *Perf. 13¼x13½*

1243-1246 A238 Set of 4 9.00 9.00

Souvenir Sheet

1247 A238 £3 multi 8.25 8.25

Reign of Queen Elizabeth II, 70th Anniv. — A239

Queen Elizabeth II wearing: £1.60, Crown. £2, Hat.

£3, Queen Elizabeth II, vert.

2022, Apr. 14 Litho. *Perf. 13*

1248-1249 A239 Set of 2 9.00 9.00

Souvenir Sheet

Perf. 13x13¼

1250 A239 £3 multi 7.50 7.50

No. 1250 contains one 29x48mm stamp.

Liberation of the Falkland Islands, 40th Anniv. — A240

British military aircraft and ship used in the Falklands War: 20p, Victor refueling airplanes. 35p, RFA Sir Percivale. 50p, Chinook helicopter carrying cargo container. £3, Harrier GR 3 jet.

2022, June 22 Litho. *Perf. 13½*

1251-1254 A240 Set of 4 10.00 10.00

Civilian Rule in Ascension, Cent. — A241

Designs: 50p, HMS Zenobia. 55p, Robert Francis Peel (1874-1924), Governor of St. Helena, and first Governor of Ascension. 65p, King George V (1865-1936). £1.60, Flag of Ascension.

2022, Dec. 19 Litho. *Perf. 13¼*

1255-1258 A241 Set of 4 8.00 8.00

AIR POST STAMPS

AP1

AP2

AP3

AP4

Green Turtles
AP5 AP6

2015, Feb. 14 Litho. *Perf. 13¼*

Stamps With White Frames

C1	AP1	(50p) multi		1.40	1.40
a.	Dated "2019"			1.40	1.40
C2	AP2	(50p) multi		1.40	1.40
a.	Dated "2019"			1.40	1.40
C3	AP3	(50p) multi		1.40	1.40
a.	Dated "2019"			1.40	1.40
C4	AP4	(50p) multi		1.40	1.40
a.	Dated "2019"			1.40	1.40
C5	AP5	(50p) multi		1.40	1.40
a.	Dated "2019"			1.40	1.40
C6	AP6	(50p) multi		1.40	1.40
a.	Dated "2019"			1.40	1.40
	Nos. C1-C6 (6)			8.40	8.40

Miniature Sheet

Stamps Without White Frames

C7	Sheet of 6	8.50	8.50
a.	AP1 (50p) multi	1.40	1.40
b.	AP2 (50p) multi	1.40	1.40
c.	AP3 (50p) multi	1.40	1.40
d.	AP4 (50p) multi	1.40	1.40
e.	AP5 (50p) multi	1.40	1.40
f.	AP6 (50p) multi	1.40	1.40
g.	Sheet of 6, #C7h-C7m, dated "2019"	8.50	8.50
h.	As #C7a, dated "2019"	1.40	1.40
i.	As #C7b, dated "2019"	1.40	1.40
j.	As #C7c, dated "2019"	1.40	1.40
k.	As #C7d, dated "2019"	1.40	1.40
l.	As #C7e, dated "2019"	1.40	1.40
m.	As #C7f, dated "2019"	1.40	1.40

Issued: Nos. C1a-C6a, C7g, 12/12/19.

POSTAGE DUE STAMPS

Outline Map of Ascension — D1

1986 Litho. *Perf. 15x14*

J1	D1	1p	beige & brown	.25	*.30*
J2	D1	2p	orange & brown	.25	*.30*
J3	D1	5p	org ver & brn	.25	*.30*
J4	D1	7p	violet & black	.25	*.50*
J5	D1	10p	ultra & black	.45	*.75*
J6	D1	25p	pale green & blk	.90	*1.25*
	Nos. J1-J6 (6)			2.35	*3.40*

AUSTRALIAN STATES

NEW SOUTH WALES

'nü sauth 'wāˌəlz

LOCATION — Southeast coast of Australia in the South Pacific Ocean
GOVT. — British Crown Colony
AREA — 309,432 sq. mi.
POP. — 1,500,000 (estimated, 1900)
CAPITAL — Sydney

In 1901 New South Wales united with five other British colonies to form the Commonwealth of Australia. Stamps of Australia are now used.

12 Pence = 1 Shilling
20 Shillings = 1 Pound

Watermarks

Wmk. 12 — Crown and Single-lined A

Wmk. 13 — Large Crown and Double-lined A

Wmk. 49 — Double-lined Numerals Corresponding with the Value

Wmk. 50 — Single-lined Numeral

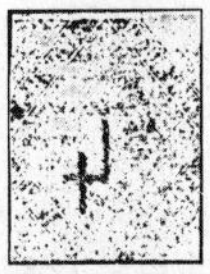
Wmk. 51 — Single-lined Numeral

Wmk. 52 — Single-lined Numeral

Wmk. 53 — 5/-

Wmk. 54 — Small Crown and NSW

Wmk. 55 — Large Crown and NSW

Wmk. 56 — NSW

Wmk. 57 — 5/- NSW in Diamond

Wmk. 58 — 20/- NSW in Circle

Wmk. 70 — V and Crown

Wmk. 199 — Crown and A in Circle

Values for unused stamps are for examples with original gum as defined in the catalogue introduction except for Nos. 1-20 which are rarely found with gum and are valued without gum. Very fine examples of Nos. 35-100, F3-F5, J1-J10 and O1-O40 will have perforations touching the framelines or design on one or more sides due to the narrow spacing of the stamps on the plates and imperfect perforation methods. Stamps with perfs clear of the design on all four sides are scarce and will command higher prices.

Seal of the Colony — A1

A1 has no clouds. A2 has clouds added to the design, except in pos. 15.

1850 Unwmk. Engr. *Imperf.*

Yellowish Wove Paper

1	A1 1p red, *yelsh wove*	16,000.	625.00
a.	1p brownish red	17,250.	650.00
c.	1p carmine	17,250.	650.00
d.	1p crimson lake	17,250.	650.00

Bluish Wove Paper

b.	1p red, *bluish wove*	15,000.	650.00
1e	A1 1p lake	16,000.	650.00

Seal of the Colony — A2

Re-engraved, with Clouds

1850, Aug. Yellowish Wove Paper

2	A2 1p red, *yelsh wove*	14,000.	550.00
f.	Hill unshaded	18,500.	850.00
g.	No clouds	18,500.	850.00
h.	No trees	18,500.	850.00
2i	A2 1p vermilion	13,750.	675.00

Bluish Wove Paper

c.	A3 1p carmine red, *bluish wove*	13,250.	750.00
j.	Hill unshaded	18,000.	750.00
k.	No clouds	18,000.	750.00
l.	No trees	18,000.	750.00
2m	A2 1p brownish lake	13,500.	750.00
2n	A2 1p crimson lake	13,500.	750.00
2o	A2 1p gooseberry red	16,500.	750.00

Laid Paper

b.	A2 1p carmine red, *yellowish laid*	18,000.	800.00
p.	Hill unshaded	—	1,275.
q.	No clouds	—	1,275.
r.	No trees	—	1,275.
e.	1p carmine red, *bluish laid*		
2s	A2 1p vermilion, *bluish*	19,000.	600.00

Printed in panes of 25 (5x5). Twenty-five varieties.

Stamps from early impressions of the plate sell at considerably higher prices.

No. 1 was reproduced by the collotype process in a souvenir sheet distributed at the London International Stamp Exhibition 1950. The paper is white.

Plate I
A3

Plate II
A4

Plate I: Vertically lined background.

Plate I re-touched: Lines above and below "POSTAGE" and "TWO PENCE" deepened. Outlines of circular band around picture also deepened.

Plate II (First re-engraving of Plate I): Horizontally lined background; the bale on the left side is dated and there is a dot in the star in each corner.

Plate II retouched: Dots and dashes added in lower spandrels.

Plate I

1850, Jan. 1 Early Impressions

a.	Early impression	20,000.	625.00
b.	Double line on bale (Pos. 2/7)		1,250.
3c	A3 2p deep blue, *yelsh wove*	*18,000.*	725.00

Intermediate Impressions

3d	A3 2p gray blue, *yelsh wove*	12,750.	425.00
3e	A3 2p deep blue, *yelsh wove*	13,750.	500.00

Late (worn plate) Impressions

3	A3 2p blue, *yelsh wove*	10,500.	225.00
3f	A3 2p deep blue, *yelsh wove*	10,500.	225.00

Printed in panes of 24 (12x2). Twenty-four varieties.

Plate I, Retouched

4	A3 2p blue, *yelsh wove*	12,750.	360.00
4a	A3 2p gray blue, *yelsh wove*	13,750.	450.00

Twelve varieties.

Plate II

1850, Apr. Early Impressions

h.	Early impression	16,500.	350.00
j.	"CREVIT" omitted (Pos. 2/1)	22,500.	1,000.
k.	Pick & shovel omitted (Pos. 1/10)	22,000.	625.00
l.	No whip (Pos. 1/4, 1/8, 2/8)	—	525.00
5m	A3 2p bright blue, *bluish wove*	16,500.	350.00
5n	A3 2p indigo blue, *yelsh wove*	16,500.	375.00
5o	A3 2p lilac blue, *yelsh wove*		*1,750.*

Late (worn plate) Impressions

5	A4 2p blue, *yelsh wove*	10,500.	175.00
a.	2p blue, *bluish wove*	10,500.	175.00
b.	2p 2p blue, *grayish wove*	10,500.	175.00
5p	A4 2p prussian blue, *bluish wove*	10,500.	225.00
c.	"CREVIT" omitted	16,500.	675.00
d.	Pick and shovel omitted	—	450.00
e.	No whip	*14,750.*	365.00

Plate II, Retouched

5F	A4 2p blue, *bluish wove*	11,500.	270.00
g.	No whip	—	425.00
i.	"CREVIT" omitted	—	585.00
5q	A4 2p prussian blue, *bluish wove*	11,500.	360.00

Eleven varieties.

Plate III
A5

Plate IV
A6

Plate III (Second re-engraving of Plate I): The bale is not dated and, with the exception of Nos. 7, 10 and 12, it is single-lined. There are no dots in the stars.

Plate IV (Third re-engraving of Plate I): The bale is double-lined and there is a circle in the center of each star.

1850-51 Wove Paper

6	A5 2p bl, *grayish wove*	11,500.	270.00
a.	Fan with 6 segments	14,500.	585.00
b.	Double-lined bale	—	375.00
c.	No whip	—	425.00
6d	A5 2p ultramarine	11,500.	270.00
7	A6 2p blue, *bluish wove* ('51)	12,500.	225.00
b.	2p blue, *grayish wove*	12,500.	250.00
c.	Fan with 6 segments (Pos. 2/8)	—	375.00
d.	No clouds (Pos. 2/10)	—	375.00
e.	Hill not shaded (Pos. 1/12)	—	400.00
f.	No waves (Pos. 1/9, 2/5)	—	*550.00*
7g	A6 2p 2p ultramarine	12,500.	270.00
7h	A6 2p 2p prussian blue	12,500.	225.00

Laid Paper

7a	A6 2p 2p ultra, *white laid*	13,500.	275.00
7i	A6 2p prussian blue	14,500.	340.00
j.	Fan with 6 segments (Pos. 2/8)	—	450.00
k.	No clouds (Pos. 2/10)	17,500.	450.00
l.	Hill not shaded (Pos. 1/12)		450.00
m.	No waves (Pos. 1/9, 2/5)		400.00
n.	"PENOE" (Pos. 1/10, 2/12)		450.00

Twenty-four varieties.

Plate V — A7

A8

Plate V (Fourth re-engraving of Plate I): There is a pearl in the fan-shaped ornament below the central design.

1850-51 Wove Paper

8	A7 2p blue, *grayish wove* ('51)	12,500.	270.00
b.	Fan with 6 segments (Pos. 2/8)	—	450.00
c.	Pick and shovel omitted (Pos. 2/5)	—	475.00
8d	A7 2p ultramarine	12,500.	270.00

Laid Paper

a.	2p ultra, *yellowish laid*	15,500.	450.00
e.	Fan with 6 segments (Pos. 2/8)	—	650.00
f.	Pick and shovel omitted (Pos. 2/5)	—	650.00

Yellowish Wove Paper

a.	3p green, *yellowish wove*	12,500.	350.00
9h	A8 3p emerald green	14,500.	375.00
e.	No whip	—	550.00
f.	"SIGIIIUM" for "SIGILLUM" (Pos. 5/3)	—	725.00
9g	A8 3p myrtle green	*23,500.*	*1,500.*

Bluish Wove Paper

9	A8 3p green, *bluish wove*	12,500.	325.00
9d	A8 3p emerald green	13,500.	325.00
i.	No whip (Pos. 4/3, 4/4)	—	450.00
j.	"SIGIIIUM" for "SIGILLUM" (Pos. 5/3)	—	650.00

Laid Paper

b.	3p green, *yellowish laid*	17,500.	825.00
k.	No whip (Pos. 4/3, 4/4)	—	*1,000.*
l.	"SIGIIIUM" for "SIGILLUM" (Pos. 5/3)	—	*1,200.*
c.	3p green, *bluish laid*	17,500.	825.00
9m	A8 3p bright green, *yellowish laid*	*19,000.*	*900.00*

Twenty-four varieties of No. 8, twenty-five of No. 9.

Queen Victoria — A9

TWO PENCE
Plate I — Background of wavy lines.
Plate II — Stars in corners.
Plate III (Plate I re-engraved) — Background of crossed lines.

1851 Yellowish Wove Paper

10	A9 1p carmine	*4,500.*	360.00
b.	No leaves to right of "SOUTH"	*6,000.*	900.00
c.	Two leaves to right of "SOUTH"	*6,000.*	1,000.
d.	"WALE"	*6,000.*	1,000.
11	A9 2p ultra, Plate I	*2,250.*	135.00

1852 Bluish Laid Paper

12	A9 1p orange brown	7,500.	540.00
a.	1p claret	7,500.	525.00
b.	As "a," no leaves to right of "SOUTH"		1,125.
c.	As "a," two leaves to right of "SOUTH"		1,250.
d.	As "a," "WALE"		1,250.

Queen Victoria — A10

SIX PENCE
Plate I — Background of fine lines.
Plate II (Plate I re-engraved) — Background of coarse lines.

1852-55

Bluish or Grayish Wove Paper

13	A9 1p red	2,250.	180.00
a.	1p carmine	2,250.	180.00
b.	1p scarlet	2,250.	225.00
c.	1p brick red	2,250.	180.00
d.	As "c," no leaves to right of "SOUTH"	4,500.	375.00
e.	As "c," two leaves to right of "SOUTH"		500.00
f.	As "c," "WALE"		500.00
14	A9 2p blue, Plate I	1,700.	42.50
a.	2p ultramarine	1,800.	42.50
b.	2p slate	1,750.	42.50
c.	2p chalky blue	1,750.	42.50
d.	2p prussian blue	1,250.	42.50
15	A10 2p blue, Plate II ('53)	2,600.	120.00
a.	"WAEES"	*3,000.*	525.00
b.	2p deep ultramarine	2,600.	150.00
c.	2p prussian blue	2,600.	135.00
d.	As "c," "WAEES"	—	550.00
16	A9 2p blue, Plate III ('55)	1,450.	85.00
a.	"WALES" partly covered with wavy lines	5,500.	325.00
b.	2p blue, *white paper* ('55)	1,450.	85.00
c.	As "b," "WALES" partly covered with wavy lines	—	300.00
17	A9 3p green	5,500.	190.00
a.	3p emerald	*6,250.*	270.00
b.	As "a," "WACES"	—	*725.00*
c.	3p deep green	6,250.	270.00
d.	3p yellow green	6,250.	250.00
e.	As "d," "WACES"	—	575.00
f.	3p blue green, *thick paper*	6,250.	300.00
g.	As "f," "WACES"		825.00
18	A9 6p brown, Plate I	5,000.	400.00
a.	"WALLS"	*5,750.*	1,250.
b.	6p black brown	5,000.	*1,250.*
c.	6p yellow brown	5,750.	325.00
d.	6p chocolate brown	5,250.	325.00
e.	6p yellow brown, *white paper*		*1,200.*
f.	As "e," ""WALLS"		*2,700.*
19	A9 6p brown, Plate II	5,750.	375.00
a.	6p bister brown	5,250.	375.00
20	A9 8p yellow ('53)	19,000.	1,000.
a.	8p orange	20,000.	1,000.
b.	No leaves to right of "SOUTH"	—	*2,250.*
c.	No bow at back of head	—	*2,250.*
d.	No lines in spandrel	—	*1,350.*

The plates of the 1, 2, 3 and 8p each contained 50 varieties and those of the 6p 25 varieties.

The 2p, plate II, 6p, plate II, and 8p have been reprinted on grayish blue wove paper. The reprints of the 2p have the spandrels and background much worn. Most of the reprints of the 6p have no floreate ornaments to the right and left of "South." On all the values the wreath has been retouched.

Type of 1851 and

A11

A12

A13

A14

1854-55 Wmk. 49 *Imperf.*

23	A9 1p orange	575.00	52.50
a.	No leaves to right of "SOUTH"	1,100.	180.00
b.	Two leaves to right of "SOUTH"	1,450.	200.00
c.	"WALE"	1,450.	200.00
d.	1d orange vermilion	525.00	52.50
24	A9 2p blue	475.00	15.00
a.	2p ultramarine	475.00	17.50
b.	2p Prussian blue	475.00	17.50
25	A9 3p green	800.00	55.00
a.	"WACES"	*2,150.*	225.00
b.	Watermarked "2"	*7,250.*	*2,000.*

Value for No. 25b is for copy with the design cut into.

26	A11 5p green	1,600.	725.00
27	A12 6p sage green	2,000.	42.50
28	A12 6p brown	1,950.	42.50
a.	Watermarked "8"	*4,750.*	160.00
29	A12 6p gray	750.00	85.00
a.	6p greenish gray	1,950.	75.00
b.	6p bluish gray	1,950.	85.00
c.	6p deep slate	2,150.	75.00
d.	As "c," wmk sideways		*1,250.*
e.	6p fawn	1,950.	160.00
f.	As "e," watermarked "8"	*4,750.*	145.00
g.	As "f," wmk sideways		*540.00*
30	A13 8p orange ('55)	*25,000.*	1,750.
a.	8p yellow	*25,000.*	1,575.
31	A14 1sh pale red brown	*5,250.*	125.00
a.	1sh red	*5,000.*	100.00
b.	1sh rose vermilion	*7,750.*	100.00
c.	As "b," watermarked "8"	*10,000.*	225.00

See Nos. 38-42, 56, 58, 65, 67.

Nos. 38-42 exist with wide margins. Stamps with perforations trimmed are often offered as Nos. 26, 30, and 30a.

A15

1856 *Imperf.*

32	A15 1p red	350.00	27.50
a.	1p orange red	425.00	27.50
b.	As "a," printed on both sides	*4,250.*	*2,500.*
c.	Watermarked "2"		*9,500.*
d.	1p carmine vermilion	400.00	27.50
33	A15 2p blue	350.00	12.50
a.	Watermarked "1"		*9,500.*
b.	Watermarked "5"	1,250.	95.00
c.	Watermarked "8"		*8,250.*
d.	2p dp turquoise blue	375.00	15.00
e.	2p ultramarine	350.00	15.00
f.	2p pale blue	350.00	16.00
34	A15 3p green	2,000.	125.00
a.	3p yellow green	1,850.	125.00
b.	Watermarked "2"		*5,000.*
c.	3p bluish green ('56)	1,950.	125.00
	Nos. 32-34 (3)	2,700.	165.00

The two known examples of No. 33c are in museums. Both are used.

The 1p has been reprinted in orange on paper watermarked Small Crown and NSW, and the 2p in deep blue on paper watermarked single lined "2." These reprints are usually overprinted "SPECIMEN."

See Nos. 34C-37, 54, 63, 90.

1859 Litho.

34C	A15 2p light blue	—	925.00
	On cover		*4,500.*

1860-63 Engr. Wmk. 49 *Perf. 13*

35	A15 1p red	175.00	25.00
a.	1p orange	175.00	25.00
b.	Perf. 12x13		*2,400.*
c.	Perf. 12	310.00	25.00
36	A15 2p blue, perf. 12	275.00	16.00
a.	Watermarked "1"		*4,500.*
c.	Perf. 12x13	*3,400.*	425.00
37	A15 3p blue green	110.00	14.00
a.	3p yellow green	125.00	11.00
b.	3p deep green	125.00	10.00
c.	Watermarked "6"	250.00	16.00
d.	Perf. 12	1,000.	52.50
38	A11 5p dark green	110.00	27.50
a.	5p yellow green	325.00	85.00
b.	Perf. 12	475.00	125.00
39	A12 6p brown, perf. 12	875.00	75.00
a.	6p gray, perf. 12	875.00	65.00
40	A12 6p violet	200.00	8.00
a.	6p aniline lilac	1,500.	160.00
b.	Watermarked "5"	850.00	30.00
c.	Watermarked "12"	800.00	25.00
e.	Perf. 12	775.00	20.00
f.	As "b," wmk sideways		*1,250.*
41	A13 8p yellow	575.00	50.00
a.	8p orange	600.00	50.00
b.	As "a," perf. 12	*7,750.*	1,450.
c.	8p red orange	575.00	65.00
d.	As "c," perf 12	*7,750.*	1,450.
42	A14 1sh rose	400.00	10.00
a.	1sh carmine	390.00	10.00
b.	As "a," perf. 12	400.00	30.00
c.	1sh crimson lake	400.00	10.00
d.	1sh brownish red, perf 12	1,750.	75.00
e.	As "a," pair, imperf. between		—
	Nos. 35-42 (8)	2,720.	225.50

1864 Wmk. 50 *Perf. 13*

43	A15 1p red	135.00	67.50

A16

1861-80 Wmk. 53 *Perf. 13*

44	A16 5sh dull violet	365.00	60.00
a.	5sh purple	410.00	85.00
b.	5sh dull violet, perf. 12	2,275.	350.00
c.	5sh purple, perf. 12	—	90.00
d.	5sh purple, perf. 10	325.00	90.00
e.	5sh purple, perf. 12x10	450.00	90.00
f.	5sh royal purple, perf 13 ('72)	900.00	77.50
g.	5sh deep rose lilac, perf 13 ('75)	250.00	47.50
h.	5sh rose lilac, perf 10 ('83)	300.00	60.00
i.	5sh purple, perf 10x12 ('85)	—	225.00
j.	5sh reddish purple, perf 10 ('86)	310.00	67.50
k.	5sh rose lilac, perf 11 ('88)	—	150.00

See No. 101. For overprint see No. O11.

Reprints are perf. 10 and overprinted "REPRINT" in black.

A17

A18

1862-65 Typo. Unwmk. *Perf. 13*

45	A17 1p red ('65)	225.00	47.50
a.	Perf. 14	240.00	80.00
b.	1p brick red ('65)	225.00	47.50
46	A18 2p blue	140.00	9.00
a.	Perf. 14	240.00	95.00

1863-64 Wmk. 50 *Perf. 13*

47	A17 1p red	85.00	11.00
a.	Watermarked "2"	270.00	37.50
b.	1p dark red brown	325.00	50.00
c.	1p brick red	85.00	12.00
d.	1p brick red, shiny surfaced paper ('65)	335.00	175.00
e.	Horiz. pair, imperf between		*2,500.*
48	A18 2p blue	65.00	3.50
a.	Watermarked "1"	260.00	6.50
b.	2p cobalt blue	65.00	3.50
c.	2p Prussian blue	67.50	4.00

1862 Wmk. 49 *Perf. 13*

49	A18 2p blue	135.00	40.00
a.	Watermarked "5"	135.00	42.50
b.	Perf. 12x13	*675.00*	250.00
c.	Perf. 12	240.00	55.00

See Nos. 52-53, 61-62, 70-71.

A19

A20

1867, Sept. Wmk. 51, 52 *Perf. 13*

50	A19 4p red brown	*125.00*	9.00
a.	Imperf.		
b.	4p pale red brown	*125.00*	9.00
51	A20 10p lilac	55.00	9.00
	Ovptd. "SPECIMEN"	30.00	
a.	Imperf.		
b.	Horiz. pair, imperf between	*3,250.*	

See Nos. 55, 64, 91, 97, 117, 129.

A21

A22

A23

Typo.; Engr. (3p, 5p, 8p)

1871-84 Wmk. 54 *Perf. 13*

52	A17 1p red	42.50	3.75
a.	Perf. 10	275.00	40.00
b.	Perf. 13x10	36.00	3.25
c.	Horiz. pair, imperf between		*2,900.*
d.	1p scarlet, perf. 10	—	190.00
53	A18 2p blue	47.50	2.00
a.	Imperf.		
b.	Horiz. pair, imperf vert.		*3,250.*
c.	Perf. 10	*275.00*	27.50
d.	Perf. 13x10	35.00	1.25
e.	Perf. 12x13		
f.	2p Prussian blue, perf. 11x12	*275.00*	*40.00*
g.	As "f," perf. 10	145.00	22.50
54	A15 3p green ('74)	75.00	5.00
a.	Perf. 11	180.00	115.00
b.	Perf. 12	—	*200.00*
c.	Perf. 10x12	160.00	50.00
d.	Perf. 11x12	135.00	42.50
e.	Perf. 10	95.00	12.00
f.	3p bright green, perf. 13x10	110.00	25.00
g.	As "f," perf. 10	130.00	22.50
55	A19 4p red brown ('77)	120.00	17.50
a.	Perf. 10	240.00	60.00
b.	Perf. 13x10	135.00	7.50
c.	Perf. 10x13	175.00	27.50
56	A11 5p dk grn, perf. 10 ('84)	42.50	45.00
a.	Horiz. pair, imperf between		2,250.
b.	Perf. 12	275.00	110.00
c.	Perf. 10x12	125.00	65.00
d.	Perf. 10x13		
e.	12x10	60.00	47.50
57	A21 6p lilac ('72)	105.00	2.50
a.	Horiz. pair, imperf. between	—	*3,000.*
b.	Perf. 13x10	120.00	2.50
c.	Perf. 10	125.00	2.50
58	A13 8p yellow ('77)	225.00	17.50
a.	Imperf.		
b.	Perf. 10	375.00	25.00
c.	Perf. 13x10	250.00	24.00
59	A22 9p on 10p red brown, perf. 12 (Bk)	25.00	5.50
a.	Double surcharge, blk & bl	*400.00*	
b.	Perf. 12x10	*300.00*	*225.00*
c.	Perf. 10	17.50	12.50
d.	Perf. 12x11	17.50	7.50
e.	Perf. 11x12	—	—
f.	Perf. 13	75.00	15.00
g.	Perf. 11	62.50	12.50
h.	Perf. 10x11	75.00	24.00
60	A23 1sh black ('76)	165.00	15.00
b.	Perf. 13x10	210.00	17.50
c.	Perf. 10	225.00	27.50
d.	Perf. 11	—	—
e.	Vert. pair, imperf between		*3,000.*
f.	Pair, imperf		*2,750.*
	Nos. 52-60 (9)	847.50	113.75

The surcharge on No. 59 measures 15mm.

See Nos. 66, 68. For overprints see Nos. O1-O10.

Typo.; Engr. (3p, 5p, 8p)

1882-91 Wmk. 55 *Perf. 11x12*

61	A17 1p red	11.00	1.50
a.	Perf. 10	25.00	3.00
b.	Perf. 10x13	125.00	9.50
c.	Perf. 10x12	275.00	70.00
d.	Perf. 12x11		130.00
e.	Perf. 10x11	*500.00*	130.00
f.	Perf. 11		160.00
g.	Perf. 13	1,000.	475.00
h.	Perf. 13x10	72.50	3.00
i.	Perf. 12x10	—	225.00
j.	Perf. 11x10	—	—
k.	Horiz. pair, imperf between		*2,100.*
62	A18 2p blue	12.50	1.00
a.	Perf. 10	62.50	1.00
b.	Perf. 13x10	160.00	7.50
c.	Perf. 13	500.00	115.00
d.	Perf. 12x10	425.00	100.00
e.	Perf. 11		100.00
f.	Perf. 12x11	450.00	100.00
g.	Perf. 11x10	500.00	160.00
h.	Perf. 12		250.00
i.	Double impression	—	800.00
63	A15 3p green	6.00	1.00
a.	Imperf., pair	500.00	
b.	Vert. pair, imperf. btwn.	—	
c.	Horiz. pair, imperf. vert.	750.00	675.00
d.	Double impression	—	—
e.	Perf. 10	35.00	2.50
f.	Perf. 11	10.00	1.00
g.	Perf. 12	15.00	2.50
h.	Perf. 12x11	7.25	1.00
i.	Perf. 10x12	32.50	3.00
m.	Perf. 10x11	40.00	3.25
n.	Perf. 12x10	55.00	4.50
o.	Wmk sideways	65.00	12.50
64	A19 4p red brown	85.00	3.00
a.	Perf. 10	125.00	5.50
b.	Perf. 10x12	225.00	70.00
c.	Perf. 12	325.00	190.00
65	A11 5p dk blue green	11.00	1.25
a.	Imperf., pair	500.00	
b.	Perf. 11	12.00	1.25
c.	Perf. 10	27.50	1.75
d.	Perf. 12	27.50	1.75
e.	Perf. 10x12	175.00	45.00
f.	5p green, perf. 12x11	12.00	1.25
g.	5p green, perf. 11x10	85.00	15.00
h.	5p green, perf. 12x10	90.00	10.00
i.	5p green, perf. 10x11	80.00	12.50
j.	5p green, perf. 11	12.00	1.25
k.	Wmk sideways	25.00	8.00
66	A21 6p lilac, perf. 10	90.00	1.50
a.	Horiz. pair, imperf. between		*3,000.*
b.	Perf. 10x12	65.00	2.00
c.	Perf. 11x12	135.00	17.50
d.	Perf. 12	135.00	10.00
e.	Perf. 11x10	125.00	2.25
f.	Perf. 11	135.00	7.75
g.	Perf. 10x13		360.00
67	A13 8p yellow, perf. 10	250.00	20.00
a.	Perf. 11	250.00	25.00
b.	Perf. 12	340.00	30.00
c.	Perf. 10x12	310.00	27.50
68	A23 1sh black	145.00	7.50
a.	Perf. 10x13	—	—
b.	Perf. 10	150.00	7.50
c.	Perf. 11	275.00	20.00
d.	Perf. 10x12	—	290.00
	Nos. 61-68 (8)	610.50	36.75

Nos. 63 and 65 exist with two types of watermark 55 — spacings of 1mm or 2mm between crown and NSW.

See No. 90. For surcharges and overprints see Nos. 92-94, O12-O19.

The 1, 2, 4, 6, 8p and 1sh have been reprinted on paper watermarked Large Crown and NSW. The 1, 2, 4p and 1sh are perforated 11x12, the 6p is perforated 10 and the 8p 11. All are overprinted "REPRINT," the 1sh in red and the others in black.

Perf. 11x12

1886-87 Typo. Wmk. 56

Bluish Revenue Stamp Paper

70	A17 1p scarlet	22.00	10.00
a.	Perf. 10	60.00	18.00
71	A18 2p dark blue	45.00	8.00
a.	Perf. 10	105.00	24.00
b.	Imperf.		*3,250.*

For overprint, see No. O20.

A24

Perf. 12 (#73-75), 12x10 (#72, 75A) and Compound

1885-86 "POSTAGE" in Black

72 A24 5sh green & vio 850.00 150.00
 a. Perf. 10 — —
 b. Perf. 13 — —
73 A24 10sh rose & vio 1,750. 275.00
 a. Perf. 13 — —
74 A24 £1 rose & vio *11,500.* *4,750.*
 a. Perf. 13 — *8,250.*

"POSTAGE" in Blue

Bluish Paper

75 A24 10sh rose & vio 325.00 75.00
 b. Perf. 10 1,950. 250.00
 c. Perf. 12x11 — —

White Paper

75A A24 £1 rose & vio 9,750. *4,750.*

For overprints, see Nos. O21-O23.

The 5sh with black overprint and the £1 with blue overprint have been reprinted on paper watermarked NSW. They are perforated 12x10 and are overprinted "REPRINT" in black.

"POSTAGE" in Blue

1894 White Paper

76 A24 10sh rose & violet, perf 12 350.00 60.00
 a. Double overprint
 b. 10sh mauve & claret, perf 10 625.00 180.00
 c. 10sh mauve & violet, perf 11 475.00 100.00
 d. 10sh mauve & violet, perf 12x11 350.00 75.00

See No. 108B.

View of Sydney
A25

Emu
A26

Captain Cook
A27

Victoria and Coat of Arms
A28

Lyrebird
A29

Kangaroo
A30

1888-89 Wmk. 55 *Perf. 11x12*

77 A25 1p violet 15.00 1.00
 a. Perf. 12 16.00 .50
 b. Perf. 12x11½ 27.50 1.25
78 A26 2p blue 22.00 .50
 a. Imperf., pair 375.00 525.00
 b. Perf. 12 22.00 .50
 c. Perf. 12x11½ 22.00 .50
79 A27 4p brown 30.00 5.50
 a. Perf. 12x11½ 55.00 8.00
 b. Perf. 12 55.00 5.00
 c. Perf. 11 350.00 115.00
 d. Imperf.
80 A28 6p carmine rose 37.50 4.50
 a. Perf. 12 40.00 10.50
 b. Perf. 12x11½ 50.00 5.00
81 A29 8p red violet 25.00 9.50
 a. Perf. 12 25.00 9.50
 b. Perf. 12x11½ 60.00 16.00
82 A30 1sh maroon ('89) 55.00 2.50
 a. Imperf., pair 1,450.
 b. Perf. 12x11½ 57.50 3.00
 c. Perf. 12 65.00 2.50
 d. 1sh violet brown, perf 11x12 55.00 3.00
 e. 1sh violet brown, perf 12x11½ 75.00 5.00
 f. 1sh violet brown, perf 12 75.00 2.75
 Nos. 77-82 (6) 184.50 23.50
 Set, ovptd. "SPECIMEN" 210.00

First British settlement in Australia, cent.
For overprints see Nos. O24-O29.

1888 Wmk. 56 *Perf. 11x12*

83 A25 1p violet 45.00 8.00
84 A26 2p blue 100.00 7.50

See Nos. 104B-106C, 113-115, 118, 125-127, 130.

Map of Australia
A31

Governors Capt. Arthur Phillip (above) and Lord Carrington
A32

1888-89 Wmk. 53 *Perf. 10*

85 A31 5sh violet ('89) 425.00 60.00
 a. 5sh deep purple 400.00 55.00
86 A32 20sh ultra 750.00 175.00

See Nos. 88, 120. For overprints see Nos. O30-O31.

1890 Wmk. 57 *Perf. 10*

87 A31 5sh violet 300.00 40.00
 a. Perf. 11 375.00 50.00
 b. Perf. 10x11 400.00 40.00
 c. Perf. 12 450.00 60.00
 d. 5sh mauve, perf 10 375.00 40.00
 e. 5sh mauve, perf 11 375.00 50.00
 f. Horiz. pair, imperf btwn. —

Perf. 11x12, 12x11

Wmk. 58

88 A32 20sh ultra 400.00 90.00
 a. Perf. 11 450.00 90.00
 b. Perf. 12 475.00 160.00
 c. 20sh cobalt blue, perf 10 525.00 170.00
 d. As "c," perf 11 500.00 90.00
 Nos. 87-88, ovptd. "SPECIMEN" 240.00

For overprints see Nos. O32-O33.

"Australia" — A33

1890, Dec. 22 Wmk. 55 *Perf. 11x12*

89 A33 2½p ultra 19.00 2.50
 a. Perf. 12 25.00 4.00
 b. Perf. 12x11½ 55.00 *50.00*
 Overprinted "SPECIMEN" 35.00

For overprint see No. O35.

Type of 1856

1891 Engr. Wmk. 52 *Perf. 10*

90 A15 3p green 6.75 *50.00*
 a. Double impression —
 b. 3p light green 16.00 *62.50*

Type of 1867

1893 Typo. *Perf. 11*

91 A20 10p lilac 20.00 11.00
 a. Perf. 10 22.50 13.00
 b. Perf. 11x10 or 10x11 27.50 13.00
 c. Perf. 12x11 160.00 17.00

Types of 1862-84 Surcharged in Black

a

b

1891, Jan. 5 Wmk. 55 *Perf. 11x12*

92 A17(a) ½p on 1p gray 10.50 *7.00*
 a. Imperf. —
 b. Surcharge omitted
 c. Double surcharge *850.00*
93 A21(b) 7½p on 6p brown 6.50 4.00
 a. Perf. 10 5.50 11.00
 b. Perf. 11 5.00 4.00
 c. Perf. 12 15.00 5.00
 d. Perf. 10x12 7.00 7.00

Perf. 12x11½

94 A23(b) 12½p on 1sh red 10.50 8.00
 a. Perf. 11x12 11.50 8.00
 b. Perf. 10 11.50 8.50
 c. Perf. 11 12.25 8.50
 d. Perf. 12 14.00 8.00
 Nos. 92-94 (3) 27.50 19.00
 Nos. 92-94 overprinted "SPECIMEN" 90.00

For overprints see Nos. O34, O36-O37.

Victoria — A37

1892-97 *Perf. 11x12*

95 A37 ½p slate ('97) 5.00 .50
 a. Perf. 12x11½ 5.00 .65
 b. Perf. 12 5.00 .50
 c. As #95, horiz. pair, imperf between *2,000.*
 d. ½p gray, perf. 10 65.00 2.50
 e. As "d," perf. 10x12 90.00 12.50
 f. As "d," perf. 11 100.00 7.25
 g. As "d," perf. 11x12 6.00 .50
 As "g," overprinted "SPECIMEN" 25.00

See Nos. 102, 109, 121. For overprint see No. O38.

Types of 1867-71

1897 *Perf. 11x12*

96 A22 9p on 10p red brn (Bk) 20.00 25.00
 a. 9p on 10p org brn (Bk) 20.00 25.00
 b. Surcharge omitted —
 c. Double surcharge 325.00 450.00
 d. Perf. 11 12.50 25.00
 e. Perf. 12 13.00 25.00
97 A20 10p violet 35.00 30.00
 a. Perf. 12x11½ 12.00 25.00
 b. Perf. 11 27.50 35.00
 c. Perf. 12 24.00 32.50
 Nos. 96-97, overprinted "SPECIMEN" 60.00

The surcharge on No. 96 measures 13½mm.
For overprints see Nos. O39-O40.

Seal
A38

Victoria
A39

A40

ONE PENNY:
Die I — The first pearl in the crown at the left is merged into the arch, the shading under the fleur-de-lis is indistinct, and the "s" of "WALES" is open.
Die II — The first pearl is circular, the vertical shading under the fleur-de-lis is clear, and the "s" of "WALES" not so open.

2½ PENCE:
Die I — There are 12 radiating lines in the star on the Queen's breast.
Die II — There are 16 radiating lines in the star. The eye is nearly full of color.

1897 *Perf. 12*

98 A38 1p rose red, II 5.00 .50
 a. Die I, perf. 11x12 5.00 1.00
 b. Imperf., pair *750.00*
 c. Imperf. horiz., pair *850.00*
 d. Die I, perf. 12x11½ 5.00 1.00
 e. Die I, perf. 12 11.00 2.00
 f. Die II, perf. 12x11½ 4.00 1.00
 g. Die II, perf. 11x12 5.00 1.00
99 A39 2p deep blue 17.50 1.50
 a. Perf. 11x12 18.00 1.50
 b. Perf. 12x11½ 9.00 1.50
100 A40 2½p dp purple, II 42.50 2.50
 a. Die I, perf. 12x11 30.00 2.50
 b. Die I, perf. 11 32.50 4.00
 c. Die I, perf. 11½x12 32.50 2.75
 d. Die II, perf. 11x12 42.50 2.75
 e. Die II, perf. 11½x12 32.50 2.75
 Nos. 98-100 (3) 65.00 4.50
 Nos. 98-100 overprinted "SPECIMEN" 75.00

Sixtieth year of Queen Victoria's reign.
See Nos. 103-104, 110-112, 122-124.

Type of 1861

1897 Engr. Wmk. 53 *Perf. 11*

101 A16 5sh red violet 60.00 16.00
 a. Horiz. pair, imperf. btwn. *11,000.*
 b. Perf. 11x12 or 12x11 60.00 24.00
 c. Perf. 12 80.00 45.00

Perf. 12x11½, 11½x12

1899, Oct. Typo. Wmk. 55

HALF PENNY:
Die I — Narrow "H" in "HALF."

102 A37 ½p blue green, I 4.00 1.50
 a. Imperf., pair 250.00 *350.00*
103 A39 2p ultra 5.75 1.00
 a. Imperf., pair 325.00
104 A40 2½p dk blue, II 9.00 1.75
 a. Imperf., pair 350.00
104B A27 4p org brown 18.00 7.50
 c. 4p red brown 35.00 17.00
 d. As "c," imperf. pair 600.00
105 A28 6p emerald 100.00 27.50
 a. Imperf., pair 600.00
106 A28 6p orange 50.00 5.00
 a. 6p yellow 18.00 10.00
 b. Imperf., pair 600.00
106C A29 8p magenta 47.50 6.00
 Nos. 102-106C (7) 234.25 50.25

Lyrebird — A41

1903 *Perf. 12x11½*

107 A41 2sh6p blue green 55.00 22.50
 Overprinted "SPECIMEN" 85.00

See Nos. 119, 131.

"Australia" — A42

1903 Wmk. 70 *Perf. 12½*

108 A42 9p org brn & ultra 20.00 3.50
 Overprinted "SPECIMEN" 50.00
 a. Perf. 11 *5,250.* *1,850.*

See No. 128.

Type of 1885-86

1904 Wmk. 56 *Perf. 12x11*

"POSTAGE" in Blue

108B A24 10sh brt rose & vio 425.00 90.00
 c. Perf. 11 400.00 75.00
 d. Perf. 14 375.00 85.00
 e. 10sh aniline crimson & violet, perf 12 425.00 95.00
 f. As "e," perf 12x11 325.00 55.00
 g. 10sh claret & violet, chalky paper, perf 12x11 *475.00* 95.00

The watermark (NSW) of No. 108B is 20x7mm, with rounded angles in "N" and "W." On No. 75, the watermark is 21x7mm, with sharp angles in the "N" and "W."

HALF PENNY:
Die II — Wide "H" in "HALF."

Perf. 11, 11x12½, 12x11½ and Compound

1905-06 Wmk. 12

109 A37 ½p blue grn, II 3.00 1.50
 a. ½p blue green, I 4.50 1.00
 b. Booklet pane of 12 —
110 A38 1p car rose, II 2.75 .25
 a. Booklet pane of 6 —
 b. Booklet pane of 12 —
111 A39 2p deep ultra 2.25 .40
112 A40 2½p dk blue, II 4.50 3.00
113 A27 4p org brown 10.50 4.50
 a. 4p red brown 13.75 5.50
114 A28 6p orange 17.00 3.00
 a. 6p yellow 19.00 4.50
 b. Perf. 11 350.00
115 A29 8p magenta 27.50 8.00
117 A20 10p violet 16.25 6.00
118 A30 1sh vio brown 28.75 1.75
119 A41 2sh6p blue green 80.00 20.00

Wmk. 199

Perf. 12x11 or 11x12

120 A32 20sh ultra 375.00 75.00
 a. Perf 12 400.00 90.00
 b. Perf 11 375.00 85.00
 Nos. 109-115,117-120 (11) 567.50 123.40

1906-07 Wmk. 13

121 A37 ½p green, I 5.00 7.50
122 A38 1p rose, II 27.00 5.00
123 A39 2p ultra 8.50 5.00
124 A40 2½p blue, II 70.00 *130.00*
125 A27 4p org brown 35.00 35.00
126 A28 6p orange 50.00 50.00
 a. 6p yellow 50.00 50.00
127 A29 8p red violet 32.00 50.00
128 A42 9p yel brn & ultra, perf. 12x12½ ('06) 28.00 2.00
 a. Perf. 11 120.00 75.00
 b. 9p org brn & ultra, perf. 12x12½ 19.00 2.00
129 A20 10p violet 35.00 *60.00*
130 A30 1sh vio brown 75.00 12.00
 a. Perf. 11 — 1,700.
131 A41 2sh6p blue green 130.00 130.00
 Nos. 121-131 (11) 495.50 486.50

Portions of some of the sheets on which the above are printed show the watermark "COMMONWEALTH OF AUSTRALIA." Stamps may also be found from portions of the sheet without watermark.

SEMI-POSTAL STAMPS

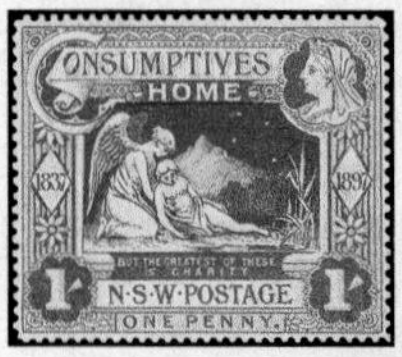

SP1

Allegory of Charity — SP2

1897, June **Wmk. 55** ***Perf. 11***

B1	SP1	1p (1sh) grn & brn	50.00	50.00
B2	SP2	2½p (2sh6p) rose, bl & gold	250.00	240.00
		Nos. B1-B2 overprinted "SPECIMEN"	300.00	

Diamond Jubilee of Queen Victoria.

The difference between the postal and face values of these stamps was donated to a fund for a home for consumptives.

REGISTRATION STAMPS

Queen Victoria — R1

Unwmk.

1856, Jan. 1 **Engr.** ***Imperf.***

F1	R1	(6p) orange & blue	*1,900.*	250.00
F2	R1	(6p) red & blue	*2,000.*	210.00
a.		Frame printed on back	*12,500.*	*5,250.*

1860 ***Perf. 12, 13***

F3	R1	(6p) orange & blue	1,150.	80.00
F4	R1	(6p) red & blue	1,200.	85.00

Nos. F1 to F4 exist also on paper with papermaker's watermark in sheet.

1863 **Wmk. 49**

F5	R1	(6p) red & blue	375.00	25.00
a.		(6p) red & Prussian blue	375.00	27.50
b.		(6p) red & indigo	475.00	35.00
c.		Double impression of frame	—	*850.00*

Fifty varieties.

Nos. F1-F2 were reprinted on thin white wove unwatermarked paper and on thick yellowish wove unwatermarked paper; the former are usually overprinted "SPECIMEN."

No. F4 was reprinted on thin white wove unwatermarked paper; perf. 10 and overprinted "REPRINT" in black.

POSTAGE DUE STAMPS

D1

Perf. 10, 11, 11½, 12 and Compound

1891-92 **Typo.** **Wmk. 55**

J1	D1	½p grn, perf 10	3.60	37.00
a.		Chalky paper	—	
J2	D1	1p green	35.00	4.00
a.		Perf 12	80.00	40.00
b.		Chalky paper	30.00	4.50
J3	D1	2p green	24.00	4.00
a.		Perf 12x10	80.00	40.00
b.		Chalky paper	27.00	6.50
J4	D1	3p green	65.00	14.00
b.		Chalky paper	90.00	28.00
J5	D1	4p green	60.00	3.75
a.		Chalky paper	60.00	13.00
J6	D1	6p grn, perf 10	60.00	15.00
J7	D1	8p grn, perf 10	125.00	27.00
J8	D1	5sh grn, perf 10	300.00	60.00
a.		Perf 11	750.00	180.00
b.		Perf 11x12	—	375.00

Perf. 12x10

J9	D1	10sh green	550.00	—
a.		Perf. 10	750.00	80.00
J10	D1	20sh green	650.00	—
a.		Perf. 10	850.00	125.00
b.		Perf. 12	1,500.	
		Nos. J1-J10 (10)	1,873.	164.75

Used values for Nos. J8-J10 are for c-t-o stamps.

Nos. J1-J5 exist on both ordinary and chalky paper.

Used values for Nos. J8-J10 are for c-t-o stamps.

OFFICIAL STAMPS

Regular Issues Overprinted in Black or Red

Perf. 10, 11, 12, 13 and Compound

1879-80 **Wmk. 54**

O1	A17	1p red	55.00	3.00
a.		Perf. 10	225.00	40.00
b.		Perf. 10x13	65.00	5.00
O2	A18	2p blue	55.00	2.75
a.		Perf. 11x12		275.00
b.		Perf. 10	275.00	40.00
O3	A15	3p green (R)	1,000.	375.00
O4	A15	3p green	200.00	32.50
a.		Watermarked "6"	—	600.00
b.		Double overprint	—	*925.00*
c.		3p yel grn, perf 10	200.00	32.50
d.		3p yel grn, perf 12	250.00	60.00
O5	A19	4p red brown	325.00	10.00
a.		Perf. 10x13	350.00	110.00
O6	A11	5p dark green	27.50	37.50
O7	A21	6p lilac	300.00	9.00
a.		Perf. 10	475.00	52.50
b.		Perf. 13x10	275.00	52.50
O8	A13	8p yellow (R)	*1,500.*	*675.00*
O9	A13	8p yellow	—	50.00
a.		Perf. 10	500.00	92.50
O10	A23	1sh black (R)	500.00	25.00
a.		Perf. 10	—	40.00
b.		Perf. 10x13	—	50.00
c.		Perf. 13x10	—	15.00

1880 **Wmk. 53**

O11	A16	5sh lilac, perf. 11	475.00	100.00
a.		Double overprint	*4,500.*	*2,250.*
b.		Perf. 10	600.00	125.00
c.		Perf. 12x10	775.00	130.00
d.		Perf. 13	875.00	110.00
e.		Perf. 10x12		—

Two No. O14 overprint types: Type I, "O" and "S" 7mm apart. Type II, "O" and "S" 5.5mm apart.

1881 **Wmk. 55**

O12	A17	1p red	27.50	2.00
a.		Perf. 10x13		140.00
O13	A18	2p blue	42.50	1.00
a.		Perf. 10x13	275.00	90.00
O14	A15	3p green	15.00	5.50
a.		Double overprint		675.00
b.		Perf. 12	225.00	110.00
c.		Perf. 11		
d.		Type II ovpt	40.00	15.00
e.		As "b," type II ovpt	25.00	15.00
f.		Wmk sideways	350.00	250.00
O15	A19	4p red brown	25.00	8.00
a.		Perf. 10x12	22.50	4.00
b.		Perf. 12	250.00	100.00
O16	A11	5p dark green	275.00	*175.00*
a.		Perf. 12	125.00	120.00
b.		Perf. 12x10		
c.		Perf. 12x11 ('85)	65.00	16.00
O17	A21	6p lilac	22.00	7.00
a.		Perf. 12		45.00
b.		Perf. 11x12	—	—
c.		Perf. 12x11 ('85)	90.00	20.00
O18	A13	8p yellow	27.50	12.50
a.		Double overprint	—	—
b.		Perf. 12	175.00	45.00
c.		Perf. 11 ('85)	27.50	29.00
d.		Perf. 10x12 or 12x10 ('85)	26.00	11.00
e.		Triple overprint	—	—
O19	A23	1sh black (R)	60.00	*15.00*
a.		Double overprint		*500.00*
b.		Perf. 10x13		60.00
c.		Perf. 11x12, comb.	30.00	8.00
		Nos. O12-O19 (8)	494.50	226.00

Beware of other red overprints on watermark 55 stamps.

No. O14 exists with two overprint types: "O" and "S" 7mm and 5.5mm apart. For detailed listings, see the Scott Classic Specialized catalogue.

1881 **Wmk. 56**

O20	A17	1p red	105.00	9.00

1887-90

O21	A24	10sh on #75	—	*3,500.*
O22	A24	£1 on #75A	*38,000.*	*17,500.*

No. 75 Overprinted

1889

O23	A24	10sh rose & vio	*5,750.*	*1,450.*
		Overprinted "SPECIMEN"	125.00	
a.		Perf. 10	*7,500.*	*3,750.*

Overprinted

1888-89 **Wmk. 55**

O24	A25	1p violet	6.50	2.00
a.		Overprinted "O" only		
O25	A26	2p blue	5.00	.75
O26	A27	4p red brown	11.00	4.25
O27	A28	6p carmine	10.00	11.00
O28	A29	8p red lilac	27.50	12.00
a.		Perf 12	60.00	17.00
O29	A30	1sh vio brown	42.50	4.75
a.		Double overprint		
b.		1sh purple brown, perf 12	45.00	7.00
c.		1sh maroon, perf 11x12 ('90)	45.00	4.00
d.		1sh maroon, perf 12	45.00	4.50
		Nos. O24-O29 (6)	102.50	34.75

Wmk. 53

O30	A31	5sh violet (R)	*2,100.*	*800.00*
O31	A32	20sh ultra	*20,000.*	*1,100.*

1890 **Wmk. 57**

O32	A31	5sh violet	*400.00*	110.00
a.		5sh, dull lilac, perf. 12	850.00	175.00
b.		5sh lilac, perf 10	675.00	175.00

Wmk. 58

O33	A32	20sh ultra	*21,000.*	*1,150.*
		O32b, O33 ovpted. "SPECIMEN"	325.00	

Centenary of the founding of the Colony (Nos. O24-O33).

1891 **Wmk. 55**

O34	A17(a)	½p on 1p gray & black	75.00	80.00
a.		Double overprint	2,500.	
O35	A33	2½p ultra	15.00	11.00
O36	A21(b)	7½p on 6p brn & black	55.00	70.00
O37	A23(b)	12½p on 1sh red & black	75.00	*115.00*

1892

O38	A37	½p gray, perf 11x12	6.00	*20.00*
a.		Perf 10	14.00	*20.00*
b.		Perf 12	13.00	*13.00*
c.		Perf 12x11½	35.00	18.00
		Overprinted "SPECIMEN"	35.00	

1894 **Wmk. 54**

O39	A22	9p on 10p red brn	1,250.	1,150.
		Overprinted "SPECIMEN"	85.00	

Wmk. 52

O40	A20	10p lilac, perf. 13	425.00	*120.00*
a.		Perf. 11x10 or 10x11	450.00	*225.00*
b.		Perf 10	450.00	
c.		Double overprint, one albino	475.00	
		Overprinted "SPECIMEN"	75.00	

The official stamps became obsolete on Dec. 31, 1894. In Aug., 1895, sets of 32 varieties of "O.S." stamps, together with some envelopes and postal cards, were placed on sale at the Sydney post office at £2 per set.

These sets contained most of the varieties listed above and a few which are not known in the original issues. An obliteration consisting of the letters G.P.O. or N.S.W. in three concentric ovals was lightly applied to the center of each block of four stamps.

It is understood that the earlier stamps and many of the overprints were reprinted to make up these sets.

QUEENSLAND

'kwēnz-ˌland

LOCATION — Northeastern part of Australia

GOVT. — British Crown Colony

AREA — 670,500 sq. mi.

POP. — 498,129 (1901)

CAPITAL — Brisbane

Originally a part of New South Wales, Queensland was constituted a separate colony in 1859. It was one of the six British Colonies that united in 1901 to form the Commonwealth of Australia.

12 Pence = 1 Shilling

20 Shillings = 1 Pound

MORETON BAY

Until 1860, Queensland, then known as Moreton Bay, utilized the postal service of New South Wales, and stamps of New South Wales were used until November 1, 1860. The New South Wales post offices in Queensland, with their opening dates and assigned canceler numbers, were:

Post Office	Opened
Brisbane	1834 (#95)
Burnett's Inn (became Goodes Inn)	1850 (#108)
Callandoon	1850 (#74)
Condamine	1856 (#151)
Dalby	1854 (#133)
Drayton	1846 (#85)
Gayndah	1850 (#86)
Gladstone	1854 (#131)
Goodes Inn	1858 (#108)
Ipswich	1846 (#87)
Maryborough	1849 (#96)
Rockhampton	1858 (#201)
Surat	1852 (#110)
Taroom	1856 (#152)
Toowoombs	1858 (#214)
Warwick	1848 (#81)

Values for unused stamps are for examples with original gum as defined in the catalogue introduction. Very fine examples of Nos. 4-73, 84-125, 128-140, and F1-F3b will have perforations touching the design on at least one or more sides due to the narrow spacing of the stamps on the plates. Stamps with perfs clear of the design on all four sides are scarce and will command higher prices.

Watermarks

Wmk. 5 — Small Star

Wmk. 6 — Large Star

Wmk. 12 — Crown and Single-lined A

Wmk. 13 — Crown and Double-lined A

Wmk. 65 — "Queensland Postage Stamps" in Sheet in Script Capitals

Wmk. 66

Wmks. 66 & 67 — "Queensland" in Large Single-lined Roman Capitals in the Sheet and Short-pointed Star to Each Stamp (Stars Vary Slightly in Size and Shape)

Wmk. 68 — Crown and Q

Wmk. 69 — Large Crown and Q

There are two varieties of the watermark 68, differing slightly in the position and shape of the crown and the tongue of the "Q."

Wmk. 70 — V and Crown

Queen Victoria — A1

Wmk. 6

1860, Nov. 1 Engr. *Imperf.*

1 A1 1p deep rose 6,600. 775.00
2 A1 2p deep blue *18,500. 1,950.*
3 A1 6p deep green *10,750.* 825.00

Clean-Cut Perf. 14 to 16

4 A1 1p deep rose 3,100. 290.00
5 A1 2p deep blue 1,650. 115.00
a. Horiz. pair, imperf between — *5,500.*
6 A1 6p deep green 1,850. 75.00

Clean-Cut Perf. 14 to 16

1860-61 Wmk. 5

6A A1 2p blue 1,150. 105.00
b. Horiz. pair, imperf. between 11,000.
6D A1 3p brown ('61) 875.00 77.50
6E A1 6p deep green 1,550. 77.50
6F A1 1sh gray violet 1,750. 115.00

Regular Perf. 14

6H A1 1p rose 475.00 57.50
6I A1 2p deep blue *1,100.* 62.50

Rough Perf. 14 to 16

7 A1 1p deep rose 115.00 47.50
8 A1 2p blue 350.00 27.50
a. Horiz. pair, imperf between *10,250.* —
9 A1 3p brown ('61) 90.00 30.00
a. Horiz. pair, imperf. vert. *10,250.* —
10 A1 6p deep green 675.00 27.50
a. 6p yellow green 775.00 27.50
11 A1 1sh dull violet 1,350. 90.00

Thick Yellowish Paper

Square Perf. 12½ to 13

1862-67 Unwmk.

12 A1 1p Indian red 525.00 70.00
13 A1 1p orange ('63) 120.00 16.00
a. Perf. 13, round holes ('67) 125.00 16.00
b. Horiz. pair, imperf. between —
c. Imperf., pair — *2,600.*
14 A1 2p deep blue 90.00 9.00
a. 2p pale blue 150.00 25.00
b. Perf. 13, round holes ('67) 90.00 9.00
c. Imperf., pair — *2,500.*
e. Horiz. pair, imperf. between *15,000.*
f. Vert. pair, imperf. between *5,750.*
15 A1 3p brown ('63) 125.00 42.50
a. Imperf.
b. Perf. 13, round holes ('67) 125.00 42.50
16 A1 6p yellow grn ('63) 190.00 11.00
a. 6p green 300.00 42.50
b. Perf. 13, round holes ('67) 195.00 13.50
c. Imperf., pair — *2,600.*
d. Horiz. pair, imperf. between — *16,000.*
e. 6p apple green ('63) 190.00 14.00
17 A1 1sh gray ('63) 400.00 22.50
b. Imperf. horizontally
c. Horiz. pair, imperf. between — *17,000.*
d. Perf. 13, round holes ('67) 400.00 24.00
e. Vert. pair, imperf between —

White Wove Paper

1865 Wmk. 5 *Rough Perf. 13*

18 A1 1p orange 125.00 57.50
a. Horiz. pair, imperf. between *6,250.*
19 A1 2p light blue 125.00 16.00
a. Vert. pair, imperf. between *8,500.*
b. Half used as 1p on cover *4,250.*
d. 2p deep blue 130.00 17.00
20 A1 6p yellow green 240.00 21.50
a. 6p deep green 290.00 21.50
Nos. 18-20 (3) 490.00 95.00

1865 *Perf. 12½x13*

18B A1 1p orange vermilion 165.00 77.50
19C A1 2p blue 280.00 77.50

Perf. 13, Round Holes

1866 Wmk. 65

21 A1 1p orange vermilion 210.00 42.50
22 A1 2p blue 105.00 16.50
b. Diagonal half used as 1p on cover —

1865 *Perf. 12½x13*

21A A1 1p orange vermilion 290.00 72.50
22C A1 2p blue 290.00 72.50

1866 Unwmk. Litho. *Perf. 13*

23 A1 4p lilac 525.00 21.50
a. 4p slate 525.00 21.00
Handstamped "SPECIMEN" 65.00
24 A1 5sh pink 1,350. 135.00
a. 5sh bright rose 1,450. 175.00
Handstamped "SPECIMEN" 80.00
b. Vert. pair, imperf between *8,750.*

Wmk. 66, 67

1868-74 Engr. *Perf. 13*

25 A1 1p orange ('71) 100.00 7.00
26 A1 2p blue 77.50 3.25
a. 2p pale blue 82.50 5.75
b. 2p bright blue 87.50 2.50
c. 2p greenish blue 155.00 2.50
d. 2p dark blue 87.50 2.50
27 A1 3p grnsh brn ('71) 240.00 6.25
a. 3p brown 125.00 5.25
b. 3p olive brown 210.00 6.50
28 A1 6p yel grn ('71) 275.00 7.00
a. 6p deep green 325.00 16.50
b. 6p green 240.00 9.50
30 A1 1sh grnsh gray ('72) 950.00 47.50
31 A1 1sh violet ('74) 425.00 22.50
a. 1sh brownish gray 950.00 47.50

Perf. 12

32 A1 1p orange 525.00 27.50
33 A1 2p blue *1,000.* 72.50
34 A1 3p brown 775.00 215.00
a. 3p greenish gray — 215.00
35 A1 6p deep green 1,850. 47.50
36 A1 1sh violet 900.00 52.50

Perf. 13x12

36A A1 1p orange 195.00
37 A1 2p blue *1,675.* 42.50
37A A1 3p brown *350.00*

The reprints are perforated 13 and the colors differ slightly from those of the originals.

1868-75 Wmk. 68 *Perf. 13*

38 A1 1p orange 115.00 5.75
a. Imperf pair 825.00
39 A1 1p rose ('74) 95.00 15.00
a. 1p deep rose red 170.00 15.00
40 A1 2p blue 85.00 4.50
a. Vert. pair, imperf between —
b. Imperf., pair *600.00*
c. 2p pale blue ('74) 90.00 2.00
41 A1 3p brown ('75) 140.00 15.00
42 A1 6p yel green ('69) 200.00 6.00
a. 6p apple green 240.00 8.50
b. 6p deep green 210.00 8.50
c. As "a," imperf pair 725.00
43 A1 1sh violet ('75) 425.00 67.50
Nos. 38-43 (6) 1,060. 113.75

1876-78 *Perf. 12*

44 A1 1p orange 77.50 6.00
a. Imperf. *450.00*
b. 1p pale org vermilion 87.50 6.00
c. Vert. pair, imperf between —
45 A1 1p rose 87.50 10.00
a. 1p salmon 125.00 12.50
46 A1 2p blue 75.00 1.75
a. 2p pale blue 135.00 14.00
b. 2p deep blue 75.00 2.00
47 A1 3p brown 125.00 9.00
48 A1 6p yellow green 275.00 4.25
a. 6p apple green 300.00 7.00
b. 6p deep green 275.00 9.50
c. 6p green 210.00 4.00
49 A1 1sh violet 110.00 8.50
m. Vert. pair, imperf between —
n. 1sh purple 275.00 5.00
Nos. 44-49 (6) 750.00 39.50

Perf. 13x12

49B A1 1p orange 145.00
49C A1 2p blue *1,450.* 240.00
49D A1 4p yellow 625.00
49E A1 6p deep green 525.00

Perf. 12½x13

49G A1 1p org ver 575.00
49H A1 2p deep blue 575.00
49J A1 6p yellow green *1,350.*

Perf. 12½

49K A1 2p deep blue *725.00*

The reprints are perforated 12 and are in paler colors than the originals.

1879 Unwmk. *Perf. 12*

50 A1 6p pale emerald 475.00 30.00
a. Horiz. pair, imperf. vert. *2,250.*

A2

1875-81 Litho. Wmk. 68 *Perf. 13*

50B A1 4p yellow ('75) *2,450.* 115.00
a. Handstamped "SPECIMEN" 115.00

Perf. 12

51 A1 4p buff ('76) 1,750. 50.00
a. 4p yellow 1,750. 52.50
52 A1 2sh pale blue ('81) 170.00 57.50
Fiscal cancellation 5.75
a. 2sh deep blue 200.00 57.50
b. Imperf. —
c. 2sh blue 165.00 57.50
d. As "c" horiz. pair, imperf. vert. *9,000.* —
53 A2 2sh6p lt red ('81) 375.00 75.00
Fiscal cancellation 5.75
a. 2sh6p bright scarlet 375.00 77.50
54 A1 5sh org brn ('81) 575.00 115.00
Fiscal cancellation 7.00
a. 5sh fawn 575.00 115.00
55 A1 10sh brown ('81) 975.00 190.00
Fiscal cancellation 7.00
a. Imperf., pair *950.00*
b. 10sh bister brown 975.00 190.00
56 A1 20sh rose ('81) *2,600. 275.00*
Fiscal cancellation 7.00
Nos. 50B-56 (7) 8,895. 877.50

Nos. 53-56, 62-64, 74-83 with pen (revenue) cancellations removed are often offered as unused.

A3

1879-81 Typo. Wmk. 68 *Perf. 12*

57 A3 1p rose red 62.50 11.50
a. 1p red orange 67.50 12.00
b. 1p brown orange 87.50 9.00
c. "QOEENSLAND" *350.00 42.50*
d. Imperf. —
e. Vert. pair, imperf. horiz. *750.00*
f. As "a" "QOGENSLAND" 350.00 62.50
g. As "b" "QOGENSLAND" 650.00 62.50
58 A3 2p gray blue 90.00 3.25
a. 2p deep ultra 95.00 3.00
b. Imperf. —
c. "PENGE" 425.00 47.50
d. "TW" joined 90.00 1.75
e. Vert. pair, imperf. horiz. *1,000.*
f. "QUEENSbAND" *425.00 47.50*
g. As "a", "QUEENSbAND" *425.00 47.50*
59 A3 4p orange yellow 475.00 22.50
a. Imperf. —
b. Horiz. pair, imperf. vert. *12,750.* —
60 A3 6p yellow green 200.00 7.00
a. Imperf. —
b. Horiz. pair, imperf. vert. —
c. 6p deep green 190.00 7.50
61 A3 1sh pale violet ('81) 190.00 17.50
a. 1sh deep violet 200.00 11.50
Nos. 57-61 (5) 1,018. 61.75

The stamps of type A3 were electrotyped from plates made up of groups of four types, differing in minor details. Two dies were used for the 1p and 2p, giving eight varieties for each of those values.

Nos. 59-60 exist imperf. vertically.

For surcharge see No. 65.

Moiré on Back

1878-79 Unwmk.

62 A3 1p brown org ('79) 825.00 115.00
a. "QOEENSLAND" *1,850.*
63 A3 2p deep ultra ('79) 825.00 57.50
a. "PENGE" *4,400.* 675.00
64 A1 1sh red violet 240.00 105.00
Fiscal cancellation 5.00
Nos. 62-64 (3) 1,890. 277.50

No. 57b Surcharged Vertically in Black

1880 Wmk. 68

65 A3 ½p on 1p brn org 425.00 240.00
a. "QOEENSLAND" *2,400. 1,250.*

On No. 65, the surcharge reads from bottom to top. Stamps with surcharges reading downward are fakes.

A4

1882-83 Typo. *Perf. 12*

66 A4 1p pale red 12.50 1.00
a. 1p rose 12.50 1.00
b. Imperf. pair —
c. 1p deep vermilion 12.50 1.00
67 A4 2p gray blue 25.00 1.00
a. 2p deep ultra 25.00 1.00
b. Horiz. pair, imperf between —
68 A4 4p yellow ('83) 55.00 3.50
a. "PENGE" *350.00* 47.50
b. Imperf., single —
69 A4 6p yellow green 37.50 2.00
70 A4 1sh violet ('83) 57.50 13.50
a. 1sh lilac 30.00 8.00
b. 1sh deep purple 26.00 8.00
c. 1sh pale mauve 13.50 8.00
Nos. 66-70 (5) 187.50 21.00

There are eight minor varieties of the 1p, twelve of the 2p and four each of the other values. On the 1p there is a period after "PENNY." On all values the lines of shading on the neck extend from side to side.

Compare design A4 with A6, A10, A11, A15, A16.

1883 *Perf. 9½x12*

71 A4 1p rose 170.00 60.00
72 A4 2p gray blue 575.00 80.00
73 A4 1sh pale violet 300.00 75.00
Nos. 71-73 (3) 1,045. 215.00

Beware of faked perfs.

See Nos. 94, 95, 100.

A5

Wmk. 68 Twice Sideways

1882-85 Engr. *Perf. 12*

Thin Paper

74 A5 2sh ultra 325.00 62.50
75 A5 2sh6p vermilion 140.00 26.00
76 A5 5sh car rose ('85) 140.00 26.50
77 A5 10sh brown 275.00 55.00
78 A5 £1 dk grn ('83) 575.00 130.00
Nos. 74-78 (5) 1,455. 300.00

The 2sh, 5sh and £1 exist imperf.

There are two varieties of the watermark on Nos. 74-78, as in the 1879-81 issue.

Stamps with revenue cancels sell for $3.25-6.50.

1886 Wmk. 69 *Perf. 12*

Thick Paper

79 A5 2sh ultra 350.00 62.50
80 A5 2sh6p vermilion 60.00 26.00
81 A5 5sh car rose 60.00 40.00
82 A5 10sh dark brown 175.00 47.50
83 A5 £1 dark green 350.00 80.00
Nos. 79-83 (5) 995.00 256.00

High value stamps with cancellations removed are offered as unused.

Stamps with revenue cancels sell for $3.25-6.50.

See Nos. 126-127, 141-144.

A6

Redrawn

1887-89 Typo. Wmk. 68 ***Perf. 12***

84 A6 1p orange 19.00 1.00
85 A6 2p gray blue 19.00 1.00
a. 2p deep ultra 25.00 1.00
b. Half used as 1c on cover —
86 A6 2sh red brown ('89) 85.00 80.00
a. 2sh pale brown 75.00 72.50

Perf. 9½x12

88 A6 2p deep ultra *450.00* 85.00
Nos. 84-88 (4) *573.00* 167.00

The 1p has no period after the value.

In the redrawn stamps the shading lines on the neck are not completed at the left, leaving an irregular white line along that side.

Variety "LA" joined exists on Nos. 84-86, 88, 90, 91, 93, 97, 98, 102.

On No. 88 beware of faked perfs.

A7

A8

1890-92 ***Perf. 12½, 13***

89 A7 ½p green 16.00 2.00
a. ½p pale green 21.00 2.00
b. ½p deep blue green 8.00 2.00
90 A6 1p orange red 9.00 1.00
a. Imperf, pair 325.00 325.00
b. Double impression 675.00
91 A6 2p gray blue 10.00 .50
a. 2p pale blue 12.00 1.00
b. "FWO" for "TWO" 90.00 29.00
92 A8 2½p rose carmine 18.00 2.50
93 A6 3p brown ('92) 10.00 4.00
94 A4 4p orange 28.50 4.00
a. "PENGE" for "PENCE" 165.00 32.50
b. 4p orange yellow 32.00 7.50
c. As "b," "PENGE" for "PENCE" 180.00 45.00
d. 4p yellow 20.00 4.00
e. As "d," "PENGE" for "PENCE" 120.00 32.50
95 A4 6p green 12.00 2.00
96 A6 2sh red brown 50.00 52.50
a. 2sh pale brown 60.00 57.50
Nos. 89-96 (8) 153.50 68.50

The ½p and 3p exist imperf.

1895 Wmk. 69 ***Perf. 12½, 13***

Thick Paper

98 A6 1p orange 5.00 .50
a. 1p reddish vermilion 5.00 .50
99 A6 2p gray blue 7.00 .50
b. "FWO" for "TWO" 95.00 22.50

Perf. 12

100 A4 1sh pale violet 47.50 30.00
Nos. 98-100 (3) 59.50 31.00

A9

A10

Moiré on Back

1895 Unwmk. ***Perf. 12½, 13***

101 A9 ½p green 11.00 8.00
a. Without moire 77.50
b. ½p deep green 11.00 8.00
102 A6 1p orange 2.50 2.50
a. "PE" missing 400.00 *80.00*
b. 1p reddish vermilion 2.50 3.00

Wmk. 68

103 A9 ½p green 3.50 2.00
a. ½p deep green 3.50 2.00
b. Printed on both sides 300.00
c. Double impression *2,000.* *2,000.*
104 A10 1p orange 4.00 .50
a. 1p pale red 9.00 1.00
105 A10 2p gray blue 37.50 .50

Wmk. 69

Thick Paper

106 A9 ½p green, perf 12½ 3.00 6.50
a. Perf 13 3.00 6.50
b. Perf 12 47.50
c. 1p deep green, perf 12 47.50

1895-96 Unwmk. Thin Paper

Crown and Q Faintly Impressed

107 A9 ½p green 2.50 6.50
108 A10 1p orange 3.50 2.50
108A A6 2p gray blue 14.00 *150.00*
b. "FWO" for "TWO" *175.00*

A11

A12

A13

1895-96 Wmk. 68

109 A11 1p red 9.00 .75
110 A12 2½p rose 25.00 5.00
a. 2½p carmine 25.00 5.00
111 A13 5p violet brown 30.00 5.00
111A A11 6p yellow green *16,000.*

Only a few used examples of No. 111A are known, and readable cancels are from 1902. It is suggested that this otherwise unissued design was accidentally included in the plate of No. 120.

A14

A15

A16

A17

A18

A19

TWO PENCE:

Type I — Point of bust does not touch frame.

Type II — First redrawing. The top of the crown, the chignon and the point of the bust touch the frame. The forehead is completely shaded.

Type III — Second redrawing. The top of crown does not touch the frame, though the chignon and the point of the bust do. The forehead and the bridge of the nose are not shaded.

1897-1900 ***Perf. 12½, 13***

112 A14 ½p deep green 5.50 7.50
a. Perf. 12 145.00
113 A15 1p red 2.25 .40
a. Perf. 12 8.50 3.50
114 A16 2p gray blue (I) 9.00 .40
a. Perf. 12 725.00 7.00
115 A17 2½p rose 17.50 27.50
116 A17 2½p violet, *blue* 10.00 3.00
117 A15 3p brown 8.50 3.00
118 A15 4p bright yellow 14.00 3.00
119 A18 5p violet brown 9.50 3.00
120 A15 6p yellow green 8.00 3.25
121 A19 1sh lilac 15.00 3.50
a. 1sh light violet 15.00 3.50
122 A19 2sh turq blue 37.50 47.50
Nos. 112-122 (11) 136.75 102.05

See Nos. 130-140.

1898 ***Serrated Roulette 13***

123 A15 1p scarlet 20.00 7.00
a. Serrated and perf. 13 10.00 6.00
b. Serrated in black 20.00 13.00
c. Serrated without color and in black 22.50 *26.00*
d. Same as "b," and perf. 13 80.00 *90.00*
e. Same as "c," and perf. 13 100.00 100.00

Victoria — A20

1899 Typo. ***Perf. 12, 12½, 13***

124 A20 ½p blue green 3.50 2.50
a. ½p green, perf 12 120.00 65.00
b. ½p pale green 14.00 4.25

Unwatermarked stamps are proofs.

"Australia" — A21

NINE PENCE:

Type I — "QUEENSLAND" 18x1½mm.

Type II — "QUEENSLAND" 17½x1¼mm.

1903 Wmk. 70 ***Perf. 12½***

125 A21 9p org brn & ultra, II 60.00 7.50
a. Type I 45.00 7.50

See No. 128.

Type of 1882

1903-06 Wmk. 68 ***Perf. 12, 12½-13***

Typographed, Perf. 12½-13 Irreg. ('03)

125B A5 5sh rose 240.00 57.50
125C A5 £1 dark green *2,100.* *675.00*

Lithographed, Perf. 12 ('05-'06)

126 A5 5sh rose 180.00 95.00
127 A5 £1 dark green 575.00 125.00
c. Perf. 12½-13 Irreg. *1,150.* 165.00

1907 Typo. Wmk. 13 ***Perf. 12½***

128 A21 9p yel brn & ultra, I 24.00 4.50
a. Type II 80.00 7.00
b. Perf. 11, type II 5,500. 775.00

1907 Wmk. 68 ***Perf. 12½, 13***

129 A16 2p ultra, type II 12.00 5.50
129A A18 5p dark brown 17.50 6.50
b. 5p olive brown 17.50 4.75

1907-09 Wmk. 12

130 A20 ½p deep green 2.25 *4.50*
131 A15 1p red 3.50 .30
a. Imperf., pair *450.00*
132 A16 2p ultra, II 40.00 3.50
133 A16 2p ultra, III 5.50 .30
134 A15 3p pale brown 27.50 2.50
135 A15 4p bright yellow 12.50 4.25
136 A15 4p gray black ('09) 27.50 6.50
137 A18 5p brown 42.50 22.00
a. 5p olive brown 24.00 25.00
138 A15 6p yellow green 22.50 4.00
139 A19 1sh violet 24.00 4.00
140 A19 2sh turquoise bl 40.00 47.50

Wmk. 12 Sideways

Litho.

141 A5 2sh6p dp org 45.00 45.00
a. 2sh6p dull orange ('10) 85.00 85.00
b. 2sh6p reddish orange ('12) 190.00 *210.00*
142 A5 5sh rose 90.00 60.00
a. 5sh deep rose ('10) 110.00 85.00
b. 5sh carmine red ('12) 275.00 *260.00*
143 A5 10sh dark brown 165.00 70.00
a. 10sh sepia ('12) 450.00 300.00
144 A5 £1 blue green 425.00 125.00
a. £1 dp blue green ('10) 575.00 325.00
b. £1 yellow green ('12) *1,850.* *1,350.*
Nos. 130-144 (15) 972.75 399.35

POSTAL FISCAL STAMPS

Authorized for postal use from Jan. 1, 1880. Authorization withdrawn July 1, 1892.

Used values are for examples with postal cancellations used from Jan. 1, 1880 through June 30, 1892.

Beware of stamps with a pen cancellation removed and a fake postmark added.

Queen Victoria — PF1

1866-74 Engr. Unwmk. ***Perf. 13***

AR1 PF1 1p blue 150.00 27.50
AR2 PF1 6p violet 290.00 125.00
AR3 PF1 1sh green 250.00 85.00
AR4 PF1 2sh brown 425.00 210.00
AR5 PF1 2sh 6p red 525.00 170.00
AR6 PF1 5sh yellow 1,350. 425.00
AR7 PF1 6sh yellow *2,100.*
AR8 PF1 10sh yel grn 1,650. 575.00
AR9 PF1 20sh rose 3,250. *1,150.*

Wmk. 68

AR10 PF1 1p blue 85.00 *65.00*
AR11 PF1 6p violet 290.00 *150.00*
AR12 PF1 6p blue 825.00 450.00
AR13 PF1 1sh green 240.00 90.00
AR14 PF1 2sh brown 425.00 170.00
AR15 PF1 5sh yellow 1,400. 375.00
AR16 PF1 10sh yel grn 1,700. *575.00*
AR17 PF1 20sh rose 3,250. *1,250.*

Queen Victoria — PF2

1872-73 Wmk. 69 ***Perf. 13***

AR18 PF2 1p lilac 75.00 25.00
AR19 PF2 6p brown 135.00 52.50
AR20 PF2 1sh green 170.00 55.00
AR21 PF2 2sh blue 275.00 75.00
AR22 PF2 2sh 6p ver 450.00 160.00
AR23 PF2 5sh org brn 575.00 240.00
AR24 PF2 10sh brown 1,150. *475.00*
AR25 PF2 20sh rose 2,850. *725.00*

Perf. 12

AR26 PF2 1p lilac 75.00 25.00
AR27 PF2 6p brown 135.00 50.00
AR28 PF2 2sh blue 275.00 75.00
AR29 PF2 2sh 6p ver 450.00 160.00
AR30 PF2 5sh org brn 575.00 240.00
AR31 PF2 10sh brown 1,150. *475.00*
AR32 PF2 20sh rose 3,000. *725.00*

Unwmk.

Perf. 13

AR33 PF2 1p lilac 85.00 25.00
AR34 PF2 6p lilac 140.00 52.50
AR35 PF2 6p brown 625.00 160.00
AR36 PF2 1sh green 210.00 52.50
AR37 PF2 2sh blue 350.00 *170.00*
AR38 PF2 2sh 6p ver 575.00 190.00
AR39 PF2 5sh org brn 775.00 240.00
AR40 PF2 10sh brown 1,375. 475.00
AR41 PF2 20sh rose 2,900. 725.00

Perf. 12

AR42 PF2 1p lilac 85.00 25.00
AR43 PF2 6p lilac 135.00 52.50
AR44 PF2 6p brown 625.00 165.00
AR45 PF2 1sh green 220.00 52.50
AR46 PF2 2sh blue 350.00 170.00
AR47 PF2 2sh 6p ver 575.00 190.00
AR48 PF2 5sh org brn 800.00 240.00
AR49 PF2 10sh brown 1,400. 475.00
AR50 PF2 20sh rose 3,000. 750.00

Queen Victoria — PF3

1878-79 Engr. Unwmk. ***Perf. 12***

AR51 PF3 1p violet 100.00 19.50

Wmk. 68

AR52 PF3 1p violet 150.00 75.00

SEMI-POSTAL STAMPS

Queen Victoria, Colors and Bearers — SP1

SP2

Perf. 12, 12½

1900, June 19 Wmk. 68

B1 SP1 1p red lilac 160.00 110.00
On cover 250.00
B2 SP2 2p deep violet 375.00 290.00
On cover 500.00
Nos. B1-B2 on one cover *750.00*

These stamps were sold at 1sh and 2sh respectively. The difference was applied to a patriotic fund in connection with the Boer War.

REGISTRATION STAMPS

R1

Clean-Cut Perf. 14 to 16

1861 Wmk. 5 Engr.

F1 R1 (6p) olive yellow 1,250. 100.00
  a. Horiz. pair, imperf. vert. *13,000.*

Rough Perf. 14 to 16

F2 R1 (6p) dull yellow 125.00 37.50

1864 ***Perf. 12½ to 13***

F3 R1 (6p) golden yellow 190.00 40.00
  a. Imperf.
  b. Double impression *2,750.* —

The reprints are watermarked with a small truncated star and perforated 12.

SOUTH AUSTRALIA

'sauth o-'strāl-yə

LOCATION — Central part of southern Australia
GOVT. — British Colony
AREA — 380,070 sq. mi.
POP. — 358,346 (1901)
CAPITAL — Adelaide

South Australia was one of the six British colonies that united in 1901 to form the Commonwealth of Australia.

12 Pence = 1 Shilling
20 Shillings = 1 Pound

Values for unused stamps are for examples with original gum as defined in the catalogue introduction.

Very fine examples of Nos. 10-60 and O1-O60 will have perforations slightly cutting into the framelines or design on one or more sides due to the narrow spacing of the stamps on the plates.

Stamps with perfs clear on all sides are scarce to rare and will command higher to substantially higher prices.

Watermarks

Wmk. 6 — Star with Long Narrow Points

Wmk. 7 — Star with Short Broad Points

Wmk. 70 — Crown and V

Wmk. 72 — Crown and SA

Wmk. 73 — Crown and SA, Letters Close

Wmk. 74 — Crown and Single-lined A

Queen Victoria — A1

1855-56 Engr. Wmk. 6 ***Imperf.***
London Print

1 A1 1p dark green 12,500. 500.
2 A1 2p dull carmine 850. 90.
3 A1 6p deep blue 5,750. 180.
4 A1 1sh violet ('56) *40,000.*

No. 4 was never put in use. Nos. 1 and 3 without watermark are proofs.

1856-59 Local Print

5 A1 1p dp yel grn ('58) *10,000.* 625.00
  a. 1p yellow green ('58) *9,000.* 750.00
6 A1 2p blood red 3,500. 90.00
  a. Printed on both sides *1,250.*
  b. 2p orange red ('56) 2,600. 92.50
7 A1 2p pale red ('57) 775. 55.00
  a. Printed on both sides *850.00*
8 A1 6p slate blue ('57) 4,750. 200.00
9 A1 1sh orange ('57) 13,500. 475.00
  a. Printed on both sides — —
  b. 1sh red orange — 775.00

1858-59 ***Rouletted***

10 A1 1p yel grn ('59) 700.00 70.00
  a. Horiz. pair, imperf. between — —
  b. 1p pale yellow green ('59) 700.00 75.00
11 A1 2p pale red ('59) 140.00 22.50
  a. Printed on both sides *750.00*
12 A1 6p slate blue 500.00 40.00
13 A1 1sh orange ('59) 1,125. 45.00
  c. Printed on both sides *1,375.*

See Nos. 14-16, 19-20, 25-26, 28-29, 32, 35-36, 41-43, 47, 51-52, 69-70, 73, 113, 118. For overprints see Nos. O1-O2, O5, O7, O9, O11-O13, O17, O20, O27, O30, O32, O39-O40, O42, O52, O76, O85.

A2

A3

Surcharge on #22-24, 34, 49-50

1860-69 ***Rouletted***

14 A1 1p dl bl grn 165.00 32.50
  a. 1p deep green 600.00 85.00
  b. 1p bright green 155.00 35.00
15 A1 1p sage green 175.00 50.00
  a. 1p deep yellow green ('69) 325.00
  b. 1p pale sage green ('65) 150.00
16 A1 2p ver ('62) 165.00 5.00
  a. Horiz. pair, imperf. btwn. 4,000. 850.00
  b. Rouletted and perf. all around *2,750.* *675.00*
  c. 2p pale red 275.00 4.75
  d. As "c," printed on both sides — 575.00
  e. 2p bright vermilion ('64) 165.00 3.75
18 A2 4p dull vio ('67) 185.00 50.00
19 A1 6p grnsh bl ('63) 350.00 4.75
20 A1 6p dull blue 425.00 7.50
  a. 6p sky blue 300.00 7.75
  b. 6p Prussian blue 1,500. 57.50
  c. Horiz. pair, imperf btwn. 3,000. *3,250.*
  d. 6p ultramarine 300.00 4.75
  e. Horiz. pair, imperf. btwn. (#20f) — *2,750.*
  f. 6p indigo blue — 75.00
  g. Rouletted and perf. all around (#20f) *475.00*
  h. 6p violet blue 500.00 8.00
  i. 6p violet ultramarine ('68) 500.00 7.00
21 A3 9p gray lilac ('69) 165.00 10.50
  a. Double impression — —
  b. Horiz. pair, imperf. between 5,000.
  c. Rouletted and perf. all around *2,900.* *250.00*
22 A3 10p on 9p red org (Bl) ('66) 625.00 45.00
23 A3 10p on 9p yel (Bl) ('67) 825.00 32.50
24 A3 10p on 9p yel (Blk) ('69) 4,000. 75.00
  a. Inverted surcharge — *7,500.*
  c. Printed on both sides — *1,250.*
  d. Rouletted x perf. 10 —
24E A1 1sh yellow ('61) 1,650. 35.00
  f. Vert. pair, imperf. btwn. — 6,500.
25 A1 1sh lake brn ('65) 325.00 13.50
  a. Horiz. pair, imperf. btwn. — *2,750.*
26 A1 1sh brown ('63) 425.00 32.50
  a. 1sh chestnut ('64) 375.00 12.50
  b. 1sh gray brown ('63) 450.00 35.00
27 A2 2sh car ('67) 550.00 37.50
  a. Vert. pair, imperf. btwn. *2,900.*

There are six varieties of the surcharge "TEN PENCE" in this and subsequent issues.

Nos. 16b, 20g, 21c, 28a, 32c, 33a are rouletted remainders that were later perforated.

See Nos. 31, 33, 46, 48, 53, 63, 68, 72, 74, 112, 113B, 119-120. For surcharges & overprints see Nos. 34, 44-45, 49-50, 59, 67, 71, O4, O6, O8, O10, O16-O19, O18, O21, O26, O28-O29, O31, O33, O36-O38, O41, O41B, O43, O53. Compare with design A6a.

1867-72 ***Perf. 11½ to 12½xRoulette***

28 A1 1p blue green 625.00 65.00
  a. Rouletted and perf. all around 750.00
29 A1 1p grayish green ('70) 500.00 30.00
29a A1 1p bright green 450.00 25.00
  b. 1p pale bright green ('67) 475.00 30.00
31 A2 4p dull violet ('68) 3,500. 165.00
  a. 4p purple ('69) — 135.00
32 A1 6p Prus blue 1,150. 20.00
  a. 6p sky blue 1,250. 20.00
  b. Printed on both sides — —
  c. Rouletted and perf. all around — *400.00*
  d. 6p indigo blue ('69) 1,300. 27.50
  e. As "d," rouletted and perf. all around — *525.00*
33 A3 9p gray lilac ('72) — *275.00*
34 A3 10p on 9p yel (Bl) ('68) 1,850. 37.50
  a. Printed on both sides — *1,275.*
35 A1 1sh chestnut ('68) 575.00 26.00
36 A1 1sh lake brn ('69) 575.00 24.00
  a. Rouletted and perf. all around — —

Nos. 44-45 Surcharged

Perf. 10, 11½, 12½ and Compound

1867-74

41 A1 1p yel grn 190.00 20.00
42 A1 1p blue green 200.00 20.00
  a. Printed on both sides 1,050.
  b. Horiz. pair, imperf between 3,200.
  c. 1p pale bright green ('68) 400.00 65.00
  d. 1p gray green ('68) 350.00 65.00
43 A1 2p vermilion 1,400.
44 A2 3p on 4p sky blue (Blk) ('70) 675.00 19.00
  a. 3p on 4p ultra, black surcharge 190.00 8.75
  b. Surcharge omitted *42,500.* *19,500.*
  c. Double surcharge 3,750.
  d. Surcharged on both sides 3,250.
  e. Rouletted — *1,350.*
  f. 3p on 4p Prussian blue ('71) *925.00*
46 A2 4p dull violet 120.00 9.25
  a. 4p dull purple ('68) 130.00 17.50
47 A1 6p Prussian blue 425.00 8.00
  a. 6p sky blue 750.00 12.50
  b. Imperf. vert., pair —
  c. Horiz. pair, imperf x perf 11½ *2,400.*
  d. 6p indigo ('69) 425.00 19.00
48 A3 9p red lilac ('72) 125.00 9.00
  a. 9p violet 210.00 9.00
  b. 9p red violet 210.00 9.50
  c. Printed on both sides *925.00*
49 A3 10p on 9p yel (Bl) ('68) *2,350.* 50.00
50 A3 10p on 9p yel (Blk) ('69) 500.00 62.50
51 A1 1sh dp brn 175.00 12.50
52 A1 1sh red brown 190.00 12.50
  a. 1sh chestnut 210.00 19.50
  b. 1sh lake brown ('68) 240.00 17.50
53 A2 2sh carmine 190.00 14.00
  a. Printed on both sides 400.00
  b. Horiz. pair, imperf. vert. —
  c. 2sh pale rose pink ('69) 2,350. 185.00
  d. 2sh deep rose pink ('69) — 125.00
  e. 2sh carmine red ('69) 200.00 22.50

Perf. 10

42e A1 1p brt grn ('71) 350.00 24.00
42f A1 1p pale br grn ('70) 350.00 24.00
42g A1 1p gray green ('70) 400.00 27.50
44g A2 3p on 4p pale ultra (Blk) ('71) 675.00 22.00
44h A2 3p on 4p ultra (Blk) ('71) 190.00 10.50
44i A2 3p on 4p Pruss bl (Blk) ('71) *1,000.*
45 A2 3p on 4p sl bl (Red) ('70) 1,700. 125.00
46b A2 4p dull lilac ('70) 240.00 12.50
46c A2 4p dull pur ('71) 210.00 12.50
47e A1 6p br blue ('70) 425.00 20.00
47f A1 6p indigo ('71) 625.00 18.50
52c A1 1sh chest ('71) 400.00 45.00

Perf. 10x11½-12½, 11½-12½x10, or Compound

42h A1 1p pale br grn 400.00 27.50
  i. Printed on both sides —
42j A1 1p deep green 240.00 11.50
42k A1 1p gray green 375.00 19.00
44j A2 3p on 4p ultra (Blk) 650.00 85.00
46d A2 4p dull lilac — 23.00
46e A2 4p slate lilac 240.00 22.50
47g A1 6p Prus blue 350.00 9.50
47h A1 6p br Pruss blue 375.00 12.00
50a A3 10p on 9p yel (Blk) ('69) 375.00 75.00
52d A1 1sh chestnut 450.00 85.00
53f A2 2sh carmine 400.00 75.00
53g A2 2sh rose pink — 240.00

See Nos. 67, O14, O28, O36.

A6

A6a

1868 Typo. Wmk. 72 ***Rouletted***

54 A6a 2p orange red 165.00 3.50
  a. Imperf.
  b. Printed on both sides 775.00
  c. Horiz. pair, imperf. btwn. 1,750.
  d. 2p deep brick red 175.00 7.50

1869 ***Perf. 11½ to 12½xRoulette***

55 A6a 2p orange red *180.00*

1870 ***Perf. 10xRoulette***

56 A6a 2p orange red 575.00 42.50

Perf. 10, 11½, 12½ and Compound

1868-75

57 A6 1p bl grn ('75) 110.00 8.00
58 A6a 2p orange red 27.50 1.25
  a. Printed on both sides 425.00
  b. Horiz. pair, imperf. vert.

Engr.

59 A3 10p on 9p yel (Bl) *1,650.*

1869 Typo. Wmk. 6 ***Rouletted***

60 A6a 2p orange red 190.00 27.50
  a. Imperf.
  b. Printed on both sides

Perf. 11½ to 12½xRoulette

61 A6a 2p orange red *2,100.* 125.00

Perf. 11½ to 12½

61B A6a 2p orange red — *1,250.*

See Nos. 62, 64-66, 97-98, 105-106, 115-116, 133-134, 145-146. For surcharges & overprints see Nos. 75, O3, O22-O25, O34-O35, O44-O47, O49, O55-O56, O62-O63, O68-O69, O74, O78-O79.

1871 Wmk. 70 ***Perf. 10***

62 A6a 2p orange red 200.00 50.00

Engr.

63 A2 4p dull violet 5,750. 325.00
  a. Printed on both sides *4,750.*

Examples of the 4p from edge of sheet sometimes lack watermark.

Perf. 10, 11½, 12½ and Compound

1876-80 Typo. Wmk. 73

64 A6 1p green 45.00 1.50
65 A6a 2p orange 57.50 1.00
66 A6a 2p blood red ('80) 325.00 5.00
  Nos. 64-66 (3) 427.50 7.50

See Nos. 97-98, 105-106, 115-116, 133-134, 145-146.

No. 71

1876-84 Engr. Wmk. 7

67 A2 3p on 4p ultra (Blk) 200.00 32.50
  a. 3p on 4p deep blue 140.00 32.50
  b. Double surcharge *1,950.*
68 A2 4p reddish violet 100.00 6.00
  a. 4p dull violet 100.00 7.50
  b. 4p slate violet ('79) 175.00 16.00

69 A1 6p deep blue 200.00 4.50
a. Horiz. pair, imperf. between —
b. Imperf.
c. 6p bright blue, perf 10 275.00 20.00
d. 6p Prussian blue, perf 10 250.00 25.00
70 A1 6p pale ultra ('84) 160.00 3.00
71 A3 8p on 9p bister brn 275.00 13.00
a. 8p on 9p yellow brown 290.00 11.00
b. 8p on 9p gray brown ('80) 240.00 7.00
d. Double surcharge 2,900.
e. Vert. pair, imperf between 5,000.
72 A3 9p rose lilac 21.00 5.00
a. Printed on both sides 650.00
73 A1 1sh red brown 100.00 3.25
a. 1sh brown 100.00 4.00
b. 1sh chocolate 27.50 4.00
c. As "b," horiz. pair, imperf. btwn. 475.00
d. 1sh sepia 29.00 6.75
e. As "d," vert. pair, imperf. btwn. 675.00
f. 1sh reddish lake brown, perf 10 575.00
74 A2 2sh carmine 65.00 8.00
a. Horiz. pair, imperf. vert. *3,250.*
b. Imperf., pair

For overprint see No. O41.

Surcharged in Black

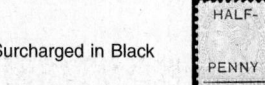

1882 Wmk. 73 *Perf. 10*
75 A6 ½p on 1p green 15.00 15.00

A9

A10

A11

A12

Perf. 10, 11½, 12½ and Compound
1883-93 Typo.
76 A9 ½p chocolate brown 20.00 2.00
a. ½p red brown ('89) 11.00 2.00
b. ½p bister brown 6.00 4.50
78 A10 3p deep green ('93) 24.00 5.75
a. 3p olive green ('90) 27.50 5.75
b. 3p sage green ('86) 42.50 2.50
79 A11 4p violet ('90) 62.50 2.75
a. 4p aniline violet ('93) 57.50 8.00
80 A12 6p pale blue ('87) 77.50 3.50
a. 6p blue ('87) 62.50 1.50
Nos. 76-80 (4) 184.00 14.00

See Nos. 96, 100-101, 104, 108-109, 111. For surcharges & overprints see Nos. 94-95, 99, O48, O50-O51, O54, O57-O61, O64, O66-O67, O71, O73, O75, O81-O82.

A13

1886-96 *Perf. 10, 11½ to 12½*
81 A13 2sh6p violet 100.00 10.00
a. 2sh6p bright aniline violet 115.00 10.00
82 A13 5sh rose 125.00 20.00
83 A13 10sh green 275.00 75.00
84 A13 15sh buff 950.00 275.00
85 A13 £1 blue 525.00 180.00
86 A13 £2 red brn 4,600. 550.00
87 A13 50sh rose red 5,750. 675.00
88 A13 £3 ol grn 6,750. 725.00
89 A13 £4 lemon 11,500. 1,350.
90 A13 £5 gray *11,500.*
90A A13 £5 brn ('96) *6,250.* 1,150.
91 A13 £10 bronze *9,750.* *1,450.*
92 A13 £15 silver *38,500.* 2,600.
93 A13 £20 lilac *45,000.* 2,900.

Perf. 10
81b A13 2sh6p violet 145.00 17.50
82a A13 5sh rose 165.00 20.00
83a A13 10sh green 350.00 75.00
84a A13 15sh buff 900.00 375.00
85a A13 £1 blue 650.00 200.00
86a A13 £2 red brn 4,800. 575.00
87a A13 50sh rose red 6,250. 800.00
88a A13 £3 ol grn 7,250. 850.00
89a A13 £4 lemon 13,500. 525.00
90b A13 £5 gray *11,250.*
91a A13 £10 bronze *12,000.* *2,200.*
92a A13 £15 silver *40,000.*
93a A13 £20 lilac *50,000.*

For overprints see Nos. O83-O84.

#94, 99

#95

Perf. 10, 11½x12½ and Compound
1891 Brown Surcharge
94 A11 2½p on 4p green 8.00 3.00
a. "½" nearer the "2" 27.50 20.00
b. Pair, imperf. between *4,000.*
c. Fraction bar omitted 125.00 90.00

Carmine Surcharge
95 A12 5p on 6p red brn 20.00 8.00
a. No period after "D" 175.00

See No. 99. For overprints see Nos. O48, O57, O59.

Many stamps of the issues of 1855-91 have been reprinted; they are all on paper watermarked Crown and SA, letters wide apart, and are overprinted "REPRINT."

1893 Typo. *Perf. 15*
96 A9 ½p brown 12.50 1.50
a. Horiz. pair, imperf. btwn 450.00
b. Pair, perf. 12 btwn; perf. 15 around 375.00 100.00
97 A6 1p green 55.00 1.00
98 A6a 2p orange 32.50 1.00
a. Vert. pair, imperf. between 1,000.
99 A11 2½p on 4p green 65.00 3.00
a. "½" nearer the "2" 135.00 20.00
b. Fraction bar omitted
100 A11 4p gray violet 55.00 4.50
101 A12 6p blue 80.00 5.00
Nos. 96-101 (6) 300.00 16.00

Kangaroo, Palm
A16

Coat of Arms
A17

1894, Mar. 1
102 A16 2½p blue violet 20.00 2.00
103 A17 5p dull violet 21.50 2.50

See Nos. 107, 110, 117, 135-136, 147, 151. For overprints see Nos. O65, O70, O72, O80.

1895-97 *Perf. 13*
104 A9 ½p pale brown 5.50 1.00
105 A6 1p green 12.50 1.00
a. Vert. pair, imperf. between
106 A6a 2p orange 16.00 .50
107 A16 2½p blue violet 10.00 2.00
108 A10 3p ol grn ('97) 6.00 3.75
109 A11 4p bright violet 6.50 1.00
110 A17 5p dull violet 12.00 2.00
111 A12 6p blue 12.00 1.50
a. 6p pale blue ('96) 12.50 1.50
Nos. 104-111 (8) 80.50 12.75

Some authorities regard the so-called redrawn 1p stamps with thicker lettering (said to have been issued in 1897) as impressions from a new or cleaned plate.

Perf. 11½, 12½, Clean-Cut, Compound
1896 Engr. Wmk. 7
112 A3 9p lilac rose 20.00 5.75
113 A1 1sh dark brown 27.50 5.00
a. Horiz. pair, imperf. vert. 475.00
c. Vert. pair, imperf. btwn. 675.00
113B A2 2sh carmine 42.50 8.00
Nos. 112-113B (3) 90.00 18.75

Adelaide Post Office — A18

1899 Typo. Wmk. 73 *Perf. 13*
114 A18 ½p yellow green 8.00 1.50
115 A6 1p carmine 10.00 1.50
a. 1p scarlet 9.00 1.50
116 A6a 2p purple 7.50 .50
117 A16 2½p dark blue 11.00 2.00
Nos. 114-117 (4) 36.50 5.50

See Nos. 132, 144. For overprint see No. O77.

Perf. 11½, 12½
1901 Engr. Wmk. 72
118 A1 1sh dark brown 24.00 17.50
a. 1sh red brown 27.50 40.00
b. Horiz. pair, imperf. vert.
119 A2 2sh carmine 27.50 13.50

1902
120 A3 9p magenta 21.00 25.00

A19

The measurements given in parentheses are the length of the value inscription in the bottom panel.

Perf. 11½, 12½ and Compound
1902-03 Typo. Wmk. 73
121 A19 3p olive grn 20.00 3.00
a. 3p olive grn (20mm), perf 12 32.50 3.75
b. Wmk sideways *1,850.*
122 A19 4p red org 42.50 5.00
a. 4p red org (17.5-18mm), perf 12 25.00 3.00
123 A19 6p blue grn 15.00 3.75
a. 6p blue grn (15mm), perf 12 27.50 20.00
124 A19 8p ultra (value 19mm long) 9.00 20.00
124A A19 8p ultra (value 16½mm long) ('03) 12.50 17.50
b. "EIGNT" 2,600. *3,250.*
125 A19 9p claret 19.00 15.00
a. Vert. pair, imperf. between 3,000.
b. Horiz. pair, imperf. between
c. 9p claret, perf 12 135.00 37.50
126 A19 10p org buff 18.00 20.00
127 A19 1sh brn ('03) 27.50 9.00
a. Horiz. pair, imperf. btwn.
b. Vert. pair, imperf. btwn. 2,900.
c. "Postage" and denomination in red brown *1,100.* *1,000.*
128 A19 2sh6p purple 45.00 15.00
a. 2sh6p pale violet 90.00 50.00
129 A19 5sh rose 135.00 80.00
130 A19 10sh grn ('03) 225.00 100.00
131 A19 £1 blue 525.00 275.00
Nos. 121-131 (12) 1,094. 563.25

1904 *Perf. 12x11½*
132 A18 ½p yellow green 8.50 3.00
133 A6 1p rose 8.75 1.00
134 A6a 2p purple 15.00 1.00
135 A16 2½p dark blue 16.00 6.50
136 A17 5p dull violet 22.50 3.00
Nos. 132-136 (5) 70.75 14.50

A20

1904-08 *Perf. 12 and 12x11½*
137 A20 6p blue grn 42.50 3.00
a. Vert. pair, imperf. between *5,000.*
138 A20 8p ultra ('06) 20.00 9.00
139 A20 9p claret ('09) 11.00 4.25
139A A20 10p org buff ('07) 18.00 25.00
b. Vert. pair, imperf. between 4,500.
c. Horiz. pair, imperf. between 3,500. 3,500.
140 A20 1sh brown 30.00 4.00
a. Vert. pair, imperf between 3,000.
b. Horiz. pair, imperf between 3,250.
141 A20 2sh6p pur ('05) 75.00 32.50
142 A20 5sh scarlet 85.00 50.00
a. 5sh pale rose, Perf 12½, small holes ('10) 140.00 75.00
142B A20 10sh grn ('08) 200.00 *150.00*
143 A20 £1 dp blue 250.00 150.00
a. Perf 12½, small holes ('10) 350.00 175.00
Nos. 137-143 (9) 731.50 427.75

See Nos. 148-150, 152-157.

1906-12 Wmk. 74
144 A18 ½p green 18.00 1.20
145 A6 1p carmine 7.50 .25
146 A6a 2p purple 8.00 1.25
a. Horiz. pair, imperf. between 2,500.
147 A16 2½p dk blue ('11) 9.00 15.00
148 A20 3p ol grn (value 19mm long) 15.00 5.00
a. Horiz. pair, imperf. between *5,750.*
149 A20 3p ol grn (value 17mm long) ('09) 17.50 12.00
150 A20 4p red org 25.00 9.00
151 A17 5p dl vio ('08) 30.00 6.75
152 A20 6p bl grn ('07) 7.50 11.00
a. Vert. pair, imperf. between 2,500. 2,750.
153 A20 8p ultra ('09) 12.00 *24.00*
154 A20 9p claret 22.50 5.00
a. Vert. pair, imperf. between 2,250.
b. Horiz. pair, imperf. between *5,000.*
155 A20 1sh brown 12.50 5.50
a. Horiz. pair, imperf. between *3,750.*
b. Vert. pair, imperf. between 3,750.
156 A20 2sh6p pur ('09) 80.00 32.50
a. 2sh6p pale violet, perf 12 ('10) 80.00 37.50
b. 2sh6p pale violet, perf 12½ ('12) 125.00 125.00
157 A20 5sh lt red ('12) 145.00 145.00
Nos. 144-157 (14) 409.50 273.45

OFFICIAL STAMPS

For Departments
Regular Issues Overprinted in Red, Black or Blue:

A. (Architect), A. G. (Attorney General), A. O. (Audit Office), B. D. (Barracks Department), B. G. (Botanical Gardens), B. M. (Bench of Magistrates), C. (Customs), C. D. (Convict Department), C. L. (Crown Lands), C. O. (Commissariat Officer), C. S. (Chief Secretary), C. Sgn. (Colonial Surgeon), C. P. (Commissioner of Police), C. T. (Commissioner of Titles), D. B. (Destitute Board), D. R. (Deed Registry), E. (Engineer), E. B. (Education Board),

G. P. (Government Printer), G. S. (Government Storekeeper), G. T. (Goolwa Tramway), G. F. (Gold Fields), H. (Hospital), H. A. (House of Assembly), I. A. (Immigration Agent), I. E. (Intestate Estates), I. S. (Inspector of Sheep), L. A. (Lunatic Asylum), L. C. (Legislative Council), L. L. (Legislative Library), L. T. (Land Titles), M. (Military), M. B. (Marine Board), M. R. (Manager of Railways), M. R. G. (Main Roads Gambierton), N. T. (Northern Territory),

O. A. (Official Assignee), P. (Police), P. A. (Protector of Aborigines), P. O. (Post Office), P. S. (Private Secretary), P. W. (Public Works), R. B. (Road Board), R. G. (Registrar General of Births, &c.), S. (Sheriff), S. C. (Supreme Court), S.G. (Surveyor General), S. M. (Stipendiary Magistrate), S. T. (Superintendent of Telegraph), T. (Treasurer), T. R. (Titles Registry), V. (Volunteers), V. A. (Valuator), V. N. (Vaccination), W. (Waterworks).

1868-74 Wmk. 6 *Rouletted*
O1 A1 1p green *350.00*
O2 A1 2p pale red *275.00*
O3 A6a 2p vermilion *150.00*
O4 A2 4p dull violet *300.00*
O5 A1 6p slate blue *300.00*
O6 A3 9p gray lilac *500.00*
O7 A1 1sh brown *300.00*
O8 A2 2sh carmine *275.00*

Perf. 11½ to 12½ x Roulette
O9 A1 1p green *275.00*
O10 A2 4p dull violet *850.00*
O11 A1 6p blue *210.00*
O12 A1 1sh brown *200.00*

Perf. 10, 11½, 12½ and Compound
O13 A1 1p green *150.00*
O14 A2 3p on 4p sl bl (Red) *750.00*
O15 A2 3p on 4p sl bl (Blk) *275.00*
O16 A2 4p dull violet *250.00*
O17 A1 6p deep blue *275.00*
O18 A3 9p violet *500.00*
O19 A3 10p on 9p yel (Blk) *500.00*
O20 A1 1sh brown 175.00 *175.00*
O21 A2 2sh carmine *125.00*

Rouletted
Wmk. 72
O22 A6a 2p orange *135.00*

Perf. 11 ½ x Roulette

O23 A6a 2p orange *175.00*
a. Perf 10 x Roulette *300.00*

Perf. 10, 11½, 12½ and Compound

O24 A6a 2p orange *50.00*

Wmk. 70

Perf. 10

O25 A6a 2p orange *125.00*
O26 A2 4p dull violet *275.00*

For General Use

Overprinted in Black

Perf. 10, 11½, 12½ and Compound

1874 Wmk. 6

O27 A1 1p green — *500.00*
a. 1p dp yel green, perf 11½-12½x10 3,500. *400.00*
b. As "a," printed on both sides 1,275.
O28 A2 3p on 4p ultra 9,000. *3,500.*
a. No period after "S" *4,250.*
O29 A2 4p dull violet 90.00 9.50
a. Inverted overprint
b. No period after "S" 85.00
c. Perf. 11½-12½x10 3,000. 600.00
O30 A1 6p deep blue 275.00 9.50
a. No period after "S" 125.00
b. 6p Prussian blue, perf 11½-12½x10 200.00 12.50
O31 A3 9p violet *4,500.* *2,000.*
a. No period after "S" *5,000.* *2,500.*
O32 A1 1sh red brown 115.00 14.00
a. Double overprint 350.00
b. No period after "S" 400.00 90.00
O33 A2 2sh carmine 375.00 32.50
a. Double overprint
b. No period after "S" 165.00
c. 2sh carmine, perf 11½-12½x10 160.00

1874-75 Wmk. 72

O34 A6 1p blue green 240.00 47.50
a. Inverted overprint
O35 A6a 2p orange 65.00 9.50

1876-86 Wmk. 7

O37 A2 4p dull violet 75.00 5.00
O38 A2 4p reddish vio 75.00 3.00
a. Double overprint
b. Inverted overprint 1,000. 350.00
c. Dbl. ovpt., one inverted
O39 A1 6p dark blue 165.00 6.00
a. Double overprint 225.00
b. Inverted overprint 1,500.
O40 A1 6p ultramarine 150.00 5.50
a. Double overprint
b. Inverted overprint
O41 A1 8p on 9p yel brn 6,500. 3,500.
a. Double overprint 7,750.
O41B A3 9p violet *9,500.*
O42 A1 1sh red brown 55.00 9.00
a. Inverted overprint 1,000. 300.00
b. Double overprint
O43 A2 2sh carmine 325.00 9.00
a. Double overprint — 400.00
b. Inverted overprint — 425.00
c. No period after "S" — 100.00

1880-91 Wmk. 73

O44 A6 1p blue green 35.00 1.75
a. Inverted overprint 140.00
b. Double overprint 275.00 140.00
c. Dbl. ovpt., one inverted *750.00*
O45 A6 1p yellow green 55.00 1.00
O46 A6a 2p orange 18.00 1.00
a. Inverted overprint 85.00
b. Double overprint 275.00 150.00
c. Overprinted sideways
d. Dbl. ovpt., one inverted
e. Dbl. ovpt., both inverted — 425.00
O47 A6a 2p blood red 110.00 35.00
O48 A11 2½p on 4p green 130.00 14.00
a. "½" nearer the "2" — 55.00
b. Double overprint
c. Pair, one without ovpt. 4,750.
Nos. O44-O48 (5) 348.00 52.75

1882-90 *Perf. 10*

O49 A6 ½p on 1p green 130.00 25.00
a. Inverted overprint
O50 A11 4p violet 140.00 13.00
O51 A12 6p blue 60.00 1.50
a. Double overprint
b. No period after "S"
Nos. O49-O51 (3) 330.00 39.50

Overprinted in Black

Perf. 10, 11½, 12½ and Compound

1891 Wmk. 7

O52 A1 1sh red brown 80.00 5.50
a. No period after "S" — 100.00
b. 1sh lake brown, perf 11½-12½ 90.00 10.00
c. 1sh Van Dyke brown 160.00 10.00
O53 A2 2sh carmine 90.00 10.00
a. Double overprint
b. No period after "S" *550.00*

1891-95 Wmk. 73

O54 A9 ½p brown 50.00 7.50
a. No period after "S" 175.00 55.00
O55 A6 1p blue green 70.00 2.00
a. Double overprint 275.00 100.00
b. No period after "S" 125.00 15.00
O56 A6a 2p orange 30.00 .50
a. No period after "S" — 45.00
O57 A11 2½p on 4p green 45.00 35.00
a. "½" nearer the "2" 120.00 60.00
b. Inverted overprint 575.00
O58 A11 4p violet 70.00 5.00
a. Double overprint —
O59 A12 5p on 6p red brn 50.00 18.00
O60 A12 6p blue 45.00 2.50
a. Double overprint —
b. No period after "S" —
Nos. O54-O60 (7) 360.00 70.50

1893 *Perf. 15*

O61 A9 ½p brown 80.00 22.50
O62 A6 1p green 10.00 1.25
O63 A6a 2p orange 32.50 .60
a. Inverted overprint 30.00 80.00
b. Double overprint 110.00
O64 A11 4p gray violet 100.00 7.00
a. Double overprint 550.00 180.00
O65 A17 5p dull violet 130.00 25.00
O66 A12 6p blue 65.00 4.00
Nos. O61-O66 (6) 417.50 60.35

1896 *Perf. 13*

O67 A9 ½p brown 65.00 5.75
a. Triple overprint *500.00*
O68 A6 1p green 45.00 1.50
a. No period after "S" 200.00 14.00
O69 A6a 2p orange 55.00 .50
a. No period after "S" 180.00 10.00
O70 A16 2½p blue violet 120.00 9.00
a. No period after "S" 80.00
O71 A11 4p brt violet 130.00 3.00
a. Double overprint *750.00* 150.00
b. No period after "S" 375.00 55.00
O72 A17 5p dull violet 130.00 32.50
a. No period after "S" 500.00
O73 A12 6p blue 70.00 3.00
a. No period after "S" 275.00 80.00
Nos. O67-O73 (7) 615.00 55.25

On No. O67a, one overprint is upright, two sideways.

Same Overprint in Dark Blue

1891-95 *Perf. 10*

O74 A6 1p green 250.00 5.00
O75 A12 6p blue —

Black Overprint

Perf. 11½, 12½, Clean-Cut

1897 Wmk. 7

O76 A1 1sh brown 75.00 5.50
a. Double overprint — *550.00*
b. No period after "S" 375.00

Overprinted in Black

1900 Wmk. 73 *Perf. 13*

O77 A18 ½p yellow green 25.00 10.00
a. Inverted overprint 200.00
b. No period after "S" 100.00
c. As "b," inverted overprint —
O78 A6 1p carmine rose 30.00 1.60
a. Inverted overprint 200.00 125.00
b. Double overprint 650.00
c. No period after "S" 125.00 22.50
O79 A6a 2p purple 40.00 1.00
a. Inverted ovpt. 200.00 90.00
b. No period after "S" 110.00 20.00
O80 A16 2½p dark blue 85.00 20.00
a. Inverted overprint *600.00* 225.00
b. No period after "S" 325.00 110.00
O81 A11 4p violet 85.00 6.00
a. Inverted overprint *650.00*
b. No period after "S" 275.00 85.00
O82 A12 6p blue 50.00 5.50
a. No period after "S" 180.00 90.00
Nos. O77-O82 (6) 315.00 44.10

1901 *Perf. 10*

O83 A13 2sh6p violet *8,750.* *6,500.*
O84 A13 5sh rose *9,000.* *7,500.*

On Nos. O77-O82 the letters "O.S." are 11½mm apart; on Nos. O83-O84, 14½mm apart.

Overprinted in Black

1903 Wmk. 72 *Perf. 11½, 12½*

O85 A1 1sh red brown 110.00 50.00

TASMANIA

taz-ˈmā-nē-ə

LOCATION — An island off the southeastern coast of Australia
GOVT. — British Colony
AREA — 26,215 sq. mi.
POP. — 172,475 (1901)
CAPITAL — Hobart

Tasmania was one of the six British colonies that united in 1901 to form the Commonwealth of Australia. The island was originally named Van Diemen's Land by its discoverer, Abel Tasman, the present name having been adopted in 1853. Stamps of Australia are now used.

12 Pence = 1 Shilling
20 Shillings = 1 Pound

Watermarks

Wmk. 6 — Large Star

Wmk. 139 Double-lined Numeral

Wmk. 49 Double-lined Numeral

Wmk. 50 Single-lined "2"

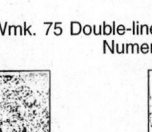

Wmk. 75 Double-lined Numeral

Wmk. 51 Single-lined "4"

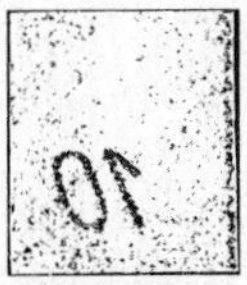

Wmk. 52 — Single-lined "10"

Wmk. 70 — V and Crown

Wmk. 13 — Crown & Double-lined A

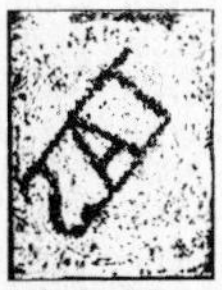

Wmk. 76 — TAS

Wmk. 77 — TAS

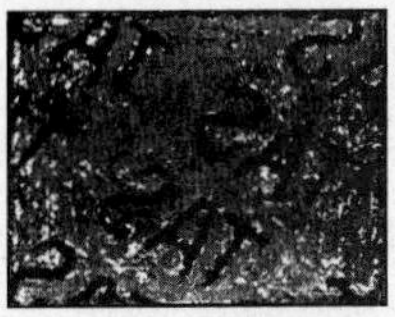

Wmk. 78 — Multiple TAS

Values for unused stamps are for examples with original gum as defined in the catalogue introduction except for Nos. 1-2b and 10 which are valued without gum as few examples exist with any remaining original gum. Very fine examples of Nos. 17-75a will have perforations touching the design on one or more sides due to the narrow spacing of the stamps on the plates. Stamps with perfs clear of the design on all four sides are scarce and command higher prices.

Queen Victoria
A1 A2

Unwmk.

1853, Nov. 1 Engr. *Imperf.*

1 A1 1p blue, fine impression, soft paper 13,000. 1,600.
1a A1 1p blue, blurred impression, hard paper 12,000. 1,350.
2 A2 4p red orange 7,500. 550.00
a. 4p yellow orange 7,000. 425.00
Cut to shape 25.00
b. 4p orange, blurred impression ('55) 7,000. 425.00
Cut to shape 25.00

Twenty-four varieties of each.
The 4p on vertically laid paper is believed to be a proof. Value, unused, $7,500.

The reprints are made from defaced plates and show marks across the face of each stamp. They are on thin and thick, unwatermarked paper and thin cardboard; only the first are perforated. Nearly all the reprints of Tasmania may be found with and without the overprint "REPRINT."

Nos. 1-47A with pen or revenue cancellations sell for a small fraction of the price of postally used examples. Stamps are found with pen cancellation removed.

Queen Victoria — A3

1855 Wmk. 6 Wove Paper

4 A3 1p dark carmine 10,500. 1,000.
5 A3 2p green 5,750. 500.00
a. 2p deep green 5,750. 600.00
6 A3 4p deep blue 5,000. 145.00
a. 4p blue 5,000. 145.00

1856-57 Unwmk.

7 A3 1p pale red 13,500. 700.00
8 A3 2p emerald ('57) 16,500. 1,000.
9 A3 4p blue ('57) 3,500. 140.00
a. 4p deep blue ('57) 3,500. 140.00
b. 4p pale blue ('57) — 180.00

1856 Pelure Paper

10 A3 1p brown red 10,000. 800.00

1857-69 Wmk. 49, 75, 139

11 A3 1p carmine ('67) 375.00 32.50
a. 1p orange red ('65) 400.00 40.00
b. 1p brown red 650.00 42.50
c. Double impression 650.00 300.00
d. 1p brick red ('63) 500.00 42.50
e. Wmk. 50 (error) ('69) —
12 A3 2p sage green ('60) 450.00 95.00
a. 2p yellow green 1,200. 125.00
b. 2p green — 67.50
c. 2p dull emerald green 150.00
d. As "b," double impression 325.00

13 A3 4p pale blue 500.00 30.00
- a. 4p blue 425.00 32.50
- b. Printed on both sides —
- c. 4p deep blue — 95.00
- d. As "a," double impression 275.00
- e. As "c," double impression 315.00
- g. 4p cobalt blue — 95.00

Nos. 11-13 (3) 1,325. 157.50

See Nos. 17-19, 23-25, 29-31, 35-37, 39-41, 45-47A.

A4

A4a

1858-67

14 A4 6p gray lilac ('63) 950.00 95.00
- a. 6p red violet ('67) 1,400. 200.00
- b. Double impression ('63) 450.00
- c. 6p dull lilac 1,500. 100.00

15 A4 6p blue gray ('65) 1,150. 150.00

16 A4a 1sh vermilion *825.00* 90.00

Nos. 14-16 (3) 2,925. 335.00

No. 15 watermarked large star was not regularly issued.

Issued: No. 14c, 16, 1/58; No. 14, 4/63; No. 15, 2/65; No. 14a, 4/67.

1864 ***Rouletted***

17 A3 1p carmine *950.00* 325.00
- a. 1p brick red — 500.00

18 A3 2p yellow grn — 1,250.

19 A3 4p blue — 475.00

21 A4 6p gray lilac — 525.00

22 A4a 1sh vermilion — 1,350.

Values for Nos. 17-22 are for stamps showing rouletting on two or three sides. Examples with full roulettes on all four sides are rare.

1864-69 ***Perf. 10***

23 A3 1p brick red 210.00 70.00
- a. 1p carmine 160.00 60.00
- b. 1p orange red 200.00 60.00
- c. As "b," double impression —

24 A3 2p yellow green 900.00 200.00
- a. 2p sage green 850.00 240.00

25 A3 4p blue 450.00 22.50
- a. Double impression 240.00

26 A4 6p lilac 650.00 30.00
- a. 6p red lilac 850.00 110.00

27 A4 6p slate blue 900.00 110.00

28 A4a 1sh vermilion 700.00 65.00
- a. Horiz. pair, imperf. vert.

Nos. 23-28 (6) 3,810. 497.50

1864-91 ***Perf. 12, 12½***

29 A3 1p carmine 140.00 25.00
- a. 1p orange red 175.00 *40.00*
- b. 1p brick red 140.00 62.50
- c. Double impression —
- d. Wmkd. "2" *3,000.*
- As "d," pen cancel 325.00

30 A3 2p yellow green 650.00 110.00

31 A3 4p blue 400.00 26.00
- a. 4p deep blue 400.00 25.00
- b. 4p cobalt blue — 65.00

32 A4 6p red lilac 200.00 47.50
- a. Horiz. pair, imperf between —
- b. Vert. pair, imperf between —
- c. 6p violet 500.00 32.50
- d. As "c," Vert. pair, imperf between —
- e. 6p purple ('84) 175.00 22.50
- f. Horiz. pair, imperf between *2,900.* —
- g. 6p dull claret ('91) 52.50 15.00

34 A4a 1sh vermilion 500.00 75.00
- a. Double impression — 200.00
- b. Horiz. pair, imperf. between *3,500.*

Perf. 10x12

29e A3 1p carmine *3,250.*
31c A3 4p blue *2,750.*

Perf. 12½

29f A3 1p carmine 120.00 27.50
29g A3 1p orange red 190.00 52.50
29h A3 1p brick red 175.00 52.50
30a A3 2p yellow green 850.00 180.00
30b A3 2p sage green 750.00 190.00
31d A3 4p blue 500.00 57.50
31e A3 4p bright blue 500.00 60.00
32h A4 6p purple 900.00 145.00
32i A4 6p slate violet 650.00 67.50

33 A4 6p slate blue 850.00 110.00
34c A4a 1sh vermilion 800.00 140.00

Perf. 11½

32j A4 6p dull lilac 300.00 25.00
32k A4 6p lilac 275.00 25.00
- l. Pair, imperf between 1,750.

32m A4 6p dp slate lil ('75) 275.00 25.00
- n. Imperf, pair — 1,400.

32o A4 6p brt vio ('78) 300.00 37.50
- p. Double impression 160.00
- q. Horiz. pair, imperf between *4,750.*

32r A4 6p dl reddish lil ('79) 200.00 45.00

34d A4a 1sh dl ver ('73) 375.00 70.00
- e. Horiz. pair, imperf between —

34f A4a 1sh brnsh ver ('73) 375.00 70.00

The reprints are on unwatermarked paper, perforated 11½, and on thin cardboard, imperforate and perforated.

Perf. Pin-perf. 5½ to 9½, 13½ to 14½

1867

35 A3 1p carmine 1,250. 400.00
36 A3 2p yel grn 975.00
37 A3 4p blue 650.00
38 A4 6p gray 650.00
38A A4 6p red lilac 1,500.
38B A4a 1sh vermilion —

Pin-perf. 13½ to 14½

35a A3 1p brick red 800.00
35b A3 1p dull vermilion 800.00
35c A3 1p carmine
36a A3 2p yel grn 1,500.
37a A3 4p pale blue 700.00
38Ac A4 6p gray violet 2,750.
38Bd A4a 1sh vermilion —

Oblique Roulette 14-15

39 A3 1p carmine 1,200.
- a. 1p brick red 1,200.
- b. 1p dull vermilion 1,250.

40 A3 2p yel grn 1,600.
41 A3 4p blue 1,250.
42 A4 6p gray 2,400.
43 A4 6p red lilac —
44 A4a 1sh vermilion 2,900.

Oblique Roulette 10-10½

39c A3 1p carmine *3,000.* 800.00
39d A3 1p brick red 1,000.
40a A3 2p yellow green 1,500.
41a A3 4p blue 1,100.
43a A4 6p gray lilac 2,400.

Oblique Roulette Imperf 10-10½

41b A3 4p blue 1,100.

1868 ***Serrate Perf. 19***

45 A3 1p carmine 1,000. 300.00
46 A3 2p yellow green 1,100.
47 A3 4p blue *2,100.* 300.00
47A A3 6p purple — 1,250.
47B A3 1sh vermilion —

Queen Victoria — A5

1870-71 **Typo.** **Wmk. 50** ***Perf. 11½***

48 A5 2p blue green 200.00 12.50
- a. Double impression 5,500. 2,000.
- b. Perf. 12 210.00 12.50
- c. 2p green 325.00 20.00
- d. As "c," perf. 12 200.00 11.00
- e. As "d," imperf, pair —

See Nos. 49-75, 98, 108-109.

Wmk. 51 ***Perf. 12***

49 A5 1p rose ('71) 150.00 67.50
- a. Imperf., pair 1,300. 1,200.

50 A5 4p blue 1,350. 525.00

Wmk. 52

51 A5 1p rose 130.00 24.00
- a. Imperf. pair 1,350. 1,350.
- c. Perf. 11½ 1,350.

52 A5 10p black 27.50 52.50
- a. Imperf. pair 750.00
- b. Perf. 11½ 52.50 52.50

The reprints are on unwatermarked paper. The 4p has also been reprinted on thin cardboard, imperf and perf.

1871-76 **Wmk. 76** ***Perf. 11½***

53 A5 1p rose 18.00 2.50
- a. Imperf.
- c. Perf. 12 155.00 35.00
- d. 1p carmine 25.00 3.50
- e. 1p pink 25.00 4.00
- f. As "d," perf. 12 170.00 40.00
- g. As "e," perf. 12 170.00 14.00

53B A5 1p ver ('73) 300.00 80.00

54 A5 2p dp grn ('72) 80.00 2.75
- a. 2p yellow green 275.00 5.00
- b. 2p blue green 57.50 2.75
- c. Imperf. pair 1,750.
- d. 2p green, perf. 12 700.00 150.00
- e. Double impression

55 A5 3p brown 80.00 5.00
- a. 3p purple brown 80.00 5.00
- b. As "a," imperf. pair 1,150.
- c. 3p brownish purple 70.00 5.00

56 A5 3p red brn ('71) 90.00 5.00
- a. 3p indian red 75.00 5.00
- b. Imperf. pair 140.00
- c. Vert. pair, imperf. horiz.
- d. Perf. 12 145.00 24.00
- e. 3p deep red brown, perf. 12 145.00 24.00
- f. As "e," pair, imperf. between

57 A5 4p dull yel ('76) 175.00 60.00
- a. Perf. 12 375.00 27.50
- b. 4p ocher 100.00 10.00
- c. 4p buff 85.00 12.00

58 A5 9p blue 32.50 9.00
- a. Imperf. pair 575.00
- b. Perf. 12 60.00 52.50
- c. Double impression *3,500.*

59 A5 5sh bright violet 375.00 85.00
- a. Imperf.
- b. Horiz. pair, imperf. vert.
- c. Perf. 12 600.00 475.00
- d. 5sh purple 375.00 85.00
- e. 5sh purple, perf. 12 575.00
- Pen cancel 11.00

Nos. 53-59 (8) 1,151. 249.25

The reprints are on unwatermarked paper, the 5sh has also been reprinted on thin cardboard; all are perforated.

1878 **Wmk. 77** ***Perf. 14***

60 A5 1p rose 12.00 1.25
61 A5 2p deep green 12.00 1.25
62 A5 8p violet brown 15.00 10.00

Nos. 60-62 (3) 39.00 12.50

The 8p has been reprinted on thin unwatermarked paper, perforated 11½.

1880-83 ***Perf. 12, 11½***

63 A5 3p indian red, perf. 12 10.00 9.00
- a. Imperf. pair 475.00
- b. Horiz. pair, imperf. between *2,500.*
- c. Perf. 11½ 25.00 5.50

64 A5 4p lem, perf. 11½ ('83) 85.00 20.00
- a. 4p olive yellow, perf. 11½ 160.00 30.00
- b. Printed on both sides *1,600.*
- c. Imperf.
- d. 4p deep yellow, perf. 12 150.00 32.50

Type of 1871 Surcharged in Black

1889 ***Perf. 14***

65 A5 ½p on 1p carmine 11.00 *25.00*
- a. "al" sideways in surcharge *2,400.* *2,100.*

No. 65 has been reprinted on thin cardboard, perforated 12, with the surcharge "Halfpenny" 19mm long.

1889-96 ***Perf. 11½***

66 A5 ½p red orange 3.25 3.50
- a. ½p yellow orange 3.25 3.50
- b. Perf. 12 6.00 *7.50*

67 A5 1p dull red 17.50 3.50
- a. 1p vermilion 14.00 3.00

68 A5 1p car, perf. 12 8.25 3.25
- a. 1p pink, perf. 12 45.00 20.00
- b. 1p salmon rose, perf. 12 42.50 15.00
- c. Imperf. pair 400.00 *375.00*

Perf. 12

69 A5 4p bister ('96) 16.00 7.50
70 A5 9p chalky bl ('96) 10.00 3.50

Nos. 66-70 (5) 55.00 21.25

1891 **Wmk. 76** ***Perf. 11½***

71 A5 ½p orange 80.00 60.00
- a. ½p brown orange 60.00 55.00
- b. Imperf. pair 325.00
- c. Perf. 12 70.00 55.00

72 A5 1p salmon rose 25.00 11.00
- a. 1p carmine, perf. 12 50.00 50.00

73 A5 4p ol bis, perf. 12 25.00 40.00

Nos. 71-73 (3) 130.00 111.00

See Nos. 98, 108-109.

Surcharged in Black

1891 **Wmk. 77** ***Perf. 11½***

Surcharge 14mm High

74 A5 2½p on 9p lt blue 24.00 4.50
- a. Dbl. surcharge, one invtd. 800.00 *900.00*
- b. Imperf. pair —

Perf. 12

Surcharge 15mm High

75 A5 2½p on 9p lt blue 5.50 4.00
- a. Surcharged in blue

No. 74 has been reprinted on thin unwatermarked paper, imperforate. There is also a reprint on thin cardboard, in deep ultramarine, with surcharge 16½mm high, and perforated 12.

A8

A9

1892-99 **Typo.** ***Perf. 14***

76 A8 ½p orange & vio 3.00 1.50
77 A9 2½p magenta 3.00 2.00
78 A8 5p pale bl & brn 9.00 4.00
79 A8 6p blue vio & blk 17.50 5.00
80 A8 10p red brn & grn ('99) 12.50 15.00
81 A8 1sh rose & green 13.00 3.50
82 A8 2sh6p brown & blue 40.00 42.50
83 A8 5sh brn vio & red 100.00 30.00
84 A8 10sh brt vio & brn 225.00 125.00
85 A8 £1 green & yel 600.00 550.00

Nos. 76-85 (10) 1,023. 778.50

No. 80 shows the numeral on white tablet. See Nos. 99, 110-111.

Lake Marion A10

Mt. Wellington A11

View of Hobart — A12

Tasman's Arch — A13

Spring River, Port Davey — A14

Russell Falls — A15

Mt. Gould and Lake St. Clair — A16

Dilston Falls — A17

1899-1900 **Engr.** **Wmk. 78** ***Perf. 14***

86 A10 ½p dark green 10.00 7.00
87 A11 1p carmine 7.00 2.00
88 A12 2p violet 29.00 2.00
89 A13 2½p dark blue 27.50 4.00
90 A14 3p dark brown 25.00 6.50
91 A15 4p ocher 30.00 10.00
92 A16 5p ultramarine 50.00 12.50
93 A17 6p lake 35.00 45.00

Nos. 86-93 (8) 213.50 89.00

See Nos. 94-97, 102-107, 114-117.

Perf. 11, 12½, 11x12½

1902-03 **Litho., Typo.** **Wmk. 70**

94 A10 ½p green 6.50 1.75
95 A11 1p carmine 22.50 2.00
96 A11 1p dull red 22.50 5.00
97 A12 2p violet 16.00 .80
98 A5 9p blue 25.00 4.00
- a. 9p ultramarine 450.00
- b. 9p indigo 240.00
- c. Perf. 11 9.00 20.00
- d. Perf 12½, wmkd. sideways 40.00 17.00

99 A8 1sh rose & green 55.00 10.50
- a. Perf. 11 100.00 85.00

Nos. 94-99 (6) 147.50 24.05

Nos. 94, 97 are litho., Nos. 96, 98-99 typo. No. 95 was printed both ways.

No. 78 Surcharged in Black

1904 **Wmk. 77** ***Perf. 14***

100 A8 1½p on 5p blue & brn 2.75 2.75

Perf. 11, 12, 12½ and Compound

1905-08 **Typo.** **Wmk. 13**

102 A10 ½p dull green 3.50 1.40
- a. Booklet pane of 12
- b. Perf. 11 3.50 .80
- c. Compound perf. 12½, 11 140.00 35.00
- d. Compound perf. 11, 12 350.00

103 A11 1p carmine 9.00 .60
a. Booklet pane of 18
b. Perf. 11 8.00 .35
c. Compound perf. 12½, 11 6.00 7.50
d. Compound perf. 12½, 12 195.00 70.00
e. Compound perf. 11, 12 215.00 70.00
104 A12 2p violet 21.00 2.00
a. Booklet pane of 18
b. Perf. 11 7.50 .35
c. Compound perf. 12½, 11 45.00 20.00
d. Compound perf. 12½, 12 490.00 150.00
e. Compound perf. 11, 12 300.00 120.00
105 A14 3p dark brown 16.00 6.00
a. Perf. 11 37.50 50.00
b. Compound perf. 12½, 11 300.00 300.00
106 A15 4p ocher 25.00 5.00
a. Perf. 11 70.00 24.00
107 A17 6p lake 85.00 10.00
a. Perf. 11 105.00 10.00
b. Compound perf. 12½, 11 540.00 540.00
108 A5 8p violet brown 22.50 9.00
a. Perf. 11 23.00 9.00
109 A5 9p blue 9.00 8.00
a. Perf. 11 9.00 12.00
b. Compound perf. 12½, 11 130.00
c. Compound perf. 12½, 12 460.00
d. Compound perf. 11, 12 600.00
110 A8 1sh rose & green 15.00 10.00
a. Perf. 11 32.50 55.00
b. Compound perf. 12½, 11 25.00 60.00
c. Compound perf. 12½, 12 300.00
111 A8 10sh brt vio & brn 325.00 *350.00*
a. Perf. 11 475.00 475.00
b. Compound perf. 12½, 12 515.00 515.00
Nos. 102-111 (10) 531.00 402.00

Nos. 104-107 also printed litho.

1911 **Redrawn**

114 A12 2p bright violet 22.50 7.50
a. Perf. 11 10.00 6.00
b. Compound perf. 11, 12½ 140.00 45.00
c. Compound perf. 12, 12½ 575.00
115 A15 4p dull yellow 72.50 72.50
a. Perf. 11 70.00 35.00
116 A17 6p lake 30.00 *55.00*
a. Perf. 11 30.00 75.00
b. Compound perf. 11, 12½ 500.00
Nos. 114-116 (3) 125.00 135.00

The redrawn 2p measures 33½x25mm instead of 32½x24½mm. There are many slight changes in the clouds and other parts of the design.

The 4p is much lighter, especially the waterfall and trees above it. This appears to be a new or cleaned plate rather than a redrawn one.

In the redrawn 6p there are more colored lines in the waterfall and the river and more white dots in the trees.

No. 114 Surcharged in Red

1912

117 A12 1p on 2p brt vio 2.25 2.25
a. Perf. 11 3.50 5.00
b. Compound perf. 12½ 11 300.00 *325.00*

POSTAL FISCAL STAMPS

Authorized for postal use by Act of November 1, 1882. Authorization withdrawn Nov. 30, 1900.

Used values are for examples with postal cancellations used from Nov. 1, 1882 through Nov. 30, 1900.

Beware of stamps with a pen cancellation removed, often regummed or with a fake postmark added.

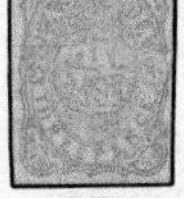
PF1

PF2

St. George and the Dragon
PF3 PF4

1863-80 **Engr.** **Wmk. 139** ***Imperf.***

AR1 PF1 3p green *800.00 300.00*
AR2 PF2 2sh 6p car *800.00 300.00*
AR3 PF3 5sh green *1,000. 450.00*
AR4 PF3 5sh brown *1,500. 800.00*
AR5 PF4 10sh sal ('80) *1,500. 800.00*
a. 10sh orange *1,800. 800.00*

For overprint see No. AR32.

Perf. 10

AR6 PF1 3p green *550.00 225.00*
AR7 PF2 2sh 6p car *450.00*
AR8 PF3 5sh brown *650.00*
AR9 PF4 10sh orange *600.00*

Perf. 12

AR10 PF1 3p green *225.00 375.00*
AR11 PF2 2sh 6p car *350.00 200.00*
AR12 PF3 5sh green *500.00 225.00*
AR13 PF3 5sh brown *650.00*
AR14 PF4 10sh orange *600.00 300.00*

Perf. 12½

AR15 PF1 3p green *650.00*
AR16 PF2 2sh 6p car *600.00*
AR17 PF3 5sh brown *900.00*
AR18 PF4 10sh orange *750.00*

Perf. 11½

AR19 PF1 3p green *800.00*
AR20 PF2 2sh 6p car *400.00 200.00*
AR21 PF3 5sh green *500.00 200.00*
AR22 PF4 10sh salmon *600.00 350.00*
a. 10sh orange *300.00 140.00*

Wmk. 77

Perf. 12

AR23 PF2 2sh 6p car 160.00 90.00
a. Horiz. pair, imperf. btwn. 2,500.

For overprint see No. AR33.

Duck-billed Platypus — PF5

1880 **Engr.** **Wmk. 77** ***Perf. 14***

AR24 PF5 1p slate 60.00 12.00
AR25 PF5 3p brown 32.50 5.50
AR26 PF5 6p lilac 110.00 2.75
AR27 PF5 1sh rose 175.00 32.50

For overprints see Nos. AR28-AR31.

Nos. AR24-AR27, AR2, AR23, 85 Overprinted "REVENUE"

1900, Nov. 15

AR28 PF5 1p slate 30.00 35.00
AR29 PF5 3p brown 42.50 *40.00*
AR30 PF5 6p lilac *125.00*
AR31 PF5 1sh rose *400.00* 350.00
AR32 PF2 2sh 6p car (#AR2) *550.00* 550.00
AR33 PF2 2sh 6p car (#AR23) *450.00*
AR34 PF4 10sh orange 850.00 800.00
AR35 A8 £1 grn & yel (#85) 300.00 *250.00*

Nos. AR28-AR35 were not supposed to be postally used. Because of imprecise terminology, postal use was tolerated until all postal use of revenues ceased on Nov. 30, 1900.

Other denominations and watermarks were overprinted after postal use was no longer allowed.

VICTORIA

vik-'tōr-ē-ə

LOCATION — In the extreme southeastern part of Australia
GOVT. — British Colony
AREA — 87,884 sq. mi.
POP. — 1,201,341 (1901)
CAPITAL — Melbourne

Victoria was one of the six former British colonies which united on Jan. 1, 1901, to form the Commonwealth of Australia.

12 Pence = 1 Shilling
20 Shillings = 1 Pound

Unused values for Nos. 1-16 are for stamps without gum as these stamps are seldom found with original gum. Otherwise, unused values are for stamps with original gum as defined in the catalogue introduction.

Very fine examples of all rouletted, perforated and serrate perforated stamps from Nos. 9-109 and F2 will have roulettes, perforations or serrate perforations touching the design. Examples clear on four sides range from scarce to rare and will command higher prices.

Watermarks

Wmk. 6 — Large Star

Wmk. 80

Wmk. 50

Wmk. 80a

Wmk. 81

Wmk. 139

Wmk. 49

Wmk. 75

Wmk. 70 — V and Crown

Wmk. 13 — Crown & Double-lined A

Queen Victoria — A1

A1 TYPES

1p:

Type I — "VICTORIA" very close to top of design, with very thin line of color between "VICTORIA" and frameline.

Type II — Thicker line of color between "VICTORIA" and frameline at top.

2p:

Type I — Border, two sets of nine wavy lines crisscrossing. Background, 22 groups of wavy triple lines below "VICTORIA."

Type II — Border, same. Background, 15 groups of wavy triple lines below "VICTORIA."

Type III — Border, two sets of five wavy lines crisscrossing. Background, same as type II.

3p:

Type I — Orb poorly defined, with white area at right and thicker at left. Central band of orb does not protrude at left.

Type II — Orb clearly defined, with white outlines at left and right. Central band of orb protrudes at left.

1850 **Litho.** **Unwmk.** ***Imperf.***

1 A1 1p dull red, II 4,000. 225.00
a. 1p dull org ver, II 5,500. 750.00
b. 1p brownish red, II ('51) 1,500. 210.00
c. 1p dull brown, I *19,000.* 2,500.
d. 1p orange vermilion, I *30,000.* 5,500.
e. 1p orange brown, I 2,100.
2 A1 1p rose, II *3,500.* 200.00
a. 1p pink, II *1,750.* 190.00
b. 1p reddish brown, II ('51) *5,500.* 190.00
3 A1 3p blue, I *6,500.* 450.00
a. 3p light blue, II ('52) *2,250.* 110.00
b. 3p bright blue, I 7,500. 625.00
4 A1 3p indigo, II *3,000.* 100.00
a. 3p pale grnsh blue, II ('52) *3,500.* 210.00
Nos. 1-4 (4) 17,000. 975.00

Nos. 1-4 exist with and without frame line.

5 A1 2p lilac, I *7,500.* 550.00
a. 2p brn lilac, I *7,000.* 550.00
b. 2p orange brown, I *2,500.*
6 A1 2p brn lilac, II 2,500. 250.00
a. 2p gray lilac, II *6,000.* 200.00
7 A1 2p brn lilac, III *7,250.* 200.00
a. 2p gray lilac, III *11,000.* 500.00
b. Value omitted, III *17,500.*
8 A1 2p yel brn, III 3,000. 200.00

Rouletted 7

9 A1 1p vermilion *3,350.*
10 A1 3p blue 2,500. 250.00
a. 3p deep blue *2,500.* 300.00

Perf. 12

12 A1 3p blue *2,000.* 175.00
a. 3p deep blue *2,000.* 175.00

Victoria on Throne — A2

1852 **Engr.** ***Imperf.***

14 A2 2p reddish brn 900.00 35.00
a. 2p chestnut 150.00
b. 2p purple brown 1,000. 30.00

No. 14 was reprinted on paper with watermark 70, imperf. & perf. 12½, overprinted "REPRINT."

1854 **Litho.**

15 A2 2p gray brown 1,200. 45.00
a. 2p purple black 45.00
16 A2 2p brown lilac 300.00 40.00
a. 2p red lilac — 37.50
b. As "a," "TVO" for "TWO" *10,000.* 1,500.

Fifty varieties.

A3

A4

1854-58 **Typo.**

17 A3 6p yellow orange 750.00 20.00
a. 6p dull orange 750.00 20.00
b. 6p reddish brown 1,250. 75.00

See Nos. 19-20, 22-24A, 26-28.

Lithographed

18 A4 1sh blue 450.00 17.50
a. 1sh greenish blue 450.00 14.00
b. 1sh indigo blue — 50.00

See Nos. 21, 25.

Typographed

19 A3 2sh green 3,000. 250.00

1857-58 ***Rouletted 7, 9½***

20 A3 6p orange — 87.50
a. 6p yellow orange — 100.00
b. 6p reddish brown — 115.00

Lithographed

21 A4 1sh blue — 160.00
a. 1sh greenish blue — 160.00

Typographed

22 A3 2sh green ('58) *7,000.* 675.00

Small Serrate Perf. 19

23 A3 6p orange — 125.00

Large Serpentine Perf. 10½
24 A3 6p orange — 125.00

Serrate x Serpentine Perf.
24A A3 6p orange — 200.00

1859 Litho. *Perf. 12*
25 A4 1sh blue 250.00 25.00
a. 1sh greenish blue 275.00 27.50
b. 1sh indigo blue — 52.50

Typographed
26 A3 2sh green 525.00 70.00

1861 Wmk. "SIX PENCE" (80)
27 A3 6p black 300.00 80.00

Wmk. Single-lined "2" (50)
1864 *Perf. 12, 13*
28 A3 2sh blue, *green* 350.00 13.00

A5

Wmk. Large Star (6)
1856, Oct. Engr. *Imperf.*
29 A5 1p green 250.00 42.50

1858 *Rouletted 5½-6½*
30 A5 6p blue 350.00 28.00
a. 6p light blue 450.00 45.00

Nos. 29 and 30 have been reprinted on paper watermarked V and Crown. They are imperforate and overprinted "REPRINT."

A6

1857-61 Typo. *Imperf.*
Wove Paper
31 A6 1p yellow green 175.00 25.00
a. Printed on both sides 2,750.
b. 1p deep green 230.00 47.50
32 A6 4p vermilion 450.00 15.00
a. Printed on both sides 2,750.
b. 4p brownish vermilion 425.00 15.00
33 A6 4p rose 375.00 15.00
a. 4p dull red 260.00 12.00

Rouletted 7 to 9½
34 A6 1p yellow green 625.00 140.00
35 A6 4p rose — 57.50
a. 4p vermilion 160.00
b. 4p dull red 60.00
35A A6 4p vermilion 575.00

Perf. 12
36 A6 1p yellow green — 500.00

Unwmk. *Imperf.*
37 A6 1p blue green 425.00 22.50
a. 1p emerald green 22.50
38 A6 2p lilac 400.00 21.00
a. 2p gray lilac 400.00 20.00
39 A6 4p rose 575.00 47.50
a. 4p rose pink 575.00 42.50
b. 4p reddish pink 47.50

Examples of No. 39 printed in dull carmine on thin paper are regarded as printer's waste and of little value. They are also found printed on both sides.

Rouletted 7 to 9½
40 A6 1p emerald green 575.00 37.50
a. 1p pale emerald 525.00 35.00
41 A6 2p lilac 1,150. 725.00
42 A6 4p rose pink 400.00 11.50
a. Vert. pair, imperf. btwn. 750.00
b. 4p reddish pink 20.00
c. 4p bright rose 400.00 11.50

Perf. 12
43 A6 1p blue green 225.00 20.00
a. 1p yellow green 325.00 24.00
b. Horiz. pair, imperf. btwn. —
c. As "a," on thin, glazed "Bordeaux" paper 240.00
44 A6 2p lilac 450.00
a. 2p gray lilac 400.00
45 A6 4p rose 300.00 8.00
b. Vert. pair, imperf. btwn. —

Rouletted 5½-6½
45C A6 4p dull rose 1,250.

Serrate Rouletted 19
45A A6 2p lilac 1,100. 600.00

Laid Paper
Imperf
46 A6 4p rose 825.00 35.00

Rouletted 5 to 7
47 A6 2p violet 275.00 10.50
a. 2p brown lilac 225.00 15.00
b. 2p dark lilac 300.00 25.00
48 A6 4p rose 250.00 7.25
a. 4p pale dull red, vertically laid paper 260.00 7.25
b. 4p pale dull red, horizontally laid paper 1,250.
c. 4p dull rose red 225.00 6.25

Serrate Rouletted 19
48D A6 4p rose red 825.00

Perf. 12
49 A6 1p green 300.00 25.00
a. Laid lines close together 35.00
50 A6 4p rose 200.00 15.00
a. Laid lines close together 13.00

Wove Paper
1860 Wmk. Value in Words (80)
51 A6 1p pale yellowish green 130.00 10.50
a. Wmk. "FOUR PENCE" (error) 9,750.
b. 1p yellow green 125.00 7.25
52 A6 2p gray lilac 200.00 10.00
a. 2p brown lilac ('61) — 52.50
b. 2p bluish slate ('61) 200.00 9.50
c. 2p slate gray ('62) 9.50
d. 2p bluish gray ('63) 230.00 35.00

Wmk. "THREE PENCE" (80)
53 A6 2p bluish gray ('63) 225.00 25.00
a. 2p gray lilac ('62) 325.00 22.50

Single-lined "2" (50)
54 A6 2p lilac 300.00 18.00
a. 2p gray lilac 275.00 22.50
b. 2p brown lilac 225.00 21.00
c. As "a," wmkd. single-lined "6" 7,750.
d. 2p gray violet ('63) 220.00 20.00
e. 2p slate ('63) 290.00 35.00

A7

1860 Unwmk. Laid Paper
56 A7 3p deep blue 650.00 77.50

Wmk. Value in Words (80)
Perf. 11½ to 12
1860-64 Wove Paper
57 A7 3p blue ('63) 350.00 7.00
a. "TRREE" instead of "THREE" in watermark 750.00
b. 3p pale blue ('61) 350.00 8.00
c. 3p bright blue ('61) 350.00 10.00
d. 3p deep blue ('64) 350.00 7.00
58 A7 3p claret 425.00 32.50
a. Perf. 13 450.00 35.00
59 A7 4p rose 200.00 5.00
a. 4p rose pink 10.00
b. 4p rose red 200.00 5.00
c. 4p rose carmine 10.00
60 A7 6p orange 8,500. 400.00
61 A7 6p black 500.00 10.50
a. 6p gray black 500.00 10.50

Wmk. "FIVE SHILLINGS" (80)
62 A7 4p rose 3,750. 25.00

Wmk. Single-lined "4" (80a)
1863 *Imperf.*
63 A7 4p rose — 80.00

Rouletted
64 A7 4p rose 2,500. 275.00

Perf. 11½ to 12
65 A7 4p rose 180.00 10.50

1863 Unwmk. *Perf. 12*
66 A7 4p rose 625.00 50.00
a. 4p rose pink, thin glazed "Bordeaux" paper 50.00
b. 4p rose, thick coarse paper 625.00 50.00

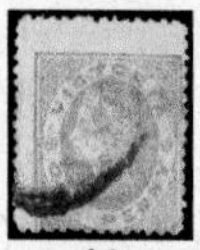
A8

A9

1861-63 Wmk. 80 *Perf. 11½ to 12*
67 A8 1p green 190.00 27.50
a. 1p olive green 30.00
68 A9 6p black 275.00 24.00
a. 6p gray black 275.00 25.00
b. 6p jet black 300.00 27.50

Wmk. Double-lined "1" (139)
69 A8 1p green 300.00 30.00
a. 1p dull green — 30.00

b. Horiz. pair, imperf between —

Wmk. Single-lined Figures (50)
70 A8 1p green 160.00 22.50
a. 1p apple green 160.00 21.00
b. 1p olive green 160.00 30.00
71 A9 6p gray black 200.00 8.00
a. 6p jet black — 10.00
b. 6p jet black, perf 13 250.00 10.00
c. 6p gray black, perf 13 200.00 8.00

The 1p and 6p of 1861-63 are known on paper without watermark but were probably impressions on the margins of watermarked sheets.

A10

A11

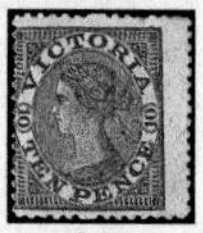
A12

A13

Wmk. Single-lined Figures (50, 80a, 81)
1863-67 *Perf. 11½ to 13*
74 A10 1p green 120.00 9.00
a. Double impression 1,500.
75 A10 2p gray lilac 140.00 10.00
a. 2p violet 160.00 15.00
76 A10 4p rose 190.00 4.00
a. Double impression 1,500.
77 A11 6p blue 150.00 5.00
78 A10 8p orange 900.00 140.00
79 A12 10p brn, *rose* 350.00 8.00
80 A13 1sh blue, *blue* 200.00 5.00
Nos. 74-80 (7) 2,050. 181.00

See Nos. 81-82, 84-96, 99-101, 108-112, 115-119, 124-126, 144, 188. Compare type A11 with type A54.

A14

Wmk. Double-lined "1" (139)
81 A10 1p green 125.00 7.00
82 A10 2p gray lilac 325.00 10.50
83 A14 3p lilac 325.00 100.00
84 A11 6p blue 115.00 9.50
Nos. 81-84 (4) 890.00 127.00

See Nos. 97, 113, 114, 155, 186. Compare type A14 with type A51.

Wmk. Double-lined "2" (49)
85 A11 6p blue 4,250.

Wmk. Single-lined "4" (80a)
86 A10 1p green 200.00 30.00
87 A10 2p gray lilac 250.00 10.50
88 A11 6p blue 2,750.

Wmk. Double-lined "4" (75)
89 A10 1p green 2,500. 160.00
90 A10 2p gray lilac 250.00 8.00
91 A10 4p rose 300.00 9.50
92 A11 6p blue 325.00 35.00

Wmk. Single-lined "6" (50)
93 A10 1p green 325.00 42.50
94 A10 2p gray lilac 350.00 11.50

Wmk. Single-lined "8" (50)
95 A10 1p green 300.00 27.50
96 A10 2p gray lilac 325.00 10.50
97 A14 3p lilac 250.00 57.50
99 A12 10p slate 1,000. 200.00

Wmk. "SIX PENCE" (80)
100 A10 1p green 1,150. 57.50
100A A10 2p slate gray 16,000.
101 A11 6p blue 800.00 42.50
a. 6p indigo blue 42.50

All values of the 1864-67 series except the 3p and 8p are known on unwatermarked paper. They are probably varieties from watermarked sheets which have been so placed on the printing press that some of the stamps escaped the watermark.

One example of the 2p gray lilac, type A10, is reported to exist with only "PENCE" of watermark 80 showing. Some believe this is part of the "SIX PENCE" watermark.

1870 Wmk. "THREE PENCE" (80)
108 A11 6p blue 525.00 37.50

Wmk. "FOUR PENCE" (80)
109 A11 6p blue 800.00 55.00

A15

1867-78 Wmk. (70) *Perf. 11½ to 13*
110 A10 1p green 125.00 4.50
a. 1p bright olive green 190.00 25.00
111 A10 2p lilac 120.00 4.00
a. 2p gray lilac 150.00 6.50
112 A10 2p lilac, *lilac* 140.00 7.00
113 A14 3p red lilac 550.00 60.00
a. 3p lilac 550.00 60.00
114 A14 3p orange 185.00 12.00
a. 3p yellow 100.00 20.00
b. 3p org brn, glazed paper ('78) 75.00 35.00
115 A10 4p rose 150.00 9.00
a. 4p dl rose, glazed paper ('79) 150.00 7.00
b. Wmk sideways 80.00
116 A11 6p blue 100.00 7.00
117 A11 6p ultra 120.00 9.00
a. 6p lilac blue 130.00 17.50
b. 6p light Prussian blue ('75) 160.00 9.00
118 A10 8p brn, *rose* 140.00 9.00
a. 8p choc, *pink* ('78) 300.00 11.50
b. Perf. 13x12 350.00
119 A13 1sh bl, *blue* 300.00 25.00
120 A15 5sh bl, *yel* 4,500. 500.00
121 A15 5sh bl & rose 700.00 25.00
a. Without blue line under crown 700.00 30.00
b. 5sh ind bl & car 850.00 60.00
122 A15 5sh ultra & rose 750.00 30.00

See Nos. 126, 144, 188. For surcharge see No. 124.

For additional stamps of type A15, see No. 191. Compare type A15 with type A58.

A16

1870 *Perf. 13*
123 A16 2p lilac 115.00 4.00
a. Perf. 12 125.00 3.50

No. 110 Surcharged in Red

1873, July 19 *Perf. 13, 12*
124 A10 ½p on 1p green 100.00 24.00
a. Perf. 12 125.00 24.00

No. 79 Surcharged in Blue

1871 Wmk. Single-lined "10" (81)
125 A12 9p on 10p brn, *rose* 950.00 20.00
a. Double surcharge 3,500.

A19

1873-78 Typo.
126 A10 8p brown, *rose* ('78) 250.00 6.50
127 A19 9p brown, *rose* 225.00 50.00

For additional stamps of type A19, see Nos. 128-129, 174-175. Compare type A19 with type A55.

1875 Wmk. V and Crown (70)
128 A19 9p brown, *rose* 225.00 50.00

No. 128 Surcharged in Blue

1876
129 A19 8p on 9p brn, *rose* 700.00 40.00

Revenue cancel 8.75
b. Perf. 12½ 150.00 —
AR32 PF5 1p brown 80.00 15.00
Revenue cancel 1.40
a. Perf. 12 80.00 16.00
Revenue cancel 1.40
b. Perf. 12½ — —
AR33 PF6 6p blue 225.00 45.00
Revenue cancel 5.75
a. Perf. 12 225.00 55.00
Revenue cancel 5.75
b. Perf. 12½ — —
AR34 PF7 1sh blue, *blue* 290.00 8.00
Revenue cancel 5.75
a. Perf. 12 290.00 13.00
Revenue cancel 5.75
b. Perf. 12½ 290.00 9.00
Revenue cancel 5.75
AR35 PF7 1sh blue, *yel,* perf 12½ 350.00 35.00
Revenue cancel 17.50
AR36 PF8 1sh 6p pink 325.00 40.00
Revenue cancel 17.50
AR37 PF9 2sh blue, *grn* 500.00 40.00
Revenue cancel 13.00
a. Perf. 12 — 50.00
Revenue cancel 13.00
b. Perf. 12½ 500.00 50.00
Revenue cancel 13.00
AR38 PF10 2sh 6p org, perf 12½ 240.00 40.00
a. 2sh6p yellow ('85) 160.00 17.50
b. 2sh6p lemon yellow ('92) 160.00 25.00
Revenue cancel 5.75
AR39 PF11 3sh maroon, *bl,* perf 12½ 950.00 90.00
Revenue cancel 14.00
AR40 PF11 3sh bister 160.00 17.50
Revenue cancel 21.00
AR41 PF12 4sh org, perf 12½ 160.00 17.50
Revenue cancel 7.25
AR42 PF13 5sh claret, *yel* 140.00 8.00
Revenue cancel 5.75
a. Perf. 12 160.00 20.00
Revenue cancel 5.75
b. Perf. 12½ 190.00 22.50
Revenue cancel 5.75
AR43 PF13 5sh car rose 140.00 20.00
Revenue cancel 7.25
AR44 PF14 6sh green 375.00 70.00
Revenue cancel 16.00
AR45 PF15 10sh brn, *pink* — 140.00
Revenue cancel 57.50
a. Perf. 12 — —
b. Perf. 12½ — —
AR46 PF15 10sh green 1,500. 75.00
Revenue cancel 20.00
AR47 PF16 15sh brown 2,600. 110.00
Revenue cancel 42.50
AR48 PF17 £1 org, *yel,* perf 12½ 1,400. 75.00
Revenue cancel 25.00
a. Perf. 12 1,500. 90.00
Revenue cancel 30.00
AR49 PF18 £1 5sh pink 7,500. 210.00
Revenue cancel 75.00
AR50 PF19 £1 10sh olive 7,500. 190.00
Revenue cancel 50.00
AR51 PF21 £2 blue 2,750. 140.00
Revenue cancel 27.50
a. Perf. 12 — 200.00
Revenue cancel 27.50
AR52 PF22 45sh gray lil 14,000. 240.00
Revenue cancel 62.50
AR53 PF23 £5 rose, perf. 12 — 1,750.
Revenue cancel 105.00
a. perf. 12½ — 1,800.
Revenue cancel 150.00
AR54 PF28 £10 lilac 19,000. 300.00
Revenue cancel 62.50
a. Perf. 12 19,000. 475.00
Revenue cancel 62.50

Nos. AR49-AR52, AR54, used, are valued cto.

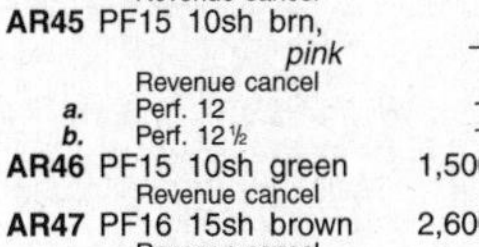

PF29

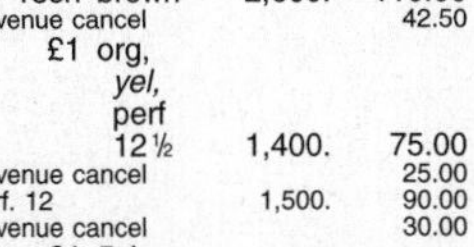

PF30

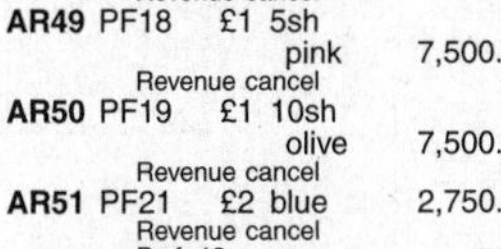

PF31

Wmk. V and Crown (70)

1879-1900 Engr. *Perf. 12½*

AR55 PF29 £25 green *65,000.* 1,500.
Revenue cancel 110.00
a. Perf. 13 —
b. Perf. 12 —
AR56 PF30 £50 violet *75,000.* 1,500.
Revenue cancel 125.00
a. Perf. 13 —
AR57 PF31 £100 red — —
Revenue cancel 225.00
a. Perf. 13 —
b. Perf. 12 —
Revenue cancel 225.00

Typo.

AR58 PF29 £25 green — 525.00
a. Lithographed —
Revenue cancel 100.00
AR59 PF30 £50 violet — 700.00
a. Lithographed —
Revenue cancel 140.00
AR60 PF31 £100 red — 1,200.
a. Lithographed —
Revenue cancel 225.00

Nos. AR55-AR60, used, are valued cto.

PF32

1887-90 Typo.

AR61 PF32 £5 cl & ultra *17,000.* 210.00
Revenue cancel 82.50
AR62 PF32 £6 blue & yel *17,500.* 240.00
Revenue cancel 90.00
AR63 PF32 £7 blk & red *20,000.* 300.00
Revenue cancel 110.00
AR64 PF32 £8 org & lil *20,000.* 325.00
Revenue cancel 110.00
AR65 PF32 £9 red & green *21,000.* 350.00
Revenue cancel 135.00

Nos. AR61-AR65, used, are valued cto.

SEMI-POSTAL STAMPS

SP1

Queen Victoria and Figure of Charity — SP2

Wmk. V and Crown (70)

1897, Oct. Typo. *Perf. 12½*

B1 SP1 1p deep blue 27.50 27.50
B2 SP2 2½p red brown 140.00 110.00

These stamps were sold at 1sh and 2sh6p respectively. The premium was given to a charitable institution.

Victoria Cross — SP3

Scout Reporting — SP4

1900

B3 SP3 1p brown olive 175.00 110.00
B4 SP4 2p emerald 325.00 250.00

These stamps were sold at 1sh and 2sh respectively. The premium was given to a patriotic fund in connection with the South African War.

REGISTRATION STAMPS

R1

Unwmk.

1854, Dec. 1 Typo. *Imperf.*

F1 R1 1sh rose & blue 5,250. 225.00

1857 *Rouletted 7*

F2 R1 1sh rose & blue 12,500. 425.00

LATE FEE STAMP

LF1

Unwmk.

1855, Jan. 1 Typo. *Imperf.*

I1 LF1 6p lilac & green 3,750. 275.00

POSTAGE DUE STAMPS

D1

Wmk. V and Crown (70)

1890 Typo. *Perf. 12½*

J1 D1 ½p claret & blue 12.00 9.00
J2 D1 1p claret & blue 10.00 2.60
J3 D1 2p claret & blue 18.00 2.50
J4 D1 4p claret & blue 37.50 7.50
J5 D1 5p claret & blue 26.00 5.50
J6 D1 6p claret & blue 30.00 12.00
J7 D1 10p claret & blue 80.00 60.00
J8 D1 1sh claret & blue 60.00 12.00
J9 D1 2sh claret & blue 160.00 75.00
J10 D1 5sh claret & blue 225.00 120.00
Nos. J1-J10 (10) 658.50 306.10

1891-94

J11 D1 ½p lake & blue 10.00 7.50
J12 D1 1p brn red & blue ('93) 22.50 2.75
J13 D1 2p brn red & blue ('93) 30.00 2.75
J14 D1 4p lake & blue ('94) 40.00 12.50
Nos. J11-J14 (4) 102.50 25.50

1894-96

J15 D1 ½p bl grn & rose 12.50 3.00
J16 D1 1p bl grn & rose 17.50 2.25
J17 D1 2p bl grn & rose 32.50 3.50
J18 D1 4p bl grn & rose 15.00 1.75
J19 D1 5p bl grn & rose 50.00 42.50
J20 D1 6p bl grn & rose 27.50 27.50
J21 D1 10p bl grn & rose 60.00 12.00
J22 D1 1sh bl grn & rose 32.50 3.75
J23 D1 2sh yel grn & rose 100.00 27.50
J24 D1 5sh yel grn & rose 150.00 45.00
Nos. J15-J24 (10) 497.50 168.75

1897-99

J15a D1 ½p yel grn & pale scar 7.00 4.50
J16a D1 1p yel grn & pale scar 8.00 3.00
J17a D1 2p yel grn & pale scar 30.00 1.75
J18a D1 4p yel grn & pale scar 12.50 3.00
J19a D1 5p yel grn & pale scar 22.50 *27.50*
J20a D1 6p yel grn & pale scar 16.00 9.00
Nos. J15a-J20a (6) 96.00 48.75

1905-09 Wmk. 13

J25 D1 ½p yel grn & rose 7.00 *15.00*
a. ½p pale green & pink 32.50 25.00
J26 D1 1p yel grn & rose 7.50 3.00
a. 1p pale green & pink 75.00 11.50
J27 D1 2p yel grn & rose 55.00 7.00
J28 D1 4p yel grn & rose 27.50 30.00
Nos. J25-J28 (4) 97.00 55.00

A 5p with wmk. 13 exists but was not issued.

WESTERN AUSTRALIA

ˈwes-tərn o-ˈstrāl-yə

LOCATION — Western part of Australia, occupying about a third of that continent
GOVT. — British Colony
AREA — 975,920 sq. mi.
POP. — 184,124 (1901)
CAPITAL — Perth

Western Australia was one of the six British colonies that united on January 1, 1901, to form the Commonwealth of Australia.

12 Pence = 1 Shilling
20 Shillings = 1 Pound

Unused values for Nos. 1-10 are for stamps without gum as these stamps are seldom found with original gum. Otherwise, unused values are for stamps with original gum as defined in the catalogue introduction.

Very fine examples of all rouletted and perforated stamps from Nos. 6-34 have roulettes or perforations touching the design. Examples clear on all four sides range from scarce to rare and will command higher prices.

Watermarks

Wmk. 82 — Swan

Wmk. 83 — Crown and W A

Wmk. 70 — V and Crown

Wmk. 13 — Crown & Double-lined A

Wmk. 74 — Crown and Single-lined A

Swan

A1 A2

1854-57 Engr. Wmk. 82 *Imperf.*

1 A1 1p black 1,700. 350.

Litho.

2 A2 2p brown, *red* ('57) 9,500. 600.
a. 2p brown, *deep red* ('57) 9,500. 900.
b. Printed on both sides 12,000. 900.

See Nos. 4, 6-7, 9, 14-39, 44-52, 54, 59-61.
For surcharges see Nos. 41, 55-56.

A3

A4

3	A3	4p blue	400.	225.
a.		Frame inverted		*200,000.*
		As "a," cut to shape		*27,500.*
b.		4p slate blue	4,500.	1,400.
4	A2	6p bronze ('57)	*15,000.*	*700.*
5	A4	1sh pale brown	550.	350.
a.		1sh dark brown	700.	450.
b.		1sh dark red brown	2,250.	1,100.
c.		1sh pale red brown	26,500.	5,000.

Engraved

Rouletted

6	A1	1p black	5,500.	750.

Lithographed

7	A2	2p brn, *red* ('57)	*15,000.*	2,000.
a.		Printed on both sides		2,300.
8	A3	4p blue	—	800.
9	A2	6p bronze ('57)	*22,500.*	2,500.
10	A4	1sh brown	8,000.	1,250.

The 1p, 2p, 4p and 6p are known with pin-perforation but this is believed to be unofficial. No. 7a is only recorded used and with pin perforations.

1860 Engr. *Imperf.*

14	A1	2p vermilion	160.00	90.00
a.		2p pale orange	140.00	90.00
15	A1	4p blue	350.	*2,500.*
16	A1	6p dull green	3,250.	425.00

Rouletted

17	A1	2p vermilion	950.00	275.00
a.		2p pale orange	900.00	300.00
18	A1	4p deep blue	6,500.	—
19	A1	6p dull green	6,500.	750.00

1861 *Clean-Cut Perf. 14 to 16*

20	A1	1p rose	750.00	150.00
a.		Imperf.		
21	A1	2p blue	240.00	45.00
a.		Imperf., pair		
b.		Horiz. pair, imperf. vert.		
22	A1	4p vermilion	2,000.	*2,250.*
a.		Imperf.		
23	A1	6p purple brn	1,200.	120.00
a.		Imperf.		
24	A1	1sh green	2,250.	275.00
a.		Imperf.		

Rough Perf. 14 to 16

24B	A1	1p rose	375.00	55.00
24C	A1	6p pur brn, *bluish*	5,000.	525.00
24D	A1	1sh deep green	5,500.	400.00

Perf. 14

25	A1	1p rose	400.00	70.00
25A	A1	2p blue	180.00	50.00
25B	A1	4p vermilion	500.00	200.00

Unwmk. *Perf. 13*

26	A1	1p lake	85.00	6.00
28	A1	6p violet	375.00	55.00

1865-79 Wmk. 1 *Perf. 12½*

29	A1	1p bister	95.00	11.00
30	A1	1p yel ocher	125.00	17.50
31	A1	2p yellow	125.00	9.00
a.		2p lilac (error) ('79)	*22,500.*	*17,500.*
b.		2p chrome yellow	110.00	8.00
32	A1	4p carmine	160.00	8.00
a.		Double impression	*32,500.*	
33	A1	6p violet	190.00	6.50
a.		6p lilac	325.00	7.00
b.		6p red lilac	300.00	7.00
c.		Double impression		*24,000.*
34	A1	1sh brt grn	300.00	22.50
		Handstamped "SPECIMEN"	225.00	
a.		1sh sage green	500.00	40.00
		Nos. 29-34 (6)	995.00	74.50

1872-78 *Perf. 14*

35	A1	1p bister	180.00	6.00
36	A1	1p yellow ocher	115.00	3.00
37	A1	2p yellow	125.00	2.00
38	A1	4p carmine	700.00	130.00
39	A1	6p lilac	240.00	4.50
		Nos. 35-39 (5)	1,360.	145.50

A5

1872 Typo.

40	A5	3p red brown	65.00	6.00
a.		3p brown	65.00	8.50
		Handstamped "SPECIMEN"	150.00	

See Nos. 53, 92. For surcharges see Nos. 57, 69-72A.

No. 31 Surcharged in Green

1875 Engr. *Perf. 12½*

41	A1	1p on 2p yellow	850.00	60.00
a.		Pair, one without surcharge		
b.		"O" of "ONE" omitted		
c.		Triple surcharge		*7,500.*

Forged surcharges exist.

1882 Wmk. 2 *Perf. 12*

44	A1	1p ocher yellow	110.00	6.50
46	A1	2p yellow	175.00	6.00
47	A1	4p carmine	300.00	60.00
48	A1	6p pale violet	575.00	60.00
		Nos. 44-48 (4)	1,160.	132.50

1882 *Perf. 14*

49	A1	1p ocher yellow	35.00	2.25
50	A1	2p yellow	45.00	2.25
51	A1	4p carmine	200.00	17.50
52	A1	6p pale violet	150.00	3.50
a.		6p violet	150.00	4.50
		Handstamped "SPECIMEN"	160.00	

Typographed

53	A5	3p red brown	11.00	4.50
a.		3p brown	19.00	4.50
		Nos. 49-53 (5)	441.00	30.00

1883 Engr. *Perf. 12x14*

54	A1	1p ocher yellow	3,000.	300.00

Nos. 44 and 49 Surcharged in Red

1884 *Perf. 12*

55	A1	½p on 1p ocher yel	18.00	*32.50*

Perf. 14

56	A1	½p on 1p ocher yel	32.50	*50.00*
a.		Thin fraction bar	120.00	*175.00*

No. 40 Surcharged in Green

1885 Typo. Wmk. 1

57	A5	1p on 3p red brown	90.00	40.00
a.		1p on 3p brown	100.00	40.00
b.		"1" with straight top	190.00	75.00
c.		As "a," "1" with straight top	210.00	75.00

A8

Wmk. Crown and C A (2)

1885 Typo. *Perf. 14*

58	A8	½p green	6.00	1.25

See No. 89.

1888 Engr.

59	A1	1p rose	37.50	4.50
60	A1	2p slate	90.00	2.00
61	A1	4p red brown	90.00	37.50
		Nos. 59-61 (3)	217.50	44.00

A9

A10

A11

A12

1890-93 Typo.

62	A9	1p carmine rose	55.00	1.25
63	A10	2p slate	37.50	4.50
64	A11	2½p blue	32.50	2.50
65	A12	4p orange brown	20.00	2.75
66	A12	5p bister	21.00	4.50
67	A12	6p violet	24.00	2.25
68	A12	1sh olive green	55.00	6.00
		Nos. 62-68 (7)	245.00	23.75

See Nos. 73-74, 76, 80, 90, 94.

Nos. 40 and 53a Surcharged in Green

1893 Wmk. Crown and C C (1)

69	A5	1p on 3p red brown	20.00	11.00
a.		1p on 3p brown	20.00	11.00
b.		Double surcharge	*2,100.*	

Wmkd. Crown and C A (2)

70	A5	1p on 3p brown	90.00	19.00

Nos. 40a and 53a Surcharged in Green

1895 Wmk. Crown and C C (1)

71	A5	½p on 3p brown	13.00	*45.00*
a.		Double surcharge	*1,750.*	

No. 72 Surcharged in Green and Red

72	A5	½p on 3p brown	120.00	*350.00*

Wmk. Crown and C A (2)

72A	A5	½p on 3p brown	90.00	*200.00*

After the supply of paper watermarked Crown and C C was exhausted, No. 72A was printed. Ostensibly this was to provide samples for Postal Union distribution, but a supply for philatelic demands was also made.

Types of 1890-93 and

A15

1899-1901 Typo. Wmk. 83

73	A9	1p carmine rose	12.50	.30
74	A10	2p yellow	40.00	3.50
75	A15	2½p blue ('01)	21.00	1.25
		Nos. 73-75 (3)	73.50	5.05

A16

A17

A18

A19

A20

A21

A22

Southern Cross — A23

Queen Victoria

A24 A25

Perf. 12½, 12x12½

1902-05 Wmk. 70

76	A9	1p car rose	30.00	1.00
a.		1p salmon		
b.		Perf. 11	400.00	50.00
c.		Perf. 12½x11	1,350.	675.00
77	A16	2p yellow	30.00	5.00
a.		Perf. 11	450.00	65.00
b.		Perf. 12½x11	*1,900.*	*1,100.*
79	A17	4p org brn	450.00	4.50
a.		Perf. 11	1,400.	450.00
80	A12	5p ol bis, perf 12½ ('05)	160.00	100.00
a.		Perf. 11	55.00	*80.00*
81	A18	8p pale yel grn	22.50	4.75
82	A19	9p orange	55.00	40.00
b.		Perf. 11	180.00	*180.00*
83	A20	10p red	35.00	12.00
84	A21	2sh org red, *yel* ('06)	60.00	13.00
a.		Perf. 11	450.00	225.00
b.		2sh orange brown, *yel* ('11)	50.00	32.50
c.		2sh bright red, *yel*	90.00	50.00
d.		As "c," perf. 11	325.00	200.00
85	A22	2sh6p dk bl, *rose*	60.00	25.00
86	A23	5sh blue green	90.00	50.00
87	A24	10sh violet	190.00	110.00
a.		10sh bright purple	950.00	450.00
88	A25	£1 brown org	450.00	210.00
a.		£1 orange	750.00	350.00
		Nos. 76-88 (12)	1,633.	575.25

Perf. 12½, 12x12½

1905-12 Wmk. 13

89	A8	½p dp grn ('10)	5.00	*9.00*
a.		Perf 11	*3,000.*	
90	A9	1p rose	25.00	4.00
e.		Perf. 11	55.00	35.00
f.		Perf. 12½x11	*1,250.*	500.00
91	A16	2p yellow	9.00	2.25
a.		Perf. 11	55.00	50.00
b.		Perf. 12½x11	*1,250.*	550.00
92	A5	3p brown	65.00	6.00
a.		Perf. 11	25.00	19.00
b.		Perf. 12½x11	1,500.	1,500.
93	A17	4p orange brn	50.00	20.00
a.		4p bister brown	60.00	20.00
b.		Perf. 11	1,250.	290.00
94	A12	5p olive bis	40.00	32.50
a.		Perf. 11, pale olive bister	60.00	12.00
b.		Perf. 11, olive green	30.00	22.50
95	A18	8p pale yel grn ('12)	25.00	*82.50*
96	A19	9p orange	37.50	6.50
b.		Perf. 11	200.00	*200.00*
97	A20	10p red orange	25.00	30.00
98	A23	5s blue green	200.00	150.00
		Nos. 89-98 (10)	481.50	342.75

For surcharge see No. 103.

A26

A27

1906-07 Wmk. 83 *Perf. 14*

99	A26	6p bright violet	55.00	5.00
100	A27	1sh olive green	60.00	7.00

1912 Wmk. 74 *Perf. 11½x12*

101	A26	6p bright violet	21.00	19.00
102	A27	1sh gray green	35.00	50.00
a.		Perf. 12½		*2,750.*

No. 91 Surcharged

1912 Wmk. 13 *Perf. 12½*

103	A16	1p on 2p yellow	4.25	*4.25*
a.		Perf compound 12½x11	*750.00*	*450.00*

Stamps of Western Australia were replaced by those of Australia.

POSTAL-FISCAL STAMPS

Postal use of the 1p telegraph stamp was authorized beginning Oct. 25, 1886.

Used values are for examples with postal cancellations.

Beware of stamps with a pen cancellation removed and a fake postmark added.

PF1

1886 Wmk. 1 *Perf. 14*

AR1	PF1	1p bister	110.00	25.00

Perf. 12½

AR2	PF1	1p bister	110.00	25.00

Authorized for postal use by the Post and Telegraph Act of Sept. 5, 1893 were the current revenue stamps through the 1sh value.

Beware of stamps with a pen cancellation removed and a fake postmark added.

Because the Act specified current stamps, postally used examples from the provisional issue of of 1881 are not included here.

PF2

1882		Wmk. 2		*Perf. 14*
AR3	PF2	1p purple	35.00	9.00
AR4	PF2	2p purple	350.00	90.00
AR5	PF2	3p purple	125.00	10.00
AR6	PF2	6p purple	190.00	17.50
AR7	PF2	1sh purple	350.00	40.00

The 6p is known postally used but was not authorized.

Wmk. 83

AR8	PF2	1p purple	42.50	10.00
AR9	PF2	3p purple	125.00	11.00
AR10	PF2	6p purple	175.00	15.00
AR11	PF2	1sh purple	350.00	50.00

Nos. AR7, AR11 have a rectangular outer frame and a circular frame around the swan.

Higher values are known with postal cancels, some postally used, but these were not authorized.

AUSTRALIA

o-'strāl-yə

LOCATION — Oceania, south of Indonesia, bounded on the west by the Indian Ocean

GOVT. — Self-governing dominion of the British Commonwealth

AREA — 2,967,909 sq. mi.

POP. — 17,892,423 (1996)

CAPITAL — Canberra

Australia includes the former British colonies of New South Wales, Victoria, Queensland, South Australia, Western Australia and Tasmania.

12 Pence = 1 Shilling
20 Shillings = 1 Pound
100 Cents = 1 Dollar (1966)

Catalogue values for unused stamps in this country are for Never Hinged items, beginning with Scott 197 in the regular postage section, Scott B1 in the semi-postal section, Scott C6 in the air post section, Scott J71 in the postage due section, and all of the Australian Antarctic Territory.

Watermarks

Wmk. 8 — Wide Crown and Wide A

Wmk. 9 — Wide Crown and Narrow A

Wmk. 10 — Narrow Crown and Narrow A

Wmk. 11 — Multiple Crown and A

Wmk. 12 — Crown and Single-lined A

Wmk. 13 — Large Crown and Double-lined A

Wmk. 55 — Large Crown and NSW

Wmk. 203 — Small Crown and A Multiple

Wmk. 228 — Small Crown and C of A Multiple

Kangaroo and Map — A1

Die I — The inside frameline has a break at left, even with the top of the letters of the denomination.

Die II — The frameline does not show a break (repaired die).

Die III — The left inside frameline shows a break opposite the face of the kangaroo.

Die IV — As Die III, with a break in the top outside frameline above the "ST" of "AUSTRALIA." The upper right inside frameline has an incomplete corner.

Dies are only indicated when there are more than one for any denomination.

1913	Typo.	Wmk. 8		*Perf. 11½, 12*
1	A1	½p green	11.50	7.50
		Never hinged	17.00	
2	A1	1p car (I)	17.50	1.75
		Never hinged	24.00	
h.		1p carmine (III)	24.00	2.25
		Never hinged	40.00	
3	A1	2p gray	70.00	10.00
		Never hinged	140.00	
4	A1	2½p dark blue	70.00	25.00
		Never hinged	140.00	
5	A1	3p ol bis, die I	140.00	17.50
		Never hinged	280.00	
a.		Die II	450.00	85.00
		Never hinged	*725.00*	
6	A1	4p orange	150.00	40.00
		Never hinged	*300.00*	
7	A1	5p org brn	135.00	50.00
		Never hinged	270.00	
8	A1	6p ultra (II)	125.00	30.00
		Never hinged	*250.00*	
b.		As #8, (III)	*4,650.*	*1,625.*
9	A1	9p purple	140.00	37.50
		Never hinged	280.00	
10	A1	1sh blue green	130.00	22.50
		Never hinged	260.00	
11	A1	2sh brown	300.00	140.00
		Never hinged	575.00	
12	A1	5sh yel & gray	550.00	260.00
		Never hinged	1,100.	
13	A1	10sh pink & gray	1,600.	800.00
		Never hinged	*3,500.*	
14	A1	£1 ultra & brn	3,250.	2,400.
		Never hinged	*6,500.*	
15	A1	£2 dp rose & blk	*6,000.*	*3,400.*
		Never hinged	*12,000.*	
		Nos. 1-12 (12)	1,839.	641.75

On No. 4, "2½d" is colorless in solid blue background.

See Nos. 38-59, 96-102, 121-129, 206.

King George V
A2

Kookaburra (Kingfisher)
A3

1913-14	Unwmk.	Engr.		*Perf. 11*
17	A2	1p carmine	5.25	*6.50*
		Never hinged	8.00	
a.		Vert. pair, imperf. between	*2,750.*	
b.		Horiz. pair, imperf. between	*4,250.*	
18	A3	6p lake brown ('14)	100.00	62.50
		Never hinged	160.00	

See No. 95.

A4

ONE PENNY

Die I — Normal die, having outside the oval band with "AUSTRALIA" a white line and a heavy colored line.

Die Ia — As die I with a small white spur below the right serif at foot of the "1" in left tablet.

Die II — A heavy colored line between two white lines back of the emu's neck. A white scratch crossing the vertical shading lines at the lowest point of the bust.

TWO PENCE

Die I — The numeral "2" is thin. The upper curve is 1mm. across and a very thin line connects it with the foot of the figure.

Die II — The "2" is thicker than in die I. The top curve is 1½mm across and a strong white line connects it with the foot of the figure. There are thin vertical lines across the ends of the groups of short horizontal lines at each side of "TWO PENCE."

THREE PENCE

Die I — The ends of the thin horizontal lines in the background run into the solid color of the various parts of the design. The numerals are thin and the letters of "THREE PENCE" are thin and irregular.

Die II — The oval about the portrait, the shields with the numerals, etc., are outlined by thin white lines which separate them from the horizontal background lines. The numerals are thick and the letters of "THREE PENCE" are heavy and regular.

FIVE PENCE

Die I — The top of the flag of the "5" is slightly curved.

Die II — The top of the flag of the "5" is flat. There are thin white vertical lines across the ends of the short horizontal lines at each side of "FIVE PENCE."

1914-24	Typo.	Wmk. 9		*Perf. 14*
19	A4	½p emer ('15)	3.75	1.60
		Never hinged	7.50	
a.		Thin "½" at right	*18,000.*	*9,000.*
20	A4	½p org ('23)	4.50	3.50
		Never hinged	7.00	
21	A4	1p red (I)	20.00	1.75
		Never hinged	30.00	
a.		1p carmine rose (I)	37.50	6.00
		Never hinged	45.00	
b.		1p red (Ia)	500.00	9.00
		Never hinged	1,000.	
c.		1p carmine (II) ('18)	80.00	10.00
		Never hinged	160.00	
d.		1p scar (I), rough paper	22.50	6.00
e.		1p rose red (Ia), rough paper	600.00	22.50
f.		1p brt rose (Ia), rough paper	1,275.	150.00
22	A4	1p vio (I) ('22)	7.00	1.60
		Never hinged	11.50	
a.		1p red violet	9.50	4.75
		Never hinged	14.00	
23	A4	1p grn (I) ('24)	5.25	2.25
		Never hinged	9.50	
24	A4	1½p choc ('18)	8.50	2.00
		Never hinged	12.50	
a.		1½p red brown	13.00	2.25
		Never hinged	18.00	
b.		1½p black brown	7.25	2.25
		Never hinged	11.50	
25	A4	1½p emer ('23)	6.75	2.50
		Never hinged	12.50	
a.		Rough paper	350.00	145.00
26	A4	1½p scar ('24)	3.75	1.10
		Never hinged	7.00	
27	A4	2p brn org (I) ('20)	16.00	2.75
		Never hinged	30.00	
a.		2p orange (I) ('20)	16.00	2.25
		Never hinged	30.00	
b.		Booklet pane of 6	—	
28	A4	2p red (I) ('22)	16.00	2.75
		Never hinged	30.00	
29	A4	2p red brn (I) ('24)	20.00	11.00
		Never hinged	35.00	
30	A4	3p ultra (I) ('24)	29.00	7.00
		Never hinged	57.50	
31	A4	4p org ('15)	40.00	5.50
		Never hinged	80.00	
a.		4p yellow	125.00	17.00
		Never hinged	300.00	
32	A4	4p violet ('21)	20.00	16.00
		Never hinged	30.00	
33	A4	4p lt ultra ('22)	60.00	12.00
		Never hinged	100.00	
34	A4	4p ol bis ('24)	32.50	12.00
		Never hinged	60.00	
35	A4	4½p violet ('24)	25.00	6.00
		Never hinged	50.00	
36	A4	5p org brn (I) ('15)	42.50	6.50
		Never hinged	85.00	
37	A4	1sh4p lt blue ('20)	100.00	30.00
		Never hinged	180.00	
		Nos. 19-37 (19)	460.50	127.80

See Nos. 60-76, 113-120, 124.

1915				*Perf. 11½, 12*
38	A1	2p gray	90.00	16.00
		Never hinged	180.00	
39	A1	2½p dark blue	80.00	32.50
		Never hinged	140.00	
40	A1	6p ultra (II)	170.00	25.00
		Never hinged	325.00	
a.		Die III	*6,250.*	*2,500.*
41	A1	9p violet	170.00	52.50
		Never hinged	450.00	
42	A1	1sh blue green	160.00	30.00
		Never hinged	360.00	
43	A1	2sh brown	600.00	110.00
		Never hinged	1,500.	
44	A1	5sh yellow & gray	850.00	300.00
		Never hinged	2,250.	
		Nos. 38-44 (7)	2,120.	566.00

1915-24				Wmk. 10
45	A1	2p gray (I)	42.50	7.50
		Never hinged	62.50	
a.		Die II, shiny paper	45.00	17.50
		Never hinged	67.50	
46	A1	2½p dark blue	25.00	10.00
		Never hinged	40.00	
a.		"1" of fraction omitted	*47,500.*	*30,000.*
47	A1	3p ol bis (I)	35.00	8.50
		Never hinged	60.00	
a.		Die II	190.00	52.50
		Never hinged	325.00	
b.		3p lt olive (IV)	52.50	13.00
		Never hinged	92.50	
48	A1	6p ultra (II)	100.00	8.75
		Never hinged	190.00	
a.		6p chalky blue (III)	100.00	22.50

Never hinged 190.00
c. 6p ultra (IV) 100.00 19.00
Never hinged 180.00
49 A1 6p yel brn (IV, '23) 25.00 3.75
Never hinged 45.00
50 A1 9p violet (IV) 70.00 16.00
Never hinged 140.00
a. 9p lilac (II) 60.00 11.00
Never hinged 120.00
51 A1 1sh blue grn (II, '16) 55.00 7.00
Never hinged 110.00
b. Die IV 65.00 3.50
52 A1 2sh brn ('16) 240.00 15.00
Never hinged 500.00
53 A1 2sh vio brn (II, '24) 70.00 30.00
Never hinged 160.00
54 A1 5sh yel & gray ('18) 240.00 100.00
Never hinged 480.00
55 A1 10sh brt pink & gray ('17) 650.00 300.00
Never hinged 1,350.
56 A1 £1 ultra & brn org ('16) 3,000. 1,750.
Never hinged 6,500.
a. £1 ultra & brn ('16) 3,000. 1,750.
Never hinged 6,500.
57 A1 £1 gray (IV, '24) 800.00 350.00
Never hinged 1,750.
58 A1 £2 dp rose & blk ('19) 5,500. 3,250.
Never hinged 12,500.
59 A1 £2 rose & vio brn ('24) 4,250. 2,500.
Never hinged 11,000.
Nos. 45-54 (10) 902.50 206.50

Perf. 14, 14½, 14½x14

1918-23 Wmk. 11
60 A4 ½p emerald 7.25 2.50
Never hinged 12.50
a. Thin "½" at right 100.00 125.00
61 A4 1p rose (I) 26.00 17.00
Never hinged 45.00
62 A4 1p dl grn (I) ('24) 13.00 9.25
Never hinged 24.00
63 A4 1½p choc ('19) 11.00 2.25
Never hinged 17.50
a. 1½p red brown ('19) 11.50 4.00
Never hinged 23.00
Nos. 60-63 (4) 57.25 31.00

1924 Unwmk. *Perf. 14*
64 A4 1p green (I) 6.50 9.50
Never hinged 12.50
65 A4 1½p carmine 22.50 8.00
Never hinged 45.00

Perf. 14, 13½x12½

1926-30 Wmk. 203
66 A4 ½p orange 3.50 2.00
Never hinged 7.00
a. Perf. 14 ('27) 6.75 7.25
Never hinged 11.00
67 A4 1p green (I) 4.25 1.00
Never hinged 8.00
a. 1p green (Ia) 50.00 *70.00*
Never hinged 75.00
b. Perf. 14 4.25 1.75
Never hinged 8.25
68 A4 1½p rose red ('27) 4.00 1.75
Never hinged 8.00
c. Perf. 14 ('26) 11.00 2.25
Never hinged 21.00
69 A4 1½p red brn ('30) 5.50 5.50
Never hinged 9.75
70 A4 2p red brn (II, '28) 14.50 8.00
Never hinged 29.00
a. Perf. 14 (I, '27) 40.00 40.00
Never hinged 75.00
71 A4 2p red (II) ('30) 9.00 .90
Never hinged 20.00
a. Tête bêche pair 175,000.
c. Unwmkd. (II) ('31) *1,350.* *2,400.*
72 A4 3p ultra (II) ('29) 30.00 5.00
Never hinged 52.50
a. 3p ultra (I) 62.50 20.00
Never hinged 125.00
b. Perf. 14 40.00 10.00
Never hinged 72.50
73 A4 4p ol bis ('29) 27.50 3.50
Never hinged 50.00
a. Perf. 14 ('28) 62.50 40.00
Never hinged 125.00
74 A4 4½p dk vio ('27) 22.50 5.25
Never hinged 40.00
a. Perf. 13½x12½ ('28) 75.00 29.00
Never hinged 135.00
75 A4 5p brn buff (II) ('30) 40.00 7.00
Never hinged 75.00
76 A4 1sh4p pale turq bl ('28) 110.00 27.50
Never hinged 225.00
a. Perf. 14 ('27) 125.00 70.00
Never hinged 275.00
Nos. 66-76 (11) 270.75 67.40

For surcharges & overprints see Nos. 106-107, O3-O4.

Parliament House, Canberra — A5

Unwmk.

1927, May 9 Engr. *Perf. 11*
94 A5 1½p brown red .60 .55
Never hinged 1.10
a. Vert. pair, imperf. btwn. *4,750.* *4,250.*
b. Horiz. pair, imperf. btwn. *10,000.* *10,000.*

Opening of Parliament House at Canberra.

Melbourne Exhibition Issue
Kookaburra Type of 1914

1928, Oct. 29
95 A3 3p deep blue 5.00 7.25
Never hinged 7.25
a. Pane of 4 175.00 *225.00*
Never hinged 260.00

No. 95a was issued at the Melbourne Intl. Phil. Exhib. No marginal inscription. Printed in sheets of 60 stamps (15 panes). No. 95a exists imperf. Value, $300,000.

No. 95 was printed in sheets of 120 and issued Nov. 2 throughout Australia.

Kangaroo-Map Type of 1913
Perf. 11½, 12

1929-30 Wmk. 203 Typo.
96 A1 6p brown 32.50 11.00
Never hinged 57.50
97 A1 9p violet 35.00 25.00
Never hinged 80.00
98 A1 1sh blue green 45.00 12.50
Never hinged 90.00
99 A1 2sh red brown 75.00 17.00
Never hinged 200.00
100 A1 5sh yel & gray 240.00 100.00
Never hinged 500.00
101 A1 10sh pink & gray 500.00 475.00
Never hinged 1,000.
102 A1 £2 dl red & blk ('30) 4,000. 800.00
Never hinged 8,000.
Nos. 96-102 (7) 4,928. 1,441.

For overprint see No. O5.

Black Swan — A6

Unwmk.

1929, Sept. 28 Engr. *Perf. 11*
103 A6 1½p dull red 2.00 2.00
Never hinged 3.25

Centenary of Western Australia.

Capt. Charles Sturt — A7

1930, June 2
104 A7 1½p dark red 1.25 1.25
Never hinged 2.50
105 A7 3p dark blue 8.00 *10.00*
Never hinged 11.00

Capt. Charles Sturt's exploration of the Murray River, cent.

Nos. 68 and 74a surcharged

1930 Wmk. 203 *Perf. 13½x12½*
106 A4 2p on 1½p rose red 2.50 1.25
Never hinged 4.00
107 A4 5p on 4½p dark violet 14.00 *15.00*
Never hinged 21.00

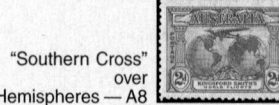

"Southern Cross" over Hemispheres — A8

Perf. 11, 11½

1931, Mar. 19 Unwmk.
111 A8 2p dull red 2.00 1.25
Never hinged 3.00
112 A8 3p blue 7.25 6.25
Never hinged 12.50
Nos. 111-112,C2 (3) 17.25 15.50

Trans-oceanic flights (1928-1930) of Sir Charles Edward Kingsford-Smith (1897-1935).

See No. C3 for similar design. For overprints see Nos. CO1, O1-O2.

Types of 1913-23 Issues
Perf. 13½x12½

1931-36 Typo. Wmk. 228
113 A4 ½p org ('32) 9.50 6.75
Never hinged 13.50
114 A4 1p green (I) 3.00 .40
Never hinged 5.00
115 A4 1½p red brn ('36) 8.00 13.50
Never hinged 12.50
116 A4 2p red (II) 2.50 .30
Never hinged 4.50
117 A4 3p ultra (II) ('32) 22.50 2.00
Never hinged 45.00
118 A4 4p ol bis ('33) 22.50 2.00
Never hinged 45.00
120 A4 5p brn buff (II) ('32) 22.50 1.00
Never hinged 35.00

Perf. 11½, 12; 13½x12½ (1sh4p)

121 A1 6p yel brn ('36) 35.00 *37.50*
Never hinged 55.00
122 A1 9p violet ('32) 40.00 3.00
Never hinged 65.00
124 A4 1sh4p lt blue ('32) 60.00 9.00
Never hinged 145.00
125 A1 2sh red brn ('35) 10.00 2.75
Never hinged 20.00
126 A1 5sh yel & gray ('32) 175.00 20.00
Never hinged 400.00
127 A1 10sh pink & gray ('32) 400.00 200.00
Never hinged 1,000.
128 A1 £1 gray ('35) 700.00 275.00
Never hinged 1,400.
129 A1 £2 dl rose & blk ('34) 4,000. 800.00
Never hinged 9,250.
Nos. 113-129 (15) 5,511. 1,373.

For redrawn 2sh see No. 206. For overprints see Nos. O6-O11.

Sydney Harbor Bridge — A9

Unwmk.

1932, Mar. 14 Engr. *Perf. 11*
130 A9 2p red 2.00 *1.60*
Never hinged 5.00
131 A9 3p blue 5.00 *4.00*
Never hinged 10.00
132 A9 5sh gray green 460.00 275.00
Never hinged 1,300.

Wmk. 228
Perf. 10½
Typo.

133 A9 2p red 2.50 2.25
Never hinged 5.00

Opening of the Sydney Harbor Bridge on Mar. 19, 1932.

Value for 5sh, used, is for CTO examples.

For overprints see Nos. O12-O13.

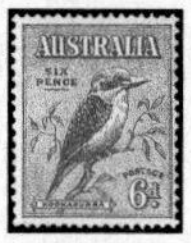

Kookaburra — A14

1932, June 1 *Perf. 13½x12½*
139 A14 6p light brown 15.00 1.25
Never hinged 27.50

Male Lyrebird — A16

1932, Feb. 15 Unwmk. *Perf. 11*
Size: 21½x25mm
141 A16 1sh dark green 35.00 4.50
Never hinged 90.00

See No. 175, 300. For overprint see No. O14.

Yarra Yarra Tribesman, Yarra River and View of Melbourne — A17

Wmk. 228

1934, July 2 Engr. *Perf. 10½*
142 A17 2p vermilion 3.75 1.75
Never hinged 6.50
a. Perf. 11½ 5.00 4.50
Never hinged 10.00
143 A17 3p blue 4.50 *4.00*
Never hinged 10.00
a. Perf. 11½ 5.00 *5.00*
Never hinged 9.00
144 A17 1sh black 52.50 27.50
Never hinged 110.00
a. Perf. 11½ 62.50 35.00
Never hinged 120.00
Nos. 142-144 (3) 60.75 33.25

Centenary of Victoria.

Merino Sheep — A18

1934, Nov. 1 *Perf. 11½*
147 A18 2p copper red 3.00 1.50
Never hinged 7.00
a. Die II 16.00 7.25
Never hinged 32.00
148 A18 3p dark blue 12.00 *12.00*
Never hinged 20.00
149 A18 9p dark violet 40.00 *35.00*
Never hinged 75.00
Nos. 147-149 (3) 55.00 48.50

Capt. John Macarthur (1767-1834), "father of the New South Wales woolen industry."

Two dies of 2p: I, shading on hill in background uneven from light to dark. II, shading is uniformly dark.

Cenotaph in Whitehall, London — A19

1935, Mar. 18 *Perf. 13½x12½*
150 A19 2p red 1.50 .50
Never hinged 3.00

Perf. 11
151 A19 1sh black 42.50 40.00
Never hinged 85.00

Anzacs' landing at Gallipoli, 20th anniv.

The 1sh perf 13½x12½ is a plate proof. Value, unused $2,250, mint never hinged $3,500.

George V on His Charger "Anzac" — A20

1935, May 2 *Perf. 11½*
152 A20 2p red 2.00 .35
Never hinged 4.00
153 A20 3p blue 5.00 *5.00*
Never hinged 10.00
154 A20 2sh violet 42.50 *40.00*
Never hinged 85.00
Nos. 152-154 (3) 49.50 45.35

25th anniv. of the reign of King George V.

Amphitrite Joining Cables between Australia and Tasmania — A21

1936, Apr. 1
157 A21 2p red 1.00 .60
Never hinged 2.75
158 A21 3p dark blue 4.00 3.75
Never hinged 6.50

Australia/Tasmania telephone link.

Edward VIII

A unique block of six unissued 2-penny King Edward VIII stamps realized the equivalent of U.S. $387,000 when it was sold at a London auction in 2014. A single stamp was separated from the block and sold at a Melbourne auction in 2015 for the equivalent of U.S. $123,600.

Proclamation Tree and View of Adelaide, 1936 — A22

1936, Aug. 3

159 A22 2p red 1.00 .60
Never hinged 2.40
160 A22 3p dark blue 4.00 3.75
Never hinged 6.50
161 A22 1sh green 14.00 11.00
Never hinged 27.50
Nos. 159-161 (3) 19.00 15.35

Centenary of South Australia.

Gov. Arthur Phillip at Sydney Cove — A23

1937, Oct. 1 ***Perf. 13x13½***

163 A23 2p red 1.50 .80
Never hinged 3.00
164 A23 3p ultra 3.75 3.25
Never hinged 6.50
165 A23 9p violet 14.00 12.00
Never hinged 25.00
Nos. 163-165 (3) 19.25 16.05

150th anniversary of New South Wales.

Kangaroo A24

Queen Elizabeth A25

King George VI A26 A27

Koala A28

Merino Sheep A29

Kookaburra (Kingfisher) A30

Platypus A31

Queen Elizabeth and King George VI in Coronation Robes
A32 A33

King George VI and Queen Elizabeth — A34

Type I

Type II

Two Types of A25 and A26:
Type I — Highlighted background. Lines around letters of Australia Postage and numerals of value.
Type II — Background of heavy diagonal lines without the highlighted effect. No lines around letters and numerals.

Perf. 13½x14, 14x13½

1937-46 Engr. Wmk. 228

166 A24 ½p org, perf. 15x14 ('42) .85 .70
Never hinged 1.90
a. Perf. 13½x14 ('38) 1.40 .60
Never hinged 3.00
167 A25 1p emerald (I) 1.10 1.00
Never hinged 2.25
168 A26 1½p dull red brn (II) 4.00 3.50
Never hinged 7.00
a. Perf. 15x14 ('41) 4.75 5.00
Never hinged 8.00
169 A26 2p scarlet (I) 2.00 .80
Never hinged 2.25
170 A27 3p ultramarine 37.50 5.00
Never hinged 65.00
a. 3p dp ultra, thin paper ('38) 30.00 5.00
Never hinged 55.00
171 A28 4p grn, perf. 15x14 ('42) 1.00 .30
Never hinged 2.00
a. Perf. 13½x14 ('38) 3.25 2.50
Never hinged 9.00
172 A29 5p pale rose vio, perf. 14x15 ('46) 1.00 .80
Never hinged 2.00
a. Perf. 14x13½ ('38) 3.00 2.50
Never hinged 4.75
173 A30 6p vio brn, perf. 15x14 ('42) 1.00 .30
Never hinged 2.00
a. Perf. 13½x14 12.50 2.40
Never hinged 25.00
b. 6p chocolate, perf. 15x14 1.40 .55
Never hinged 2.25
174 A31 9p sep, perf. 14x15 ('43) 2.00 .45
Never hinged 3.00
a. Perf. 14x13½ ('38) 4.50 2.40
Never hinged 9.00
175 A16 1sh gray grn, perf. 15x14 ('41) 1.40 .40
Never hinged 2.40
a. Perf. 13½x14 27.50 3.00
Never hinged 72.50
176 A27 1sh4p mag ('38) 1.60 *1.60*
Never hinged 3.50

Perf. 13½

177 A32 5sh dl red brn ('38) 9.75 4.75
Never hinged 20.00
178 A33 10sh dl gray vio ('38) 28.00 20.00
Never hinged 40.00
179 A34 £1 bl gray ('38) 70.00 42.50
Never hinged 115.00
Nos. 166-179 (14) 161.20 82.10

No. 175 measures 17½x21½mm.
See Nos.223A, 293, 295, 298, 300. For surch. & overprints see Nos. 190, M1, M4-M5, M7.

1938-42 ***Perf. 15x14***

180 A25 1p emerald (II) 1.00 .70
181 A25 1p dl red brn (II) ('41) .70 .60
181B A26 1½p bl grn (II) ('41) .70 *.80*
182 A26 2p scarlet (II) 1.00 .30
182B A26 2p red vio (II) ('41) .40 .30
183 A27 3p dk ultra ('40) 29.00 3.00
Never hinged 57.50
183A A27 3p dk vio brn ('42) .40 .30
Nos. 180-183A (7) 33.20 6.00
Set, never hinged 72.50

No. 183 differs from Nos. 170-170a in the shading lines on the king's left eyebrow which go downward, left to right, instead of the reverse. Also, more of the left epaulette shows.
For surcharges & ovpt. see Nos. 188-189, M3.

Coil Perforation

A special perforation was applied to stamps intended for use in coils to make separation easier. It consists of small and large holes (2 small, 10 large, 2 small) on the stamps' narrow side. Some of the stamps so perforated were sold in sheets.
This coil perforation may be found on Nos. 166, 181, 182, 182B, 193, 215, 223A, 231, 257, 315-316, 319, 319a and others.

Nurse, Sailor, Soldier and Aviator — A35

Perf. 13½x13

1940, July 15 Engr. Wmk. 228

184 A35 1p green 1.50 *1.50*
Never hinged 3.00
185 A35 2p red 1.60 *1.50*
Never hinged 3.25
186 A35 3p ultra 5.00 *7.00*
Never hinged 10.00
187 A35 6p chocolate 15.00 *13.00*
Never hinged 30.00
Nos. 184-187 (4) 23.10 23.00

Australia's participation in WWII.

No. 182 Surcharged in Blue

1941, Dec. 10 ***Perf. 15x14***

188 A26 2½p on 2p red .80 *.80*
Never hinged 1.50

No. 183 Surcharged in Black and Yellow

189 A27 3½p on 3p dk ultra .90 *.90*
Never hinged 1.75

No. 172a Surcharged in Purple

Perf. 14x13½

190 A29 5½p on 5p pale rose vio 3.25 *3.25*
Never hinged 5.25
Nos. 188-190 (3) 4.95 4.95

Queen Elizabeth
A36 A37

King George VI
A38 A39

George VI and Blue Wrens A40

Emu A41

1942-44 Engr. ***Perf. 15x14***

191 A36 1p brown vio ('43) .45 .25
192 A37 1½p green .70 .25
193 A38 2p lt rose vio ('44) .70 .25
194 A39 2½p red .70 .30
195 A40 3½p ultramarine .90 .70
196 A41 5½p indigo 1.25 1.00
Nos. 191-196 (6) 4.70 2.75
Set, never hinged 8.00

See Nos. 224-225. For overprint see No. M2.

Catalogue values for unused stamps in this section, from this point to the end of the section, are for Never Hinged items.

Duke and Duchess of Gloucester — A42

1945, Feb. 19 Engr. ***Perf. 14½***

197 A42 2½p brown red .30 .25
198 A42 3½p bright ultra .45 *.50*
199 A42 5½p indigo .55 *.50*
Nos. 197-199 (3) 1.30 *1.25*

Inauguration of the Duke of Gloucester as Governor General.

Official Crest and Inscriptions A43

Dove and Australian Flag A44

Angel of Peace; "Motherhood" and "Industry" — A45

1946, Feb. 18 Wmk. 228 ***Perf. 14½***

200 A43 2½p carmine .25 .25
201 A44 3½p deep ultra .65 *.50*
202 A45 5½p deep yellow green .70 *.50*
Nos. 200-202 (3) 1.60 *1.25*

End of WWII. See Nos. 1456-1458.

Sir Thomas Mitchell and Map of Queensland — A46

1946, Oct. 14

203 A46 2½p dark carmine .25 .25
204 A46 3½p deep ultra .50 .40
205 A46 1sh olive green .50 .40
Nos. 203-205 (3) 1.25 1.05

Sir Thomas Mitchell's exploration of central Queensland, cent.

Kangaroo-Map Type of 1913 Redrawn

1945, Dec. Typo. ***Perf. 11½***

206 A1 2sh dk red brown 5.50 5.50

The R and A of AUSTRALIA are separated at the base and there is a single line between the value tablet and "Two Shillings." On No. 125 the tail of the R touches the A, while two lines appear between value tablet and "Two Shillings." There are many other minor differences in the design.
For overprint see No. M6.

John Shortland A47

Pouring Steel A48

Loading Coal — A49

1947, Sept. Engr. ***Perf. 14½x14***

207 A47 2½p brown red .35 .25

Perf. 14½

208 A48 3½p deep blue .65 *.65*
209 A49 5½p deep green .65 *.40*
Nos. 207-209 (3) 1.65 1.30

150th anniv. of the discovery of the Hunter River estuary, site of Newcastle by Lieut. John Shortland. By error the 2½p shows his father, Capt. John Shortland.

Princess Elizabeth — A50

Perf. 14x14½

1947, Nov. 20 **Wmk. 228**
210 A50 1p brown violet .40 .40

See No. 215.

Hereford Bull A51

Crocodile A52

1948, Feb. 16 ***Perf. 14½***
211 A51 1sh3p violet brown 2.50 1.25
212 A52 2sh chocolate 2.50 1.00

See No. 302.

William J. Farrer — A53

Design: No. 214, Ferdinand von Mueller.

1948 ***Perf. 14½x14***
213 A53 2½p red .50 .25
214 A53 2½p dark red .45 .25

William J. Farrer (1845-1906), wheat researcher, and Ferdinand von Mueller (1825-1896), German-born botanist.
Issue dates: No. 213, July 12. No. 214, Sept. 13.

Elizabeth Type of 1947

1948, Aug. **Unwmk.** ***Perf. 14x14½***
215 A50 1p brown violet .40 .25

Scout in Uniform — A55

1948, Nov. 15 **Engr.** **Wmk. 228**
216 A55 2½p brown red .45 .25

Pan-Pacific Scout Jamboree, Victoria, Dec. 29, 1948 to Jan. 9, 1949. See No. 249.

Arms of Australia — A56

1949-50 **Wmk. 228** ***Perf. 14x13½***
218 A56 5sh dark red 4.50 1.25
219 A56 10sh red violet 29.00 2.00
220 A56 £1 deep blue 45.00 8.50
221 A56 £2 green ('50) 175.00 26.00
Nos. 218-221 (4) 253.50 37.75

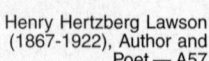

Henry Hertzberg Lawson (1867-1922), Author and Poet — A57

Perf. 14½x14

1949, June 17 **Unwmk.**
222 A57 2½p rose brown .50 .25

Outback Mail Carrier and Plane — A58

1949, Oct. 10
223 A58 3½p violet blue .40 .40

UPU, 75th anniv.

Types of 1938, 1942-44 and

Aborigine — A59

1948-50 **Unwmk.** ***Perf. 14½x14***
223A A24 ½p orange ('49) .45 .25
224 A37 1½p green ('49) .35 .45
225 A38 2p lt rose violet 1.00 .55

Wmk. 228

226 A59 8½p dark brown ('50) .40 .40
Nos. 223A-226 (4) 2.20 1.65

Issued: 2p, Dec.; ½p, Sept.; 1½p, 8/29; 8½p, 8/14.
See Nos. 248, 303.

John Forrest — A60

1949, Nov. 28 **Wmk. 228**
227 A60 2½p brown red .40 .25

Forrest (1847-1918), explorer & statesman.

New South Wales A61

Victoria A62

First stamp designs.

Perf. 14½x14

1950, Sept. 27 **Unwmk.**
228 A61 2½p rose brown .40 .25
229 A62 2½p rose brown .40 .25
a. Pair, #228-229 1.60 1.25

Cent. of Australian adhesive postage stamps. Issued in sheets of 160 stamps containing alternate copies of Nos. 228 and 229.

Elizabeth A63

George VI A64

1950-51 **Engr.** **Unwmk.**
230 A63 1½p deep green .80 .75
231 A63 2p yellow grn ('51) .30 .25
232 A64 2½p violet brn ('51) .30 *.45*
233 A64 3p dull green ('51) .35 .25
Nos. 230-233 (4) 1.75 1.70

Issued: 1½p, 6/19; 2p, 3/28; 2½p, 5/23; 3p, 11/14.

A65

A66

1950-52 **Wmk. 228**
234 A64 2½p red .25 .25
235 A64 3p red ('51) .35 *.35*
236 A65 3½p red brown ('51) .35 .25
237 A65 4½p scarlet ('52) .45 *.45*
238 A65 6½p choc ('52) .35 .35
238A A65 6½p blue green ('52) .45 .25
239 A66 7½p deep blue ('51) .50 .50
Nos. 234-239 (7) 2.70 2.40

Issued: 2½p, 4/12; 3p, 2/28; 7½p, 10/31; 3½p, 11/28; 4½p, No. 238, 2/20; No. 238A, 4/9.

A67

Founding of the Commonwealth of Australia, 50th Anniv. — A68

Designs: No. 240, Sir Edmund Barton. No. 241, Sir Henry Parkes, bearded. 5½p, Duke of York opening first Federal Parliament. 1sh6p, Parliament House, Canberra.

Perf. 14½x14

1951, May 1 **Engr.** **Unwmk.**
240 A67 3p carmine 1.00 .25
241 A67 3p carmine 1.00 .25
a. Pair, #240, 241 2.00 2.00
242 A68 5½p deep blue 1.20 *1.50*
243 A68 1sh6p red brown 1.60 1.40
Nos. 240-243 (4) 4.80 3.40

Edward Hammond Hargraves — A69

Design: No. 245, Charles Joseph Latrobe (1801-1875), first governor of Victoria.

1951, July 2
244 A69 3p rose brown .80 .25
245 A69 3p rose brown .80 .25
a. Pair, #244, 245 2.00 1.60

Discovery of gold in Australia, cent. (No. 244); Establishment of representative government in Victoria, cent. (No. 245). Sheets contain alternate rows of Nos. 244 and 245.

King George VI — A70

1952, Mar. 19 **Wmk. 228** ***Perf. 14½***
247 A70 1sh½p slate blue 2.50 .85

Aborigine Type of 1950 Redrawn
Size: 20½x25mm

248 A59 2sh6p dark brown 5.75 1.25

Portrait as on A59; lettering altered and value repeated at lower left. See No. 303.

Scout Type of 1948
Dated "1952-53"

Perf. 14x14½

1952, Nov. 19 **Wmk. 228**
249 A55 3½p red brown .45 .25

Pan-Pacific Scout Jamboree, Greystanes, Dec. 30, 1952, to Jan. 9, 1953.

Modern Dairy, Butter Production — A71

Perf. 14½

1953, Feb. 11 **Unwmk.** **Typo.**
250 A71 3p shown .90 .40
251 A71 3p Wheat .90 .40
252 A71 3p Beef .90 .40
a. Strip of 3, #250-252 8.00 8.00
253 A71 3½p shown .90 .40
254 A71 3½p Wheat .90 .40
255 A71 3½p Beef .90 .40
a. Strip of 3, #253-255 7.50 *7.50*
Nos. 250-255 (6) 5.40 2.40

Both the 3p and 3½p were printed in panes of 50 stamps: 17 Butter, 17 Wheat and 16 Beef. The stamps were issued to encourage food production.

Queen Elizabeth II — A72

Perf. 14½x14

1953-54 **Unwmk.** **Engr.**
256 A72 1p purple .30 .30
256A A72 2½p deep blue ('54) .45 .30
257 A72 3p dark green .45 .25

Wmk. 228

258 A72 3½p dark red .55 .45
258B A72 6½p orange ('54) 1.50 .75
Nos. 256-258B (5) 3.25 2.05

Issued: 3½p, 4/21; 3p, 6/17; 1p, 8/19; 2½p, 6½p, 6/23.
See Nos. 292, 296.

Coronation Issue

Queen Elizabeth II A73

1953, May 25 **Unwmk.**
259 A73 3½p rose red .60 .25
260 A73 7½p violet 1.00 1.00
261 A73 2sh dull green 2.00 1.50
Nos. 259-261 (3) 3.60 2.75

Boy and Girl with Calf — A74

1953, Sept. 3 ***Perf. 14½***
262 A74 3½p dp green & red brn .50 .25

Official establishment of Young Farmers' Clubs, 25th anniv.

Lieut. Gov. David Collins A75

Sullivan Cove, Hobart A76

Design: No. 264, Lieut. Gov. William Paterson (facing left).

1953, Sept. 23 ***Perf. 14½x14***
263 A75 3½p red brown .45 .25
264 A75 3½p red brown .60 .25
a. Pair, #263-264 1.60 1.60
265 A76 2sh green 4.00 2.50
Nos. 263-265 (3) 5.05 3.00

Settlement in Tasmania, 150th anniv. Sheets contain alternate rows of Nos. 263 and 264.

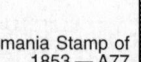

Tasmania Stamp of 1853 — A77

1953, Nov. 11 ***Perf. 14½***
266 A77 3p red .40 .40

Tasmania's first postage stamps, cent.

Elizabeth II and Duke of Edinburgh — A78

Elizabeth II — A79

1954, Feb. 2 ***Perf. 14½x14, 14x14½***

267 A78 3½p rose red .35 .25
268 A79 7½p purple .80 *.80*
269 A78 2sh green 1.60 1.00
Nos. 267-269 (3) 2.75 2.05

Visit of Queen Elizabeth II and the Duke of Edinburgh, 1954.

Telegraph Pole and Key — A80

1954, Apr. 7 **Engr.** ***Perf. 14***

270 A80 3½p dark red .45 .25

Inauguration of the telegraph in Australia, cent.

Red Cross and Globe — A81

1954, June 9 ***Perf. 14½x14***

271 A81 3½p deep blue & red .40 .25

Australian Red Cross Society.

Swan — A82

1954, Aug. 2 **Unwmk.** ***Perf. 14½***

274 A82 3½p black .40 .25

Western Australia's first postage stamp, cent.

Diesel and Early Steam Locomotives A83

1954, Sept. 13 ***Perf. 14x14½***

275 A83 3½p red brown .45 .25

Centenary of Australian railroads.

Antarctic Flora and Fauna and Map — A84

1954, Nov. 17 ***Perf. 14***

276 A84 3½p black .40 .25

Australia's interest in the Antarctic continent.

Olympic Circles and Arms of Melbourne — A85

1954, Dec. 1

277 A85 2sh dark blue 5.75 3.25

16th Olympic Games to be held in Melbourne Nov.-Dec. 1956. See No. 286.

Globe, Flags and Rotary Emblem — A86

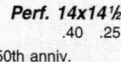

1955, Feb. 23 ***Perf. 14x14½***

278 A86 3½p carmine .40 .25

Rotary International, 50th anniv.

Elizabeth II — A87

1955, Mar. 9 **Wmk. 228** ***Perf. 14½***

279 A87 1sh½p dk gray blue 3.25 1.00

See No. 301.

Top of US Monument, Canberra — A88

1955, May 4 **Unwmk.** ***Perf. 14x14½***

280 A88 3½p deep ultra .50 .25

Friendship between Australia and the US.

Cobb and Company Mail Coach — A89

1955, July 6 ***Perf. 14½x14***

281 A89 3½p dark brown .50 .25
282 A89 2sh brown 2.25 2.25

Pioneers of Australia's coaching era.

World Map, YMCA Emblem — A90

Engr. and Typo.

1955, Aug. 10 ***Perf. 14***

283 A90 3½p Prus green & red .40 .25
a. Red omitted *25,000.*

Centenary of YMCA.

Florence Nightingale and Modern Nurse — A91

1955, Sept. 21 **Engr.** ***Perf. 14x14½***

284 A91 3½p red violet .40 .25

Centenary of Florence Nightingale's work in the Crimea and of the founding of modern nursing.

Queen Victoria — A92

1955, Oct. 17 ***Perf. 14½***

285 A92 3½p green .40 .25

South Australia's first postage stamps, cent.

Olympic Type of 1954

1955, Nov. 30 **Unwmk.** ***Perf. 14***

286 A85 2sh deep green 3.25 2.40

16th Olympic Games at Melbourne, Nov. 22-Dec. 8, 1956.

Queen Victoria, Queen Elizabeth II and Badges of Victoria, New South Wales and Tasmania — A93

1956, Sept. 26 ***Perf. 14½x14***

287 A93 3½p brown carmine .40 .25

Centenary of responsible government in Victoria, New South Wales and Tasmania.

Melbourne Coat of Arms A94

Southern Cross, Olympic Torch A95

Collins Street, Melbourne — A96

Design: 2sh, Melbourne across Yarra River.

1956, Oct. 31 **Engr.** ***Perf. 14½, 14***

288 A94 4p dark carmine .50 .25
289 A95 7½p ultramarine .75 *1.00*

Photo.

Perf. 14x14½

290 A96 1sh multicolored .95 .50

Perf. 12x11½

Granite Paper

291 A96 2sh multicolored 1.60 1.25
Nos. 288-291 (4) 3.80 3.00

16th Olympic Games, Melbourne, 11/22-12/8.

A lithographed souvenir sheet incorporating reproductions of Nos. 288-291 in reduced size was of private origin and not postally valid.

Types of 1938-55 and

Queen Elizabeth II — A97

Perf. 14½x14, 14x15, 15x14, 14½

1956-57 **Engr.** **Unwmk.**

292 A72 3½p dark red 1.40 .55
293 A28 4p green 2.00 .45
294 A97 4p claret ('57) .45 .25
a. Booklet pane of 6 ('57) 12.50
295 A30 6p brown violet 3.50 .55
296 A72 6½p orange 3.50 .25
297 A97 7½p violet ('57) 1.60 .55
298 A31 9p sepia 17.00 2.00
299 A97 10p gray blue ('57) 1.25 .55
300 A16 1sh gray green 7.25 1.10
301 A87 1sh7p redsh brn ('57) 5.25 .70
302 A52 2sh chocolate 14.00 1.10
303 A59 2sh6p brown ('57) 10.50 1.10
Nos. 292-303 (12) 67.70 9.15

No. 300 measures 17½x21½mm. No. 303 measures 20½x25mm and is the redrawn type of 1952.

Issued: 3½p, 7/2; 2sh, 7/21; No. 293, 6p, 8/18; 6½p, Sept. 9p, 1sh, 12/13; 2sh6p, 1/30; 10p, 3/6; No. 294, 1sh7p, 3/13; 7½p, 11/13.

South Australia Coat of Arms — A99

1957, Apr. 17 **Unwmk.** ***Perf. 14½***

304 A99 4p brown red .40 .25

Centenary of responsible government in South Australia.

No. 304 exists in two types on alternate rows of the sheet. Type I — The scroll just passes through the hyphen between the dates. Type II — The scroll passing through the hyphen between "1857-1957" is longer. Both types are of equal value.

Caduceus and Map of Australia — A100

1957, Aug. 21 ***Perf. 14½x14***

305 A100 7p violet blue .60 .30

Royal Flying Doctor Service of Australia.

Star of Bethlehem and Praying Child — A101

1957, Nov. 6 **Engr.**

306 A101 3½p dull rose .35 .25
307 A101 4p pale purple .35 .25

Christmas.

Canberra War Memorial, Sailor and Airman — A102

Design: No. 309, As No. 308 with soldier and service woman. Printed in alternate rows in sheet.

1958, Feb. 10 **Unwmk.**

308 A102 5½p brown carmine 1.60 .70
309 A102 5½p brown carmine 1.60 .70
a. Pair, #308-309 4.00 3.50

Sir Charles Kingsford-Smith and "Southern Cross" — A103

1958, Aug. 27 ***Perf. 14x14½***

310 A103 8p brt violet blue 1.25 1.00

1st air crossing of the Tasman Sea, 30th anniv. See New Zealand No. 321.

Broken Hill Mine — A104

1958, Sept. 10 ***Perf. 14½x14***

311 A104 4p brown .40 .25

Broken Hill mining field, 75th anniv.

Nativity — A105

1958, Nov. 5 ***Perf. 14½x15***

312 A105 3½p dark red .30 .25
313 A105 4p dark purple .30 .25

Christmas.

A106

A107

A108

A109

A110

Platypus
A111

Tasmanian Tiger
A112

Flannel Flower
A113

Aboriginal Stockman Cutting Out a Steer
A114

Die I

Die II

Designs: 3p, Queen Elizabeth II facing right. 6p, Banded anteater. 8p, Tiger cat. 9p, Kangaroos. 11p, Rabbit bandicoot. 1sh6p, Christmas bells (flower). 2sh3p, Wattle (flower). 2sh5p, Banksia (flower). 3sh, Waratah (flower).

FIVE PENCE

Die I — Four short lines inside "5" at right of ball; six short lines left of ball; full length line above ball is seventh from bottom. Odd numbered horizontal rows in each sheet are in Die I.

Die II — Five short lines inside "5" at right of ball; seven at left; full length line above ball is eighth from bottom. Even numbered horizontal rows in each sheet are in Die II.

Perf. 14½x14, 14x14½, 14½

1959-64 Engr. Unwmk.

314	A106	1p dull violet	.25	.25
315	A107	2p red brn ('62)	.40	.35
316	A108	3p bluish green	.35	.25
317	A108	3½p dark green	.25	.25
318	A109	4p carmine	1.00	.25
a.		Booklet pane of 6	29.00	
319	A110	5p dark blue (I)	1.00	.25
a.		5p dark blue (II)	1.00	.25
b.		Booklet pane of 6 ('60)	17.00	
320	A111	6p chocolate ('60)	1.50	.25
321	A111	8p red brn ('60)	1.50	.25
322	A111	9p brown black	1.90	.75
323	A111	11p dk blue ('61)	1.90	.25
324	A111	1sh slate green	4.50	.70
325	A112	1sh2p dk purple ('62)	1.90	.35
326	A113	1sh6p red, *yel* ('60)	3.00	1.20
327	A113	2sh dark blue	2.00	.25
328	A113	2sh3p green, *yel*	2.25	.25
328A	A113	2sh3p yel grn ('64)	6.00	3.25
329	A113	2sh5p brn, *yel* ('60)	7.50	1.10
330	A113	3sh crimson	3.25	.45

Wmk. 228

331	A114	5sh red brown, *cream* ('61)	24.00	2.25
a.		red brown, *white* ('64)	120.00	12.00
		Nos. 314-331 (19)	64.45	12.90

Issued: 1p, 4p, 2/2; 3½p, 3/18; 2sh, 4/8; 3p, 5/20; 3sh, 7/15; 1sh, No. 328, 9/9; 5p, 10/1; 9p, 10/21; 1sh6p, 2/3/60; 2sh5p, 3/16/60; 8p, 5/11/60; 6p, 9/30/60; 11p, 5/3/61; 5sh, 7/26/61; 2p, 1sh2p, 3/21/62; No. 328A, 10/28/64.

Luminescent Printings

Paper with an orange red phosphorescence (surface coating), was used for some printings of the Colombo Plan 1sh, No. 340, the Churchill 5p, No. 389, and several regular postage stamps. These include 2p, 3p, 6p, 8p, 9p, 11p, 1sh2p, 1sh6p and 2sh3p (Nos. 315, 316, 365, 367, 321, 368, 323, 325, 369, 328A).

Stamps printed only on phosphorescent paper include the Monash 5p, Hargrave 5p, ICY 2sh3p and Christmas 5p (Nos. 388, 390-393) and succeeding commemoratives; the 2sh, 2sh6p and 3sh regular birds (Nos. 370, 372, 373); and most of the regular series in decimal currency.

Ink with a phosphorescent content was used in printing most of the 5p red, No. 366, almost all of the 5p red booklets, No. 366a, most of the decimal 4c regular, No. 397, and its booklet pane, No. 397a, and all of No. 398.

Postmaster Isaac Nichols Boarding Vessel to Receive Mail — A115

1959, Apr. 22 ***Perf. 14½x14***
332 A115 4p dark gray blue .40 .25

First post office, Sydney, 150th anniv.

Parliament House, Brisbane, and Queensland Arms — A116

1959, June 5 ***Perf. 14x14½***
333 A116 4p dk green & violet .40 .25

Cent. of Queensland self-government.

Approach of the Magi — A117

1959, Nov. 4 ***Perf. 15x14½***
334 A117 5p purple .40 .25

Christmas.

Girl Guide and Lord Baden-Powell A118

1960, Aug. 18 ***Perf. 14½x14***
335 A118 5p dark blue .45 .25

50th anniversary of the Girl Guides.

The Overlanders by Sir Daryl Lindsay — A119

1960, Sept. 21 ***Perf. 14½***
336 A119 5p lilac rose .40 .25

Exploration of Australia's Northern Territory, cent.

No. 336 exists in two types. Type I: Top edge of the mane is broken and right ear is not closed. Type II: Mane is smooth and the lines in the ear are closed.

Melbourne Cup and Archer, 1861 Winner — A120

1960, Oct. 12 **Unwmk.**
337 A120 5p sepia .40 .25

Centenary of the Melbourne Cup.

Queen Victoria — A121

1960 Nov. 2 **Engr.** ***Perf. 14½***
338 A121 5p dark green .40 .25

Centenary of the first Queensland stamps.

Open Bible and Candle — A122

1960, Nov. 9 **Unwmk.**
339 A122 5p maroon .40 .25

Christmas; beginning of 350th anniv. year of the publication of the King James translation of the Bible.

Colombo Plan Emblem — A123

1961, June 30 ***Perf. 14x14½***
340 A123 1sh red brown 1.60 .30

Colombo Plan for the peaceful development of South East Asia countries, 10th anniv.

Dame Nellie Melba, by Sir Bertram Mackennal — A124

1961, Sept. 20 ***Perf. 14½***
341 A124 5p deep blue .45 .30

Dame Nellie Melba, singer, birth cent.

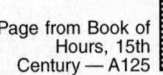

Page from Book of Hours, 15th Century — A125

1961, Nov. 8 ***Perf. 14½x14***
342 A125 5p reddish brown .40 .25

Christmas; end of the 350th anniv. year of the publication of the King James translation of the Bible.

John McDouall Stuart — A126

1962, July 25 **Unwmk.** ***Perf. 14½***
345 A126 5p carmine .40 .25

First south-north crossing of Australia by John McDouall Stuart, cent.

Nurse and Rev. Flynn's Grave — A127

1962, Sept. 5 **Photo.** ***Perf. 13½***
346 A127 5p multicolored .50 .30
a. Red omitted *450.00*

Australian Inland Mission founded by Rev. John Flynn, 50th anniv.

Woman and Globe — A128

1962, Sept. 26 **Engr.** ***Perf. 14x14½***
347 A128 5p dark green .40 .25

World Conf. of the Associated Country Women of the World, Melbourne, Oct. 2-12.

Madonna and Child — A129

1962, Oct. 17 ***Perf. 14½***
348 A129 5p deep violet .40 .25

Christmas.

View of Perth and Kangaroo Paw — A130

Arms of Perth — A131

1962, Nov. 1 **Photo.** ***Perf. 14***
349 A130 5p multicolored .75 .25
a. Red omitted *5,500.*

Perf. 14½x14
350 A131 2sh3p emer, blk, red & ultra 4.00 3.50

British Empire and Commonwealth Games, Perth, Nov. 22-Dec. 1.

Perf 14x14¾ examples of Nos. 349-350 are from a booklet pane issued for the 2006 Commonwealth Games. These stamps were not valid for postage.

Elizabeth II A132

Elizabeth II and Prince Philip A133

1963, Feb. 18 **Engr.** ***Perf. 14½***
351 A132 5p dark green .50 .25
352 A133 2sh3 red brown 4.00 3.00

Visit of Elizabeth II and Prince Philip.

Perf 14½x14 lithographed examples of Nos. 351-352 come from the booklet footnoted under No. 2507. These stamps were not valid for postage.

Walter Burley Griffin and Arms of Canberra — A134

1963, Mar. 8 **Unwmk.** ***Perf. 14½x14***
353 A134 5p dark green .40 .25

50th anniv. of Canberra; Walter Burley Griffin, American architect, who laid out plan for Canberra.

Red Cross Centenary Emblem — A135

1963, May 8 Photo. ***Perf. 13½x13***

354 A135 5p dk blue, red & gray .50 .25

Centenary of the International Red Cross.

Explorers Blaxland, Lawson and Wentworth Looking West from Mt. York — A136

1963, May 28 Engr. ***Perf. 14½x14***

355 A136 5p dark blue .40 .25

1st crossing of the Blue Mts., 150th anniv.

Globe, Ship, Plane and Map of Australia — A137

1963, Aug. 28 Unwmk.

356 A137 5p red .40 .25

Importance of exports to Australian economy.

Elizabeth II A138

Black-backed Magpie and Eucalyptus A139

Abel Tasman and Ship A144

George Bass, Whaleboat A145

Designs: 6p, Yellow-tailed thornbill, horiz. 1sh6p, Galah on tree stump. 2sh, Golden whistler. 2sh5p, Blue wren and bracken fern. 2sh6p, Scarlet robin, horiz. 3sh, Straw-necked ibis. 5sh, William Dampier and "Roebuck" sailing ship. 7sh6p, Capt. James Cook. 10sh, Matthew Flinders and three-master "Investigator." £2, Admiral Philip Parker King.

Perf. 15x14

1963-65 Unwmk. Engr.

365 A138 5p green .90 .25
a. Booklet pane of 6 ('64) 35.00
b. Pair, imperf. btwn. 2.75 2.00
366 A138 5p red .90 .25
a. Booklet pane of 6 45.00

Photo.

Perf. 13½

367 A139 6p multi 1.10 .35
a. Vert. pair, imperf. btwn.
368 A139 9p multi 2.00 *1.75*
369 A139 1sh6p multi 1.75 *1.40*
370 A139 2sh multi 2.25 .55
371 A139 2sh5p multi 5.75 *3.25*
372 A139 2sh6p multi 4.75 3.00
a. Red omitted *12,000. 12,000.*
373 A139 3sh multi 3.25 2.00

Engr.

Perf. 14½x14, 14½x15

374 A144 4sh violet blue 3.75 .95

Wmk. 228

375 A145 5sh red brown 5.25 2.50
376 A144 7sh6p olive green 18.00 13.00
377 A144 10sh deep claret 32.50 8.00
378 A145 £1 purple 65.00 30.00
379 A145 £2 brn blk 97.50 80.00
Nos. 365-379 (15) 244.65 147.25

No. 365a was printed in sheets of 288 which were sold intact by the Philatelic Bureau. These sheets have been broken to obtain pairs and blocks which are imperf. between (see No. 365b).

Issued: No. 365, 4sh, 10/9/63; 10sh, £1, 2/26/64; 9p, 1sh6p, 2sh5p, 3/11/64; 6p, 8/19/64; 7sh6p, £2, 8/26/64; 5sh, 11/25/64; 2sh, 2sh6p, 3sh, 4/21/65; No. 366, 6/30/65.

See Nos. 400-401, 406-417, 1727-1728.

Star of Bethlehem — A146

1963, Oct. 25 Unwmk. ***Perf. 14½***

380 A146 5p blue .40 .25

Christmas.

Cable Around World and Under Sea — A147

1963, Dec. 3 Photo. ***Perf. 13½***

381 A147 2sh3p gray, ver, blk & blue 4.50 3.50

Opening of the Commonwealth Pacific (telephone) cable service (COMPAC).

See New Zealand No. 364.

Bleriot 60 Plane, 1914 — A148

1964, July 1 Engr. ***Perf. 14½x14***

382 A148 5p olive green .50 .25
383 A148 2sh3p red 3.25 3.25

50th anniv. of the first air mail flight in Australia; Maurice Guillaux, aviator.

Child Looking at Nativity Scene — A149

1964, Oct. 21 Photo. ***Perf. 13½***

384 A149 5p bl, blk, red & buff .40 .25
a. Red omitted *6,250. 2,750.*
b. Black omitted *2,750.*
c. Buff omitted *3,500.*

Christmas.

No. 384a used is valued on cover. The red ink can be removed from No. 384 by bleaching.

"Simpson and His Donkey" by Wallace Anderson — A150

1965, Apr. 14 Engr. ***Perf. 14x14½***

385 A150 5p olive bister .50 .25
386 A150 8p dark blue .90 .80
387 A150 2sh3p rose claret 2.80 3.00
Nos. 385-387 (3) 4.20 4.05

50th anniv. of the landing of the Australian and New Zealand Army Corps (ANZAC) at Gallipoli, Turkey, Apr. 25, 1915. Private John Simpson Kirkpatrick saved the lives of many wounded soldiers. The statue erected in his honor stands in front of Melbourne's Shrine of Remembrance.

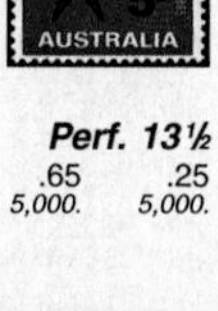

Radio Mast and Satellite Orbiting Earth — A151

1965, May 10 Photo. ***Perf. 13½***

388 A151 5p multicolored .65 .25
a. Gray omitted *5,000. 5,000.*

ITU, cent.

Winston Churchill — A152

1965, May 24

389 A152 5p lt bl, pale gray, dk gray & blk .40 .25
a. Pale gray omitted (white face) *5,500.*
b. Dark gray ("Australia") omitted *7,500.*

Sir Winston Spencer Churchill (1874-1965), statesman and WWII leader.

Two examples of No. 389b recorded, one damaged. Value is for sound example.

See New Zealand No. 371.

John Monash and Transmission Tower — A153

1965, June 23 Photo. ***Perf. 13½***

390 A153 5p red, yel, blk & lt brn .40 .25

Birth cent. of General Sir John Monash (1865-1931), soldier, Vice-Chancellor of University of Melbourne and chairman of the Victoria state electricity commission.

Lawrence Hargrave and Sketch for 1902 Seaplane — A154

1965, Aug. 4 Unwmk. ***Perf. 13½***

391 A154 5p multicolored .40 .25
a. Purple (5d) omitted *600.00 600.00*

50th anniv. of the death of Lawrence Hargrave (1850-1915), aviation pioneer.

ICY Emblem — A155

1965, Sept. 1 Photo. ***Perf. 13½***

392 A155 2sh3p lt blue & green 3.25 3.00

International Cooperation Year.

Nativity — A156

1965, Oct. 20 Unwmk. ***Perf. 13½***

393 A156 5p multicolored .40 .25
a. Gold omitted *5,500.*
b. Ultramarine omitted *1,000.*
c. Brown omitted (white faces) *5,000.*

Christmas.

Types of 1963-65 and

Elizabeth II A157

Humbug Fish A158

Designs: No. 400, Yellow-tailed thornbill, horiz. 6c, blue-faced honeyeater, horiz. 8c, Coral fish. 9c, Hermit crab. 10c Anemone fish. 13c, Red-necked avocet. 15c, Galah on tree stump. 20c, Golden whistler. 24c Azure kingfisher, horiz. 25c, Scarlet robin, horiz. 30c Straw-necked ibis. 40c Abel Tasman and ship. 50c, William Dampier and "Roebuck" sailing ship. 75c, Capt. James Cook. $1, Matthew Flinders and three-master "Investigator." $2, George Bass and whaleboat. $4, Admiral Philip Parker King.

Perf. 14½x14 (A157); 13½ (A158, A139)

Engr. (A157), Photo. (A158, A139)

1966-71

394 A157 1c red brown .45 .25
395 A157 2c olive green .75 .25
396 A157 3c Prus green .75 .25
397 A157 4c red .30 .25
a. Booklet pane of 5 + label 35.00
398 A157 5c on 4c red ('67) .40 .25
a. Booklet pane of 5 + label ('67) 7.00
399 A157 5c dk blue ('67) .75 .25
a. Booklet pane of 5 + label 12.50
400 A139 5c lt grn, blk, brn & yel .55 .25
a. Brown omitted *3,500.* —
401 A139 6c gray, blk, lem & bl .80 .35
b. Blue omitted *2,500.*
401A A157 6c orange ('70) .50 .25
402 A158 7c brn, ver, blk & gray 1.25 .25
402A A157 7c dp rose lilac ('71) .75 .40
403 A158 8c multicolored 1.25 .40
404 A158 9c multicolored 1.25 .35
405 A158 10c lt brn, blk, org & bl 1.25 .25
a. Orange omitted *4,250.*
b. Blue omitted *3,000. 2,000.*
406 A139 13c lt bl grn, blk, gray & red 2.25 .40
a. Red omitted *2,250.*
b. Gray omitted *2,100.*
407 A139 15c lt grn, blk, gray & rose 2.25 .90
a. Rose omitted *4,500.*
b. Gray omitted *2,750. 750.00*
408 A139 20c pink, blk, yel & gray 5.25 .30
a. Yellow omitted *2,900.*
b. Gray omitted *750.00*
409 A139 24c tan, blk, vio bl & org 1.10 *1.10*
410 A139 25c gray, grn, blk & red 4.00 .55
a. Red omitted *5,750.*
411 A139 30c lt grn, buff, blk & red 16.00 .85
a. Red omitted *3,000.*

Engr.

Perf. 14½x14, 14½x15

412 A144 40c violet blue 12.00 .25
413 A145 50c brown red 16.00 .25
414 A144 75c olive green 2.00 1.40
415 A144 $1 deep claret 3.25 .45
a. Perf 15x14 125.00 32.50
416 A145 $2 purple 8.00 2.25
417 A145 $4 sepia 8.00 5.00
Nos. 394-417 (26) 91.10 17.70

No. 398 issued in booklets only.

Booklet panes of 10 of No. 399, and of 5 No. 400, are torn from sheets. They were issued for the use of "Australian Defence Forces," as the covers read, in Viet Nam.

Issued: Nos. 398, 399, 9/29/67; No. 401A, 9/28/70; No. 402A, 10/1/71; No. 415a, 1973; others, 2/14/66.

Coil Stamps

1966-67 Photo. ***Perf. 15 Horiz.***

418 A157 3c emerald, blk & buff .60 .50
419 A157 4c org red, blk & buff .70 .50
420 A157 5c blue, black & buff .85 .25
Nos. 418-420 (3) 2.15 1.25

Issued: 5c, 9/29/67; others, 2/14/66.

Rescue — A159

1966, July 6 Photo. ***Perf. 13½***

421 A159 4c blue, ultra & black .30 .25

Royal Life Saving Society, 75th anniv.

Adoration of the Shepherds — A160

1966, Oct. 19 Photo. ***Perf. 13½***

422 A160 4c olive & black .30 .25
a. Olive omitted *7,250.*

Christmas.

Dutch Sailing Ship, 17th Century — A161

1966, Oct. 24 Photo. *Perf. 13½*
423 A161 4c bl, blk, dp org & gold .30 .25
a. Deep orange omitted *6,000.*
b. Gold omitted *2,000.*

350th anniv. of Dirk Hartog's discovery of the Australian west coast, and his landing on the island named after him.

Hands Reaching for Bible — A162

1967, Mar. 7 Photo. *Perf. 13½*
424 A162 4c multicolored .30 .25

British and Foreign Bible Soc., 150th anniv.

Combination Lock and Antique Keys — A163

1967, Apr. 5 Photo. *Perf. 13½*
425 A163 4c emerald, blk & lt blue .30 .25

150th anniv. of banking in Australia (Bank of New South Wales).

Lions Intl., 50th Anniv. — A164

1967, June 7 Photo. *Perf. 13½*
426 A164 4c ultra, black & gold .30 .25

YWCA Emblems and Flags — A165

1967, Aug. 21 Photo. *Perf. 13½*
427 A165 4c dk blue, lt bl & lilac .30 .25

World Council Meeting of the YWCA, Monash University, Victoria, Aug. 14-Sept. 1.

A166

Design: Seated women symbolizing obstetrics and gynecology, female symbol.

1967, Sept. 20 Photo. *Perf. 13½*
428 A166 4c lilac, dk blue & blk .30 .25

5th World Congress of Gynecology and Obstetrics, Sydney, Sept. 23-30.

Gothic Arches and Christmas Bell Flower A167

Cross, Stars of David and Yin Yang Forming Mandala A168

1967 Photo. *Perf. 13½*
429 A167 5c multicolored .30 .25
430 A168 25c multicolored 2.25 2.00

Christmas.
Issue dates: 5c, Oct. 18; 25c, Nov. 27.

Satellite Orbiting Earth A169

Satellite and Antenna, Moree, N.S.W. A170

Design: 20c, World weather map connecting Washington, Moscow and Melbourne, and computer and teleprinter tape spools.

1968, Mar. 20 Photo. *Perf. 13½*
431 A169 5c dull yel, red, bl & dk blue .90 .50
432 A169 20c blue, blk & red 2.50 2.40
a. Red omitted *3,000.*
433 A170 25c Prus blue, blk & lt green 4.00 4.00
Nos. 431-433 (3) 7.40 6.90

Use of satellites for weather observations and communications.

Kangaroo Paw, Western Australia — A171

State Flowers: 13c, Pink heath, Victoria. 15c, Tasmanian blue gum, Tasmania. 20c, Sturt's desert pea, South Australia. 25c, Cooktown orchid, Queensland. 30c, Waratah, New South Wales.

1968, July 10 Photo. *Perf. 13½*
Flowers in Natural Colors
434 A171 6c multicolored .55 .50
435 A171 13c multicolored .65 .55
436 A171 15c multicolored 2.25 .45
437 A171 20c multicolored 5.00 .75
438 A171 25c multicolored 4.75 .75
439 A171 30c multicolored 1.25 .25
a. Green omitted *3,750.*
Nos. 434-439 (6) 14.45 3.25

A 1971 reprinting of No. 439 shows more areas of white in the pink petals. This is scarcer than the first printing. Value, $4.75.

Sturt's Desert Rose, Northern Territory — A171a

Designs: 5c, Golden wattle, national flower. 7c, 10c, Sturt's desert pea.

Coil Stamps

1970-75 *Perf. 14½ Horiz.*
439A A171a 2c dk grn & multi .25 .25
i. Lettering and value bolder .25 .25
439B A171a 4c gray & multi .70 .45
439C A171a 5c gray & multi .25 .25
439D A171a 6c gray & multi 1.40 .55
h. Green omitted *2,250.*
439E A171a 7c blk, red & grn .40 .25
f. Green omitted 110.00
439G A171a 10c blk, red & grn .35 .25
Nos. 439A-439G (6) 3.35 2.00

Issued: 4c, 5c, 4/27; 6c, 10/28; 2c, 7c, 10/1/71; 10c, 1/15/75; No. 439Ai, 11/73.

Soil Testing Through Chemistry & by Computer A172

Hippocrates & Hands Holding Hypodermic A173

1968, Aug. 6 Photo. *Perf. 13½*
440 A172 5c multicolored .30 .25
441 A173 5c multicolored .30 .25

9th Intl. Congress of Soil Science, University of Adelaide, Aug. 6-16 (No. 440); General Assembly of World Medical Associations, Sydney, Aug. 6-9 (No. 441). Nos. 440-441 printed in sheets of 100 in two separate panes of 50 connected by a gutter. Each sheet contains 10 gutter pairs.

Runner and Aztec Calendar Stone — A174

Design: 25c, Aztec calendar stone and Mexican flag, horiz.

1968, Oct. 2
442 A174 5c multicolored .55 .25
443 A174 25c multicolored 2.00 1.75
a. Green omitted *3,500.*

19th Olympic Games, Mexico City, Oct. 12-27. Nos. 442-443 printed in sheets of 100 in two separate panes of 50 connected by a gutter. Each sheet contains 10 gutter pairs.

Symbolic House and Money — A175

1968, Oct. 16
444 A175 5c multicolored .35 .35

11th Triennial Congress of the Intl. Union of Building Societies and Savings Associations, Sydney, Oct. 20-27.

View of Bethlehem and Church Window — A176

1968, Oct. 23 Photo. *Perf. 13½*
445 A176 5c lt bl, red, grn & gold .30 .25
a. Red omitted *3,500. 2,000.*
b. Gold omitted *850.00 500.00*

Christmas.

Edgeworth David (1858-1934), Geologist — A177

Famous Australians: No. 447, Caroline Chisholm (1808-77), social worker, reformer. No. 448, Albert Namatjira (1902-59), aborigine, artist. No. 449, Andrew Barton (Banjo) Paterson 1864-1941), poet, writer.

1968, Nov. 6 Engr. *Perf. 15x14*
446 A177 5c green, *greenish* 1.20 .35
a. Booklet pane of 5 + label 6.50
447 A177 5c purple, *pink* 1.20 .35
a. Booklet pane of 5 + label 6.50
448 A177 5c dark brown, *buff* 1.20 .35
a. Booklet pane of 5 + label 6.50
449 A177 5c indigo, *lt blue* 1.20 .35
a. Booklet pane of 5 + label 6.50
Nos. 446-449 (4) 4.80 1.40

Sir Edmund Barton (1849-1920) — A178

Prime Ministers: No. 451, Alfred Deakin (1856-1919). No. 452, John C. Watson (1867-1941). No. 453, Sir George H. Reid (1845-1918).

1969, Oct. 22 Engr. *Perf. 15x14*
450 A178 5c indigo, *greenish* 1.20 .35
a. Booklet pane of 5 + label 6.50
451 A178 5c indigo, *greenish* 1.20 .35
a. Booklet pane of 5 + label 6.50
452 A178 5c indigo, *greenish* 1.20 .35
a. Booklet pane of 5 + label 6.50
453 A178 5c indigo, *greenish* 1.20 .35
a. Booklet pane of 5 + label 6.50
Nos. 450-453 (4) 4.80 1.40

Reginald C. and John R. Duigan, Aviators — A179

Famous Australians: No. 455, Lachlan Macquarie (1761-1824), Governor of New South Wales. No. 456, Adam Lindsay Gordon (1833-70), poet. No. 457, Edward John Eyre (1815-1901), explorer.

1970, Nov. 16 Engr. *Perf. 15x14*
454 A179 6c dark blue 1.20 .50
a. Booklet pane of 5 + label 6.50
455 A179 6c dk brn, *salmon* 1.20 .50
a. Booklet pane of 5 + label 6.50
456 A179 6c magenta, *brt pink* 1.20 .50
a. Booklet pane of 5 + label 6.50
457 A179 6c brown red, *salmon* 1.20 .50
a. Booklet pane of 5 + label 6.50
Nos. 454-457 (4) 4.80 2.00

Nos. 446-457 were issued in booklet panes only; all stamps have 1 or 2 straight edges.

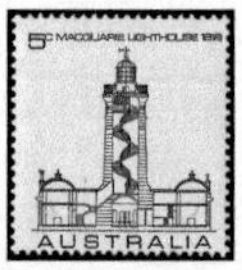

Macquarie Lighthouse — A180

1968, Nov. 27 Engr. *Perf. 14½x13½*
458 A180 5c indigo, *buff* .45 .50

Macquarie Lighthouse, Outer South Head, Sydney, 150th anniv.

Surveyor George W. Goyder and Assistants, 1869; Building in Darwin, 1969 — A181

1969, Feb. 5 Photo. *Perf. 13½*
459 A181 5c black brn & dull yel .30 .25

First permanent settlement of the Northern Territory of Australia, cent.

Melbourne Harbor Scene — A182

1969, Feb. 26 Photo. *Perf. 13½*
460 A182 5c dull blue & multi .30 .25

6th Biennial Conference of the Intl. Assoc. of Ports and Harbors, Melbourne, March 3-8.

Overlapping Circles — A183

1969, June 5 Photo. *Perf. 13½*
461 A183 5c gray, vio bl, bl & gold .30 .25
a. Gold omitted *3,000.*

ILO, 50th anniv.

Sugar Cane — A184

Primary industries: 15c, Eucalyptus (timber). 20c, Wheat. 25c, Ram, ewe, lamb (wool).

1969, Sept. 17 ***Perf. 13½x13***

462 A184 7c blue & multi 1.60 1.00
463 A184 15c emerald & multi 4.75 3.00
a. Black omitted *1,750.* —
464 A184 20c org brn & multi 2.40 1.20
465 A184 25c gray, black & yel 3.25 1.20
Nos. 462-465 (4) 12.00 6.40

Nativity A185 Tree of Life A186

Perf. 13½x13, 13x13½

1969, Oct. 15 **Photo.**

466 A185 5c multicolored .40 .25
a. Yellow omitted *1,800.*
b. Magenta omitted *1,800.*
467 A186 25c multicolored 3.00 2.75

Christmas.

Vickers Vimy Flown by Ross Smith, England to Australia — A187

Designs: No. 469, B.E. 2E plane, automobile, spectators. No. 470, Ford truck, surveyors Lieuts. Hudson Fysh & P.J. McGinness.

1969, Nov. 12 ***Perf. 13x13½***

468 A187 5c bl, blk, cop red & ol .75 .35
469 A187 5c bl, blk, cop red & ol .75 .35
470 A187 5c cop red, black & ol .75 .35
a. Strip of 3, #468-470 3.75 3.50
Nos. 468-470 (3) 2.25 1.05

1st England to Australia flight by Capt. Ross Smith & Lieut. Keith Smith, 50th anniv.

No. 470a has various combinations possible.

A188

Design: Diesel locomotive and new track linking Melbourne, Sydney and Brisbane with Perth.

1970, Feb. 11 **Photo.** ***Perf. 13x13½***

471 A188 5c multicolored .35 .25

Completion of the standard gauge railroad between Sydney and Perth.

EXPO '70 Australian Pavilion — A189

Design: 20c, Southern Cross and Japanese inscription: "From the country of the south with warm feeling."

1970, Mar. 16 **Photo.** ***Perf. 13x13½***

472 A189 5c bl, blk, red & brnz .30 .25
473 A189 20c red & black .75 .45

EXPO '70 Intl. Exhib., Osaka, Japan, Mar. 15-Sept. 13.

Queen Elizabeth II and Prince Philip — A190 Australian Flag — A191

1970, Mar. 31

474 A190 5c yel bister & black .50 .30
475 A191 30c vio blue & multi 2.25 1.50

Visit of Queen Elizabeth II, Prince Philip and Princess Anne to Australia.

Steer, Alfalfa and Native Spear Grass — A192

1970, Apr. 13 **Photo.** ***Perf. 13x13½***

476 A192 5c emerald & multi .30 .35

11th Intl. Grasslands Congress, Surfers Paradise, Queensland, Apr. 13-23.

Capt. James Cook and "Endeavour" — A193

Designs: No. 478, Sextant, "Endeavour." No. 479, "Endeavour," landing party, kangaroo. No. 480, Daniel Charles Solander, Sir Joseph Banks, Cook, map, botanical drawing. No. 481, Cook taking possession with Union Jack; "Endeavour," coral. 30c, Cook, "Endeavour," sextant, kangaroo, aborigines.

1970, Apr. 20 ***Perf. 13½x13***

Size: 24x35½mm

477 A193 5c org brn & multi .35 .25
478 A193 5c org brn & multi .35 .25
479 A193 5c org brn & multi .35 .25
480 A193 5c org brn & multi .35 .25
481 A193 5c org brn & multi .35 .25
a. Strip of 5, #477-481 2.40 2.40

Size: 62x29mm

482 A193 30c org brn & multi 2.40 2.25
a. Souv. sheet, #477-482, imperf 16.00 12.00
Nos. 477-482 (6) 4.15 3.50

Cook's discovery and exploration of the eastern coast of Australia, 200th anniv.

No. 481a has continuous design.

No. 482a with brown marginal overprint "Souvenir Sheet ANPEX 1970. . ." is of private origin. Value $27.50.

Snowy Mountains Hydroelectric Project — A194

Designs: 8c, Ord River hydroelectric project (dam, cotton plant and boll). 9c, Bauxite and aluminum production (mine, conveyor belt and aluminum window frame). 10c, Oil and natural gas (off-shore drilling rig and pipelines).

1970, Aug. 31 **Photo.** ***Perf. 13x13½***

483 A194 7c multicolored 1.20 .40
484 A194 8c multicolored .25 .25
485 A194 9c multicolored .50 .25
486 A194 10c multicolored .60 .30
Nos. 483-486 (4) 2.55 1.20

Australian economic development.

Flame Symbolizing Democracy and Freedom of Speech — A195

1970, Oct. 2 **Photo.** ***Perf. 13½x13***

487 A195 6c green & multi .30 .25

16th Commonwealth Parliamentary Assoc. Conference, Canberra, Oct. 2-9.

Herd of Illawarra Shorthorns and Laboratory — A196

1970, Oct. 7 ***Perf. 13x13½***

488 A196 6c multicolored .30 .25

18th Intl. Dairy Cong., Sydney, Oct. 12-16.

Madonna and Child, by William Beasley — A197

1970, Oct. 14 ***Perf. 13½x13***

489 A197 6c multicolored .30 .25

Christmas.

UN Emblem, Dove and Symbols — A198

1970, Oct. 19

490 A198 6c blue & multi .30 .25

25th anniversary of the United Nations.

Qantas Boeing 707, and Avro 504 — A199

30c, Sunbeam Dyak powered Avro 504 on ground and Qantas Boeing 707 in the air.

1970, Nov. 2 ***Perf. 13x13½***

491 A199 6c multicolored .40 .25
492 A199 30c multicolored 1.25 1.25

Qantas, Australian overseas airlines, 50th anniv.

Japanese Noh Actor, Australian Dancer and Chinese Opera Character A200

15c, Chinese pipe, trumpet, Australian aboriginal didgeridoo, Thai fiddle, Indian double oboe, Tibetan drums. 20c, Red Sea dhow, Chinese junk, Australian lifeguard's surfboat, Malaysian & South Indian river boats.

1971, Jan. 6 **Photo.** ***Perf. 13½x13***

493 A200 7c multicolored 1.20 *.55*
494 A200 15c multicolored 1.60 *1.25*
495 A200 20c multicolored 1.45 *.70*
Nos. 493-495 (3) 4.25 2.50

Link between Australia and Asia; 28th Intl. Congress of Orientalists, Canberra, Jan. 6-12.

Southern Cross — A201

1971, Apr. 21 **Photo.** ***Perf. 13x13½***

496 A201 6c multicolored .30 .25

Australian Natives Assoc., cent.

Symbolic Market Graphs — A202

1971, May 5 ***Perf. 13½x13***

497 A202 6c silver & multi .30 .25

Centenary of Sydney Stock Exchange.

Rotary Emblem — A203

1971, May 17 ***Perf. 13x13½***

498 A203 6c multicolored .30 .25

First Intl. Rotary Convention held in Australia, Sydney, May 16-20.

DH-9A, Australian Mirage Jet Fighters — A204

1971, June 9 ***Perf. 13½x13***

499 A204 6c multicolored .55 .25

Royal Australian Air Force, 50th anniv.

RSPCA Centenary — A205

Designs: 12c, Man and lamb (animal science). 18c, Kangaroo (fauna conservation). 24c, Seeing eye dog (animals' aid to man).

1971, July 5 **Photo.** ***Perf. 13½x13***

500 A205 6c blk, brown & org .25 .25
501 A205 12c blk, dk grn & yel .45 .25
502 A205 18c brown & multi .65 .35
a. Litho., perf. 14¾x14, dated "2013" (#1003b) .45 .45
503 A205 24c blue & multi 1.20 .70
Nos. 500-503 (4) 2.55 1.55

Royal Society for Prevention of Cruelty to Animals in Australia, cent.

Issued: No. 502a, 5/10/2013.

Longnecked Tortoise, Painted on Bark — A206

Aboriginal Art: 25c, Mourners' body paintings, Warramunga tribe. 30c, Cave painting, Western Arnhem Land, vert. 35c, Graveposts, Bathurst and Melville Islands, vert.

Perf. 13x13½, 13½x13

1971, Sept. 29

504 A206 20c multicolored .45 .30
505 A206 25c multicolored .45 .45
506 A206 30c multicolored 1.50 .45
507 A206 35c multicolored .55 .45
Nos. 504-507 (4) 2.95 1.65

Three Kings and Star — A207

1971, Oct. 13 **Photo.** ***Perf. 13½x13***

508 Block of 7 45.00 35.00
a. A207 7c brt grn, dk bl (Kings) & lil 12.00 1.50
b. A207 7c lil, red brn, grn & dk bl 3.25 .70
c. A207 7c red brown & lilac 4.00 .80
d. A207 7c lilac, red brn & brt grn 3.25 .70
e. A207 7c red brown & dark blue 3.25 .70
f. A207 7c lilac, green & dk blue 15.00 3.00
g. A207 7c brt grn, dk bl & lilac (Kings) 3.25 .70

Christmas. Nos. 508a-508g printed se-tenant in sheets of 50. Each sheet contains 2 green crosses formed by 4 No. 508g and three No. 508a.

Andrew Fisher (1862-1928) — A208

Prime Ministers: No. 515, Joseph Cook (1860-1947). No. 516, William Morris Hughes (1864-1952). No. 517, Stanley Melbourne Bruce (1883-1967).

1972, Mar. 8 Engr. *Perf. 15x14*

514	A208 7c dark blue	.70	.40
a.	Booklet pane of 5 + label	3.50	
515	A208 7c dark red	.70	.40
a.	Booklet pane of 5 + label	3.50	
516	A208 7c dark blue	.70	.40
a.	Booklet pane of 5 + label	3.50	
517	A208 7c dark red	.70	.40
a.	Booklet pane of 5 + label	3.50	
	Nos. 514-517 (4)	2.80	1.60

Nos. 514-517 were issued in booklets only; all stamps have one or two straight edges.

Cameo Brooch — A209

1972, Apr. 18 Photo. *Perf. 13½*

518	A209 7c multicolored	.35	.25

Country Women's Assoc., 50th anniv.

Apple and Banana — A210

1972, June 14

519	A210 20c shown	2.40	1.50
520	A210 25c Rice	2.40	1.75
521	A210 30c Fish	1.75	1.75
522	A210 35c Cattle	4.00	3.00
	Nos. 519-522 (4)	10.55	8.00

Worker in Sheltered Workshop — A211

18c, Amputee assembling electrical circuit. 24c, Boy wearing Toronto splint, playing ball.

1972, Aug. 2 *Perf. 13½x13*

523	A211 12c grn & brn	.30	.25
524	A211 18c org & ol, horiz.	1.25	.60
525	A211 24c brn & ultra	.50	.25
	Nos. 523-525 (3)	2.05	1.10

Rehabilitation of the handicapped.

Overland Telegraph Line — A212

1972, Aug. 22 Photo. *Perf. 13x13½*

526	A212 7c dk red, blk & lemon	.30	.30

Centenary of overland telegraph line.

Athlete, Olympic Rings — A213

1972, Aug. 28 *Perf. 13½x13*

527	A213 7c shown	.45	.45
528	A213 7c Swimming	.45	.45
529	A213 7c Rowing	.45	.45
530	A213 35c Equestrian	3.25	2.75
	Nos. 527-530 (4)	4.60	4.10

20th Olympic Games, Munich, 8/26-9/11.

Abacus, Numerals, Computer Circuits — A214

1972, Oct. 16 Photo. *Perf. 13x13½*

531	A214 7c multicolored	.30	.30

10th Intl. Congress of Accountants.

19th Cent. Combine Harvester — A215

5c, Pioneer family, vert. 10c, Water pump, vert. 40c, Pioneer house. 50c, Cobb & Co. coach. 60c, Early Morse key, vert. 80c, Paddle-wheel steamer.

Perf. 13½x13, 13x13½

1972, Nov. 15 Photo.

532	A215 5c multicolored	.25	.25
533	A215 10c multicolored	.35	.25
534	A215 15c shown	.30	.25
535	A215 40c multicolored	.60	.25
536	A215 50c multicolored	1.00	.25
537	A215 60c multicolored	.90	.55
538	A215 80c multicolored	1.25	.65
	Nos. 532-538 (7)	4.65	2.45

Australian pioneer life.

Jesus and Children A216

Dove, Cross and "Darkness into Light" A217

Perf. 14½x14, 13½x13

1972, Nov. 29

539	A216 7c tan & multi	.35	.25
540	A217 35c blue & multi	8.00	6.50

Christmas.

Metric Conversion, Mass — A218

Metric conversion: No. 542, Temperature, horiz. No. 543, Length. No. 544, Volume.

1973, Mar. 7 Photo. *Perf. 14x14½*

541	A218 7c pale vio & multi	.60	.40
542	A218 7c yellow & multi	.60	.40
543	A218 7c yel green & multi	.60	.40
544	A218 7c brt rose & multi	.60	.40
	Nos. 541-544 (4)	2.40	1.60

Conversion to metric system.

Stylized Caduceus and Laurel — A219

1973, Apr. 4 Photo. *Perf. 14½x14*

545	A219 7c dk bl, emer & lil rose	.40	.30

WHO, 25th anniv.

Dame Mary Gilmore, Writer — A220

Famous Australians: No. 547, William Charles Wentworth, explorer. No. 548, Sir Isaac Isaacs, lawyer, 1st Australian-born Governor-General. No. 549, Marcus Clarke, writer.

Engr. & Litho.

1973, May 16 *Perf. 15x14*

546	A220 7c bister & black	.80	.30
547	A220 7c bister & black	.80	.30
548	A220 7c black & violet	.80	.30
549	A220 7c black & violet	.80	.30
a.	Block of 4, #546-549	4.00	4.00

Shipping Industry — A221

Designs: 25c, Iron ore and steel. 30c, Truck convoy (beef road). 35c, Aerial mapping.

1973, June 6 Photo. *Perf. 13½x13*

550	A221 20c ultra & multi	1.75	1.40
551	A221 25c red & multi	1.50	1.40
552	A221 30c ol brn & multi	3.00	1.75
553	A221 35c olive & multi	2.00	1.75
	Nos. 550-553 (4)	8.25	6.30

Australian economic development.

Banded Coral Shrimp — A222

Chrysoprase A223

Helichrysum Thomsonii A223a

Wombat A224

Radio Astronomy — A225

Red Gums of the Far North, by Hans Heysen A226

Coming South (Immigrants), by Tom Roberts — A226a

2c, Fiddler crab. 3c, Coral crab. 4c, Mauve stinger. 7c, Agate. 8c, Opal. 9c, Rhodonite. 10c, Star sapphire. 11c, Atomic absorption spectrophotometry. 25c, Spiny anteater. 30c, Brushtail possum. 33c, Immunology. 45c, Callistemon teretifolius, horiz. 48c, Oceanography. 75c, Feather-tailed glider.

Paintings: $1, Sergeant of Light Horse, by George Lambert. No. 575, On the Wallaby Track. $4, Shearing the Rams, by Tom Roberts. No. 577, McMahon's Point, by Arthur Streeton. No. 578, Mentone.

Perf. 14x15, 15x14 (A222, A223, A223a); Perf. 14x14½ (A224); Perf. 13x13½ (A225, A226, $1)

1973-84 Photo.

554	A222	1c shown	.25	.25
555	A222	2c multi	.25	.25
556	A222	3c multi	.25	.25
557	A222	4c multi	.25	.25
558	A223	6c shown	.25	.25
559	A223	7c multi	.30	.25
560	A223	8c multi	.30	.25
561	A223	9c multi	.30	.25
562	A223	10c multi ('74)	.35	.25
563	A225	11c multi ('75)	.65	.30
564	A223a	18c shown ('75)	.60	.25
565	A224	20c shown ('74)	.45	.25
566	A225	24c shown ('75)	1.00	.45
567	A224	25c multi ('74)	1.25	.60
568	A224	30c multi ('74)	.65	.25
569	A225	33c multi ('75)	1.00	.80
570	A223a	45c multi ('75)	.80	.35
571	A225	48c multi ('75)	1.25	1.00
572	A224	75c multi ('74)	1.25	.60
573	A226a	$1 multi ('74)	1.60	.40
574	A226	$2 shown ('74)	3.25	.75
575	A226	$2 multi ('81)	3.25	.75
576	A226	$4 multi ('74)	6.00	2.75

Litho.

Perf. 14½

577	A226a	$5 multi ('79)	8.00	2.75
578	A226	$5 multi ('84)	7.50	3.50
579	A226a	$10 shown ('77)	16.00	4.00
		Nos. 554-579 (26)	57.00	22.00

Issued: 1c-9c, 7/11; 20c, 25c, 30c, 75c, 2/13; $1, No. 574, $4, 4/24; 10c, 10/16; 11c, 24c, 33c, 48c, 5/14; 18c, 45c, 8/27; $10, 10/19; No. 577, 3/14; No. 575, 6/17; No. 578, 4/4.

No. 560 Surcharged in Red

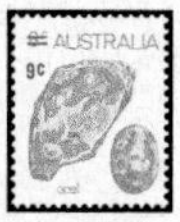

Perf. 15x14

580	A223 9c on 8c multi ('74)	.30	.35

Hand Protecting Playing Children — A227

1973, Sept. 5 Photo. *Perf. 13x13½*

581	A227 7c bis brn, grn & plum	.30	.25

50th anniv. of Legacy, an ex-servicemen's organization concerned with the welfare of widows and children of servicemen.

Baptism of Christ A228

The Good Shepherd A229

1973, Oct. 3 *Perf. 14x14½*

582	A228 7c gold & multi	.30	.25
a.	Perf. 14x15	3.00	.75

Perf. 13½

583	A229 30c gold & multi	2.25	2.25

Christmas.

Buchanan's Hotel, Townsville A230

St. James' Church, Sydney A231

Designs: 7c, Opera House, Sydney. 40c, Como House, Melbourne.

1973, Oct. 17 Photo. *Perf. 14½x14*

584	A230 7c lt blue & ultra	.35	.25
a.	Perf. 15x14	4.50	.90
585	A230 10c bister & black	.50	.35

Perf. 13x13½, 13½x13

586	A230 40c dl pink, gray & blk	.65	.75
587	A231 50c gray & multi	1.60	1.25
	Nos. 584-587 (4)	3.10	2.60

Australian architecture; opening of the Sydney Opera House, Oct. 14, 1973 (No. 584).

Radio and Gramophone Speaker — A232

1973, Nov. 21 Photo. *Perf. 13½x13*

588	A232 7c dull blue, blk & brn	.35	.25

Broadcasting in Australia, 50th anniv.

Supreme Court Judge on Bench — A233

1974, May 15 Photo. ***Perf. 14x14½***
589 A233 7c multicolored .35 .25

150th anniv. of the proclamation of the Charter of Justice in New South Wales and Van Diemen's Land (Australia's Third Charter).

Australian Football — A234

1974, July 24 Photo. ***Perf. 14x14½***
590 A234 7c shown .35 .25
591 A234 7c Cricket .35 .25
a. Booklet pane of 1, litho., perf. 14¾x14, dated "2007" .25 —
592 A234 7c Golf .35 .25
593 A234 7c Surfing .35 .25
594 A234 7c Tennis .35 .25
595 A234 7c Bowls, horiz. .35 .25
596 A234 7c Rugby, horiz. .35 .25
Nos. 590-596 (7) 2.45 1.75

No. 591a issued 11/14/2007.

Carrier Pigeon — A235

Designs: 30c, Carrier pigeons, vert.

1974, Oct. 9 Photo. ***Perf. 14½x14***
597 A235 7c multicolored .60 .25
a. Perf. 15x14 .60 .35

Perf. 13½x13

598 A235 30c multicolored 1.60 1.20

UPU, cent. A booklet containing a strip of 5 each of Nos. 597-598 was produced and sold for $4 Australian by the National Stamp Week Promotion Council with government approval.

William Charles Wentworth — A236

Typo. & Litho.

1974, Oct. 9 ***Perf. 14x15***
599 A236 7c bister & black .40 .25
a. Perf. 14x14½ 1.60 .40

Sesquicentennial of 1st Australian independent newspaper. W. C. Wentworth and Dr. Robert Wardell were the editors and the "A" is type from masthead of "The Australian."

Adoration of the Kings, by Dürer — A237

Christmas: 35c, Flight into Egypt, by Albrecht Dürer.

1974, Nov. 13 Engr. ***Perf. 14x14½***
600 A237 10c buff & black .40 .25
601 A237 35c buff & black .90 .90

Pre-school Education — A238

Correspondence Schools — A239

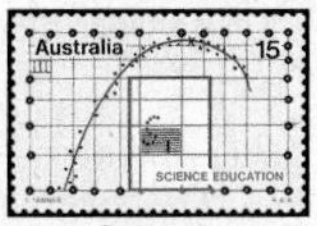

Science Education — A240

Advanced Education — A241

Perf. 13x13½, 13½x13

1974, Nov. 20 Photo.
602 A238 5c multicolored .60 .25
603 A239 11c multicolored .60 .25
604 A240 15c multicolored .60 .40
605 A241 60c multicolored 1.60 1.20
Nos. 602-605 (4) 3.40 2.10

"Avoid Pollution" A242

"Road Safety" A243

Design: No. 607, "Avoid bush fires."

1975, Jan. 29 Photo. ***Perf. 14½x14***
606 A242 10c multicolored .55 .45
a. Perf. 15x14 9.50 5.00
607 A242 10c multicolored .55 .45
a. Perf. 15x14 1.50 1.10

Perf. 14x14½

608 A243 10c multicolored .55 .45
Nos. 606-608 (3) 1.65 1.35

Environmental dangers.

Symbols of Womanhood, Sun, Moon — A244

1975, Mar. 12 Photo. ***Perf. 14x14½***
609 A244 10c dk vio blue & grn .35 .25

International Women's Year.

Joseph B. Chifley (1885-1951) — A245

No. 611, John Curtin, 1885-1945. No. 612, Arthur W. Fadden, 1895-1973. No. 613, Joseph A. Lyons, 1879-1939. No. 614, Earle Page, 1880-1963. No. 615, John H. Scullin, 1876-1953.

1975, Mar. 26
610 A245 10c shown .35 .25
611 A245 10c multicolored .35 .25
612 A245 10c multicolored .35 .25
613 A245 10c multicolored .35 .25
614 A245 10c multicolored .35 .25
615 A245 10c multicolored .35 .25
Nos. 610-615 (6) 2.10 1.50

Australian Prime Ministers.

Australian Postal Commission A246

Design: No. 617, Australian Telecommunications Commission.

1975, July 1 Photo. ***Perf. 14½x14***
616 A246 10c red, black & gray .65 .45
a. Perf. 15x14 .85 .45
617 A246 10c yel, black & gray .65 .45
a. Pair, #616-617 1.60 1.25
b. Perf. 15x14 .85 .45
c. Pair, #616a, 617b 3.50 3.50

Formation of Australian Postal and Telecommunications Commissions. Printed checkerwise.

Edith Cowan, Judge and Legislator A247

Truganini, Last Tasmanian Aborigine A248

Portraits: No. 619, Louisa Lawson (1848-1920), journalist. No. 620, Ethel Florence (Henry Handel) Richardson (1870-1946), novelist. No. 621, Catherine Spence (1825-1910), teacher, journalist, voting reformer. No. 622, Emma Constance Stone (1856-1902), first Australian woman physician.

1975, Aug. 6 Photo. ***Perf. 14x14½***
618 A247 10c olive grn & multi .60 .30
a. Perf. 14x15 .60 .30
619 A247 10c yel bister & multi .60 .30
a. Perf. 14x15 .60 .30
620 A248 10c olive & multi .60 .30
a. Perf. 14x15 .60 .30
621 A248 10c gray & multi .60 .30
a. Perf. 14x15 .60 .30
622 A247 10c violet & multi .60 .30
a. Perf. 14x15 .60 .30
623 A248 10c brown & multi .60 .30
a. Perf. 14x15 .60 .30
Nos. 618-623 (6) 3.60 1.80

Famous Australian women.

Spirit House (PNG) and Sydney Opera House A249

Bird in Flight and Southern Cross A250

1975, Sept. 16 Photo. ***Perf. 13½***
624 A249 18c multicolored .45 .25
625 A250 25c multicolored .80 .65

Papua New Guinea independence, Sept. 16, 1975.

Adoration of the Kings A251

"The Light Shineth in the Darkness" A252

1975, Oct. 29 Photo. ***Perf. 14½x14***
626 A251 15c multicolored .40 .25
627 A252 45c silver & multi 1.60 1.50

Christmas.

Australian Coat of Arms — A253

Type I

Type II

Type I — Kangaroo: eye is dot, right paw has 1 toe, left foot has 1 toe. Emu: feet have 1 toe.

Type II — Kangaroo: eye is line, right paw has 3 toes, left foot has 2 toes. Emu: feet have 2 toes.

Other differences exist.

1976, Jan. 5 Photo. ***Perf. 14½x14***
628 A253 18c multicolored, type I .40 .25
a. Type II .95 .40

"Williams' Coffin" Telephone, 1878 — A254

1976, Mar. 10 Photo. ***Perf. 13½***
629 A254 18c buff & multi .40 .30

Centenary of first telephone call by Alexander Graham Bell, Mar. 10, 1876.

John Oxley — A255

Australian explorers: No. 631, Hamilton Hume and William Hovell. No. 632, John Forrest. No. 633, Ernest Giles. No. 634, Peter Warburton. No. 635, William Gosse.

1976, June 9 Photo. ***Perf. 13½***
630 A255 18c shown .35 .25
631 A255 18c multicolored .35 .25
632 A255 18c multicolored .35 .25
633 A255 18c multicolored .35 .25
634 A255 18c multicolored .35 .25
635 A255 18c multicolored .35 .25
Nos. 630-635 (6) 2.10 1.50

Survey Rule, Graph, Punched Tape — A256

1976, June 15 ***Perf. 15x14***
636 A256 18c multicolored .40 .25

Commonwealth Scientific and Industrial Research Organization, 50th anniv.

Soccer Goalkeeper A257

Olympic Rings and: No. 638, Woman gymnast, vert. 25c, Woman diver, vert. 40c, Bicycling.

Perf. 13x13½, 13½x13

1976, July 14 Photo.
637 A257 18c multicolored .30 .25
638 A257 18c multicolored .30 .25
639 A257 25c multicolored .40 .40
640 A257 40c multicolored .60 .50
Nos. 637-640 (4) 1.60 1.40

21st Olympic Games, Montreal, Canada, July 17-Aug. 1.

Richmond Bridge, Tasmania A258

Mt. Buffalo, Victoria A259

Designs: 25c, Broken Bay, New South Wales. 35c, Wittenoom Gorge, Western Australia. 70c, Barrier Reef, Queensland. 85c, Ayers Rock, Northern Territory.

Perf. 14½x14, 14x14½

1976, Aug. 25 Photo.
641 A258 5c multicolored .30 .25
642 A258 25c multicolored .45 .25
643 A258 35c multicolored .50 .30
644 A259 50c multicolored .70 .30
645 A258 70c multicolored 1.00 .40
646 A258 85c multicolored 1.10 .70
Nos. 641-646 (6) 4.05 2.20

Blamire Young and Australia No. 59 — A260

1976, Sept. 27 Photo. *Perf. 13½*

647 A260 18c apple grn & multi .40 .25

Miniature Sheet

648 Sheet of 4 1.60 1.60
- *a.* A260 18c yellow & dark brown .40 .40
- *b.* A260 18c rose, dk brown & yel .40 .40
- *c.* A260 18c bl, dk brn, rose & yel .40 .40

Natl. Stamp Week, Sept. 27-Oct. 3. Blamire Young (1862-1935), designer of Australia's 1st issue. No. 648 shows different stages of 4-color printing. The 4th stamp in sheet is identical with No. 647.

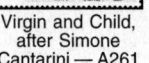

Virgin and Child, after Simone Cantarini — A261

Holly, Toy Koala, Christmas Tree and Decoration, Partridge — A262

1976, Nov. 1 Photo. *Perf. 14½x14*

649 A261 15c brt car & lt blue .40 .25

Perf. 13½

650 A262 45c multicolored .80 .80

Christmas.

John Gould (1804-1881) Ornithologist — A263

Famous Australians: No. 652, Thomas Laby (1880-1946), nuclear scientist. No. 653, Sir Baldwin Spencer (1860-1929), anthropologist (aborigines). No. 654, Griffith Taylor (1880-1963), geographer and antarctic explorer.

1976, Nov. 10 *Perf. 15x14*

651 A263 18c shown .35 .25
652 A263 18c Laby .35 .25
653 A263 18c Spencer .35 .25
654 A263 18c Taylor .35 .25
Nos. 651-654 (4) 1.40 1.00

Violinists — A264

1977, Jan. 19 Photo. *Perf. 14x14½*

655 A264 20c shown .30 .25
656 A264 30c Dramatic scene .35 .25
657 A264 40c Dancer .45 .30
658 A264 60c Opera singer .90 .40
Nos. 655-658 (4) 2.00 1.20

Performing arts in Australia.

Elizabeth II — A265

Design: 45c, Elizabeth II and Prince Philip.

1977, Feb. 2 *Perf. 14x14½*

659 A265 18c multicolored .40 .30
660 A265 45c multicolored .75 .75

Reign of Queen Elizabeth II, 25th anniv.

Perf 14½x14 examples of Nos. 659-660 are from a booklet pane containing 2 of each stamp, found in the booklet footnoted under No. 2507.

Wicket Keeper, Slip Fieldsman — A266

Cricket match, 19th century: No. 662, Umpire and batsman. No. 663, Two fieldsmen. No. 664, Batsman and umpire. No. 665, Bowler and fieldsman. 45c, Batsman facing bowler.

1977, Mar. 9 Photo. *Perf. 13½*

661 A266 18c gray & multi .45 .45
- *a.* Litho., perf. 14¾x14, dated "2007" .55 .55

662 A266 18c gray & multi .45 .45
- *a.* Litho., perf. 14¾x14, dated "2007" .55 .55

663 A266 18c gray & multi .45 .45
- *a.* Litho., perf. 14¾x14, dated "2007" .55 .55

664 A266 18c gray & multi .45 .45
- *a.* Litho., perf. 14¾x14, dated "2007" .55 .55

665 A266 18c gray & multi .45 .45
- *a.* Strip of 5, #661-665 3.00 3.00
- *b.* Litho., perf. 14¾x14, dated "2007" .55 .55

666 A266 45c gray & multi 1.00 1.00
- *a.* Litho., imperf., dated "2007" 1.25 1.25
- *b.* Booklet pane of 6, #661a, 662a, 663a, 664a, 665b, 666a 4.00 —

Nos. 661-666 (6) 3.25 3.25

Nos. 661a, 662a, 663a, 664a, 665b, 666a, 666b issued 11/14/2007.

Parliament House, Canberra — A267

1977, Apr. 13 *Perf. 14½x14*

667 A267 18c multicolored .40 .25

Parliament House, Canberra, 50th anniv.

Trade Union Workers — A268

1977, May 9 Photo. *Perf. 13*

668 A268 18c multicolored .40 .25

Australian Council of Trade Unions (ACTU), 50th anniv.

Surfing Santa A269

Virgin and Child A270

1977, Oct. 31 Photo. *Perf. 14x14½*

669 A269 15c multicolored .40 .25

Perf. 13½x13

670 A270 45c multicolored .75 .75

Christmas.

Australian Flag — A271

1978, Jan. 26 Photo. *Perf. 13x13½*

671 A271 18c multicolored .40 .30

Australia Day, 190th anniversary of first permanent settlement in New South Wales.

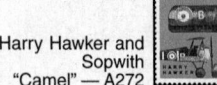

Harry Hawker and Sopwith "Camel" — A272

Australian Aviators and their Planes: No. 673, Bert Hinkler and Avro Avian. No. 674, Charles Kingsford-Smith and Fokker "Southern Cross." No. 675, Charles Ulm and "Southern Cross."

1978, Apr. 19 Litho. *Perf. 15½*

672 A272 18c ultra & multi .40 .30
673 A272 18c blue & multi .40 .30
674 A272 18c orange & multi .40 .30
675 A272 18c yellow & multi .40 .30
- *a.* Souv. sheet, 2 each #674-675, imperf. 2.25 2.00

Nos. 672-675 (4) 1.60 1.20

No. 675a for 50th anniv. of first Trans-Pacific flight from Oakland, Cal., to Brisbane.

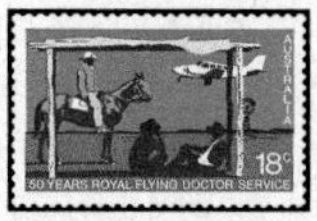

Beechcraft Baron Landing — A273

1978, May 15 Photo. *Perf. 13½*

676 A273 18c multicolored .40 .30

Royal Flying Doctor Service, 50th anniv.

Illawarra Flame Tree — A274

Australian trees: 25c, Ghost gum. 40c, Grass tree. 45c, Cootamundra wattle.

1978, June 1

677 A274 18c multicolored .25 .25
678 A274 25c multicolored .50 .50
679 A274 40c multicolored .65 .65
680 A274 45c multicolored .70 .70
Nos. 677-680 (4) 2.10 2.10

Sturt's Desert Rose, Map of Australia — A275

1978, June 19 Litho. *Perf. 15½*

681 A275 18c multicolored .40 .25

Establishment of Government of the Northern Territory.

Hooded Dotterel — A276

Australian birds: 20c, Little grebe. 25c, Spur-wing Plover. 30c, Pied oystercatcher. 55c, Lotus bird.

1978 Photo. *Perf. 13½*

682 A276 5c multicolored .25 .25
683 A276 20c multicolored .40 .25
684 A276 25c multicolored .45 .25
685 A276 30c multicolored .70 .35
686 A276 55c multicolored .90 .60
Nos. 682-686 (5) 2.70 1.70

Issued: Nos. 683, 686, July 3; others, July 17. See Nos. 713-718, 732-739, 768.

Australia No. 95 on Album Page — A277

1978, Sept. 25 Litho. *Perf. 15½*

687 A277 20c multicolored .40 .25
- *a.* Miniature sheet of 4 1.60 1.60

National Stamp Week; 50th anniv. of Melbourne Intl. Phil. Exhib., Oct. 1928.

Virgin and Child, by Simon Marmion — A278

Paintings from National Gallery, Victoria: 15c, Virgin and Child, after Van Eyck. 55c, Holy Family, by Perino del Vaga.

1978 *Perf. 15*

688 A278 15c multicolored .40 .25
689 A278 25c multicolored .55 .55
690 A278 55c multicolored 1.00 .80
Nos. 688-690 (3) 1.95 1.60

Christmas. Issued: 25c, 10/3; others, 11/1.

Tulloch — A279

Race horses: 35c, Bernborough, vert. 50c, Phar Lap, vert. 55c, Peter Pan.

Perf. 15x14, 14x15

1978, Oct. 18 Photo.

691 A279 20c multicolored .40 .30
692 A279 35c multicolored .60 .40
693 A279 50c multicolored .80 .80
694 A279 55c multicolored 1.00 .90
Nos. 691-694 (4) 2.80 2.40

Australian horse racing.

Flag Raising at Sydney Cove — A280

1979, Jan. 26 Litho. *Perf. 15½*

695 A280 20c multicolored .40 .30

Australia Day, Jan. 26.

Passenger Steamer Canberra — A281

Ferries and Murray River Steamers: 35c, M.V. Lady Denman. 50c, P.S. Murray River Queen. 55c, Hydrofoil Curl Curl.

Perf. 13½, 15x14 (20c)

1979, Feb. 14 Photo.

696 A281 20c multicolored .40 .30
697 A281 35c multicolored .60 .40
698 A281 50c multicolored .80 .80
699 A281 55c multicolored .90 .90
Nos. 696-699 (4) 2.70 2.40

Port Campbell — A282

Designs: Australian National Parks.

1979, Apr. 9 Litho. *Perf. 15½*

700 A282 20c shown .35 .35
701 A282 20c Uluru .35 .35
702 A282 20c Royal .35 .35
703 A282 20c Flinders Ranges .35 .35
704 A282 20c Nambung .35 .35
- *a.* Strip of 5, #700-704 2.00 2.00

705 A282 20c Girraween, vert. .35 .35
706 A282 20c Mount Field, vert. .35 .35
- *a.* Pair, #705-706 .75 .75

Nos. 700-706 (7) 2.45 2.45

Double Fairlie — A283

Australian steam locomotives: 35c, Puffing Billy. 50c, Pichi Richi. 55c, Zig Zag.

Perf. 13½, 15x14 (20c)

1979, May 16 **Photo.**

707	A283 20c multicolored	.40	.30
708	A283 35c multicolored	.75	.40
709	A283 50c multicolored	.90	.80
710	A283 55c multicolored	.95	.80
	Nos. 707-710 (4)	3.00	2.30

"Black Swan" — A284

1979, June 6 **Photo.** ***Perf. 13½***

711	A284 20c multicolored	.40	.25

150th anniversary of Western Australia.

Children Playing, IYC Emblem — A285

1979, Aug. 13 **Litho.** ***Perf. 13½x13***

712	A285 20c multicolored	.40	.25

International Year of the Child.

Bird Type of 1978

Australian birds: 1c, Zebra finch. 2c, Crimson finch. 15c, Forest kingfisher, vert. 20c, Eastern yellow robin. 40c, Lovely wren, vert. 50c, Flame robin, vert.

1979, Sept. 17 **Photo.** ***Perf. 13½***

713	A276 1c multicolored	.25	.25
714	A276 2c multicolored	.25	.25
715	A276 15c multicolored	.35	.25
716	A276 20c multicolored	.45	.25
717	A276 40c multicolored	.75	.35
718	A276 50c multicolored	1.00	.40
	Nos. 713-718 (6)	3.05	1.75

Christmas Letters, Flag-wrapped Parcels — A286

Christmas: 15c, Nativity, icon. 55c, Madonna and Child, by Buglioni.

1979 **Litho.** ***Perf. 13***

719	A286 15c multicolored	.35	.25
720	A286 25c multicolored	.45	.30
721	A286 55c multicolored	1.00	.90
	Nos. 719-721 (3)	1.80	1.45

Issue dates: 25c, Sept. 24. Others, Nov. 1.

Trout Fishing — A287

Sport fishing: 35c, Angler. 50c, Black marlin fishing. 55c, Surf fishing.

1979, Oct. 24 **Photo.** ***Perf. 14x14½***

722	A287 20c multicolored	.35	.30
723	A287 35c multicolored	.50	.35
724	A287 50c multicolored	.80	.65
725	A287 55c multicolored	1.20	.80
	Nos. 722-725 (4)	2.85	2.10

Matthew Flinders, Map of Australia — A288

1980, Jan. 23 **Litho.** ***Perf. 13½***

726	A288 20c multicolored	.40	.25

Australia Day, Jan. 28.

Dingo — A289

1980, Feb. 20 **Litho.** ***Perf. 13½x13***

727	A289 20c shown	.35	.25
728	A289 25c Border collie	.45	.45
729	A289 35c Australian terrier	.55	.50
730	A289 50c Australian cattle dog	.75	.70
731	A289 55c Australian kelpie	.85	.80
	Nos. 727-731 (5)	2.95	2.70

Bird Type of 1978

10c, Golden-shoulder parrot, vert. 22c, White-tailed kingfisher, vert. 28c, Rainbow bird, vert. 35c, Regent bower bird, vert. 45c, Masked woodswallow. 60c, King parrot, vert. 80c, Rainbow pitta. $1, Western magpie, vert.

Perf. 13x12½ (10c, 28c, 35c, 60c, $1), 14x15 (22c), 12½x13 (45c, 80c)

1980 **Litho., Photo. (22c)**

732	A276 10c multicolored	.30	.25
a.	Perf. 14½x14	1.75	.60
733	A276 22c multicolored	.40	.30
734	A276 28c multicolored	.60	.45
735	A276 35c multicolored	.70	.45
736	A276 45c multicolored	.95	.60
a.	Perf. 14x14½	3.50	2.00
737	A276 60c multicolored	1.25	.60
738	A276 80c multicolored	1.60	1.00
739	A276 $1 multicolored	2.00	.45
	Nos. 732-739 (8)	7.80	4.10

Issued: Nos. 733, 734, 737, 3/31; others, 7/1.

Queen Elizabeth II, 54th Birthday — A290

1980, Apr. 21 **Litho.** ***Perf. 13x13½***

740	A290 22c multicolored	.35	.25

Wanderer — A291

1980, May 7 **Litho.** ***Perf. 13x13½***

741	Strip of 5	2.00	2.00
a.	A291 22c shown	.35	.35
b.	A291 22c Stealing sheep	.35	.35
c.	A291 22c Squatter on horseback	.35	.35
d.	A291 22c Three troopers	.35	.35
e.	A291 22c Wanderer's ghost	.35	.35

"Waltzing Matilda", poem by Andrew Barton Patterson (1864-1941). No. 741 in continuous design.

High Court Building, Canberra — A292

1980, May 19

742	A292 22c multicolored	.40	.25

Opening of High Court of Australia Building, Canberra, May 26.

Salvation Army Officers — A294

No. 748, St. Vincent de Paul Society, vert. No. 749, Meals on Wheels, vert. No. 750, "Life. Be in it." (Joggers, bicyclists).

Perf. 13x13½, 13½x13

1980, Aug. 11

747	A294 22c shown	.40	.30
748	A294 22c multicolored	.40	.30
749	A294 22c multicolored	.40	.30
750	A294 22c multicolored	.40	.30
	Nos. 747-750 (4)	1.60	1.20

Mailman c. 1900 — A295

1980, Sept. 29 **Litho.** ***Perf. 13x13½***

751	A295 22c Mailbox	.40	.25
752	A295 22c shown	.40	.25
753	A295 22c Mail truck	.40	.25
754	A295 22c Mailman, mailbox	.40	.25
755	A295 22c Mailman, diff.	.40	.25
a.	Souvenir sheet of 3	1.50	1.50
b.	Strip of 5, #751-755	2.00	2.00
	Nos. 751-755 (5)	2.00	1.25

Natl. Stamp Week, Sept. 29-Oct. 5. Nos. 755a contains stamps similar to #751, 753, 755.

No. 755a overprinted "SYDPEX 80" was privately produced.

Holy Family, by Prospero Fontana — A296

Christmas: 15c, Virgin Enthroned, by Justin O'Brien. 60c, Virgin and Child, by Michael Zuern the Younger, 1680.

1980 ***Perf. 13x13½***

756	A296 15c multicolored	.30	.25
757	A296 28c multicolored	.55	.45
758	A296 60c multicolored	.90	.65
	Nos. 756-758 (3)	1.75	1.35

Issued: 15c, 60c, Nov. 3; 28c, Oct. 1.

CA-6 Wackett Trainer, 1941 — A297

Designs: Australian military training planes.

1980, Nov. 19 ***Perf. 13½x14***

759	A297 22c shown	.40	.30
760	A297 40c Winjeel, 1955	.65	.40
761	A297 45c Boomerang, 1944	.75	.50
762	A297 60c Nomad, 1975	.95	.80
	Nos. 759-762 (4)	2.75	2.00

Bird Type of 1978

1980, Nov. 17 **Litho.** ***Perf. 13½***

768	A276 18c Spotted catbird, vert.	.50	.25

Flag on Map of Australia — A298

1981, Jan. 21 ***Perf. 13½x13***

771	A298 22c multicolored	.40	.25

Australia Day, Jan. 21.

Jockey Darby Munro (1913-1966), by Tony Rafty — A299

Australian sportsmen (Caricatures by Tony Rafty): 35c, Victor Trumper (1877-1915), cricket batsman. 55c, Norman Brookes (1877-1968), tennis player. 60c, Walter Lindrum (1898-1960), billiards player.

1981, Feb. 18 ***Perf. 14x13½***

772	A299 22c multicolored	.40	.25
773	A299 35c multicolored	.65	.60
a.	Booklet pane of 1, perf. 14¾x14, dated "2007"	1.10	—
774	A299 55c multicolored	1.00	.90
775	A299 60c multicolored	1.10	1.00
	Nos. 772-775 (4)	3.15	2.75

No. 773a issued 11/14/2007.

Australia No. C2 and Cover — A300

22c, Australia No. C2, vert.

Perf. 13x13½, 13½x13

1981, Mar. 25 **Litho.**

776	A300 22c multicolored	.45	.45
777	A300 60c shown	1.10	.80

Australia-United Kingdom official airmail service, 50th anniv.

Map of Australia, APEX Emblem — A301

1981, Apr. 6 **Photo.** ***Perf. 13x13½***

778	A301 22c multicolored	.40	.25

50th anniv. of APEX (young men's service club).

Queen Elizabeth's Personal Flag of Australia — A302

1981, Apr. 21 **Litho.** ***Perf. 13***

779	A302 22c multicolored	.40	.25

Queen Elizabeth II, 55th birthday.

Perf 14x14¾ examples in a booklet pane of 4 come from the booklet footnoted under No. 2507.

License Inspected, Forrest Creek, by S.T. Gill — A303

Gold Rush Era (Sketches by S.T. Gill): No. 781, Puddling. No. 782, Quality of Washing Stuff. No. 783, Diggers on Route to Deposit Gold.

1981, May 20 ***Perf. 13x13½***

780	A303 22c multicolored	.40	.30
781	A303 22c multicolored	.40	.30
782	A303 22c multicolored	.40	.30
783	A303 22c multicolored	.40	.30
	Nos. 780-783 (4)	1.60	1.20

Lace Monitor — A303a

Tasmanian Tiger — A304

Two Types of A304:

Type I — Indistinct line at right of ear, stripes even with base of tail.

Type II — Heavy line at right of ear, stripes longer.

3c, Corroboree frog. 5c, Queensland hairy-nosed wombat, vert. 15c, Eastern snake-necked tortoise. 25c, Greater bilby, vert. 27c, Blue Mountains tree frog. 30c, Bridled nail-tailed wallaby, vert. 40c, Smooth knob-tailed gecko. 50c, Leadbeater's opossum. 55c, Stick-nest rat, vert. 65c, Yellow-faced whip snake. 70c, Crucifix toad. 75c, Eastern water dragon. 85c, Centralian blue-tongued lizard. 90c, Freshwater crocodile. 95c, Thorny devil.

1981-83 **Litho.**

784	A303a 1c shown	.25	.25
785	A303a 3c multicolored	.40	.25
786	A304 5c multicolored	.35	.35
b.	Imperf., dated "2007"	.25	.25

787 A303a 15c multicolored .40 .25
788 A304 24c Type I, photo. & litho. .50 .40
a. Shown, type II, litho. .70 .40
b. Imperf., dated "2007" .50 .50
789 A304 25c multicolored .65 .45
b. Imperf., dated "2007" .60 .60
790 A303a 27c multicolored .60 .25
791 A304 30c multicolored .90 .60
a. Imperf., dated "2007" .70 .70
792 A303a 40c multicolored .85 .45
793 A304 50c multicolored 1.10 .70
b. Imperf., dated "2007" 1.10 1.10
c. Booklet pane, 2 each #788b, 793b 3.50 —
794 A304 55c multicolored 1.10 .70
a. Imperf., dated "2007" 1.25 1.25
b. Booklet pane, #786b, 789b, 791a, 794a 2.75 —
795 A303a 65c multicolored 1.40 .70
796 A303a 70c multicolored 1.40 .75
797 A303a 75c multicolored 1.60 .75
798 A303a 85c multicolored 1.75 1.00
799 A303a 90c multicolored 1.90 .95
800 A303a 95c multicolored 2.00 1.00
Nos. 784-800 (17) 17.15 9.80

Perfs: 1c, 70c, 85c, 95c, 13½; 3c, 15c, 27c, 40c, 50c, 65c, 75c, 90c, 12½x13; 5c, 25c, 30c, 55c, 13x12½; 24c, 13x13½.

Issued: 24c, 7/1/81; 5c, 25c, 30c, 50c, 55c, 7/15/81; 3c, 27c, 65c, 75c, 4/19/82; 15c, 40c, 90c, 6/16/82. 1c, 70c, 85c, 95c, 2/2/83.

Nos. 786b, 788b, 789b, 791a, 793b. 793c, 794a, 794b issued 6/26/07. No. 788b has wider spacing between text lines than on the original stamps.

1982-84 ***Perf. 14x14½, 14½x14***
785a A303a 3c ('84) .70 .45
786a A304 5c ('84) 1.40 .50
787a A303a 15c ('84) 1.25 .60
789a A304 25c ('83) 1.40 .60
790a A303a 27c 1.10 .30
792a A303a 40c ('84) 3.00 1.10
793a A304 50c ('83) 2.25 1.10
795a A303a 65c ('84) 2.25 1.40
797a A303a 75c ('84) 2.60 1.40
Nos. 785a-797a (9) 15.95 7.45

Prince Charles and Lady Diana — A305

1981, July 29 **Litho.** ***Perf. 13***
804 A305 24c multicolored .45 .25
805 A305 60c multicolored 1.25 *1.25*

Royal Wedding.

Fungi — A306

24c, Cortinarius cinnabarinus. 35c, Coprinus comatus. 55c, Armillaria luteobubalina. 60c, Cortinarius austro-venetus.

1981, Aug. 19 **Litho.** ***Perf. 13***
806 A306 24c multicolored .55 .40
807 A306 35c multicolored .70 .70
808 A306 55c multicolored 1.00 .80
809 A306 60c multicolored 1.00 1.00
Nos. 806-809 (4) 3.25 2.90

Intl. Year of the Disabled — A307

1981, Sept. 16 ***Perf. 14x13½***
810 A307 24c multicolored .45 .30

Christmas Bush for His Adorning — A308

Christmas (Carols by William James and John Wheeler): 30c, The Silver Stars are in the Sky. 60c, Noeltime.

1981 **Litho.** ***Perf. 13x13½***
811 A308 18c multicolored .35 .25
812 A308 30c multicolored .60 .60
813 A308 60c multicolored 1.00 1.00
Nos. 811-813 (3) 1.95 1.85

Issue dates: 30c, Sept. 28; others, Nov. 2.

Globe — A309

1981, Sept. 30
814 A309 24c multicolored .55 .40
815 A309 60c multicolored 1.00 .95

Commonwealth Heads of Government Meeting, Melbourne, Sept. 30-Oct. 7.

Yacht — A310

24c, Ocean racer. 35c, Lightweight sharpie. 55c, 12-Meter. 60c, Sabot.

1981, Oct. 14 **Litho.** ***Perf. 13x13½***
816 A310 24c multicolored .45 .30
817 A310 35c multicolored .60 .50
818 A310 55c multicolored .85 .80
819 A310 60c multicolored 1.00 .85
Nos. 816-819 (4) 2.90 2.45

Australia Day, Jan. 26 — A311

1982, Jan. 20 **Litho.** ***Perf. 13x13½***
820 A311 24c multicolored .45 .30

Sperm Whale — A312

35c, Southern right whale, vert. 55c, Blue whale, vert. 60c, Humpback whale.

1982, Feb. 17 ***Perf. 13x13½, 13½x13***
821 A312 24c shown .50 .40
822 A312 35c multicolored .75 .70
823 A312 55c multicolored 1.00 1.00
824 A312 60c multicolored 1.20 1.10
Nos. 821-824 (4) 3.45 3.20

A trial printing of No. 824 exists with a greenish blue background and no white streaks at the UL. A small number of these stamps were sold by mistake.

Elizabeth II, 56th Birthday — A313

1982, Apr. 21 ***Perf. 13½***
825 A313 27c multicolored .50 .40

Roses — A314

27c, Marjorie Atherton. 40c, Imp. 65c, Minnie Watson. 75c, Satellite.

1982, May 19 ***Perf. 13x13½***
826 A314 27c multicolored .50 .30
827 A314 40c multicolored .60 .60
828 A314 65c multicolored 1.00 1.00
829 A314 75c multicolored 1.20 1.10
Nos. 826-829 (4) 3.30 3.00

50th Anniv. of Australian Broadcasting Commission A315

No. 830, Announcer, microphone. No. 831, Emblem.

1982, June 16 ***Perf. 13½x13***
830 A315 27c multicolored .45 .35
831 A315 27c multicolored .45 .35
a. Pair, #830-831 1.60 1.30

Nos. 830-831 se-tenant in continuous design.

Alice Springs Post Office, 1872 — A316

No. 833, Kingston, 1869. No. 834, York, 1893. No. 835, Flemington, 1890, vert. No. 836, Forbes, 1881, vert. No. 837, Launceston, 1889, vert. No. 838, Rockhampton, 1892, vert.

1982, Aug. 4 ***Perf. 13½x14, 14x13½***
832 A316 27c shown .40 .30
833 A316 27c multicolored .40 .30
834 A316 27c multicolored .40 .30
835 A316 27c multicolored .40 .30
836 A316 27c multicolored .40 .30
837 A316 27c multicolored .40 .30
838 A316 27c multicolored .40 .30
Nos. 832-838 (7) 2.80 2.10

Christmas — A317

1st Australian Christmas cards, 1881. 21c, horiz.

1982 **Litho.** ***Perf. 14½***
839 A317 21c multicolored .35 .25
840 A317 35c multicolored .60 .35
841 A317 75c multicolored 1.20 1.00
Nos. 839-841 (3) 2.15 1.60

Issue dates: 35c, Sept. 15; others, Nov. 1.

12th Commonwealth Games, Brisbane, Sept. 30-Oct. 9 — A318

1982, Sept. 22 **Litho.** ***Perf. 14x14½***
842 A318 27c Archery .50 .25
843 A318 27c Boxing .50 .25
844 A318 27c Weightlifting .50 .25
a. Souvenir sheet of 3, #842-844 1.75 1.75
845 A318 75c Pole vault 1.25 1.25
a. Booklet pane of 4, #842-845, perf. 14x14¾ ('06) 3.00 —
Nos. 842-845 (4) 2.75 2.00

Nos. 842-842 are perf 14½. No. 844a is perf 13½x13.

No. 845a issued 3/1/2006.

Natl. Stamp Week — A319

1982, Sept. 27 ***Perf. 13x13½***
846 A319 27c No. 132 .50 .30

A320

Design: Gurgurr (Moon Spirit), Bark Painting by Yirawala Gunwinggu Tribe.

1982, Oct. 12 ***Perf. 14½***
847 A320 27c multicolored .50 .30

Opening of Natl. Gallery, Canberra.

A321

Various eucalypts (gum trees): 1c, Pink-flowered marri. 2c, Gungurru. 3c, Red-flowering gum. 10c, Tasmanian blue gum. 27c, Forrest's marlock.

Perf. 12½x13½
1982, Nov. 17 **Photo.**
848 A321 1c multicolored .25 .25
849 A321 2c multicolored .25 .25
850 A321 3c multicolored .65 *.35*
851 A321 10c multicolored .65 *.40*
852 A321 27c multicolored .65 .40
a. Bklt. pane, #850-851, 2 #848-849, 3 #852 + label 4.00
b. Bklt. pane, 2 ea #848-849, 852 2.00
Nos. 848-852 (5) 2.45 1.65

Nos. 848-852 issued in booklets only.

Mimi Spirits Singing and Dancing, by David Milaybuma — A322

Aboriginal Bark Paintings: Music and dance of the Mimi Spirits, Gunwinggu Tribe. 40c, Lofty Nabardayal. 65c, Jimmy Galareya. 75c, Dick Nguleingulei Murrumurru.

1982, Nov. 17 **Litho.** ***Perf. 13½x14***
853 A322 27c shown .50 .30
854 A322 40c multicolored .60 .40
855 A322 65c multicolored 1.00 .80
856 A322 75c multicolored 1.25 .90
Nos. 853-856 (4) 3.35 2.40

Historic Fire Engines — A323

27c, Shand Mason Steam, 1891. 40c, Hotchkiss, 1914. 65c, Ahrens-Fox PS2, 1929. 75c, Merryweather Manual, 1851.

1983, Jan. 12 ***Perf. 13½x14***
857 A323 27c multicolored .50 .30
858 A323 40c multicolored .75 .50
859 A323 65c multicolored 1.00 .80
860 A323 75c multicolored 1.20 1.20
Nos. 857-860 (4) 3.45 2.80

Australia Day — A324

1983, Jan. 26 **Litho.** ***Perf. 14½***
861 A324 27c Sirius .45 .30
862 A324 27c Supply .45 .30
a. Pair, #861-862 1.10 1.10

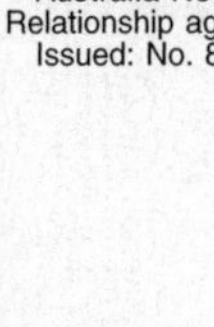
A325

1983, Feb. 2 ***Perf. 14x13½***
863 A325 27c multicolored .50 .30
863a Perf. 14¾x14, dated "2013" (#1003b) .70 .70

Australia-New Zealand Closer Economic Relationship agreement (ANZCER).

Issued: No. 863a, 5/10/2013.

A326

No. 864, Equality, dignity. No. 865, Social justice, cooperation. No. 866, Liberty, freedom. No. 867, Peace, harmony.

1983, Mar. 9 Litho. *Perf. 14½*

864	A326	27c multicolored	.45	.30
865	A326	27c multicolored	.45	.30
866	A326	27c multicolored	.45	.30
867	A326	75c multicolored	1.20	1.00
		Nos. 864-867 (4)	2.55	1.90

Commonwealth day.

Queen Elizabeth II, 57th Birthday — A327

1983, Apr. 20 *Perf. 14½*

868	A327	27c Britannia	.45	.35

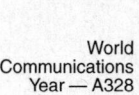

World Communications Year — A328

1983, May 18 Litho. *Perf. 13½x14*

869	A328	27c multicolored	.45	.35

50th Anniv. of Australian Jaycees Youth Organization A329

1983, June 8

870	A329	27c multicolored	.45	.35

St. John Ambulance Cent. — A330

1983, June 8 *Perf. 13½x14*

871	A330	27c multicolored	.45	.35

Regent Skipper — A331

10c, Cairn's birdwing. 20c, Macleay's swallowtail. 27c, Ulysses. 30c, Chlorinda hairstreak. 35c, Blue tiger. 45c, Big greasy. 60c, Wood white. 80c, Amaryllis azure. $1, Sword grass brown.

1983 *Perf. 13½, 14½x14 (30c)*

872	A331	4c shown	.60	.40
873	A331	10c multicolored	.60	.40
874	A331	20c multicolored	.45	.25
875	A331	27c multicolored	.65	.25
875A	A331	30c multicolored	.80	.25
876	A331	35c multicolored	.80	.35
877	A331	45c multicolored	1.00	.45
878	A331	60c multicolored	1.20	.55
879	A331	80c multicolored	1.40	.80
880	A331	$1 multicolored	2.25	1.00
		Nos. 872-880 (10)	9.75	4.70

Issue dates: 30c, Oct. 24; others, June 15.

The Sentimental Bloke, by C.J. Dennis, 1909 — A332

Folktale scenes: a, The bloke. b, Doreen-the intro. c, The stror at coot. d, Hitched. e, The mooch of life.

1983, Aug. 3 *Perf. 14½*

881		Strip of 5	2.50	2.50
a.-e.	A332	27c multi, any single	.45	.40

Kookaburra Bird Wearing Santa Hat — A333

24c, Nativity. 85c, Holiday beach scene.

1983 Litho. *Perf. 13½x14*

882	A333	24c multicolored	.40	.30
883	A333	35c multicolored	.60	.35
884	A333	85c multicolored	1.30	.90
		Nos. 882-884 (3)	2.30	1.55

Christmas. Issued: No. 883, 9/14; Nos. 882, 884, 11/2.

Inland Explorers — A334

Clay sculptures by Dianne Quinn: No. 885, Ludwig Leichhardt (1813-48). No. 886, William John Wills (1834-61), Robert O'Hara Burke (1821-61). No. 887, Paul Edmund de Strzelecki (1797-1873). No. 888, Alexander Forrest (1849-1901).

1983, Sept. 26 *Perf. 14½*

885	A334	30c multicolored	.50	.35
886	A334	30c multicolored	.50	.35
887	A334	30c multicolored	.50	.35
888	A334	30c multicolored	.50	.35
		Nos. 885-888 (4)	2.00	1.40

Australia Day — A335

1984, Jan. 26 Litho. *Perf. 13½x14*

889	A335	30c Cooks' Cottage	.45	.30

50th Anniv. of Official Air Mail Service A336

Pilot Charles Ulm (1898-1934); his plane, "Faith in Australia," and different flight covers: No. 890, Australia-New Zealand. No. 891, Australia-Papua New Guinea.

1984, Feb. 22 Litho. *Perf. 13½*

890	A336	45c multicolored	.75	*.75*
891	A336	45c multicolored	.75	*.75*
a.		Pair, #890-891	2.25	*2.25*

Thomson, 1898 — A337

Australian-made vintage cars: b, Tarrant, 1906. c, Australian Six, 1919. d, Summit, 1923. e, Chic, 1924.

1984, Mar. 14 *Perf. 14½*

892		Strip of 5	2.40	2.40
a.-e.	A337	30c any single	.45	.35

Queen Elizabeth II, 58th Birthday — A338

1984, Apr. 18 *Perf. 14½*

893	A338	30c multicolored	.45	.30

Clipper Ships — A339

30c, Cutty Sark, 1869, vert. 45c, Orient, 1853. 75c, Sobraon, 1866. 85c, Thermopylae, 1868, vert.

1984, May 23 *Perf. 14x13½, 13½x14*

894	A339	30c multicolored	.45	.35
895	A339	45c multicolored	.80	.80
896	A339	75c multicolored	1.25	1.00
897	A339	85c multicolored	1.40	1.25
		Nos. 894-897 (4)	3.90	3.40

Freestyle Skiing — A340

No. 899, Slalom, horiz. No. 900, Cross-country, horiz. No. 901, Downhill.

1984, June 6 Litho. *Perf. 14½*

898	A340	30c shown	.50	.35
899	A340	30c multicolored	.50	.35
900	A340	30c multicolored	.50	.35
901	A340	30c multicolored	.50	.35
		Nos. 898-901 (4)	2.00	1.40

Coral Hopper — A341

3c, Jimble. 5c, Tasseled anglerfish. 10c, Stonefish. 20c, Red handfish. 25c, Orange-tipped cowrie. 30c, Choat's wrasse. 33c, Leafy sea dragon. 40c, Red velvet fish. 45c, Textile cone shell. 50c, Blue-lined surgeonfish. 55c, Bennett's nudibranch. 60c, Lionfish. 65c, Stingray. 70c, Blue-ringed octopus. 80c, Pine-apple fish. 85c, Regal angelfish. 90c, Crab-eyed goby. $1, Crown of thorns starfish.

Perf. 13½, 14x14½ (30c, 33c)

1984-86 Litho.

902	A341	2c shown	.25	.25
903	A341	3c multicolored	.25	.25
904	A341	5c multicolored	.40	.40
905	A341	10c multicolored	.25	.25
906	A341	20c multicolored	.40	.35
907	A341	25c multicolored	.40	.35
908	A341	30c multicolored	.65	.25
909	A341	33c multicolored	.80	.25
910	A341	40c multicolored	.80	.35
911	A341	45c multicolored	.80	.35
912	A341	50c multicolored	1.00	.40
913	A341	55c multicolored	1.10	.80
914	A341	60c multicolored	1.00	.80
915	A341	65c multicolored	1.05	.80
916	A341	70c multicolored	1.15	1.00
917	A341	80c multicolored	1.50	1.00
918	A341	85c multicolored	1.60	1.00
919	A341	90c multicolored	1.40	1.00
920	A341	$1 multicolored	1.60	1.10
		Nos. 902-920 (19)	16.40	10.95

Issued: 2c, 25c, 30c, 50c, 55c, 85c, 6/18; 33c, 1/20/85; 5c, 20c, 40c, 80c, 90c, 6/12/85; 3c, 10c, 45c, 60c, 65c, 70c, $1, 6/11/86.

1984 Summer Olympics — A342

Event stages: No. 922, Start (facing down). No. 923, Competing (facing right). No. 924, Finish, vert.

Perf. 13½x14, 14x13½

1984, July 25 Litho.

922	A342	30c multicolored	.60	.35
923	A342	30c multicolored	.60	.35
924	A342	30c multicolored	.60	.35
		Nos. 922-924 (3)	1.80	1.05

Ausipex '84 — A343

Designs: No. 926: a, Victoria #3. b, New South Wales #1. c, Tasmania #1. d, South Australia #1. e, Western Australia #1. f, Queensland #3.

1984 Litho. *Perf. 14½*

925	A343	30c No. 2	.50	.35

Souvenir Sheet

926		Sheet of 7	4.00	*4.75*
a.-f.	A343	30c any single	.50	.40

No. 926 contains Nos. 925, 926a-926f. Issued: No. 925, Aug. 22; No. 926, Sept. 21.

Christmas — A344

24c, Angel and Child. 30c, Veiled Virgin and Child. 40c, Angel. 50c, Three Kings. 85c, Madonna and Child.

1984 Litho. *Perf. 14x13½*

927	A344	24c multicolored	.40	.25
928	A344	30c multicolored	.45	.30
929	A344	40c multicolored	.60	.65
930	A344	50c multicolored	.80	.60
931	A344	85c multicolored	1.40	1.25
		Nos. 927-931 (5)	3.65	3.05

Stained-glass windows. Issue dates: 40c, Sept. 17; others, Oct. 30.

European Settlement Bicentenary — A345

Design: No. 932, Bicentennial Emblem.

Rock paintings: No. 933, Stick figures, Cobar Region, New South Wales. No. 934, Bunjil's Cave, Grampians, Western Victoria. No. 935, Quinkan Gallery, Cape York, Queensland. No. 936, Wandjina Spirit and Snake Babies, Gibb River, Western Australia. No. 937, Rock Python, Western Australia. No. 938, Silver Barramundi, Kakadu Natl. Park, Northern Territory. 85c, Rock Possum, Kakadu Natl. Park.

1984, Nov. 7 Litho. *Perf. 14½*

932	A345	30c multicolored	.55	.30
933	A345	30c multicolored	.55	.30
934	A345	30c multicolored	.55	.30
935	A345	30c multicolored	.55	.30
936	A345	30c multicolored	.55	.30
937	A345	30c multicolored	.55	.30
938	A345	30c multicolored	.55	.30
939	A345	85c multicolored	1.75	*1.90*
		Nos. 932-939 (8)	5.60	4.00

Settlement of Victoria Sesquicentenary — A346

No. 940, Helmeted honeyeater. No. 941, Leadbeater's possum.

1984, Nov. 19

940	A346	30c multicolored	.50	.40
941	A346	30c multicolored	.50	.40
a.		Pair, #940-941	1.25	1.25

Australia Day — A347

No. 942, Musgrave Ranges, by Sidney Nolan. No. 943, The Walls of China, by Russell Drysdale.

1985, Jan. 25 Litho.

942		30c multicolored	.55	.35
a.		Pair, #942 tete-beche	2.50	2.50

943 30c multicolored .55 .35
a. A347 Pair, #942-943 1.50 1.40
b. Pair, #943 tete-beche 2.50 2.50

Intl. Youth Year — A348

1985, Feb. 13 Litho. ***Perf. 14x13½***
944 A348 30c multicolored .55 .35

Royal Victorian Volunteer Artillery — A349

Colonial military uniforms: b, Western Australian Pinjarrah Cavalry. c, New South Wales Lancers. d, New South Wales Contingent to the Sudan. e, Victorian Mounted Rifles.

1985, Feb. 25 ***Perf. 14½***
945 Strip of 5 2.50 2.40
a.-e. A349 33c any single .50 .30

District Nursing Service Centenary — A350

1985, Mar. 13
946 A350 33c multicolored .60 .35

Australian Cockatoo A351

Perf. 14 Horiz. on 1 or 2 sides
1985, Mar. 13
947 A351 1c apple grn, yel & buff 1.40 *1.25*
948 A351 33c apple grn, yel, & lt grnsh blue 1.40 *.75*
a. Bklt. pane, 1 #947, 3 #948 6.50

Issued in booklets only.

A352

No. 949, Abel Tasman, explorer. No. 950, The Eendracht. No. 951, William Dampier. No. 952, Globe and hand.

1985, Apr. 10 ***Perf. 13***
949 A352 33c multicolored .60 .40
950 A352 33c multicolored .60 .40
951 A352 33c multicolored .60 .40
952 A352 90c multicolored 1.90 *1.90*
a. Souvenir sheet of 4, #949-952 5.00 5.00
Nos. 949-952 (4) 3.70 3.10

Queen Elizabeth II, 59th Birthday — A353

33c, Queen's Badge, Order of Australia.

1985, Apr. 22 ***Perf. 14x13½***
953 A353 33c multicolored .50 .35
a. Perf. 14¾x14, dated "2013" (#1003b) .85 .85

Issued: No. 953a, 5/10/2013.

A354

1985, May 15 Litho. ***Perf. 14x13***
954 A354 33c Soil .50 .25
955 A354 50c Air 1.00 *.75*
956 A354 80c Water 1.20 1.00
957 A354 90c Energy 1.40 1.25
Nos. 954-957 (4) 4.10 3.25

Environmental conservation.

A356

Illustrations from classic children's books: a, Elves & Fairies, by Annie Rentoul. b, The Magic Pudding, text and illustrations by Norman Lindsay. c, Ginger Meggs, by James Charles Bancks. d, Blinky Bill, by Dorothy Wall. e, Snugglepot and Cuddlepie, by May Gibbs.

1985, July 17 Litho. ***Perf. 14½***
960 A356 Strip of 5 3.25 3.00
a.-e. 33c any single .50 .35

Electronic Mail — A357

1985, Sept. 18 **Litho.**
961 A357 33c multicolored .55 .30

Christmas — A358

Angel in a ship, detail from a drawing by Albrecht Durer (1471-1528).

1985, Sept. 18 **Litho.**
962 A358 45c multicolored .80 .35

See Nos. 967-970.

Coastal Shipwrecks — A359

Salvaged antiquities: 33c, Astrolabe from Batavia, 1629. 50c, German beardman (Bellarmine) jug from Vergulde Draeck, 1656. 90c, Wooden bobbins from Batavia, and scissors from Zeewijk, 1727. $1, Silver buckle from Zeewijk.

1985, Oct. 2 Litho. ***Perf. 13***
963 A359 33c multicolored .65 .25
964 A359 50c multicolored 1.00 .95
965 A359 90c multicolored 1.90 1.75
966 A359 $1 multicolored 2.40 2.00
Nos. 963-966 (4) 5.95 4.95

Christmas Type of 1985

Illustrations by Scott Hartshorne.

1985, Nov. 1 Litho. ***Perf. 14***
967 A358 27c Angel with trumpet .50 .25
968 A358 33c Angel with bells .60 .35
969 A358 55c Angel with star 1.00 .80
970 A358 90c Angel with ornament 1.40 1.40
Nos. 967-970 (4) 3.50 2.80

Australia Day — A360

1986, Jan. 24 Litho. ***Perf. 14½***
971 A360 33c Aboriginal painting .55 .35

AUSSAT — A361

Various communications satellites.

1986, Jan. 24
972 A361 33c multicolored .65 .30
973 A361 80c multicolored 1.25 1.25

South Australia, Sesquicent. A362

No. 974, Sailing ship Buffalo. No. 975, City Sign, sculpture by O.H. Hajek.

1986, Feb. 12 ***Perf. 13½x14***
974 A362 33c multicolored .50 .40
975 A362 33c multicolored .50 .40
a. Pair, #974-975 1.40 1.40

Cook's New Holland Expedition — A363

No. 976, Hibiscus merankensis. No. 977, Banksia serrata. No. 978, Dillenia alata. No. 979, Corria reflexa. No. 980, Parkinson. No. 981, Banks.

1986, Mar. 12 ***Perf. 13***
976 A363 33c multicolored .65 .35
977 A363 33c multicolored .65 .35
978 A363 50c multicolored 1.10 *1.25*
979 A363 80c multicolored 1.60 1.40
980 A363 90c multicolored 1.75 1.75
981 A363 90c multicolored 1.75 1.75
Nos. 976-981 (6) 7.50 6.85

Australian bicentennial. Sydney Parkinson (d. 1775), artist. Sir Joseph Banks (1743-1820), naturalist.

Halley's Comet — A364

33c, Radio telescope, trajectory diagram.

1986, Apr. 9 ***Perf. 14x13½***
982 A364 33c multicolored .60 .40

Elizabeth II, 60th Birthday — A365

1986, Apr. 21 ***Perf. 14½***
983 A365 33c multicolored .60 .40

Horses — A366

33c, Brumbies. 80c, Stock horse mustering. 90c, Show-jumping. $1, Australian pony.

1986, May 21
984 A366 33c multicolored .60 .30
985 A366 80c multicolored 1.40 1.25
986 A366 90c multicolored 1.60 1.40
987 A366 $1 multicolored 2.00 1.60
Nos. 984-987 (4) 5.60 4.55

Click Go the Shears, Folk Song — A366a

Lines from the song: b, Old shearer stands. c, Ringer looks around. d, Boss of the board. e, Tar-boy is there. f, Shearing is all over.

1986, July 21 Litho. ***Perf. 14½***
987A Strip of 5 3.00 3.00
b.-f. A366a 33c, any single .50 .40

Amalgamated Shearers' Union, predecessor of the Australian Workers' Union, cent.

Australia Bicentennial — A367

Settling of Botany Bay penal colony: No. 988, King George III, c. 1767, by A. Ramsay. No. 989, Lord Sydney, secretary of state, 1783-1789, by Gilbert Stuart. No. 990, Capt. Arthur Phillip, 1st penal colony governor, by F. Wheatley, 1786. $1, Capt. John Hunter, governor, 1795-1800, by W. B. Bennett, 1815.

1986, Aug. 6 Litho. ***Perf. 13***
988 A367 33c multicolored .80 .45
989 A367 33c multicolored .80 .45
990 A367 33c multicolored .80 .45
991 A367 $1 multicolored 2.25 2.25
Nos. 988-991 (4) 4.65 3.60

Wildlife — A368

Designs: a, Red kangaroo. b, Emu. c, Koala. d, Kookaburra. e, Platypus.

1986, Aug. 13 ***Perf. 14½x14***
992 Strip of 5 3.50 3.50
a.-e. A368 36c any single .70 .60

Alpine Wildflowers — A369

3c, Royal bluebell. 5c, Alpine marsh marigold. 25c, Mount Buffalo sunray. 36c, Silver snow daisy.

Roulетted 9½ Vert. on 1 or 2 sides
1986, Aug. 25 **Booklet Stamps**
993 A369 3c multicolored 1.10 *1.25*
994 A369 5c multicolored 1.60 *1.60*
995 A369 25c multicolored 1.60 *1.60*
996 A369 36c multicolored 1.00 .80
a. Bklt. pane, #993, #994, 2 #996 5.00
b. Bklt. pane, #993, #995, 2 #996 5.25
Nos. 993-996 (4) 5.30 5.25

Orchids — A370

36c, Elythranthera emarginata. 55c, Dendrobium nindii. 90c, Caleana major. $1, Thelymitra variegata.

1986, Sept. 18 ***Perf. 14½***

997	A370	36c multicolored	.60	.25
998	A370	55c multicolored	.90	.90
999	A370	90c multicolored	1.75	1.75
1000	A370	$1 multicolored	2.00	2.00
		Nos. 997-1000 (4)	5.25	4.90

America's Cup Triumph '83 — A371

No. 1001, Australia II crossing finish line. No. 1002, Trophy. No. 1003, Boxing kangaroo.

1986, Sept. 26 ***Perf. 14x13½***

1001	A371	36c multicolored	.60	.40
1002	A371	36c multicolored	.60	.40
1003	A371	36c multicolored	.60	.40
a.		Perf. 14¾x14, dated "2013" (#1003b)	.95	.95
b.		Booklet pane of 4, #502a, 863a, 953a, 1003a	3.50	—
		Nos. 1001-1003 (3)	1.80	1.20

Issued: Nos. 1003a, 1003b, 5/10/2013. No. 1003b was issued in a booklet also containing Nos. 1284b, 3534d and 3918.

Intl. Peace Year — A372

1986, Oct. 22 Litho. ***Perf. 14x13½***

1004	A372	36c multicolored	.55	.35

Christmas — A373

Kindergarten nativity play: No. 1005, Holy Family, vert. No. 1006, Three Kings, vert. No. 1007, Angels. No. 1008a, Angels, peasants. No. 1008b, Holy Family, angels, vert. No. 1008c, Shepherd, angels, vert. No. 1008d, Three Kings. No. 1008e, Shepherds.

1986, Nov. 3 **Litho.**

1005	A373	30c multicolored	.60	.35
a.		Perf 14x13½	1.25	1.25
1006	A373	36c multicolored	.60	.40
1007	A373	60c multicolored	1.10	1.10
		Nos. 1005-1007 (3)	2.30	1.85

Souvenir Sheet

1008		Sheet of 5	2.75	2.75
a.-e.		A373 30c any single	.55	.45

Perfs: Nos. 1005-1006, 1008c, 15x14½; Nos. 1007, 1008a 1008e, 14½x15.

No. 1008b, 15x14½x15x15; No. 1008d, 14½x15x14½x14½.

Australia Day — A374

No. 1009, Flag, circuit board. No. 1010, Made in Australia campaign emblem.

1987, Jan. 23 Litho. ***Perf. 13½x14***

1009	A374	36c multicolored	.60	.40
1010	A374	36c multicolored	.60	.40

America's Cup — A375

Views of yachts racing.

1987, Jan. 28 ***Perf. 15x14½***

1011	A375	36c multicolored	.60	.30
1012	A375	55c multicolored	1.00	*1.10*
1013	A375	90c multicolored	1.60	*1.60*
1014	A375	$1 multicolored	1.90	1.75
		Nos. 1011-1014 (4)	5.10	4.75

Fruits — A376

36c, Melons, grapes. 65c, Tropical fruit. 90c, Pears, apples, oranges. $1, Berries, peaches.

1987, Feb. 11 ***Perf. 14x13½***

1015	A376	36c multicolored	.60	.30
1016	A376	65c multicolored	1.00	1.00
1017	A376	90c multicolored	1.40	1.40
1018	A376	$1 multicolored	2.00	1.75
		Nos. 1015-1018 (4)	5.00	4.45

Agricultural Shows — A377

1987, Apr. 10 Litho. ***Perf. 14x13½***

1019	A377	36c Livestock	.60	.30
1020	A377	65c Produce	1.00	1.00
1021	A377	90c Carnival	1.40	1.40
1022	A377	$1 Farmers	2.00	2.00
		Nos. 1019-1022 (4)	5.00	4.70

Queen Elizabeth II, 61st Birthday — A378

1987, Apr. 21 ***Perf. 13½x14***

1023	A378	36c multicolored	.60	.40

First Fleet Leaving England — A379

Continuous design: No. 1024a, Convicts awaiting transportation. b, Capt. Arthur Phillip, Mrs. Phillip, longboat on shore. c, Sailors relaxing and working. d, Longboats heading from and to fleet. 4e, Fleet in harbor.

No. 1025a, Longboat approaching Tenerife, The Canary Isls. b, Fishing in Tenerife Harbor. $1, Fleet, dolphins.

1987 ***Perf. 13***

1024		Strip of 5	3.75	3.75
a.-e.		A379 36c any single	.70	.40
1025		Pair	1.60	1.50
a.-b.		A379 36c any single	.70	.40
1026	A379	$1 multicolored	2.25	2.00
		Nos. 1024-1026 (3)	7.60	7.25

Australia bicent.; departure of the First Fleet, May 13, 1787; arrival at Tenerife, June 1787.

Issued: No. 1024, 5/13; Nos. 1025-1026, 6/3.

1987, Aug. 6

First Fleet arrives at Rio de Janeiro, Aug. 1787: a, Whale, storm in the Atlantic. b, Citrus grove. c, Market. d, Religious procession. e, Fireworks over harbor.

1027		Strip of 5	3.75	3.75
a.-e.		A379 37c any single	.60	.40

No. 1027 has a continuous design.

1987, Oct. 13

First Fleet arrives at Cape of Good Hope, Oct. 1787: No. 1028a, British officer surveys livestock and supplies, Table Mountain. No. 1028b, Ships anchored in Table Bay. No. 1029, Fishermen pull in nets as the Fleet approaches the Cape.

1028		Pair	1.75	1.75
a.-b.		A379 37c any single	.75	.40
1029	A379	$1 multicolored	1.90	1.40

No. 1028 has a continuous design.

1988, Jan. 26

Arrival of the First Fleet, Sydney Cove, Jan. 1788: a, Five aborigines on shore. b, Four aborigines on shore. c, Kangaroos. d, White cranes. e, Flag raising.

1030		Strip of 5	4.00	3.75
a.-e.		A379 37c any single	.60	.40

Printed se-tenant in a continuous design.

The Early Years: Sydney Cove and Parramatta Colonies — A380

Details from panorama "View of Sydney from the East Side of the Cove," 1808, painted by convict artist John Eyre to illustrate The Present Picture of New South Wales, published in London in 1811, and paintings in British and Australian museums: a, Government House, 1790, Sydney, by midshipman George Raper. b, Government Farm, Parramatta, 1791, attributed to the Port Jackson Painter. c, Parramatta Road, 1796, attributed to convict artist Thomas Watling. d, The Rocks and Sydney Cove, 1800, an aquatint engraving by Edward Dayes. e, Sydney Hospital, 1803, by George William Evans, an explorer and surveyor-general of New South Wales. Printed se-tenant in a continuous design.

1988, Apr. 13 Litho. ***Perf. 13***

1031		Strip of 5	3.75	3.50
a.-e.		A380 37c any single	.60	.40

Australia Bicentennial.

The Man from Snowy River, 1890, Ballad by A.B. Paterson — A381

Excerpts: a, At the station. b, Mountain bred. c, Terrible descent. d, At their heels. e, Brought them back.

1987, June 24 ***Perf. 14x13½***

1034		Strip of 5	4.00	4.00
a.-e.		A381 36c any single	.60	.40

Printed se-tenant in a continuous design.

Fauna — A382

Designs: a, Possum. b, Cockatoo. c, Wombat. d, Rosella. e, Echidna.

1987, July 1 ***Perf. 14½x14***

1035		Strip of 5	3.75	3.75
a.-e.		A382 37c any single	.60	.40

Printed se-tenant in a continuous design.

Technology — A383

1987, Aug. 19 ***Perf. 14½***

1036	A383	37c Bionic ear	.60	.30
1037	A383	53c Microchips	1.00	.60
1038	A383	63c Robotics	1.25	1.00
1039	A383	68c Zirconia ceramics	1.40	1.25
		Nos. 1036-1039 (4)	4.25	3.15

Children — A384

37c, Crayfishing. 55c, Cat's cradle. 90c, Eating meat pies. $1, Playing with a joey.

1987, Sept. 16

1040	A384	37c multicolored	.60	.25
1041	A384	55c multicolored	1.00	*1.10*
1042	A384	90c multicolored	1.60	1.40
1043	A384	$1 multicolored	2.10	1.60
		Nos. 1040-1043 (4)	5.30	4.35

Christmas — A385

Carolers: a, Woman, two girls. b, Man, two girls. c, Four children. d, Man, two women, boy. e, Six youths. 37c, three women, two men. Nos. 1044a-1044e are vert.

1987, Nov. 2 Litho. ***Perf. 14½***

1044		Strip of 5	3.75	3.50
a.-e.		A385 30c any single	.60	.35

Perf. 13½x14

1045	A385	37c multicolored	.60	.40
1046	A385	63c shown	1.50	1.00
		Nos. 1044-1046 (3)	5.85	4.90

Carols by Candlelight, Christmas Eve, Sidney Myer Bowl, Melbourne.

Aboriginal Crafts — A386

Designs: 3c, Spearthrower, Western Australia. 15c, Shield, New South Wales. No. 1049, Basket, Queensland. No. 1050, Bowl, Central Australia. No. 1051, Belt, Northern Territory.

Perf. 15½ Horiz.

1987, Oct. 13 **Photo.**

1047	A386	3c multicolored	1.60	1.50
1048	A386	15c multicolored	4.00	4.00
1049	A386	37c multicolored	1.00	1.00
a.		Bklt. pane, 2 ea #1047, 1049	5.75	
1050	A386	37c multicolored	1.00	1.00
1051	A386	37c multicolored	1.00	1.00
a.		Bklt. pane, #1048, 3 #1050, 2 #1051	9.00	
		Nos. 1047-1051 (5)	8.60	8.50

Issued only in booklets.

Caricature of Australian Koala and American Bald Eagle — A387

1988, Jan. 26 ***Perf. 13***

1052	A387	37c multicolored	.75	.40

Australia bicentennial. See No. 1086 and US No. 2370.

Living Together — A388

Cartoons: 1c, Religion. 2c, Industry. 3c, Local government. 4c, Trade unions. 5c, Parliament. 10c, Transportation. 15c, Sports. 20c, Commerce. 25c, Housing. 30c, Welfare. 37c, Postal services. 39c, Tourism. 40c, Recreation. 45c, Health. 50c, Mining. 53c, Primary industry. 55c, Education. 60c, Armed Forces. 63c, Police. 65c, Telecommunications. 68c, The media. 70c, Science and technology. 75c, Visual arts. 80c, Performing arts. 90c, Banking. 95c, Law. $1, Rescue and emergency services.

1988 ***Perf. 14***

1053	A388	1c multi	.25	.25
1054	A388	2c multi	.25	.25
1055	A388	3c multi	.25	.25
1056	A388	4c multi	.25	.25
1057	A388	5c multi	.30	.25
1058	A388	10c multi	.30	.25
1059	A388	15c multi	.40	.25
1060	A388	20c multi	.60	.25
1061	A388	25c multi	.60	.25
1062	A388	30c multi	.60	.25
1063	A388	37c multi	.75	.25
a.		Booklet pane of 10	10.50	
1063B	A388	39c multi	.80	.35
c.		Booklet pane of 10	9.00	
1064	A388	40c multi	.80	.45
1065	A388	45c multi	.90	.45
1066	A388	50c multi	1.00	.50
1067	A388	53c multi	1.60	1.00
1068	A388	55c multi	1.30	.65
1069	A388	60c multi	1.25	.80
1070	A388	63c multi	2.00	1.60
1071	A388	65c multi	1.60	.80
1072	A388	68c multi	2.00	1.10
1073	A388	70c multi	1.60	.80
1074	A388	75c multi	1.60	.80

1075	A388	80c multi	1.60	.80
1076	A388	90c multi	1.90	1.00
1077	A388	95c multi	2.00	1.10
1078	A388	$1 multi	2.00	1.25
		Nos. 1053-1078 (27)	28.50	16.20

Issued: 1c, 2c, 3c, 5c, 30c, 40c, 55c, 60c, 63c, 65c, 68c, 75c, 95c, 3/16; 39c, 9/28; others, 2/17.

Queen Elizabeth II, 62nd Birthday — A389

1988, Apr. 21 ***Perf. 14½***

1079	A389	37c multicolored	1.00	.50

EXPO '88, Brisbane, Apr. 30-Oct. 30 — A390

1988, Apr. 29 ***Perf. 13***

1080	A390	37c multicolored	1.00	.50

Opening of Parliament House, Canberra — A391

1988, May 9 ***Perf. 14½***

1081	A391	37c multicolored	1.00	.50

Australia Bicentennial — A392

Designs: No. 1082, Colonist, clipper ship. No. 1083, British and Australian parliaments, Queen Elizabeth II. No. 1084, Cricketer W.G. Grace. No. 1085, John Lennon (1940-1980), William Shakespeare (1564-1616) and Sydney Opera House. Nos. 1083a, 1085a have continuous design picturing flag of Australia.

1988, June 21 Litho. ***Perf. 13***

1082	A392	37c multicolored	.85	.40
1083	A392	37c multicolored	.85	.40
a.		Pair, #1082-1083	2.00	1.60
1084	A392	$1 multicolored	1.75	*1.40*
a.		Booklet pane of 1, imperf., dated "2007"	3.25	—
1085	A392	$1 multicolored	1.75	*1.40*
a.		Pair, #1084-1085	4.00	4.00
		Nos. 1082-1085 (4)	5.20	3.60

No. 1084a issued 11/14/2007.

See Great Britain Nos. 1222-1225.

Caricature Type of 1988

Design: Caricature of an Australian koala and New Zealand kiwi.

1988, June 21 Litho. ***Perf. 13½***

1086	A387	37c multicolored	1.00	.60

Australia bicentennial. See New Zealand No. 907.

"Dream" Lore on Art of the Desert — A393

Aboriginal paintings from Papunya Settlement in the Flinders University Art Museum: 37c, Bush Potato Country, by Turkey Tolsen Tjupurrula with by David Corby Tjapaltjarri. 55c, Courtship Rejected, by Limpi Puntungka Tjapangati. 90c, Medicine Story, anonymous. $1, Ancestor Dreaming, by Tim Leura Tjapaltjarri.

1988, Aug. 1 Litho. ***Perf. 13***

1087	A393	37c multicolored	.80	.40
1088	A393	55c multicolored	1.25	1.00
1089	A393	90c multicolored	2.00	2.00
1090	A393	$1 multicolored	2.25	2.00
		Nos. 1087-1090 (4)	6.30	5.40

1988 Summer Olympics, Seoul — A394

37c, Basketball. 65c, Running. $1, Rhythmic gymnastics.

1988, Sept. 14 ***Perf. 14½***

1091	A394	37c multicolored	.80	.50
1092	A394	65c multicolored	1.60	1.25
1093	A394	$1 multicolored	2.00	2.00
		Nos. 1091-1093 (3)	4.40	3.75

34th Commonwealth Parliamentary Conference, Canberra — A395

37c, Scepter and mace.

1988, Sept. 19

1094	A395	37c multicolored	.80	.40

Works in the Contemporary Decorative Arts Collection at the Natl. Gallery — A396

2c, "Australian Fetish," by Peter Tully. 5c, Vase by Colin Levy. 39c, Teapot by Frank Bauer.

Roulette 9 Horiz.

1988, Sept. 28 Litho.

1095	A396	2c multicolored	3.75	*4.00*
1096	A396	5c multicolored	4.00	*4.00*
1097	A396	39c multicolored	1.60	.60
a.		Bklt. pane of 3 (2c, 2 39c)	6.75	
b.		Bklt. pane of 6 (5c, 5 39c)	8.00	
		Nos. 1095-1097 (3)	9.35	8.60

Nos. 1095-1097 issued in booklets only.

Views — A397

1988, Oct. 17 Photo. ***Perf. 13***

1098	A397	39c The Desert	.80	.40
1099	A397	55c The Top End	1.20	.80
1100	A397	65c The Coast	1.60	1.20
1101	A397	70c The Bush	1.90	1.60
		Nos. 1098-1101 (4)	5.50	4.00

Christmas — A398

Children's design contest winning drawings: 32c, Nativity scene, by Danielle Hush, age 7. 39c, Koala wearing a Santa hat, by Kylie Courtney, age 6. 63c, Cockatoo wearing a Santa hat, by Benjamin Stevenson, age 10.

1988, Oct. 31 ***Perf. 13½x13***

1102	A398	32c multicolored	.80	.30
1103	A398	39c multicolored	.80	.40
1104	A398	63c multicolored	1.60	1.20
		Nos. 1102-1104 (3)	3.20	1.90

Sir Henry Parkes (1815-1896), Advocate of the Federation of the Six Colonies — A399

1989, Jan. 25 Litho. ***Perf. 14x13½***

1105	A399	39c multicolored	.80	.40

Australia Day.

Sports — A400

1989, Feb. 13 ***Perf. 14x14½***

1106	A400	1c Bowls	.30	.25
a.		Perf. 13¼x13¾ ('90)	.40	.35
1107	A400	2c Bowling	.25	.25
a.		Perf. 13¼x13¾ ('91)	.25	.25
1108	A400	3c Football	.35	.25
1109	A400	39c Fishing	1.00	.35
a.		Booklet pane of 10	12.00	
d.		Perf. 13¼x13¾ on sides ('90)	2.25	*3.00*
e.		Booklet pane of 10, #1109d	22.50	
1109B	A400	41c Cycling	.80	.25
c.		Booklet pane of 10	8.00	
1110	A400	55c Kite-flying	1.10	.85
1111	A400	70c Cricket	1.60	1.10
a.		Imperf., dated "2007" (from booklet pane No. 1302b)	2.25	2.25
1112	A400	$1.10 Golf	2.00	1.40

No. 1109d also exists perfed on 4 sides from sheets. These are scarcer. Value, unused or used $17.50.

No. 1111a issued 11/14/2007.

1990-94

1114	A400	5c Kayaking, canoeing	1.00	1.00
a.		Perf. 13¼x13¾	.35	.25
1115	A400	10c Windsurfing	1.00	1.00
a.		Perf. 13¼x13¾	.70	.70
1116	A400	20c Tennis	1.00	.35
a.		Perf. 13¼x13¾	2.00	.35
1117	A400	65c Rock climbing	2.60	1.00
a.		Perf. 13¼x13¾	3.50	1.40
1118	A400	$1 Running	2.25	1.60
a.		Perf. 13¼x13¾	4.75	3.50

Issued: Nos. 1114a, 1115a, 1116a, 1117a, 1118, 1/17/90; No. 1118a, 1/91; Nos. 1115, 1117, 2/92; No. 1116, 7/93; No. 1114, 3/94.

The 1990 year date on the original printing of No. 1117 is in serif type. The date on the 4 koala reprint of 2005 is in san-serif type.

1990, Aug. 27

1119	A400	43c Skateboarding	.85	.60
a.		Booklet pane of 10	8.50	

Perf. 13½

1120	A400	$1.20 Hang-gliding	2.00	1.10

1991, Aug. 22 ***Perf. 14x14½***

1121	A400	75c Netball	1.25	.80
1122	A400	80c Squash	1.25	.80
1123	A400	85c Diving	1.40	.80
1124	A400	90c Soccer	1.60	.80
		Nos. 1106-1124 (19)	23.60	14.55

For self-adhesive stamps see Nos. 1185-1186.

Botanical Gardens A401

Designs: $2, Nooroo, New South Wales. $5, Mawarra, Victoria. $10, Palm House, Adelaide Botanical Garden. $20, A View of the Artist's House and Garden in Mills Plains, Van Diemen's Land by John Glover.

1989-90 Litho. & Engr. ***Perf. 14***

1132	A401	$2 multicolored	4.00	1.60
a.		Perf. 13¼x13¾ ('91)	7.50	4.00
1133	A401	$5 multicolored	8.00	2.40
a.		Perf. 13¼x13¾	20.00	9.25
1134	A401	$10 multicolored	15.00	5.75

Litho with Foil Application

Perf. 14½x14

1135	A401	$20 multicolored	30.00	14.00
		Nos. 1132-1135 (4)	57.00	23.75

Issued: $10, 4/12; $2, $5, 9/13; $20, 8/15/90.

Sheep — A402

1989, Feb. 27 Litho. ***Perf. 13½x14***

1136	A402	39c Merino	.80	.40
1137	A402	39c Poll Dorset	.80	.40
1138	A402	85c Polwarth	1.75	1.60
1139	A402	$1 Corriedale	2.00	1.60
		Nos. 1136-1139 (4)	5.35	4.00

World Sheep and Wool Congress, Tasmania, Feb. 27-Mar. 6.

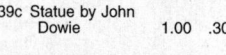

Queen Elizabeth II, 63rd Birthday — A403

1989, Apr. 21 Litho. ***Perf. 14½***

1140	A403	39c Statue by John Dowie	1.00	.30

Colonial Australia — A404

Pastoral Era: a, Immigrant ship in port, c. 1835. b, Pioneer's hut, wool bales in dray. c, Squatter's homestead. d, Shepherds. e, Explorers.

1989, May 10

1141	A404	Strip of 5	5.00	4.75
a.-e.		39c any single	.80	.40

Stars of Stage and Screen — A405

Performers and directors: 39c, Gladys Moncrieff and Roy Rene, the stage, 1920's. 85c, Charles Chauvel and Chips Rafferty, talking films. $1, Nellie Stewart and James Cassius Williamson, the stage, 1890's. $1.10, Lottie Lyell and Raymond Longford, silent films.

1989, July 12 Litho. ***Perf. 14½***

1142	A405	39c multicolored	.80	.25
a.		Perf. 14x13½	11.50	11.50
1143	A405	85c multicolored	1.75	*1.60*
1144	A405	$1 multicolored	2.10	1.50
1145	A405	$1.10 multicolored	2.10	1.60
		Nos. 1142-1145 (4)	6.75	4.95

Impressionist Paintings — A406

Paintings by Australian artists: No. 1146, *Impression for Golden Summer*, by Sir Arthur Streeton. No. 1147, *All on a Summer's Day*, by Charles Conder, vert. No. 1148, *Petit Dejeuner*, by Frederick McCubbin. No. 1149, *Impression*, by Tom Roberts.

Perf. 13½x14, 14x13½

1989, Aug. 23 Litho.

1146	A406	41c shown	.80	.40
1147	A406	41c multicolored	.80	.40
1148	A406	41c multicolored	.80	.40
1149	A406	41c multicolored	.80	.40
		Nos. 1146-1149 (4)	3.20	1.60

The Urban Environment A407

1989, Sept. 1 Litho. *Perf. 15½*

Booklet Stamps

1150 A407 41c Freeways .80 .45
1151 A407 41c Architecture .80 .45
1152 A407 41c Commuter train .80 .45
a. Bklt. pane, 2 ea #1150, 1152, 3 #1151 7.50
Nos. 1150-1152 (3) 2.40 1.35

No. 1152a sold for $3.

Australian Youth Hostels, 50th Anniv. — A408

1989, Sept. 13 *Perf. 14½*

1153 A408 41c multicolored 1.00 .40

Street Cars — A409

Designs: No. 1154, Horse-drawn tram, Adelaide, 1878. No. 1155, Steam tram, Sydney, 1884. No. 1156, Cable car, Melbourne, 1886. No. 1157, Double-deck electric tram, Hobart, 1893. No. 1158, Combination electric tram, Brisbane, 1901.

1989, Oct. 11 Litho. *Perf. 13½x14*

1154 A409 41c multicolored .90 .40
1155 A409 41c multicolored .90 .40
1156 A409 41c multicolored .90 .40
a. Perf. 14½ on 3 sides 3.25 3.25
b. Booklet pane of 10, #1156a 32.50
1157 A409 41c multicolored .90 .40
1158 A409 41c multicolored .90 .40
Nos. 1154-1158 (5) 4.50 2.00

Purchase of booklet containing No. 1156b included STAMPSHOW '89 admission ticket and a Melbourne one-day transit pass. Sold for $8.

Christmas — A410

Illuminations: 36c, Annunciation, from the Nicholai Joseph Foucault Book of Hours, c. 1510-20. 41c, Annunciation to the Shepherds, from the Wharncliffe Hours, c. 1475. 80c, Adoration of the Magi, from Parisian Book of Hours, c. 1490-1500.

1989, Nov. 1 *Perf. 14x13½*

1159 A410 36c multicolored .60 .40
a. Booklet pane of 10 7.25

Perf. 15x14½

1160 A410 41c multicolored .80 .40
1161 A410 80c multicolored 1.40 1.20
Nos. 1159-1161 (3) 2.80 2.00

Radio Australia, 50th Anniv. — A411

1989, Nov. 1 *Perf. 14x13½*

1162 A411 41c multicolored 1.00 .40

Australia Day — A412

1990, Jan. 17 Litho. *Perf. 15x14½*

1163 A412 41c Golden wattle 1.00 .40

Special Occasions — A413

1990, Feb. 7 *Perf. 14x13½*

1164 A413 41c Thinking of You .80 .40
a. Booklet pane of 10 8.00
b. Perf. 14½ on 3 sides 3.50 1.10
c. Booklet pane of 10, #1164b 35.00

See No. 1193.

Women Practicing Medicine in Australia, Cent. — A414

1990, Feb. 7 *Perf. 14½x15*

1165 A414 41c Constance Stone .80 .40

Dr. Constance Stone, Australia's first woman doctor.

A415

Fauna of the High Country: 41c, Greater glider. 65c, Spotted-tailed quoll. 70c, Mountain pygmy-possum. 80c, Brush-tailed rock-wallaby.

1990, Feb. 21 *Perf. 14x13½*

1166 A415 41c multicolored .80 .40
1167 A415 65c multicolored 1.40 1.20
1168 A415 70c multicolored 1.50 1.20
1169 A415 80c multicolored 1.60 1.40
Nos. 1166-1169 (4) 5.30 4.20

A416

No. 1170, Quit smoking. No. 1171, Don't drink and drive. No. 1172, Eat right. No. 1173, Medical check-ups.

1990, Mar. 14

1170 A416 41c multicolored .80 .40
1171 A416 41c multicolored .80 .40
1172 A416 41c multicolored .80 .40
1173 A416 41c multicolored .80 .40
Nos. 1170-1173 (4) 3.20 1.60

Community health.

A417

Scenes from WW II, 1940-41: No. 1174, Anzacs at the front. No. 1175, Women working in factories, aircraft at the ready. 65c, Veterans and memorial parade. $1, Helicopters picking up wounded, cemetery. $1.10, Anzacs reading mail from home, 5 women watching departure of 2 ships.

1990-2005 Litho. *Perf. 14½*

1174 A417 41c shown .80 .35
1175 A417 41c multicolored .80 .35
1176 A417 65c multicolored 1.25 1.00
a. Booklet pane of 2, perf. 14½x14 ('05) 9.75 —
1177 A417 $1 multicolored 1.75 1.40
1178 A417 $1.10 multicolored 2.10 1.60
Nos. 1174-1178 (5) 6.70 4.70

Australia and New Zealand Army Corps (ANZAC).

Issued: Nos. 1174-1178, 4/12/90. No. 1176a, Apr. 2005.

A418

1990, Apr. 19 *Perf. 14½*

1179 A418 41c multicolored 1.00 .40

Queen Elizabeth's 64th birthday.

Penny Black, 150th Anniv. — A419

Stamps on stamps: a, New South Wales #44. b, South Australia #4. c, Tasmania #2. d, Victoria #120. e, Queensland #111A. f, Western Australia #3a.

1990, May 1 *Perf. 13½x14*

1180 Block of 6 5.25 4.75
a.-f. A419 41c any single .80 .40
g. Souvenir sheet of 6 5.75 5.50
h. As "g," with Stamp World London '90 emblem ovpt. in silver in sheet margin *16.00 16.00*

No. 1180h issued 5/3.

The Gold Rush — A420

a, Off to the diggings. b, The diggings. c, Panning for gold. d, Commissioner's tent. e, Gold escort.

1990, May 16 *Perf. 13*

1181 Strip of 5 3.75 3.75
a.-e. A420 41c any single .80 .40

Cooperation in Antarctic Research — A421

41c, Glaciology. $1.10, Krill (marine biology).

1990, June 13 Litho. *Perf. 14½x14*

1182 A421 41c multi .80 .40
1183 A421 $1.10 multi 1.75 1.10
a. Min. sheet of 2, #1182-1183 2.75 2.75
b. #1183a overprinted 8.00 8.00

No. 1183 is overprinted in gold, in sheet margin only, for NZ 1990 International Stamp Exhibition, Auckland, Aug. 24-Sept. 2, 1990.

See Russia Nos. 5902-5903.

Colonial Australia — A422

Boom Time: a, Land boom. b, Building boom. c, Investment boom. d, Retail boom. e, Factory boom.

1990, July 12 Litho. *Perf. 13*

1184 Strip of 5 4.50 4.50
a.-e. A422 41c any single .80 .40

Sports Type of 1989

1990-91 Typo. *Die Cut Perf. 11½*

Self-Adhesive

1185 A400 41c Cycling 1.00 .75
1186 A400 43c Skateboarding 1.00 .25
a. Litho. 1.10 .25

Blue background has large dots on No. 1186 and smaller dots on No. 1186a. No. 1186 is on waxed paper backing printed with 0 to 4 koalas. No. 1186a is on plain paper backing printed with one kangaroo.

Issued: 41c, 5/16; No. 1186, 8/27; No. 1186a, 1991.

Salmon Gums by Robert Juniper — A423

43c, The Blue Dress by Brian Dunlop.

Perf. 15½ Vert.

1990, Sept. 3 Litho.

Booklet Stamps

1191 A423 28c multicolored 2.00 1.25
a. Perf. 14½ vert. 2.00 1.50
1192 A423 43c multicolored 1.00 .85
a. Bklt. pane, #1191, 4 #1192 9.50
b. Perf. 14½ vert. 1.20 .60
c. Bklt. pane, #1191a, 4 #1192b 5.00

Thinking Of You Type

1990, Sept. 3 *Perf. 14½*

1193 A413 43c multicolored .85 .50
a. Booklet pane of 10 8.00

Christmas — A424

1990, Oct. 31 Litho. *Perf. 14½*

1194 A424 38c Kookaburras .75 .35
a. Booklet pane of 10 8.00
1195 A424 43c Nativity, vert. .80 .40
a. Perf. 14¾x14, additionally dated "2013" (#3534d) 1.25 1.25
1196 A424 80c Opossum 1.60 1.60
Nos. 1194-1196 (3) 3.15 2.35

Issued: No. 1195a, 5/10/2013.

Local Government in Australia, 150th Anniv. — A425

43c, Town Hall, Adelaide.

1990, Oct. 31

1197 A425 43c multi 1.00 .40

Flags — A426

43c, National flag. 90c, White ensign. $1, Air Force ensign. $1.20, Red ensign.

1991, Jan. 10 Litho. *Perf. 14½*

1199 A426 43c multi .80 .45
1200 A426 90c multi 1.40 1.40
1201 A426 $1 multi 1.75 1.40
1202 A426 $1.20 multi 2.10 1.60
Nos. 1199-1202 (4) 6.05 4.85

Australia Day.

Water Birds — A427

No. 1203, Black swan. No. 1204, Black-necked stork, vert. No. 1205, Cape Barren goose, vert. No. 1206, Chestnut teal.

1991, Feb. 14

1203 A427 43c multicolored .80 .40
1204 A427 43c multicolored .80 .40
1205 A427 85c multicolored 2.00 1.50
1206 A427 $1 multicolored 1.75 1.60
Nos. 1203-1206 (4) 5.35 3.90

Women's Wartime Services, 50th Anniv. — A428

50th Anniv: No. 1208, Siege of Tobruk. $1.20, Australian War Memorial, Canberra.

1991-2005 Litho. *Perf. 14½*

1207 A428 43c shown .80 .40
a. Booklet pane of 4, perf. 14x14½ ('05) 9.75 —
1208 A428 43c multicolored .80 .40
1209 A428 $1.20 multicolored 2.10 1.60
Nos. 1207-1209 (3) 3.70 2.40

Issued: Nos. 1207-1209, 3/14/91. No. 1207a, Apr. 2005.

Queen Elizabeth II's 65th Birthday — A429

1991, Apr. 11 Litho. *Perf. 14½*

1210 A429 43c multicolored 1.00 .80

Insects — A430

No. 1211, Hawk moth. No. 1212, Cotton harlequin bug. No. 1213, Leichhardt's grasshopper. No. 1214, Jewel beetle.

1991, Apr. 11

1211 A430 43c multicolored .80 .40
1212 A430 43c multicolored .80 .40
1213 A430 80c multicolored 1.75 1.50
1214 A430 $1 multicolored 1.75 1.60
Nos. 1211-1214 (4) 5.10 3.90

Australian Photography, 150th Anniv. — A431

Designs: No. 1215a, Bondi, by Max Dupain, 1939. No. 1215b, Gears for the Mining Industry, Vickers Ruwolt Melbourne, by Wolfgang Sievers, 1967. 70c, Wheel of Youth, by Harold Cazneaux, 1929. $1.20, Teacup Ballet, by Olive Cotton, 1935.

1991, May 13 Litho. *Perf. 14½*

1215 Pair 2.00 1.60
a.-b. A431 43c any single .85 .40
1216 A431 70c blk, olive & cl 1.50 1.25
1217 A431 $1.20 blk, gray & Prus bl 2.00 1.60
Nos. 1215-1217 (3) 5.50 4.45

Golden Days of Radio — A432

No. 1218, Music & variety shows. No. 1219, Soap operas. No. 1220, Quiz shows. No. 1221, Children's stories.

1991, June 13 Litho. *Perf. 14½*

1218 A432 43c multicolored .80 .40
1219 A432 43c multicolored .80 .40
1220 A432 85c multicolored 1.25 1.60
1221 A432 $1 multicolored 2.10 1.75
Nos. 1218-1221 (4) 4.95 4.15

Pets — A433

1991, July 25 Litho. *Perf. 14½*

1222 A433 43c Puppy .80 .40
1223 A433 43c Kitten .80 .40
1224 A433 70c Pony 1.50 1.25
1225 A433 $1 Cockatoo 1.75 1.60
Nos. 1222-1225 (4) 4.85 3.65

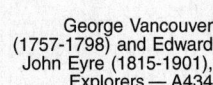

George Vancouver (1757-1798) and Edward John Eyre (1815-1901), Explorers — A434

1991, Sept. 26 Litho. *Perf. 14½*

1226 A434 $1.05 multicolored 1.75 1.25
a. Souvenir sheet of 1 2.25 2.25
b. As "a," overprinted in gold 7.50 7.50

Vancouver's visit to Western Australia, 200th anniv. and Eyre's journey to Albany, Western Australia, 150th anniv.

No. 1226b overprinted in sheet margin with show emblem and: "PHILANIPPON / WORLD STAMP / EXHIBITION / TOKYO / 16-24 NOV 1991" followed by Japanese inscription.

Issued: No. 1226b, Nov. 16.

Australian Literature of the 1890's — A435

Designs: 43c, Seven Little Australians by Ethel Turner. 75c, On Our Selection by Steele Rudd. $1, Clancy of the Overflow by A.B. "Banjo" Paterson, vert. $1.20, The Drover's Wife by Henry Lawson, vert.

1991, Oct. 10

1227 A435 43c multicolored .80 .40
1228 A435 75c multicolored 1.10 1.00
1229 A435 $1 multicolored 1.75 1.25
1230 A435 $1.20 multicolored 2.10 1.40
Nos. 1227-1230 (4) 5.75 4.05

Christmas — A436

38c, Shepherd. 43c, Baby Jesus. 90c, Wise man, camel.

1991, Nov. 1

1231 A436 38c multi .60 .30
a. Booklet pane of 20 12.50
1232 A436 43c multi .65 .30
1233 A436 90c multi 1.60 1.60
Nos. 1231-1233 (3) 2.85 2.20

Thinking of You — A437

1992, Jan. 2 Litho. *Perf. 14½*

1234 A437 45c Wildflowers .85 .30
a. Booklet pane of 10 8.75

Threatened Species — A438

Designs: Nos. 1235a, 1241, Parma wallaby. Nos. 1235b, 1242, Ghost bat. Nos. 1235c, 1243, Long-tailed dunnart. Nos. 1235d, 1244, Little pygmy possum. Nos. 1235e, 1245, Dusky hopping mouse. Nos. 1235f, 1246, Squirrel glider.

1992, Jan. 2 Litho. *Perf. 14x14½*

1235 Block of 6 5.25 5.25
a.-f. A438 45c any single .80 .40

Die Cut

Perf. 11½

Self-Adhesive

Size: 31x22mm

1241 A438 45c multicolored 1.00 .40
a. Typo. 1.00 .40
1242 A438 45c multicolored 1.00 .40
a. Typo. 1.00 .40
1243 A438 45c multicolored 1.00 .40
a. Typo. 1.00 .40
1244 A438 45c multicolored 1.00 .40
a. Typo. 1.00 .40
1245 A438 45c multicolored 1.00 .40
a. Typo. 1.00 .40
1246 A438 45c multicolored 1.00 .40
a. Typo. 1.00 .40
b. Bklt. pane, 2 each #1241-1244, 1 each #1245-1246 10.00
c. Pane of 5, #1242-1246 6.00
d. Strip of 6, #1241-1246 6.00
e. Strip of 6, #1241a-1246a 6.00
f. #1246c overprinted 6.00
g. As "f," no die cutting 210.00
Nos. 1241-1246 (6) 6.00 2.40

Litho. stamps are sharper in appearance than typo. stamps, most notably on the black lettering. Nos. 1246b and 1246c have tagging bars which make the right portion of the stamps appear toned.

No. 1246f — overprinted in Gold on sheet margin of No. 1246c with emblem of "WORLD COLUMBIAN / STAMP EXPO '92 / MAY 22-31, 1992 - CHICAGO." Issued in May.

See Nos. 1271-1293.

Wetlands A439

20c, Noosa River, Queensland. 45c, Lake Eildon, Victoria.

Perf. 14½ Horiz.

1992, Jan. 2 Litho.

Booklet Stamps

1247 A439 20c multi 1.20 .85
a. Perf. 14 horiz. 2.50 .85
1248 A439 45c multi .80 .80
a. Bklt. pane, #1247, 4 #1248 5.50
Complete booklet, #1248a 5.50
b. Perf. 14 horiz. 2.00 .65
c. Bklt. pane, #1247a, 4 #1248b 6.50
Complete booklet, #1248c 6.50

Sailing Ships — A440

No. 1249, Young Endeavour. No. 1250, Britannia, vert. No. 1251, Akarana, vert. No. 1252, John Louis.

1992, Jan. 15 Litho. *Perf. 14½*

1249 A440 45c multi .80 .40
1250 A440 45c multi .80 .40
1251 A440 $1.05 multi 1.75 1.60
1252 A440 $1.20 multi 2.10 1.60
a. Sheet of 4, #1249-1252 6.50 6.50
b. As "a," overprinted 6.50 9.25
c. As "a," overprinted 13.00 10.50
Nos. 1249-1252 (4) 5.45 4.00

Australia Day. Discovery of America, 500th anniv. (No. 1252a).

Overprint in gold on sheet margin of No. 1252b contains emblem and "WORLD COLUMBIAN / STAMP EXPO '92 / MAY 22-31, 1992-CHICAGO." No. 1252b issued in May.

Overprint in gold on sheet margin of No. 1252c contains emblem and "GENOVA '92 / 18-27 SEPTEMBER." No. 1252c issued in Sept.

Australian Battles, 1942 — A441

No. 1253, Bombing of Darwin. No. 1254, Milne Bay. No. 1255, Kokoda Trail. No. 1256, Coral Sea. No. 1257, El Alamein.

1992-2005 Litho. *Perf. 14½*

1253 A441 45c multi .80 .40
1254 A441 75c multi 1.25 .80
1255 A441 75c multi 1.25 .80
1256 A441 $1.05 multi 1.75 1.25
a. Booklet pane, #1253-1256, perf. 14x14½ ('05) 11.00 —
1257 A441 $1.20 multi 2.00 1.25
Nos. 1253-1257 (5) 7.05 4.50

No. 1256a issued Apr. 2005.

Intl. Space Year — A442

45c, Helix Nebula. $1.05, The Pleiades. $1.20, Spiral Galaxy NGC 2997.

1992, Mar. 19

1258 A442 45c multi .80 .40
1259 A442 $1.05 multi 1.60 1.25
1260 A442 $1.20 multi 2.40 1.60
a. Sheet of 3, #1258-1260 5.00 5.00
b. As "a," overprinted 9.00 9.00
Nos. 1258-1260 (3) 4.80 3.25

Overprint on sheet margin of No. 1260b contains emblem of "WORLD COLUMBIAN / STAMP EXPO '92 / MAY 22-31, 1992-CHICAGO." No. 1260b issued in May.

Queen Elizabeth II, 66th Birthday — A443

1992, Apr. 9 *Perf. 14x14½*

1261 A443 45c Wmk. 228 & #258 .90 .25

Vineyard Regions — A444

Designs: No. 1262, Hunter Valley New South Wales. No. 1263, North Eastern Victoria. No. 1264, Barossa Valley South Australia. No. 1265, Coonawarra South Australia. No. 1266, Margaret River Western Australia.

1992, Apr. 9

1262 A444 45c multicolored .80 .55
1263 A444 45c multicolored .80 .55
1264 A444 45c multicolored .80 .55
1265 A444 45c multicolored .80 .55
1266 A444 45c multicolored .80 .55
Nos. 1262-1266 (5) 4.00 2.75

Land Care — A445

a, Salt action. b, Farm planning. c, Erosion control. d, Tree planting. e, Dune care.

1992, June 11 Litho. *Perf. 14½x14*

1267 Strip of 5 4.25 4.00
a.-e. A445 45c Any single .80 .40

1992 Summer Olympics and Paralympics, Barcelona — A446

1992, July 2 *Perf. 14½*

1268 A446 45c Cycling 1.40 .70
1269 A446 $1.20 Weight lifting 2.40 2.00
1270 A446 $1.20 High jump 2.40 2.00
Nos. 1268-1270 (3) 6.20 4.70

Threatened Species Type of 1992

Designs: 30c, Saltwater crocodile. 35c, Echidna. 40c, Platypus. No. 1274, Kangaroo. No. 1275, Adult kangaroo with joey. No. 1276, Two adult kangaroos. No. 1277, Four koalas. No. 1278, Koala walking. No. 1279, Koala in tree. 50c, Koala. 60c, Common brushtail possum. 70c, Kookaburra. Nos. 1283, 1283A, Pelican. 90c, Eastern gray kangaroo. 95c, Common wombat. $1.20, Pink cockatoo. $1.35, Emu.

1992-98 Litho. *Perf. 14x14½*

1271 A438 30c multi .80 .40
1272 A438 35c multi .70 .35
1273 A438 40c multi .80 .30
1274 A438 45c orange & multi .80 .25
a. Brown panel 6.00 5.00
b. Bright orange panel 4.00 3.50
c. Additionally dated "2013" (#1284b) 1.50 1.50
1275 A438 45c orange & multi .80 .25
a. Brown panel 6.00 5.00
b. Bright orange panel 4.00 3.50
c. Additionally dated "2013" (#1284b) 1.50 1.50
1276 A438 45c orange & multi .80 .25
a. Sheet of 3, #1274-1276 10.00 10.00
b. Brown panel 6.00 5.00
c. Bright orange panel 4.00 3.50
d. Additionally dated "2013" (#1284b) 1.50 1.50
1277 A438 45c orange & multi .80 .25
a. Brown panel 6.00 5.00
b. Bright orange panel 4.00 3.50
1278 A438 45c orange & multi .80 .25
a. Brown panel 6.00 5.00
b. Bright orange panel 4.00 3.50
1279 A438 45c orange & multi .80 .25
a. Block of 6, #1274-1279 6.50 6.50
b. Souv. sheet, #1274-1279 20.00 20.00
c. Brown panel 6.00 5.00

d. Block, #1274a-1275a, 1276b, 1277a-1278a, 1279c 36.00 36.00
e. Bright orange panel 4.00 3.50
f. Block, #1274b-1275b, 1276c, 1277b-1278b, 1279e 24.00 24.00

On No. 1279a Australia and denomination are orange, "KANGAROO" is 9mm long, and date is 1½mm long. Date is 1mm long and "KANGAROO" 8mm long on Nos. 1279d and 1279f. No. 1279d comes from 2 Koala printing. No. 1279f comes from 3 Koala printing.

1280 A438 50c multi .80 .35
1281 A438 60c multi 1.00 .65
1282 A438 70c multi 1.00 .50
a. "Australia 70c" in brn ('96) 2.75 2.50
1283 A438 85c peach panel at bottom 1.60 .80
1283A A438 85c yellow panel at bottom 3.25 3.00
1284 A438 90c multi 1.35 .80
a. Additionally dated "2013" (#1284b) 3.25 3.00
b. Booklet pane of 4, #1274c, 1275c, 1276d, 1284a 6.50 —
1285 A438 95c multi 1.60 .80
1286 A438 $1.20 multi 1.90 1.60
a. "Australia $1.20" in brown ('98) 3.75 3.25
1287 A438 $1.35 multi 2.40 2.00
Nos. 1271-1287 (18) 22.00 13.05

PHILAKOREA '94 (No. 1279b).

"Australia" and denominations on Nos. 1282, 1286 are in orange.

No. 1276a inscribed in sheet margin with "CHINA '96 — 9th Asian International Exhibition" in Chinese and English and exhibition emblems.

No. 1282a comes from 3 Koala or 1 Kangaroo and 1 Koala printing. No. 1286a comes from 1 Kangaroo printing.

No. 1283A is from the three koala printing.

Issued: 35c, 50c, 60c, 95c, 8/13; 40c, 70c, 90c, $1.20, 8/12/93; 30c, 85c, $1.35, 3/10/94; 45c, 5/12/94; No. 1279b, 8/94; No. 1282a, 3/96; No. 1276a, 5/18/96; No. 1283A, 1997; No. 1286a, 12/98; Nos. 1274c, 1275c, 1276d, 1284a, 1284b, 5/10/13. No. 1284b was issued in a booklet also containing Nos. 1003b, 3534d and 3918.

Die Cut Perf. 11

1994, May 12 Litho.

Self-Adhesive

1288 A438 45c like #1274 1.75 .75
1289 A438 45c like #1275 1.75 .75
1290 A438 45c like #1276 1.75 .75
1291 A438 45c like #1277 1.75 .75
1292 A438 45c like #1278 1.75 .75
1293 A438 45c like #1279 1.75 .75
a. Bklt. pane, #1290, 1293, 2 each #1288-1289, 1291-1292 17.50
b. Strip of 6, #1288-1293 11.50
Nos. 1288-1293 (6) 10.50 4.50

Serpentine Die Cut 11½

1995 Typo. Self-Adhesive

Coil Stamps

1294 A438 45c Like #1274 1.00 .40
1294A A438 45c Like #1275 1.00 .40
1294B A438 45c Like #1276 1.00 .40
1294C A438 45c Like #1277 1.00 .40
1294D A438 45c Like #1278 1.00 .40
1295 A438 45c Like #1279 1.00 .40
a. Strip of 6, #1294, 1294A-1294D, 1295 8.00
Nos. 1294-1295 (6) 6.00 2.40

Nos. 1294-1295 come from the third through seventh Koala printings by Pemara.

Opening of Sydney Harbor Tunnel, August 29 — A447

Sydney Harbor Bridge and Tunnel: a, Left side. b, Right side.

1992, Aug. 28 Litho. *Perf. 14½*

1296 A447 45c Pair, #a.-b. 4.50 4.50
c. Pair, #d.-e., perf 15½ 4.00 4.00

Buildings in Western Australia Goldfield Towns — A448

Designs: No. 1297, Warden's Courthouse, Coolgardie. No. 1298, Post Office, Kalgoorlie. $1.05, York Hotel, Kalgoorlie. $1.20, Town Hall, Kalgoorlie.

1992, Sept. 17 Litho. *Perf. 14x14½*

1297 A448 45c multicolored .80 .40
1298 A448 45c multicolored .80 .40
1299 A448 $1.05 multicolored 1.60 1.60
1300 A448 $1.20 multicolored 2.00 1.60
Nos. 1297-1300 (4) 5.20 4.00

Sheffield Shield Cricket Competition, Cent. — A449

Cricket match, 1890s: 45c, Bowler. $1.20, Batsman, wicket keeper.

1992, Oct. 15 Litho. *Perf. 14½*

1301 A449 45c multicolored .75 .40
a. Perf. 14¾x14, dated "2007" 1.40 1.40
1302 A449 $1.20 multicolored 2.00 1.60
a. Perf. 14¾x14, dated "2007" 3.75 3.75
b. Booklet pane of 3, #1111a, 1301a, 1302a 7.50 —

Nos. 1301a, 1302a, 1302b issued 11/14/2007.

Christmas — A450

Designs: 40c, Children dressed as Mary and Joseph with baby carriage. 45c, Boy jumping from bed Christmas morning. $1, Boy and girl singing Christmas carol.

1992, Oct. 30 Litho. *Perf. 14x14½*

1303 A450 40c multicolored .75 .35
a. Booklet pane of 20 14.00
1304 A450 45c multicolored .75 .35
1305 A450 $1 multicolored 1.60 1.25
Nos. 1303-1305 (3) 3.10 1.95

Watercolor Paintings by Albert Namatjira — A451

Designs: No. 1306a, Ghost Gum, Central Australia. b, Across the Plain to Mount Giles.

1993, Jan. 14 Litho. *Perf. 14x15*

1306 A451 45c Pair, #a.-b. 1.90 1.90

Australia Day.

Dreamings — A452

Aboriginal paintings: 45c, Wild Onion Dreaming, by Pauline Nakamarra Woods. 75c, Yam Plants, by Jack Wunuwun, vert. 85c, Goose Egg Hunt, by George Milpurrurru, vert. $1, Kalumpiwarra-Ngulalintji, by Rover Thomas.

Perf. 14x14½, 14½x14

1993, Feb. 4 Litho.

1307 A452 45c red & multi .80 .40
1308 A452 75c org yel & multi 1.40 .80
1309 A452 85c buff & multi 1.60 1.10
1310 A452 $1 salmon & multi 1.75 1.50
Nos. 1307-1310 (4) 5.55 3.80

World Heritage Sites in Australia A453

1993, Mar. 4 Litho. *Perf. 14½x14*

1311 A453 45c Uluru (Ayers Rock) .80 .40
1312 A453 85c Fraser Island 1.60 .80
1313 A453 95c Shark Bay 1.90 1.00
1314 A453 $2 Kakadu 3.25 2.00
Nos. 1311-1314 (4) 7.55 4.20

See Nos. 1485-1488.

World War II Ships — A454

45c, Cruiser HMAS Sydney II. 85c, Corvette HMAS Bathurst. $1.05, Destroyer HMAS Arunta. $1.20, Hospital Ship Centaur.

1993-2005 Litho. *Perf. 14x14½*

1315 A454 45c multicolored .80 .40
1316 A454 85c multicolored 1.25 1.00
1317 A454 $1.05 multicolored 1.60 1.60
a. Booklet pane, #1315, 1317 ('05) *11.75* —
1318 A454 $1.20 multicolored 2.40 1.60
Nos. 1315-1318 (4) 6.05 4.60

Issued: Nos. 1315-1318, 4/7/93. No. 1317a, April 2005.

Queen Elizabeth II, 67th Birthday — A455

1993, Apr. 7 *Perf. 14½x14*

1319 A455 45c multicolored .90 .40

A456

Designs based on 19th cent. trade union banners: No. 1320, Baker, shoe maker. No. 1321, Stevedore, seamstresses. $1, Blacksmith, telephone operator, cook. $1.20, Carpenters.

1993, May 7 Litho. *Perf. 14½x14*

1320 A456 45c multicolored .90 .40
1321 A456 45c multicolored .90 .40
1322 A456 $1 multicolored 1.60 1.20
1323 A456 $1.20 multicolored 2.40 1.60
Nos. 1320-1323 (4) 5.80 3.60

Working life in the 1890s.

Trains — A457

Designs: No. 1324, Centenary Special, Tasmania. No. 1325, Spirit of Progress. No. 1326, Western Endeavour. No. 1327, Silver City Comet. No. 1328, Kuranda Tourist Train. No. 1329, The Ghan.

1993, June 1 *Perf. 14x14½*

1324 A457 45c multicolored .80 .80
1325 A457 45c multicolored .80 .80
1326 A457 45c multicolored .80 .80
1327 A457 45c multicolored .80 .80
1328 A457 45c multicolored .80 .80
1329 A457 45c multicolored .80 .80
a. Block of 6, #1324-1329 7.75 7.75
Nos. 1324-1329 (6) 4.80 4.80

Die Cut Perf. 11½x12

Self-Adhesive

1330 A457 45c like No. 1324 1.60 .40
1331 A457 45c like No. 1325 1.60 .40
1332 A457 45c like No. 1326 1.60 .40
1333 A457 45c like No. 1327 1.60 .40
1334 A457 45c like No. 1328 1.60 .40
1335 A457 45c like No. 1329 1.60 .40
a. Strip of 6, #1330-1335 10.50
b. Bklt. pane, #1332, 1335, 2 ea #1330-1331, 1333-1334 12.00
Nos. 1330-1335 (6) 9.60 2.40

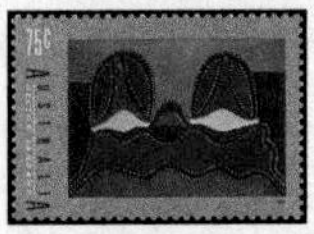

Aboriginal Art — A458

Aboriginal paintings: 45c, Black Cockatoo Feather, by Fiona Foley, vert. 75c, Ngarrgooroon Country, by Hector Jandany. $1, Ngak Ngak, by Ginger Riley. $1.05, Untitled work, by Robert Cole, vert.

Perf. 14½x14, 14x14½

1993, July 1 Litho.

1336 A458 45c henna brown & multi .80 .40
1337 A458 75c brown & multi 1.25 .80
1338 A458 $1 gray & multi 1.75 1.25
1339 A458 $1.05 olive & multi 2.00 1.40
Nos. 1336-1339 (4) 5.80 3.85

Dame Enid Lyons, MP, and Sen. Dorothy Tangney — A459

No. 1340, Stylized globe, natl. arms, Inter-Parliamentary Conf. emblem.

1993, Sept. 2 Litho. *Perf. 14½*

1340 A459 45c multicolored .80 .80
1341 A459 45c multicolored .80 .80
a. Pair, #1340-1341 2.25 2.00

90th Inter-Parliamentary Union Conference (No. 1340). First women in Australian Federal Parliament, 50th anniv. (No. 1341). Nos. 1340-1341 printed in panes of 25 with 16 #1340 and 9 #1341. Panes with 16 #1341 and 9 #1340 were issued Nov. 19, but were available only through Philatelic Agency.

A460

A461

Dinosaurs: Nos. 1342, 1348, Ornithocheirus. Nos. 1343, 1349, Leaellynasaura. No. 1344, Allosaurus. No. 1345, Timimus. No. 1346, Muttaburrasaurus. No. 1347, Minmi.

1993, Oct. 1 *Perf. 14x14½, 14½x14*

1342 A460 45c multi, horiz. .80 .40
1343 A460 45c multi .80 .40
1344 A461 45c multi .80 .40
1345 A461 45c multi .80 .40

Size: 30x50mm

1346 A461 75c multi 1.25 .80
1347 A461 $1.05 multi horiz. 1.60 1.60
a. Souvenir sheet of 6, #1342-1347, perf. 14¼ 6.00 6.00
b. As "a," overprinted 10.00 10.00
c. As "a," overprinted 10.00 10.00
Nos. 1342-1347 (6) 6.05 4.00

Self-Adhesive

Die Cut Perf. 11½

1348 A460 45c multi horiz. 2.10 .80
1349 A460 45c multi 2.10 .80
a. Bklt. pane, 5 each #1348-1349 22.00

Overprint in gold on sheet margin of No. 1347b contains "BANGKOK 1993" show emblem and "WORLD PHILATELIC / EXHIBITION / BANGKOK 1-10 OCTOBER 1993."

Overprint in gold on sheet margin of No. 1347c contains dinosaur and "Sydney / STAMP & COIN / SHOW / 15-17 October 1993."

Christmas — A462

1993, Nov. 1 Litho. *Perf. 14½x14*

1354 A462 40c Goodwill .70 .40
a. Booklet pane of 20 14.00
1355 A462 45c Joy .80 .40
1356 A462 $1 Peace 1.60 1.20
Nos. 1354-1356 (3) 3.10 2.00

Australia Day — A463

Landscape paintings: 45c, Shoalhaven River Bank-Dawn, by Arthur Boyd. 85c, Wimmera (from Mt. Arapiles), by Sir Sidney Nolan. $1.05, Lagoon, Wimmera, by Nolan. $2, White

Cockatoos in Paddock with Flame Trees, by Boyd, vert.

Perf. 14½x14, 14x14½

1994, Jan. 13 Litho.

1357 A463 45c multicolored .80 .40
1358 A463 85c multicolored 1.40 .80
1359 A463 $1.05 multicolored 2.10 2.10
1360 A463 $2 multicolored 4.00 2.40
Nos. 1357-1360 (4) 8.30 5.70

See Nos.1418-1421, 1476-1479, 1572-1574.

Royal Life Saving Society, Cent. — A464

1994, Jan. 20 Litho. *Perf. 14x14½*

1361 A464 45c Vigilance .80 .40
1362 A464 45c Education .80 .40
1363 A464 95c Drill 1.60 1.20
1364 A464 $1.20 Fitness 2.00 1.40
Nos. 1361-1364 (4) 5.20 3.40

Die Cut Perf. 11½

Self-Adhesive

1365 A464 45c like #1361 1.60 .80
1366 A464 45c like #1362 1.60 .80
a. Pair, #1365-1366 3.75
b. Booklet pane, 5 #1366a 19.00

Thinking of You — A465

1994, Feb. 3 Litho. *Perf. 14½x14*

1367 A465 45c Rose .90 .40
1368 A465 45c Tulips .80 .40
1369 A465 45c Poppies .80 .40
a. Pair, #1368-1369 2.00 1.75
b. Booklet pane, 5 #1369a 10.00
Nos. 1367-1369 (3) 2.50 1.20

A466

1994, Apr. 8 Litho. *Perf. 14½*

1370 A466 45c multicolored 1.25 .80

Queen Elizabeth II, 68th birthday.

A467

1994, Apr. 8 *Perf. 14½x14*

1371 A467 95c multicolored 1.90 1.60

Opening of Friendship Bridge, Thailand-Laos.

Intl. Year of the Family — A468

Children's paintings of their families: 45c, Bobbie Lea Blackmore. 75c, Kathryn Teoh. $1, Maree McCarthy.

1994, Apr. 14 Litho. *Perf. 14x14½*

1372 A468 45c multicolored .80 .40
1373 A468 75c multicolored 1.40 .80
1374 A468 $1 multicolored 1.90 1.20
Nos. 1372-1374 (3) 4.10 2.40

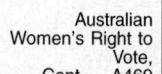

Australian Women's Right to Vote, Cent. — A469

1994, June 9 Litho. *Perf. 14x14½*

1375 A469 45c multicolored 1.00 .55

Bunyips Folklore Creatures — A470

Types of Bunyips: No. 1376, Aboriginal legend. No. 1377, Nature Spirit. 90c, Berkeley's Creek. $1.35, Natural history.

1994, July 14 Litho. *Perf. 14x14½*

1376 A470 45c multicolored .80 .80
1377 A470 45c multicolored .80 .80
a. Pair, #1376-1377 1.60 1.60
1378 A470 90c multicolored 2.00 1.60
1379 A470 $1.35 multicolored 2.40 2.40
Nos. 1376-1379 (4) 6.00 5.60

World War II Prime Ministers — A471

Designs: a, Robert Menzies. b, Arthur Fadden. c, John Curtin. d, Francis (Frank) Forde. e, Joseph Benedict (Ben) Chifley.

1994-2005

1380 Strip of 5 6.00 6.00
a.-e. A471 45c any single .80 .80
f. Booklet pane, #1380a, 1380c ('05) *9.75* —

Issued: No. 1380, 8/11/94. No. 1380f, April 2005.

Aviation Pioneers — A472

Designs: No. 1381, Lawrence Hargrave, box kites. No. 1382, Ross and Keith Smith, Vickers Vimy. $1.35, Ivor McIntyre, Stanley Goble, Fairey IIID A10-3 seaplane. $1.80, Freda Thompson, DeHavilland Moth Major.

1994, Aug. 29 Engr. *Perf. 12*

1381 A472 45c multicolored .80 .80
1382 A472 45c multicolored .80 .80
1383 A472 $1.35 multicolored 2.40 1.60
1384 A472 $1.80 multicolored 3.00 2.40
Nos. 1381-1384 (4) 7.00 5.60

First England-Australia flight within 30-day time span (No. 1382). First aerial circumnavigation of Australia (No. 1383). First woman to fly solo from England-Australia (No. 1384).

A473

Australian Zoo Animals — A474

Perf. 14x14½, 14½x14

1994, Sept. 28 Litho.

1385 A473 45c Scarlet macaw .80 .80
1386 A473 45c Cheetah, vert. .80 .80
1387 A474 45c Fijian crested iguana .80 .80
1388 A474 45c Orangutan .80 .80

Size: 50x30mm

Perf. 14½x14

1389 A473 $1 Asian elephant 1.60 1.20
a. Souv. sheet of 5, #1385-1389, perf. 14½ 6.00 6.00
b. As "a," ovptd. 13.50 13.50
c. As "a," ovptd. 13.50 13.50
d. As "a," ovptd. 13.00 13.00
e. As "a," ovptd. 12.00 12.00
Nos. 1385-1389 (5) 4.80 4.40

Self-Adhesive

Die Cut Perf. 11½

1390 A473 45c like #1385 3.00 .80
1391 A473 45c like #1386 3.00 .80
a. Bklt. pane, 6 #1390, 4 #1391 25.00

Denomination is in LL corner on No. 1391.

Overprint in gold on sheet margin:

No. 1389b, show emblem and "Brisbane Stamp Show Zoos / October 21-23, 1994."

No. 1389c, show emblem and "SYDNEY / STAMP / AND / COIN / SHOW / 30/9/94 TO 2/10/94."

No. 1389d, show emblem and "Stampshow '94 Melbourne October 27-30 / National/State Centennial Exhibition 1894-1994."

No. 1389e, show emblem and "STAMP SHOW 94 / Fremantle Convention Centre / 5-6 November 1994."

Christmas — A475

Details from Adoration of the Magi, by Giovanni Toscani: 40c, Madonna and Child, vert. 45c, One of Magi, horse and groom. $1, Joseph receiving frankincense from Magi. $1.80, Entire painting.

1994, Oct. 31 Litho. *Perf. 14½x14*

1392 A475 40c multicolored .80 .35
a. Booklet pane of 20 16.00
Complete booklet, #1392a 16.00

Perf. 14x14½

1393 A475 45c multicolored .80 .35
1394 A475 $1 multicolored 1.60 1.25

Size: 50x30mm

1395 A475 $1.80 multicolored 2.80 2.40
Nos. 1392-1395 (4) 6.00 4.35

50th Sydney-Hobart Yacht Race — A476

Designs: a, Yachts bow-on, Sydney Opera House, Harbor Bridge. b, Two yachts abeam.

1994, Oct. 31 *Perf. 14½*

1396 Pair 3.25 3.25
a.-b. A476 45c any single 1.10 .80

Self-Adhesive

Die Cut Perf. 11½

1397 A476 45c like #1396a 3.00 .60
1397A A476 45c like #1396b 3.00 .60

A477

Self-Adhesive Booklet Stamps Background Color

Die Cut Perf. 17

1994, Nov. 2 Litho.

1398 A477 45c bluish green 1.20 1.00
1399 A477 45c blue 1.20 1.00
1400 A477 45c purple 1.20 1.00
1401 A477 45c yellow green 1.20 1.00
1402 A477 45c pale yel green 1.20 1.00
1403 A477 45c pale red brown 1.20 1.00
1404 A477 45c rose 1.20 1.00
1405 A477 45c orange yellow 1.20 1.00
a. Booklet pane of 20 24.00
Nos. 1398-1405 (8) 9.60 8.00

No. 1405a contains 3 each of Nos.1399, 1401, 1403, 1405 and 2 each of Nos. 1398, 1400, 1402, 1404. No. 1405a was sold in ATM machines, at the Natl. Philatelic Center, and Australian Philatelic Bureau.

Two printings differ slightly in shade and advertisement on back of pane.

Nos. 1406-1417 were deleted from the 2003 Standard catalogue. These self-adhesive stamps of design No. A438 have computer-generated denominations and exist with a large variety of different inscriptions for shows and other purposes.

Australia Day Type of 1994

Paintings: No. 1418, Back Verandah, by Russell Drysdale. No. 1419, Skull Springs Country, by Guy Grey-Smith. $1.05, Outcamp, by Robert Juniper. $1.20, Kite Flying, by Ian Fairweather.

1995, Jan. 12 Litho. *Perf. 15x14½*

1418 A463 45c multicolored .80 .80
1419 A463 45c multicolored .80 .80
1420 A463 $1.05 multicolored 2.00 1.60
1421 A463 $1.20 multicolored 2.40 1.60
Nos. 1418-1421 (4) 6.00 4.80

St. Valentine's Day — A478

Various designs: a, Red heart. b, Red & gold heart. c, Gold heart.

1995, Feb. 6 Litho. *Perf. 14½x14*

1422 Strip of 3 2.75 2.40
a.-c. A478 45c any single .80 .40

See No. 1480.

Endeavour — A479

No. 1423: a, Captain Cook's Endeavour. b, Replica.

1995, Feb. 9 Litho. *Perf. 14x14½*

1423 Pair 2.75 2.75
a.-b. A479 45c any single .80 .80

Booklet Stamps

Size: 44x26mm

Perf. 14 Horiz.

1424 A479 20c like #1423b 2.40 2.40
1425 A479 45c like #1423a 2.40 2.40
a. Bklt. pane, #1424, 4 #1425 8.50 4.00
Complete booklet, #1425a 8.50

Natl. Trust, 50th Anniv. — A480

Designs: No. 1426a, Coalport plate, Regency style bracket clock. No. 1426b, 15th-16th cent. x-frame Italian style chair, 19th cent. Steiner doll. $1, Advance Australia teapot, neo-classical parian-ware statuette. $2, China urn, silver bowl.

1995, Mar. 16 Engr. *Perf. 14x14½*

1426 Pair 2.00 1.60
a.-b. A480 45c any single .75 .40
1427 A480 $1 red brn & bl 2.00 1.60
1428 A480 $2 blue & green 3.00 2.00
Nos. 1426-1428 (3) 7.00 5.20

Opals A481

1995, Apr. 5 Litho. *Perf. 14½x14*

1429 A481 $1.20 Light opal 2.00 1.60
1430 A481 $2.50 Black opal 4.00 3.25

Nos. 1429-1430 each contain a holographic image. Soaking in water may affect the hologram.

See Nos. 1554-1555.

A482

1995, Apr. 20 Litho. *Perf. 14½*

1431 A482 45c multicolored .80 .40

Queen Elizabeth II, 69th birthday.

A483

Famous Australians from World War II — No. 1432, Sir Edward Dunlop. No. 1433, Mrs. Jessie Vasey. No. 1434, Tom Derrick. No. 1435, Rawdon Hume Middleton.

1995, Apr. 20 Litho. *Perf. 14½x14*

1432 A483 45c multi	1.00	.80
1433 A483 45c multi	1.00	.80
1434 A483 45c multi	1.00	.80
1435 A483 45c multi	1.00	.80
a. Block of 4, #1432-1435	4.75	4.75
Nos. 1432-1435 (4)	4.00	3.20

Self-Adhesive

Die Cut Perf. 11½

1436 A483 45c like #1432	1.60	.80
1437 A483 45c like #1433	1.60	.80
1438 A483 45c like #1434	1.60	.80
1439 A483 45c like #1435	1.60	.80
a. Booklet pane, 4 #1436, 2 each #1437-1439	16.00	
b. Strip of 4, #1436-1439	12.00	
Nos. 1436-1439 (4)	6.40	3.20

See Nos. 1452-1455.

UN, 50th Anniv. — A484

1995, May 11 Litho. *Perf. 14x14½*

1440 A484 45c + label, multi	1.10	.40
a. Block of 4 + 4 labels	5.75	5.25

No. 1440 was issued se-tenant with label in blocks of 4 + 4 labels in four designs. In alternating rows, labels appear on left or right side of stamp.

A485

Poster, scene from: No. 1441, The Story of the Kelly Gang, 1906. No. 1442, On Our Selection, 1932. No. 1443, Jedda, 1955. No. 1444, Picnic at Hanging Rock, 1970s. No. 1445, Strictly Ballroom, 1992.

1995, June 8 Litho. *Perf. 14½x14*

1441 A485 45c multicolored	.80	.80
1442 A485 45c multicolored	.80	.80
1443 A485 45c multicolored	.80	.80
1444 A485 45c multicolored	.80	.80
1445 A485 45c multicolored	.80	.80
a. Strip of 5, #1441-1445	5.75	5.75
Nos. 1441-1445 (5)	4.00	4.00

Self-Adhesive

Die Cut Perf. 11½

1446 A485 45c like #1441	.80	.80
1447 A485 45c like #1442	.80	.80
1448 A485 45c like #1443	.80	.80
1449 A485 45c like #1444	.80	.80
1450 A485 45c like #1445	.80	.80
a. Strip of 5, #1446-1450	20.00	
b. Bklt. pane, 2 ea #1446-1450	16.00	
Nos. 1446-1450 (5)	4.00	4.00

Motion Pictures, cent.

By its nature No. 1450b constitutes a complete booklet. The peelable backing serves as a booklet cover.

A486

People with Disabilities: No. 1451a, Person flying kite from wheelchair. b, Blind person playing violin, guide dog.

1995, July 13 Litho. *Perf. 14½x14*

1451 Pair	2.25	2.25
a.-b. A486 45c any single	.80	.40

Famous Australians from World War II Type of 1995

1995-2005 Litho. *Perf. 14½x14*

1452 A483 45c Leon Goldsworthy	.80	.80
a. Booklet pane, #1432, 1434, 1435, 1452 ('05)	9.75	—
1453 A483 45c Len Waters	.80	.80
1454 A483 45c Ellen Savage	.80	.80
a. Booklet pane, #1433, 1454 ('05)	10.75	—
1455 A483 45c Percy Collins	.80	.80
a. Block of 4, #1452-1455	6.00	6.00
Nos. 1452-1455 (4)	3.20	3.20

Issued: Nos. 1452-1455, 8/10/95. Nos 1452a and 1454a, April 2005.

Peace Types of 1946

Perf. 14x14½, 14½x14

1995, Aug. 10 Engr.

1456 A43 45c red brown	.95	.40
1457 A45 45c dark green	.95	.40
1458 A44 $1.50 dark blue	2.75	2.00
Nos. 1456-1458 (3)	4.65	2.80

End of World War II, 50th anniv.

Wildlife — A487

Designs: a, Koalas. b, Pandas.

1995, Sept. 1 Litho. *Perf. 14*

1459 Pair	2.25	2.25
a.-b. A487 45c any single	.80	.80
c. Souv. sheet #1459a, perf. 11x11½	2.25	2.25
d. Souv. sheet #1459b, perf. 11x11½	2.50	2.50
e. #1459c Ovptd. in sheet margin	4.50	4.50
f. #1459d Ovptd. in sheet margin	4.50	4.50

Overprints read: No. 1459e: "AUSTRALIAN STAMP EXHIBITION." No. 1459f: "INTERNATIONAL STAMP & COIN EXPO. / BEIJING '95."

Issued: No. 1459f, 9/14/95.

See People's Republic of China Nos. 2597-2598.

Australian Medical Discoveries A488

Designs: No. 1461a, Joseph Slattery, Thomas Lyle, Walter Filmer, x-ray pioneers. No. 1461b, Jean Macnamara, Macfarlane Burnet, viruses and immunology. No. 1461C, Fred Hollows, eye care, vert. $2.50, Howard Florey, co-discoverer of penicillin, vert.

1995, Sept. 7 *Perf. 14x14½, 14½x14*

1461 Pair	2.40	1.60
a.-b. A488 45c any single	.85	.80
1461C A488 45c multicolored	1.10	.75
1461D A488 $2.50 multicolored	4.00	4.00
Nos. 1461-1461D (3)	7.50	6.35

No. 1461D exists in sheetlets of 10.

The World Down Under — A489

Designs: Nos. 1462a, 1465a, Flatback turtle. Nos. 1462b, 1465b, Flame angelfish, nudibranch. Nos. 1463a, 1465c, Potato cod, giant maori wrasse. Nos. 1463b, 1465d, Giant trevally. Nos. 1464a, 1465e, Black marlin. Nos. 1464b, 1465f, Mako & tiger sharks.

1995, Oct. 3 Litho. *Perf. 14x14½*

1462 Pair	2.25	2.25
a.-b. A489 45c any single	.80	.80
1463 Pair	2.25	2.25
a.-b. A489 45c any single	.80	.80
1464 Pair	2.25	2.25
a.-b. A489 45c any single	.80	.80
Nos. 1462-1464 (3)	6.75	6.75

Miniature Sheet of 6

1465 A489 45c #a.-f.	6.50	6.50
g. Ovptd. in sheet margin	9.00	9.00
h. Ovptd. in sheet margin	9.00	9.00
i. Ovptd. in sheet margin	9.00	9.00
j. Ovptd. in sheet margin	9.00	9.00
k. Ovptd. in sheet margin	9.00	9.00

Nos. 1462-1464 have pale blue border on three sides. No. 1465 is a continuous design and does not have the pale border. Fish on No. 1465 are printed with additional phosphor ink producing a glow-in-the-dark effect under ultraviolet light.

Overprints in gold in sheet margin of No. 1465 include show emblems and text:

No. 1465g: "ADELAIDE / STAMP AND / COLLECTIBLES / FAIR / 14/10/95 - / 15/10/95."

No. 1465h: "SYDNEY / CENTREPOINT 95 / STAMPSHOW."

No. 1465i: "Brisbane Stamp Show / 20-22 October 1995."

No. 1465j: "Melbourne Stamp & Coin Fair / 27-29 October 1995."

No. 1465k: "Swanpex WA / 28-29 October 1995."

Booklet Stamps

Self-Adhesive

Die Cut Perf. 11½

1466 A489 45c like #1462a	1.20	.40
1467 A489 45c like #1462b	1.20	.40
1468 A489 45c like #1463a	1.20	.40
1469 A489 45c like #1463b	1.20	.40
1470 A489 45c like #1464a	1.20	.40
1471 A489 45c like #1464b	1.60	.40
a. Booklet pane, #1470-1471, 2 each #1466-1469	14.00	
b. Strip of 6, #1466-1471	14.00	
Nos. 1466-1471 (6)	7.60	2.40

By its nature, No. 1471a constitutes a complete booklet. The peelable backing serves as a booklet cover.

Christmas — A490

Stained glass windows, Our Lady Help of Christians Church, Melbourne: 40c, Madonna and Child. 45c, Angel carrying banner. $1, Three rejoicing angels.

1995, Nov. 1 Litho. *Perf. 14½x14*

1472 A490 40c multicolored	.80	.40
1473 A490 45c multicolored	1.25	.40
1474 A490 $1 multicolored	1.60	1.20
Nos. 1472-1474 (3)	3.65	2.00

Booklet Stamp

Self-Adhesive

Die Cut Perf. 11½

1475 A490 40c multicolored	1.25	.40
a. Booklet pane of 20	25.00	

Madonna and Child on No. 1475 are printed with additional phosphor ink giving parts of the stamp a rough texture.

By its nature, No. 1475a constitutes a complete booklet. The peelable backing serves as a booklet cover, which also contains 20 labels. The complete booklet is available with backing showing two different advertisements.

Australia Day Type of 1994

Paintings by Australian women: 45c, West Australian Banksia, by Margaret Preston, vert. 85c, The Babe is Wise, by Lina Bryans, vert. $1, The Bridge in Curve, by Grace Cossington Smith. $1.20, Beach Umbrellas, by Vida Lahey.

Perf. 14x14½, 14½x14

1996, Jan. 16 Litho.

1476 A463 45c multicolored	1.00	.35
1477 A463 85c multicolored	1.25	1.10
1478 A463 $1 multicolored	2.00	1.25
1479 A463 $1.20 multicolored	2.40	1.60
a. Block of 4, #1476-1479	8.00	6.50
Nos. 1476-1479 (4)	6.65	4.30

Heart and Roses — A491

1996, Jan. 30 *Perf. 14x14½*

1480 A491 45c gold & multi	1.00	.40

See No. 1422.

Military Aviation — A492

Airplanes: No. 1481, Firefly, Sea Fury. No. 1482, Beaufighter, Kittyhawk. No. 1483, Hornet. No. 1484, Kiowa.

1996-2005 Litho. *Perf. 14x14½*

1481 A492 45c multicolored	.80	.80
1482 A492 45c multicolored	.80	.80
a. Booklet pane, #1481, 1482 ('05)	*10.00*	—
1483 A492 45c multicolored	.80	.80
1484 A492 45c multicolored	.80	.80
a. Block of 4, #1481-1484	4.00	4.00

Issued: 1481-1484, 2/26/96. No. 1482a, April 2005.

Australian World Heritage Sites Type of 1993

Designs: 45c, Tasmanian Wilderness. 75c, Willandra Lakes. 95c, Fossil Cave, Naracoorte. $1, Lord Howe Island.

1996, Mar. 14 Litho. *Perf. 14½x14*

1485 A453 45c multicolored	.75	.75
1486 A453 75c multicolored	1.25	1.25
1487 A453 95c multicolored	1.60	1.25
1488 A453 $1 multicolored	2.00	1.60
a. Booklet pane, #1311, 1314, 1485, 1488 ('06)	8.25	—
Nos. 1485-1488 (4)	5.60	4.85

No. 1488a issued 3/15/2006.

Indonesian Bear Cuscus — A493

No. 1489, Australian Spotted Cuscus.

1996, Mar. 22

1489 A493 45c multicolored	.80	.80
1490 A493 45c multicolored	.80	.80
a. Pair, Nos. 1489-1490	2.50	2.50
b. Souvenir sheet, No. 1490a	4.00	4.00
c. As "b," but with World Philatelic Youth Exhibition emblem in sheet margin	9.25	9.25

No. 1490a has continuous design.

See Indonesia Nos. 1640-1642.

Queen Elizabeth II, 70th Birthday — A494

Litho. & Engr.

1996, Apr. 11 *Perf. 14x14½*

1491 A494 45c multicolored	1.00	.40

North Melbourne Kangaroos A495

Brisbane Bears A496

Sydney Swans A497

Carlton Blues A498

Adelaide Crows A499

Fitzroy Lions A500

Richmond Tigers A501

St. Kilda Saints A502

Melbourne Demons A503

Collingwood Magpies A504

Fremantle Dockers A505

Footscray Bulldogs A506

West Coast Eagles A507

Essendon Bombers A508

Geelong Cats A509

Hawthorn Hawks A510

1996, Apr. 23 Litho. *Perf. 14½x14*

1492	A495	45c multicolored	.75	.75
1493	A496	45c multicolored	.75	.75
1494	A497	45c multicolored	.75	.75
1495	A498	45c multicolored	.75	.75
1496	A499	45c multicolored	.75	.75
1497	A500	45c multicolored	.75	.75
1498	A501	45c multicolored	.75	.75
1499	A502	45c multicolored	.75	.75
1500	A503	45c multicolored	.75	.75
1501	A504	45c multicolored	.75	.75
1502	A505	45c multicolored	.75	.75
1503	A506	45c multicolored	.75	.75
1504	A507	45c multicolored	.75	.75
1505	A508	45c multicolored	.75	.75
1506	A509	45c multicolored	.75	.75
1507	A510	45c multicolored	.75	.75
a.		Min. sheet of 16, #1492-1507	15.00	
		Nos. 1492-1507 (16)	12.00	12.00

Booklet Stamps
Self-Adhesive
Serpentine Die Cut 11½

1508	A495	45c multicolored	1.00	.40
a.		Booklet pane of 10	10.00	
1509	A496	45c multicolored	1.00	.40
a.		Booklet pane of 10	10.00	
1510	A497	45c multicolored	1.00	.40
a.		Booklet pane of 10	10.00	
1511	A498	45c multicolored	1.00	.40
a.		Booklet pane of 10	10.00	
1512	A499	45c multicolored	1.00	.40
a.		Booklet pane of 10	10.00	
1513	A500	45c multicolored	1.00	.40
a.		Booklet pane of 10	10.00	
1514	A501	45c multicolored	1.00	.40
a.		Booklet pane of 10	10.00	
1515	A502	45c multicolored	1.00	.40
a.		Booklet pane of 10	10.00	
1516	A503	45c multicolored	1.00	.40
a.		Booklet pane of 10	10.00	
1517	A504	45c multicolored	1.00	.40
a.		Booklet pane of 10	10.00	
1518	A505	45c multicolored	1.00	.40
a.		Booklet pane of 10	10.00	
1519	A506	45c multicolored	1.00	.40
a.		Booklet pane of 10	10.00	
1520	A507	45c multicolored	1.00	.40
a.		Booklet pane of 10	10.00	
1521	A508	45c multicolored	1.00	.40
a.		Booklet pane of 10	10.00	
1522	A509	45c multicolored	1.00	.40
a.		Booklet pane of 10	10.00	
1523	A510	45c multicolored	1.00	.40
a.		Booklet pane of 10	10.00	
		Nos. 1508-1523 (16)	16.00	6.40

By their nature, Nos. 1508a-1523a are complete booklets. The peelable paper backing serves as a booklet cover.

Australian Football League, cent.

Flora and Fauna — A511

Designs: 5c, Leadbeater's possum. 10c, Powerful owl. 20c, Saltwater crocodile, Kangkong flower. 25c, Northern dwarf tree frog, red lily. No. 1528, Little kingfisher. No. 1529, Jacana. No. 1530, Jabiru. No. 1531, Brolga. $1, Big greasy butterfly, water lily. $2, Blackwood wattle. $5, Mountain ash, fern. $10, Kakadu Wetlands during lightning storm, great egret, red lily.

Perf. 14x14½, 14½x14 (#1535)

1996-99 Litho.

1524	A511	5c multi	.25	.25
1525	A511	10c multi	.30	.25
1526	A511	20c multi	.40	.40
1527	A511	25c multi	.55	.40
1528	A511	45c multi	.95	.40
1529	A511	45c multi	.95	.40
1530	A511	45c multi	.95	.40
1531	A511	45c multi	.95	.40
a.		Block of 4, #1528-1531	4.50	4.00
b.		Souvenir sheet of 2, #1530-1531	7.50	
1532	A511	$1 multi	2.10	.65
1533	A511	$2 multi	3.25	1.25

Size: 30x50mm

1534	A511	$5 multi, vert.	7.50	3.25

Size: 50x30mm

1535	A511	$10 multi	15.00	5.75
a.		Souvenir sheet of 1	18.00	18.00
b.		As "a," ovptd. in sheet margin	30.00	30.00
c.		As "a," ovptd in sheet margin	25.00	25.00
d.		As "a," ovptd in sheet margin	29.00	21.00
		Nos. 1524-1535 (12)	33.15	13.80

Self-Adhesive
Serpentine Die Cut 11½, 11¼ (#1539i)

1536	A511	45c like #1529	1.00	.35
1537	A511	45c like #1528	1.00	.35
1538	A511	45c like #1531	1.00	.35
1539	A511	45c like #1530	1.00	.35
a.		Booklet pane, 3 ea #1536, #1538, 2 ea #1537, #1539	10.00	
b.		Strip of 4, #1536-1539	4.75	
h.		Sheet of 5, #1537-1539, 2 #1536	6.00	
i.		Booklet pane, 5 each #1536-1539	28.00	

Serpentine Die Cut 12½x13

1539C	A511	45c like #1529	1.50	.55
1539D	A511	45c like #1528	1.50	.55
1539E	A511	45c like #1531	1.50	.55
1539F	A511	45c like #1530	1.50	.55
g.		Strip of 4, #1539C-1539F	8.50	
		Nos. 1536-1539F (8)	10.00	3.60

Nos. 1536-1539 are booklet stamps.

No. 1531b is inscribed in sheet margin with Shanghai '97 emblem and "International Stamp & Coin Exposition Shanghai '97" in Chinese and English.

No. 1535b is overprinted in silver in sheet margin with PACIFIC 97 emblem and "Australia Post Exhibition Sheet No. 4."

No. 1535c is overprinted in sheet margin for "Italia '98" in Milan.

No. 1535d is overprinted in copper in sheet margin with "PHILA NIPPON '01" and show emblem. Issued: No. 1535c, 8/1/01.

By its nature No. 1539a is a complete booklet. The peelable backing serves as a booklet cover.

Issued: 5c, 10c, $2, $5, 5/9/96; 20c, 25c, $1, $10, #1538a, 4/10/97; #1528-1531, 1536-1539, 6/2/97; #1531b, 11/17/97; #1539C-1539F, 11/13/99; No. 1539i, 9/1/98.

No. 1539i is a complete booklet.

See Nos. 1734-1746L, 1984-1995, 2060-2063, 2111-2114, 2159-2170, 2235-2238.

Modern Olympic Games, Cent. — A512

Designs: No. 1540, Edwin Flack, 1st Australian gold medalist, runners. No. 1541, Fanny Durack, 1st Australian woman gold medalist, swimmers. $1.05, Paralympics, Atlanta.

Litho. & Engr.

1996, June 6 *Perf. 14x14½*

1540	A512	45c multicolored	.75	.30
1541	A512	45c multicolored	.75	.30
a.		Pair, #1540-1541	2.25	1.75
1542	A512	$1.05 multicolored	2.40	1.20
		Nos. 1540-1542 (3)	3.90	1.80

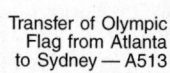

Transfer of Olympic Flag from Atlanta to Sydney — A513

1996, July 22 Litho.

1543	A513	45c multicolored	1.10	.40

Issued in sheets of 10.

Children's Book Council, 50th Anniv. — A514

Covers from "Book of the Year" books: No. 1544, "Animalia." No. 1545, "Greetings from Sandy Beach." No. 1546, "Who Sank the Boat?" No. 1547, "John Brown, Rose and the Midnight Cat."

1996, July 4 Litho. *Perf. 14x14½*

1544	A514	45c multicolored	1.00	1.00
1545	A514	45c multicolored	1.00	1.00
1546	A514	45c multicolored	1.00	1.00
1547	A514	45c multicolored	1.00	1.00
a.		Block of 4, #1544-1547	4.50	4.50
		Nos. 1544-1547 (4)	4.00	4.00

Serpentine Die Cut 11½
Self-Adhesive

1548	A514	45c like #1544	1.10	.40
1549	A514	45c like #1546	1.10	.40
1550	A514	45c like #1547	1.10	.40
1551	A514	45c like #1545	1.10	.40
a.		Booklet pane, 4 #1548, 2 each #1549-1551	12.00	
b.		Strip of 4, #1548-1551	8.00	
		Nos. 1548-1551 (4)	4.40	1.60

By its nature, No. 1551a is a complete booklet. The peelable paper backing serves as a booklet cover.

National Council of Women, Cent. — A515

Designs: 45c, Margaret Windeyer (1866-1939), honorary life president. $1, Rose Scott (1847-1925), founding executive member.

1996, Aug. 8 Litho. *Perf. 14½x14*

1552	A515	45c claret & yellow	.80	.30
1553	A515	$1 blue & yellow	2.00	1.10

Gems Type of 1995

1996, Sept. 5 Litho. *Perf. 14½x14*

1554	A481	45c Pearl	1.60	.30
1555	A481	$1.20 Diamond	3.00	2.50

No. 1555 contains a round foil design. Soaking in water may affect the design.

Arts Councils in Regional Australia A516

Silhouettes of performing artists, outdoor scene: 20c, Ballet dancer, violinist, field, bales, trees. 45c, Violinist, hand holding flower, dancer, tree in field.

Perf. 14 Horiz.

1996, Sept. 12 Litho.

Booklet Stamps

1556	A516	20c multicolored	1.75	1.50
1557	A516	45c multicolored	1.50	.60
a.		Bklt. pane, #1556, 4 #1557	5.75	
		Complete booklet, #1557a	5.75	

A517

Pets — A518

1996-97 *Perf. 14x14½, 14½x14*

1558	A517	45c Cockatoo	.75	.75
1559	A517	45c Ducks, vert.	.75	.75
1560	A517	45c Dog, cat, vert.	.75	.40
a.		Pair, #1559-1560	2.00	2.00
1561	A518	45c Dog, puppy	.75	.75
1562	A518	45c Kittens	.75	.75
a.		Pair, #1561-1562	2.60	2.60

Size: 30x50mm

1563	A518	45c Pony mare, foal	.75	.40
a.		Souvenir sheet, #1558-1563, perf. 14¼	6.00	6.00
b.		As "a," ovptd.	8.00	8.00
c.		As "a," ovptd.	8.00	8.00
d.		As "a," ovptd.	8.00	8.00
e.		As "a," ovptd.	8.00	8.00
f.		As "a," ovptd.	8.00	8.00
g.		As "a," ovptd.	8.00	8.00
h.		As "a," ovptd.	8.00	8.00
		Nos. 1558-1563 (6)	4.50	3.80

Self-Adhesive
Serpentine Die Cut 11½

1564	A518	45c like #1561	1.60	.80
1565	A518	45c like #1562	1.60	.80
a.		Bklt. pane, 6 #1564, 4 #1565	15.00	

No. 1563a is a continuous design.

Overprints in gold on sheet margin: No. 1563b, show emblem and "10TH ASIAN INTERNATIONAL PHILATELIC EXHIBITION 1996" in Chinese and English. No. 1563c, pets emblem and, "ASDA CENTREPOINT '96 STAMP AND COIN SHOW / 5-7 October 1996." No. 1563d, pets emblem and "ST PETERS STAMP & COLLECTIBLE FAIR / 12-13 OCTOBER 1996." No. 1563e, pets emblem and "MELBOURNE '96 NATIONAL PHILATELIC EXHIBITION / 17-20 OCTOBER 1996." No. 1563f, pets emblem and "QUEENSLAND SPRING STAMP AND COIN SHOW / 25-27 OCTOBER 1996." No. 1563g, pets emblem and "SWANPEX '96 / 26-27 OCTOBER 1996." No. 1563h: Hong Kong '97 emblem and "11TH ASIAN INTERNATIONAL STAMP EXHIBITION / 12-16 FEBRUARY 1997."

By its nature, No. 1565a is a complete booklet. The peelable paper backing serves as a booklet cover.

Issued: Nos. 1558-1563, 1563a, 1564-1565, 10/1/96; Nos. 1563b-1563g, 10/3/96; No. 1563h, 2/12/97.

Baron Ferdinand von Mueller (1825-96), Botanist — A519

1996, Oct. 9 *Perf. 14*

1566	A519	$1.20 multicolored	2.40	2.40

See Germany No. 1949.

Christmas — A520

40c, Madonna and Child. 45c, Wise man. $1, Shepherd boy, lamb.

1996, Nov. 1 *Perf. 14½x14*

1567	A520	40c multicolored	.80	.35
1568	A520	45c multicolored	.90	.35
1569	A520	$1 multicolored	1.60	1.25
		Nos. 1567-1569 (3)	3.30	1.95

Self-Adhesive
Serpentine Die Cut 12

1570	A520	40c like #1567	2.00	.40
a.		Booklet pane of 20	40.00	

By its nature, No. 1570a is a complete booklet. The peelable paper backing serves as a booklet cover.

Exploration of Australian Coast & Christmas Island by Willem de Vlamingh, 300th Anniv. — A521

Portrait of a Dutch Navigator, by Jan Verkolje.

1996, Nov. 1 *Perf. 14x14½*
1571 A521 45c multicolored .90 .30
a. Pair, #1571 & Christmas Is. #404 2.25 2.25

Australia Day Type of 1994

Paintings: 85c, Landscape '74, by Fred Williams. 90c, The Balcony 2, by Brett Whiteley. $1.20, Fire Haze at Gerringong, by Lloyd Rees.

1997, Jan. 16 Litho. *Perf. 14½x14*
1572 A463 85c multicolored 1.50 .75
1573 A463 90c multicolored 1.60 1.25
1574 A463 $1.20 multicolored 2.50 1.60
Nos. 1572-1574 (3) 5.60 3.60

Sir Donald Bradman, Cricketer — A522

1997, Jan. 23 Litho. *Perf. 14¼*
1575 A522 45c Portrait .80 .40
a. Without gold highlights, dated "2007" 1.40 1.40
1576 A522 45c At bat .80 .40
a. Pair, No. 1575-1576 2.40 2.25
b. Booklet pane, #1575-1576 1.90 —
c. Without gold highlights, dated "2007" 1.40 1.40

No. 1576b issued 1/24/07. Nos. 1575a, 1576c issued 11/14/2007.

See Nos. 1634-1646, 1719-1722, 1800-1807, 1933-1936, 1941-1942, 2021-2030, 2125-2132, 2207-2210.

Greetings — A523

1997, Jan. 29 *Perf. 14½x14*
1577 A523 45c Rose .80 .40

Serpentine Die Cut 11½
Booklet Stamp
Self-Adhesive

1578 A523 45c like #1577 1.50 .30
a. Booklet pane of 10 15.00

By its nature, No. 1578a is a complete booklet. The peelable paper backing, which also contains 12 labels, serves as a booklet cover.

Classic Cars — A524

Automobiles: No. 1579, 1934 Ford Coupe Utility. No. 1580, 1948 GMH Holden 48-215 (FX). No. 1581, 1958 Austin Lancer. No. 1582, 1962 Chrysler Valiant R Series.

1997, Feb. 27 Litho. *Perf. 14x14½*
1579 A524 45c multicolored .90 .90
a. Booklet pane of 4 3.75
1580 A524 45c multicolored .90 .90
a. Booklet pane of 4 3.75
1581 A524 45c multicolored .90 .90
a. Booklet pane of 4 3.75
1582 A524 45c multicolored .90 .90
a. Booklet pane of 4 3.75
b. Block of 4, #1579-1582 4.50 4.50
Complete booklet, #1579a, 1580a, 1581a, 1582a 19.00
Nos. 1579-1582 (4) 3.60 3.60

Complete booklet contains 2 postal cards and 16 self-adhesive labels.

Serpentine Die Cut 12
Booklet Stamps
Self-Adhesive

1583 A524 45c like #1579 1.25 .40
1584 A524 45c like #1580 1.25 .40
1585 A524 45c like #1581 1.25 .40
1586 A524 45c like #1582 1.25 .40
a. Bklt. pane, 2 ea #1583, 1585, 3 ea #1584, 1586 12.50
b. Strip of 4, #1583-1586 12.50
Nos. 1583-1586 (4) 5.00 1.60

By its nature, No. 1586a is a complete booklet. The peelable backing serves as a booklet cover. The backing for No. 1586b is inscribed with a 3x8mm black vertical box and "SNP CAMBEC."

Circuses in Australia, 150th Anniv. — A525

Designs: No. 1591, Queen of the Arena, May Wirth (1894-1978). No. 1592, Wizard of the Wire, Con Colleano (1899-1973). No. 1593, Clowns. No. 1594, Tumblers.

1997, Mar. 13 Litho. *Perf. 14½x14*
1591 A525 45c multicolored .80 .35
1592 A525 45c multicolored .80 .35
1593 A525 45c multicolored .80 .35
1594 A525 45c multicolored .80 .35
a. Block of 4, #1591-1594 4.50 4.50
Nos. 1591-1594 (4) 3.20 1.40

A526

1997, Apr. 17 Engr. *Perf. 14x14½*
1595 A526 45c Design A50 1.00 .40

Queen Elizabeth II, 71st birthday, 50th wedding anniv.

A527

1997, Apr. 17 *Perf. 14½x14*
1596 A527 45c multicolored 1.00 .40

Lions Clubs of Australia, 50th anniv.

A528

Dolls and Teddy Bears: No. 1597, Doll wearing red hat. No. 1598, Bear standing. No. 1599, Doll wearing white dress holding teddy bear. No. 1600, Doll in brown outfit. No. 1601, Teddy bear seated.

1997, May 8 Litho. *Perf. 14½x14*
1597 A528 45c multicolored .80 .80
1598 A528 45c multicolored .80 .80
1599 A528 45c multicolored .80 .80
1600 A528 45c multicolored .80 .80
1601 A528 45c multicolored .80 .80
a. Strip of 5, #1597-1601 5.50 5.50
Nos. 1597-1601 (5) 4.00 4.00

Nos. 1597-1601 were printed in sheets containing two strips of five. Some sheets exist overprinted in margin with picture of teddy bear and inscription "Brisbane Stamp & Coin Expo / 7-9 June 1997."

Emergency Services — A529

Designs: No. 1602, Disaster victim evacuated. No. 1603, Police rescue hiker. $1.05, Rapid response saves home. $1.20, Ambulance dash saves life.

1997, July 10 Litho. *Perf. 14x14½*
1602 A529 45c multicolored .80 .80
1603 A529 45c multicolored .80 .80
a. Pair, #1602-1603 2.00 1.60
1604 A529 $1.05 multicolored 1.75 1.50
1605 A529 $1.20 multicolored 2.40 1.60
Nos. 1602-1605 (4) 5.75 4.70

Arrival of Merino Sheep in Australia, Bicent. — A530

Designs: No. 1606, George Peppin, Junior (1827-76), breeder, Merino sheep. No. 1607, "Pepe" chair, uses of wool.

1997, Aug. 7 Litho. *Perf. 14x14½*
1606 A530 45c multicolored .80 .40
1607 A530 45c multicolored .80 .40
a. Pair, #1606-1607 2.00 2.00

Scenes from "The Dreaming," Animated Stories for Children — A531

Designs: 45c, Dumbi the Owl. $1, The Two Willy-Willies. $1.20, How Brolga Became a Bird. $1.80, Tuggan-Tuggan.

1997, Aug. 21 *Perf. 14½*
1608 A531 45c multicolored .80 .40
1609 A531 $1 multicolored 1.75 1.25
1610 A531 $1.20 multicolored 2.40 1.60
1611 A531 $1.80 multicolored 3.25 2.00
Nos. 1608-1611 (4) 8.20 5.25

Prehistoric Animals — A532

Designs: No. 1612, Rhoetosaurus brownei. No. 1613, Mcnamaraspis kaprios. No. 1614, Ninjemys oweni. No. 1615, Paracyclotosaurus davidi. No. 1616, Woolungasaurus glendowerensis.

1997, Sept. 4 Litho. *Perf. 14½x14*
1612 A532 45c multicolored .80 .40
1613 A532 45c multicolored .80 .40
1614 A532 45c multicolored .80 .40
1615 A532 45c multicolored .80 .40
1616 A532 45c multicolored .80 .40
a. Strip of 5, #1612-1616 6.50 5.00
Nos. 1612-1616 (5) 4.00 2.00

Printed in sheets of 10 stamps.

A533

Nocturnal Animals — A534

No. 1617, Barking owl. No. 1618, Spotted-tailed quoll. No. 1619, Platypus. No. 1620, Brown antechinus. No. 1621, Dingo. No. 1622, Yellow-bellied glider.

Perf. 14½x14, 14x14½

1997, Oct. 1 **Litho.**
1617 A533 45c multicolored .80 .80
1618 A533 45c multicolored .80 .80
a. Pair, #1617-1618 2.00 1.60
1619 A534 45c multicolored .80 .80
1620 A534 45c multicolored .80 .80
1621 A534 45c multicolored .80 .80
a. Strip of 3, #1619-1621 3.25 3.25

Size: 50x30mm

1622 A534 45c multicolored 1.40 .80
a. Souvenir sheet, #1617-1622, perf. 14¼ 6.00 6.00
Nos. 1617-1622 (6) 5.40 4.80

No. 1622a is printed with additional phosphor ink revealing a glow-in-the-dark spider and web under ultraviolet light.

Size: 21x32mm
Serpentine Die Cut Perf. 11½
Self-Adhesive

1623 A533 45c like #1617 1.25 .40
1624 A533 45c like #1618 1.25 .40
a. Booklet pane, 5 each #1623-1624 12.50
b. Pair, #1623-1624 4.00

By its nature No. 1624a is a complete booklet. The peelable paper backing serves as a booklet cover.

Breast Cancer Awareness — A535

1997, Oct. 27 Litho. *Perf. 14x14½*
1625 A535 45c multicolored 1.00 .40

Christmas — A536

Children in Christmas Nativity pageant: 40c, Angels. 45c, Mary holding Baby Jesus. $1, Three Wise Men.

1997, Nov. 3
1626 A536 40c multicolored .65 .35
1627 A536 45c multicolored .75 .35
1628 A536 $1 multicolored 1.60 1.25
Nos. 1626-1628 (3) 3.00 1.95

Booklet Stamps
Serpentine Die Cut Perf. 11½
Self-Adhesive

1629 A536 40c multicolored .75 .40
a. Booklet pane of 20 15.00

By its nature No. 1629a is a complete booklet. The peelable paper backing serves as a booklet cover, which also contains 20 labels.

Maritime Heritage — A537

1998, Jan. 15 Litho. *Perf. 14½x14*
1630 A537 45c Flying Cloud .80 .40
a. Pane of 10 9.00 9.00
1631 A537 85c Marco Polo 1.25 .80
a. Sheet of 2, #1631 perf. 13½ & Canada #1779b 7.00 7.00
1632 A537 $1 Chusan 1.60 .80
1633 A537 $1.20 Heather Belle 2.00 1.25
Nos. 1630-1633 (4) 5.65 3.25

Australia '99 (No. 1630a). World Stamp Expo. (No. 1631a).

See Canada No. 1779a.

Issued: No. 1630a, 6/17/98; No. 1631a, 3/19/99.

Legends Type of 1997

Olympians: No. 1634: a, Betty Cuthbert. b, Cuthbert running. c, Herb Elliott. d, Elliott running. e, Dawn Fraser. f, Fraser swimming. g, Marjorie Jackson. h, Jackson running. i, Murray Rose. j, Rose swimming. k, Shirley Strickland. l, Strickland clearing hurdle.

1998, Jan. 21 *Perf. 14x14½*

Size: 34x26mm

1634 Sheet of 12 14.00 14.00
a.-l. A522 45c any single .80 .80
m. Booklet pane, #1634a-1634d 5.50 —
n. Booklet pane, #1634e-1634h 5.50 —
o. Booklet pane, #1634i-1634l 5.50 —

Booklet Stamps
Self-Adhesive
Serpentine Die Cut 11½
Size: 34x25mm

1635	A522	45c like #1634a	1.10	.40
1636	A522	45c like #1634b	1.10	.40
1637	A522	45c like #1634c	1.10	.40
1638	A522	45c like #1634d	1.10	.40
1639	A522	45c like #1634e	1.10	.40
1640	A522	45c like #1634f	1.10	.40
1641	A522	45c like #1634g	1.10	.40
1642	A522	45c like #1634h	1.10	.40
1643	A522	45c like #1634i	1.10	.40
1644	A522	45c like #1634j	1.10	.40
1645	A522	45c like #1634k	1.10	.40
1646	A522	45c like #1634l	1.10	.40
a.		Bklt. pane of 12, #1635-1646	20.00	
		Nos. 1635-1646 (12)	13.20	4.80

By its nature, No. 1646a is a complete booklet. The peelable backing serves as a booklet cover.

Nos. 1634m-1634o issued 1/24/07.

Greetings — A538

1998, Feb. 12 Litho. *Perf. 14½x14*

1647	A538	45c Champagne roses	.90	.40

Booklet Stamp
Self-Adhesive
Serpentine Die Cut 11½

1648	A538	45c like #1647	.90	.65
a.		Booklet pane of 10	11.00	

By its nature No. 1648a is a complete booklet. The peelable paper backing, which contains 12 labels, serves as a booklet cover.

Queen Elizabeth II, 72nd Birthday — A539

1998, Apr. 9 Litho. *Perf. 14x14½*

1649	A539	45c multicolored	1.10	.65

Royal Australian Navy Fleet Air Arm, 50th Anniv. — A540

1998, Apr. 9

1650	A540	45c multicolored	1.10	.40

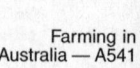

Farming in Australia — A541

Designs: No. 1651, Sheep for producing wool. No. 1652, Sheaves of wheat. No. 1653, Herding cattle on horseback. No. 1654, Harvesting sugar cane. No. 1655, Dairy cattle, man on motorcycle.

1998, Apr. 21

1651	A541	45c multicolored	.80	.40
1652	A541	45c multicolored	.80	.40
1653	A541	45c multicolored	.80	.40
1654	A541	45c multicolored	.80	.40
1655	A541	45c multicolored	.80	.40
a.		Strip of 5, #1651-1655	4.75	4.75
		Nos. 1651-1655 (5)	4.00	2.00

Booklet Stamps
Self-Adhesive
Serpentine Die Cut 11½
Size: 37x25mm

1656	A541	45c like #1651	1.25	.40
1657	A541	45c like #1652	1.25	.40
1658	A541	45c like #1653	1.25	.40
1659	A541	45c like #1654	1.25	.40
1660	A541	45c like #1655	1.25	.40
a.		Bklt. pane, 2 ea #1656-1660	16.00	
		Nos. 1656-1660 (5)	6.25	2.00

The peelable backing of No. 1660a serves as a booklet cover.

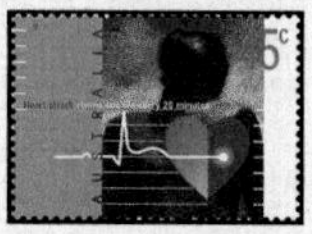
Heart Health — A542

1998, May 4 Litho. *Perf. 14x14½*

1661	A542	45c multicolored	1.10	.40

Rock and Roll in Australia — A543

a, "The Wild One," by Johnny O'Keefe, 1958. b, "Oh Yeah Uh Huh," by Col Joye and the Joye Boys, 1959. c, "He's My Blonde-headed Stompie Wompie Real Gone Surfer Boy," by Little Pattie, 1963. d, "Shakin' All Over," by Normie Rowe, 1965. e, "She's So Fine," by The Easybeats, 1965. f, "The Real Thing," by Russell Morris, 1969. g, "Turn Up Your Radio," by The Masters Apprentices, 1970. h, "Eagle Rock," by Daddy Cool, 1971. i, "Most People I Know Think That I'm Crazy," by Billy Thorpe & the Aztecs, 1972. j, "Horror Movie," by Skyhooks, 1974. k, "It's a Long Way to the Top," by AC/DC, 1975. l, "Howzat," by Sherbet, 1976.

1998, May 26

1662	A543	Sheet of 12	12.00	12.00
a.-l.		45c any single	.80	.80

Coil Stamps
Self-Adhesive
Serpentine Die Cut 11½
Size: 37x25mm

1663	A543	45c like #1662a	1.10	.50
1664	A543	45c like #1662b	1.10	.50
1665	A543	45c like #1662c	1.10	.50
1666	A543	45c like #1662d	1.10	.50
1667	A543	45c like #1662e	1.10	.50
1668	A543	45c like #1662f	1.10	.50
1669	A543	45c like #1662g	1.10	.50
1670	A543	45c like #1662h	1.10	.50
1671	A543	45c like #1662i	1.10	.50
1672	A543	45c like #1662j	1.10	.50
1673	A543	45c like #1662k	1.10	.50
1674	A543	45c like #1662l	1.10	.50
a.		Strip of 12 + label	18.00	
		Nos. 1663-1674 (12)	13.20	6.00

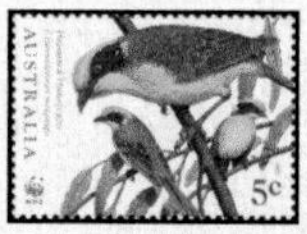
Endangered Birds — A544

World Wildlife Fund: No. 1675, Helmeted honeyeater. No. 1676, Orange-bellied parrot. No. 1677, Red-tailed black cockatoo. No. 1678, Gouldian finch.

1998, June 25 *Perf. 14x14½*

1675	A544	5c multicolored	.40	.40
1676	A544	5c multicolored	.40	.40
a.		Pair, #1675-1676	1.60	1.60
1677	A544	45c multicolored	.80	.80
1678	A544	45c multicolored	.80	.80
a.		Pair, #1677-1678	2.40	2.40

Performing and Visual Arts — A545

Young people: No. 1679, Playing French horn. No. 1680, Dancing.

1998, July 16 Litho. *Perf. 14x14½*

1679	A545	45c multicolored	.80	.80
1680	A545	45c multicolored	.80	.80
a.		Pair, #1679-1680	2.25	2.25

Orchids — A546

Designs: 45c, Phalaenopsis rosenstromii. 85c, Arundina graminifolia. $1, Grammatophyllum speciosum. $1.20, Dendrobium phalaenopsis.

1998, Aug. 6 Litho. *Perf. 14½x14*

1681	A546	45c multicolored	.80	.40
1682	A546	85c multicolored	1.30	.75
1683	A546	$1 multicolored	1.60	1.00
1684	A546	$1.20 multicolored	2.00	1.75
a.		Souvenir sheet, #1681-1684	6.50	6.50
		Nos. 1681-1684 (4)	5.70	3.90

See Singapore Nos. 858-861b.

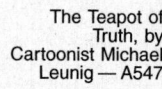

The Teapot of Truth, by Cartoonist Michael Leunig — A547

Designs: No. 1685, Angel carrying teapot, bird with flower. No. 1686, Birds perched on heart-shaped vine. No. 1687, Characters using their heads to pour tea into cup. $1, Stylized family. $1.20, Stylized teapot with face & legs.

1998, Aug. 13 *Perf. 14x14½*

1685	A547	45c multicolored	1.60	1.25
a.		Booklet pane of 4	6.50	
1686	A547	45c multicolored	1.60	1.25
a.		Booklet pane of 4	6.50	
1687	A547	45c multicolored	1.60	1.25
a.		Booklet pane of 4	6.50	

Size: 30x25mm

1688	A547	$1 multicolored	2.60	2.60
a.		Booklet pane of 2	5.25	
1689	A547	$1.20 multicolored	3.25	3.25
a.		Booklet pane of 2	6.25	
		Complete booklet, #1685a, 1686a, 1687a, 1688a, 1689a, 1 postal card & 16 self-adhesive labels	35.00	
		Nos. 1685-1689 (5)	10.65	9.60

A548

Butterflies — No. 1690, Red lacewing. No. 1691, Dull oakblue. No. 1692, Meadow argus. No. 1693, Ulysses. No. 1694, Common red-eye.

1998, Sept. 3 Litho. *Perf. 14½x14*

1690	A548	45c multicolored	.80	.80
1691	A548	45c multicolored	.80	.80
1692	A548	45c multicolored	.80	.80
1693	A548	45c multicolored	.80	.80
1694	A548	45c multicolored	.80	.80
a.		Strip of 5, #1690-1694	5.50	5.25
b.		Souv. sheet of 5, #1690-1694	7.00	7.00
		Nos. 1690-1694 (5)	4.00	4.00

No. 1694b for China 1999 World Philatelic Exhibition. Issued 8/21/99.

Self-Adhesive
Serpentine Die Cut 11½

1695	A548	45c like #1690	1.00	.40
1696	A548	45c like #1691	1.00	.40
1697	A548	45c like #1692	1.00	.40
1698	A548	45c like #1693	1.00	.40
1699	A548	45c like #1694	1.00	.40
a.		Strip of 5, #1695-1699	8.75	
		Nos. 1695-1699 (5)	5.00	2.00

A549

Designs: No. 1700, Sextant, map of Bass Strait. No. 1701, Telescope, map of Van Diemen's Land (Tasmania).

1998, Sept. 10 *Perf. 14½x14*

1700	A549	45c multicolored	1.00	.40
1701	A549	45c multicolored	1.00	.40
a.		Pair, #1700-1701	2.40	2.25

Circumnavigation of Tasmania by George Bass (1771-c. 1803) and Matthew Flinders (1774-1814), bicent.

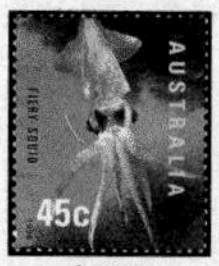
A550

Marine Life — A551

Designs: No. 1702, Fiery squid. No. 1703, Manta ray. No. 1704, Bottlenose dolphin. No. 1705, Weedy seadragon. No. 1706, Southern right whale. No. 1707, White pointer shark.

Perf. 14½x14, 14x14½

1998, Oct. 1 Litho.

1702	A550	45c multi	.80	.80
1703	A550	45c multi, horiz.	.80	.80
1704	A551	45c multi	.80	.80
1705	A551	45c multi	.80	.80
a.		Pair, #1704-1705	2.25	2.25

Size: 50x30mm

1706	A551	45c multi, horiz.	.80	.80
1707	A551	45c multi	.80	.80
a.		Souvenir sheet, #1702-1707	6.00	5.75
		Nos. 1702-1707 (6)	4.80	4.80

Booklet Stamps
Self-Adhesive
Serpentine Die Cut Perf. 11½

1708	A551	45c like #1704	1.10	.40
1709	A551	45c like #1705	1.10	.40
a.		Bklt. pane, 5 ea #1708-1709	11.00	

No. 1709a is a complete booklet. The peelable paper backing serves as a booklet cover.

Nos. 1708-1709 also exist in coils, issued in rolls of 100 with surrounding selvage removed. Value, set of singles $4.50.

Universal Declaration of Human Rights, 50th Anniv. — A552

1998, Oct. 22 Litho. *Perf. 14½x14*

1712	A552	45c multicolored	1.10	.60

Christmas — A553

40c, Magi. 45c, Nativity. $1, Journey to Bethlehem.

1998, Nov. 2 *Perf. 14x14½*

1713	A553	40c multicolored	.80	.55
1714	A553	45c multicolored	.90	.80
1715	A553	$1 multicolored	2.00	2.00
		Nos. 1713-1715 (3)	3.70	3.35

Booklet Stamp
Self-Adhesive
Serpentine Die Cut Perf. 11½

1716	A553	40c multicolored	1.10	.55
a.		Booklet pane of 20	22.00	

No. 1716a is a complete booklet.

Nationality and Citizenship Act, 50th Anniv. — A554

1999, Jan. 14 Litho. *Perf. 14x14½*

1717	A554	45c multicolored	1.10	.50

Die Cut Perf. 11¾
Self-Adhesive

1718	A554	45c multicolored	1.10	.55

Legends Type of 1997

Designs: Nos. 1719, 1721, Arthur Boyd, artist. Nos. 1720, 1722, "Nebuchadnezzar on Fire Falling over a Waterfall," by Boyd.

1999, Jan. 22 Litho. *Perf. 14x14½*

1719	A522	45c multicolored	.80	.80
1720	A522	45c multicolored	.80	.80
a.		Pair, #1719-1720	2.25	2.25
b.		Booklet pane, #1719-1720	3.00	—

Booklet Stamps
Self-Adhesive
Serpentine Die Cut Perf. 11½

1721 A522 45c multicolored 1.10 .55
1722 A522 45c multicolored 1.10 .55
a. Bklt. pane, 5 ea #1721-1722 11.00

No. 1722a is a complete booklet.
No. 1720b issued 1/24/07.

Love — A555

1999, Feb. 4 ***Perf. 14x14½***
1723 A555 45c Red roses .75 .65

Booklet Stamp
Self-adhesive
Serpentine Die Cut Perf. 11½

1724 A555 45c like #1723 1.10 .55
a. Booklet pane of 10 11.00

No. 1724a is a complete booklet.

Intl. Year of Older Persons — A556

Designs: No. 1725, Woman walking with girl, man up close. No. 1726, Woman up close, man playing soccer with boy.

1999, Feb. 11 ***Perf. 14x14½***
1725 A556 45c multicolored .80 .40
1726 A556 45c multicolored .80 .40
a. Pair, #1725-1726 1.60 2.25

Early Navigators Type of 1963

No. 1727: a, like #374. b, like #376. c, like #377.
No. 1728: a, like #375. b, like #379. c, like #378.

Perf. 14x14½, 14½x14

1999, Mar. 19 **Litho.**
1727 Sheet of 3 5.25 5.00
a.-c. A144 45c any single 1.00 1.00
d. As #1727, imperf. 12.00 12.00
e. As #1727, perfin "A99" in sheet margin 45.00 45.00
1728 Sheet of 3 5.25 5.00
a.-c. A145 45c any single 1.00 1.00
d. As #1728, imperf. 12.00 12.00
e. As #1728, perfin "A99" in sheet margin 45.00 45.00

Australia '99, World Stamp Expo.
Nos. 1727e-1728e were made from Nos. 1727d-1728d at Australia '99. Examples different perforations or with the perforating and "A99" inverted were intentionally misperfed personally by patrons of the show.

Sailing Ships — A557

1999, Mar. 19 ***Perf. 14½x14***
1729 A557 45c Polly Woodside .90 .55
a. Perf 14x14½ 3.00 3.00
b. Souvenir sheet of 2, #1729a, Ireland #1173a 6.00 6.00
1730 A557 85c Alma Doepel 1.75 1.60
1731 A557 $1 Enterprize 1.90 1.60
1732 A557 $1.05 Lady Nelson 2.00 1.60
Nos. 1729-1732 (4) 6.55 5.35

Australia '99, World Stamp Expo (No. 1729a). See Ireland No. 1173.
No. 1729 was issued in sheets of 20 with a se-tenant label showing Australia '99 logo. Panes of 10 No. 1729 with labels were sold only at the show, where patrons could have their photos printed on the label.

Olympic Torch — A558

1999, Mar. 22
1733 A558 $1.20 #289 2.00 2.00

Flora & Fauna Type of 1996

Flowers: Nos. 1734, 1742A, 1743, 1746B, 1746I, Correa reflexa. Nos. 1735, 1742B, 1744, 1746C, 1746J, Hibbertia scandens. Nos. 1736, 1742C, 1745, 1746D, 1746K, Ipomoea pes-caprae. Nos. 1737, 1742D, 1746, 1746E, 1746L, Wahlenbergia stricta.
70c, Humpback whales, zebra volute. No. 1739, Brahminy kite, checkerboard helmet shell. No. 1740, Fraser Island, chambered nautilus. $1.05, Loggerhead turtle, baler. $1.20, White-bellied sea eagle, Campbell's stromb.

1999 **Litho.** ***Perf. 14x14½***
1734 A511 45c multicolored .80 .40
1735 A511 45c multicolored .80 .40
1736 A511 45c multicolored .80 .40
1737 A511 45c multicolored .80 .40
a. Block of 4, #1734-1737 3.75 3.75
1738 A511 70c multicolored 1.40 1.40
1739 A511 90c multicolored 1.60 1.25
1740 A511 90c multicolored 1.60 1.25
a. Pair, #1739-1740 3.50 3.25
1741 A511 $1.05 multicolored 2.10 1.90
1742 A511 $1.20 multicolored 2.40 2.40
Nos. 1734-1742 (9) 12.30 9.80

Booklet Stamps
Serpentine Die Cut 11, 11¼ (#1742Df)
Self-Adhesive

1742A A511 45c like #1734 1.00 .40
1742B A511 45c like #1735 1.00 .40
1742C A511 45c like #1736 1.00 .40
1742D A511 45c like #1737 1.00 .40
e. Booklet pane, 3 each #1742A, 1742C, 2 each #1742B, 1742D 10.00
f. Booklet pane, 5 each #1742A-1742D 19.00

Die Cut perf. 12½x12¾

1743 A511 45c like #1734 1.00 .40
1744 A511 45c like #1735 1.00 .40
1745 A511 45c like #1736 1.00 .40
1746 A511 45c like #1737 1.00 .40
a. Booklet pane, 3 each #1743, 1745, 2 each #1744, #1746 10.00
g. Strip of 4, #1743-1746 4.50
Nos. 1742A-1746 (8) 8.00 3.20

Nos. 1742De, 1746a are complete booklets.

Coil Stamps
Serpentine Die Cut 11½

1746B A511 45c like #1734 1.10 .40
1746C A511 45c like #1735 1.10 .40
1746D A511 45c like #1736 1.10 .40
1746E A511 45c like #1737 1.10 .40
f. Strip of 4, #1746B-1746E 5.25
h. Pane, #1746B, 1746D-1746E, 2 #1746C 5.75

Serpentine Die Cut 13

1746I A511 45c like #1734 1.10 .40
1746J A511 45c like #1735 1.10 .40
1746K A511 45c like #1736 1.10 .40
1746L A511 45c like #1737 1.10 .40
m. Strip of 4, #1746I-1746K 5.25
Nos. 1746B-1746L (8) 8.80 3.20

Issued: Nos. 1738-1742, 7/8; 1746B-1746E, 1746I-1746L, 4/8.
No. 1742Df is a complete booklet.

Queen Mother and Queen Elizabeth II — A559

1999, Apr. 15 ***Perf. 14x14½***
1747 A559 45c multicolored 1.00 .75

Queen Elizabeth II, 73rd birthday.

Children's Television Programs — A560

Designs: Nos. 1748, 1753, "Here's Humphrey." Nos. 1749, 1754, "Bananas in Pajamas." Nos. 1750, 1755, "Mr. Squiggle." Nos. 1751, 1756, Teddy bears from "Play School." Nos. 1752, 1757, Clock, dog, boy from "Play School."

1999, May 6 **Litho.** ***Perf. 14½x14***
1748 A560 45c multicolored 1.00 .75
1749 A560 45c multicolored 1.00 .75
1750 A560 45c multicolored 1.00 .75
1751 A560 45c multicolored 1.00 .75
1752 A560 45c multicolored 1.00 .75
a. Strip of 5, #1748-1752 5.75 5.75
Nos. 1748-1752 (5) 5.00 3.75

Self-Adhesive
Serpentine Die Cut 11½x11¼

1753 A560 45c like #1748 1.10 .40
1754 A560 45c like #1749 1.10 .40
1755 A560 45c like #1750 1.10 .40
1756 A560 45c like #1751 1.10 .40
1757 A560 45c like #1752 1.10 .40
a. Bklt. pane, 2 ea #1753-1757 18.00
Nos. 1753-1757 (5) 5.50 2.00

No. 1757a is a complete booklet.

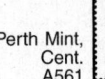

Perth Mint, Cent. A561

1999, May 13 **Litho.** ***Perf. 14¼x14***
1758 A561 $2 gold & multi 4.00 3.75

Test Rugby in Australia, Cent. — A562

Designs: Nos. 1759, 1763, Kicking ball, vert. Nos. 1760, 1764, Catching ball. $1, Diving with ball. $1.20, Being tackled.

1999, June 8 **Litho.** ***Perf. 14½x14***
1759 A562 45c multi 1.00 .75
1760 A562 45c multi, vert. 1.00 .75
a. Pair, #1759-1760 2.25 2.25

Perf. 14x14½

1761 A562 $1 multi 2.25 2.25
1762 A562 $1.20 multi 2.50 2.50

Serpentine Die Cut 11½
Self-Adhesive
Coil Stamps

1763 A562 45c like #1759 1.75 .60
1764 A562 45c like #1760 1.75 .60
a. Pair, #1763-1764 3.50

Snowy Mountains Hydroelectric Projects, 50th Anniv. — A563

Designs: No. 1765, Rock bolters at Tumut 2 Power Station Hall, driller at Tooma-Tumut Tunnel. No. 1766, English class for migrant workers at Cooma. No. 1767, Eucumbene Dam, Tumut 2 Tailwater Tunnel. No. 1768, Island Bend Dam, German carpenters.

1999, Aug. 12 **Litho.** ***Perf. 14x14½***
1765 A563 45c multicolored 1.00 .75
1766 A563 45c multicolored 1.00 .75
1767 A563 45c multicolored 1.00 .75
1768 A563 45c multicolored 1.00 .75
a. Block of 4, #1765-1768 4.50 4.50
Nos. 1765-1768 (4) 4.00 3.00

Self-Adhesive
Coil Stamps
Litho.
Serpentine Die Cut 11¾

1769 A563 45c Like #1765 1.25 .40
1770 A563 45c Like #1766 1.25 .40
1771 A563 45c Like #1767 1.25 .40
1772 A563 45c Like #1768 1.25 .40
a. Strip of 4, #1769-1772 6.00 5.25
Nos. 1769-1772 (4) 5.00 1.60

Teddy Bear — A564

Birthday cake — A564a

Roses, Rings — A564b

Pen, Letter — A564c

Christmas Ornament — A564d

Koala — A564e

1999-2003 **Litho.** ***Perf. 14½x14***
1773 A564 45c multicolored .90 .65
1774 A564a 45c multicolored .90 .65
1775 A564b 45c multicolored .90 .65
a. Booklet pane of 4 + 4 labels ('02) 3.75 —
Booklet, 5 #1775a 27.50
1776 A564c 45c multicolored .90 .65
1777 A564d 45c multicolored .90 .75
a. Booklet pane of 4 + 4 labels 3.75 —
Complete booklet, 5 #1777a 27.50
1778 A564e $1 multicolored 2.60 2.60
Nos. 1773-1778 (6) 7.10 5.95

Greetings.
Nos. 1773-1778 each were printed with a se-tenant label at right in sheets of 20. Size of label is 24mm wide on No. 1777, 19mm wide on No. 1775a, 17mm on others. Labels were inscribed with phrases appropriate to the stamp design, or blank, upon which Australia Post printed photographs, sent to them through special orders. No. 1775a and 1777a each come with five different margins, each of which is found in the respective booklet, which sold for $9.95.
Issued: Nos. 1773-1778, 9/1/99; No. 1775a, 3/12/02. No. 1777a, 10/31/03.
See No. 1926.
Compare with types A631, A633, A634.

2000 Olympic Games, Sydney — A565

1999, Sept. 14 **Litho.** ***Perf. 14½x14***
1779 A565 45c multicolored 1.00 .75

Sydney Design 99, Intl. Design Congress — A566

Designs: 45c, Australia Post emblem. 90c, Embryo chair. $1.35, Possum skin textile design. $1.50, Storey Hall, Royal Melbourne Institute of Technology.

1999, Sept. 16 **Litho.** ***Perf. 14x14½***
1780 A566 45c multicolored 1.25 .75
1781 A566 90c multicolored 1.60 1.25
1782 A566 $1.35 multicolored 2.40 2.00
1783 A566 $1.50 multicolored 2.75 2.75
Nos. 1780-1783 (4) 8.00 6.75

Pond Fauna — A567

Designs: Nos. 1784, 1790c, Roth's tree frog. Nos. 1785, 1790d, Dragonfly. Nos. 1786, 1790b, Sacred kingfisher. Nos. 1787, 1790f, Magnificent tree frog. Nos. 1788, 1790e, 1791, Northern dwarf tree frog. Nos. 1789, 1790a, 1792, Javelin frog.
No. 1793, Sacred kingfisher. No. 1794, Magnificent tree frog.

1999, Oct. 1 **Litho.** ***Perf. 14x14½***
1784 A567 45c multicolored .95 .80
1785 A567 45c multicolored .95 .80
a. Pair, #1784-1785 2.25 2.25

Size: 26x38mm
Perf. 14½x14

1786 A567 45c multicolored .95 .80
1787 A567 45c multicolored .95 .80
a. Pair, #1786-1787 2.25 2.25

Size: 25x30mm

1788 A567 50c multicolored 1.10 .90
1789 A567 50c multicolored 1.10 .90
a. Pair, #1788-1789 2.40 2.40
Nos. 1784-1789 (6) 6.00 5.00

Souvenir Sheet

Perf. 14½

1790 A567 Sheet of 6, #a-f 7.00 7.00
g. Ovptd. in sheet margin for Bangkok 2000 Exhibition 12.00 12.00
h. Ovptd. in gold in sheet margin for Adelaide Stamp '99 Exhibition 15.00 15.00

No. 1790d has foil impression on dragonfly's wings.

No. 1790 with overprints for Victorian and South Australian Philatelic Congresses in 1999 are unofficial.

No. 1790h was issued by Australia Post. Another, unofficial, overprint in black (with an orange and black sticker affixed) was applied to other souvenir sheets by the event organizers using the same logo.

Self-Adhesive

Serpentine Die Cut 11¼

Size: 25x30mm

1791 A567 50c multicolored 1.40 .60
1792 A567 50c multicolored 1.40 .60
a. Bklt. pane, 5 ea #1791-1792 17.00

Nos. 1791-1792 are booklet stamps. No. 1792a is a complete booklet.

Die Cut Perf. 11¾

Size: 26x38mm

1793 A567 45c multicolored 1.25 .60
1794 A567 45c multicolored 1.25 .60
a. Pair, #1793-1794 4.25 4.25

Christmas — A568

1999, Nov. 1 *Perf. 14½x14*

1795 A568 40c Madonna and child, vert. 1.00 .75

Perf. 14x14½

1796 A568 $1 Tree 2.25 2.25

Booklet Stamp
Self-Adhesive

Serpentine Die Cut 11¾

1797 A568 40c Like #1795 1.00 .40
a. Booklet pane of 20 20.00

Celebrate 2000 — A569

1999, Nov. 1 Litho. *Perf. 14½x14*

1798 A569 45c multicolored 1.10 .75

No. 1798 has a holographic image. Soaking in water may affect hologram.

Sheets of 10 exist with 10 labels inscribed "Celebrate 2000."

No. 1798 was also printed with a se-tenant label at right in sheets of 20. Labels were inscribed "Celebrate 2000" or blank, upon which Australia Post printed photographs, sent to them through special orders.

Sheets of 10 stamps plus 10 photo labels have been available at special events. These have the sheet selvage inscribed for each event. Most of these have been available only at the event and exist in very limited quantities.

Faces of Australia A570

Ordinary people: a, Nicholle and Meghan Triandis, baby twins. b, David Willis, cattleman with hat. c, Natasha Bramley, with snorkel gear. d, Cyril Watson, Aboriginal boy. e, Mollie Dowdall, with red hat. f, Robin Dicks, in khaki uniform. g, Mary Simons, with gray hair. h, Peta and Samantha Nieuwerth, mother and daughter. i, Dr. John Matthews, with stethoscope. j, Edith Dizon-Fitzsimmons, with large earrings. k, Philippa Weir, with brown hat. l, John Thurgar, with suit, tie and hat. m, Miguel Alzona, with large, multicolored hat. n, Rachael Thomson, girl with wavy hair. o, Necip Akarsu, with mustache. p, Justin Allan, with HMAS Brisbane cap. q, Wadad Dennaoui, with checked blouse. r, Jack Laity, with hat and jacket. s, Kelsey Stubbin, with Australia cap. t, Gianna Rossi, with hand on chin. u, Paris Hansch, young girl. v, Donald George Whatham, in shirt and tie. w, Stacey Coull, Aboriginal girl in patterned blouse. x, Alex Payne, with bicycle helmet. y, John Lodge, with Salvation Army hat.

2000, Jan. 1 Litho. *Perf. 14¾x13¾*

1799 A570 Sheet of 25 24.00 24.00
a.-y. 45c Any single .95 .80

Legends Type of 1997

Aging veterans of World War I: Nos. 1800, 1804, Walter Parker. Nos. 1801, 1805, Roy Longmore. Nos. 1802, 1806, Alec Campbell. Nos. 1803, 1807, 1914-15 Star.

2000, Jan. 21 Litho. *Perf. 14x14¾*

Size: 34x26mm

1800 A522 45c multi .95 .80
1801 A522 45c multi .95 .80
1802 A522 45c multi .95 .80
1803 A522 45c multi .95 .80
a. Block of 4, #1800-1803 4.00 3.60
b. Booklet pane, #1800-1803 *6.00* —
Nos. 1800-1803 (4) 3.80 3.20

Self-Adhesive

Die Cut Perf. 11¾

1804 A522 45c multi 1.00 .75
1805 A522 45c multi 1.00 .75
1806 A522 45c multi 1.00 .75
1807 A522 45c multi 1.00 .75
a. Complete booklet, 2 each #1804-1806, 4 #1807 13.00
Nos. 1804-1807 (4) 4.00 3.00

No. 1803b issued 1/24/07.

A571

Arts festivals.

2000, Feb. 24 Litho. *Perf. 14¾x14*

1808 A571 45c Perth .95 .75
1809 A571 45c Adelaide .95 .75
1810 A571 45c Sydney .95 .75
1811 A571 45c Melbourne .95 .75
1812 A571 45c Brisbane .95 .75
a. Strip of 5, #1808-1812 4.75 4.75
Nos. 1808-1812 (5) 4.75 3.75

A572

Gardens: Nos. 1813, 1818, 1823, Coast banksia, false sarsaparilla, swamp bloodwood (denomination at UR). Nos. 1814, 1819, 1824, Swamp bottlebrush, Eastern spinebill (denomination at UL). Nos. 1815, 1820, 1825, Canna X generalis varieties (denomination at LL). Nos. 1816, 1821, 1826, Pond, roses, purple swamphen (denomination at UR). Nos. 1817, 1822, 1827, Pond, hibiscus, nerium oleander (denomination at UL).

2000, Mar. 23 Litho. *Perf. 14¾x14*

1813 A572 45c multi .95 .95
1814 A572 45c multi .95 .95
1815 A572 45c multi .95 .95
1816 A572 45c multi .95 .95
1817 A572 45c multi .95 .95
a. Horiz. strip, #1813-1817 4.75 4.75
Nos. 1813-1817 (5) 4.75 4.75

Booklet Stamps
Self-Adhesive

Serpentine Die Cut 11½x11¼

Pale Green Frames

1818 A572 45c multi 1.10 .75
1819 A572 45c multi 1.10 .75
1820 A572 45c multi 1.10 .75
1821 A572 45c multi 1.10 .75
1822 A572 45c multi 1.10 .75
a. Booklet, 2 each #1818-1822 11.50
Nos. 1818-1822 (5) 5.50 3.75

Coil Stamps
Self-Adhesive

Serpentine Die Cut 11¾

Pale Green Frames

1823 A572 45c multi 1.25 .75
1824 A572 45c multi 1.25 .75
1825 A572 45c multi 1.25 .75
1826 A572 45c multi 1.25 .75
1827 A572 45c multi 1.25 .75
a. Strip of 5, #1823-1827 7.50
Nos. 1823-1827 (5) 6.25 3.75

Queen Elizabeth II, 74th Birthday — A573

2000, Apr. 13 Litho. *Perf. 14x14¾*

1828 A573 45c multi 1.00 .75

Korean War, 50th Anniv. — A574

2000, Apr. 18

1829 A574 45c multi 1.00 .75

Daisy — A575

Australia on Globe, Southern Cross — A576

Kangaroo and Flag — A577

Sand, Sea and Sky — A578

Rainforest — A579

2000, May 11 *Perf. 14½x14*

1830 A575 45c multi + label 1.20 .75
1831 A576 45c multi + label 1.20 .75
1832 A577 45c multi + label 1.20 .75
1833 A578 45c multi + label 1.20 .75
1834 A579 45c multi + label 1.20 .75
Nos. 1830-1834 (5) 6.00 3.75

Nos. 1830-1834 each issued in sheets of 20 stamps and labels, with and without decorative selvage.

Sheets containing 10 No. 1831 with margins and ten labels that could be personalized were sold for $12, $2 of which was donated to volunteer organizations of the purchaser's choice. Volunteer organizations could purchase these sheets and offer them for resale in fundraising projects.

No. 1832 exists in a sheet of 10+10 labels that sold sold for $16. Sheet has decorative selvage and labels showing stock photo.

The Move Towards Federation — A580

Designs: No. 1835, Taking the vote. No. 1836, Waiting for the results. No. 1837, The fair new nation. No. 1838, Queen Victoria.

2000, May 22 *Perf. 14¾x14*

1835 A580 45c multi .90 .75
1836 A580 45c multi .90 .75
a. Pair, #1835-1836 2.00 2.00

Size: 30x50mm

Perf. 14x14½

1837 A580 $1.50 multi 2.40 2.40
1838 A580 $1.50 multi 2.40 2.40
a. Pair, #1837-1838 5.00 5.00
b. Souvenir sheet, #1836a, 1838a 7.25 7.25
c. As "b," with marginal inscription for The Stamp Show 2000, London 14.00 14.00
Nos. 1835-1838 (4) 6.60 6.30

Tourist Attractions A581

Designs: 50c, Sydney Opera House. $1, Nandroya Falls. $1.50, Sydney Harbour Bridge. $2, Cradle Mountain. $3, The Pinnacles. $4.50, Flinders Ranges. $5, Twelve Apostles. $10, Devils Marbles.

2000, June 20 Litho. *Perf. 14½x14*

1839 A581 50c multi .80 .75
1840 A581 $1 multi 1.60 1.50
1841 A581 $1.50 multi 2.40 2.25
1842 A581 $2 multi 3.25 2.75
1843 A581 $3 multi 4.75 4.50

Size: 56x25mm

Perf. 14x14½

1844 A581 $4.50 multi 7.25 6.75
1845 A581 $5 multi 8.00 7.25
1846 A581 $10 multi 16.00 14.40
Nos. 1839-1846 (8) 44.05 40.15

See Nos. 1925, 1979-1983, 2055-2059, 2077-2080, 2280-2283.

2000 Paralympics, Sydney — A582

Designs: Nos. 1847, 1855, Wheelchair tennis. Nos. 1848, 1856, Amputee running. Nos. 1849, 1853, Wheelchair basketball. Nos. 1850, 1852, Cycling for the visually impaired. Nos. 1851, 1854, Amputee shot put.

2000, July 3 Litho. *Perf. 14¾x14*

1847 A582 45c multi .75 .75
1848 A582 45c multi .75 .75
a. Pair, #1847-1848 2.00 2.00
1849 A582 49c multi 1.00 1.00
1850 A582 49c multi 1.00 1.00
1851 A582 49c multi 1.00 1.00
a. Strip of 3, #1849-1851 3.25 3.25
Nos. 1847-1851 (5) 4.50 4.50

Booklet Stamps
Self-Adhesive

Die Cut Perf. 11½x11¾

1852 A582 49c multi 1.25 .75
1853 A582 49c multi 1.25 .75
1854 A582 49c multi 1.25 .75
a. Bklt., 4 ea #1852-1853, 2 #1854 14.50

Coil Stamps
Self-Adhesive

Serpentine Die Cut 11¾

1855 A582 45c multi 1.10 .85
1856 A582 45c multi 1.10 .85
a. Pair, #1855-1856 3.00 3.00
Nos. 1852-1856 (5) 5.95 3.95

No. 1851 exists without Tasmania in the map of Australia at LL. Value $20.

Australian Victoria Cross, Cent. — A583

Designs: No. 1857, Sir Neville Howse. No. 1858, Sir Arthur Roden Cutler. No. 1859, Victoria Cross. No. 1860, Edward Kenna. No. 1861, Keith Payne.

2000, July 24 Litho. *Perf. 14¾x14*

1857 A583 45c multi .95 .75
1858 A583 45c multi .95 .75
1859 A583 45c multi .95 .75
1860 A583 45c multi .95 .75
1861 A583 45c multi .95 .75
a. Horiz. strip of 5, #1857-1861 5.00 5.00
Nos. 1857-1861 (5) 4.75 3.75

Olympic Sports — A584

Designs: Nos. 1862a, 1869, Water polo. Nos. 1862b, 1870, Women's field hockey. Nos. 1862c, 1863, Swimming. Nos. 1862d, 1865, Basketball. Nos. 1862e, 1866, Triathlon cycling. Nos. 1862f, 1871, Equestrian. Nos. 1862g, 1872, Tennis. Nos. 1862h, 1864, Rhythmic gymnastics. Nos. 1862i, 1867, Runner. Nos. 1862j, 1868, Rowing.

2000, Aug. 17 Litho. *Perf. 14¾x14*

1862	Sheet of 10	11.50	11.50
a.-j.	A584 45c Any single	.80	.80
k.	As #1862, with inscription added in sheet margin	20.00	20.00

No. 1862k was issued 9/15/00 and has additional multicolored inscription in upper sheet margin reading "15-28 / September / 2000 / OLYMPHILEX 2000" and show emblem.

Booklet Stamps

Self-Adhesive

Serpentine Die Cut 11½x11¼

1863	A584 45c multi	1.00	.70
1864	A584 45c multi	1.00	.70
1865	A584 45c multi	1.00	.70
1866	A584 45c multi	1.00	.70
1867	A584 45c multi	1.00	.70
1868	A584 45c multi	1.00	.70
1869	A584 45c multi	1.00	.70
1870	A584 45c multi	1.00	.70
1871	A584 45c multi	1.00	.70
1872	A584 45c multi	1.00	.70
a.	Booklet, #1863-1872	14.00	
	Nos. 1863-1872 (10)	10.00	7.00

Sydney and Athens — A585

Olympic torch, flag and: 45c, Parthenon. $1.50, Sydney Opera House.

2000, Sept. 15 Litho. *Perf. 14½x14*

1873	A585 45c multi + label	1.00	.60
1874	A585 $1.50 multi + label	2.40	2.40

Nos. 1873-1874 were issued in sheets of 20 stamps and 20 se-tenant labels. Labels were inscribed "Sydney Athens." These sheets could be ordered with personalized labels, as could sheets with a stock photo.

See Greece Nos. 1968-1969.

Australian Gold Medalists at 2000 Olympics A586

Cathy Freeman Lighting Olympic Flame A587

Medal Winners: Nos. 1875, 1891, Ian Thorpe. Nos. 1876, 1892, Men's 4x100-meter freestyle relay swimming team. Nos. 1877, 1893, Michael Diamond. Nos. 1878, 1894, Three day event equestrian team. Nos. 1879, 1895, Susie O'Neill. Nos. 1880, 1896, Men's 4x200-meter freestyle relay swimming team. Nos. 1881, 1897, Simon Fairweather. Nos. 1882, 1898, Brett Aitken, Scott McGrory. Nos. 1883, 1899, Grant Hackett. Nos. 1884, 1900, Women's water polo team. Nos. 1885, 1901, Natalie Cook, Kerri Pottharst. Nos. 1886, 1902, Cathy Freeman. Nos. 1887, 1903, Lauren Burns. Nos. 1888, 1904, Women's field hockey team. Nos. 1889, 1905, Jenny Armstrong, Belinda Stowell. Nos. 1890, 1906, Tom King, Mark Turnbull.

2000 Digitally Printed *Perf. 14¼*

1875	A586 45c multi	1.00	.80
1876	A586 45c multi	1.00	.80
1877	A586 45c multi	1.00	.80
1878	A586 45c multi	1.00	.80
1879	A586 45c multi	1.00	.80
1880	A586 45c multi	1.00	.80
1881	A586 45c multi	1.00	.80
1882	A586 45c multi	1.00	.80
1883	A586 45c multi	1.00	.80
1884	A586 45c multi	1.00	.80
1885	A586 45c multi	1.00	.80
1886	A586 45c multi	1.00	.80
1887	A586 45c multi	1.00	.80
1888	A586 45c multi	1.00	.80
1889	A586 45c multi	1.00	.80
1890	A586 45c multi	1.00	.80

Litho.

1891	A586 45c multi	1.10	1.10
1892	A586 45c multi	1.10	1.10
1893	A586 45c multi	1.10	1.10
1894	A586 45c multi	1.10	1.10
1895	A586 45c multi	1.10	1.10
1896	A586 45c multi	1.10	1.10
1897	A586 45c multi	1.10	1.10
1898	A586 45c multi	1.10	1.10
1899	A586 45c multi	1.10	1.10
1900	A586 45c multi	1.10	1.10
1901	A586 45c multi	1.10	1.10
1902	A586 45c multi	1.10	1.10
1903	A586 45c multi	1.10	1.10
1904	A586 45c multi	1.10	1.10
1905	A586 45c multi	1.10	1.10
1906	A586 45c multi	1.10	1.10
1907	A587 45c multi	1.60	1.60
	Nos. 1875-1907 (33)	35.20	32.00

Issued: Nos. 1875-1876, 9/17; No. 1877, 9/18; Nos. 1891-1892, 9/19; Nos. 1878-1880, 1893, 9/20; No. 1881, 9/21; Nos. 1882, 1894-1896, 9/22; No. 1897, 9/23; Nos. 1883-1884, 1898, 9/24; Nos. 1885-1886, 1899-1900, 9/26; Nos. 1887, 1901-1902, 9/28; Nos. 1888, 1903, 9/30; Nos. 1889-1890, 10/1; No. 1904, 10/2; Nos. 1905-1906, 10/3; No. 1907, 10/10.

Nos. 1875-1890 have shinier appearance than Nos. 1891-1906. Olympic rings, flag stars and flag edge on Nos. 1875-1890 has a more ragged appearance than Nos. 1891-1906, which have crisp details.

Nos. 1875-1907 printed in sheets of 10. Sheets of Nos. 1875-1890 exist rouletted at either the right or left and have one of six red animal imprints in lower right margin representing where the sheets were made (Platypus, Sydney; Kookaburra, Canberra; Koala, Brisbane; Swan, Perth; Kangaroo, Adelaide; Opossum, Melbourne). Sheets of Nos. 1875-1890 were placed on sale at 67 outlets within 24 hours of the awarding of the medals to the athletes. Sheets of Nos. 1891-1906, which have a straight-edged right margin and a red Australia map imprint in lower right margin, gradually became available nationwide as stocks were printed and shipped.

A sheet containing Nos. 1891-1907 and 8 labels was available only in the Australia Post annual collection. Value, $50.

Space — A588

Designs: Nos. 1908, 1914a, Flight crew. Nos. 1909, 1914b, Robots, vert. Nos. 1910, 1914c, 1915, 1917, Astronaut, vert. Nos. 1911, 1914d, 1916, 1918, Terrain, vert. Nos. 1912, 1914e, Spacecraft. Nos. 1913, 1914f, Launch site, vert.

Perf. 14x14½, 14½x14

2000, Oct. 3 Litho.

1908	A588 45c multi	.95	.95
1909	A588 45c multi	.95	.95

Size: 26x38mm

1910	A588 45c multi	.95	.95
1911	A588 45c multi	.95	.95
a.	Pair, #1910-1911	2.25	2.25

Size: 50x30mm

1912	A588 45c multi	.95	.95

Size: 30x50mm

1913	A588 45c multi	.95	.95
	Nos. 1908-1913 (6)	5.70	5.70

Souvenir Sheet

Litho. with Translucent Foil

Perf. 14½

1914	Sheet of 6	5.00	5.00
a.-f.	A588 45c any single	.80	.80
g.	As #1914, ovptd. in margin in gold	14.00	14.00

Booklet Stamps

Litho.

Self-Adhesive

Serpentine Die Cut 11½x11¼

1915	A588 45c multi	1.00	.60
1916	A588 45c multi	1.00	.60
a.	Booklet, 5 each #1915-1916	12.00	

Coil Stamps

Serpentine Die Cut 11½

1917	A588 45c multi	1.10	.60
1918	A588 45c multi	1.10	.60
a.	Pair, #1917-1918	2.50	2.00

Nos. 1915-1918 have pink and gray frames.

No 1914g overprinted with emblem of Hong Kong 2001 Stamp Exhibition. Issued 2/1/01.

2000 Paralympics, Sydney — A589

Designs: No. 1919, Paralympics emblem. No. 1920, Runner with torch.

2000, Oct. 18 Litho. *Perf. 14½x14*

1919	A589 45c multi + label	1.25	1.00
1920	A589 45c multi + label	1.25	1.00

Siobhan Paton, Paralympian of the Year — A590

2000, Oct. 31 *Perf. 14¼*

1921	A590 45c multi	1.00	.75

Christmas — A591

40c, Madonna and child. 45c, Manger.

2000, Nov. 1 Litho. *Perf. 14½x14*

1922	A591 40c multi	.75	.50
1923	A591 45c multi	.75	.50
a.	Souvenir sheet, #1922-1923	2.25	2.25

Booklet Stamp

Serpentine Die Cut 11¾

1924	A591 40c multi	.85	.70
a.	Booklet of 20 + 20 stickers	17.25	

Tourist Attractions Type of 2000

2000, Nov. 1 *Perf. 14½x14*

1925	A581 80c Byron Bay	1.75	1.50

No. 1778 Digitally Overprinted in Dark Blue

2001, Jan. Litho. *Perf. 14½x14*

1926	A564 $1 multi + label	*17.50*	*17.50*

Federation of Australia, Cent. — A592

Designs: Nos. 1927, 1931, Federation Arch, Sydney. Nos. 1928, 1932, Sir Edmund Barton, first prime minister. No. 1929, National celebrations, horiz (50x30mm). No. 1930, State banquet (30x50mm).

Perf. 14¾x14, 14x14¾

2001, Jan. 1 Litho.

1927	A592 49c multi	1.00	.80
1928	A592 49c multi	1.00	.80
a.	Pair, #1927-1928	3.00	2.50
1929	A592 $2 multi	3.25	2.75
1930	A592 $2 multi	3.25	2.75
a.	Souvenir sheet, #1927-1930, perf. 14½	10.00	10.00
	Nos. 1927-1930 (4)	8.50	7.10

Self-Adhesive

Booklet Stamps

Serpentine Die Cut 11½x11

1931	A592 49c multi	1.00	.30
a.	Serpentine die cut 11½x11¾	—	—
1932	A592 49c multi	1.00	.30
a.	Booklet, 5 each # 1931-1932	11.50	

Australian Legends Type of 1997

Slim Dusty, musician: Nos. 1933, 1935, With guitar. Nos. 1934, 1936, Wearing blue shirt.

2001, Jan. 25 *Perf. 14x14¾*

Size: 34x26mm

1933	A522 45c multi	1.10	1.00
1934	A522 45c multi	1.10	1.00
a.	Pair, #1933-1934	2.50	2.00
b.	Booklet pane, #1933-1934	*3.00*	—

Self-Adhesive

Booklet Stamps

Serpentine Die Cut 11x11½

1935	A522 45c multi	1.10	.75
1936	A522 45c multi	1.10	.75
a.	Booklet, 5 each #1935-1936	11.50	
	Nos. 1933-1936 (4)	4.40	3.50

No. 1934b issued 1/24/07.

Australian Army, Cent. — A593

Rising Sun badge and: No. 1937, Light Horse Brigade, 1940, soldiers in New Guinea, 1943. No. 1938, Soldier in UN peacekeeping mission carrying Rwandan child, 1995, soldiers on commando officer selection course, 1997.

2001-05 *Perf. 14x14¾*

1937	A593 45c multi	1.10	.75
1938	A593 45c multi	1.10	.75
a.	Pair, #1937-1938	2.50	2.00
b.	Booklet pane, #1937-1938	*16.00*	—
	Complete booklet, #1176a, 1207a, 1256a, 1317a, 1380f, 1452a, 1454a, 1482a, 1938b	100.00	

Issued: Nos. 1937-1938, 2/15/01. No. 1938b, 4/05. Complete booklet sold for $14.95.

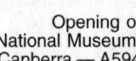

Opening of National Museum, Canberra — A594

Designs: No. 1939, Museum floor plan. No. 1940, Pangk (wallaby sculpture), by George MacNaught and Joe Ngallametta.

2001, Mar. 8

1939	A594 49c multi	1.00	.85
a.	Additionally dated "2013" (#1940c)	1.10	1.10
1940	A594 49c multi	1.00	.85
a.	Pair, #1939-1940	2.25	2.00
b.	Additionally dated "2013" (#1940c)	1.10	1.10
c.	Booklet pane of 2, #1939a, 1940b	2.25	—

Issued: Nos. 1939a, 1940b, 1940c, 3/5/13. No. 1938d was issued in booklet along with Nos. 2710c, 2869e, 3107c, 3349b and 3877a.

Australian Legends Type of 1997

Similar to Nos. 1575-1576, but with cropped designs and "1908-2001" inscription added.

2001, Mar. 13 *Perf. 14¼*

1941	A522 45c Like #1575	1.00	.80
a.	Without gold highlights, dated "2007"	1.40	1.40
1942	A522 45c Like #1576	.80	.80
a.	Pair, #1941-1942	2.25	2.00
b.	Without gold highlights, dated "2007"	1.40	1.40

Nos. 1941a, 1942b issued 11/14/07.

Rock Music — A595

Designs: Nos. 1943a, 1953, Khe Sanh, by Cold Chisel, 1978. Nos. 1943b, 1952, Down Under, by Men at Work, 1981. Nos. 1943c, 1951, Power and the Passion, by Midnight Oil, 1983. Nos. 1943d, 1950, Original Sin, by INXS. Nos. 1943e, 1949, You're the Voice, by John Farnham, 1986. Nos. 1943f, 1948, Don't Dream It's Over, by Crowded House, 1986. Nos. 1943g, 1947, Treaty, by Yothu Yindi, 1991. Nos. 1943h, 1946, Tomorrow, by Silverchair, 1994. Nos. 1943i, 1945, Confide in Me, by Kylie Minogue, 1994. Nos. 1943j, 1944, Truly, Madly, Deeply, by Savage Garden, 1997.

2001, Mar. 20 Litho. *Perf. 14x14¾*

1943	Sheet of 10	10.00	10.00
a.-j.	A595 45c Any single	1.00	.80

Self-Adhesive

Serpentine Die Cut 11¼x11½

1944 A595 45c multi 1.00 .80
1945 A595 45c multi 1.00 .80
1946 A595 45c multi 1.00 .80
1947 A595 45c multi 1.00 .80
1948 A595 45c multi 1.00 .80
1949 A595 45c multi 1.00 .80
1950 A595 45c multi 1.00 .80
1951 A595 45c multi 1.00 .80
1952 A595 45c multi 1.00 .80
1953 A595 45c multi 1.00 .80
a. Horiz. strip of 10, #1944-1953 14.50
b. Booklet, #1944-1953 10.00
Nos. 1944-1953 (10) 10.00 8.00

Queen Elizabeth II, 75th Birthday — A596

2001, Apr. 12 Litho. *Perf. 14¾x14*
1954 A596 45c multi 1.00 .75

Flower A597

Balloons A598

Streamers A599

Kangaroos A600

Bayulu Banner A601

Litho., Litho with Hologram (#1957)

2001-03 *Perf. 14½x14*
1955 A597 45c multi + label .80 .80
1956 A598 45c multi + label .80 .80
1957 A599 45c multi + label .80 .80
1958 A600 $1 multi + label 2.00 1.60
a. Booklet pane of 4 + 4 labels 8.75 —
Complete booklet, 2 #1958a 22.00
1959 A601 $1.50 multi + label 2.50 2.50
Nos. 1955-1959 (5) 6.90 6.50

Issued: Nos. 1955-1959, 4/24/01. No. 1958a, 10/31/03.

The complete booklet, which sold for $10.95, contains two panes of No. 1958a with different margins.

Federal Parliament, Cent. — A602

Designs: No. 1960, The Opening of the First Federal Parliament, 9 May 1901, by Charles Nuttall. No. 1961, Opening of the First Parliament of the Commonwealth of Australia by H.R.H. The Duke of Cornwall and York (Later King George V), May 9, 1901, by Tom Roberts.

2001, May 3 Litho. *Perf. 14¼*
1960 A602 45c multi 1.00 .65
a. Souvenir sheet of 1 2.00 2.00
1961 A602 $2.45 multi 4.00 4.00
a. Souvenir sheet of 1 5.50 5.50

Outback Services — A603

Designs: Nos. 1962, 1967, 1972, Telecommunications. Nos. 1963, 1968, 1973, Transport. Nos. 1964, 1969, 1974, School of the Air. Nos. 1965, 1970, 1975, Postal service. Nos., 1966, 1971, 1976, Royal flying Doctor Service.

2001, June 5 *Perf. 14x14½*
1962 A603 45c multi 1.00 .75
1963 A603 45c multi 1.00 .75
1964 A603 45c multi 1.00 .75
1965 A603 45c multi 1.00 .75
1966 A603 45c multi 1.00 .75
a. Horiz. strip, #1962-1966 5.00 4.75
Nos. 1962-1966 (5) 5.00 3.75

Self-Adhesive

Coil Stamps

Serpentine Die Cut 11¼

1967 A603 45c multi 1.25 .95
1968 A603 45c multi 1.25 .95
1969 A603 45c multi 1.25 .95
1970 A603 45c multi 1.25 .95
1971 A603 45c multi 1.25 .95
a. Horiz. strip, #1967-1971 8.00

Booklet Stamps

Serpentine Die Cut 11¾

1972 A603 45c multi 1.00 .75
1973 A603 45c multi 1.00 .75
1974 A603 45c multi 1.00 .75
1975 A603 45c multi 1.00 .75
1976 A603 45c multi 1.00 .75
a. Booklet, 2 each #1972-1976 11.00
Nos. 1967-1976 (10) 11.25 8.50

Dragon Boat Races — A604

Dragon boats and: 45c, Hong Kong Convention and Exhibition Center. $1, Sydney Opera House.

2001, June 25 *Perf. 14x14½*
1977 A604 45c multi 1.10 .85
1978 A604 $1 multi 2.25 2.25
a. Souvenir sheet, #1977-1978 3.50 3.50

See Hong Kong Nos. 938-939.

Tourist Attraction Type of 2000

Designs: 50c, Blue Mountains. $1, Murrumbidgee River. $1.50, Port Douglas. $20, Uluru.

Litho., Litho with Foil Application ($20)

2001, July 12 *Perf. 14½x14*
1979 A581 50c multi 1.00 1.00
1980 A581 $1 multi 2.00 2.00
1981 A581 $1.50 multi 3.00 3.00

Size: 56x25mm

Perf. 14x14½

1982 A581 $20 multi 24.00 24.00
Nos. 1979-1982 (4) 30.00 30.00

Booklet Stamp

Self-Adhesive

Serpentine Die Cut 11¼x10½

1983 A581 50c multi 1.10 1.00
a. Booklet, 10 #1983 11.50

Flora & Fauna Type of 1996

Birds: Nos. 1984, 1988, 1992, Variegated fairy wren. Nos. 1985, 1989, 1993, Painted firetail. Nos. 1986, 1990, 1994, Crimson chat. Nos. 1987, 1991, 1995, Budgerigar.

2001-02 Litho. *Perf. 14x14½*
1984 A511 45c multi 1.00 .75
1985 A511 45c multi 1.00 .75
1986 A511 45c multi 1.00 .75
1987 A511 45c multi 1.00 .75
a. Block of 4, #1984-1987 4.25 4.25
Nos. 1984-1987 (4) 4.00 3.00

Self-Adhesive

Coil Stamps

Die Cut Perf. 12½x12¾

1988 A511 45c multi 1.25 .75
1989 A511 45c multi 1.25 .75
1990 A511 45c multi 1.25 .75
1991 A511 45c multi 1.25 .75
a. Horiz. strip of 4, #1988-1991 5.25 5.25

Booklet Stamps

Serpentine Die Cut 11¼

1992 A511 45c multi 1.25 .75
1993 A511 45c multi 1.25 .75
1994 A511 45c multi 1.25 .75
1995 A511 45c multi 1.25 .75
a. Booklet pane, #1993, 1995 4.50
b. Booklet pane, #1992-1995, rouletted at bottom 7.50
Booklet, #1995a, 2 #1995b 12.00
c. Booklet pane, #1992-1995, rouletted at side 15.00
Booklet, 5 #1995c 85.00
d. Pane, #1992-1994, 2 #1995 9.50
e. Coil strip, #1992-1995 5.50
f. As "d," with Philakorea 2002 ovpt. in margin ('02) 15.00
g. As "d," with China 2002 Stamp & Coin Expo ovpt. in margin ('02) 15.00
h. As "d," with Hafnia '01 ovpt. in margin 27.50
Nos. 1988-1995 (8) 10.00 6.00

Issued: No. 1995f, 8/2/02; No. 1995g, 9/28/02. No. 1995h, 10/16/01. Rest of set, 8/9/01.

Daniel Solander (1733-82), Botanist on Endeavour A605

Designs: 45c, Barringtonia calyptrata and Solander. $1.50, Cachlospermum gillivraei and Endeavour.

Perf. 12½x12¾

2001, Aug. 16 Litho. & Engr.
1996 A605 45c multi 1.25 .90
1997 A605 $1.50 multi 3.25 3.25

See Sweden No. 2419.

Commonwealth Heads of Government Meeting, Brisbane — A606

2001, Sept. 4 Litho. *Perf. 14½x14*
1998 A606 45c Southern Cross 1.00 .75
1999 A606 45c Australia on globe 1.00 .75
a. Pair, #1998-1999 2.25 2.25

Christmas A607

2001, Sept. 4 *Perf. 14½x14*

Stamp + Label

2000 A607 40c Christmas tree .85 .70
2001 A607 80c Star 1.60 1.60

Nos. 2000-2001 were each printed in sheets of 20 + 20 labels. The labels could be personalized.

Birds of Prey — A608

Designs: No. 2002, Wedge-tailed eagle. No. 2003, Nankeen kestrel. No. 2004, Red goshawk, vert. No. 2005, Spotted harrier, vert.

Perf. 14x14½, 14½x14

2001, Sept. 11
2002 A608 49c multi 1.00 .80
2003 A608 49c multi 1.00 .80
a. Pair, #2002-2003 2.50 2.50
2004 A608 98c multi 1.60 1.60
2005 A608 98c multi 1.60 1.60
a. Pair, #2004-2005 4.00 2.50
Nos. 2002-2005 (4) 5.20 4.80

Caricatures of Australian Wildlife by Roland Harvey — A609

Designs: Nos. 2006, 2012, Bilby and antechinus musicians, dancing cockatoo. Nos. 2007, 2013, Koala with birthday cake. Nos. 2008, 2014, Ring-tailed possums with drinks and food. Nos. 2009, 2015, Bilbies, crocodile, emu, koala and gifts. Nos. 2010, 2016, Wombat and ladder. Nos. 2011, 2017, Wallabies, echidnas, platypus and ladder.

2001, Oct. 2 *Perf. 14½x14*
2006 A609 45c multi 1.00 .80
2007 A609 45c multi 1.00 .80
2008 A609 45c multi 1.00 .80
a. Horiz. strip of 3, #2006-2008 3.00 3.00
b. Souvenir sheet, #2006-2008 3.50 3.50
2009 A609 45c multi 1.00 .80
2010 A609 45c multi 1.00 .80
2011 A609 45c multi 1.00 .80
a. Horiz. strip, #2009-2011 3.00 3.00
b. Souvenir sheet, #2009-2011 3.00 3.00
Nos. 2006-2011 (6) 6.00 4.80

Self-Adhesive

Serpentine Die Cut 11½x11

2012 A609 45c multi 1.00 .80
2013 A609 45c multi 1.00 .80
2014 A609 45c multi 1.00 .80
2015 A609 45c multi 1.00 .80
2016 A609 45c multi 1.00 .80
2017 A609 45c multi 1.00 .80
a. Coil strip, 2012-2017 7.50
b. Booklet, #2014-2015, 2 each #2012-2013, 2016-2017 12.00
Nos. 2012-2017 (6) 6.00 4.80

Christmas — A610

Illuminations from the Wharncliffe Hours, by Maitre Francois: 40c, Adoration of the Magi. 45c, Flight into Egypt.

2001, Nov. 1 *Perf. 14½x14*
2018 A610 40c multi 1.00 .60
2019 A610 45c multi 1.25 .65

Self-Adhesive

Serpentine Die Cut 11½x11¼

2020 A610 40c multi 1.10 .25
a. Booklet of 20 + 20 labels 22.00

Australian Legends Type of 1997

Medical researchers: Nos. 2021, 2026, Sir Gustav Nossal. Nos. 2022, 2027, Nancy Mills. No. 2023, 2028, Peter Doherty. Nos. 2024, 2029, Fiona Stanley. Nos. 2025, 2030, Donald Metcalf.

2002, Jan. 23 Litho. *Perf. 14x14¾*

Size: 34x26mm

2021 A522 45c multi .95 .75
2022 A522 45c multi .95 .75
2023 A522 45c multi .95 .75
2024 A522 45c multi .95 .75
2025 A522 45c multi .95 .75
a. Vert. strip, #2021-2025 5.00 5.00
b. Booklet pane, #2021-2025 *8.00 8.00*
Nos. 2021-2025 (5) 4.75 3.75

Booklet Stamps

Self-Adhesive

Serpentine Die Cut 11x11½

2026 A522 45c multi 1.00 1.00
2027 A522 45c multi 1.00 1.00
2028 A522 45c multi 1.00 1.00
2029 A522 45c multi 1.00 1.00
2030 A522 45c multi 1.00 1.00
a. Booklet, 2 each #2026-2030 12.50
Nos. 2026-2030 (5) 5.00 5.00

No. 2025b issued 1/24/07.

Reign of Queen Elizabeth II, 50th Anniv. — A611

Queen: 45c, As young woman. $2.45, In 2000.

2002, Feb. 6 ***Perf. 14¾x14***
2031 A611 45c multi .95 .70
2032 A611 $2.45 multi 5.00 5.00
a. Souvenir sheet, #2031-2032 6.25 6.25

A booklet pane containing 2 each of Nos. 2031-2032 is found in the booklet footnoted under No. 2507.

Gold Medalists at 2002 Winter Olympics, Salt Lake City — A612

Designs: No. 2033, Steven Bradbury. No. 2034, Alisa Camplin.

2002 ***Perf. 14¼***
2033 A612 45c multi 1.10 1.00
2034 A612 45c multi 1.10 1.00

Issued: No. 2033, 2/20; No. 2034, 2/22.

Race Cars — A613

Designs: Nos. 2035, 2041, Victoria Austin 7 and Bugatti Type 40, Phillip Island, Victoria, 1928. Nos. 2036, 2042, Jaguar Mark II, Mallala, South Australia, 1963. Nos. 2037, 2043, Repco-Brabham, Sandown, Victoria, 1966. Nos. 2038, 2044, Holden Torana XU1 and Ford Falcon XY GTHO, Bathurst, New South Wales, 1972. Nos. 2039, 2045, Williams FW07 Ford, Calder, Victoria, 1980. Nos. 2040, 2046, Benetton-Renault, Albert Park, Victoria, 2001.

2002, Feb. 27 ***Perf. 14x14¾***
2035 A613 45c multi 1.00 .75
2036 A613 45c multi 1.00 .75
2037 A613 45c multi 1.00 .75
2038 A613 45c multi 1.00 .75
2039 A613 45c multi 1.00 .75
2040 A613 45c multi 1.00 .75
a. Block of 6, #2035-2040 7.00 7.00
Nos. 2035-2040 (6) 6.00 4.50

Self-Adhesive

Serpentine Die Cut 11¼x11½
2041 A613 45c multi 1.00 .80
2042 A613 45c multi 1.00 .80
2043 A613 45c multi 1.00 .80
2044 A613 45c multi 1.00 .80
2045 A613 45c multi 1.00 .80
2046 A613 45c multi 1.00 .80
a. Coil strip, #2041-2046 9.00
b. Booklet, #2045-2046, 2 each #2041-2044 10.00
Nos. 2041-2046 (6) 6.00 4.80

Lighthouses and Maps — A614

Designs: 45c, Macquarie, New South Wales. Nos. 2048, 2051, Troubridge Island, South Australia. Nos. 2049, 2052, Cape Naturaliste, Western Australia. $1.50, Cape Bruny, Tasmania.

2002, Mar. 12 ***Perf. 14½x14***
2047 A614 45c multi 1.40 .60
a. Booklet pane of 4 5.75 —
2048 A614 49c multi 1.40 .90
a. Booklet pane of 2 2.75 —
2049 A614 49c multi 1.40 .90
a. Horiz. pair, #2048-2049 2.75 2.00
b. Booklet pane of 2 2.75 —
2050 A614 $1.50 multi 2.25 2.00
a. Booklet pane of 2 7.00 —
b. Booklet pane, #2047-2050 7.75 —
Booklet, #2047a, 2048a, 2049b, 2050a, 2050b 25.75

Booklet Stamps

Self-Adhesive

Serpentine Die Cut 11¾
2051 A614 49c multi 1.00 .50
2052 A614 49c multi 1.00 .50
a. Booklet, 5 each #2051-2052 13.50
Nos. 2047-2052 (6) 8.45 5.40

Booklet containing Nos. 2047a-2050b sold for $9.95.

Encounter of Matthew Flinders and Nicolas Baudin, Bicent. — A615

Map, ship and: 45c, Baudin and kangaroo. $1.50, Flinders and Port Lincoln parrot.

2002, Apr. 4 ***Perf. 14x14¾***
2053 A615 45c multi 1.25 .75
2054 A615 $1.50 multi 2.50 2.10

See France Nos. 2882-2883.

Tourist Attractions Type of 2000

Designs: 50c, Walker Flat. $1, Mt. Roland. $1.50, Cape Leveque.

2002, May 1 ***Perf. 14½x14***
2055 A581 50c multi 1.10 1.00
2056 A581 $1 multi 2.25 2.25
2057 A581 $1.50 multi 3.25 3.25

Booklet Stamps

Self-Adhesive

Serpentine Die Cut 11¼x10½
2058 A581 50c multi 1.40 .85
2059 A581 $1 multi 2.25 2.00
a. Booklet, 6 #2058, 4 #2059 18.00
Nos. 2055-2059 (5) 10.25 9.35

Flora & Fauna Type of 1996

Designs: 50c, Desert star flower. $1, Bilby. $1.50, Thorny devil. $2, Great Sandy Desert.

2002, June 4 Litho. ***Perf. 14x14½***
2060 A511 50c multi .75 .55
2061 A511 $1 multi 1.50 1.25
2062 A511 $1.50 multi 2.25 1.75

Perf. 14½x14

Size: 50x30mm
2063 A511 $2 multi 3.00 2.40
Nos. 2060-2063 (4) 7.50 5.95

See Nos. 2112-2114 for self-adhesive versions of 50c stamp.

Paintings by Albert Namatjira (1902-59) — A616

Designs: Nos. 2064, 2068, Ghost Gum Mt. Sonder, MacDonnel Ranges. Nos. 2065, 2069, Mt. Hermannsburg. Nos. 2066, 2070, Glen Helen Country. Nos. 2067, 2071, Simpsons Gap.

2002, July 2 Litho. ***Perf. 14x14¾***
2064 A616 45c multi .95 .75
a. Booklet pane of 4 4.00 4.00
2065 A616 45c multi .95 .75
a. Booklet pane of 4 4.00 4.00
2066 A616 45c multi .95 .75
a. Booklet pane of 4 4.00 4.00
2067 A616 45c multi .95 .75
a. Block of 4, #2064-2067 4.25 3.75
b. Souvenir sheet of 4, #2064-2067 4.25 3.75
c. Booklet pane of 4 4.00 4.00
d. Booklet pane, #2067b 4.25 4.25
Booklet, #2064a, 2065a, 2066a, 2067c, 2067d 20.75
Nos. 2064-2067 (4) 3.80 3.00

Serpentine Die Cut 11x11½

Self-Adhesive
2068 A616 45c multi 1.00 .75
2069 A616 45c multi 1.00 .75
2070 A616 45c multi 1.00 .75
2071 A616 45c multi 1.00 .75
a. Booklet pane of 10, 3 each #2068-2069, 2 each #2070-2071 10.00
b. Coil strip of 4, #2068-2071 4.50
Nos. 2068-2071 (4) 4.00 3.00

Australia — Thailand Diplomatic Relations, 50th Anniv. — A617

Designs: 45c, Nelumbo nucifera. $1, Nymphaea immutabilis.

2002, Aug. 6 Litho. ***Perf. 14x14½***
2072 A617 45c multi 1.00 .75
2073 A617 $1 multi 2.25 2.00
a. Souvenir sheet, #2072-2073 3.25 2.75
b. As "a," overprinted in gold in margin 8.50 8.50

Overprint on margin of No. 2073b has IFSDA and APTA emblems and text reading "50th Anniversary International Federation / of Stamp Dealers Associations."

See Thailand Nos. 2028-2029.

Christmas A618

Koala — A619

Puja, by Ngarralja Tommy May — A620

2002 ***Perf. 14¼x14***
2074 A618 90c multi + label 1.90 1.90
2075 A619 $1.10 multi + label 2.25 2.25
2076 A620 $1.65 multi + label 3.50 3.50
a. Booklet pane of 4 + 4 labels 13.75 —
Complete booklet, 3 #2076a 50.00
Nos. 2074-2076 (3) 7.65 7.65

Issued: 2074-2076, 8/23. No. 2076a, 10/31.

Nos. 2074-2076 were each printed in sheets of 20 stamps + 20 labels. Labels on some sheets could be personalized for an additional fee.

The complete booklet, which sold for $20.75, contains three panes of No. 2076a with different margins.

Tourist Attractions Type of 2000

Designs: $1.10, Coonawarra. $1.65, Gariwerd-Grampians Natl. Park. $2.20, National Library. $3.30, Cape York.

2002, Aug. 23 Litho. ***Perf. 14½x14***
2077 A581 $1.10 multi 2.25 2.25
2078 A581 $1.65 multi 3.50 3.50
2079 A581 $2.20 multi 4.50 4.50
2080 A581 $3.30 multi 7.00 6.00
Nos. 2077-2080 (4) 17.25 16.25

Aboriginal Food Plants — A621

Designs: Nos. 2081, 2088, Murnong. Nos. 2082, 2087, Acacia seeds. Nos. 2083, 2086, Quandong. Nos. 2084, 2090, Honey grevillea. Nos. 2085, 2089, Lilly-pilly.

2002, Sept. 3 Litho. ***Perf. 14¾x14***
2081 A621 49c multi 1.00 .75
2082 A621 49c multi 1.00 .75
2083 A621 49c multi 1.00 .75
2084 A621 49c multi 1.00 .75
2085 A621 49c multi 1.00 .75
a. Horiz. strip of 5, #2081-2085 5.00 4.75
b. Tete beche block of 10, 2 each # 2081-2085 10.00 11.50
Nos. 2081-2085 (5) 5.00 3.75

Booklet Stamps

Self-Adhesive

Serpentine Die Cut 11¾
2086 A621 49c multi 1.00 .80
2087 A621 49c multi 1.00 .80
2088 A621 49c multi 1.00 .80
2089 A621 49c multi 1.00 .80
2090 A621 49c multi 1.00 .80
a. Booklet pane, 2 each #2086-2090 11.00
Nos. 2086-2090 (5) 5.00 4.00

Bunyip A622

Fairy A623

Gnome A624

Goblin A625

Wizard A626

Sprite A627

2002, Sept. 25 ***Perf. 14¾x14***
2091 A622 45c multi 1.00 .75
2092 A623 45c multi 1.00 .75
2093 A624 45c multi 1.00 .75
a. Horiz. strip of 3, #2091-2093 3.00 3.00
2094 A625 45c multi 1.00 .75
2095 A626 45c multi 1.00 .75
2096 A627 45c multi 1.00 .75
a. Horiz. strip of 3, #2094-2096 3.00 3.00
b. Souvenir sheet, #2091-2096 6.50 6.50
Nos. 2091-2096 (6) 6.00 4.50

Self-Adhesive

Serpentine Die Cut 11½x11
2097 A622 45c multi 1.00 .75
2098 A623 45c multi 1.00 .75
2099 A624 45c multi 1.00 .75
2100 A625 45c multi 1.00 .75
2101 A626 45c multi 1.00 .75
2102 A627 45c multi 1.00 .75
a. Vert. coil strip of 6, #2097-2102 6.00
b. Booklet pane, #2097, 2102, 2 each #2098-2101 10.00
Nos. 2097-2102 (6) 6.00 4.50

Characters from The Magic Rainforest, by John Marsden.

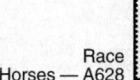

Race Horses — A628

2002, Oct. 15 Litho. ***Perf. 14x14½***
2103 A628 45c Wakeful 1.00 .75
2104 A628 45c Rising Fast 1.00 .75
2105 A628 45c Manikato 1.00 .75
2106 A628 45c Might and Power 1.00 .75
2107 A628 45c Sunline 1.00 .75
a. Horiz. strip of 5, #2103-2107 5.25 5.25
Nos. 2103-2107 (5) 5.00 3.75

Christmas — A629

2002, Nov. 1 ***Perf. 14½x14***
2108 A629 40c Nativity 1.00 .80
2109 A629 45c Magi 1.00 .70

Self-Adhesive

Booklet Stamp

Serpentine Die Cut 11¼
2110 A629 40c Nativity 1.00 .70
a. Booklet pane of 20 + 20 labels 20.00
Nos. 2108-2110 (3) 3.00 2.20

Flora and Fauna Type of 1996

Designs: 50c, Desert star flower. $1.45, Blue orchid.

2003 Litho. ***Perf. 14x14½***
2111 A511 $1.45 multi 3.25 3.25

Self-Adhesive

Coil Stamps

Serpentine Die Cut 11¼
2112 A511 50c multi 1.00 .50

Serpentine Die Cut 12¾
2113 A511 50c multi 1.00 .50

Booklet Stamp

Serpentine Die Cut 11¼x11

2114 A511 50c multi 1.00 .50
a. Booklet pane of 10 10.00
b. Booklet pane of 20 22.50
Nos. 2111-2114 (4) 6.25 4.75

Issued: 50c, 1/7; $1.45, 2/11.

Flowers A630

Roses and Wedding Rings A631

Roses and Hearts A632

Birthday Cake, Balloons and Gifts — A633

Teddy Bear — A634

Balloons and Streamers A635

Kangaroo and Australian Flag — A636

Australia on Globe A637

Automobile A638

Rose and Wedding Rings A639

2003 ***Perf. 14½x14***

2115 A630 50c multi + label 1.50 .85
a. Booklet pane of 4 + 4 labels 6.00
Booklet, 5 #2115a 30.00
2116 A631 50c multi + label 1.50 .85
a. Booklet pane of 4 + 4 labels 6.00
Booklet, 5 #2116a 30.00
2117 A632 50c multi + label 1.50 .85
a. Booklet pane of 4 + 4 labels 6.00
Booklet, 5 #2117a 30.00
b. Strip of 3, #2115-2117, + 3 labels 4.50
2118 A633 50c multi + label 1.50 .85
a. Booklet pane of 4 + 4 labels 6.00
Booklet, 5 #2118a 30.00
2119 A634 50c multi + label 1.50 .85
a. Booklet pane of 4 + 4 labels 6.00 —
Complete booklet, 5 #2119a 30.00
2120 A635 50c multi + label 1.50 .85
a. Booklet pane of 4 + 4 labels 6.00
Booklet, 5 #2120a 30.00
b. Strip of 3, #2118-2120, + 3 labels 3.50
2121 A636 50c multi + label 1.50 .85
2122 A637 50c multi + label 1.50 .85
a. Booklet pane of 4 + 4 labels 6.00 —
Complete booklet, 5 #2122a 30.00
2123 A638 50c multi + label 1.50 .85
a. Strip of 3, #2121-2123, + 3 labels 4.50
2124 A639 $1 multi + label 1.75 1.75
a. Booklet pane of 4 + 4 labels 7.00
Booklet, 5 #2124a 35.00
Nos. 2115-2124 (10) 15.25 9.40

Issued: No. 2119a, 10/31/03; No. 2122a, 3/16/04. Rest of set, 1/7/03.

Panes of 20 stamps containing the same design could have labels personalized. The personalized panes sold for a higher price.

Nos. 2115a, 2116a, 2117a, 2118a, 2119a, 2120a, 2122a and 2124a come in complete booklets, each containing 5 panes, each pane having different margins. Some panes are found in a number of different booklets.

Australian Legends Type of 1997

Tennis players: Nos. 2125, 2129, Margaret Court with Wimbledon trophy. Nos. 2126, 2131, Court in action. Nos. 2127, 2130, Rod Laver with Wimbledon trophy. Nos. 2128, 2132, Laver in action.

2003, Jan. 24 ***Perf. 14x14¾***

Size: 34x26mm

2125 A522 50c multi 1.00 .70
2126 A522 50c multi 1.00 .70
2127 A522 50c multi 1.00 .70
2128 A522 50c multi 1.00 .70
a. Block of 4, #2125-2128 5.25 4.75
b. Booklet pane, #2125-2128 *6.00* —
Nos. 2125-2128 (4) 4.00 2.80

Self-Adhesive

Booklet Stamps

Serpentine Die Cut 11x11½

2129 A522 50c multi 1.00 .50
2130 A522 50c multi 1.00 .50
2131 A522 50c multi 1.00 .50
2132 A522 50c multi 1.00 .50
a. Booklet pane, 3 each #2129-2130, 2 each #2131-2132 10.00
Nos. 2129-2132 (4) 4.00 2.00

No. 2128b issued 1/24/07.

Fish — A640

2003, Feb. 11 ***Perf. 14½x14***

2133 A640 50c Snapper 1.00 .60
2134 A640 50c Murray cod 1.00 .60
2135 A640 50c Brown trout 1.00 .60
2136 A640 50c Yellowfin tuna 1.00 .60
2137 A640 50c Barramundi 1.00 .60
a. Horiz. strip of 5, #2133-2137 5.75 4.50
Nos. 2133-2137 (5) 5.00 3.00

Australian Cultivars — A641

Designs: Nos. 2138, 2143, Hari Withers camellia. Nos. 2139, 2144, Victoria Gold rose. Nos. 2140, 2145, Superb grevillea. Nos. 2141, 2146, Bush Tango kangaroo paw. Nos. 2142, 2147, Midnight rhododendron.

2003, Mar. 25 ***Perf. 14¾x14***

2138 A641 50c multi .95 .70
2139 A641 50c multi .95 .70
2140 A641 50c multi .95 .70
2141 A641 50c multi .95 .70
2142 A641 50c multi .95 .70
a. Horiz. strip of 5, #2138-2142 5.75 5.00
Nos. 2138-2142 (5) 4.75 3.50

Self-Adhesive

Serpentine Die Cut 11½x11¼

2143 A641 50c multi 1.00 .35
2144 A641 50c multi 1.00 .35
2145 A641 50c multi 1.00 .35
2146 A641 50c multi 1.00 .35
2147 A641 50c multi 1.00 .35
a. Coil strip of 5, #2143-2147 5.00
b. Booklet pane, 2 each #2143-2147 10.00
Nos. 2143-2147 (5) 5.00 1.75

Paintings A642

Designs: No. 2148, Ned Kelly, by Sidney Nolan. No. 2149, Family Home, Suburban Exterior, by Howard Arkley. $1.45, Cord Drawn Long, Expectant, by Robert Jacks. $2.45, Girl, by Joy Hester.

2003, May 6 Litho. ***Perf. 14½x14***

2148 A642 $1 multi 1.75 1.50
2149 A642 $1 multi 1.75 1.50
a. Horiz. pair, #2148-2149 3.50 3.25
2150 A642 $1.45 multi 3.25 2.75
2151 A642 $2.45 multi 4.75 4.00
Nos. 2148-2151 (4) 11.50 9.75

Coronation of Queen Elizabeth II, 50th Anniv. — A643

Designs: 50c, Queen Elizabeth II, 1953. $2.45, St. Edward's Crown.

2003, June 2 Litho. ***Perf. 14¾x14***

2152 A643 50c multi 1.00 1.00
2153 A643 $2.45 multi 4.00 3.25
a. Souvenir sheet, #2152-2153 6.50 6.50

Booklet Stamp

Self-Adhesive

Serpentine Die Cut 11½x11¼

2154 A643 50c multi .90 .40
a. Booklet pane of 10 9.00
Nos. 2152-2154 (3) 5.90 4.65

Papunya Tula Aboriginal Art — A644

Untitled works by: $1.10, Ningura Napurrula. $1.65, Naata Nungurrayi. $2.20, Graham Tjupurrula. $3.30, Dini Campbell Tjampitjinpa.

2003, June 17 ***Perf. 14½x14***

2155 A644 $1.10 multi 2.00 2.00
2156 A644 $1.65 multi 3.00 3.00

Size: 56x25mm

Perf. 14x14½

2157 A644 $2.20 multi 4.00 4.00
2158 A644 $3.30 multi 5.75 5.75
Nos. 2155-2158 (4) 14.75 14.75

Flora & Fauna Type of 1996

Designs: Nos. 2159, 2163, 2167, Orange-thighed tree frog. Nos. 2160, 2164, 2168, Green-spotted triangle butterfly. Nos. 2161, 2165, 2169, Striped possum. Nos. 2162, 2166, 2170, Yellow-bellied sunbird.

2003, July 8 Litho. ***Perf. 14x14¼***

2159 A511 50c multi .85 .40
2160 A511 50c multi .85 .40
2161 A511 50c multi .85 .40
2162 A511 50c multi .85 .40
a. Block of 4, #2159-2162 3.75 3.75
Nos. 2159-2162 (4) 3.40 1.60

Self-Adhesive

Serpentine Die Cut 11¼

2163 A511 50c multi 1.00 .40
2164 A511 50c multi 1.00 .40
a. Booklet pane of 2, #2163-2164 2.25
2165 A511 50c multi 1.00 .40
2166 A511 50c multi 1.00 .40
a. Booklet pane of 4, #2163-2166, rouletted at bottom 4.50
Complete booklet, #2164a, 2 #2166a 10.25
b. Booklet pane of 4, #2163-2166, rouletted at side 4.50
Complete booklet, 5 #2166b 23.00
c. Coil strip of 4, #2163-2166 4.50

Coil Stamps

Serpentine Die Cut 12¾

2167 A511 50c multi 1.10 .40
2168 A511 50c multi 1.10 .40
2169 A511 50c multi 1.10 .40
2170 A511 50c multi 1.10 .40
a. Strip of 4, #2167-2170 5.25
Nos. 2163-2170 (8) 8.40 3.20

Genetics — A645

Map of Australia and: No. 2171, DNA molecule. No. 2172, Kangaroo chromosomes in cell division.

2003, July 8 Litho. ***Perf. 14x14¾***

2171 A645 50c red & multi 1.00 .80
2172 A645 50c grn & multi 1.00 .80
a. Horiz. pair, #2171-2172 2.50 2.50

Murray River Shipping, 150th Anniv. — A646

Murray River vessels: Nos. 2173, 2178, Oscar W. Nos. 2174, 2179, Marion. Nos. 2175, 2180, Ruby. Nos. 2176, 2181, Pyap. Nos. 2177, 2182, Adelaide.

2003, Aug. 5 Litho. ***Perf. 14x14¾***

2173 A646 50c multi .90 .70
a. Booklet pane of 4 3.75 —
2174 A646 50c multi .90 .70
a. Booklet pane of 4 3.75 —
2175 A646 50c multi .90 .70
a. Booklet pane of 4 3.75 —
2176 A646 50c multi .90 .70
a. Booklet pane of 4 3.75 —
2177 A646 50c multi .90 .70
a. Booklet pane of 4 3.75 —
Complete booklet, #2173a-2177a 20.00
b. Horiz. strip of 5, #2173-2177 4.50 4.00
Nos. 2173-2177 (5) 4.50 3.50

Self-Adhesive

Serpentine Die Cut 11¼x11½

2178 A646 50c multi 1.10 .45
2179 A646 50c multi 1.10 .45
2180 A646 50c multi 1.10 .45
2181 A646 50c multi 1.10 .45
2182 A646 50c multi 1.10 .45
a. Horiz. coil strip of 5, #2178-2182 5.75
b. Booklet pane, 2 each #2178-2182 11.00
Nos. 2178-2182 (5) 5.50 2.25

The booklet containing Nos. 2173a-2177a sold for $10.95.

Christmas — A647

2003, Aug. 5 Litho. ***Perf. 14½x14***

2183 A647 50c Christmas tree .80 .60
a. Sheet of 20 + 20 labels 35.00 —
2184 A647 90c Star 1.60 1.50
a. Sheet of 20 + 20 labels 50.00 —

Labels on Nos. 2183a and 2184a could be personalized. No. 2183a sold for $23 on day of issue; No. 2184a for $32.

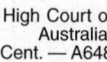

High Court of Australia, Cent. — A648

Designs: 50c, Sir Samuel Griffith (1845-1920), first Chief Justice, text from Constitution about High Court. $1.45, "Justice," names of significant cases.

2003, Sept. 2 Litho. ***Perf. 14x14¾***

2185 A648 50c multi .80 .80
2186 A648 $1.45 multi 2.50 2.50
a. Souvenir sheet, #2185-2186 4.00 *4.25*

Insects — A649

Designs: Nos. 2187, 2198, Ulysses butterfly. Nos. 2188, 2197, Leichhardt's grasshopper. Nos. 2189, 2196, Vedalia ladybird. Nos. 2190, 2195, Green mantid and damselfly. Nos. 2191, 2194, Emperor gum moth caterpillar. Nos. 2192, 2193, Fiddler beetle.

2003, Sept. 24 *Perf. 14x14¾*
2187 A649 50c multi .80 .60
2188 A649 50c multi .80 .60
2189 A649 50c multi .80 .60
a. Horiz. strip, #2187-2189 3.25 3.25
2190 A649 50c multi .80 .60
2191 A649 50c multi .80 .60
2192 A649 50c multi .80 .60
a. Horiz. strip, #2190-2192 3.25 3.25
b. Souvenir sheet, #2187-2192 5.75 5.75
c. As "b," with Bangkok 2003 emblem in margin in gold 8.00 8.00
Nos. 2187-2192 (6) 4.80 3.60

Self-Adhesive

Serpentine Die Cut 11x11¼

2193 A649 50c multi 1.00 .40
2194 A649 50c multi 1.00 .40
2195 A649 50c multi 1.00 .40
2196 A649 50c multi 1.00 .40
2197 A649 50c multi 1.00 .40
2198 A649 50c multi 1.00 .40
a. Horiz. coil strip, #2193-2198 6.75
b. Booklet pane, #2193-2194, 2 each #2195-2198 12.00
Nos. 2193-2198 (6) 6.00 2.40

No. 2193c issued 10/4.

2003 Rugby World Cup — A650

Designs: 50c, Players running with ball, hands and ball. $1.10, Webb Ellis Cup, Telstra Stadium. $1.65, Player kicking at goal, ball in hand.

2003, Oct. 8 Litho. *Perf. 14½x14*
2199 A650 50c multi 1.00 .85
a. Booklet pane of 3 3.50 —
2200 A650 $1.10 multi 2.25 2.25
a. Booklet pane of 3 7.00 —
2201 A650 $1.65 multi 3.25 3.25
a. Booklet pane of 3 10.50 —
Complete booklet, #2199a, 2200a, 2201a 24.00
b. Souvenir sheet, #2199-2201 7.00 7.00
Nos. 2199-2201 (3) 6.50 6.35

Booklet sold for $10.95.

Active With Asthma — A651

2003, Oct. 14 *Perf. 14x14½*
2202 A651 50c multi 1.00 .70

Christmas — A652

Designs: 45c, Madonna and Child with Angels. 50c, Three Wise Men. 90c, Angel Appearing to the Shepherds.

2003, Oct. 31 *Perf. 14½x14*
2203 A652 45c multi .75 .80
2204 A652 50c multi .80 .80
2205 A652 90c multi 1.60 1.60

Booklet Stamp

Self-Adhesive

Serpentine Die Cut 11½x11¼

2206 A652 45c multi .95 .60
a. Booklet pane of 20 + 20 labels 20.00
Nos. 2203-2206 (4) 4.10 3.80

Australian Legends Type of 1997

Dame Joan Sutherland, opera singer: Nos. 2207, 2209, In costume. Nos. 2208, 2210, In black and red dress.

2004, Jan. 23 Litho. *Perf. 14x14¾*

Size: 37x26mm

2207 A522 50c multi .90 .70
2208 A522 50c multi .90 .70
a. Horiz. pair, #2207-2208 2.00 2.00
b. Booklet pane, #2207-2208 *3.00* —

Booklet Stamps

Self-Adhesive

Serpentine Die Cut 11x11½

2209 A522 50c multi 1.00 .40
2210 A522 50c multi 1.00 .40
a. Booklet pane, 5 each #2209-2210 11.00
Nos. 2207-2210 (4) 3.80 2.20

No. 2208b issued 1/24/07.

Settlement of Hobart Town, Tasmania, Bicent. — A653

Segment of shell necklace, map of Tasmania and: No. 2211, Cheshunt House, Deloraine. No. 2212, Complete shell necklace. No. 2213, Mount Wellington. No. 2214, Hobart Town from Kangaroo Point, by John Glover.

2004, Feb. 3 Litho. *Perf. 14x14½*
2211 A653 50c multi 1.00 .70
2212 A653 50c multi 1.00 .70
a. Pair, #2211-2212 2.00 1.60
2213 A653 $1 multi 2.00 1.60
2214 A653 $1 multi 2.00 1.60
a. Pair, #2213-2214 4.00 3.50
b. Souvenir sheet, #2211-2214 6.25 6.25
c. As "b," optd. for Paris Exhib. 2004 *35.00 35.00*
d. As "b," optd. for China 2005 exhibition *20.00 20.00*
Nos. 2211-2214 (4) 6.00 4.60

Historic Bridges — A654

Designs: Nos. 2215, 2220, Ross Bridge, Tasmania, 1836. Nos. 2216, 2221, Lockyer Creek Bridge, Queensland, 1911. Nos. 2217, 2222, Sydney Harbour Bridge, 1932. Nos. 2218, 2223, Birkenhead Bridge, Adelaide, 1940. Nos. 2219, 2224, Bolte Bridge, Melbourne, 1999.

2004, Mar. 2 Litho. *Perf. 14x14½*
2215 A654 50c multi .90 .70
a. Booklet pane of 4 4.00 —
2216 A654 50c multi .90 .70
a. Booklet pane of 4 4.00 —
2217 A654 50c multi .90 .70
a. Booklet pane of 4 4.00 —
2218 A654 50c multi .90 .70
a. Booklet pane of 4 4.00 —
2219 A654 50c multi .90 .70
a. Booklet pane of 4 4.00 —
Complete booklet, #2215a, 2216a, 2217a, 2218a, 2219a 21.00
b. Horiz. strip of 5, #2215-2219 5.25 4.00
c. Booklet pane of 6 ('06) 6.25 —
Nos. 2215-2219 (5) 4.50 3.50

The complete booklet No. 2219a sold for $10.95.

No. 2219c issued 3/1/06.

Self-Adhesive

Serpentine Die Cut 11x11½

2220 A654 50c multi 1.40 .90
2221 A654 50c multi 1.40 .90
2222 A654 50c multi 1.40 .90
2223 A654 50c multi 1.40 .90
2224 A654 50c multi 1.40 .90
a. Horiz. coil strip of 5, #2220-2224 7.25
b. Booklet pane, 2 each #2220-2224 14.50
Nos. 2220-2224 (5) 7.00 4.50

Southern Cross — A655

2004-05 *Perf. 14½x14*
2225 A655 50c multi .90 .70
a. Booklet pane of 4 + 4 labels 4.25 —
Complete booklet, 5 #2225a 22.00

Issued: No. 2225, 3/16/04. No. 2225a, Jan. 2005. No. 2225a was issued in a variety of complete booklets, each containing 5 panes with different margins. Each complete booklet sold for $10.95.

Renewable Energy — A656

Designs: Nos. 2226, 2230, Solar energy. Nos. 2227, 2231, Wind energy. Nos. 2228, 2232, Hydroelectric energy. Nos. 2229, 2233, Biomass energy.

2004, Mar. 30 *Perf. 14x14½*
2226 A656 50c multi .90 .70
2227 A656 50c multi .90 .70
2228 A656 50c multi .90 .70
2229 A656 50c multi .90 .70
a. Block of 4, #2226-2229 3.75 3.75
Nos. 2226-2229 (4) 3.60 2.80

Coil Stamps

Self-Adhesive

Serpentine Die Cut 11x11½

2230 A656 50c multi 1.00 .50
2231 A656 50c multi 1.00 .50
2232 A656 50c multi 1.00 .50
2233 A656 50c multi 1.00 .50
a. Horiz. strip of 4, #2230-2233 4.25
Nos. 2230-2233 (4) 4.00 2.00

Royal Visit, 50th Anniv. — A657

2004, Apr. 13 *Perf. 14½x14*
2234 A657 50c multi .90 .70
a. Booklet pane of 4 4.25 —
Complete booklet, 5 #2234a 22.00

The booklet, which contains five panes with different margins, sold for $10.95. Another booklet pane, with a different margin, is found in the booklet footnoted under No. 2507.

Flora & Fauna Type of 1996

Designs: 5c, Red lacewing butterfly. 10c, Blue-banded eggfly butterfly. 75c, Cruiser butterfly. $2, Butterflies, Daintree National Park rainforest.

2004, May 4 Litho. *Perf. 14x14½*
2235 A511 5c multi .25 .25
2236 A511 10c multi .25 .25
2237 A511 75c multi 1.60 .95

Size: 50x30mm

Perf. 14½x14

2238 A511 $2 multi 3.50 3.00
Nos. 2235-2238 (4) 5.60 4.45

Australian Innovations A658

Designs: Nos. 2239, 2248, Black box flight recorder, 1961. Nos. 2240, 2247, Ultrasound imaging equipment, 1976. Nos. 2241, 2246, Racecam television sports coverage, 1979. Nos. 2242, 2245, Baby safety capsule, 1984. Nos. 2243, 2244, Polymer banknotes, 1988.

2004, May 18 *Perf. 14x14½*
2239 A658 50c multi 1.00 .70
2240 A658 50c multi 1.00 .70
2241 A658 50c multi 1.00 .70
2242 A658 50c multi 1.00 .70
2243 A658 50c multi 1.00 .70
a. Horiz. strip, #2239-2243 5.00 5.00
Nos. 2239-2243 (5) 5.00 3.50

Booklet Stamps

Self-Adhesive

Serpentine Die Cut 11x11½

2244 A658 50c multi 1.10 .50
2245 A658 50c multi 1.10 .50
2246 A658 50c multi 1.10 .50
2247 A658 50c multi 1.10 .50
2248 A658 50c multi 1.10 .50
a. Booklet pane, 2 each #2244-2248 11.00
Nos. 2244-2248 (5) 5.50 2.50

Passenger Ship Travel Posters — A659

Designs: 50c, Shaw Savill Lines. $1, Awatea, Union Steam Ship Co. $1.45, Orient Line. $2, Aberdeen & Commonwealth Line.

2004, June 1 Litho. *Perf. 14½x14*
2249 A659 50c multi 1.00 .70
2250 A659 $1 multi 1.60 1.25
2251 A659 $1.45 multi 2.40 1.75
2252 A659 $2 multi 3.25 2.40
Nos. 2249-2252 (4) 8.25 6.10

Serpentine Die Cut 11½x11¼

Syncopated

2252A A659 50c Like #2249, *2005* 5.00 2.50

Booklet Stamp

Self-Adhesive

Serpentine Die Cut 11½x11¼

2253 A659 50c multi 1.10 .50
a. Booklet pane of 10 11.00

Issued: Nos. 2249-2252, 2253, 6/1/04. No. 2252A, 2/22/05. No. 2252A issued in sheet of 10.

Eureka Stockade, 150th Anniv. — A660

Designs: 50c, Eureka flag. $2.45, Peter Lalor (1827-89), leader of rebellious gold diggers.

2004, June 29 *Perf. 14x14½*
2254 A660 50c multi 1.00 .70
a. Booklet pane of 2 2.25 —
2255 A660 $2.45 multi 4.00 3.25
a. Booklet pane of 2 10.25 —
b. Booklet pane, #2254-2255 6.25
Complete booklet, #2255a, 2255b, 2 #2254a 25.00
c. Souvenir sheet, #2254-2255 5.75 5.75

No. 2255b has perfs that extend to the right margin. No. 2255c does not have perfs that extend through the margin. The margin is larger on No. 2255b than on No. 2255c. The complete booklet sold for $10.95.

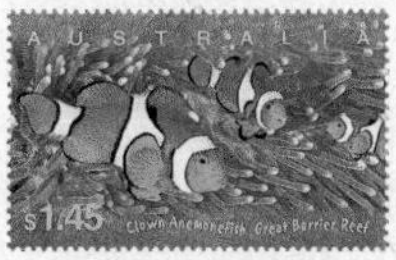

Tourist Attractions A661

Designs: No. 2256, Koala, Eastern Australia, vert. No. 2257, Little penguin, Phillip Island, vert. $1.45, Clown anemonefish, Great Barrier Reef. $2.45, Beach, Gold Coast.

Perf. 14x14½, 14½x14

2004, July 13 Litho.
2256 A661 $1 multi 1.50 1.25
2257 A661 $1 multi 1.60 1.25
a. Horiz. pair, #2256-2257 4.50 4.50
2258 A661 $1.45 multi 3.00 2.00

Litho. With Foil Application

2259 A661 $2.45 multi 5.00 4.75
Nos. 2256-2259 (4) 11.10 9.25

2004 Summer Olympics and Paralympics, Athens — A662

2004, Aug. 3 Litho. *Perf. 14x14½*
2260 A662 50c Swimmer 1.00 .70
2261 A662 $1.65 Runner 2.75 2.75
2262 A662 $1.65 Cyclist 2.75 2.75
Nos. 2260-2262 (3) 6.50 6.20

Gold Medalists at 2004 Summer Olympics, Athens — A663

Designs: No. 2263, Ian Thorpe, Men's swimming 400m freestyle. No. 2264, Women's 4x100m medley relay swimming team. No. 2265, Sara Carrigan, Women's cycling road race. No. 2266, Petria Thomas, Women's swimming 100m butterfly. No. 2267, Suzanne Balogh, Women's trap shooting. No. 2268, Ian Thorpe, Men's swimming 200m freestyle. No. 2269, Jodie Henry, Women's swimming 100m freestyle. No. 2270, Anna Meares, Women's cycling 500m time trial. No. 2271, James Tomkins and Drew Ginn, Men's rowing pairs. No. 2272, Grant Hackett, Men's swimming 1500m freestyle. No. 2273, Women's 4x100 freestyle relay swimming team. No. 2274, Chantelle Newbery, Women's diving 10m platform. No. 2275, Men's 4000m team pursuit cycling team. No. 2276, Ryan Bayley, Men's cycling individual sprint. No. 2277, Graeme Brown and Stuart O'Grady, Men's cycling Madison. No. 2278, Ryan Bayley, Men's cycling Keirin. No. 2279, Men's field hockey team.

2004 Litho. *Perf. 14¼*

2263	A663 50c multi	1.00	.80
2264	A663 50c multi	1.00	.80
2265	A663 50c multi	1.00	.80
2266	A663 50c multi	1.00	.80
2267	A663 50c multi	1.00	.80
2268	A663 50c multi	1.00	.80
2269	A663 50c multi	1.00	.80
2270	A663 50c multi	1.00	.80
2271	A663 50c multi	1.00	.80
2272	A663 50c multi	1.00	.80
2273	A663 50c multi	1.00	.80
2274	A663 50c multi	1.00	.80
2275	A663 50c multi	1.00	.80
2276	A663 50c multi	1.00	.80
2277	A663 50c multi	1.00	.80
2278	A663 50c multi	1.00	.80
2279	A663 50c multi	1.00	.80
	Nos. 2263-2279 (17)	17.00	13.60

Issued: Nos. 2263-2264, 8/16; Nos. 2265-2266, 8/17; Nos. 2267-2268, 8/18; Nos. 2269-2273, 8/23; No. 2274, 8/24; No. 2275, 8/25; No. 2276. 8/26; Nos. 2277-2278, 8/27; No. 2279, 8/30.

A sheet containing Nos. 2263-2279 was available only in the Australia Post annual collection. Value, $50.

Tourist Attractions Type of 2000

Designs: $1.20, Entrance Beach, Broome, Western Australia. $1.80, Mt. William National Park, Tasmania. $2.40, Potato Point, Bodalla, New South Wales. $3.60, Point Gibbon, South Australia.

2004, Sept. 6 *Perf. 14½x14*

2280	A581 $1.20 multi	2.40	1.75
2281	A581 $1.80 multi	3.25	2.75
2282	A581 $2.40 multi	4.00	4.00
2283	A581 $3.60 multi	5.50	5.50
	Nos. 2280-2283 (4)	15.15	14.00

Block of £2 Kangaroo & Map Stamps from Australia Post Archives — A664

2004, Sept. 7 *Perf. 14¼*

2284	A664 $5 multi	11.00	9.25

Souvenir Sheet
Self-Adhesive
Serpentine Die Cut 11¼

2285	A664 $5 multi	11.00	11.00

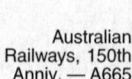

Australian Railways, 150th Anniv. — A665

Designs: Nos. 2286, 2291, Melbourne to Sandridge line, 1854. Nos. 2287, 2292, Sydney to Parramatta line, 1855. Nos. 2288, 2293, Helidon to Toowoomba line, 1867. Nos. 2289, 2294, Kalgoorlie to Port Augusta line, 1917. Nos. 2290, 2295, Alice Springs to Darwin line, 2004.

2004, Sept. 7 *Perf. 14x14¾*

2286	A665 50c multi	.95	.70
a.	Booklet pane of 4	4.25	—
2287	A665 50c multi	.95	.70
a.	Booklet pane of 4	4.25	—
2288	A665 50c multi	.95	.70
a.	Booklet pane of 4	4.25	—
2289	A665 50c multi	.95	.70
a.	Booklet pane of 4	4.25	—
2290	A665 50c multi	.95	.70
a.	Booklet pane of 4	4.25	—
	Complete booklet, #2286a-2290a	22.00	
b.	Horiz. strip, #2286-2290	5.25	5.25
	Nos. 2286-2290 (5)	4.75	3.50

Complete booklet of Nos. 2286a-2290a sold for $10.95.

Self-Adhesive
With Designs Lightened at Stamp Edges
Serpentine Die Cut 11¼x11½

2291	A665 50c multi	1.00	.60
2292	A665 50c multi	1.00	.60
2293	A665 50c multi	1.00	.60
2294	A665 50c multi	1.00	.60
2295	A665 50c multi	1.00	.60
a.	Horiz. coil strip, #2291-2295	5.50	
b.	Booklet pane, 2 each #2291-2295	11.00	
	Nos. 2291-2295 (5)	5.00	3.00

Cats and Dogs — A666

Designs: Nos. 2296, 2302, Cat (fish background). Nos. 2297, 2304, Cat (mouse background). Nos. 2298, 2301, Labrador retriever puppy (ball background). Nos. 2299, 2303, West Highland terriers (paw print background). $1, Jack Russell terrier (bone background).

2004, Sept. 21 *Perf. 14¾x14*

2296	A666 50c multi	1.00	.70
a.	Booklet pane of 4	4.25	—
2297	A666 50c multi	1.00	.70
a.	Horiz. pair, #2296-2297	2.25	1.60
b.	Booklet pane of 4	4.25	—
c.	Booklet pane, 2 each #2296-2297	4.50	—
	Complete booklet, #2296a, 2297b, 3 #2297c	21.00	
2298	A666 50c multi	1.00	.70
a.	Booklet pane of 4	4.25	—
2299	A666 50c multi	1.00	.70
a.	Horiz. pair, #2298-2299	2.25	1.60
b.	Booklet pane of 4	4.25	—
c.	Booklet pane, 2 each #2298-2299	4.50	—
2300	A666 $1 multi	2.00	1.60
a.	Booklet pane of 2	4.25	—
	Complete booklet, #2298a, 2299b, 2300a, 2 #2299c	21.00	
b.	Souvenir sheet, #2296-2300	5.50	5.50
	Nos. 2296-2300 (5)	6.00	4.40

The complete booklets each sold for $10.95. The Cat booklet contains three examples of No. 2297c, each with different margins and stamp arrangements. The Dog booklet contains two examples of No. 2299c with different margins and stamp arrangements.

Self-Adhesive
Booklet Stamps
Serpentine Die Cut 11¼ Syncopated

2301	A666 50c multi	.80	.60
2302	A666 50c multi	.80	.60
2303	A666 50c multi	.80	.60
a.	Booklet pane, 3 #2301, 2 #2303	5.25	
2304	A666 50c multi	.80	.60
a.	Booklet pane, 3 each #2301-2302, 2 each #2303-2304	9.00	
b.	Booklet pane, 3 #2302, 2 #2304	5.25	
2305	A666 $1 multi	2.25	1.25
a.	Booklet pane of 5	11.00	
	Nos. 2301-2305 (5)	5.45	3.65

Grand Prix Motorcycle Racing — A667

Designs: Nos. 2306, 2311, Mick Doohan (motorcycle #1, red panel). Nos. 2307, 2312, Wayne Gardner (motorcycle #1, blue panel). Nos. 2308, 2313, Troy Bayliss (motorcycle #12, orange red panel). Nos. 2309, 2314, Daryl Beattie (motorcycle #4, green panel). Nos. 2310, 2315, Garry McCoy (motorcycle #8, yellow orange panel).

2004, Oct. 12 Litho. *Perf. 14x14¾*

2306	A667 50c multi	.95	.70
2307	A667 50c multi	.95	.70
2308	A667 50c multi	.95	.70
2309	A667 50c multi	.95	.70
2310	A667 50c multi	.95	.70
a.	Horiz. strip of 5, #2306-2310	5.25	4.00
	Nos. 2306-2310 (5)	4.75	3.50

Self-Adhesive
Serpentine Die Cut 11¼ Syncopated

2311	A667 50c multi	1.00	.70
2312	A667 50c multi	1.00	.70
2313	A667 50c multi	1.00	.70
2314	A667 50c multi	1.00	.70
2315	A667 50c multi	1.00	.70
a.	Horiz. coil strip, #2311-2315	6.00	
b.	Booklet pane, 2 each #2311-2315	11.00	
	Nos. 2311-2315 (5)	5.00	3.50

Christmas — A668

Designs: 45c, Madonna and Child. 50c, Shepherds. $1, Magi, horiz.

2004, Nov. 1 *Perf. 14¾x14, 14x14¾*

2316	A668 45c multi	.80	.65
2317	A668 50c multi	.85	.75
2318	A668 $1 multi	1.60	1.60
	Nos. 2316-2318 (3)	3.25	3.00

Self-Adhesive
Booklet Stamps
Serpentine Die Cut 11¼ Syncopated

2319	A668 45c multi	.95	.85
a.	Booklet pane of 20 + 20 etiquettes	20.00	
2320	A668 $1 multi	2.00	1.60
a.	Booklet pane of 5	10.00	

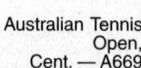

Australian Tennis Open, Cent. — A669

Designs: 50c, Male player, tennis court and stands, 1905. $1.80, Female player, tennis court and stands, 2005.

2005, Jan. 11 Litho. *Perf. 14x14¾*

2321	A669 50c multi	1.00	.65
a.	Booklet pane of 2	2.25	—
2322	A669 $1.80 multi	3.50	2.00
a.	Booklet pane of 2	8.50	—
	Complete booklet, 2 each #2321a, 2322a	25.00	

The complete booklet contains two examples of Nos. 2321a and 2322a, each with different margins.

Australian Legends — Fashion Designers — A670

Designs: Nos. 2323, 2329, Prue Acton. Nos. 2324, 2330, Jenny Bannister. Nos. 2325, 2331, Collette Dinnigan. Nos. 2326, 2332, Akira Isogawa. Nos. 2327, 2333, Joe Saba. Nos. 2328, 2334, Carla Zampatti.

2005, Jan. 21 *Perf. 14¾x14*

2323	A670 50c multi	.80	.70
2324	A670 50c multi	1.00	.70
a.	Horiz. pair, #2323-2324	1.75	1.60
b.	Booklet pane, #2323-2324	3.00	—
2325	A670 50c multi	.80	.70
2326	A670 50c multi	.80	.70
a.	Horiz. pair, #2325-2326	1.75	1.60
b.	Booklet pane, #2325-2326	3.00	—
2327	A670 50c multi	.80	.70
2328	A670 50c multi	.80	.70
a.	Horiz. pair, #2327-2328	1.75	1.60
b.	Booklet pane, #2327-2328	3.00	—
	Nos. 2323-2328 (6)	5.00	4.20

Self-Adhesive
Booklet Stamps
Serpentine Die Cut 11¼ Syncopated

2329	A670 50c multi	.90	.60
2330	A670 50c multi	.90	.60
a.	Booklet pane, 5 each #2329-2330	10.00	
2331	A670 50c multi	.90	.60
2332	A670 50c multi	.90	.60
a.	Booklet pane, 5 each #2331-2332	10.00	
2333	A670 50c multi	.90	.60
2334	A670 50c multi	.90	.60
a.	Booklet pane, 5 each #2333-2334	10.00	
	Nos. 2329-2334 (6)	5.40	3.60

Nos. 2324b, 2326b, 2328b, 1/24/07.

Parrots — A671

Designs: Nos. 2335, 2340, Princess parrot. Nos. 2336, 2344, Rainbow lorikeet. Nos. 2337, 2343, Green rosella. Nos. 2338, 2342, Red-capped parrot. Nos. 2339, 2341, Purple-crowned lorikeet.

2005, Feb. 8 *Perf. 14¾x14*

2335	A671 50c multi	1.00	.70
2336	A671 50c multi	1.00	.70
2337	A671 50c multi	1.00	.70
2338	A671 50c multi	1.00	.70
2339	A671 50c multi	1.00	.70
a.	Horiz. strip of 5, #2335-2339	5.50	4.75
	Nos. 2335-2339 (5)	5.00	3.50

A sheet containing Nos. 2335-2339 + 4 labels was available only with purchase of the "2005 Collection of Australian Stamps." Value $24.

Self-Adhesive
Coil Stamps
Serpentine Die Cut 11¼ Syncopated

2340	A671 50c multi	1.10	.60
2341	A671 50c multi	1.10	.60
2342	A671 50c multi	1.10	.60
2343	A671 50c multi	1.10	.60
2344	A671 50c multi	1.10	.60
a.	Vert. strip of 5, #2340-2344	6.00	
	Nos. 2340-2344 (5)	5.50	3.00

Sports Memorabilia — A672

Designs: No. 2345, Sir Donald Bradman's cricket cap. No. 2346, Lionel Rose's boxing gloves. No. 2347, Marjorie Jackson's running spikes. No. 2348, Racing silks of Phar Lap's jockeys.

2005, Mar. 8 Litho. *Perf. 14¾x14*

2345	A672 50c multi	.90	.70
a.	Booklet pane of 5, #1575a, 1576c, 1941a, 1942b, 2345 dated "2007"	7.50	—
2346	A672 50c multi	.90	.70
a.	Horiz. pair, #2345-2346	2.25	2.00
2347	A672 $1 multi	1.60	1.20
2348	A672 $1 multi	1.60	1.20
a.	Horiz. pair, #2347-2348	4.50	4.50
	Nos. 2345-2348 (4)	5.00	3.80

No. 2345a issued 11/14/2007.

Child's Plush Toy A673

Red Roses A674

Gifts A675

Kangaroos A676

White Roses A677

Yellow Roses and Woman's Hand A678

Koala
A679

Shell on Beach
A680

Sydney Opera House — A681

2005, Mar. 22 *Perf. 14¾x14*

2349	A673 50c multi		.90	.70
2350	A674 50c multi		.90	.70
2351	A675 50c multi		.90	.70
2352	A676 50c multi		.90	.70
a.	Additionally dated "2013" (#3534d)		1.25	1.25
2353	A677 50c multi		.90	.70
a.	Horiz. strip, #2349-2353		5.00	5.00
2354	A678 $1 multi		1.60	1.60
2355	A679 $1.10 multi		2.25	2.25
2356	A680 $1.20 multi		2.40	2.40
2357	A681 $1.80 multi		3.50	3.50
	Nos. 2349-2357 (9)		14.25	13.25

Issued: No. 2352a, 5/10/2013.

Booklet Stamps
Self-Adhesive
Serpentine Die Cut 11x11¼ Syncopated

2358	A673 50c multi	3.75	*3.25*
a.	Booklet pane of 4	15.00	
	Complete booklet, 5 #2358a	75.00	
2359	A674 50c multi	3.75	*3.25*
a.	Booklet pane of 4	15.00	
	Complete booklet, 5 #2359a	75.00	
2360	A675 50c multi	3.75	*3.25*
a.	Booklet pane of 4	15.00	
	Complete booklet, 5 #2360a	75.00	
2361	A677 50c multi	3.75	*3.25*
a.	Booklet pane of 4	15.00	
	Complete booklet, 5 #2361a	75.00	
2362	A678 $1 multi	6.25	*6.25*
a.	Booklet pane of 4	25.00	
	Complete booklet, 5 #2362a	125.00	
2363	A679 $1.10 multi	6.50	*8.00*
a.	Booklet pane of 4	26.00	
	Complete booklet, 2 #2363a	130.00	
2364	A680 $1.20 multi	7.00	*9.00*
a.	Booklet pane of 2	14.00	
2365	A681 $1.80 multi	7.50	*13.00*
a.	Booklet pane of 2	15.00	
	Complete booklet, 2 each #2364a, 2365a	30.00	
	Nos. 2358-2365 (8)	42.25	49.25

Each pane in the various complete booklets has a different margin. The complete booklets containing Nos. 2358-2361 each sold for $10.95, the complete booklet containing No. 2362 sold for $20.95, and the complete booklets containing Nos. 2363-2365 sold for $12.95.

See Nos. 2439-2447.

First Australian Coin, 150th Anniv. — A682

1855 One sovereign coin: Nos. 2366, 2368a, Obverse. Nos. 2367, 2368b, Reverse.

2005, Apr. 21 **Litho.** *Perf. 14x14¾*

2366	A682 50c multi	1.00	.75
2367	A682 $2.45 multi	4.00	3.60
a.	Booklet pane, #2366-2367	7.75	—

Litho. & Embossed with Foil Application

2368	Sheet of 2	6.00	6.00
a.	A682 50c multi	.90	.90
b.	A682 $2.45 multi	5.00	5.00

UNESCO World Heritage Sites in Australia and Great Britain — A683

Designs: No. 2369, Wet Tropics of Queensland, Australia. No. 2370, Stonehenge, England. No. 2371, Greater Blue Mountains Area, New South Wales, Australia. No. 2372, Blenheim Castle, England. No. 2373, Purnululu National Park, Western Australia. No. 2374, Heart of Neolithic Orkney, Scotland. No. 2375, Ayers Rock, Uluru-Kata Tjuta National Park, Northern Territory, Australia. No. 2376, Hadrian's Wall, England.

2005, Apr. 21 **Litho.** *Perf. 14¼*

2369	A683 50c multi	.95	.70
2370	A683 50c multi	.95	.70
a.	Horiz. pair, #2369-2370	2.00	2.00
2371	A683 50c multi	1.00	.70
2372	A683 50c multi	1.00	.70
a.	Horiz. pair, #2371-2372	2.00	2.00
2373	A683 $1 multi	1.60	1.20
2374	A683 $1 multi	1.60	1.20
a.	Horiz. pair, #2373-2374	3.60	3.60
b.	Booklet pane, #2369-2370, 2373-2374, + 4 labels	7.75	—
2375	A683 $1.80 multi	3.75	3.25
2376	A683 $1.80 multi	3.75	3.25
a.	Horiz. pair, #2375-2376	7.50	7.50
b.	Booklet pane, #2371-2372, 2375-2376, + 4 labels	11.50	—
	Nos. 2369-2376 (8)	14.60	11.70

See Great Britain Nos. 2280-2287.

Creatures of the Slime — A684

2005, Apr. 21 *Perf. 14x14¾*

2377	A684 50c Tribrachidium	.90	.70
2378	A684 50c Dickinsonia	.90	.70
2379	A684 50c Spriggina	.90	.70
2380	A684 50c Kimberella	.90	.70
2381	A684 50c Inaria	.90	.70
a.	Horiz. strip of 5, #2377-2381	5.00	4.75
2382	A684 $1 Charnodiscus	1.75	1.60
a.	Souvenir sheet, #2377-2382	7.50	7.50
b.	Booklet pane, #2377-2382	9.00	—
	Nos. 2377-2382 (6)	6.25	5.10

Rotary International, Cent. — A685

2005, Apr. 21 *Perf. 14¾x14*

2383	A685 50c multi	.90	.65
a.	Imperf.	8.00	8.00

Self-Adhesive
Serpentine Die Cut 11½x11¼ Syncopated

2384	A685 50c multi	.90	.65
a.	Booklet pane of 10	10.25	
b.	Booklet pane of 1	1.40	—
	Complete booklet, #2367a, 2374b, 2376b, 2382b, 2384b	40.00	

No. 2383a was sold at the Pacific Explorer Intl. Philatelic Exhibition 2005.

Queen Elizabeth II, 79th Birthday — A686

2005, May 10 *Perf. 14x14¾*

2385	A686 50c multi	1.00	.70
a.	Booklet pane of 4	4.00	—
	Complete booklet, 5 #2385a	29.00	

2006 Commonwealth Games, Melbourne. No. 2385a was issued in a booklet that sold for $10.95, with the 5 panes having different margins.

Bush Wildlife — A687

No. 2386, Superb lyrebird. Nos. 2387, 2390, Laughing kookaburra. Nos. 2388, 2391, Koala. Nos. 2389, 2392, Red kangaroo.

2005, June 7 *Perf. 14x14¾*

2386	A687 $1 multi	1.75	1.20
2387	A687 $1.10 multi	1.90	1.50
2388	A687 $1.20 multi	2.10	1.60
2389	A687 $1.80 multi	3.25	2.40
	Nos. 2386-2389 (4)	9.00	6.70

Serpentine Die Cut 11¼x11½ Syncopated
Self-Adhesive
Booklet Stamps

2390	A687 $1.10 multi	1.75	1.60
a.	Booklet pane of 5	10.00	
2391	A687 $1.20 multi	2.40	2.25
a.	Booklet pane of 5	12.00	
2392	A687 $1.80 Red kangaroo	3.25	3.25
a.	Booklet pane of 5	17.00	
	Nos. 2390-2392 (3)	7.40	7.10

Wild Flowers — A688

Designs: Nos. 2393, 2397, 2401, Sturt's desert pea. Nos. 2394, 2398, 2402, Coarse-leaved mallee. Nos. 2395, 2399, 2403, Common fringe lily. Nos. 2396, 2400, 2404, Swamp daisy.

2005, July 5 *Perf. 14x14½*

2393	A688 50c multi	1.00	.40
2394	A688 50c multi	1.00	.40
2395	A688 50c multi	1.00	.40
2396	A688 50c multi	1.00	.40
a.	Horiz. strip of 4, #2393-2396	4.00	3.75
	Nos. 2393-2396 (4)	4.00	1.60

Self-Adhesive
Serpentine Die Cut 11¼x11

2397	A688 50c multi	1.25	.70
2398	A688 50c multi	1.25	.70
2399	A688 50c multi	1.25	.70
2400	A688 50c multi	1.25	.70
a.	Horiz. coil strip of 4, #2397-2400	5.00	
b.	Booklet pane of 10, 3 each #2397-2398, 2 each #2399-2400	11.00	
c.	Booklet pane of 20, 5 each #2397-2400	20.00	
d.	Booklet pane of 5, #2398-2400, 2 #2397	6.50	

Coil Stamps
Die Cut Perf. 12¾

2401	A688 50c multi	1.35	.70
2402	A688 50c multi	1.35	.70
2403	A688 50c multi	1.35	.70
2404	A688 50c multi	1.35	.70
a.	Horiz. coil strip of 4, #2401-2404	5.50	
	Nos. 2397-2404 (8)	10.40	5.60

Australian Wine — A689

Designs: Nos. 2405, 2410, Grapevine, vineyard. Nos. 2406, 2411, Grapes, grape leaves. No. 2407, Grape pickers, basket of grapes, wine bottle. No. 2408, Wine bottle, corkscrew, wine barrels. $1.45, Wine glasses, cheese.

2005, July 19 *Perf. 14x14¾*

2405	A689 50c multi	.90	.70
2406	A689 50c multi	.90	.70
a.	Horiz. pair, #2405-2406	2.00	1.60
b.	Booklet pane, #2406a	2.25	—
c.	Booklet pane, 2 #2406a	4.50	—
2407	A689 $1 multi	1.60	1.25
2408	A689 $1 multi	1.60	1.25
a.	Horiz. pair, #2407-2408	3.75	2.75
b.	Booklet pane, 2 #2408a	9.25	—
2409	A689 $1.45 multi	2.75	2.40
a.	Booklet pane of 2	6.25	—
	Complete booklet, #2406b, 2406c, 2408b, 2409a	22.50	
	Nos. 2405-2409 (5)	7.75	6.30

Booklet Stamps
Self-Adhesive
Serpentine Die Cut 11¼x11½ Syncopated

2410	A689 50c multi	1.00	.65
2411	A689 50c multi	1.00	.65
a.	Booklet pane, 5 each #2410-2411	11.00	

Complete booklet sold for $10.95.

Trees — A690

Designs: Nos. 2412, 2417, Snowgum. Nos. 2413, 2418, Wollemi pine. Nos. 2414, 2419, Boab. Nos. 2415, 2420, Karri. Nos. 2416, 2421, Moreton Bay fig.

2005, Aug. 8 *Perf. 14x14¾*

2412	A690 50c multi	1.00	.70
2413	A690 50c multi	1.00	.70
2414	A690 50c multi	1.00	.70
2415	A690 50c multi	1.00	.70
2416	A690 50c multi	1.00	.70
a.	Horiz. strip of 5, #2412-2416	5.00	4.00
	Nos. 2412-2416 (5)	5.00	3.50

Coil Stamps
Serpentine Die Cut 11¼x11½ Syncopated

2417	A690 50c multi	1.00	.70
2418	A690 50c multi	1.00	.70
2419	A690 50c multi	1.00	.70
2420	A690 50c multi	1.00	.70
2421	A690 50c multi	1.00	.70
a.	Horiz. strip of 5, #2417-2421	6.00	
	Nos. 2417-2421 (5)	5.00	3.50

Nos. 2417-2421 have "frames" that are faded portions of the design.

Portion of Specimen Pane of New South Wales No. 86 from Australia Post Archives — A691

2005, Sept. 6 **Litho.** *Perf. 14¼*

2422	A691 $5 multi	10.00	10.00

No. 2422 exists imperf.

Southern Cross — A692

Southern Cross and: 45c, Christmas tree. 50c, Map of Oceania and East Asia.

2005 *Perf. 14½x14*

2423	A692 45c multi	.90	.35
a.	Booklet pane of 4	5.75	—
	Complete booklet (see footnote)	24.00	
2424	A692 50c multi	1.00	.60

Issued: Nos. 2423, 2424, 9/6. No. 2423a, 11/1. No. 2423a exists with three different margins, each of which appear in a booklet also containing two examples of Christmas Island No. 452a. The complete booklet sold for $9.95.

Southern Cross With Personalized Picture — A692a

Serpentine Die Cut 11½x11¼ Syncopated
2005, Sept. 6 **Litho.**
Self-Adhesive

2425	A692a 45c Like #2423	2.50	2.50
2426	A692a 50c Like #2424	2.50	2.50

Nos. 2425-2426 were sold in sheets of 20 and have personalized pictures and a straight edge at right, and lack separations between the stamp and the picture. Sheets of 20 of No. 2425 sold for $22, and of No. 2426, $23.

Down on the Farm — A693

Designs: Nos. 2427, 2433, Hen and chicks. Nos. 2428, 2434, Lambs and insects. Nos. 2429, 2437, Goats and rabbit. Nos. 2430, 2435, Pigs and frog. Nos. 2431, 2436, Cow and bird. $1, Horse, dogs, birds, lizard.

2005, Oct. 4 Litho. *Perf. 14x14¾*

2427	A693 50c multi		1.00	.70
	a.	Booklet pane of 1	1.40	—
2428	A693 50c multi		1.00	.70
	a.	Booklet pane of 1	1.40	—
2429	A693 50c multi		1.00	.70
	a.	Booklet pane of 1	1.40	—
2430	A693 50c multi		1.00	.70
	a.	Booklet pane of 1	1.40	—
2431	A693 50c multi		1.00	.70
	a.	Booklet pane of 1	1.40	—
	b.	Horiz. strip of 5, #2427-2431	5.00	4.00
2432	A693 $1 multi		2.00	1.60
	a.	Booklet pane of 1	2.75	—
	b.	Souvenir sheet, #2427-2432	7.00	7.00
	c.	Booklet pane of 1 #2432b (120x190mm)	10.00	—
		Complete booklet, #2427a-2432a, 2432c	20.00	
		Nos. 2427-2432 (6)	7.00	5.10

The complete booklet containing Nos. 2427a-2432a and 2432c sold for $9.95.

Booklet Stamps

Self-Adhesive

Serpentine Die Cut 11¼ Syncopated

2433	A693 50c multi		1.00	.70
2434	A693 50c multi		1.00	.70
2435	A693 50c multi		1.00	.70
2436	A693 50c multi		1.00	.70
2437	A693 50c multi		1.00	.70
	a.	Booklet pane of 5, #2433-2437	6.75	—
	b.	Booklet pane of 10, 2 each #2433-2437	10.00	
	c.	Booklet pane of 20, 4 each #2433-2437	20.00	
2438	A693 $1 multi		2.00	1.60
	a.	Booklet pane of 5	12.00	—
		Nos. 2433-2438 (6)	7.00	5.10

Greetings Types of 2005 With Personalized Photo at Right Like Type A692a

Serpentine Die Cut 11½x11¼ Syncopated

2005 Self-Adhesive

2439	A673	50c multi	5.00	5.00
2440	A674	50c multi	5.00	5.00
2441	A675	50c multi	5.00	5.00
2442	A676	50c multi	5.00	5.00
2443	A677	50c multi	5.00	5.00
2444	A678	$1 multi	8.00	8.00
2445	A679	$1.10 multi	5.75	7.25
2446	A680	$1.20 multi	6.50	8.00
2447	A681	$1.80 multi	5.50	5.50
		Nos. 2439-2447 (9)	50.75	53.75

Nos. 2439-2447 were sold in sheets of 20 and have personalized pictures and a straight edge at right, and lack separations between the stamp and the picture. Sheets of 20 of Nos. 2439-2443 sold for $23 each, of No. 2444, $33.50, of No. 2445, $35, of No. 2446, $37, of No. 2447, $48.

Christmas — A694

Designs: Nos. 2448, 2450, Madonna and Child. Nos. 2449, 2451, Angel, horiz.

2005, Nov. 1 Litho. *Perf. 14½x14*

2448	A694 45c multi		.80	.35

Perf. 14x14½

2449	A694 $1 multi		1.60	1.60

Booklet Stamps

Self-Adhesive

Serpentine Die Cut 11½x11¼ Syncopated

2450	A694 45c multi		1.00	.75
	a.	Booklet pane of 20	20.00	

Serpentine Die Cut 11¼x11½ Syncopated

2451	A694 $1 multi		2.25	2.00
	a.	Booklet pane of 5	11.00	
		Nos. 2448-2451 (4)	5.65	4.70

Emblem of 2006 Commonwealth Games, Melbourne A695

Commonwealth Games Athletes A696

Highlights of Commonwealth Games — A697

Medalists at Commonwealth Games — A698

"Equality, Humanity, Destiny" A699

"Destiny, Equality, Humanity" A700

"Humanity, Destiny, Equality" A701

Designs: Nos. 2455, 2458, Runner crouching before race. $1.25, Cyclist. $1.85, Athlete holding ball.

No. 2459 — Sheet #1: a, Trolley car with wings. b, Fish sculpture. c, Cat and mouse puppets. d, Queen Elizabeth II. e, Opening ceremony crowd and fireworks.

No. 2460 — Sheet #2: a, Anna Meares. b, Equality, Humanity, destiny. c, Stephanie Rice swimming. d, Destiny, Equality, Humanity. e, Ben Kersten.

No. 2461 — Sheet #3: a, Ryan Bayley holding flag. b, Adam Vella & Michael Diamond. c, Sean Finning. d, Deserie Baynes & Suzanne Balogh. e, Danni Miatke. f, Women's Artistic Gymnastics team. g, Kate Bates. h, Leisel Jones wearing swim cap and waving. i, David Moore & Daniel Repacholi.

No. 2462 — Sheet #4: a, Brad Kahlfeldt. b, Libby Lenton, lane marker in background. c, Josh Jefferis on pommel horse. d, Emma Snowsill.

No. 2463 — Sheet #5: a, Leisel Jones wearing sweatsuit. b, Ryan Bayley wearing cycling helmet. c, Matthew Cowdrey in water. d, Chloe Sims. e, Sophie Edington in water. f, Women's 4x200m freestyle swim team. g, Ben Turner.

No. 2464 — Sheet #6: a, Katie Mactier. b, Russell Mark & Craig Trembath. c, Jessicah Schipper in water. d, Kerryn McCann. e, Lalita Yauhleuskaya & Dina Aspandiyarova.

No. 2465 — Sheet #7: a, Lauryn Mark & Natalia Rahman. b, Jane Saville. c, Libby Lenton, pushing on lane marker. d, Nathan Deakes in 20km walk. e, Lisa McIntosh.

No. 2466 — Sheet #8: a, Leisel Jones with fist raised. b, Men's triples lawn bowling team. c, Sophie Edington holding medal. d, Matthew Cowdrey wearing sweatsuit. e, Brooke Krueger-Billett. f, Josh Jefferis kissing medal. g, Natalie Grinham. h, Women's 4x100m freestyle swim team. i, Joanna Fargus.

No. 2467 — Sheet #9: a, Alex Karapetyan. b, Jessicah Schipper wearing sweatsuit. c, Nathan O'Neill. d, Lalita Yauhleuskaya holding medal.

No. 2468 — Sheet #10: a, Hollie Dykes. b, Men's 4x100m medley swim team. c, Oenone Wood. d, Women's 4x100m medley swim team. e, Stephanie Rice with arm raised. f, Damian Istria. g, Deborah Lovely.

No. 2469 — Sheet #11: a, Chantelle Newbery & Loudy Tourky. b, John Steffensen. c, Bree Cole & Sharleen Stratton. d, Lynsey Armitage & Karen Murphy.

No. 2470 — Sheet #12: a, Heath Francis. b, Jana Pittman. c, Lalita Yauhleuskaya wearing sight. d, Scott Martin. e, Loudy Tourky. f, Women's basketball team. g, Chris Rae. h, Bruce Scott.

No. 2471 — Sheet #13: a, Nathan Deakes in 50km walk. b, Bronwyn Thompson. c, Robert Newbery & Mathew Helm. d, Steven Hooker. e, Stuart Rendell. f, Kelvin Kerkow. g, Men's basketball team.

No. 2472 — Sheet #14: a, Women's 4x400m relay team. b, Kym Howe. c, Women's field hockey team. d, Mathew Helm. e, Men's 4x400m relay team. f, Bradley Pitt. g, Jarrod Fletcher.

No. 2473 — Sheet #15: a, Natalie Bates. b, Natalie Grinham & Joe Kneipp. c, Men's field hockey team. d, Rachael Grinham & Natalie Grinham. e, Mathew Hayman.

No. 2474 — Sheet #16: a, Dancer on hoops. b, Women wearing hats. c, Dancer. d, Lit-up stadium and fireworks. e, Darkened stadium and fireworks.

No. 2475 — Sheet #17 — Kerryn McCann: a, Running, with opponents in background. b, Drinking from water bottle. c, Running past opponent, profile. d, Running on track with opponent. e, With hands over mouth. f, Collapsed on track. g, With both arms raised. h, Holding flag. i, Raising flower bouquet. j, Holding medal.

2006 Litho. *Perf. 14¾x14*

2452	A695 50c shown		.90	.75
	a.	Sheet of 9 + 9 labels	27.50	—
	b.	Booklet pane of 4	4.25	—

Self-Adhesive (#2453-2454)

Serpentine Die Cut 11¼ Syncopated

2453	A695 50c multi		.75	.75
	a.	Booklet pane of 4	4.50	

With Personalized Photo at Right Like Type A692a

Booklet Stamp

Serpentine Die Cut 11½x11¼ on 3 Sides, Syncopated

2454	A695 50c multi		1.50	*1.50*
	a.	Booklet pane of 4	7.00	

Perf. 14x14¾

2455	A696 50c shown		.80	.60
2456	A696 $1.25 multi		2.00	2.00
2457	A696 $1.85 multi		2.75	2.75
	a.	Souvenir sheet, #2455-2457, 142x75mm sheet	5.50	5.50
	b.	Booklet pane, #2455-2457, in 168x118mm pane	7.75	—
		Complete booklet, #1488a, 2457b, 2 each #2453a, 2454a, + 3 postal cards	37.50	
	c.	Booklet pane, #2455-2457, in 156x103mm pane	7.75	—
		Complete booklet, #845a, 2219c, 2452b, 2457c	22.00	
		Nos. 2455-2457 (3)	5.55	5.35

Booklet Stamp

Self-Adhesive

Serpentine Die Cut 11¼ Syncopated

2458	A696 50c multi		.90	.75
	a.	Booklet pane of 10	10.00	

Miniature Sheets

Perf. 14½x14

2459		Sheet of 5	7.25	*15.00*
	a.-e.	A697 50c any single	1.40	*3.00*
2460		Sheet of 5	7.25	*11.00*
	a.	A698 50c multi	1.40	*3.00*
	b.	A699 50c multi	1.40	1.00
	c.	A698 50c multi	1.40	*3.00*
	d.	A700 50c multi	1.40	1.00
	e.	A698 50c multi	1.40	*3.00*
2461		Sheet of 10, #2460b, 2461a-2461i	14.50	*28.00*
	a.-i.	A698 50c any single	1.40	*3.00*
2462		Sheet of 5, #2460b, 2462a-2462d	7.25	*13.00*
	a.-d.	A698 50c any single	1.40	*3.00*
2463		Sheet of 10, #2460b, 2460d, 2463a-2463h	14.50	*24.00*
	a.-g.	A698 50c any single	1.40	*3.00*
	h.	A701 50c multi	1.40	1.00
2464		Sheet of 5	7.25	*15.00*
	a.-e.	A698 50c any single	1.40	*3.00*
2465		Sheet of 5	7.25	*15.00*
	a.-e.	A698 50c any single	1.40	*3.00*
2466		Sheet of 10, #2460b, 2466a-2466i	14.50	*28.00*
	a.-i.	A698 50c any single	1.40	*3.00*
2467		Sheet of 5, #2460b, 2467a-2467d	7.25	*13.00*
	a.-d.	A698 50c any single	1.40	*3.00*
2468		Sheet of 10, #2460b, 2460d, 2463h, 2468a-2468g	14.50	*24.00*
	a.-g.	A698 50c any single	1.40	*3.00*
2469		Sheet of 5, #2460b, 2469a-2469d	7.25	*13.00*
	a.-d.	A698 50c any single	1.40	*3.00*
2470		Sheet of 10, #2460b, 2460d, 2470a-2470h	14.50	*26.00*
	a.-h.	A698 50c any single	1.40	*3.00*
2471		Sheet of 10, #2460b, 2460d, 2463h, 2471a-2471g	14.50	*24.00*
	a.-g.	A698 50c any single	1.40	*3.00*
2472		Sheet of 10, #2460b, 2460d, 2463h, 2472a-2472g	14.50	*24.00*
	a.-g.	A698 50c any single	1.40	*3.00*
2473		Sheet of 5	7.25	*15.00*
	a.-e.	A698 50c any single	1.40	*3.00*
2474		Sheet of 5	7.25	*15.00*
	a.-e.	A697 50c any single	1.40	*3.00*
2475		Sheet of 10	14.50	*30.00*
	a.-j.	A697 50c any single	1.40	*3.00*
		Nos. 2459-2475 (17)	181.25	*333.00*

Issued: Nos. 2452-2453, 1/12; Nos. 2454, 2457b, 3/15; Nos. 2452b, 2455-2458, 2457c, 3/1; No. 2459, 3/16; No. 2460, 3/17; No. 2461, 3/18; Nos. 2462, 2463, 3/19; No. 2464, 3/20; Nos. 2465, 2466, 3/21; Nos. 2467, 2468, 3/22; No. 2469, 3/23; No. 2470, 3/24; No. 2471, 3/25; No. 2472, 3/26; Nos. 2473, 2474, 3/27; No. 2475, 3/28.

No. 2452a sold for $15.95. Labels could be personalized.

Complete booklet containing No. 2454 sold for $19.95. Labels could be personalized.

Complete booklet containing No. 2457c sold for $10.95 and included a booklet pane with perf. 14x14¾ lithographed examples of Nos. 349-350 which were not valid for postage.

A booklet issued 2/1, containing #2452b, an imperf booklet pane of 4 #2452, a booklet pane of 2 #2453, a booklet pane of 1 #2453 and four 50c coins, sold for $24.95.

Dame Edna Everage in 2004 A702

Barry Humphries A703

Inscriptions: Nos. 2476, 2481, Mrs. Norm Everage, 1969. Nos. 2477, 2482, Mrs. Edna Everage, 1973. Nos. 2478, 2483, Dame Edna Everage, 1982.

2006, Jan. 20 Litho. *Perf. 14½x14*

2476	A702 50c multi		.80	.70
2477	A702 50c multi		.80	.70
2478	A702 50c multi		.80	.70
2479	A702 50c shown		.80	.70
2480	A703 50c shown		.80	.70
	a.	Horiz. strip of 5, #2476-2480	4.75	4.00
	b.	Booklet pane, #2476-2480	5.25	—
		Complete booklet	45.00	
		Nos. 2476-2480 (5)	4.00	3.50

Booklet Stamps

Self-Adhesive

Serpentine Die Cut 11¼ Syncopated

2481	A702 50c multi		.75	.75
2482	A702 50c multi		.75	.75
2483	A702 50c multi		.75	.75
	a.	Booklet pane, 4 #2481, 3 each #2482-2483	9.00	
2484	A702 50c multi		.75	.75
2485	A703 50c multi		.75	.75
	a.	Booklet pane, 5 each #2484-2485	9.00	
		Nos. 2481-2485 (5)	3.75	3.75

Edna Everage, stage character played by Barry Humphries.

No. 2480b issued 1/24/07. Complete booklet, which sold for $22.95, contains Nos. 1576b, 1634m, 1634n, 1634o, 1720b, 1803b, 1934b, 2025b, 2128b, 2208b, 2324b, 2326b, 2328b, and 2480b.

Rose — A704

2006, Jan. 27 Litho. *Perf. 14x14¾*

2486	A704 50c multi		1.00	1.00

With White Border

Self-Adhesive

Litho. & Typo.

Serpentine Die Cut 11¼ Syncopated

2487	A704 50c multi		1.60	1.60

Booklet Stamp

Litho.

2488	A704 50c multi		1.00	1.00
	a.	Booklet pane of 10	10.00	

No. 2487 has a scratch-and-sniff area with a rose scent applied to the center of the rose, has a denomination composed of small black dots, and was printed in sheets of 10. No. 2488 lacks the scrach and sniff panel and has a solid gray denomination.

Flowers — A705

Designs: $1, Pincushion hakea. $2, Donkey orchid. $5, Mangles kangaroo paw. $10, Waratah.

2006, Feb. 7 Litho. *Perf. 14x14½*

2489 A705 $1 multi 2.00 1.40
2490 A705 $2 multi 3.25 2.50

Perf. 14½x14

Size:50x30mm

2491 A705 $5 multi 7.75 6.50
a. Souvenir sheet of 1 6.50 6.50
2492 A705 $10 multi 15.50 13.00
Nos. 2489-2492 (4) 28.50 23.40

Souvenir Sheet

Litho. & Embossed

2493 A705 $10 multi 20.00 20.00

Issued: No. 2491a, 9/30/22. 2022 Perth Stamp & Coin Show (No. 2491a).

Dale Begg-Smith, Men's Moguls Gold Medalist at 2006 Winter Olympics, Turin — A706

2006, Feb. 15 Litho. *Perf. 14½*

2494 A706 50c multi 2.75 2.00

Animals A707

Royal Exhibition Building, Melbourne A708

Designs: 2495, 5c, Platypus. 2496, 25c, Short-beaked echidna. No. 2497, $1.25, Common wombat. Nos. 2498, $1.25, Koala, vert. No. 2499, $1.85, Tasmanian devil. 2501, $2.50, Greater bilby. 2502, $3.70, Dingo.

2006 *Perf. 14x14¾, 14¾x14*

2495 A707 5c multi .25 .25
2496 A707 25c multi .50 .35
2497 A707 $1.25 multi 2.00 2.00
2498 A707 $1.25 multi 2.50 2.50
a. Souvenir sheet of 1, with China 2006 emblem and Great Wall of China in sheet margin 2.25 2.25
b. As "a," with Sydney landmarks in sheet margin 2.25 2.25
2499 A707 $1.85 multi 3.25 3.25
2500 A708 $1.85 multi 3.75 3.75
2501 A707 $2.50 multi 4.00 4.00
2502 A707 $3.70 multi 6.50 6.50
Nos. 2495-2502 (8) 22.75 22.60

Self-Adhesive

Booklet Stamps

Serpentine Die Cut 11¼ Syncopated

2503 A707 $1.25 multi 2.50 2.50
a. Booklet pane of 5 12.75
b. Booklet pane of 2 5.75
Complete booklet, 4 #2503b 23.00
c. As "a," with Washington 2000 Exhib. emblem added to lower right margin of bklt. pane 13.75
2504 A708 $1.85 multi 3.75 3.75
a. Booklet pane of 5 19.00
b. Booklet pane of 2 7.50
Complete booklet, 4 #2504b 30.00

Issued: Nos. 2498, 2500, 2503, 2504, 5/2; No. 2503c, 5/27; others, 3/6.

Each of the four panes of Nos. 2503b and 2504b in the complete booklets have different margins. The complete booklet containing No. 2503b sold for $12.95; the booklet containing No. 2504b sold for $14.95.

Nos. 2498a-2498b issued 10/26.

See Nos. 2542-2543, 2674, 2676, 2678, 5010.

Queen Elizabeth II, 80th Birthday

A709 A710

2006, Apr. 19 *Perf. 14¾x14*

2505 A709 50c multi 1.00 1.00
a. Booklet pane of 2 2.00 —
b. Dated "2010" 2.00 1.00
2506 A710 $2.45 multi 4.75 4.75
a. Booklet pane of 2 10.00 —
b. Booklet pane, #2505-2506, 153x104mm pane size 6.00 —
Complete booklet, #2506a, 2506b, 2 #2505a 20.00
c. Souvenir sheet, #2505-2506, 105x70mm sheet size 6.50 6.50

Self-Adhesive

Booklet Stamp

Serpentine Die Cut 11¼ Syncopated

2507 A709 50c multi 1.00 .75
a. Booklet pane of 10 10.00

Complete booklet containing Nos. 2505-2506 sold for $10.95.

A booklet commemorating royal visits to Australia containing a booklet pane of 2 each of lithographed, perf. 14x14¾ example of Nos. 474-475, a booklet pane of 4 lithographed, perf. 14x14¾ examples of No. 779, a booklet pane of 2 each of lithographed perf. 14½x14 examples of Nos. 659-660, a booklet pane of 2 each Nos. 2031-2032, a booklet pane of No. 2234a with a different margin, a booklet pane of 2 each of perf. 14½x14 examples of Nos. 351-352 (not valid for postage), and a 50c coin was released in 2006. It sold for $15.95.

Lighthouses — A711

Designs: Nos. 2508, 2513, Point Lonsdale Lighthouse, Victoria. Nos. 2509, 2514, Cape Don Lighthouse, Northern Territory. Nos. 2510, 2515, Wollongong Head Lighthouse, New South Wales. Nos. 2511, 2516, Casuarina Point Lighthouse, Western Australia. Nos. 2512, 2517, Point Cartwright Lighthouse, Queensland.

2006, May 2 *Perf. 14¾x14*

2508 A711 50c multi .80 .70
2509 A711 50c multi .80 .70
2510 A711 50c multi .80 .70
a. Booklet pane, #2509, 2510, 2 #2508 4.25 —
b. Booklet pane, #2508, 2509, 2 #2510 4.25 —
2511 A711 50c multi .80 .70
2512 A711 50c multi .80 .70
a. Horiz. strip, #2508-2512 4.50 4.50
b. Booklet pane, #2511, 2512, 2 #2509 4.25 —
c. Booklet pane, #2510, 2512, 2 #2511 4.25 —
d. Booklet pane, #2508, 2511, 2 #2512 4.25 —
Complete booklet, #2510a, 2510b, 2512b, 2512c, 2512d 20.00
Nos. 2508-2512 (5) 4.00 3.50

Coil Stamps

Self-Adhesive

Serpentine Die Cut 11¼ Syncopated

2513 A711 50c multi .75 .75
2514 A711 50c multi .75 .75
2515 A711 50c multi .75 .75
2516 A711 50c multi .75 .75
2517 A711 50c multi .75 .75
a. Vert. strip, #2513-2517 5.75

Complete booklet sold for $10.95.

2006 World Cup Soccer Championships, Germany — A712

Soccer player, 2006 World Cup emblem and word: Nos. 2518, 2522, "Play." Nos. 2519, 2523, "Goal." $1.25, "Save." $1.85, "Shot."

2006, May 9 *Perf. 14x14¾*

2518 A712 50c multi .80 .70
2519 A712 50c multi .80 .70
a. Horiz. pair, #2518-2519 2.25 2.25
2520 A712 $1.25 multi 1.90 1.75
2521 A712 $1.85 multi 3.00 3.00
a. Souvenir sheet, #2518-2521 8.00 8.00
b. As "a," with 2006 Paris Exhib. ovpt. 9.25 9.25
Nos. 2518-2521 (4) 6.50 6.15

Booklet Stamps

Self-Adhesive

Serpentine Die Cut 11¼ Syncopated

2522 A712 50c multi 1.00 .75
2523 A712 50c multi 1.00 .75
a. Booklet pane, 5 each #2522-2523 11.00

No. 2521b issued 6/17.

Postie Kate — A713

Kate: Nos. 2524, 2529, Writing address on letter. Nos. 2525, 2530, On motorcycle, delivering letter. Nos. 2526, 2531, With van, delivering package. Nos. 2527, 2532, Riding motorcycle in rain. Nos. 2528, 2533, Waving.

2006, June 1 Litho. *Perf. 14x14¾*

2524 A713 50c multi .75 .60
a. Booklet pane of 1 1.75 —
2525 A713 50c multi .75 .60
a. Booklet pane of 1 1.75 —
2526 A713 50c multi .75 .60
a. Booklet pane of 1 1.75 —
2527 A713 50c multi .75 .60
a. Booklet pane of 1 1.75 —
2528 A713 50c multi .75 .60
a. Horiz. strip of 5, #2524-2528 4.00 3.60
b. Booklet pane of 1 1.75 —
Nos. 2524-2528 (5) 3.75 3.00

Booklet Stamps

Self-Adhesive

Serpentine Die Cut 11¼ Syncopated

2529 A713 50c multi 1.00 .60
2530 A713 50c multi 1.00 .60
2531 A713 50c multi 1.00 .60
2532 A713 50c multi 1.00 .60
2533 A713 50c multi 1.00 .60
a. Booklet pane, 2 each #2529-2533 11.00
b. Booklet pane, 4 each #2529-2533 20.00
c. Booklet pane, #2529-2533 5.00
Complete booklet, #2524a, 2525a, 2526a, 2527a, 2528b, 2533c 20.00
Nos. 2529-2533 (5) 5.00 3.00

Complete booklet sold for $9.95.

Worldwide Fund for Nature (WWF) — A714

Designs: Nos. 2534, 2538, Humpback whale. Nos. 2535, 2539, Blue whale. $1.25, Fin whale. $1.85, Southern bottlenose whale.

2006, June 6 *Perf. 14x14¾*

2534 A714 50c multi .75 .60
2535 A714 50c multi .75 .60
a. Horiz. pair, #2534-2535 2.00 2.00
2536 A714 $1.25 multi 2.50 2.50
2537 A714 $1.85 multi 3.00 3.00
a. Souvenir sheet, #2534-2537 6.00 5.25
Nos. 2534-2537 (4) 7.00 6.70

Self-Adhesive

Serpentine Die Cut 11¼ Syncopated

Coil Stamps

2538 A714 50c multi 1.10 .95
2539 A714 50c multi 1.10 .95
a. Horiz. pair, #2538-2539 2.25

Booklet Stamps

2540 A714 $1.25 multi 6.50 6.50
a. Booklet pane of 5 32.50
2541 A714 $1.85 multi 7.25 7.25
a. Booklet pane of 5 37.50
Nos. 2538-2541 (4) 15.95 15.65

Types of 2006 With Personalized Photo at Right Like Type A692a

Designs: $1.25, Koala. $1.85, Royal Exhibition Building.

Serpentine Die Cut 11½x11¼ Syncopated

2006 Litho.

Self-Adhesive

2542 A707 $1.25 multi *8.00 8.00*
2543 A708 $1.85 multi *12.00 12.00*

Nos. 2542-2543 were sold in sheets of 20 and have personalized pictures and a straight edge at right, and lack separations between the stamp and the pictures. Sheets of 20 of No. 2542 sold for $38, and of No. 2543, $49.

Extreme Sports — A715

Designs: 50c, Surfing. $1, Snowboarding. $1.45, Skateboarding. $2, Freestyle motocross.

2006, July 18 Litho. *Perf. 14x14¾*

2544 A715 50c multi .75 .70
2545 A715 $1 multi 1.50 1.25
2546 A715 $1.45 multi 2.50 2.50
2547 A715 $2 multi 3.25 3.25
Nos. 2544-2547 (4) 8.00 7.70

Cars and Trucks — A716

Designs: Nos. 2548, 2553, 1917 Ford TT Truck. Nos. 2549, 2554, 1956 Holden FE. Nos. 2550, 2555, 1961 Morris 850. Nos. 2551, 2556, 1976 Holden Sandman HX. Nos. 2552, 2557, 1985 Toyota Land Cruiser FJ60.

2006, Aug. 15 *Perf. 14x14¾*

2548 A716 50c multi .75 .70
a. Booklet pane of 4 3.50 —
2549 A716 50c multi .75 .70
a. Booklet pane of 4 3.50 —
2550 A716 50c multi .75 .70
a. Booklet pane of 4 3.50 —
2551 A716 50c multi .75 .70
a. Booklet pane of 4 3.50 —
2552 A716 50c multi .75 .70
a. Booklet pane of 4 3.50 —
Complete booklet, #2548a-2552a 18.00
b. Horiz. strip of 5, #2548-2552 4.75 4.00
Nos. 2548-2552 (5) 3.75 3.50

Booklet Stamps

Self-Adhesive

Serpentine Die Cut 11¼ Syncopated

2553 A716 50c multi .90 .70
a. Booklet pane of 10 11.00
b. Missing 2006 date
2554 A716 50c multi .90 .70
a. Booklet pane of 10 11.00
2555 A716 50c multi .90 .70
a. Booklet pane of 10 11.00
2556 A716 50c multi .90 .70
a. Booklet pane of 10 11.00
2557 A716 50c multi .90 .70
a. Booklet pane of 10 11.00
b. Booklet pane, 2 each #2553-2557 16.00
Nos. 2553-2557 (5) 4.50 3.50

Complete booklet containing Nos. 2548a-2552a sold for $10.95.

Rock Posters — A717

Designs: Nos. 2558a, 2559a, Sunbury Rock Festival, 1972. Nos. 2558b, 2559b, Magic Dirt Tour, 2002. Nos. 2558c, 2559c, The Masters Apprentices Parramatta concert, 1972. Nos. 2558d, 2559d, Goanna's Spirit of Place album, 1983. Nos. 2558e, 2559e, Angels, Sports and Paul Kelly and the Dots Latrobe concert, 1979. Nos. 2558f, 2559f, Midnight Oil, 1979. Nos. 2558g, 2559g, Big Day Out Festival, 2003. Nos. 2558h, 2559h, Apollo Bay Music Festival, 1999. Nos. 2558i, 2559i, Rolling Stones Australian Tour, 1973. Nos. 2558j, 2559j, Mental as Anything's Another Falcon Tour, 1990.

2006, Sept. 12 Litho. *Perf. 14½x14*

2558 Sheet of 10 16.00 16.00
a.-j. A717 50c Any single .95 .95
k. Booklet pane of 2 #2558a 2.25 —
l. Booklet pane of 2 #2558b 2.25 —
m. Booklet pane of 2 #2558c 2.25 —
n. Booklet pane of 2 #2558d 2.25 —
o. Booklet pane of 2 #2558e 2.25 —
p. Booklet pane of 2 #2558f 2.25 —
q. Booklet pane of 2 #2558g 2.25 —
r. Booklet pane of 2 #2558h 2.25 —
s. Booklet pane of 2 #2558i 2.25 —
t. Booklet pane of 2 #2558j 2.25 —
Complete booklet, #2558k-2558t 22.00

Self-Adhesive

Serpentine Die Cut 11½x11¼ Syncopated

2559 Booklet pane of 10 16.00
a.-j. A717 50c Any single 1.00 1.00

Complete booklet containing Nos. 2558k-2558t sold for $10.95.

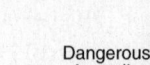

Dangerous Australian Wildlife — A718

Designs: Nos. 2560, 2566, White shark. Nos. 2561, 2567, Eastern brown snake. Nos. 2562, 2568, Box jellyfish. Nos. 2563, 2569, Saltwater crocodile. Nos. 2564, 2570, Blue-ringed octopus. Nos. 2565, 2571, Yellow-bellied sea snake.

2006, Oct. 3 Litho. *Perf. 14x14¾*

2560 A718 50c multi 1.00 .70
a. Booklet pane of 2 2.25 —
2561 A718 50c multi 1.00 .70
2562 A718 50c multi 1.00 .70
a. Booklet pane of 2 2.25 —
2563 A718 50c multi 1.00 .70
a. Booklet pane of 2 2.25 —
2564 A718 50c multi 1.00 .70
a. Horiz. strip of 5, #2560-2564 5.00 5.00
b. Booklet pane of 2 2.25 —
2565 A718 $1 multi 1.90 1.90
a. Booklet pane, 2 each #2561, 2565 6.50 —
b. Booklet pane, #2560-2565 (page 26) 7.50 —
c. Souvenir sheet, #2560-2565 7.75 7.75
Complete booklet, #2560a, 2562a, 2563a, 2564b, 2565a, 2565b 25.00
Nos. 2560-2565 (6) 6.90 5.40

Self-Adhesive

Serpentine Die Cut 11 Syncopated

2566 A718 50c multi 1.00 .70
2567 A718 50c multi 1.00 .70
2568 A718 50c multi 1.00 .70
2569 A718 50c multi 1.00 .70
2570 A718 50c multi 1.00 .70
a. Horiz. coil strip of 5, #2566-2570 5.75
b. Booklet pane, #2566-2570 7.00
2571 A718 $1 multi 1.75 1.75
a. Booklet pane of 5 9.00
Nos. 2566-2571 (6) 6.75 5.25

Complete booklet sold for $10.95. A souvenir sheet similar to No. 2565c containing partially perforated examples of Nos. 2560-2564 and a stamp that is assumed to be invalid depicting a red-back spider sold for $9.95. Value $25.

Television in Australia, 50th Anniv. — A719

Television shows: Nos. 2572, 2577, IMT (In Melbourne Tonight). Nos. 2573, 2578, Homicide. Nos. 2574, 2579, Dateline. Nos. 2575, 2580, Neighbours. Nos. 2576, 2581, Kath & Kim.

2006, Oct. 24 Litho. *Perf. 14x14¾*

2572 A719 50c multi .75 .60
2573 A719 50c multi .75 .60
2574 A719 50c multi .75 .60
2575 A719 50c multi .75 .60
2576 A719 50c multi .75 .60
a. Horiz. strip of 5, #2572-2576 4.50 4.50
Nos. 2572-2576 (5) 3.75 3.00

Self-Adhesive

Serpentine Die Cut 11¼x11½ Syncopated

2577 A719 50c multi .90 .30
a. Booklet pane of 10 #2577 9.00
2578 A719 50c multi .90 .30
2579 A719 50c multi .90 .30
2580 A719 50c multi .90 .30
2581 A719 50c multi .90 .30
a. Booklet pane of 10 #2581 9.25
b. Booklet pane of 10, 2 each #2577-2581 9.25
c. Horiz. coil strip of 5, #2577-2581 5.25
Nos. 2577-2581 (5) 4.50 1.50

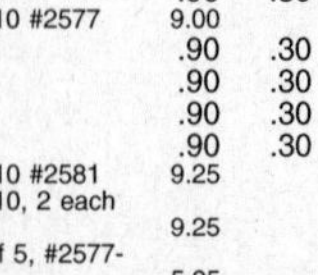

Melbourne Summer Olympics, 50th Anniv. — A720

1956 Melbourne Olympics emblem and: No. 2582, Australia #291, Olympic torch. No. 2583, View of Melbourne across Yarra River, 2006, Olympic torch. No. 2584, Australia #290, runners. No. 2585, Collins Street, Melbourne, 2006, runners.

2006, Nov. 1 *Perf. 14¾x14*

2582 A720 50c multi .90 .70
2583 A720 50c multi .90 .70
a. Horiz. pair, #2582-2583 2.00 2.00
2584 A720 $1 multi 1.90 1.20
2585 A720 $1 multi 1.90 1.20
a. Horiz. pair, #2584-2585 4.80 2.75
Nos. 2582-2585 (4) 5.60 3.80

Christmas — A721

Designs: 45c, Madonna and Child. 50c, Magus with gift. $1.05, Shepherd and lamb.

2006, Nov. 1 *Perf. 14¾x14*

2586 A721 45c multi .80 .40
2587 A721 50c multi .80 .50
2588 A721 $1.05 multi 1.60 1.60
Nos. 2586-2588 (3) 3.20 2.50

Self-Adhesive

Booklet Stamps

Serpentine Die Cut 11½x11¼ Syncopated

2589 A721 45c multi .80 .30
a. Booklet pane of 20 16.00
2590 A721 $1.05 multi 1.90 .30
a. Booklet pane of 5 9.25

Australian Victory in 2006 Ashes Cricket Match — A722

Designs: 50c, Players celebrating. $1.85, Players with Ashes Urn.

2007, Jan. 16 Litho. *Perf. 14½x14*

2591 A722 50c multi .75 .65
a. Imperf. 2.00 2.00
2592 A722 $1.85 multi 2.75 2.40
a. Souvenir sheet, #2591-2592 4.50 4.50
b. Imperf. *15.00 12.00*
c. Booklet pane of 2, #2591a, 2592b 7.50 —
Complete booklet, #591a, 666b, 773a, 1084a, 1302b, 2345a, 2592c 32.00

Booklet Stamps

Self-Adhesive

Serpentine Die Cut 10¾x11¼ Syncopated

2593 A722 50c multi 1.50 .75
a. Booklet pane of 5 7.50
2594 A722 $1.85 multi 5.00 2.50
a. Booklet pane of 5 25.00
Nos. 2591-2594 (4) 10.00 6.30

Nos. 2591a, 2592b, 2592c issued 11/14/07. Complete booklet sold for $14.95 and was not made available to foreign addresses.

Horse Racing Personalities — A723

Designs: Nos. 2595, 2607, Scobie Breasley, jockey, in silks. No. 2596, Breasley on horse. Nos. 2597, 2608, Bart Cummings, horse trainer, with binoculars. No. 2598, Cummings holding trophy. No. 2599, Roy Higgins, jockey, in silks. Nos. 2600, 2609, Higgins on horse. No. 2601, Bob Ingham, horse breeder. Nos. 2602, 2610, Ingham with horse. Nos. 2603, 2611, George Moore, jockey, in silks. No. 2604, Moore on horse. Nos. 2605, 2612, John Tapp, horse race announcer. No. 2606, Tapp with binoculars.

2007, Jan. 24 *Perf. 14½x14*

2595 A723 50c multi .90 .75
2596 A723 50c multi .90 .75
2597 A723 50c multi .90 .75
2598 A723 50c multi .90 .75
a. Block of 4, #2595-2598 3.75 3.00
2599 A723 50c multi .90 .75
2600 A723 50c multi .90 .75
2601 A723 50c multi .90 .75
2602 A723 50c multi .90 .75
a. Block of 4, #2599-2602 3.75 3.00
2603 A723 50c multi .90 .75
2604 A723 50c multi .90 .75
2605 A723 50c multi .90 .75
2606 A723 50c multi .90 .75
a. Block of 4, #2603-2606 3.75 3.00
Nos. 2595-2606 (12) 10.80 9.00

Booklet Stamps

Self-Adhesive

Serpentine Die Cut 11x11¼ Syncopated

2607 A723 50c multi .90 .30
2608 A723 50c multi .90 .30
a. Booklet pane of 10, 5 each #2607-2608 9.25
2609 A723 50c multi .90 .30
2610 A723 50c multi .90 .30
a. Booklet pane of 10, 5 each #2609-2610 9.25
2611 A723 50c multi .90 .30
2612 A723 50c multi .90 .30
a. Booklet pane of 10, 5 each #2611-2612 9.25
Nos. 2607-2612 (6) 5.40 1.80

Flowers — A724

Designs: Nos. 2613, 2617, 2621, Tasmanian Christmas bell. Nos. 2614, 2618, 2622, Green spider flower. Nos. 2615, 2619, 2623, Sturt's desert rose. Nos. 2616, 2620, 2624, Phebalium whitei.

2007, Feb. 13 Litho. *Perf. 14x14½*

2613 A724 50c multi .90 .40
2614 A724 50c multi .90 .40
2615 A724 50c multi .90 .40
2616 A724 50c multi .90 .40
a. Horiz. strip of 4, #2613-2616 3.75 3.00
Nos. 2613-2616 (4) 3.60 1.60

Self-Adhesive

Serpentine Die Cut 11¼

2617 A724 50c multi .90 .30
2618 A724 50c multi .90 .30
2619 A724 50c multi .90 .30
2620 A724 50c multi .90 .30
a. Horiz. coil strip of 4, #2617-2620 3.75
b. Booklet pane of 10, 3 each #2617-2618, 2 each #2619-2620 9.25
c. Booklet pane of 20, 5 each #2617-2620 18.50

Coil Stamps

Die Cut Perf. 12¾

2621 A724 50c multi .90 .30
2622 A724 50c multi .90 .30
2623 A724 50c multi .90 .30
2624 A724 50c multi .90 .30
a. Horiz. strip of 4, #2621-2624 3.75
Nos. 2617-2624 (8) 7.20 2.40

12th FINA World Swimming Championships, Melbourne — A725

2007, Feb. 20 *Perf. 14½x14*

2625 A725 50c multi 1.00 1.00

Coil Stamp

Self-Adhesive

Serpentine Die Cut 11¼ Syncopated

2626 A725 50c multi 1.10 .30

Islands — A726

Designs: 10c, Maria Island, Tasmania. 30c, Rottnest Island, Western Australia. $1.30, Green Island, Queensland. $1.95, Fraser Island, Queensland. $2.60, Kangaroo Island, South Australia. $3.85, Lord Howe Island, New South Wales.

2007, Mar. 5 *Perf. 14x14½*

2627 A726 10c multi .25 .25
2628 A726 30c multi .60 .30
2629 A726 $1.30 multi 2.25 1.60
2630 A726 $1.95 multi 3.50 2.40
2631 A726 $2.60 multi 4.50 2.25
2632 A726 $3.85 multi 7.00 3.50
Nos. 2627-2632 (6) 18.10 10.30

Booklet Stamps

Self-Adhesive

Serpentine Die Cut 11¼ Syncopated

2633 A726 $1.30 multi 2.25 .30
a. Booklet pane of 5 30.00
2634 A726 $1.95 multi 3.50 .30
a. Booklet pane of 5 40.00

Surf Life Saving Australia, Cent. — A727

Designs: Nos. 2635, 2639, Female lifeguard. Nos. 2636, 2640, Male lifeguards. $1, Surf boat crew. $2, Nippers (junior lifeguards). $2.45, Inflatable rescue boat and crew, vert. (30x50mm).

2007, Mar. 6 Litho. *Perf. 14x14½*

2635 A727 50c multi .90 .90
a. Booklet pane of 1 1.25 —
2636 A727 50c multi .90 .90
a. Horiz. pair, #2635-2636 1.90 1.90
b. Booklet pane of 1 1.25 —
2637 A727 $1 multi 1.90 1.40
a. Booklet pane of 1 2.50 —
2638 A727 $2 multi 3.75 2.75
a. Booklet pane of 1 5.25 —
Nos. 2635-2638 (4) 7.45 5.95

Self-Adhesive

Coil Stamps (#2639-2640)

Serpentine Die Cut 11¼ Syncopated

2639 A727 50c multi .90 .30
2640 A727 50c multi .90 .30
a. Horiz. pair, #2639-2640 1.90

Litho. With Three-Dimensional Plastic Affixed

2641 A727 $2.45 multi 4.25 4.25
a. Souvenir sheet of 2 8.50
b. Booklet pane, as "a," with rouletting at left of pane 12.50
Complete booklet, #2635a, 2636b, 2637a, 2638a, 2641b 23.00

Complete booklet sold for $12.95. No. 2641a does not have rouletting at left side of sheet.

Signs of the Zodiac — A728

Designs: Nos. 2642, 2654, 2665B, Aries. Nos. 2643, 2655, 2665C, Taurus. Nos. 2644, 2656, 2665D, Gemini. Nos. 2645, 2657, 2665E, Cancer. Nos. 2646, 2658, 2665F, Leo. Nos. 2647, 2659, 2665G, Virgo. Nos. 2648, 2660, 2665H, Libra. Nos. 2649, 2661, 2665I, Scorpio. Nos. 2650, 2662, 2665J, Sagittarius. Nos. 2651, 2663, 2665K, Capricorn. Nos. 2652, 2664, 2665L, Aquarius. Nos. 2653, 2665, 2665M, Pisces.

2007, Apr. 3 Litho. *Perf. 14½x14*

2642 A728 50c multi .95 .95
2643 A728 50c multi .95 .95
2644 A728 50c multi .95 .95
2645 A728 50c multi .95 .95
a. Block of 4, #2642-2645 4.00
2646 A728 50c multi .95 .95
2647 A728 50c multi .95 .95
2648 A728 50c multi .95 .95
2649 A728 50c multi .95 .95
a. Block of 4, #2646-2649 4.00
2650 A728 50c multi .95 .95
2651 A728 50c multi .95 .95
2652 A728 50c multi .95 .95
2653 A728 50c multi .95 .95
a. Block of 4, #2650-2653 4.00
Nos. 2642-2653 (12) 11.40 11.40

Booklet Stamps

Self-Adhesive

Serpentine Die Cut 11¼ Syncopated

2654 A728 50c multi 1.00 .30
a. Booklet pane of 10 10.50
2655 A728 50c multi 1.00 .30
a. Booklet pane of 10 10.50
2656 A728 50c multi 1.00 .30
a. Booklet pane of 10 10.50
2657 A728 50c multi 1.00 .30
a. Booklet pane of 10 10.50
2658 A728 50c multi 1.00 .30
a. Booklet pane of 10 10.50
2659 A728 50c multi 1.00 .30
a. Booklet pane of 10 10.50
2660 A728 50c multi 1.00 .30
a. Booklet pane of 10 10.50
2661 A728 50c multi 1.00 .30
a. Booklet pane of 10 10.50
2662 A728 50c multi 1.00 .30
a. Booklet pane of 10 10.50
2663 A728 50c multi 1.00 .30
a. Booklet pane of 10 10.50

2664 A728 50c multi 1.00 .30
a. Booklet pane of 10 10.50
2665 A728 50c multi 1.00 .30
a. Booklet pane of 10 10.50
Nos. 2654-2665 (12) 12.00 3.60

With Personalized Photo at Right Like Type A692a
Serpentine Die Cut 11½x11¼ Syncopated
Self-Adhesive

2665B A728 50c multi 2.50 *2.50*
2665C A728 50c multi 2.50 *2.50*
2665D A728 50c multi 2.50 *2.50*
2665E A728 50c multi 2.50 *2.50*
2665F A728 50c multi 2.50 *2.50*
2665G A728 50c multi 2.50 *2.50*
2665H A728 50c multi 2.50 *2.50*
2665I A728 50c multi 2.50 *2.50*
2665J A728 50c multi 2.50 *2.50*
2665K A728 50c multi 2.50 *2.50*
2665L A728 50c multi 2.50 *2.50*
2665M A728 50c multi 2.50 *2.50*
Nos. 2665B-2665M (12) 30.00 *30.00*

Nos. 2665B-2665M were sold in sheets of 20 and have personalized pictures and a straight edge at right, and lack separations between the stamp and the pictures. Sheets of 20 of Nos. 2665B-2665M each sold for $23.

Travel Posters of the 1930s — A729

Designs: 50c, At the Beach, by Percy Trompf. $1, Fishing, by John Vickery. $2, Riding in the Country, by James Northfield. $2.45, Winter Sport, by Northfield.

2007, Apr. 10 *Perf. 14½x14*
2666 A729 50c multi .95 .75
2667 A729 $1 multi 2.00 1.60
a. Booklet pane of 2, #2666-2667 3.25 —
2668 A729 $2 multi 4.00 3.00
2669 A729 $2.45 multi 5.00 3.75
a. Booklet pane of 4, #2666-2669 12.00 —
b. Booklet pane of 2, #2666, 2669 6.00 —
Complete booklet, #2667a, 2669a, 2669b 21.00
Nos. 2666-2669 (4) 11.95 9.10

Queen Elizabeth II, 81st Birthday — A730

2007, Apr. 18 *Perf. 14x14½*
2670 A730 50c multi .95 .75

Shipwrecks A731

Designs: 50c, Admella, 1859. $1, Loch Ard, 1878. $2, Dunbar, 1857.

2007, May 1 Litho. *Perf. 14x14½*
2671 A731 50c multi .95 .70
2672 A731 $1 multi 2.00 1.60
2673 A731 $2 multi 4.00 3.25
Nos. 2671-2673 (3) 6.95 5.55

Animals Type of 2006 and

Sydney Harbour Bridge — A732

Design: $1.30, Yellow-footed rock wallaby, vert.

2007 Litho. *Perf. 14½x14*
2674 A707 $1.30 multi 2.50 2.50
2675 A732 $1.95 multi 3.75 3.75
a. Imperf. x perf. 14 x imperf. x imperf. 3.75 3.75
b. Souvenir sheet, #2675, 2675a 7.50 7.50
c. Souvenir sheet, 2 #2675 7.75 7.75
d. As "b," with Sberatel Exhib., Prague ovpt. 9.75 9.75
e. As "c," with Bangkok 2007 Exhib. ovpt. 9.75 9.75

Self-Adhesive
Booklet Stamps
Serpentine Die Cut 11¼ Syncopated

2676 A707 $1.30 multi 3.25 3.25
a. Booklet pane of 2 6.25
Complete booklet, 4 #2676a 25.00
2677 A732 $1.95 multi 4.00 4.00
a. Booklet pane of 1 4.00
b. Booklet pane of 2 8.00
Complete booklet, #2677a, 3 #2677b 29.00

With Personalized Photo at Right Like Type A692a
Serpentine Die Cut 11½x11¼

2678 A707 $1.30 multi 4.50 4.50
2679 A732 $1.95 multi 5.75 5.75

Issued: Nos. 2674-2679, 5/8; No. 2675b, 6/15. Complete booklet containing No. 2676 sold for $12.95. It contains four different examples of No. 2676a. The booklet containing No. 2677 sold for $14.95, and it contains three different examples of No. 2677b.

No. 2675c issued 6/15. Margin of No. 2675c is overprinted in gold with emblem for Sydney Philatelic Show.

Nos. 2678-2679 were sold in sheets of 20 and have personalized pictures and a straight edge at right, and lack separations between the stamp and the picture. A sheet of 20 of No. 2678 sold for $39; of No. 2679, $51.

Circus Performers — A733

Circus acts: Nos. 2680, 2685, 2690, Torch juggler. Nos. 2681, 2686, 2691, Contortionist. Nos. 2682, 2687, 2692, Trapeze artists. Nos. 2683, 2688, 2693, Acrobats. Nos. 2684, 2689, 2694, Human cannonball.

2007, May 15 Litho. *Perf. 14½x14*
2680 A733 50c multi .95 .95
2681 A733 50c multi .95 .95
a. Booklet pane of 2 2.50 —
2682 A733 50c multi .95 .95
a. Booklet pane of 2 2.50 —
2683 A733 50c multi .95 .95
a. Booklet pane of 2 2.50 —
2684 A733 50c multi .95 .95
a. Horiz. strip of 5, #2680-2684 5.00 5.00
b. Booklet pane, #2680-2684 6.25 —
c. Booklet pane, 2 each # 2680, 2684 5.25 —
Nos. 2680-2684 (5) 4.75 4.75

Booklet Stamps
Self-Adhesive
Serpentine Die Cut 11¼ Syncopated

2685 A733 50c multi 1.10 .40
2686 A733 50c multi 1.10 .40
2687 A733 50c multi 1.10 .40
2688 A733 50c multi 1.10 .40
2689 A733 50c multi 1.10 .40
a. Booklet pane, 2 each #2685-2689 11.50

Litho. With Foil Application

2690 A733 50c multi 1.40 1.40
2691 A733 50c multi 1.40 1.40
2692 A733 50c multi 1.40 1.40
2693 A733 50c multi 1.40 1.40
2694 A733 50c multi 1.40 1.40
a. Booklet pane, #2690-2694 7.25
Complete booklet, #2681a, 2682a, 2683a, 2684b, 2684c, 2694a 25.00
Nos. 2685-2694 (10) 12.50 9.00

Complete booklet sold for $12.95. Nos. 2690-2694 each have gold stars and a portion of stamp covered by varnish.

Tourist Attractions — A734

Designs: Nos. 2695, 2700, Big Guitar, Tamworth, New South Wales. Nos. 2696, 2701, Big Lobster, Kingston Southeast, South Australia. Nos. 2697, 2702, Big Banana, Coffs Harbour, New South Wales. Nos. 2698, 2703, Big Merino Sheep, Goulburn, New South Wales. Nos. 2699, 2704, Big Pineapple, Nambour, Queensland.

2007, June 5 *Perf. 14½x14*
2695 A734 50c multi .95 .95
2696 A734 50c multi .95 .95
2697 A734 50c multi .95 .95
2698 A734 50c multi .95 .95
2699 A734 50c multi .95 .95
a. Horiz. strip of 5, #2695-2699 5.00 5.00
Nos. 2695-2699 (5) 4.75 4.75

Booklet Stamps
Self-Adhesive
Serpentine Die Cut 11¼ Syncopated

2700 A734 50c multi 1.10 .40
2701 A734 50c multi 1.10 .40
2702 A734 50c multi 1.10 .40
2703 A734 50c multi 1.10 .40
2704 A734 50c multi 1.10 .40
a. Booklet pane, 2 each #2700-2704 11.50
Nos. 2700-2704 (5) 5.50 2.00

Endangered Animals — A735

Designs: No. 2705, Gray-headed flying fox. No. 2706, Mountain pygmy possum. $1.25, Flatback turtle, horiz. $1.30, Wandering albatross, horiz.

2007, June 26 *Perf. 14½x14*
2705 A735 50c multi .95 .70
a. Booklet pane of 2 #2705 2.25 —
2706 A735 50c multi .95 .70
a. Horiz. pair, #2705-2706 2.00 1.40
b. Booklet pane of 2 #2706 2.25 —

Perf. 14x14½

2707 A735 $1.25 multi 2.40 1.90
a. Booklet pane of 2 5.75 —
2708 A735 $1.30 multi 2.50 2.00
a. Booklet pane of 2 6.00 —
Complete booklet, #793c, 794b, 2705a, 2706b, 2707a, 2708a 23.00

Complete booklet sold for $10.95.

Modern Architecture A736

Designs: No. 2709, Former ICI House, Melbourne. No. 2710, Academy of Science, Canberra. $1, Council House, Perth. $2.45, Sydney Opera House.

2007, July 10 *Perf. 14x14¾*
2709 A736 50c multi .95 .70
2710 A736 50c multi .95 .70
a. Horiz. pair, #2709-2710 2.00 1.40
b, Additionally dated "2013" (#2710c) 1.10 1.10
c. Booklet pane of 2 #2710b 2.25 —
2711 A736 $1 multi 2.00 1.60
2712 A736 $2.45 multi 5.00 3.75
a. Souvenir sheet, #2709-2712 9.00 9.00

Due to the arrangement of the stamps on No. 2712a, the left side of the top row of perfs on each of the stamps is perf. 14 and the right side of the top row is perf. 14¾.

No. 2712a exists imperf from a telephone drawing at a substantial premium over face value. Value for single souvenir sheet, $17.50.

Issued: Nos. 2710b, 2710c, 3/5/13. No. 2710c was issued in booklet along with Nos. 1940c, 2869e, 3107c, 3349b and 3877a.

Markets — A737

Designs: Nos. 2713, 2718, Queen Victoria Market, Melbourne. Nos. 2714, 2719, Rusty's Market, Cairns. Nos. 2715, 2720, Sydney Fish Market. Nos. 2716, 2721, Adelaide Central Market. Nos. 2717, 2722, Hume Murray Farmers Market, Albury Wodonga.

2007, July 24 *Perf. 14½x14*
2713 A737 50c multi .95 .95
2714 A737 50c multi .95 .95
2715 A737 50c multi .95 .95
2716 A737 50c multi .95 .95
2717 A737 50c multi .95 .95
a. Horiz. strip of 5, #2713-2717 5.00 5.00
Nos. 2713-2717 (5) 4.75 4.75

Booklet Stamps
Self-Adhesive
Serpentine Die Cut 11¼ Syncopated

2718 A737 50c multi 1.10 .40
a. Booklet pane of 10 11.50
2719 A737 50c multi 1.10 .40
a. Booklet pane of 10 11.50
2720 A737 50c multi 1.10 .40
a. Booklet pane of 10 11.50
2721 A737 50c multi 1.10 .40
a. Booklet pane of 10 11.50
2722 A737 50c multi 1.10 .40
a. Booklet pane of 10 11.50
Nos. 2718-2722 (5) 5.50 2.00

Asia-Pacific Economic Cooperation Forum, Sydney — A738

2007, Aug. 28 *Perf. 14x14½*
2723 A738 50c multi .95 .95

Coil Stamp
Self-Adhesive
Serpentine Die Cut 11¼x11½ Syncopated

2724 A738 50c multi .95 .30

Special Air Service, 50th Anniv. — A739

2007, Sept. 4 *Perf. 14x14½*
2725 A739 50c multi .95 .75

This stamp exists with "SAS" insignia embossed with gold foil. This was a restricted issue sold at far more than face value by the Philatelic Bureau.

Botanical Gardens — A740

Designs: Nos. 2726, 2731, Brisbane Botanic Gardens, Mt. Coot-tha. Nos. 2727, 2732, Kings Park and Botanic Gardens, Perth. Nos. 2728, 2733, Royal Botanic Gardens and Domain, Sydney. Nos. 2729, 2734, Royal Botanic Gardens, Melbourne. Nos. 2730, 2735, Botanic Gardens of Adelaide.

2007, Sept. 12 *Perf. 14x14½*
2726 A740 50c multi .95 .95
a. Booklet pane of 4 4.25 —
2727 A740 50c multi .95 .95
a. Booklet pane of 4 4.25 —
2728 A740 50c multi .95 .95
a. Booklet pane of 4 4.25 —
2729 A740 50c multi .95 .95
a. Booklet pane of 4 4.25 —
2730 A740 50c multi .95 .95
a. Booklet pane of 4 4.25 —
Complete booklet, #2726a-2730a 22.00
b. Horiz. strip of 5, #2726-2730 5.00 5.00
Nos. 2726-2730 (5) 4.75 4.75

Self-Adhesive
Serpentine Die Cut 11¼x11½ Syncopated

2731 A740 50c multi .95 .30
2732 A740 50c multi .95 .30
2733 A740 50c multi .95 .30
2734 A740 50c multi .95 .30
2735 A740 50c multi .95 .30
a. Horiz. coil strip of 5, #2731-2735 5.00
b. Booklet pane of 20, 5 each #2731-2735, + 10 labels 19.50
Nos. 2731-2735 (5) 4.75 1.50

Complete booklet sold for $10.95.

Space Age, 50th Anniv. — A741

Designs: Nos. 2736, 2743, Sputnik, 1957. Nos. 2737, 2744, First space walk, 1965. Nos. 2738, 2745, First Moon walk, 1969. Nos. 2739, 2746, Voyager, 1977. Nos. 2740, 2747, International Space Station, 1998. Nos. 2741, 2742a, Hubble Space Telescope, 1990, horiz.

2007, Oct. 2 Litho. *Perf. 14½x14*
2736 A741 50c multi 1.00 1.00
a. Booklet pane of 2 2.40 —
2737 A741 50c multi 1.00 1.00
a. Booklet pane of 2 2.40 —

2738 A741 50c multi 1.00 1.00
a. Booklet pane of 2 2.40 —
2739 A741 50c multi 1.00 1.00
a. Booklet pane of 2 2.40 —
2740 A741 50c multi 1.00 1.00
a. Horiz. strip of 5, #2736-2740 5.25 5.25
b. Booklet pane of 2 2.40 —
c. Booklet pane of 5, #2736-2740 6.00 —
2741 A741 $1 multi, 50x30mm 2.25 2.25
a. Booklet pane of 2 5.00 —
Complete booklet, #2736a, 2737a, 2738a, 2739a, 2740b, 2740c, 2741a 23.00
Nos. 2736-2741 (6) 7.25 7.25

Souvenir Sheet

2742 Sheet of 6, #2736-2740, 2742a 7.50 7.50
a. A741 $1 multi, 52x43mm 2.25 2.25

A souvenir sheet in the 50c denomination exists. It was sold in a restricted sale with a normal souvenir sheet and a coin at a price far in advance of face value.

Self-Adhesive
Booklet Stamps
Serpentine Die Cut 11¼ Syncopated

2743 A741 50c multi 1.00 .30
2744 A741 50c multi 1.00 .30
2745 A741 50c multi 1.00 .30
2746 A741 50c multi 1.00 .30
2747 A741 50c multi 1.00 .30
a. Coil strip of 5, #2743-2747 5.25
b. Booklet pane, 2 each #2743-2747 10.00
Nos. 2743-2747 (5) 5.00 1.50

Complete booklet sold for $10.95.

Trailer Campers — A742

People and trailer campers from: Nos. 2748, 2753, 1950s. Nos. 2749, 2754, 1960s. Nos. 2750, 2755, 1970s. Nos. 2751, 2756, 1980s. Nos. 2752, 2757, Today.

2007, Oct. 16 ***Perf. 14x14½***

2748 A742 50c multi 1.10 1.10
a. Booklet pane of 4 5.00 —
2749 A742 50c multi 1.10 1.10
a. Booklet pane, 2 each #2748-2749 5.00 —
2750 A742 50c multi 1.10 1.10
a. Booklet pane of 4 5.00 —
2751 A742 50c multi 1.10 1.10
a. Booklet pane, 2 each #2750-2751 5.00 —
2752 A742 50c multi 1.10 1.10
a. Horiz. strip of 5, #2748-2752 5.50 5.50
b. Booklet pane of 4 5.00 —
Complete booklet, #2748a, 2749a, 2750a, 2751a, 2752b 25.00
Nos. 2748-2752 (5) 5.50 5.50

Self-Adhesive
Booklet Stamps
Serpentine Die Cut 11¼ Syncopated

2753 A742 50c multi 1.10 .30
a. Booklet pane of 10 11.00 —
2754 A742 50c multi 1.10 .30
a. Booklet pane of 10 11.00 —
2755 A742 50c multi 1.10 .30
a. Booklet pane of 10 11.00 —
2756 A742 50c multi 1.10 .30
a. Booklet pane of 10 11.00 —
2757 A742 50c multi 1.10 .30
a. Booklet pane of 10 11.00 —
b. Booklet pane, 2 each #2753-2757 11.00 —
Nos. 2753-2757 (5) 5.50 1.50

Complete booklet sold for $10.95.

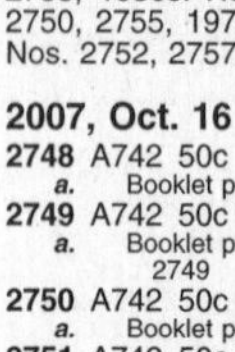

Christmas — A743

Designs of past Australian Christmas stamps with original denominations removed: Nos. 2758, 2763, 2768, #669. Nos. 2759, 2764, 2769, #1195. Nos. 2760, 2765, #1567. Nos. 2761, 2766, #306, horiz. Nos. 2762, 2767, 2770, #931.

Perf. 14½x14, 14x14½

2007, Nov. 1 **Litho.**

2758 A743 45c multi .95 .95
a. Booklet pane of 4 4.25 —
2759 A743 45c multi .95 .95
a. Booklet pane of 4 4.25 —
2760 A743 45c multi .95 .95
a. Horiz. pair, #2759-2760 2.00 2.00
b. Booklet pane of 4 4.25 —
2761 A743 50c multi 1.10 1.10
a. Booklet pane of 2 2.25 —
2762 A743 $1.10 multi 2.40 2.40
a. Booklet pane of 1 2.50 —
Nos. 2758-2762 (5) 6.35 6.35

Self-Adhesive
Serpentine Die Cut 11¼ Syncopated

2763 A743 45c multi .95 .30
a. With varnish block over stamp vignette .95 .30
2764 A743 45c multi .95 .30
a. Booklet pane of 20 20.00
2765 A743 45c multi .95 .95
a. Booklet pane of 20 20.00
2766 A743 50c multi 1.10 1.10
a. Booklet pane of 5 5.50
2767 A743 $1.10 multi 2.40 2.40
a. Booklet pane of 5 12.00
b. Souvenir sheet, #2763-2767 6.50
c. Booklet pane, #2763-2767 7.00
Complete booklet, #2758a, 2759a, 2760b, 2761a, 2762a, 2767c 25.00
Nos. 2763-2767 (5) 6.35 5.05

Complete booklet sold for $10.95. Size of No. 2767b is 156x100mm. Size of No. 2767c is 156x104mm.

With Personalized Photo at Right Like Type A692a
Serpentine Die Cut 11½x11¼ Syncopated

2768 A743 45c multi 2.40 2.40
2769 A743 45c multi 2.40 2.40
2770 A743 $1.10 multi 3.75 3.75
Nos. 2768-2770 (3) 8.55 8.55

Nos. 2768-2770 were sold in sheets of 20 and have personalized pictures and a straight edge at right, and lack separations between the stamp and the pictures. Sheets of 20 of Nos. 2768 and 2769 sold for $22, and of No. 2770, $35.

A booklet titled "Behind the Stamp," which contained four panes, sold for $19.95. The panes were in two designs, one containing Nos. 740, 1164, 1193, 1891 and a litho. reproduction of No. 277, the other containing Nos. 400, 616-617, 882, 1063 and a reproduction of No. 367. The stamps within both panes were dated "2007" and the panes were either perforated at a different gauge than the original stamps or imperforate.

Red Rose — A744

2008, Jan. 15 **Litho.** ***Perf. 14***

2771 A744 50c multi 1.00 1.00

Litho. With Foil Application
Serpentine Die Cut 11¼ Syncopated
Self-Adhesive

2772 A744 50c multi 1.00 .30

Booklet Stamp
Litho.

2773 A744 50c multi 1.10 .30
a. Booklet pane of 4 4.50
Complete booklet, 5 #2773a 22.50

With Personalized Photo at Right Like Type A692a
Serpentine Die Cut 11½x11¼ Syncopated

2774 A744 50c multi 2.40 2.40

No. 2772 was printed in a sheet of 10 + 10 labels, having rose-scented scratch and sniff areas on the rose and the labels. No. 2773 lacks the scratch and sniff areas. The complete booklet, which sold for $10.95, contains five examples of No. 2773a, each with a different margin.

No. 2774 was sold in sheets of 20 for $23 and have personalized pictures and a straight edge at right, and lack separations between the stamp and the personalized photo.

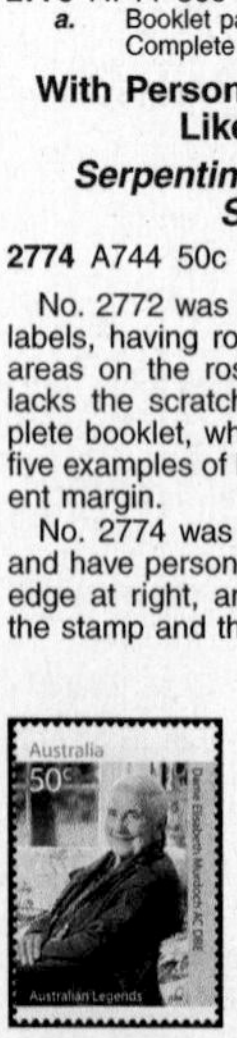

Philanthropists — A745

Designs: Nos. 2775, 2782, Dame Elisabeth Murdoch. Nos. 2776, 2781, Victor and Loti Smogron. Nos. 2777, 2780, Lady Mary Fairfax. Nos. 2778, 2779, Frank Lowy.

2008, Jan. 23 **Litho.** ***Perf. 14¾x14***

2775 A745 50c multi 1.25 1.25
2776 A745 50c multi 1.25 1.25
2777 A745 50c multi 1.25 1.25
2778 A745 50c multi 1.25 1.25
a. Horiz. strip of 4, #2775-2778 5.00 5.00
Nos. 2775-2778 (4) 5.00 5.00

Coil Stamps
Self-Adhesive
Serpentine Die Cut 11¼ Syncopated

2779 A745 50c multi 1.00 .30
2780 A745 50c multi 1.00 .30
2781 A745 50c multi 1.00 .30
2782 A745 50c multi 1.00 .30
a. Vert. strip of 4, #2779-2782 4.00
Nos. 2779-2782 (4) 4.00 1.20

Organ and Tissue Donation — A746

2008, Feb. 5 ***Perf. 14¾x14***

2783 A746 50c multi 1.10 1.10

Booklet Stamp
Self-Adhesive
Serpentine Die Cut 11¼ Syncopated

2784 A746 50c multi 1.10 .30
a. Booklet pane of 10 11.00

Scouting in Australia, Cent. — A747

Australian Scouting emblem and: 50c, Four scouts near tent. $1.35, Scouts from various nations. $2, Lord Robert Baden-Powell.

2008, Feb. 19 ***Perf. 14***

2785 A747 50c multi 1.10 1.10
2786 A747 $1.35 multi 2.75 2.75
2787 A747 $2 multi 4.25 4.25
a. Perf. 14x14½ 4.25 4.25
b. Souvenir sheet, 2 #2787a 8.50 8.50
Nos. 2785-2787 (3) 8.10 8.10

Self-Adhesive
Serpentine Die Cut 11¼ Syncopated
Coil Stamp

2788 A747 50c multi 1.10 .30

Booklet Stamps

2789 A747 $1.35 multi 2.75 1.40
a. Booklet pane of 5 14.50
2790 A747 $2 multi 4.25 2.25
a. Booklet pane of 5 22.00
Nos. 2788-2790 (3) 8.10 3.95

Canberra Stamp Show (No. 2787b).

Gorges — A748

Designs: $1.35, Grose River Gorge, New South Wales. $2, Walpa Gorge, Northern Territory. $2.70, Katherine Gorge, Northern Territory, horiz. $4, Geikie Gorge, Western Australia, horiz.

2008, Mar. 3 **Litho.** ***Perf. 14***

2791 A748 $1.35 multi 2.75 2.75
2792 A748 $2 multi 4.25 4.25
2793 A748 $2.70 multi 5.75 2.75
2794 A748 $4 multi 8.50 4.25
Nos. 2791-2794 (4) 21.25 14.00

Booklet Stamps (#2795-2796)
Self-Adhesive
Serpentine Die Cut 11½x11¼ Syncopated

2795 A748 $1.35 multi 7.50 5.00
a. Booklet pane of 5 37.50
b. Booklet pane of 2 15.00 —
Complete booklet, 4 #2795b 68.00
2796 A748 $2 multi 9.00 7.50
a. Booklet pane of 5 45.00
b. Booklet pane of 2 18.00 —
Complete booklet, 4 #2796b 72.00

With Personalized Photo at Right Like Type A692a

2797 A748 $1.35 multi *8.00 8.00*
2798 A748 $2 multi *12.00 12.00*

Nos. 2797-2798 each were sold in sheets of 20 and have personalized pictures and a straight edge at right, and lack separations between the stamp and the personalized photo. Sheets of 20 of No. 2797 sold for $40, and of No. 2798, $52.

Complete booklet containing No. 2795b sold for $10.95, and containing No. 2796b, $16.95. Each booklet contains four panes with differing margins.

World Youth Day — A749

Various depictions of Pope Benedict XVI with "08" in: 50c, Light blue. $1.35, Pink. $2, Light green.

2008, Mar. 4 ***Perf. 14***

2799 A749 50c multi 1.10 .85
2800 A749 $1.35 multi 2.75 2.75
2801 A749 $2 multi 4.25 4.25
Nos. 2799-2801 (3) 8.10 7.85

Booklet Stamps (#2802-2803)
Self-Adhesive
Serpentine Die Cut 11½x11¼ Syncopated

2802 A749 $1.35 multi 4.75 .40
a. Booklet pane of 5 22.50
2803 A749 $2 multi 7.50 2.50
a. Booklet pane of 5 37.50

With Personalized Photo at Right Like Type A692a

2804 A749 50c multi 5.00 3.00
2805 A749 $1.35 multi 8.00 8.00
2806 A749 $2 multi 10.00 10.00
Nos. 2804-2806 (3) 23.00 21.00

Nos. 2804-2806 each were sold in sheets of 20 and have personalized pictures and a straight edge at right, and lack separations between the stamp and the personalized photo. Sheets of 20 of No. 2804 sold for $23, No. 2805, sold for $40, and No. 2806 sold for $52.

Rugby League, Cent. — A750

Players and teams: Nos. 2807, 2823, Andrew Ryan, Bulldogs. Nos. 2808, 2824, Scott Prince, Titans. Nos. 2809, 2825, Brett Kimmorley, Sharks. Nos. 2810, 2826, Danny Buderus, Knights. Nos. 2811, 2827, Johnathan Thurston, Cowboys. Nos. 2812, 2828, Darren Lockyer, Broncos. Nos. 2813, 2829, Matt Orford, Sea Eagles. Nos. 2814, 2830, Cameron Smith, Storm. Nos. 2815, 2831, Craig Fitzgibbon, Roosters. Nos. 2816, 2832, Alan Tongue, Raiders. Nos. 2817, 2833, Dean Widders, Rabbitohs. Nos. 2818, 2834, Tony Puletua, Panthers. Nos. 2819, 2835, Mark Gasnier, Dragons. Nos. 2820, 2836, Nathan Cayless, Eels. Nos. 2821, 2837, Robbie Farah, Wests Tigers. Nos. 2822, 2838, Steve Price, Warriors.

2008, Mar. 24 ***Perf. 14***

2807 A750 50c multi 1.10 1.10
2808 A750 50c multi 1.10 1.10
2809 A750 50c multi 1.10 1.10
2810 A750 50c multi 1.10 1.10
a. Block of 4, #2807-2810 4.50 4.50
2811 A750 50c multi 1.10 1.10
2812 A750 50c multi 1.10 1.10
2813 A750 50c multi 1.10 1.10
2814 A750 50c multi 1.10 1.10
a. Block of 4, #2811-2814 4.50 4.50
2815 A750 50c multi 1.10 1.10
2816 A750 50c multi 1.10 1.10
2817 A750 50c multi 1.10 1.10
2818 A750 50c multi 1.10 1.10
a. Block of 4, #2815-2818 4.50 4.50
2819 A750 50c multi 1.10 1.10
2820 A750 50c multi 1.10 1.10
2821 A750 50c multi 1.10 1.10
2822 A750 50c multi 1.10 1.10
a. Block of 4, #2819-2822 4.50 4.50
Nos. 2807-2822 (16) 17.60 17.60

Booklet Stamps
Self-Adhesive
Serpentine Die Cut 11 Syncopated

2823 A750 50c multi 1.10 .30
a. Booklet pane of 10 11.00
2824 A750 50c multi 1.10 .30
a. Booklet pane of 10 11.00
2825 A750 50c multi 1.10 .30
a. Booklet pane of 10 11.00
2826 A750 50c multi 1.10 .30
a. Booklet pane of 10 11.00
2827 A750 50c multi 1.10 .30
a. Booklet pane of 10 11.00
2828 A750 50c multi 1.10 .30
a. Booklet pane of 10 11.00
2829 A750 50c multi 1.10 .30
a. Booklet pane of 10 11.00
2830 A750 50c multi 1.10 .30
a. Booklet pane of 10 11.00
2831 A750 50c multi 1.10 .30
a. Booklet pane of 10 11.00
2832 A750 50c multi 1.10 .30
a. Booklet pane of 10 11.00
2833 A750 50c multi 1.10 .30
a. Booklet pane of 10 11.00
2834 A750 50c multi 1.10 .30
a. Booklet pane of 10 11.00
2835 A750 50c multi 1.10 .30
a. Booklet pane of 10 11.00
2836 A750 50c multi 1.10 .30
a. Booklet pane of 10 11.00
2837 A750 50c multi 1.10 .30
a. Booklet pane of 10 11.00
2838 A750 50c multi 1.10 .30
a. Booklet pane of 10 11.00
b. Booklet pane of 20, #2823-2829, 2831-2838, 5 #2830 22.00
Nos. 2823-2838 (16) 17.60 4.80

A booklet containing one Rugby League dollar coin, and panes containing Nos. 2810a, 2814a, 2818a, 2822a, and four No. 2814, each in perf. 14½x14, sold for $15.95.

Heavy Haulers — A751

Designs: Nos. 2839, 2844, 2849, Excavator. Nos. 2840, 2845, 2850, Dump truck. Nos. 2841, 2846, 2851, Road train. Nos. 2842, 2847, 2852, Locomotive and ore cars. Nos. 2843, 2848, 2853, Ore carrier MS Berge Stahl.

2008, Apr. 1 ***Perf. 14***
Without White Frames

2839 A751 50c multi 1.10 1.10
2840 A751 50c multi 1.10 1.10
2841 A751 50c multi 1.10 1.10
2842 A751 50c multi 1.10 1.10
2843 A751 50c multi 1.10 1.10
a. Horiz. strip of 5, #2839-2843 5.50 5.50
Nos. 2839-2843 (5) 5.50 5.50

Booklet Stamps
Self-Adhesive
Serpentine Die Cut 11 Syncopated

2844 A751 50c multi 1.10 .60
2845 A751 50c multi 1.10 .60
2846 A751 50c multi 1.10 .60
2847 A751 50c multi 1.10 .60
2848 A751 50c multi 1.10 .60
a. Booklet pane, 4 each #2844-2848 22.00

Coil Stamps
With White Frames

2849 A751 50c multi 1.10 .60
2850 A751 50c multi 1.10 .60
2851 A751 50c multi 1.10 .60
2852 A751 50c multi 1.10 .60
2853 A751 50c multi 1.10 .60
a. Vert. strip of 5, #2849-2853 5.50
Nos. 2844-2853 (10) 11.00 6.00

ANZAC Day — A752

Designs: Nos. 2854, 2863, Veterans marching. Nos. 2855, 2862, Laying of wreaths at memorial. Nos. 2856, 2861, Buglers. Nos. 2857, 2860, Veteran holding child. Nos. 2858, 2859, Young people at Gallipoli.

2008, Apr. 16 ***Perf. 14***

2854 A752 50c multi 1.10 1.10
a. Perf. 14¾x14 1.10 1.10
b. Booklet pane, 4 #2854a 5.00 —
2855 A752 50c multi 1.10 1.10
a. Perf. 14¾x14 1.10 1.10
b. Booklet pane, 4 #2855a 5.00 —
c. Souvenir sheet, 2 each #2854-2855, perf. 14 4.50 4.50
2856 A752 50c multi 1.10 1.10
a. Perf. 14¾x14 1.10 1.10
b. Booklet pane, 4 #2856a 5.00 —
c. Souvenir sheet of 4 #2856a 4.50 4.50
d. Souvenir sheet, 2 each #2855-2856, perf. 14 4.50 4.50
2857 A752 50c multi 1.10 1.10
a. Perf. 14¾x14 1.10 1.10
b. Booklet pane, 4 #2857a 5.00 —
2858 A752 50c multi 1.10 1.10
a. Perf. 14¾x14 1.10 1.10
b. Booklet pane, 4 #2858a 5.00 —
Complete booklet, #2854b-2858b 25.00
c. Souvenir sheet, #2854a-2858a 5.50
d. Horiz. strip of 5, #2854-2858 5.50 5.50
Nos. 2854-2858 (5) 5.50 5.50

Coil Stamps
Self-Adhesive
Serpentine Die Cut 11 Syncopated

2859 A752 50c multi 1.10 .60
2860 A752 50c multi 1.10 .60
2861 A752 50c multi 1.10 .60
2862 A752 50c multi 1.10 .60
2863 A752 50c multi 1.10 .60
a. Vert. strip of 5, #2859-2863 5.50
Nos. 2859-2863 (5) 5.50 3.00

Complete booklet sold for $10.95.
2008 World Stamp Championships, Israel (No. 2856c). Issued: No. 2855c, 11/3; No. 2856d, 11/5.

Queen's Birthday — A753

Designs: 50c, Queen Elizabeth II. $2, Order of Australia badge.

2008, Apr. 18 ***Perf. 14***

2864 A753 50c multi 1.10 .85
a. Perf. 14¾x14 1.10 .85
b. Dated "2010" 2.00 1.00
2865 A753 $2 multi 4.25 2.25
a. Perf. 14¾x14 4.25 2.25
b. Souvenir sheet, #2864a, 2865a 5.50 5.50

First Hot-air Balloon Flight in Australia, 150th Anniv. — A754

Hot-air balloons over: Nos. 2866, 2870, Sydney Harbour Bridge and Sydney Opera House. Nos. 2867, 2871, Mount Feathertop, Victoria (red denomination). Nos. 2868, 2873, Western MacDonnell Ranges, Northern Territory (lilac denomination). Nos. 2869, 2872, Canberra.

2008, May 6 Litho. ***Perf. 14x14¾***

2866 A754 50c multi 1.10 1.10
a. Booklet pane of 4 5.00 —
2867 A754 50c multi 1.10 1.10
a. Booklet pane of 4 5.00 —
2868 A754 50c multi 1.10 1.10
a. Booklet pane of 4 5.00 —
2869 A754 50c multi 1.10 1.10
a. Booklet pane of 4 5.00 —
b. Booklet pane of 4, #2866-2869 5.00 —
Complete booklet, #2866a-2869a, 2869b 25.00
c. Horiz. strip of 4, #2866-2869 4.50 4.50
d. Additionally dated "2013" (#2869e) 1.10 1.10
e. Booklet pane of 2 #2869d 2.25 —
Nos. 2866-2869 (4) 4.40 4.40

Issued: Nos. 2869d, 2869e, 3/5/13. No. 2869e was issued in booklet along with Nos. 1940c, 2710c, 3107c, 3349b and 3877a.

Booklet Stamps
Self-Adhesive
Serpentine Die Cut 11 Syncopated

2870 A754 50c multi 1.10 .30
2871 A754 50c multi 1.10 .30
2872 A754 50c multi 1.10 .30
2873 A754 50c multi 1.10 .30
a. Booklet pane, 4 #2870, 2 each #2871-2873 11.00
Nos. 2870-2873 (4) 4.40 1.20

Complete booklet sold for $10.95.

Working Dogs — A755

Designs: Nos. 2874, 2879, German shepherd. Nos. 2875, 2880, Australian cattle dog. Nos. 2876, 2881, Beagle. Nos. 2877, 2882, Border collie. Nos. 2878, 2883, Labrador retriever.

2008, June 10 Litho. ***Perf. 14¾x14***

2874 A755 50c multi 1.10 1.10
a. Booklet pane of 4 5.00 —
2875 A755 50c multi 1.10 1.10
a. Booklet pane of 4 5.00 —
2876 A755 50c multi 1.10 1.10
a. Booklet pane of 4 5.00 —
2877 A755 50c multi 1.10 1.10
a. Booklet pane of 4 5.00 —
2878 A755 50c multi 1.10 1.10
a. Booklet pane of 4 5.00 —
Complete booklet, #2874a-2878a 25.00
b. Horiz. strip of 5, #2874-2878 5.50 5.50
Nos. 2874-2878 (5) 5.50 5.50

Booklet Stamps
Self-Adhesive
Serpentine Die Cut 11 Syncopated

2879 A755 50c multi 1.10 .30
a. Booklet pane of 10 + 5 stickers 11.00
2880 A755 50c multi 1.10 .30
a. Booklet pane of 10 + 5 stickers 11.00
2881 A755 50c multi 1.10 .30
a. Booklet pane of 10 + 5 stickers 11.00
2882 A755 50c multi 1.10 .30
a. Booklet pane of 10 + 5 stickers 11.00
2883 A755 50c multi 1.10 .30
a. Booklet pane of 10 + 5 stickers 11.00
b. Booklet pane of 10, 2 each #2879-2883, + 5 stickers 11.00
Nos. 2879-2883 (5) 5.50 1.50

Complete booklet sold for $10.95.

2008 Summer Olympics, Beijing — A756

2008, June 24 ***Perf. 14¾x14***

2884 A756 50c multi 1.10 1.10

Coil Stamp
Self-Adhesive
Serpentine Die Cut 11 Syncopated

2885 A756 50c multi 1.10 .30

Ecology — A757

Slogans: Nos. 2886, 2890, Save water. Nos. 2887, 2891, Reduce waste. Nos. 2888, 2892, Travel smart. Nos. 2889, 2893, Save energy.

2008, July 8 Litho. ***Perf. 14x14¾***

2886 A757 50c multi 1.10 1.10
2887 A757 50c multi 1.10 1.10
2888 A757 50c multi 1.10 1.10
2889 A757 50c multi 1.10 1.10
a. Block of 4, #2886-2889 4.50 4.50
Nos. 2886-2889 (4) 4.40 4.40

Self-Adhesive
Serpentine Die Cut 11¼x11 Syncopated

2890 A757 50c multi 1.10 .30
a. Booklet pane of 2 2.25
2891 A757 50c multi 1.10 .30
a. Booklet pane of 2 2.25
2892 A757 50c multi 1.10 .30
a. Booklet pane of 2 2.25
2893 A757 50c multi 1.10 .30
a. Booklet pane of 2 2.25
b. Booklet pane of 4, #2890-2893 4.50
c. Double-sided booklet pane of 8, 2 each #2890-2893 9.25
Complete booklet, #2890a, 2891a, 2892a, 2893a, 2893b, 2893c 24.00
d. Double-sided booklet of 20, 5 each #2890-2893 22.00
e. Horiz. coil strip of 4, #2890-2893 4.50
Nos. 2890-2893 (4) 4.40 1.20

Complete booklet sold for $10.95.

Quarantine Laws, Cent. — A758

2008, July 15 ***Perf. 14¾x14***

2894 A758 50c multi 1.10 1.10

Coil Stamp
Self-Adhesive
Serpentine Die Cut 11x11¼ Syncopated

2895 A758 50c multi 1.10 .30

Australian Football, 150th Anniv. — A759

2008, July 29 ***Perf. 14¾x14***

2896 A759 50c multi 1.10 .85

2008 Summer Olympics, Beijing — A760

No. 2897, Basketball. Nos. 2898, 2900, Cycling. Nos. 2899, 2901, Rhythmic gymnastics.

2008, Aug. 1

2897 A760 50c multi 1.10 .85
2898 A760 $1.30 multi 2.75 2.75
2899 A760 $1.35 multi 2.75 2.75
Nos. 2897-2899 (3) 6.60 6.35

Litho.
Serpentine Die Cut 11¼ Syncopated
Booklet Stamps
Self-Adhesive

2900 A760 $1.30 multi 2.75 .30
a. Booklet pane of 5 14.00
2901 A760 $1.35 multi 2.75 .30
a. Booklet pane of 5 14.50

Scenes From World Youth Day — A761

Designs: No. 2902, Pilgrims at opening mass. No. 2903, Papal welcome. No. 2904, Stations of the Cross. No. 2905, Pilgrimage walk. No. 2906, Pope Benedict XVI at final mass.

2008, July 24 Litho. ***Perf. 14½x14***

2902 A761 50c multi 2.00 *2.00*
2903 A761 50c multi 2.00 *2.00*
2904 A761 50c multi 2.00 *2.00*
2905 A761 50c multi 2.00 *2.00*
2906 A761 50c multi 2.00 *2.00*
a. Vert. strip of 5, #2902-2906 12.00 *12.00*
Nos. 2902-2906 (5) 10.00 10.00

Aircraft — A762

Designs: No. 2907, Bristol Tourer. No. 2908, Short S.30 Empire Flying Boat. No. 2909, Lockheed Super Constellation. $2, Airbus A380.

2008, Aug. 5 ***Perf. 14***

2907 A762 50c multi 1.00 .80
a. Perf. 14x14¾ 1.25 1.25
b. Booklet pane of 2, #2907a 2.50 —
2908 A762 50c multi 1.00 .80
a. Perf. 14x14¾ 1.25 1.25
b. Booklet pane of 2, #2907a 2.50 —
2909 A762 50c multi 1.00 .80
a. Perf. 14x14¾ 1.25 1.25
b. Booklet pane of 2, #2907a 2.50 —
c. Horiz. strip of 3, #2907-2909 3.00 2.40

2910 A762 $2 multi 4.00 2.00
a. Perf. 14x14¾ 5.50 5.50
b. Booklet pane of 1, #2907a 5.50 —
c. Booklet pane of 4, #2907a-2910a 9.50 —
Complete booklet, #2907b, 2908b, 2909b, 2910b, 2910c 23.00
d. Souvenir sheet, 2 each #2868, 2910a 9.50 9.50
Nos. 2907-2910 (4) 7.00 4.40

Booklet Stamp
Self-Adhesive
Serpentine Die Cut 11¼ Syncopated

2911 A762 $2 multi 4.00 2.00
a. Booklet pane of 5 20.00

Complete booklet sold for $10.95. Issued: No./ 2910d, 8/22. SunStamp 2008 Philatelic Exhibition, Brisbane (No. 2910d).

Gold Medalists at 2008 Summer Olympics, Beijing — A763

Designs: No. 2912, Stephanie Rice, Women's swimming 400m individual medley. No. 2913, Lisbeth Trickett, Women's swimming 100m butterfly. No. 2914, Leisel Jones, Women's swimming, 100m breaststroke. No. 2915, Stephanie Rice, Women's swimming 200m individual medley. No. 2916, Women's 4x200m freestyle relay swimming team. No. 2917, Drew Ginn and Duncan Free, Men's rowing pairs. No. 2918, David Crawshay and Scott Brennan, Men's rowing double sculls. No. 2919, Women's 4x100m medley relay swimming team. No. 2920, Emma Snowsill, Women's triathlon. No. 2921, Malcolm Page and Nathan Wilmot, Men's sailing 470 crew. No. 2922, Tessa Parkinson and Elise Rechichi, Women's sailing 470 crew. No. 2923, Ken Wallace, Men's single kayak 500m. No. 2924, Steven Hooker, Men's pole vault. No. 2925, Matthew Mitcham, Men's 10m platform diving.

2008, Aug. Litho. *Perf. 14¼*
2912 A763 50c multi .95 .75
2913 A763 50c multi .95 .75
2914 A763 50c multi .95 .75
2915 A763 50c multi .95 .75
2916 A763 50c multi .95 .75
2917 A763 50c multi .95 .75
2918 A763 50c multi .95 .75
2919 A763 50c multi .95 .75
2920 A763 50c multi .95 .75
2921 A763 50c multi .95 .75
2922 A763 50c multi .95 .75
2923 A763 50c multi .95 .75
2924 A763 50c multi .95 .75
2925 A763 50c multi .95 .75
Nos. 2912-2925 (14) 13.30 10.50

Issued: Nos. 2912, 8/11; No. 2913, 8/12; No. 2914, 8/13; No. 2915, 8/14; No. 2916, 8/15; Nos. 2917-2919, 8/18; Nos. 2920-2922, 8/19; Nos. 2923-2925, 8/25. Nos. 2912-2925 were printed in sheets of 10. Digitally printed versions of Nos. 2912-2925 were printed in Beijing in sheets of 10. The digitally printed stamps were only available in complete sets of 14 sheets to collectors in Australia who preordered the sets, and purchasers at the Olympex Stamp Exhibition in China. The digitally printed stamps have a larger dot pattern, most evident in the background and the Olympic rings, and a browner cast to the orange background.

Waterfalls — A764

Designs: $1.40, Russell Falls, Tasmania. $2.05, Jim Jim Falls, Northern Territory. $2.80, Spa Pool, Hammersley Gorge, Western Australia. $4.10, Mackenzie Falls, Victoria.

2008, Sept. 8 Litho. *Perf. 14¾x14*
2926 A764 $1.40 multi 2.50 2.50
2927 A764 $2.05 multi 3.75 3.75
2928 A764 $2.80 multi 5.25 2.50
2929 A764 $4.10 multi 7.50 3.75
Nos. 2926-2929 (4) 19.00 12.50

Booklet Stamps
Self-Adhesive
Serpentine Die Cut 11¼ Syncopated

2930 A764 $1.40 multi 2.50 .30
a. Booklet pane of 5 13.00
b. Booklet pane of 2 5.50
Complete booklet, 4 #2930b 22.00
2931 A764 $2.05 multi 3.75 1.90
a. Booklet pane of 5 19.00
b. Booklet pane of 2 7.75
Complete booklet, 4 #2931b 30.00

With Personalized Photo at Right Like Type A692a
Serpentine Die Cut 11½x11¼ Syncopated
Self-Adhesive

2932 A764 $1.40 multi 3.75 3.75
2933 A764 $2.05 multi 5.00 5.00

Complete booklet containing No. 2930 sold for $11.95; booklet containing No. 2931, $16.95. Margins for each pane in the complete booklets differ.

Nos. 2932-2933 each were sold in sheets of 20 and have personalized pictures and a straight edge at right, and lack separations between the stamp and the personalized photo. Sheets of 20 of No. 2932 sold for $41, and No. 2933 sold for $53.

Tourist Areas of Cities — A765

Designs: Nos. 2934, 2941, 2945, Luna Park, Melbourne. Nos. 2935, 2942, 2946, South Bank, Brisbane. Nos. 2936, 2943, 2947, The Rocks, Sydney. Nos. 2937, 2944, 2948, Fishermans Wharf, Fremantle. $1.10, Foreshore, Cairns. $1.65, Salamanca Place, Hobart. $2.75, Glenelg, Adelaide (50x30mm).

2008, Sept. 8 Litho. *Perf. 14x14½*
2934 A765 55c multi .95 .95
2935 A765 55c multi .95 .95
2936 A765 55c multi .95 .95
2937 A765 55c multi .95 .95
a. Block of 4, #2934-2937 4.00 4.00
b. Sheet of 4, #2934-2937 4.00 4.00
c. Block of 4, #2934-2937, perf. 13½x14 *18.00 18.00*
2938 A765 $1.10 multi 2.00 1.60
2939 A765 $1.65 multi 3.00 2.25

Perf. 14½x14

2940 A765 $2.75 multi 5.00 2.40
Nos. 2934-2940 (7) 13.80 10.05

Self-Adhesive
Coil Stamps
Die Cut Perf. 12¾

2941 A765 55c multi .95 .30
2942 A765 55c multi .95 .30
2943 A765 55c multi .95 .30
2944 A765 55c multi .95 .30
a. Horiz. strip of 4, #2941-2944 4.00

Booklet Stamps
Serpentine Die Cut 11¼

2945 A765 55c multi .95 .30
a. Booklet pane of 10 9.75
2946 A765 55c multi .95 .30
a. Booklet pane of 10 9.75
2947 A765 55c multi .95 .30
a. Booklet pane of 10 9.75
2948 A765 55c multi .95 .30
a. Booklet pane of 10 9.75
b. Booklet pane of 20, 5 each #2945-2948 20.00
Nos. 2941-2948 (8) 7.60 2.40

Issued: No. 2937b, 5/14/09. Hong Kong 2009 Intl. Stamp Exhibition (No. 2937b).

Australia and Southern Cross
A766

Balloons
A767

Bird and Beach
A768

Stylized Map
A769

Sparklers
A770

Flowers and Silver Wedding Rings
A771

Gold Wedding Rings
A772

Baby's Feet
A773

Heart and Roses
A774

Roses and Wedding Gown
A775

2008, Sept. 23 *Perf. 14½x14*
2949 A766 55c multi .95 .95

Perf. 14¾x14

2950 A767 55c multi .95 .95
2951 A768 55c multi .95 .95
2952 A769 55c multi .95 .95
a. Souvenir sheet of 2 + 2 labels, Chips Rafferty in margin 4.25 4.25
b. As "a," Errol Flynn in margin 4.25 4.25
2953 A770 55c multi .95 .95
a. Block of 4, #2950-2953 4.00 4.00
2954 A771 55c multi .95 .95
2955 A772 55c multi .95 .95
2956 A773 55c multi .95 .95
2957 A774 55c multi .95 .95
a. Block of 4, #2954-2957 4.00 4.00
2958 A775 $1.10 multi 2.00 1.60
Nos. 2949-2958 (10) 10.55 10.15

Nos. 2952a and 2952b were sold with Nos. 3009b and 3010d in a set for $12.95.

Booklet Stamps
Self-Adhesive
Serpentine Die Cut 11¼ Syncopated

2959 A767 55c multi 1.00 .30
a. Booklet pane of 4 4.25
Complete booklet, 5 #2959a 22.00
b. Booklet pane of 10 10.50
2960 A770 55c multi 1.00 .30
a. Booklet pane of 4 4.25
Complete booklet, 5 #2960a 22.00
b. Booklet pane of 10 10.50
2961 A771 55c multi 1.00 .30
a. Booklet pane of 4 4.25
Complete booklet, 5 #2961a 22.00
2962 A772 55c multi 1.00 .30
a. Booklet pane of 4 4.25
Complete booklet, 5 #2962a 22.00
b. Booklet pane of 10 10.50
2963 A773 55c multi 1.00 .30
a. Booklet pane of 4 4.25
Complete booklet, 5 #2963a 22.00
b. Booklet pane of 10 10.50
2964 A774 55c multi 1.00 .30
a. Booklet pane of 4 4.25
Complete booklet, 5 #2964a 22.00
2965 A775 $1.10 multi 2.00 2.00
a. Booklet pane of 4 8.00
Complete booklet, 5 #2965a 41.00
b. Booklet pane of 10 20.00
Nos. 2959-2965 (7) 8.00 3.80

With Personalized Photo at Right Like Type A692a
Serpentine Die Cut 11½x11¼ Syncopated
Self-Adhesive

2966 A767 55c multi 2.25 2.25
2967 A768 55c multi 2.25 2.25
2968 A769 55c multi 2.25 2.25
2969 A770 55c multi 2.25 2.25
2970 A771 55c multi 2.25 2.25
2971 A772 55c multi 2.25 2.25
2972 A773 55c multi 2.25 2.25
2973 A774 55c multi 2.25 2.25
2974 A775 $1.10 multi 3.25 3.25
Nos. 2966-2974 (9) 21.25 21.25

Issued: Nos. 2959b, 2960b, 2962b, 2963b, 2965b, 3/2/09.

Complete booklet containing No. 2965 sold for $22.95; booklets containing Nos. 2959-2964 each sold for $11.95. Each booklet contained panes with five different margins.

Nos. 2966-2974 each were sold in sheets of 20 and have personalized pictures and a straight edge at right, and lack separations between the stamp and the personalized photo. Sheets of 20 of Nos. 2966-2973 each sold for $24, and No. 2974 sold for $35.

Large Extinct Animals — A776

Designs: Nos. 2975, 2981, Genyornis. Nos. 2976, 2982, Diprotodon. Nos. 2977, 2983, Thylacoleo. Nos. 2978, 2984, Thylacine. No. 2979, Megalania, horiz. (52x37mm). No. 2980, Procoptodon, horiz. (52x37mm).

2008, Oct. 1 Litho. *Perf. 14½x14*
2975 A776 55c multi .95 .95
a. Perf. 14 .95 .95
b. Booklet pane of 2 #2975 2.25 —
2976 A776 55c multi .95 .95
a. Perf. 14 .95 .95
b. Booklet pane of 2 #2976 2.25 —
2977 A776 55c multi .95 .95
a. Perf. 14 .95 .95
b. Booklet pane of 2 #2977 2.25 —
2978 A776 55c multi .95 .95
a. Perf. 14 .95 .95
b. Horiz. strip of 4, #2975-2978 4.00 4.00
c. Booklet pane of 2 #2978 2.25 —
d. Booklet pane of 4, #2975-2978 4.25 —
2979 A776 $1.10 multi 2.00 1.60
a. Perf. 14 .95 .95
b. Booklet pane of 2 #2979 4.25 —
2980 A776 $1.10 multi 2.00 1.60
a. Perf. 14 .95 .95
b. Horiz. pair, #2979-2980 4.00 4.00
c. Souvenir sheet, #2975a-2980a 8.00 8.00
d. Booklet pane of 2 #2980 4.25 —
e. Booklet pane of 2, #2979-2980 4.25 —
Complete booklet, #2975b, 2976b, 2977b, 2978c, 2978d, 2979b, 2980d, 2980e 26.50
f. As "c," overprinted with Beijing 2008 Stamp Exposition emblem in margin 7.00 7.00
Nos. 2975-2980 (6) 7.80 7.00

Self-Adhesive
Serpentine Die Cut 11¼ Syncopated

2981 A776 55c multi .95 .30
2982 A776 55c multi .95 .30
2983 A776 55c multi .95 .30
2984 A776 55c multi .95 .30
a. Vert. coil strip of 4, #2981-2984 4.00
b. Booklet pane of 10, 3 each #2981-2982, 2 each #2983-2984 9.75
Nos. 2981-2984 (4) 3.80 1.20

Complete booklet sold for $13.95. Issued: No. 2980f, 10/24.

Matthew Cowdrey, Paralympian of the Year — A777

2008, Oct. 24 Litho. *Perf. 14¼*
2985 A777 55c multi .85 .70

Christmas
A778 A779

Star of Bethlehem and: Nos. 2987, 2992, 2995, Madonna and child. No. 2988, 2996, Angel. Nos. 2989, 2993, Magus.

2008, Oct. 31 Litho. *Perf. 14¾x14*
2986 A778 50c multi .80 .80
2987 A779 50c multi .80 .80
2988 A779 55c multi .85 .70
2989 A779 $1.20 multi 1.90 1.90
Nos. 2986-2989 (4) 4.35 4.20

Booklet Stamps
Self-Adhesive
Litho. & Typo.
Serpentine Die Cut 11¼ Syncopated

2990 A778 50c multi .80 .30
a. Booklet pane of 10 8.00

Litho.

2991 A778 50c multi .80 .30
a. Booklet pane of 20 16.00
2992 A779 50c multi .80 .30
a. Booklet pane of 20 16.00
2993 A779 $1.20 multi 1.90 .30
a. Booklet pane of 5 9.25
Nos. 2990-2993 (4) 4.30 1.20

With Personalized Photo at Right Like Type A692a
Serpentine Die Cut 11½x11¼ Syncopated
Self-Adhesive

2994 A778 50c multi 1.75 1.75
2995 A779 50c multi 1.75 1.75
2996 A779 55c multi 1.75 1.75
Nos. 2994-2996 (3) 5.25 5.25

Nos. 2994-2996 each were sold in sheets of 20 and have personalized pictures and a straight edge at right, and lack separations between the stamp and the personalized photo. Sheets of 20 of Nos. 2994-2995 each sold for $23, and No. 2996 sold for $24.

Posters for Popular Australian Films — A780

Poster for: Nos. 2997, 3002, The Adventures of Priscilla, Queen of the Desert. Nos. 2998, 3003, The Castle. Nos. 2999, 3004, Muriel's Wedding. Nos. 3000, 3005, Lantana. Nos. 3001, 3006, Gallipoli.

2008, Nov. 3 Litho. *Perf. 14¾x14*

2997 A780 55c multi .85 .85
2998 A780 55c multi .85 .85
2999 A780 55c multi .85 .85
3000 A780 55c multi .85 .85
3001 A780 55c multi .85 .85
a. Horiz. strip of 5, #2997-3001 4.25 4.25
Nos. 2997-3001 (5) 4.25 4.25

Self-Adhesive
Serpentine Die Cut 11¼ Syncopated

3002 A780 55c multi .85 .30
a. Booklet pane of 10 8.50
3003 A780 55c multi .85 .30
a. Booklet pane of 10 8.50
3004 A780 55c multi .85 .30
a. Booklet pane of 10 8.50
3005 A780 55c multi .85 .30
a. Booklet pane of 10 8.50
3006 A780 55c multi .85 .30
a. Booklet pane of 10 8.50
b. Booklet pane of 10, 2 each #3002-3006 8.50
c. Vert. coil strip of 5, #3002-3006 4.25
d. Souvenir sheet of 10, 1 ea #3002, 3004-3006, 6 #3003 11.00
Nos. 3002-3006 (5) 4.25 1.50

Academy Award-winning Actors and Actresses — A781

Designs: Nos. 3007, 3015, Nicole Kidman. Nos. 3008, 3016, Russell Crowe. Nos. 3009, 3018, Geoffrey Rush. Nos. 3010, 3017, Cate Blanchett. Nos. 3011, 3020, Crowe in *Gladiator*. Nos. 3012, 3019, Kidman in *Moulin Rouge!* Nos. 3013, 3021, Blanchett in *Elizabeth: The Golden Age*. Nos. 3014, 3022, Rush in *Shine*.

2009, Jan. 22 Litho. *Perf. 14¾x14*

3007 A781 55c multi .80 .80
a. Booklet pane of 4 4.25 —
3008 A781 55c multi .80 .80
a. Booklet pane of 4 4.25 —
b. Sheet of 10 + 10 labels 14.00 14.00
3009 A781 55c multi .80 .80
a. Booklet pane of 4 4.25 —
b. Souvenir sheet of 4 8.25 8.25
3010 A781 55c multi .85 .85
a. Booklet pane of 4 4.25 —
b. Block of 4, #3007-3010 3.50 3.50
c. Booklet pane of 4, #3007-3010 4.25 —
d. Souvenir sheet of 4, #3007-3010 8.25 8.25
3011 A781 55c multi .85 .85
a. Booklet pane of 4 4.25 —
b. Booklet pane of 4, 2 each #3008, 3011 4.25 —
Complete booklet, #3008a, 3010c, 3011a, 3011b 17.00
3012 A781 55c multi .85 .85
a. Booklet pane of 4 4.25 —
b. Booklet pane of 4, 2 each #3007, 3012 4.25 —
Complete booklet, #3007a, 3010c, 3012a, 3012b 17.00
3013 A781 55c multi .85 .85
a. Booklet pane of 4 4.25 —
b. Booklet pane of 4, 2 each #3010, 3013 4.25 —
Complete booklet, #3010a, 3010c, 3013a, 3013b 17.00
3014 A781 55c multi .85 .85
a. Booklet pane of 4 4.25 —
b. Booklet pane of 4, 2 each #3009, 3014 4.25 —
Complete booklet, #3009a, 3010c, 3014a, 3014b 17.50
c. Block of 4, #3011-3014 3.50 3.50
Nos. 3007-3014 (8) 6.65 6.65

Issued: No. 3008b, 5/6/10. Two sheets of 3008b, each sheet having different labels, were sold together as a set for $13.50. Nos. 3009b and 3010d were sold with Nos. 2952a and 2952b in a set for $12.95.

Self-Adhesive
Booklet Stamps
Serpentine Die Cut 11¼ Syncopated

3015 A781 55c multi .85 .30
3016 A781 55c multi .85 .30
3017 A781 55c multi .85 .30
3018 A781 55c multi .85 .30
3019 A781 55c multi .85 .30
a. Booklet pane of 10, 5 each #3015, 3019 8.50
3020 A781 55c multi .85 .30
a. Booklet pane of 10, 5 each #3016, 3020 8.50
3021 A781 55c multi .85 .30
a. Booklet pane of 10, 5 each #3017 3021 8.50
3022 A781 55c multi .85 .30
a. Booklet pane of 20, 3 each #3015-3018, 2 each #3019-3022 17.00
b. Booklet pane of 10, 5 each #3019, 3022 8.50
Nos. 3015-3022 (8) 6.80 2.40

Each complete booklet sold for $10.95.

Roses A782

Heart A783

Flowers With Heart-Shaped Petals — A784

2009, Feb. 3 Litho. *Perf. 14¾x14*

3023 A782 55c multi .80 .80
3024 A783 55c gray blue .80 .80
3025 A784 55c multi .80 .80
a. Pair, #3024-3025 1.60 1.60
Nos. 3023-3025 (3) 2.40 2.40

Booklet Stamps
Self-Adhesive
Serpentine Die Cut 11¼ Syncopated

3026 A782 55c multi .80 .80
a. Booklet pane of 10 8.00
3027 A783 55c gray blue .80 .80
a. Booklet pane of 10 8.00
3028 A784 55c multi .80 .80
a. Booklet pane of 10 8.00

Litho. With Foil Application

3029 A784 55c multi .80 .80

Litho. With Flocking

3030 A783 55c gray blue .80 .80
a. Booklet pane of 10, 2 each #3029-3030 8.00
Nos. 3026-3030 (5) 4.00 4.00

With Personalized Photo at Right Like Type A692a
Syncopated Die Cut 11½x11¼ Syncopated
Self-Adhesive

3031 A782 55c multi 1.75 1.75
3032 A783 55c multi 1.75 1.75
3033 A784 55c multi 1.75 1.75
Nos. 3031-3033 (3) 5.25 5.25

Nos. 3031-3033 each were sold in sheets of 20 and have personalized pictures and a straight edge at right and lack separations between the stamp and the personalized photo. Sheets of 20 of each stamp sold for $24.

Australian Inventions — A785

Designs: Nos. 3034, 3039, Esky (insulated cooler), wine cask. Nos. 3035, 3040, Hills hoist (rotatable clothes line frame). Nos. 3036, 3041, Speedos (swim wear), zinc oxide cream. Nos. 3037, 3042, Ute (utility vehicle), B&D Roll-A-Door (garage door). Nos. 3038, 3043, Victa rotary lawnmower.

2009, Feb. 19 Litho. *Perf. 14¾x14*

3034 A785 55c multi .80 .80
a. Booklet pane of 4 4.00 —
b. As #3034, perf. 14 .80 .80
3035 A785 55c multi .80 .80
a. Booklet pane of 4 4.00 —
b. As #3035, perf. 14 .80 .80
3036 A785 55c multi .80 .80
a. Booklet pane of 4 4.00 —
b. As #3036, perf. 14 .80 .80
3037 A785 55c multi .80 .80
a. Booklet pane of 4 4.00 —
b. As #3037, perf. 14 .80 .80
3038 A785 55c multi .80 .80
a. Booklet pane of 4 4.00 —
Complete booklet, #3034a, 3035a, 3036a, 3037a, 3038a 19.50
b. As #3038, perf. 14 .80 .80
c. Souvenir sheet, #3034b-3038b 4.00 4.00
d. Horiz. strip of 5, #3034-3038 4.00 4.00
Nos. 3034-3038 (5) 4.00 4.00

Self-Adhesive
Serpentine Die Cut 11¼ Syncopated

3039 A785 55c multi .80 .30
3040 A785 55c multi .80 .30
3041 A785 55c multi .80 .30
3042 A785 55c multi .80 .30
3043 A785 55c multi .80 .30
a. Vert. coil strip of 5, #3039-3043 4.00
b. Booklet pane of 10, 2 each #3039-3043 8.00
Nos. 3039-3043 (5) 4.00 1.50

Complete booklet sold for $12.95.

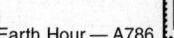

Earth Hour — A786

Animals and slogan: Nos. 3044, 3047, Lights out. No. 3045, 3048, Switch off. $2.05, Save energy.

2009, Mar. 11 *Perf. 14¾x14*

3044 A786 55c multi .90 .90
3045 A786 55c multi .90 .90
a. Horiz. pair, #3044-3045 1.90 1.90
3046 A786 $2.05 multi 3.50 3.50
Nos. 3044-3046 (3) 5.30 5.30

Booklet Stamps
Self-Adhesive
Serpentine Die Cut 11¼ Syncopated

3047 A786 55c multi .90 .30
3048 A786 55c multi .90 .30
a. Booklet pane of 20, 10 each #3047-3048 18.50

Australia Post, Bicent. — A787

Inscriptions: Nos. 3049a, 3050, First postmaster. Nos. 3049b, 3051, Early post office. Nos. 3049c, 3052, Early posting box. Nos. 3049d, 3053, News from home. Nos. 3049e, 3054, Early air mail. Nos. 3049f, 3055, Home delivery. Nos. 3049g, 3056, Post-war immigration. Nos. 3049h, 3057, Retail post shop. Nos. 3049i, 3058, Express post. Nos. 3049j, 3059, Part of every day.

2009, Mar. 25 *Perf. 14¾x14*

3049 Sheet of 10 9.25 9.25
a.-j. A787 55c Any single .90 .90
k. Booklet pane of 10, #3049a-3049j 11.00 —
l. As "k," imperf. 11.00
Complete booklet, #3049l, 2 #3049k 32.50

Self-Adhesive
Serpentine Die Cut 11¼ Syncopated

3050 A787 55c multi .90 .30
3051 A787 55c multi .90 .30
3052 A787 55c multi .90 .30
3053 A787 55c multi .90 .30
3054 A787 55c multi .90 .30
3055 A787 55c multi .90 .30
3056 A787 55c multi .90 .30
3057 A787 55c multi .90 .30
3058 A787 55c multi .90 .30
3059 A787 55c multi .90 .30
a. Vert. coil strip of 10, #3050-3059 9.00
b. Booklet pane of 10, #3050-3059 9.00
Nos. 3050-3059 (10) 9.00 3.00

Complete booklet sold for $19.95. Compare with type A806.

Aboriginal Art — A788

Designs: No. 3060, Mamu, by Nura Rupert. No. 3061, All the Jila, by Jan Billycan. No. 3062, Mina Mina, by Judy Napangardi Watson. $1.40, Untitled work from the Mission Series, by Elaine Russell. $2.05, Natjula, by Tjuruparu Watson.

2009, Apr. 1 *Perf. 14x14¾*

3060 A788 55c multi .90 .70
3061 A788 55c multi .90 .70
3062 A788 55c multi .90 .70
a. Horiz. strip of 3, #3060-3062 2.75 2.00
3063 A788 $1.40 multi 2.25 1.10
3064 A788 $2.05 multi 3.50 1.75
Nos. 3060-3064 (5) 8.45 4.95

Self-Adhesive
Booklet Stamps
Serpentine Die Cut 11¼ Syncopated

3065 A788 $1.40 multi 2.25 1.10
a. Booklet pane of 5 11.50
3066 A788 $2.05 multi 3.50 1.75
a. Booklet pane of 5 17.50

Queen's Birthday — A789

Queen Elizabeth II: 55c, In uniform. $2.05, Wearing green coat and hat.

2009, Apr. 15 *Perf. 14¾x14*

3067 A789 55c multi .90 .70
a. Booklet pane of 2 2.25 —
b. Dated "2010" 2.00 1.00
3068 A789 $2.05 multi 3.50 1.75
a. Booklet pane of 2 8.50 —
b. Souvenir sheet of 2, #3067-3068 4.50 2.40
c. Booklet pane, #3068b 5.25 —
Complete booklet, #3068a, 3068c, 2 #3067a 18.50

Complete booklet sold for $10.95.

Eponymous Desserts — A790

Designs: Nos. 3069, 3073, Anna Pavlova and Pavlova. Nos. 3070, 3074, Dame Nellie Melba and Peach Melba. Nos. 3071, 3075, Baron and Lady Lamington and Lamingtons. Nos. 3072, 3076, ANZAC soldiers and ANZAC biscuits.

2009, May 15 Litho. *Perf. 14x14¾*

3069 A790 55c multi 1.00 1.00
a. Booklet pane of 4 5.25 —
3070 A790 55c multi 1.00 1.00
a. Booklet pane of 4 5.25 —
3071 A790 55c multi 1.00 1.00
a. Booklet pane of 4 5.25 —
3072 A790 55c multi 1.00 1.00
a. Booklet pane of 4 5.25 —
Complete booklet, #3069a-3072a 20.75
b. Horiz. strip of 4, #3069-3072 4.25 4.25
Nos. 3069-3072 (4) 4.00 4.00

Booklet Stamps
Self-Adhesive
Serpentine Die Cut 11¼ Syncopated

3073 A790 55c multi 1.00 .30
3074 A790 55c multi 1.00 .30
3075 A790 55c multi 1.00 .30
3076 A790 55c multi 1.00 .30
a. Booklet pane of 10, 3 each #3073-3074, 2 each #3075-3076 11.00
Nos. 3073-3076 (4) 4.00 1.20

Complete booklet sold for $10.95.

Worldwide Fund for Nature (WWF) — A791

Designs: 55c, Spotted bottlenose dolphins. $1.35, Hourglass dolphins. $1.40, Southern right whale dolphins. $2.05, Dusky dolphins.

2009, May 26 ***Perf. 14x14¾***

3077 A791 55c multi 1.00 .80
3078 A791 $1.35 multi 2.50 2.50
3079 A791 $1.40 multi 2.50 2.50
3080 A791 $2.05 multi 3.75 3.75
a. Souvenir sheet, #3077-3080 10.00 10.00
Nos. 3077-3080 (4) 9.75 9.55

Booklet Stamps
Self-Adhesive
Serpentine Die Cut 11¼ Syncopated

3081 A791 $1.35 multi 2.50 2.50
a. Booklet pane of 5 13.00
3082 A791 $1.40 multi 2.50 2.50
a. Booklet pane of 5 13.00
3083 A791 $2.05 multi 3.75 3.75
a. Booklet pane of 5 19.00
Nos. 3081-3083 (3) 8.75 8.75

Queensland, 150th Anniv. — A792

Designs: 55c, Queensland Parliament, windmill. $2.75, Great Barrier Reef, red-eyed tree frog.

2009, June 9 Litho. ***Perf. 14¾x14***

3084 A792 55c multi 1.00 .80
3085 A792 $2.75 multi 5.25 4.00
a. Souvenir sheet, #3084-3085 6.25 6.25

Australia's Favorite Stamps — A793

Designs: Nos. 3086, 3091, 3095B, Australia #15. Nos. 3087, 3092, Australia #132. Nos. 3088, 3093, Australia #200. Nos. 3089, 3094, Australia #226. Nos. 3090, 3095, Australia #18.

2009, June 26 Litho. ***Perf. 14x14¾***

3086 A793 55c multi 1.00 1.00
a. Booklet pane of 4 4.50 —
3087 A793 55c multi 1.00 1.00
a. Booklet pane of 4 4.50 —
3088 A793 55c multi 1.00 1.00
a. Booklet pane of 4 4.50 —
3089 A793 55c multi 1.00 1.00
a. Booklet pane of 4 4.50 —
3090 A793 55c multi 1.00 1.00
a. Booklet pane of 4 4.50 —
Complete booklet, #3086a-3090a 23.00
b. Horiz. strip of 5, #3086-3090 5.25 5.25
Nos. 3086-3090 (5) 5.00 5.00

Self-Adhesive
Serpentine Die Cut 11¼ Syncopated

3091 A793 55c multi 1.00 .30
3092 A793 55c multi 1.00 .30
3093 A793 55c multi 1.00 .30
3094 A793 55c multi 1.00 .30
3095 A793 55c multi 1.00 .30
a. Horiz. coil strip of 5, #3091-3095 5.25
Nos. 3091-3095 (5) 5.00 1.50

Litho. & Embossed
Serpentine Die Cut 11¼ Syncopated
Self-Adhesive

3095B A793 55c multi 1.00 .30
c. Sheet of 13, #3091-3095, 8 #3095B 14.00

The complete booklet sold for $12.95. Nos. 3091-3095 each were printed by two different printers. There is no noticeable difference between single coil stamps, but Pemara-printed stamps are slightly closer to each other on the strip compared to the McKellar Renown-printed stamps.

Marsupials and Their Young — A794

Designs: $1.45, Koalas. $2.10, Eastern gray kangaroos. $2.90, Brushtail possums, horiz. $4.20, Common wombats, horiz.

2009, July 1 ***Perf. 14¾x14***

3096 A794 $1.45 multi 2.75 2.75
3097 A794 $2.10 multi 4.00 4.00
a. Additionally dated "2013" (#3534d) 5.50 5.50

Perf. 14x14¾

3098 A794 $2.90 multi 5.50 2.75
3099 A794 $4.20 multi 7.75 4.00
Nos. 3096-3099 (4) 20.00 13.50

Issued: No. 3097a, 5/10/13.

Booklet Stamps
Self-Adhesive
Serpentine Die Cut 11¼ Syncopated

3100 A794 $1.45 multi 2.75 1.40
a. Booklet pane of 5 14.00
3101 A794 $2.10 multi 4.00 2.00
a. Booklet pane of 5 20.00

With Personalized Photo at Right Like Type A692a
Serpentine Die Cut 11¼ Syncopated
Self-Adhesive

3102 A794 $1.45 multi 4.00 4.00
3103 A794 $2.10 multi 5.25 5.25

Nos. 3102-3103 each were sold in sheets of 20 and have personalized pictures and a straight edge at right and lack separations between the stamp and the personalized photo. Sheets of 20 of No. 3102 sold for $42; No. 3103, for $54.

Parks and Gardens — A795

Designs: Nos. 3104, 3109, Fitzroy Gardens, Melbourne. Nos. 3105, 3110, Roma Street Parkland, Brisbane. Nos. 3106, 3111, St. David's Park, Hobart. Nos. 3107, 3112, Commonwealth Park, Canberra. Nos. 3108, 3113, Hyde Park, Sydney.

2009, July 14 Litho. ***Perf. 14x14¾***

3104 A795 55c multi 1.10 1.10
a. Booklet pane of 4 5.25 —
b. Sheet of 4, #3072, 3086, 3090, 3104 4.25 4.25
3105 A795 55c multi 1.10 1.10
a. Booklet pane of 4 5.25 —
3106 A795 55c multi 1.10 1.10
a. Booklet pane of 4 5.25 —
3107 A795 55c multi 1.10 1.10
a. Booklet pane of 4 5.25 —
b. Additionally dated "2013" (#3107c) 1.25 1.25
c. Booklet pane of 2 #3107b 2.50 —
3108 A795 55c multi 1.10 1.10
a. Booklet pane of 4 5.25 —
Complete booklet, #3104a-3108a 26.00
b. Horiz. strip of 5, #3104-3108 5.50 5.50
Nos. 3104-3108 (5) 5.50 5.50

Issued: Nos. 3107b, 3107c, 3/5/13. No. 3107c was issued in booklet along with Nos. 1940c, 2710c, 2869e, 3349b and 3877a.

Coil Stamps
Self-Adhesive
Serpentine Die Cut 11¼ Syncopated

3109 A795 55c multi 1.10 .30
3110 A795 55c multi 1.10 .30
3111 A795 55c multi 1.10 .30
3112 A795 55c multi 1.10 .30
3113 A795 55c multi 1.10 .30
a. Horiz. strip of 5, #3109-3113 5.25
b. Booklet pane of 10, 2 each # 3109-3113 11.00
Nos. 3109-3113 (5) 5.50 1.50

The complete booklet sold for $12.95.
Issued: No. 3104b, 7/23. Melbourne Stamp Show 09 (No. 3104b).

Insects and Spiders — A796

Designs: Nos. 3114, 3120a, 3121, Hatchet wasp. Nos. 3115, 3120b, 3122, Praying mantis. Nos. 3116, 3120c, 3123, Ground beetle. Nos. 3117, 3120d, 3124, Jumping spider. Nos. 3118, 3120e, 3125, Ant. $1.10, Weevil.

2009, July 28 Litho. ***Perf. 14x14¾***

3114 A796 55c multi 1.10 1.10
3115 A796 55c multi 1.10 1.10
3116 A796 55c multi 1.10 1.10
3117 A796 55c multi 1.10 1.10
3118 A796 55c multi 1.10 1.10
b. Horiz. strip of 5, #3114-3118 5.25 5.25
3119 A796 $1.10 multi 2.25 1.60
Nos. 3114-3119 (6) 7.75 7.10

Miniature Sheet
With Square of Thermochromic Ink Covering Magnification Squares

3120 Sheet of 6 7.75 7.75
a.-e. A796 55c Any single 1.10 1.10
f. A796 $1.10 multi 2.25 2.25

Coil Stamps
Self-Adhesive
Serpentine Die Cut 11¼ Syncopated

3121 A796 55c multi 1.10 .30
3122 A796 55c multi 1.10 .30
3123 A796 55c multi 1.10 .30
3124 A796 55c multi 1.10 .30
3125 A796 55c multi 1.10 .30
a. Horiz. strip of 5, #3121-3125 5.25
Nos. 3121-3125 (5) 5.50 1.50

Endangered Wildlife — A797

Designs: Nos. 3126, 3132, Bridled nailtail wallaby. Nos. 3127, 3133, Norfolk Island green parrot. Nos. 3128, 3134, Subarctic fur seal. Nos. 3129, 3135, Christmas Island blue-tailed skink. Nos. 3130, 3136, Green turtle.

2009, Aug. 4 Litho. ***Perf. 14¾x14***
"Australia" Above Denomination

3126 A797 55c multi 1.10 1.10
3127 A797 55c multi 1.10 1.10
3128 A797 55c multi 1.10 1.10
3129 A797 55c multi 1.10 1.10
3130 A797 55c multi 1.10 1.10
a. Horiz. strip of 5, #3126-3130 5.25 5.25
Nos. 3126-3130 (5) 5.50 5.50
3131 A797 55c Sheet of 5, #3126, 3128-3130, Norfolk Island #980 5.25 5.25

Booklet Stamps
Self-Adhesive
Serpentine Die Cut 11¼ Syncopated

3132 A797 55c multi 1.10 .30
3133 A797 55c multi 1.10 .30
3134 A797 55c multi 1.10 .30
3135 A797 55c multi 1.10 .30
3136 A797 55c multi 1.10 .30
a. Booklet pane of 20, 4 each #3132-3136 22.00
Nos. 3132-3136 (5) 5.50 1.50

Inscribed on the left side of Nos. 3128 and 3134 is "Australian Antarctic Territory"; on Nos. 3129 and 3135, "Christmas Island"; and on Nos. 3130 and 3136, "Cocos (Keeling) Islands." All recent stamps of the Australian possessions of Australian Antarctic Territory, Christmas Island and Cocos Islands are doubly-inscribed with "Australia" and the territory's name, and all stamps inscribed "Australia," "Australian Antarctic Territory," "Christmas Island," or "Cocos Islands," are valid for postage anywhere in those four areas. However, because Nos. 3128-3130 and 3134-3136 have the territorial inscriptions at the side rather than above the denomination like similar Norfolk Island stamps, Nos. 979-983, they will be listed here only and not in the listings for each of these territories. No. 3131 is identical to Norfolk Island No. 984. Norfolk Island No. 980 has "Norfolk Island" above the denomination, which differentiates it from Australia No. 3127.

Corrugated Iron Water Tank, Fleurieu Peninsula, South Australia — A798

Corrugated Iron House, Broken Hill, New South Wales — A799

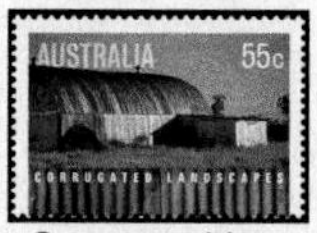

Corrugated Iron Shearing Shed, Bushy Park Cattle Station, Queensland A800

Magney House, Bingie Bingie Point, New South Wales A801

2009, Aug. 11 ***Perf. 14x14¾***

3137 A798 55c multi 1.10 1.10
a. Booklet pane of 4 5.25 —
3138 A799 55c multi 1.10 1.10
a. Booklet pane of 4 5.25 —
3139 A800 55c multi 1.10 1.10
a. Booklet pane of 4 5.25 —
3140 A801 55c multi 1.10 1.10
a. Booklet pane of 4 5.25 —
Complete booklet, #3137a-3140a 22.00
b. Horiz. strip of 4, #3137-3140 4.50 4.50
Nos. 3137-3140 (4) 4.40 4.40

Self-Adhesive
Serpentine Die Cut 11¼ Syncopated

3141 A798 55c multi 1.10 .30
3142 A799 55c multi 1.10 .30
3143 A800 55c multi 1.10 .30
3144 A801 55c multi 1.10 .30
a. Horiz. coil strip of 4, #3141-3144 4.50
b. Booklet pane of 20, 5 each #3141-3144 22.00
Nos. 3141-3144 (4) 4.40 1.20

Complete booklet sold for $10.95.

Intl. Year of Astronomy — A802

Designs: 55c, Sombrero Galaxy (M104). $1.45, Reflection Nebula (M78). $2.10, Spiral Galaxy (M83).

2009, Aug. 25 ***Perf. 14x14¾***

3145 A802 55c multi 1.10 .85
3146 A802 $1.45 multi 2.75 2.25
3147 A802 $2.10 multi 4.00 3.00
a. Souvenir sheet, #3145-3147 8.00 6.00
Nos. 3145-3147 (3) 7.85 6.10

No. 3147a exists imperf from a telephone drawing at a substantial premium over face value. Value for a single sheet, $22.

Birds — A803

Designs: 55c, Green catbird. $1.10, Noisy scrub-bird. $1.65, Mangrove golden whistler. $2.75, Scarlet honeyeater.

2009, Sept. 9 Litho. ***Perf. 14¾x14***

3148 A803 55c multi 1.10 1.10
a. Additionally dated "2013" 1.10 1.10
3149 A803 $1.10 multi 2.25 1.60
a. Booklet pane of 2, #3148-3149 4.25 —
b. Additionally dated "2013" 2.10 2.10
3150 A803 $1.65 multi 3.50 2.50
a. Booklet pane of 2, #3149-3150 7.25 —
b. Booklet pane of 2, #3148, 3150 6.75 —
c. Additionally dated "2013" 3.25 3.25
3151 A803 $2.75 multi 5.50 4.25
a. Booklet pane of 2, #3148, 3151 8.50 —
Complete booklet, #3149a, 3150a, 3150b, 3151a 26.00
b. Additionally dated "2013" 5.50 5.50
c. Booklet pane of 4, #3148a, 3149b, 3150c, 3151d 12.00 —
Nos. 3148-3151 (4) 12.35 9.45

Issued: Nos. 3148a, 3149b, 3150c, 3151b, 3151c, 5/11/13. No. 3151c was issued in a booklet also containing Nos. 3376b, 3665b and 3925a.

Self-Adhesive

Serpentine Die Cut 11¼ Syncopated

3152 A803 55c multi .95 .25
a. Booklet pane of 20 19.00

Complete booklet sold for $12.95.

Toys — A804

Children and: Nos. 3153, 3158, Cyclops pedal car. Nos. 3154, 3159, Test Match board game. Nos. 3155, 3160, Barbie doll. Nos. 3156, 3161, Malvern Star Dragstar bicycle. Nos. 3157, 3162, Cabbage Patch Kids doll.

2009, Sept. 25 ***Perf. 14¾x14***

3153 A804 55c multi 1.10 1.10
a. Booklet pane of 4 5.25 —
3154 A804 55c multi 1.10 1.10
a. Booklet pane of 4 5.25 —
3155 A804 55c multi 1.10 1.10
a. Booklet pane of 4 5.25 —
b. Sheet of 10 #3155 + 10 labels 22.00 22.00
3156 A804 55c multi 1.10 1.10
a. Booklet pane of 4 5.25 —
3157 A804 55c multi 1.10 1.10
a. Booklet pane of 4 5.25 —
Complete booklet, #3153a, 3154a, 3155a, 3156a, 3157a 26.00
b. Horiz. strip of 5, #3153-3157 5.50 5.50
Nos. 3153-3157 (5) 5.50 5.50

No. 3155b sold for $10.95.

Booklet Stamps

Self-Adhesive

Serpentine Die Cut 11¼ Syncopated

3158 A804 55c multi 1.10 .30
3159 A804 55c multi 1.10 .30
3160 A804 55c multi 1.10 .30
3161 A804 55c multi 1.10 .30
3162 A804 55c multi 1.10 .30
a. Booklet pane of 10, 2 each #3158-3162 11.00
Nos. 3158-3162 (5) 5.50 1.50

Complete booklet sold for $12.95.

Children Playing Sports — A805

"Let's get active" and children playing: Nos. 3163, 3169, Australian rules football. Nos. 3164, 3170, Basketball. Nos. 3165, 3171, Soccer. Nos. 3166, 3172, Netball. Nos. 3167, 3173, Cricket. Nos. 3168, 3174, Tennis.

2009, Oct. 6 ***Perf. 14¾x14***

3163 A805 55c multi 1.10 1.10
3164 A805 55c multi 1.10 1.10
3165 A805 55c multi 1.10 1.10
3166 A805 55c multi 1.10 1.10
3167 A805 55c multi 1.10 1.10
3168 A805 55c multi 1.10 1.10
a. Block of 6, #3163-3168 7.00 7.00
b. Souvenir sheet, #3163-3168 7.00 7.00
Nos. 3163-3168 (6) 6.60 6.60

Booklet Stamps

Self-Adhesive

Serpentine Die Cut 11¼ Syncopated

3169 A805 55c multi 1.10 .30
a. Booklet pane of 10 11.50
3170 A805 55c multi 1.10 .30
a. Booklet pane of 10 11.50
3171 A805 55c multi 1.10 .30
a. Booklet pane of 10 11.50
3172 A805 55c multi 1.10 .30
a. Booklet pane of 10 11.50
3173 A805 55c multi 1.10 .30
a. Booklet pane of 10 11.50
3174 A805 55c multi 1.10 .30
a. Booklet pane of 10 11.50
b. Booklet pane of 10, #3172, 3174, 2 each #3169-3171, 3173 11.50
Nos. 3169-3174 (6) 6.60 1.80

Miniature Sheet

Australia Post Employees — A806

No. 3175: a, Patrica Crabb (with white blouse with red dots). b, Shirley Freeman (at counter, with brochures at left). c, Vinko Romank (lifting mail tubs). d, Valda Knott (sorting boxes in background). e, Gordon Morgan (motorcycle in background). f, Vongpradith Phongsavan (with conveyor belt in background). g, Norma Thomas (with contractor delivery automobile). h, John Marsh (with blue shirt and tie). i, Anne Brun (at desk, with computer keyboard at left). j, Russell Price (with beard).

2009, Oct. 13 ***Perf. 14¾x14***

3175 A806 Sheet of 10 11.50 8.50
a.-j. 55c Any single 1.10 .85

Australia Post, bicent. Compare with Type A787.

Christmas
A807 A808

Designs: Nos. 3176, 3183, Madonna and Child. Nos. 3177, 3184, 3190, 3195, Candles in star frame. Nos. 3178, 3185, 3191, 3196, Tree ornaments in Christmas tree frame. Nos. 3179, 3186, 3192, 3197, Gifts in stocking cap frame. Nos. 3180, 3187, 3193, 3198, Ornaments in bell frame. Nos. 3181, 3188, 3194, 3199, Candy canes in stocking frame. $1.25, Magi.

2009, Nov. 2 Litho. ***Perf. 14¾x14***

3176 A807 50c multi 1.10 1.10
3177 A808 50c multi 1.10 1.10
3178 A808 50c multi 1.10 1.10
3179 A808 50c multi 1.10 1.10
3180 A808 50c multi 1.10 1.10
3181 A808 50c multi 1.10 1.10
a. Horiz. strip of 5, #3177-3181 5.50 5.50
3182 A807 $1.25 multi 2.75 2.75
a. Souvenir sheet of 2, #3176, 3182 4.00 4.00
Nos. 3176-3182 (7) 9.35 9.35

Booklet Stamps (#3183-3194)

Self-Adhesive

Serpentine Die Cut 11¼ Syncopated

3183 A807 50c multi 1.10 .30
a. Booklet pane of 20 22.00
3184 A808 50c multi 1.10 .30
3185 A808 50c multi 1.10 .30
3186 A808 50c multi 1.10 .30
3187 A808 50c multi 1.10 .30
3188 A808 50c multi 1.10 .30
a. Booklet pane of 10, 2 each #3184-3188 11.00
3189 A807 $1.25 multi 2.75 .30
a. Booklet pane of 5 14.00

Litho. With Foil Application Frames in Gold

3190 A808 50c multi 1.10 .30
3191 A808 50c multi 1.10 .30
3192 A808 50c multi 1.10 .30
3193 A808 50c multi 1.10 .30
3194 A808 50c multi 1.10 .30
a. Booklet pane of 10, 2 each #3190-3194 11.00
Nos. 3183-3194 (12) 14.85 3.60

With Personalized Photo at Right Like Type A692a

3195 A808 50c multi 2.40 2.40
3196 A808 50c multi 2.40 2.40
3197 A808 50c multi 2.40 2.40
3198 A808 50c multi 2.40 2.40
3199 A808 50c multi 2.40 2.40
Nos. 3195-3199 (5) 12.00 12.00

Nos. 3195-3199 were sold in sheets of 20 containing 4 of each stamp, have personalized pictures and a straight edge at right and lack separations between the stamp and the personalized photo. Sheets of 20 of sold for $23.

No. 3197 exists without "Australia" and the denomination.

Authors — A809

Designs: Nos, 3200, 3212, Color photograph of Peter Carey. No. 3201, Black-and-white photograph of Carey. No. 3202, Black-and-white photograph of David Malouf. Nos. 3203, 3213, Color photograph of Malouf. Nos, 3204, 3214, Color photograph of Colleen McCullough. No. 3205, Black-and-white photograph of McCullough. No. 3206, Black-and-white photograph of Bryce Courtenay. Nos. 3207, 3215, Color photograph of Courtenay. Nos, 3208, 3216, Color photograph of Thomas Keneally. No. 3209, Black-and-white photograph of Keneally. No. 3210, Black-and-white photograph of Tim Winton. Nos. 3211, 3217, Color photograph of Winton.

2010, Jan. 21 Litho. ***Perf. 14¾x14***

3200 A809 55c multi 1.10 1.10
3201 A809 55c black & gray 1.10 1.10
3202 A809 55c black & gray 1.10 1.10
3203 A809 55c multi 1.10 1.10
a. Block of 4, #3200-3203 4.50 4.50
b. Booklet pane of 4, #3203-3203 8.50 —
c. As "b," with color separations of stamps 8.50 —
3204 A809 55c multi 1.10 1.10
3205 A809 55c black & gray 1.10 1.10
3206 A809 55c black & gray 1.10 1.10
3207 A809 55c multi 1.10 1.10
a. Block of 4, #3204-3207 4.50 4.50
b. Booklet pane of 4, #3204-3207 8.50 —
c. As "b," with color separations of stamps 8.50 —
3208 A809 55c multi 1.10 1.10
3209 A809 55c black & gray 1.10 1.10
3210 A809 55c black & gray 1.10 1.10
3211 A809 55c multi 1.10 1.10
a. Block of 4, #3208-3211 4.50 4.50
b. Booklet pane of 4, #3208-3211 8.50 —
c. As "b," with color separations of stamps 8.50 —
Complete booklet, #3203b, 3203c, 3207b, 3207c, 3211b, 3211c 52.00
Nos. 3200-3211 (12) 13.20 13.20

Booklet Stamps

Self-Adhesive

Serpentine Die Cut 11¼ Syncopated

3212 A809 55c multi 1.10 .30
3213 A809 55c multi 1.10 .30
3214 A809 55c multi 1.10 .30
3215 A809 55c multi 1.10 .30
3216 A809 55c multi 1.10 .30
3217 A809 55c multi 1.10 .30
a. Booklet pane of 20, 5 #3214, 3 each #3212-3213, 3215-3217 23.00
Nos. 3212-3217 (6) 6.60 1.80

Complete booklet sold for $24.95. Color separations were not valid for postage.

Rule of Governor Lachlan Macquarie, Bicent. — A810

Designs: No. 3218, Macquarie (1762-1824) and north view of Sydney. No. 3219, Port Jackson and Sydney Town. No. 3220, Parramatta Female Penitentiary. No. 3221, Governor's Sydney Stables.

2010, Feb. 16 ***Perf. 14x14¾***

3218 A810 55c multi 1.10 .85
a. Booklet pane of 4 5.75 —
3219 A810 55c multi 1.10 .85
a. Booklet pane of 4 5.75 —
3220 A810 55c multi 1.10 .85
a. Booklet pane of 4 5.75 —
3221 A810 55c multi 1.10 .85
a. Booklet pane of 4 5.75 —
Complete booklet, #3218a-3221a 23.00
b. Block of 4, #3218-3221 4.50 3.50
Nos. 3218-3221 (4) 4.40 3.40

Complete booklet sold of $10.95.

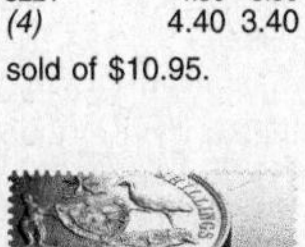

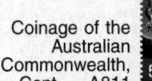

Coinage of the Australian Commonwealth, Cent. — A811

1910 two shilling coin: Nos. 3222, 3224a, Reverse depicting Australian coat of arms. Nos. 3223, 3224b, Obverse depicting King Edward VII.

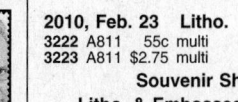

2010, Feb. 23 Litho. ***Perf. 14x14¾***

3222 A811 55c multi 1.10 .85
3223 A811 $2.75 multi 5.75 2.75

Souvenir Sheet

Litho. & Embossed With Foil Application

3224 Sheet of 2 7.00 3.75
a. A811 55c multi 1.10 .85
b. A811 $2.75 multi 5.75 2.75

No. 3224 exists imperf from a telephone drawing at a substantial premium over face value. Value for single souvenir sheet, $14.

Gold Medalists at 2010 Winter Olympics, Vancouver — A812

Designs: No. 3225, Torah Bright, Snowboard halfpipe. No. 3226, Lydia Lassila, Freestyle skiing aerials.

2010 Litho. ***Perf. 14¼***

3225 A812 55c multi 1.10 .85
3226 A812 55c multi 1.10 .85

Issued: No. 3225, 2/25; No. 3226, 3/3.

Powered Flight in Australia, Cent. (in 2009) — A813

Airplane of: 55c, Colin Defries. $1.45, John Duigan. $2.10, Harry Houdini.

2010, Mar. 9 ***Perf. 14x14¾***

3227 A813 55c multi 1.10 .85
3228 A813 $1.45 multi 3.25 1.60
a. Souvenir sheet, #3218, 3223, 3227, 3228 11.00 11.00
b. Sheet of 4, 2 each #3227-3228 9.00 6.75
3229 A813 $2.10 multi 4.50 2.25
Nos. 3227-3229 (3) 8.85 4.70

Booklet Stamps

Self-Adhesive

Serpentine Die Cut 11¼ Syncopated

3230 A813 $1.45 multi 3.25 1.60
a. Booklet pane of 5 16.00
3231 A813 $2.10 multi 4.50 2.25
a. Booklet pane of 5 23.00

2010 Canberra Stamp Show (No. 3228a). London 2010 Festival of Stamps (No. 3228b). Issued: No. 3228a, 3/12. No. 3228b, 5/8.

Agricultural Shows — A814

Designs: Nos. 3232, 3237, Prize bull. Nos. 3233, 3238, Cake decorating competition. Nos. 3234, 3239, Horse competition. Nos. 3235, 3240, Wood chopping competition. Nos. 3236, 3241, Dog show.

2010, Mar. 23 Litho. ***Perf. 14¾x14***

3232 A814 55c multi 1.10 1.10
a. Booklet pane of 4 5.50 —
3233 A814 55c multi 1.10 1.10
a. Booklet pane of 4 5.50 —
3234 A814 55c multi 1.10 1.10
a. Booklet pane of 4 5.50 —
3235 A814 55c multi 1.10 1.10
a. Booklet pane of 4 5.50 —
3236 A814 55c multi 1.10 1.10
a. Booklet pane of 4 5.50 —
Complete booklet, #3232a-3236a 27.50
b. Horiz. strip of 5, #3232-3236 5.75 5.75
c. Souvenir sheet, #3232-3236 5.75 5.75
Nos. 3232-3236 (5) 5.50 5.50

Booklet Stamps

Self-Adhesive

Serpentine Die Cut 11¼ Syncopated

3237 A814 55c multi 1.10 .30
3238 A814 55c multi 1.10 .30
3239 A814 55c multi 1.10 .30
3240 A814 55c multi 1.10 .30
3241 A814 55c multi 1.10 .30
a. Booklet pane of 10, 2 each #3237-3241 11.50 —
Nos. 3237-3241 (5) 5.50 1.50

Complete booklet sold for $12.95.

Queen's Birthday — A815

2010, Apr. 6 ***Perf. 14¾x14***

3242 A815 55c multi 1.25 1.25
a. Sheet of 4, #2505b, 2864b, 3067b, 3242 8.00 4.00

Booklet Stamp
Self-Adhesive
Serpentine Die Cut 11¼ Syncopated

3243 A815 55c multi 1.25 .30
a. Booklet pane of 10 12.75

Issued: No. 3242a, 5/8. London 2010 Festival of Stamps (No. 3242a).

Kokoda Campaign, 68th Anniv. — A816

Designs: Nos. 3244, 3249, Soldiers in battle. Nos. 3245, 3250, Injured Australian soldier, Papuan natives. Nos. 3246, 3251, Veterans of Kokoda Campaign, Papuan houses. Nos. 3247, 3252, Tourists at Kokoda. $1.45, Veterans at Kokoda Campaign Memorial, Isurava, Papua New Guinea.

2010, Apr. 20 ***Perf. 14¾x14***

3244 A816 55c multi 1.10 1.10
3245 A816 55c multi 1.10 1.10
a. Booklet pane of 4, 2 each #3244-3245 6.25 —
3246 A816 55c multi 1.10 1.10
3247 A816 55c multi 1.10 1.10
a. Booklet pane of 4 6.25 —
b. Horiz. strip of 4, #3244-3247 4.50 4.50
3248 A816 $1.45 multi 3.25 2.40
a. Booklet pane of 4, 2 each #3246, 3248 11.50
Complete booklet, #3245a, 3247a, 3248a 24.00
b. Souvenir sheet, #3244-3248 7.75 7.75
Nos. 3244-3248 (5) 7.65 6.80

Self-Adhesive
Serpentine Die Cut 11¼ Syncopated

3249 A816 55c multi 1.10 .30
3250 A816 55c multi 1.10 .30
3251 A816 55c multi 1.10 .30
3252 A816 55c multi 1.10 .30
a. Vert. coil strip of 4, #3249-3252 4.50
b. Booklet pane of 10, 2 each #3250, 3252, 3 each #3249, 3251 11.50
Nos. 3249-3252 (4) 4.40 1.20

Complete booklet sold for $10.95. See Papua New Guinea Nos. 1455-1456.

Queen Victoria ("Chalon Head") Portrait of Tasmania and Queensland Stamps) — A817

2010, May 7 Litho. ***Perf. 14x13½***

3253 A817 $5 multi 10.00 5.25
a. Souvenir sheet of 1 10.00 5.25
b. As "a," with London 2010 emblem in gold in sheet margin 8.25 8.25

No. 3253 has simulated toning. A souvenir sheet with a litho. and engraved stamp sold for $15.

Issued: No. 3253b, 5/8.

Railway Journeys — A818

Designs: Nos. 3254, 3258, The Ghan. Nos. 3255, 3259, West Coast Wilderness Railway, Tasmania. Nos. 3256, 3260, The Indian Pacific. $2.10, Kuranda Scenic Railway, Queensland (50x30mm).

2010, May 7 ***Perf. 14x14¾***

3254 A818 55c multi 1.10 1.10
3255 A818 55c multi 1.10 1.10
3256 A818 55c multi 1.10 1.10
a. Booklet pane of 4, #3254, 3255, 2 #3256 6.50 —
b. Booklet pane of 4, #3255, 3256, 2 #3254 6.50 —
c. Booklet pane of 4, #3254, 3256, 2 #3255 6.50 —

Perf. 13½x14

3257 A818 $2.10 multi 4.25 2.25
a. Booklet pane of 1 6.25 —
Complete booklet, #3256a-3256c, 3257a 26.50
b. Souvenir sheet of 1 4.25 2.25
c. As "b," with London 2010 emblem in gold in sheet margin 3.50 3.50
Nos. 3254-3257 (4) 7.55 5.55

Self-Adhesive
Serpentine Die Cut 11¼ Syncopated

3258 A818 55c multi 1.10 .30
3259 A818 55c multi 1.10 .30
3260 A818 55c multi 1.10 .30
a. Horiz. coil strip of 3, #3258-3260 3.50
b. Booklet pane of 20, 8 each #3258-3259, 4 #3260 23.00

Serpentine Die Cut 11¼

3261 A818 $2.10 multi 4.25 2.25
a. Booklet pane of 5 22.00
Nos. 3258-3261 (4) 7.55 3.15

No. 3257a has blue panels at the sides. Complete booklet sold for $12.95.

Issued: No. 3257c, 5/8.

Expo 2010, Shanghai — A819

Designs: No. 3262, Australian Pavilion. No. 3263, Australian kookaburra mascot, Peng Peng.

2010, May 18 ***Perf. 14¾x14***

3262 A819 55c multi 1.00 .80
3263 A819 55c multi 1.00 .80
a. Pair, #3262-3263 2.00 1.60

UNESCO World Heritage Sites in Australia — A820

Designs: Nos. 3264, 3268, Purnululu National Park. Nos. 3265, 3269, Kakadu National Park. No. 3266, Gondwana Rainforests, horiz. No. 3267, Tasmanian Wilderness, horiz.

2010, May 25 ***Perf. 14¾x14***

3264 A820 55c multi 1.00 1.00
3265 A820 55c multi 1.00 1.00
a. Horiz. pair, #3264-3265 2.00 2.00

Perf. 14x14¾

3266 A820 $1.10 multi 2.25 1.60
3267 A820 $1.10 multi 2.25 1.60
a. Horiz. pair, #3266-3267 4.50 3.25
Nos. 3264-3267 (4) 6.50 5.20

Self-Adhesive
Serpentine Die Cut 11¼ Syncopated

3268 A820 55c multi 1.00 1.00
3269 A820 55c multi 1.00 1.00
a. Vert. coil pair, #3268-3269 2.00
b. Booklet pane of 10, 5 each #3268-3269 10.00

Fish — A821

Designs: 5c, Coral rabbitfish. Nos. 3271, 3278, 3283, Clown triggerfish. Nos. 3272, 3279, 3284, Spotted sweetlips. Nos. 3273, 3280, 3285, Golden damsel. Nos. 3274, 3281, 3286, Regal angelfish. $1.20, Saddle butterflyfish. $1.80, Chevron butterflyfish. $3, Orangefin anemonefish.

2010, June 21 Litho. ***Perf. 14x14½***

3270 A821 5c multi .25 .25
3271 A821 60c multi 1.00 .25
3272 A821 60c multi 1.00 .25
a. Souvenir sheet, #3271, 3272, 2 #3270 2.40 2.40
3273 A821 60c multi 1.00 .25
3274 A821 60c multi 1.00 .25
a. Block or strip of 4, #3271-3274 4.00 1.00
3275 A821 $1.20 multi 2.00 1.00
3276 A821 $1.80 multi 3.00 1.50

Perf. 14½x14
Size: 50x30mm (#3277)

3277 A821 $3 multi 5.00 2.50
Nos. 3270-3277 (8) 14.25 6.25

Coil Stamps
Self-Adhesive
Die Cut Perf. 12¾

3278 A821 60c multi 1.00 .25
3279 A821 60c multi 1.00 .25
3280 A821 60c multi 1.00 .25
3281 A821 60c multi 1.00 .25
a. Horiz. strip of 4, #3278-3281 4.00

Booklet Stamps
Serpentine Die Cut 11¼

3282 A821 5c multi .25 .25
a. Booklet pane of 20 4.00
3283 A821 60c multi 1.00 .25
3284 A821 60c multi 1.00 .25
3285 A821 60c multi 1.00 .25
3286 A821 60c multi 1.00 .25
a. Booklet pane of 10, 3 each #3283-3284, 2 each #3285-3286 10.00
b. Booklet pane of 20, 5 each #3283-3286 20.00
Nos. 3278-3286 (9) 8.25 2.25

Issued: No. 3272a, 8/4/10. Bangkok 2010 Intl. Stamp Exhibition (No. 3272a).

Beaches — A822

Designs: $1.50, Bay of Fires, Tasmania. $2.20, Cape Tribulation, Queensland. $4.30, Hellfire Bay, Western Australia, horiz.

2010, June 28 ***Perf. 14¾x14***

3287 A822 $1.50 multi 2.50 1.25
3288 A822 $2.20 multi 3.75 1.90

Size: 50x30mm (#3289)
Perf. 14½x14

3289 A822 $4.30 multi 7.25 3.75
Nos. 3287-3289 (3) 13.50 6.90

Booklet Stamps
Self-Adhesive
Serpentine Die Cut 11¼ Syncopated

3290 A822 $1.50 multi 2.50 1.25
a. Booklet pane of 5 12.50
3291 A822 $2.20 multi 3.75 1.90
a. Booklet pane of 5 19.00

With Personalized Photo at Right Like Type A692a
Serpentine Die Cut 11½x11¼ Syncopated

3292 A822 $1.50 multi 3.75 3.75
3293 A822 $2.20 multi 4.75 4.75

Nos. 3292-3293 each were printed in sheets of 20 and have personalized pictures and a straight edge at right, and lack separations between the stamp and the personalized photo. Sheets of 20 of No. 3292 sold for $43, and No. 3293 sold for $56.

Adopted Dogs — A823

Designs: Nos. 3294, 3299, Piper. Nos. 3295, 3300, Jessie. Nos. 3296, 3301, Buckley. Nos. 3297, 3302, Daisy. Nos. 3298, 3303, Tigger.

2010, June 29 ***Perf. 14¾x14***

3294 A823 60c multi 1.00 1.00
3295 A823 60c multi 1.00 1.00
3296 A823 60c multi 1.00 1.00
3297 A823 60c multi 1.00 1.00
3298 A823 60c multi 1.00 1.00
a. Horiz. strip of 5, #3294-3298 5.00 5.00
Nos. 3294-3298 (5) 5.00 5.00

Self-Adhesive
Serpentine Die Cut 11¼ Syncopated

3299 A823 60c multi 1.00 .25
3300 A823 60c multi 1.00 .25
3301 A823 60c multi 1.00 .25
3302 A823 60c multi 1.00 .25
3303 A823 60c multi 1.00 .25
a. Vert. coil strip of 5, #3299-3303 5.00
b. Booklet pane of 10, 2 each #3299-3303 10.00
Nos. 3299-3303 (5) 5.00 1.25

No. 3303a was produced by two different printers, Pemara and McKellar Renown. The stamps have the printer's name on the backing paper, but are essentially identical to each other.

Emergency Services — A824

000 Emergency Services emblem and: Nos. 3304, 3308, "Stay Focused, Stay Relevant, Stay on Line." Nos. 3305, 3309, Police Helicopter. Nos. 3306, 3310, Fire. Nos. 3307, 3311, Ambulance Cross.

2010, July 13 ***Perf. 14¾x14***

3304 A824 60c multi 1.10 1.10
3305 A824 60c multi 1.10 1.10
3306 A824 60c multi 1.10 1.10
3307 A824 60c multi 1.10 1.10
a. Horiz. strip of 4, #3304-3307 4.40 4.40
Nos. 3304-3307 (4) 4.40 4.40

Self-Adhesive
Serpentine Die Cut 11¼ Syncopated

3308 A824 60c multi 1.10 .25
3309 A824 60c multi 1.10 .25
3310 A824 60c multi 1.10 .25
3311 A824 60c multi 1.10 .25
a. Vert. coil strip of 4, #3308-3311 4.40
b. Booklet pane of 20, 5 each #3308-3311 22.00
Nos. 3308-3311 (4) 4.40 1.00

Southern Cross — A825

2010, July 19 ***Perf. 14½x14***

3312 A825 60c Blue sky 1.10 1.10
a. Sheet of 20 + 20 labels 27.00 27.00
3313 A825 60c Purple & orange sky 1.10 1.10
a. Horiz. pair, #3312-3313 2.25 2.25
b. Sheet of 20 + 20 labels 27.00 27.00
c. Perf. 14x14½, + label at bottom 1.40 1.40

Nos. 3312a and 3313b each sold for $12.95 and have labels depicting various National Rugby League and Australian Football League team emblems that could not be personalized. No. 3313c was issued in sheet of 10 + 10 labels depicting race horse Black Caviar that were sold in groups of 2 sheets that sold for $12.95.

Balloons A826

Teddy Bear A827

Wattle A828

Flowers A829

Tulips A830

Roses A831

Flowers and Champagne Flutes A832

Wedding Rings A833

2010, July 19 *Perf. 14¾x14*

3314 A826 60c multi 1.10 1.10
3315 A827 60c multi 1.10 1.10
3316 A828 60c multi 1.10 1.10
a. Horiz. strip of 3, #3314-3316 3.30 3.30
3317 A829 60c multi 1.10 1.10
3318 A830 60c multi 1.10 1.10
3319 A831 60c multi 1.10 1.10
3320 A832 60c multi 1.10 1.10
a. Block of 4, #3317-3320 4.40 4.40
3321 A833 $1.20 multi 2.25 2.25
Nos. 3314-3321 (8) 9.95 9.95

Booklet Stamps
Self-Adhesive
Serpentine Die Cut 11¼ Syncopated

3322 A826 60c multi 1.10 .25
a. Booklet pane of 10 11.00
3323 A827 60c multi 1.10 .25
a. Booklet pane of 10 11.00
3324 A828 60c multi 1.10 .25
a. Booklet pane of 10 11.00
3325 A830 60c multi 1.10 .25
a. Booklet pane of 10 11.00
3326 A831 60c multi 1.10 .25
a. Booklet pane of 10 11.00
3327 A833 $1.20 multi 2.25 1.10
a. Booklet pane of 10 22.50
Nos. 3322-3327 (6) 7.75 2.35

With Personalized Photo at Right Like Type A692a
Serpentine Die Cut 11½x11¼ Syncopated

3328 A826 60c multi 2.25 2.25
3329 A827 60c multi 2.25 2.25
3330 A828 60c multi 2.25 2.25
3331 A829 60c multi 2.25 2.25
3332 A830 60c multi 2.25 2.25
3333 A831 60c multi 2.25 2.25
3334 A832 60c multi 2.25 2.25
3335 A833 $1.20 multi 3.50 3.50
Nos. 3328-3335 (8) 19.25 19.25

Nos. 3328-3335 each were printed in sheets of 20 and have personalized pictures and a straight edge at right, and lack separations between the stamp and the personalized photo. Sheets of 20 of Nos. 3328-3334 each sold for $25, and No. 3335 sold for $37.

See No. 3401.

Australian Taxation Office, Cent. — A834

2010, July 27 Litho. *Perf. 14x14¾*

3336 A834 60c multi 1.10 .85

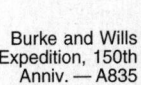

Burke and Wills Expedition, 150th Anniv. — A835

Designs: Nos. 3337, 3341, Explorers Robert Burke (1820-61) and William J. Wills (1834-61). Nos. 3338, 3342, Burke and Wills on horses leaving Melbourne. No. 3339, Expedition members returning from Gulf of Carpenteria. No. 3340, Expedition members heading towards Mt. Hopeless.

2010, Aug. 3 Litho. *Perf. 14x14¾*

3337 A835 60c multi 1.10 1.10
a. Booklet pane of 4 5.00 —
3338 A835 60c multi 1.10 1.10
a. Horiz. pair, #3337-3338 2.20 2.20
b. Booklet pane of 4 5.00 —
3339 A835 $1.20 multi 2.25 2.25
a. Booklet pane of 2 5.00 —
3340 A835 $1.20 multi 2.25 2.25
a. Horiz. pair, #3339-3340 4.50 4.50
b. Booklet pane of 2 5.00 —
Complete booklet, #3337a, 3338b, 3339a, 3340b 20.00
Nos. 3337-3340 (4) 6.70 6.70

Coil Stamps
Self-Adhesive
Serpentine Die Cut 11¼ Syncopated

3341 A835 60c multi 1.10 .25
3342 A835 60c multi 1.10 .25
a. Horiz. pair, #3341-3342 2.20

Complete booklet sold for $10.95.

See Australian Antarctic Territory No. L149b.

Girl Guides, Cent. — A836

Emblem, early Girl Guides and: 60c, Girl Guide with helmet and climbing rope. $1.50, Girl Guides wearing hats. $2.20, Olave Baden-Powell.

2010, Aug. 31 Litho. *Perf. 14x14¾*

3343 A836 60c multi 1.10 1.10
3344 A836 $1.50 multi 2.75 2.75
3345 A836 $2.20 multi 4.00 4.00
Nos. 3343-3345 (3) 7.85 7.85

Self-Adhesive
Serpentine Die Cut 11¼ Syncopated

3346 A836 60c multi 1.10 .25
a. Booklet pane of 20 22.00

Booklet Stamps

3347 A836 $1.50 multi 2.75 1.40
a. Booklet pane of 5 14.00
3348 A836 $2.20 multi 4.00 2.00
a. Booklet pane of 5 20.00
Nos. 3346-3348 (3) 7.85 3.65

Dedication of National Service Memorial, Canberra — A837

2010, Sept. 8 Litho. *Perf. 14x14¾*

3349 A837 60c multi 1.10 1.10
a. Additionally dated "2013" (#3349b) 1.25 1.25
b. Booklet pane of 4 #3349a 5.00 —

Issued: Nos. 3349a, 3349b, 3/5/13. No. 3349b was issued in booklet along with Nos. 1940b, 2710c, 2869e, 3107c and 3877a.

Booklet Stamp
Self-Adhesive
Serpentine Die Cut 11¼ Syncopated

3350 A837 60c multi 1.10 .25
a. Booklet pane of 10 11.00

Long Weekend Vacations — A838

People on weekend vacations: Nos. 3351, 3356, Boating at beach, 1950s. Nos. 3352, 3357, Camping, 1960s. Nos. 3353, 3358, Surfing at beach, 1970s. Nos. 3354, 3359, Houseboating on river, 1980s. Nos. 3355, 3360, At winter resort, 1990s.

2010, Sept. 22 *Perf. 14x14¾*

3351 A838 60c multi 1.25 1.25
a. Booklet pane of 4 5.50 —
3352 A838 60c multi 1.25 1.25
a. Booklet pane of 4 5.50 —
3353 A838 60c multi 1.25 1.25
a. Booklet pane of 4 5.50 —
3354 A838 60c multi 1.25 1.25
a. Booklet pane of 4 5.50 —
3355 A838 60c multi 1.25 1.25
a. Booklet pane of 4 5.50 —
Complete booklet, #3351a-3355a 27.50
b. Horiz. strip of 5, #3351-3355 6.25 6.25
Nos. 3351-3355 (5) 6.25 6.25

Self-Adhesive
Serpentine Die Cut 11¼ Syncopated

3356 A838 60c multi 1.25 .25
3357 A838 60c multi 1.25 .25
3358 A838 60c multi 1.25 .25
3359 A838 60c multi 1.25 .25
3360 A838 60c multi 1.25 .25
a. Horiz. coil strip of 5, #3356-3360 6.25
b. Booklet pane of 10, 2 each #3356-3360 12.50
Nos. 3356-3360 (5) 6.25 1.25

Complete booklet sold for $13.95.

Care for Wildlife — A839

Designs: Nos. 3361, 3367, Common wombat. Nos. 3362, 3368, Eastern gray kangaroo. Nos. 3363, 3369, Koala. Nos. 3364, 3370, Gray-headed flying fox. Nos. 3365, 3371, Southern boobook. $1.20, Ringtail possum.

2010, Oct. 5 Litho. *Perf. 14¾x14*
Denomination Color

3361 A839 60c orange brown 1.25 1.25
3362 A839 60c blue 1.25 1.25
3363 A839 60c green 1.25 1.25
3364 A839 60c red brown 1.25 1.25
3365 A839 60c bister 1.25 1.25
a. Horiz. strip of 5, #3361-3365 6.25 6.25
3366 A839 $1.20 red 2.40 1.75
a. Souvenir sheet of 6, #3361-3366 8.75 8.75
Nos. 3361-3366 (6) 8.65 8.00

Self-Adhesive
Serpentine Die Cut 11¼ Syncopated

3367 A839 60c orange brown 1.25 .25
3368 A839 60c blue 1.25 .25
3369 A839 60c green 1.25 .25
3370 A839 60c red brown 1.25 .25
3371 A839 60c bister 1.25 .25
a. Vert. coil strip of 5, #3367-3371 6.25
b. Booklet pane of 10, 2 each #3367-3371 12.50
Nos. 3367-3371 (5) 6.25 1.25

Canonization of St. Mary MacKillop (1842-1909) — A840

2010, Oct. 18 *Perf. 14¾x14*

3372 A840 60c multi 1.25 .95

Kingfishers — A841

Designs: 60c, Red-backed kingfisher. $1.20, Sacred kingfisher. $1.80, Blue-winged kookaburra. $3, Yellow-billed kingfisher.

2010, Oct. 26 *Perf. 14¾x14*

3373 A841 60c multi 1.25 1.25
a. Additionally dated "2013" 1.25 1.25
3374 A841 $1.20 multi 2.50 1.90
a. Additionally dated "2013" 2.40 2.40
3375 A841 $1.80 multi 3.75 1.90
a. Additionally dated "2013" 3.50 3.50
3376 A841 $3 multi 6.25 3.25
a. Additionally dated "2013" 5.75 5.75
b. Booklet pane of 4, #3373a, 3374a, 3375a, 3376a 13.00 —
Nos. 3373-3376 (4) 13.75 8.30

Issued: Nos. 3373a, 3374a, 3375a, 3376a, 3376b, 5/11/13. No. 3376b was issued in a booklet also containing Nos. 3151c, 3665b and 3925a.

Self-Adhesive
Serpentine Die Cut 11¼ Syncopated

3377 A841 60c multi 1.25 .25
a. Booklet pane of 10 12.50

150th Running of the Melbourne Cup Horse Race — A842

Designs: No. 3378, Melbourne Cup. Nos. 3379, 3382, Carbine, 1890 winner, horiz. Nos. 3380, 3383, Phar Lap, 1930 winner, horiz. Nos. 3381, 3384, Saintly, 1996 winner, horiz.

2010, Nov. 1 Litho. *Perf. 14¾x14*

3378 A842 60c multi 1.25 .95
a. Booklet pane of 4 7.25 —

Perf. 14x14¾

3379 A842 60c multi 1.25 1.25
a. Booklet pane of 4 7.25 —
3380 A842 60c multi 1.25 1.25
a. Booklet pane of 4 7.25 —
3381 A842 60c multi 1.25 1.25
a. Booklet pane of 4 7.25 —
Complete booklet, #3378a, 3379a, 3380a, 3381a 29.00
b. Souvenir sheet, #3378-3381 5.00 5.00
Nos. 3378-3381 (4) 5.00 4.70

No. 3381b exists imperf from a telephone drawing at a substantial premium over face value. Value for single souvenir sheet, $15.

Booklet Stamps
Self-Adhesive
Serpentine Die Cut 11¼ Syncopated

3382 A842 60c multi 1.25 .25
3383 A842 60c multi 1.25 .25
3384 A842 60c multi 1.25 .25
a. Booklet pane of 20, 7 each #3382-3383, 6 #3384 25.00
Nos. 3382-3384 (3) 3.75 75.00

Complete booklet sold for $13.95 and also included imperforate and gummed lithographed pages reproducing pairs of Nos. 337, 693, 694, 2104 and 2106 that were not valid for postage.

Christmas
A843 A844

Designs: Nos. 3385, 3390, 3393, 3396, Girl writing letter to Santa Claus. Nos. 3386, 3389, 3394, 3395, Santa Claus reading letter. Nos. 3387, 3391, Adoration of the Magi. $1.30, Adoration of the Shepherds.

2010, Nov. 1 Litho. *Perf. 14¾x14*

3385 A843 55c multi 1.10 1.10
3386 A843 55c multi 1.10 1.10
a. Horiz. pair, #3385-3386 2.25 2.25
3387 A844 55c multi 1.10 1.10
3388 A844 $1.30 multi 2.75 2.75
Nos. 3385-3388 (4) 6.05 6.05

Booklet Stamps
Self-Adhesive
Serpentine Die Cut 11¼ Syncopated

3389 A843 55c multi 1.10 .25
3390 A843 55c multi 1.10 .25
a. Booklet pane of 20, 10 each #3389-3390 22.00
3391 A844 55c multi 1.10 .25
a. Booklet pane of 20 22.00
3392 A844 $1.30 multi 2.75 1.40
a. Booklet pane of 5 14.00

Litho. With Foil Application

3393 A843 55c multi 1.10 .25
a. Booklet pane of 10 11.00
3394 A843 55c multi 1.10 .25
a. Booklet pane of 10 11.00
Nos. 3389-3394 (6) 8.25 2.65

With Personalized Photo at Right Like Type A692a
Litho.
Self-Adhesive
Serpentine Die Cut 11½x11¼ Syncopated

3395 A843 55c multi 2.50 2.50
3396 A843 55c multi 2.50 2.50

Nos. 3395-3396 were printed together in sheets of 20 (10 of each design), and have personalized pictures and a straight edge at right and lack separations between the stamp and the personalized photo. Sheets of 20 sold for $24.

Champagne Flutes Type of 2010 and

Roses A845

Hearts and Flowers A846

2011, Jan. 18 *Perf. 14¾x14*

3397 A845 60c multi 1.25 1.25
3398 A846 60c multi 1.25 1.25
a. Horiz. pair, #3397-3398 2.50 2.50

Booklet Stamps
Self-Adhesive
Serpentine Die Cut 11¼ Syncopated

3399 A845 60c multi 1.25 .25
a. Booklet pane of 12 12.50
3400 A846 60c multi 1.25 .25
a. Booklet pane of 12 12.50
3401 A832 60c multi 1.25 .60
a. Booklet pane of 12 12.50
Nos. 3399-3401 (3) 3.75 1.10

With Personalized Photo at Right Like Type A692a
Serpentine Die Cut 11½x11¼ Syncopated

3402 A845 60c multi 2.50 2.50
3403 A846 60c multi 2.50 2.50

Nos. 3395-3396 each were printed in sheets of 20 and have personalized pictures and a straight edge at right and lack separations between the stamp and the personalized photo. Sheets of 20 of Nos. 3402-3403 each sold for $25.

No. 3401 dated 2010.

Famous Women — A848

Designs: Nos. 3404, 3408, Eva Cox, feminist. Nos. 3405, 3409, Germaine Greer, writer on feminist topics. Nos. 3406, 3410, Elizabeth Evatt, jurist. Nos. 3407, 3411, Anne Summers, writer.

2011, Jan. 20 *Perf. 14¾x14*

3404 A848 60c multi 1.25 1.25
3405 A848 60c multi 1.25 1.25
3406 A848 60c multi 1.25 1.25
3407 A848 60c multi 1.25 1.25
a. Horiz. strip of 4, #3404-3407 5.00 5.00
Nos. 3404-3407 (4) 5.00 5.00

Booklet Stamps
Self-Adhesive
Serpentine Die Cut 11¼ Syncopated

3408 A848 60c multi 1.25 .25
3409 A848 60c multi 1.25 .25
3410 A848 60c multi 1.25 .25
3411 A848 60c multi 1.25 .25
a. Booklet pane of 20, 5 each #3408-3411 25.00
Nos. 3408-3411 (4) 5.00 1.00

Intl. Women's Day, Cent. — A849

2011, Feb. 15 *Perf. 14x14¾*

3412 A849 60c multi 1.25 .95
a. Miniature sheet of 10 12.50 12.50

Military Aircraft — A850

Designs: Nos. 3413, 3417, F-111. Nos. 3414, 3418, F/A-18F. $1.20, Wedge Tail. $3, C-17.

2011, Feb. 22 *Perf. 14x14¾*

3413 A850 60c multi 1.25 1.25
3414 A850 60c multi 1.25 1.25
3415 A850 $1.20 multi 2.40 1.90
a. Souvenir sheet of 4, #3337, 3339, 3413, 3415 7.75 7.75
3416 A850 $3 multi 6.00 4.50
a. Souvenir sheet of 4, #3413-3416 11.00 11.00
Nos. 3413-3416 (4) 10.90 8.90

Booklet Stamps
Self-Adhesive
Serpentine Die Cut 11¼ Syncopated

3417 A850 60c multi 1.25 .25
3418 A850 60c multi 1.25 .25
a. Booklet pane of 10, 5 each #3417-3418 12.50

Issued: No. 3415a, 3/31. Sydney Stamp Expo 2011 (No. 3415a).

Flowers — A851

Designs: Nos. 3419, 3424, Gerbera daisy. Nos. 3420, 3425, Jacarandas. Nos. 3421, 3426, Australian everlasting. Nos. 3422, 3427, Violet. Nos. 3423, 3428, Tulip.

2011, Mar. 8 **Litho.** *Perf. 14¾x14*

3419 A851 60c multi 1.25 1.25
a. Booklet pane of 4 5.25 —
3420 A851 60c multi 1.25 1.25
a. Booklet pane of 4 5.25 —
3421 A851 60c multi 1.25 1.25
a. Booklet pane of 4 5.25 —
3422 A851 60c multi 1.25 1.25
a. Booklet pane of 4 5.25 —
3423 A851 60c multi 1.25 1.25
a. Booklet pane of 4 5.25 —
Complete booklet, #3419a, 3420a, 3421a, 3422a, 3423a 27.00
b. Horiz. strip of 5, #3419-3423 6.25 6.25
Nos. 3419-3423 (5) 6.25 6.25

Self-Adhesive
Serpentine Die Cut 11¼ Syncopated

3424 A851 60c multi 1.25 .25
3425 A851 60c multi 1.25 .25
3426 A851 60c multi 1.25 .25
3427 A851 60c multi 1.25 .25
3428 A851 60c multi 1.25 .25
a. Vert. coil strip of 5, #3424-3428 6.25
b. Booklet pane of 20, 4 each #3424-3428 25.00
Nos. 3424-3428 (5) 6.25 1.25

Complete booklet sold for $12.95.

Paintings of Flowers in National Gallery of Victoria — A852

Paintings: Nos. 3429, 3434, A Bunch of Flowers, by Nora Heysen. Nos. 3430, 3435, Camellias, by Arnold Shore. Nos. 3431, 3436, Fruit and Flowers, by Vida Lahey. Nos. 3432, 3437, Still Life, Zinnias, by Roy de Maistre. Nos. 3433, 3438, A Cottage Bunch, by Hans Heysen.

2011, Mar. 22 *Perf. 14x14¾*

3429 A852 60c multi 1.25 1.25
3430 A852 60c multi 1.25 1.25
3431 A852 60c multi 1.25 1.25
3432 A852 60c multi 1.25 1.25
3433 A852 60c multi 1.25 1.25
a. Horiz. strip of 5, #3429-3433 6.25 6.25
Nos. 3429-3433 (5) 6.25 6.25

Self-Adhesive
Serpentine Die Cut 11¼ Syncopated

3434 A852 60c multi 1.25 .25
3435 A852 60c multi 1.25 .25
3436 A852 60c multi 1.25 .25
3437 A852 60c multi 1.25 .25
3438 A852 60c multi 1.25 .25
a. Horiz. coil strip of 5, #3434-3438 6.25
b. Booklet pane of 10, 2 each #3434-3438 12.50
Nos. 3434-3438 (5) 6.25 1.25

Lake Eyre — A853

Lake Eyre: 60c, In dry season. $1.55, With new growth. $2.25, Bird life. $3.10, In flood.

2011, Apr. 4 *Perf. 14½x14*

3439 A853 60c multi 1.25 .65
3440 A853 $1.55 multi 3.25 3.25
3441 A853 $2.25 multi 4.75 4.75
3442 A853 $3.10 multi 6.50 3.25
Nos. 3439-3442 (4) 15.75 11.90

Booklet Stamps
Self-Adhesive
Serpentine Die Cut 11¼

3443 A853 $1.55 multi 3.25 1.60
a. Booklet pane of 5 16.50
3444 A853 $2.25 multi 4.75 2.40
a. Booklet pane of 5 24.00

A854

Portraits of Queen Elizabeth II by: 60c, Brian Dunlop, 1984. $2.25, Rolf Harris, 2005.

2011, Apr. 5 *Perf. 14¾x14*

3445 A854 60c multi 1.25 .65
3446 A854 $2.25 multi 4.75 2.40
a. Souvenir sheet of 2, #3445-3446 6.00 6.00

Queen Elizabeth II, 85th birthday.

A855

Background color: 60c, Pale olive green. $2.25, White.

2011, Apr. 12 *Perf. 14¾x14*

3447 A855 60c multi 1.25 1.25
3448 A855 $2.25 multi 4.75 2.40
a. Souvenir sheet of 2, #3447-3448 6.00 6.00

Booklet Stamp
Self-Adhesive
Serpentine Die Cut 11¼ Syncopated

3449 A855 60c multi 1.25 .25
a. Booklet pane of 10 12.50

Wedding of Prince William and Catherine Middleton.

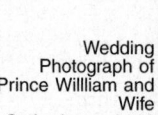

Wedding Photograph of Prince Willliam and Wife Catherine — A856

2011, May 4 *Perf. 14¼*

3450 A856 60c multi 1.25 1.25

Booklet Stamp
Self-Adhesive
Serpentine Die Cut 11¼ Syncopated

3451 A856 60c multi 1.25 .25
a. Booklet pane of 10 12.50

Dame Nellie Melba (1861-1931), Operatic Soprano — A857

2011, May 10 *Perf. 14¾x14*

3452 A857 60c multi 1.25 1.25

Booklet Stamp
Self-Adhesive
Serpentine Die Cut 11¼ Syncopated

3453 A857 60c multi 1.25 .25
a. Booklet pane of 20 25.00

Native Agricultural Products — A858

Designs: Nos. 3454, 3458, Eucalyptus oil. Nos. 3455, 3459, Australian honey. Nos. 3456, 3460, Macadamia nuts. Nos. 3457, 3461, Tea tree oil.

2011, May 17 *Perf. 14x14¾*

3454 A858 60c multi 1.25 1.25
3455 A858 60c multi 1.25 1.25
3456 A858 60c multi 1.25 1.25
3457 A858 60c multi 1.25 1.25
a. Horiz. strip of 4, #3454-3457 5.00 5.00
Nos. 3454-3457 (4) 5.00 5.00

Self-Adhesive
Serpentine Die Cut 11¼ Syncopated

3458 A858 60c multi 1.25 .25
3459 A858 60c multi 1.25 .25
3460 A858 60c multi 1.25 .25
3461 A858 60c multi 1.25 .25
a. Horiz. coil strip of 4, #3458-3461 5.00
b. Booklet pane of 10, 4 #3458, 2 each #3459-3461 12.50
Nos. 3458-3461 (4) 5.00 1.00

Southern Cross With Sports Team Emblem A859

Booklet Stamps
Self-Adhesive
Blue Sky
With Emblem of Australian Rules Football Team
Adelaide Crows
Serpentine Die Cut 10¾x11¼ Syncopated

2011, Apr. 12 **Litho.**

3462 A859 60c Emblem at R 1.50 .75
3463 A859 60c Emblem at L 1.50 .75
a. Booklet pane of 10, 5 each #3462-3463 15.00

Carlton Blues

3464 A859 60c Emblem at R 1.50 .75
3465 A859 60c Emblem at L 1.50 .75
a. Booklet pane of 10, 5 each #3464-3465 15.00

Essendon Bombers

3466 A859 60c Emblem at R 1.50 .75
3467 A859 60c Emblem at L 1.50 .75
a. Booklet pane of 10, 5 each #3466-3467 15.00

Geelong Cats

3468 A859 60c Emblem at R 1.50 .75
3469 A859 60c Emblem at L 1.50 .75
a. Booklet pane of 10, 5 each #3468-3469 15.00

Gold Coast Suns

3470 A859 60c Emblem at R 1.50 .75
3471 A859 60c Emblem at L 1.50 .75
a. Booklet pane of 10, 5 each #3470-3471 15.00

North Melbourne Kangaroos

3472 A859 60c Emblem at R 1.50 .75
3473 A859 60c Emblem at L 1.50 .75
a. Booklet pane of 10, 5 each #3472-3473 15.00

Port Adelaide Power

3474 A859 60c Emblem at R 1.50 .75
3475 A859 60c Emblem at L 1.50 .75
a. Booklet pane of 10, 5 each #3474-3475 15.00

West Coast Eagles

3476 A859 60c Emblem at R 1.50 .75
3477 A859 60c Emblem at L 1.50 .75
a. Booklet pane of 10, 5 each #3476-3477 15.00

Western Bulldogs

3478 A859 60c Emblem at R 1.50 .75
3479 A859 60c Emblem at L 1.50 .75
a. Booklet pane of 10, 5 each #3478-3479 15.00

Purple & Orange Sky
Brisbane Lions

3480 A859 60c Emblem at R 1.50 .75
3481 A859 60c Emblem at L 1.50 .75
a. Booklet pane of 10, 5 each #3480-3481 15.00

Collingwood Magpies

3482 A859 60c Emblem at R 1.50 .75
3483 A859 60c Emblem at L 1.50 .75
a. Booklet pane of 10, 5 each #3482-3483 15.00

Fremantle Dockers

3484 A859 60c Emblem at R 1.50 .75
3485 A859 60c Emblem at L 1.50 .75
a. Booklet pane of 10, 5 each #3484-3485 15.00

Hawthorn Hawks

3486 A859 60c Emblem at R 1.50 .75
3487 A859 60c Emblem at L 1.50 .75
a. Booklet pane of 10, 5 each #3486-3487 15.00

Melbourne Demons

3488 A859 60c Emblem at R 1.50 .75
3489 A859 60c Emblem at L 1.50 .75
a. Booklet pane of 10, 5 each #3488-3489 15.00

Richmond Tigers

3490 A859 60c Emblem at R 1.50 .75
3491 A859 60c Emblem at L 1.50 .75
a. Booklet pane of 10, 5 each #3490-3491 15.00

St. Kilda Saints

3492 A859 60c Emblem at R 1.50 .75
3493 A859 60c Emblem at L 1.50 .75
a. Booklet pane of 10, 5 each #3492-3493 15.00

Sydney Swans

3494 A859 60c Emblem at R 1.50 .75
3495 A859 60c Emblem at L 1.50 .75
a. Booklet pane of 10, 5 each #3494-3495 15.00

Blue Sky With National Rugby League Emblems

North Queensland Cowboys

3496 A859 60c Emblem at R 1.50 .75
3497 A859 60c Emblem at L 1.50 .75
a. Booklet pane of 10, 5 each #3496-3497 15.00

St. George Illawarra Dragons

3498 A859 60c Emblem at R 1.50 .75
3499 A859 60c Emblem at L 1.50 .75
a. Booklet pane of 10, 5 each #3498-3499 15.00

Parramatta Eels

3500 A859 60c Emblem at R 1.50 .75
3501 A859 60c Emblem at L 1.50 .75
a. Booklet pane of 10, 5 each #3500-3501 15.00

Newcastle Knights

3502 A859 60c Emblem at R 1.50 .75
3503 A859 60c Emblem at L 1.50 .75
a. Booklet pane of 10, 5 each #3502-3503 15.00

Penrith Panthers

3504 A859 60c Emblem at R 1.50 .75
3505 A859 60c Emblem at L 1.50 .75
a. Booklet pane of 10, 5 each #3504-3505 15.00

Canberra Raiders

3506 A859 60c Emblem at R 1.50 .75
3507 A859 60c Emblem at L 1.50 .75
a. Booklet pane of 10, 5 each #3506-3507 15.00

Sydney Roosters

3508 A859 60c Emblem at R 1.50 .75
3509 A859 60c Emblem at L 1.50 .75
a. Booklet pane of 10, 5 each #3508-3509 15.00

Cronulla Sutherland Sharks

3510 A859 60c Emblem at R 1.50 .75
3511 A859 60c Emblem at L 1.50 .75
a. Booklet pane of 10, 5 each #3510-3511 15.00

Gold Coast Titans

3512 A859 60c Emblem at R 1.50 .75
3513 A859 60c Emblem at L 1.50 .75
a. Booklet pane of 10, 5 each #3512-3513 15.00

Purple & Orange Sky Brisbane Broncos

3514 A859 60c Emblem at R 1.50 .75
3515 A859 60c Emblem at L 1.50 .75
a. Booklet pane of 10, 5 each #3514-3515 15.00

Canterbury-Bankstown Bulldogs

3516 A859 60c Emblem at R 1.50 .75
3517 A859 60c Emblem at L 1.50 .75
a. Booklet pane of 10, 5 each #3516-3517 15.00

South Sydney Rabbitohs

3518 A859 60c Emblem at R 1.50 .75
3519 A859 60c Emblem at L 1.50 .75
a. Booklet pane of 10, 5 each #3518-3519 15.00

Manly Warringah Sea Eagles

3520 A859 60c Emblem at R 1.50 .75
3521 A859 60c Emblem at L 1.50 .75
a. Booklet pane of 10, 5 each #3520-3521 15.00

Melbourne Storm

3522 A859 60c Emblem at R 1.50 .75
3523 A859 60c Emblem at L 1.50 .75
a. Booklet pane of 10, 5 each #3522-3523 15.00

New Zealand Warriors

3524 A859 60c Emblem at R 1.50 .75
3525 A859 60c Emblem at L 1.50 .75
a. Booklet pane of 10, 5 each #3524-3525 15.00

Wests Tigers

3526 A859 60c Emblem at R 1.50 .75
3527 A859 60c Emblem at L 1.50 .75
a. Booklet pane of 10, 5 each #3526-3527 15.00
Nos. 3462-3527 (66) 99.00 49.50

Each booklet, Nos. 3463a-3527a, sold for $6.95. Stamps with team emblem at right have straight edge at right, and stamps with team emblem at left have straight edge at left.

Australian Navy, Cent. — A860

Sailor and: Nos. 3528, 3530, HMAS Australia and biplane. Nos. 3529, 3531, HMAS Sydney and helicopter.

2011, June 14 *Perf. 14x14¾*

3528 A860 60c multi 1.40 1.40
3529 A860 60c multi 1.40 1.40
a. Horiz. pair, #3528-3529 2.80 2.80

Booklet Stamps Self-Adhesive

Serpentine Die Cut 11¼ Syncopated

3530 A860 60c multi 1.40 .25
3531 A860 60c multi 1.40 .25
a. Booklet pane of 20, 10 each #3530-3531 28.00

A861

Baby animals: 60c, Bilby. $1.60, Dingo. $1.65, Kangaroo. $2.35, Koala. $4.70, Sugar glider.

2011, July 1 Litho. *Perf. 14¾x14*

3532 A861 60c multi 1.40 1.10
3533 A861 $1.60 multi 3.50 1.75
a. Souvenir sheet of 1 3.50 3.50
3534 A861 $1.65 multi 3.50 3.50
a. Souvenir sheet of 2, #3533-3534 7.00 7.00
b. Souvenir sheet of 1 3.50 3.50
c. Additionally dated "2013" 4.25 4.25
d. Booklet pane of 4, #1195a, 2352a, 3097a, 3534c 12.50 —
3535 A861 $2.35 multi 5.00 5.00
a. Souvenir sheet of 2 9.75 9.75
3536 A861 $4.70 multi 10.00 5.00
Nos. 3532-3536 (5) 23.40 16.35

Issued: No. 3534a, 7/28; No. 3535a, 6/18/12. Nos. 3533a, 3534b, 11/11. PhilaNippon '11 World Stamp Exhibition, Yokohama (No. 3534a). 2012 World Stamp Championship, Indonesia (No. 3535a). China 2011 Intl. Stamp Exhibition, Wuxi (Nos. 3533a, 3534b). Nos. 3534c, 3534d, 5/10/13. No. 3534d was issued in a booklet also containing Nos. 1003b, 1284b, and 3918.

Booklet Stamps Self-Adhesive

Serpentine Die Cut 11¼ Syncopated

3537 A861 $1.65 multi 3.50 1.75
a. Booklet pane of 5 17.50
3538 A861 $2.35 multi 5.00 2.50
a. Booklet pane of 5 25.00

With Personalized Photo at Right Like Type A692a

Serpentine Die Cut 11½x11¼ Syncopated

3539 A861 $1.60 multi 4.75 4.75
3540 A861 $1.65 multi 5.00 5.00
3541 A861 $2.35 multi 11.50 11.50
Nos. 3539-3541 (3) 21.25 21.25

Nos. 3539-3541 each were printed in sheets of 20 and have personalized pictures and at straight edge at right, and lack separations between the stamp and the personalized photo. Sheets of 20 of No. 3539 sold for $45; No. 3540, $46; No. 3541, $106.

A862

2011, July 5 *Perf. 14¾x14*

3542 A862 60c yellow & black 1.40 1.10

Amnesty International, 50th anniv.

Living Australian — A863

Photographs of Australian scenes: Nos. 3543, 3548, Boy and dog on beach. Nos. 3544, 3549, Children with flags painted on faces hugging. Nos. 3545, 3550, Reflection in sunglasses of sports fans in stadium. Nos. 3546, 3551, Aboriginal boy performing wedge tail eagle dance. Nos. 3547, 3552, Kangaroo resting on beach.

2011, July 5 *Perf. 14x14¾*

Denomination Color

3543 A863 60c orange 1.40 1.40
3544 A863 60c purple 1.40 1.40
3545 A863 60c green 1.40 1.40
3546 A863 60c red violet 1.40 1.40
3547 A863 60c blue 1.40 1.40
a. Horiz. strip of 5, #3543-3547 7.00 7.00

Self-Adhesive

Serpentine Die Cut 11¼ Syncopated

3548 A863 60c orange 1.40 .25
3549 A863 60c purple 1.40 .25
3550 A863 60c green 1.40 .25
3551 A863 60c red violet 1.40 .25
3552 A863 60c blue 1.40 .25
a. Horiz. coil strip of 5, #3548-3552 7.00
b. Booklet pane of 10, 2 each #3548-3552 14.00
Nos. 3548-3552 (5) 7.00 1.25

Skiing — A864

Designs: 60c, Child learning to ski. $1.60, Snowboarder, horiz. $1.65, Downhill skier, horiz.

2011, July 19 *Perf. 14¾x14*

3553 A864 60c multi 1.25 1.25

Perf. 14x14¾

3554 A864 $1.60 multi 3.50 3.50
3555 A864 $1.65 multi 3.50 3.50
Nos. 3553-3555 (3) 8.25 8.25

Self-Adhesive Coil Stamp

Serpentine Die Cut 11¼ Syncopated

3556 A864 60c multi 1.25 .25

Booklet Stamps

3557 A864 $1.60 multi 3.50 1.75
a. Booklet pane of 5 17.50
3558 A864 $1.65 multi 3.50 1.75
a. Booklet pane of 5 17.50
Nos. 3556-3558 (3) 8.25 3.75

Items Depicted on Australian States Stamps — A865

Designs: No. 3559, Kangaroo and lyrebird. No. 3560, Black swan and Southern Cross.

2011, July 28 *Perf. 14x13½*

3559 A865 $2 pale grn & blue 4.25 2.10
3560 A865 $2 pink & blue 4.25 2.10
a. Pair, #3559-3560 8.50 4.25
b. Souvenir sheet of 2, #3559-3560 8.50 4.25

A limited edition of No. 3560b with a gold overprint in the sheet margin exists.

Worldwide Fund for Nature (WWF), 50th Anniv. — A866

Designs: No. 3561, Quokka. No. 3562, Southern elephant seal. No. 3563, Dugong. No. 3564, Christmas Island shrew.

2011, Aug. 30 Litho. *Perf. 14x14¾*

3561 A866 60c multi 1.25 .95
3562 A866 60c multi 1.25 .95
3563 A866 60c multi 1.25 .95
3564 A866 60c multi 1.25 .95
a. Block of 4, #3561-3564 5.00 4.00
b. Souvenir sheet of 4, #3561-3564, #3561 at UL 5.00 5.00
c. Souvenir sheet of 4, #3561-3564, #3562 at UL 5.00 5.00
d. Souvenir sheet of 4, #3561-3564, #3563 at UL 5.00 5.00
e. Souvenir sheet of 4, #3561-3564, #3564 at UL 5.00 5.00
Nos. 3561-3564 (4) 5.00 3.80

Along with the "Australia" inscription at left, inscribed at the bottom above the animal's name is "Australian Antarctic Territory" on No. 3562, "Cocos (Keeling) Islands" on No. 3563, and "Christmas Island" on No. 3564. All recent stamps of the Australian possessions of Australian Antarctic Territory, Cocos Islands and Christmas Island are doubly-inscribed with "Australia" and the possession's name, and all stamps inscribed "Australia," "Australian Antarctic Territory," "Cocos Islands," or "Christmas Island" are valid for postage anywhere in those four areas. As there was no attempt to make the stamps bearing the names of these possessions in this set available separately in those locations they will be listed here only and not in the listings for each of the possessions.

2011 Presidents Cup Golf Tournament, Melbourne — A867

Designs: Nos. 3565, 3570, Hand on golf club. Nos. 3566, 3569B, 3571, Presidents Cup. Nos. 3567, 3572, Golf shoes, glove and ball. $1.65, Golf club and ball. $2.35, Clubs in golf bag.

2011, Sept. 27 *Perf. 14¾x14*

3565 A867 60c multi 1.25 1.25
3566 A867 60c multi 1.25 1.25
3567 A867 60c multi 1.25 1.25
a. Horiz. strip of 3, #3565-3567 3.75 3.75
3568 A867 $1.65 multi 3.25 3.25
3569 A867 $2.35 multi 4.75 4.75
a. Souvenir sheet of 5, #3565-3569 12.00 12.00
Nos. 3565-3569 (5) 11.75 11.75

Litho. & Embossed With Foil Application

3569B A867 60c multi 1.25 1.25

No. 3569B was printed in sheets of 15 that sold for $9.45.

Litho. Self-Adhesive

Serpentine Die Cut 11¼ Syncopated

3570 A867 60c multi 1.25 .25
3571 A867 60c multi 1.25 .25
3572 A867 60c multi 1.25 .25
a. Booklet pane of 10, 4 each # 3570-3571, 2 #3572 12.50
b. Vert. coil strip of 3, #3570-3572 3.75
3573 A867 $1.65 multi 3.25 1.60
a. Booklet pane of 5 16.50
3574 A867 $2.35 multi 4.75 2.40
a. Booklet pane of 5 24.00
Nos. 3570-3574 (5) 11.75 4.75

Mythical Creatures — A868

Designs: Nos. 3575, 3581, Fairy. Nos. 3576, 3582, Troll. Nos. 3577, 3583, Mermaid. Nos. 3578, 3584, Griffin. Nos. 3579, 3585, Unicorn. $1.20, Dragon.

2011, Oct. 4 Litho. *Perf. 14¾x14*

3575 A868 60c multi 1.25 1.25
3576 A868 60c multi 1.25 1.25
3577 A868 60c multi 1.25 1.25
3578 A868 60c multi 1.25 1.25
3579 A868 60c multi 1.25 1.25
a. Horiz. strip of 5, #3575-3579 6.25 6.25
3580 A868 $1.20 multi 2.40 1.90
a. Souvenir sheet of 6, #3575-3580 8.75 8.75
Nos. 3575-3580 (6) 8.65 8.15

Booklet Stamps
Self-Adhesive

Serpentine Die Cut 11¼ Syncopated

3581	A868 60c multi		1.25	.25
3582	A868 60c multi		1.25	.25
3583	A868 60c multi		1.25	.25
3584	A868 60c multi		1.25	.25
3585	A868 60c multi		1.25	.25
a.	Booklet pane of 10, 2 each #3581-3585		12.50	
b.	Booklet pane of 20, 4 each #3581-3585		25.00	
	Nos. 3581-3585 (5)		6.25	1.25

Commonwealth Heads of Government Meeting, Perth — A869

2011, Oct. 18 ***Perf. 14½x14***

3586	A869 60c multi	1.25	.95

Diplomatic Relations Between Australia and South Korea, 50th Anniv. — A870

Designs: 60c, Korean woman playing haegeum. $1.65, Australian aborigine playing didgeridoo.

2011, Oct. 31 ***Perf. 13¼x13***

3587	A870 60c multi	1.25	.95
3588	A870 $1.65 multi	3.50	1.75

Booklet Stamp
Self-Adhesive

Serpentine Die Cut 11¼ Syncopated

3589	A870 $1.65 multi	3.50	1.75
a.	Booklet pane of 5	17.50	

See South Korea No. 2373.

Christmas
A871 A872

Designs: Nos. 3590, 3595, Madonna and Child. Nos. 3591, 3596, 3599, 3601, Star on Christmas tree. Nos. 3592, 3597, 3600, 3602, Star and gift. 60c, Star and fruit tree branches. $1.50, Magi and camels, horiz.

2011, Oct. 31 Litho. ***Perf. 14¾x14***

3590	A871 55c multi	1.10	1.10
3591	A872 55c multi	1.10	1.10
3592	A872 55c multi	1.10	1.10
a.	Horiz. pair, #3591-3592	2.20	2.20
3593	A872 60c multi	1.25	1.25

Perf. 14x14¾

3594	A871 $1.50 multi	3.25	3.25
	Nos. 3590-3594 (5)	7.80	7.80

Booklet Stamps
Self-Adhesive

Serpentine Die Cut 11¼ Syncopated

3595	A871 55c multi	1.10	.25
a.	Booklet pane of 20 + 20 etiquettes	22.00	
3596	A872 55c multi	1.10	.25
3597	A872 55c multi	1.10	.25
a.	Booklet pane of 20, 10 each #3596-3597 + 20 etiquettes	22.00	
3598	A871 $1.50 multi	3.25	1.60
a.	Booklet pane of 5	16.50	

Litho. With Foil Application

3599	A872 55c multi	1.10	.25
a.	Booklet pane of 10	11.00	
3600	A872 55c multi	1.10	.25
a.	Booklet pane of 10	11.00	
	Nos. 3595-3600 (6)	8.75	2.85

Litho.
With Personalized Photo at Right Like Type A692a

Serpentine Die Cut 11½x11¼ Syncopated

3601	A872 55c multi	2.50	2.50
3602	A872 55c multi	2.50	2.50
3603	A872 60c multi	2.60	2.60
	Nos. 3601-3603 (3)	7.60	7.60

Nos. 3601-3603 each were printed in sheets of 20 and have personalized pictures and a straight edge at right, and lack separations between the stamp and the personalized photo. Sheets of 20 of Nos. 3601 and 3602 each sold for $24, for No. 3603, $25.

Remembrance Day — A873

Lines from "In Flanders Fields," poem by John McCrae, and: 60c, Poppy, bugler. $1.20, Two poppies, two soldiers.

2011, Nov. 2 Litho. ***Perf. 14x14¾***

3604	A873 60c multi	1.25	1.25
3605	A873 $1.20 multi	2.50	1.90
a.	Souvenir sheet of 2, #3604-3605	3.75	3.25

Self-Adhesive

Serpentine Die Cut 11¼ Syncopated

3606	A873 60c multi	1.25	.25
a.	Booklet pane of 10	12.50	

No. 3606 was issued in coils and booklets.

ANZUS Treaty, 60th Anniv. — A874

Design: Australian Lieutenant General Sydney F. Rowell, New Zealand Major General William Gentry, and U.S. Admiral Arthur Radford.

2011, Nov. 16 ***Perf. 14x14¾***

3607	A874 60c multi	1.25	.95

Cupcake and Birthday Candle
A875

Teddy Bear
A876

Balloons and Streamers
A877

"Love" and Hearts
A878

Birds
A879

Rose
A880

2012, Jan. 17 ***Perf. 14¾x14***

3608	A875 60c multi	1.25	1.25
3609	A876 60c multi	1.25	1.25
3610	A877 60c multi	1.25	1.25
3611	A878 60c multi	1.25	1.25
3612	A879 60c multi	1.25	1.25
a.	Horiz. strip of 5, $3608-3612	6.25	6.25
3613	A880 $1.20 multi	2.60	2.60
	Nos. 3608-3613 (6)	8.85	8.85

Booklet Stamps
Self-Adhesive

Serpentine Die Cut 11¼ Syncopated

3614	A875 60c multi	1.25	.25
a.	Booklet pane of 10 + 5 stickers	12.50	
3615	A876 60c multi	1.25	.25
a.	Booklet pane of 10 + 5 stickers	12.50	
3616	A877 60c multi	1.25	.25
a.	Booklet pane of 10 + 5 stickers	12.50	
3617	A878 60c multi	1.25	.25
a.	Booklet pane of 10 + 5 stickers	12.50	
3618	A879 60c multi	1.25	.25
a.	Booklet pane of 10 + 5 stickers	12.50	
3619	A880 $1.20 multi	2.75	1.40
a.	Booklet pane of 4	11.00	
	Complete booklet, 5 #3619a	55.00	
	Nos. 3614-3619 (6)	9.00	2.65

With Personalized Photo at Right Like Type A692a

Serpentine Die Cut 11½x11¼ Syncopated

3620	A875 60c multi	2.75	2.75
3621	A876 60c multi	2.75	2.75
3622	A877 60c multi	2.75	2.75
3623	A878 60c multi	2.75	2.75
3624	A879 60c multi	2.75	2.75
3625	A880 $1.20 multi	4.00	4.00
	Nos. 3620-3625 (6)	17.75	17.75

Complete booklet sold for $24.95 and contains five booklet panes of No. 3619a, each with a different margin.

Nos. 3620-3625 each were printed in sheets of 20 and have personalized pictures and a straight edge at right, and lack separations between the stamp and the personalized photo. Sheets of 20 of Nos. 3620-3624 each sold for $25, for No. 3625, $37.

Athletes — A881

Designs: Nos. 3626, 3634, Ron Barassi, Australian Rules Football player. Nos. 3627, 3635, Gary Ablett, Jr., Australian Rules Football player. Nos. 3628, 3636, John Raper, Rugby League player. Nos. 3629, 3637, Billy Slater, Rugby League player. Nos. 3630, 3638, David Campese, Rugby Union player. Nos. 3631, 3639, David Pocock, Rugby Union player. Nos. 3632, 3640, Joe Marston, soccer player. Nos. 3633, 3641, Mark Schwarzer, soccer player.

2012, Jan. 20 ***Perf. 14¾x14***

3626	A881 60c multi	1.25	1.25
a.	Booklet pane of 4	5.50	—
3627	A881 60c multi	1.25	1.25
a.	Booklet pane of 4	5.50	—
3628	A881 60c multi	1.25	1.25
a.	Booklet pane of 4	5.50	—
3629	A881 60c multi	1.25	1.25
a.	Booklet pane of 4	5.50	—
3630	A881 60c multi	1.25	1.25
a.	Booklet pane of 4	5.50	—
3631	A881 60c multi	1.25	1.25
a.	Booklet pane of 4	5.50	—
3632	A881 60c multi	1.25	1.25
a.	Booklet pane of 4	5.50	—
3633	A881 60c multi	1.25	1.25
a.	Booklet pane of 4	5.50	—
	Complete booklet, #3626a-3633a	44.00	
	Nos. 3626-3633 (8)	10.00	10.00

Booklet Stamps
Self-Adhesive

Serpentine Die Cut 11¼ Syncopated

3634	A881 60c multi	1.25	.25
a.	Booklet pane of 10	12.50	
3635	A881 60c multi	1.25	.25
a.	Booklet pane of 10	12.50	
3636	A881 60c multi	1.25	.25
a.	Booklet pane of 10	12.50	
3637	A881 60c multi	1.25	.25
a.	Booklet pane of 10	12.50	
3638	A881 60c multi	1.25	.25
a.	Booklet pane of 10	12.50	
3639	A881 60c multi	1.25	.25
a.	Booklet pane of 10	12.50	
3640	A881 60c multi	1.25	.25
a.	Booklet pane of 10	12.50	
3641	A881 60c multi	1.25	.25
a.	Booklet pane of 10	12.50	
	Nos. 3634-3641 (8)	10.00	2.00

Complete booklet sold for $19.95.

Technological Changes Through the Years — A882

Designs: Nos. 3642, 3647, Woman on pay telephone, 4G phone. Nos. 3643, 3648, Man carrying ice to icebox, modern refrigerator. Nos. 3644, 3649, Family watching black-and-white television, flat-screen television. Nos. 3645, 3650, Man with vinyl records and record player, digital media player. Nos. 3646, 3651, Man reading paper road map, global positioning system.

2012, Feb. 7 ***Perf. 14x14¾***

3642	A882 60c multi	1.40	1.40
3643	A882 60c multi	1.40	1.40
3644	A882 60c multi	1.40	1.40
3645	A882 60c multi	1.40	1.40
3646	A882 60c multi	1.40	1.40
a.	Horiz. strip of 5, #3642-3646	7.00	7.00
b.	Souvenir sheet of 5, #3642-3646	7.00	7.00

Self-Adhesive

Serpentine Die Cut 11¼ Syncopated

3647	A882 60c multi	1.40	.25
3648	A882 60c multi	1.40	.25
3649	A882 60c multi	1.40	.25
3650	A882 60c multi	1.40	.25
3651	A882 60c multi	1.40	.25
a.	Horiz. coil strip of 5, #3647-3651	7.00	
b.	Booklet pane of 10, 2 each #3647-3651	14.00	
	Nos. 3647-3651 (5)	7.00	1.25

Transportation in State Capitals — A883

Designs: Nos. 3652, 3657, O-Bahn bus system, Adelaide. Nos. 3653, 3658, Ferry in Sydney Harbor. Nos. 3654, 3659, Train in Perth. Nos. 3655, 3660, St. Kilda-bound tram, Melbourne. Nos. 3656, 3661, North Sydney-bound double-decker train, Sydney.

2012, Feb. 21 ***Perf. 14x14¾***

3652	A883 60c multi	1.40	1.40
a.	Booklet pane of 4	5.75	—
3653	A883 60c multi	1.40	1.40
a.	Booklet pane of 4	5.75	—
3654	A883 60c multi	1.40	1.40
a.	Booklet pane of 4	5.75	—
3655	A883 60c multi	1.40	1.40
a.	Booklet pane of 4	5.75	—
3656	A883 60c multi	1.40	1.40
a.	Booklet pane of 4	5.75	—
	Complete booklet, #3652a-3656a	29.00	
b.	Horiz. strip of 5, #3652-3656	7.00	7.00

Booklet Stamps
Self-Adhesive

Serpentine Die Cut 11¼ Syncopated

3657	A883 60c multi	1.40	.25
3658	A883 60c multi	1.40	.25
3659	A883 60c multi	1.40	.25
3660	A883 60c multi	1.40	.25
3661	A883 60c multi	1.40	.25
a.	Booklet pane of 20, 4 each #3657-3661	28.00	
	Nos. 3657-3661 (5)	7.00	1.25

Complete booklet sold for $12.95.

Ducks — A884

Designs: Nos. 3662, 3666, Radjah shelduck. Nos. 3663, 3667, Pink-eared duck. $1.65, Australian shelduck. $2.35, Plumed whistling duck.

2012, Mar. 6 ***Perf. 14x14¾***

3662	A884 60c multi	1.25	1.25
a.	Additionally dated "2013"	1.25	1.25
3663	A884 60c multi	1.25	1.25
a.	Additionally dated "2013"	1.25	1.25
3664	A884 $1.65 multi	3.50	3.50
a.	Additionally dated "2013"	3.25	3.25
3665	A884 $2.35 multi	5.00	5.00
a.	Additionally dated "2013"	4.50	4.50
b.	Booklet pane of 4, #3662a, 3663a, 3664a, 3665a	10.50	—
	Nos. 3662-3665 (4)	11.00	11.00

Issued: Nos. 3662a, 3663a, 3664a, 3665a, 3665b, 5/11/13. No. 3665b was issued in a booklet also containing Nos. 3151c, 3376b and 3925a.

Self-Adhesive

Serpentine Die Cut 11¼ Syncopated

3666	A884 60c multi	1.25	.25
3667	A884 60c multi	1.25	.25
a.	Horiz. coil pair, #3666-3667	2.50	
b.	Booklet pane of 10, 5 each #3666-3667	25.00	

Booklet Stamps

3668	A884 $1.65 multi	3.50	1.75
a.	Booklet pane of 5	17.50	

3669 A884 $2.35 multi 5.00 2.50
a. Booklet pane of 5 25.00
Nos. 3666-3669 (4) 11.00 4.75

Farm Products — A885

Designs: 10c, Dairy cows. 20c, Pineapples. $1, Wine grapes. $3, Sunflowers. $5, Apples.

2012, Mar. 20 *Perf. 14x14½*
3670 A885 10c multi .25 .25
3671 A885 20c multi .40 .25
a. As No. 3671, with part of design and 1mm wide white space separating designs at left side 1.10 1.10

Size: 50x30mm

Perf. 14½x14

3672 A885 $1 multi 2.10 1.10
3673 A885 $3 multi 6.25 3.25
3674 A885 $5 multi 10.50 5.25
Nos. 3670-3674 (5) 19.50 10.10

No. 3671 has a white margin extending to the perforation tips at left. Four of the five stamps in the bottom row of the bottom pane in the sheet of 100 stamps (composed of two panes of 50) are No. 3671a.
See Nos. 3712-3723.

Compulsory Voting Enrollment, Cent. — A886

2012, Mar. 27 Litho. *Perf. 14¾x14*
3675 A886 60c multi 1.25 .95

Reign of Queen Elizabeth II, 60th Anniv. — A887

Photograph of Queen Elizabeth II in: 60c, 1952. $2.35, 2012.

2012, Apr. 3 *Perf. 14¾x14*
3676 A887 60c multi 1.25 .95
3677 A887 $2.35 multi 5.00 5.00
a. Souvenir sheet of 2, #3676-3677 6.25 6.00

Booklet Stamp
Self-Adhesive

Serpentine Die Cut 11¼ Syncopated

3678 A887 $2.35 multi 5.00 2.50
a. Booklet pane of 5 25.00

Medical Doctors — A888

Designs: Nos. 3679, 3684, Dr. Jane Stocks Greig (1872-1939), public health specialist. Nos. 3680, 3685, Dame Kate Campbell (1899-1986), pediatrician. Nos. 3681, 3686, Dr. Victor Chang (1936-91), cardiac surgeon. Nos. 3682, 3687, Dr. Fred Hollows (1929-93), ophthalmologist. Nos. 3683, 3688, Dr. Chris O'Brien (1952-2009), surgeon.

2012, Apr. 10 *Perf. 14¾x14*
3679 A888 60c multi 1.25 1.25
3680 A888 60c multi 1.25 1.25
3681 A888 60c multi 1.25 1.25
3682 A888 60c multi 1.25 1.25
3683 A888 60c multi 1.25 1.25
Nos. 3679-3683 (5) 6.25 6.25

Coil Stamps
Self-Adhesive

Serpentine Die Cut 11¼ Syncopated

3684 A888 60c multi 1.25 .25
3685 A888 60c multi 1.25 .25
3686 A888 60c multi 1.25 .25
3687 A888 60c multi 1.25 .25
3688 A888 60c multi 1.25 .25
a. Vert. coil strip of 5, #3684-3688 6.25
Nos. 3684-3688 (5) 6.25 1.25

Rising Sun Badge — A889

Rising Sun Badge in use from: Nos. 3689, 3694, 1902-04. Nos. 3690, 3695, 1904-49. Nos. 3691, 3696, 1954-69. Nos. 3692, 3697, 1969-91. Nos. 3693, 3698, 1991-present.

2012, Apr. 17 *Perf. 14x14¾*
3689 A889 60c multi 1.25 1.25
3690 A889 60c multi 1.25 1.25
3691 A889 60c multi 1.25 1.25
3692 A889 60c multi 1.25 1.25
3693 A889 60c multi 1.25 1.25
a. Horiz. strip of 5, #3689-3693 6.25 6.25
b. Souvenir sheet of 5, #3689-3693 6.25 6.25

Booklet Stamps
Self-Adhesive

Serpentine Die Cut 11¼ Syncopated

3694 A889 60c multi 1.25 .25
3695 A889 60c multi 1.25 .25
3696 A889 60c multi 1.25 .25
3697 A889 60c multi 1.25 .25
3698 A889 60c multi 1.25 .25
a. Booklet pane of 10, 2 each #3694-3698 12.50
Nos. 3694-3698 (5) 6.25 1.25

Limited editions exist of No. 3698a with a gold overprint in the margin, and a part-perforate sheet of seven stamps (five similar to Nos. 3689-3693, and two different $1 stamps).

Nudibranchs A890

Designs: Nos. 3699, 3705, Chromodoris westraliensis. Nos. 3700, 3706, Godiva sp. Nos. 3701, 3707, Flabellina rubrolineata. No. 3702, Phyllidia ocellata. No. 3703, Thorunna florens. $1.80, Nembrotha purpureolineata.

2012, May 8 *Perf. 14x14¾*
3699 A890 60c multi 1.25 1.25
a. Booklet pane of 4 5.25 —
3700 A890 60c multi 1.25 1.25
a. Booklet pane of 4 5.25 —
3701 A890 60c multi 1.25 1.25
a. Booklet pane of 4 5.25 —
3702 A890 $1.20 multi 2.40 1.90
3703 A890 $1.20 multi 2.40 1.90
a. Booklet pane of 4, #3699-3702 6.50 —
3704 A890 $1.80 multi 3.75 1.90
a. Booklet pane of 4, #3699-3701, 3704 7.75 —
Complete booklet, #3699a, 3700a, 3701a, 3703a, 3704a 30.00
b. Souvenir sheet of 6, #3699-3704 12.50 12.50
Nos. 3699-3704 (6) 12.30 9.45

Booklet Stamps
Self-Adhesive

Serpentine Die Cut 11¼ Syncopated

3705 A890 60c multi 1.25 .25
3706 A890 60c multi 1.25 .25
3707 A890 60c multi 1.25 .25
a. Booklet pane of 20, 7 each #3705-3706, 6 #3707 25.00
Nos. 3705-3707 (3) 3.75 .75

Complete booklet sold for $14.95.

Australian Flag, Olympic Rings, London Tourist Attractions — A891

2012, June 5 *Perf. 14¾x14*
3708 A891 60c multi 1.25 1.25

Self-Adhesive

Serpentine Die Cut 11¼ Syncopated

3709 A891 60c multi 1.25 .25
a. Booklet pane of 10 12.50

2012 Summer Olympics, London.

Colonial Heritage — A892

Designs: No. 3710, Redrawn vignette of New South Wales #1. No. 3710, Redrawn vignette of Tasmania #88.

2012, June 19 *Perf. 14x14½*
3710 A892 $2 yellow & blue 4.25 2.10
a. Perf. 14x13½ 4.25 2.10
3711 A892 $2 lt blue & blue 4.25 2.10
a. Perf. 14x13½ 4.25 2.10
b. Horiz. pair, #3710-3711 8.50 4.25
c. Souvenir sheet of 2, #3710a, 3711a 8.50 4.25

Farm Products Type of 2012

Designs: Nos. 3712, 3716, 3720, Beef cattle. Nos. 3713, 3717, 3721, Oranges. Nos. 3714, 3718, 3722, Sugar. Nos. 3715, 3719, 3723, Wool.

2012, June 26 Litho. *Perf. 14x14½*
3712 A885 60c multi 1.25 .25
3713 A885 60c multi 1.25 .25
3714 A885 60c multi 1.25 .25
3715 A885 60c multi 1.25 .25
a. Block of 4, #3712-3715 5.00 2.50
Nos. 3712-3715 (4) 5.00 1.00

Coil Stamps
Self-Adhesive

Serpentine Die Cut 12¾

3716 A885 60c multi 1.25 .25
3717 A885 60c multi 1.25 .25
3718 A885 60c multi 1.25 .25
3719 A885 60c multi 1.25 .25
a. Horiz. strip of 4, #3716-3719 5.00

Booklet Stamps

Serpentine Die Cut 11¼

3720 A885 60c multi 1.25 .25
3721 A885 60c multi 1.25 .25
3722 A885 60c multi 1.25 .25
3723 A885 60c multi 1.25 .25
a. Booklet pane of 10, 2 each #3720, 3722-3723, 4 #3721 12.50
b. Booklet pane of 20, 5 each #3720-3723 25.00
Nos. 3716-3723 (8) 10.00 2.00

Inland Exploration A893

Designs: No. 3724, Explorers crossing Blue Mountains, 1813. No. 3725, Explorers William Lawson, William Charles Wentworth and Gregory Blaxland. No. 3726, Explorer John McDouall Stuart. No. 3727, Stuart Overland Crossing Expedition planting flag on Indian Ocean coast.

2012, July 3 *Perf. 14x14¾*
3724 A893 60c multi 1.25 .95
3725 A893 60c multi 1.25 .95
a. Horiz. pair, #3724-3725 2.50 1.90
3726 A893 $1.20 multi 2.50 2.00
3727 A893 $1.20 multi 2.50 2.00
a. Horiz. pair, #3726-3727 5.00 4.00
b. Souvenir sheet of 4, #3724-3727 7.50 6.00
Nos. 3724-3727 (4) 7.50 5.90

Sports of the Summer Olympics — A894

Designs: 60c, Swimming. $1.60, Pole vault. $2.30, Rowing.

2012, July 17 *Perf. 14x14¾*
3728 A894 60c multi 1.25 1.25
3729 A894 $1.60 multi 3.50 3.50
3730 A894 $2.35 multi 5.00 5.00
Nos. 3728-3730 (3) 9.75 9.75

Coil Stamp
Self-Adhesive

Serpentine Die Cut 11¼ Syncopated

3731 A894 60c multi 1.25 .25

Booklet Stamps

3732 A894 $1.60 multi 3.50 1.75
a. Booklet pane of 5 17.50
3733 A894 $2.35 multi 5.00 2.50
a. Booklet pane of 5 25.00
Nos. 3731-3733 (3) 9.75 4.50

Photographs of Everyday Life in Australia — A895

Designs: Nos. 3734, 3740, Little Wonders, by Ann Clark (children on beach). Nos. 3735, 3742, The Godfathers, by Chevelle Williams (sheep in pen). Nos. 3736, 3741, Is There a Letter for Me?, by Wanda Lach (row of mailboxes in rural area). Nos. 3737, 3743, Lunch on the Harbor, by Damian Madden (seagull with French fry in beak). Nos. 3738, 3739, Fuel Ask at the Store Across the Road, by Ronald Rockman (rural gas station).

2012, July 24 *Perf. 14x14¾*
3734 A895 60c multi 1.25 1.25
3735 A895 60c multi 1.25 1.25
3736 A895 60c multi 1.25 1.25
3737 A895 60c multi 1.25 1.25
3738 A895 60c multi 1.25 1.25
a. Horiz. strip of 5, #3734-3738 6.25 6.25
Nos. 3734-3738 (5) 6.25 6.25

Booklet Stamps
Self-Adhesive

Serpentine Die Cut 11¼ Syncopated

3739 A895 60c multi 1.25 .25
3740 A895 60c multi 1.25 .25
3741 A895 60c multi 1.25 .25
3742 A895 60c multi 1.25 .25
3743 A895 60c multi 1.25 .25
a. Booklet pane of 20, 4 each #3739-3742 25.00
Nos. 3739-3743 (5) 6.25 1.25

Souvenir Sheet

Emblem of Australia 2013 World Stamp Expo and Royal Exhibition Building, Melbourne — A896

2012, June 18 Litho. *Perf. 14¾x14*
3744 A896 $1.85 multi 3.75 1.90

A limited edition of No. 3744 with a gold overprint in the sheet margin exists.

Australian Gold Medalists at 2012 Summer Olympics, London — A897

Designs: No. 3745, Women's 4x100 meter freestyle swimming relay team. No. 3746, Tom Slingsby, men's Laser class sailing. No. 3747, Anna Meares, women's sprint cycling. No. 3748, Iain Jensen and Nathan Outteridge, men's 49er class sailing. No. 3749, Sally Pearson, women's 100 meter hurdles. No. 3750, Men's 1000 meter kayak fours team. No. 3751, Mathew Belcher and Malcolm Page, men's 470 class sailing.

2012 *Perf. 14¼*
3745 A897 60c multi 1.25 .95
3746 A897 60c multi 1.25 .95
3747 A897 60c multi 1.25 .95
3748 A897 60c multi 1.25 .95
3749 A897 60c multi 1.25 .95
3750 A897 60c multi 1.25 .95
3751 A897 60c multi 1.25 .95
Nos. 3745-3751 (7) 8.75 6.65

Nos. 3745-3751 each were printed in sheets of 10. Issued: No. 3745, 7/31; No. 3746, 8/9; No. 3747, 8/10; others, 8/13.
See No. 4506B.

Portraits of Autralian Nobel Prize Winners — A898

Portrait of: Nos. 3752, 3757, Sir Frank Macfarlane Burnet, by Clifton Pugh. Nos. 3753, 3758, Sir John Carew Eccles, by Judy Cassab. Nos. 3754, 3759, Patrick White, by Brett Whiteley. Nos. 3755, 3760, Sir Howard Walter Florey, by Allan Gwynne-Jones. Nos. 3756, 3761, William Lawrence Bragg, by Sir William Dargie.

2012, Aug. 28 Litho. *Perf. 14¾x14*

3752	A898	60c multi	1.25	1.25
3753	A898	60c multi	1.25	1.25
3754	A898	60c multi	1.25	1.25
3755	A898	60c multi	1.25	1.25
3756	A898	60c multi	1.25	1.25
a.		Horiz. strip of 5, #3752-3756	6.25	6.25
		Nos. 3752-3756 (5)	6.25	6.25

Self-Adhesive

Serpentine Die Cut 11¼ Syncopated

3757	A898	60c multi	1.25	.25
3758	A898	60c multi	1.25	.25
3759	A898	60c multi	1.25	.25
3760	A898	60c multi	1.25	.25
3761	A898	60c multi	1.25	.25
a.		Vert. coil strip of 5, #3757-3761	6.25	
b.		Booklet pane of 10, 2 each #3757-3761	12.50	
		Nos. 3757-3761 (5)	6.25	1.25

Road Trips — A899

Designs: Nos. 3762, 3769, Station wagon at Port Arthur, Tasmania. Nos. 3763, 3767, Volkswagen Bus at Great Barrier Reef, Queensland. Nos. 3764, 3768, Motorcyclists picnicking near Margaret River, Western Australia. $1.65, Station wagon at Phillip Island, Victoria. $2.35, Car at camel race, Alice Springs, Northern Territory.

2012, Sept. 18 *Perf. 14¼*

3762	A899	60c multi	1.25	1.25
3763	A899	60c multi	1.25	1.25
3764	A899	60c multi	1.25	1.25
a.		Horiz. strip of 3, #3762-3764	3.75	3.75
3765	A899	$1.65 multi	3.50	1.75
3766	A899	$2.35 multi	4.75	2.40
a.		Souvenir sheet of 5, #3762-3766	12.00	12.00
		Nos. 3762-3766 (5)	12.00	7.90

Booklet Stamps
Self-Adhesive

Serpentine Die Cut 11¼ Syncopated

3767	A899	60c multi	1.25	.25
3768	A899	60c multi	1.25	.25
3769	A899	60c multi	1.25	.25
a.		Booklet pane of 10, 3 each #3767, 3769, 4 #3768	12.50	
3770	A899	$1.65 multi	3.50	1.75
a.		Booklet pane of 5	17.50	
3771	A899	$2.35 multi	4.75	2.40
a.		Booklet pane of 5	24.00	
		Nos. 3767-3771 (5)	12.00	4.90

Compare with type A933.

Wilderness Areas — A900

Designs: $1.65, Nullarbor Plain, Western Australia. $2.35, Daintree National Park, Queensland. $4.50, Cradle Mountain, Tasmania.

2012, Sept. 25 *Perf. 14¾x14*

3772	A900	$1.65 multi	3.50	1.75
3773	A900	$2.35 multi	4.75	2.40
3774	A900	$4.50 multi	9.25	4.75
		Nos. 3772-3774 (3)	17.50	8.90

Booklet Stamps
Self-Adhesive

Serpentine Die Cut 11¼ Syncopated

3775	A900	$1.65 multi	3.50	1.75
a.		Booklet pane of 5	17.50	
3776	A900	$2.35 multi	4.75	2.40
a.		Booklet pane of 5	24.00	

Animals in Australian Zoos — A901

Designs: No. 3777, Sumatran tiger, Melbourne Zoo, Victoria. Nos. 3778, 3789, Wedge-tailed hawk, Healesville Sanctuary, Victoria. Nos. 3779, 3787. Sumatran orangutan, Perth Zoo, Western Australia. Nos. 3780, 3786, Giant panda, Adelaide Zoo, South Australia. Nos. 3781, 3785, Giraffe, Taronga Zoo, Sydney, New South Wales. Nos. 3782, 3788, Saltwater crocodile, Australia Zoo, Sunshine Coast, Queensland. Nos. 3783, 3784, Black rhinoceros, Taronga Western Plains Zoo, Dubbo, New South Wales.

2012, Sept. 28 *Perf. 13¾x14*

3777	A901	60c multi	1.25	.95

Size: 37x26mm

Perf. 14x14¾

3778	A901	60c multi	1.25	1.25
3779	A901	60c multi	1.25	1.25
3780	A901	60c multi	1.25	1.25
3781	A901	60c multi	1.25	1.25
3782	A901	60c multi	1.25	1.25
3783	A901	60c multi	1.25	1.25
a.		Souvenir sheet of 7, #3777-3783	8.75	8.75
		Nos. 3777-3783 (7)	8.75	8.45

Self-Adhesive

Serpentine Die Cut 11¼ Syncopated

3784	A901	60c multi	1.25	.25
3785	A901	60c multi	1.25	.25
3786	A901	60c multi	1.25	.25
3787	A901	60c multi	1.25	.25
3788	A901	60c multi	1.25	.25
3789	A901	60c multi	1.25	.25
a.		Horiz. coil strip of 6, #3784-3789	7.50	
b.		Booklet pane of 20, 4 each #3784-3785, 3 each #3786-3789	25.00	
		Nos. 3784-3789 (6)	7.50	1.50

Auto Racing at Bathurst, 50th Anniv. — A902

Designs: Nos. 3790, 3794, Race car, country name in red. Nos. 3791, 3797, Mount Panorama Race Track, country name in yellow green. Nos. 3792, 3796, Race car, country name in blue. Nos. 3793, 3795, Race car, country name in yellow.

2012, Oct. 2 *Perf. 14x14¾*

3790	A902	60c multi	1.25	1.25
3791	A902	60c multi	1.25	1.25
3792	A902	60c multi	1.25	1.25
3793	A902	60c multi	1.25	1.25
a.		Block of 4, #3790-3793	5.00	5.00
b.		Souvenir sheet of 4, #3790-3793	5.00	5.00
		Nos. 3790-3793 (4)	5.00	5.00

Booklet Stamps
Self-Adhesive

Serpentine Die Cut 11¼ Syncopated

3794	A902	60c multi	1.25	.25
3795	A902	60c multi	1.25	.25
3796	A902	60c multi	1.25	.25
3797	A902	60c multi	1.25	.25
a.		Booklet pane of 10, 2 each #3794-3796, 4 #3797	12.50	
		Nos. 3794-3797 (4)	5.00	1.00

Susie O'Neill, Swimmer — A903

O'Neill: No. 3798, Wearing black jacket. No. 3799, Swimming in pool.

2012, Oct. 12 *Perf. 14¾x14*

3798	A903	60c multi	1.25	.95
3799	A903	60c multi	1.25	.95
a.		Pair, #3798-3799	2.50	1.90

Australian Ballet, 50th Anniv. — A904

Designs: Nos. 3800, 3802, One dancer. Nos. 3801, 3803, Two dancers.

2012, Oct. 16 *Perf. 14¾x14*

3800	A904	60c multi	1.25	1.25
3801	A904	60c multi	1.25	1.25
a.		Pair, #3800-3801	2.50	2.50

Coil Stamps
Self-Adhesive

Serpentine Die Cut 11¼ Syncopated

3802	A904	60c multi	1.25	.25
3803	A904	60c multi	1.25	.25
a.		Vert. pair, #3802-3803	2.50	

Lawn Bowling — A905

Designs: 60c, Female bowlers. $1.20, Male bowlers.

2012, Nov. 1 *Perf. 14x14¾*

3804	A905	60c multi	1.25	.95
3805	A905	$1.20 multi	2.50	1.90
a.		Souvenir sheet of 2, #3804-3805	3.75	3.00

Christmas
A906 A907

Designs: Nos. 3806, 3811, Detail of Madonna and Child from Adoration of the Magi tapestry. Nos. 3807, 3812, 3815, 3817, Reindeer. Nos. 3808, 3813, 3816, 3818, Gifts. 60c, Bells. $1.60, Entire Adoration of the Magi tapestry (50x30mm), horiz.

2012, Nov. 1 *Perf. 14¾x14*

3806	A906	55c multi	1.25	1.25
3807	A907	55c multi	1.25	1.25
3808	A907	55c multi	1.25	1.25
3809	A907	60c multi	1.25	.60

Perf. 14½x14

3810	A906	$1.60 multi	3.50	1.75
		Nos. 3806-3810 (5)	8.50	6.10

Booklet Stamps
Self-Adhesive

Serpentine Die Cut 11¼ Syncopated

3811	A906	55c multi	1.25	.25
a.		Booklet pane of 20	25.00	
3812	A907	55c multi	1.25	.25
3813	A907	55c multi	1.25	.25
a.		Booklet pane of 20, 10 each #3812-3813	25.00	
3814	A906	$1.60 multi	3.50	1.75
a.		Booklet pane of 5	17.50	

Litho. With Foil Application

3815	A907	55c multi	1.25	.25
a.		Booklet pane of 10	12.50	

Litho. & Embossed With Foil Application

3816	A907	55c multi	1.25	.25
a.		Booklet pane of 10	12.50	
		Nos. 3811-3816 (6)	9.75	3.00

With Personalized Photo at Right Like Type A692a
Litho.

Serpentine Die Cut 11½x11¼ Syncopated

3817	A907	55c multi	2.50	2.50
3818	A907	55c multi	2.50	2.50

Nos. 3817-3818 each were printed in sheets of 20 and have personalized pictures and straight edge at right, and lack separations between the stamp an the personalized photo. Sheets of 20 of each stamp sold for $24.

Jacqueline Freney, Paralympian of the Year — A908

2012, Nov. 9 *Perf. 14¼*

3819	A908	60c multi	1.25	.95

Musical Legends — A909

Designs: Nos. 3820, 3830, AC/DC (rock band). Nos. 3821, 3831, Cold Chisel (rock band). Nos. 3822, 3832, INXS (rock band). Nos. 3823, 3833, John Farnham (singer). Nos. 3824, 3834, Kylie Minogue (singer). Nos. 3825, 3835, Men At Work (rock band). Nos. 3826, 3836, Ian "Molly" Meldrum (record producer). Nos. 3827, 3837, Olivia Newton-John (singer). No. 3828, 3838, Paul Kelly (singer). Nos. 3829, 3839, The Seekers (rock band).

2013, Jan. 18 *Perf. 14¾x14*

3820	A909	60c multi	1.25	1.25
a.		Booklet pane of 4	5.25	—
3821	A909	60c multi	1.25	1.25
a.		Booklet pane of 4	5.25	—
b.		Horiz. pair, #3820-3821	2.50	2.50
3822	A909	60c multi	1.25	1.25
a.		Booklet pane of 4	5.25	—
3823	A909	60c multi	1.25	1.25
a.		Booklet pane of 4	5.25	—
3824	A909	60c multi	1.25	1.25
a.		Booklet pane of 4	5.25	—
3825	A909	60c multi	1.25	1.25
a.		Booklet pane of 4	5.25	—
3826	A909	60c multi	1.25	1.25
a.		Booklet pane of 4	5.25	—
b.		Horiz. pair, #3824, 3826	2.50	2.50
3827	A909	60c multi	1.25	1.25
a.		Booklet pane of 4	5.25	—
b.		Horiz. pair, #3823, 3827	2.50	2.50
3828	A909	60c multi	1.25	1.25
a.		Booklet pane of 4	5.25	—
b.		Horiz. pair, #3822, 3828	2.50	2.50
3829	A909	60c multi	1.25	1.25
a.		Booklet pane of 4	5.25	—
b.		Horiz. pair, #3825, 3829	2.50	2.50
		Complete booklet, #3820a-3829a	52.50	
		Nos. 3820-3829 (10)	12.50	12.50

Booklet Stamps
Self-Adhesive

Serpentine Die Cut 11¼ Syncopated

3830	A909	60c multi	1.25	.25
a.		Booklet pane of 10	12.50	
3831	A909	60c multi	1.25	.25
a.		Booklet pane of 10	12.50	
3832	A909	60c multi	1.25	.25
a.		Booklet pane of 10	12.50	
3833	A909	60c multi	1.25	.25
a.		Booklet pane of 10	12.50	
3834	A909	60c multi	1.25	.25
a.		Booklet pane of 10	12.50	
3835	A909	60c multi	1.25	.25
a.		Booklet pane of 10	12.50	
3836	A909	60c multi	1.25	.25
a.		Booklet pane of 10	12.50	
3837	A909	60c multi	1.25	.25
a.		Booklet pane of 10	12.50	
3838	A909	60c multi	1.25	.25
a.		Booklet pane of 10	12.50	
3839	A909	60c multi	1.25	.25
a.		Booklet pane of 10	12.50	
		Nos. 3830-3839 (10)	12.50	2.50

Complete booklet sold for $24.95.

Eucalyptus Leaves
A910

Map of Australia
A911

Rose Petal
A912

Orchid
A913

Gifts and Champagne Flutes — A914

2013, Feb. 5 Litho. *Perf. 14¾x14*

3840	A910	60c multi	1.25	1.25
3841	A911	60c blue & multi	1.25	1.25
3842	A911	60c org & multi	1.25	1.25
3843	A912	60c multi	1.25	1.25
3844	A913	60c multi	1.25	1.25
a.		Horiz. strip of 5, #3840-3844	6.25	6.25
3845	A914	$1.20 multi	2.50	2.50
		Nos. 3840-3845 (6)	8.75	8.75

Booklet Stamps
Self-Adhesive

Serpentine Die Cut 11¼ Syncopated

3846 A910 60c multi 1.25 .25
a. Booklet pane of 10 + 5 stickers 12.50
3847 A911 60c blue & multi 1.25 .25
3848 A911 60c org & multi 1.25 .25
a. Booklet pane of 10, 5 each #3847-3848, + 5 stickers 12.50
3849 A912 60c multi 1.25 .25
a. Booklet pane of 10 + 5 stickers 12.50
3850 A913 60c multi 1.25 .25
a. Booklet pane of 10 + 5 stickers 12.50
3851 A914 $1.20 multi 2.50 1.25
a. Booklet pane of 10 + 5 stickers 25.00
b. Booklet pane of 4 10.50
Complete booklet, 5 #3851b 52.50
Nos. 3846-3851 (6) 8.75 2.50

Complete booklet sold for $24.95 and contains five examples of No. 3851b, each with a different image in pane margin.

With Personalized Photo at Right Like Type A692a

Serpentine Die Cut 11½x11¼ Syncopated

3852 A910 60c multi 2.60 2.60
3853 A911 60c blue & multi 2.60 2.60
3854 A911 60c org & multi 2.60 2.60
3855 A912 60c multi 2.60 2.60
3856 A913 60c multi 2.60 2.60
3857 A914 $1.20 multi 3.75 3.75
Nos. 3852-3857 (6) 16.75 16.75

Nos, 3852-3857 each were printed in sheets of 20 and have personalized pictures and a straight edge at right and lack separations between the stamp and the personalized photo. Sheets of 20 of Nos. 3852-3856 sold for $25 each, No. 3857, $37.

Women and Surfboards A915

Surfer and Stylized Waves A916

Surfboards on Automobile Roof — A917

Surfer — A918

2013, Feb. 12 Litho. ***Perf. 14x14¾***

3858 A915 60c multi 1.25 1.25
a. Booklet pane of 4 5.25 —
3859 A916 60c multi 1.25 1.25
a. Booklet pane of 4 5.25 —
3860 A917 60c multi 1.25 1.25
a. Booklet pane of 4 5.25 —
3861 A918 60c multi 1.25 1.25
a. Booklet pane of 4 5.25 —
b. Booklet pane of 4, #3858-3861, #3859 in UL 5.25 —
Complete booklet, #3858a, 3859a, 3860a, 3861a, 3861b 26.50
c. Block of 4, #3851-3861 5.00 5.00
d. Souvenir sheet of 4, #3858-3861, #3858 in UL 5.00 5.00
Nos. 3858-3861 (4) 5.00 5.00

Self-Adhesive

Serpentine Die Cut 11¼ Syncopated

3862 A915 60c multi 1.25 .25
3863 A916 60c multi 1.25 .25
3864 A917 60c multi 1.25 .25
3865 A918 60c multi 1.25 .25
a. Horiz. coil strip of 4, #3862-3865 5.00
b. Booklet pane of 10, 3 each #3862, 3865, 2 each #3863-3864 12.50
Nos. 3862-3865 (4) 5.00 1.00

Complete booklet sold for $12.95.

Dogs — A919

Designs: Nos. 3866, 3871, Miniature schnauzer. Nos. 3867, 3872, Miniature dachshund. Nos. 3868, 3873, Cavalier King Charles spaniel. Nos. 3869, 3874, Pug. Nos. 3870, 3875, Australian terrier.

2013, Feb. 19 ***Perf. 14¾x14***

3866 A919 60c multi 1.25 1.25
3867 A919 60c multi 1.25 1.25
3868 A919 60c multi 1.25 1.25
3869 A919 60c multi 1.25 1.25
3870 A919 60c multi 1.25 1.25
a. Horiz. strip of 5, #3866-3870 6.25 6.25
Nos. 3866-3870 (5) 6.25 6.25

Booklet Stamps
Self-Adhesive

Serpentine Die Cut 11¼ Syncopated

3871 A919 60c multi 1.25 .25
a. Booklet pane of 10 + 5 stickers 12.50
3872 A919 60c multi 1.25 .25
a. Booklet pane of 10 + 5 stickers 12.50
3873 A919 60c multi 1.25 .25
a. Booklet pane of 10 + 5 stickers 12.50
3874 A919 60c multi 1.25 .25
a. Booklet pane of 10 + 5 stickers 12.50
3875 A919 60c multi 1.25 .25
a. Booklet pane of 10 + 5 stickers 12.50
Nos. 3871-3875 (5) 6.25 1.25

Canberra, Cent. — A920

Map and: 60c, National Portrait Gallery. $2.35, Parliament House.

2013, Mar. 5 ***Perf. 14x14¾***

3876 A920 60c multi 1.25 1.25
3877 A920 $2.35 multi 4.75 2.40
a. Booklet pane of 4, 2 each #3876-3877 13.00 —
Complete booklet, #1940c, 2710c, 2869e, 3107c, 3349b, 3877a 27.50

Self-Adhesive

Serpentine Die Cut 11¼ Syncopated

3878 A920 60c multi 1.25 .25
a. Booklet pane of 20 25.00

Complete booklet sold for $12.95. No. 3878 was issued in coils and booklet panes.

Paintings in National Gallery of Australia — A921

Designs: Nos. 3879, 3884, Dandenong Ranges from 'Beleura,' by Eugene von Guérard. Nos. 3880, 3885, In the Flinders - Far North, by Hans Heysen. Nos. 3881, 3886, Land of the Golden Fleece, by Arthur Streetson. Nos. 3882, 3887, Mr. Robinson's House on the Derwent, Van Diemen's Land, by John Glover. Nos. 3883, 3888, Studley Park at Sunrise, by Nicholas Chevalier.

2013, Mar. 19 ***Perf. 14¾x14***

3879 A921 60c multi 1.25 1.25
3880 A921 60c multi 1.25 1.25
3881 A921 60c multi 1.25 1.25
3882 A921 60c multi 1.25 1.25
3883 A921 60c multi 1.25 1.25
a. Horiz. strip of 5, #3879-3883 6.25 6.25
Nos. 3879-3883 (5) 6.25 6.25

Booklet Stamps
Self-Adhesive

Serpentine Die Cut 11¼ Syncopated

3884 A921 60c multi 1.25 .25
3885 A921 60c multi 1.25 .25
3886 A921 60c multi 1.25 .25
3887 A921 60c multi 1.25 .25
3888 A921 60c multi 1.25 .25
a. Booklet pane of 10, 2 each #3884-3888 12.50
Nos. 3884-3888 (5) 6.25 1.25

Baby Animals — A922

Designs: $1.70, Kookaburra. $1.75, Wombat. $2.60, Echidna. $4.65, Platypus. $6.45, Possum.

2013, Apr. 2 ***Perf. 14¾x14***

3889 A922 $1.70 multi 3.50 3.50
3890 A922 $1.75 multi 3.75 3.75
3891 A922 $2.60 multi 5.50 5.50
3892 A922 $4.65 multi 9.75 7.50
3893 A922 $6.45 multi 13.50 10.00
Nos. 3889-3893 (5) 36.00 30.25

Booklet Stamps
Self-Adhesive

Serpentine Die Cut 11¼ Syncopated

3894 A922 $1.70 multi 3.50 1.75
a. Booklet pane of 5 17.50
3895 A922 $1.75 multi 3.75 1.90
a. Booklet pane of 5 19.00
3896 A922 $2.60 multi 5.50 2.75
a. Booklet pane of 5 27.50
Nos. 3894-3896 (3) 12.75 6.40

With Personalized Photo at Right Like Type A692a

Serpentine Die Cut 11½x11¼ Syncopated

3898 A922 $1.75 multi 5.00 5.00
3899 A922 $2.60 multi 6.75 6.75

Nos, 3898-3899 each were printed in sheets of 20 and have personalized pictures and a straight edge at right and lack separations between the stamp and the personalized photo. Sheets of 20 of No. 3898 sold for $48, No. 3899, $65.

Coach — A923

Queen Elizabeth II — A924

2013, Apr. 9 Litho. ***Perf. 14¾x14***

3900 A923 60c multi 1.25 .95
a. Booklet pane of 1 1.25 —
3901 A924 $2.60 multi 5.50 5.50
a. Souvenir sheet of 2, #3900-3901 6.75 6.75
b. Booklet pane of 1 5.50 —
c. Booklet pane of 3 16.50 —
Complete booklet, #3901b, 2 each #3900a, 3901c, + 50c coin 41.00

Complete booklet sold for $19.95.

Booklet Stamp
Self-Adhesive

Serpentine Die Cut 11¼ Syncopated

3902 A924 $2.60 multi 5.50 2.75
a. Booklet pane of 5 27.50

Litho. & Embossed

Perf. 14¾x14

3903 A923 60c multi 1.40 1.40

Coronation of Queen Elizabeth II, 60th anniv. Examples of No. 3901a with an overprint for the Australia 2013 World Stamp Expo were made given to the show organizers and sold only by them. No. 3903 was printed in sheets of 10 that sold for $6.45.

Botanical Gardens — A925

Designs: Nos. 3904, 3909, Royal Tasmanian Botanical Gardens, Hobart. Nos. 3905, 3910, Australian National Botanic Gardens, Canberra. Nos. 3906, 3911, Blue Mountains Botanic Garden, Mount Tomah, New South Wales. Nos. 3907, 3912, Darwin Botanic Gardens, Darwin, Northern Territory. No. 3908, 3913, Royal Botanic Gardens, Cranbourne, Victoria.

2013, Apr. 23 Litho. ***Perf. 14x14¾***

3904 A925 60c multi 1.25 1.25
a. Booklet pane of 4 + 2 labels 5.50 —
3905 A925 60c multi 1.25 1.25
a. Booklet pane of 4 + 2 labels 5.50 —
3906 A925 60c multi 1.25 1.25
a. Booklet pane of 4 + 2 labels 5.50 —
3907 A925 60c multi 1.25 1.25
a. Booklet pane of 4 + 2 labels 5.50 —
3908 A925 60c multi 1.25 1.25
a. Booklet pane of 4 + 2 labels 5.50 —
Complete booklet, #3904a, 3905a, 3906a, 3907a, 3908a 27.50
b. Horiz. strip of 5, #3904-3908 6.25 6.25
Nos. 3904-3908 (5) 6.25 6.25

Coil Stamps
Self-Adhesive

Serpentine Die Cut 11¼ Syncopated

3909 A925 60c multi 1.25 .25
3910 A925 60c multi 1.25 .25
3911 A925 60c multi 1.25 .25
3912 A925 60c multi 1.25 .25
3913 A925 60c multi 1.25 .25
a. Horiz. strip of 5, #3909-3913 6.25
Nos. 3909-3913 (5) 6.25 1.25

Complete booklet sold for $12.95. Examples of complete booklets with overprints for the Australia 2013 World Stamp Expo were made given to the show organizers and sold only by them.

Battle of Beersheba, 96th Anniv. — A926

Designs: 60c, Statue of Australian Light Horseman, by Peter Corlett, Beersheva, Israel. $2.60, Australian Light Horsemen, photograph of battle re-enactment.

2013, May 10 ***Perf. 13x13½***

3914 A926 60c multi 1.25 .95
3915 A926 $2.60 multi 5.00 3.75

See Israel Nos. 1975-1976.

Black Caviar, Undefeated Racehorse — A927

2013, May 10 ***Perf. 14¾x14***

3916 A927 60c multi 1.25 1.25

Booklet Stamp
Self-Adhesive

Serpentine Die Cut 11¼ Syncopated

3917 A927 60c multi 1.25 .25
a. Booklet pane of 10 12.50

Stamps like No. 3916 but with a white frame were printed in limited-quantity sheets of 10 that were sold in special packages only at the Australia 2013 World Stamp Expo.

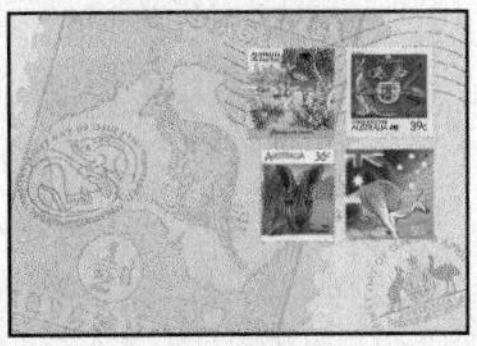

Stamps Depicting Kangaroos — A928

2013, May 10 Litho. ***Imperf.***

3918 A928 $1.62 Booklet pane 3.50 —
Complete booklet, #1003b, 1284b, 3534d, 3918 25.00

No. 3918 contains imperforate examples of Nos. 992a, 1030c, 1063B and 2121, but these stamps were not valid for postage individually as cutouts from the entire booklet pane. Complete booklet sold for $12.95, and also contains a perforated booklet pane containing lithographed reproductions of Nos. 166 and 322 that is invalid for postage.

Kangaroo and Map Stamps, Cent. — A929

2013, May 10 Litho. ***Perf. 14¼x14***

3919 A929 $10 red 19.00 9.50
a. Souvenir sheet of 1 19.00 9.50

A booklet containing an imperforate example of No. 3919 sold for $24.95.

First Commonwealth of Australia Banknotes, Cent. — A930

Designs: 60c, Scene from ceremony for numbering first banknote. $2.60, Arms of Australia.

2013, May 11 Litho. *Perf. 14x13½*

3920 A930 60c multi 1.25 .95
3921 A930 $2.60 multi 5.00 3.75
a. Souvenir sheet of 2, #3920-3921 6.25 4.75

Examples of No. 3921a overprinted in the margin with the emblem of the 2013 Melbourne World Stamp Expo were sold by the exhibitions organizers for $15.

Pardalotes — A931

Designs: 60c, Forty-spotted pardalote. $1.20, Spotted pardalotes. $1.80, Red-browed pardalote. $3, Striated pardalote.

2013, May 11 Litho. *Perf. 14x14¾*

3922 A931 60c multi 1.25 1.25
3923 A931 $1.20 multi 2.25 2.25
3924 A931 $1.80 multi 3.50 2.60
3925 A931 $3 multi 5.75 4.50
a. Booklet pane of 4, #3922-3925 13.00 —
Complete booklet, #3151c, 3376b, 3665b, 3925a 48.50
Nos. 3922-3925 (4) 12.75 10.60

Coil Stamp
Self-Adhesive

Serpentine Die Cut 11¼ Syncopated

3926 A931 60c multi 1.25 .25

Booklet Stamp

3927 A931 $1.20 multi 2.25 .50
a. Booklet pane of 5 11.50

Complete booklet sold for $24.95.

State Government Houses — A932

Government House of: Nos. 3928, 3932, South Australia. Nos. 3929, 3933, Western Australia. Nos. 3930, 3934, New South Wales. Nos. 3931, 3935, Tasmania.

2013, June 11 Litho. *Perf. 14x14¾*

3928 A932 60c multi 1.25 1.25
3929 A932 60c multi 1.25 1.25
3930 A932 60c multi 1.25 1.25
3931 A932 60c multi 1.25 1.25
a. Block of 4, #3928-3931 5.00 5.00
Nos. 3928-3931 (4) 5.00 5.00

Self-Adhesive

Serpentine Die Cut 11¼ Syncopated

3932 A932 60c multi 1.25 .25
3933 A932 60c multi 1.25 .25
3934 A932 60c multi 1.25 .25
3935 A932 60c multi 1.25 .25
a. Horiz. coil strip of 4, #3932-3935 5.00
b. Booklet pane of 20, 5 each #3932-3935 25.00
Nos. 3932-3935 (4) 5.00 1.00

Road Trips — A933

Designs: Nos. 3936, 3942, Utility vehicle in Sydney. Nos. 3937, 3941, Station wagon in Melbourne. Nos, 3938, 3945, Car on roller coaster tracks, Gold Coast. Nos. 3939, 3943, Utility vehicle and camper in Adelaide. Nos. 3940, 3944, Car and camper in Canberra.

2013, July 2 Litho. *Perf. 14¼*

3936 A933 60c multi 1.10 1.10
3937 A933 60c multi 1.10 1.10
3938 A933 60c multi 1.10 1.10
3939 A933 60c multi 1.10 1.10
3940 A933 60c multi 1.10 1.10
a. Souvenir sheet of 5, #3936-3940 5.50 5.50
Nos. 3936-3940 (5) 5.50 5.50

Booklet Stamps
Self-Adhesive

Serpentine Die Cut 11¼ Syncopated

3941 A933 60c multi 1.10 .25
3942 A933 60c multi 1.10 .25
a. Booklet pane of 10, 5 each #3941-3942 11.00
3943 A933 60c multi 1.10 .25
3944 A933 60c multi 1.10 .25
3945 A933 60c multi 1.10 .25
a. Booklet pane of 20, 7 each #3943, 3945, 6 #3944 22.00
Nos. 3941-3945 (5) 5.50 1.25

Aboriginal Leaders — A934

Designs: Nos. 3946, 3951, Shirley Smith (1921-98), justice and welfare advocate. Nos. 3947, 3952, Neville Bonner (1922-99), first Aboriginal member of Australian Parliament. Nos. 3948, 3953, Oodgeroo Noonuccal (1920-93), poet. Nos. 3949, 3954, Eddie "Koiki" Mabo (1936-92), plaintiff in historic Aboriginal land rights lawsuit. Nos. 3950, 3955, Charles Perkins (1936-2000), Secretary of the Department of Aboriginal Affairs.

2013, July 9 Litho. *Perf. 14¾x14*

3946 A934 60c multi 1.10 1.10
a. Booklet pane of 4 4.75 —
3947 A934 60c multi 1.10 1.10
a. Booklet pane of 4 4.75 —
3948 A934 60c multi 1.10 1.10
a. Booklet pane of 4 4.75 —
3949 A934 60c multi 1.10 1.10
a. Booklet pane of 4 4.75 —
3950 A934 60c multi 1.10 1.10
a. Booklet pane of 4 4.75 —
Complete booklet, #3946a, 3947a, 3948a, 3949a, 3950a 24.00
b. Horiz. strip of 5, #3946-3950 5.50 5.50
Nos. 3946-3950 (5) 5.50 5.50

Coil Stamps
Self-Adhesive

Serpentine Die Cut 11¼ Syncopated

3951 A934 60c multi 1.10 .25
3952 A934 60c multi 1.10 .25
3953 A934 60c multi 1.10 .25
3954 A934 60c multi 1.10 .25
3955 A934 60c multi 1.10 .25
a. Vert. coil strip of 5, #3951-3955 5.50
Nos. 3951-3955 (5) 5.50 1.25

Complete booklet sold for $12.95.

Birth of Prince George of Cambridge — A935

2013, July 22 Litho. *Perf. 14¼*

3956 A935 60c multi 1.10 1.10

Booklet Stamp
Self-Adhesive

Serpentine Die Cut 11¼ Syncopated

3957 A935 60c multi 1.10 .25
a. Booklet pane of 10 11.00

Headline News — A936

News stories of: Nos. 3958, 3962, August 15, 1945 (end of World War II). Nos. 3959, 3963, July 21, 1969 (first man on the Moon). Nos. 3960, 3964, December 25, 1974 (destruction of Darwin by Cyclone Tracy). Nos. 3961, 3965, September 27, 1983 (victory of Australia in America's Cup yacht races).

2013, July 23 Litho. *Perf. 14¾x14*

3958 A936 60c multi 1.10 1.10
3959 A936 60c multi 1.10 1.10
3960 A936 60c multi 1.10 1.10
3961 A936 60c multi 1.10 1.10
a. Block of 4, #3958-3961 4.40 4.40
b. Souvenir sheet of 4, #3958-3961 4.40 4.40
Nos. 3958-3961 (4) 4.40 4.40

Self-Adhesive

Serpentine Die Cut 11¼ Syncopated

3962 A936 60c multi 1.10 .25
3963 A936 60c multi 1.10 .25
3964 A936 60c multi 1.10 .25
3965 A936 60c multi 1.10 .25
a. Vert. coil strip of 4, #3962-3965 4.40
b. Booklet pane of 20, 5 each #3962-3965 22.00
Nos. 3962-3965 (4) 4.40 1.00

Carnivorous Plants — A937

Designs: Nos. 3966, 3970, Cephalotus follicularis and ants. Nos. 3967, 3971, Drosera rupicola and fly. Nos. 3968, 3972, Drosera lowriei and butterfly. Nos. 3969, 3973, Nepenthes rowanae and frog.

2013, Aug. 13 Litho. *Perf. 14¾x14*

3966 A937 60c multi 1.10 1.10
3967 A937 60c multi 1.10 1.10
3968 A937 60c multi 1.10 1.10
3969 A937 60c multi 1.10 1.10
a. Block of 4, #3966-3969 4.40 4.40
Nos. 3966-3969 (4) 4.40 4.40

Booklet Stamps
Self-Adhesive

Serpentine Die Cut 11¼ Syncopated

3970 A937 60c multi 1.10 .25
3971 A937 60c multi 1.10 .25
3972 A937 60c multi 1.10 .25
3973 A937 60c multi 1.10 .25
a. Booklet pane of 10, 3 each #3970, 3972, 2 each #3971, 3973 11.00
Nos. 3970-3973 (4) 4.40 1.00

Coral Reefs A938

Designs: Nos. 3974, 3979, Underwater view of Ningaloo Reef, Western Australia. Nos. 3975, 3978, Underwater view of Great Barrier Reef, Queensland. Nos. 3976, 3981, Aerial veiw of Ningaloo Reef. Nos. 3977, 3980, Aerial view of Great Barrier Reef.

2013, Aug. 20 Litho. *Perf. 14½x14*

3974 A938 60c multi 1.10 1.10
a. Perf. 13½x14 1.10 1.10
3975 A938 60c multi 1.10 1.10
a. Horiz. pair, #3974-3975 2.20 2.20
b. Perf. 13½x14 1.10 1.10
3976 A938 $1.20 multi 2.25 2.25
a. Perf. 13½x14 2.25 2.25
3977 A938 $1.20 multi 2.25 2.25
a. Horiz. pair, #3976-3977 4.50 4.50
b. Perf. 13½x14 2.25 2.25
c. Souvenir sheet of 4, #3974a, 3975b, 3976a, 3977b 6.75 6.75
Nos. 3974-3977 (4) 6.70 6.70

Booklet Stamps
Self-Adhesive

Serpentine Die Cut 10½ Syncopated

3978 A938 60c multi 1.10 .25
3979 A938 60c multi 1.10 .25
a. Booklet pane of 20, 10 each #3978-3979 22.00
3980 A938 $1.20 multi 2.25 .50
3981 A938 $1.20 multi 2.25 .50
a. Booklet pane of 5, 3 #3980, 2 #3981 11.50
Nos. 3978-3981 (4) 6.70 1.50

Poultry Breeds — A939

Designs: No. 3982, Australian Game hen and rooster. No. 3983, Australian Pit Game hen and chicks. Nos. 3984, 3985, Australorp hens (37x26mm).

2013, Sept. 3 Litho. *Perf. 14x13½*

3982 A939 60c multi 1.10 .85
a. Booklet pane of 4 4.75 —
3983 A939 60c multi 1.10 .85
a. Booklet pane of 4 4.75 —
b. Booklet pane of 4, 2 each #3982-3983 4.75 —

Perf. 14x14¾

3984 A939 60c multi 1.10 1.10
a. Booklet pane of 4 4.75 —
b. Souvenir sheet of 3, #3982-3984 3.30 3.30
Complete booklet, #3982a, 3983a, 3983b, 2 #3984a 24.00
Nos. 3982-3984 (3) 3.30 2.80

Booklet Stamp
Self-Adhesive

Serpentine Die Cut 11¼ Syncopated

3985 A939 60c multi 1.10 .25
a. Booklet pane of 10 11.00

Complete booklet sold for $12.95 and contains two examples of No. 3984a having different margins.

Dinosaurs — A940

Designs: Nos. 3986, 3992, Koolasuchus. Nos. 3987, 3995, Serendipaceratops (26x37mm). No. 3988, Timimus (30x50mm). Nos. 3989, 3993, Diamantinasaurus, horiz. No. 3990, Qantassaurus, horiz. (50x30mm). Nos. 3991, 3994, Australovenator (26x37mm).

2013, Sept. 24 Litho. *Perf. 14½x14*

3986 A940 60c multi 1.25 1.25
a. Booklet pane of 4 5.00 —
b. Perf. 14½ 1.25 1.25

Perf. 14¾x14

3987 A940 60c multi 1.25 1.25
a. Booklet pane of 4 5.00 —
b. Perf. 14½ 1.25 1.25

Perf. 14x14½

3988 A940 60c multi 1.25 1.25
a. Perf. 14x13½ 1.25 1.25
b. Booklet pane of 2 #3988a 2.50 —
c. Perf. 14½ 1.25 1.25

Perf. 14x14½

3989 A940 60c multi 1.25 1.25
a. Booklet pane of 4 5.00 —
b. Perf. 14½ 1.25 1.25

Perf. 14½x14

3990 A940 60c multi 1.25 1.25
a. Perf. 13½x14 1.25 1.25
b. Booklet pane of 2 #3990a 2.50 —
c. Perf. 14½ 1.25 1.25

Perf. 14¾x14

3991 A940 60c multi 1.25 1.25
a. Booklet pane of 4 5.00 —
Complete booklet, #3986a, 3987a, 3988b, 3989a, 3990b, 3991a 25.00
b. Perf. 14½ 1.25 1.25
c. Souvenir sheet of 6, #3986b, 3987b, 3988c, 3989b, 3990c, 3991b 7.50 7.50
Nos. 3986-3991 (6) 7.50 7.50

Booklet Stamps
Self-Adhesive

Serpentine Die Cut 11¼

3992 A940 60c multi 1.25 .25
3993 A940 60c multi 1.25 .25
a. Booklet pane of 10, 5 each #3992-3993 12.50

Serpentine Die Cut 11¼ Syncopated

3994 A940 60c multi 1.25 .25
3995 A940 60c multi 1.25 .25
a. Booklet pane of 20, 10 each #3994-3995 25.00
Nos. 3992-3995 (4) 5.00 1.00

Complete booklet sold for $12.95.

Historic Railroad Stations — A941

Station at: Nos. 3996, 4000, Maryborough, Victoria. Nos. 3997, 4001, Quorn, South Australia. Nos. 3998, 4002, Hay, New South Wales. Nos. 3999, 4003, Normanton, Queensland.

2013, Oct. 8 Litho. *Perf. 14x14¾*

3996 A941 60c multi 1.25 1.25
3997 A941 60c multi 1.25 1.25
3998 A941 60c multi 1.25 1.25
3999 A941 60c multi 1.25 1.25
a. Block of 4, #3996-3999 5.00 5.00
Nos. 3996-3999 (4) 5.00 5.00

Self-Adhesive

Serpentine Die Cut 11¼ Syncopated

4000 A941 60c multi 1.25 .25
4001 A941 60c multi 1.25 .25
4002 A941 60c multi 1.25 .25
4003 A941 60c multi 1.25 .25
a. Horiz. coil strip of 4, #4000-4003 5.00
b. Booklet pane of 10, 3 each #4000-4001, 2 each #4002-4003 12.50
Nos. 4000-4003 (4) 5.00 1.00

Ludwig Leichhardt (1813-48), Explorer of Outback Region — A942

2013, Oct. 15 Litho. ***Perf. 14¼***
4004 A942 60c multi 1.25 .95

See Germany No. 2752.

Early Australian Coinage — A943

Designs: 60c, Holey dollar and dumps. $3, Holey dollars.

2013, Oct. 22 Litho. ***Perf. 14x14¾***
4005 A943 60c multi 1.25 .95
4006 A943 $3 multi 5.75 4.50

Souvenir Sheet

Litho. & Embossed With Foil Application

4007 Sheet of 2 7.00 7.00
a. A943 60c multi 1.25 .95
b. A943 $3 multi 5.75 4.50

Christmas
A944 A945

Designs: Nos. 4008, 4014, Madonna and Child. Nos. 4009, 4015, 4019, Christmas tree. Nos. 4010, 4016, 4020, Gift. 60c, Candle. Nos. 4012, 4017, Bell. Nos. 4013, 4018, Adoration of the Shepherds.

2013, Nov. 1 Litho. ***Perf. 14¾x14***
4008 A944 55c multi 1.10 1.10
4009 A945 55c multi 1.10 1.10
4010 A945 55c multi 1.10 1.10
a. Horiz. pair, #4009-4010 2.20 2.20
4011 A945 60c multi 1.25 .95
4012 A945 $1.70 multi 3.25 1.60
4013 A944 $2.55 multi 4.75 2.40
a. Souvenir sheet of 2, #4008, 4013 6.00 6.00
Nos. 4008-4013 (6) 12.55 8.25

Booklet Stamps Self-Adhesive

Serpentine Die Cut 11¼ Syncopated

4014 A944 55c multi 1.10 .25
a. Booklet pane of 20 + 10 etiquettes 22.00
4015 A945 55c multi 1.10 .25
4016 A945 55c multi 1.10 .25
a. Booklet pane of 20, 10 each #4015-4016, + 10 etiquettes 22.00
4017 A945 $1.70 multi 3.25 1.60
a. Booklet pane of 5 16.50
4018 A944 $2.55 multi 4.75 2.40
a. Booklet pane of 5 24.00

Litho. & Embossed With Foil Application

4019 A945 55c multi 1.10 .25
a. Booklet pane of 10 11.00
4020 A945 55c multi 1.10 .25
a. Booklet pane of 10 11.00
Nos. 4014-4020 (7) 13.50 5.25

Christening of Prince George of Cambridge — A946

Duke and Duchess of Cambridge with Prince George: 60c, White background. $2.60, Yellow background.

2014, Jan. 7 Litho. ***Perf. 14¾x14***
4022 A946 60c multi 1.10 1.10
4023 A946 $2.60 multi 4.75 4.75
a. Souvenir sheet of 2, #4022-4023 6.00 6.00

Booklet Stamps Self-Adhesive

Serpentine Die Cut 11¼ Syncopated

4024 A946 60c multi 1.10 .25
a. Booklet pane of 10 11.00
4025 A946 $2.60 multi 4.75 2.40
a. Booklet pane of 5 24.00

Orchids — A947

Designs: Nos. 4026, 4030, Golden rock orchid. Nos. 4027, 4031, Bee orchid. Nos. 4028, 4032, Orange blossom orchid. Nos. 4029, 4033, Shirt orchid.

2014, Jan. 14 Litho. ***Perf. 14¾x14***
4026 A947 60c multi 1.10 1.10
4027 A947 60c multi 1.10 1.10
4028 A947 60c multi 1.10 1.10
4029 A947 60c multi 1.10 1.10
a. Horiz. strip of 4, #4026-4029 4.40 4.40
Nos. 4026-4029 (4) 4.40 4.40

Booklet Stamps Self-Adhesive

Serpentine Die Cut 11¼ Syncopated

4030 A947 60c multi 1.10 .25
4031 A947 60c multi 1.10 .25
4032 A947 60c multi 1.10 .25
4033 A947 60c multi 1.10 .25
a. Booklet pane of 10, 2 each #4030, 4032, 3 each #4031, 4033 11.00
b. Booklet pane of 20, 5 each #4030-4033 22.00
Nos. 4030-4033 (4) 4.40 1.00

Cooking Celebrities — A948

Designs: Nos. 4034, 4039, Margaret Fulton. Nos. 4035, 4040, Maggie Beer. Nos. 4036, 4041, Stephanie Alexander. Nos. 4037, 4042, Neil Perry. Nos. 4038, 4043, Kylie Kwong.

2014, Jan. 17 Litho. ***Perf. 14¾x14***
4034 A948 60c multi 1.10 1.10
a. Booklet pane of 4 5.25 —
4035 A948 60c multi 1.10 1.10
a. Booklet pane of 4 5.25 —
4036 A948 60c multi 1.10 1.10
a. Booklet pane of 4 5.25 —
4037 A948 60c multi 1.10 1.10
a. Booklet pane of 4 5.25 —
4038 A948 60c multi 1.10 1.10
a. Booklet pane of 4 5.25 —
Complete booklet, #4034a, 4035a, 4036a, 4037a, 4038a 22.00
Nos. 4034-4038 (5) 5.50 5.50

Booklet Stamps Self-Adhesive

Serpentine Die Cut 11¼ Syncopated

4039 A948 60c multi 1.10 .25
a. Booklet pane of 10 11.00
4040 A948 60c multi 1.10 .25
a. Booklet pane of 10 11.00
4041 A948 60c multi 1.10 .25
a. Booklet pane of 10 11.00
4042 A948 60c multi 1.10 .25
a. Booklet pane of 10 11.00
4043 A948 60c multi 1.10 .25
a. Booklet pane of 10 11.00
Nos. 4039-4043 (5) 5.50 1.25

Complete booklet sold for $14.95.

Victory of Australian Cricket Team in 2013-14 Ashes Test Matches A949

Designs: 60c, Ashes urn. $2.60, Australian cricket team.

2014, Jan. 20 Litho. ***Perf. 14¾x14***
4044 A949 60c multi 1.10 .85
4045 A949 $2.60 multi 4.75 4.75
a. Souvenir sheet of 2, #4044-4045 6.00 6.00

Booklet Stamp Self-Adhesive

Serpentine Die Cut 11½x11¼

4046 A949 $2.60 multi 4.75 2.40
a. Booklet pane of 5 24.00

Hearts A950 Rose A951

2014, Feb. 4 Litho. ***Perf. 14¾x14***
4047 A950 60c multi 1.10 1.10
4048 A951 60c multi 1.10 1.10
a. Pair, #4047-4048 2.20 2.20

Booklet Stamps Self-Adhesive

Serpentine Die Cut 11¼ Syncopated

4049 A950 60c multi 1.10 .25
a. Booklet pane of 10 11.00
4050 A951 60c multi 1.10 .25
a. Booklet pane of 20 22.00

With Personalized Photo at Right Like Type A692a

Serpentine Die Cut 11½x11¼ Syncopated

4051 A950 60c multi 2.25 2.25
4052 A951 60c multi 2.25 2.25

Nos, 4051-4052 each were printed in sheets of 20 and have personalized pictures and a straight edge at right and lack separations between the stamp and the personalized photo. Sheets of 20 of each stamp sold for $25.

National and State Floral Emblems — A952

Designs: Nos. 4053, 4060, 4064, Tasmanian blue gum (Tasmania). Nos. 4054, 4061, 4065, Waratah (New South Wales). Nos. 4055, 4062, 4066, Golden wattle (Australia). Nos. 4056, 4063, 4067, Common heath (Victoria). $1.40, Cooktown orchid (Queensland). $2.10, Kangaroo paw (Western Australia). $3.50, Sturt's desert pea (South Australia).

2014, Mar. 24 Litho. ***Perf. 14½x14***
4053 A952 70c multi 1.40 1.40
4054 A952 70c multi 1.40 1.40
4055 A952 70c multi 1.40 1.40
4056 A952 70c multi 1.40 1.40
a. Horiz. strip of 4, #4053-4056 5.60 5.60
4057 A952 $1.40 multi 2.60 1.40
4058 A952 $2.10 multi 4.00 2.00
4059 A952 $3.50 multi 6.50 3.25
Nos. 4053-4059 (7) 18.70 12.25

Coil Stamp Self-Adhesive

Serpentine Die Cut 12¾

4060 A952 70c multi 1.40 .25
4061 A952 70c multi 1.40 .25
4062 A952 70c multi 1.40 .25
4063 A952 70c multi 1.40 .25
a. Vert. strip of 4, #4060-4063 5.60

Booklet Stamps

Serpentine Die Cut 11¼

4064 A952 70c multi 1.40 .25
4065 A952 70c multi 1.40 .25
4066 A952 70c multi 1.40 .25
4067 A952 70c multi 1.40 .25
a. Booklet pane of 10, 3 each #4064-4065, 2 each #4066-4067 14.00
b. Booklet pane of 20, 5 each #4064-4067 28.00
Nos. 4060-4067 (8) 11.20 2.00

Map of Australia on Beach A953 Kangaroo A954

Serpentine Die Cut 11¼ Syncopated

2014, Mar. 24 Litho.

Booklet Stamps Self-Adhesive

4068 A953 (70c) multi 1.40 .25
4069 A954 (70c) multi 1.40 .25
a. Booklet pane of 5, 2#4068, 3 #4069 7.25

No. 4069a was made available to holders of Australia Post My Post Concession Account card and the general public. Pensioners, veterans, the disabled, and others typically on low or fixed incomes, could apply at their local post office to receive a Concession Account card. Those eligible to receive the card were sent a free example of No. 4069a, which was mailed with the card. Card holders, when showing the card at the post office and having the information recorded, could purchase up to ten No. 4069a every year for $3 (60c per stamp, lower than the 70c letter rate instituted on March 31). 10,000 examples of No. 4069a were made available to the public through the philatelic bureau, but these were sold for $3.95 (79c per stamp). There are no differences between the stamps offered to card holders and the general public, aside from the selling price. Nos. 4068 and 4069 were valid only on letters, and could not be used on parcels or international mail.

Queen Elizabeth II, 88th Birthday — A955

Queen Elizabeth II facing: 70c, Left. $2.60, Right.

2014, Apr. 8 Litho. ***Perf. 14¾x14***
4070 A955 70c multi 1.40 1.10
4071 A955 $2.60 multi 5.00 2.50
a. Souvenir sheet of 2, #4070-4071 6.50 3.75

Booklet Stamp Self-Adhesive

Serpentine Die Cut 11¼ Syncopated

4072 A955 $2.60 multi 5.00 2.50
a. Booklet pane of 5 25.00

Map of Australia A956 Balloons and Streamers A957

Baby's Mobile A958 Fireworks A959

Rose A960 Stylized Flowers A961

Champagne Flutes
A962

Wedding Rings and Roses
A963

Wedding Rings — A964

2014, Apr. 15 Litho. *Perf. 14¾x14*

4073 A956 70c blue & multi 1.40 .70
4074 A956 70c red & multi 1.40 .70
a. Horiz. pair, #4073-4074 2.80 1.40
4075 A957 70c multi 1.40 1.40
4076 A958 70c multi 1.40 1.40
4077 A959 70c multi 1.40 1.40
4078 A960 70c multi 1.40 1.40
4079 A961 70c multi 1.40 1.40
4080 A962 70c multi 1.40 1.40
4081 A963 70c multi 1.40 1.40
4082 A964 $1.40 multi 2.60 1.40
Nos. 4073-4082 (10) 15.20 12.60

Booklet Stamps
Self-Adhesive

Serpentine Die Cut 11¼ Syncopated

4083 A957 70c multi 1.40 .25
a. Booklet pane of 10 14.00
4084 A958 70c multi 1.40 .25
a. Booklet pane of 10 14.00
4085 A959 70c multi 1.40 .25
a. Booklet pane of 10 14.00
4086 A960 70c multi 1.40 .25
a. Booklet pane of 10 14.00
4087 A961 70c multi 1.40 .25
a. Booklet pane of 10 14.00
4088 A962 70c multi 1.40 .25
a. Booklet pane of 10 14.00
4089 A963 70c multi 1.40 .25
a. Booklet pane of 10 14.00
4090 A964 $1.40 multi 2.60 1.40
a. Booklet pane of 4 10.50
Complete booklet, 5 #4090a 52.50
Nos. 4083-4090 (8) 12.40 3.15

Complete booklet contains 5 examples of No. 4090a, each with different pane margins.

With Personalized Photo at Right Like Type A692a

Serpentine Die Cut 11½x11¼ Syncopated

4091 A956 70c blue & multi 2.50 2.50
4092 A957 70c multi 2.50 2.50
4093 A958 70c multi 2.50 2.50
4094 A959 70c multi 2.50 2.50
4095 A960 70c multi 2.50 2.50
4096 A961 70c multi 2.50 2.50
4097 A962 70c multi 2.50 2.50
4098 A963 70c multi 2.50 2.50
4099 A964 $1.40 multi 3.75 3.75
Nos. 4091-4099 (9) 23.75 23.75

Nos, 4091-4099 each were printed in sheets of 20 and have personalized pictures and a straight edge at right and lack separations between the stamp and the personalized photo. Sheets of 20 of Nos. 4091-4098 sold for $27 each, No. 4099, $41.

World War I, Cent. — A965

Inscriptions: Nos. 4100, 4105, War Declared! Nos. 4101, 4106, Australians in Action. Nos. 4102, 4107, Troops Depart. Nos. 4103, 4108, Training, Mena Camp (Egypt). Nos. 4104, 4109, Our Boys.

2014, Apr. 22 Litho. *Perf. 14¼*

4100 A965 70c multi 1.40 1.40
4101 A965 70c multi 1.40 1.40
4102 A965 70c multi 1.40 1.40
4103 A965 70c multi 1.40 1.40
4104 A965 70c multi 1.40 1.40
a. Souvenir sheet of 5, #4100-4104 7.00 7.00
Nos. 4100-4104 (5) 7.00 7.00

Booklet Stamps
Self-Adhesive

Serpentine Die Cut 11¼ Syncopated

4105 A965 70c multi 1.40 .25
4106 A965 70c multi 1.40 .25
4107 A965 70c multi 1.40 .25
4108 A965 70c multi 1.40 .25
4109 A965 70c multi 1.40 .25
a. Booklet pane of 10, 2 each #4105-4109 14.00
Nos. 4105-4109 (5) 7.00 1.25

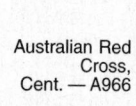

Australian Red Cross, Cent. — A966

2014, May 6 Litho. *Perf. 14x14¾*

4110 A966 70c multi 1.40 1.40

Coil Stamp
Self-Adhesive

Serpentine Die Cut 11¼ Syncopated

4111 A966 70c multi 1.40 .25

Poems by Andrew Barton "Banjo" Paterson (1864-1941)
A967

Designs: Nos. 4112, 4116, Clancy of the Overflow. Nos. 4113, 4117, The Man from Snowy River. Nos. 4114, 4118, Waltzing Matilda. Nos. 4115, 4119, Mulga Bill's Bicycle.

2014, May 13 Litho. *Perf. 14x14¾*

4112 A967 70c multi 1.40 1.40
a. Booklet pane of 4 5.60 —
4113 A967 70c multi 1.40 1.40
a. Booklet pane of 4 5.60 —
4114 A967 70c multi 1.40 1.40
a. Booklet pane of 4 5.60 —
4115 A967 70c multi 1.40 1.40
a. Block of 4, #4112-4115 5.60 5.60
b. Souvenir sheet of 4, #4112-4115 5.60 5.60
c. Booklet pane of 4 #4115 5.60 —
d. Booklet pane of 4, #4112-4115 5.60 —
Complete booklet, #4112a, 4113a, 4114a, 4115c, 2 #4115d 34.00
Nos. 4112-4115 (4) 5.60 5.60

Self-Adhesive

Serpentine Die Cut 11¼ Syncopated

4116 A967 70c multi 1.40 .25
4117 A967 70c multi 1.40 .25
4118 A967 70c multi 1.40 .25
4119 A967 70c multi 1.40 .25
a. Horiz. coil strip of 4, #4116-4119 5.60
b. Booklet pane of 10, 3 each #4116-4117, 2 each #4118-4119 14.00
Nos. 4116-4119 (4) 5.60 1.00

The complete booklet sold for $16.95. In the complete booklet, one of the two examples of No. 4115d has a booklet pane margin similar to No. 4115b.

G20 Summit, Brisbane — A968

2014, June 3 Litho. *Perf. 14¾x14*

4120 A968 70c multi 1.40 1.10

King George V Typographed Stamps, Cent. — A969

2014, June 17 Litho. *Perf. 14½x14*

4121 A969 70c red 1.40 1.10
a. Booklet pane of 4 5.60 —
4122 A969 70c red brown 1.40 1.10
a. Booklet pane of 4 5.60 —
4123 A969 70c purple 1.40 1.10
a. Booklet pane of 4 5.60 —
4124 A969 70c green 1.40 1.10
a. Booklet pane of 4 5.60 —
b. Booklet pane of 4, #4121-4124 5.60 —
c. Booklet pane of 4, #4121-4124, imperf. 5.60 —
Complete booklet, #4121a, 4122a, 4123a, 4124a, 4124b, 4124c 34.00
d. Block or strip of 4, #4121-4124 5.60 4.40
e. Souvenir sheet of 4, #4121-4124 5.60 4.40
f. Sheet of 10, 4 #4121, 2 each #4122-4124 14.00 11.00

Typo.

4125 A969 70c red 1.40 1.10
4126 A969 70c purple 1.40 1.10
4127 A969 70c green 1.40 1.10
4128 A969 70c red brown 1.40 1.10
a. Horiz. strip of 4, #4125-4128 5.60 4.40
b. Sheet of 10, 4 #4125, 2 each #4126-4128 14.00 11.00
Nos. 4121-4128 (8) 11.20 8.80

Complete booklet sold for $16.95. Nos. 4124f and 4128b were sold together for $14.45.

First Air Mail in Australia, Cent. — A970

Designs: 70c, Spectators watching airplane in flight. $2.60, Maurice Guillaux piloting Bleriot XI airplane.

2014, July 1 Litho. *Perf. 14¼*

4129 A970 70c multi 1.40 1.10
a. Booklet pane of 4 5.75 —
4130 A970 $2.60 multi 5.00 2.50
a. Booklet pane of 4 20.50 —
b. Booklet pane of 2, #4129-4130 6.50 —
Complete booklet, #4130a, 4130b, 2 #4129a 38.50
c. Souvenir sheet of 2, #4129-4130 6.50 —

Complete booklet sold for $19.95. The two examples of No. 4129a in the booklet have different pane margins.

Visit of Duke and Duchess of Cambridge and Prince George — A971

Designs: 70c, Duke and Duchess, Sydney Harbour Bridge. $2.60, Duke and Duchess, Prince George, and bilby.

2014, July 8 Litho. *Perf. 14¼*

4131 A971 70c multi 1.40 1.40
4132 A971 $2.60 multi 5.00 5.00
a. Souvenir sheet of 2, #4131-4132 6.50 6.50

Booklet Stamps
Self-Adhesive

Serpentine Die Cut 11¼ Syncopated

4133 A971 70c multi 1.40 .25
a. Booklet pane of 10 14.00
4134 A971 $2.60 multi 5.00 2.50
a. Booklet pane of 5 25.00

Equestrian Events — A972

Designs: Nos. 4135, 4140, Pony Club. Nos. 4136, 4141, Polocrosse. Nos. 4137, 4142, Show jumping. Nos. 4138, 4143, Cross-country. Nos. 4139, 4144, Dressage.

2014, July 15 Litho. *Perf. 14¾x14*

4135 A972 70c multi 1.40 1.40
4136 A972 70c multi 1.40 1.40
4137 A972 70c multi 1.40 1.40
4138 A972 70c multi 1.40 1.40
4139 A972 70c multi 1.40 1.40
Nos. 4135-4139 (5) 7.00 7.00

Self-Adhesive

Serpentine Die Cut 11¼ Syncopated

4140 A972 70c multi 1.40 .25
a. Booklet pane of 10 14.00
4141 A972 70c multi 1.40 .25
a. Booklet pane of 10 14.00
4142 A972 70c multi 1.40 .25
a. Booklet pane of 10 14.00
4143 A972 70c multi 1.40 .25
a. Booklet pane of 10 14.00
4144 A972 70c multi 1.40 .25
a. Booklet pane of 10 14.00
b. Vert. coil strip of 5, #4140-4144 7.00
Nos. 4140-4144 (5) 7.00 1.25

Norfolk Island Pine — A973

Norfolk Island Pine and: 70c, Cottesloe Beach, Western Australia. $1.40, Old Military Barracks, Kingston, Norfolk Island.

2014, July 22 Litho. *Perf. 14x14¾*

4145 A973 70c multi 1.40 1.10
4146 A973 $1.40 multi 2.60 2.00

See Norfolk Island Nos. 1090-1091.

Australian Military Centenaries
A974

Designs: Nos. 4147, 4149, Military aviation, cent. Nos. 4148, 4150, Submarines, cent.

2014, Aug. 5 Litho. *Perf. 14x14¾*

4147 A974 70c multi 1.40 1.40
4148 A974 70c multi 1.40 1.40
a. Vert. pair, #4147-4148 2.80 2.80
b. Souvenir sheet of 2, #4147-4148 2.80 2.80

Booklet Stamps
Self-Adhesive

Serpentine Die Cut 11¼ Syncopated

4149 A974 70c multi 1.40 .25
4150 A974 70c multi 1.40 .25
a. Booklet pane of 20, 10 each #4149-4150 28.00

Mid-20th Century Advertisements — A975

Advertisement for: Nos. 4151, 4156, Phillip Island Tourism. Nos. 4152, 4157, Harper's Empire Self-Raising Flour. Nos. 4153, 4158, Trans-Australian Airways. Nos. 4154, 4159, Jacko Shoe Polish. Nos. 4155, 4160, Swallow & Ariell's Teddy Bear Biscuits.

2014, Aug. 19 Litho. *Perf. 14¾x14*

4151 A975 70c multi 1.40 1.40
4152 A975 70c multi 1.40 1.40
4153 A975 70c multi 1.40 1.40
4154 A975 70c multi 1.40 1.40
4155 A975 70c multi 1.40 1.40
a. Horiz. strip of 5, #4151-4155 7.00 7.00
b. Souvenir sheet of 5, #4151-4155 7.00 7.00
Nos. 4151-4155 (5) 7.00 7.00

Coil Stamps
Self-Adhesive

Serpentine Die Cut 11¼ Syncopated

4156 A975 70c multi 1.40 .25
4157 A975 70c multi 1.40 .25
4158 A975 70c multi 1.40 .25
4159 A975 70c multi 1.40 .25
4160 A975 70c multi 1.40 .25
a. Vert. strip of 5, #4156-4160 7.00
Nos. 4156-4160 (5) 7.00 1.25

Aurora Australis (Southern Lights) — A976

Various photographs of auroras with denomination at: Nos. 4161, 4163, 4165, LL. Nos. 4162, 4164, 4166, LR.

2014, Aug. 26 Litho. *Perf. 14x14¾*

4161 A976 70c multi 1.40 1.40
4162 A976 70c multi 1.40 1.40
a. Horiz. pair, #4161-4162 2.80 2.80
4163 A976 $1.40 multi 2.60 2.00
4164 A976 $1.40 multi 2.60 2.00
a. Horiz. pair, #4163-4164 5.20 4.00
b. Souvenir sheet of 4, #4161-4164 8.00 8.00
Nos. 4161-4164 (4) 8.00 6.80

Booklet Stamps
Self-Adhesive

4165 A976 70c multi 1.40 .25
4166 A976 70c multi 1.40 .25
a. Booklet pane of 10, 5 each #4165-4166 14.00

On. No. 4164b, Nos. 4162a and 4164a are tete-beche in relationship to each other.

Gardens — A977

Designs: Nos. 4167, 4172, Cruden Farm, Victoria. Nos. 4168, 4173, Mendel Gardens, Western Australia. Nos. 4169, 4176, Niwajiri, South Australia. Nos. 4170, 4174, Walcott Gardens, Australian Capital Territory. Nos. 4171, 4175, Wychwood, Tasmania.

2014, Sept. 2 Litho. *Perf. 14x14¾*

4167	A977	70c multi	1.40	1.40
4168	A977	70c multi	1.40	1.40
4169	A977	70c multi	1.40	1.40
4170	A977	70c multi	1.40	1.40
4171	A977	70c multi	1.40	1.40
a.		Horiz. strip of 5, #4167-4171	7.00	7.00
		Nos. 4167-4171 (5)	7.00	7.00

Booklet Stamps
Self-Adhesive
Serpentine Die Cut 11¼ Syncopated

4172	A977	70c multi	1.40	.25
4173	A977	70c multi	1.40	.25
4174	A977	70c multi	1.40	.25
4175	A977	70c multi	1.40	.25
4176	A977	70c multi	1.40	.25
a.		Booklet pane of 20, 4 each #4172-4176	28.00	
		Nos. 4172-4176 (5)	7.00	1.25

Venomous Creatures — A978

Designs: Nos. 4177, 4186, European wasp. Nos. 4178, 4185, Lionfish. Nos. 4179, 4183, Bull ant. Nos. 4180, 4187, Tiger snake. Nos. 4181, 4188, Stonefish. Nos. 4182, 4184, Stingray.

2014, Sept. 23 Litho. *Perf. 14x14¾*

4177	A978	70c multi	1.25	1.25
4178	A978	70c multi	1.25	1.25
4179	A978	70c multi	1.25	1.25
4180	A978	70c multi	1.25	1.25
a.		Souvenir sheet of 6, 2 each #4177, 4179, 4180, + 6 labels	7.75	7.75
4181	A978	70c multi	1.25	1.25
4182	A978	70c multi	1.25	1.25
a.		Souvenir sheet of 6, #4177-4182	7.50	7.50
b.		Souvenir sheet of 6, 2 each #4176, 4181, 4182, + 6 labels	7.75	7.75
		Nos. 4177-4182 (6)	7.50	7.50

Booklet Stamps
Self-Adhesive
Serpentine Die Cut 11¼ Syncopated

4183	A978	70c multi	1.25	.25
4184	A978	70c multi	1.25	.25
4185	A978	70c multi	1.25	.25
4186	A978	70c multi	1.25	.25
4187	A978	70c multi	1.25	.25
4188	A978	70c multi	1.25	.25
a.		Booklet pane of 10, #4185, 4188, 2 each #4183-4184, 4186-4187	12.50	
b.		Booklet pane of 20, 3 each #4183, 4185, 4187, 4188, 4 each #4184, 4186	25.00	
		Nos. 4183-4188 (6)	7.50	1.50

A souvenir sheet of six containing one each of Nos. 4177-4182 + six labels was sold with a die and game pieces that sold for $9.95. Nos. 4180a and 4182b sold together as a set in a folder for $8.85.

National Parks — A979

Designs: $2.75, Alpine National Park, Victoria. $5.35, Blue Mountains National Park, New South Wales. $7.40, Judbarra/Gregroy National Park, Northern Territory.

2014, Oct. 1 Litho. *Perf. 14¾x14*

4189	A979	$2.75 multi	5.00	2.50
4190	A979	$5.35 multi	9.50	4.75
4191	A979	$7.40 multi	13.00	6.50
		Nos. 4189-4191 (3)	27.50	13.75

Booklet Stamp
Self-Adhesive
Serpentine Die Cut 11¼ Syncopated

4192	A979	$2.75 multi	5.00	2.50
a.		Booklet pane of 5	25.00	

National Parks Type of 2014 With Personalized Photo at Right Like Type A692a
Serpentine Die Cut 11½x11¼ Syncopated

2014, Oct. 1 Litho.

Self-Adhesive

4193	A979	$2.75 multi	6.00	6.00

No. 4193 was printed in sheets of 20 and has personalized picture and a straight edge at right and lack separations between the stamp and personalized photo. Sheets of 20 of No. 4193 sold for $68.

Horse Racing Tracks — A980

Designs: Nos. 4194, 4198, Eagle Farm, Queensland. Nos. 4195, 4199, Royal Randwick, New South Wales. Nos. 4196, 4200, Morphettville, South Australia. Nos. 4197, 4201, Flemington, Victoria.

2014, Oct. 7 Litho. *Perf. 14x14¾*

4194	A980	70c multi	1.25	1.25
4195	A980	70c multi	1.25	1.25
4196	A980	70c multi	1.25	1.25
4197	A980	70c multi	1.25	1.25
a.		Horiz. strip of 4, #4194-4197	5.00	5.00
		Nos. 4194-4197 (4)	5.00	5.00

Self-Adhesive
Serpentine Die Cut 11¼ Syncopated

4198	A980	70c multi	1.25	.25
4199	A980	70c multi	1.25	.25
4200	A980	70c multi	1.25	.25
4201	A980	70c multi	1.25	.25
a.		Horiz. coil strip of 4, #4198-4201	5.00	
b.		Booklet pane of 10, 3 each #4198-4199, 2 each #4200-4201	12.50	
		Nos. 4198-4201 (4)	5.00	1.00

Australian Defense Force, Cent. — A981

Poppies and: Nos. 4202, 4206, Cap of Royal Australian Navy. Nos. 4203, 4209, Hat of Australian Army. Nos. 4204, 4207, Cap of Royal Australian Air Force. Nos. 4205, 4208, Australian Defense Force badge.

2014, Oct. 21 Litho. *Perf. 14¼*

4202	A981	70c multi	1.25	1.25
4203	A981	70c multi	1.25	1.25
4204	A981	70c multi	1.25	1.25
4205	A981	70c multi	1.25	1.25
a.		Souvenir sheet of 4, #4202-4205	5.00	5.00
		Nos. 4202-4205 (4)	5.00	5.00

Booklet Stamps
Self-Adhesive
Serpentine Die Cut 11¼ Syncopated

4206	A981	70c multi	1.25	.25
4207	A981	70c multi	1.25	.25
4208	A981	70c multi	1.25	.25
4209	A981	70c multi	1.25	.25
a.		Booklet pane of 10, 2 each #4206, 4207, 4209, 4 #4208	12.50	

Christmas
A982 A983

Designs: Nos. 4210, 4216, Madonna and Child. Nos. 4211, 4217, 4221, Snowflake, ornament, Christmas tree, reindeer. Nos. 4212, 4218, 4222, Star, ornament, gift. 70c, Snowflake, ornament, holly leaves, dove, star. Nos. 4214, 4219, Snowflake and bells. Nos. 4215, 4220, Angels.

2014, Oct. 31 Litho. *Perf. 14¾x14*

4210	A982	65c multi	1.10	1.10
4211	A983	65c green	1.10	1.10
4212	A983	65c red	1.10	1.10
a.		Horiz. pair, #4211-4212	2.20	2.20
4213	A983	70c blue green	1.25	.95
4214	A983	$1.70 pur & dk bl	3.00	1.50
4215	A982	$2.55 multi	4.50	2.25
a.		Souvenir sheet of 2, #4210, 4215	5.75	5.75
		Nos. 4210-4215 (6)	12.05	8.00

Self-Adhesive
Booklet Stamps
Serpentine Die Cut 11¼ Syncopated

4216	A982	65c multi	1.10	.25
a.		Booklet pane of 20 + 20 etiquettes	22.00	
4217	A983	65c green	1.10	.25
4218	A983	65c red	1.10	.25
a.		Booklet pane of 20, 10 each #4217-4218, + 20 etiquettes	22.00	
4219	A983	$1.70 pur & dk bl	3.00	1.50
a.		Booklet pane of 5	15.00	
4220	A982	$2.55 multi	4.50	2.25
a.		Booklet pane of 5	22.50	

Litho. With Foil Application

4221	A983	65c green	1.10	.25
a.		Booklet pane of 10	11.00	
4222	A983	65c red	1.10	.25
a.		Booklet pane of 10	11.00	
		Nos. 4216-4222 (7)	13.00	5.00

Marsupials — A984

Designs: Nos. 4225, 4234, Echidna. Nos. 4226, 4233, Common wombat. Nos. 4227, 4231, Eastern gray kangaroo. Nos. 4228, 4232, Koala. No. 4229, Numbat. No. 4230, Tasmanian devil.

2015, Jan. 13 Litho. *Perf. 14x14¾*

4225	A984	70c multi	1.10	1.10
4226	A984	70c multi	1.10	1.10
4227	A984	70c multi	1.10	1.10
4228	A984	70c multi	1.10	1.10
a.		Block of 4, #4225-4228	4.40	4.40
4229	A984	$1.40 multi	2.25	1.75
4230	A984	$1.40 multi	2.25	1.75
a.		Vert. pair, #4229-4230	4.50	3.50
b.		Souvenir sheet of 6, #4225-4230	9.00	9.00
		Nos. 4225-4230 (6)	8.90	7.90

Booklet Stamps
Self-Adhesive
Serpentine Die Cut 11¼ Syncopated

4231	A984	70c multi	1.10	.25
4232	A984	70c multi	1.10	.25
4233	A984	70c multi	1.10	.25
4234	A984	70c multi	1.10	.25
a.		Booklet pane of 10, 3 each #4231-4232, 2 each #4233-4234	11.00	
b.		Booklet pane of 20, 5 each #4231-4234	22.00	
		Nos. 4231-4234 (4)	4.40	1.00

Victoria Cross Recipients — A985

Designs: Nos. 4235, 4240, Ben Roberts-Smith. Nos. 4236, 4241, Cameron Baird (1981-2013). Nos. 4237, 4242, Mark Donaldson. Nos. 4238, 4243, Dan Keighran. Nos. 4239, 4244, Keith Payne.

2015, Jan. 22 Litho. *Perf. 14¾x14*

4235	A985	70c multi	1.10	1.10
4236	A985	70c multi	1.10	1.10
4237	A985	70c multi	1.10	1.10
4238	A985	70c multi	1.10	1.10
4239	A985	70c multi	1.10	1.10
a.		Souvenir sheet of 5, #4235-4239	5.50	5.50
		Nos. 4235-4239 (5)	5.50	5.50

Booklet Stamps
Self-Adhesive
Serpentine Die Cut 11¼ Syncopated

4240	A985	70c multi	1.10	.25
a.		Booklet pane of 10	11.00	
4241	A985	70c multi	1.10	.25
a.		Booklet pane of 10	11.00	
4242	A985	70c multi	1.10	.25
a.		Booklet pane of 10	11.00	
4243	A985	70c multi	1.10	.25
a.		Booklet pane of 10	11.00	
4244	A985	70c multi	1.10	.25
a.		Booklet pane of 10	11.00	
		Nos. 4240-4244 (5)	5.50	1.25

Souvenir Sheet

Victoria Cross A986

2015, Jan. 22 Litho. *Perf. 14x14¾*

4245	A986	Sheet of 2	9.00	9.00
a.		70c olive green	1.10	.85
b.		$5 violet	7.75	5.75

Heart-Shaped Items — A987

Designs: Nos. 4246, 4251, Kite. Nos. 4247, 4252, Airplane contrail. Nos. 4248, 4250, Hot-air balloon. Nos. 4249, 4253, Cloud.

2015, Feb. 3 Litho. *Perf. 14¾x14*

4246	A987	70c multi	1.10	1.10
4247	A987	70c multi	1.10	1.10
4248	A987	70c multi	1.10	1.10
4249	A987	70c multi	1.10	1.10
a.		Horiz. strip of 4, #4246-4249	4.40	4.40
		Nos. 4246-4249 (4)	4.40	4.40

Booklet Stamps
Self-Adhesive
Serpentine Die Cut 11¼ Syncopated

4250	A987	70c multi	1.10	.25
4251	A987	70c multi	1.10	.25
4252	A987	70c multi	1.10	.25
4253	A987	70c multi	1.10	.25
a.		Booklet pane of 20, 7 each #4250-4251, 3 each #4252-4253	22.00	
b.		Booklet pane of 10, 5 each #4252-4253	11.00	
		Nos. 4250-4253 (4)	4.40	1.00

Clipper Ships — A988

Designs: No. 4254, Frances Henty. No. 4255, Phoenician. No. 4256, Arabian. No. 4257, Monkchester.

2015, Feb. 17 Litho. *Perf. 14x14¾*

4254	A988	70c multi	1.10	.85
4255	A988	70c multi	1.10	.85
a.		Horiz. pair, #4254-4255	2.20	1.70
4256	A988	$1.40 multi	2.25	1.75
4257	A988	$1.40 multi	2.25	1.75
a.		Horiz. pair, #4256-4257	4.50	3.50
		Nos. 4254-4257 (4)	6.70	5.20

Tourist Attractions — A989

Designs: Nos. 4258, 4262, Horse-drawn tram, Victor Harbour, South Australia. Nos. 4259, 4263, Seaplane, Whitsunday Islands, Queensland. Nos. 4260, 4264, Steam train, Dandenong Ranges, Victoria. Nos. 4261, 4265, Cruise boat, Katherine Gorge, Northern Territory.

2015, Mar. 3 Litho. *Perf. 14¾x14*

4258	A989	70c multi	1.10	1.10
4259	A989	70c multi	1.10	1.10
4260	A989	70c multi	1.10	1.10
4261	A989	70c multi	1.10	1.10
a.		Horiz. strip of 4, #4258-4261	4.40	4.40
		Nos. 4258-4261 (4)	4.40	4.40

Self-Adhesive
Serpentine Die Cut 11¼ Syncopated

4262	A989	70c multi	1.10	.25
4263	A989	70c multi	1.10	.25
4264	A989	70c multi	1.10	.25
4265	A989	70c multi	1.10	.25
a.		Vert. coil strip of 4, #4262-4265	4.40	
b.		Booklet pane of 10, 3 each #4262, 4264, 2 each #4263, 4265	11.00	
		Nos. 4262-4265 (4)	4.40	1.00

Trees — A990

Designs: 70c, Lemon-scented gum tree. $1.40, Queensland bottle tree. No. 4268, Green fig tree. No. 4269, Moonah tree.

2015, Mar. 17 Litho. *Perf. 14x14¾*

4266	A990 70c multi		1.10	.85
4267	A990 $1.40 multi		2.25	1.75
4268	A990 $2.10 multi		3.25	2.50
4269	A990 $2.10 multi		3.25	2.50
	a.	Horiz. pair, #4268-4269	6.50	5.00
	b.	Souvenir sheet of 4, #4266-4269	10.00	10.00
	Nos. 4266-4269 (4)		9.85	7.60

Self-Adhesive
Printed on Wood Veneer
Serpentine Die Cut 11¼ Syncopated

4270	A990 70c multi	1.25	1.25

No. 4270 was printed in sheets of 10. The sheet was sold only in a package, together with a sheet of 10 of No. 4266. The package sold for $14.95.

Australian and New Zealand Army Corps, Cent. — A991

Soldier and bugler with bugler facing: 70c, Right. $1.85, Left.

2015, Apr. 7 Litho. *Perf. 14¾x14*

4271	A991 70c multi		1.10	1.10
4272	A991 $1.85 multi		3.00	3.00
	a.	Souvenir sheet of 2, #4271-4272	4.25	4.25

Booklet Stamps
Self-Adhesive
Serpentine Die Cut 11¼ Syncopated

4273	A991 70c multi		1.10	.25
	a.	Booklet pane of 10	11.00	
4274	A991 $1.85 multi		3.00	1.50
	a.	Booklet pane of 5	15.00	

See New Zealand Nos. 2584-2585.

Queen Elizabeth II, 89th Birthday — A992

Hat color: 70c, Red. $2.75, Blue.

2015, Apr. 7 Litho. *Perf. 14¾x14*

4275	A992 70c multi		1.10	.85
	a.	Booklet pane of 4	4.75	—
4276	A992 $2.75 multi		4.50	2.25
	a.	Souvenir sheet of 2, #4275-4276	5.75	5.75
	b.	Booklet pane of 2	9.00	—
	c.	Booklet pane of 2, #4275-4276	5.75	—
		Complete booklet, #4276b, 4276c, 2 #4275a	24.50	

Booklet Stamp
Self-Adhesive
Serpentine Die Cut 11¼ Syncopated

4277	A992 $2.75 multi		4.50	2.25
	a.	Booklet pane of 5	22.50	

Complete booklet sold for $14.95.

World War I, Cent. — A993

Australian soldiers involved in Gallipoli campaign: Nos. 4278, 4283, Landing at Gallipoli. Nos. 4279, 4284, Lance Corporal Albert Jacka and Victoria Cross. Nos. 4280, 4285, At Lone Pine. Nos. 4281, 4286, With donkey used for recovering wounded soldiers. Nos. 4282, 4287, Near cannon before evacuation.

2015, Apr. 14 Litho. *Perf. 14¼*

4278	A993 70c multi		1.10	1.10
	a.	Booklet pane of 4	4.75	—
4279	A993 70c multi		1.10	1.10
	a.	Booklet pane of 4	4.75	—
4280	A993 70c multi		1.10	1.10
	a.	Booklet pane of 4	4.75	—
4281	A993 70c multi		1.10	1.10
	a.	Booklet pane of 4	4.75	—
4282	A993 70c multi		1.10	1.10
	a.	Booklet pane of 4	4.75	—
		Complete booklet, #4278a, 4279a, 4280a, 4281a, 4282a	24.00	
	b.	Horiz. strip of 5, #4278-4282	5.50	5.50
	c.	Souvenir sheet of 5, #4278-4282	5.50	5.50
	Nos. 4278-4282 (5)		5.50	5.50

Booklet Stamps
Self-Adhesive
Serpentine Die Cut 11¼ Syncopated

4283	A993 70c multi		1.10	.25
4284	A993 70c multi		1.10	.25
4285	A993 70c multi		1.10	.25
4286	A993 70c multi		1.10	.25
4287	A993 70c multi		1.10	.25
	a.	Booklet pane of 10, 2 each #4283-4287	11.00	
	Nos. 4283-4287 (5)		5.50	1.25

Complete booklet sold for $14.95.

Cats — A994

Cats named: Nos. 4288, 4293, Charo. Nos. 4289, 4294, Bubu. Nos. 4290, 4295, Sweeie. Nos. 4291, 4296, Cato. Nos. 4292, 4297, Briony.

2015, May 5 Litho. *Perf. 14¾x14*

4288	A994 70c multi		1.10	1.10
4289	A994 70c multi		1.10	1.10
4290	A994 70c multi		1.10	1.10
4291	A994 70c multi		1.10	1.10
4292	A994 70c multi		1.10	1.10
	a.	Horiz. strip of 5, #4288-4292	5.50	5.50
	Nos. 4288-4292 (5)		5.50	5.50

Self-Adhesive
Serpentine Die Cut 11¼ Syncopated

4293	A994 70c multi		1.10	.25
	a.	Booklet pane of 10	11.00	
4294	A994 70c multi		1.10	.25
	a.	Booklet pane of 10	11.00	
4295	A994 70c multi		1.10	.25
	a.	Booklet pane of 10	11.00	
4296	A994 70c multi		1.10	.25
	a.	Booklet pane of 10	11.00	
4297	A994 70c multi		1.10	.25
	a.	Booklet pane of 10	11.00	
	b.	Vert. coil strip of 5, #4293-4297	5.50	
	Nos. 4293-4297 (5)		5.50	1.25

Items in Australian Museums — A995

Designs: Nos. 4298, 4303, 1907 Model automatic totalizer, from Museum of Applied Arts and Sciences, Sydney. Nos. 4299, 4302, Turtle sculpture by Ellarose Savage, Australian Museum, Sydney. Nos. 4300, 4305, Anchor of HMS Endeavour, National Musseum of Australia, Canberra. Nos. 4301, 4304, Replica of "Welcome Stranger" gold nugget, Gold Museum, Sovereign Hill, Victoria.

2015, May 19 Litho. *Perf. 14¾x14*

4298	A995 70c multi		1.10	1.10
4299	A995 70c multi		1.10	1.10
4300	A995 70c multi		1.10	1.10
4301	A995 70c multi		1.10	1.10
	a.	Block of 4, #4298-4301	4.40	4.40
	b.	Souvenir sheet of 4, #4298-4301	4.40	4.40
	Nos. 4298-4301 (4)		4.40	4.40

Coil Stamps
Self-Adhesive
Serpentine Die Cut 11¼ Syncopated

4302	A995 70c multi		1.10	.25
4303	A995 70c multi		1.10	.25
4304	A995 70c multi		1.10	.25
4305	A995 70c multi		1.10	.25
	a.	Vert. strip of 4, #4302-4305	4.40	
	Nos. 4302-4305 (4)		4.40	1.00

Islands — A996

Designs: Nos. 4306, 4310, Phillip Island, Victoria. Nos. 4307, 4311, Lady Musgrave Island, Queensland. $1.40, Bruny Island, Tasmania. $2.10, Buccaneer Archipelago, Western Australia.

2015, June 2 Litho. *Perf. 14x14¾*

4306	A996 70c multi		1.10	1.10
4307	A996 70c multi		1.10	1.10
	a.	Horiz. pair, #4306-4307	2.20	2.20
4308	A996 $1.40 multi		2.25	1.10
4309	A996 $2.10 multi		3.25	1.60
	Nos. 4306-4309 (4)		7.70	4.90

Booklet Stamps
Self-Adhesive
Serpentine Die Cut 11¼ Syncopated

4310	A996 70c multi		1.10	.25
4311	A996 70c multi		1.10	.25
	a.	Booklet pane of 10, 5 each #4310-4311	11.00	

Walter and Eliza Hall Institute of Medical Research, Cent. — A997

2015, June 30 Litho. *Perf. 14¾x14*

4312	A997 70c multi		1.10	.85
	a.	Booklet pane of 4	4.50	—
		Complete booklet, 5 #4312a	22.50	

Complete booklet sold for $14.95.

Lighthouses — A998

Designs: Nos. 4313, 4317, Cape Byron Lighthouse, New South Wales. Nos. 4314, 4318, Cape Leeuwin Lighthouse, Western Australia. Nos. 4315, 4319, North Reef Lighthouse, Queensland. Nos. 4316, 4320, Tasman Island Lighthouse, Tasmania.

2015, July 7 Litho. *Perf. 14¾x14*

4313	A998 70c multi		1.10	1.10
	a.	Booklet pane of 4	4.50	—
4314	A998 70c multi		1.10	1.10
	a.	Booklet pane of 4	4.50	—
4315	A998 70c multi		1.10	1.10
	a.	Booklet pane of 4	4.50	—
4316	A998 70c multi		1.10	1.10
	a.	Booklet pane of 4	4.50	—
	b.	Booklet pane of 4, #4313-4316	4.50	—
		Complete booklet, #4313a, 4314a, 4315a, 4316a, 4316b	22.50	
	c.	Block of 4, #4313-4316	4.40	4.40
	Nos. 4313-4316 (4)		4.40	4.40

Self-Adhesive
Serpentine Die Cut 11¼ Syncopated

4317	A998 70c multi		1.10	.25
4318	A998 70c multi		1.10	.25
4319	A998 70c multi		1.10	.25
4320	A998 70c multi		1.10	.25
	a.	Booklet pane of 20, 5 each #4317-4320	22.00	
	b.	Vert. coil strip of 4, #4317-4320	4.40	
	Nos. 4317-4320 (4)		4.40	1.00

Complete booklet sold for $14.95.

Hiking Trails — A999

Designs: Nos. 4321, 4326, National Pass Track, New South Wales. Nos. 4322, 4328, Cape to Cape Track, Western Australia. Nos. 4323, 4325, Larapinta Trail, Northern Territory. Nos. 4324, 4327, Overland Track, Tasmania.

2015, July 14 Litho. *Perf. 14x14¾*

4321	A999 70c multi		1.10	1.10
4322	A999 70c multi		1.10	1.10
4323	A999 70c multi		1.10	1.10
4324	A999 70c multi		1.10	1.10
	a.	Horiz. strip of 4, #4321-4324	4.40	4.40
	b.	Souvenir sheet of 4, #4321-4324	4.40	4.40
	Nos. 4321-4324 (4)		4.40	4.40

Self-Adhesive
Serpentine Die Cut 11¼ Syncopated

4325	A999 70c multi		1.10	.25
4326	A999 70c multi		1.10	.25
4327	A999 70c multi		1.10	.25
4328	A999 70c multi		1.10	.25
	a.	Booklet pane of 10, 3 each #4325, 4327, 2 each #4326, 4328	11.00	
	b.	Horiz. coil strip of 4, #4325-4328	4.40	
	Nos. 4325-4328 (4)		4.40	1.00

2015 Netball World Cup, Sydney — A1000

2015, Aug. 8 Litho. *Perf. 14¾x14*

4329	A1000 70c multi	1.10	.85

Booklet Stamp
Self-Adhesive
Serpentine Die Cut 11¼ Syncopated

4330	A1000 70c multi		1.10	.25
	a.	Booklet pane of 20	20.00	

Houses of Parliament — A1001

Houses of Parliament in: 70c, Australia. $1.85, New Zealand. $1.95, Singapore.

2015, Aug. 14 Litho. *Perf. 14¼*

4331	A1001 70c multi		1.10	.85
4332	A1001 $1.85 multi		2.75	1.40
4333	A1001 $1.95 multi		3.00	1.50
	a.	Souvenir sheet of 3, #4331-4333	7.00	7.00
	Nos. 4331-4333 (3)		6.85	3.75

Diplomatic relations of Singapore with Australia and New Zealand, 50th anniv.

See New Zealand No. 2600, Singapore Nos. 1743-1745.

Birth of Princess Charlotte of Cambridge — A1002

2015, Aug. 25 Litho. *Perf. 14¼*

4334	A1002 70c multi	1.00	1.00

Booklet Stamp
Self-Adhesive
Serpentine Die Cut 11¼ Syncopated

4335	A1002 70c multi		1.00	.25
	a.	Booklet pane of 10	10.00	

Neon Signs — A1003

Designs: Nos. 4336, 4339, Skipping Girl Vinegar sign, Abbotsford, Victoria, 1936. Nos. 4337, 4340, Pink Poodle Motel sign, Surfers Paradise, Queensland, 1967. $1.40, Dandy Pig sign for Gippsland Co-operative Bacon Curing Company, Dandenong, Victoria, 1950s.

2015, Sept. 1 Litho. *Perf. 14¾x14*

4336	A1003 70c multi		1.00	1.00
4337	A1003 70c multi		1.00	1.00
4338	A1003 $1.40 multi		2.00	1.50
	a.	Souvenir sheet of 3, #4336-4338	4.00	4.00
	Nos. 4336-4338 (3)		4.00	3.50

Self-Adhesive
Serpentine Die Cut 11¼ Syncopated

4339	A1003 70c multi		1.00	1.00
4340	A1003 70c multi		1.00	1.00
	a.	Vert. coil pair, #4339-4340	2.00	
	b.	Booklet pane of 10, 5 each #4339-4340	10.00	

A1004

A1005

A1006

A1007

Queen Elizabeth II, Longest-Reigning British Monarch — A1008

2015, Sept. 9 Litho. *Perf. 14¾x14*

4341 A1004 70c black 1.00 .75
a. Booklet pane of 4 4.25 —
4342 A1005 70c multi 1.00 .75
a. Booklet pane of 4 4.25 —
4343 A1006 70c multi 1.00 .75
a. Booklet pane of 4 4.25 —
b. Horiz. strip of 3, #4341-4343 3.00 2.25
4344 A1007 $2.75 multi 4.00 4.00
a. Booklet pane of 2 8.00 —
4345 A1008 $2.75 multi 4.00 4.00
a. Booklet pane of 2 8.00 —
Complete booklet, #4341a, 4342a, 4343a, 4344a, 4345a 29.00
b. Horiz. pair, #4344-4345 8.00 8.00
c. Souvenir sheet of 5, #4341-4345 11.00 11.00
Nos. 4341-4345 (5) 11.00 10.25

Booklet Stamps
Self-Adhesive
Serpentine Die Cut 11¼ Syncopated

4346 A1007 $2.75 multi 4.00 4.00
4347 A1008 $2.75 multi 4.00 4.00
a. Booklet pane of 5, 2 #4346, 3 #4347 20.00

Complete booklet sold for $19.95.

Planets — A1009

Designs: Nos. 4348, 4356a, Mercury. Nos. 4349, 4356b, Mars, horiz. Nos. 4350, 4356c, 4357, Earth. Nos. 4351, 4356d, 4358, Uranus. Nos. 4352, 4356e, 4359, Neptune, horiz. Nos. 4353, 4356f, 4360, Venus, horiz. Nos. 4354, 4356g, Jupiter. Nos. 4355, 4356h, Saturn, horiz.

Litho., Litho. & Silk-Screened (#4356)

2015, Sept. 22 *Perf. 14½x14*

Stamps With White Frames on Two Sides

4348 A1009 35c multi .50 .40

Perf. 14x14½

4349 A1009 35c multi .50 .40
a. Pair, #4348-4349 1.00 .80

Size: 26x38mm
Perf. 14¾x14

4350 A1009 70c multi 1.00 1.00
4351 A1009 70c multi 1.00 1.00

Size:36x28mm
Perf. 14x14¾

4352 A1009 70c multi 1.00 1.00
4353 A1009 70c multi 1.00 1.00

Size: 30x50mm
Perf. 14x14½

4354 A1009 70c multi 1.00 1.00

Size: 50x30mm
Perf. 14½x14

4355 A1009 70c multi 1.00 1.00
Nos. 4348-4355 (8) 7.00 6.80

Miniature Sheet
Stamps Without White Frames
Perf. 14½, 14x14½ (#4356e, 4356f)

4356 Sheet of 8 7.00 7.00
a. A1009 35c multi .50 .40
b. A1009 35c multi .50 .40
c. A1009 70c multi, 26x38mm 1.00 .75
d. A1009 70c multi, 26x38mm 1.00 .75
e. A1009 70c multi, 38x26mm 1.00 .75
f. A1009 70c multi, 38x26mm 1.00 .75
g. A1009 70c multi, 30x50mm 1.00 .75
h. A1009 70c multi, 50x30mm 1.00 .75

Litho.
Serpentine Die Cut 11¼ Syncopated
Booklet Stamps
Self-Adhesive
Size: 26x38mm
Stamps With White Frames on Two Sides

4357 A1009 70c multi 1.00 .25
4358 A1009 70c multi 1.00 .25
a. Booklet pane of 20, 10 each #4357-4358 20.00

Size: 38x26mm

4359 A1009 70c multi 1.00 .25
4360 A1009 70c multi 1.00 .25
a. Booklet pane of 10, 5 each #4359-4360 10.00
Nos. 4357-4360 (4) 4.00 1.00

Humanitarians Honored by Australia — A1010

Designs: Nos. 4361, 4364, Mother Teresa (1910-97), Honorary Companion of the Order of Australia. Nos. 4362, 4365, Nelson Mandela (1918-2013), Honorary Companion of the Order of Australia. Nos. 4363, 4366, Raoul Wallenberg (1912-45), Honorary Citizen of Australia.

2015, Oct. 5 Litho. *Perf. 14x14¾*

4361 A1010 70c multi 1.00 1.00
4362 A1010 70c multi 1.00 1.00
4363 A1010 70c multi 1.00 1.00
Nos. 4361-4363 (3) 3.00 3.00

Booklet Stamps
Self-Adhesive
Serpentine Die Cut 11¼ Syncopated

4364 A1010 70c multi 1.00 .25
a. Booklet pane of 10 10.00
4365 A1010 70c multi 1.00 .25
a. Booklet pane of 10 10.00
4366 A1010 70c multi 1.00 .25
a. Booklet pane of 10 10.00
Nos. 4364-4366 (3) 3.00 .75

Bicycles — A1011

Designs: Nos. 4367, 4371, 1888 Basset & Co. penny-farthing. Nos. 4368, 4372, Sutherland ladies' safety bicycle, c. 1910. $1.85, Finlay Bros. men's sprung-frame saftey bicycle, 1930s. $2.75, Baum Cycles custom-made road bicycle, 2015.

2015, Oct. 13 Litho. *Perf. 14¼*

4367 A1011 70c multi 1.00 1.00
a. Booklet pane of 4 4.00 —
4368 A1011 70c multi 1.00 1.00
a. Booklet pane of 4 4.00 —
b. Horiz. pair, #4367-4368 2.00 2.00
4369 A1011 $1.85 multi 2.75 1.40
a. Booklet pane of 2 5.50 —
4370 A1011 $2.75 multi 4.00 4.00
a. Booklet pane of 2 8.00 —
Complete booklet, #4367a, 4368a, 4369a, 4370a 21.50
Nos. 4367-4370 (4) 8.75 7.40

Booklet Stamps
Self-Adhesive
Serpentine Die Cut 11¼ Syncopated

4371 A1011 70c multi 1.00 .25
4372 A1011 70c multi 1.00 .25
a. Booklet pane of 20, 10 each #4371-4372 20.00
4373 A1011 $2.75 multi 4.00 2.00
a. Booklet pane of 5 20.00
Nos. 4371-4373 (3) 6.00 2.50

Complete booklet sold for $14.95.

Animals in War — A1012

Poppies, soldiers and: Nos. 4374, 4379, Donkeys. Nos. 4375, 4380, Dogs. Nos. 4376, 4381, Horses. Nos. 4377, 4383, Pigeons. Nos. 4378, 4382, Camels.

2015, Oct. 27 Litho. *Perf. 14¼*

4374 A1012 70c multi 1.00 1.00
4375 A1012 70c multi 1.00 1.00
4376 A1012 70c multi 1.00 1.00
4377 A1012 70c multi 1.00 1.00
4378 A1012 70c multi 1.00 1.00
a. Souvenir sheet of 5, #4374-4378 5.00 5.00
Nos. 4374-4378 (5) 5.00 5.00

Booklet Stamps
Self-Adhesive
Serpentine Die Cut 11¼ Syncopated

4379 A1012 70c multi 1.00 .25
4380 A1012 70c multi 1.00 .25
4381 A1012 70c multi 1.00 .25
4382 A1012 70c multi 1.00 .25
4383 A1012 70c multi 1.00 .25
a. Booklet pane of 10, 2 each #4379-4383 10.00
Nos. 4379-4383 (5) 5.00 1.25

Christmas
A1013 A1014

Designs: Nos. 4384, 4389, 4394, Gift box with ribbon. Nos. 4385, 4390, 4395, Green doves. Nos. 4386, 4391, Nativity. Nos. 4387, 4392, Blue doves. Nos. 4388, 4393, Magi.

2015, Oct. 30 Litho. *Perf. 14¾x14*

4384 A1013 65c multi .95 .95
4385 A1013 65c multi .95 .95
a. Horiz. pair, #4384-4385 1.90 1.90
4386 A1014 65c multi .95 .95
4387 A1013 $1.70 multi 2.50 2.50
4388 A1014 $2.55 multi 3.75 3.75
a. Souvenir sheet of 2, #4386, 4388 4.75 4.75
Nos. 4384-4388 (5) 9.10 9.10

Booklet Stamps
Self-Adhesive
Serpentine Die Cut 11¼ Syncopated

4389 A1013 65c multi .95 .25
4390 A1013 65c multi .95 .25
a. Booklet pane of 20, 10 each #4389-4390 19.00
4391 A1014 65c multi .95 .25
a. Booklet pane of 20 19.00
4392 A1013 $1.70 multi 2.50 1.25
a. Booklet pane of 5 12.50
4393 A1014 $2.55 multi 3.75 1.90
a. Booklet pane of 5 19.00

Litho. & Silk-Screened

4394 A1013 65c multi .95 .25
a. Booklet pane of 10 9.50

Litho. With Foil Application

4395 A1013 65c multi .95 .25
a. Booklet pane of 10 9.50
Nos. 4389-4395 (7) 11.00 4.40

Wildflowers — A1015

Designs: Nos. 4398, 4402, 4405, Rose coneflower. Nos. 4399, 4403, 4406, Spiny mirbelia. Nos. 4400, 4404, 4407, Blue devil. $2, Golden rainbow.

2015, Dec. 15 Litho. *Perf. 14¾x14*

4398 A1015 $1 multi 1.50 1.50
4399 A1015 $1 multi 1.50 1.50
4400 A1015 $1 multi 1.50 1.50
a. Horiz. strip of 3, #4398-4400 4.50 4.50
4401 A1015 $2 multi 3.00 1.50
Nos. 4398-4401 (4) 7.50 6.00

Self-Adhesive
Serpentine Die Cut 11¼ Syncopated

4402 A1015 $1 multi 1.50 .25
4403 A1015 $1 multi 1.50 .25
4404 A1015 $1 multi 1.50 .25
a. Vert. coil strip of 3, #4402-4404 4.50
b. Booklet pane of 10, 4 #4402, 3 each #4403-4404 15.00
c. Booklet pane of 20, 8 #4402, 5 #4403, 7 #4404 30.00
Nos. 4402-4404 (3) 4.50 .75

With Personalized Photo at Right Like Type A692a
Serpentine Die Cut 11½x11¼ Syncopated
Self-Adhesive

4405 A1015 $1 multi 2.40 2.40
4406 A1015 $1 multi 2.40 2.40
4407 A1015 $1 multi 2.40 2.40
4408 A1015 $2 multi 4.00 4.00
Nos. 4405-4408 (4) 11.20 11.20

Nos. 4405-4408 were each printed in sheets of 20 and have personalized pictures and a straight edge at right and lack separations between the stamp and the personalized photo. Sheets of 20 of Nos. 4405-4407 sold for $33 each, No. 4408, $53.

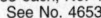

See No. 4653.

Tennis Players — A1016

Designs: Nos. 4409, 4412, Tony Roche. Nos. 4410, 4413, Fred Stolle. Nos. 4411a, 4414, Pat Cash. Nos. 4411b, 4415, Ashley Cooper. Nos. 4411c, 4416, Roy Emerson. Nos. 4411d, 4417, Neale Fraser. Nos. 4411e, 4418, Evonne Goolagong Cawley. Nos. 4411f, 4419, John Newcombe. Nos. 4411g, 4420, Patrick Rafter. Nos. 4411h, 4421, Ken Rosewall. Nos. 4411i, 4422, Frank Sedgman. Nos. 4411j, 4423, Lleyton Hewitt.

2016, Jan. 21 Litho. *Perf. 14¾x14*

4409 A1016 $1 multi 1.50 1.50
4410 A1016 $1 multi 1.50 1.50
a. Vert. pair, #4409-4410 3.00 3.00
4411 Sheet of 10 15.00 15.00
a.-j. A1016 $1 Any single 1.50 1.50

Booklet Stamps
Self-Adhesive
Serpentine Die Cut 11¼ Syncopated

4412 A1016 $1 multi 1.50 .25
a. Booklet pane of 10 15.00
4413 A1016 $1 multi 1.50 .25
a. Booklet pane of 10 15.00
4414 A1016 $1 multi 1.50 .25
a. Booklet pane of 10 15.00
4415 A1016 $1 multi 1.50 .25
a. Booklet pane of 10 15.00
4416 A1016 $1 multi 1.50 .25
a. Booklet pane of 10 15.00
4417 A1016 $1 multi 1.50 .25
a. Booklet pane of 10 15.00
4418 A1016 $1 multi 1.50 .25
a. Booklet pane of 10 15.00
4419 A1016 $1 multi 1.50 .25
a. Booklet pane of 10 15.00
4420 A1016 $1 multi 1.50 .25
a. Booklet pane of 10 15.00
4421 A1016 $1 multi 1.50 .25
a. Booklet pane of 10 15.00
4422 A1016 $1 multi 1.50 .25
a. Booklet pane of 10 15.00
4423 A1016 $1 multi 1.50 .25
a. Booklet pane of 10 15.00
Nos. 4412-4423 (12) 18.00 3.00

White Roses
A1017

Champagne Flutes
A1018

Heart of Red Roses
A1019

Cake
A1020

Balloons
A1021

Handprints
A1022

Map of Australia
A1023

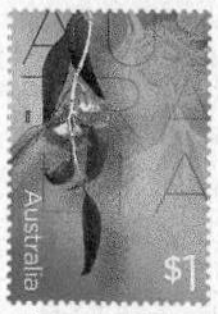
Flowering Gum
A1024

Wattle
A1025

Engagement and Wedding Rings
A1026

2016, Jan. 25 Litho. *Perf. 14¾x14*

4424	A1017 $1 multi		1.50	1.50
4425	A1018 $1 multi		1.50	1.50
4426	A1019 $1 multi		1.50	1.50
4427	A1020 $1 multi		1.50	1.50
4428	A1021 $1 multi		1.50	1.50
4429	A1022 $1 multi		1.50	1.50
4430	A1023 $1 multi		1.50	1.10
4431	A1024 $1 multi		1.50	1.10
4432	A1025 $1 multi		1.50	1.10
4433	A1026 $2 multi		3.00	3.00
	Nos. 4424-4433 (10)		16.50	15.30

Booklet Stamps
Self-Adhesive

Serpentine Die Cut 11¼ Syncopated

4434	A1017 $1 multi	1.50	.25
a.	Booklet pane of 10 + 5 stickers	15.00	
4435	A1018 $1 multi	1.50	.25
a.	Booklet pane of 10 + 5 stickers	15.00	
4436	A1019 $1 multi	1.50	.25
a.	Booklet pane of 10 + 5 stickers	15.00	
4437	A1020 $1 multi	1.50	.25
a.	Booklet pane of 10 + 5 stickers	15.00	
4438	A1021 $1 multi	1.50	.25
a.	Booklet pane of 10 + 5 stickers	15.00	
4439	A1022 $1 multi	1.50	.25
a.	Booklet pane of 10 + 5 stickers	15.00	
4440	A1026 $2 multi	3.00	1.50
a.	Booklet pane of 4	12.00	
	Complete booklet, 4 #4440a	48.00	
	Nos. 4434-4440 (7)	12.00	3.00

Complete booklet sold for $32.95 and contains four examples of No. 4440a, each with a different pane margin.

With Personalized Photo at Right Like Type A692a
Serpentine Die Cut 11½x11¼ Syncopated
Self-Adhesive

4441	A1017 $1 multi	2.40	2.40
4442	A1018 $1 multi	2.40	2.40
4443	A1019 $1 multi	2.40	2.40
4444	A1020 $1 multi	2.40	2.40
4445	A1021 $1 multi	2.40	2.40
4446	A1022 $1 multi	2.40	2.40
4447	A1023 $1 multi	2.40	2.40
4448	A1024 $1 multi	2.40	2.40
4449	A1025 $1 multi	2.40	2.40
4450	A1026 $2 multi	3.75	3.75
	Nos. 4441-4450 (10)	25.35	25.35

Nos. 4441-4450 were each printed in sheets of 20 and have personalized pictures and a straight edge at right and lack separations between the stamp and the personalized photo. Sheets of 20 of Nos. 4441-4449 sold for $33 each, No. 4450, $53.

Australian One Pound Banknote, One Dollar Banknote and Coin
A1027

2016, Feb. 9 Litho. *Perf. 14½x14*

4451	A1027 $1 multi	1.50	1.10
a.	Perf. 13½x14	1.50	1.10
b.	Booklet pane of 4 #4451a	6.00	—
	Complete booklet, 5 #4451b	30.00	

Complete booklet sold for $20.95, and contained five examples of No. 4451b, each with different pane margins.

Items Starting With Same Letter — A1028

Designs: Nos. 4452, 4457, Numbat, nippers (junior lifeguards) on surfboard, New South Wales map. Nos. 4453, 4458, Quokka, quoll, queue sign, Quokkair plane, Queensland map. Nos. 4454, 4459, Surf, surfboard, sand castle, starfish, sausage, shark toy, shell, snail, South Australia map. Nos. 4455, 4460, Vegetables, Victa lawnmower, violins, Vegemite sandwich, Victoria map. Nos. 4456, 4461, Wombat, wattle, waratah, water hose, Western Australia Cricket Association bat and ball, Western Australia map.

2016, Mar. 1 Litho. *Perf. 14¾x14*

4452	A1028 $1 multi	1.50	1.50
4453	A1028 $1 multi	1.50	1.50
4454	A1028 $1 multi	1.50	1.50
4455	A1028 $1 multi	1.50	1.50
4456	A1028 $1 multi	1.50	1.50
a.	Horiz. strip of 5, #4452-4456	7.50	7.50
	Nos. 4452-4456 (5)	7.50	7.50

Booklet Stamps
Self-Adhesive

Serpentine Die Cut 11¼ Syncopated

4457	A1028 $1 multi	1.50	.25
a.	Booklet pane of 10	15.00	
4458	A1028 $1 multi	1.50	.25
a.	Booklet pane of 10	15.00	
4459	A1028 $1 multi	1.50	.25
a.	Booklet pane of 10	15.00	
4460	A1028 $1 multi	1.50	.25
a.	Booklet pane of 10	15.00	
4461	A1028 $1 multi	1.50	.25
a.	Booklet pane of 10	15.00	
	Nos. 4457-4461 (5)	7.50	1.25

See Nos. 4520-4529, 4697-4706, 4853-4862, 5027-5038.

Bridges — A1029

Designs: Nos. 4462, 4465, Gladesville Bridge, New South Wales. Nos. 4463, 4467, Story Bridge, Queensland. Nos. 4464, 4466, Tasman Bridge, Tasmania.

2016, Mar. 15 Litho. *Perf. 14x14¾*

4462	A1029 $1 multi	1.60	1.60
4463	A1029 $1 multi	1.60	1.60
4464	A1029 $1 multi	1.60	1.60
a.	Horiz. strip of 3, #4462-4464	4.80	4.80
	Nos. 4462-4464 (3)	4.80	4.80

Booklet Stamps
Self-Adhesive

Serpentine Die Cut 11¼ Syncopated

4465	A1029 $1 multi	1.60	.25
4466	A1029 $1 multi	1.60	.25
4467	A1029 $1 multi	1.60	.25
a.	Booklet pane of 20, 7 each #4465-4466, 6 #4467	32.00	
	Nos. 4465-4467 (3)	4.80	.75

Queen Elizabeth II, 90th Birthday — A1030

Designs: $1, Queen Elizabeth II. $2.75, Golden wattle diamond brooch.

2016, Apr. 5 Litho. *Perf. 14¾x14*

4468	A1030 $1 multi	1.60	1.25
4469	A1030 $2.75 multi	4.25	4.25
a.	Souvenir sheet of 2, #4468-4469	6.00	6.00

Booklet Stamp
Self-Adhesive

Serpentine Die Cut 11¼ Syncopated

4470	A1030 $2.75 multi	4.25	2.10
a.	Booklet pane of 5	21.50	

World War I, Cent. — A1031

Poppy and: Nos. 4471, 4476, Soldiers arriving on the Western Front. Nos. 4472, 4477, Somme Offensive. Nos. 4473, 4478, Referendum on conscription. Nos. 4474, 4479, Matron Grace Wilson of Australian Army Nursing Service, and Royal Red Cross, First Class. Nos. 4475, 4480, Soldier writing letter home.

2016, Apr. 12 Litho. *Perf. 14¼*

4471	A1031 $1 multi	1.60	1.60
4472	A1031 $1 multi	1.60	1.60
4473	A1031 $1 multi	1.60	1.60
4474	A1031 $1 multi	1.60	1.60
a.	Booklet pane of 4, #4471-4474	6.50	—
4475	A1031 $1 multi	1.60	1.60
a.	Booklet pane of 4, #4472-4475	6.50	—
b.	Booklet pane of 4, #4471, 4473-4475	6.50	—
c.	Booklet pane of 4, #4471-4472, 4474-4475	6.50	—
d.	Booklet pane of 4, #4471-4473, 4475	6.50	—
	Complete booklet, #4474a, 4475a, 4475b, 4475c, 4475d	32.50	
e.	Souvenir sheet of 5, #4471-4475	8.00	8.00
	Nos. 4471-4475 (5)	8.00	8.00

Booklet Stamps
Self-Adhesive

Serpentine Die Cut 11¼ Syncopated

4476	A1031 $1 multi	1.60	.25
4477	A1031 $1 multi	1.60	.25
4478	A1031 $1 multi	1.60	.25
4479	A1031 $1 multi	1.60	.25
4480	A1031 $1 multi	1.60	.25
a.	Booklet pane of 10, 2 each #4476-4480	16.00	
	Nos. 4476-4480 (5)	8.00	1.25

Complete booklet sold for $20.95.

Butterflies — A1032

Designs: Nos. 4481, 4485, Pale triangle butterfly. Nos. 4482, 4487, Bordered rustic butterfly. Nos. 4483, 4486, Cairns birdwing butterfly. $2.75, Chequered swallowtail butterfly.

2016, May 3 Litho. *Perf. 14x14¾*

4481	A1032 $1 multi	1.50	1.50
4482	A1032 $1 multi	1.50	1.50
4483	A1032 $1 multi	1.50	1.50
4484	A1032 $2.75 multi	4.00	4.00
a.	Souvenir sheet of 4, #4481-4484	8.50	8.50
	Nos. 4481-4484 (4)	8.50	8.50

Self-Adhesive

Serpentine Die Cut 11¼ Syncopated

4485	A1032 $1 multi	1.50	.25
4486	A1032 $1 multi	1.50	.25
4487	A1032 $1 multi	1.50	.25
a.	Horiz. coil strip of 3, #4485-4487	4.50	
b.	Booklet pane of 20, 7 each #4485, 4487, 6 #4486	30.00	

Booklet Stamp

4488	A1032 $2.75 multi	4.00	2.00
a.	Booklet pane of 5	20.00	
	Nos. 4485-4488 (4)	8.50	2.75

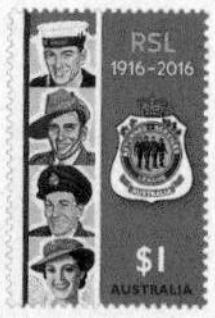
Returned and Services League of Australia, Cent. — A1033

2016, May 31 Litho. *Perf. 14¾x14*

4489	A1033 $1 multi	1.50	1.50

Booklet Stamp
Self-Adhesive

Serpentine Die Cut 11¼ Syncopated

4490	A1033 $1 multi	1.50	.25
a.	Booklet pane of 20	30.00	

Early 20th Century Fruit Crate Labels — A1034

Labels for: Nos. 4491, 4495, Paterson & Co. "Red Gum Pack" Apples. Nos. 4492, 4496, The River's Pride Navel Oranges. Nos. 4493, 4497, L. H. Kile "Robin" Apples. Nos. 4494, 4498, W. H. Price Ltd. Special Ohanez Grapes.

2016, June 7 Litho. *Perf. 14x14¾*

4491	A1034 $1 multi	1.50	1.50
a.	Booklet pane of 4	6.50	—
4492	A1034 $1 multi	1.50	1.50
a.	Booklet pane of 4	6.50	—
4493	A1034 $1 multi	1.50	1.50
a.	Booklet pane of 4	6.50	—
4494	A1034 $1 multi	1.50	1.50
a.	Booklet pane of 4	6.50	—
	Complete booklet, #4491a, 4492a, 4493a, 4494a	26.00	

Self-Adhesive

Serpentine Die Cut 11¼ Syncopated

4495	A1034 $1 multi	1.50	.25
4496	A1034 $1 multi	1.50	.25
4497	A1034 $1 multi	1.50	.25
4498	A1034 $1 multi	1.50	.25
a.	Horiz. coil strip of 4, #4495-4498	6.00	
b.	Booklet pane of 10, 3 each #4496-4497, 2 each #4497-4498	15.00	
	Nos. 4495-4498 (4)	6.00	1.00

Complete booklet sold for $16.95.

Owls — A1035

Designs: Nos. 4499, 4505, Rufous owl. Nos. 4500, 4503, Eastern grass owl. Nos. 4501, 4504, Sooty owl. Nos. 4502, 4506, Southern boobook owl.

2016, July 5 Litho. *Perf. 14x13½*

4499	A1035 $1 multi	1.50	1.50
a.	Booklet pane of 2	3.25	—
4500	A1035 $1 multi	1.50	1.50
a.	Booklet pane of 2	3.25	—
b.	Booklet pane of 2, #4499-4500	3.25	—
4501	A1035 $1 multi	1.50	1.50
a.	Booklet pane of 2	3.25	—
b.	Booklet pane of 2, #4500-4501	3.25	—
4502	A1035 $1 multi	1.50	1.50
a.	Booklet pane of 2	3.25	—
b.	Booklet pane of 2, #4501-4502	3.25	—
c.	Booklet pane of 2, #4499, 4502	3.25	—
	Complete booklet, #4499a, 4500a, 4500b, 4501a, 4501b, 4502a, 4502b, 4502c	26.00	
d.	Souvenir sheet of 4, #4499-4502	6.00	6.00
	Nos. 4499-4502 (4)	6.00	6.00

Booklet Stamps
Self-Adhesive

Serpentine Die Cut11¼x10¾ Syncopated

4503	A1035 $1 multi	1.50	.25
4504	A1035 $1 multi	1.50	.25
4505	A1035 $1 multi	1.50	.25
4506	A1035 $1 multi	1.50	.25
a.	Booklet pane of 10, 2 each #4503, 4506, 3 each #4504-4505	15.00	

Complete booklet sold for $16.95.

Olympic Gold Medalist Type of 2012

Design: $1, Jared Tallent, men's 50-kilometer walk.

2016, July 23 Litho. *Perf. 14½*

4506B	A897 $1 multi	1.50	1.10

Tallent originally received a 2012 Olympic silver medal, but was awarded a gold medal in 2016 after Sergey Kirdyapkin was stripped of his medal for doping.

Play School Children's Television Program, 50th Anniv. — A1036

Designs: $1, Jemima and Humpty. $2, Big Ted and Little Ted.

2016, July 26 Litho. *Perf. 14¾x14*

4507 A1036 $1 multi 1.50 1.50
4508 A1036 $2 multi 3.00 2.25
a. Souvenir sheet of 2, #4507-4508 4.50 4.50

Booklet Stamp
Self-Adhesive
Serpentine Die Cut 11¼ Syncopated

4509 A1036 $1 multi 1.50 .25
a. Booklet pane of 10 15.00

With Personalized Photo at Right Like Type A692a
Serpentine Die Cut 11½x11¼ Syncopated
Self-Adhesive

4510 A1036 $1 multi 2.50 2.50

No. 4510 was printed in a sheet of 20 and has personalized pictures and a straight edge at right and lack separations between the stamp and the personalized photo. Sheets of 20 sold for $33 each.

2016 Summer Olympics, Rio de Janeiro — A1037

2016, Aug. 2 Litho. *Perf. 14x14¾*

4511 A1037 $1 multi 1.50 1.10

Australian Gold Medalists at 2016 Summer Olympics, Rio de Janeiro — A1038

Designs: No. 4512, Mack Horton, men's 400-meter freestyle. No. 4513, Women's 4x100 meter freestyle relay team. No. 4514, Catherine Skinner, women's trap shooting. No. 4515, Women's rugby sevens team. No. 4516, Kyle Chalmers, men's 100-meter freestyle. No. 4517, Kimberley Brennan, women's single sculls. No. 4518, Tom Burton, men's Laser class sailing. No. 4519, Chloe Esposito, women's individual modern pentathlon.

2016 Litho. *Perf. 14¼*

4512 A1038 $1 multi 1.50 1.10
4513 A1038 $1 multi 1.50 1.10
4514 A1038 $1 multi 1.50 1.10
4515 A1038 $1 multi 1.50 1.10
4516 A1038 $1 multi 1.50 1.10
4517 A1038 $1 multi 1.50 1.10
4518 A1038 $1 multi 1.50 1.10
4519 A1038 $1 multi 1.50 1.10
Nos. 4512-4519 (8) 12.00 8.80

Nos. 4512-4519 were each printed in sheets of 10. Issued: Nos. 4512-4514, 8/8; No. 4515, 8/9; No. 4516, 8/11; No. 4517, 8/15; No. 4518, 8/17; No. 4519, 8/18.

Items Starting With Same Letter Type of 2016

Designs: Nos. 4520, 4525, Ant, Australian Rules Footballer players and ball, ANZAC memorial. Nos. 4521, 4526, Couple at campfire with Canberra map, crocodile, cockatoo. Nos. 4522, 4527, Lace monitor, lyrebird on lounge, Lamingtons on log. Nos. 4523, 4528, Rugby ball, refrigerator, rocket, reel, ruler, rope, Red Center poster. Nos. 4524, 4529, Tasmania map, Tasmanian devil, tradesman in tinnie (boat) with toolbelt.

2016, Aug. 16 Litho. *Perf. 14¾x14*

4520 A1028 $1 multi 1.50 1.50
4521 A1028 $1 multi 1.50 1.50
4522 A1028 $1 multi 1.50 1.50
4523 A1028 $1 multi 1.50 1.50
4524 A1028 $1 multi 1.50 1.50
Nos. 4520-4524 (5) 7.50 7.50

Self-Adhesive
Serpentine Die Cut 11¼ Syncopated

4525 A1028 $1 multi 1.50 .25
a. Booklet pane of 10 15.00
4526 A1028 $1 multi 1.50 .25
a. Booklet pane of 10 15.00
4527 A1028 $1 multi 1.50 .25
a. Booklet pane of 10 15.00
4528 A1028 $1 multi 1.50 .25
a. Booklet pane of 10 15.00
4529 A1028 $1 multi 1.50 .25
a. Booklet pane of 10 15.00
b. Vert. coil strip of 5, #4525-4529 7.50
Nos. 4525-4529 (5) 7.50 1.25

Jewel Beetles — A1039

Designs: Nos. 4530, 4534, Stigmodera gratiosa. Nos. 4531, 4535, Castiarina klugii. No. 4532, Temognatha alternata. No. 4533, Julodimorpha bakewellii.

2016, Sept. 6 Litho. *Perf. 14¾x14*

4530 A1039 $1 multi 1.60 1.60
4531 A1039 $1 multi 1.60 1.60
a. Horiz. pair, #4530-4531 3.20 3.20
4532 A1039 $2 multi 3.25 2.40
4533 A1039 $2 multi 3.25 2.40
a. Horiz. pair, #4532-4533 6.50 4.80
Nos. 4530-4533 (4) 9.70 8.00

Self-Adhesive
Serpentine Die Cut 11¼ Syncopated

4534 A1039 $1 multi 1.60 .25
4535 A1039 $1 multi 1.60 .25
a. Vert. coil pair, #4534-4535 3.20
b. Booklet pane of 20, 10 each #4534-4535 32.00

Landing of Dirk Hartog in Western Australia, 400th Anniv. — A1040

2016, Sept. 13 Litho. *Perf. 14¾x14*

4536 A1040 $2 multi 3.25 2.40

A1041

Endangered Animals A1042

Designs: No. 4537, Orange-bellied parrots. No. 4538, Northern quolls. Nos. 4539, 4544, Snow leopards. Nos. 4540, 4545, Western swamp tortoise. Nos. 4541, 4546, Western lowland gorillas. Nos. 4542, 4547, Asian elephants. Nos. 4543, 4548, Southern corroboree frog.

2016, Sept. 20 Litho. *Perf. 14x14¾*

4537 A1041 50c multi .80 .60
4538 A1041 50c multi .80 .60
a. Horiz. pair, #4537-4538 1.60 1.20
4539 A1041 $1 multi 1.60 1.60
4540 A1041 $1 multi 1.60 1.60
4541 A1041 $1 multi 1.60 1.60
4542 A1041 $1 multi 1.60 1.60

Perf. 13¾x14

4543 A1042 $1 multi 1.60 1.60
a. Souvenir sheet of 7, #4537-4543 9.75 9.75
Nos. 4537-4543 (7) 9.60 9.20

Self-Adhesive
Serpentine Die Cut 11¼ Syncopated

4544 A1041 $1 multi 1.60 .25
4545 A1041 $1 multi 1.60 .25
4546 A1041 $1 multi 1.60 .25
4547 A1041 $1 multi 1.60 .25
a. Horiz. coil strip of 4, #4544-4547 6.40
b. Booklet pane of 20, 6 each #4544-4545, 4 each #4546, 4547 32.00

Booklet Stamp
Serpentine Die Cut 10¾x11 Syncopated

4548 A1042 $1 multi 1.60 .25
a. Booklet pane of 10 16.00
Nos. 4544-4548 (5) 8.00 1.25

Taronga Zoo, cent. (Nos. 4543, 4548).

Monotremes — A1043

Designs: $2.10, Platypus. $2.95, Short-beaked echidna.

2016, Sept. 26 Litho. *Perf. 14¾x14*

4549 A1043 $2.10 multi 3.25 3.25
4550 A1043 $2.95 multi 4.50 4.50
a. Souvenir sheet of 2, #4549-4550 7.75 7.75

Booklet Stamps
Self-Adhesive
Serpentine Die Cut 11¼ Syncopated

4551 A1043 $2.10 multi 3.25 1.60
a. Booklet pane of 5 16.50
4552 A1043 $2.95 multi 4.50 2.25
a. Booklet pane of 5 22.50

With Personalized Photo at Right Like Type A692a
Serpentine Die Cut 11½x11¼ Syncopated

4553 A1043 $2.10 multi 4.25 4.25
4554 A1043 $2.95 multi 5.50 5.50

Nos. 4553-4554 were each printed in sheets of 20 and have personalized pictures and a straight edge at right and lack separations between the stamp and the personalized photo. Sheets of 20 of No. 4553 sold for $55 each, No. 4554, $72.

Australian Involvement in Viet Nam War — A1044

Poppies and inscription: Nos. 4555, 4560, In the field. Nos. 4556, 4561, Long Tan Cross. Nos. 4557, 4562, Aid and recreation. Nos. 4558, 4563, Opposition and withdrawal. Nos. 4559, 4564, Commemoration.

2016, Oct. 11 Litho. *Perf. 14¼*

4555 A1044 $1 multi 1.60 1.60
a. Booklet pane of 4 6.50 —
4556 A1044 $1 multi 1.60 1.60
a. Booklet pane of 4 6.50 —
4557 A1044 $1 multi 1.60 1.60
a. Booklet pane of 4 6.50 —
4558 A1044 $1 multi 1.60 1.60
a. Booklet pane of 4 6.50 —
4559 A1044 $1 multi 1.60 1.60
a. Booklet pane of 4 6.50 —
Complete booklet, #4555a, 4556a, 4557a, 4558a, 4559a 32.50
b. Souvenir sheet of 5, #4555-4559 8.00 8.00
Nos. 4555-4559 (5) 8.00 8.00

Booklet Stamps
Self-Adhesive
Serpentine Die Cut 11¼ Syncopated

4560 A1044 $1 multi 1.60 .25
4561 A1044 $1 multi 1.60 .25
4562 A1044 $1 multi 1.60 .25
4563 A1044 $1 multi 1.60 .25
4564 A1044 $1 multi 1.60 .25
a. Booklet pane of 10, 2 each #4560-4564 16.00
Nos. 4560-4564 (5) 8.00 1.25

Complete booklet sold for $20.95.

Dylan Alcott, Paralympian of the Year — A1045

2016, Oct. 18 Litho. *Perf. 14¼*

4565 A1045 $1 multi 1.60 1.25

No. 4565 exists in sheets of 10.

Christmas
A1046 A1047

Designs: Nos. 4566, 4571, 4576, 4578, Star and "Goodwill." Nos. 4567, 4572, 4577, 4579, Gift and "Joy." Nos. 4568, 4573, 4580, Madonna and Child. Nos. 4569, 4574, 4581, Angel, Nos. 4570, 4575, Magi.

2016, Oct. 31 Litho. *Perf. 14¾x14*

4566 A1046 65c multi 1.00 1.00
4567 A1046 65c multi 1.00 1.00
a. Horiz. pair, #4566-4567 2.00 2.00
4568 A1047 65c multi 1.00 1.00
4569 A1047 $1.70 multi 2.60 2.60
4570 A1047 $2.55 multi 4.00 4.00
a. Souvenir sheet of 3, #4568-4570 7.75 7.75
Nos. 4566-4570 (5) 9.60 9.60

Booklet Stamps
Self-Adhesive
Serpentine Die Cut 11¼ Syncopated

4571 A1046 65c multi 1.00 .25
4572 A1047 65c multi 1.00 .25
a. Booklet pane of 20, 10 each #4971-4972, + 20 etiquettes 20.00
4573 A1047 65c multi 1.00 .25
a. Booklet pane of 20 + 20 etiquettes 20.00
4574 A1047 $1.70 multi 2.60 1.40
a. Booklet pane of 5 13.00
4575 A1047 $2.55 multi 4.00 2.00
a. Booklet pane of 5 20.00

Litho. & Embossed With Foil Application

4576 A1046 65c multi 1.00 .25
a. Booklet pane of 10 10.00
4577 A1046 65c multi 1.00 .25
a. Booklet pane of 10 10.00
Nos. 4571-4577 (7) 11.60 4.65

With Personalized Photo at Right Like Type A692a
Litho.
Serpentine Die Cut 11½x11¼ Syncopated

4578 A1046 65c multi 2.00 2.00
4579 A1046 65c multi 2.00 2.00
4580 A1047 65c multi 2.00 2.00
4581 A1047 $1.70 multi 3.50 3.50
Nos. 4578-4581 (4) 9.50 9.50

Nos. 4578-4581 were each printed in sheets of 20 and have personalized pictures and a straight edge at right and lack separations between the stamp and the personalized photo. Sheets of 20 of No. 4578-4580 each sold for $26 each, No. 4581, $47.

Rose
A1048

Heart
A1049

2017, Feb. 7 Litho. *Perf. 14¾x14*

4582 A1048 $1 multi 1.60 1.60
4583 A1049 $1 multi 1.60 1.60

Booklet Stamps
Self-Adhesive
Serpentine Die Cut 11¼ Syncopated

4584 A1048 $1 multi 1.60 .25
a. Booklet pane of 10 16.00
4585 A1049 $1 multi 1.60 .25
a. Booklet pane of 10 16.00

With Personalized Photo at Right Like Type A692a
Litho.
Serpentine Die Cut 11½x11¼ Syncopated
Self-Adhesive

4586 A1048 $1 multi 2.60 2.60
4587 A1049 $1 multi 2.60 2.60

Nos. 4586-4587 were each printed in sheets of 20 and have personalized pictures and a straight edge at right and lack separations between the stamp and the personalized photo. Sheets of 20 of Nos. 4586-4587 sold for $33 each.

Jetties — A1050

Designs: Nos. 4588, 4592, Busselton Jetty, Western Australia. Nos. 4589, 4593, Tumby Bay Jetty, South Australia. $2.10, Shelley Beach Jetty, Victoria. $2.95, Kincumber Jetty, New South Wales.

2017, Feb. 21 Litho. *Perf. 14x14¾*

4588 A1050 $1 multi 1.60 1.60
4589 A1050 $1 multi 1.60 1.60
a. Horiz. pair, #4588-4589 3.20 3.20
4590 A1050 $2.10 multi 3.25 3.25
4591 A1050 $2.95 multi 4.50 4.50
Nos. 4588-4591 (4) 10.95 10.95

Self-Adhesive

Serpentine Die Cut 11¼ Syncopated

4592 A1050 $1 multi 1.60 1.60
4593 A1050 $1 multi 1.60 1.60
a. Horiz. coil pair, #4592-4593 3.20
b. Booklet pane of 10, 5 each #4592-4593 16.00

Booklet Stamps

4594 A1050 $2.10 multi 3.25 1.60
a. Booklet pane of 5 16.50
4595 A1050 $2.95 multi 4.50 4.50
a. Booklet pane of 5 22.50
Nos. 4592-4595 (4) 10.95 9.30

Paintings and Artists — A1051

Designs: No. 4596, Near Heidelberg, by Sir Arthur Streeton (1867-1943). No. 4597, Footballer, by Sir Sidney Nolan (1917-92).

2017, Mar. 30 Litho. *Perf. 14x13½*

4596 A1051 $1 multi 1.60 1.25
4597 A1051 $1 multi 1.60 1.25
a. Horiz. pair, #4596-4597 3.20 2.50

Gems — A1052

Designs: Nos. 4598, 4602, Golden sapphire. Nos. 4599, 4603, Rhodonite. No. 4600, Fluorite. No. 4601, Pink diamond.

2017, Mar. 30 Litho. *Perf. 14¾x14*

4598 A1052 $1 multi 1.60 1.60
a. Booklet pane of 4 6.50 —
4599 A1052 $1 multi 1.60 1.60
a. Horiz. pair, #4598-4599 3.20 3.20
b. Booklet pane of 4 6.50 —
4600 A1052 $2 multi 3.00 2.25
a. Booklet pane of 4 12.50 —
4601 A1052 $2 multi 3.00 2.25
a. Horiz. pair, #4600-4601 6.00 4.50
b. Booklet pane of 4 12.50 —
c. Booklet pane of 4, #4598-4601 9.50 —
Complete booklet, #4598a, 4599b, 4600a, 4601b, 4601c 47.50
d. Souvenir sheet of 4, #4598-4601 9.25 7.75
Nos. 4598-4601 (4) 9.20 7.70

Self-Adhesive

Serpentine Die Cut 11¼ Syncopated

4602 A1052 $1 multi 1.60 1.60
4603 A1052 $1 multi 1.60 1.60
a. Vert. coil pair, #4602-4603 3.20
b. Booklet pane of 10, 5 each #4602-4603 16.00

Complete booklet sold for $30.95.

A1053

Queen Elizabeth II, 91st Birthday A1054

2017, Apr. 4 Litho. *Perf. 14¾x14*

4604 A1053 $1 multi 1.50 1.50
4605 A1054 $2.95 multi 4.50 4.50
a. Souvenir sheet of 2, #4604-4605 6.00 6.00

Booklet Stamps
Self-Adhesive

Serpentine Die Cut 11¼ Syncopated

4606 A1053 $1 multi 1.50 .25
a. Booklet pane of 10 15.00

Serpentine Die Cut 11¼

4607 A1054 $2.95 multi 4.50 2.25
a. Booklet pane of 5 22.50

World War I, Cent. — A1055

Poppy and: Nos. 4608, 4613, War in the air. Nos. 4609, 4614, Third Battle of Ypres. Nos. 4610, 4616, Support for the troops. Nos. 4611, 4615, Sinai-Palestine campaign. Nos. 4612, 4617, War correspondent Charles Bean.

2017, Apr. 18 Litho. *Perf. 14¼*

4608 A1055 $1 multi 1.50 1.50
4609 A1055 $1 multi 1.50 1.50
4610 A1055 $1 multi 1.50 1.50
4611 A1055 $1 multi 1.50 1.50
a. Booklet pane of 4, #4608-4611 6.50 —
4612 A1055 $1 multi 1.50 1.50
a. Booklet pane of 4, #4608-4610, 4612 6.50 —
b. Booklet pane of 4, #4609-4612 6.50 —
c. Booklet pane of 4, #4608, 4610-4612 6.50 —
d. Booklet pane of 4, #4608-4609, 4611-4612 6.50 —
Complete booklet, #4611a, 4612a, 4612b, 4612c, 4612d 32.50
e. Souvenir sheet of 5, #4608-4612 7.50 7.50
Nos. 4608-4612 (5) 7.50 7.50

Booklet Stamps
Self-Adhesive

Serpentine Die Cut 11¼ Syncopated

4613 A1055 $1 multi 1.50 .25
4614 A1055 $1 multi 1.50 .25
4615 A1055 $1 multi 1.50 .25
4616 A1055 $1 multi 1.50 .25
4617 A1055 $1 multi 1.50 .25
a. Booklet pane of 10, 2 each #4613-4617 15.00
Nos. 4613-4617 (5) 7.50 1.25

Complete booklet sold for $20.95.

Caves — A1056

Designs: Nos. 4618, 4622, Cliefden Caves, New South Wales. Nos. 4619, 4623, Weebubbie Cave, Western Australia. $2, Undara Lava Tube, Queensland. $3, Kubla Khan Cave, Tasmania.

2017, May 2 Litho. *Perf. 14x14¾*

4618 A1056 $1 multi 1.50 1.50
4619 A1056 $1 multi 1.50 1.50
a. Horiz. pair, #4618-4619 3.00 3.00
4620 A1056 $2 multi 3.00 2.25
4621 A1056 $3 multi 4.50 2.25
Nos. 4618-4621 (4) 10.50 7.50

Self-Adhesive

Serpentine Die Cut 11¼ Syncopated

4622 A1056 $1 multi 1.50 .25
4623 A1056 $1 multi 1.50 .25
a. Horiz. coil pair, #4622-4623 3.00
b. Booklet pane of 20, 10 each #4622-4623 30.00

Street Art — A1057

Art: Nos. 4624, 4628, Indigenous Boy, by Adnate, Hosier Lane, Melbourne. Nos. 4625, 4631, Woman, by Vans the Omega, Railway Terrace, Adelaide. Nos. 4626, 4630, Forever Curious, by Rone and Phibs, Rutledge Lane, Melbourne. Nos. 4627, 4629, Shinka, by Fin DAC, Little Rundle Street, Adelaide.

2017, May 16 Litho. *Perf. 14¾x14*

4624 A1057 $1 multi 1.50 1.50
4625 A1057 $1 multi 1.50 1.50
4626 A1057 $1 multi 1.50 1.50
4627 A1057 $1 multi 1.50 1.50
a. Souvenir sheet of 4, #4624-4627 6.00 6.00
Nos. 4624-4627 (4) 6.00 6.00

Booklet Stamps
Self-Adhesive

Serpentine Die Cut 11¼ Syncopated

4628 A1057 $1 multi 1.50 .25
4629 A1057 $1 multi 1.50 .25
4630 A1057 $1 multi 1.50 .25
4631 A1057 $1 multi 1.50 .25
a. Booklet pane of 10, 2 each #4628, 4631, 3 each #4629-4630 15.00
Nos. 4628-4631 (4) 6.00 1.00

1967 Constitutional Amendment Referendum, 50th Anniv. — A1058

2017, May 24 Litho. *Perf. 14¾x14*

4632 A1058 $1 multi 1.50 1.10

Distinguished Aborigines A1059

Designs: Nos. 4633, 4636, Tom Calma, University of Canberra Chancellor. Nos. 4634, 4637, Lowitja O'Donoghue, nurse, and first chairperson of Aboriginal and Torres Strait Islander Commission. Nos. 4635, 4638, Galarrwuy Yunupingu, Aboriginal land rights activist.

2017, May 29 Litho. *Perf. 14x14¾*

4633 A1059 $1 multi 1.50 1.50
4634 A1059 $1 multi 1.50 1.50
4635 A1059 $1 multi 1.50 1.50
Nos. 4633-4635 (3) 4.50 4.50

Booklet Stamps
Self-Adhesive

Serpentine Die Cut 11¼ Syncopated

4636 A1059 $1 multi 1.50 .25
4637 A1059 $1 multi 1.50 .25
4638 A1059 $1 multi 1.50 .25
a. Booklet pane of 20, 7 each #4636-4637, 6 #4638 30.00
Nos. 4636-4638 (3) 4.50 .75

Lions Clubs International, Cent. — A1060

2017, June 7 Litho. *Perf. 14x14¾*

4639 A1060 $1 multi 1.60 1.60

Booklet Stamp
Self-Adhesive

Serpentine Die Cut 11¼ Syncopated

4640 A1060 $1 multi 1.60 .25
a. Booklet pane of 20 32.00

Scenes from Works Written by Henry Lawson (1867-1922) A1061

Scene from: $1, *The Drover's Wife.* $2.95, *Mitchell: A Character Sketch.*

2017, June 13 Litho. *Perf. 14x14¾*

4641 A1061 $1 multi 1.60 1.60
4642 A1061 $2.95 multi 4.50 4.50
a. Souvenir sheet of 2, #4641-4642 6.25 6.25

Booklet Stamps
Self-Adhesive

Serpentine Die Cut 11¼ Syncopated

4643 A1061 $1 multi 1.60 1.60
a. Booklet pane of 20 32.00
4644 A1061 $2.95 multi 4.50 4.50
a. Booklet pane of 5 22.50

Succulent Plants — A1062

Designs: Nos. 4645, 4649, Portulaca cyclophylla. Nos. 4646, 4650, Tecticornia verrucosa. Nos. 4647, 4651, Calandrinia creethae. Nos. 4648, 4652, Gunniopsis quadrifida.

2017, June 20 Litho. *Perf. 14x14¾*

4645 A1062 $1 multi 1.60 1.60
4646 A1062 $1 multi 1.60 1.60
4647 A1062 $1 multi 1.60 1.60
4648 A1062 $1 multi 1.60 1.60
Nos. 4645-4648 (4) 6.40 6.40

Self-Adhesive

Serpentine Die Cut 11¼ Syncopated

4649 A1062 $1 multi 1.60 .25
4650 A1062 $1 multi 1.60 .25
4651 A1062 $1 multi 1.60 .25
4652 A1062 $1 multi 1.60 .25
a. Horiz. coil strip of 4, #4649-4652 6.40
b. Booklet pane of 10, 3 each #4649-4650, 2 each #4651-4652 16.00
Nos. 4649-4652 (4) 6.40 1.00

Wildflowers Type of 2015

Serpentine Die Cut 11¼ Syncopated

2017, July 4 Self-Adhesive Litho.

Booklet Stamp

4653 A1015 $2 Golden rainbow 3.25 1.60
a. Booklet pane of 5 16.50

Dated 2016.

Trans-Australian Railway Travel Posters
A1063 A1064

2017, July 4 Litho. *Perf. 14¾x14*

4654 A1063 $1 multi 1.60 1.60
4655 A1064 $1 multi 1.60 1.60
a. Souvenir sheet of 2, #4654-4655 3.25 3.25

Booklet Stamps
Self-Adhesive

Serpentine Die Cut 11¼ Syncopated

4656 A1063 $1 multi 1.60 .25
4657 A1064 $1 multi 1.60 .25
a. Booklet pane of 10, 5 each #4656-4657 16.00

A1065

Dragonflies A1066

Designs: Nos. 4658, 4663, Scarlet percher. Nos. 4659, 4664, Arrowhead rockmaster. Nos. 4660, 4666, Australian tiger. Nos. 4661, 4667, Jewel flutterer. Nos. 4662, 4665, Beautiful petaltail.

2017, Aug. 1 Litho. *Perf. 14x14¾*

4658 A1065 $1 multi 1.60 1.60
a. Perf. 14x14¾x13¾x14¾ 1.60 1.60

4659 A1065 $1 multi 1.60 1.60
a. Perf. 14x14¾x13¾x14¾ 1.60 1.60

Perf. 13¾x14

4660 A1066 $1 multi 1.60 1.60
4661 A1066 $1 multi 1.60 1.60
4662 A1066 $1 multi 1.60 1.60
a. Souvenir sheet of 5, #4658a, 4659a, 4660-4662 8.00 8.00
Nos. 4658-4662 (5) 8.00 8.00

Self-Adhesive

Serpentine Die Cut 11¼ Syncopated

4663 A1065 $1 multi 1.60 .25
4664 A1065 $1 multi 1.60 .25
a. Horiz. coil pair, #4663-4664 3.20
b. Booklet pane of 20, 10 each #4663-4664 32.00

Booklet Stamps

Serpentine Die Cut 10¾ Syncopated

4665 A1066 $1 multi 1.60 .25
4666 A1066 $1 multi 1.60 .25
4667 A1066 $1 multi 1.60 .25
a. Booklet pane of 10, 3 each #4665, 4667, 4 #4666 16.00
Nos. 4663-4667 (5) 8.00 1.25

Shipwrecks
A1067

Wreck of: Nos. 4668, 4671, HMS Pandora, 1791, and pistol. Nos. 4669, 4672, PS Clonmel, 1841, and decanter. Nos. 4670, 4673, Zuytdorp, 1712, and silver coin.

2017, Aug. 29 Litho. *Perf. 14x14¾*

4668 A1067 $1 multi 1.60 1.60
4669 A1067 $1 multi 1.60 1.60
4670 A1067 $1 multi 1.60 1.60
a. Booklet pane of 4, #4669, 4670, 2 #4668 6.75 —
b. Booklet pane of 4, #4668, 4670, 2 #4669 6.75 —
c. Booklet pane of 4, #4668, 4669, 2 #4670 (#4670 at UL and LR) 6.75 —
d. Booklet pane of 4, #4668, 4669, 2 #4670 (#4670 at UR and LL) 6.75 —
Complete booklet, #4670a, 4670c, 4670d, 2 #4670b 34.00
Nos. 4668-4670 (3) 4.80 4.80

Self-Adhesive

Serpentine Die Cut 11¼ Syncopated

4671 A1067 $1 multi 1.60 .25
4672 A1067 $1 multi 1.60 .25
4673 A1067 $1 multi 1.60 .25
a. Horiz. coil strip of 3, #4671-4673 4.80
b. Booklet pane of 10, 4 #4671, 3 each #4672-4673 16.00
Nos. 4671-4673 (3) 4.80 .75

Complete booklet sold for $20.95. The pane margins differ on the two examples of No. 4670b in the complete booklet.

Heard Island — A1068

Designs: No. 4674, Southern elephant seals. No. 4675, Kerguelen cabbage. No. 4676, King penguins. No. 4677, Baudissin Glacier.

2017, Sept. 5 Litho. *Perf. 14¼*

4674 A1068 $1 multi 1.60 1.25
4675 A1068 $1 multi 1.60 1.25
4676 A1068 $1 multi 1.60 1.25
4677 A1068 $1 multi 1.60 1.25
a. Souvenir sheet of 4, #4674-4677 6.50 5.00
Nos. 4674-4677 (4) 6.40 5.00

Launch of Weapons Research Satellite, 50th Anniv. — A1069

2017, Sept. 12 Litho. *Perf. 14¾x14*

4678 A1069 $1 multi 1.60 1.60

Booklet Stamp
Self-Adhesive

Serpentine Die Cut 11¼ Syncopated

4679 A1069 $1 multi 1.60 .25
a. Booklet pane of 20 32.00

Water Plants — A1070

Designs: $2.10, Entire marshwort. $2.30, Giant waterlily. $3, Lotus lily.

2017, Sept. 27 Litho. *Perf. 14x14¾*

4680 A1070 $2.10 multi 3.25 3.25
4681 A1070 $2.30 multi 3.75 3.75
4682 A1070 $3 multi 4.75 4.75
Nos. 4680-4682 (3) 11.75 11.75

Booklet Stamps
Self-Adhesive

Serpentine Die Cut 11¼ Syncopated

4683 A1070 $2.10 multi 3.25 1.60
a. Booklet pane of 5 16.50
4684 A1070 $2.30 multi 3.75 1.90
a. Booklet pane of 5 19.00
4685 A1070 $3 multi 4.75 2.40
a. Booklet pane of 5 24.00
Nos. 4683-4685 (3) 11.75 5.90

"Australia" — A1071

Serpentine Die Cut 11¼ Syncopated
2017, Oct. 2 Self-Adhesive Litho.
Booklet Stamps

4686 A1071 ($1) multi 1.75 .25
a. Booklet pane of 5 8.75

No. 4686a was made available to holders of Australia Post My Post Concession Account card and the general public. Pensioners, veterans, the disabled, and others typically on low or fixed incomes, could apply at their local post office to receive a Concession Account card. Those eligible to receive the card were sent a free example of No. 4686a, which was mailed with the card. Card holders, when showing the card at the post office and having the information recorded, could purchase up to ten No. 4686a every year for $3 (60c per stamp, lower than the $1 letter rate). The examples of No. 4686a made available to the public through the philatelic bureau sold for $5.45 ($1.09 per stamp). There are no differences between the stamps offered to card holders and the general public, aside from the selling price. No. 4686 was valid only on domestic letters and could not be used on parcels or international mail.

Women at War — A1072

Poppies and women in: Nos. 4687, 4692, World War I. Nos. 4688, 4693, World War II. Nos. 4689, 4694, Korea and Viet Nam. Nos. 4690, 4695, Afghanistan and Iraq. Nos. 4691, 4696, Peacekeeping.

2017, Oct. 6 Litho. *Perf. 14¼*

4687 A1072 $1 multi 1.60 1.60
4688 A1072 $1 multi 1.60 1.60
4689 A1072 $1 multi 1.60 1.60
4690 A1072 $1 multi 1.60 1.60
4691 A1072 $1 multi 1.60 1.60
a. Souvenir sheet of 5, #4687-4691 8.00 8.00
Nos. 4687-4691 (5) 8.00 8.00

Booklet Stamps
Self-Adhesive

Serpentine Die Cut 11¼ Syncopated

4692 A1072 $1 multi 1.60 .25
4693 A1072 $1 multi 1.60 .25
4694 A1072 $1 multi 1.60 .25
4695 A1072 $1 multi 1.60 .25
4696 A1072 $1 multi 1.60 .25
a. Booklet pane of 10, 2 each #4692-4696 16.00
Nos. 4692-4696 (5) 8.00 1.25

Items Starting With Same Letter Type of 2016

Designs: Nos. 4697, 4702, Barramundi in billy on barbecue, blowflies, and budgie-smugglers (bathing suit). Nos. 4698, 4703, Galahs, gasket, gecko, gnome, man in gumboots, signs to Gladstone, Great Barrier Reef and Gulargambone. Nos. 4699, 4704, Jabiru, jillaroo, jam and jumbucks. No. 4700, 4705, Kangaroo, koala, kelpie. Nos. 4701, 4706, Ulysses butterfly, ute, uggs, umpire with ukulele, umbrella.

2017, Oct. 17 Litho. *Perf. 14¾x14*

4697 A1028 $1 multi 1.60 1.60
4698 A1028 $1 multi 1.60 1.60
4699 A1028 $1 multi 1.60 1.60
4700 A1028 $1 multi 1.60 1.60
4701 A1028 $1 multi 1.60 1.60
Nos. 4697-4701 (5) 8.00 8.00

Self-Adhesive

Serpentine Die Cut 11¼ Syncopated

4702 A1028 $1 multi 1.60 .25
a. Booklet pane of 10 16.00
4703 A1028 $1 multi 1.60 .25
a. Booklet pane of 10 16.00
4704 A1028 $1 multi 1.60 .25
a. Booklet pane of 10 16.00
4705 A1028 $1 multi 1.60 .25
a. Booklet pane of 10 16.00
4706 A1028 $1 multi 1.60 .25
a. Booklet pane of 10 16.00
b. Vert. coil strip of 5, #4702-4706 8.00
Nos. 4702-4706 (5) 8.00 1.25

Aboriginal Art — A1073

Designs: Nos. 4707, 4711, Pukumani Poles, by Bede Tungutalum. Nos. 4708, 4712, Waterlili and Gaya, by Banduk Marika. No. 4709, Untitled, by Tungutalum. No. 4710, Guyamala, by Marika.

2017, Oct. 24 Litho. *Perf. 14¾x14*

4707 A1073 $1 multi 1.60 1.60
4708 A1073 $1 multi 1.60 1.60
4709 A1073 $2 multi 3.25 3.25
4710 A1073 $2 multi 3.25 3.25
Nos. 4707-4710 (4) 9.70 9.70

Booklet Stamps
Self-Adhesive

Serpentine Die Cut 11¼ Syncopated

4711 A1073 $1 multi 1.60 .25
4712 A1073 $1 multi 1.60 .25
a. Booklet pane of 20, 10 each #4711-4712 32.00

Christmas
A1074 A1075

Designs: Nos. 4713, 4718, Madonna and Child projected on St. Mary's Cathedral, Sydney. Nos. 4714, 4719, 4723, Christmas gift boxes. Nos. 4715, 4720, 4724, Star and Christmas tree. $2, Bells. $2.30, Small Cowper Madonna projected on St. Mary's Cathedral.

2017, Nov. 1 Litho. *Perf. 14¾x14*

4713 A1074 65c multi 1.00 1.00
4714 A1075 65c multi 1.00 1.00
4715 A1075 65c multi 1.00 1.00
a. Horiz. pair, #4714-4715 2.00 2.00
4716 A1075 $2 multi 3.25 1.60
4717 A1074 $2.30 multi 3.50 1.75
a. Souvenir sheet of 2, #4713, 4717 4.50 2.75
Nos. 4713-4717 (5) 9.75 6.35

Booklet Stamps
Self-Adhesive

Serpentine Die Cut 11¼ Syncopated

4718 A1074 65c multi 1.00 .25
a. Booklet pane of 20 + 20 labels 20.00
4719 A1075 65c multi 1.00 .25
4720 A1075 65c multi 1.00 .25
a. Booklet pane of 20, 10 each #4719-4720 + 20 labels 20.00
4721 A1075 $2 multi 3.25 1.60
a. Booklet pane of 5 16.50
4722 A1074 $2.30 multi 3.50 1.75
a. Booklet pane of 5 17.50

Litho. With Foil Application

4723 A1075 65c gold & multi 1.00 .25
a. Booklet pane of 10 10.00
4724 A1075 65c gold & multi 1.00 .25
a. Booklet pane of 10 10.00
Nos. 4718-4724 (7) 11.75 4.60

Australian Convict Heritage — A1076

Designs: Nos. 4730, 4733, Hyde Park Barracks, Sydney, New South Wales Colony, ticket of leave, and chain gang. Nos. 4731, 4734, Penitentiary, Van Diemen's Land, convict love token. $3, Convict Establishment (Fremantle Prison), Swan River Colony, article from newspaper about life on convict transport ships.

2018, Jan. 16 Litho. *Perf. 14x14¾*

4730 A1076 $1 multi 1.60 1.60
4731 A1076 $1 multi 1.60 1.60
4732 A1076 $3 multi 5.00 2.50
Nos. 4730-4732 (3) 8.20 5.70

Self-Adhesive

Serpentine Die Cut 11¼ Syncopated

4733 A1076 $1 multi 1.60 .25
4734 A1076 $1 multi 1.60 .25
a. Horiz. coil pair, #4733-4734 3.20
b. Booklet pane of 10, 5 each #4733-4734 16.00

Booklet Stamp

4735 A1076 $3 multi 5.00 2.50
a. Booklet pane of 5 25.00
Nos. 4733-4735 (3) 8.20 3.00

Nos. 4732 & 4735 are inscribed: "International Post".

Television Personalities — A1077

Designs: Nos. 4736, 4741, Daryl Somers, television host. Nos. 4737, 4742, Denise Drysdale, singer and dancer. Nos. 4738, 4743, Bert Newton, television host. Nos. 4739, 4744, Kerri-Anne Kennerley, television host. Nos. 4740-4745, Ray Martin, television journalist.

2018, Jan. 18 Litho. *Perf. 14¾x14*

4736 A1077 $1 multi 1.60 1.60
4737 A1077 $1 multi 1.60 1.60
4738 A1077 $1 multi 1.60 1.60
4739 A1077 $1 multi 1.60 1.60
4740 A1077 $1 multi 1.60 1.60
Nos. 4736-4740 (5) 8.00 8.00

Booklet Stamps
Self-Adhesive

Serpentine Die Cut 11¼ Syncopated

4741 A1077 $1 multi 1.60 .25
a. Booklet pane of 10 16.00
4742 A1077 $1 multi 1.60 .25
a. Booklet pane of 10 16.00
4743 A1077 $1 multi 1.60 .25
a. Booklet pane of 10 16.00
4744 A1077 $1 multi 1.60 .25
a. Booklet pane of 10 16.00
4745 A1077 $1 multi 1.60 .25
a. Booklet pane of 10 16.00
Nos. 4741-4745 (5) 8.00 1.25

Bird
A1078

Flower
A1079

2018, Feb. 6 Litho. *Perf. 14¾x14*

4746 A1078 $1 multi 1.60 1.60
4747 A1079 $2 multi 3.25 1.60

Booklet Stamp
Self-Adhesive

Serpentine Die Cut 11¼ Syncopated

4748 A1078 $1 multi 1.60 .25
a. Booklet pane of 10 16.00

With Personalized Photo at Right Like Type A692a

Serpentine Die Cut 11½x11¼ Syncopated

4749 A1078 $1 multi 2.50 2.50
4750 A1079 $1 multi 2.50 2.50

Nos. 4749-4750 were each printed in sheets of 20 and have personalized pictures and a straight edge at right and lack separations between the stamp and the personalized photo. Sheets of 20 of Nos. 4749-4750 sold for $33 each.

Banksia Flowers — A1080

Designs: Nos. 4751, 4755, 4759, Banksia speciosa. Nos. 4752, 4756, 4760, Banksia grossa. Nos. 4753, 4757, 4761, Baksia coccinea. Nos. 4754, 4758, 4762, Banksia cuneata.

2018, Feb. 20 Litho. *Perf. 14¾x14*

4751 A1080 $1 multi 1.60 1.60
4752 A1080 $1 multi 1.60 1.60
4753 A1080 $1 multi 1.60 1.60
4754 A1080 $1 multi 1.60 1.60
a. Souvenir sheet of 4, #4751-4754 6.50 6.50
Nos. 4751-4754 (4) 6.40 6.40

Booklet Stamps
Self-Adhesive

Serpentine Die Cut 11¼ Syncopated

4755 A1080 $1 multi 1.60 .25
4756 A1080 $1 multi 1.60 .25
4757 A1080 $1 multi 1.60 .25
4758 A1080 $1 multi 1.60 .25
a. Booklet pane of 20, 5 each #4755-4758 32.00
Nos. 4755-4758 (4) 6.40 1.00

With Personalized Photo at Right Like Type A692a

Serpentine Die Cut 11½x11¼ Syncopated

4759 A1080 $1 multi 2.50 2.50
4760 A1080 $1 multi 2.50 2.50
4761 A1080 $1 multi 2.50 2.50
4762 A1080 $1 multi 2.50 2.50
Nos. 4759-4762 (4) 10.00 10.00

Nos. 4759-4762 were each printed in sheets of 20 and have personalized pictures and a straight edge at right and lack separations between the stamp and the personalized photo. Sheets of 20 of Nos. 4759-4762 sold for $33 each.

19th and 20th Century Jam Can Labels — A1081

Label for: Nos. 4763, 4767, Kingurli Prince Engelbert Plum Jam. Nos. 4764, 4768, Peacock's Apricot Jam. Nos. 4765, 4769, Melray Blackberry Jam. Nos. 4766, 4770, Alva Dark Plum Jam.

2018, Mar. 6 Litho. *Perf. 14¾x14*

4763 A1081 $1 multi 1.60 1.60
4764 A1081 $1 multi 1.60 1.60
4765 A1081 $1 multi 1.60 1.60
4766 A1081 $1 multi 1.60 1.60
Nos. 4763-4766 (4) 6.40 6.40

Booklet Stamps
Self-Adhesive

Serpentine Die Cut 11¼ Syncopated

4767 A1081 $1 multi 1.60 .25
a. Booklet pane of 10 16.00
4768 A1081 $1 multi 1.60 .25
a. Booklet pane of 10 16.00
4769 A1081 $1 multi 1.60 .25
a. Booklet pane of 10 16.00
4770 A1081 $1 multi 1.60 .25
a. Booklet pane of 10 16.00
Nos. 4767-4770 (4) 6.40 1.00

Finches — A1082

Designs: Nos. 4771, 4775, Blue-faced parrot-finch. Nos. 4772, 4776, Double-barred finches. Nos. 4773, 4777, Star finches. Nos. 4774, 4778, Zebra finches.

2018, Mar. 16 Litho. *Perf. 14x14¾*

4771 A1082 $1 multi 1.60 1.60
4772 A1082 $1 multi 1.60 1.60
4773 A1082 $1 multi 1.60 1.60
4774 A1082 $1 multi 1.60 1.60
Nos. 4771-4774 (4) 6.40 6.40

Self-Adhesive

Serpentine Die Cut 11¼ Syncopated

4775 A1082 $1 multi 1.60 .25
4776 A1082 $1 multi 1.60 .25
4777 A1082 $1 multi 1.60 .25
4778 A1082 $1 multi 1.60 .25
a. Horiz. coil strip of 4, #4775-4778 6.40
b. Booklet pane of 10, 3 each #4775-4776, 2 each #4777-4778 16.00
Nos. 4775-4778 (4) 6.40 1.00

See Nos. 4811-4813.

2018 Commonwealth Games, Gold Coast, Queensland — A1083

2018, Mar. 20 Litho. *Perf. 14¾x14*

4779 A1083 $1 multi 1.60 1.25

War Memorials — A1084

Poppies, silhouette of soldier and: Nos. 4780, 4788, Legacy Memorial, Melbourne. Nos. 4781, 4785, Avenue of Honor, Ballarat. Nos. 4782, 4789, Cobbers Statue, Fromelles, France. Nos. 4783, 4787, Cenotaph, Darwin. Nos. 4784, 4786, Tomb of the Unknown Australian Soldier, Canberra.

2018, Apr. 10 Litho. *Perf. 14¼*

4780 A1084 $1 multi 1.50 1.50
a. Booklet pane of 4 7.50 —
4781 A1084 $1 multi 1.50 1.50
a. Booklet pane of 4 7.50 —
4782 A1084 $1 multi 1.50 1.50
a. Booklet pane of 4 7.50 —
4783 A1084 $1 multi 1.50 1.50
a. Booklet pane of 4 7.50 —
4784 A1084 $1 multi 1.50 1.50
a. Booklet pane of 4 7.50 —
Complete booklet, #4780a, 4781a, 4782a, 4783a, 4784a 31.50
b. Souvenir sheet of 5, #4780-4784 7.50 7.50
Nos. 4780-4784 (5) 7.50 7.50

Booklet Stamps
Self-Adhesive

Serpentine Die Cut 11¼ Syncopated

4785 A1084 $1 multi 1.50 .25
4786 A1084 $1 multi 1.50 .25
4787 A1084 $1 multi 1.50 .25
4788 A1084 $1 multi 1.50 .25
4789 A1084 $1 multi 1.50 .25
a. Booklet pane of 10, 2 each #4785-4789 15.00
Nos. 4785-4789 (5) 7.50 1.25

Complete booklet sold for $20.95.

Queen Elizabeth II, 92nd Birthday — A1085

Queen Elizabeth II: $1, And Queen Elizabeth rose. $3, Holding bouquet of flowers.

2018, Apr. 17 Litho. *Perf. 14¾x14*

4790 A1085 $1 multi 1.50 1.50
4791 A1085 $3 multi 4.50 2.25
a. Souvenir sheet of 2, #4790-4791 6.00 3.75

Booklet Stamps
Self-Adhesive

Serpentine Die Cut 11¼ Syncopated

4792 A1085 $1 multi 1.50 .25
a. Booklet pane of 10 15.00
4793 A1085 $3 multi 4.50 2.25
a. Booklet pane of 5 22.50

1868 Aboriginal XI Cricket Team — A1086

2018, May 1 Litho. *Perf. 14x14¾*

4794 A1086 $1 multi 1.50 1.10

First overseas tour of an Australian cricket team, 150th anniv.

Clouds — A1087

Cloud type: Nos. 4795, 4799, Lenticularis. Nos. 4796, 4800, Mammatus. Nos. 4797, 4801, Cumulonimbus. Nos. 4798, 4802, Arcus.

2018, May 1 Litho. *Perf. 14¼x14*

4795 A1087 $1 multi 1.50 1.50
4796 A1087 $1 multi 1.50 1.50
4797 A1087 $1 multi 1.50 1.50
4798 A1087 $1 multi 1.50 1.50
a. Souvenir sheet of 4, #4795-4798 6.00 6.00
Nos. 4795-4798 (4) 6.00 6.00

Booklet Stamps
Self-Adhesive

Serpentine Die Cut 11¼ Syncopated

4799 A1087 $1 multi 1.50 .25
a. Booklet pane of 10 15.00
4800 A1087 $1 multi 1.50 .25
a. Booklet pane of 10 15.00
4801 A1087 $1 multi 1.50 .25
a. Booklet pane of 10 15.00
4802 A1087 $1 multi 1.50 .25
a. Booklet pane of 10 15.00
Nos. 4799-4802 (4) 6.00 1.00

Silo Art — A1088

Silo from: Nos. 4803, 4807, Brim, Victoria. Nos. 4804, 4808, Ravensthorpe, Western Australia. Nos. 4805, 4809, Thallon, Queensland. Nos. 4806, 4810, Weethalle, New South Wales.

2018, May 21 Litho. *Perf. 14x14¾*

4803 A1088 $1 multi 1.50 1.50
4804 A1088 $1 multi 1.50 1.50
a. Booklet pane of 4, 2 each #4803, 4804 6.25 —
4805 A1088 $1 multi 1.50 1.50
a. Booklet pane of 4, 2 each #4803, 4805 6.25 —
4806 A1088 $1 multi 1.50 1.50
a. Booklet pane of 4, #4803-4806 6.25 —
b. Booklet pane of 4, 2 each #4804, 4806 6.25 —
c. Booklet pane of 4, 2 each #4805, 4806 6.25 —
Complete booklet, #4804a, 4805a, 4806a, 4806b, 4806c 31.50
d. Souvenir sheet of 4, #4803-4806 6.00 6.00
Nos. 4803-4806 (4) 6.00 6.00

Booklet Stamps
Self-Adhesive

Serpentine Die Cut 11¼ Syncopated

4807 A1088 $1 multi 1.50 .25
a. Booklet pane of 10 15.00
4808 A1088 $1 multi 1.50 .25
a. Booklet pane of 10 15.00
4809 A1088 $1 multi 1.50 .25
a. Booklet pane of 10 15.00
4810 A1088 $1 multi 1.50 .25
a. Booklet pane of 10 15.00
Nos. 4807-4810 (4) 6.00 1.00

Complete booklet sold for $20.95.

Finches Type of 2018

Designs: No. 4811, Gouldian finches. No. 4812, Beautiful firetail. $2, Black-throated finches.

2018, June 5 Litho. *Perf. 14x13¾*

4811 A1082 $1 multi 1.50 1.10
4812 A1082 $1 multi 1.50 1.10
4813 A1082 $2 multi 3.00 2.25
a. Souvenir sheet of 3, #4811-4813 6.00 4.50
Nos. 4811-4813 (3) 6.00 4.45

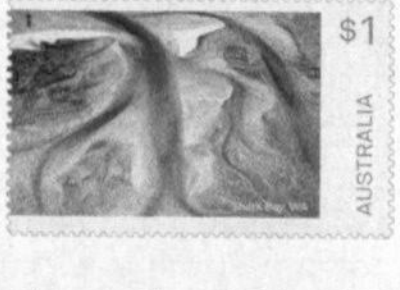

Art in Nature A1089

Aerial photographs of: Nos. 4814, 4818, Shark Bay, Western Australia. Nos. 4815, 4819, Lake MacDonnell, South Australia. Nos. 4816, 4820, Wyadup Rocks, Western Australia. Nos. 4817, 4821, Cape Capricorn, Queensland.

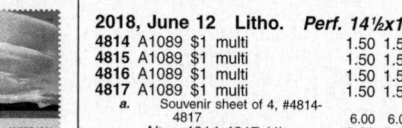

2018, June 12 Litho. *Perf. 14½x14*

4814 A1089 $1 multi 1.50 1.50
4815 A1089 $1 multi 1.50 1.50
4816 A1089 $1 multi 1.50 1.50
4817 A1089 $1 multi 1.50 1.50
a. Souvenir sheet of 4, #4814-4817 6.00 6.00
Nos. 4814-4817 (4) 6.00 6.00

Booklet Stamps
Self-Adhesive

Serpentine Die Cut 10¾x11 Syncopated

4818 A1089 $1 multi 1.50 .25
a. Booklet pane of 10 15.00
4819 A1089 $1 multi 1.50 .25
a. Booklet pane of 10 15.00
4820 A1089 $1 multi 1.50 .25
a. Booklet pane of 10 15.00
4821 A1089 $1 multi 1.50 .25
a. Booklet pane of 10 15.00
Nos. 4818-4821 (4) 6.00 1.00

Birth of Prince Louis of Cambridge — A1090

2018, July 3 Litho. *Perf. 14¼*

4822 A1090 $1 multi 1.50 1.10

Frogs — A1091

Designs: No. 4823, Armored mist frog. No. 4824, Australian lace-lid. No. 4825, Baw baw frog. No. 4826, Tasmanian tree frog.

2018, July 10 Litho. *Perf. 14x14¾*

4823 A1091 $1 multi 1.50 1.10
4824 A1091 $1 multi 1.50 1.10
4825 A1091 $1 multi 1.50 1.10
4826 A1091 $1 multi 1.50 1.10
a. Souvenir sheet of 4, #4823-4826 6.00 4.50
Nos. 4823-4826 (4) 6.00 4.40

Reef Animals — A1092

Designs: Nos. 4827, 4832a, 4833, Nautilus. Nos. 4828, 4832b, 4834, Green sea turtle. Nos. 4829, 4832c, 4835, Olive sea snake. Nos. 4830, 4832d, 4836, Emperor angelfish. Nos. 4831, 4832e, Gray reef shark (50x30mm).

Perf. 14x14¾, 14¼x14 (#4431, 4432e)

2018, Aug. 1 Litho.

Stamps With White Frames on Two Sides

4827 A1092 $1 multi 1.50 1.50
a. Booklet pane of 4 6.25 —
4828 A1092 $1 multi 1.50 1.50
a. Booklet pane of 4 6.25 —
4829 A1092 $1 multi 1.50 1.50
a. Booklet pane of 4 6.25 —
4830 A1092 $1 multi 1.50 1.50
a. Booklet pane of 4 6.25 —
4831 A1092 $2 multi 3.00 3.00
a. Booklet pane of 2 6.25 —
Complete booklet, #4827a, 4828a, 4829a, 4830a, 4831a 31.50
Nos. 4827-4831 (5) 9.00 9.00

Souvenir Sheet
Stamps Without White Frames

4832 Sheet of 5 9.00 6.75
a.-d. A1092 $1 Any single 1.50 1.10
e. A1092 $2 multi 3.00 2.25

Booklet Stamps
Self-Adhesive
Stamps With White Frames on Two Sides

Serpentine Die Cut 11¼ Syncopated

4833 A1092 $1 multi 1.50 .25
4834 A1092 $1 multi 1.50 .25
4835 A1092 $1 multi 1.50 .25
4836 A1092 $1 multi 1.50 .25
a. Booklet pane of 10, 3 each #4833-4834, 2 each #4835-4836 15.00
b. Booklet pane of 20, 5 each #4833-4836 30.00
Nos. 4833-4836 (4) 6.00 1.00

Complete booklet sold for $20.95.

Winx, Winner of 27 Consecutive Stakes Races — A1093

2018, Aug. 18 Litho. *Perf. 14x14¾*

4837 A1093 $1 multi 1.50 1.50

Booklet Stamp
Self-Adhesive

Serpentine Die Cut 11¼ Syncopated

4838 A1093 $1 multi 1.50 .25
a. Booklet pane of 10 15.00

Illustrations From Children's Novels About the Australian Bush — A1094

Illustration from: No. 4839, *The Magic Pudding*, by Norman Lindsay. No. 4840, *Tales of Snugglepot and Cuddlepie: Their Adventures Wonderful*, by May Gibbs.

2018, Aug. 21 Litho. *Perf. 14x14¾*

4839 A1094 $1 multi 1.50 1.10
4840 A1094 $1 multi 1.50 1.10
a. Souvenir sheet of 2, #4839-4840 3.00 2.25

Motorcycles A1095

Designs: Nos. 4841, 4845, 4849, 1904 Kelecom. Nos. 4842, 4846, 4850, 1912 The Precision. Nos. 4843, 4847, 4851, 1919 Whiting V4. Nos. 4844, 4848, 4852, 1923 Invincible J.A.P.

2018, Sept. 4 Litho. *Perf. 14x14¾*

4841 A1095 $1 multi 1.50 1.50
a. Booklet pane of 4 6.00 —
4842 A1095 $1 multi 1.50 1.50
a. Booklet pane of 4 6.00 —
4843 A1095 $1 multi 1.50 1.50
a. Booklet pane of 4 6.00 —
4844 A1095 $1 multi 1.50 1.50
a. Booklet pane of 4 6.00 —
b. Booklet pane of 4, #4841-4844 6.00 —
Complete booklet, #4841a, 4842a, 4843a, 4844a, 4844b 30.00
Nos. 4841-4844 (4) 6.00 6.00

Booklet Stamps
Self-Adhesive

Serpentine Die Cut 11¼ Syncopated

4845 A1095 $1 multi 1.50 .25
a. Booklet pane of 10 15.00
4846 A1095 $1 multi 1.50 .25
a. Booklet pane of 10 15.00
4847 A1095 $1 multi 1.50 .25
a. Booklet pane of 10 15.00
4848 A1095 $1 multi 1.50 .25
a. Booklet pane of 10 15.00
Nos. 4845-4848 (4) 6.00 1.00

Typo.
Coil Stamps

4849 A1095 $1 multi 1.50 .25
4850 A1095 $1 multi 1.50 .25
4851 A1095 $1 multi 1.50 .25
4852 A1095 $1 multi 1.50 .25
a. Horiz. strip of 4, #4849-4852 6.00
Nos. 4849-4852 (4) 6.00 1.00

Complete booklet sold for $20.95. Typographed coil stamps have larger dots in images than lithographed booklet stamps.

Items Starting With Same Letter
Type of 2016

Designs: Nos. 4853, 4858, Emu, egg. echidna, Eureka flag. Nos. 4854, 4859, Organ, obelisk, oar, oven, octopus, owl, oil heater, oilskin coat, opal opera house. Nos. 4855, 4860, X-ray, xylophone, Xanthorrhea grass tree. XXXX beer, Xerox machine. Nos. 4856, 4861, Yacht, yo-yo, yowie, yabbies (crawfish). Nos. 4857, 4862, Zombie on zebra crossing (crosswalk), zoologist, zebra finches.

2018, Sept. 18 Litho. *Perf. 14¾x14*

4853 A1028 $1 multi 1.50 1.50
4854 A1028 $1 multi 1.50 1.50
4855 A1028 $1 multi 1.50 1.50
4856 A1028 $1 multi 1.50 1.50
4857 A1028 $1 multi 1.50 1.50
Nos. 4853-4857 (5) 7.50 7.50

Booklet Stamps
Self-Adhesive

Serpentine Die Cut 11¼ Syncopated

4858 A1028 $1 multi 1.50 .25
a. Booklet pane of 10 15.00
4859 A1028 $1 multi 1.50 .25
a. Booklet pane of 10 15.00
4860 A1028 $1 multi 1.50 .25
a. Booklet pane of 10 15.00
4861 A1028 $1 multi 1.50 .25
a. Booklet pane of 10 15.00
4862 A1028 $1 multi 1.50 .25
a. Booklet pane of 10 15.00
Nos. 4858-4862 (5) 7.50 1.25

Farmers Inspecting Parched Land — A1095a

Serpentine Die Cut 11¼ Syncopated
2018, Sept. 20 Litho.

Booklet Stamp
Self-Adhesive

4862B A1095a $1 multi 1.50 .75
c. Booklet pane of 5 7.50

With the sale of each booklet pane of No. 4862Bc, Australia Post donated $2 to Rural Aid Limited to provide drought assistance to farms and communities.

Australian Cities A1096

Designs: $3, Melbourne. $4.60, Adelaide. $7.50, Brisbane.

2018, Sept. 25 Litho. *Perf. 14¼x14*

4863 A1096 $3 multi 4.50 4.50
4864 A1096 $4.60 multi 6.75 3.50
4865 A1096 $7.50 multi 11.00 5.50
Nos. 4863-4865 (3) 22.25 13.50

Booklet Stamp
Self-Adhesive

Serpentine Die Cut 10¾x11 Syncopated

4866 A1096 $3 multi 4.50 2.25
a. Booklet pane of 5 22.50

See Nos. 5011-5013.

World War I, Cent. — A1097

Poppy and: Nos. 4867, 4872, Soldiers resting in last hundred days of war. Nos. 4868, 4873, Lieutenant General Sir John Monash (1865-1931). Nos. 4869, 4874, Armistice declaration. Nos. 4870, 4875, Australian women awaiting return of troops. Nos. 4871, 4876, Children honoring fallen soldiers at cemetery.

2018, Oct. 2 Litho. *Perf. 14¼*

4867 A1097 $1 multi 1.50 1.50
4868 A1097 $1 multi 1.50 1.50
4869 A1097 $1 multi 1.50 1.50
4870 A1097 $1 multi 1.50 1.50
a. Booklet pane of 4, #4867-4870 6.00 —
4871 A1097 $1 multi 1.50 1.50
a. Booklet pane of 4, #4868-4871 6.00 —
b. Booklet pane of 4, #4867, 4869-4871 6.00 —
c. Booklet pane of 4, #4867-4868, 4870-4871 6.00 —
d. Booklet pane of 4, #4867-4869, 4871 6.00 —
Complete booklet, #4870a, 4871a, 4871b, 4871c, 4871d 30.00
e. Souvenir sheet of 5, #4867-4871 7.50 7.50
Nos. 4867-4871 (5) 7.50 7.50

Booklet Stamps
Self-Adhesive

Serpentine Die Cut 11¼ Syncopated

4872 A1097 $1 multi 1.50 .25
4873 A1097 $1 multi 1.50 .25
4874 A1097 $1 multi 1.50 .25
4875 A1097 $1 multi 1.50 .25
4876 A1097 $1 multi 1.50 .25
a. Booklet pane of 10, 2 each #4872-4876 15.00
Nos. 4872-4876 (5) 7.50 1.25

Complete booklet sold for $20.95.

Wedding of Prince Harry and Meghan Markle — A1098

2018, Oct. 2 Litho. *Perf. 14¼*

4877 A1098 $1 multi 1.50 1.10

Veteran A1099

Two Veterans A1100

2018, Oct. 23 Litho. *Perf. 14¾x14*

4878 A1099 $1 multi 1.50 1.10
4879 A1100 $1 multi 1.50 1.10
a. Pair, #4878-4879 3.00 2.25

Repatriation of veterans by Department of Veterans' Affairs, cent.

Lighthouses Near Sydney — A1101

Designs: Nos. 4880, 4883, Hornby Lighthouse. Nos. 4881, 4884, Robertsons Point Lighthouse. Nos. 4882, 4885, Macquarie Lighthouse.

2018, Oct. 23 Litho. *Perf. 14x14¾*

4880 A1101 $1 multi 1.50 1.50
4881 A1101 $1 multi 1.50 1.50
4882 A1101 $1 multi 1.50 1.50
a. Booklet pane of 4, #4881-4882, 2 #4880 6.00 —
b. Booklet pane of 4, #4880, 4882, 2 #4881 6.00 —
c. Booklet pane of 4, #4880-4881, 2 #4882 (#4480 at UR) 6.00 —
d. Booklet pane of 4, 2 each #4880-4881 6.00 —
e. Booklet pane of 4, #4880-4881, 2 #4882 (#4480 at UL) 6.00 —
Complete booklet, #4882a, 4882b, 4882c, 4882d, 4882e 30.00
f. Souvenir sheet of 3, #4880-4882 4.50 4.50
Nos. 4880-4882 (3) 4.50 4.50

Self-Adhesive

Serpentine Die Cut 11¼ Syncopated

4883 A1101 $1 multi 1.50 .25
4884 A1101 $1 multi 1.50 .25
4885 A1101 $1 multi 1.50 .25
a. Horiz. coil strip of 3, #4883-4885 4.50
b. Booklet pane of 10, 4 #4883, 3 each #4884-4885 15.00
Nos. 4883-4885 (3) 4.50 .75

Complete booklet sold for $20.95.

Christmas
A1102 A1103

Designs: Nos. 4886, 4891, Madonna and Child. Nos. 4887, 4892, 4896, "Jingle Bells" and bell. Nos. 4888, 4893, 4897, "Glad Tidings" and Christmas tree. $2, "Noel" and star. $2.30, Angels.

2018, Nov. 1 Litho. *Perf. 14¾x14*

4886 A1102 65c multi .95 .95
4887 A1103 65c multi .95 .95
4888 A1103 65c multi .95 .95
a. Horiz. pair, #4887-4888 1.90 1.90
4889 A1103 $2 multi 3.00 3.00
4890 A1102 $2.30 multi 3.50 3.50
a. Souvenir sheet of 2, #4886, 4890 4.50 4.50
Nos. 4886-4890 (5) 9.35 9.35

Booklet Stamps
Self-Adhesive

Serpentine Die Cut 11¼ Syncopated

4891 A1102 65c multi .95 .25
a. Booklet pane of 20 + 20 etiquettes 19.00
4892 A1103 65c multi .95 .25
4893 A1103 65c multi .95 .25
a. Booklet pane of 20, 10 each #4892-4893, + 20 etiquettes 19.00
4894 A1103 $2 multi 3.00 1.50
a. Booklet pane of 5 15.00
4895 A1102 $2.30 multi 3.50 1.75
a. Booklet pane of 5 17.50

Litho. With Foil Application

4896 A1103 65c multi .95 .25
a. Booklet pane of 10 + 10 etiquettes 9.50
4897 A1103 65c multi .95 .25
a. Booklet pane of 10 + 10 etiquettes 9.50
Nos. 4891-4897 (7) 11.25 4.50

Writers of Children's Books and Their Works — A1104

Designs: Nos. 4903, 4908, Mem Fox, *Where is the Green Sheep?* Nos. 4904, 4909, Morris Gleitzman, *Once.* Nos. 4905, 4910, Leigh Hobbs, *Mr. Chicken Goes to Paris.* Nos. 4906, 4911, Alison Lester, *Magic Beach.* Nos. 4907, 4912, Shaun Tan, *The Lost Thing.*

2019, Jan. 17 Litho. *Perf. 14x14¾*

4903 A1104 $1 multi 1.50 1.50
4904 A1104 $1 multi 1.50 1.50
4905 A1104 $1 multi 1.50 1.50
4906 A1104 $1 multi 1.50 1.50
4907 A1104 $1 multi 1.50 1.50
Nos. 4903-4907 (5) 7.50 7.50

Booklet Stamps
Self-Adhesive

Serpentine Die Cut 11¼ Syncopated

4908 A1104 $1 multi 1.50 .25
a. Booklet pane of 10 15.00
4909 A1104 $1 multi 1.50 .25
a. Booklet pane of 10 15.00
4910 A1104 $1 multi 1.50 .25
a. Booklet pane of 10 15.00
4911 A1104 $1 multi 1.50 .25
a. Booklet pane of 10 15.00
4912 A1104 $1 multi 1.50 .25
a. Booklet pane of 10 15.00
Nos. 4908-4912 (5) 7.50 1.25

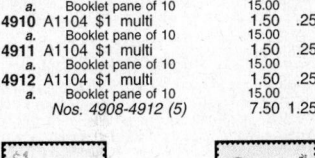

Wedding Rings A1105

Bird Carrying Flower A1106

Roses A1107

Decorated Cake A1108

Teddy Bear A1109

Party Balloons A1110

Sparkler
A1111

White Rose
A1112

2019, Feb. 5 Litho. *Perf. 14¾x14*

4913 A1105 $1 multi 1.50 1.50
4914 A1106 $1 multi 1.50 1.50
4915 A1107 $1 multi 1.50 1.50
4916 A1108 $1 multi 1.50 1.50
4917 A1109 $1 multi 1.50 1.50
4918 A1110 $1 multi 1.50 1.50
4919 A1111 $1 multi 1.50 1.50
4920 A1112 $2 multi 3.00 3.00
Nos. 4913-4920 (8) 13.50 13.50

Booklet Stamps
Self-Adhesive

Serpentine Die Cut 11¼ Syncopated

4921 A1105 $1 multi 1.50 .25
a. Booklet pane of 10 15.00
4922 A1106 $1 multi 1.50 .25
a. Booklet pane of 10 15.00
4923 A1107 $1 multi 1.50 .25
a. Booklet pane of 10 15.00
4924 A1108 $1 multi 1.50 .25
a. Booklet pane of 10 15.00
4925 A1109 $1 multi 1.50 .25
a. Booklet pane of 10 15.00
4926 A1110 $1 multi 1.50 .25
a. Booklet pane of 10 15.00
4927 A1111 $1 multi 1.50 .25
a. Booklet pane of 10 15.00
4928 A1112 $2 multi 3.00 1.50
a. Booklet pane of 4 12.00
Complete booklet, 4 #4928a 48.00
Nos. 4921-4928 (8) 13.50 3.25

With Personalized Photo at Right Like Type A692a

Serpentine Die Cut 11½x11¼ Syncopated

4929 A1105 $1 multi 2.40 2.40
4930 A1106 $1 multi 2.40 2.40
4931 A1107 $1 multi 2.40 2.40
4932 A1108 $1 multi 2.40 2.40
4933 A1109 $1 multi 2.40 2.40
4934 A1110 $1 multi 2.40 2.40
4935 A1111 $1 multi 2.40 2.40

Complete booklet sold for $32.95 and contains four examples of No. 4928a with different pane margins.

An additional stamp was issued in this set. The editors would like to see any example of it.

Nos. 4929-4935 were each printed in sheets of 20 and have personalized pictures and a straight edge at right and lack separations between the stamp and the personalized photo. Sheets of 20 of Nos. 4929-4935 sold for $33 each.

Boyd House II, South Yarra, Victoria, Designed by Robin Boyd (1919-71) — A1113

2019, Feb. 12 Litho. *Perf. 14x14¾*

4937 A1113 $1 multi 1.40 1.10

Discovery of Welcome Stranger Gold Nugget, 150th Anniv. — A1114

2019, Feb. 26 Litho. *Perf. 14x14¾*

4938 A1114 $1 multi 1.40 1.10

Booklet Stamp
Self-Adhesive

Serpentine Die Cut 11¼ Syncopated

4939 A1114 $1 multi 1.40 .25
a. Booklet pane of 20 28.00

Australian Animals — A1115

Designs: Nos. 4940, 4944, Galah. Nos. 4941, 4945, Red kangaroo. Nos. 4942, 4946, Tasmanian devil. Nos. 4943, 4947, Blue-tongue lizard.

2019, Mar. 5 Litho. *Perf. 14x14¾*

4940 A1115 $1 multi 1.40 1.40
4941 A1115 $1 multi 1.40 1.40
4942 A1115 $1 multi 1.40 1.40
4943 A1115 $1 multi 1.40 1.40
Nos. 4940-4943 (4) 5.60 5.60

Self-Adhesive

Serpentine Die Cut 11¼ Syncopated

4944 A1115 $1 multi 1.40 .25
a. Booklet pane of 10 14.00
4945 A1115 $1 multi 1.40 .25
a. Booklet pane of 10 14.00
4946 A1115 $1 multi 1.40 .25
a. Booklet pane of 10 14.00
4947 A1115 $1 multi 1.40 .25
a. Booklet pane of 10 14.00
b. Hoirz. coil strip of 4, #4944-4947 5.60
Nos. 4944-4947 (4) 5.60 1.00

Sustainable Fish — A1116

Designs: Nos. 4948, 4951, Patagonian toothfish and fishing boat with bird exclusion device. Nos. 4949, 4952, Blue grenadier and fishing boat with seal excluder device. Nos. 4950, 4953, Tiger flathead and fishing boat with mesh net.

2019, Mar. 14 Litho. *Perf. 14¼*

4948 A1116 $1 multi 1.50 1.50
4949 A1116 $1 multi 1.50 1.50
4950 A1116 $1 multi 1.50 1.50
a. Souvenir sheet of 3, #4948-4950 4.50 4.50
Nos. 4948-4950 (3) 4.50 4.50

Booklet Stamps
Self-Adhesive

Serpentine Die Cut 11¼ Syncopated

4951 A1116 $1 multi 1.50 .25
4952 A1116 $1 multi 1.50 .25
4953 A1116 $1 multi 1.50 .25
a. Booklet pane of 10, 4 #4951, 3 each #4952-4953 15.00
Nos. 4951-4953 (3) 4.50 .75

Queen Elizabeth II, 93rd Birthday
A1117 A1118

2019, Apr. 9 Litho. *Perf. 14¾x14*

4954 A1117 $1 multi 1.40 1.10
4955 A1118 $3 multi 4.25 4.25
a. Souvenir sheet of 2, #4954-4955 5.75 5.75

Booklet Stamp
Self-Adhesive

Serpentine Die Cut 11¼ Syncopated

4956 A1118 $3 multi 4.25 2.10
a. Booklet pane of 5 21.50

ANZAC Day — A1119

Cover of: $1, 1919 ANZAC Memorial Day souvenir program. $3, 1919 ANZAC Day souvenir program for Australian Depots in France.

2019, Apr. 16 Litho. *Perf. 14¾x14*

4957 A1119 $1 blue & multi 1.40 1.40
4958 A1119 $3 red & multi 4.25 3.25
a. Souvenir sheet of 2, #4957-4958 5.75 5.75

Booklet Stamp
Self-Adhesive

Serpentine Die Cut 11¼ Syncopated

4959 A1119 $1 blue & multi 1.40 .25
a. Booklet pane of 20 28.00

International Year of Indigenous Languages A1120

2019, Apr. 30 Litho. *Perf. 14x14¾*

4960 A1120 $1 multi 1.40 1.10

A1121

Flightless Birds — A1122

Designs: No. 4961, Emu. No. 4962, Southern cassowary. $2.30, Little penguin.

2019, May 7 Litho. *Perf. 14x14½*

4961 A1121 $1 multi 1.40 1.10
4962 A1121 $1 multi 1.40 1.10

Perf. 14x14¾

4963 A1122 $2.30 multi 3.25 3.25

Booklet Stamp
Self-Adhesive

Serpentine Die Cut 11¼ Syncopated

4964 A1122 $2.30 multi 3.25 1.60
a. Booklet pane of 5 16.50

Native Bees — A1123

Designs: Nos. 4965, 4969, Green and gold nomia bee. Nos. 4966, 4970, Neon cuckoo bee. Nos. 4967, 4971, Wasp-mimic bee. Nos. 4968, 4972, Resin bee.

2019, May 14 Litho. *Perf. 14x14¾*

4965 A1123 $1 multi 1.40 1.40
4966 A1123 $1 multi 1.40 1.40
4967 A1123 $1 multi 1.40 1.40
4968 A1123 $1 multi 1.40 1.40
Nos. 4965-4968 (4) 5.60 5.60

Booklet Stamps
Self-Adhesive

Serpentine Die Cut 11¼ Syncopated

4969 A1123 $1 multi 1.40 .25
a. Booklet pane of 10 14.00
4970 A1123 $1 multi 1.40 .25
a. Booklet pane of 10 14.00
4971 A1123 $1 multi 1.40 .25
a. Booklet pane of 10 14.00
4972 A1123 $1 multi 1.40 .25
a. Booklet pane of 10 14.00
Nos. 4969-4972 (4) 5.60 1.00

Sports Stadiums — A1124

Designs: Nos. 4973, 4977, AAMI Park, Melbourne. Nos. 4974, 4978, Optus Stadium, Perth. Nos. 4975, 4979, Sydney Cricket Ground. No. 4976, 4980, Melbourne Cricket Ground.

2019, June 4 Litho. *Perf. 14x14¾*

4973 A1124 $1 multi 1.40 1.40
4974 A1124 $1 multi 1.40 1.40
4975 A1124 $1 multi 1.40 1.40
4976 A1124 $1 multi 1.40 1.40
Nos. 4973-4976 (4) 5.60 5.60

Booklet Stamps
Self-Adhesive

Serpentine Die Cut 11¼ Syncopated

4977 A1124 $1 multi 1.40 .25
a. Booklet pane of 10 14.00
4978 A1124 $1 multi 1.40 .25
a. Booklet pane of 10 14.00
4979 A1124 $1 multi 1.40 .25
a. Booklet pane of 10 14.00
4980 A1124 $1 multi 1.40 .25
a. Booklet pane of 10 14.00
Nos. 4977-4980 (4) 5.60 1.00

Principle of Gender Pay Parity in Australia, 50th Anniv. — A1125

2019, June 18 Litho. *Perf. 14x14¾*

4981 A1125 $1 multi 1.40 1.10

Crayfish — A1126

Designs: No. 4982, Cherax cainii. No. 4983, Astacopsis gouldi. No. 4984, Euastacus sulcatus.

2019, July 2 Litho. *Perf. 14x14¾*

4982 A1126 $1 multi 1.40 1.10
4983 A1126 $1 multi 1.40 1.10
4984 A1126 $1 multi 1.40 1.10
Nos. 4982-4984 (3) 4.20 3.30

First Man on the Moon, 50th Anniv. — A1127

Designs: Nos. 4985, 4990, Apollo 11 Lunar Module "Eagle". Nos. 4986, 4991, Parkes Radio Telescope, Parkes, New South Wales. Nos. 4987, 4992, First Moon walk. Nos. 4988, 4993, Telecast of moon walk via Honeysuckle Creek Tracking Station, Australian Capital Territory.

2019, July 16 Litho. *Perf. 14¾x14*

4985 A1127 $1 multi 1.40 1.40
4986 A1127 $1 multi 1.40 1.40
4987 A1127 $1 multi 1.40 1.40
4988 A1127 $1 multi 1.40 1.40
Nos. 4985-4988 (4) 5.60 5.60
4989 Souvenir sheet of 4, #4985, 4987, 4989a, 4989b 5.60 5.60
a. A1127 $1 As #4986, Litho. with silver foil application 1.40 1.40
b. A1127 $1 As #4988, Litho. with silver foil application 1.40 1.40

Self-Adhesive

Serpentine Die Cut 11¼ Syncopated

4990 A1127 $1 multi 1.40 .25
a. Booklet pane of 10 14.00
4991 A1127 $1 multi 1.40 .25
a. Booklet pane of 10 14.00
4992 A1127 $1 multi 1.40 .25
a. Booklet pane of 10 14.00
4993 A1127 $1 multi 1.40 .25
a. Booklet pane of 10 14.00
b. Vert. coil strip of 4, #4990-4993 5.60
Nos. 4990-4993 (4) 5.60 1.00

Gardening — A1128

Designs: Nos. 4994, 4999, Rainwater garden. Nos. 4995, 5000, Worm farm. Nos. 4996, 5001, Nest box. Nos. 4997, 5002, Pollinators. $2, Vegetable garden.

2019, Aug. 1 Litho. *Perf. 14x14¾*

4994 A1128 $1 multi 1.40 1.40
a. Booklet pane of 4 5.75 —
4995 A1128 $1 multi 1.40 1.40
a. Booklet pane of 4 5.75 —
4996 A1128 $1 multi 1.40 1.40
a. Booklet pane of 4 5.75 —

Size: 50x30mm

Perf. 14½x14

4997 A1128 $1 multi 1.40 1.40
a. Booklet pane of 4 5.75 —
4998 A1128 $2 multi 2.75 2.10
a. Booklet pane of 2 5.75 —
Complete booklet, #4994a, 4995a, 4996a, 4997a, 4998s 29.00
b. Souvenir sheet of 5, #4994-4998 8.50 7.75
Nos. 4994-4998 (5) 8.35 7.70

Booklet Stamps
Self-Adhesive
Size: 38x26mm

Serpentine Die Cut 11¼ Syncopated

4999 A1128 $1 multi 1.40 .25
5000 A1128 $1 multi 1.40 .25
5001 A1128 $1 multi 1.40 .25
a. Booklet pane of 20, 6 each #4999, 5001, 7 #5000 28.00

Size: 50x30mm

Serpentine Die Cut 10¾ Syncopated

5002 A1128 $1 multi 1.40 .25
a. Booklet pane of 10 14.00
Nos. 4999-5002 (4) 5.60 1.00

Complete booklet sold for $20.95.

Bush Citrus — A1129

Designs: Nos. 5003, 5006, Desert lime. Nos. 5004, 5007, Finger lime. Nos. 5005, 5008, Lemon aspen.

2019, Aug. 13 Litho. *Perf. 14x14¾*

5003 A1129 $1 multi 1.40 1.40
5004 A1129 $1 multi 1.40 1.40
5005 A1129 $1 multi 1.40 1.40
a. Souvenir sheet of 3, #5003-5005 4.25 4.25
Nos. 5003-5005 (3) 4.20 4.20

Coil Stamps
Self-Adhesive

Serpentine Die Cut 11¼ Syncopated

5006 A1129 $1 multi 1.40 .25
5007 A1129 $1 multi 1.40 .25
5008 A1129 $1 multi 1.40 .25
a. Horiz. coil strip of 3, #5006-5008 4.25
Nos. 5006-5008 (3) 4.20 .75

Fall to Earth of Murchison Meteorite, 50th Anniv. — A1130

2019, Sept. 10 Litho. *Perf. 14¾x14*

5009 A1130 $1 multi 1.40 1.10

Animals Type of 2006

Design: $2.50, Greater bilby.

Serpentine Die Cut 11¼ Syncopated
2019, Sept. 23 Litho.

Booklet Stamp
Self-Adhesive

5010 A707 $2.50 multi 3.50 1.75
a. Booklet pane of 5 17.50

Australian Cities Type of 2018

Designs: $3.20, Sydney. $5, Perth.

2019, Sept. 23 Litho. *Perf. 14¼x14*

5011 A1096 $3.20 multi 4.25 4.25
5012 A1096 $5 multi 6.75 3.00

Booklet Stamp
Self-Adhesive

Serpentine Die Cut 10¾x11 Syncopated

5013 A1096 $3.20 multi 4.25 2.10
a. Booklet pane of 5 21.50

Australian Team for 2019 The Ashes Test Cricket Series With Trophy — A1131

2019, Oct. 1 Litho. *Perf. 14¼*

5014 A1131 $1 multi 1.40 1.10

Marriage Equality
A1132 A1133

2019, Oct. 1 Litho. *Perf. 14¾x14*

5015 A1132 $1 multi 1.40 1.10
5016 A1133 $1 multi 1.40 1.10

Vickers Vimy and Crew — A1134

Label and Handstamp for First Great Britain to Australia Airmail Flight A1135

2019, Oct. 1 Litho. *Perf. 14¾x14*

5017 A1134 $1 multi 1.40 1.40
a. Booklet pane of 4 5.75 —
5018 A1135 $3.20 multi 4.25 4.25
a. Booklet pane of 2 9.25 —
Complete booklet, #5018a, 4 #5017a 32.50
b. Souvenir sheet of 2, #5017-5018 5.75 5.75

Booklet Stamps
Self-Adhesive

Serpentine Die Cut 11¼ Syncopated

5019 A1134 $1 multi 1.40 .25
a. Booklet pane of 20 28.00 —

Serpentine Die Cut 11¾x11½ Syncopated

5020 A1135 $3.20 multi 4.25 2.10
a. Booklet pane of 5 21.50 —

First Great Britain-Australia airmail flight, captained by Ross Smith, cent. Complete booklet contains four examples of No. 5017a, each with different pane margins, and sold for $23.95.

Seeds of Endangered Plant Species in Seed Banks — A1136

Designs: Nos. 5021, 5024, Rytidosperma clelandii. Nos. 5022, 5025, Epacris petrophila. Nos. 5023, 5026, Petrophile latericola.

2019, Oct. 8 Litho. *Perf. 14¾x14*

5021 A1136 $1 multi 1.40 1.40
5022 A1136 $1 multi 1.40 1.40
5023 A1136 $1 multi 1.40 1.40
Nos. 5021-5023 (3) 4.20 4.20

Booklet Stamps
Self-Adhesive

Serpentine Die Cut 11¼ Syncopated

5024 A1136 $1 multi 1.40 .25
a. Booklet pane of 10 14.00
5025 A1136 $1 multi 1.40 .25
a. Booklet pane of 10 14.00
5026 A1136 $1 multi 1.40 .25
a. Booklet pane of 10 14.00
Nos. 5024-5026 (3) 4.20 .75

Items Starting With Same Letter Type of 2016

Designs: Nos. 5027, 5033, Dog, digger, Daily News, dentures, dunny (outhouse). Nos. 5028, 5034, Father, fish in fish creel, fishing pole and gear, child with football. Nos. 5029, 5035, Housewife hanging laundry on Hills Hoist, hibiscus. Nos. 5030, 5036, Ibis, ironing board, ironman triathlete holding iron. Nos. 5031, 5037, Mechanic feeding macadamia nuts to mud crab, milk carton, mallet. Nos. 5032, 5038, Platypus eating peach and pineapple pavlova, presents, possum, python, pelican, picket fence.

2019, Oct. 22 Litho. *Perf. 14¾x14*

5027 A1028 $1 multi 1.40 1.40
5028 A1028 $1 multi 1.40 1.40
5029 A1028 $1 multi 1.40 1.40
5030 A1028 $1 multi 1.40 1.40
5031 A1028 $1 multi 1.40 1.40
5032 A1028 $1 multi 1.40 1.40
a. Souvenir sheet of 6, #5027-5032 8.50 8.50
Nos. 5027-5032 (6) 8.40 8.40

Booklet Stamps
Self-Adhesive

Serpentine Die Cut 11¼ Syncopated

5033 A1028 $1 multi 1.40 .25
a. Booklet pane of 10 14.00
5034 A1028 $1 multi 1.40 .25
a. Booklet pane of 10 14.00
5035 A1028 $1 multi 1.40 .25
a. Booklet pane of 10 14.00
5036 A1028 $1 multi 1.40 .25
a. Booklet pane of 10 14.00
5037 A1028 $1 multi 1.40 .25
a. Booklet pane of 10 14.00
5038 A1028 $1 multi 1.40 .25
a. Booklet pane of 10 14.00
Nos. 5033-5038 (6) 8.40 1.50

Christmas
A1137 A1138

Designs: Nos. 5039, 5044, 5051Flight into Egypt. Nos. 5040, 5046, 5049, 5052, Christmas tree. Nos. 5041, 5045, 5050, Star. Nos. 5042, 5047, 5053, Adoration of the Magi. Nos. 5043, 5048, 5054, Christmas gift.

2019, Nov. 1 Litho. *Perf. 14¾x14*

5039 A1137 65c multi .90 .90
5040 A1138 65c multi .90 .90
5041 A1138 65c multi .90 .90
a. Horiz. pair, #5040-5041 1.80 1.80
5042 A1137 $2.20 multi 3.00 3.00
a. Souvenir sheet of 2, #5039, 5042 4.00 4.00
5043 A1138 $2.20 multi 3.00 3.00
Nos. 5039-5043 (5) 8.70 8.70

Booklet Stamps
Self-Adhesive

Serpentine Die Cut 11¼ Syncopated

5044 A1137 65c multi .90 .25
a. Booklet pane of 20 + 20 etiquettes 18.00
5045 A1138 65c multi .90 .25
5046 A1138 65c multi .90 .25
a. Booklet pane of 20, 10 each #5045-5046, + 20 etiquettes 18.00
5047 A1137 $2.20 multi 3.00 1.50
a. Booklet pane of 5 15.00
5048 A1138 $2.20 multi 3.00 1.50
a. Booklet pane of 5 15.00

Litho. With Foil Application

5049 A1138 65c multi .90 .25
a. Booklet pane of 10 + 10 etiquettes 9.00
5050 A1138 65c multi .90 .25
a. Booklet pane of 10 + 10 etiquettes 9.00
Nos. 5044-5050 (7) 10.50 4.25

With Personalized Photo at Right Like Type A692a

Litho.

Serpentine Die Cut 11½x11¼ Syncopated

5051 A1137 65c multi 2.00 2.00
5052 A1138 65c multi 2.00 2.00
5053 A1137 $2.20 multi 6.75 6.75
5054 A1138 $2.20 multi 6.75 6.75
Nos. 5051-5054 (4) 17.50 17.50

Nos. 5051-5054 were each printed in sheets of 20 and have personalized pictures and a straight edge at right and lack separations between the stamp and the personalized photo. Sheets of 20 of Nos. 5051-5052 sold for $26 each, and sheets of 20 of Nos. 5053-5054 sold for $57 each.

On Dec. 16, 2019, Australia Post began issuing self-adhesive personalizable stamps in nine different shapes (Australia, speech bubble, teddy bear, heart, present, star, house, curved frame and decorative frame), with each shape available initially with six different denominations (65c, $1.10, $2.20, $3.30, $5.50, and $2.20 for international use). These stamps could only be purchased in sheets of 20.

Marsupials A1139

Designs: Nos. 5055, 5059, Koala. Nos. 5056, 5060, Wombat. $2.20, Echidna. $3.30, Sugar glider.

2019, Dec. 16 Litho. *Perf. 14x14¾*

5055 A1139 $1.10 multi 1.60 1.60
a. Souvenir sheet of 4 6.50 6.50
5056 A1139 $1.10 multi 1.60 1.60
a. Souvenir sheet of 4 6.50 6.50
5057 A1139 $2.20 multi 3.25 1.60
a. Souvenir sheet of 2 6.50 6.50
5058 A1139 $3.30 multi 4.75 2.40
a. Souvenir sheet of 2 9.50 5.00
Nos. 5055-5058 (4) 11.20 7.20

Self-Adhesive

Serpentine Die Cut 11¼ Syncopated

5059 A1139 $1.10 multi 1.60 .25
a. Booklet pane of 10 16.00
5060 A1139 $1.10 multi 1.60 .25
a. Booklet pane of 20 32.00
b. Horiz. coil pair, #5059-5060 3.20

NZ 2020 Stamp Exhibition, Auckland, New Zealand (Nos. 5055a, 5056a, 5057a, 5058a). Issued: Nos. 5055a, 5056a, 5057a, 5058a, Mar. 2020. The NZ 2020 Stamp Exhibition was halted on Mar. 21, 2020 because of the COVID-19 pandemic.

Teddy Bear A1140

Party Balloons A1141

Gifts A1142

"Let's Party!" A1143

Flowers A1144

Champagne Flutes A1145

Bridal Bouquet A1146

Map of Australia and Southern Cross Constellation A1147

Kangaroo's Paw Flower and Southern Cross Constellation A1148

Wedding Ring A1149

2020, Jan. 2 Litho. *Perf. 14¾x14*

5061 A1140 $1.10 multi 1.60 1.60
5062 A1141 $1.10 multi 1.60 1.60
5063 A1142 $1.10 multi 1.60 1.60
5064 A1143 $1.10 multi 1.60 1.60
5065 A1144 $1.10 multi 1.60 1.60
5066 A1145 $1.10 multi 1.60 1.60
5067 A1146 $1.10 multi 1.60 1.60
5068 A1147 $1.10 multi 1.60 1.25
5069 A1148 $1.10 multi 1.60 1.25
5070 A1149 $2.20 multi 3.25 3.25
a. Souvenir sheet of 10, #5061-5070 18.00 18.00
Nos. 5061-5070 (10) 17.65 16.95

Booklet Stamps
Self-Adhesive

Serpentine Die Cut 11¼ Syncopated

5071 A1140 $1.10 multi 1.60 .25
a. Booklet pane of 10 + 5 stickers 16.00
5072 A1141 $1.10 multi 1.60 .25
a. Booklet pane of 10 + 5 stickers 16.00
5073 A1142 $1.10 multi 1.60 .25
a. Booklet pane of 10 + 5 stickers 16.00
5074 A1143 $1.10 multi 1.60 .25
a. Booklet pane of 10 + 5 stickers 16.00
5075 A1144 $1.10 multi 1.60 .25
a. Booklet pane of 10 + 5 stickers 16.00
5076 A1145 $1.10 multi 1.60 .25
a. Booklet pane of 10 + 5 stickers 16.00
5077 A1146 $1.10 multi 1.60 .25
a. Booklet pane of 10 + 5 stickers 16.00
5078 A1149 $2.20 multi 3.25 1.60
a. Booklet pane of 4 13.00
Complete booklet, 4 #5078a 52.00
Nos. 5071-5078 (8) 14.45 3.35

Complete booklet sold for $35.95 and the four panes in it have different pane margins.

Tree-dwelling Mammals — A1150

Designs: No. 5089, Bennett's tree kangaroo. No. 5090, Spectacled flying fox. No. 5091, Lemuroid ringtail possum.

2020, Jan. 21 Litho. *Perf. 14¾x14*

5089 A1150 $1.10 multi 1.50 1.10
5090 A1150 $1.10 multi 1.50 1.10
5091 A1150 $1.10 multi 1.50 1.10
a. Souvenir sheet of 3, #5089-5091 4.50 3.50
Nos. 5089-5091 (3) 4.50 3.30

Sports Broadcasters A1151

Designs: No. 5092, Richie Benaud (1930-2015), cricket commentator. No. 5093, Reg Gasnier (1939-2014), rugby commentator. No. 5094, Les Murray (1945-2017), soccer commentator. $2.20, Lou Richards (1923-2017), Jack Dyer (1913-2003), and Bob Davis (1928-2011), Australia rules football commentators.

2020, Feb. 4 Litho. *Perf. 14x14¾*

5092 A1151 $1.10 multi 1.50 1.10
a. Booklet pane of 4 6.00 —
5093 A1151 $1.10 multi 1.50 1.10
a. Booklet pane of 4 6.00 —
5094 A1151 $1.10 multi 1.50 1.10
a. Booklet pane of 4 6.00 —

Size: 50x30mm

Perf. 14¼x14

5095 A1151 $2.20 multi 3.00 2.25
a. Booklet pane of 2 6.00 —
Complete booklet, #5092a, 5093a, 5094a, 3 #5095a 36.00
Nos. 5092-5095 (4) 7.50 5.55

Complete booklet sold for $26.95 and the three panes of No. 5095a in it have different pane margins.

Completion of Standard Gauge Transcontinental Rail Line, 50th Anniv. — A1152

2020, Feb. 11 Litho. *Perf. 14x14¾*

5096 A1152 $1.10 multi 1.50 1.50
a. Souvenir sheet of 4 6.00 6.00

Booklet Stamp
Self-Adhesive

Serpentine Die Cut 11¼ Syncopated

5097 A1152 $1.10 multi 1.50 .25
a. Booklet pane of 20 30.00

Canberra Stampshow 2020 (No. 5096a). Issued: No. 5096a, 3/13/20.

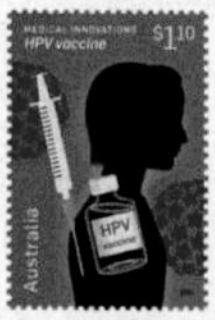

Medical Innovations — A1153

Designs: Nos. 5098, 5102, Human papillomavirus vaccine. Nos. 5099, 5103, Implanted cardiac pacemaker. Nos. 5100, 5104, Spray-on skin cells. $3.20, Medical use of penicillin.

2020, Feb. 18 Litho. *Perf. 14¾x14*

5098 A1153 $1.10 multi 1.50 1.50
5099 A1153 $1.10 multi 1.50 1.50
5100 A1153 $1.10 multi 1.50 1.50
5101 A1153 $3.20 multi 4.25 4.25
Nos. 5098-5101 (4) 8.75 8.75

Booklet Stamps
Self-Adhesive

Serpentine Die Cut 11¼ Syncopated

5102 A1153 $1.10 multi 1.50 .25
5103 A1153 $1.10 multi 1.50 .25
5104 A1153 $1.10 multi 1.50 .25
a. Booklet pane of 20, 8 #5102, 7 #5103, 5 #5104 30.00
5105 A1153 $3.20 multi 4.25 2.10
a. Booklet pane of 5 21.50
Nos. 5102-5105 (4) 8.75 2.85

S.S. Wonga Wonga — A1154

2020, Mar. 3 Litho. *Perf. 14x14¾*

5106 A1154 $1.10 multi 1.50 1.10

Mail steamer service between Sydney and San Francisco, 150th anniv.

Sports Stadiums — A1155

Designs: Nos. 5107, 5111, Rod Laver Arena, Melbourne. Nos. 5108, 5112, Adelaide Oval, Adelaide. Nos. 5109, 5113, Anne Meares Velodrome, Brisbane. Nos. 5110, 5114, Sydney Olympic Park Aquatic Center, Sydney.

2020, Mar. 24 Litho. *Perf. 14x14¾*

5107 A1155 $1.10 multi 1.40 1.40
5108 A1155 $1.10 multi 1.40 1.40
5109 A1155 $1.10 multi 1.40 1.40
5110 A1155 $1.10 multi 1.40 1.40
Nos. 5107-5110 (4) 5.60 5.60

Self-Adhesive

Serpentine Die Cut 11¼ Syncopated

5111 A1155 $1.10 multi 1.40 .25
a. Booklet pane of 10 14.00
5112 A1155 $1.10 multi 1.40 .25
a. Booklet pane of 10 14.00
5113 A1155 $1.10 multi 1.40 .25
a. Booklet pane of 10 14.00
5114 A1155 $1.10 multi 1.40 .25
a. Booklet pane of 10 14.00
b. Horiz. coil strip of 4, #5111-5114 5.60
Nos. 5111-5114 (4) 5.60 1.00

Queen Elizabeth II, 94th Birthday
A1156 A1157

2020, Apr. 7 Litho. *Perf. 14¾x14*

5115 A1156 $1.10 multi 1.40 1.10
5116 A1157 $3.20 multi 4.25 4.25
a. Souvenir sheet of 2, #5115-5116 5.75 5.75

Booklet Stamp
Self-Adhesive

Serpentine Die Cut 11¼ Syncopated

5117 A1157 $3.20 multi 4.25 2.10
a. Booklet pane of 5 21.50

ANZAC Day — A1158

Paintings: Nos. 5118, 5122, The Sock Knitter, by Grace Cossington Smith (1892-1984). Nos. 5119, 5123, A Man, by Hilda Rix Nicholas (1884-1961). Nos. 5120, 5124, Group of VADS, by William Dargie (1912-2003). Nos. 5121, 5125, Bomber Crew, by Stella Bowen (1893-1947).

2020, Apr. 14 Litho. *Perf. 14¾x14*

5118 A1158 $1.10 multi 1.40 1.40
5119 A1158 $1.10 multi 1.40 1.40
5120 A1158 $1.10 multi 1.40 1.40
5121 A1158 $1.10 multi 1.40 1.40
a. Souvenir sheet of 4, #5118-5121 5.75 5.75
Nos. 5118-5121 (4) 5.60 5.60

Coil Stamps
Self-Adhesive

Serpentine Die Cut 11¼ Syncopated

5122 A1158 $1.10 multi 1.40 .25
5123 A1158 $1.10 multi 1.40 .25
5124 A1158 $1.10 multi 1.40 .25
5125 A1158 $1.10 multi 1.40 .25
a. Vert. coil strip of 4, #5122-5125 5.60
Nos. 5122-5125 (4) 5.60 1.00

Comedians A1159

Designs: Nos. 5126, 5130, Noeline Brown. Nos. 5127, 5131, Adam Hills. Nos. 5128, 5132, Garry McDonald. Nos. 5129, 5133, Magda Szubanski.

2020, Apr. 15 Litho. *Perf. 14x14¾*

5126 A1159 $1.10 multi 1.40 1.40
5127 A1159 $1.10 multi 1.40 1.40
5128 A1159 $1.10 multi 1.40 1.40
5129 A1159 $1.10 multi 1.40 1.40
Nos. 5126-5129 (4) 5.60 5.60

Booklet Stamps
Self-Adhesive

Serpentine Die Cut 11¼ Syncopated

5130 A1159 $1.10 multi 1.40 .25
a. Booklet pane of 10 14.00
5131 A1159 $1.10 multi 1.40 .25
a. Booklet pane of 10 14.00
5132 A1159 $1.10 multi 1.40 .25
a. Booklet pane of 10 14.00
5133 A1159 $1.10 multi 1.40 .25
a. Booklet pane of 10 14.00
Nos. 5130-5133 (4) 5.60 1.00

State and Territory Birds — A1160

Designs: Nos. 5134, 5140, Gang-gang cockatoo, Australian Capital Territory. Nos. 5135, 5141, Helmeted honeyeater, Victoria. Nos. 5136, 5142, Wedge-tailed eagle, Northern Territory. Nos. 5137, 5143, Laughing kookaburra, New South Wales. Nos. 5138, 5144, Brolga, Queensland. Nos. 5139, 5145, Black swan, Western Australia, horiz.

2020, Apr. 21 Litho. *Perf. 14¾x14*

5134 A1160 $1.10 multi 1.40 1.40
5135 A1160 $1.10 multi 1.40 1.40
5136 A1160 $1.10 multi 1.40 1.40
5137 A1160 $1.10 multi 1.40 1.40
5138 A1160 $1.10 multi 1.40 1.40

Perf. 14x14¾

5139 A1160 $1.10 multi 1.40 1.40
a. Souvenir sheet of 4 #5139 5.75 5.75
b. Souvenir sheet of 4 with Perth 2022 Stamp and Coin Show emblem in sheet margin 6.75 5.25
Nos. 5134-5139 (6) 8.40 8.40

Booklet Stamps
Self-Adhesive

Serpentine Die Cut 11¼ Syncopated

5140 A1160 $1.10 multi 1.40 .25
a. Booklet pane of 10 14.00
5141 A1160 $1.10 multi 1.40 .25
a. Booklet pane of 10 14.00
5142 A1160 $1.10 multi 1.40 .25
a. Booklet pane of 10 14.00
5143 A1160 $1.10 multi 1.40 .25
a. Booklet pane of 10 14.00
5144 A1160 $1.10 multi 1.40 .25
a. Booklet pane of 10 14.00
5145 A1160 $1.10 multi 1.40 .25
a. Booklet pane of 10 14.00
Nos. 5140-5145 (6) 8.40 1.50

Issued: No. 5139a, 9/19. No. 5139b, 3/4/22. 2020 Perth Stamp and Coin Show (No. 5139a). 2022 Perth Stamp and Coin Show (No. 5139b).

Miniature Sheet

First Pacific Voyage of the HMS Endeavour, 250th Anniv. — A1161

Nos. 5146 and 5147: a, Southern Cross constellation. b, HMS Endeavour. c, Silhouettes of indigenous Australians. d, Flower and needle. e, Map of Australian coast and Torres Strait Islands. f, Lieutenant James Cook using sextant. g, Map of Australia. h, Expedition member sitting. i, Naturalists Joseph Banks and Daniel Solander. j, Compass rose.

Perf. 14 Syncopated

2020, Apr. 29 Litho.

5146 A1161 Sheet of 10 7.00 7.00
a.-j. 55c Any single .70 .70

Booklet Stamps
Self-Adhesive

Serpentine Die Cut 11¾ Syncopated on 3 Sides

5147 A1161 Booklet pane of 10 7.00
a.-j. 55c Any single .70 .25

Citizen Science — A1162

Inscriptions: Nos. 5148, 5152, QuestaGame. Nos. 5149, 5153, Ngukurr Wi Stadi Bla Kantri (We study the country). Nos. 5150, 5154, Butterflies Australia. Nos. 5151, 5155, Zika Mozzie Seeker.

2020, May 19 Litho. *Perf. 14x14¾*

5148 A1162 $1.10 multi 1.50 1.50
5149 A1162 $1.10 multi 1.50 1.50
5150 A1162 $1.10 multi 1.50 1.50
5151 A1162 $1.10 multi 1.50 1.50
Nos. 5148-5151 (4) 6.00 6.00

Booklet Stamps
Self-Adhesive

Serpentine Die Cut 11¼ Syncopated

5152 A1162 $1.10 multi 1.50 .25
a. Booklet pane of 10 15.00
5153 A1162 $1.10 multi 1.50 .25
a. Booklet pane of 10 15.00
5154 A1162 $1.10 multi 1.50 .25
a. Booklet pane of 10 15.00
5155 A1162 $1.10 multi 1.50 .25
a. Booklet pane of 10 15.00
Nos. 5152-5155 (4) 6.00 1.00

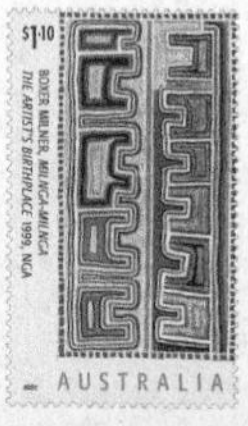

Art by Western Desert Aboriginals — A1163

Designs: No. 5156, Milnga-Milnga, The Artist's Birthplace, by Boxer Milner (c.1935-2009). No. 5157, Tingarri Mamultjulkulakutu, by Fred Ward Tjungurrayi. No. 5158, Untitled painting by Eubena Nampitjin (c. 1925-2013). $2.20, Kangaroo Dreaming, by Walter Tjampitjinpa (c. 1912-81).

2020, June 9 Litho. ***Perf. 14x14¼***

5156 A1163 $1.10 multi 1.50 1.10
5157 A1163 $1.10 multi 1.50 1.10
5158 A1163 $1.10 multi 1.50 1.10
5159 A1163 $2.20 multi 3.00 3.00
Nos. 5156-5159 (4) 7.50 6.30

Booklet Stamp
Self-Adhesive
Serpentine Die Cut 11x10¾ Syncopated

5160 A1163 $2.20 multi 3.00 1.50
a. Booklet pane of 5 15.00

Fashion Photography — A1164

Photograph from: No. 5161, 1949, by Athol Shmith (1914-90). No. 5162, 1959, by Helmut Newton (1920-2004). No. 5163, 1960s, by Henry Talbot (1920-99). No. 5164, 1972, Bruno Benini (1925-2001).

2020, June 16 Litho. ***Perf. 14¾x14***

5161 A1164 $1.10 multi 1.50 1.10
5162 A1164 $1.10 multi 1.50 1.10
5163 A1164 $1.10 multi 1.50 1.10
5164 A1164 $1.10 multi 1.50 1.10
a. Souvenir sheet of 4, #5161-5164 6.00 4.50
Nos. 5161-5164 (4) 6.00 4.40

Royal Children's Hospital Melbourne, 150th Anniv. — A1165

2020, July 7 Litho. ***Perf. 14x14¾***

5165 A1165 $1.10 multi 1.60 1.60

Booklet Stamp
Self-Adhesive
Serpentine Die Cut 11¼ Syncopated

5166 A1165 $1.10 multi 1.60 .25
a. Booklet pane of 10 16.00

Australian Alps — A1166

Designs: Nos. 5167, 5170, Snow gum trees, Namadgi National Park, Australian Capital Territory. Nos. 5168, 5171, The Cathedral, Mount Buffalo National Park, Victoria. Nos. 5169, 5172, Swampy Plain River, Kosciuszko National Park, New South Wales.

2020, July 21 Litho. ***Perf. 14x14¾***

5167 A1166 $1.10 multi 1.60 1.60
5168 A1166 $1.10 multi 1.60 1.60
5169 A1166 $1.10 multi 1.60 1.60
a. Souvenir sheet of 3, #5167-5169 4.80 4.80
Nos. 5167-5169 (3) 4.80 4.80

Coil Stamps
Self-Adhesive
Serpentine Die Cut 11¼ Syncopated

5170 A1166 $1.10 multi 1.60 .25
5171 A1166 $1.10 multi 1.60 .25
5172 A1166 $1.10 multi 1.60 .25
a. Horiz. strip of 3, #5170-5172 4.80
Nos. 5170-5172 (3) 4.80 .75

A1167

Wildlife Recovery A1168

Animals severly affected by loss of habitat in Australian bushfires: Nos. 5173, 5179, Bathurst copper butterfly. Nos. 5174, 5180, Davies' tree frog. Nos. 5175, 5181, Kangaroo Island dunnart. Nos. 5176, 5182, Regent honeyeater. Nos. 5177, 5183, Blue Mountains water skink. No. 5178, Koala.

2020, Aug. 4 Litho. ***Perf. 14x14¾***

5173 A1167 $1.10 multi 1.60 1.60
5174 A1167 $1.10 multi 1.60 1.60
5175 A1167 $1.10 multi 1.60 1.60
5176 A1167 $1.10 multi 1.60 1.60
5177 A1167 $1.10 multi 1.60 1.60

Perf. 14¼x14

5178 A1168 $1.10 multi 1.60 1.60
a. Souvenir sheet of 6, #5173-5178 9.75 9.75
Nos. 5173-5178 (6) 9.60 9.60

Booklet Stamp
Self-Adhesive
Serpentine Die Cut 11¼ Syncopated

5179 A1167 $1.10 multi 1.60 .25
a. Booklet pane of 10 16.00
5180 A1167 $1.10 multi 1.60 .25
a. Booklet pane of 10 16.00
5181 A1167 $1.10 multi 1.60 .25
a. Booklet pane of 10 16.00
5182 A1167 $1.10 multi 1.60 .25
a. Booklet pane of 10 16.00
5183 A1167 $1.10 multi 1.60 .25
a. Booklet pane of 10 16.00
Nos. 5179-5183 (5) 8.00 1.25

Princes Highway, Cent. — A1169

Automobile and travel poster for: No. 4184, Mount Gambier. No. 4185, Geelong. No. 4186, Melbourne. No. 4187, Sydney.

2020, Aug. 11 Litho. ***Perf. 14¾x14***

5184 A1169 $1.10 multi 1.60 1.25
5185 A1169 $1.10 multi 1.60 1.25
5186 A1169 $1.10 multi 1.60 1.25
5187 A1169 $1.10 multi 1.60 1.25
Nos. 5184-5187 (4) 6.40 5.00

Opalized Fossils — A1170

Fossil of: Nos. 5188, 5194, Pine cone. Nos. 5189, 5193, Theropod tooth. Nos. 5190, 5192, Moon snail. Nos. 5191, 5195, Wood.

2020, Aug. 17 Litho. ***Perf. 14x14¾***

5188 A1170 $1.10 multi 1.60 1.60
5189 A1170 $1.10 multi 1.60 1.60
5190 A1170 $1.10 multi 1.60 1.60
5191 A1170 $1.10 multi 1.60 1.60
a. Souvenir sheet of 4, #5188-5191 6.50 6.50
Nos. 5188-5191 (4) 6.40 6.40

Booklet Stamps
Self-Adhesive
Serpentine Die Cut 11¼ Syncopated

5192 A1170 $1.10 multi 1.60 .25
5193 A1170 $1.10 multi 1.60 .25
5194 A1170 $1.10 multi 1.60 .25
5195 A1170 $1.10 multi 1.60 .25
a. Booklet pane of 10, 3 each #5192-5193, 2 each #5194-5195 16.00
b. Booklet pane of 20, 5 each #5192-5195 32.00
Nos. 5192-5195 (4) 6.40 1.00

Art on Water Towers — A1171

Designs: Nos. 5196, 5200, Lucky Dip, by Jenny McCracken on Gulargambone, New South Wales water tower. Nos. 5197, 5201, Man's Face, by Guido van Helten on Winton, Victoria water tower. Nos. 5198, 5202, Eastern Bearded Dragon, by Apparition Media on Narrandera, New South Wales water tower. No. 5199, 5203, Man with Safety Helmet, by Vans the Omega, on Snowtown, South Australia water tower.

2020, Sept. 7 Litho. ***Perf. 14¾x14***

5196 A1171 $1.10 multi 1.60 1.60
5197 A1171 $1.10 multi 1.60 1.60
5198 A1171 $1.10 multi 1.60 1.60
5199 A1171 $1.10 multi 1.60 1.60
a. Souvenir sheet of 4, #5196-5199 6.50 6.50
Nos. 5196-5199 (4) 6.40 6.40

Booklet Stamps
Self-Adhesive
Serpentine Die Cut 11¼ Syncopated

5200 A1171 $1.10 multi 1.60 .25
a. Booklet pane of 10 16.00
5201 A1171 $1.10 multi 1.60 .25
a. Booklet pane of 10 16.00
5202 A1171 $1.10 multi 1.60 .25
a. Booklet pane of 10 16.00
5203 A1171 $1.10 multi 1.60 .25
a. Booklet pane of 10 16.00
Nos. 5200-5203 (4) 6.40 1.00

Pencil and "G'day" — A1172

Pen and "Hello" — A1173

Serpentine Die Cut 11¼ Syncopated
2020, Oct. 1 Litho.
Self-Adhesive

5204 A1172 $1.10 multi 1.60 .80
5205 A1173 $1.10 multi 1.60 .80
a. Horiz. pair, #5204-5205 3.20

Civil Aviation in Australia, Cent. A1174

Designs: $1.10, Qantas Dreamliner at Sydney Airport. $2.20, Biplane and 1920 Act concerning civil aviation.

2020, Oct. 6 Litho. ***Perf. 14½x14***

5206 A1174 $1.10 multi 1.60 1.60
5207 A1174 $2.20 multi 3.25 2.40
a. Souvenir sheet of 2, #5206-5207 5.00 3.75

Booklet Stamp
Self-Adhesive
Serpentine Die Cut 10¾ Syncopated

5208 A1174 $1.10 multi 1.60 .25
a. Booklet pane of 10 16.00

Australian National Botanic Gardens, Canberra, 50th Anniv. — A1175

Designs: Nos. 5209, 5211, 5213, Grevillea iaspicula. Nos. 5210, 5212, 5214, Banksia marginata.

2020, Oct. 13 Litho. ***Perf. 14x14¾***

5209 A1175 $1.10 multi 1.60 1.60
5210 A1175 $1.10 multi 1.60 1.60
a. Souvenir sheet of 2, #5209-5210 3.25 3.25

Self-Adhesive
Country Name in Gray Green
Consistent Shading on "50"
Serpentine Die Cut 11¼ Syncopated

5211 A1175 $1.10 multi 1.60 .25
5212 A1175 $1.10 multi 1.60 .25
a. Horiz. coil pair, #5211-5212 3.20
b. Booklet pane of 10, 5 each #5211-5212 16.00

Digitally Printed
Booklet Stamps
Country Name in Green
Lighter Color on Edges of "50"
Than in Center of Numbers

5213 A1175 $1.10 multi 1.60 .25
5214 A1175 $1.10 multi 1.60 .25
a. Booklet pane of 10, 5 each #5213-5214 16.00

The covers and pictures at the bottoms of the opened booklet panes differ on Nos. 5212b and 5214a.

UNESCO World Heritage Sites in Australia — A1176

Designs: Nos. 5215, 5219, Royal Exhibition Building and Carlton Gardens, Melbourne, Victoria. Nos. 5216, 5220, Budj Bim Cultural Landscape, Victoria. Nos. 5217, 5221, Cascades Female Factory, Tasmania. Nos. 5218, 5222, Sydney Opera House, Sydney, New South Wales.

2020, Oct. 20 Litho. ***Perf. 14¾x14***

5215 A1176 $1.10 multi 1.60 1.60
5216 A1176 $1.10 multi 1.60 1.60
5217 A1176 $1.10 multi 1.60 1.60
5218 A1176 $1.10 multi 1.60 1.60
Nos. 5215-5218 (4) 6.40 6.40

Booklet Stamps
Self-Adhesive
Serpentine Die Cut 11¼ Syncopated

5219 A1176 $1.10 multi 1.60 .25
a. Booklet pane of 10 16.00
5220 A1176 $1.10 multi 1.60 .25
a. Booklet pane of 10 16.00
5221 A1176 $1.10 multi 1.60 .25
a. Booklet pane of 10 16.00
5222 A1176 $1.10 multi 1.60 .25
a. Booklet pane of 10 16.00
Nos. 5219-5222 (4) 6.40 1.00

100th Running of the W. S. Cox Plate Horse Race — A1177

Litho. & Embossed With Foil Application

2020, Oct. 22 ***Perf. 14¼***

5223 A1177 $1.10 dk blue & gold 1.60 1.25

A1178

Christmas — A1179

Designs: Nos. 5224, 5229, Painting of Madonna and Child, by Leopoldine Mimovich (1920-2019). Nos. 5225, 5230, Christmas wreath. Nos. 5226, 5231, Christmas stocking with flowers. Nos. 5227, 5232, Painting of Holy Family, by Mimovich. Nos. 5228, 5233, Christmas ornament, flowers and holly.

2020, Oct. 30 Litho. ***Perf. 14¾x14***

5224 A1178 65c multi .95 .95
5225 A1179 65c multi .95 .95
5226 A1179 65c multi .95 .95
a. Horiz. pair, #5225-5226 1.90 1.90
5227 A1178 $2.20 multi 3.25 3.25
a. Souvenir sheet of 2, #5224, 5227 4.25 4.25
5228 A1179 $2.20 multi 3.25 3.25
Nos. 5224-5228 (5) 9.35 9.35

Booklet Stamps
Self-Adhesive
Serpentine Die Cut 11¼ Syncopated

5229 A1178 65c multi .95 .25
a. Booklet pane of 20 + 20 etiquettes 19.00
5230 A1179 65c multi .95 .25
a. With glossier varnish .95 .25
b. Booklet pane of 10 #5230a + 10 etiquettes 9.50
5231 A1179 65c multi .95 .25
a. Booklet pane of 20 10 each #5230-5231, + 20 etiquettes 19.00
b. With glossier varnish .95 .25
c. Booklet pane of 10 #5231b + 10 etiquettes 9.50
5232 A1178 $2.20 multi 3.25 1.60
a. Booklet pane of 5 16.50
5233 A1179 $2.20 multi 3.25 1.60
a. Booklet pane of 5 16.50
Nos. 5229-5233 (5) 9.35 3.95

Three Stuffed Rabbit Dolls A1180

"Thank You" A1181

Bunch of Balloons A1182

Heart A1183

White Flowers — A1184

2021, Jan. 25 Litho. ***Perf. 14¾x14***

5234 A1180 $1.10 multi 1.75 1.75
5235 A1181 $1.10 multi 1.75 1.75
5236 A1182 $1.10 multi 1.75 1.75
5237 A1183 $1.10 multi 1.75 1.75
5238 A1184 $2.20 multi 3.50 3.50
a. Souvenir sheet of 5, #5234-5238 10.50 10.50
Nos. 5234-5238 (5) 10.50 10.50

Booklet Stamps
Self-Adhesive

Serpentine Die Cut 11¼ Syncopated

5239 A1180 $1.10 multi 1.75 .25
a. Booklet pane of 10 17.50
5240 A1181 $1.10 multi 1.75 .25
a. Booklet pane of 10 17.50
5241 A1182 $1.10 multi 1.75 .25
a. Booklet pane of 10 17.50
5242 A1183 $1.10 multi 1.75 .25
a. Booklet pane of 10 17.50
5243 A1184 $2.20 multi 3.50 1.75
a. Booklet pane of 4 14.00
Complete booklet, 4 #5243a 56.00
Nos. 5239-5243 (5) 10.50 2.75

Complete booklet sold for $35.95 and includes a pane of 20 stickers. Each booklet pane in complete booklet has a different booklet pane margin.

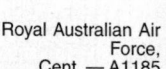

Royal Australian Air Force, Cent. — A1185

Designs: $1.10, F-35. $3.30, SE5A.

2021, Feb. 9 Litho. ***Perf. 14x14¾***

5244 A1185 $1.10 multi 1.75 1.75
5245 A1185 $3.30 multi 5.25 2.60
a. Souvenir sheet of 2, #5244-5245 7.00 4.50
b. Souvenir sheet of 2, #5244-5245, with Perth Stamp and Coin Show emblem in sheet margin 7.00 4.50

Coil Stamp
Self-Adhesive
Inkjet Printed

Serpentine Die Cut 11¼ Syncopated

5246 A1185 $1.10 multi 1.75 .25

Issued: No. 5245b, 3/12. 2021 Perth Stamp and Coin Show (No. 5245b).

Medical Personnel A1186

Ambulance Driver and Health Care Worker A1187

Police and Defense Force Personnel A1188

Postal Worker and Grocery Deliveryman A1189

Store Cashier and Teacher on Computer — A1190

2021, Feb. 16 Litho. ***Perf. 14¾x14***

5247 A1186 $1.10 multi 1.75 1.75
a. Souvenir sheet of 4 with 2022 Canberra Stampshow emblem in sheet margin 6.75 5.25
5248 A1187 $1.10 multi 1.75 1.75
5249 A1188 $1.10 multi 1.75 1.75
5250 A1189 $1.10 multi 1.75 1.75
5251 A1190 $1.10 multi 1.75 1.75
a. Horiz. strip of 5, #5247-5251 8.75 8.75
b. Souvenir sheet of 5, #5247-5251 8.75 8.75
Nos. 5247-5251 (5) 8.75 8.75

Booklet Stamps
Self-Adhesive

Serpentine Die Cut 11¼ Syncopated

5252 A1186 $1.10 multi 1.75 .25
5253 A1187 $1.10 multi 1.75 .25
5254 A1188 $1.10 multi 1.75 .25
5255 A1189 $1.10 multi 1.75 .25
5256 A1190 $1.10 multi 1.75 .25
a. Booklet pane of 10, 2 each #5252-5256 17.50
Nos. 5252-5256 (5) 8.75 1.25

Frontline workers during the COVID-19 pandemic. Issued: No. 5247a, 3/18/22. 2022 Canberra Stampshow (No. 5247a).

Ramsar Convention Wetlands — A1191

Designs: 20c, Cobourg Peninsula Wetland, Northern Territory. $2.70, Moreton Bay Wetland, Queensland. $3.40, Blue Lake Wetland, New South Wales. $3.50, Riverland Wetland, South Australia.

2021, Feb. 22 Litho. ***Perf. 14x14¾***

5257 A1191 20c multi .35 .25
5258 A1191 $2.70 multi 4.25 4.25
5259 A1191 $3.40 multi 5.25 5.25
5260 A1191 $3.50 multi 5.50 5.50
Nos. 5257-5260 (4) 15.35 15.25

Booklet Stamps
Self-Adhesive

Serpentine Die Cut 11¼ Syncopated

5261 A1191 $2.70 multi 4.25 2.10
a. Booklet pane of 5 21.50
5262 A1191 $3.40 multi 5.25 2.60
a. Booklet pane of 5 26.50
5263 A1191 $3.50 multi 5.50 2.75
a. Booklet pane of 5 27.50
Nos. 5261-5263 (3) 15.00 7.45

Edith Cowan (1861-1932), First Woman Member of Western Australia Parliament — A1192

2021, Mar. 2 Litho. ***Perf. 14¾x14***

5264 A1192 $1.10 multi 1.75 1.30

Arrival in Australia of HMVS Cerberus, 150th Anniv. — A1193

2021, Mar. 22 Litho. ***Perf. 14¾x14***

5265 A1193 $1.10 multi 1.75 1.30

Holden Automobiles A1194

Designs: Nos. 5266, 5271, 1948 Holden 48-215. Nos. 5267, 5272, 1963 Holden EH Premier. Nos. 5268, 5273, 1968 Holden HK Monaro GTS 327. Nos. 5269, 5274, 1971 Holden HQ Kinswood Ute. Nos. 5270, 5275, 2006 Holden VE Commodore SS V.

2021, Mar. 22 Litho. ***Perf. 14x14¾***

5266 A1194 $1.10 multi 1.75 1.75
5267 A1194 $1.10 multi 1.75 1.75
5268 A1194 $1.10 multi 1.75 1.75
5269 A1194 $1.10 multi 1.75 1.75
5270 A1194 $1.10 multi 1.75 1.75
a. Souvenir sheet of 5, #5266-5270 8.75 8.75
Nos. 5266-5270 (5) 8.75 8.75

Booklet Stamps
Self-Adhesive

Serpentine Die Cut 11¼ Syncopated

5271 A1194 $1.10 multi 1.75 .25
a. Booklet pane of 10 17.50
5272 A1194 $1.10 multi 1.75 .25
a. Booklet pane of 10 17.50
5273 A1194 $1.10 multi 1.75 .25
a. Booklet pane of 10 17.50
5274 A1194 $1.10 multi 1.75 .25
a. Booklet pane of 10 17.50
5275 A1194 $1.10 multi 1.75 .25
a. Booklet pane of 10 17.50
Nos. 5271-5275 (5) 8.75 1.25

Cricket Players — A1195

Designs: Nos. 5276, 5282, Adam Gilchrist. Nos. 5277, 5283, Ricky Ponting. Nos. 5278, 5284, Ellyse Perry. Nos. 5279, 5285, Jason Gillespie. Nos. 5280, 5286, Allan Border. Nos. 5281, 5287, Dennis Lillee.

2021, Mar. 26 Litho. ***Perf. 14¾x14***

5276 A1195 $1.10 multi 1.75 1.75
5277 A1195 $1.10 multi 1.75 1.75
a. Horiz. pair, #5276-5277 3.50 3.50
5278 A1195 $1.10 multi 1.75 1.75
5279 A1195 $1.10 multi 1.75 1.75
a. Horiz. pair, #5278-5279 3.50 3.50
5280 A1195 $1.10 multi 1.75 1.75
5281 A1195 $1.10 multi 1.75 1.75
a. Horiz. pair, #5280-5281 3.50 3.50
Nos. 5276-5281 (6) 10.50 10.50

Booklet Stamps
Self-Adhesive

Serpentine Die Cut 11¼ Syncopated

5282 A1195 $1.10 multi 1.75 .25
a. Booklet pane of 10 17.50
5283 A1195 $1.10 multi 1.75 .25
a. Booklet pane of 10 17.50
5284 A1195 $1.10 multi 1.75 .25
a. Booklet pane of 10 17.50
5285 A1195 $1.10 multi 1.75 .25
a. Booklet pane of 10 17.50
5286 A1195 $1.10 multi 1.75 .25
a. Booklet pane of 10 17.50
5287 A1195 $1.10 multi 1.75 .25
a. Booklet pane of 10 17.50
Nos. 5282-5287 (6) 10.50 1.50

Rotary International in Australia, Cent. — A1196

2021, Apr. 6 Litho. ***Perf. 14¾x14***

5288 A1196 $1.10 multi 1.75 1.30

ANZAC Day Wreaths
A1197 A1198

2021, Apr. 13 Litho. ***Perf. 14¾x14***

5289 A1197 $1.10 multi 1.75 1.75
5290 A1198 $1.10 multi 1.75 1.75
a. Souvenir sheet of 2, #5289-5290 3.50 3.50

Booklet Stamps
Self-Adhesive

Serpentine Die Cut 11¼ Syncopated

5291 A1197 $1.10 multi 1.75 .25
5292 A1198 $1.10 multi 1.75 .25
a. Booklet pane of 20, 10 each #5291-5292 35.00

Landmarks on Australian National Heritage List — A1199

Designs: No. 5293, Sydney Harbour Bridge and toll token. No. 5294, Queen Victoria Market, Melbourne and various foodstuffs. No. 5295, Old Parliament House, Canberra and ceremonial mace.

2021, May 10 Litho. ***Perf. 14¾x14***

5293 A1199 $1.10 multi 1.75 1.30
5294 A1199 $1.10 multi 1.75 1.30
5295 A1199 $1.10 multi 1.75 1.30
Nos. 5293-5295 (3) 5.25 3.90

Migratory Shorebirds A1200

Designs: Nos. 5296, 5299, Bar-tailed godwit. Nos. 5297, 5300, Great knot. Nos. 5298, 5301, Eastern curlew.

2021, May 18 Litho. ***Perf. 14x14¾***

5296 A1200 $1.10 multi 1.75 1.75
5297 A1200 $1.10 multi 1.75 1.75
5298 A1200 $1.10 multi 1.75 1.75
a. Souvenir sheet of 3, #5296-5298 5.25 5.25
Nos. 5296-5298 (3) 5.25 5.25

Booklet Stamps
Self-Adhesive

Serpentine Die Cut 11¼ Syncopated

5299 A1200 $1.10 multi 1.75 .25
a. Booklet pane of 10 17.50
5300 A1200 $1.10 multi 1.75 .25
a. Booklet pane of 10 17.50
5301 A1200 $1.10 multi 1.75 .25
a. Booklet pane of 10 17.50
Nos. 5299-5301 (3) 5.25 .75

Pigeons and Doves — A1201

Designs: Nos. 5302, 5306, Topknot pigeons. Nos. 5303, 5307, Superb fruit-doves. Nos. 5304, 5308, White-headed pigeons. Nos. 5305, 5309, Squatter pigeons.

2021, June 1 Litho. ***Perf. 14x14¾***

5302 A1201 $1.10 multi 1.75 1.75
5303 A1201 $1.10 multi 1.75 1.75
5304 A1201 $1.10 multi 1.75 1.75
5305 A1201 $1.10 multi 1.75 1.75
a. Souvenir sheet of 4, #5302-5305 7.00 7.00
Nos. 5302-5305 (4) 7.00 7.00

Coil Stamps
Self-Adhesive

Serpentine Die Cut 11¼ Syncopated

5306 A1201 $1.10 multi 1.75 .25
5307 A1201 $1.10 multi 1.75 .25
5308 A1201 $1.10 multi 1.75 .25
5309 A1201 $1.10 multi 1.75 .25
a. Horiz. strip of 4, #5306-5309 7.00
Nos. 5306-5309 (4) 7.00 1.00

2020 Summer Olympics, Tokyo — A1202

2021, July 6 Litho. ***Perf. 14x14¾***

5310 A1202 $1.10 multi 1.75 1.30

The 2020 Summer Olympics were postponed until 2021 because of the COVID-19 pandemic.

Contemporary Sculptures A1203

Designs: No. 5311, 5315, Smiley Blue Eye, by Lex Namponan. Nos. 5312, 5316, Planet, by Inge King (1915-2016). Nos. 5313, 5317, Rigel, by Lenton Parr (1924-2003). Nos. 5314, 5318, Eel Trap, by Yvonne Koolmatrie.

2021, July 6 Litho. *Perf. 14x14¾*

5311 A1203 $1.10 multi 1.75 1.75
5312 A1203 $1.10 multi 1.75 1.75
5313 A1203 $1.10 multi 1.75 1.75
5314 A1203 $1.10 multi 1.75 1.75
a. Souvenir sheet of 4, #5311-5314 7.00 7.00
Nos. 5311-5314 (4) 7.00 7.00

Booklet Stamps
Self-Adhesive

Serpentine Die Cut 11¼ Syncopated

5315 A1203 $1.10 multi 1.75 .25
5316 A1203 $1.10 multi 1.75 .25
5317 A1203 $1.10 multi 1.75 .25
5318 A1203 $1.10 multi 1.75 .25
a. Booklet pane of 10, 3 each #5315-5316, 2 each #5317-5318 17.50
Nos. 5315-5318 (4) 7.00 1.00

Extinct Volcanoes A1204

Designs: Nos. 5319, 5323, Table Cape, Tasmania. Nos. 5320, 5324, Wollumbin Mount Warning, New South Wales. Nos. 5321, 5325, Mount Elephant, Victoria. Nos. 5322, 5326, Lord Howe Island, New South Wales.

2021, July 13 Litho. *Perf. 14x14¾*

5319 A1204 $1.10 multi 1.75 1.75
5320 A1204 $1.10 multi 1.75 1.75
5321 A1204 $1.10 multi 1.75 1.75
5322 A1204 $1.10 multi 1.75 1.75
Nos. 5319-5322 (4) 7.00 7.00

Self-Adhesive

Serpentine Die Cut 11¼ Syncopated

5323 A1204 $1.10 multi 1.75 .25
5324 A1204 $1.10 multi 1.75 .25
5325 A1204 $1.10 multi 1.75 .25
5326 A1204 $1.10 multi 1.75 .25
a. Horiz. coil strip of 4, #5323-5326 7.00
b. Booklet pane of 20, 5 each #5323-5326 35.00
Nos. 5323-5326 (4) 7.00 1.00

Native Bonsai Trees — A1205

Designs: No. 5327, Callistemon viminalis. No. 5328, Ficus rubiginosa. Nos. 5329, 5330, Melaleuca linariifolia.

2021, July 27 Litho. *Perf. 14¾x14*

5327 A1205 $1.10 multi 1.75 1.30
5328 A1205 $1.10 multi 1.75 1.30
5329 A1205 $2.70 multi 4.00 4.00
a. Souvenir sheet of 3, #5327-5329 7.50 6.75
Nos. 5327-5329 (3) 7.50 6.60

Booklet Stamp
Self-Adhesive

Serpentine Die Cut 11¼ Syncopated

5330 A1205 $2.70 multi 4.00 2.00
a. Booklet pane of 5 20.00

Australian Gold Medalists at the 2020 Summer Olympics, Tokyo — A1206

Designs: No. 5331, Kaylee McKeown, women's 200-meter backstroke. No. 5332, McKeown, women's 100-meter backstroke. No. 5333, Women's 4x100-meter freestyle relay team. No. 5334, Ariarne Titmus, women's 400-meter freestyle. No. 5335, Titmus, Women's 200-meter freestyle. No. 5336, Men's four-man rowing team. No. 5337, Women's four-woman rowing team. No. 5338, Zac Stubblety-Cook, men's 200-meter backstroke. No. 5339, Jessica Fox, women's canoe slalom. No. 5340, Logan Martin, men's BMX freestyle cycling. No. 5341, Matt Wearn, men's laser sailing. No. 5342, Emma McKeon, women's 50-meter freestyle. No. 5343, McKeon, women's 100-meter freestyle. No. 5344, Women's 4x100-meter medley relay team. No. 5345, Keegan Palmer, men's park skateboarding. No. 5346, Mathew Belcher and Will Ryan, men's 470 sailing. No. 5347, Tom Green and Jean van der Westhuyzen, men's 1000-meter 2-man canoe sprint.

2021 Litho. *Perf. 14¼*

5331 A1206 $1.10 multi 1.75 1.30
5332 A1206 $1.10 multi 1.75 1.30
5333 A1206 $1.10 multi 1.75 1.30
5334 A1206 $1.10 multi 1.75 1.30
5335 A1206 $1.10 multi 1.75 1.30
5336 A1206 $1.10 multi 1.75 1.30
5337 A1206 $1.10 multi 1.75 1.30
5338 A1206 $1.10 multi 1.75 1.30
5339 A1206 $1.10 multi 1.75 1.30
5340 A1206 $1.10 multi 1.75 1.30
5341 A1206 $1.10 multi 1.75 1.30
5342 A1206 $1.10 multi 1.75 1.30
5343 A1206 $1.10 multi 1.75 1.30
5344 A1206 $1.10 multi 1.75 1.30
5345 A1206 $1.10 multi 1.75 1.30
5346 A1206 $1.10 multi 1.75 1.30
5347 A1206 $1.10 multi 1.75 1.30
Nos. 5331-5347 (17) 29.75 22.10

Nos. 5331-5347 were each issued in sheets of 10. Issued: No. 5331, 7/27; Nos. 5332-5334, 7/28; Nos. 5335-5337, 7/29; Nos. 5338-5339, 7/30; Nos. 5340-5344, 8/2; Nos. 5345-5347, 8/6. The 2020 Summer Olympics were postponed until 2021 because of the COVID-19 pandemic.

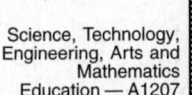

Science, Technology, Engineering, Arts and Mathematics Education — A1207

Designs: Nos. 5348, 5353, Virtual reality. Nos. 5349, 5354, Hydroponics. Nos. 5350, 5355, Space study. Nos. 5351, 5356, Robotics. Nos. 5352, 5357, Urban design.

2021, Aug. 3 Litho. *Perf. 14¾x14*

5348 A1207 $1.10 multi 1.75 1.75
5349 A1207 $1.10 multi 1.75 1.75
5350 A1207 $1.10 multi 1.75 1.75
5351 A1207 $1.10 multi 1.75 1.75
5352 A1207 $1.10 multi 1.75 1.75
a. Souvenir sheet of 5, #5348-5352 8.75 8.75
Nos. 5348-5352 (5) 8.75 8.75

Booklet Stamps
Self-Adhesive

Serpentine Die Cut 11¼ Syncopated

5353 A1207 $1.10 multi 1.75 .25
5354 A1207 $1.10 multi 1.75 .25
5355 A1207 $1.10 multi 1.75 .25
5356 A1207 $1.10 multi 1.75 .25
5357 A1207 $1.10 multi 1.75 .25
a. Booklet pane of 10, 2 each #5353-5357 17.50
Nos. 5353-5357 (5) 8.75 1.25

A1208

A1209

Ginger Meggs Comic Strips, Cent. — A1210

2021, Sept. 7 Litho. *Perf. 14¾x14*

5358 A1208 $1.10 multi 1.60 1.25
5359 A1209 $1.10 multi 1.60 1.25
5360 A1210 $1.10 multi 1.60 1.25
a. Souvenir sheet of 3, #5358-5360 4.80 3.75
Nos. 5358-5360 (3) 4.80 3.75

Wattle Blossoms — A1211

Designs: Nos. 5361, 5364, Acacia leprosa "Scarlet Blaze." Nos. 5362, 5365, Acacia purpureopetala. Nos. 5363, 5366, Acacia alata var. biglandulosa.

2021, Sept. 14 Litho. *Perf. 14¾x14*

5361 A1211 $1.10 multi 1.60 1.60
5362 A1211 $1.10 multi 1.60 1.60
5363 A1211 $1.10 multi 1.60 1.60
a. Souvenir sheet of 3, #5361-5363 4.80 4.80
Nos. 5361-5363 (3) 4.80 4.80

Booklet Stamps
Self-Adhesive

Serpentine Die Cut 11¼ Syncopated

5364 A1211 $1.10 multi 1.60 .25
5365 A1211 $1.10 multi 1.60 .25
5366 A1211 $1.10 multi 1.60 .25
a. Booklet pane of 10, 4 #5364, 3 each #5365-5366 16.00
Nos. 5364-5366 (3) 4.80 .75

A1212

Queen Elizabeth II, 95th Birthday — A1213

2021, Sept. 21 Litho. *Perf. 14x14¾*

5367 A1212 $1.10 multi 1.60 1.25

Perf. 14x14¼

5368 A1213 $3.50 multi 5.25 2.60
a. Souvenir sheet of 2, #5367-5368 7.00 4.00

Booklet Stamp
Self-Adhesive

Serpentine Die Cut 11x10¾ Syncopated

5369 A1213 $3.50 multi 5.25 2.60
a. Booklet pane of 5 26.50

Archibald Prize, Cent. — A1214

Archibald Prize-winning portrait of: No. 5370, Margaret Olley, 1948 winner, by William Dobell (1899-1970). No. 5371, Albert Namatjira, 1956 winner, by William Dargie (1912-2003). No. 5372, Hugo Weaving, 2013 winner, by Del Kathryn Barton.

2021, Sept. 28 Litho. *Perf. 14x14¼*

5370 A1214 $1.10 multi 1.60 1.25
5371 A1214 $1.10 multi 1.60 1.25
5372 A1214 $1.10 multi 1.60 1.25
Nos. 5370-5372 (3) 4.80 3.75

Animals Using Mimicry — A1215

Designs: No. 5373, Leafy seadragon. No. 5374, Tawny frogmouth. $2.20, Macleay's spectre.

2021, Oct. 5 Litho. *Perf. 14¼*

5373 A1215 $1.10 multi 1.75 1.30
5374 A1215 $1.10 multi 1.75 1.30
5375 A1215 $2.20 multi 3.50 1.75
a. Souvenir sheet of 3, #5373-5375 7.00 4.50
Nos. 5373-5375 (3) 7.00 4.35

Retirement of Holden Automobiles Brand — A1216

Designs: Nos. 5376, 5381, 1972 Holden LJ Torana XU-1. Nos. 5377, 5382, 1993, Holden VP Commodore. Nos. 5378, 5383, 1996 Holden VR Commodore. Nos. 5379, 5384, 2001 Holden VX Commodore. Nos. 5380, 5385, 2020 Holden ZB Commodore.

2021, Oct. 7 Litho. *Perf. 14x14¾*

5376 A1216 $1.10 multi 1.75 1.75
5377 A1216 $1.10 multi 1.75 1.75
5378 A1216 $1.10 multi 1.75 1.75
5379 A1216 $1.10 multi 1.75 1.75
5380 A1216 $1.10 multi 1.75 1.75
a. Souvenir sheet of 5, #5376-5380 8.75 8.75
Nos. 5376-5380 (5) 8.75 8.75

Booklet Stamps
Self-Adhesive

Serpentine Die Cut 11¼ Syncopated

5381 A1216 $1.10 multi 1.75 .25
a. Booklet pane of 10 17.50
5382 A1216 $1.10 multi 1.75 .25
a. Booklet pane of 10 17.50
5383 A1216 $1.10 multi 1.75 .25
a. Booklet pane of 10 17.50
5384 A1216 $1.10 multi 1.75 .25
a. Booklet pane of 10 17.50
5385 A1216 $1.10 multi 1.75 .25
a. Booklet pane of 10 17.50
Nos. 5381-5385 (5) 8.75 1.25

Royal Society for Prevention of Cruelty to Animals, 150th Anniv. — A1217

Designs: Nos. 5386, 5391, "R," marsupial and flower. Nos. 5387, 5392, "S," cat. Nos. 5388, 5393, "P," dog. Nos. 5389, 5394, "C," pig. Nos. 5390, 5395, "A," horse.

2021, Oct. 19 Litho. *Perf. 14¾x14*

5386 A1217 $1.10 multi 1.75 1.75
5387 A1217 $1.10 multi 1.75 1.75
5388 A1217 $1.10 multi 1.75 1.75
5389 A1217 $1.10 multi 1.75 1.75
5390 A1217 $1.10 multi 1.75 1.75
a. Souvenir sheet of 5, #5386-5390 8.75 8.75
Nos. 5386-5390 (5) 8.75 8.75

Self-Adhesive

Serpentine Die Cut 11¼ Syncopated

5391 A1217 $1.10 multi 1.75 .25
a. Booklet pane of 10 17.50
5392 A1217 $1.10 multi 1.75 .25
a. Booklet pane of 10 17.50
5393 A1217 $1.10 multi 1.75 .25
a. Booklet pane of 10 17.50
5394 A1217 $1.10 multi 1.75 .25
a. Booklet pane of 10 17.50
5395 A1217 $1.10 multi 1.75 .25
a. Booklet pane of 10 17.50
b. Vert. coil strip of 5, #5391-5395 8.75
Nos. 5391-5395 (5) 8.75 1.25

First Regular Airmail Flights, Cent. — A1218

2021 Litho. *Perf. 14¾x14*

5396 A1218 $1.10 multi 1.75 1.30
a. Souvenir sheet of 4 with text for Newcastle Stamp and Coin Expo 2022 in sheet margin 6.50 5.00
b. Souvenir sheet of 4, Perth Stamp & Coin show emblem in sheet margin 7.00 5.25

Issued: No. 5396, 10/22; No. 5396a, 5/27/22; No. 5396b, 10/29/21 . Newcastle Stamp and Coin Expo 2022 (No. 5396a).

Christmas
A1219 A1220

Designs: Nos. 5397, 5402, Rectangular glazed terracotta plaque depicting Madonna and Child, by Della Robbia family of artists. Nos. 5398, 5404, 5407, Gingerbread cookie in shape of Christmas tree. Nos. 5399, 5403, 5408, Gingerbread cookie in shape of gift box with bow. Nos. 5400, 5405, Round glazed terracotta plaque depicting Madonna and Child, by Figli de Giuseppe Cantagalli. Nos. 5401, 5406, Gingerbread cookie in shape of star.

2021, Nov. 1 Litho. *Perf. 14¾x14*

5397 A1219 65c multi 1.00 1.00
5398 A1220 65c multi 1.00 1.00
5399 A1220 65c multi 1.00 1.00
a. Horiz. pair, #5398-5399 2.00 2.00
5400 A1219 $2.40 multi 3.75 1.90
a. Souvenir sheet of 2, #5397-5400 4.75 3.00
5401 A1220 $2.40 multi 3.75 1.90
Nos. 5397-5401 (5) 10.50 6.80

Booklet Stamps
Self-Adhesive

Serpentine Die Cut 11¼ Syncopated

5402 A1219 65c multi 1.00 .25
a. Booklet pane of 20 + 20 etiquettes 20.00
5403 A1220 65c multi 1.00 .25
5404 A1220 65c multi 1.00 .25
a. Booklet pane of 20, 10 each #5403-5404 + 20 etiquettes 20.00
5405 A1219 $2.40 multi 3.75 1.90
a. Booklet pane of 5 19.00
5406 A1220 $2.40 multi 3.75 1.90
a. Booklet pane of 5 19.00

Litho. With Foil Application

5407 A1220 65c multi 1.00 .25
a. Booklet pane of 10 + 10 etiquettes 10.00
5408 A1220 65c multi 1.00 .25
a. Booklet pane of 10 + 10 etiquettes 10.00
Nos. 5402-5408 (7) 12.50 5.05

Boats Under Sail — A1221

Designs: No. 5409, Sailors competing in Sydney-Hobart Yacht Race. No. 5410, Sailors hanging off side of catamaran during the Australian Sailing Youth Championships. $2.20, Crew using trapeze to counterbalance wind on a 16-foot skiff.

2022, Jan. 11 Litho. *Perf. 14x14¾*

5409 A1221 $1.10 multi 1.60 1.25
5410 A1221 $1.10 multi 1.60 1.25
5411 A1221 $2.20 multi 3.25 2.50
Nos. 5409-5411 (3) 6.45 5.00

Legislation Requiring Use of Seat Belts, 50th Anniv. — A1222

2022, Jan. 2 Litho. *Perf. 14¾x14*

5412 A1222 $1.10 multi 1.60 1.60

Coil Stamp
Self-Adhesive

Serpentine Die Cut 11¼ Syncopated

5413 A1222 $1.10 multi 1.60 .25

Flowers and "Happy Birthday" A1224

Rubber Duck A1225

Tic-Tac-Toe Game A1226

Roses A1227

Wedding Rings — A1228

2022, Feb. 8 Litho. *Perf. 14¾x14*

5415 A1224 $1.10 multi 1.60 1.60
5416 A1225 $1.10 multi 1.60 1.60
5417 A1226 $1.10 multi 1.60 1.60
5418 A1227 $1.10 multi 1.60 1.60
5419 A1228 $2.20 multi 3.25 3.25
a. Souvenir sheet of 5, #5415-5419 10.00 10.00
Nos. 5415-5419 (5) 9.65 9.65

Booklet Stamps
Self-Adhesive

Serpentine Die Cut 11¼ Syncopated

5420 A1224 $1.10 multi 1.60 .25
a. Booklet pane of 10 + 5 stickers 16.00
5421 A1225 $1.10 multi 1.60 .25
a. Booklet pane of 10 + 5 stickers 16.00
5422 A1226 $1.10 multi 1.60 .25
a. Booklet pane of 10 + 5 stickers 16.00
5423 A1227 $1.10 multi 1.60 .25
a. Booklet pane of 10 + 5 stickers 16.00
5424 A1228 $2.20 multi 3.25 .50
a. Booklet pane of 4 13.00
Complete booklet, 4 #5424a 52.00
Nos. 5420-5424 (5) 9.65 1.50

Complete booklet sold for $35.95 and contains four panes, each with different pane margins, and a pane of 20 stickers.

UNESCO World Heritage Sites in Australia — A1229

Designs: Nos. 5425, 5429, Blue Mountains, New South Wales. Nos. 5426, 5430, Flinders Ranges, South Australia. Nos. 5427, 5431, Ningaloo Coast, Western Australia. Nos. 5428, 5432, Gondwana Rainforests, New South Wales.

2022, Feb. 22 Litho. *Perf. 14x14¾*

5425 A1229 $1.10 multi 1.60 1.60
5426 A1229 $1.10 multi 1.60 1.60
5427 A1229 $1.10 multi 1.60 1.60
5428 A1229 $1.10 multi 1.60 1.60
Nos. 5425-5428 (4) 6.40 6.40

Booklet Stamps
Self-Adhesive

Serpentine Die Cut 11¼ Syncopated

5429 A1229 $1.10 multi 1.60 .25
5430 A1229 $1.10 multi 1.60 .25
5431 A1229 $1.10 multi 1.60 .25
5432 A1229 $1.10 multi 1.60 .25
a. Booklet pane of 10, 3 each #5429-5430, 2 each #5431-5432 16.00
Nos. 5429-5432 (4) 6.40 1.00

A1230

A1231

National Sheepdog Trials, 150th Anniv. — A1232

2022, Mar. 8 Litho. *Perf. 14¾x14*

5433 A1230 $1.10 multi 1.75 1.75
5434 A1231 $1.10 multi 1.75 1.75
5435 A1232 $1.10 multi 1.75 1.75
a. Souvenir sheet of 3, #5433-5435 5.25 5.25
Nos. 5433-5435 (3) 5.25 5.25

Self-Adhesive

Serpentine Die Cut 11¼ Syncopated

5436 A1230 $1.10 multi 1.75 .25
a. Booklet pane of 10 17.50
5437 A1231 $1.10 multi 1.75 .25
a. Booklet pane of 10 17.50
5438 A1232 $1.10 multi 1.75 .25
a. Booklet pane of 10 17.50
b. Vert. coil strip of 3, #5436-5438 5.25
Nos. 5436-5438 (3) 5.25 .75

Australian Film Directors — A1233

Designs: Nos. 5439, 5444, Baz Luhrmann. Nos. 5440, 5445, Peter Weir. Nos. 5441, 5446, Warwick Thornton. Nos. 5442, 5447, Gillian Armstrong. Nos. 5443, 5448, George Miller.

2022, Mar. 15 Litho. *Perf. 14x14¾*

5439 A1233 $1.10 multi 1.75 1.75
5440 A1233 $1.10 multi 1.75 1.75
5441 A1233 $1.10 multi 1.75 1.75
5442 A1233 $1.10 multi 1.75 1.75
5443 A1233 $1.10 multi 1.75 1.75
Nos. 5439-5443 (5) 8.75 8.75

Booklet Stamps
Self-Adhesive

Serpentine Die Cut 11¼ Syncopated

5444 A1233 $1.10 multi 1.75 .25
a. Booklet pane of 10 17.50
5445 A1233 $1.10 multi 1.75 .25
a. Booklet pane of 10 17.50
5446 A1233 $1.10 multi 1.75 .25
a. Booklet pane of 10 17.50
5447 A1233 $1.10 multi 1.75 .25
a. Booklet pane of 10 17.50
5448 A1233 $1.10 multi 1.75 .25
a. Booklet pane of 10 17.50
Nos. 5444-5448 (5) 8.75 1.25

Reign of Queen Elizabeth II, 70th Anniv.
A1234 A1235

2022, Apr. 5 Litho. *Perf. 14¾x14*

5449 A1234 $1.10 multi 1.60 1.60
5450 A1235 $3.50 multi 5.00 5.00
a. Souvenir sheet of 2, #5449-5450 6.75 6.75

Booklet Stamps
Self-Adhesive

Serpentine Die Cut 11¼ Syncopated

5451 A1234 $1.10 multi 1.60 .25
a. Booklet pane of 10 16.00
5452 A1235 $3.50 multi 5.00 2.50
a. Booklet pane of 5 25.00

Country Women's Association, Cent. — A1236

2022, Apr. 26 Litho. *Perf. 14¾x14*

5453 A1236 $1.10 multi 1.60 1.25

Aboriginal Fiber Art — A1237

Designs: Nos. 5454, 5457, Coiled baby basket, by Lucy Malirrimurruwuy. Nos. 5455, 5458, Conical basket, by Mary Djupuduwuy (1945-2005). Nos. 5456, 5459, Flat-bottomed basket, by Nancy Walinyinawuy (1940-2017).

2022, May 3 Litho. *Perf. 14x14¾*

5454 A1237 $1.10 multi 1.60 1.60
5455 A1237 $1.10 multi 1.60 1.60
5456 A1237 $1.10 multi 1.60 1.60
Nos. 5454-5456 (3) 4.80 4.80

Booklet Stamps
Self-Adhesive

Serpentine Die Cut 11¼ Syncopated

5457 A1237 $1.10 multi 1.60 .25
a. Booklet pane of 10 16.00
5458 A1237 $1.10 multi 1.60 .25
a. Booklet pane of 10 16.00
5459 A1237 $1.10 multi 1.60 .25
a. Booklet pane of 10 16.00
Nos. 5457-5459 (3) 4.80 .75

A1238

A1239

World War I Era Postcards Depicting Kookaburras Sent to Servicemen Abroad — A1240

2022, May 12 Litho. *Perf. 14¾x14*

5460 A1238 $1.10 multi 1.60 1.60
5461 A1239 $1.10 multi 1.60 1.60
5462 A1240 $1.10 multi 1.60 1.60
a. Souvenir sheet of 3, #5460-5462 4.80 4.80
Nos. 5460-5462 (3) 4.80 4.80

Booklet Stamps
Self-Adhesive

Serpentine Die Cut 11¼ Syncopated

5463 A1238 $1.10 multi 1.60 .25
5464 A1239 $1.10 multi 1.60 .25
5465 A1240 $1.10 multi 1.60 .25
a. Booklet pane of 20, 7 each #5463-5464, 6 #5465 32.00
Nos. 5463-5465 (3) 4.80 .75

Anzac Day.

Bush Seasonings — A1241

Designs: No. 5466, River mint. No. 5467, Mountain pepper. No. 5468, Lemon myrtle.

2022, May 24 Litho. *Perf. 14¾x14*

5466 A1241 $1.10 multi 1.60 1.25
a. Tete-beche pair 3.20 2.50
b. Booklet pane of 4 6.75 —
c. Booklet pane of 4 (two tete-beche pairs) 6.75 —
5467 A1241 $1.10 multi 1.60 1.25
a. Tete-beche pair 3.20 2.50
b. Booklet pane of 4 6.75 —
c. Booklet pane of 4 (two tete-beche pairs) 6.75 —
5468 A1241 $2.20 multi 3.25 2.40
a. Tete-beche pair 6.50 4.80
b. Booklet pane of 4 13.50 —
c. Booklet pane of 4 (two tete-beche pairs) 13.50 —
Complete booklet, #5466b, 5466c, 5467b, 5467c, 5468b, 5468c 54.00
d. Souvenir sheet of 6, 2 each #5466-5468 (three tete-beche pairs) 13.00 13.00
Nos. 5466-5468 (3) 6.45 4.90

Complete booklet sold for $36.95.

Megapodes A1242

Designs: Nos. 5469, 5472, Malleefowl. Nos. 5470, 5473, Australian brush-turkey. Nos. 5471, 7474, Orange-footed scrubfowl.

2022, June 7 Litho. *Perf. 14x14¾*

5469 A1242 $1.10 multi 1.60 1.60
5470 A1242 $1.10 multi 1.60 1.60
5471 A1242 $1.10 multi 1.60 1.60
a. Souvenir sheet of 3, #5469-5471 4.80 4.80
Nos. 5469-5471 (3) 4.80 4.80

Booklet Stamps
Self-Adhesive

Serpentine Die Cut 11¼ Syncopated

5472 A1242 $1.10 multi 1.60 .25
a. Booklet pane of 10 16.00
5473 A1242 $1.10 multi 1.60 .25
a. Booklet pane of 10 16.00
5474 A1242 $1.10 multi 1.60 .25
a. Booklet pane of 10 16.00
Nos. 5472-5474 (3) 4.80 .75

Prince Philip (1921-2021) A1244

2022, June 14 Litho. *Perf. 14x14¾*

Stamp With Cream Frame

5477 A1244 $1.10 multi 1.60 1.25

Souvenir Sheet
Stamp Without Cream Frame

5478 A1244 $1.10 multi 1.60 1.25

Sir Douglas Nicholls (1906-88), Pastor and Governor of South Australia — A1245

2022, July 5 Litho. *Perf. 14x14¾*

5479 A1245 $1.10 multi 1.60 1.25

A1246

A1247

Budgerigars — A1248

2022, July 11 Litho. *Perf. 14¾x14*

5480 A1246 $1.10 multi 1.60 1.60
5481 A1247 $1.10 multi 1.60 1.60
5482 A1248 $1.10 multi 1.60 1.60
a. Souvenir sheet of 3, #5480-5482 4.80 4.80
Nos. 5480-5482 (3) 4.80 4.80

Booklet Stamps
Self-Adhesive

Serpentine Die Cut 11¼ Syncopated

5483 A1246 $1.10 multi 1.60 .25
a. Booklet pane of 10 16.00
5484 A1247 $1.10 multi 1.60 .25
a. Booklet pane of 10 16.00
5485 A1248 $1.10 multi 1.60 .25
a. Booklet pane of 10 16.00
Nos. 5483-5485 (3) 4.80 .75

Australian Men's National Soccer Team, Cent. — A1249

Players from: No. 5486, 1922. No. 5487, 2022.

2022, July 19 Litho. *Perf. 14x14¾*

5486 A1249 $1.10 multi 1.60 1.25
5487 A1249 $1.10 multi 1.60 1.25
a. Souvenir sheet of 2, #5486-5487 3.25 2.50

Cicadas — A1250

Designs: No. 5488, Masked devil cicada. No. 5489, Golden emperor cicada. No. 5490, Sandgrinder cicada.

2022, Aug. 2 Litho. *Perf. 14x14¾*

5488 A1250 $1.10 multi 1.50 1.10
5489 A1250 $1.10 multi 1.50 1.10
5490 A1250 $1.10 multi 1.50 1.10
a. Souvenir sheet of 3, #5488-5490 4.50 3.50
Nos. 5488-5490 (3) 4.50 3.30

Adelaide-Darwin Overland Telegraph Line, 150th Anniv. — A1251

2022, Aug. 23 Litho. *Perf. 14x14¾*

5491 A1251 $1.10 multi 1.50 1.10

Aerial Views — A1252

Designs: $2.90, Cradle Mountain, Tasmania. $3.50, Kakadu National Park, Northern Territory. $3.70, Bungle Bungle Range, Western Australia. $4, Great Barrier Reef, Queensland.

2022, Aug. 23 Litho. *Perf. 14x14¾*

5492 A1252 $2.90 multi 4.00 4.00
5493 A1252 $3.50 multi 4.75 4.75
5494 A1252 $3.70 multi 5.00 5.00
5495 A1252 $4 multi 5.50 2.75
Nos. 5492-5495 (4) 19.25 16.50

Booklet Stamps
Self-Adhesive

Serpentine Die Cut 11¼ Syncopated

5496 A1252 $2.90 multi 4.00 2.00
a. Booklet pane of 5 20.00
5497 A1252 $3.50 multi 4.75 2.40
a. Booklet pane of 5 24.00
5498 A1252 $3.70 multi 5.00 2.50
a. Booklet pane of 5 25.00
Nos. 5496-5498 (3) 13.75 6.90

A1253

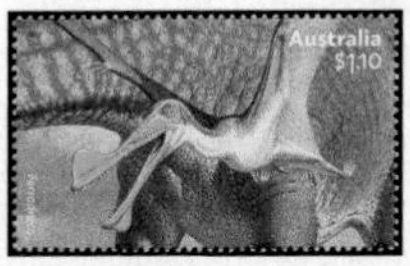

Dinosaurs A1254

Designs: Nos. 5499, 5504, Diamantinasaurus. Nos. 5500, 5505, Elaphrosaurine. Nos. 5501, 5506, Australovenator. Nos. 5502, 5507, Ferrodraco. Nos. 5503, 5508, Kunbarrasaurus.

2022, Sept. 5 Litho. *Perf. 14x14¾*

5499 A1253 $1.10 multi 1.50 1.50
5500 A1253 $1.10 multi 1.50 1.50
5501 A1253 $1.10 multi 1.50 1.50

Perf. 14¼x14

5502 A1254 $1.10 multi 1.50 1.50
5503 A1254 $1.10 multi 1.50 1.50
a. Souvenir sheet of 5, #5499-5503 7.50 7.50
Nos. 5499-5503 (5) 7.50 7.50

Booklet Stamps
Self-Adhesive

Serpentine Die Cut 11¼ Syncopated

5504 A1253 $1.10 multi 1.50 .25
a. Booklet pane of 10 15.00
5505 A1253 $1.10 multi 1.50 .25
a. Booklet pane of 10 15.00
5506 A1253 $1.10 multi 1.50 .25
a. Booklet pane of 10 15.00

Serpentine Die Cut 10¾x11 Syncopated

5507 A1254 $1.10 multi 1.50 .25
a. Booklet pane of 10 15.00
5508 A1254 $1.10 multi 1.50 .25
a. Booklet pane of 10 15.00
Nos. 5504-5508 (5) 7.50 1.25

Rose Varieties — A1255

Designs: Nos. 5509, 5515, Lorraine Lee. Nos. 5510, 5514, Lady of Australia. Nos. 5511, 5516, Governor Marie Bashir. Nos. 5512, 5513, Dusky Moon.

2022, Sept. 13 Litho. *Perf. 14x14¾*

5509 A1255 $1.10 multi 1.50 1.50
5510 A1255 $1.10 multi 1.50 1.50
5511 A1255 $1.10 multi 1.50 1.50
5512 A1255 $1.10 multi 1.50 1.50
a. Souvenir sheet of 4, #5509-5512 6.00 6.00
Nos. 5509-5512 (4) 6.00 6.00

Booklet Stamps
Self-Adhesive

Serpentine Die Cut 11¼ Syncopated

5513 A1255 $1.10 multi 1.50 .25
5514 A1255 $1.10 multi 1.50 .25
5515 A1255 $1.10 multi 1.50 .25
5516 A1255 $1.10 multi 1.50 .25
a. Booklet pane of 20, 5 each #5513-5516 30.00
Nos. 5513-5516 (4) 6.00 1.00

A1256

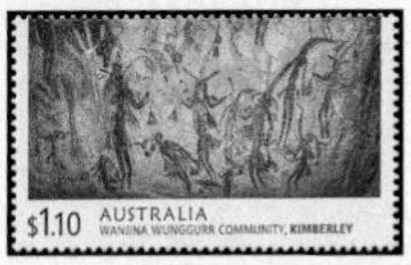

Rock Art of the Wanjina Wunggurr Community in the Kimberley Region A1257

2022, Sept. 20 Litho. *Perf. 14¼x14*

5517 A1256 $1.10 multi 1.50 1.10
5518 A1257 $1.10 multi 1.50 1.10
a. Souvenir sheet of 2, #5517-5518 3.00 2.25

Peter Geoffrey Brock (1945-2006), Race Car Driver, and His Cars — A1258

Brock and: Nos. 5519, 5524, 1972 Holden LJ Torana GTR XU-1. Nos. 5520, 5525, 1979 Holden LX Torana SS A9X. Nos. 5521, 5526, 1980 Holden VC Commodore. Nos. 5522, 5527, 1984 Holden VK Commodore. Nos. 5523, 5528, 1987 Holden VL Commodore SS Group A.

2022, Oct. 3 Litho. *Perf. 14x14¾*

5519 A1258 $1.10 multi 1.50 1.50
a. Perf. 14 1.50 1.50
5520 A1258 $1.10 multi 1.50 1.50
a. Perf. 14 1.50 1.50
5521 A1258 $1.10 multi 1.50 1.50
a. Perf. 14 1.50 1.50
5522 A1258 $1.10 multi 1.50 1.50
a. Perf. 14 1.50 1.50
5523 A1258 $1.10 multi 1.50 1.50
a. Perf. 14 1.50 1.50
b. Souvenir sheet of 5, #5519a-5523a 7.50 7.50
Nos. 5519-5523 (5) 7.50 7.50

Booklet Stamps
Self-Adhesive

Serpentine Die Cut 11¼ Syncopated

5524 A1258 $1.10 multi 1.50 .25
a. Booklet pane of 10 15.00
5525 A1258 $1.10 multi 1.50 .25
a. Booklet pane of 10 15.00
5526 A1258 $1.10 multi 1.50 .25
a. Booklet pane of 10 15.00
5527 A1258 $1.10 multi 1.50 .25
a. Booklet pane of 10 15.00
5528 A1258 $1.10 multi 1.50 .25
a. Booklet pane of 10 15.00
Nos. 5524-5528 (5) 7.50 1.25

Free, Secular and Compulsory Education, 150th Anniv. — A1259

2022, Oct. 11 Litho. *Perf. 14x14¾*

5529 A1259 $1.10 multi 1.50 1.50

Coil Stamp
Self-Adhesive

Serpentine Die Cut 11¼ Syncopated

5530 A1259 $1.10 multi 1.50 .25

Rivers — A1260

Designs: No. 5531, Diamantina River, Queensland. No. 5532, Murrumbidgee River, Australian Capital Territory. No. 5533, Murray River, South Australia. No. 5534, Gordon River, Tasmania.

2022, Oct. 25 Litho. *Perf. 14x14¾*

5531 A1260 $1.10 multi 1.50 1.10
5532 A1260 $1.10 multi 1.50 1.10
5533 A1260 $1.10 multi 1.50 1.10
5534 A1260 $1.10 multi 1.50 1.10
Nos. 5531-5534 (4) 6.00 4.40

Christmas
A1261 A1262

Designs: Nos. 5535, 5540, Madonna and Child. Nos. 5536, 5541, 5545, "Joy." Nos. 5537, 5542, 5546, "Peace." Nos. 5538, 5543, Angel. Nos. 5539, 5544, "Noel."

2022, Nov. 1 Litho. *Perf. 14¾x14*

5535 A1261 65c multi .85 .85
5536 A1262 65c multi .85 .85
5537 A1262 65c multi .85 .85
a. Horiz. pair, #5536-5537 1.70 1.70
5538 A1261 $2.60 multi 3.50 3.50
a. Souvenir sheet of 2, #5535, 5538 4.50 4.50
5539 A1262 $2.60 multi 3.50 3.50
Nos. 5535-5539 (5) 9.55 9.55

Booklet Stamps
Self-Adhesive

5540 A1261 65c multi .85 .25
a. Booklet pane of 20 + 20 etiquettes 17.00
5541 A1262 65c multi .85 .25
5542 A1262 65c multi .85 .25
a. Booklet pane of 20, 10 each #5541-5542 + 20 etiquettes 17.00
5543 A1261 $2.60 multi 3.50 1.75
a. Booklet pane of 5 17.50
5544 A1262 $2.60 multi 3.50 1.75
a. Booklet pane of 5 17.50

Litho. With Foil Application

5545 A1262 65c multi .85 .25
a. Booklet pane of 10 + 10 etiquettes 8.50
5546 A1262 65c multi .85 .25
a. Booklet pane of 10 + 10 etiquettes 8.50
Nos. 5540-5546 (7) 11.25 4.75

SEMI-POSTAL STAMPS

Catalogue values in this section are for Never Hinged items.

Queensland Flood Relief — SP1

Designs: No. B1, Rescuer holding baby. No. B2, Flooded buildings, ground-level view. No. B3, Rescuers taking pet from house. No. B4, Kangaroo stranded on island in flood. No. B5, Flooded buildings, aerial view.

Serpentine Die Cut 11¼ Syncopated

2011, Jan. 27 Litho.

Self-Adhesive

B1 SP1 60c+(20c) multi 1.75 1.75
B2 SP1 60c+(20c) multi 1.75 1.75
B3 SP1 60c+(20c) multi 1.75 1.75
B4 SP1 60c+(20c) multi 1.75 1.75
B5 SP1 60c+(20c) multi 1.75 1.75
a. Sheet of 10, 2 each #B1-B5 17.50
Nos. B1-B5 (5) 8.75 8.75

Surtax for Premier's Flood Relief Appeal.

Leaves in Ring and Hands — SP2

2012, June 26 **Self-Adhesive**
B6 SP2 60c+(20c) multi 1.75 1.75

Printed in sheets of 10. Surtax for Olivia Newton-John Cancer and Wellness Center.

AIR POST STAMPS

Airplane over Bush Lands — AP1

Unwmk.

1929, May 20 **Engr.** ***Perf. 11***
C1 AP1 3p deep green 9.25 8.50
Never hinged 14.50
a. Booklet pane of 4 ('30) 450.00

Kingsford-Smith Type of 1931

1931, Mar. 19
C2 A8 6p gray violet 8.00 8.00
Never hinged 11.50

AP3

1931, Nov. 4
C3 AP3 6p olive brown 17.00 14.00
Never hinged 35.00

For overprint see No. CO1.

Mercury and Hemispheres AP4

1934, Dec. 1 ***Perf. 11***
C4 AP4 1sh6p violet brown 40.00 8.00
Never hinged 97.50

Perf. 13½x14

1937, Oct. 22 **Wmk. 228**
C5 AP4 1sh6p violet brown 8.50 1.40
Never hinged 14.50

Catalogue values for unused stamps in this section, from this point to the end of the section, are for Never Hinged items.

Mercury and Globe — AP5

1949, Sept. 1 ***Perf. 14½***
C6 AP5 1sh6p sepia 2.25 .60

1956, Dec. 6 **Unwmk.**
C7 AP5 1sh6p sepia 18.50 1.10

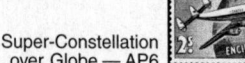

Super-Constellation over Globe — AP6

1958, Jan. 6 ***Perf. 14½x14***
C8 AP6 2sh dark violet blue 2.75 2.25

Inauguration of Australian "Round the World" air service.

AIR POST OFFICIAL STAMP

No. C3 Overprinted

Perf. 11, 11½

1931, Nov. 17 **Unwmk.**
CO1 AP3 6p olive brown 35.00 *35.00*
Never hinged 57.50

Issued primarily for official use, but to prevent speculation, a quantity was issued for public distribution.

POSTAGE DUE STAMPS

Very fine examples of Nos. J1-J38 will have perforations touching the design on one or more sides due to the narrow spacing of the stamps on the plates. Stamps with perfs clear of the design on all four sides are scarce and will command higher prices.

D1

1902 **Typo.** **Wmk. 55** ***Perf. 11½, 12***
J1 D1 ½p emerald 5.75 7.00
J2 D1 1p emerald 27.00 14.00
a. Perf. 11 *2,650.* *1,000.*
b. Perf. 11x11½ 400.00 160.00
J3 D1 2p emerald 67.50 11.50
a. Perf. 11x11½ 525.00 190.00
J4 D1 3p emerald 52.50 32.50
J5 D1 4p emerald 52.50 15.00
J6 D1 6p emerald 62.50 12.50
J7 D1 8p emerald 105.00 90.00
J8 D1 5sh emerald 210.00 80.00
Nos. J1-J8 (8) 582.75 262.50

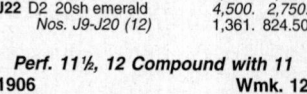

D2

Perf. 11½, 12, Compound with 11

1902-04
J9 D2 ½p emerald 22.00 *18.00*
a. Perf. 11 575.00 325.00
J10 D2 1p emerald, Perf 12x11 21.00 5.00
a. Perf. 11 170.00 32.50
b. Perf 11½ 200.00 140.00
c. Perf 11x11½ 37.50 11.50
J11 D2 2p emerald 52.50 3.50
a. Perf. 11 240.00 30.00
b. Perf 12 — 180.00
c. Perf 11x11½ 120.00 37.50
d. Perf 11x12 140.00 45.00
J12 D2 3p emerald 95.00 18.00
a. Perf. 11 160.00 62.50
b. Perf 12 375.00 110.00
J13 D2 4p emerald 80.00 27.50
a. Perf. 11 275.00 75.00
J14 D2 5p emerald 70.00 25.00
a. Perf. 11 400.00 57.50
b. Perf 12 75.00 20.00
J15 D2 6p emerald 75.00 12.50
a. Perf. 11 130.00 17.50
J16 D2 8p emerald 150.00 60.00
J17 D2 10p emerald 100.00 25.00
a. Perf 12x11½ 125.00 20.00
J18 D2 1sh emerald 85.00 20.00
a. Perf. 11 500.00 45.00
b. Perf 12x11½ 120.00 30.00
J19 D2 2sh emerald 135.00 135.00
a. Perf 11½, 12 200.00 200.00
J20 D2 5sh emerald 475.00 475.00
a. Perf. 11 1,700. 300.00

Perf. 11

J21 D2 10sh emerald *2,250.* *1,900.*
J22 D2 20sh emerald *4,500.* *2,750.*
Nos. J9-J20 (12) 1,361. 824.50

Perf. 11½, 12 Compound with 11

1906 **Wmk. 12**
J23 D2 ½p emerald 16.00 18.00
J24 D2 1p emerald 30.00 5.75
a. Perf. 11 *3,250.* *1,150.*
J25 D2 2p emerald 80.00 10.00
J26 D2 3p emerald 950.00 350.00
J27 D2 4p emerald 77.50 24.00
a. Perf. 11 *5,750.* *3,500.*
J28 D2 6p emerald 77.50 25.00
Nos. J23-J28 (6) 1,231. 432.75

1907 **Wmk. 13** ***Perf. 11½x11***
J29 D2 ½p emerald 37.50 *80.00*
J30 D2 1p emerald 150.00 80.00
J31 D2 2p emerald 300.00 175.00
J32 D2 4p emerald 300.00 165.00
J33 D2 6p emerald 350.00 250.00
Nos. J29-J33 (5) 1,138. 750.00

D3

Perf. 11 (2sh, 10sh, 20sh), 11½x11 (1sh, 5sh)

1908-09 **Wmk. 12**
J34 D3 1sh emer ('09) 125.00 17.50
J35 D3 2sh emerald *1,050.* *18,000.*
J36 D3 5sh emerald 275.00 52.50
J37 D3 10sh emerald *2,750.* *27,500.*
J38 D3 20sh emerald *7,500.* *52,500.*

D4

1909-23 **Wmk. 13** ***Perf. 12x12½***
J39 D4 ½p grn & car 32.00 *45.00*
a. Perf 11, grn & rose ('14) 20.00 17.00
b. Perf 12½, grn & scar ('13) 37.50 29.00
c. Perf 14 ('19) 20.00 10.00
J40 D4 1p grn & car 23.00 9.75
a. Perf 11, yel grn & rose, thicker paper, thick yellowish gum 4,000. 1,500.
b. Perf 11, brt apple grn & rose, thin paper, thin white gum ('14) 20.00 8.50
c. Perf 14 ('14) 70.00 17.00
J41 D4 2p grn & car 40.00 6.00
a. Perf 11 *25,000.* *15,750.*
b. Perf 14 ('18) 29.00 7.50
J42 D4 3p grn & car 35.00 14.50
a. Perf 14, green & rose ('16) 150.00 52.00
J43 D4 4p grn & car 24.00 11.50
a. Perf 14 ('21) 200.00 70.00
J44 D4 6p grn & car 30.00 4.50
a. Perf 11 *37,000.* *25,000.*
J45 D4 1sh grn & car 33.00 9.25
a. Perf 14, yel grn & scarlet ('23) 45.00 23.00
J46 D4 2sh grn & car 115.00 16.00
J47 D4 5sh grn & car 175.00 17.00
J48 D4 10sh grn & car 275.00 170.00
a. Perf 14, yel grn & scarlet ('21) 1,500.
J49 D4 £1 grn & car 525.00 325.00
a. Perf 14, yel grn & scar ('21) 1,000.
Nos. J39-J49 (11) 1,307. 628.50

Nos. J39-J48 and J40a, J41a, J44a are from the 1909 printings and have thicker paper and thick yellowish gum. The other listings are from the 1912-23 printings on thinner paper with thin white gum.

1922-30 **Wmk. 10** ***Perf. 14, 11 (4p)***
J50 D4 ½p grn & car ('23) 9.25 7.50
J51 D4 1p green & car 7.50 2.25
J52 D4 1½p grn & rose ('25) 4.25 7.50
J53 D4 2p green & car 9.25 4.25
J54 D4 3p green & car 17.00 3.25
J55 D4 4p grn & car ('30) 17.00 8.00
a. Perf 14 52.00 23.00
J56 D4 6p green & car 37.50 18.50
Nos. J50-J56 (7) 101.75 51.25
Set, never hinged 200.00

1931-36 **Wmk. 228** ***Perf. 11***
J57 D4 ½p yel grn & rose ('34) 23.00 23.00
J58 D4 1p yel grn & rose ('32) 9.00 2.25
a. Perf 14 14.00 11.50
J59 D4 2p yel grn & rose ('33) 10.50 2.25
a. Perf 14 11.50 11.50
J60 D4 3p yel grn & rose ('36) 140.00 115.00
J61 D4 4p yel grn & rose ('34) 29.00 4.50
J62 D4 6p yel grn & rose ('36) 550.00 500.00
J63 D4 1sh yel grn & rose ('34) 70.00 30.00
Nos. J57-J63 (7) 831.50 677.00
Set, never hinged 1,400.

D5

Engraved; Value Typo.

1938 ***Perf. 14½x14***
J64 D5 ½p green & car 3.50 *3.50*
J65 D5 1p green & car 12.50 1.10
J66 D5 2p green & car 12.50 2.25
J67 D5 3p green & car 55.00 23.00
J68 D5 4p green & car 16.00 1.10
J69 D5 6p green & car 100.00 45.00
J70 D5 1sh green & car 57.50 20.00
Nos. J64-J70 (7) 257.00 95.95
Set, never hinged 400.00

Catalogue values for unused stamps in this section, from this point to the end of the section, are for Never Hinged items.

Type of 1938
Value Tablet Redrawn

Original

Redrawn

Pence denominations: "D" has melon-shaped center in redrawn tablet. The 1909-45 3p differs slightly, having no vertical white stroke half filling the right side of "D" center.

1sh. 1938: Numeral "1" narrow, with six background lines above.

1sh. 1947: Numeral broader, showing more white space around dotted central ornament. Three lines above.

1946-57 **Wmk. 228**
J71 D5 ½p grn & car ('56) 7.00 5.75
J72 D5 1p grn & car ('47) 4.50 1.10
J73 D5 2p green & car 8.00 1.10
J74 D5 3p green & car 10.00 1.10
J75 D5 4p grn & car ('52) 14.00 1.40
J76 D5 5p grn & car ('48) 18.50 2.25
J77 D5 6p grn & car ('47) 18.50 2.90
J78 D5 7p grn & car ('53) 8.00 7.00
J79 D5 8p grn & car ('57) 26.00 23.00
J80 D5 1sh grn & car ('47) 29.00 4.50
Nos. J71-J80 (10) 143.50 50.10

D5a

1953-54

White Tablet, Carmine Numeral

J81 D5a 1sh grn & car ('54) 10.00 6.25
J82 D5a 2sh green & car 16.00 14.50
J83 D5a 5sh green & car 15.00 8.50
Nos. J81-J83 (3) 41.00 29.25

Issued: 2sh, 5sh, Aug. 26; 1sh, Feb. 17.

Redrawn Type of 1947-57

Two Types of Some Pence Values:

Type I — Background lines touch numeral, "D" and period.

Type II — Lines do not touch numeral, etc.

Second engraving of 1sh has sharper and thicker lines.

The ½p type II has 7 dots under the "2."

The 8p type II has distinct lines in centers of "8" and between "8" and "D."

Engr.; Value Typo.

1958-60 **Unwmk.** ***Perf. 14½x14***
J86 D5 ½p grn & car, II 7.00 4.25
a. Six dots under the "2" 9.25 2.25
J87 D5 1p grn & car, II 5.75 1.10
a. Type I 5.75 2.25
J88 D5 3p grn & car, II 5.75 4.50
J89 D5 4p grn & car, I 11.50 10.00
a. Type II ('59) 9.25 *9.25*
J90 D5 5p grn & car, I 29.00 17.50
a. Type II ('59) 100.00 40.00
J91 D5 6p grn & car, II 10.00 5.25
J92 D5 8p grn & car, II 29.00 *29.00*
a. Indistinct lines 23.00 23.00
J93 D5 10p grn & car, II 17.00 6.25

White Tablet, Carmine Numeral

J94 D5a 1sh green & car 29.00 7.00
a. 2nd redrawing ('60) 29.00 5.75
J95 D5a 2sh grn & car 35.00 21.00
Nos. J86-J95 (10) 179.00 105.85

Issued: 1sh, 9/8/58; 10p, 12/9/59; 2sh, 3/8/60; 3p, 6p, 5/25/60; others, 2/27/58.

MILITARY STAMPS

Nos. 166, 191, 183A, 173, 175, 206 and 177 Overprinted in Black

a

b

c

Perf. 14½x14, 15x14, 11½, 13½x13

1946-47 **Wmk. 228**

M1	A24(a)	½p orange	3.50	3.50
		Never hinged	5.75	
M2	A36(b)	1p brown vio	3.50	3.50
		Never hinged	5.75	
a.		Blue overprint	115.00	77.50
		Never hinged	140.00	
M3	A27(b)	3p dk vio brn	3.50	*3.50*
		Never hinged	5.75	
a.		Double overprint	*1,250.*	
M4	A30(a)	6p brn violet	12.00	11.50
		Never hinged	18.00	
M5	A16(a)	1sh gray green	12.00	11.50
		Never hinged	18.00	
M6	A1(c)	2sh dk red brn	35.00	45.00
		Never hinged	70.00	
M7	A32(c)	5sh dl red brn	140.00	*200.00*
		Never hinged	250.00	
		Nos. M1-M7 (7)	209.50	278.50

"B.C.O.F." stands for "British Commonwealth Occupation Force."

Issue dates: Nos. M1-M3, Oct. 11, 1946, Nos. M4-M7, May 8, 1947.

OFFICIAL STAMPS

Overprinted Official stamps are comparatively more difficult to find well centered than the basic issues on which they are printed. This is because poorly centered sheets that had been discarded were purposely chosen to be overprinted to save money.

Perforated Initials

In 1913-31, postage stamps were perforated "OS" for federal official use. The Scott Standard Catalogues do not list officials with perforated initials, but listings for these Australian stamps will be found in the *Scott Classic Specialized Catalogue.*

Overprinted

On Regular Issue of 1931

1931, May 4 **Unwmk.** ***Perf. 11, 11½***

O1	A8	2p dull red	60.00	22.50
O2	A8	3p blue	225.00	35.00

These stamps were issued primarily for official use but to prevent speculation a quantity was issued for public distribution.

Used values are for CTO examples.

Counterfeit overprints exist.

On Regular Issues of 1928-32

1932 **Wmk. 203** ***Perf. 13½x12½***

O3	A4	2p red (II)	25.00	13.00
O4	A4	4p olive bister	40.00	26.00

Perf. 11½, 12

O5	A1	6p brown	97.50	90.00

1932-33 **Wmk. 228** ***Perf. 13½x12½***

O6	A4	½p orange	11.00	1.65
a.		Inverted overprint	*30,000.*	*21,000.*
O7	A4	1p green (I)	6.00	.50
O8	A4	2p red (II)	25.00	.60
a.		Inverted overprint		*47,500.*
O9	A4	3p ultra (II) ('33)	10.00	5.00
O10	A4	5p brown buff	52.50	30.00

Perf. 11½, 12

O11	A1	6p yel brn	42.50	22.50
a.		Inverted overprint		*72,500.*
		Nos. O6-O11 (6)	147.00	60.25
		Set, never hinged	275.00	

1932 **Unwmk.** ***Perf. 11, 11½***

O12	A9	2p red	7.25	6.00
O13	A9	3p blue	24.00	24.00
O14	A16	1sh gray green	72.50	52.50
		Nos. O12-O14 (3)	103.75	82.50
		Set, never hinged	160.00	

AUSTRALIAN ANTARCTIC TERRITORY

Catalogue values for all unused stamps in this section are for Never Hinged items.

All stamps, except Nos. L1-L7, are also valid for postage in Australia.

Edgeworth David, Douglas Mawson and A.F. McKay (1908-09 South Pole Expedition) A1

Australian Explorers and Map of Antarctica A2

Designs: 8p, Loading weasel (snow truck). 1sh, Dog team and iceberg, vert. 2sh3p, Emperor penguins and map, vert.

Perf. 14½, 14½x14, 14x14½

1957-59 **Engr.** **Unwmk.**

L1	A1	5p brown	.65	.30
L2	A2	8p dark blue	2.25	1.00
L3	A2	1sh dark green	2.75	1.75
L4	A2	2sh ultra ('57)	1.50	.90
L5	A2	2sh3p green	7.50	3.50
		Nos. L1-L5 (5)	14.65	7.45
		Set, hinged	8.50	

Nos. L1 and L2 were printed as 4p and 7p stamps and surcharged typographically in black and dark blue before issuance.

Sizes of stamps: No. L2, 34x21mm; Nos. L3, L5, 21x34mm; No. L4, 43½x25½mm.

1961, July 5 ***Perf. 14½***

L6	A1	5p dark blue	1.00	.45

The denomination on No. L6 is not within a typographed circle, but is part of the engraved design.

Sir Douglas Mawson — A3

1961, Oct. 18

L7	A3	5p dark green	.50	.40

50th anniv. of the 1911-14 Australian Antarctic Expedition.

Lookout and Iceberg — A4

Designs: 1c, Aurora australis and camera dome. 2c, Banding penguins. 5c, Branding of elephant seals. 7c, Measuring snow strata. 10c, Wind gauges. 15c, Weather balloon. 20c, Helicopter. 25c, Radio operator. 50c, Ice compression tests. $1, "Mock sun" (parahelion) and dogs. 20c, 25c, 50c and $1 horizontal.

Perf. 13½x13, 13x13½

1966-68 **Photo.** **Unwmk.**

L8	A4	1c multicolored	.50	.30
L9	A4	2c multicolored	.50	*.75*
L10	A4	4c multicolored	.60	.50
L11	A4	5c multicolored	1.40	.50
L12	A4	7c multicolored	.75	.50
L13	A4	10c multicolored	1.00	1.00
L14	A4	15c multicolored	4.75	1.40
L15	A4	20c multicolored	8.00	2.75
L16	A4	25c multicolored	2.00	2.00
L17	A4	50c multicolored	5.00	4.00
L18	A4	$1 multicolored	20.00	12.00
		Nos. L8-L18 (11)	44.50	25.70
		Set, hinged	34.00	

Issued: 5c, 9/25/68; others, 9/28/66.

Nos. L8-L18 are on phosphorescent helecon paper. Fluorescent orange is one of the colors used in printing the 10c, 15c, 20c and 50c.

Sastrugi Snow Formation — A5

1971, June 23 **Photo.** ***Perf. 13x13½***

L19	A5	6c shown	.85	.65
L20	A5	30c Pancake ice	4.50	*3.50*

10th anniv. of the Antarctic Treaty pledging peaceful uses of and scientific cooperation in Antarctica.

Capt. Cook, Sextant, Azimuth Compass — A6

Design: 35c, Chart of Cook's circumnavigation of Antarctica, and "Resolution."

1972, Sept. 13 **Photo.** ***Perf. 13x13½***

L21	A6	7c bister & multi	1.05	.75
L22	A6	35c buff & multi	4.25	4.25

Bicentenary of Capt. James Cook's circumnavigation of Antarctica.

Plankton and Krill Shrimp A7

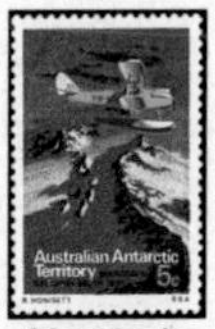

Mawson's D.H. Gipsy Moth, 1931 A8

Food Chain (Essential for Survival): 7c, Adelie penguin feeding on krill shrimp. 9c, Leopard seal pursuing fish, horiz. 10c, Killer whale hunting seals, horiz. 20c, Wandering albatross, horiz. $1, Sperm whale attacking giant squid.

Explorers' Aircraft: 8c, Rymill's DH Fox Moth returning to Barry Island. 25c, Hubert Wilkins Lockheed Vega, horiz. 30c, Lincoln Ellsworth's Northrop Gamma. 35c, Lars Christensen's Avro Avian and Framnes Mountains, horiz. 50c, Richard Byrd's Ford Tri-Motor dropping US flag over South Pole.

Perf. 13½x13, 13x13½

1973, Aug. 15

L23	A7	1c multicolored	.25	.25
L24	A8	5c multicolored	.25	.25
L25	A7	7c multicolored	1.00	.90
L26	A8	8c multicolored	.25	*.50*
L27	A7	9c multicolored	.25	.25
L28	A7	10c multicolored	2.50	1.75
L29	A7	20c multicolored	.70	.60
L30	A8	25c multicolored	.55	.60
L31	A8	30c multicolored	.55	*.70*
L32	A8	35c multicolored	.55	*.70*
L33	A8	50c multicolored	1.00	*.75*
L34	A7	$1 multicolored	1.75	*2.00*
		Nos. L23-L34 (12)	9.60	9.25

Adm. Byrd, Plane, Mountains — A9

Design: 20c, Adm. Byrd, Floyd Bennett trimotored plane, map of Antarctica.

1979, June 20 **Litho.** ***Perf. 15½***

L35	A9	20c multicolored	.40	*.60*
L36	A9	55c multicolored	.85	*1.10*

50th anniv. of first flight over South Pole by Richard Byrd (1888-1957).

"S.Y. Nimrod" — A10

Designs: 1c, S.Y. Aurora. 2c, R.Y. Penola. 5c, M.V. Thala Dan. 10c, H.M.S. Challenger. No. L41, S.S. Morning. No. L42, S.Y. Nimrod, stern view. 20c, R.R.S. Discovery II. 22c, R.Y.S. Terra Nova. 25c, S.S. Endurance. 30c, S.S. Fram. 35c, M.S. Nella Dan. 40c, M.S. Kista Dan. 45c, L'Astrolabe. 50c, S.S. Norvegia. 55c, S.Y. Discovery. $1, H.M.S. Resolution.

2c, 5c, 22c, 25c, 40c, 55c, $1 are vertical.

Perf. 13½x13, 13x13½

1979-81 **Litho.**

L37	A10	1c multi	.25	.25
L38	A10	2c multi	.25	.25
L39	A10	5c multi	.25	*.25*
L40	A10	10c multi	.30	*.25*
L41	A10	15c multi	1.15	*2.60*
L42	A10	15c shown	.25	*.30*
L43	A10	20c multi	.30	*1.00*
L44	A10	22c multi	.50	*.30*
L45	A10	25c multi	.50	*.70*
L46	A10	30c multi	.50	*1.30*
L47	A10	35c multi	.60	*1.30*
L48	A10	40c multi	.80	*1.30*
L49	A10	45c multi	.80	*1.30*
L50	A10	50c multi	.80	*1.00*
L51	A10	55c multi	1.00	*2.60*
L52	A10	$1 multi	2.00	*3.25*
		Nos. L37-L52 (16)	10.25	*17.95*

Issued: 5c, 20c, 25c, 30c, 55c, 8/29; 1c, No. L41, 22c, 35c, $1, 5/21/80; 2c, 10c, No. L42, 40c, 45c, 50c, 9/9/81.

A11

1982, May 5 **Litho.** ***Perf. 14x13½***

L53	A11	27c Mawson, landscape	.35	*.25*
L54	A11	75c Mawson, map	1.00	*1.40*

Sir Douglas Mawson (1882-1958), explorer.

A12

Local Wildlife: a, Light-mantled sooty albatross. b, Macquarie Isld. shags. c, Elephant seals. d, Royal penguins. e, Antarctic prions.

1983, Apr. 6 **Litho.** ***Perf. 14½***

L55	Strip of 5, multi	3.50	3.50
a.-e.	A12 27c, any single	.70	.50

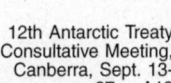

12th Antarctic Treaty Consultative Meeting, Canberra, Sept. 13-27 — A13

1983, Sept. 7 **Litho.** ***Perf. 14½***

L56	A13	27c multicolored	.45	.50

South Magnetic Pole Expedition, 75th Anniv. — A14

1984, Jan. 16

L57	A14	30c Prismatic compass	.50	.50
L58	A14	85c Aneroid barometer	1.50	*2.00*

Dog Team, Mawson Station — A15

2c, Summer afternoon. 10c, Evening. 15c, Prince Charles Mts. 20c, Morning. 25c, Sea ice, iceberg. 30c, Mt. Coates. 33c, Iceberg Alley, Mawson. 36c, Winter evening. 45c, Brash ice, vert. 60c, Midwinter shadows. 75c, Coastline. 85c, Landing field. 90c, Pancake ice, vert. $1, Emperor penguins, Auster Rookery.

1984-87 Litho. *Perf. 14½x15*

L60	A15	2c multi	.25	.25
L61	A15	5c shown	.25	.25
L62	A15	10c multi	.25	.25
L63	A15	15c multi	.30	.25
L64	A15	20c multi	.35	.30
L65	A15	25c multi	.40	.35
L66	A15	30c multi	.50	.45
L67	A15	33c multi	.55	.45
L68	A15	36c multi	.60	.30
L69	A15	45c multi	.75	.65
L70	A15	60c multi	1.00	.80
L71	A15	75c multi	1.25	1.10
L72	A15	85c multi	1.50	1.25
L73	A15	90c multi	1.50	1.25
L74	A15	$1 multi	1.75	1.40
		Nos. L60-L74 (15)	11.20	9.30

Issued: 5, 25, 30, 75, 85c, 7/18/84; 15, 33, 45, 90c, $1, 8/7/85; 2, 10, 20, 36, 60c, 3/11/87.

Antarctic Treaty, 25th Anniv. — A16

1986, Sept. 17 Litho. *Perf. 14x13½*

L75	A16	36c multicolored	1.00	.85

Environment, Conservation and Technology — A17

No. L76: a, Hour-glass dolphins and the *Nella Dan*. b, Emperor penguins and Davis Station. c, Crabeater seal and helicopters. d, Adelie penguins and snow-ice transport vehicle. e, Gray-headed albatross and photographer.

1988, July 20 Litho. *Perf. 13*

L76		Strip of 5	6.00	6.00
a.-e.		A17 37c any single	1.05	1.05

Paintings by Sir Sidney Nolan (b. 1917) — A18

No. L77, Antarctica. No. L78, Iceberg Alley. No. L79, Glacial Flow. No. L80, Frozen Sea.

1989, June 14 Litho. *Perf. 14x13½*

L77	A18	39c multicolored	.90	.60
L78	A18	39c multicolored	.90	.60
L79	A18	60c multicolored	1.50	1.50
L80	A18	80c multicolored	2.25	2.25
		Nos. L77-L80 (4)	5.55	4.95

Aurora Australis — A19

Design: $1.20, Research ship Aurora Australis.

1991, June 20 Litho. *Perf. 14½*

L81	A19	43c multicolored	.80	.80
L82	A19	$1.20 multicolored	2.25	1.50

Antarctic Treaty, 30th anniv. (No. L81).

Regional Wildlife — A20

45c, Adelie penguin. 75c, Elephant seal. 85c, Northern giant petrel. 95c, Weddell seal. $1, Royal penguins. $1.20, Emperor penguin, vert. $1.40, Fur seals. $1.50, King penguins, vert.

Perf. 14x14½, 14½x14

1992-93 Litho.

L83	A20	45c multi	.75	.65
L84	A20	75c multi	1.25	1.10
L85	A20	85c multi	1.50	1.40
L86	A20	95c multi	1.60	1.50
L86A	A20	$1 multi	1.75	1.60
L87	A20	$1.20 multi	1.90	1.75
L88	A20	$1.40 multi	2.40	2.00
L89	A20	$1.50 multi	2.60	2.25
		Nos. L83-L89 (8)	13.75	12.25

Issued: $1, $1.40, $1.50, 1/14/93; others, 5/14/92.

The Last Huskies — A21

45c, Dog up close, vert. 75c, Sled team. 85c, Dog seated, vert. $1.05, Three dogs.

1994, Jan. 13 Litho. *Perf. 14½*

L90	A21	45c multi	1.00	.75
L91	A21	75c multi	1.50	1.50
L92	A21	85c multi	2.25	2.25
L93	A21	$1.05 multi	2.50	2.50
		Nos. L90-L93 (4)	7.25	7.00

Whales & Dolphins — A22

1995, June 15 Litho. *Perf. 14½*

L94	A22	45c Humpback whale	.95	.85
L95	A22	45c Hourglass dolphin, vert.	.95	.85
L96	A22	45c Minke whale, vert.	.95	.85
a.		Pair, #L95-L96	2.25	2.25
L97	A22	$1 Killer whale	2.50	2.50
a.		Souvenir sheet of 4, #L94-L97	7.75	7.75
b.		As "a," overprinted	*65.00*	*65.00*
c.		As "a," overprinted	*40.00*	*40.00*
		Nos. L94-L97 (4)	5.35	5.05

No. L97b is overprinted in gold in sheet margin with Singapore '95 emblem and: "Australia Post Exhibition Sheet No. 2," and, in both Chinese and English, with "Singapore 95 World Stamp Exhibition."

No. L97c is overprinted in gold in sheet margin with exhibition emblem, "Australian Post Exhibition Sheet No. 3" and CAPEX '96 WORLD PHILATELIC EXHIBITION / EXPOSITION PHILATELIQUE MONDIALE

Issued: No. L97b, 9/1/95; No. L97c, 6/15/96.

Landscapes, by Christian Clare Robertson — A23

Designs: No. L98, Rafting sea ice. No. L99, Shadow on the Plateau. $1, Ice cave. $1.20, Twelve Lake.

1996, May 16 Litho. *Perf. 14½x14*

L98	A23	45c multicolored	1.25	.95
L99	A23	45c multicolored	1.25	.95
a.		Pair, Nos. L98-L99	2.50	2.25
L100	A23	$1 multicolored	2.25	2.50
L101	A23	$1.20 multicolored	3.00	2.40
		Nos. L98-L101 (4)	7.75	6.80

Australian Natl. Antarctic Research Expeditions, 50th Anniv. — A24

Designs: No. L102, Apple field huts. No. L103, Inside an apple hut. 95c, Summer surveying. $1.05, Sea ice research. $1.20, Remote field camp.

1997, May 15 Litho. *Perf. 14x14½*

L102	A24	45c multicolored	1.10	.90
L103	A24	45c multicolored	1.10	.90
a.		Pair, #L102-L103	2.25	2.25
L104	A24	95c multicolored	2.50	2.25
L105	A24	$1.05 multicolored	2.10	2.40
L106	A24	$1.20 multicolored	2.75	2.50
		Nos. L102-L106 (5)	9.55	8.95

Modes of Transportion — A25

Designs: No. L107, Snowmobile. No. L108, Ship, "Aurora Australis." $1, Helicopter airlifting a four-wheel drive ATV, vert. $2, Antarctic Hagglunds (rubber-tracked vehicles with fiberglass cabins), vert.

Perf. 14x14½, 14½x14

1998, Mar. 5 Litho.

L107	A25	45c multicolored	1.00	1.00
L108	A25	45c multicolored	1.00	1.00
a.		Pair, #L107-L108	2.50	2.50
L109	A25	$1 multicolored	2.50	3.00
L110	A25	$2 multicolored	5.25	4.50
		Nos. L107-L110 (4)	9.75	9.50

Preservation of Huts used During Mawson's Antarctic Expedition — A26

Designs: No. L111, Photograph of Mawson, sailing ship Aurora. No. L112, Photograph, "Home of the Blizzard," by Frank Hurley. 90c, Photograph, "Huskie Team," by Xavier Mertz. $1.35, Huts restoration.

1999, May 13 Litho. *Perf. 14x14½*

L111	A26	45c multicolored	1.00	1.00
L112	A26	45c multicolored	1.00	1.00
a.		Pair, #L111-L112	2.40	2.40
L113	A26	90c multicolored	2.75	3.00
L114	A26	$1.35 multicolored	4.00	3.50
		Nos. L111-L114 (4)	8.75	8.50

Penguins — A27

2000, July 24 Litho. *Perf. 13¾x14½*

L115	A27	45c Emperor penguins	1.25	1.25
L116	A27	45c Adélie penguins	1.25	1.25
a.		Pair, #L115-L116	4.75	4.75

Australians in the Antarctic, Cent. — A28

No. L117: a, Penguins and icicles. b, Louis Bernacchi, physicist. c, Nimrod. d, Scientists at South Magnetic Pole. e, Griffith Taylor and Frank Debenham, geologists. f, First radio used in Antarctica. g, First flight over Antarctica. h, Sir Douglas Mawson, explorer. i, BANZARE (British, Australian and New Zealand Antarctic Research Expedition). j, Australia's claim to territory. k, Establishment of ANARE (Australian National Antarctic Research Expeditions). l, Transport. m, Aurora Australis. n, Climate research. o, Cold-weather clothing. p, Nella Dan. q, First women on Antarctica. r, Communications. s, Tourism. t, Satellite view of Antarctica.

2001, May 17 Litho. *Perf. 14¾x14*

L117		Sheet of 20	18.50	18.50
a.-e.		A28 5c Any single	.40	.40
f.-j.		A28 10c Any single	.50	.50
k.-o.		A28 25c Any single	.60	.60
p.-t.		A28 45c Any single	.75	.75

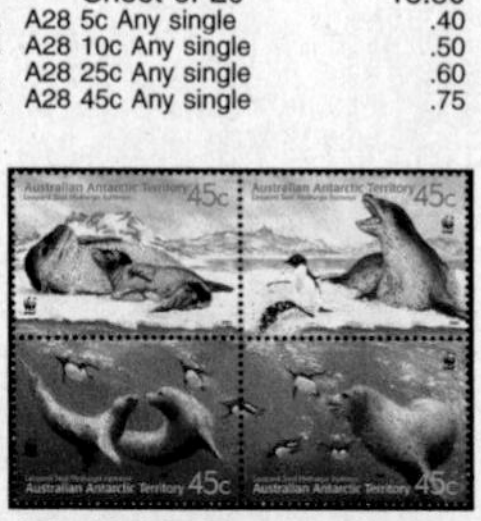

Worldwide Fund for Nature (WWF) — A29

No. L118: a, Leopard seal and pup on ice. b, Leopard seal and penguin on ice. c, Penguins, two leopard seals in water. d, Penguins, leopard seal in water.

2001, Sept. 11 Litho. *Perf. 14x14½*

L118	A29	Block of 4	6.75	8.00
a.-d.		45c Any single	1.00	1.00

Antarctic Base Stations — A30

Maps showing station locations and: a, Light Detection and Ranging Instrument, aurora australis, Davis Station. b, Diatom, Casey Station. c, Wandering albatross, Macquarie Island Station. d, Adèlie penguin, Mawson Station.

2002, July 2 Litho. *Perf. 14x14¾*

L119	A30	Block of 4, #a-d	7.00	7.00
a.-d.		45c Any single	1.00	1.00

Ships — A31

Designs: No. L120, Kista Dan, No. L121, Magga Dan. $1, Thala Dan, vert. $1.45, Nella Dan, vert.

Perf. 14x14½, 14½x14

2003, Apr. 29 Litho.

L120	A31	50c multi	1.00	1.00
L121	A31	50c multi	1.00	1.00
a.		Horiz. pair, #L120-L121	2.25	2.25
L122	A31	$1 multi	2.25	2.25
L123	A31	$1.45 multi	3.75	3.75
		Nos. L120-L123 (4)	8.00	8.00

Mawson Station, 50th Anniv. — A32

Designs: No. L124, Naming ceremony, 1954. No. L125, Station buildings. $1, Barge and airplane. $1.45, Auster Emperor Penguin Rookery.

2004, Feb. 13 Litho. *Perf. 14x14½*

L124	A32	50c multi	1.00	1.00
L125	A32	50c multi	1.00	1.00
a.		Horiz. pair, #L124-L125	2.50	2.50
L126	A32	$1 multi	3.00	3.00
L127	A32	$1.45 multi	4.00	4.00
		Nos. L124-L127 (4)	9.00	9.00

Aircraft — A33

Designs: No. L128, Hughes 500 helicopter. No. L129, De Havilland DHC-2 Beaver. $1, Pilatus PC-6 Porter. $1.45, Douglas DC-3/Dakota C-47.

2005, Sept. 6 Litho. *Perf. 14x14½*

L128	A33	50c multi	1.00	1.00
L129	A33	50c multi	1.00	1.00
a.		Horiz. pair, #L128-L129	2.25	2.25
L130	A33	$1 multi	2.75	2.75
L131	A33	$1.45 multi	4.50	4.50
		Nos. L128-L131 (4)	9.25	9.25

Fish — A34

Designs: No. L132, Mackerel icefish. No. L133, Lanternfish. No. L134, Eaton's skate. No. L135, Patagonian toothfish.

2006, Aug. 1 Litho. *Perf. 14x14¾*

L132	A34	50c multi	.90	.90
L133	A34	50c multi	.90	.90
a.		Horiz. pair, #L132-L133	2.50	2.50
L134	A34	$1 multi	2.00	2.00
L135	A34	$1 multi	2.00	2.00
a.		Horiz. pair, #L134-L135	5.00	5.00
		Nos. L132-L135 (4)	5.80	5.80

Worldwide Fund For Nature (WWF) — A35

Royal penguins: No. L136, Four marching. No. L137, Nesting. No. L138, Two contesting territory (denomination at bottom), horiz. No. L139, Two courting (denomination at left), horiz.

2007, Aug. 7 Litho. *Perf. 14½x14*

L136 A35 50c multi 1.00 1.00
L137 A35 50c multi 1.00 1.00
a. Horiz. pair, #L136-L137 2.75 2.00

Perf. 14x14½

L138 A35 $1 multi 1.50 1.50
L139 A35 $1 multi 1.50 1.50
a. Vert. pair, #L138-L139 5.75 4.75
Nos. L136-L139 (4) 5.00 5.00

International Polar Year — A36

Designs: No. L140, Astronomy. No. L141, Glaciology. No. L142, Marine biology. No. L143, Oceanography.

2008, Sept. 16 Litho. *Perf. 14x14½*

L140 A36 55c multi 1.00 1.00
L141 A36 55c multi 1.00 1.00
a. Vert. pair, #L140-L141 3.00 2.75
L142 A36 $1.10 multi 1.75 1.75
L143 A36 $1.10 multi 1.75 1.75
a. Vert. pair, #L142-L143 6.00 6.00
b. Souvenir sheet, #L140-L143 11.50 12.50
Nos. L140-L143 (4) 5.50 5.50

Discovery of South Magnetic Pole, Cent. — A37

Designs: No. L144, Crew unloading the Nimrod. No. L145, Crew depositing expedition provisions by automobile. No. L146, Men at Northern Party camp. No. L147, Alistair Mackay, Douglas Mawson,and Edgeworth David with flag at South Magnetic Pole.

2009, Jan. 8 Litho. *Perf. 14½x14*

L144 A37 55c lt bl & blk 1.00 .75
L145 A37 55c lt bl & multi 1.00 .75
a. Horiz. pair, #L144-L145 2.40 2.60
L146 A37 $1.10 lt bl & blk 2.40 1.60
L147 A37 $1.10 lt bl & blk 2.40 1.60
a. Horiz. pair, #L146-L147 5.00 5.00
b. Souvenir sheet, #L144-L147 7.50 8.00
Nos. L144-L147 (4) 6.80 4.70

International Polar Year — A38

Designs: 55c, Snow petrel. $2.05, Jade iceberg.

2009, Mar. 4 Litho. *Perf. 14x14¾*

L148 A38 55c multi 1.60 1.30
L149 A38 $2.05 multi 5.00 3.25
a. Souvenir sheet, #L148-L149 8.00 4.50
b. Sheet of 2, Australia #3337, Australian Antarctic Terr. #L149 10.00 10.00

Issued: No. L149b, 8/20/10. Stampex 2010, Adelaide (No. L149b).

For Endangered Wildlife stamps inscribed "Australian Antarctic Territory" see Australia Nos. 3128 and 3134.

Macquarie Island — A39

Designs: No. L150, Pleurophyllum hookeri (flower). No. L151, Southern elephant seal. No. L152, Mawson Point Stacks (green terrain). No. L153, Caroline Cove (brown terrain).

2010, Oct. 26 Litho. *Perf. 14¼*

L150 A39 60c multi 1.00 1.00
L151 A39 60c multi 1.00 1.00
a. Horiz. pair, #L150-L151 3.00 3.00
L152 A39 $1.20 multi 1.90 1.90
L153 A39 $1.20 multi 1.90 1.90
a. Horiz. pair, #L152-L153 6.00 6.00
b. Souvenir sheet, #L150-L153 12.00 12.00
Nos. L150-L153 (4) 5.80 5.80

A40

A41

A42

Icebergs — A43

2011, June 7 Litho. *Perf. 14x14¾*

L154 Block of 4 5.00 5.00
a. A40 60c multi 1.00 1.00
b. A41 60c multi 1.00 1.00
c. A42 60c multi 1.00 1.00
d. A43 60c multi 1.00 1.00
e. Souvenir sheet of 4, #L154a-L154d 8.00 8.00

Booklet Stamps
Self-Adhesive
Stamps With Grayed Frame

Serpentine Die Cut 11¼ Syncopated

L155 A40 60c multi 1.00 .30
L156 A41 60c multi 1.00 .30
L157 A42 60c multi 1.00 .30
L158 A43 60c multi 1.00 .30
a. Booklet pane of 10, 3 each #L155-L156, 2 each #L157-L158 12.00
Nos. L155-L158 (4) 4.00 1.20

Australasian Antarctic Expedition, Cent. — A44

No. L159: a, Map and mast of SY Aurora. b, John King Davis (1884-1967), captain of the SY Aurora. c, SY Aurora and postmark. d, Expedition members landing at Macquarie Island. e, Birds on Macquarie Island.

2011, Aug. 2 *Perf. 14¾x14*

L159 Horiz. strip of 5 7.00 7.25
a.-e. A44 60c Any single 1.00 1.00
f. Souvenir sheet of 5, #L159a-L159e 9.50 7.25

For WWF stamp inscribed "Australian Antarctic Territory" see Australia No. 3562.

Dr. Philip Law (1912-2010), Polar Explorer — A45

Designs: 60c, Law. $1.20, Map of Antarctica, Law and helicopter at Arthurson Bluff. $1.80, Map of Antarctica, opening of Mawson Station.

2012, Mar. 6 Litho. *Perf. 14¾x14*

L160 A45 60c multi 1.75 1.40
L161 A45 $1.20 multi 3.50 2.75
L162 A45 $1.80 multi 5.50 2.75
a. Souvenir sheet of 3, #L160-L162 11.00 8.50
Nos. L160-L162 (3) 10.75 6.90

Australasian Antarctic Expedition, Cent. — A46

Designs: No. L163, Main hut. No. L164, Xavier Mertz and dogs. No. L165, Belgrave Ninnis and dogs. No. L166, Bow of SY Aurora, map of Cape Denison, penguins. No. L167, Stern of SY Aurora, expedition members carrying supplies from ship.

2012, Sept. 4

L163 A46 60c multi 1.00 1.00
L164 A46 60c multi 1.00 1.00
L165 A46 60c multi 1.00 1.00
a. Horiz. strip of 3, #L163-L165 5.00 4.00
L166 A46 $1.20 multi 1.50 1.50
L167 A46 $1.20 multi 1.50 1.50
a. Horiz. pair, #L166-L167 6.75 5.50
b. Souvenir sheet of 5, #L163-L167 12.00 9.50
Nos. L163-L167 (5) 6.00 6.00

Mountains — A47

Designs: No. L168, Mt. Parsons. No. L169, Mawson Escarpment. $1.20, South Masson Range. $1.80, David Range.

2013, Mar. 12 Litho. *Perf. 14x14¾*

L168 A47 60c multi .90 .95
L169 A47 60c multi .90 .95
a. Horiz. pair, #L168-L169 2.50 1.90
L170 A47 $1.20 multi 2.50 1.90
L171 A47 $1.80 multi 3.75 3.00
a. Souvenir sheet of 4, #L168-L171 8.75 8.75
Nos. L168-L171 (4) 8.05 6.80

Australasian Antarctic Expedition, Cent. — A48

Designs: No. L172, Men walking in blizzard. No. L173, Man checking wind recorder. No. L174, Weddell seal, Cape petrels. No. L175, Wireless operator Walter Hannam. No. L176, Frank Wild, leader of Western Party of Expedition.

2013, Sept. 10 *Perf. 14¾x14*

L172 A48 60c multi 1.10 .85
L173 A48 60c multi 1.10 .85
L174 A48 60c multi 1.10 .85
a. Horiz. strip of 3, #L172-L174 3.30 2.60
L175 A48 $1.20 multi 2.25 1.75
L176 A48 $1.20 multi 2.25 1.75
a. Horiz. pair, #L175-L176 4.50 3.50
b. Souvenir sheet of 5, #L172-L176 8.00 8.00
Nos. L172-L176 (5) 7.80 6.05

Australasian Antarctic Expedition, Cent. — A49

Designs: No. L177, Scientific researchers with large net. No. L178, Expedition members on SY Aurora. No. L179, Sir Douglas Mawson (1882-1958), expedition leader. No. L180, Mawson on motor launch, Cape Denison. No. L181, Frank Hurley with movie camera.

2014, Feb. 18 Litho. *Perf. 14¾x14*

L177 A49 60c multi 1.10 .85
L178 A49 60c multi 1.10 .85
L179 A49 60c multi 1.10 .85
a. Horiz. strip of 3, #L177-L179 3.30 2.60
L180 A49 $1.20 multi 2.25 1.75
L181 A49 $1.20 multi 2.25 1.75
a. Horiz. pair, #L180-L181 4.50 3.50
b. Souvenir sheet of 5, #L177-L181 8.00 8.00
Nos. L177-L181 (5) 7.80 6.05

Husky — A50

Designs: Nos. L182, L186, Gray husky (shown). Nos. L183, L186, Brown husky. No. L184, Dog team with drivers in orange parkas, horiz. No. L185, Dog team with drivers in black parkas, horiz.

Perf. 14¾x14, 14x14¾

2014, Sept. 9 Litho.

L182 A50 70c multi 1.25 1.25
L183 A50 70c multi 1.25 1.25
a. Horiz. pair, #L182-L183 2.50 2.50
L184 A50 $1.40 multi 2.50 2.00
L185 A50 $1.40 multi 2.50 2.00
a. Horiz. pair, #L184-L185 5.00 4.00
b. Souvenir sheet of 4, #L182-L185 7.50 7.50
Nos. L182-L185 (4) 7.50 6.50

Booklet Stamps
Self-Adhesive

Serpentine Die Cut 11¼ Syncopated

L186 A50 70c multi 1.25 .25
L187 A50 70c multi 1.25 .25
a. Booklet pane of 10, 5 each #L186-L187 12.50

Antarctic Atmospheric Conditions — A51

Various Antarctic landscapes and atmospheric conditions with denomination at: No. L188, UR. No. L189, UL. No. L190, UR. No. L191, UL.

2015, May 26 Litho. *Perf. 14x14¾*

L188 A51 70c multi 1.10 .85
L189 A51 70c multi 1.10 .85
a. Horiz. pair, #L188-L189 2.20 1.70
L190 A51 $1.40 multi 2.25 1.75
L191 A51 $1.40 multi 2.25 1.75
a. Horiz. pair, #L190-L191 4.50 3.50
b. Souvenir sheet of 4, #L188-L191 6.75 6.75
Nos. L188-L191 (4) 6.70 5.20

Dogs Involved in Macquarie Island Pest Eradication — A52

Dogs and: No. L192, Penguins. No. L193, Man with backpack. No. L194, Woman. No. L195, Man in winter coat.

2015, Sept. 9 Litho. *Perf. 14x14¾*

L192 A52 70c multi 1.00 .75
L193 A52 70c multi 1.00 .75
a. Horiz. pair, #L192-L193 2.00 1.50
L194 A52 $1.40 multi 2.00 1.50
L195 A52 $1.40 multi 2.00 1.50
a. Horiz. pair, #L194-L195 4.00 3.00
b. Souvenir sheet of 4, #L192-L195 6.00 6.00
Nos. L192-L195 (4) 6.00 4.50

Photographs of Ernest Shackleton's Imperial Trans-Antarctic Expedition by Frank Hurley (1885-1962) — A53

Inscriptions: No. L196, Weddell Sea. No. L197, Ice-bound. No. L198, Ocean Camp. No. L199, Rescue Mission. $3, At Work.

2016, June 21 Litho. *Perf. 14¾x14*

L196 A53 $1 multi 1.50 1.10
L197 A53 $1 multi 1.50 1.10
a. Horiz. pair, #L196-L197 3.00 2.25
L198 A53 $2 multi 3.00 2.25
L199 A53 $2 multi 3.00 2.25
a. Horiz. pair, #L198-L199 6.00 4.50
L200 A53 $3 multi 4.50 3.50
a. Souvenir sheet of 5, #L196-L200 13.50 13.50
Nos. L196-L200 (5) 13.50 10.20

Ice Flowers (Frost Formations) — A54

Various ice flowers. Denomination at UR on Nos. L201, L203, L205a, L205c, L206, Denomination at UL on Nos. L202, L204, L205b, L205d, L207.

Litho., Litho & Embossed With Foil Application (#L205)

2016, Sept. 20 *Perf. 14¼*

L201 A54 $1 multi 1.60 1.60
L202 A54 $1 multi 1.60 1.60
a. Horiz. pair, #L201-L202 3.20 3.20
L203 A54 $2 multi 3.25 1.60
L204 A54 $3 multi 4.75 2.40
Nos. L201-L204 (4) 11.20 7.20

Miniature Sheet

L205 Sheet of 4 11.50 6.50
a.-b. A54 $1 Either single 1.60 1.25
c. A54 $2 multi 3.25 1.60
d. A54 $3 multi 4.75 2.40

Booklet Stamps Self-Adhesive

Serpentine Die Cut 11¼ Syncopated

L206 A54 $1 multi 1.60 .25
L207 A54 $1 multi 1.60 .25
a. Booklet pane of 10, 5 each #L206-L207 16.00

A55

A56

A57

East Antarctic Deep Sea Creatures — A58

2017, Mar. 7 **Litho.** *Perf. 14¼*

L208 A55 $1 multi 1.60 1.25
L209 A56 $1 multi 1.60 1.25
a. Horiz. pair, #L208-L209 3.20 2.50
L210 A57 $2 multi 3.00 2.25
L211 A58 $2 multi 3.00 2.25
a. Horiz. pair, #L210-L211 6.00 4.50
b. Souvenir sheet of 4, #L208-L211 9.25 7.00
Nos. L208-L211 (4) 9.20 7.00

Cultural Heritage — A59

Designs: No. L212, Aneroid barometer and ship. No. L213, Proclamation of Sir Douglas Mawson and map of Antarctica. $2, Weasel M29 vehicle and mountains.

2017, Sept. 19 **Litho.** *Perf. 14¾x14*

L212 A59 $1 multi 1.60 1.25
L213 A59 $1 multi 1.60 1.25
L214 A59 $2 multi 3.25 1.60
a. Souvenir sheet of 3, #L212-L214 6.50 4.25
Nos. L212-L214 (3) 6.45 4.10

Crabeater Seals — A60

Designs: No. L215, Two seals. No. L216, Seal in water. No. L217, Two seals, diff. No. L218, One seal.

2018, Mar. 27 **Litho.** *Perf. 14x14¾*

L215 A60 $1 multi 1.60 1.25
L216 A60 $1 multi 1.60 1.25
L217 A60 $2 multi 3.25 1.60
L218 A60 $2 multi 3.25 1.60
a. Souvenir sheet of 4, #L215-L218 9.75 5.75
Nos. L215-L218 (4) 9.70 5.70

RSV Aurora Australis, 30th Anniv. — A61

Designs: No. L219, Ship in ice. No. L220, Ship and penguins. No. L221, Wave approaching ship. No. L222, Aerial view of ship in ice.

2018, Sept. 25 **Litho.** *Perf. 14x14¾*

L219 A61 $1 multi 1.50 1.10
L220 A61 $1 multi 1.50 1.10
L221 A61 $2 multi 3.00 2.25
L222 A61 $2 multi 3.00 2.25
a. Souvenir sheet of 4, #L219-L222 9.00 6.75
Nos. L219-L222 (4) 9.00 6.70

Carey Research Station, 50th Anniv. — A62

Designs: No. L223, Scientist holding equipment at Aurora Basin North, 2013. No. L224, Casey Repstat, 1971. No. L225, Tents at Aurora Basin North, 2013. No. L226, Casey Station, 2015.

2019, Mar. 26 **Litho.** *Perf. 14x14¾*

L223 A62 $1 multi 1.50 1.10
L224 A62 $1 multi 1.50 1.10
L225 A62 $2 multi 3.00 2.25
L226 A62 $2 multi 3.00 2.25
a. Souvenir sheet of 4, #L223-L226 9.00 6.75
Nos. L223-L226 (4) 9.00 6.70

Mapping the Australian Antarctic Territory — A63

Maps by: No. L227, Douglas Mawson, 1911. No. L228, Department of the Interior, 1939. No. L229, Division of National Mapping, 1971. No. L230, Australian Antarctic Division, 1993.

2019, Aug. 20 **Litho.** *Perf. 14¼*

L227 A63 $1 multi 1.40 1.10
L228 A63 $1 multi 1.40 1.10
L229 A63 $2 multi 2.75 2.10
L230 A63 $2 multi 2.75 2.10
a. Souvenir sheet of 4, #L227-L230 8.50 6.50
Nos. L227-L230 (4) 8.30 6.40

1948 HMAS Wyatt Earp Expedition — A64

Designs: No. L231, HMAS Wyatt Earp. No. L232, Royal Australian Air Force Vought Kingfisher. $3.30, HMAS Wyatt Earp and Royal Australian Air Force Vought Kingfisher.

Perf. 12¼x13¼

2020, Mar. 31 **Litho. & Engr.**

L231 A64 $1.10 multi 1.40 1.10
L232 A64 $1.10 multi 1.40 1.10
L233 A64 $3.30 multi 4.00 3.00
a. Souvenir sheet of 3, #L231-L233 7.00 5.25
Nos. L231-L233 (3) 6.80 5.20

A65

A66

A67

Arrival of New Icebreaker RSV Nuyina — A68

2020, Sept. 29 **Litho.** *Perf. 14x14¾*

L234 A65 $1.10 multi 1.60 1.25
L235 A66 $1.10 multi 1.60 1.25
L236 A67 $2.20 multi 3.25 2.40
L237 A68 $2.20 multi 3.25 2.40
a. Souvenir sheet of 4, #L234-L237 9.75 9.75
Nos. L234-L237 (4) 9.70 7.30

Australian Antarctic Arts Fellowship — A69

Designs: No. L238, Music performance. No. L239, Painting. No. L240, Sound recording. No. L241, Photography.

2021, Mar. 16 **Litho.** *Perf. 14x14¾*

L238 A69 $1.10 multi 1.75 1.30
L239 A69 $1.10 multi 1.75 1.30
L240 A69 $2.20 multi 3.50 2.60
L241 A69 $2.20 multi 3.50 2.60
a. Souvenir sheet of 4, #L238-L241 10.50 8.00
Nos. L238-L241 (4) 10.50 7.80

Lichens — A70

Designs: No. L242, Buellia frigida. No. L243, Xanthoria mawsonii. $2.20, Umbilicaria decussata. $3.30, Xanthoria elegans.

2021, Oct. 5 **Litho.** *Perf. 14¼*

L242 A70 $1.10 multi 1.75 1.30
L243 A70 $1.10 multi 1.75 1.30
L244 A70 $2.20 multi 3.50 2.60
L245 A70 $3.30 multi 5.00 3.75
a. Souvenir sheet of 4, #L242-L245 12.00 9.00
Nos. L242-L245 (4) 12.00 8.95

Penguins — A71

Designs: No. L246, Head of Emperor penguin. No. L247, Emperor penguins. No. L248, Head of Adélie penguin. No. L249, Adélie penguins.

2022, Mar. 22 **Litho.** *Perf. 14x14¾*

L246 A71 $1.10 multi 1.75 1.30
L247 A71 $1.10 multi 1.75 1.30
L248 A71 $2.20 multi 3.25 2.50
L249 A71 $2.20 multi 3.25 2.50
a. Souvenir sheet of 4, #L246-L249 10.00 7.75
Nos. L246-L249 (4) 10.00 7.60

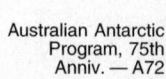

Australian Antarctic Program, 75th Anniv. — A72

Designs: No. L250, Flag raising cermony, building and equipment. No. L251, Australian National Antarctic Research Expedition team members, sled and flag, vehicle for Antarctic transportation, vert. No. L252, Researcher with microscope, researcher in snow, vert. No. L253, Airplanes.

Perf. 14x14¾, 14¾x14

2022, Aug. 9 **Litho.**

L250 A72 $1.10 multi 1.50 1.10
L251 A72 $1.10 multi 1.50 1.10
L252 A72 $2.20 multi 3.00 2.25
L253 A72 $2.20 multi 3.00 2.25
a. Souvenir sheet of 4, #L250-L253 9.00 6.75
Nos. L250-L253 (4) 9.00 6.70

INDEX AND IDENTIFIER

All page numbers shown are those in this Volume 1A. Postage stamps that do not have English words on them are shown in the Illustrated Identifier.

Appraisals

DR. ROBERT FRIEDMAN & SONS STAMP & COIN BUYING CENTER
2029 W. 75th St.
Woodridge, IL 60517
PH: 800-588-8100
FAX: 630-985-1588
stampcollections@drbobstamps.com
www.drbobfriedmanstamps.com

Auctions

DUTCH COUNTRY AUCTIONS
The Stamp Center
4115 Concord Pike
Wilmington, DE 19803
PH: 302-478-8740
FAX: 302-478-8779
auctions@dutchcountryauctions.com
www.dutchcountryauctions.com

Australia

COLONIAL STAMP COMPANY
5757 Wilshire Blvd. PH #8
Los Angeles, CA 90036
PH: 323-933-9435
FAX: 323-939-9930
info@colonialstamps.com
www.colonialstamps.com

Austria

HENRY GITNER PHILATELISTS, INC.
PO Box 3077-S
Middletown, NY 10940
PH: 845-343-5151
PH: 800-947-8267
FAX: 845-343-0068
hgitner@hgitner.com
www.hgitner.com

Bangkok

COLONIAL STAMP COMPANY
5757 Wilshire Blvd. PH #8
Los Angeles, CA 90036
PH: 323-933-9435
FAX: 323-939-9930
info@colonialstamps.com
www.colonialstamps.com

Bermuda

COLONIAL STAMP COMPANY
5757 Wilshire Blvd. PH #8
Los Angeles, CA 90036
PH: 323-933-9435
FAX: 323-939-9930
info@colonialstamps.com
www.colonialstamps.com

British Asia

THE STAMP ACT
PO Box 1136
Belmont, CA 94002
PH: 650-703-2342
thestampact@sbcglobal.net

British Commonwealth

ARON R. HALBERSTAM PHILATELISTS, LTD.
PO Box 150168
Van Brunt Station
Brooklyn, NY 11215-0168
PH: 718-788-3978
arh@arhstamps.com
www.arhstamps.com

British Commonwealth

ROY'S STAMPS
PO Box 28001
600 Ontario Street
St. Catharines, ON
CANADA L2N 7P8
Phone: 905-934-8377
Email: roystamp@cogeco.ca
www.roysstamps.com

THE STAMP ACT
PO Box 1136
Belmont, CA 94002
PH: 650-703-2342
thestampact@sbcglobal.net

British E. Africa

COLONIAL STAMP COMPANY
5757 Wilshire Blvd. PH #8
Los Angeles, CA 90036
PH: 323-933-9435
FAX: 323-939-9930
info@colonialstamps.com
www.colonialstamps.com

British Guiana

COLONIAL STAMP COMPANY
5757 Wilshire Blvd. PH #8
Los Angeles, CA 90036
PH: 323-933-9435
FAX: 323-939-9930
info@colonialstamps.com
www.colonialstamps.com

Buying

DR. ROBERT FRIEDMAN & SONS STAMP & COIN BUYING CENTER
2029 W. 75th St.
Woodridge, IL 60517
PH: 800-588-8100
FAX: 630-985-1588
stampcollections@drbobstamps.com
www.drbobfriedmanstamps.com

Canada

CANADA STAMP FINDER LLC
2800 N 6th Street, Unit 1-708
St. Augustine, FL 32084
PH: 904-217-2166
Canadian Address:
PO Box 92591
Brampton, ON L6W 4R1
PH: 514-238-5751
Toll Free in North America:
877-412-3106
FAX: 323-315-2635
canadastampfinder@gmail.com
www.canadastampfinder.com

ROY'S STAMPS
PO Box 28001
600 Ontario Street
St. Catharines, ON
CANADA L2N 7P8
Phone: 905-934-8377
Email: roystamp@cogeco.ca
www.roysstamps.com

China - PRC

THE STAMP ACT
PO Box 1136
Belmont, CA 94002
PH: 650-703-2342
thestampact@sbcglobal.net

Collections

DR. ROBERT FRIEDMAN & SONS STAMP & COIN BUYING CENTER
2029 W. 75th St.
Woodridge, IL 60517
PH: 800-588-8100
FAX: 630-985-1588
stampcollections@drbobstamps.com
www.drbobfriedmanstamps.com

Ducks

MICHAEL JAFFE
PO Box 61484
Vancouver, WA 98666
PH: 360-695-6161
PH: 800-782-6770
FAX: 360-695-1616
mjaffe@brookmanstamps.com
www.brookmanstamps.com

Europe-Western

HENRY GITNER PHILATELISTS, INC.
PO Box 3077-S
Middletown, NY 10940
PH: 845-343-5151
PH: 800-947-8267
FAX: 845-343-0068
hgitner@hgitner.com
www.hgitner.com

German Colonies

COLONIAL STAMP COMPANY
5757 Wilshire Blvd. PH #8
Los Angeles, CA 90036
PH: 323-933-9435
FAX: 323-939-9930
info@colonialstamps.com
www.colonialstamps.com

Great Britain

COLONIAL STAMP COMPANY
5757 Wilshire Blvd. PH #8
Los Angeles, CA 90036
PH: 323-933-9435
FAX: 323-939-9930
info@colonialstamps.com
www.colonialstamps.com

New Issues

DAVIDSON'S STAMP SERVICE
Personalized Service since 1970
PO Box 36355
Indianapolis, IN 46236-0355
PH: 317-826-2620
ed-davidson@earthlink.net
www.newstampissues.com

Stamp Stores

California

COLONIAL STAMP COMPANY
5757 Wilshire Blvd. PH #8
Los Angeles, CA 90036
PH: 323-933-9435
FAX: 323-939-9930
info@colonialstamps.com
www.colonialstamps.com

Connecticut

MILLER'S STAMP COMPANY
P.O. Box 1011
Niantic, CT 06357
www.millerstamps.com
PH: 860-908-6200

Delaware

DUTCH COUNTRY AUCTIONS
The Stamp Center
4115 Concord Pike
Wilmington, DE 19803
PH: 302-478-8740
FAX: 302-478-8779
auctions@dutchcountryauctions.com
www.dutchcountryauctions.com

British Commonwealth

Stamp Stores

Florida

DR. ROBERT FRIEDMAN & SONS STAMP & COIN BUYING CENTER
PH: 800-588-8100
FAX: 630-985-1588
stampcollections@drbobstamps.com
www.drbobfriedmanstamps.com

Illinois

DR. ROBERT FRIEDMAN & SONS STAMP & COIN BUYING CENTER
2029 W. 75th St.
Woodridge, IL 60517
PH: 800-588-8100
FAX: 630-985-1588
stampcollections@drbobstamps.com
www.drbobfriedmanstamps.com

Indiana

KNIGHT STAMP & COIN CO.
237 Main St.
Hobart, IN 46342
PH: 219-942-4341
PH: 800-634-2646
knight@knightcoin.com
www.knightcoin.com

New Jersey

BERGEN STAMPS & COLLECTIBLES
306 Queen Anne Rd.
Teaneck, NJ 07666
PH: 201-836-8987
bergenstamps@gmail.com

TRENTON STAMP & COIN
Thomas DeLuca
Store: Forest Glen Plaza
1800 Highway #33, Suite 103
Hamilton Square, NJ 08690
Mail: PO Box 8574
Trenton, NJ 08650
PH: 609-584-8100
FAX: 609-587-8664
TOMD4TSC@aol.com
www.trentonstampandcoin.com

New York

CHAMPION STAMP CO., INC.
432 West 54th St.
New York, NY 10019
PH: 212-489-8130
FAX: 212-581-8130
championstamp@aol.com
www.championstamp.com

Stamp Stores

Ohio

HILLTOP STAMP SERVICE
Richard A. Peterson
PO Box 626
Wooster, OH 44691
PH: 330-262-8907 (0)
PH: 330-201-1377 (H)
hilltop@bright.net
hilltopstamps@sssnet.com
www.hilltopstamps.com

Supplies

BROOKLYN GALLERY COIN & STAMP, INC.
8725 4th Ave.
Brooklyn, NY 11209
PH: 718-745-5701
FAX: 718-745-2775
info@brooklyngallery.com
www.brooklyngallery.com

Topicals

E. JOSEPH MCCONNELL, INC.
PO Box 683
Monroe, NY 10949
PH: 845-783-9791
ejstamps@gmail.com
www.EJMcConnell.com

Topicals - Columbus

MR. COLUMBUS
PO Box 1492
Fennville, MI 49408
PH: 269-543-4755
David@MrColumbus1492.com
www.MrColumbus1492.com

United Nations

HENRY GITNER PHILATELISTS, INC.
PO Box 3077-S
Middletown, NY 10940
PH: 845-343-5151
PH: 800-947-8267
FAX: 845-343-0068
hgitner@hgitner.com
www.hgitner.com

United States

ACS STAMP COMPANY
2914 W 135th Ave
Broomfield, Colorado 80020
303-841-8666
www.ACSStamp.com

United States

BROOKMAN STAMP CO.
PO Box 90
Vancouver, WA 98666
PH: 360-695-1391
PH: 800-545-4871
FAX: 360-695-1616
info@brookmanstamps.com
www.brookmanstamps.com

HENRY GITNER PHILATELISTS, INC.
PO Box 3077-S
Middletown, NY 10940
PH: 845-343-5151
PH: 800-947-8267
FAX: 845-343-0068
hgitner@hgitner.com
www.hgitner.com

MILLER'S STAMP COMPANY
P.O. Box 1011
Niantic, CT 06357
www.millerstamps.com
PH: 860-908-6200

U.S. Classics/Moderns

BARDO STAMPS
PO Box 7437
Buffalo Grove, IL 60089
PH: 847-634-2676
jfb7437@aol.com
www.bardostamps.com

U.S.-Collections Wanted

DUTCH COUNTRY AUCTIONS
The Stamp Center
4115 Concord Pike
Wilmington, DE 19803
PH: 302-478-8740
FAX: 302-478-8779
auctions@dutchcountryauctions.com
www.dutchcountryauctions.com

DR. ROBERT FRIEDMAN & SONS STAMP & COIN BUYING CENTER
2029 W. 75th St.
Woodridge, IL 60517
PH: 800-588-8100
FAX: 630-985-1588
stampcollections@drbobstamps.com
www.drbobfriedmanstamps.com

Want Lists - British Empire 1840-1935 German Cols./Offices

COLONIAL STAMP COMPANY
5757 Wilshire Blvd. PH #8
Los Angeles, CA 90036
PH: 323-933-9435
FAX: 323-939-9930
info@colonialstamps.com
www.colonialstamps.com

Wanted - Worldwide Collections

DUTCH COUNTRY AUCTIONS
The Stamp Center
4115 Concord Pike
Wilmington, DE 19803
PH: 302-478-8740
FAX: 302-478-8779
auctions@dutchcountryauctions.com
www.dutchcountryauctions.com

Websites

ACS STAMP COMPANY
2914 W 135th Ave
Broomfield, Colorado 80020
303-841-8666
www.ACSStamp.com

Wholesale - Dealers

HENRY GITNER PHILATELISTS, INC.
PO Box 3077-S
Middletown, NY 10940
PH: 845-343-5151
PH: 800-947-8267
FAX: 845-343-0068
hgitner@hgitner.com
www.hgitner.com

Worldwide

GUILLERMO JALIL
Maipu 466, local 4
1006 Buenos Aires
Argentina
guillermo@jalilstamps.com
philatino@philatino.com
www.philatino.com (worldwide stamp auctions)
www.jalilstamps.com (direct sale, worldwide stamps)

Worldwide-Collections

DR. ROBERT FRIEDMAN & SONS STAMP & COIN BUYING CENTER
2029 W. 75th St.
Woodridge, IL 60517
PH: 800-588-8100
FAX: 630-985-1588
stampcollections@drbobstamps.com
www.drbobfriedmanstamps.com

Supplies

The Finest Stamp Mount Money Can Buy!

Showgard® SUPERSAFE Original Hagner hawid

www.showgard.com

VIDIFORMS COMPANY, INC.
Showgard House
115 N. Rt. 9W, Congers, NY 10920
845-268-4005
Toll Free 877-507-5758

United States

Large Selection of U.S. and Worldwide Stamps

Over 400 Countries & Colonies in stock, A-Z. Mint and Used. Fast Service and Low Prices.

FOR A PRICE LIST WRITE TO:

ALMAZ CO. Dept. V1
P.O. Box 100-812 • Vanderveer Station
Brooklyn, NY 11210
Phone/Fax (718) 241-6360
AlmazStamps@aol.com

INDEX TO ADVERTISERS 2024 VOLUME 1A

2024 VOLUME 1A DEALER DIRECTORY YELLOW PAGE LISTINGS

This section of your Scott Catalogue contains advertisements to help you conveniently find what you need, when you need it...!